Washington Information Directory

1998–1999

Washington

Information Directory

1998–1999

CONGRESSIONAL QUARTERLY INC.

Washington Information Directory 1998–1999
Editor: Paul McClure
Associate Editor: James DeAngelis
Senior Researchers: Christopher J. Davey, Lincoln M. Farr
Contributing Editor: Talia Greenberg
Book Design: Anne Theilgard, Kachergis Book Design
Illustrators: Debra Naylor, Deborah Ismond
Subject Index: Patricia R. Ruggiero
Electronic Composition: Jessica S. Forman

The Library of Congress cataloged the first edition of this
    title as follows:
Washington information directory. 1975/76—
Washington. Congressional Quarterly Inc.
  1. Washington, D.C.—Directories. 2. Washington metropol-
    itan area—Directories. 3. United States—Executive
    departments—Directories. I. Congressional Quarterly
    Inc.
F192.3.W33 975.3'0025 75-646321

ISBN 1-56802-082-1
ISSN 0887-8064

Contents

Boxes and Illustrations

Preface

Now in its twenty-third edition, the *Washington Information Directory* remains an indispensable guide to the key players and organizations in the nation's capital. The book provides fully updated listings for agencies, congressional committees, and nonprofit groups; it includes descriptions of each organization in a format that lets you search by topic of interest. The directory remains your best one-volume resource for getting the information you need in—or about—Washington.

CQ editors and researchers have added several new features to the book. These include thousands of current Internet addresses, more than 200 new listings for organizations, and more than thirty new or expanded subject headings. The first section in most chapters is now devoted to general policy. More specific sections follow, and these also have had a careful review to keep them comprehensive and timely. Chief among the significant changes to chapters:

• **Military Personnel and Veterans.** A new chapter covering active duty, reserve, and civilian employees of the military, from recruitment to retirement and beyond. New listings focus on emerging topics, such as women in the services and military justice.

• **Housing and Development.** Expanded to provide extensive information on the construction and real estate industries as well as on housing programs and domestic development efforts.

• **Social Services and Disabilities.** Increased focus on services for people with disabilities, including agencies and committees with jurisdiction over the Americans with Disabilities Act.

• **Economics and Business.** A new section on sales and services focuses on wholesale, retail, and advertising; the section on industrial production and manufacturing now covers more specific industries.

In updating the directory, we work to improve and expand the information we present. Hence the list of state officials now includes state treasurers. Information on labor unions and the AFL-CIO, formerly an appendix, has been expanded and integrated into the subject-based chapters. And since national affairs and local resources are interconnected in Washington, we have added information on local governments, airports and commuter rail, and national park sites in the capital region.

At the core of our business is the research method itself. Every name, number, and address in this book—including electronic information—has been verified and double-checked by CQ staff, on a schedule that permits updates right up to press time. We know that you count on us for accurate, up-to-date information, and our commitment to providing it remains as strong as ever.

Our goal is to produce the most comprehensive, useful, and authoritative directory of its kind. We welcome your comments and suggestions.

Paul McClure, Editor
James DeAngelis, Associate Editor

How to Use This Directory

The *Washington Information Directory* is designed to make your search for information fast and easy.

Each chapter covers a broad topic; within the chapters, information is grouped in more specific subject areas. This subject arrangement allows you to find in one place the departments and agencies of the federal government, congressional committees, and nonprofit organizations that have the information you need.

The directory divides information sources into three categories: (1) agencies, (2) Congress, and (3) nonprofit organizations. Each entry includes the name, address, and telephone number of the organization; the name and title of the director or the best person to contact for information; fax and press numbers, hotlines, and Internet addresses whenever available; and a description of the work performed by the organization.

How Information Is Presented

Here are examples of the three main categories of entries, and of the other resources the directory provides. They are drawn from Parks and Recreation Areas, a subsection in chapter 9, Environment and Natural Resources.

AGENCIES

The first entry—the National Park Service—is a federal agency. It is listed in bold type under its commonly known name, with its government parent, the Interior Dept., shown in parentheses.

National Park Service *(Interior Dept.), 1849 C St. N.W., #3316 20240 (mailing address: P.O. Box 37127, Washington, DC 20013-7127); (202) 208-4621. Fax, (202) 208-7889. Robert Stanton, director. Press, (202) 208-6843. Washington area activities, (202) 619-7275 (recording). Internet, http://www.nps.gov.*

Administers national parks, monuments, historic sites, and recreation areas. Oversees coordination, planning, and financing of public outdoor recreation programs at all levels of government. Conducts recreation research surveys; administers financial assistance program to states for planning and development of outdoor recreation programs.

CONGRESS

Entries under the Congress heading are usually Senate or House committees. (Also included here are agencies under congressional jurisdiction, such as the General Accounting Office and Library of Congress.) Committee entries include the chair and a key staff member. The descriptions give the committee's jurisdiction or its activities relating to the particular subject. Here is the entry for the Senate committee with jurisdiction over the national park system:

Senate Energy and Natural Resources Committee, *Subcommittee on National Parks, Historic Preservation, and Recreation, SD-354 20510; (202) 224-6969. Fax, (202) 228-0459. Craig Thomas, R-Wyo., chair; Jim O'Toole, professional staff member. Internet, http://www.senate.gov/~energy.*

Jurisdiction over legislation on national parks, recreation and wilderness areas, trails, wild and scenic rivers, historic sites, and military parks and battlefields.

NONPROFIT

Thousands of nonprofit private and special-interest groups have headquarters or legislative offices in or near Washington. Their staffs are often excellent information sources, and these organizations typically maintain special libraries or information centers. Here is an example of a group with an interest in parks and recreation areas:

Rails-to-Trails Conservancy, *1100 17th St. N.W., 10th Floor 20036; (202) 331-9696. Fax, (202) 331-9680. David G. Burwell, president. Internet, rtrails@transact.org or http://www.railtrails.org.*
Promotes the conversion of abandoned railroad corridors into hiking and biking trails for public use. Provides public education programs and technical and legal assistance. Publishes trail guides. Monitors legislation and regulations.

BOXES AND CHARTS

The directory includes organization charts to make the hierarchy of federal agencies easier to grasp, as well as boxes that provide essential agency contacts and other quick reference information. On the topic of parks, for example, you can locate the National Park Service within the Interior Dept. (see chart on p. 301) or consult a list of contacts at National Park Service Sites in the Capital Region (see box on p. 120). A general organization chart for the federal government appears on p. xv.

Reference Resources

TABLES OF CONTENTS

The summary table of contents (p. v) lists the directory's chapters and their major subheadings. A list of information boxes and organization charts within the chapters is given on p. viii. At the beginning of each chapter you will find a detailed table of contents that breaks the chapter into general and specific sections; for convenience, here again we list the boxes and charts that appear in the chapter.

CONGRESSIONAL INFORMATION

A special section on the 105th Congress, beginning on p. 720, provides extensive information about members and committees:

State Delegations. Here (p. 722) you can look up senators, representatives, and delegates by state (or territory) and congressional district.

Members' Offices. For both the House (p. 751) and Senate (p. 819), we provide each member's Capitol Hill office address, telephone and fax, Internet address, key professional aide, committee assignments, and district offices.

Committees. These sections provide the jurisdiction and membership for committees and subcommittees of the House (p. 727) and Senate (p. 805), as well as the joint committees of Congress (p. 803). Also included here are partisan committees.

Leadership. New to this edition are separate sections listing the party leadership of the House (p. 749) and Senate (p. 818).

READY REFERENCE LISTS

A special section of reference lists, beginning on p. 838, gives information on the following subjects:

Federal Regional Offices. This section (p. 839) gives addresses and telephone numbers for regional offices of federal departments and agencies throughout the country.

State Government. The list of state officials (p. 871) gives the name, address, and telephone number for each governor, lieutenant governor, secretary of state, and attorney general. U.S. territories are included. New to this edition is a list of state treasurers.

Diplomats. The foreign embassies section (p. 880) gives the names, official addresses, and telephone numbers of foreign diplomats in Washington; the names of the ranking U.S. diplomatic officials abroad; and the names and phones of State Dept. and Commerce Dept. desk officers.

Federal Laws on Information. Here you will find concise explanations of the Freedom Information of Act (p. 897), which includes the Electronic Freedom of Information Act of 1996, and of the Privacy Act (p. 899).

Map of Capitol Hill

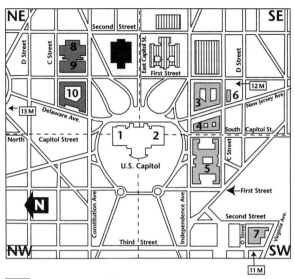

U.S. Capitol, Washington, D.C. 20510 or 20515*
1. Senate Wing   2. House Wing

House Office Buildings, Washington, D.C. 20515
3. Cannon   4. Longworth
5. Rayburn   6. O'Neill
7. Ford

Senate Office Buildings, Washington, D.C. 20510
8. Hart   9. Dirksen
10. Russell

Supreme Court, Washington, D.C. 20543

Library of Congress, Washington, D.C. 20540

M Subway System
11. Federal Center SW   12. Capitol South
13. Union Station

* Mail sent to the U.S. Capitol should bear the ZIP code of the chamber to which it is addressed.

Note: Dotted line indicates the city's quadrants, which are noted in the corners of the map.

INDEXES

Use the name index (p. 900) to look up any person mentioned in the directory.

Use the subject index (p. 947) to look up a subject area or a specific organization or agency. If you need information on a particular topic but do not know a specific source, the index has subject entries to help you find where that topic is covered. For example, on the subject of equal employment for women, you can find index entries under both Women and Equal Employment Opportunity.

Reaching Your Information Source

PHONING AND FAXING

Call the information or toll-free number first. Often you can get the answer you need without going further. If not, a quick explanation of your query should put you in touch with the person who can answer your question. Rarely will you need to talk to the top administrator.

Offer to fax your query if it is difficult to explain over the phone, but make sure that the person helping you knows to expect your fax. Faxing promptly and limiting your transmission to a single page should bring the best results.

Remember that publications and documents are often available from a special office (for federal agencies, see p. 79) or, increasingly, via Web sites or special fax-on-demand services. Ask whether there is a faster way than by mail to receive the information you need.

Keep in mind the agency or organization, not the name of the director. Personnel changes are common, but for most inquiries you will want to stay with the organization you call, rather than track down a person who may have moved on to a new job.

With congressional questions, contact your own member of Congress first: your representative has staff people assigned to answer questions from constituents. Contact a committee only if you have a technical question that cannot be answered elsewhere.

WRITING

Address letters to the director of an office or organization—the contact person listed here. Your letter will be directed to the person who can answer your question. Be prepared to follow up by phone.

USING THE INTERNET

Most agencies and nonprofits now have sites on the World Wide Web (for federal agencies, see p. 84), as well as e-mail addresses for general inquiries. Information available from these sources is expanding rapidly and is usually free once you are online. If you have Internet access, try the Web site, but bear in mind that this approach is not always faster or better than a phone call: connections can be slow, menus can be complex or confusing, information can be incomplete or out-of-date.

As with faxing, reserve e-mail for inquiries that may be too complex for a phone call, but phone first to establish that someone is ready to help.

Addresses and Area Codes

Listings in the directory include full contact information, including telephone area code and, when available, room or suite number and nine-digit ZIP code. If an office has a mailing address that is different from the physical location, we provide both. Note that a few listings are not a local call from Washington—the Social Security Administration headquarters in Baltimore and a small number of nonprofits in outlying suburbs. Other special cases to take note of:

WASHINGTON, D.C., ADDRESSES

For brevity, entries for agencies, organizations, and congressional offices in the District of Columbia (area code 202) do not include the city and state as part of the address. Here is the beginning of a typical Washington entry:

Federal Communications Commission, *1919 M St. N.W. 20554; (202) 418-1000.*

To complete the mailing address, add "Washington, DC."

BUILDING ADDRESSES

Departments and agencies generally have their own ZIP codes; however, updates to our directory reflect the increasing use of street addresses by the federal government. Federal offices that we list by building name or abbreviation are at the following locations:

The White House. Located at 1600 Pennsylvania Ave. N.W. 20500.

Old Executive Office Building. Located at 17th St. and Pennsylvania Ave. N.W. 20500.

New Executive Office Building. Located at 725 17th St. N.W. 20505.

Main State Building. Located at 2201 C St. N.W. 20520.

The Pentagon. Located in Arlington, Va., but has a Washington mailing address and special ZIP codes for each branch of the military.

Navy Annex. Located at Columbia Pike and Southgate Rd., Arlington, VA 20370, but most offices use a Washington mailing address.

U.S. Capitol. Abbreviated as CAP; the letters *H* and *S* before the room number indicate the House or Senate side of the building. ZIP codes are 20510 for the Senate, 20515 for the House.

Senate Office Buildings. The ZIP code is 20510. Abbreviations, building names, and street addresses:

SD	Dirksen Senate Office Bldg., Constitution Ave. between 1st and 2nd Sts. N.E.
SR	Russell Senate Office Bldg., Constitution Ave. between Delaware Ave. and 1st St. N.E.
SH	Hart Senate Office Bldg., 2nd St. and Constitution Ave. N.E.

House Office Buildings. The ZIP code is 20515. Abbreviations, building names, and street addresses:

CHOB	Cannon House Office Bldg., Independence Ave. between New Jersey Ave. and 1st St. S.E.
FHOB	Ford House Office Bldg., 2nd and D Sts. S.W.
LHOB	Longworth House Office Bldg., Independence Ave. between S. Capitol St. and New Jersey Ave. S.E.
OHOB	O'Neill House Office Bldg., 300 New Jersey Ave. S.E.
RHOB	Rayburn House Office Bldg., Independence Ave. between S. Capitol and 1st Sts. S.W.

GOVERNMENT OF THE UNITED STATES

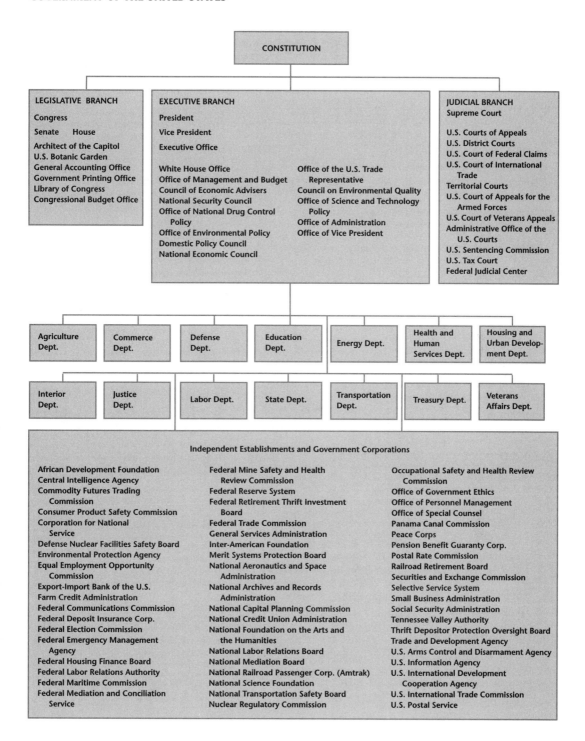

CONSTITUTION

LEGISLATIVE BRANCH

Congress

Senate   House

Architect of the Capitol
U.S. Botanic Garden
General Accounting Office
Government Printing Office
Library of Congress
Congressional Budget Office

EXECUTIVE BRANCH

President

Vice President

Executive Office

White House Office
Office of Management and Budget
Council of Economic Advisers
National Security Council
Office of National Drug Control
    Policy
Office of Environmental Policy
Domestic Policy Council
National Economic Council

Office of the U.S. Trade
    Representative
Council on Environmental Quality
Office of Science and Technology
    Policy
Office of Administration
Office of Vice President

JUDICIAL BRANCH
Supreme Court

U.S. Courts of Appeals
U.S. District Courts
U.S. Court of Federal Claims
U.S. Court of International
    Trade
Territorial Courts
U.S. Court of Appeals for the
    Armed Forces
U.S. Court of Veterans Appeals
Administrative Office of the
    U.S. Courts
U.S. Sentencing Commission
U.S. Tax Court
Federal Judicial Center

Agriculture Dept.

Commerce Dept.

Defense Dept.

Education Dept.

Energy Dept.

Health and Human Services Dept.

Housing and Urban Development Dept.

Interior Dept.

Justice Dept.

Labor Dept.

State Dept.

Transportation Dept.

Treasury Dept.

Veterans Affairs Dept.

Independent Establishments and Government Corporations

African Development Foundation
Central Intelligence Agency
Commodity Futures Trading
    Commission
Consumer Product Safety Commission
Corporation for National
    Service
Defense Nuclear Facilities Safety Board
Environmental Protection Agency
Equal Employment Opportunity
    Commission
Export-Import Bank of the U.S.
Farm Credit Administration
Federal Communications Commission
Federal Deposit Insurance Corp.
Federal Election Commission
Federal Emergency Management
    Agency
Federal Housing Finance Board
Federal Labor Relations Authority
Federal Maritime Commission
Federal Mediation and Conciliation
    Service

Federal Mine Safety and Health
    Review Commission
Federal Reserve System
Federal Retirement Thrift Investment
    Board
Federal Trade Commission
General Services Administration
Inter-American Foundation
Merit Systems Protection Board
National Aeronautics and Space
    Administration
National Archives and Records
    Administration
National Capital Planning Commission
National Credit Union Administration
National Foundation on the Arts and
    the Humanities
National Labor Relations Board
National Mediation Board
National Railroad Passenger Corp. (Amtrak)
National Science Foundation
National Transportation Safety Board
Nuclear Regulatory Commission

Occupational Safety and Health Review
    Commission
Office of Government Ethics
Office of Personnel Management
Office of Special Counsel
Panama Canal Commission
Peace Corps
Pension Benefit Guaranty Corp.
Postal Rate Commission
Railroad Retirement Board
Securities and Exchange Commission
Selective Service System
Small Business Administration
Social Security Administration
Tennessee Valley Authority
Thrift Depositor Protection Oversight Board
Trade and Development Agency
U.S. Arms Control and Disarmament Agency
U.S. Information Agency
U.S. International Development
    Cooperation Agency
U.S. International Trade Commission
U.S. Postal Service

1 ⚖

Advocacy and Public Service

⚖ CIVIL RIGHTS

See also Constitutional Law and Civil Liberties (chap. 14); Equal Employment Opportunity (chap. 7); Public Interest Law (this chapter); Special Groups in Education (chap. 6)

AGENCIES

Commission on Civil Rights, *624 9th St. N.W., #700 20425; (202) 376-7700. Fax, (202) 376-7672. Mary Frances Berry, chair; Cruz Reynoso, vice chair. Press, (202) 376-8312. Library, (202) 376-8110. TDD, (202) 376-8116. Locator, (202) 376-8177. Complaints, (800) 552-6843; in Washington, (202) 376-8582. Internet, http://www.usccr. gov.*

Assesses federal laws and policies of government agencies and studies legal developments to determine the nature and extent of denial of equal protection under the law on the basis of race, color, religion, sex, national origin, age, or disability in many areas, including employment, voting rights, education, administration of justice, and housing. Reports and makes recommendations to the president and Congress; serves as national clearinghouse for civil rights information. Conducts studies relating to discrimination against certain groups, including women, African Americans, Hispanics, Asians, Native Americans, and Pacific Island Americans. Library open to the public.

Equal Employment Opportunity Commission, *1801 L St. N.W., #10006 20507; (202) 663-4001. Fax, (202) 663-4110. Paul M. Igasaki, chair. Information, (202) 663-4900. Library, (202) 663-4630. TDD, (202) 663-4141. Internet, http://www.eeoc.gov.*

Works to end job discrimination by private and government employers based on race, color, religion, sex, national origin, or age. Works to protect employees against reprisal for protest of employment practices alleged to be unlawful in hiring, promotion, firing, wages, and other terms and conditions of employment. Enforces Title VII of the Civil Rights Act of 1964, as amended, which includes the Pregnancy Discrimination Act; Americans with Disabilities Act; Age Discrimination in Employment Act; Equal Pay Act; and, in the federal sector, rehabilitation laws. Receives charges of discrimination; attempts conciliation or settlement; can bring court action to force compliance; has review and appeals responsibility in the federal sector.

Executive Office of the President, *Public Liaison, Old Executive Office Bldg., #122 20502; (202) 456-2930. Fax, (202) 456-6218. Maria Echaveste, director. Press, (202) 456-2100.*

Serves as liaison between the administration and the public on issues of domestic and international concern, including women, minorities, and the elderly.

Health and Human Services Dept., *Civil Rights, 200 Independence Ave. S.W., #522A 20201; (202) 619-0403. Fax, (202) 619-3818. Dennis Hayashi, director. Information, (202) 619-0403. TDD, (800) 537-7697. Toll-free hotline, (800) 368-1019. Internet, http://www.os.dhhs.gov/ progorg/ocr/ocrhmpg.html.*

Administers and enforces laws prohibiting discrimination on the basis of race, color, sex, national origin, religion, age, or disability in programs receiving federal funds from the department; authorized to discontinue funding.

Justice Dept., *Civil Rights, 601 D St. N.W., #4040 20530; (202) 514-2151. Fax, (202) 514-0293. Bill Lann Lee, acting assistant attorney general. Information, (202) 514-2007. Library, (202) 514-4098. TDD, (800) 514-0383.*

Enforces federal civil rights laws prohibiting discrimination on the basis of race, color, religion, sex, disability, age, or national origin in voting, education, employment, credit, housing, public accommodations and facilities, and federally assisted programs.

CONGRESS

House Government Reform and Oversight Committee, *Subcommittee on Human Resources, B372 RHOB 20515; (202) 225-2548. Fax, (202) 225-2382. Christopher Shays, R-Conn., chair; Larry Halloran, staff director. Internet, http://www.house.gov/reform.*

Oversees operations of the Equal Employment Opportunity Commission.

House Government Reform and Oversight Committee, *Subcommittee on National Security, International Affairs, and Criminal Justice, B373 RHOB 20515; (202) 225-2577. Fax, (202) 225-1154. Dennis Hastert, R-Ill., chair; Robert Charles, staff director. Internet, http://www.house.gov/reform.*

Oversees operations of the Commission on Civil Rights.

House Judiciary Committee, *Subcommittee on the Constitution, 362 Ford Bldg. 20515; (202) 226-7680. Fax, (202) 225-3746. Charles T. Canady, R-Fla., chair; Keri Folmar, counsel. Internet, http://www.house.gov/judiciary.*

Jurisdiction over constitutional rights and civil liberties legislation. Oversees the U.S. Commission on Civil Rights and the Justice Dept.'s Civil Rights Division.

Senate Judiciary Committee, *Subcommittee on the Constitution, Federalism, and Property Rights, SD-164*

20510; (202) 224-8081. John Ashcroft, R-Mo., chair; David Miller, chief counsel. Internet, http://www.senate.gov/committee/judiciary.html.

Jurisdiction over civil and constitutional rights legislation; oversees operations of the Commission on Civil Rights.

Senate Labor and Human Resources Committee, SD-428 20510; (202) 224-5375. Fax, (202) 224-6510. James M. Jeffords, R-Vt., chair; Mark Powden, staff director. Internet, http://www.senate.gov/~labor.

Oversees operations of the Equal Employment Opportunity Commission.

NONPROFIT

Citizens' Commission on Civil Rights, 2000 M St. N.W., #400 20036-3307; (202) 659-5565. Fax, (202) 223-5302. Corrine M. Yu, director and counsel. Internet, yu@cccr.com.

Bipartisan commission of former federal officials. Monitors compliance of federal agencies and judicial bodies with civil rights laws; conducts social science research and provides technical and legal assistance to other civil rights and public interest groups; interests include low- and moderate-income housing, voting rights, employment, school desegregation, and education of the disadvantaged.

Leadership Conference on Civil Rights, 1629 K St. N.W., #1010 20006; (202) 466-3311. Fax, (202) 466-3435. Wade Henderson, executive director.

Coalition of national organizations representing minorities, women, labor, older Americans, people with disabilities, and religious groups. Works for enactment and enforcement of civil rights and social welfare legislation; acts as clearinghouse for information on civil rights legislation and regulations.

NAACP Legal Defense and Educational Fund, 1275 K St. N.W., #301 20005; (202) 682-1300. Fax, (202) 682-1312. Vacant, director, Washington Office.

Civil rights litigation group that provides legal information on civil rights issues, including employment, housing, and educational discrimination; monitors federal enforcement of civil rights laws. Not affiliated with the National Assn. for the Advancement of Colored People (NAACP). (Headquarters in New York.)

Poverty and Race Research Action Council, 1711 Connecticut Ave. N.W., #207 20009; (202) 387-9887. Fax, (202) 387-0764. Chester W. Hartman, executive director. Internet, prrac@aol.com.

Facilitates cooperative links between researchers and activists who work on race and poverty issues. Provides nonprofit organizations with funding for research on race and poverty.

See also Lawyers' Committee for Civil Rights Under Law (p. 29)

African Americans

See also Caucuses (chap. 20)

NONPROFIT

Blacks in Government, 1820 11th St. N.W. 20001-5015; (202) 667-3280. Fax, (202) 667-3705. Oscar Eason Jr., president. Internet, http://www.bignet.org.

Advocacy organization for public employees. Promotes equal opportunity and career advancement for African American government employees; provides career development information; seeks to eliminate racism in the federal work force; sponsors programs, business meetings, and social gatherings; represents interests of African American government workers to Congress and the executive branch; promotes voter education and registration.

Congressional Black Caucus Foundation, 1004 Pennsylvania Ave. S.E. 20003; (202) 675-6730. Fax, (202) 547-3806. Ramona Edelin, interim executive director. Internet, http://www.cbcfnet.org.

Conducts research and programs on public policy issues of concern to African Americans. Sponsors fellowship programs in which professionals and academic candidates work on congressional committees and subcommittees. Holds issue forums and leadership seminars. Provides elected officials, organizations, and researchers with statistical, demographic, public policy, and political information. Sponsors internship and scholarship programs.

Joint Center for Political and Economic Studies, 1090 Vermont Ave. N.W., #1100 20005-4961; (202) 789-3500. Fax, (202) 789-6390. Eddie N. Williams, president. Internet, http://www.jointctr.org.

Researches and analyzes issues of concern to African Americans, focusing on economic and social policy issues and African American political participation. Publishes a biannual profile of African American elected officials in federal, state, and local government; holds forums on public policy issues.

Lincoln Institute for Research and Education, 1001 Connecticut Ave. N.W., #1135 20036; (202) 223-5112. J. A. Parker, president.

Public policy research group that studies issues of interest to middle-class African Americans, including business, economics, employment, education, national defense, health, and culture. Sponsors seminars.

National African American Leadership Summit, *145 Kennedy St. N.W. 20011; (202) 726-5111. Fax, (202) 882-1681. Benjamin F. Chavis Jr., chief executive officer. Internet, http://www.melanet.com/naals.*

Promotes the economic, moral, and spiritual development of African Americans; encourages political mobilization. Interests include education, health, the environment, communications, international affairs, and human rights, particularly as these issues affect the African American community.

National Assn. for the Advancement of Colored People (NAACP), *1025 Vermont Ave. N.W., #1120 20005; (202) 638-2269. Fax, (202) 638-5936. Hilary Shelton, deputy director. Internet, http://www.naacp.org.*

Membership: persons interested in civil rights for all minorities. Works for the political, educational, social, and economic equality and empowerment of minorities through legal, legislative, and direct action. (Headquarters in Baltimore.)

National Assn. of Colored Women's Clubs, *5808 16th St. N.W. 20011-2898; (202) 726-2044. Fax, (202) 726-0023. Patricia L. Fletcher, president. Internet, http://www.webspawner.com/nacwc.*

Conducts programs in education, social service, and philanthropy. Works to protect and enforce civil rights and to raise the family living standard; promotes interracial understanding; enhances leadership development.

National Black Caucus of Local Elected Officials, *c/o National League of Cities, 1301 Pennsylvania Ave. N.W., #550 20004; (202) 626-3169. Fax, (202) 626-3103. Paul Richards, president. Press, (202) 626-3000.*

Membership: elected officials at the local level and other interested individuals. Concerned with issues affecting African Americans, including housing, economics, the family, and human rights.

National Black Caucus of State Legislators, *444 N. Capitol St. N.W., #622 20001; (202) 624-5457. Fax, (202) 508-3826. Ivan Lanier, executive director.*

Membership: African American state legislators. Promotes effective leadership among African American state legislators; serves as an information network and clearinghouse for members.

National Center for Neighborhood Enterprise, *1424 16th St. N.W., 300 20036; (202) 518-6500. Fax, (202) 588-*0314. Robert L. Woodson Sr., chair. Internet, http://www.ncne.com.

Seeks new approaches to the problems confronting the African American community. Interests include economic development, the encouragement of entrepreneurship, housing, family development, and education.

National Council of Negro Women, *633 Pennsylvania Ave. N.W. 20004; (202) 737-0120. Fax, (202) 737-0476. Dr. Jane Elaine Smith, president. Internet, http://www.ncnw.org.*

Coalition of domestic and international organizations and individuals interested in issues that affect African American women. Encourages the development of African American women; sponsors programs on family health care, career development, child care, juvenile offenders, housing discrimination against women, teenage pregnancy, and literacy improvement among female heads of households; promotes social and economic well-being of African American women through its Development Projects training program.

National Urban League, *1111 14th St. N.W., #1001 20005-5603; (202) 898-1604. Fax, (202) 408-1965. Robert McAlpine, director, Policy and Government Relations. Internet, http://www.nul.org.*

Federation of affiliates concerned with the social welfare of African Americans and other minorities. Seeks elimination of racial segregation and discrimination; monitors legislation, policies, and regulations to determine impact on minorities; interests include employment, health, welfare, education, housing, and community development. (Headquarters in New York.)

Project 21, *300 Eye St. N.E., #3 20002; (202) 543-1286. Fax, (202) 543-4779. Rodrick Conrad, coordinator. Internet, http://www.nationalcenter.org.*

Emphasizes spirit of entrepreneurship, sense of family, and traditional values among African Americans. (Initiative of the National Center for Public Policy Research.)

See also Concerned Black Men (p. 26); Minority Business Enterprise Legal Defense and Education Fund (p. 169)

Hispanics

See also Caucuses (chap. 20)

NONPROFIT

Congressional Hispanic Caucus Institute, *504 C St. N.E. 20002; (202) 543-1771. Fax, (202) 546-2143. Rita*

Elizondo, executive director. Toll-free college scholarship information, (800) 392-3532.

Addresses issues of concern to Hispanic Americans and fosters awareness of the contributions of Hispanics to American society. Develops programs to familiarize Hispanic students with policy-related careers and to encourage their professional development. Acts as an information clearinghouse on educational opportunities.

League of United Latin American Citizens, *1133 20th St. N.W., #750 20036; (202) 408-0060. Fax, (202) 408-0064. Richard Roybal, executive director, National Educational Service Centers. Internet, lulac@aol.com or http://www.lulac.org.*

Seeks full social, political, economic, and educational rights for Hispanics in the United States. Programs include housing projects for the poor, employment and training for youth and women, and political advocacy on issues affecting Hispanics, including immigration. Operates National Educational Service Centers (NESCs) and awards scholarships. (Headquarters in El Paso, Texas.)

Mexican American Legal Defense and Educational Fund, *1518 K St. N.W., #410 20005; (202) 628-4074. Fax, (202) 393-4206. Georgina Verdugo, regional counsel, Washington Office. Internet, http://www.maldef.org.*

Gives legal assistance to Mexican-Americans and other Hispanics in such areas as equal employment, voting rights, bilingual education, and immigration; awards scholarship funds to Hispanic law students. Monitors legislation and regulations. (Headquarters in Los Angeles.)

National Conference of Catholic Bishops/U.S. Catholic Conference, *Secretariat for Hispanic Affairs, 3211 4th St. N.E., 4th Floor 20017-1194; (202) 541-3152. Fax, (202) 722-8717. Ronaldo Cruz, director. Internet, http://www.nccbuscc.org.*

Acts as an information clearinghouse on communications and pastoral and liturgical activities; serves as liaison for other church institutions, and government and private agencies concerned with Hispanics; provides information on legislation; acts as advocate for Hispanics within the National Conference of Catholic Bishops.

National Conference of Puerto Rican Women, *5 Thomas Circle N.W. 20005; (202) 387-4716. Fax, (305) 592-6601. Lisa Torres, president. Internet, chicotorre@ aol.com.*

Promotes equal participation of Puerto Rican and other Hispanic women in the economic, social, and political aspects of life in both the United States and Puerto Rico.

National Council of La Raza, *1111 19th St. N.W., #1000 20036; (202) 785-1670. Fax, (202) 776-1792. Raul Yzaguirre, president. Internet, http://www.nclr.org.*

Offers technical assistance to Hispanic community organizations; operates policy analysis center with interests in education, employment and training, immigration, language issues, civil rights, and housing and community development. Special projects focus on the Hispanic elderly, teen-age pregnancy, health, and AIDS. Monitors legislation and regulations.

National Puerto Rican Coalition, *1700 K St. N.W., #500 20006; (202) 223-3915. Fax, (202) 429-2223. Manuel Mirabal, president. Internet, nprc@aol.com or http://www.incacorp.com/nprc.*

Membership: Puerto Rican organizations and individuals. Analyzes and advocates for public policy that benefits Puerto Ricans; offers training and technical assistance to Puerto Rican organizations and individuals; develops national communication network for Puerto Rican community-based organizations and individuals.

See also Aspira Assn. (p. 201); National Coalition of Hispanic Health and Human Services Organizations (p. 377)

Lesbians and Gays

NONPROFIT

Dignity USA, *1500 Massachusetts Ave. N.W., #11 20005; (202) 861-0017. Fax, (202) 429-9808. Robert F. Miailovich, president. Toll-free, (800) 877-8797. Internet, dignity@aol.com or http://www.dignityusa.org.*

Membership: gay, lesbian, bisexual, and transgender Catholics, their families, and friends. Works to promote spiritual development, social interaction, educational outreach, and feminist issues.

Gay and Lesbian Activists Alliance, *P.O. Box 75265 20013-5265; (202) 667-5139. Rick Rosendall, president. Internet, equal@glaa.org or http://www.glaa.org.*

Advances the rights of gays and lesbians within the Washington community. (Affiliated with International Lesbian and Gay Assn., Brussels, Belgium.)

Gay and Lesbian Alliance Against Defamation (GLAAD), *1875 Connecticut Ave. N.W., #800 20009; (202) 986-1360. Fax, (202) 667-0902. Gene Falk, ; Steve Weisman, co-chairs. Internet, glaad@glaad.org or http://www.glaad.org.*

Monitors coverage of gay, lesbian, and bisexual issues in the media. Organizes protests and campaigns against homophobic reporting and stereotyping. Publishes and distributes a media guide.

Gay and Lesbian Victory Fund, *1012 14th St. N.W., #1000 20005; (202) 842-8679. Fax, (202) 289-3863. Brian K. Bond, executive director. Internet, victoryf@aol.com or http://www.victoryfund.org.*

Supports the candidacy of openly gay and lesbian individuals in federal, state, and local elections.

Human Rights Campaign, *1101 14th St. N.W., #200 20005; (202) 628-4160. Fax, (202) 347-5323. Elizabeth Birch, executive director. Internet, hrc@hrc.org or http://www.hrc.org.*

Promotes legislation affirming the rights of lesbians and gays. Interests include civil rights; funding for AIDS research; lesbian health issues; and discrimination in housing, immigration, employment, and the military.

Log Cabin Republicans, *1633 Q St. N.W., #210 20009; (202) 347-5306. Fax, (202) 347-5224. Rich Tafel, executive director. Internet, logcabin@cais.com or http://www.lcr.org.*

Membership: lesbian and gay Republicans. Educates conservative politicians and voters on gay and lesbian issues; disseminates information; conducts seminars for members. Monitors legislation and regulations.

National Gay and Lesbian Task Force and Policy Institute, *2320 17th St. N.W. 20009-2702; (202) 332-6483. Fax, (202) 332-0207. Kerry Lobel, executive director. TDD, (202) 332-6219. Internet, ngltf@ngltf.org or http://www.ngltf.org.*

Educates the media and the public on issues affecting the lesbian and gay community. Interests include grass-roots organizations, civil rights, antigay violence, sodomy law reform, and gays on campus. Monitors legislation.

National Lesbian and Gay Journalists Assn., *1718 M St. N.W., #245 20036; (202) 588-9888. Fax, (202) 588-1818. Karen-Louise Boothe, president. Internet, nlgja@aol.com or http://www.nlgja.org.*

Fosters fair and accurate coverage of lesbian and gay issues. Provides professional support and networking services; sponsors conferences, seminars, and workshops.

National Organization for Women (NOW), *1000 16th St. N.W., #700 20036; (202) 331-0066. Fax, (202) 785-8576. Patricia Ireland, president. TDD, (202) 331-9002. Internet, now@now.org or http://www.now.org.*

Membership: women and men interested in feminist civil rights. Works to end discrimination against lesbians and gays. Promotes the development and enforcement of legislation prohibiting discrimination on the basis of sexual orientation.

Parents, Families, and Friends of Lesbians and Gays (PFLAG), *1101 14th St. N.W., #1030 20005; (202) 638-4200. Fax, (202) 638-0243. Nancy McDonald, president. Internet, info@pflag.org or http://www.pflag.org.*

Promotes the health and well-being of gay, lesbian, and bisexual persons, their families, and their friends through support, education, and advocacy. Works to change public policies and attitudes toward gay, lesbian, and bisexual persons. Monitors legislation and regulations.

Servicemembers Legal Defense Network, *P.O. Box 65301 20035-5301; (202) 328-3244. Fax, (202) 797-1635. Michelle M. Benecke and C. Dixon Osburn, co-directors. Internet, sldn@sldn.org or http://www.sldn.org.*

Provides legal assistance to individuals affected by the military's policy on gays and lesbians. Monitors legislation and regulations.

Native Americans

AGENCIES

Administration for Native Americans *(Health and Human Services Dept.), 200 Independence Ave. S.W., #348F 20201; (202) 690-7776. Fax, (202) 690-7441. Gary N. Kimble, commissioner.*

Awards grants for locally determined social and economic development strategies; promotes Native American economic and social self-sufficiency; funds tribes and Native American and native Hawaiian organizations. Commissioner chairs the Intradepartmental Council on Indian Affairs, which coordinates Native American-related programs.

Bureau of Indian Affairs *(Interior Dept.), 1849 C St. N.W., #4160, MSC 4140 20240; (202) 208-7163. Fax, (202) 208-6334. Kevin Grover, assistant secretary. Information, (202) 208-3711. Press, (202) 219-4150. Internet, http://www.usgs.gov/doi/bureau-indian-affairs.html.*

Works with federally recognized Indian tribal governments and Alaska native communities in a government-to-government relationship. Encourages and supports tribes' efforts to govern themselves and to provide needed programs and services on the reservations. Manages land held in trust for Indian tribes and individuals. Funds educational benefits, road construction and maintenance, social services, police protection, economic development efforts, and special assistance to develop governmental and administrative skills.

CONGRESS

House Resources Committee, *1324 LHOB 20515-6201; (202) 225-2761. Fax, (202) 225-5929. Don Young,*

R-Alaska, chair; Lloyd Jones, staff director. Internet, resource@hr.house.gov or http://www.house.gov/resources.

Jurisdiction over all matters regarding relations with and welfare of Native Americans, including land management and trust responsibilities, education, health, special services, loan programs, and claims against the United States.

Senate Committee on Indian Affairs, SH-838 20510; (202) 224-2251. Fax, (202) 224-2309. Ben Nighthorse Campbell, R-Colo., chair; Gary Bohnee, staff director.

Jurisdiction over legislation on Native Americans; oversight of all programs that affect Native Americans.

JUDICIARY

U.S. Court of Federal Claims, 717 Madison Pl. N.W. 20005; (202) 219-9668. Fax, (202) 219-9630. Loren A. Smith, chief judge; David A. Lampen, clerk, (202) 219-9657.

Deals with Native American tribal claims against the government that are founded upon the Constitution, congressional acts, government regulations, and contracts. Examples include claims for land, water, and mineral rights and for the accounting of funds held for Native Americans under various treaties.

NONPROFIT

National Congress of American Indians, 2010 Massachusetts Ave. N.W., #200 20036; (202) 466-7767. Fax, (202) 466-7797. JoAnn K. Chase, executive director. Internet, http://www.ncai.org.

Membership: Native American and Alaska native governments and individuals. Provides information and serves as general advocate for tribes. Monitors legislative and regulatory activities affecting Native American affairs.

Native American Rights Fund, 1712 N St. N.W. 20036; (202) 785-4166. Fax, (202) 822-0068. Vacant, managing attorney, Washington Office.

Provides Native Americans and Alaskan natives with legal assistance in land claims, water rights, hunting, and other areas. (Headquarters in Boulder.)

Navajo Nation, 1101 17th St. N.W., #250 20036; (202) 775-0393. Fax, (202) 775-8075. Sharon Clahchischilliage, director, Washington Office.

Monitors legislation and regulations affecting the Navajo people; serves as an information clearinghouse on the Navajo Nation. (Headquarters in Window Rock, Ariz.)

See also Americans for the Restitution and Righting of Old Wrongs (p. 201); Friends Committee on National Legislation (p. 32)

Senior Citizens

See also Fair Housing/Special Groups (chap. 12); Health Services for Special Groups (chap. 11); Pensions and Benefits (chap. 7); Social Services and Disabilities (chap. 18)

AGENCIES

Administration on Aging (Health and Human Services Dept.), 330 Independence Ave. S.W., #4760 20201; (202) 401-4634. Fax, (202) 619-3759. Jeanette C. Takamura, assistant secretary. Press, (202) 401-4541. Internet, http://www.aoa.dhhs.gov.

Acts as advocate for the elderly; serves as the principal agency for implementing programs under the Older Americans Act. Develops programs to promote the economic welfare and personal independence of older people; provides advice and assistance to promote the development of state-administered, community-based social services for older people; supports curriculum development and training in gerontology.

CONGRESS

House Education and the Workforce Committee, Subcommittee on Early Childhood, Youth, and Families, 2181 RHOB 20515; (202) 225-4527. Fax, (202) 225-9571. Frank Riggs, R-Calif., chair; Kevin Talley, staff director. Internet, http://www.house.gov/eeo.

Jurisdiction over legislation on all matters dealing with programs and services for the elderly, including nutrition programs and the Older Americans Act.

Senate Special Committee on Aging, SD-G31 20510; (202) 224-5364. Fax, (202) 224-8660. Charles E. Grassley, R-Iowa, chair; Ted Totman, staff director.

Oversight of all matters affecting older Americans. Studies and reviews public and private policies and programs that affect the elderly, including retirement income and maintenance, housing, health, welfare, employment, education, recreation, and participation in family and community life; provides other Senate committees with information. Cannot report legislation.

NONPROFIT

American Assn. of Retired Persons, 601 E St. N.W. 20049; (202) 434-2277. Fax, (202) 434-2320. Horace B. Deets, executive director. Press, (202) 434-2560. Library, (202) 434-6240. TDD, (202) 434-6554. Internet, http://www.aarp.org.

Membership organization for persons aged 50 and older. Provides members with training, employment information, and volunteer programs; offers financial services, including insurance, investment programs, and consumer discounts; makes grants through AARP Andrus Foundation for research on aging. Monitors legislation and regulations on issues affecting older Americans, including age discrimination, Social Security, Medicaid and Medicare, pensions and retirement, and consumer protection.

Gray Panthers Project Fund, *2025 Pennsylvania Ave. N.W., #821 20006; (202) 466-3132. Fax, (202) 466-3133. Tim Fuller, director.*

Educational and advocacy organization that promotes national health care and economic and social justice for people of all ages, including the elderly.

National Alliance of Senior Citizens, *1744 Riggs Pl. N.W., 3rd Floor 20009-2508; (202) 986-0117. Fax, (202) 986-2974. Peter J. Luciano, chief executive officer.*

Membership: persons of any age who want to improve the quality of life for senior Americans. Interests include Social Security, health care, Medicare, pensions, crime against older Americans, intergenerational support, and improvement of care for the dying.

National Caucus and Center on Black Aged, *1424 K St. N.W., #500 20005-2410; (202) 637-8400. Fax, (202) 347-0895. Samuel J. Simmons, president.*

Concerned with issues that affect elderly African Americans. Sponsors employment and housing programs for the elderly and education and training for professionals in gerontology. Monitors legislation and regulations.

National Council of Senior Citizens, *8403 Colesville Rd., #1200, Silver Spring, MD 20910-3314; (301) 578-8800. Fax, (301) 578-8999. Steve Protulis, executive director. Internet, http://www.ncscinc.org.*

Federation of senior citizen clubs, associations, councils, and other groups. Seeks to nationalize health care services and to strengthen benefits to the elderly, including improved Social Security payments, increased employment, and education and health programs. Offers prescription drug program, Medicare supplement, and group travel.

National Council on the Aging, *409 3rd St. S.W., 2nd Floor 20024; (202) 479-1200. Fax, (202) 479-0735. James Firman, president. Information, (202) 479-6653. Press, (202) 479-6610. Library, (202) 479-6669. TDD, (202) 479-6674. Internet, info@ncoa.org or http://www.ncoa.org.*

Serves as an information clearinghouse on training, technical assistance, advocacy, and research on every aspect of aging. Provides information on social services for older persons. Monitors legislation and regulations. Library open to the public.

National Hispanic Council on Aging, *2713 Ontario Rd. N.W. 20009; (202) 265-1288. Fax, (202) 745-2522. Marta Sotomayor, president. Internet, nhcoa@worldnet. att.net or http://www.incacorp.com/nhcoa.*

Membership: senior citizens, health care workers, professionals in the field of aging, and others in the United States and Puerto Rico who are interested in topics related to Hispanics and aging. Provides research training, consulting, and technical assistance; sponsors seminars, workshops, and management internships.

National Senior Citizens Law Center, *1101 14th St. N.W., #400 20005; (202) 289-6976. Fax, (202) 289-7224. Burton D. Fretz, executive director. Internet, nsclc@nsclc. org or http://www.nsclc.org.*

Organization funded by the Legal Services Corp. Litigates on behalf of legal services programs and elderly poor clients and client groups. Represents clients before Congress and federal departments and agencies. Interests include Social Security, Medicare, Medicaid, nursing home residents' rights, home health care, pensions, and protective services.

60 Plus, *1655 N. Fort Myer Dr., #355, Arlington, VA 22209; (703) 807-2070. Fax, (703) 807-2073. James L. Martin, president. Internet, http://www.60plus.org.*

Advocates rights of senior citizens. Interests include free enterprise, less government regulation, and tax reform. Seeks the abrogation of the estate tax. Publishes rating system of members of Congress. Monitors legislation and regulations.

United Seniors Assn., Inc., *3900 Jermantown Rd., #450, Fairfax, VA 22030; (703) 359-6500. Fax, (703) 803-6853. Sandra L. Butler, president. Toll-free, (800) 887-2872. Internet, http://www.unitedseniors.org.*

Advocates the rights of older Americans. Works to lower taxes, reduce wasteful government spending, and preserve the rights and benefits of senior citizens.

Women

NONPROFIT

Assn. for Women in Science, *1200 New York Ave. N.W., #650 20005; (202) 326-8940. Fax, (202) 326-8960. Catherine Didion, executive director. Internet, awis@awis. org or http://www.awis.org.*

Promotes equal opportunity for women in scientific professions; provides career and funding information. Interests include international development.

Center for Women Policy Studies, *1211 Connecticut Ave. N.W., #312 20036; (202) 872-1770. Fax, (202) 296-8962. Leslie R. Wolfe, president. Internet, HN4066@ handsnet.org.*

Policy and advocacy organization concerned with women's issues, including educational and employment equity for women, women and AIDS, violence against women, economic opportunity for low-income women, women's health, and reproductive laws.

Church Women United, *110 Maryland Ave. N.E., #108 20002; (202) 544-8747. Fax, (202) 544-9133. Ann Delorey, legislative director. Internet, cwu_washington.parti@ ecunet.org or http://www.churchwomen.org.*

Ecumenical women's organization. Interests include defense policy, employment, family stability, health, human rights, justice, world peace, and hunger and poverty issues, especially as they affect women and children.

Independent Women's Forum, *1319 18th St. N.W. 20036; (202) 833-4553. Fax, (202) 833-4543. Barbara Ledeen, executive director. Internet, iwf@iwf.org or http://www.iwf.org.*

Membership: women and men interested in promoting individual responsibility, strong families, freedom, and opportunity. Conducts litigation; publishes periodical and media directory; maintains speakers bureau. Interests include maintaining single-sex schools and eliminating affirmative action programs. Monitors legislation and regulations.

Jewish Women International, *1828 L St. N.W., #250 20036; (202) 857-1300. Fax, (202) 857-1380. Gail Rubinson, executive director. Internet, jewishwomen@ charitiesusa.com or http://www.jewishwomen.org.*

Organization of Jewish women in the United States and Canada. Interests include emotional health of children and youth; family issues such as choice, family violence, and women's health care; civil and constitutional rights; community services; and anti-Semitism.

Leadership America, Inc., *700 N. Fairfax St., #610, Alexandria, VA 22314; (703) 549-1102. Fax, (703) 836-9205. Rita Harmon, executive director. Internet, info@ leadershipamerica.com or http://www.leadershipamerica. com.*

Educational program designed to increase women's influence in the national decisionmaking process. Con-

ducts seminars on public policy issues for women in leadership positions.

National Organization for Women (NOW), *1000 16th St. N.W., #700 20036; (202) 331-0066. Fax, (202) 785-8576. Patricia Ireland, president. TDD, (202) 331-9002. Internet, now@now.org or http://www. now.org.*

Membership: women and men interested in feminist civil rights. Uses traditional and nontraditional forms of political activism, including nonviolent civil disobedience, to improve the status of all women regardless of age, income, sexual orientation, or race.

National Women's Law Center, *11 Dupont Circle N.W., #800 20036; (202) 588-5180. Fax, (202) 588-5185. Marcia Greenberger and Nancy D. Campbell, co-presidents.*

Works to expand and protect women's legal rights through advocacy and public education. Interests include reproductive rights, health, education, employment, women in prison, income security, and family support.

Older Women's League, *666 11th St. N.W., #700 20001; (202) 783-6686. Fax, (202) 638-2356. Deborah Briceland-Betts, executive director.*

Grassroots organization concerned with the social and economic problems of middle-aged and older women. Interests include health care, Social Security, pension rights, housing, employment, women as care givers, effects of budget cuts, and issues relating to death and dying.

Quota International, *1420 21st St. N.W. 20036; (202) 331-9694. Fax, (202) 331-4395. Kathleen Treiber, executive director. Internet, staff@quota.org or http://www. quota.org.*

International service organization that links members in fourteen countries in a worldwide network of service. Interests include deaf, hard-of-hearing, and speech-impaired individuals and disadvantaged women and children.

The Woman Activist, *2310 Barbour Rd., Falls Church, VA 22043; (703) 573-8716. Flora Crater, president.*

Advocacy group that conducts research on individuals and groups in elective and appointive office, especially those who make decisions affecting women and minorities. Publishes annual ratings of these officials.

Women's Action for New Directions, *110 Maryland Ave. N.E., #205 20002; (202) 543-8505. Fax, (202) 675-6469. Kimberly Robson, director of policy and programs. Legislative hotline, (800) 444-9263. Internet, wandwill@ wand.org or http://www.wand.org.*

Monitors legislation affecting women. Interests include the redirection of military spending toward domestic priorities. (Headquarters in Arlington, Mass.)

Women's Legal Defense Fund, *1875 Connecticut Ave. N.W., #710 20009-5728; (202) 986-2600. Fax, (202) 986-2539. Judith L. Lichtman, president. Internet, info@wlds. org.*

Advocacy organization that advances legal rights of women, primarily in the areas of employment and family leave; conducts research and provides technical expertise and analysis; litigates selected cases.

Women's Research and Education Institute, *1750 New York Ave. N.W., #350 20006; (202) 628-0444. Fax, (202) 628-0458. Betty Dooley, president. Internet, wrei@ix.netcom.com or http://www.wrei.org.*

Provides data, research, and policy analyses on women's issues. Sponsors fellowships in congressional offices; promotes public education through conferences, symposia, and briefings; serves as an information clearinghouse; publishes periodic report on the status of women in the United States. Interests include health care, housing, women and tax policy, military women, alternative work options, employment, older women, and home-based work.

See also Fund for the Feminist Majority Foundation (p. 715)

Other Minority Groups

See also Religion and Ethics (this chapter); Social Services and Disabilities (chap. 18)

NONPROFIT

American-Arab Anti-Discrimination Committee, *4201 Connecticut Ave. N.W., #300 20008-1158; (202) 244-2990. Fax, (202) 244-3196. Naila Asali, chair; Hala Maksoud, president. Internet, adc@adc.org or http://www. adc.org.*

Nonsectarian organization that seeks to protect the rights and heritage of Americans of Arab descent. Works to combat discrimination against Arab Americans in employment, education, and political life and to prevent stereotyping of Arabs in the media.

American Muslim Council, *1212 New York Ave. N.W., #400 20005; (202) 789-2262. Fax, (202) 789-2550. Atif Harden, director. Internet, http://www.amermuslim.org.*

Promotes equal rights and political empowerment for Muslims in the United States. Opposes discrimination against Muslims; fosters cultural understanding and cooperation among organizations.

Anti-Defamation League, *1100 Connecticut Ave. N.W., #1020 20036; (202) 452-8320. Fax, (202) 296-2371. David Freedman, regional director. Internet, adlwashdc@aol.com or http://www.adl.org.*

Jewish organization interested in civil rights and liberties. Seeks to combat anti-Semitism and other forms of bigotry. Interests include discrimination in employment, housing, voting, and education; U.S. foreign policy in the Middle East; and the treatment of Jews worldwide. Monitors legislation and regulations affecting Jewish interests and the civil rights of all Americans. (Headquarters in New York.)

Japanese American Citizens League, *1001 Connecticut Ave. N.W., #704 20036; (202) 223-1240. Fax, (202) 296-8082. Bob Sakanawa, Washington representative. Internet, http://jacl.org.*

Monitors legislative and regulatory activities affecting the rights of Japanese Americans. Supports civil rights of all Americans, with a focus on Asian and Asian-Pacific Americans.

Organization of Chinese American Women, *4641 Montgomery Ave., #208, Bethesda, MD 20814; (301) 907-3898. Fax, (301) 907-3899. Pauline W. Tsui, acting executive director.*

Seeks to overcome racial and sexual discrimination and to ensure equal education and employment opportunities in professional and nonprofessional fields; provides members with leadership, skills, and employment training; assists newly arrived immigrants.

Organization of Chinese Americans, *1001 Connecticut Ave. N.W., #707 20036; (202) 223-5500. Fax, (202) 296-0540. Daphne Kwok, executive director. Internet, http://www.ari.net/oca.*

Advocacy group seeking equal opportunities for Chinese Americans and other Asian Americans. Interests include cultural heritage, education, voter registration, hate crimes, immigration, and civil rights issues; opposes adoption of English as official U.S. language.

⚖ CONSUMER PROTECTION

See also Consumer Education (chap. 6); Food and Nutrition (chap. 2); Public Interest Law (this chapter); Sales and Services (chap. 5)

AGENCIES

Consumer Affairs Council, *750 17th St. N.W., 6th Floor 20006; (202) 395-7900. Fax, (202) 395-7901. Leslie Burne,*

CONSUMER PRODUCT SAFETY COMMISSION

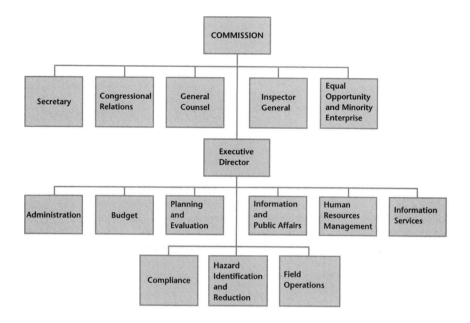

director; Howard Seltzer, executive secretary. Main phone is voice and TDD accessible.

Composed of consumer representatives from federal agencies. Reviews policy and provides leadership in improving the effectiveness of government consumer programs.

Consumer Product Safety Commission, *4330 East-West Hwy., Bethesda, MD 20814; (301) 504-0990. Fax, (301) 504-0281. Ann Brown, chair; Pamela Gilbert, executive director. Information, (301) 504-0580. Library, (301) 504-0044. TDD, (800) 638-8270. Locator, (301) 504-0100. Product safety hotline, (800) 638-2772. Internet, info@ cpsc.gov or http://www.cpsc.gov.*

Establishes and enforces product safety standards; collects data; studies the causes and prevention of product-related injuries; identifies hazardous products and recalls them from the marketplace. Library open to the public.

Federal Trade Commission, *Advocacy Office, 6th St. and Pennsylvania Ave. N.W., #458 20580; (202) 326-3344. Fax, (202) 326-2050. Vacant, coordinator.*

Promotes the interests of consumers by encouraging market competition. Conducts research and advises government agencies and bodies on consumer and competition issues.

Federal Trade Commission, *Consumer Protection, 6th and Pennsylvania Ave. N.W., #466H 20580; (202) 326-*

3238. Fax, (202) 326-3799. Joan Z. Bernstein, director. Internet, http://www.ftc.gov.

Enforces regulations dealing with unfair or deceptive business practices in advertising, marketing, and service industries; educates consumers and businesses about these regulations; conducts investigations and litigation.

General Services Administration, *Consumer Information Center, 1800 F St. N.W.. #G142 20405; (202) 501-1794. Fax, (202) 501-4281. Teresa N. Nasif, director. Internet, http://www.pueblo.gsa.gov.*

Publishes quarterly consumer information catalog that lists free and low-cost federal publications. Copies may be obtained from the Consumer Information Centers, Pueblo, CO 81009. Copies also available at Federal Information Centers.

U.S. Office of Consumer Affairs *(Health and Human Services Dept.), 750 17th St. N.W., 6th Floor 20006; (202) 395-7900. Fax, (202) 395-7901. Leslie Burne, director. Main phone is voice and TDD accessible. Internet, http://www.os.dhhs.gov.*

Coordinates federal consumer programs and serves as a resource center for government agencies; advises state and local governments on administration of consumer programs; assists agencies and businesses in developing consumer complaint mechanisms. Publishes *Consumer's Resource Handbook* and *Consumer News.*

CONSUMER AND EMERGENCY HOTLINES

DEPARTMENTS

Agriculture

Meat and poultry safety inquiries, (800) 535-4555; (202) 720-3333 in Washington

Commerce

Export enforcement hotline, (800) 424-2890

Trade Information Center, (800) 872-8723

Defense

Army espionage hotline, (800) 225-5779

Veterans nuclear test info., (800) 462-3683

Education

Student financial aid info., (800) 433-3243

Energy

Environmental hotline, (800) 541-1625

Renewable energy conservation info., (800) 523-2929

Health and Human Services

AIDS info., (800) 342-2437; 332-2437 in Washington; TDD, (800) 243-7889. Spanish speaking, (800) 344-7432; (202) 328-0697 in Washington

Cancer info., (800) 422-6237

Civil rights info., (800) 368-1019; (202) 863-0100 in Washington

Domestic violence hotline, (800) 799-7233

General health info., (800) 336-4797

Inspector general hotline, (800) 368-5779

Medicare hotline, (800) 638-6833

National Adoption Center, (800) 862-3678

National Runaway Switchboard, (800) 621-4000

Housing and Urban Development

Housing discrimination hotline, (800) 669-9777

Justice

Americans With Disabilities Act information, (800) 514-0301; TDD, (800) 514-0383

FBI Information Center, (800) 877-1461

Immigration and Naturalization Service regulations hotline, (800) 755-0777; forms request, (800) 870-3676

Juvenile justice info., (800) 638-8736

Office of Justice Programs
Drug and crime data, (800) 666-3332
National Victims Resource Center, (800) 627-6873

Unfair employment hotline, (800) 255-7688

Transportation

Airline safety hotline, (800) 255-1111

Auto safety hotline, (800) 424-9393; (202) 366-0123 in Washington

Boating hotline, (800) 368-5647

Federal Aviation Administration consumer hotline, (800) 322-7873

Hazardous material, chemical, and oil spills, (800) 424-8802; (202) 426-2675 in Washington

Treasury

Comptroller of the Currency customer assistance hotline, (800) 613-6743

Drug smuggling reports, (800) 232-5378

Explosive materials discovery theft, loss reports, (800) 3855; (202) 927-7777 in Washington

Tax form requests, (800) 829-3676

Tax refund info., (800) 829-4477

Taxpayer assistance, (800) 829-1040; (410) 962-2590 in Baltimore

---

AGENCY AND DEPARTMENT CONSUMER CONTACTS

Agriculture Dept., *Consumer Affairs,* 3101 Park Center Dr., #813-B, Alexandria, VA 22302; (703) 305-2281. Fax, (703) 305-2230. Joyce Willis, director. Internet, http://www.usda.gov/fcs.

Commerce Dept., *Consumer Affairs,* 14th St. and Constitution Ave. N.W., #5718 20230; (202) 482-5001. Fax, (202) 482-6007. Lajuan Johnson, director. Internet, CAffairs@doc.gov.

Commission on Civil Rights, *Public Affairs,* 624 9th St. N.W. 20425; (202) 376-8312. Fax, (202) 376-8315.

Charles Rivera, chief. TDD, (202) 376-8116. Internet, http://www.usccr.gov.

Consumer Product Safety Commission, *Information and Public Affairs,* 4330 East-West Hwy., Bethesda, MD; (301) 504-0580. Fax, (301) 504-0862. Kathleen Begala, director. TDD, (800) 638-8270. Product safety hotline, (800) 638-2772. Internet, info@cpsc.gov or http://www.cpsc.gov.

Defense Dept., *Morale, Welfare, and Recreation,* The Pentagon 20301-4000; (703) 697-7197. Fax, (703) 614-3375. Steve Rossetti, director.

CONSUMER AND EMERGENCY HOTLINES (continued)

Veterans Affairs

Benefits hotline, (800) 827-1000

Debt Management Center, (800) 827-0648

Fraud, waste, and mismanagement hotline, (800) 488-8244

Life insurance information, (800) 669-8477

Persian Gulf hotline, (800) 749-8387

AGENCIES

Consumer Product Safety Commission

Product safety info., (800) 638-2772

Environmental Protection Agency

Asbestos ombudsman, (800) 368-5888; (202) 260-0490; in Washington

Electromagnetic field infoline, (800) 363-2383

Endangered species hotline, (800) 447-3813

National Lead Information Center, (800) 532-3394

National radon hotline, (800) 767-7236

Ozone information hotline, (800) 296-1996

Pesticides and related medical info., (800) 858-7378

Safe drinking water hotline, (800) 426-4791

Superfund hotline, (800) 424-9346; (703) 412-9810 in Washington

Wetlands information hotline, (800) 832-7828

Export-Import Bank

Export finance hotline, (800) 565-3946; (202) 565-3946 in Washington

Federal Deposit Insurance Corporation

Banking complaints and inquiries, (800) 934-3342

Federal Election Commission

Fundraising laws info., (800) 424-9530; (202) 219-3420 in Washington

Federal Emergency Management Agency

Emergency management and training info., (800) 638-1821; (301) 447-1030 in Maryland

Flood insurance service, (800) 638-6620

General Services Administration

Federal Information Center, (800) 688-9889

National Archives and Records Administration

Audiovisual material sales and info., (800) 788-6282

Nuclear Regulatory Commission

Nuclear power info., (800) 368-5642

Office of Special Counsel

Prohibited personnel practices info., (800) 872-9855; (202) 653-7188 in Washington

Small Business Administration

Small business assistance, (800) 827-5722

Social Security Administration

Fraud and abuse hotline, (800) 767-0385

Social Security benefits info., (800) 772-1213

PRIVATE ORGANIZATIONS

GED Hotline on Adult Education, (800) 626-9433

National Center for Missing and Exploited Children, (800) 843-5678

National Insurance Consumer Helpline, (800) 942-4242

National Literacy Hotline, (800) 228-8813

National Organization for Victim Assistance, (800) 879-6682; (202) 232-6682 in Washington

Project Vote Smart, (800) 622-7627

United Network for Organ Sharing, (800) 243-6667

Education Dept., *Intergovernmental and Interagency Affairs,* 600 *Independence Ave. S.W., #6442 20202-3500; (202) 401-0404. Fax, (202) 401-8607. G. Mario Moreno, assistant secretary. Press, (202) 401-1304. TDD, (202) 205-5507.*

Energy Dept., *Consumer and Public Liaison,* 1000 *Independence Ave. S.W., CI-10 20585; (202) 586-5373. Fax, (202) 586-0539. Betty Nolan, director.*

Environmental Protection Agency, *Public Information Center,* 401 *M St. S.W., #3404 20460; (202) 260-5922. Fax, (202) 260-6257. Carol DeAngelo, head librarian. Internet, public-access@epamail.epa.gov.*

Federal Communications Commission, *Public Service,* 1919 *M St. N.W., #254 20554; (202) 418-0191. Fax, (202) 418-0232. Martha Contee, chief. TDD, (202) 418-2555.*

Federal Deposit Insurance Corp., *Compliance and Consumer Affairs,* 1730 *Pennsylvania Ave., 7th Floor 20429; (202) 942-3100. Fax, (202) 942-3427. Carmen Sullivan, director. Toll-free, (800) 934-3342. TDD, (800) 925-4618. Internet, consumer@fdic.gov.*

Federal Maritime Commission, *Informal Inquiries & Complaints,* 800 *N. Capitol St. N.W., #1052 20573; (202) 523-5807. Fax, (202) 523-0014. Joseph Farrell, director.*

Federal Reserve System, *Consumer and Community Affairs,* 20th and C Sts. N.W. 20551-0001; (202) 452-2631. Fax, (202) 872-4995. Griffith L. Garwood, director. Complaints, (202) 452-3693.

Food and Drug Administration *(Health and Human Services Dept.), Consumer Affairs,* 5600 Fishers Lane, Rockville, MD 20857; (301) 827-5006. Fax, (301) 443-9767. Charles Gaylord, acting associate commissioner. Consumer inquiries, (800) 532-4440. Internet, http://www.fda.gov.

General Services Administration, *Consumer Information Center,* 1800 F St. N.W., #G142 20405; (202) 501-1794. Fax, (202) 501-4281. Teresa N. Nasif, director. Internet, http://www.pueblo.gsa.gov.

Interior Dept., *Communications,* 1849 C St. N.W., #6013 20240; (202) 208-6416. Fax, (202) 208-5311. Michael Gauldin, director. TDD, (202) 208-4817.

Justice Dept., *Civil Division,* 1331 Pennsylvania Ave., #950N 20004; (202) 307-0066. Fax, (202) 514-8742. Eugene M. Thirolf, director, Consumer Litigation.

Merit Systems Protection Board, 1120 Vermont Ave. N.W., #806 20419; (202) 653-7200. Fax, (202) 653-7130. Robert E. Taylor, clerk of the board. TDD, (202) 653-8896.

National Institute of Standards and Technology *(Commerce Dept.), Inquiries,* Route I-270 and Quince Orchard Rd., Administrative Bldg., #A-903, Gaithersburg, MD 20899; (301) 975-3058. Fax, (301) 926-1630. Sharon Shaffer, head. Reference Desk, (301) 975-3052. Internet, inquiries@nist.gov.

Nuclear Regulatory Commission, *Public Affairs,* 11555 Rockville Pike, Rockville, MD; (301) 415-8200. Fax, (301) 415-3716. Mindy Landau, coordinator, Consumer Affairs. Internet, nrc@nrc.gov or http://www.nrc.gov/opa.

Postal Rate Commission, *Consumer Advocate,* 1333 H St. N.W. 20268-0001; (202) 789-6830. Fax, (202) 789-6886. W. Gail Willette, director.

Securities and Exchange Commission, *Filings and Information Services,* 450 5th St. N.W. 20549; (202) 942-8938. Fax, (703) 914-1005. Wilson Butler, director.

Small Business Administration, 409 3rd St. S.W. 20416; (202) 205-6657. Fax, (202) 205-7230. Jeanne Sclater, associate deputy director, Economic Development.

State Dept., *Coordinator for Business Affairs,* Main State Bldg., #2318 20520; (202) 647-1625. Fax, (202) 647-

3953. Marshal Adair, acting senior coordinator. Internet, http://www.state.gov/www/about_state/business/index/html.

Transportation Dept., *Consumer Affairs,* 400 7th St. S.W., #10405 (mailing address: Transportation Dept., C75, Washington, DC 20590); (202) 366-2220. Fax, (202) 366-7907. Hoyte Decker, assistant director.

Treasury Dept., *Public Affairs,* 1500 Pennsylvania Ave. N.W., #2321 20220; (202) 622-2960. Fax, (202) 622-2808. Howard Schloss, assistant secretary.

U.S. Postal Service, *Consumer Affairs,* 475 L'Enfant Plaza S.W. 20260-2200; (202) 268-2284. Fax, (202) 268-2304. Michael Shinay, vice president. TDD, (202) 268-2310.

Veterans Affairs Dept., *Consumer Affairs,* 810 Vermont Ave. N.W., #915 20420; (202) 273-5772. Fax, (202) 273-5716. Clayton Cochran, Shirley Mathis, program analysts.

CONGRESS

House Appropriations Committee, *Subcommittee on Commerce, Justice, State, and Judiciary,* H309 Capitol 20515; (202) 225-3351. Harold Rogers, R-Ky., chair; Jim Kulikowski, staff director. Internet, http://www.house.gov/appropriations.

Jurisdiction over legislation to appropriate funds for the Federal Trade Commission.

House Appropriations Committee, *Subcommittee on VA, HUD, and Independent Agencies,* H143 CAP 20515; (202) 225-3241. Jerry Lewis, R-Calif., chair; Frank Cushing, staff director. Internet, http://www.house.gov/appropriations.

Jurisdiction over legislation to appropriate funds for the Consumer Information Center of the General Services Administration, the Consumer Product Safety Commission, and the U.S. Office of Consumer Affairs of the Health and Human Services Dept.

House Banking and Financial Services Committee, *Subcommittee on Financial Institutions and Consumer Credit,* 2129 RHOB 20515; (202) 225-2258. Fax, (202) 225-6984. Marge Roukema, R-N.J., chair; Laurie Schaffer, staff director. Internet, http://www.house.gov/banking.

Jurisdiction over legislation on consumer protection, including fair lending and regulatory issues.

House Commerce Committee, *Subcommittee on Health and the Environment,* 2125 RHOB 20515; (202) 225-2927. Fax, (202) 225-1919. Michael Bilirakis, R-Fla., chair; James E. Derderian, staff director. Internet, http://www.house.gov/commerce/health.html.

Jurisdiction over legislation on vaccines; labeling and packaging, including tobacco products and alcohol beverages; and the use of vitamins. Oversight of the Food and Drug Administration.

House Commerce Committee, *Subcommittee on Telecommunications, Trade, and Consumer Protection,* *2125 RHOB 20515; (202) 225-2927. Fax, (202) 225-1919. W. J. "Billy" Tauzin, R-La., chair; James E. Derderian, staff director. Internet, http://www.house.gov/commerce.*

Jurisdiction over product liability and consumer protection legislation, the Consumer Product Safety Commission, the Federal Trade Commission, and interstate and foreign commerce, including general trade matters within the jurisdiction of the full committee.

House Government Reform and Oversight Committee, *Subcommittee on National Economic Growth, Natural Resources, and Regulatory Affairs, B377 RHOB 20515; (202) 225-4407. Fax, (202) 225-2441. David M. McIntosh, R-Ind., chair; Mildred Webber, staff director. Internet, http://www.house.gov/reform.*

Oversight of the Federal Trade Commission and the Consumer Product Safety Commission.

House Science Committee, *Subcommittee on Basic Research, B374 RHOB 20515; (202) 225-7858. Fax, (202) 225-7815. Vacant, chair; Steve Eule, staff director. Press, (202) 225-0584. Internet, http://www.house.gov/science.*

Jurisdiction over legislation related to the U.S. Fire Administration and Building and Fire Research Laboratory of the National Institute of Standards and Technology; oversight of federal fire prevention and the Earthquake Hazards Reduction Act. Jurisdiction over research and development involving government nutritional programs.

Senate Appropriations Committee, *Subcommittee on Commerce, Justice, State, and Judiciary, SR-393 20510; (202) 224-7277. Judd Gregg, R-N.H., chair, (202) 224-3324; Vas Alexopoulos, legislative assistant. Chair's fax, (202) 224-4952. Internet, http://www.senate.gov/~appropriations.*

Jurisdiction over legislation to appropriate funds for the Federal Trade Commission.

Senate Appropriations Committee, *Subcommittee on VA, HUD, and Independent Agencies, SD-127 20510; (202) 224-7211. Christopher S. Bond, R-Mo., chair; John*

K. Mark, staff director. Internet, http://www.senate.gov/~appropriations.

Jurisdiction over legislation to appropriate funds for the Consumer Information Center of the General Services Administration, the Consumer Product Safety Commission, and the U.S. Office of Consumer Affairs.

Senate Banking, Housing, and Urban Affairs Committee, *SD-534 20510; (202) 224-7391. Fax, (202) 224-5137. Alfonse M. D'Amato, R-N.Y., chair; Howard Menell, staff director. Internet, http://www.senate.gov/~banking.*

Jurisdiction over legislation on consumer protection, including the Community Reinvestment Act and the Fair Credit Reporting Act, and regulatory oversight issues.

Senate Commerce, Science, and Transportation Committee, *SD-508 20510; (202) 224-5115. Fax, (202) 224-1259. John McCain, R-Ariz., chair; John Raidt, staff director. Internet, http://www.senate.gov/~commerce.*

Jurisdiction over regulation of consumer products and services, including testing related to toxic substances. Jurisdiction over legislation related to the U.S. Fire Administration and the Building and Fire Research Laboratory of the National Institute of Standards and Technology; oversight of federal fire prevention and the Earthquake Hazards Reduction Act.

Senate Commerce, Science, and Transportation Committee, *Subcommittee on Consumer Affairs, Foreign Commerce, and Tourism, SH-425 (mailing address: SD-508, Washington, DC 20510); (202) 224-5183. Fax, (202) 228-0326. John Ashcroft, R-Mo., chair, (202) 224-6154; Kevin Sabo, senior counsel. Internet, http://www.senate.gov/~commerce.*

Jurisdiction over legislation on the Federal Trade Commission, the Consumer Product Safety Commission, the Food and Drug Administration, the National Highway Traffic Safety Administration, and the U.S. Fire Administration. Jurisdiction over product safety and liability; flammable products; insurance; and labeling and packaging legislation, including advertising and packaging of tobacco products and alcohol beverages.

Senate Labor and Human Resources Committee, *SD-428 20510; (202) 224-5375. Fax, (202) 224-6510. James M. Jeffords, R-Vt., chair; Mark Powden, staff director. Internet, http://www.senate.gov/~labor.*

Jurisdiction over legislation on vaccines, drug labeling and packaging, inspection and certification of fish and processed food, and the use of vitamins.

NONPROFIT

Automotive Consumer Action Program, *8400 West-park Dr., McLean, VA 22102; (703) 821-7144. Fax, (703) 821-7075. Lesley J. Hardesty, national manager. Press, (703) 827-7407.*

Third-party mediation program that promotes national standards and procedures in resolving auto dealer/manufacturer and consumer disputes.

Center for Auto Safety, *2001 S St. N.W., #410 20009; (202) 328-7700. Clarence M. Ditlow III, executive director. Internet, http://www.essential.org/orgs/cas.*

Public interest organization that receives written consumer complaints against auto manufacturers; monitors federal agencies responsible for regulating and enforcing auto and highway safety rules.

Citizen Action, *1730 Rhode Island Ave. N.W., #403 20036; (202) 775-1580. Fax, (202) 296-4054. Ira Arlook, executive director. Internet, http://www.citizenaction.org.*

Coalition of statewide citizens' groups working for state and national legislative reform. Interests include health care, insurance reform, global warming, energy policy, and toxics right-to-know. Monitors legislation and regulations.

Consumer Alert, *1001 Connecticut Ave. N.W., #1128 20036; (202) 467-5809. Fax, (202) 467-5814. Frances B. Smith, executive director. Internet, info@consumeralert.org or http://www.consumeralert.org.*

Membership: individual consumers. Promotes consumer choice and economic competition to advance consumers' interests.

Consumer Federation of America, *1424 16th St. N.W., #604 20036; (202) 387-6121. Fax, (202) 265-7989. Stephen Brobeck, executive director.*

Federation of national, regional, state, and local pro-consumer organizations. Promotes consumer interests in banking, credit, and insurance; telecommunications; housing; food, drugs, and medical care; safety; energy and natural resources development; and indoor air quality.

Consumer Federation of America's Insurance Group, *1424 16th St. N.W., #604 20036; (202) 387-6121. Fax, (202) 265-7989. Robert Hunter, director.*

Public interest organization that conducts research and provides consumers with information on buying insurance. Interests include auto, homeowner, renter, and life insurance. Monitors legislation and regulations.

Consumers Union of the United States, Inc., *1666 Connecticut Ave. N.W., #310 20009-1039; (202) 462-6262.*

Fax, (202) 265-9548. Gene Kimmelman, co-director, Washington Office.

Consumer advocacy group that represents consumer interests before Congress and regulatory agencies and litigates consumer affairs cases involving the government. Interests include consumer impact of world trade. Publishes *Consumer Reports* magazine. (Headquarters in Yonkers, N.Y.)

Council of Better Business Bureaus, Inc., *4200 Wilson Blvd., #800, Arlington, VA 22203; (703) 276-0100. Fax, (703) 525-8277. James L. Bast, president. Internet, bbb@bbb.org or http://www.bbb.org.*

Membership: businesses and Better Business Bureaus in the United States and Canada. Promotes ethical business practices and truth in national advertising; mediates disputes between consumers and businesses.

National Assn. of Consumer Agency Administrators, *1010 Vermont Ave. N.W., #514 20005; (202) 347-7395. Fax, (202) 347-2563. Wendy Weinberg, executive director. Internet, nacaa@erols.com.*

Membership: federal, state, and local government consumer affairs professionals. Seeks to enhance consumer services available to the public. Acts as a clearinghouse for consumer information and legislation. Serves as liaison with federal agencies and Congress. Offers training programs, seminars, and conferences.

National Consumers League, *1701 K St. N.W., #1200 20006; (202) 835-3323. Fax, (202) 835-0747. Linda F. Golodner, president. Internet, http://www. natlconsumersleague.org.*

Citizens' interest group that engages in research and educational activities related to consumer issues. Interests include health care; child labor; food, drug, and product safety; environment; telecommunications; and financial services.

National SAFE KIDS Campaign, *1301 Pennsylvania Ave. N.W., #1000 20004; (202) 662-0600. Fax, (202) 393-2072. Heather Paul, executive director. Internet, http://www.safekids.org.*

Promotes awareness among adults that unintentional injury is the leading cause of death among children ages 14 and under. Conducts educational programs on childhood injury prevention; sponsors National SAFE KIDS Week.

Public Citizen, *1600 20th St. N.W. 20009; (202) 588-1000. Fax, (202) 588-7798. Joan Claybrook, president. Internet, http://www.citizen.org.*

Public interest consumer advocacy organization comprising the following projects: Buyers Up, Congress

Watch, Critical Mass Energy Project, Health Research Group, Litigation Group, and Global Trade Watch.

Trial Lawyers for Public Justice, *1717 Massachusetts Ave. N.W., #800 20036; (202) 797-8600. Fax, (202) 232-7203. Arthur H. Bryant, executive director. Internet, http://www.tlpj.org.*

Membership: consumer activists, trial lawyers, and public interest lawyers. Litigates to influence corporate and government decisions about products or activities adversely affecting health or safety. Interests include toxic torts, environmental protection, civil rights and civil liberties, workers' safety, consumer protection, and the preservation of the civil justice system.

U.S. Chamber of Commerce, *Business and Government Policy, 1615 H St. N.W., #500 20062-2000; (202) 463-5500. Fax, (202) 887-3445. Randy Johnson, vice president, Labor Policy. Internet, http://www.uschamber.org.*

Monitors legislation and regulations regarding business and consumer issues, including legislation and policies affecting the Federal Trade Commission, Consumer Product Safety Commission, and other agencies.

U.S. Public Interest Research Group (USPIRG), *218 D St. S.E. 20003; (202) 546-9707. Fax, (202) 546-2461. Gene Karpinski, executive director. Internet, uspirg@pirg.org or http://www.pirg.org.*

Conducts research and advocacy on consumer and environmental issues, including banking practices, campaign finance reform, product safety, toxic waste, and safe drinking water; monitors private and governmental actions affecting consumers; supports efforts to challenge consumer fraud and illegal business practices. Serves as national office for state groups.

See also National Consumer Law Center (p. 29)

Credit Practices

See also Real Estate (chap. 12)

AGENCIES

Comptroller of the Currency *(Treasury Dept.),* **Community and Consumer Policy,** *250 E St. S.W. 20219; (202) 874-5216. Fax, (202) 874-5221. Stephen Cross, deputy comptroller.*

Develops policy for enforcing consumer laws and regulations that affect national banks, including the Truth-in-Lending, Community Reinvestment, and Equal Credit Opportunity acts.

Comptroller of the Currency *(Treasury Dept.),* **Law Dept.,** *250 E St. S.W., 8th Floor 20219; (202) 874-5200.*

Fax, (202) 874-5374. Julie L. Williams, chief counsel. Library, (202) 874-4720.

Enforces and oversees compliance by nationally chartered banks with laws prohibiting discrimination in credit transactions on the basis of sex or marital status. Enforces regulations concerning bank advertising; may issue cease-and-desist orders.

Comptroller of the Currency *(Treasury Dept.),* **Public Affairs,** *250 E St. S.W. 20219; (202) 874-4910. Fax, (202) 874-4950. Lenora Cross, acting senior deputy comptroller. Internet, http://www.occ.treas.gov.*

Advises the comptroller on relations with the media, the banking industry, Congress, and consumer and community development groups.

Federal Deposit Insurance Corp., *Compliance and Consumer Affairs, 1730 Pennsylvania Ave., 7th Floor 20429; (202) 942-3100. Fax, (202) 942-3427. Carmen Sullivan, director. Toll-free, (800) 934-3342. TDD, (800) 925-4618. Internet, consumer@fdic.gov.*

Coordinates and monitors complaints filed by consumers against federally insured state banks that are not members of the Federal Reserve System; handles complaints concerning truth-in-lending and other fair credit provisions, including charges of discrimination on the basis of sex or marital status; responds to general banking inquiries; answers questions on deposit insurance coverage.

Federal Deposit Insurance Corp., *Supervision, 550 17th St. N.W. 20429; (202) 898-8510. Fax, (202) 898-3638. Nicholas J. Ketcha Jr., director.*

Examines and supervises federally insured state banks that are not members of the Federal Reserve System for violations of truth-in-lending and other fair credit provisions.

Federal Reserve System, *Consumer and Community Affairs, 20th and C Sts. N.W. 20551-0001; (202) 452-2631. Fax, (202) 872-4995. Griffith L. Garwood, director. Complaints, (202) 452-3693.*

Receives consumer complaints concerning truth-in-lending, fair credit billing, equal credit opportunity, electronic fund transfer, home mortgage disclosure, consumer leasing, and advertising; receives complaints about unregulated practices; refers complaints to district banks. The Federal Reserve monitors enforcement of fair lending laws with regard to state-chartered banks that are members of the Federal Reserve System.

Federal Trade Commission, *Credit Practices, 601 Pennsylvania Ave. N.W. 20580; (202) 326-3224. Fax, (202)*

326-2558. *David Medine, associate director. TDD, (202) 326-2502.*

Enforces truth-in-lending and fair credit billing provisions for creditors not handled by other agencies, such as retail stores and small loan companies; enforces the Fair Credit Reporting Act, which protects consumers from unfair credit ratings and practices; enforces the Fair Debt Collection Practices Act, Electronic Funds Transfer Act, Equal Credit Opportunity Act, Consumer Leasing Act, Holder in Due Course Rule, and Credit Practices Rule.

Justice Dept., *Civil Division, 1331 Pennsylvania Ave., #950N 20004; (202) 307-0066. Fax, (202) 514-8742. Eugene M. Thirolf, director, Consumer Litigation.*

Files suits to enforce the Truth-in-Lending Act and other federal statutes protecting consumers, generally upon referral by client agencies.

National Credit Union Administration, *Examination and Insurance, 1775 Duke St., Alexandria, VA 22314-3428; (703) 518-6360. Fax, (703) 518-6499. David M. Marquis, director. Toll-free investment hotline, (800) 755-5999.*

Oversees and enforces compliance by federally chartered credit unions with the Truth-in-Lending Act, the Equal Credit Opportunity Act, and other federal statutes protecting consumers.

Office of Thrift Supervision *(Treasury Dept.), Consumer Programs, 1700 G St. N.W., 6th Floor 20552; (202) 906-6237. Fax, (202) 906-6326. Gilda Morse, manager. Consumer complaints, (800) 842-6929.*

Receives and processes complaints filed against savings and loan institutions, including charges of false and deceptive advertising and of discrimination against minorities and women.

Small Business Administration, *Civil Rights Compliance, 409 3rd St. S.W., #6400 20416; (202) 205-6751. Fax, (202) 205-7580. Carol L. Walker, deputy chief. TDD, (202) 205-7150.*

Reviews complaints against the Small Business Administration by recipients of its assistance in cases of alleged discrimination in credit transactions; monitors recipients for civil rights compliance.

NONPROFIT

American Bankers Assn., *Communications, 1120 Connecticut Ave. N.W. 20036; (202) 663-7501. Fax, (202) 296-9258. Virginia Dean, executive director. Library, (202) 663-5513. Internet, http://www.aba.com.*

Provides information on a wide range of banking issues and financial management. Library open to the public by appointment.

American Financial Services Assn., *919 18th St. N.W., #300 20006; (202) 296-5544. Fax, (202) 223-0321. Randolph Lively, president. Internet, http://www. americanfinsvcs.com.*

Membership: consumer installment credit industry including consumer finance, sales finance, and industrial banking companies. Conducts research; provides consumer finance education. Monitors legislation and regulations.

National Retail Federation, *325 7th St. N.W., #1000 20004-2802; (202) 783-7971. Fax, (202) 737-2849. Tracy Mullin, president. Internet, nrf@mcimail.com or http:// www.nrf.com.*

Membership: national and state associations of retailers and major retail corporations. Provides information on credit, truth-in-lending laws, and other fair credit practices.

Fire Prevention and Control

See also Caucuses (chap. 20); Clothing and Textiles (chap. 5)

AGENCIES

Consumer Product Safety Commission, *Hazard Identification and Reduction, 4330 East-West Hwy., #702, Bethesda, MD 20814; (301) 504-0554. Fax, (301) 504-0407. Ronald L. Medford, assistant executive director.*

Proposes, evaluates, and develops standards and test procedures for safety and fire resistance in accordance with the Flammable Fabrics Act and the Federal Hazardous Substances Act. Reports injuries resulting from use of products.

Federal Emergency Management Agency, *National Fire Academy, 16825 S. Seton Ave., Emmitsburg, MD 21727-8998; (301) 447-1117. Fax, (301) 447-1173. Denis Onieal, superintendent. Internet, http://www.fema.gov/ netc/usfa.htm.*

Trains fire officials and related professionals in fire prevention and management, current firefighting technologies, and the administration of fire prevention organizations.

Forest Service *(Agriculture Dept.), Fire and Aviation Management, 201 14th St. S.W. (mailing address: P.O. Box 96090, Washington, DC 20090-6090); (202) 205-1483. Fax, (202) 205-1272. Mary Jo Lavin, director.*

Responsible for aviation and fire management programs, including fire control planning and prevention, suppression of fires, and the use of prescribed fires. Provides state foresters with financial and technical assistance for fire protection in forests and on rural lands.

National Institute of Standards and Technology *(Commerce Dept.), Building and Fire Research Laboratory, Route I-270 and Quince Orchard Rd., Gaithersburg, MD 20899; (301) 975-5900. Fax, (301) 975-4032. Richard N. Wright, director. Library, (301) 975-6859. Internet, http://www.bfrl.nist.gov.*

Conducts basic and applied research on fire and fire resistance of construction materials; develops testing methods, standards, design concepts, and technologies for fire protection and prevention.

National Institute of Standards and Technology *(Commerce Dept.), Fire Safety Engineering, Route I-270 and Quince Orchard Rd., Gaithersburg, MD 20899; (301) 975-6863. Fax, (301) 975-4052. David D. Evans, chief.*

Conducts research on fire safety. Develops models to measure the behavior and mitigate the impact of large-scale fires. Operates the Fire Research Information Service and a large-scale fire test facility.

National Institute of Standards and Technology *(Commerce Dept.), Fire Science, Route I-270 and Quince Orchard Rd., Bldg. 224, #B250, Gaithersburg, MD 20899; (301) 975-6864. Fax, (301) 975-4052. Richard G. Gann, chief.*

Conducts research on fire and metrology. Studies smoke components of flames, the burning of polymeric materials, and fire detection and suppression systems.

Occupational Safety and Health Administration *(Labor Dept.), Safety Standards, 200 Constitution Ave. N.W., #N3605 20210; (202) 219-8061. Fax, (202) 219-7477. John F. Martonik, acting director.*

Administers regulations for fire safety standards; sponsors programs for maritime, fire protection, construction, mechanical, and electrical industries.

U.S. Fire Administration *(Federal Emergency Management Agency), 16825 S. Seton Ave., Emmitsburg, MD 21727; (301) 447-1018. Fax, (301) 447-1270. Carrye B. Brown, administrator. Internet, http://www.usfa.fema.gov.*

Conducts research and collects, analyzes, and disseminates data on combustion, fire prevention, firefighter safety, and the management of fire prevention organizations; studies and develops arson prevention programs and fire prevention codes; maintains the National Fire Data System.

NONPROFIT

International Assn. of Fire Chiefs, *4025 Fair Ridge Dr., Fairfax, VA 22033-2868; (703) 273-0911. Fax, (703) 273-9363. Garry L. Briese, executive director. Internet, iafchq@iafc.org or http://www.iafc.org.*

Membership: firefighting chiefs and managers. Conducts research on fire control; testifies before congressional committees. Monitors legislation and regulations affecting fire safety codes.

International Assn. of Fire Fighters, *1750 New York Ave. N.W., 3rd Floor 20006; (202) 737-8484. Fax, (202) 737-8418. Alfred K. Whitehead, president. Internet, http://www.iaff.org.*

Membership: more than 225,000 professional fire fighters and emergency medical personnel. Assists members with contract negotiation and grievances; conducts training programs and workshops. Monitors legislation and regulations. (Affiliated with the AFL-CIO and the Canadian Labour Congress.)

National Fire Protection Assn., *1110 N. Glebe Rd., #560, Arlington, VA 22201; (703) 516-4346. Fax, (703) 516-4350. Anthony R. O'Neill, vice president, Government Affairs. Internet, wdc@nfpa.org.*

Membership: individuals and organizations interested in fire protection. Develops and updates fire protection codes and standards; sponsors technical assistance programs; collects fire data statistics. Monitors legislation and regulations. (Headquarters in Quincy, Mass.)

Labeling and Packaging

See also Food and Nutrition (chap. 2); Medical Devices and Technology (chap. 11); Pharmaceuticals (chap. 11); Tobacco (this chapter)

AGENCIES

Consumer Product Safety Commission, *Hazard Identification and Reduction, 4330 East-West Hwy., #702, Bethesda, MD 20814; (301) 504-0554. Fax, (301) 504-0407. Ronald L. Medford, assistant executive director.*

Establishes labeling and packaging regulations. Develops standards in accordance with the Poison Prevention Packaging Act, the Federal Hazardous Substances Act, and the Consumer Products Safety Act.

Federal Trade Commission, *Consumer Protection, 6th and Pennsylvania Ave. N.W., #466H 20580; (202) 326-3238. Fax, (202) 326-3799. Joan Z. Bernstein, director. Internet, http://www.ftc.gov.*

Enforces labeling acts for textile, wool, and fur fiber products and for energy appliances; enforces packaging and labeling acts requiring identification of the manufacturer and listing of correct weight and other identifying information for most products, excluding food, drugs, and cosmetics.

Food and Drug Administration *(Health and Human Services Dept.), Center for Food Safety and Applied Nutrition,* 200 C St. S.W. 20204; (202) 205-4850. Fax, (202) 205-5025. Fred R. Shank, director. Press, (202) 205-4241. TDD, (202) 205-4863. Internet, http://vm.cfsan.da.gov.

Develops and enforces labeling regulations for foods (except meat and poultry but including fish) and cosmetics; develops and enforces standards on form and fill of packaging for foods and cosmetics; develops and enforces safety regulations for food and cosmetic packaging materials; recommends action to Justice Dept.

Food and Drug Administration *(Health and Human Services Dept.), Drug Marketing, Advertising, and Communications,* 5600 Fishers Lane, HFD-40, #17B-20, Rockville, MD 20857; (301) 827-2828. Fax, (301) 594-6771. Minnie Baylor-Henry, director. Internet, http://www.fda.gov/cder.

Monitors prescription drug advertising and labeling; investigates complaints; conducts market research on health care communications and drug issues.

Food Safety and Inspection Service *(Agriculture Dept.),* 1400 Independence Ave. S.W., #331E 20250; (202) 720-7025. Fax, (202) 205-0158. Thomas J. Billy, administrator. Press, (202) 720-9113. Consumer inquiries, (800) 535-4555; in Washington, (202) 720-3333. Internet, http://www.usda.gov/fsis.

Inspects meat and poultry products and provides safe handling and labeling guidelines.

National Institute of Standards and Technology *(Commerce Dept.), Weights and Measures,* 820 W. Diamond St., #223, Gaithersburg, MD 20899; (301) 975-4004. Fax, (301) 926-0647. Gilbert M. Ugiansky, chief, (301) 975-4005.

Promotes uniform standards among the states for packaging and labeling products and for measuring devices, including scales and commercial measurement instruments; advises manufacturers on labeling and packaging laws and on measuring device standards.

NONPROFIT

Flexible Packaging Assn., 1090 Vermont Ave. N.W., #500 20005-4960; (202) 842-3880. Fax, (202) 842-3841. Glenn E. Braswell, president. Internet, fpa@flexpack.org.

Membership: companies that supply or manufacture flexible packaging. Conducts programs to teach students practical applications of science and design; coordinates programs on reducing solid waste for schools.

Glass Packaging Institute, 1627 K St. N.W., #800 20006; (202) 887-4850. Fax, (202) 785-5377. Joseph Cattaneo, executive vice president. Internet, http://www.gpi.org.

Membership: manufacturers of glass containers and their suppliers. Administers the Nickel Solution Trust with interests in recycling, legislation and government regulations, and research affecting glass packaging. Promotes conservation of natural resources in the industry.

Packaging Machinery Manufacturers Institute, 4350 N. Fairfax Dr., #600, Arlington, VA 22203; (703) 243-8555. Fax, (703) 243-8556. Chuck Yuska, president. Internet, http://www.packexpo.com.

Membership: manufacturers of packaging and packaging-related converting machinery. Provides industry information and statistics; offers educational programs to members.

Privacy

See also Privacy Act (appendix)

AGENCIES

Federal Communications Commission, *Common Carrier Bureau Network Services,* 2000 M St. N.W., #235 20554; (202) 418-2320. Fax, (202) 418-2345. Geraldine Matise, chief.

Establishes federal policy governing interstate caller identification services.

Federal Trade Commission, *Credit Practices,* 601 Pennsylvania Ave. N.W. 20580; (202) 326-3224. Fax, (202) 326-2558. David Medine, associate director.

Enforces the Fair Credit Reporting Act, which requires credit bureaus to furnish correct and complete information to businesses evaluating credit, insurance, or job applications.

Office of Management and Budget *(Executive Office of the President), Information Policy and Technology,* 725 17th St. N.W., #10236 20503; (202) 395-3785. Fax, (202) 395-5167. Bruce W. McConnell, chief.

Oversees implementation of the Privacy Act of 1974. Issues guidelines and regulations.

CONGRESS

House Judiciary Committee, *Subcommittee on the Constitution,* 362 Ford Bldg. 20515; (202) 226-7680. Fax, (202) 225-3746. Charles T. Canady, R-Fla., chair; Keri Folmar, counsel. Internet, http://www.house.gov/judiciary.

Jurisdiction over legislation on the release of personal information by government agencies.

Senate Judiciary Committee, *Subcommittee on the Constitution, Federalism, and Property Rights, SD-164 20510; (202) 224-8081. John Ashcroft, R-Mo., chair; David Miller, chief counsel. Internet, http://www.senate.gov/ committee/judiciary.html.*

Jurisdiction over legislation on the release of personal information by government agencies.

NONPROFIT

American Civil Liberties Union, *Privacy and Technology, 122 Maryland Ave. N.E. 20002; (202) 544-1681. Fax, (202) 546-0738. Laura W. Murphy, director, Washington Office.*

Studies the ways in which technology affects privacy. Interests include the Privacy Act of 1974, telecommunications, video and library lists, credit and medical records, criminal justice systems, drug testing, DNA database security, and patient confidentiality. (Headquarters in New York.)

American Society for Industrial Security, *1655 N. Fort Myer Dr., #1200, Arlington, VA 22209-3198; (703) 522-5800. Fax, (703) 243-4954. Michael Stack, executive director. Internet, http://www.asisonline.org.*

Membership: security professionals worldwide. Interests include all aspects of security, with emphases on counterterrorism, computer security, privacy issues, government security, and the availability of job-related information for employers determining an employee's suitability for employment.

Assn. of Direct Response Fundraising Counsel, *1612 K St. N.W., #510 20006-2802; (202) 293-9640. Fax, (202) 887-9699. Robert S. Tigner, general counsel. Internet, adrfco@aol.com.*

Membership: businesses in the direct response fundraising industry. Establishes standards of ethical practice in such areas as ownership of direct mail donor lists and mandatory disclosures by fundraising counsel. Educates nonprofit organizations and the public on direct mail fundraising.

Center for Democracy and Technology, *1634 Eye St. N.W., #1100 20006; (202) 637-9800. Fax, (202) 637-0968. Jerry Berman, executive director. Internet, info@cdt.org or http://www.cdt.org.*

Promotes civil liberties and democratic values in new computer and communications media. Interests include free speech, privacy, freedom of information, electronic commerce, and design of the information infrastructure. Monitors legislation and regulations.

Communications Workers of America, *501 3rd St. N.W. 20001; (202) 434-1100. Fax, (202) 434-1279.*

Morton Bahr, president. Internet, http://www. cwa-union.org.

Membership: telecommunications, broadcast, and printing and publishing workers. Opposes electronic monitoring of productivity, eavesdropping by employers, and misuse of drug and polygraph tests.

Consumers Union of the United States, *1666 Connecticut Ave. N.W., #310 20009; (202) 462-6262. Fax, (202) 265-9548. Mark Silbergeld, director, Washington Office.*

Consumer advocacy group active in protecting the privacy of consumers. Interests include credit report accuracy. (Headquarters in Yonkers, N.Y.)

Direct Marketing Assn., *1111 19th St. N.W., #1100 20036; (202) 955-5030. Fax, (202) 955-0085. Jerry Cerasale, senior vice president, Government Affairs. Internet, http://www.the-dma.org.*

Membership: telemarketers; users, creators, and producers of direct mail; and suppliers to the industry. Evaluates direct marketing methods that make use of personal consumer information. Offers free service whereby consumers may remove their names from national mailing and telephone marketing lists. (Headquarters in New York.)

Electronic Privacy Information Center, *666 Pennsylvania Ave. S.E., #301 20003; (202) 544-9240. Fax, (202) 547-5482. Marc Rotenberg, director. Internet, info@epic.org or http://www.epic.org.*

Conducts research and conferences on domestic and international civil liberties issues, including privacy, information access, computer security, and encryption; litigates cases. Monitors legislation and regulations. (Affiliated with the Fund for Constitutional Government.)

National Assn. of State Utility Consumer Advocates, *1133 15th St. N.W., #550 20005; (202) 727-3908. Fax, (202) 727-3911. Charles Acquard, executive director. Internet, nasuca@nasuca.org or http://www.nasuca.org.*

Membership: public advocate offices authorized by states to represent ratepayer interests before state and federal utility regulatory commissions. Supports privacy protection for telephone customers.

National Consumers League, *1701 K St. N.W., #1200 20006; (202) 835-3323. Fax, (202) 835-0747. Linda F. Golodner, president. Internet, http://www. natlconsumersleague.org.*

Citizens' interest group concerned with privacy rights of consumers. Interests include credit and financial records, medical records, direct marketing, telecommunications, and workplace privacy.

U.S. Public Interest Research Group (USPIRG), *218 D St. S.E. 20003; (202) 546-9707. Fax, (202) 546-2461. Gene Karpinski, executive director. Internet, uspirg@pirg. org or http://www.pirg.org.*

Coordinates grassroots efforts to advance consumer protection laws. Works for the protection of privacy rights, particularly in the area of fair credit reporting.

See also Information Industry Assn. (p. 87)

Product Safety/Testing

AGENCIES

Consumer Product Safety Commission, *4330 East-West Hwy., Bethesda, MD 20814; (301) 504-0990. Fax, (301) 504-0281. Ann Brown, chair. Information, (301) 504-0580. Library, (301) 504-0044. TDD, (800) 638-8270. Locator, (301) 504-0100. Product safety hotline, (800) 638-2772. Internet, info@cpsc.gov or http://www.cpsc.gov.*

Establishes and enforces product safety standards; collects data; studies causes and prevention of product-related injuries; identifies hazardous products and recalls them from the marketplace. Library open to the public.

Consumer Product Safety Commission, *Compliance, 4330 East-West Hwy., Bethesda, MD; (301) 504-0621. Fax, (301) 504-0359. Alan H. Schoem, director.*

Identifies and acts on any defective consumer product already in distribution; conducts surveillance and enforcement programs to ensure industry compliance with existing safety standards; works to ensure that products imported to the United States comply with existing safety standards; conducts enforcement litigation. Participates in developing standards to ensure that the final result is enforceable; monitors recall of defective products and issues warnings to consumers when appropriate.

Consumer Product Safety Commission, *Engineering Sciences, 4330 East-West Hwy., Bethesda, MD; (301) 504-0504. Fax, (301) 504-0533. Andrew G. Stadnik, associate executive director.*

Develops and evaluates consumer product safety standards, test methods, performance criteria, design specifications, and quality standards; conducts and evaluates engineering tests. Collects scientific and technical data to determine potential hazards of consumer products.

Consumer Product Safety Commission, *Epidemiology and Health Sciences, 4330 East-West Hwy., Bethesda, MD 20814; (301) 504-0957. Fax, (301) 504-0079. Mary Ann Danello, associate executive director.*

Collects data on consumer product-related hazards and potential hazards; determines the frequency, severity, and distribution of various types of injuries and investigates their causes; assesses the effects of product safety standards and programs on consumer injuries; conducts epidemiological studies and research in the field of consumer product-related injuries.

National Injury Information Clearinghouse *(Consumer Product Safety Commission), 4330 East-West Hwy., Bethesda, MD; (301) 504-0424. Fax, (301) 504-0124. Ann Montalbano, director. Fax-on-demand, (301) 504-0051. To report consumer product-related accidents or injuries, (800) 638-2772.*

Analyzes types and frequency of injuries resulting from consumer and recreational products. Collects injury information from consumer complaints, investigations, coroners' reports, death certificates, newspaper clippings, and statistically selected hospital emergency rooms nationwide.

NONPROFIT

American Academy of Pediatrics, *601 13th St. N.W., #400N 20005; (202) 347-8600. Fax, (202) 393-6137. Jackie Noyes, director. Toll-free, (800) 336-5475. Internet, kids1st@aap.org or http://www.aap.org.*

Promotes legislation and regulations concerning child health and safety. Committee on Injury and Poison Prevention drafts policy statements and publishes information on toy safety, poisons, and other issues that affect children and adolescents. (Headquarters in Elk Grove Village, Ill.)

Cosmetic Ingredient Review, *1101 17th St. N.W., #310 20036-4702; (202) 331-0651. Fax, (202) 331-1969. F. Alan Andersen, director. Internet, cirinfo@ctfa-cir.org or http:// www.ctfa-cir.org.*

Voluntary self-regulatory program funded by the Cosmetic, Toiletry, and Fragrance Assn. Reviews and evaluates published and unpublished data to assess the safety of cosmetic ingredients.

Product Liability Alliance, *1725 K St. N.W. 20006; (202) 872-0885. Fax, (202) 296-5940. James A. Anderson Jr., vice president, Government Relations.*

Membership: manufacturers, product sellers and their insurers, and trade associations. Promotes enactment of federal product liability tort reform legislation.

Product Liability Coordinating Committee, *1001 19th St. North, #800, Arlington, VA 22209; (703) 276-5045. Fax, (703) 276-5166. Pat Rowland, executive director.*

Membership: major corporations. Represents members' views concerning reform of national product liability legislation.

Tobacco

See also Caucuses (chap. 20); Commodities/Farm Produce (chap. 2)

AGENCIES

Bureau of Alcohol, Tobacco, and Firearms *(Treasury Dept.), Field Operations,* 650 Massachusetts Ave. N.W., #8100 20226; (202) 927-7970. Fax, (202) 927-7756. Andrew L. Vita, assistant director. Information, (202) 927-7777. Press, (202) 927-9510. Internet, http://www.atf. treas.gov.

Enforces and administers revenue laws relating to tobacco.

Centers for Disease Control and Prevention *(Health and Human Services Dept.), Smoking and Health/Liaison,* 200 Independence Ave. S.W., #317B 20201; (202) 205-8500. Fax, (202) 205-8313. Michele Chang, acting associate director, Liaison Office. Internet, http://www.cdc. gov/tobacco.

Produces and issues the surgeon general's annual report on smoking and health; conducts public information and education programs on smoking and health. Conducts epidemiological studies, surveys, and analyses on tobacco use. Serves as liaison between governmental and nongovernmental organizations that work on tobacco initiatives. (Headquarters in Atlanta.)

Federal Trade Commission, *Advertising Practices,* 601 Pennsylvania Ave. N.W., #S4002 20580; (202) 326-3090. Fax, (202) 326-3259. C. Lee Peeler, associate director.

Regulates advertising of tobacco products under the Federal Cigarette Labeling and Advertising Act and the Comprehensive Smokeless Tobacco Health Education Act. Regulates labeling and advertising of tobacco products; administers health warnings on packages; monitors and tests claims on tobacco products for validity. Works with the Justice Dept. in enforcing the ban on tobacco advertising in the broadcast media; investigates deceptive claims and violations of laws and may refer violations to the Justice Dept. for criminal prosecution.

Food and Drug Administration *(Health and Human Services Dept.),* 5600 Fishers Lane, Rockville, MD 20857; (301) 827-2410. Fax, (301) 443-3100. Michael Friedman, deputy commissioner. Information, (301) 443-3170. Press, (301) 827-6242. Internet, http://www.fda.gov.

Considers nicotine an addictive drug and issues regulations on the advertising and sale of tobacco products,

especially to minors. Regulates other products containing nicotine, such as skin patches and chewing gum, which are designed to help people stop smoking. Library open to the public.

NONPROFIT

Action on Smoking and Health, *2013 H St. N.W. 20006; (202) 659-4310. Fax, (202) 833-3921. John F. Banzhaf III, executive director. Internet, http://ash.org.*

Educational and legal organization that works to ensure protection of nonsmokers from cigarette smoking; provides information about smoking hazards and nonsmokers' rights.

Bakery, Confectionery, and Tobacco Workers International, *10401 Connecticut Ave., Kensington, MD 20895; (301) 933-8600. Fax, (301) 946-8452. Frank Hurt, president.*

Membership: approximately 120,000 workers from the bakery and tobacco industries. Helps members negotiate pay, benefits, and better working conditions; conducts training programs and workshops. Monitors legislation and regulations. (Affliated with the AFL-CIO.)

National Center for Tobacco-Free Kids, *1707 L St. N.W., #800 20036; (202) 296-5469. Fax, (202) 296-5427. William D. Novelli, president. Toll-free, (800) 284-5437. Internet, http://www.tobaccofreekids.org.*

Seeks to reduce tobacco use by children through public policy change and educational programs. Provides technical assistance to state and local programs.

National Smokers Alliance, *901 N. Washington St., #400, Alexandria, VA 22314; (703) 739-1324. Fax, (703) 739-1328. Thomas Humber, president. Toll-free, (800) 224-3322. Internet, http://www.spcakup.org.*

Membership: adult smokers. Promotes accommodation of smokers and nonsmokers in public places and at work; opposes discrimination against smokers, government-imposed smoking bans, and excessive taxation and regulation of tobacco products.

🏛 PHILANTHROPY, PUBLIC SERVICE, AND VOLUNTARISM

See also Political Advocacy (chap. 20)

AGENCIES

AmeriCorps *(Corporation for National Service),* 1201 New York Ave. N.W. 20525; (202) 606-5000. Fax, (202)

565-2784. Vacant, executive director. TDD, (202) 565-2799. Volunteer recruiting information, (800) 942-2677. Internet, http://www.cns.gov/americorps.html.

Provides Americans age 17 or older with opportunities to serve their communities on a full- or part-time basis. Participants work in the areas of education, public safety, human needs, and the environment and earn education awards for college or vocational training.

AmeriCorps *(Corporation for National Service), National Civilian Community Corps, 1201 New York Ave. N.W. 20525; (202) 606-5000. Fax, (202) 565-2792. Andrew Chambers, director. TDD, (202) 565-2799. Volunteer recruiting information, (800) 942-2677.*

Provides a residential service and leadership program for young men and women of all social, economic, and educational backgrounds. Works to restore and preserve the environment. Members provide intensive disaster relief, fight forest fires, and restore homes and habitats after natural disasters.

AmeriCorps *(Corporation for National Service), Volunteers in Service to America (VISTA), 1201 New York Ave. N.W., 9th Floor 20525; (202) 606-5000. Fax, (202) 565-2789. Diana London, deputy director. Volunteer recruiting information, (800) 942-2677; TDD, (800) 833-3722. Internet, http://www.cns.gov/americorps/ac_vista. html.*

Assigns full-time volunteers to public and private nonprofit organizations to alleviate poverty in local communities. Volunteers receive stipends.

Corporation for National Service, *1201 New York Ave. N.W. 20525; (202) 606-5000. Fax, (202) 565-2784. Harris L. Wofford, chief executive officer; Shirley Sagawa, executive director. TDD, (202) 565-2799. Volunteer recruiting information, (800) 942-2677. Internet, http://www.cns.gov.*

Independent corporation that administers federally sponsored domestic volunteer programs to provide disadvantaged citizens with services. Engages Americans of all ages and backgrounds in community-based service. Addresses U.S. education, human, public safety, and environmental needs. Works to foster civic responsibility and provide educational opportunity for those who make a substantial commitment to service. Programs include AmeriCorps, AmeriCorps-VISTA (Volunteers in Service to America), AmeriCorps-NCCC (National Civilian Community Corps), Learn and Serve America, and the National Senior Service Corps.

Internal Revenue Service *(Treasury Dept.), Employee Plans and Exempt Organizations, 1111 Constitution Ave. N.W., #1311 20224; (202) 622-6720. Fax, (202) 622-6873. Evelyn Petschek, assistant commissioner.*

Provides rules for the uniform interpretation and application of federal tax laws affecting tax-exempt organizations and private foundations.

Learn and Serve America *(Corporation for National Service), 1201 New York Ave. N.W. 20525; (202) 606-5000. Fax, (202) 565-2787. Susan Stroud, director. TDD, (202) 565-2799. Volunteer recruiting information, (800) 942-2677.*

Coordinates school-based community service programs, including the K-12 Program, for school-age children; the Higher Education Program, for undergraduate and graduate students; and School and Community-based Programs, which support schools and nonprofits that provide school-age children with community service opportunities.

National Senior Service Corps *(Corporation for National Service), Retired and Senior Volunteer Program, Foster Grandparent Program, and Senior Companion Program, 1201 New York Ave. N.W. 20525; (202) 606-5000. Fax, (202) 565-2789. Tom Endres, director. TDD, (202) 565-2799. Volunteer recruiting information, (800) 942-2677.*

Network of programs that help older Americans find service opportunities in their communities, including the Retired and Senior Volunteer Program, which encourages older citizens to use their talents and experience in community service; the Foster Grandparent Program, which gives older citizens opportunities to work with exceptional children and children with special needs; and the Senior Companion Program, which recruits older citizens to help homebound adults, especially seniors, with special needs.

Peace Corps, *1990 K St. N.W. 20526; (202) 606-3970. Fax, (202) 606-4458. Mark D. Gearan, director; Charles R. Baquet III, deputy director. Toll-free, (800) 424-8580. Press, (202) 606-3010. Locator, (202) 606-3886. Internet, http://www.peacecorps.gov.*

Promotes world peace and mutual understanding between the United States and developing nations. Administers volunteer programs to assist developing countries in education, the environment, health, small business and urban development, and agriculture.

CONGRESS

General Accounting Office, *Health, Education, and Human Services, 441 G St. N.W. 20548; (202) 512-6806. Fax, (202) 512-5806. Richard L. Hembra, assistant comptroller general.*

Independent, nonpartisan agency in the legislative branch. Audits, analyzes, and evaluates programs of the

Corporation for National Service; makes reports available to the public.

House Appropriations Committee, *Subcommittee on VA, HUD, and Independent Agencies, H143 CAP 20515; (202) 225-3241. Jerry Lewis, R-Calif., chair; Frank Cushing, staff director. Internet, http://www.house.gov/ appropriations.*

Appropriates funds for programs of the Corporation for National Service.

House Government Reform and Oversight Committee, *Subcommittee on Human Resources, B372 RHOB 20515; (202) 225-2548. Fax, (202) 225-2382. Christopher Shays, R-Conn., chair; Larry Halloran, staff director. Internet, http://www.house.gov/reform.*

Oversight of the Corporation for National Service.

House Ways and Means Committee, *1102 LHOB 20515; (202) 225-3625. Bill Archer, R-Texas, chair; Peter Singleton, chief of staff. Internet, http://www.house.gov/ ways_means.*

Jurisdiction over legislation on tax-exempt foundations and charitable trusts.

Senate Appropriations Committee, *Subcommittee on Labor, Health and Human Services, and Education, SD-184 20510; (202) 224-7230. Arlen Specter, R-Pa., chair; Craig A. Higgins, staff director. Internet, http://www. senate.gov/~appropriations/labor.*

Jurisdiction over legislation to appropriate funds for programs of the Corporation for National Service.

Senate Finance Committee, *SD-219 20510; (202) 224-4515. Fax, (202) 224-5920. William V. Roth Jr., R-Del., chair; Lindy L. Paull, staff director. Internet, http://www. senate.gov/ finance.*

Jurisdiction over legislation on tax-exempt foundations and charitable trusts.

Senate Labor and Human Resources Committee, *SD-428 20510; (202) 224-5375. Fax, (202) 224-6510. James M. Jeffords, R-Vt., chair; Mark Powden, staff director. Internet, http://www.senate.gov/~labor.*

Oversight of the Corporation for National Service and domestic activities of the Red Cross.

NONPROFIT

See also Arts and Humanities (chap. 4); Consumer Protection (this chapter); International Trade and Development (chap. 13); Mail Rates and Classification (chap. 10); Small and Disadvantaged Business (chap. 5)

Advocacy Institute, *1707 L St. N.W., #400 20036; (202) 659-8475. Fax, (202) 659-8484. Michael Pertschuk, David Cohen, and Kathleen Sheekey, co-directors. Internet, aiinfo@advocacy.org or http://www.advocacy.org.*

Public interest organization that offers counseling and training in advocacy skills and strategies to nonprofit groups interested in such issues as civil and human rights, public health, arms control, and environmental and consumer affairs. Aids groups in making better use of resources, such as access to the media and coalition building.

Assn. of Junior Leagues International, *1319 F St. N.W., #604 20004; (202) 393-3364. Fax, (202) 393-4517. Mary Douglass, director, Washington Office.*

Educational and charitable women's organization that promotes voluntarism and works for community improvement through leadership of trained volunteers; includes leagues in Canada, Mexico, and Great Britain. Interests include children, women, domestic violence, aging, education, and child health issues. (Headquarters in New York.)

Capital Research Center, *1513 16th St. N.W. 20005; (202) 483-6900. Fax, (202) 483-6902. Terrence Scanlon, president. Internet, http://www.capitalresearch.org.*

Researches funding sources of public interest and advocacy groups; analyzes the impact these groups have on public policy; publishes findings in newsletters and reports.

Caring Institute, *228 7th St. S.E., 20003; (202) 547-4273. Fax, (202) 547-3540. Val Halamandaris, president. Internet, caringins@nmaa.org.*

Promotes selflessness and public service. Recognizes the achievements of individuals who have demonstrated a commitment to serving others. Operates the Frederick Douglass Museum and Hall of Fame for Caring Americans. Sponsors the National Caring Award and offers internships and scholarships to high school and college students.

Center for Corporate Public Involvement, *1001 Pennsylvania Ave. N.W., #500 20004-2599; (202) 624-2425. Fax, (202) 624-2319. Shawn Hausman, director.*

Membership: life and health insurance companies and associations. Encourages members to become involved in community projects and voluntarism; provides information on model programs in corporate community involvement. Interests include education, arts and culture, children's health and safety, and crime and violence prevention.

Concerned Black Men, Inc., *1511 K St. N.W., #1100 20005; (202) 783-5414. Fax, (202) 783-4842. Kelvin Glymph, president.*

Membership: African American men interested in volunteering with African American youth. Programs include a Youth Recognition Awards Banquet, an African American History Bee, Teenage Pregnancy Prevention Workshops, the Adopt-a-School Program, and the Youth Offender Outreach Project.

The Congressional Award, *379 Ford Bldg. (mailing address: P.O. Box 77440, Washington, DC 20013-8440); (202) 226-0130. Fax, (202) 226-0131. Kendall S. Hartman, national director.*

Noncompetitive program established by Congress that recognizes the achievements of young people ages 14 to 23. Participants are awarded gold, silver, and bronze medals for setting and achieving goals in four areas: volunteer public service, personal development, physical fitness, and expeditions.

Council of Better Business Bureaus, Inc., *Philanthropic Advisory Service, 4200 Wilson Blvd., #800, Arlington, VA 22203-1804; (703) 276-0100. Fax, (703) 525-8277. Bennett M. Weiner, vice president. Internet, http://www.bbb.org/about/pas.html.*

Serves as a donor information service on charities that solicit nationally or have national or international program services; issues reports on the operations of national charitable organizations; provides charities with counseling and educational materials on compliance with the standards for charitable solicitations.

Council on Foundations, *1828 L St. N.W., #300 20036; (202) 466-6512. Fax, (202) 785-3926. Dorothy Ridings, president. Internet, http://www.cof.org.*

Membership: independent community, family, and public and company-sponsored foundations; corporate giving programs; and foundations in other countries. Promotes responsible and effective philanthropy through educational programs, publications, government relations, and promulgation of a set of principles and practices for effective grant making.

Earth Share, *3400 International Dr. N.W., #2K 20008; (202) 537-7100. Fax, (202) 537-7101. Kalman Stein, president. Toll-free, (800) 875-3863. Internet, info@earthshare.org or http://www.earthshare.org.*

Federation of environmental and conservation organizations. Works with government and private payroll deduction programs to solicit contributions to member organizations for environmental research, education, and community programs. Provides information on establishing environmental giving options in the workplace.

Evangelical Council for Financial Accountability, *P.O. Box 17456 20041-0456; (703) 713-1414. Fax, (703) 713-1133. Paul D. Nelson, president. Toll-free, (800) 323-9473. Internet, webmaster@ecfa.org or http://www.ecfa.org.*

Membership: charitable, religious, and educational nonprofit organizations committed to evangelical Christianity. Assists members in making appropriate public disclosure of their financial practices and accomplishments. Certifies organizations that conform to standards of financial integrity and Christian ethics.

Foundation Center, *1001 Connecticut Ave. N.W., #938 20036; (202) 331-1400. Fax, (202) 331-1739. Patricia Pasqual, director, Washington Office. Internet, http://www.fdncenter.org.*

Publishes foundation guides. Serves as a clearinghouse on foundations and corporate giving, nonprofit management, fundraising, and grants for individuals. Provides training and seminars on fundraising and grantwriting. Operates libraries in Atlanta, Cleveland, New York, San Francisco, and Washington, D.C.; libraries open to the public. (Headquarters in New York.)

General Federation of Women's Clubs, *1734 N St. N.W. 20036-2990; (202) 347-3168. Fax, (202) 835-0246. Judith Maggrett, executive director. Internet, gfwc@gfwc.org or http://www.gfwc.org.*

Nondenominational, nonpartisan international organization of women volunteers. Interests include conservation, education, international and public affairs, and the arts.

Gifts In Kind America, *333 N. Fairfax St., Alexandria, VA 22314; (703) 836-2121. Fax, (703) 549-1481. Susan Corrigan, president. Internet, ProductDonations@giftsinkind.org or http://www.giftsinkind.org.*

Encourages corporations to donate newly manufactured products to domestic and international charities. Works with companies to develop in-kind programs, coordinates the distribution of gifts to nonprofit agencies, collects tax documentation from recipients, and conducts communitywide public relations activities to encourage product giving. Serves schools and health, recreational, housing, arts, and environmental groups.

Grantmakers in Health, *1100 Connecticut Ave. N.W., 12th Floor 20036; (202) 452-8331. Fax, (202) 452-8340. Lauren LeRoy, president. Internet, http://www.gih.org.*

Seeks to increase the capacity of private sector grantmakers to enhance public health. Fosters information exchange among grantmakers. Publications include a bulletin on current news in health and human services and the *Directory of Health Philanthropy.* (Headquarters in New York.)

Habitat for Humanity International, *1511 K St. N.W., #605 20005; (202) 628-9171. Fax, (202) 628-9169. Thomas L. Jones, managing director. Internet, public_ info@habitat.org or http://www.habitat.org.*

Ecumenical housing ministry that, with the help of volunteers, donors, and its own affiliate offices, builds affordable homes worldwide for low-income persons. (Headquarters in Americus, Ga.)

Independent Sector, *1828 L St. N.W., #1200 20036; (202) 223-8100. Fax, (202) 416-0580. Sara E. Melendez, president. Internet, http://www.indepsec.org.*

Membership: corporations, foundations, and national voluntary, charitable, and philanthropic organizations. Encourages volunteering, giving, and not-for-profit initiatives by the private sector for public causes.

Institute for Justice, *1717 Pennsylvania Ave. N.W., #200 20006; (202) 955-1300. Fax, (202) 955-1329. Chip Mellor, president. Internet, general@instituteforjustice.org or http://www.instituteforjustice.org.*

Sponsors seminars to train law students, grass-roots activists, and practicing lawyers in applying advocacy strategies in public interest litigation. Seeks to protect from arbitrary government interference free speech, private property rights, parental school choice, and economic liberty. Litigates cases.

Lutheran Volunteer Corps, *1226 Vermont Ave. N.W. 20005; (202) 387-3222. Fax, (202) 667-0037. Robert H. Holum, executive director. Internet, http://www.his. com/lvc.*

Administers volunteer program in selected U.S. cities; coordinates activities with health and social service agencies, educational institutions, and environmental groups.

National Assembly of National Voluntary Health and Social Welfare Organizations, *1319 F St. N.W., #601 20004; (202) 347-2080. Fax, (202) 393-4517. Gordon A. Raley, executive director. Internet, nassembly@ nassembly.org or http://www.nassembly.org.*

Membership: national voluntary health and human service organizations. Provides collective leadership in the areas of health and human service. Provides members' professional staff and volunteers with a forum to share information. Supports public policies, programs, and resources that advance the effectiveness of health and human service organizations and their service delivery.

National Center for Nonprofit Boards, *2000 L St. N.W., #510 20036-4907; (202) 452-6262. Fax, (202) 452-6299. Judith O'Connor, president. Internet, ncnb@ncnb.org or http://www.ncnb.org.*

Works to improve the effectiveness of nonprofit organizations by strengthening their boards of directors. Operates an information clearinghouse; publishes materials on governing nonprofit organizations; assists organizations in conducting training programs, workshops, and conferences for board members and chief executives.

National Committee for Responsive Philanthropy, *2001 S St. N.W., #620 20009; (202) 387-9177. Fax, (202) 332-5084. Robert O. Bothwell, president. Internet, ncrp@ aol.com or http://www.primenet.com/~ncrp.*

Directs philanthropic giving to benefit the socially, economically, and politically disenfranchised; advocates for groups that represent the poor, minorities, and women. Conducts research; organizes local coalitions; assists philanthropic groups in other countries. Monitors legislation and regulations.

National Society of Fund Raising Executives, *1101 King St., #700, Alexandria, VA 22314; (703) 684-0410. Fax, (703) 684-0540. Patricia F. Lewis, president. Toll-free, (800) 666-3863. Internet, http://www.nsfre.org.*

Membership: individuals who serve as fund-raising executives for nonprofit institutions or as members of counseling firms engaged in fund-raising management. Promotes ethical standards; offers workshops; certifies members; monitors legislation and regulations. NSFRE Foundation promotes philanthropy and voluntarism. Library open to the public by appointment.

Points of Light Foundation, *1737 H St. N.W. 20006; (202) 223-9186. Fax, (202) 223-9256. Robert Goodwin, president. Internet, http://www.pointsoflight.org.*

Promotes mobilization of people for volunteer community service aimed at solving social problems. Offers technical assistance, training, and information services to nonprofit organizations, public agencies, corporations, and others interested in volunteering.

Progressive Policy Institute, *518 C St. N.E. 20002; (202) 547-0001. Fax, (202) 544-5014. Will Marshall, president. Internet, info@dlcppi.org or http://www.dlcppi.org.*

Encourages civic participation in solving U.S. problems through voluntary national service, community-based institutions, and public-private partnerships.

Public Allies, *1015 18th St. N.W., #200 20036; (202) 822-1180. Fax, (202) 822-1199. Chuck J. Supple, president.*

Works in partnership with nonprofit organizations, business, and government to place young adults aged 18-30 in challenging paid positions, provide them with leadership training, and engage them in team projects that serve needs in local neighborhoods.

Support Center of Washington, *2001 O St. N.W. 20036-5955; (202) 833-0300. Fax, (202) 857-0077. Oliver Tessier, executive director. Internet, http://pobox.com/~ supportcenter.*

Works to increase the effectiveness and efficiency of nonprofit organizations by providing financial management, accounting, and fund-raising assistance. Other services include legal and tax information, marketing and resource development, and training programs.

United Way of America, *701 N. Fairfax St., Alexandria, VA 22314; (703) 836-7100. Fax, (703) 683-7840. Betty Stanley Beene, president. Internet, http://www.unitedway. org.*

Service association for independent local United Way organizations in the United States. Services include staff training; fund-raising, planning, and communications assistance; resource management; and national public service advertising.

Youth Service America, *1101 15th St. N.W., #200 20005; (202) 296-2992. Fax, (202) 296-4030. Steve Culvertson, president. Internet, info@usa.org or http://www. servenet.org.*

Advocates youth service at national, state, and local levels. Promotes opportunities for young people to be engaged in community service. Provides service and conservation corps and school- and university-based programs with technical assistance; acts as a clearinghouse on youth service.

⚖ PUBLIC INTEREST LAW

See also Civil Rights (this chapter); Consumer Protection (this chapter); Law and Justice (chap. 14)

AGENCIES

Legal Services Corp., *750 1st St. N.E., 10th Floor 20002-4250; (202) 336-8800. Fax, (202) 336-8959. John McKay, president; John Tull, vice president. Information, (202) 336-8892. Library, (202) 336-8804.*

Independent federal corporation established by Congress. Awards grants to local agencies that provide the poor with legal services. Library open to the public.

CONGRESS

House Government Reform and Oversight Committee, *Subcommittee on National Security, International Affairs, and Criminal Justice, B373 RHOB 20515; (202) 225-2577. Fax, (202) 225-1154. Dennis*

Hastert, R-Ill., chair; Robert Charles, staff director. Internet, http://www.house.gov/reform.

Oversees operations of the Legal Services Corp.

House Judiciary Committee, *Subcommittee on Commercial and Administrative Law, B353 RHOB 20515; (202) 225-2825. Fax, (202) 225-4299. George W. Gekas, R-Pa., chair; Ray Smietanka, counsel.*

Jurisdiction over legislation on legal services. Oversees the Legal Services Corp.

Senate Labor and Human Resources Committee, *SD-428 20510; (202) 224-5375. Fax, (202) 224-6510. James M. Jeffords, R-Vt., chair; Mark Powden, staff director. Internet, http://www.senate.gov/~labor.*

Legislative and oversight jurisdiction over operations of the Legal Services Corp.

NONPROFIT

Alliance for Justice, *2000 P St. N.W., #712 20036; (202) 822-6070. Fax, (202) 822-6068. Nan Aron, president. Internet, alliance@afj.org or http://www.afj.org.*

Membership: public interest lawyers and advocacy, environmental, civil rights, and consumer organizations. Promotes reform of the legal system to ensure access to the courts; monitors selection of federal judges; works to preserve the rights of nonprofit organizations to advocate on behalf of their constituents.

American Bar Assn., *Commission on Mental and Physical Disability Law, 740 15th St. N.W. 20005; (202) 662-1570. Fax, (202) 662-1032. John Parry, director. Internet, http://www.abanet.org/disability/home.html.*

Serves as a clearinghouse for information on mental and physical disability law and offers legal research services.

Bazelon Center for Mental Health Law, *1101 15th St. N.W., #1212 20005; (202) 467-5730. Fax, (202) 223-0409. Robert Berstein, director. TDD, (202) 467-4232. Internet, hn1660@handsnet.org or http://www.bazelon.org.*

Public interest law firm. Conducts test case litigation to defend rights of persons with mental disabilities. Provides legal support for legal services offices, protection and advocacy agencies, and private attorneys. Monitors legislation and regulations.

Center for Law and Education, *1875 Connecticut Ave. N.W., #510 20009-5728; (202) 986-3000. Fax, (202) 986-6648. Paul Weckstein, director. Publications, (202) 462-7688. Internet, cledc@erols.com.*

Assists local legal services programs in matters concerning education, civil rights, and provision of legal services to low-income persons; litigates some cases for low-income individuals. (Headquarters in Boston.)

Center for Law and Social Policy, *1616 P St. N.W., #150 20036; (202) 328-5141. Fax, (202) 328-5195. Alan W. Houseman, director. Information, (202) 328-5140. Internet, http://www.class.org.*

Public interest organization with expertise in law and policy affecting low-income Americans. Seeks to improve the economic conditions of low-income families with children and to secure access for persons in poverty to the civil justice system.

Center for Study of Responsive Law, *1530 P St. N.W. (mailing address: P.O. Box 19367, Washington, DC 20036); (202) 387-8030. Fax, (202) 234-5176. John Richard, administrator. Internet, http://www.csrl.org.*

Consumer interest clearinghouse that conducts research and holds conferences on public interest law. Interests include white-collar crime, the environment, occupational health and safety, the postal system, banking deregulation, insurance, freedom of information policy, and broadcasting.

Disability Rights Education and Defense Fund, *1629 K St. N.W. 20006; (202) 986-0375. Fax, (202) 775-7465. Pat Wright, director, Governmental Affairs.*

Law and policy center working to protect and advance the civil rights of people with disabilities through legislation, litigation, advocacy, and technical assistance. Educates and trains attorneys, advocates, persons with disabilities, and parents of children with disabilities. (Headquarters in Berkeley, Calif.)

Institute for Justice, *1717 Pennsylvania Ave. N.W., #200 20006; (202) 955-1300. Fax, (202) 955-1329. Chip Mellor, president. Internet, general@instituteforjustice.org or http://www.instituteforjustice.org.*

Sponsors seminars to train law students, grassroots activists, and practicing lawyers in applying advocacy strategies in public interest litigation. Seeks to protect from arbitrary government interference free speech, private property rights, parental school choice, and economic liberty. Litigates cases.

Institute for Public Representation, *600 New Jersey Ave. N.W. 20001; (202) 662-9535. Fax, (202) 662-9634. Douglas L. Parker, director. TDD, (202) 662-9538.*

Public interest law firm funded by Georgetown University Law Center that studies federal administrative law and federal court litigation. Interests include communications law, environmental protection, and disability rights.

Lawyers' Committee for Civil Rights Under Law, *1450 G St. N.W., #400 20005; (202) 662-8600. Fax, (202) 783-0857. Barbara Arnwine, executive director.*

Provides minority groups and the poor with legal assistance in such areas as voting rights, employment discrimination, education, environment, and equal access to government services and benefits.

Migrant Legal Action Program, *P.O. Box 53308 20009; (202) 462-7744. Fax, (202) 462-7914. Roger C. Rosenthal, executive director. Internet, hn1645@ handsnet.org.*

Offers support, litigation assistance, and training to local legal services groups and other organizations and private attorneys with migrant farmworker clients. Monitors legislation and regulations.

National Consumer Law Center, *1629 K St. N.W., #600 20006; (202) 986-6060. Fax, (202) 463-9462. Margot Saunders, managing attorney.*

Provides lawyers funded by the Legal Services Corp. with research and assistance; researches problems of low-income consumers and develops alternative solutions. (Headquarters in Boston.)

National Health Law Program, *1101 14th St. N.W., #405 20005; (202) 289-7661. Fax, (202) 289-7724. Lawrence Lavin, director. Internet, nhelp@healthlaw.org or http://www.healthlaw.org.*

Organization of lawyers representing the economically disadvantaged, minorities, and the elderly in issues concerning federal, state, and local health care programs. Offers technical assistance, workshops, seminars, and training for health law specialists. (Headquarters in Los Angeles.)

National Legal Aid and Defender Assn., *1625 K St. N.W., #800 20006; (202) 452-0620. Fax, (202) 872-1031. Clinton Lyons, executive director. Internet, info@nlada.org or http://www.nlada.org.*

Membership: local organizations and individuals providing indigent clients, including prisoners, with legal aid and defender services. Serves as a clearinghouse for member organizations; publishes directory of legal aid and defender programs.

National Legal Center for the Public Interest, *1000 16th St. N.W., #301 20036; (202) 296-1683. Fax, (202) 293-2118. Ernest B. Hueter, president.*

Public interest law center and information clearinghouse. Studies judicial issues and the impact of the legal system on the private sector; sponsors seminars; does not litigate cases.

Public Citizen Litigation Group, *1600 20th St. N.W.*
20009; (202) 588-7721. Fax, (202) 588-7795. David
Vladeck, director. Internet, http://www.citizen.org.

Conducts litigation for Public Citizen, a citizens'
interest group, in the areas of consumer rights,
employee rights, health and safety, government and corporate accountability, and separation of powers; represents other individuals and citizens' groups with similar
interests.

Trial Lawyers for Public Justice, *1717 Massachusetts*
Ave. N.W., #800 20036; (202) 797-8600. Fax, (202) 232-
7203. Arthur H. Bryant, executive director. Internet,
http://www.tlpj.org.

Membership organization that litigates cases involving toxic torts, environmental protection, civil rights and
liberties, consumer safety, workers' rights, and the
preservation of the civil justice system. Serves as an
information clearinghouse.

 # RELIGION AND ETHICS

See also Constitutional Law and Civil Liberties
(chap. 14); Private, Parochial, and Home Schooling
(chap. 6)

NONPROFIT

Alban Institute, *7315 Wisconsin Ave., #1250 West,*
Bethesda, MD 20814; (301) 718-4407. Fax, (301) 718-
1958. Leslie L. Buhler, executive vice president. Toll-free,
(800) 486-1318.

Nondenominational research, consulting, and educational membership organization that provides church
and synagogue congregations with support and services.
Interests include planning and growth, conflict resolution, leadership and staff training, spiritual development,
and mission and stewardship. Conducts continuing education programs.

American Assn. of Pastoral Counselors, *9504A Lee*
Hwy., Fairfax, VA 22301-2303; (703) 385-6967. Fax, (703)
352-7725. C. Roy Woodruff, executive director. Internet,
info@aapc.org or http://www.metanoia.org/aapc.

Membership: mental health professionals with training in both religion and the behavioral sciences. Nonsectarian organization that accedits pastoral counseling
centers, certifies pastoral counselors, and approves training programs.

American Baptist Churches U.S.A., *110 Maryland*
Ave. N.E., #504 20002-5694; (202) 544-3400. Fax, (202)
544-0277. Curtis Ramsey Lucas, director, Legislative Advo-
cacy.

Serves as liaison between American Baptist churches
and government organizations. Interests include immigration, foreign and military policy, human services,
employment, the environment, and civil rights. (Headquarters in Valley Forge, Pa.)

American Ethical Union, *Washington Ethical Action,*
6214 Crathie Lane, Bethesda, MD 20816-1004; (301) 229-
3759. Fax, (301) 229-2592. Herbert Blinder, director,
Washington Office. Internet, http://www.ethicalSociety.org.

Federation of ethical culture societies in the United
States. Interests include human rights, ethics, world
peace, health, welfare, education, and civil and religious
liberties. Monitors legislation and regulations. (Headquarters in New York.)

American Friends Service Committee, *1822 R St.*
N.W. 20009-1604; (202) 483-3341. Fax, (202) 232-3197.
James Matlack, director, Washington Office. Toll-free, (800)
226-9816. Internet, afscinfo@afsc.org or http://www.
afsc.org.

Independent organization affiliated with the Religious Society of Friends (Quakers) in America. Sponsors
domestic and international service, development, justice,
and peace programs. Interests include peace education;
arms control and disarmament; social and economic justice; gay and lesbian rights; racism, sexism, and civil
rights; refugees and immigration policy; crisis response
and relief efforts; and international development efforts,
especially in Central America, the Middle East, and
southern Africa. (Headquarters in Philadelphia.)

American Jewish Committee, *1156 15th St. N.W.,*
#1201 20005; (202) 785-4200. Fax, (202) 785-4115. Jason
F. Isaacson, director, Government and International
Affairs. Internet, http://www.ajc.org.

Human relations agency devoted to protecting civil
and religious rights for all people. Interests include
church-state issues, research on human behavior, Israel
and the Middle East, Jews in the former Soviet Union,
immigration, social discrimination, civil and women's
rights, employment, education, housing, and international cooperation for peace and human rights. (Headquarters in New York.)

American Jewish Congress, *2027 Massachusetts Ave.*
N.W. 20036; (202) 332-4001. Fax, (202) 387-3434. David
Harris, Washington representative. Internet, washrep@
ajcongress.org or http://www.ajcongress.org.

Jewish community relations and civil liberties organization. Seeks to combat anti-Semitism and other
forms of bigotry in employment, education, housing,

and voting. Areas of activity include church-state relations; government involvement in education; public school prayer; constitutional, minority, women's, and human rights; world Jewry; U.S. foreign policy in the Middle East; Arab investment in the United States; and the Arab boycott of Israel. Monitors legislation. (Headquarters in New York.)

American Muslim Council, *1212 New York Ave. N.W., #400 20005; (202) 789-2262. Fax, (202) 789-2550. Atif Harden, director. Internet, http://www.amermuslim.org.*

Promotes equal rights and political empowerment for Muslims in the United States. Opposes discrimination against Muslims; fosters cultural understanding and cooperation among organizations.

Americans United for Separation of Church and State, *1816 Jefferson Pl. N.W. 20036; (202) 466-3234. Fax, (202) 466-2587. Barry W. Lynn, executive director. Internet, americansunited@au.org or http://www.au.org.*

Citizens' interest group. Opposes federal and state aid to parochial schools; works to ensure religious neutrality in public schools; supports religious free exercise; initiates litigation; maintains speakers bureau. Monitors legislation and regulations.

Baptist Joint Committee on Public Affairs, *200 Maryland Ave. N.E., 3rd Floor 20002; (202) 544-4226. Fax, (202) 544-2094. James M. Dunn, executive director. Internet, http://www.bjcpa.org.*

Membership: national Baptist conventions and conferences. Conducts research and operates an information service. Interests include religious liberty, separation of church and state, First Amendment religious issues, and government regulation of religious institutions.

Baptist World Alliance, *6733 Curran St., McLean, VA 22101-6005; (703) 790-8980. Fax, (703) 893-5160. Denton Lotz, general secretary. Internet, bwa@bwanet.org or http://www.bwanet.org.*

International Baptist organization. Conducts religious teaching and works to create a better understanding among nations. Organizes development efforts and disaster relief in less developed nations. Interests include human rights and religious liberty.

B'nai B'rith International, *1640 Rhode Island Ave. N.W. 20036; (202) 857-6500. Fax, (202) 296-0638. Sidney M. Clearfield, executive vice president. Internet, http://www.bnaibrith.org.*

Provides information and coordinates political action on public policy issues important to the international Jewish community. The B'nai B'rith Youth Organization offers educational and leadership training programs for teenagers and counseling and career guidance services. Other interests include community volunteer programs, senior citizen housing, and the security and development of Israel. Partially funds the Foundation for Jewish Campus Life, which offers educational, religious, recreational, and social programs for Jewish college and university students. Operates the B'nai B'rith Klutznick National Jewish Museum.

Catholic Charities USA, *1731 King St., #200, Alexandria, VA 22314; (703) 549-1390. Fax, (703) 549-1656. Fred Kammer SJ, president. Press, (703) 549-1390. Internet, http://catholiccharitiesusa.org.*

Member agencies and institutions provide persons of all backgrounds with social services, including adoption, education, counseling, food, and housing services. National office promotes public policies that address human needs and social injustice. Provides members with advocacy and professional support, including technical assistance, training, and resource development; disseminates publications.

Catholic Information Center, *825 15th St. N.W. 20005-2203; (202) 783-2062. Fax, (202) 783-2063. L. Michael Curtin, director.*

Provides information on Roman Catholicism and the Catholic church. Offers free counseling services. Library open to the public.

Center for Judeo-Christian Values, *1003 K St. N.W., #408 20001; (202) 682-9571. Fax, (202) 682-1848. Stan DeBoe, director. Internet, office@cjcv.erols.com.*

Works to develop shared principles for building a moral society. Promotes a greater role for religion in American life; seeks to counter the influence of popular culture. Supports public policy changes to promote the values of human life, the traditional family, personal responsibility, and free expression of faith.

Christian Life Commission of the Southern Baptist Convention, *505 2nd St. N.E. 20002; (202) 547-8105. Fax, (202) 547-8165. Will Dodson, director, Government Relations.*

Public policy office of the Southern Baptist Convention. Educates churches and members about moral/political issues in U.S. government. Interests include abortion, pornography, religious liberty, First Amendment, drugs and alcohol, hunger, and race relations. (Headquarters in Nashville.)

Christian Science Committee on Publication, *910 16th St. N.W. 20006; (202) 857-0427. Fax, (202) 331-0587. Philip G. Davis, federal representative. Internet, fedrepcs@aol.com.*

Public service organization that provides information on the religious convictions and practices of Christian Scientists; maintains a speakers bureau. Monitors legislation and regulations.

Church of the Brethren, *337 North Carolina Ave. S.E. 20003; (202) 546-3202. Fax, (202) 544-5852. Heather Nolen, coordinator. Internet, washofc@aol.com or http://members.aol.com/Washofc/main.html.*

Organizes and coordinates political activities on social policy issues of concern to the church. Interests include military spending; civil rights and liberties; health care; conditions for the poor; refugees and immigrants; world hunger; conditions in the Middle East, Sudan, and Central America; and religious freedom. Sponsors seminars. (Headquarters in Elgin, Ill.)

Council of Jewish Federations, *1640 Rhode Island Ave. N.W., #500 20036; (202) 785-5900. Fax, (202) 785-7043. Diana Aviv, director, Washington Office. Internet, http:// jewishfedna.org.*

Membership: Jewish Federations, which are community organizations serving localities in the United States and Canada. Serves federations in areas of fundraising, operations, planning, and government relations; assists Jewish communities overseas. Interests include health, welfare, immigration, and human rights. (Headquarters in New York.)

Episcopal Church, *110 Maryland Ave. N.E., #309 20002; (202) 547-7300. Fax, (202) 547-4457. Tom Hart, acting director, Government Affairs. Internet, http://www.ecusa. anglican.org.*

Informs Congress, the executive branch, and governmental agencies about the actions and resolutions of the Episcopal church. Monitors legislation and regulations. (Headquarters in New York.)

Episcopal Peace Fellowship, *1317 G St. N.W. (mailing address: P.O. Box 28156, Washington, DC 20038-8156); (202) 783-3380. Fax, (202) 393-3695. Mary H. Miller, executive secretary. Internet, epf@igc.apc.org or http://www.nonviolence.org/epf.*

Organizes Episcopalians committed to the biblical concept of peace. Supports conscientious objectors who resist military service and who refuse to pay taxes that support the military; seeks to end the death penalty. Maintains network of local chapters; serves as a clearinghouse for peace education materials.

Ethics and Public Policy Center, *Religion and Society Program, 1015 15th St. N.W., #900 20005; (202) 682-1200. Fax, (202) 408-0632. Elliott Abrams, president. Internet, ethics@eppc.org.*

Research organization that analyzes the public policy positions of organized religions.

Evangelical Lutheran Church in America, *Lutheran Office for Governmental Affairs, 122 C St. N.W., #125 20001; (202) 783-7507. Fax, (202) 783-7502. Russel Siler, director, Governmental Affairs. Internet, loga@ecunet.org or http://elca.org.*

Monitors legislation and regulations on public policy issues of interest to the Lutheran church. (Headquarters in Chicago.)

Friends Committee on National Legislation, *245 2nd St. N.E. 20002-5795; (202) 547-6000. Fax, (202) 547-6019. Joe Volk, executive secretary. Recorded information, (202) 547-4343. Internet, fcnl@igc.apc.org or http://www. fas.org/pub/gen/fcnl.*

Advocates for economic justice, world disarmament, international cooperation, and religious rights. Advocates on behalf of Native Americans in such areas as treaty rights, self-determination, and U.S. trust responsibilities. Conducts research and education activities through the FCNL Education Fund. Opposes the death penalty. Monitors national legislation and policy. Affiliated with the Religious Society of Friends (Quakers).

General Board of Church and Society of the United Methodist Church, *100 Maryland Ave. N.E. 20002; (202) 488-5600. Fax, (202) 488-5619. Thom White Wolf Fassett, general secretary. Internet, http://www.umc-gbcs. org.*

Conducts research on social, political, and economic issues. Interests include social welfare, the environment, civil liberties, criminal justice, and foreign policy; assists member churches.

General Conference of Seventh-day Adventists, *12501 Old Columbia Pike, Silver Spring, MD 20904-6600; (301) 680-6000. Fax, (301) 680-6090. Robert S. Folkenberg, president. Internet, http://www.adventist.org.*

World headquarters of the Seventh-day Adventist church. Interests include education, health care, humanitarian relief, and development. Supplies educational tools for the blind and the hearing-impaired. Operates schools worldwide. Organizes community service-oriented youth groups.

Institute on Religion and Democracy, *1521 16th St. N.W., #300 20036; (202) 986-1440. Fax, (202) 986-3159. Diane L. Knippers, president. Internet, 102676.56@compuserve.com.*

Interdenominational bipartisan organization that supports democratic and constitutional forms of government consistent with the values of Christianity. Serves as a resource center to promote Christian perspectives on U.S. foreign policy questions. Interests include international conflicts, religious liberties, and the promotion of democratic forms of government in the United States and worldwide.

International Religious Liberty Assn., *12501 Old Columbia Pike, Silver Spring, MD 20904-6600; (301) 680-6680. Fax, (301) 680-6695. John Graz, secretary general.*

Seeks to preserve and expand religious liberty and freedom of conscience; advocates separation of church and state; sponsors international and domestic meetings and congresses.

Jesuit Conference, *Social Ministries, 1616 P St. N.W., #400 20036-1405; (202) 462-7008. Fax, (202) 462-7009. British Robinson, director. Internet, jesuitusa@igc.apc.org.*

Information and advocacy organization of Jesuits and laypersons concerned with peace and social justice issues in the United States. Interests include peace and disarmament, economic justice, and issues affecting minorities, especially Native Americans, Hispanics, and African Americans.

Leadership Conference of Women Religious, *8808 Cameron St., Silver Spring, MD 20910-4169; (301) 588-4955. Fax, (301) 587-4575. Mary Christine Fellerhoff, executive director.*

Membership: Roman Catholic women religious who are the principal administrators of their congregations in the United States. Offers programs and support to members; conducts research; serves as an information clearinghouse.

Maryknoll Fathers and Brothers (Catholic Foreign Mission Society of America), *4834 16th St. N.W. 20011; (202) 726-4252. Fax, (202) 726-0466. Francis Higdon, regional director. Internet, http://www. maryknoll.org.*

Conducts religious teaching and other mission work for the poor in Africa, Asia, and Latin America.

Mennonite Central Committee, *110 Maryland Ave. N.E., #502 20002; (202) 544-6564. Fax, (202) 544-2820. J. Daryl Byler, director, Washington Office. Internet, mccwash@igc.apc.org or http://www.mennonitecc.ca/mcc.*

Christian organization engaged in service and development projects. Monitors legislation and regulations affecting issues of interest to Mennonite and Brethren in Christ churches. Interests include human rights in developing countries, military spending, the environment, world hunger, poverty, and civil and religious liberties. (Headquarters in Akron, Pa.)

National Assn. of Evangelicals, *1023 15th St. N.W., #500 20005; (202) 789-1011. Fax, (202) 842-0392. Rich Cizik, policy analyst. Internet, oga@nae.net or http://www.nae.net.*

Represents Christian evangelical denominations. Interests include religious liberty; economic policy; church-state relations; public health issues, including HIV and AIDS; and immigration and refugee policy. Monitors legislation and regulations. (Headquarters in Wheaton, Ill.)

National Catholic Conference for Interracial Justice, *1200 Varnum St. N.E. 20017; (202) 529-6480. Fax, (202) 526-1262. Joseph Conrad Jr., executive director.*

Promotes the Roman Catholic church's teachings on racial justice and multicultural and multiracial understanding.

National Conference of Catholic Bishops/U.S. Catholic Conference, *3211 4th St. N.E. 20017; (202) 541-3000. Fax, (202) 541-3323. Msgr. Dennis M. Schnurr, general secretary. Press, (202) 541-3200. Internet, http://www.nccbuscc.org.*

Serves as a forum for bishops to exchange ideas, debate concerns of the church, and draft responses to religious and social issues. Provides information on doctrine and policies of the Roman Catholic church; develops religious education and training programs; formulates policy positions on social issues, including the economy, employment, federal budget priorities, voting rights, energy, health, housing, rural affairs, international military and political matters, human rights, the arms race, global economics, and immigration and refugee policy.

National Conference on Soviet Jewry, *1640 Rhode Island Ave. N.W., #501 20036; (202) 898-2500. Fax, (202) 898-0822. Mark B. Levin, executive director. Internet, ncsj@erols.com.*

Promotes religious and personal freedom for Jews wishing to leave the former Soviet Union in accordance with international law and for those choosing to remain. Provides them with legal advice and technical assistance. Organizes conferences, rallies, vigils, commemorations, and letter-writing campaigns; monitors legislation.

National Council of Catholic Women, *1275 K St. N.W., #975 20005; (202) 682-0334. Fax, (202) 682-0338. Annette Kane, executive director. Internet, nccw@us.net.*

Federation of Roman Catholic women's organizations. Provides a forum for Catholic women to research and discuss issues affecting the church and society; monitors legislation and regulations. Interests include employment, abortion, care for the elderly, day care, genetic engineering research, pornography legislation, and substance abuse. Special programs include volunteer respite care, leadership training for women, and mentoring of mothers.

National Council of Churches, *110 Maryland Ave. N.E., #108 20002; (202) 544-2350. Fax, (202) 543-1297. Albert M. Pennybacker, acting director, Washington Office. Internet, ncc-washington.parti@ecunet.org or http://www.ncccusa.org.*

Membership: Protestant, Anglican, and Eastern Orthodox churches. Interests include racial and social equality; social welfare, economic justice, and peace issues; church-state relations; prayer in public schools; and federal aid to private schools. (Headquarters in New York.)

National Council of Jewish Women, *1707 L St. N.W., #950 20036; (202) 296-2588. Fax, (202) 331-7792. Sammie Moshenberg, director, Washington Office. Internet, ncjwdc@aol.com or http://www.ncjw.org.*

Jewish women's education, community service, and advocacy organization. Interests include economic equity for women; reproductive, civil, and constitutional rights; juvenile justice; child care; education and welfare programs; Israel; aging issues; and work and family issues. (Headquarters in New York.)

NETWORK, *801 Pennsylvania Ave. S.E., #460 20003-2167; (202) 547-5556. Fax, (202) 547-5510. Kathy Thornton, national coordinator. Internet, network@igc.apc.org or http;//www.igc.apc.org/network.*

Catholic social justice lobby that coordinates political activity on public policy issues. Interests include securing just access to economic resources, reordering federal budget priorities, and transforming global relationships.

Presbyterian Church (U.S.A.), *110 Maryland Ave. N.E., #104 20002; (202) 543-1126. Fax, (202) 543-7755. Elenora Giddings Ivory, director, Washington Office. Internet, ga_washington_office@pcusa.org or http://www.pcusa.org.*

Provides information on the views of the general assembly of the Presbyterian church on public policy issues; monitors legislation affecting issues of concern. Interests include arms control, budget priorities, foreign policy, civil rights, religious liberty, church-state relations, economic justice, and public policy issues affecting women. (Headquarters in Louisville, Ky.)

Progressive National Baptist Convention, Inc., *601 50th St. N.E. 20019; (202) 396-0558. Fax, (202) 398-4998. Tyrone S. Pitts, general secretary. Internet, http://www.pnbc.org.*

Baptist denomination that supports missionaries, implements education programs, and advocates for civil and human rights.

Sojourners, *2401 15th St. N.W. 20009; (202) 328-8842. Fax, (202) 328-8757. James E. Wallis, president. Toll-free, (800) 714-7474. Internet, sojourn@ari.net or http://www.sojourner.com.*

Membership: Catholics, Protestants, Evangelicals, and other interested Christians. Grassroots network that focuses on the intersection of faith, politics, and culture. (Affiliated with the Church of the Savior.)

Union of American Hebrew Congregations, *Religious Action Center of Reform Judaism, 2027 Massachusetts Ave. N.W. 20036; (202) 387-2800. Fax, (202) 667-9070. David Saperstein, director, Washington Office. Internet, http://rj.org/rac.*

Religious and educational organization concerned with social justice and religious liberty. Mobilizes the American Jewish community and serves as its advocate on issues concerning Jews around the world, including economic justice, civil rights, and international peace. (Headquarters in New York.)

Unitarian Universalist Assn. of Congregations in North America, *2026 P St. N.W., #3 20036-5914; (202) 296-4672. Fax, (202) 296-4673. Meg A. Riley, director. Internet, uuawo@aol.com or http://uua.org.*

Monitors public policy and legislation. Interests include civil and religious liberties; international and interfaith affairs; human rights; and public policy affecting women, including reproductive rights policy.

United Church of Christ, *110 Maryland Ave. N.E., #207 20002; (202) 543-1517. Fax, (202) 543-5994. Jay Lintner, director, Washington Office. Internet, http://www.ucc.org.*

Studies public policy issues and promotes church policy on these issues; organizes political activity to implement church views. Interests include health care, international peace, economic justice, and civil rights. (Headquarters in Cleveland.)

Women's Alliance for Theology, Ethics, and Ritual, *8035 13th St., Silver Spring, MD 20910-4803; (301) 589-2509. Fax, (301) 589-3150. Diann Neu and Mary Hunt, co-directors. Internet, water@hers.com or http://www.hers.com/water.*

Feminist theological organization that focuses on issues concerning women and religion. Interests include social issues; work skills for women with disabilities; human rights in Latin America; and liturgies, rituals, counseling, and research.

See also Center of Concern (p. 441); Ethics Resource Center (p. 135)

2

Agriculture and Nutrition

◼ GENERAL POLICY

AGENCIES

Agricultural Marketing Service *(Agriculture Dept.),* *1400 Independence Ave. S.W. #3071S (mailing address: P.O. Box 96456, Washington, DC 20090-6456); (202) 720-5115. Fax, (202) 720-8477. Enrique E. Figueroa, administrator. Information, (202) 720-8998. Internet, http://www.usda.gov/ams/lsd.htm.*

Administers marketing, standardization, grading, inspection, and regulatory programs; maintains a market news service to inform producers of market price changes; conducts agricultural marketing research and development programs; studies agricultural transportation issues.

Agriculture Dept., *1400 Independence Ave. S.W. 20250; (202) 720-3631. Fax, (202) 720-2166. Dan Glickman, secretary; Richard Rominger, deputy secretary, (202) 720-6158. Information, (202) 720-2791. Library, (202) 720-3434. Recorded news, (202) 488-8358. Locator, (202) 720-8732. Internet, http://www.usda.gov.*

Serves as principal adviser to the president on agricultural policy; works to increase and maintain farm income and to develop markets abroad for U.S. agricultural products.

Agriculture Dept., *Board of Contract Appeals, 1400 Independence Ave. S.W. #2912S 20250-0601; (202) 720-7023. Fax, (202) 720-3059. Edward Houry, chair.*

Considers appeals of decisions made by contracting officers involving agencies within the Agriculture Dept., including decisions on contracts for construction, property, and services.

Agriculture Dept., *Chief Economist, 1400 Independence Ave. S.W., #112A 20250-3810; (202) 720-5955. Fax, (202) 690-4915. Keith J. Collins, chief economist. Internet, http://www.usda.gov/oce.*

Prepares economic and statistical analyses used to plan and evaluate short- and intermediate-range agricultural policy. Evaluates Agriculture Dept. policy and legislation for their impact on the agricultural economy. Administers Agriculture Dept. economic agencies, including the Office of Risk Assessment and Cost-Benefit Analysis, and the World Agricultural Outlook Board.

Agriculture Dept., *Food, Nutrition, and Consumer Services, 1400 Independence Ave. S.W., #240E 20250; (202) 720-7711. Fax, (202) 690-3100. Shirley R. Watkins, under secretary. Internet, http://www.usda.gov/fcs.*

Oversees the Food and Consumer Service and the office of the consumer adviser for agricultural products.

Farm Service Agency *(Agriculture Dept.), 1400 Independence Ave. S.W., Mail Stop 0501 20250-0501; (202) 720-3467. Fax, (202) 720-9105. Keith Kelly, administrator. Information, (202) 720-5237. Internet, http://www.fsa.usda.gov.*

Oversees farm commodity programs that provide crop loans and purchases. Administers price support programs that provide crop payments when market prices fall below specified levels; conducts programs to help obtain adequate farm and commercial storage and drying equipment for farm products; directs conservation and environmental cost sharing projects and programs to assist farmers during natural disasters and other emergencies. Oversees the Federal Crop Insurance Corporation.

See also Domestic Policy Council (p. 328)

CONGRESS

General Accounting Office, *Food and Agriculture Issues, 441 G St. N.W., #2T23 20548; (202) 512-5138. Fax, (202) 512-9936. Robert A. Robinson, director.*

Independent, nonpartisan agency in the legislative branch that audits the Agriculture Dept. and analyzes and reports on its handling of food and agriculture issues.

House Agriculture Committee, *1301 LHOB 20515; (202) 225-0029. Fax, (202) 225-0917. Bob Smith, R-Ore., chair; Paul Unger, staff director, (202) 225-2171. Internet, http://www.house.gov/agriculture.*

Jurisdiction over legislation on agriculture and forestry in general; agricultural trade matters and international commodity agreements; inspection and certification of livestock, poultry, meat products and seafood; agricultural research; pests and pesticides; nutrition; and agricultural assistance programs. Oversees Agriculture Dept. operations.

House Agriculture Committee, *Subcommittee on Forestry, Resource Conservation, and Research, 1336 LHOB 20515; (202) 225-2342. Larry Combest, R-Texas, chair; Russell Laird, staff director. Internet, http://www.house.gov/agriculture.*

Jurisdiction over legislation on rural development; oversight of Rural Utilities Service. Jurisdiction over legislation on soil conservation, small-scale stream channelization, watershed, and flood control programs, water and air quality, and agricultural credit programs.

House Appropriations Committee, *Subcommittee on Agriculture, Rural Development, FDA, and Related Agencies, 2362 RHOB 20515; (202) 225-2638. Joe Skeen,*

AGRICULTURE DEPARTMENT

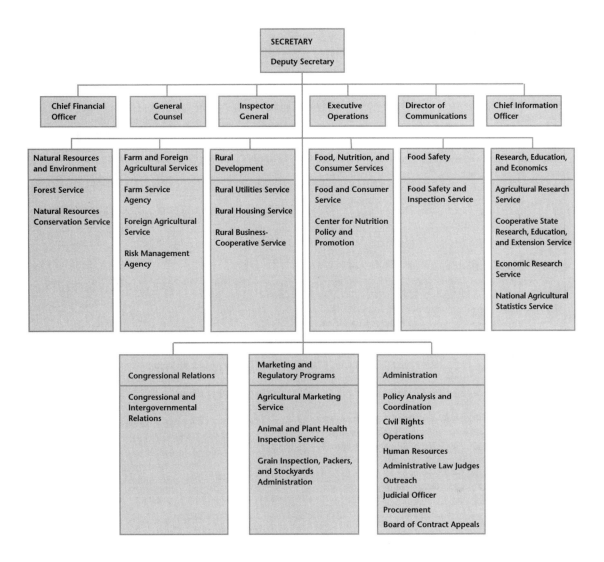

R-N.M., chair; Timothy K. Sanders, staff director. Internet, http://www.house.gov/appropriations.

Jurisdiction over legislation to appropriate funds for the Agriculture Dept. (except the Forest Service), the Commodity Futures Trading Commission, and other agriculture-related services and programs.

House Government Reform and Oversight Committee, *Subcommittee on National Economic Growth, Natural Resources, and Regulatory Affairs, B377 RHOB 20515; (202) 225-4407. Fax, (202) 225-2441. David M.*

McIntosh, R-Ind., chair; Mildred Webber, staff director. Internet, http://www.house.gov/reform.

Oversees operations of the Agriculture Dept. (except Food and Consumer Service, Food Safety and Inspection Service, and Forest Service).

Senate Agriculture, Nutrition, and Forestry Committee, SR-328A 20510; (202) 224-2035. Fax, (202) 224-1725. Richard G. Lugar, R-Ind., chair; Randy Green, staff director. Internet, http://www.senate.gov/~agriculture.

Jurisdiction over legislation on agriculture, agricultural economics and research, agricultural extension services and experiment stations, agricultural engineering, animal industry and diseases, forestry, pests and pesticides, rural issues, nutrition, and family farms; oversees Agriculture Dept. operations.

Senate Agriculture, Nutrition, and Forestry Committee, *Subcommittee on Forestry, Conservation, and Rural Revitalization, SR-328A 20510; (202) 224-2035. Rick Santorum, R-Pa., chair; David French, legislative assistant. Internet, http://www.senate.gov/~agriculture.*

Jurisdiction over legislation on family farming and rural development, including rural electrification and telephone development; oversight of the Rural Utilities Service. Jurisdiction over legislation on irrigation, soil conservation, stream channelization, watershed programs, and flood control programs involving structures of less than 4,000 acre-feet in storage capacity.

Senate Appropriations Committee, *Subcommittee on Agriculture, Rural Development, and Related Agencies, SD-136 20510; (202) 224-5270. Fax, (202) 224-9450. Thad Cochran, R-Miss., chair; Rebecca M. Davies, clerk. Internet, http://www.senate.gov/committee/appropriations. html.*

Jurisdiction over legislation to appropriate funds for the Agriculture Dept. (except the Forest Service), the Commodity Futures Trading Commission, farm credit, and other agriculture-related services and programs.

Senate Banking, Housing, and Urban Affairs Committee, *Subcommittee on Financial Institutions and Regulatory Relief, SD-534 20510; (202) 224-7391. Lauch Faircloth, R-N.C., chair; Jim Hyland, staff director. Internet, http://www.senate.gov/~banking.*

Jurisdiction over legislation on economic stabilization and growth, including regulatory relief issues, barriers to development in rural areas, price controls, and asset disposition policies.

NONPROFIT

American Farm Bureau Federation, *600 Maryland Ave. S.W., #800 20024; (202) 484-3600. Fax, (202) 484-3604. Richard W. Newpher, executive director, Washington Office. Internet, http://www.fb.com.*

Federation of state farm bureaus in fifty states and Puerto Rico. Promotes agricultural research. Interests include commodity programs, domestic production, marketing, education, research, financial assistance to the farmer, foreign assistance programs, rural development, the world food shortage, and inspection and certification of food. (Headquarters in Park Ridge, Ill.)

National Assn. of State Departments of Agriculture, *1156 15th St. N.W., #1020 20005; (202) 296-9680. Fax, (202) 296-9686. Richard W. Kirchhoff, executive vice president. Internet, nasdahq@patriot.net or http://www. nasda-hq.org/.*

Membership: agriculture commissioners from the fifty states, Puerto Rico, Guam, American Samoa, and the U.S. Virgin Islands. Serves as liaison between federal agencies and state governments to coordinate agricultural policies and laws. Seeks to protect consumers and the environment. Monitors legislation and regulations.

National Council of Agricultural Employers, *1112 16th St. N.W., #920 20036; (202) 728-0300. Fax, (202) 728-0303. Sharon M. Hughes, executive vice president. Internet, ncae@erols.com.*

Membership: employers of agricultural labor. Encourages establishment and maintenance of conditions conducive to an adequate supply of domestic and foreign farm labor.

National Farmers Union (Farmers Educational and Cooperative Union of America), *400 Virginia Ave. S.W., #710 20024-2730; (202) 554-1600. Fax, (202) 554-1654. Lynn McBride, legislative representative. Internet, http://www.nfu.org.*

Membership: family farmers belonging to state affiliates. Interests include commodity programs, domestic production, marketing, education, research, energy and natural resources, financial assistance to farmers, Social Security for farmers, foreign programs, rural development, the world food shortage, and inspection and certification of food. (Headquarters in Denver.)

National Grange, *1616 H St. N.W. 20006-4999; (202) 628-3507. Fax, (202) 347-1091. Kermit W. Richardson, master.*

Membership: farmers and others involved in agricultural production and rural community service activities. Coordinates community service programs with state grange organizations.

Rural Coalition, *110 Maryland Ave. N.E., #101 20002; (202) 544-9611. Fax, (202) 544-9613. Lorette Picciano, executive director. Internet, ruralco@aol.com.*

Alliance of organizations that develop public policies benefiting rural communities. Collaborates with community-based groups on agriculture and rural development issues, including health and the environment, minority farmers, farmworkers, native Americans' rights, and rural community development. Provides rural groups with technical assistance.

Union of Concerned Scientists, *1616 P St. N.W., #310 20036; (202) 332-0900. Fax, (202) 332-0905. Alden Meyer, director, Government Relations. Internet, ucs@ucsusa.org or http://www.ucsusa.org.*

Advocates policies to encourage low-input sustainable agricultural practices and to reduce the environmental and health effects caused by conventional agricultural practices and high-chemical inputs. Seeks to evaluate future role, risk, and benefits of biotechnology. Monitors legislation and regulations.

United Farm Workers of America, *c/o AFL-CIO, 815 16th St. N.W. 20006; (202) 637-5212. Fax, (202) 508-6924. Dan Hawes, manager. TDD, (202) 637-5012. Internet, http://www.ufw.org.*

Membership: approximately 50,000 farm workers. Helps members negotiate pay, benefits, and better working conditions; conducts training programs and workshops. Interests includes immigration and migrant workers. Monitors legislation and regulations. (Affiliated with the AFL-CIO.)

U.S. Chamber of Commerce, *Food, Agriculture, Energy, and Natural Resources Policy, 1615 H St. N.W. 20062-2000; (202) 463-5500. Fax, (202) 887-3445. Stew Hardy, manager. Internet, http://www.uschamber.org.*

Develops policy on issues affecting production, transportation, and sale of agricultural products. Interests include food safety, pesticides, nutrition labeling, seafood inspection, backhauling, and international trade.

Agricultural Research/Education

See also Botany (chap. 17)

AGENCIES

Agricultural Research Service *(Agriculture Dept.), 1400 Independence Ave. S.W., #302A 20250-0300; (202) 720-3656. Fax, (202) 720-5427. Edward B. Knipling, associate administrator. Internet, http://www.ars.usda. gov.*

Conducts research on crops, livestock, poultry, soil and water conservation, agricultural engineering, and control of insects and other pests; develops new uses for farm commodities.

Agriculture Dept., *Research, Education, and Economics, 1400 Independence Ave. S.W., #217W 20250-0110; (202) 720-5923. Fax, (202) 690-2842. Eileen Kennedy, acting deputy under secretary, (202) 720-8885.*

Coordinates agricultural research, extension, and teaching programs in the food and agricultural sciences, including human nutrition, home economics, consumer services, agricultural economics, environmental quality, natural and renewable resources, forestry and range management, animal and plant production and protection, aquaculture, and the processing, distribution, marketing, and utilization of food and agricultural products. Oversees the Agricultural Research Service; the Cooperative State Research, Education, and Extension Service; the Economic Research Service; and the National Agricultural Statistics Service.

Agriculture Dept., *Special Emphasis Outreach Program, 1400 Independence Ave. S.W., #1364S 20250-9400; (202) 720-7314. Fax, (202) 690-2345. Lloyd E. Wright, associate director.*

Works with state governments to foster participation by minority and disabled individuals and institutions in food and agricultural research, teaching programs, and related areas. Assists the Agriculture Dept. in developing and improving opportunities in agricultural enterprises for minority individuals and institutions.

Census Bureau *(Commerce Dept.), Agriculture and Financial Statistics, Iverson Mall, #437; (301) 763-8555. Fax, (301) 763-8315. Ewen M. Wilson, chief. Toll-free, (800) 523-3215. Library, (301) 763-8241.*

Conducts a quinquennial agricultural census that provides data on crops, livestock, operator characteristics, land use, farm production expenditures, machinery and equipment, and irrigation for counties, states, regions, and the nation.

Cooperative State Research, Education, and Extension Service *(Agriculture Dept.), 1400 Independence Ave. S.W., #305A 20250-2201; (202) 720-4423. Fax, (202) 720-8987. B. H. Robinson, administrator. TDD, (202) 690-1899. Internet, http://www.reeusda.gov.*

Conducts educational programs to assist farmers, processors, and others in efficient production and marketing of agricultural products. Conducts educational programs on sustainable agriculture. Serves as national headquarters for the 4-H youth programs and coordinates activities with state and local clubs.

Cooperative State Research, Education, and Extension Service *(Agriculture Dept.), Competitive Research Grants and Awards Management, 901 D St. S.W., #322 20250-2240; (202) 401-1761. Fax, (202) 401-3237. Sally Rockey, deputy administrator.*

Administers grants to colleges, universities, small businesses, and other organizations to promote research in food, agriculture, and related areas. Maintains administrative responsibility for programs in aquaculture, critical materials (domestic rubber), small-farm resource development, and higher education.

Cooperative State Research, Education, and Extension Service *(Agriculture Dept.), Science and Education Resources Development, 1400 Independence Ave. S.W., #338A 20250; (202) 720-3377. Fax, (202) 720-3945. K. Jane Coulter, deputy administrator.*

Provides national leadership and coordination on issues relating to food and agricultural research, higher education, and extension; assists colleges and universities in developing and maintaining education programs in the food and agricultural sciences. Seeks to ensure that colleges and universities produce the requisite number of graduates to satisfy the nation's need for individuals trained in the field. Maintains research information system covering all publicly supported agriculture, food, human nutrition, and forestry research.

Economic Research Service *(Agriculture Dept.), 1800 M St. N.W. 20036; (202) 694-5000. Fax, (202) 694-5757. Susan E. Offutt, administrator. Internet, http://www. econ.ag.gov.*

Analyzes factors affecting farm production and their relationship to the environment, prices and income, and the outlook for various commodities, including aquaculture and industrial crops. Studies include rural development and natural resources, agricultural trade and production, government policies, and foreign demand for agricultural products.

National Agricultural Library *(Agriculture Dept.), 10301 Baltimore Ave., Beltsville, MD 20705; (301) 504-5248. Fax, (301) 504-7042. Pamela Q. J. André, director. TDD, (301) 504-6856. Reference desk, (301) 504-5479, 8:30 a.m. to 4:30 p.m. Internet, http://www.nal.usda.gov.*

Makes agricultural information available to researchers, educators, policymakers, and the public; coordinates state land-grant and Agriculture Dept. field libraries; promotes international cooperation and exchange of information. Interests include food production, nutrition, animal and plant health, rural development, and agricultural trade.

National Agricultural Library *(Agriculture Dept.), D.C. Reference Center, 1400 Independence Ave. S.W., #1052S 20250; (202) 720-3434. Fax, (202) 720-3200. Janet Wright, chief. Reference desk fax, (202) 720-0342.*

Maintains an agricultural reference collection and online services for use by department personnel and the public. (Headquarters in Beltsville, Md.)

National Agricultural Statistics Service *(Agriculture Dept.), 1400 Independence Ave. S.W., #4117S 20250; (202) 720-2707. Fax, (202) 720-9013. Donald M. Bay, administrator. Weekly weather and crop information, bulletin subscriptions, (202) 720-4021. Internet, nass@nass.usda.gov.*

Prepares estimates and reports on production, supply, prices, and other items relating to the U.S. agricultural economy. Reports include statistics on field crops, fruits and vegetables, cattle, hogs, poultry, and related products.

National Science and Technology Council *(Executive Office of the President), Old Executive Office Bldg., #435 20500; (202) 456-6100. Fax, (202) 456-6026. John H. Gibbons, chair. Internet, http://www.whitehouse.gov/ White_House/EOP/OSTP.*

Coordinates research and development activities and programs that involve more than one federal agency. Concerns include food, agriculture, and forestry research.

Rural Business-Cooperative Service *(Agriculture Dept.), Cooperative Services, 1400 Independence Ave. S.W., #4016S, Mail Stop 3250 20250-3250; (202) 720-7558. Fax, (202) 720-4641. Randall E. Torgerson, deputy administrator. Information, (202) 720-6483.*

Conducts economic research and provides technical assistance to help farmers market their products and purchase supplies; helps people living in rural areas to obtain business services through cooperatives.

CONGRESS

House Agriculture Committee, *Subcommittee on Department Operations, Nutrition, and Foreign Agriculture, 1430 LHOB 20515; (202) 225-0171. Fax, (202) 225-4464. Robert W. Goodlatte, R-Va., chair; Kevin Kramp, staff director. Internet, http://www.house.gov/ agriculture.*

Jurisdiction over legislation on agricultural education.

House Science Committee, *Subcommittee on Basic Research, B374 RHOB 20515; (202) 225-7858. Fax, (202) 225-7815. Vacant, chair; Steve Eule, staff director. Press, (202) 225-0584. Internet, http://www.house.gov/ science.*

Jurisdiction over legislation concerning agricultural research and development.

Senate Agriculture, Nutrition, and Forestry Committee, *Subcommittee on Research, Nutrition, and General Legislation, SR-361A 20510; (202) 224-2035. Fax, (202) 224-1725. Mitch McConnell, R-Ky., chair; David Hovermale, legislative assistant. Internet, http:// www.senate.gov/~agriculture.*

Jurisdiction over legislation on agricultural education and research.

INTERNATIONAL ORGANIZATIONS

Consultative Group on International Agricultural Research (CGIAR), *701 18th St. N.W. (mailing address: 1818 H St. N.W., J-4073, Washington, DC 20433); (202) 473-8951. Fax, (202) 473-8110. Alexander von der Osten, executive secretary. Internet, cgiar@cgnet.com or http:// www.cgiar.org.*

Promotes sustainable agriculture for food security in developing countries; supports a network of sixteen international agricultural research centers. Interests include agricultural productivity, environmental protection, and biodiversity; promotes effective public policy and strong national research programs.

NONPROFIT

Academy for Educational Development, *Social Development, 1255 23rd St. N.W., #400 20037; (202) 884-8700. Fax, (202) 884-8701. William Smith, executive vice president. Internet, http://www.aed.org.*

Conducts studies of international agricultural development on a contract basis; encourages exchange of agricultural information between researchers and farmers.

Agricultural Research Institute, *9650 Rockville Pike, Bethesda, MD 20814; (301) 530-7122. Fax, (301) 530-7007. Richard A. Herrett, executive director. Internet, ari@nal.usda.gov.*

Membership: corporations, trade organizations, professional societies, universities, experiment stations, and government agencies involved in research. Identifies critical agricultural needs and problems; sponsors conferences and workshops.

Future Farmers of America, *5632 Mount Vernon Memorial Hwy., Alexandria, VA (mailing address: P.O. Box 15160, Alexandria, VA 22309); (703) 360-3600. Fax, (703) 360-5524. Larry D. Case, national adviser. Internet, http://www.ffa.org.*

Membership: local chapters of high school students enrolled in agricultural education and agribusiness programs. Coordinates leadership training and other activities with local chapters across the United States.

National Council of Farmer Cooperatives, *50 F St. N.W., #900 20001; (202) 626-8700. Fax, (202) 626-8722. David Graves, president. Internet, info@ncfc.org or http://www.access.digex.net/~ncfc/members.*

Membership: cooperative businesses owned and operated by farmers. Conducts educational programs and encourages research on agricultural cooperatives; provides statistics and analyzes trends; presents awards for research papers.

National 4-H Council, *7100 Connecticut Ave., Chevy Chase, MD 20815-4999; (301) 961-2820. Fax, (301) 961-2894. Richard J. Sauer, president. Press, (301) 961-2915. Internet, http://www.fourhcouncil.edu.*

Educational organization incorporated to strengthen and complement the 4-H program (for young people ages 7 to 19) of the Agriculture Dept.'s Cooperative Extension Service and state land-grant universities. Programs include citizenship and leadership training workforce preparation, and environmental stewardship.

Fertilizer and Pesticides

AGENCIES

Agricultural Research Service *(Agriculture Dept.),* **National Agricultural Pesticide Impact Assessment Program,** *10300 Baltimore Ave., #300, Bldg. 005, BARC-West, Beltsville, MD 20705-2350; (301) 504-7245. Fax, (301) 504-7117. Nancy N. Ragsdale, director.*

Coordinates the pesticide assessment program under the Insecticide, Fungicide, and Rodenticide Act; maintains liaison with the Environmental Protection Agency on pesticide issues.

Environmental Protection Agency, *Pesticide Programs, 1921 Jefferson Davis Hwy., Arlington, VA (mailing address: 401 M St. S.W., MC 7501C, Washington, DC 20460); (703) 305-7090. Fax, (703) 308-4776. Marcia Mulcie, director. National Pesticide Telecommunications Network, (800) 858-7378. Internet, http://www.epa.gov/ pesticides.*

Evaluates data to determine the risks and benefits of pesticides; sets standards for safe use of pesticides, including those for use on foods. Develops rules that govern labeling and literature accompanying pesticide products.

Environmental Protection Agency, *Prevention, Pesticides, and Toxic Substances, 401 M St. S.W., MC 7101 20460; (202) 260-2902. Fax, (202) 260-1847. Dr. Lynn R. Goldman, assistant administrator. Information, (202) 260-3810.*

Studies and makes recommendations for regulating chemical substances under the Toxic Substances Control Act; compiles list of chemical substances subject to the act; registers, controls, and regulates use of pesticides and toxic substances.

CONGRESS

House Agriculture Committee, *Subcommittee on Department Operations, Nutrition, and Foreign Agriculture, 1430 LHOB 20515; (202) 225-0171. Fax, (202) 225-4464. Robert W. Goodlatte, R-Va., chair; Kevin*

Kramp, staff director. Internet, http://www.house.gov/ agriculture.

Jurisdiction over legislation on pesticides.

Senate Environment and Public Works Committee, Subcommittee on Superfund, Waste Control, and Risk Assessment, SD-410 20510; (202) 224-6176. Fax, (202) 224-5167. Robert C. Smith, R-N.H., chair; Tom Gibson, staff contact. Internet, http://www.senate.gov/committee/ environment.html.

Jurisdiction over legislation on pesticides.

NONPROFIT

American Crop Protection Assn., 1156 15th St. N.W., #400 20005; (202) 296-1585. Fax, (202) 463-0474. Jay J. Vroom, president. Internet, http://www.acpa.org.

Membership: pesticide manufacturers. Provides information on pesticide safety, development, and use. Monitors legislation and regulations.

Entomological Society of America, 9301 Annapolis Rd., Lanham, MD 20706; (301) 731-4535. Fax, (301) 731-4538. Doug Kliene, executive director. Internet, info@ entsoc.org.

Scientific association that promotes the science of entomology and the interests of professionals in the field. Advises on crop protection, food chain, and individual and urban health matters dealing with insects.

Fertilizer Institute, 501 2nd St. N.E. 20002; (202) 675-8250. Fax, (202) 544-8123. Gary D. Myers, president.

Membership: manufacturers, dealers, and distributors of fertilizer. Provides statistical data and other information concerning the effects of fertilizer and its relationship to world food production, food supply, and the environment.

Migrant Legal Action Program, P.O. Box 53308 20009; (202) 462-7744. Fax, (202) 462-7914. Roger C. Rosenthal, executive director. Internet, hn1645@ handsnet.org.

Assists local legal services groups and private attorneys representing farm workers. Monitors legislation, regulations, and enforcement activities of the Environmental Protection Agency and the Occupational Safety and Health Administration in the area of pesticide use as it affects the health of migrant farm workers. Litigates cases concerning living and working conditions experienced by migrant farmworkers. Works with local groups on implementation of Medicaid block grants.

National Agricultural Aviation Assn., 1005 E St. S.E. 20003; (202) 546-5722. Fax, (202) 546-5726. James Boillot, executive director. Internet, naaa@aol.com.

Membership: qualified agricultural pilots; operating companies that seed, fertilize, and spray land by air; and allied industries. Monitors legislation and regulations.

National Coalition Against the Misuse of Pesticides, 701 E St. S.E., #200 20003; (202) 543-5450. Fax, (202) 543-4791. Jay Feldman, executive director. Internet, ncamp@igc.apc.org or http://www.csn.net/ncamp/.

Coalition of family farmers, farmworkers, consumers, home gardeners, and others concerned about pesticide hazards and safety. Issues information to increase public awareness of environmental, public health, and economic problems caused by pesticide abuse; promotes alternatives to pesticide use.

National Food Processors Assn., 1401 New York Ave. N.W., #400 20005; (202) 639-5900. Fax, (202) 639-5932. John R. Cady, president. Press, (202) 639-5919.

Maintains an information clearinghouse on environmental and crop protection; analyzes products for pesticide residue. Monitors legislation and regulations.

National Pest Control Assn., 8100 Oak St., Dunn Loring, VA 22027; (703) 573-8330. Fax, (703) 573-4116. Robert M. Rosenberg, director, Government Affairs. Internet, http://www.pestworld.org.

Membership: pest control operators. Monitors federal regulations that affect pesticide use; provides members with technical information.

Horticulture and Gardening

See also Botany (chap. 17)

AGENCIES

National Arboretum *(Agriculture Dept.),* 3501 New York Ave. N.E. 20002; (202) 245-4539. Fax, (202) 245-4575. Thomas S. Elias, director. Library, (202) 245-4967.

Maintains public display of plants on 444 acres; provides information and makes referrals concerning cultivated plants (exclusive of field crops and fruits); conducts plant breeding and research; maintains herbarium. Library open to the public by appointment.

Smithsonian Institution Libraries, *Horticulture Library,* Arts and Industries Bldg., 900 Jefferson Dr. S.W., MRC 420 20560; (202) 357-1544. Fax, (202) 786-2026. Marca L. Woodhams, chief librarian. Internet, woodhma@ ic.si.edu.

Collection includes books, periodicals, trade catalogs, and videotapes on horticulture, garden history, and landscape design. Specializes in American gardens and gardening of the late nineteenth and early twentieth centuries. Open to the public by appointment.

CONGRESS

U.S. Botanic Garden, *245 1st St. S.W. 20024; (202) 225-8333. Fax, (202) 225-1561. Jeffrey P. Cooper-Smith, executive director. Flower show information, (202) 225-7099 (recording).*

Collects, cultivates, and grows various plants for public display and study; identifies botanic specimens and furnishes information on proper growing methods. Conducts horticultural classes and tours. Sponsors four seasonal flower shows annually.

NONPROFIT

American Nursery and Landscape Assn., *1250 Eye St. N.W., #500 20005-3922; (202) 789-2900. Fax, (202) 789-1893. Robert J. Dolibois, executive vice president. Internet, http://www.anla.org.*

Membership: wholesale growers, garden center retailers, landscape firms, and suppliers to the horticultural community. Monitors legislation and regulations on agricultural, environmental, and small-business issues; conducts educational seminars on business management for members. (Affiliated with the National Assn. of Plant Patent Owners.)

American Horticultural Society, *7931 E. Boulevard Dr., Alexandria, VA 22308-1300; (703) 768-5700. Fax, (703) 768-8700. Linda Hallman, president. Toll-free, (800) 777-7931. Internet, garden@ahs.aol.com or http://members.aol.com/gardenahs.*

Promotes the expansion of horticulture in the United States through educational programs for amateur and professional horticulturists. Acts as a horticultural clearinghouse; operates the Gardener's Information Service. Oversees historic house and farm once owned by George Washington, with gardens maintained by plant societies; house and grounds are rented for special occasions.

American Society for Horticultural Science, *600 Cameron St., Alexandria, VA 22314-2562; (703) 836-4606. Fax, (703) 836-2024. Michael Neff, executive director. Internet, ashs@ashs.org or http://www.ashs.org/.*

Membership: educators, government workers, firms, associations, and individuals interested in horticultural science. Promotes scientific research and education in horticulture, including international exchange of information.

National Assn. of Plant Patent Owners, *1250 Eye St. N.W., #500 20005-3922; (202) 789-2900. Fax, (202) 789-1893. Craig Regelbrugge, administrator.*

Membership: owners of patents on newly propagated horticultural plants. Informs members of plant patents issued, provisions of patent laws, and changes in prac-tice. Promotes the development, protection, production, and distribution of new varieties of horticultural plants. Works with international organizations of plant breeders on matters of common interest. (Affiliated with the American Nursery and Landscape Assn.)

Society of American Florists, *1601 Duke St., Alexandria, VA 22314; (703) 836-8700. Fax, (703) 836-8705. Drew Gruenburg, senior vice president. Internet, http://www.safnow.org.*

Membership: growers, wholesalers, and retailers in the floriculture and ornamental horticulture industries. Interests include labor, pesticides, the environment, international trade, and toxicity of plants. Mediates industry problems.

Soil and Watershed Conservation

See also Community and Regional Development (chap. 12); Resources Management (chap. 9)

AGENCIES

Farm Service Agency *(Agriculture Dept.), Conservation and Environmental Programs, 1400 Independence Ave. S.W., Mail Stop 0513 20250-0501; (202) 720-6221. Fax, (202) 720-4619. George T. Denley, director. Internet, http://www.fsa.usda.gov/pas.*

Directs conservation and environmental projects and programs to help farmers and ranchers prevent soil erosion and contamination of natural resources.

Farm Service Agency *(Agriculture Dept.), Natural Resources Analysis, 1400 Independence Ave. S.W. (mailing address: P.O. Box 2415, Washington, DC 20013-2415); (202) 720-9685. Fax, (202) 720-8261. Thomas L. Browning, director. Internet, tbrownin@wdc.fsa.usda.gov.*

Studies economic issues relating to conservation and land-use programs.

Interior Dept., *North American Wetlands Conservation Council, 4401 N. Fairfax Dr., #110, Arlington, VA 22203; (703) 358-1784. Fax, (703) 358-2282. David A. Smith, coordinator. Internet, r9arw_nawwo@mail.fws.gov or http://www.fws.gov.*

Membership: government and private-sector conservation experts. Works to protect, restore, and manage wetlands and other habitats for migratory birds and other animals and to maintain migratory bird and waterfowl populations.

Natural Resources Conservation Service *(Agriculture Dept.), 1400 Independence Ave. S.W. (mailing address: P.O. Box 2890, Washington, DC 20013-2890); (202) 720-4525. Fax, (202) 720-7690. Pearlie Reed, chief.*

Information, (202) 720-3210. Internet, http://www. ncg.nrcs.usda.gov.

Responsible for soil and water conservation programs, including watershed protection, flood prevention, river basin surveys, and resource conservation and development. Provides landowners, operators, state and local units of government, and community groups with technical assistance in carrying out local programs. Inventories and monitors soil, water, and related resource data and resource use trends. Provides information about soil surveys, farmlands, and other natural resources.

CONGRESS

House Agriculture Committee, *Subcommittee on Forestry, Resource Conservation, and Research, 1336 LHOB 20515; (202) 225-2342. Fax, (202) 225-0951. Larry Combest, R-Tex., chair; Russell Laird, staff director. Internet, http://www.house.gov/agriculture.*

Jurisdiction over legislation on soil conservation, watershed, and flood control programs.

Senate Agriculture, Nutrition, and Forestry Committee, *Subcommittee on Forestry, Conservation, and Rural Revitalization, SR-328A 20510; (202) 224-2035. Rick Santorum, R-Pa., chair; David French, legislative assistant. Internet, http://www.senate.gov/~agriculture.*

Jurisdiction over legislation on soil conservation, watershed programs, and flood control programs involving structures of less than 4,000 acre-feet in storage capacity.

NONPROFIT

American Farmland Trust, *1920 N St. N.W., #400 20036; (202) 659-5170. Fax, (202) 659-8339. Ralph Grossi, president. Internet, http://www.farmland.org.*

Works with farmers to promote farming practices that lead to a healthy environment. Interests include preservation of farmlands from urban development, establishment of safeguards against soil erosion, and agricultural resource conservation policy development at all government levels. Initiates local preservation efforts and assists individuals and organizations engaged in safeguarding agricultural properties.

Henry A. Wallace Institute for Alternative Agriculture, *9200 Edmonston Rd., #117, Greenbelt, MD 20770-1551; (301) 441-8777. Fax, (301) 220-0164. I. Garth Youngberg, executive director. Internet, hawiaa@access. digex.net or http://www.hawiaa.org.*

Supports the adoption of low-cost, resource-conserving, and environmentally sound farming methods. Provides scientific information and sponsors

research and education programs on alternative agricultural methods. Monitors legislation and regulations.

Irrigation Assn., *8260 Willow Oaks Corporate Dr., #120, Fairfax, VA 22031; (703) 573-3551. Fax, (703) 573-1913. Thomas Kimmell, executive director. Internet, http://www. irrigation.org.*

Membership: companies and individuals involved in irrigation, drainage, and erosion control worldwide. Seeks to improve the products and practices used to manage water resources; interests include economic development and environmental enhancement.

National Assn. of Conservation Districts, *509 Capitol Court N.E. 20002-4937; (202) 547-6223. Fax, (202) 547-6450. Ernest C. Shea, chief executive officer. Internet, http://www.nacdnet.org.*

Membership: conservation districts (local subdivisions of state government). Works to promote the conservation of land, forests, and other natural resources. Interests include erosion and sediment control; water quality; forestry, water, flood plain, and range management; rural development; and urban and community conservation.

 # COMMODITIES/FARM PRODUCE

See also Caucuses (chap. 20)

AGENCIES

Agricultural Marketing Service *(Agriculture Dept.), Seed Regulatory and Testing, Bldg. 306, BARC East, #209, Beltsville, MD 20705; (301) 504-9237. Fax, (301) 504-5454. Jim Triplitt, chief. Internet, http://www.ams. usda.gov/lsg/ls-sd.htm.*

Administers interstate programs prohibiting false advertising and labeling of seeds. Regulates interstate shipment of seeds. Tests seeds for a fee under the Agricultural Marketing Act.

Agricultural Marketing Service *(Agriculture Dept.), Transportation and Marketing, 1400 Independence Ave. S.W., #4006S (mailing address: P.O. Box 96456, Washington, DC 20090-6456); (202) 690-1300. Fax, (202) 690-0338. Eileen S. Stommes, deputy administrator; James A. Caron, program manager, SEA, (202) 690-1707. Internet, http://www.usda.gov/ams/tmd.htm.*

Promotes efficient, cost-effective marketing and transportation for U.S. agricultural products; sets standards for domestic and international marketing of organic products. Shipper and Exporter Assistance (SEA) program provides exporters with market information, educational services, and regulatory representation.

Agriculture Dept., *Marketing and Regulatory Programs, 1400 Independence Ave. S.W. Stop #0109 20250-0109; (202) 720-4256. Fax, (202) 720-5775. Michael V. Dunn, assistant secretary.*

Administers inspection and grading services and regulatory programs for agricultural commodities through the Agricultural Marketing Service; Animal and Plant Health Inspection Service; and Grain Inspection, Packers, and Stockyards Administration.

Agricultural Research Service *(Agriculture Dept.), National Plant Germplasm System, #133, Bldg. 5, BARC West, Beltsville, MD 20705; (301) 504-6252. Fax, (301) 504-5467. Peter Bretting, national program leader. Internet, http://www.ars-grin.gov.*

Network of organizations and individuals interested in preserving the genetic diversity of crop plants, including cotton, wheat and other grains, fruits and vegetables, rice, sugar, tobacco, and peanuts. Collects, preserves, evaluates, and catalogs germplasm and distributes it for specific purposes.

Animal and Plant Health Inspection Service *(Agriculture Dept.), 1400 Independence Ave. S.W. (mailing address: Ag. Box 3407, Washington, DC 20250); (202) 720-3861. Fax, (202) 720-3982. Terry Medley, administrator. Information, (202) 720-2511. Internet, http://www.aphis.usda.gov.*

Administers quarantine regulations governing imports of agricultural commodities into the United States; certifies that U.S. exports are free of pests and disease.

Commodity Credit Corp. *(Agriculture Dept.), 1400 Independence Ave. S.W. (mailing address: P.O. Box 2415, Washington, DC 20013-2415); (202) 720-3467. Fax, (202) 720-8254. August Schumacher Jr., under secretary. Information, (202) 720-5237. Internet, http://wwwaix.fsa.usda.gov/kcco/ccc.htm.*

Finances commodity stabilization programs, domestic and export surplus commodity disposal, foreign assistance, storage activities, and related programs.

Commodity Futures Trading Commission, *3 Lafayette Center, 1155 21st St. N.W. 20581; (202) 418-5030. Fax, (202) 418-5525. Brooksley Born, chair; Linda J. Ferren, executive director. Information, (202) 418-5080. Library, (202) 418-5255. Internet, http://www.cftc.gov.*

Administers the Commodity Exchange Act, which regulates all commodity futures and options to prevent fraudulent trade practices.

Cooperative State Research, Education, and Extension Service *(Agriculture Dept.), 1400 Independence Ave. S.W., #305A 20250-2201; (202) 720-4423. Fax, (202) 720-8987. B. H. Robinson, administrator. TDD, (202) 690-1899. Internet, http://www.reeusda.gov.*

Conducts workshops on management of farmer cooperatives and educational programs on sustainable agriculture. Provides farmers with management and marketing programs; offers training to rural communities.

Farm Service Agency *(Agriculture Dept.), 1400 Independence Ave. S.W., Mail Stop 0501 20250-0501; (202) 720-3467. Fax, (202) 720-9105. Keith Kelly, administrator. Information, (202) 720-5237. Internet, http://www.fsa.usda.gov.*

Administers farm commodity programs providing crop loans and purchases; provides crop payments when market prices fall below specified levels; sets acreage allotments and marketing quotas. Oversees the Federal Crop Insurance Corporation.

Foreign Agricultural Service *(Agriculture Dept.), 1400 Independence Ave. S.W. 20250; (202) 720-3935. Fax, (202) 690-2159. Lon Hatamiya, administrator; Christopher E. Goldthwait, general sales manager, (202) 720-5691. Information, (202) 720-7115. TDD, (202) 690-4879. Internet, http://www.fas.usda.gov.*

Promotes exports of U.S. commodities and assists with trade negotiations; coordinates activities of U.S. representatives in foreign countries who report on crop and market conditions; sponsors trade fairs in foreign countries to promote export of U.S. agricultural products; analyzes world demand and production of various commodities; monitors sales by private exporters.

Foreign Agricultural Service *(Agriculture Dept.), Commodity and Marketing Programs, 1400 Independence Ave. S.W., #5089 20250; (202) 720-4761. Fax, (202) 690-3606. James V. Parker, deputy administrator. Internet, http://www.fas.usda.gov/commodity.html.*

Works with nonprofit commodity and trade associations to increase and maintain exports of U.S. agricultural products. Studies and reports on markets for specific commodities and food products, both worldwide and in particular countries; assists with advertising and consumer promotions abroad.

Rural Business-Cooperative Service *(Agriculture Dept.), Cooperative Services, 1400 Independence Ave. S.W., #4016S, Mail Stop 3250 20250-3250; (202) 720-7558. Fax, (202) 720-4641. Randall E. Torgerson, deputy administrator. Information, (202) 720-6483.*

Provides cooperative enterprises that process and market farm products and other cooperatively owned, rural-based industries with technical and research assistance. Helps to develop new cooperatives.

State Dept., *Agricultural and Textile Trade Affairs,* *Main State Bldg., #3526 20520; (202) 647-3090. Fax, (202) 647-1894. Nick Riegg, chief, (202) 647-2302.*

Negotiates bilateral textile trade agreements with foreign governments concerning cotton, wool, and synthetic textile and apparel products. Develops agricultural trade policy; handles questions pertaining to international negotiations on all agricultural products covered by the World Trade Organization (WTO).

CONGRESS

House Agriculture Committee, *Subcommittee on Department Operations, Nutrition, and Foreign Agriculture, 1430 LHOB 20515; (202) 225-0171. Fax, (202) 225-4464. Robert W. Goodlatte, R-Va., chair; Kevin Kramp, staff director. Internet, http://www.house.gov/agriculture.*

Jurisdiction over legislation on emergency commodity distribution. Jurisdiction over legislation on international commodity agreements, foreign agricultural trade of commodities, and foreign market development (jurisdiction shared with House International Relations Committee).

House Agriculture Committee, *Subcommittee on General Farm Commodities, 1430 LHOB 20515; (202) 225-0171. Fax, (202) 225-4464. Bill Barrett, R-Neb., chair; Mike Neruda, staff director. Internet, http://www.house. gov/agriculture.*

Jurisdiction over legislation on feed grains, wheat, oilseeds, lentils, peas, soybeans, dry edible beans, cotton, cottonseed, and rice. Jurisdiction over legislation on the Commodity Credit Corp. and agricultural trade matters.

House Agriculture Committee, *Subcommittee on Livestock, Dairy, and Poultry, 1301 LHOB 20515; (202) 225-0029. Fax, (202) 225-4369. Richard W. Pombo, R-Calif., chair; Chris D'Arcy, staff director. Internet, http://www.house.gov/agriculture/livestoc.htm.*

Jurisdiction over legislation on dairy commodity programs and wool.

House Agriculture Committee, *Subcommittee on Risk Management and Specialty Crops, 1301 LHOB 20515; (202) 225-4652. Thomas W. Ewing, R-Ill., chair; Stacy Carey, staff director.*

Jurisdiction over legislation on tobacco, peanuts, sugar, and on the inspection and certification of flowers, fruits, and vegetables. Jurisdiction over legislation on the Commodity Futures Trading Commission and the Commodity Exchange Act.

House International Relations Committee, *Subcommittee on International Economic Policy and Trade, 702 O'Neill Bldg. 20515; (202) 225-3345. Fax, (202) 225-0432. Ileana Ros-Lehtinen, R-Fla., chair; Mauricio Tamargo, staff director. Internet, http://www.house.gov/ international_relations.*

Jurisdiction over legislation on international commodity agreements, foreign agricultural trade of commodities and foreign market development (jurisdiction shared with House Agriculture Committee), and export controls on agricultural commodities.

House Small Business Committee, *Subcommittee on Tax, Finance, and Exports, B363 RHOB 20515; (202) 226-2630. Fax, (202) 225-8950. Donald Manzullo, R-Ill., chair; Philip D. Eskeland, staff director.*

Jurisdiction over legislation on export expansion and agricultural development as it relates to the small-business community.

Senate Agriculture, Nutrition, and Forestry Committee, *SR-328A 20510; (202) 224-2035. Fax, (202) 224-1725. Richard G. Lugar, R-Ind., chair; Randy Green, staff director. Internet, http://www.senate.gov/~agriculture.*

Jurisdiction over the Commodity Futures Trading Commission and the Commodity Exchange Act.

Senate Agriculture, Nutrition, and Forestry Committee, *Subcommittee on Marketing, Inspection, and Product Promotion, SR-328A 20510; (202) 224-2035. Fax, (202) 224-1725. Paul Coverdell, R-Ga., chair; Richard Gupton, legislative assistant. Internet, http://www.senate. gov/committee/agriculture.html.*

Oversight of international commodity agreements, foreign agricultural trade of commodities, foreign market development, and export controls on agricultural commodities.

Senate Agriculture, Nutrition, and Forestry Committee, *Subcommittee on Production and Price Competitiveness, SR-326 20510; (202) 224-5054. Thad Cochran, R-Miss., chair; Mark E. Keenum, legislative assistant.*

Jurisdiction over legislation on agricultural commodities, including feed grains; wheat; oilseeds, including tung nuts, flaxseed, soybeans, dry edible beans, cotton, cottonseed, and rice; dairy products; wool; tobacco; peanuts; and sugar (jurisdiction over legislation on sugar imports shared with Senate Finance Committee).

Senate Agriculture, Nutrition, and Forestry Committee, *Subcommittee on Research, Nutrition, and General Legislation, SR-361A 20510; (202) 224-2035.*

Fax, (202) 224-1725. Mitch McConnell, R-Ky., chair; David Hovermale, legislative assistant. Internet, http:// www.senate.gov/~agriculture.

Jurisdiction over legislation on the inspection and certification of flowers, fruits, and vegetables. Oversight of commodity donations and emergency commodity distribution.

Senate Finance Committee, *SD-219 20510; (202) 224-4515. Fax, (202) 224-5920. William V. Roth Jr., R-Del., chair; Lindy L. Paull, staff director. Internet, http://www. senate.gov/~finance.*

Jurisdiction over some legislation on sugar, including sugar imports (jurisdiction shared with Senate Agriculture, Nutrition, and Forestry Committee).

Senate Small Business Committee, *SR-428A 20510; (202) 224-5175. Fax, (202) 224-4885. Christopher S. Bond, R-Mo., chair; Louis Taylor, staff director. Internet, http://www.senate.gov/~sbc.*

Jurisdiction over legislation on export expansion and agricultural development as it relates to the small-business community.

NONPROFIT

Agribusiness Council, *1312 18th St. N.W., #300 20036; (202) 296-4563. Fax, (202) 887-9178. Nicholas E. Hollis, president.*

Works to strengthen U.S. competitiveness in overseas agricultural markets. Promotes cooperation between private industry and government to improve international agricultural trade and development. Sponsors trade missions to developing countries. Helps to establish state and local agribusiness councils. (U.S. affiliate of Agri-Energy Roundtable.)

Agri-Energy Roundtable, *1312 18th St. N.W., #300 20036; (202) 887-0528. Fax, (202) 887-9178. Nicholas E. Hollis, executive director.*

Membership: companies, international organizations, and affiliated agro-industry associations in emerging countries. International clearinghouse that encourages cooperation in energy and agricultural development between industrialized and developing nations.

American Seed Trade Assn., *601 13th St. N.W., #570S 20005; (202) 638-3128. Fax, (202) 638-3171. Dean Urmston, executive vice president. Internet, http://www.amseed. com.*

Membership: producers and merchandisers of seeds. Conducts seminars on research developments in corn, sorghum, soybean, garden seeds, and other farm seeds; promotes overseas seed market development.

International Assn. of Refrigerated Warehouses, *7315 Wisconsin Ave., #1200N, Bethesda, MD 20814; (301) 652-5674. Fax, (301) 652-7269. J. William Hudson, president. Internet, http://www.iarw.org.*

Membership: owners and operators of public refrigerated warehouses. Interests include labor, transportation, taxes, environment, safety, regulatory compliance, and food distribution. Monitors legislation and regulations.

National Cooperative Business Assn., *1401 New York Ave. N.W., #1100 20005-2146; (202) 638-6222. Fax, (202) 638-1374. Russell C. Notar, president. Internet, ncba@ ncba.org or http://www.cooperative.org.*

Alliance of cooperatives, businesses, and state cooperative associations. Provides information about starting and managing agricultural cooperatives in the United States and in developing nations. Monitors legislation and regulations.

National Council of Farmer Cooperatives, *50 F St. N.W., #900 20001; (202) 626-8700. Fax, (202) 626-8722. David Graves, president. Internet, info@ncfc.org or http://www.access.digex.net/~ncfc/members.*

Membership: cooperative businesses owned and operated by farmers. Encourages research on agricultural cooperatives; provides statistics and analyzes trends. Monitors legislation and regulations on agricultural trade, transportation, energy, and tax issues.

U.S. Agricultural Export Development Council, *910 17th St. N.W., #800 20006; (202) 887-8992. Fax, (202) 887-8993. John Mentis, executive director. Internet, usaedc@msn.com.*

Membership: producer and agribusiness organizations. Works with the Foreign Agricultural Service on projects to create, expand, and maintain agricultural markets abroad. Sponsors seminars and workshops.

Cotton

AGENCIES

Agricultural Marketing Service *(Agriculture Dept.),* **Cotton,** *1400 Independence Ave. S.W., #2641 (mailing address: P.O. Box 96456, Washington, DC 20090-6456); (202) 720-3193. Fax, (202) 690-1718. Mary E. Atienza, deputy administrator. Internet, http://www.usda.gov/ ams/cotton.htm.*

Administers cotton marketing programs; sets cotton grading standards and conducts quality inspections based on those standards. Maintains market news service to inform producers of daily price changes.

Farm Service Agency *(Agriculture Dept.), Fibers Analysis,* 1400 Independence Ave. S.W., Mail Stop 0515 20250-0515; (202) 720-7954. Fax, (202) 690-1346. Wayne Bjorlie, director.

Develops production adjustment and price support programs to balance supply and demand for cotton.

Farm Service Agency *(Agriculture Dept.), Price Support,* 1400 Independence Ave. S.W., Mail Stop 0512 20250-0512; (202) 720-7901. Fax, (202) 690-3307. Grady Bilberry, director.

Develops cotton price support and loan programs through the payment-in-kind program, loans and diversion payments to farmers, direct purchases of commodities from farmers, and payments to support "target prices" fixed by law for upland cotton.

INTERNATIONAL ORGANIZATIONS

International Cotton Advisory Committee, 1629 K St. N.W., #702 20006; (202) 463-6660. Fax, (202) 463-6950. Lawrence H. Shaw, executive director. Internet, secretariat@icac.org or http://www.icac.org.

Membership: cotton producing and consuming countries. Provides information on cotton production, trade, consumption, stocks, and prices.

NONPROFIT

American Cotton Shippers Assn., 1725 K St. N.W., #1404 20006; (202) 296-7116. Fax, (202) 659-5322. Neal P. Gillen, executive vice president. Internet, http://www. acsa-cotton.org.

Coalition of four regional cotton shippers' associations. Monitors legislation and regulations concerning international cotton trade. (Headquarters in Memphis.)

Cotton Council International, 1521 New Hampshire Ave. N.W. 20036; (202) 745-7805. Fax, (202) 483-4040. Allen Terhaar, executive director. Internet, http://www. cottonusa.org/index.htm.

Division of National Cotton Council of America. Promotes U.S. raw cotton exports. (Headquarters in Memphis.)

Cotton Warehouse Assn. of America, 1156 15th St. N.W., #1103 20005; (202) 331-4337. Fax, (202) 331-4330. Donald L. Wallace Jr., executive vice president. Internet, dwassoc@erols.com.

Membership: cotton compress and warehouse workers. Serves as a liaison between members and government agencies; monitors legislation and regulations.

National Cotton Council of America, 1521 New Hampshire Ave. N.W. 20036; (202) 745-7805. Fax, (202)

483-4040. John Maguire, vice president, Washington Office. Internet, http://www.cotton.org/ncc.

Membership: all segments of the U.S. cotton industry. Provides statistics and information on such topics as cotton history and processing. (Headquarters in Memphis.)

Dairy Products and Eggs

AGENCIES

Agricultural Marketing Service *(Agriculture Dept.), Dairy,* 1400 Independence Ave. S.W., #2968 (mailing address: P.O. Box 96456, Washington, DC 20090-6456); (202) 720-4392. Fax, (202) 690-3410. Richard M. McKee, deputy administrator. Internet, http://www.usda.gov/ ams/dairy.

Administers dairy product marketing and promotion programs; grades dairy products; maintains market news service on daily price changes; sets minimum price that farmers receive for milk.

Farm Service Agency *(Agriculture Dept.), Dairy,* 1400 Independence Ave. S.W., Mail Stop 0552 20250-0552; (202) 720-3385. Fax, (202) 690-0767. Bonnie Tanner, chief. Internet, http://www.fsa.usda.gov.

Administers dairy stabilization and price support programs, including purchases and dispositions of dairy products acquired under price supports.

Farm Service Agency *(Agriculture Dept.), Dairy and Sweeteners Analysis,* 1400 Independence Ave. S.W., Mail Stop 0516 20250-0516; (202) 720-6733. Fax, (202) 690-1346. Thomas Lederer, acting director.

Develops production adjustment and price support programs to balance supply and demand for dairy products and sugar.

NONPROFIT

American Butter Institute, 2101 Wilson Blvd., #400, Arlington, VA 22201; (703) 243-6111. Fax, (703) 841-9328. Jerome J. Kozak, executive director.

Membership: butter manufacturers, packagers, and distributors. Interests include dairy price supports and programs, packaging and labeling, and imports. Monitors legislation and regulations.

Egg Nutrition Center, 1819 H St. N.W., #520 20006; (202) 833-8850. Fax, (202) 463-0102. Donald McNamara, director. Internet, eggnutr@aol.com or http://www. enc-online.org.

Provides information on egg nutrition and related health issues. Disseminates information on cholesterol and heart disease.

International Dairy Foods Assn., *1250 H St. N.W., #900 20005; (202) 737-4332. Fax, (202) 331-7820. E. Linwood Tipton, president. Internet, http://www.idfa.org.*

Membership: processors, manufacturers, marketers, and distributors of dairy foods. Provides members with marketing, public relations, and management services. Monitors legislation and regulations. (Affiliated with the Milk Industry Foundation, the National Cheese Institute, and the International Ice Cream Assn.)

International Ice Cream Assn., *1250 H St. N.W., #900 20005; (202) 737-4332. Fax, (202) 331-7820. E. Linwood Tipton, president.*

Membership: manufacturers and distributors of ice cream and other frozen desserts. Conducts market research. Monitors legislation and regulations.

Milk Industry Foundation, *1250 H St. N.W., #900 20005; (202) 737-4332. Fax, (202) 331-7820. E. Linwood Tipton, president.*

Membership: processors of fluid milk and fluid-milk products. Conducts market research. Monitors legislation and regulations.

National Cheese Institute, *1250 H St. N.W., #900 20005; (202) 737-4332. Fax, (202) 331-7820. E. Linwood Tipton, president.*

Membership: cheese manufacturers, packagers, processors, and distributors. Interests include dairy price supports and programs, packaging and labeling, and imports. Monitors legislation and regulations.

National Milk Producers Federation, *2101 Wilson Blvd., #400, Arlington, VA 22201; (703) 243-6111. Fax, (703) 841-9328. Jerome J. Kozak, chief executive officer. Internet, nmpf@aol.com or http://www.nmpf.org.*

Membership: dairy farmer cooperatives. Provides information on development and modification of sanitary regulations, product standards, and marketing procedures for dairy products.

United Egg Producers, *1 Massachusetts Ave. N.W., #800 20001-1401; (202) 789-2499. Fax, (202) 682-0775. Christine Nelson, director, Government Relations. Internet, cnelson@mwmlaw.com or http://www.unitedegg.org.*

Membership: regional egg marketing cooperatives. Monitors legislation and regulations. (Headquarters in Atlanta.)

Fruits and Vegetables

AGENCIES

Agricultural Marketing Service *(Agriculture Dept.),* **Fruit and Vegetable,** *1400 Independence Ave. S.W. (mailing address: P.O. Box 96456, Washington, DC 20090-6456); (202) 720-4722. Fax, (202) 720-0016. Robert C. Keeney, director. Internet, http://www.usda.gov/ams/fruitveg.htm.*

Administers fruit and vegetable marketing service and regulatory programs, including marketing orders and research and promotional programs for fruits, vegetables, and specialty crops; sets grading standards for fresh and processed fruits and vegetables; conducts quality inspections based on those standards; maintains market news service to inform producers of daily price changes.

Economic Research Service *(Agriculture Dept.),* *1800 M St. N.W., #5120 20036; (202) 694-5200. Fax, (202) 694-5792. Joy Harwood, chief, Field Crops; Barry Krissoff, chief, Specialty Crops. Internet, http://www.econ.ag.gov.*

Conducts market research; studies and forecasts domestic supply-and-demand trends for fruits and vegetables.

NONPROFIT

International Banana Assn., *1929 39th St. N.W. 20007; (202) 223-1183. Fax, (202) 223-1194. Robert M. Moore, president.*

Works to improve global distribution and increased consumption of bananas; collects and disseminates information about the banana industry; serves as a liaison between the U.S. government and banana-producing countries on issues of concern to the industry.

United Fresh Fruit and Vegetable Assn., *727 N. Washington St., Alexandria, VA 22314; (703) 836-3410. Fax, (703) 836-7745. Thomas Stenzel, president.*

Membership: growers, shippers, wholesalers, retailers, food service operators, importers, and exporters involved in producing and marketing fresh fruits and vegetables. Represents the industry before the government and the public sector.

U.S. Apple Assn., *6707 Old Dominion Dr., #320, McLean, VA (mailing address: P.O. Box 1137, McLean, VA 22101-1137); (703) 442-8850. Fax, (703) 790-0845. Vacant, president.*

Membership: U.S. commercial apple growers and processors, distributors, exporters, importers, and retailers of apples. Compiles statistics, including imports and exports; promotes research and marketing; provides information about apples and nutrition to educators. Monitors legislation and regulations.

Wine Institute, *601 13th St. N.W., #580 South 20005; (202) 408-0870. Fax, (202) 371-0061. Robert P. Koch,* senior vice president, Federal Government Relations. Internet, http://www.wineinstitute.org.

Membership: California wineries and affiliated businesses. Seeks international recognition for California wines; conducts promotional campaigns in other countries. Monitors legislation and regulations. (Headquarters in San Francisco.)

Grains and Oilseeds

AGENCIES

Agricultural Marketing Service *(Agriculture Dept.), Livestock and Seed, 1400 Independence Ave. S.W., #2092S (mailing address: P.O. Box 96456, Washington, DC 20090-6456); (202) 720-5705. Fax, (202) 720-3499. Barry L. Carpenter, deputy administrator. Internet, http://www.usda.gov/ams/lsd.htm.*

Administers programs for marketing grain, including rice; maintains market news service to inform producers of grain market situation and daily price changes.

Farm Service Agency *(Agriculture Dept.), Feed Grains and Oilseeds Analysis, 1400 Independence Ave. S.W., Mail Stop 0532 20250; (202) 720-4417. Fax, (202) 690-1346. Phil Sronce, director.*

Develops production adjustment and price support programs to balance supply and demand for certain commodities, including corn, soybeans, and other feed grains and oilseeds.

Farm Service Agency *(Agriculture Dept.), Food Grains, 1400 Independence Ave. S.W., Mail Stop 0508 20250; (202) 720-7923. Fax, (202) 720-8261. Brad Karmen, director. Internet, http://www.fsa.usda.gov.*

Develops production adjustment and price support programs to balance supply and demand for certain commodities, including wheat and rice.

Farm Service Agency *(Agriculture Dept.), Price Support, 1400 Independence Ave. S.W., Mail Stop 0512 20250-0512; (202) 720-7901. Fax, (202) 690-3307. Grady Bilberry, director. Internet, http://www.fsa.usda.gov.*

Develops grain and oilseeds price support and loan programs through the payment-in-kind program, loans and diversion payments to farmers, direct purchases of commodities from farmers, and payments to support "target prices" fixed by law for grain and oilseeds.

Grain Inspection, Packers, and Stockyards Administration *(Agriculture Dept.), 1400 Independence Ave. S.W., Stop 3601 20250-3601; (202) 720-0219. Fax, (202) 205-9237. James Baker, administrator. Information, (202) 720-5091. Internet, http://www.usda.gov/gipsa.*

Administers inspection and weighing program for grain, soybeans, rice, sunflower seeds, and other processed commodities; conducts quality inspections based on established standards.

NONPROFIT

American Corn Millers Federation, *600 Maryland Ave. S.W., #305W 20024-2573; (202) 554-1614. Fax, (202) 554-1616. Betsy Faga, president. Internet, cornmiller@aol.com.*

Trade association representing the dry corn milling industry. Sponsors research on white corn.

American Feed Industry Assn., *1501 Wilson Blvd., #1100, Arlington, VA 22209; (703) 524-0810. Fax, (703) 524-1921. David A. Bossman, president. Internet, mailafia@tomco.net or http://www.afia.org.*

Membership: feed manufacturers and their suppliers. Conducts seminars on feed grain production, marketing, advertising, and quality control.

American Soybean Assn., *600 Pennsylvania Ave. S.E., #320 20003; (202) 969-8900. Fax, (202) 969-7036. John Gordley, Washington representative. Internet, http://www.oilseeds.org/asa.*

Membership: soybean farmers. Promotes expanded world markets and research for the benefit of soybean growers; maintains a network of state and international offices. (Headquarters in St. Louis.)

Corn Refiners Assn., *1701 Pennsylvania Ave. N.W., #950 20006; (202) 331-1634. Fax, (202) 331-2054. Charles S. Conner, president. Internet, details@corn.org or http://www.corn.org.*

Promotes research on technical aspects of corn refining and product development; acts as a clearinghouse for members who award research grants to colleges and universities. Monitors legislation and regulations.

Millers National Federation, *600 Maryland Ave. S.W., #305W 20024-2573; (202) 484-2200. Fax, (202) 488-7416. Roy Henwood, president. Internet, millersnet@aol.com.*

Membership: companies owning wheat and rye flour mills. Seeks to inform the public, the industry, and government about issues affecting the domestic flour milling industry. Monitors legislation and regulations.

National Assn. of Wheat Growers, *415 2nd St. N.E., #300 20002; (202) 547-7800. Fax, (202) 546-2638. Margie Williams, acting chief executive officer. Internet, nawg1@aol.com or http://www.wheatworld.org.*

Federation of state wheat grower associations. Sponsors annual seminar on legislative issues.

National Corn Growers Assn., *122 C St. N.W., #510 20001; (202) 628-7001. Fax, (202) 628-1933. Bruce Knight, vice president, Public Policy. Internet, corninfo@ ncga.com or http://www.ncga.com.*

Promotes the use, marketing, and efficient production of corn; conducts research and educational activities. Monitors legislation and regulations. (Headquarters in St. Louis.)

National Grain and Feed Assn., *1201 New York Ave. N.W., #830 20005; (202) 289-0873. Fax, (202) 289-5388. Kendell Keith, president. Internet, http://www.ngfa.org.*

Membership: firms that process U.S. grains and oilseeds for domestic and export markets. Arbitration panel resolves disputes over trade and commercial regulations.

National Grain Trade Council, *1300 L St. N.W., #925 20005; (202) 842-0400. Fax, (202) 789-7223. Robert R. Petersen, president.*

Federation of grain exchanges and national associations of grain processors, handlers, merchandisers, distributors, exporters, and warehouse workers.

National Institute of Oilseed Products, *1101 15th St. N.W., #202 20005; (202) 785-3232. Fax, (202) 223-9741. Richard Cristol, Washington representative. Internet, niop@assnhq.com.*

Membership: companies and individuals involved in manufacturing and trading oilseed products. Provides statistics on oilseed product imports and exports.

National Oilseed Processors Assn., *1255 23rd St. N.W., #850 20037-1174; (202) 452-8040. Fax, (202) 835-0400. Sheldon J. Hauck, president. Internet, http://www. oilseeds.org/nopa.*

Provides information on soybean crops, products, processing, and commodity programs; interests include international trade.

North American Export Grain Assn., *1300 L St. N.W., #900 20005; (202) 682-4030. Fax, (202) 682-4033. Daniel G. Amstutz, president. Internet, naega@internetmci.com.*

Membership: grain exporting firms and others interested in the grain export industry. Provides information on grain export allowances, rates, distribution, and current market trends; sponsors seminars. Monitors legislation and regulations.

Soy Protein Council, *1255 23rd St. N.W., #850 20037-1174; (202) 467-6610. Fax, (202) 833-3636. Sheldon J. Hauck, executive vice president.*

Membership: firms that process and sell vegetable proteins or food products containing vegetable proteins.

Provides information on the nutritional properties of vegetable proteins.

Terminal Elevator Grain Merchants' Assn., *1300 L St. N.W., #925 20005; (202) 842-0400. Fax, (202) 789-7223. Robert R. Petersen, secretary.*

Membership: companies owning terminal elevators. Monitors legislation and regulations concerning grain inspection programs, transportation of grain, and general farm policy.

U.S. Feed Grains Council, *1400 K St. N.W., #1200 20005; (202) 789-0789. Fax, (202) 898-0522. Kenneth Hobbie, president. Internet, grains@grains.org or http:// www.grains.org.*

Membership: feed grain producers and exporters; railroads; banks; and chemical, machinery, malting, and seed companies interested in feed grain exports. Promotes development of U.S. feed grain markets overseas.

U.S. Wheat Associates, *1620 Eye St. N.W., #801 20006; (202) 463-0999. Fax, (202) 785-1052. Alan Tracy, president. Internet, info@uswheat.org.*

Membership: wheat farmers. Develops export markets for the U.S. wheat industry; provides information on wheat production and marketing.

USA Rice Federation, *4301 N. Fairfax Dr., #305, Arlington, VA 22203; (703) 351-8161. Fax, (703) 351-8162. Ellen Terpstra, president. Internet, http://www.usarice.com.*

Membership: rice milling and related firms. Provides U.S. and foreign rice trade and industry information; assists in establishing quality standards for rice production and milling. Monitors legislation and regulations.

Sugar

AGENCIES

Economic Research Service *(Agriculture Dept.), 1800 M St. N.W., #5120 20036; (202) 694-5200. Fax, (202) 694-5792. Joy Harwood, chief, Field Crops; Barry Krissoff, chief, Specialty Crops. Internet, http://www.econ.ag.gov.*

Conducts market research; studies and forecasts domestic supply-and-demand trends for sugar and other sweeteners.

Farm Service Agency *(Agriculture Dept.), Dairy and Sweeteners Analysis, 1400 Independence Ave. S.W., Mail Stop 0516 20250-0516; (202) 720-6733. Fax, (202) 690-1346. Thomas Lederer, acting director.*

Develops production adjustment and price support programs to balance supply and demand for certain commodities, including dairy products, sugar, and honey.

American Sugar Beet Growers Assn., *1156 15th St. N.W., #1101 20005; (202) 833-2398. Fax, (202) 833-2962. Luther Markwart, executive vice president. Internet, asga@ aol.com or http://members.aol.com/asga/sugar.htm.*

Membership: sugar beet growers associations. Serves as liaison to U.S. government agencies, including the Agriculture Dept. and the U.S. Trade Representative. Monitors legislation and regulations.

Chocolate Manufacturers Assn./American Cocoa Research Institute, *7900 Westpark Dr., #A320, McLean, VA 22102; (703) 790-5011. Fax, (703) 790-5752. Lawrence T. Graham, president. Internet, http://www.candyusa.org.*

Membership: U.S. chocolate manufacturers and distributors. Sponsors educational programs; offers grants for cocoa research.

National Confectioners Assn., *7900 Westpark Dr., #A320, McLean, VA 22102; (703) 790-5750. Fax, (703) 790-5752. Lawrence T. Graham, president. Internet, http://www.candyusa.org.*

Membership: confectionery manufacturers and suppliers. Provides information on confectionery consumption and nutrition; sponsors research on candy technology. Monitors legislation and regulations.

Sugar Assn., *1101 15th St. N.W., #600 20005; (202) 785-1122. Fax, (202) 785-5019. Richard Keelor, president. Internet, sugar@sugar.org.*

Membership: sugar processors, growers, refiners, and planters. Provides nutritional information on sugar.

U.S. Beet Sugar Assn., *1156 15th St. N.W., #1019 20005; (202) 296-4820. Fax, (202) 331-2065. Van R. Olsen, president. Internet, beetsugar@aol.com.*

Membership: beet sugar processors. Library open to the public by appointment.

U.S. Cane Sugar Refiners' Assn., *1730 Rhode Island Ave. N.W., #608 20036; (202) 331-1458. Fax, (202) 785-5110. Nicholas Kominus, president. Internet, uscsra@ worldnet.att.net.*

Membership: independent sugar cane refiners. Monitors legislation and regulations.

Tobacco and Peanuts

See also Consumer Protection (chap. 1)

AGENCIES

Agricultural Marketing Service *(Agriculture Dept.), Tobacco, 300 12th St. S.W., #502 Annex (mailing address: P.O. Box 96456, Washington, DC 20090-6456); (202) 205-*
0567. Fax, (202) 205-0235. John P. Duncan III, deputy administrator. Internet, http://www.usda.gov/ams/ tobacco.htm.

Administers tobacco marketing programs; sets standards for domestic and imported tobacco; tests imports for prohibited pesticides; conducts voluntary inspections of U.S. tobacco exports; maintains market news service to inform producers of price changes.

Economic Research Service *(Agriculture Dept.), 1800 M St. N.W., #5120 20036; (202) 694-5200. Fax, (202) 694-5792. Joy Harwood, chief, Field Crops; Barry Krissoff, chief, Specialty Crops. Internet, http://www.econ.ag.gov.*

Conducts market research; studies and forecasts domestic supply-and-demand trends for tobacco.

Farm Service Agency *(Agriculture Dept.), Tobacco and Peanuts, 1400 Independence Ave. S.W., Mail Stop 0514 20250; (202) 720-7413. Fax, (202) 720-1948. Charles Hatcher, director. Internet, http://www.fsa.usda.gov.*

Develops production adjustment and price support programs to balance supply and demand for tobacco and peanuts.

Burley and Dark Leaf Tobacco Assn., *1100 17th St. N.W., #505 20036; (202) 296-6820. Fax, (202) 467-6349. Pem Pfisterer Clark, managing director.*

Membership: growers of burley and dark leaf tobacco. Promotes tobacco sales.

Cigar Assn. of America, *1100 17th St. N.W., #504 20036; (202) 223-8204. Fax, (202) 833-0379. Norman F. Sharp, president.*

Membership: growers and suppliers of cigar leaf tobacco and manufacturers, packagers, importers, and distributors of cigars. Monitors legislation and regulations.

National Peanut Council, *1500 King St., #301, Alexandria, VA 22314-2737; (703) 838-9500. Fax, (703) 838-9089. Jeannette Anderson, president. Internet, peanutsusa@aol.com.*

Membership: peanut growers, shellers, brokers, and manufacturers, as well as allied companies. Provides information on economic and nutritional value of peanuts; coordinates research; promotes U.S. peanut exports, domestic production, and market development.

Smokeless Tobacco Council, *1627 K St. N.W., #700 20006; (202) 452-1252. Fax, (202) 452-0118. Jeffery L. Schlagenhauf, president.*

Members: smokeless tobacco manufacturers. Monitors legislation and regulations.

Tobacco Associates, *1725 K St. N.W., #512 20006-1401; (202) 828-9144. Fax, (202) 828-9149. Kirk Wayne, president.*

Membership: producers of flue-cured tobacco. Promotes exports; provides information to encourage overseas market development.

Tobacco Institute, *1875 Eye St. N.W., #800 20006; (202) 457-4800. Fax, (202) 457-9350. Samuel D. Chilcote Jr., president.*

Membership: manufacturers of tobacco products. Provides information on the economics, history, and views of the U.S. tobacco industry.

FARM LOANS, INSURANCE, AND SUBSIDIES

AGENCIES

Commodity Credit Corp. *(Agriculture Dept.), 1400 Independence Ave. S.W. (mailing address: P.O. Box 2415, Washington, DC 20013); (202) 720-3467. Fax, (202) 720-8254. August Schumacher Jr., under secretary. Internet, http://wwwaix.fsa.usda.gov/kcco/ccc.htm.*

Administers and finances the commodity stabilization program through loans, purchases, and supplemental payments; sells through domestic and export markets commodities acquired by the government under this program; administers some aspects of foreign food aid through the Food for Peace program; provides storage facilities.

Farm Credit Administration, *1501 Farm Credit Dr., McLean, VA 22102-5090; (703) 883-4007. Fax, (703) 734-5784. Marsha Pyle Martin, chair. Information, (703) 883-4056. TDD, (703) 883-4444. Internet, info-line@fca.gov or http://www.fca.gov.*

Examines and regulates the cooperative Farm Credit System, which comprises federal land bank associations, production credit associations, federal land credit associations, agriculture credit associations, farm credit banks, and banks for cooperatives. Oversees credit programs and related services for harvesters of aquatic products, farmers, ranchers, producers, and their associations.

Farm Credit Administration, *Examination, 1501 Farm Credit Dr., McLean, VA 22102-5090; (703) 883-4160. Fax, (703) 893-2978. Roland E. Smith, chief examiner. Press, (703) 883-4056.*

Enforces and oversees compliance with the Farm Credit Act. Monitors cooperatively owned member

banks' and associations' compliance with laws prohibiting discrimination in credit transactions.

Farm Service Agency *(Agriculture Dept.), 1400 Independence Ave. S.W., Mail Stop 0501 20250-0501; (202) 720-3467. Fax, (202) 720-9105. Keith Kelly, administrator. Information, (202) 720-5237. Internet, http://www.fsa.usda.gov.*

Administers farm commodity programs providing crop loans and purchases; provides crop payments when market prices fall below specified levels; sets acreage allotments and marketing quotas; assists farmers in areas affected by natural disasters. Oversees the Federal Crop Insurance Corporation.

Farm Service Agency *(Agriculture Dept.), Farm Credit Programs, 1400 Independence Ave. S.W. 20250; (202) 720-4671. Fax, (202) 690-3573. Caroline B. Cooksie, deputy administrator. Internet, http://www.fsa.usda.gov.*

Provides outreach programs and technical assistance for socially disadvantaged applicants for Agriculture Dept. farm loans.

Federal Agricultural Mortgage Corp. (Farmer Mac), *919 18th St. N.W., #200 20006-5503; (202) 872-7700. Fax, (202) 872-7713. Thomas R. Clark, vice president. Internet, http://www.farmermac.com.*

Private corporation chartered by Congress to provide a secondary mortgage market for farm and rural housing loans. Guarantees principal and interest repayment on securities backed by farm and rural housing loans.

Risk Management Agency *(Agriculture Dept.), 1400 Independence Ave. S.W., #3053S 20250; (202) 690-2803. Fax, (202) 690-2818. Kenneth D. Ackerman, administrator. Internet, http://www.act.fcic.usda.gov.*

Provides farmers with insurance against crops lost because of bad weather, insects, disease, and other natural causes.

Rural Development *(Agriculture Dept.), Civil Rights, 1400 Independence Ave. S.W. (mailing address: AG Box 0703, Washington, DC 20250-0703); (202) 690-9800. Fax, (202) 690-9803. Cheryl Prejean Greaux, director.*

Enforces compliance with the Equal Credit Opportunity Act, which prohibits discrimination on the basis of sex, marital status, race, color, religion, disability, or age, in public assistance for rural housing and farm loan programs.

CONGRESS

House Agriculture Committee, *1301 LHOB 20515; (202) 225-0029. Fax, (202) 225-0917. Bob Smith, R-Ore.,* chair; Paul Unger, staff director, (202) 225-2171. Internet, http://www.house.gov/agriculture.

Jurisdiction over legislation on price supports.

House Agriculture Committee, *Subcommittee on General Farm Commodities, 1430 LHOB 20515; (202) 225-0171. Fax, (202) 225-4464. Bill Barrett, R-Neb., chair; Mike Neruda, staff director. Internet, http://www.house. gov/agriculture.*

Jurisdiction over legislation on natural disaster assistance relating to the farm industry and production adjustment programs.

House Agriculture Committee, *Subcommittee on Risk Management and Specialty Crops, 1301 LHOB 20515; (202) 225-4652. Thomas W. Ewing, R-Ill., chair; Stacy Carey, staff director.*

Jurisdiction over legislation on agricultural credit and crop insurance.

House Small Business Committee, *2361 RHOB 20515; (202) 225-5821. Fax, (202) 225-3587. James M. Talent, R-Mo., chair; Mark Strand, chief of staff. Internet, http://www.house.gov/smbiz.*

Jurisdiction over rural economy and family farming legislation as it relates to the small-business community.

House Ways and Means Committee, *Subcommittee on Oversight, 1136 LHOB 20515; (202) 225-7601. Fax, (202) 225-9680. Nancy L. Johnson, R-Conn., chair; William McKenney, staff director. Internet, http://www. house.gov/ways_means.*

Oversees government-sponsored enterprises, including the Farm Credit Banks and the Federal Agricultural Mortgage Corp., with regard to the financial risk they pose to the federal government.

Senate Agriculture, Nutrition, and Forestry Committee, *Subcommittee on Forestry, Conservation, and Rural Revitalization, SR-328A 20510; (202) 224-2035. Rick Santorum, R-Pa., chair; David French, legislative assistant. Internet, http://www.senate.gov/~agriculture.*

Jurisdiction over legislation on agricultural credit, loans, natural disaster assistance, and insurance, including crop insurance.

Senate Agriculture, Nutrition, and Forestry Committee, *Subcommittee on Production and Price Competitiveness, SR-326 20510; (202) 224-5054. Thad Cochran, R-Miss., chair; Mark E. Keenum, legislative assistant.*

Jurisdiction over legislation on price supports and production adjustment programs.

Senate Banking, Housing, and Urban Affairs Committee, *SD-534 20510; (202) 224-7391. Fax, (202) 224-5137. Alfonse M. D'Amato, R-N.Y., chair; Howard Menell, staff director. Internet, http://www.senate.gov/ ~banking.*

Oversees government-sponsored enterprises, including the Farm Credit Banks and the Federal Agricultural Mortgage Corp., with regard to the financial risk they pose to the federal government.

Senate Small Business Committee, *SR-428A 20510; (202) 224-5175. Fax, (202) 224-4885. Christopher S. Bond, R-Mo., chair; Louis Taylor, staff director. Internet, http://www.senate.gov/~sbc.*

Jurisdiction over rural economy and family farming legislation as it relates to the small-business community.

NONPROFIT

Environmental Working Group, *1718 Connecticut Ave. N.W., #600 20009; (202) 667-6982. Fax, (202) 232-2592. Kenneth A. Cook, president. Internet, info@ewg.org or http://www.ewg.org.*

Research and advocacy group that studies and publishes reports on agricultural subsidies. Monitors legislation and regulations.

Farm Credit Council, *50 F St. N.W., #900 20001; (202) 626-8710. Fax, (202) 626-8718. William R. Weber, president.*

Represents the Farm Credit System, a national financial cooperative that makes loans to agricultural producers, rural homebuyers, farmer cooperatives, and rural utilities. Finances the export of U.S. agricultural commodities.

 FOOD AND NUTRITION

See also Commodities/Farm Produce (this chapter); Livestock and Poultry (this chapter)

AGENCIES

Agricultural Marketing Service *(Agriculture Dept.), Science and Technology, 1400 Independence Ave. S.W. (mailing address: P.O. Box 96456, Washington, DC 20090-6456); (202) 720-5231. Fax, (202) 720-6496. William J. Franks Jr., deputy administrator. Internet, http://www. usda.gov/ams/science.htm.*

Provides analytical testing to AMS divisions, federal and state agencies, and the private sector food industry; participates in international food safety organizations. Tests commodities traded with specific countries and regions, including butter, honey, eggs, nuts, poultry, and meat; analyzes nutritional value of U.S. military rations.

Agricultural Research Service *(Agriculture Dept.), 1400 Independence Ave. S.W., #302A 20250-0300; (202) 720-3656. Fax, (202) 720-5427. Edward B. Knipling, associate administrator. Internet, http://www.ars.usda.gov.*

Conducts studies on agricultural problems of domestic and international concern through nationwide network of research centers. Studies include research on human nutrition; livestock production and protection; crop production, protection, and processing; postharvest technology; and food distribution and market value.

Agriculture Dept., *Food, Nutrition, and Consumer Services, 1400 Independence Ave. S.W., #240E 20250; (202) 720-7711. Fax, (202) 690-3100. Shirley R. Watkins, under secretary. Internet, http://www.usda.gov/fcs.*

Oversees the Food and Consumer Service and the office of the consumer adviser for agricultural products.

Animal and Plant Health Inspection Service *(Agriculture Dept.), 1400 Independence Ave. S.W. (mailing address: Ag. Box 3407, Washington, DC 20250); (202) 720-3861. Fax, (202) 720-3982. Terry Medley, administrator. Information, (202) 720-2511. Internet, http://www.aphis.usda.gov.*

Administers animal disease control programs in cooperation with states; inspects imported animals, flowers, and plants; licenses the manufacture and marketing of veterinary biologics to ensure purity and effectiveness.

Cooperative State Research, Education, and Extension Service *(Agriculture Dept.), 1400 Independence Ave. S.W., #305A 20250-2201; (202) 720-4423. Fax, (202) 720-8987. B. H. Robinson, administrator. TDD, (202) 690-1899. Internet, http://www.reeusda.gov.*

Oversees county agents and operation of state offices that provide information on nutrition, diet, food purchase budgeting, food safety, home gardening, and other consumer concerns.

Food and Consumer Service *(Agriculture Dept.), 3101 Park Center Dr., #803, Alexandria, VA 22302; (703) 305-2062. Fax, (703) 305-2908. Yvette S. Jackson, administrator. Information, (703) 305-2276. Internet, http://www.usda.gov/fcs.*

Administers all Agriculture Dept. domestic food assistance, including the distribution of funds and food for school breakfast and lunch programs (preschool through secondary) to public and nonprofit private schools; the food stamp program; and a supplemental nutrition program for women, infants, and children (WIC).

Food and Consumer Service *(Agriculture Dept.), Child Nutrition, 3101 Park Center Dr., #1006, Alexandria, VA 22302; (703) 305-2590. Fax, (703) 305-2879. Stanley Garnett, director. Press, (703) 305-2276.*

Administers the transfer of funds to state agencies for the National School Lunch Program; the School Breakfast Program; the Special Milk Program, which helps schools and institutions provide children who do not have access to full meals under other child nutrition programs with fluid milk; the Child and Adult Care Food Program, which provides children in nonresidential child-care centers and family day care homes with year-round meal service; and the Summer Food Service Program, which provides children from low-income families with meals during the summer months.

Food and Consumer Service *(Agriculture Dept.), Food Distribution, 3101 Park Center Dr., #503, Alexandria, VA 22302; (703) 305-2680. Fax, (703) 305-2420. Les Johnson, director. TDD, (703) 305-2800.*

Administers the Emergency Food Assistance Program, under which butter, cheese, milk, rice, and other surplus commodities are distributed to the needy. Administers the National Commodity Processing Program, which facilitates distribution, at reduced prices, of processed foods to state agencies, including charitable institutions, child-care food programs, nutrition programs for the elderly, state correctional institutions, and summer food service programs.

Food and Consumer Service *(Agriculture Dept.), Food Stamp Program, 3101 Park Center Dr., #710, Alexandria, VA 22302; (703) 305-2026. Fax, (703) 305-2454. Susan Carr Gossman, deputy administrator.*

Administers, through state welfare agencies, the Food Stamp Program, which provides needy persons with food coupons to increase food purchasing power. Provides matching funds to cover half the cost of coupon issuance.

Food and Consumer Service *(Agriculture Dept.), Nutrition and Technical Services, 3101 Park Center Dr., #607, Alexandria, VA 22302; (703) 305-2585. Fax, (703) 305-2549. Patricia Daniels, director.*

Administers the Nutrition Education and Training Program, which provides states with grants for disseminating nutrition information to children and for in-service training of food service and teaching personnel; administers the Child Nutrition Labeling Program, which certifies that foods served in school lunch and breakfast programs meet nutritional requirements; provides information and technical assistance in nutrition and food service management.

Food and Consumer Service *(Agriculture Dept.), Supplemental Food Program, 3101 Park Center Dr., #540, Alexandria, VA 22302; (703) 305-2746. Fax, (703) 305-2196. Stanley C. Garnett, director, Food and Consumer Services.*

Provides health departments and agencies with federal funding for food supplements and administrative expenses to make food, nutrition education, and health services available to infants, young children, and pregnant, nursing, and postpartum women.

Food and Drug Administration *(Health and Human Services Dept.), Center for Food Safety and Applied Nutrition, 200 C St. S.W. 20204; (202) 205-4850. Fax, (202) 205-5025. Fred R. Shank, director. Press, (202) 205-4241. TDD, (202) 205-4863. Internet, http://vm.cfsan.fda.gov.*

Develops standards of composition and quality of foods (except meat and poultry but including fish); develops safety regulations for food and color additives for foods, cosmetics, and drugs; monitors pesticide residues in foods; conducts food safety and nutrition research; develops analytical methods for measuring food additives, nutrients, pesticides, and chemical and microbiological contaminants; recommends action to Justice Dept.

Food and Drug Administration *(Health and Human Services Dept.), Special Nutritionals, 200 C St. S.W., #2804 20204; (202) 205-4168. Fax, (202) 205-5295. Elizabeth A. Yetley, director.*

Scientific and technical component of the Center for Food Safety and Applied Nutrition. Conducts research on nutrients; develops regulations and labeling requirements on infant formulas, medical foods, and dietary supplements, including herbs.

Food Safety and Inspection Service *(Agriculture Dept.), 1400 Independence Ave. S.W., #331E 20250; (202) 720-7025. Fax, (202) 205-0158. Thomas J. Billy, administrator. Press, (202) 720-9113. Consumer inquiries, (800) 535-4555; in Washington, (202) 720-3333. Internet, http://www.usda.gov/fsis.*

Inspects meat, poultry, and egg products moving in interstate commerce for use as human food to ensure that they are safe, wholesome, and accurately labeled. Provides safe handling and labeling guidelines.

National Agricultural Library *(Agriculture Dept.), Food and Nutrition Information Center, 10301 Baltimore Ave., #304, Beltsville, MD 20705-2351; (301) 504-5719. Fax, (301) 504-6409. Vacant, coordinator. Internet, fnic@nal.usda.gov or http://www.nal.usda.gov/fnic.*

Serves individuals and agencies seeking information or educational materials on food and human nutrition;

lends books and audiovisual materials for educational purposes; maintains a database of food and nutrition software and multimedia programs; provides reference services; develops resource lists of health and nutrition publications. Center open to the public.

National Institute of Diabetes and Digestive and Kidney Diseases *(National Institutes of Health), Nutritional Sciences, 45 Center Dr., Bldg. 45, #6AN-18F, Bethesda, MD 20892-6600; (301) 594-8883. Fax, (301) 480-8300. Dr. Van S. Hubbard, chief. Information, (301) 496-3583.*

Supports research on nutritional requirements, dietary fiber, obesity, eating disorders, energy regulation, clinical nutrition, trace minerals, and basic nutrient functions.

National Oceanic and Atmospheric Administration *(Commerce Dept.), Seafood Inspection Program, 1315 East-West Hwy., Silver Spring, MD 20910; (301) 713-2355. Fax, (301) 713-1081. Richard Cano, chief, Inspection Services. Internet, http://www.seafood.ssp.nmfs.gov/iss/issue.html.*

Administers voluntary inspection program for fish products and fish processing plants; certifies fish for wholesomeness, safety, and condition; grades for quality. Conducts training and workshops to help U.S. importers and foreign suppliers comply with food regulations.

CONGRESS

House Agriculture Committee, *Subcommittee on Department Operations, Nutrition, and Foreign Agriculture, 1430 LHOB 20515; (202) 225-0171. Fax, (202) 225-4464. Robert W. Goodlatte, R-Va., chair; Kevin Kramp, staff director. Internet, http://www.house.gov/agriculture.*

Jurisdiction over legislation on nutrition and hunger issues, pesticides, food safety, food stamps, and consumer programs generally.

House Agriculture Committee, *Subcommittee on Livestock, Dairy, and Poultry, 1301 LHOB 20515; (202) 225-0029. Fax, (202) 225-4369. Richard W. Pombo, R-Calif., chair; Chris D'Arcy, staff director. Internet, http://www.house.gov/agriculture/livestoc.htm.*

Jurisdiction over legislation concerning inspection of aquacultural species (seafood), dairy products, meats, poultry, and livestock.

House Appropriations Committee, *Subcommittee on Agriculture, Rural Development, FDA, and Related Agencies, 2362 RHOB 20515; (202) 225-2638. Joe Skeen, R-N.M., chair; Timothy K. Sanders, staff director. Internet, http://www.house.gov/appropriations.*

Jurisdiction over legislation to appropriate funds for the Food and Drug Administration, Food Safety and Inspection Service, and Food and Consumer Service.

House Commerce Committee, *Subcommittee on Health and the Environment,* *2125 RHOB 20515; (202) 225-2927. Fax, (202) 225-1919. Michael Bilirakis, R-Fla., chair; James E. Derderian, staff director. Internet, http:// www.house.gov/commerce/health.html.*

Jurisdiction over legislation on vaccines; labeling and packaging, including tobacco products and alcohol beverages; and the use of vitamins. Oversight of the Food and Drug Administration.

House Education and the Workforce Committee, *Subcommittee on Early Childhood, Youth, and Families, 2181 RHOB 20515; (202) 225-4527. Fax, (202) 225-9571. Frank Riggs, R-Calif., chair; Kevin Talley, staff director. Internet, http://www.house.gov/eeo.*

Jurisdiction over legislation on the National School Lunch Program, the School Breakfast Program, the Summer Food Program for Children, the Special Milk Program for Children, and the Special Supplemental Food Program for Women, Infants, and Children (WIC).

House Government Reform and Oversight Committee, *Subcommittee on Human Resources, B372 RHOB 20515; (202) 225-2548. Fax, (202) 225-2382. Christopher Shays, R-Conn., chair; Larry Halloran, staff director. Internet, http://www.house.gov/reform.*

Oversees government food and consumer services, including the Food and Nutrition Service and the Food Safety and Inspection Service.

House Science Committee, *Subcommittee on Basic Research, B374 RHOB 20515; (202) 225-7858. Fax, (202) 225-7815. Vacant, chair; Steve Eule, staff director. Press, (202) 225-0584. Internet, http://www.house.gov/ science.*

Jurisdiction over research and development involving government nutritional programs.

Senate Agriculture, Nutrition, and Forestry Committee, *Subcommittee on Research, Nutrition, and General Legislation, SR-361A 20510; (202) 224-2035. Fax, (202) 224-1725. Mitch McConnell, R-Ky., chair; David Hovermale, legislative assistant. Internet, http:// www.senate.gov/~agriculture.*

Jurisdiction over legislation on food, nutrition, and hunger; oversight of the inspection and certification of meat, flowers, fruits, vegetables, and livestock. Jurisdiction over commodity donations, food stamps, school lunch and breakfast programs, nutritional programs for the elderly, and the Special Supplemental Food Program for Women, Infants, and Children (WIC).

Senate Appropriations Committee, *Subcommittee on Agriculture, Rural Development, and Related Agencies, SD-136 20510; (202) 224-5270. Fax, (202) 224-9450. Thad Cochran, R-Miss., chair; Rebecca M. Davies, clerk. Internet, http://www.senate.gov/committee/ appropriations.html.*

Jurisdiction over legislation to appropriate funds for the Food and Drug Administration, the Food Safety and Inspection Service, the Food and Consumer Service, and other consumer-related services and programs.

Senate Commerce, Science, and Transportation Committee, *Subcommittee on Consumer Affairs, Foreign Commerce, and Tourism, SH-425 (mailing address: SD-508, Washington, DC 20510); (202) 224-5183. Fax, (202) 228-0326. John Ashcroft, R-Mo., chair, (202) 224-6154; Kevin Sabo, senior counsel. Internet, http://www. senate.gov/~commerce.*

Jurisdiction over legislation on the Food and Drug Administration and over labeling and packaging legislation, including advertising and packaging of tobacco products and alcohol beverages.

Senate Labor and Human Resources Committee, *SD-428 20510; (202) 224-5375. Fax, (202) 224-6510. James M. Jeffords, R-Vt., chair; Mark Powden, staff director. Internet, http://www.senate.gov/~labor.*

Jurisdiction over legislation on vaccines, drug labeling and packaging, inspection and certification of fish and processed food, and the use of vitamins.

INTERNATIONAL ORGANIZATIONS

Codex Alimentarius Commission, *U.S. Codex Office, 1400 Indiana Ave. S.W., South Bldg., #4861 20250; (202) 418-8852. Fax, (202) 418-8865. Patrick Clerkin, director. Internet, uscodex@aol.com or http://www.usda.gov/fsis/ codex.*

The principal U.N. agency concerned with food standards, food safety, and related regulation of international trade. Convenes committees in member countries to address specific commodities and issues including labeling, additives in food and veterinary drugs, pesticide residues and other contaminants, and systems for food inspection. (Located in the USDA Food Safety and Inspection Service; international headquarters in Geneva.)

NONPROFIT

American Dietetic Assn., *1225 Eye St. N.W., #1250 20005; (202) 371-0500. Fax, (202) 371-0840. Robin Schuhart, director. Internet, http://www.eatright.org.*

Membership: dietitians and other nutrition professionals. Promotes public health and nutrition; accredits academic programs in clinical nutrition and food service management; sets standards of professional practice. Sponsors the National Center for Nutrition and Dietetics. (Headquarters in Chicago.)

American Herbal Products Assn., *4733 Bethesda Ave., #345, Bethesda, MD 20814; (301) 951-3204. Fax, (301) 951-3205. Jeffrey M. Morrison, president. Internet, http://www.ahpa.org.*

Membership: U.S. companies and individuals that grow, import, process, or market herbs and herbal products; and associates in education, law, media, and medicine. Supports research; promotes standardization, consumer protection, competition, and self-regulation in the industry. Monitors legislation and regulations.

American Society for Clinical Nutrition, *9650 Rockville Pike, Bethesda, MD 20814-3998; (301) 530-7110. Fax, (301) 571-1863. Ann Marie Gebhart, executive officer. Internet, http://www.faseb.org/ascn.*

Membership: clinical nutritionists. Supports research on the role of human nutrition in health and disease; encourages undergraduate and graduate nutrition education. (Division of American Society for Nutritional Sciences.)

American Society for Nutritional Sciences, *9650 Rockville Pike, Bethesda, MD 20814; (301) 530-7050. Fax, (301) 571-1892. Richard G. Allison, executive officer. Internet, http://www.nutrition.org.*

Membership: nutrition scientists. Conducts research in nutrition and related fields worldwide and promotes the exchange of information; promotes nutrition education; offers awards for nutrition research.

American Society for Parenteral and Enteral Nutrition, *8630 Fenton St., #412, Silver Spring, MD 20910; (301) 587-6315. Fax, (301) 587-2365. Barney Sellers, executive director. Internet, aspen@nutr.org or http://www.clinnutr.org.*

Membership: health care professionals who provide patients with intravenous nutritional support during hospitalization and rehabilitation at home. Develops nutrition guidelines; provides educational materials; conducts annual meetings.

Center for Science in the Public Interest, *1875 Connecticut Ave. N.W., #300 20009-5728; (202) 332-9110. Fax, (202) 265-4954. Michael Jacobson, executive director. Internet, cspi@cspinet.org or http://www.cspinet.org.*

Conducts research on food and nutrition. Interests include eating habits, food safety regulations, food additives, organically produced foods, alcohol beverages, and links between diet and disease. Monitors U.S. and international policy.

Child Nutrition Forum, *1875 Connecticut Ave. N.W., #540 20009-5728; (202) 986-2200. Fax, (202) 986-2525. Ellen Teller, coordinator.*

Membership: agriculture, labor, education, and health and nutrition specialists; school food service officials; and consumer and religious groups. Supports federal nutrition programs for children; provides information on school nutrition programs; monitors legislation and regulations concerning hunger issues.

Community Nutrition Institute, *910 17th St. N.W., #413 20006; (202) 776-0595. Fax, (202) 776-0599. Rodney E. Leonard, executive director. Internet, cni@digex.net or http://www.access.digex.net/~cni.*

Citizens' interest group that provides information on nutrition, food policy issues, and federally funded food programs. Monitors legislation and regulations affecting food safety and nutrition.

Congressional Hunger Center, *229½ Pennsylvania Ave. S.E. 20003; (202) 547-7022. Fax, (202) 547-7575. John Morrill, executive director; Tony P. Hall, D-Ohio, chair. Internet, nohungr@aol.com or http://www.ghn.org/chc.*

Works to increase public awareness of hunger in the United States and abroad. Develops strategies to combat hunger and facilitates collaborative efforts between organizations.

Council for Responsible Nutrition, *1300 19th St. N.W., #310 20036; (202) 872-1488. Fax, (202) 872-9594. John Cordaro, president. Internet, http://www.crnusa.org.*

Membership: manufacturers, distributors, and suppliers of nutritional supplements and products. Provides information to members; monitors Food and Drug Administration, Federal Trade Commission, and Consumer Product Safety Commission regulations.

Food and Drug Law Institute, *1000 Vermont Ave. N.W., #200 20005-4903; (202) 371-1420. Fax, (202) 371-0649. John Villforth, president. Internet, comments@fdli.org or http://www.fdli.org.*

Membership: providers of products and services to the food, drug, medical device, and cosmetics industries, including major food and drug companies; and lawyers working in food and drug law. Arranges conferences on technological and legal developments in the industry; sponsors law courses, fellowships, and legal writing. Library open to the public.

Food Research and Action Center, *1875 Connecticut Ave. N.W., #540 20009-5728; (202) 986-2200. Fax, (202) 986-2525. James Weil, president. Internet, http://www. frac.org.*

Public interest advocacy, research, and legal center that works to end hunger and poverty in the United States; offers legal assistance, organizational aid, training, and information to groups seeking to improve or expand federal food programs, including food stamp, child nutrition, and WIC (women, infants, and children) programs; conducts studies relating to hunger and poverty; coordinates network of antihunger organizations. Monitors legislation and regulations.

International Food Information Council, *1100 Connecticut Ave. N.W., #430 20036; (202) 296-6540. Fax, (202) 296-6547. Sylvia Rowe, president. Internet, foodinfo@ific.health.org or http://ificinfo.health.org.*

Membership: food and beverage companies and manufacturers of food ingredients. Provides the media, health professionals, and consumers with scientific information about food safety and nutrition. Interests include harmonization of international food safety standards.

International Life Sciences Institute North America, *1126 16th St. N.W., #300 20036; (202) 659-0074. Fax, (202) 659-3859. Florence E. Boyce, administrator. Internet, ilsi@ilsi.org or http://www.ilsi.org.*

Acts as liaison among scientists from international government agencies, concerned industries, research institutes, and universities regarding the safety of foods and chemical ingredients. Conducts research on caffeine, food coloring, oral health, human nutrition, and other food issues. Promotes international cooperation among scientists.

Physicians Committee for Responsible Medicine, *5100 Wisconsin Ave. N.W. (mailing address: P.O. Box 6322, Washington, DC 20015); (202) 686-2210. Fax, (202) 686-2216. Dr. Neal D. Barnard, president. Internet, pcrm@ pcrm.org or http://www.pcrm.org.*

Membership: health care professionals, medical students, and other individuals. Provides individuals and institutions with nutrition information and low-fat, cholesterol-free recipes; promotes preventive medicine.

Public Citizen, *Health Research Group, 1600 20th St. N.W. 20009; (202) 588-1000. Fax, (202) 588-7796. Dr. Sidney M. Wolfe, director. Internet, http://www.citizen. org.*

Citizens' interest group that studies and reports on unsafe foods; monitors and petitions the Food and Drug Administration.

Public Voice for Food and Health Policy, *1012 14th St. N.W., #800 20005; (202) 347-6200. Fax, (202) 347-6261. Art Jaeger, executive director. Internet, hn2597@ handsnet.org.*

Research and education organization that promotes the consumer interest in food and health policy issues. Monitors legislation and regulations affecting food safety, food access and security, agriculture, health, nutrition, and the environment.

United Food and Commercial Workers International Union, *1775 K St. N.W. 20006; (202) 223-3111. Fax, (202) 466-1562. Douglas H. Dority, president. Internet, http://www.ufcw.org.*

Membership: approximately 1.4 million workers in food-related industries, including supermarkets, department stores, insurance and finance, and packing houses and processing plants. Helps members negotiate pay, benefits, and better working conditions; conducts training programs and workshops. Monitors legislation and regulations. (Affiliated with the AFL-CIO.)

Beverages

See also Substance Abuse (chap. 11); Traffic Safety (chap. 19)

AGENCIES

Bureau of Alcohol, Tobacco, and Firearms *(Treasury Dept.), Field Operations, 650 Massachusetts Ave. N.W., #8100 20226; (202) 927-7970. Fax, (202) 927-7756. Andrew L. Vita, assistant director. Information, (202) 927-7777. Press, (202) 927-9510. Internet, http://www.atf. treas.gov.*

Regulates the advertising and labeling of alcohol beverages, including the size of containers; enforces taxation of alcohol. Authorized to refer violations to Justice Dept. for criminal prosecution.

National Clearinghouse for Alcohol and Drug Information *(Health and Human Services Dept.), Center for Substance Abuse Prevention, 11426-28 Rockville Pike, #200, Rockville, MD (mailing address: P.O. Box 2345, Rockville, MD 20847-2345); (301) 468-2600. Fax, (301) 468-6433. John Noble, director. Toll-free, (800) 729-6686. TDD, (800) 487-4889. Internet, http://www.health.org.*

Provides information, publications, and grant applications for programs to prevent alcohol and drug abuse.

NONPROFIT

Beer Institute, *122 C St. N.W., #750 20001; (202) 737-2337. Fax, (202) 737-7004. Ray McGrath, president. Internet, http://www.beerinst.org.*

Membership: domestic and international brewers and suppliers to the domestic brewing industry. Monitors legislation and regulations.

Center for Science in the Public Interest, *1875 Connecticut Ave. N.W., #300 20009-5728; (202) 332-9110. Fax, (202) 265-4954. Michael Jacobson, executive director. Internet, cspi@cspinet.org or http://www.cspinet.org.*

Concerned with U.S. and international policy on alcohol, including marketing, labeling, and taxation. Opposes U.S. government promotion of alcohol products overseas.

Distilled Spirits Council of the United States, *1250 Eye St. N.W., #900 20005; (202) 628-3544. Fax, (202) 682-8888. F. A. Meister, president. Internet, http://www.discus. health.org.*

Membership: manufacturers and marketers of distilled spirits sold in the United States. Provides consumer information on alcohol-related issues and topics. Monitors legislation and regulations.

International Bottled Water Assn., *1700 Diagonal Rd., #650, Alexandria, VA 22314; (703) 683-5213. Fax, (703) 683-4074. Sylvia E. Swanson, president. Internet, http://www.bottledwater.org.*

Serves as a clearinghouse for industry-related consumer, regulatory, and technical information; interests include international trade. Monitors state and federal legislation and regulations.

Mothers Against Drunk Driving (MADD), *1001 G St. N.W., #400 East 20001; (202) 638-3735. Fax, (202) 638-3516. Tom Howarth, Washington contact.*

Concerned with alcohol policy as it relates to motor vehicle safety. Supports implementation of a nationwide legal intoxication level of 0.08 blood alcohol content. (Headquarters in Irving, Texas.)

National Alcohol Beverage Control Assn., *4216 King St. West, Alexandria, VA 22302-1507; (703) 578-4200. Fax, (703) 820-3551. James M. Sgueo, executive director.*

Membership: distilleries, trade associations, and state agencies that control the purchase, distribution, and sale of alcohol beverages. Serves as an information clearinghouse. Monitors legislation and regulations.

National Assn. of Beverage Retailers, *5101 River Rd., #108, Bethesda, MD 20816-1508; (301) 656-1494. Fax, (301) 656-7539. John B. Burcham Jr., executive director.*

Membership: state associations of on- and off-premises licensees. Monitors legislation and regulations affecting the alcohol beverage industry.

National Assn. of State Alcohol and Drug Abuse Directors, *808 17th St. N.W., #410 20006; (202) 293-0900. Fax, (202) 293-1250. John S. Gustafson, executive director.*

Provides information on treatment and prevention of alcohol abuse.

National Beer Wholesalers Assn., *1100 S. Washington St., Alexandria, VA 22314-4494; (703) 683-4300. Fax, (703) 683-8965. Ronald A. Sarasin, president.*

Sponsors programs on preventing alcohol abuse; monitors legislation and regulations for family-owned and family-operated beer distributors.

National Licensed Beverage Assn., *4214 King St. West, Alexandria, VA 22302-1507; (703) 671-7575. Fax, (703) 845-0310. Debra A. Leach, executive director. Internet, nlba@msn.com or http://www.nlba.org.*

Membership: bars, taverns, restaurants, cocktail lounges, stores, and hotels that sell alcohol beverages. Sponsors program that trains bartenders, waiters, and waitresses to serve alcohol in a responsible manner.

National Soft Drink Assn., *1101 16th St. N.W. 20036-6396; (202) 463-6732. Fax, (202) 463-8172. William L. Ball III, president. Internet, http://www.nsda.org.*

Membership: companies engaged in producing or distributing carbonated soft drinks. Acts as industry liaison with government and the public.

Wine and Spirits Wholesalers of America, *805 15th St. N.W., #430 20005; (202) 371-9792. Fax, (202) 789-2405. Douglas W. Metz, managing director. Internet, comments@wswa.org or http://www.wswa.org.*

Membership: wholesale distributors of domestic and imported wine and distilled spirits. Provides information on drinking awareness.

Wine Institute, *601 13th St. N.W., #580 South 20005; (202) 408-0870. Fax, (202) 371-0061. Robert P. Koch, senior vice president, Federal Government Relations. Internet, http://www.wineinstitute.org.*

Membership: California wineries and affiliated businesses. Seeks international recognition for California wines; conducts promotional campaigns in other countries. Monitors legislation and regulations. (Headquarters in San Francisco.)

Food Industries

NONPROFIT

American Bakers Assn., *1350 Eye St. N.W., #1290 20005; (202) 789-0300. Fax, (202) 898-1164. Paul C.*

Abenante, president. Internet, http://www.sosland. com/aba.

Membership: wholesale baking companies and their suppliers. Promotes increased consumption of baked goods; provides consumers with nutritional information; conducts conventions. Monitors legislation and regulations.

American Frozen Food Institute, *2000 Corporate Ridge, #1000, McLean, VA 22102; (703) 821-0770. Fax, (703) 821-1350. Steven C. Anderson, president. Internet, http://www.affi.com.*

Membership: frozen food packers, distributors, and suppliers. Provides production statistics.

American Meat Institute, *1700 N. Moore St., #1600, Arlington, VA (mailing address: P.O. Box 3556, Washington, DC 20007); (703) 841-2400. Fax, (703) 527-0938. J. Patrick Boyle, president. Internet, http://www. meatami.org.*

Membership: national and international meat and poultry packers, suppliers, and processors. Provides statistics on meat and poultry production and exports. Funds research projects and consumer education programs. Monitors legislation and regulations.

Bakery, Confectionery, and Tobacco Workers International, *10401 Connecticut Ave., Kensington, MD 20895; (301) 933-8600. Fax, (301) 946-8452. Frank Hurt, president.*

Membership: approximately 120,000 workers from the bakery and tobacco industries. Helps members negotiate pay, benefits, and better working conditions; conducts training programs and workshops. Monitors legislation and regulations. (Affliated with the AFL-CIO.)

Biscuit and Cracker Manufacturers' Assn., *1400 L St. N.W., #400 20005; (202) 898-1636. Fax, (202) 898-1668. Frank Rooney, president. Internet, http://www.net-link.net/bcma.*

Membership: companies in the biscuit and cracker industry. Monitors legislation and regulations.

Food Marketing Institute, *800 Connecticut Ave. N.W., #500 20006-2701; (202) 452-8444. Fax, (202) 429-4549. Timothy Hammonds, president. Library, (202) 429-8295. Internet, http://www.fmi.org.*

International organization of food retailers and wholesalers. Conducts programs in research, education, industry relations, and public affairs. Library open to the public by appointment.

Food Processing Machinery and Suppliers Assn., *200 Daingerfield Rd., Alexandria, VA 22314-2800; (703)*

684-1080. *Fax, (703) 548-6563. George O. Melnykovich, president. Internet, info@fpmsa.org or http://www. fpmsa.org.*

Membership: manufacturers and suppliers of processing and packaging equipment to the food and beverage industries. Helps members market their products and services. Monitors legislation and regulations.

Grocery Manufacturers of America, *1010 Wisconsin Ave. N.W., #900 20007; (202) 337-9400. Fax, (202) 337-4508. C. Manly Molpus, president. Internet, http://www. gmabrands.com.*

Membership: manufacturers of products sold through the retail grocery trade. Monitors legislation and regulations.

Hotel Employees and Restaurant Employees International, *1219 28th St. N.W. 20007; (202) 393-4373. Fax, (202) 333-0468. Edward T. Hanley, president. Internet, http://www.erols.com/hereiu.*

Membership: approximately 241,000 hotel and restaurant employees. Helps members negotiate pay, benefits, and better working conditions; conducts training programs and workshops. Monitors legislation and regulations. (Affiliated with the AFL-CIO.)

International Assn. of Food Industries Suppliers, *1451 Dolley Madison Blvd., McLean, VA 22101-3850; (703) 761-2600. Fax, (703) 761-4334. Charles Bray, president. Internet, http://www.iafis.org.*

Membership: equipment manufacturers, suppliers, and servicers for the food and dairy processing industry. Participates in the sanitary standards program for dairy and food processing; sponsors food engineering scholarships and biennial Food and Dairy Expo.

National-American Wholesale Grocers Assn., *201 Park Washington Court, Falls Church, VA 22046; (703) 532-9400. Fax, (703) 538-4673. John R. Block, president. Internet, http://www.nawga-ifda.org.*

Trade association of grocery wholesale distribution companies that supply and service independent grocers. Provides members with research, technical, educational, and government service programs.

National Assn. of Convenience Stores, *1605 King St., Alexandria, VA 22314-2792; (703) 684-3600. Fax, (703) 836-4564. Kerley LeBoeuf, president. Internet, NACS1@ aol.com or http://www.cstorecentral.com.*

Membership: convenience store retailers and industry suppliers. Advocates industry position on labor, tax, environment, alcohol, and food-related issues; conducts research and training programs. Monitors legislation and regulations.

National Food Processors Assn., *1401 New York Ave. N.W., #400 20005; (202) 639-5900. Fax, (202) 639-5932. John R. Cady, president. Press, (202) 639-5919.*

Membership: manufacturers and suppliers of processed and packaged food, drinks, and juice. Promotes agricultural interests of food processors; provides research, technical services, education, communications, and crisis management for members. Monitors legislation and regulations.

National Pasta Assn., *2101 Wilson Blvd., #920, Arlington, VA 22201; (703) 841-0818. Fax, (703) 528-6507. Jula J. Kinnaird, president. Internet, npa@ziplink.net or http://www.ilovepasta.org.*

Membership: U.S. pasta manufacturers and related suppliers. Represents the industry and provides information on pasta to consumers.

National Restaurant Assn., *1200 17th St. N.W. 20036-3097; (202) 331-5900. Fax, (202) 331-2429. Herman Cain, executive vice president. Internet, http://www.restaurant.org.*

Membership: restaurants, cafeterias, clubs, caterers, institutional food services, and other members of the food industry. Supports food service education and research. Monitors legislation and regulations.

Retailer's Bakery Assn., *14239 Park Center Dr., Laurel, MD 20707; (301) 725-2149. Fax, (301) 725-2187. Peter Houstle, executive vice president.*

Membership: single- and multiunit retail bakeries and bakery-delis; donut and other specialty shops; supermarket in-store bakeries and bakery-delis; allied companies that offer equipment, ingredients, supplies, or services to these retailers; and students and teachers of secondary or post-secondary school baking programs. Provides business and training aids. Monitors legislation and regulations.

Snack Food Assn., *1711 King St., #1, Alexandria, VA 22314; (703) 836-4500. Fax, (703) 836-8262. James W. Shufelt, president. Internet, http://www.snax.com.*

Membership: snack food manufacturers and suppliers. Promotes industry sales; compiles statistics; conducts research and surveys; assists members with training and education; provides consumers with industry information. Monitors legislation and regulations.

Women Grocers of America, *1825 Samuel Morse Dr., Reston, VA 22090; (703) 437-5300. Fax, (703) 437-7768. Thomas K. Zaucha, president.*

Supports the interests of women in the food distribution industry; sponsors seminars. (Affiliated with National Grocers Assn.)

World Food Assistance

See also International Trade and Development (chap. 13)

AGENCIES

Agency for International Development, *1300 Pennsylvania Ave. N.W., #609-010 20523; (202) 712-4040. Fax, (202) 216-3237. J. Brian Atwood, administrator. Information, (202) 712-4300. Press, (202) 712-4320. Internet, http://www.info.usaid.gov.*

Provides developing countries and the nations of central and eastern Europe with economic and humanitarian assistance; offers technical assistance to increase agricultural production. Jointly administers the Food for Peace program with the Agriculture Dept.'s Foreign Agricultural Service.

Foreign Agricultural Service *(Agriculture Dept.),* **Export Credits,** *1400 Independence Ave. S.W., #4077S 20250; (202) 720-6301. Fax, (202) 690-0727. Mary Chambliss, deputy administrator. Internet, http://www.fas.usda.gov.*

Administers Commodity Credit Corporation commercial export programs, including export credit guarantee and export enhancement programs. Administers, with the Agency for International Development, U.S. foreign food aid programs.

Foreign Agricultural Service *(Agriculture Dept.),* **International Cooperation and Development,** *1400 Independence Ave. S.W., #3008S 20250-1081; (202) 690-0776. Fax, (202) 720-6103. Mary Ann Keeffe, deputy administrator. Information, (202) 720-7115. Internet, http://www.fas.usda.gov/icd/icd-interests.html.*

Coordinates and conducts the department's international cooperation and development programs in agriculture and related fields. Programs include technical assistance and training, scientific and technical cooperation, administration of collaborative research, representation of Agriculture Dept. and U.S. government interests in international organization affairs, and facilitation of private sector involvement in country and regional agricultural development. Programs are conducted cooperatively with other Agriculture Dept. and U.S. government agencies, universities, and the private sector.

State Dept., *Agricultural Trade Policy and Programs, Main State Bldg., #3526 20520; (202) 647-3090. Fax, (202) 647-1894. Richard T. Miller, director.*

Makes recommendations on international food policy issues such as the effects of U.S. food aid on foreign policy; studies and drafts proposals on the U.S. role in Food for Peace and World Food programs.

World Agricultural Outlook Board *(Agriculture Dept.),* *1400 Independence Ave. S.W., #5143S 20250; (202) 720-6030. Fax, (202) 690-1805. Gerald A. Bange, chair. Internet, http://www.usda.gov/oce.*

Reports to the USDA Chief Economist. Coordinates the department's commodity forecasting program, which develops the official prognosis of supply, utilization, and prices for commodities worldwide. Works with the National Weather Service to monitor the impact of global weather on agriculture.

CONGRESS

House Agriculture Committee, *Subcommittee on Department Operations, Nutrition, and Foreign Agriculture, 1430 LHOB 20515; (202) 225-0171. Fax, (202) 225-4464. Robert W. Goodlatte, R-Va., chair; Kevin Kramp, staff director. Internet, http://www.house.gov/ agriculture.*

Jurisdiction over international commodity donations and over legislation on U.S. domestic food production for foreign assistance programs under Public Law 480, including the Food for Peace program and the Foreign Agricultural Service. (The House International Relations Committee has jurisdiction over legislation on overseas food distribution.)

House International Relations Committee, *2170 RHOB 20515; (202) 225-5021. Fax, (202) 225-2035. Benjamin A. Gilman, R-N.Y., chair; Richard J. Garon Jr., chief of staff. Internet, http://www.house.gov/international _relations.*

Jurisdiction over legislation on overseas food distribution for foreign assistance programs under Public Law 480, including the Food for Peace program and the Foreign Agricultural Service. (The House Agriculture Committee has jurisdiction over legislation on domestic food production for Public Law 480 programs.)

Senate Agriculture, Nutrition, and Forestry Committee, *Subcommittee on Marketing, Inspection, and Product Promotion, SR-328A 20510; (202) 224-2035. Fax, (202) 224-1725. Paul Coverdell, R-Ga., chair; Richard Gupton, legislative assistant. Internet, http://www.senate. gov/committee/agriculture.html.*

Jurisdiction over legislation on food production and distribution for foreign assistance programs under Public Law 480, including the Food for Peace program and the Foreign Agricultural Service.

Senate Agriculture, Nutrition, and Forestry Committee, *Subcommittee on Research, Nutrition, and General Legislation, SR-361A 20510; (202) 224-2035. Fax, (202) 224-1725. Mitch McConnell, R-Ky., chair;*

David Hovermale, legislative assistant. Internet, http:// www.senate.gov/~agriculture.

Jurisdiction over legislation on commodity donations, food, nutrition, and hunger in the United States and in foreign countries.

INTERNATIONAL ORGANIZATIONS

Food and Agriculture Organization of the United Nations, *Liaison Office for North America, 2175 K St. N.W., #300 20437; (202) 653-2400. Fax, (202) 653-5760. Charles H. Riemenschneider, director. Library, (202) 653-2402. Internet, http://www.fao.org.*

Serves as the main forum of the international community on world food, agriculture, fisheries, and forestry problems. Provides developing nations with technical assistance to improve and increase food and agricultural production; encourages sustainable agriculture and rural development; works to achieve food security, especially in low-income, food-deficient countries; and seeks to control plant and animal disease infestations. Library open to the public by appointment. (International headquarters in Rome.)

International Fund for Agricultural Development, *1775 K St. N.W., #410 20006; (202) 331-9099. Fax, (202) 331-9366. Vera P. Weill-Hallé, Washington representative. Internet, v.weillhalle@ifad.org or http://www.ifad.org.*

Specialized agency of the United Nations which provides the rural poor of developing nations with cost-effective ways of overcoming hunger, poverty, and malnutrition. Advocates a community-based approach to reducing rural poverty. (International headquarters in Rome.)

NONPROFIT

Agricultural Cooperative Development International, *50 F St. N.W., #1100 20001; (202) 638-4661. Fax, (202) 626-8726. Michael Deegan, president.*

Membership: farm supply, processing, and marketing cooperatives; farm credit banks; national farmer organizations; and insurance cooperatives. Provides cooperatives with training and technical, management, and marketing assistance; supports farm credit systems, agribusiness, and government agencies in developing countries. Contracts with the Agency for International Development to start farm cooperatives in other countries. (Affiliated with the National Council of Farmer Cooperatives.)

American Red Cross, *National Headquarters, 430 17th St. N.W., 2nd Floor 20006; (202) 737-8300. Fax, (202) 783-3432. Elizabeth Dole, president. Internet, http://www.redcross.org.*

Humanitarian relief and health education organization chartered by Congress. Provides food and supplies to assist in major disaster and refugee situations worldwide. (Public inquiries, 8111 Gatehouse Rd., Falls Church, VA 22042; 703-206-7090; fax, 703-206-7749.)

Bread for the World, *1100 Wayne Ave., #1000, Silver Spring, MD 20910; (301) 608-2400. Fax, (301) 608-2401. David Beckmann, president. Internet, bread@bread.org or http://www.bread.org.*

Christian citizens' movement that works to eradicate world hunger. Organizes and coordinates political action on issues and public policy affecting the causes of hunger. Interests include domestic food assistance programs, international famine, and hunger relief.

CARE, *1625 K St. N.W., #200 20006; (202) 223-2277. Fax, (202) 296-8695. Marianne Leach, executive director. Internet, info@care.org or http://www.care.org.*

Assists the developing world's poor through emergency assistance and community self-help programs that focus on sustainable development, agriculture, agroforestry, water and sanitation, health, family planning, and income generation. (U.S. headquarters in Atlanta; international headquarters in Brussels.)

International Food Policy Research Institute, *1200 17th St. N.W. 20036-3006; (202) 862-5600. Fax, (202) 467-4439. Per Pinstrup-Andersen, director. Library, (202) 862-5614. Internet, ifpri@cgnet.com or http://www.cgiar.org/ifpri.*

Research organization that analyzes the world food situation and suggests ways of making food more available in developing countries. Provides various governments with information on national and international food policy. Sponsors conferences; publishes research reports. Library open to the public by appointment.

National Center for Food and Agricultural Policy, *1616 P St. N.W., #100 20036; (202) 328-5074. Fax, (202) 328-5133. Dale E. Hathaway, director. Internet, ncfap@rff.org.*

Research and educational organization concerned with international food and agricultural issues. Examines public policy concerning agriculture, food safety and quality, natural resources, and the environment.

Oxfam America, *1511 K St. N.W., #640 20005; (202) 783-7302. Fax, (202) 783-8739. Bernice Romero, advocacy coordinator. Toll-free, (800) 225-5800. Internet, oxfamusa@igc.apc.org or http://www.charity.org/oxfam.html.*

Funds disaster relief and self-help development projects, including food and agriculture programs. (Headquarters in Boston.)

RESULTS, *236 Massachusetts Ave. N.E., #300 20002; (202) 543-9340. Fax, (202) 543-7512. Lynn McMullen, director. Toll-free, (800) 900-5323. Internet, results@action.org or http://results.action.org.*

Works to end world hunger; encourages grassroots and legislative support of programs and proposals dealing with hunger and hunger-related issues. Monitors legislation and regulations.

U.S. National Committee for World Food Day, *2175 K St. N.W. 20437; (202) 653-2404. Fax, (202) 653-5760. Patricia Young, national coordinator.*

Consortium of farm, religious, nutrition, education, consumer, relief, and development organizations. Coordinates widespread community participation in World Food Day. Distributes materials about food and hunger issues and encourages long-term action.

Winrock International Institute for Agricultural Development, *1611 N. Kent St., #600, Arlington, VA 22209; (703) 525-9430. Fax, (703) 525-1744. Richard Cobb, vice president. Internet, http://www.winrock.org.*

Seeks to increase the output of crops and livestock and to raise rural incomes in developing nations. Interests include agricultural planning, strengthening research systems, training personnel, and implementing production programs. (Headquarters in Morrilton, Ark.)

Worldwatch Institute, *1776 Massachusetts Ave. N.W., 8th Floor 20036; (202) 452-1999. Fax, (202) 296-7365. Lester R. Brown, president. Internet, worldwatch@worldwatch.org or http://www.worldwatch.org.*

Research organization that studies the environmental origins of world population growth and health trends; interests include the food supply and malnutrition.

 LIVESTOCK AND POULTRY

See also Animals and Plants (chap. 9); Commodities/Farm Produce (this chapter)

AGENCIES

Agricultural Marketing Service *(Agriculture Dept.),* **Livestock and Seed,** *1400 Independence Ave. S.W., #2092S (mailing address: P.O. Box 96456, Washington, DC 20090-6456); (202) 720-5705. Fax, (202) 720-3499. Barry L. Carpenter, deputy administrator. Internet, http://www.usda.gov/ams/lsd.htm.*

Administers meat marketing program; maintains market news service to inform producers of meat market situation and daily price changes; develops, establishes, and revises U.S. standards for classes and grades of livestock and meat; grades, examines, and certifies meat and meat products.

Agricultural Marketing Service *(Agriculture Dept.),* **Livestock and Seed,** *1400 Independence Ave. S.W., #2092S (mailing address: P.O. Box 96456, Washington, DC 20090-6456); (202) 720-5705. Fax, (202) 720-1112. Herbert Abraham, chief, Livestock and Meat Standardization. Internet, http://www.usda.gov/ams/lsd.htm.*

Sets meat grading standards. Writes and maintains meat purchase specifications.

Agricultural Marketing Service *(Agriculture Dept.),* **Poultry,** *1400 Independence Ave. S.W., #3932S (mailing address: P.O. Box 96456, Washington, DC 20090-6456); (202) 720-4476. Fax, (202) 720-5631. D. Michael Holbrook, deputy administrator. Internet, http://www.usda. gov/ams/poultry.htm.*

Sets poultry grading standards and conducts quality inspections based on those standards.

Food Safety and Inspection Service *(Agriculture Dept.), 1400 Independence Ave. S.W., #331E 20250; (202) 720-7025. Fax, (202) 205-0158. Thomas J. Billy, administrator. Press, (202) 720-9113. Consumer inquiries, (800) 535-4555; in Washington, (202) 720-3333. Internet, http://www.usda.gov/fsis.*

Inspects meat and poultry products and provides safe handling and labeling guidelines.

Grain Inspection, Packers, and Stockyards Administration *(Agriculture Dept.), 1400 Independence Ave. S.W., Stop 3601 20250-3601; (202) 720-0219. Fax, (202) 205-9237. James Baker, administrator. Information, (202) 720-5091. Internet, http://www.usda.gov/gipsa.*

Maintains competition in the marketing of livestock, poultry, grain, and meat by prohibiting deceptive and monopolistic marketing practices; tests market scales and conducts check weighings for accuracy.

CONGRESS

House Agriculture Committee, *Subcommittee on* **Livestock, Dairy, and Poultry,** *1301 LHOB 20515; (202) 225-0029. Fax, (202) 225-4369. Richard W. Pombo, R-Calif., chair; Chris D'Arcy, staff director. Internet, http://www.house.gov/agriculture/livestoc.htm.*

Jurisdiction over legislation on inspection and certification of meat, livestock, and poultry, and over animal welfare.

Senate Agriculture, Nutrition, and Forestry Committee, *Subcommittee on Research, Nutrition, and* **General Legislation,** *SR-361A 20510; (202) 224-2035. Fax, (202) 224-1725. Mitch McConnell, R-Ky., chair; David Hovermale, legislative assistant. Internet, http://www.senate.gov/~agriculture.*

Jurisdiction over legislation on inspection and certification of meat, livestock, and poultry, and over animal welfare.

NONPROFIT

American Meat Institute, *1700 N. Moore St., #1600, Arlington, VA (mailing address: P.O. Box 3556, Washington, DC 20007); (703) 841-2400. Fax, (703) 527-0938. J. Patrick Boyle, president. Internet, http://www. meatami.org.*

Membership: national and international meat and poultry packers and processors. Provides statistics on meat and poultry production and consumption, livestock, and feed grains. Funds meat research projects and consumer education programs; sponsors conferences and correspondence courses on meat production and processing. Monitors legislation and regulations.

American Sheep Industry Assn., *412 1st St. S.E., #1 Lobby Level 20003; (202) 484-7134. Fax, (202) 484-0770. Fran Boyd, Washington representative.*

Membership: sheep, wool, and mohair producers. Interests include sheep breeds, lamb and wool marketing, and wool research. Monitors legislation and regulations. (Headquarters in Denver.)

Animal Health Institute, *501 Wythe St., Alexandria, VA (mailing address: P.O. Box 1417-D50, Alexandria, VA 22313-1480); (703) 684-0011. Fax, (703) 684-0125. Alex Mathews, president. Internet, http://www.ahi.org.*

Membership: manufacturers of drugs and other products (including vaccines, pesticides, and vitamins) for pets and food-producing animals. Monitors legislation and regulations.

Farm Animal Reform Movement, *P.O. Box 30654, Bethesda, MD 20824; (301) 530-1737. Fax, (301) 530-5747. Alex Hershaft, president. Internet, farmusa@erols.com or http://www.envirolink.org/orgs/ farm.*

Works to end use of animals for food. Interests include consumer health, agricultural resources, and environmental quality. Conducts national educational campaigns, including World Farm Animals Day and the Great American Meatout. Monitors legislation and regulations.

National Broiler Council, *1015 15th St. N.W., #930 20005; (202) 296-2622. Fax, (202) 293-4005. George B. Watts, president. Internet, http://www.eatchicken.com.*

Membership: producers and processors of broiler chickens. Provides information on production, marketing, and consumption of broiler chickens.

National Cattlemen's Beef Assn., *1301 Pennsylvania Ave. N.W., #300 20004; (202) 347-0228. Fax, (202) 638-0607. Chandler Keys, vice president, Government Affairs. Internet, http://www.cowtown.org.*

Membership: individual cattlemen, state cattlemen's groups, and breed associations. Provides information on beef research, agricultural labor, beef grading, foreign trade, taxes, branding, animal health, and environmental management. (Headquarters in Englewood, Colo.)

National Meat Canners Assn., *1700 N. Moore St., #1600, Arlington, VA 22209; (703) 841-3680. Fax, (703) 841-9656. Jerome Breiter, executive secretary. Internet, http://www.meatami.com.*

Membership: canners of prepared meats and meat food products. Provides information on the canned meat industry.

National Pork Producers Council, *122 C St. N.W., #875 20001; (202) 347-3600. Fax, (202) 347-5265. Gary Madson, vice president. Internet, pork@nppc.org or http://www.nppc.org.*

Membership: pork producers and independent pork producer organizations. Interests include pork production, nutrition, the environment, trade, and federal regulations. Monitors legislation and regulations. (Headquarters in Des Moines, Iowa.)

National Renderers Assn., *801 N. Fairfax St., #207, Alexandria, VA 22314; (703) 683-0155. Fax, (703) 683-2626. Thomas M. Cook, president. Internet, renders@aol.com.*

Membership: manufacturers of meat meal and tallow. Compiles industry statistics; sponsors research; conducts seminars and workshops. Monitors legislation and regulations.

National Turkey Federation, *1225 New York Ave. N.W., #400 20005; (202) 898-0100. Fax, (202) 898-0203. Stuart E. Proctor Jr., president. Internet, http://www.turkeyfed.org.*

Membership: turkey growers, hatcheries, breeders, and processors. Promotes turkey consumption. Monitors legislation and regulations.

North American Meat Processors Assn., *1920 Association Dr., #400, Reston, VA 20191; (703) 758-1900. Fax, (703) 758-8001. Deven L. Scott, executive vice president. Internet, http://www.namp.com.*

Membership: meat, poultry, fish, and game companies specializing in the food service industry. Conducts seminars; interests include quality standards and procedures for handling meat, poultry, fish, and game.

U.S. Hide, Skin, and Leather Assn., *1700 N. Moore St., #1600, Arlington, VA 22209; (703) 841-5485. Fax, (703) 841-9656. Jerome Breiter, president. Internet, http://www.meatami.org.*

Membership: meatpackers, brokers, dealers, processors, and exporters of hides and skins. Maintains liaison with allied trade associations and participates in programs on export statistics, hide price reporting, and freight rates; conducts seminars and consumer information programs. (Division of American Meat Institute.)

See also Public Lands Council (p. 305)

3

Communications and the Media

■ GENERAL POLICY

AGENCIES

Federal Communications Commission, *1919 M St. N.W. 20554; (202) 418-1000. Fax, (202) 418-2801. William Kennard, chair; Andrew S. Fishel, managing director, (202) 418-1919. Press, (202) 418-0500. Library, (202) 418-0450. Locator, (202) 418-0126. Internet, http://www. fcc.gov.*

Regulates interstate and foreign communications by radio, television, wire, cable, microwave, and satellite; consults with other government agencies and departments on national and international matters involving wire and radio telecommunications and with state regulatory commissions on telegraph and telephone matters; reviews applications for construction permits and licenses for such services. Library open to the public.

Federal Communications Commission, *Complaints and Political Programming, 2025 M St. N.W., #8202 20554; (202) 418-1440. Fax, (202) 653-1124. Norman Goldstein, chief. Information, (202) 418-0200.*

Handles complaints and inquiries concerning the equal time rule, which requires equal broadcast opportunities for all legally qualified candidates for the same office. Enforces related Communications Act provisions, including the requirement for sponsorship identification of all paid broadcast announcements.

National Telecommunications and Information Administration *(Commerce Dept.), 14th St. and Constitution Ave. N.W., #4898 20230; (202) 482-1840. Fax, (202) 482-1635. Larry Irving Jr., NTIA administrator. Information, (202) 482-7002. Library, (202) 482-3999. Internet, tiiap@ntia.doc.gov or http://www.ntia.doc.gov.*

Develops domestic and international telecommunications policy for the executive branch; manages federal use of radio spectrum; conducts research on radiowave transmissions and other aspects of telecommunications; serves as information source for federal and state agencies on the efficient use of telecommunications resources; provides noncommercial telecommunications services with grants for construction of facilities.

CONGRESS

House Appropriations Committee, *Subcommittee on Commerce, Justice, State, and Judiciary, H309 Capitol 20515; (202) 225-3351. Harold Rogers, R-Ky., chair; Jim Kulikowski, staff director. Internet, http://www.house. gov/appropriations.*

Jurisdiction over legislation to appropriate funds for the Federal Communications Commission, the Board for

International Broadcasting, the National Telecommunications and Information Administration, and the U.S. Information Agency.

House Appropriations Committee, *Subcommittee on Labor, Health and Human Services, and Education, 2358 RHOB 20515; (202) 225-3508. John Edward Porter, R-Ill., chair; Tony McCann, staff director. Internet, http:// www.house.gov/appropriations.*

Jurisdiction over legislation to appropriate funds for the Corporation for Public Broadcasting.

House Commerce Committee, *Subcommittee on Telecommunications, Trade, and Consumer Protection, 2125 RHOB 20515; (202) 225-2927. Fax, (202) 225-1919. W. J. "Billy" Tauzin, R-La., chair; James E. Derderian, staff director. Internet, http://www.house.gov/commerce.*

Jurisdiction over legislation related to interstate and foreign telecommunications, including television, cable television, local and long-distance telephone service, radio, wire, microwave, and satellite communications. Jurisdiction over the Federal Communications Commission and the Corporation for Public Broadcasting.

House Government Reform and Oversight Committee, *Subcommittee on Government Management, Information, and Technology, B373 RHOB 20515; (202) 225-5147. Steve Horn, R-Calif., chair; J. Russell George, staff director. Internet, http://www.house.gov/cho.*

Oversees operations of the National Telecommunications and Information Administration, the Federal Communications Commission, the Board for International Broadcasting, and the U.S. Information Agency.

House Judiciary Committee, *2138 RHOB 20515; (202) 225-3951. Fax, (202) 225-7682. Henry J. Hyde, R-Ill., chair; Thomas Mooney, chief counsel. Internet, http:// www.house.gov/judiciary.*

Jurisdiction over legislation related to anticompetitive practices and to monopolies in communications, including cable telecommunications and network practices.

Library of Congress, *Copyright Office, 101 Independence Ave. S.E., #403 20557-6400; (202) 707-8160. Fax, (202) 707-0905. Walter D. Sampson, chief, Licensing. Information, (202) 707-8150. Internet, http://www.loc. gov/copyright.*

Licenses cable television companies and satellite carriers; collects and distributes royalty payments under the copyright law. Distributes licenses for making and distributing phonorecords and for use of certain noncommercial broadcasting. Administers Section 115 licensing for making and distributing phonorecords.

FEDERAL COMMUNICATIONS COMMISSION

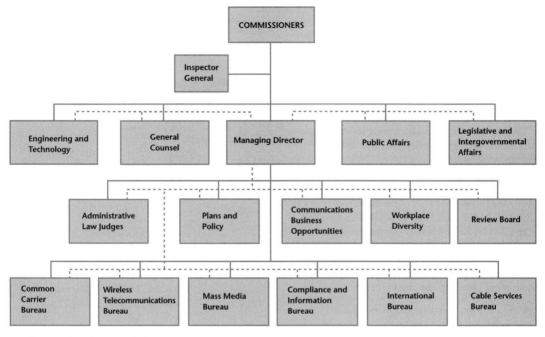

—— Lines of policy and judicial authority
···· Lines of management and administrative authority

Senate Appropriations Committee, *Subcommittee on Commerce, Justice, State, and Judiciary, SR-393 20510; (202) 224-7277. Judd Gregg, R-N.H., chair, (202) 224-3324; Vas Alexopoulos, legislative assistant. Chair's fax, (202) 224-4952. Internet, http://www.senate.gov/ ~appropriations.*

Jurisdiction over legislation to appropriate funds for the Federal Communications Commission, the Board for International Broadcasting, the National Telecommunications and Information Administration, and the U.S. Information Agency.

Senate Appropriations Committee, *Subcommittee on Labor, Health and Human Services, and Education, SD-184 20510; (202) 224-7230. Arlen Specter, R-Pa., chair; Craig A. Higgins, staff director. Internet, http://www. senate.gov/~appropriations/labor.*

Jurisdiction over legislation to appropriate funds for the Corporation for Public Broadcasting.

Senate Commerce, Science, and Transportation Committee, *Subcommittee on Communications, SH-227 20510; (202) 224-5184. Conrad Burns, R-Mont.,*

chair; Lauren Belvin, counsel. Internet, http://www. senate.gov/~commerce.

Jurisdiction over legislation related to interstate and foreign communications, including television, cable television, local and long-distance telephone service, radio, wire, microwave, and satellite communications. Oversight of the Federal Communications Commission, the National Telecommunications and Information Administration, and the Corporation for Public Broadcasting.

Senate Foreign Relations Committee, *Subcommittee on International Operations, SD-450 20510; (202) 224-4651. Fax, (202) 224-0836. Rod Grams, R-Minn., chair; Chris Walker, senior professional staff member. Internet, http://www.senate.gov/committee/foreign.html.*

Oversight of the Board for International Broadcasting and the U.S. Information Agency.

Senate Judiciary Committee, *Subcommittee on Antitrust, Business Rights, and Competition, SD-161 20510; (202) 224-9494. Fax, (202) 228-0463. Mike DeWine, R-Ohio, chair; Louie DuPart, chief counsel. Internet, http://www.senate.gov/committee/judiciary.html.*

Jurisdiction over legislation related to anticompetitive practices and to monopolies in communications, including cable telecommunication and network practices.

INTERNATIONAL ORGANIZATIONS

Inter-American Telecommunications Commission (CITEL) *(Organization of American States), 1889 F St., #250-A 20006; (202) 458-3004. Fax, (202) 458-6854. Roberto Blois Montes de Souza, executive secretary. Internet, http://www.oas.org/EN/PROG/CITEL/citel.htm.*

Works with the public and private sectors to facilitate the development of telecommunications in the Americas.

NONPROFIT

Accuracy in Media, *4455 Connecticut Ave. N.W., #330 20008; (202) 364-4401. Fax, (202) 364-4098. Reed J. Irvine, board chair. Internet, ar@aim.org or http://www.aim.org.*

Analyzes print and electronic news media for bias, omissions, and errors in news; approaches media with complaints. Maintains speakers bureau.

Alliance for Public Technology, *901 15th St. N.W., #230 20005-2327; (202) 408-1403. Fax, (202) 408-1134. Barbara O'Connor, chair. Main phone is voice and TDD accessible. Internet, apt@apt.org or http://www.apt.org.*

Membership: public groups and individuals concerned with developing affordable access to information services and telecommunications technology, particularly for the elderly, residential consumers, low-income groups, and people with disabilities.

Alliance for Telecommunications Industry Solutions, *1200 G St. N.W., #500 20005; (202) 628-6380. Fax, (202) 393-5453. George Edwards, president. Internet, http://www.atis.org.*

Promotes the timely resolution of national and international issues involving telecommunications standards and operational guidelines. Sponsors industry forums; serves as an information clearinghouse. Monitors legislation and regulations.

Center for Media and Public Affairs, *2100 L St. N.W., #300 20037-1525; (202) 223-2942. Fax, (202) 872-4014. Robert Mulligan, executive director. Internet, http://www.cmpa.com.*

Nonpartisan research and educational organization that studies media coverage of social and political issues and campaigns. Conducts surveys; publishes materials and reports.

Center for Media Education, *1511 K St. N.W., #518 20005; (202) 628-2620. Fax, (202) 628-2554. Kathryn C. Montgomery, president. Internet, http://www.cme.org/cme.*

Promotes public interest in media policies and access to new educational technologies for all children. Provides nonprofit groups with educational and informational services. Maintains a speakers bureau.

Computer and Communications Industry Assn., *666 11th St. N.W., #600 20001; (202) 783-0070. Fax, (202) 783-0534. Edward J. Black, president. Internet, ccia@aol.com or http://www.ccianet.org.*

Membership: manufacturers and suppliers of computer data processing and communications-related products and services. Interests include telecommunications policy, capital formation and tax policy, communications and computer industry standards, intellectual property policies, encryption, international trade, and antitrust reform.

Institute for Public Representation, *600 New Jersey Ave. N.W. 20001; (202) 662-9535. Fax, (202) 662-9634. Douglas L. Parker, director. TDD, (202) 662-9538.*

Public interest law firm funded by Georgetown University Law Center that specializes in communications regulatory policy. Assists citizens' groups that seek input into local and federal regulation of the electronic media; interests include freedom of information.

International Communications Industries Assn., *11242 Waples Mill Rd., #200, Fairfax, VA 22030; (703) 273-7200. Fax, (703) 278-8082. Walter Blackwell, executive director. Internet, icia@icia.org or http://www.infocomm.org.*

Membership: video, audiovisual, and microcomputer dealers; manufacturers and producers; and individuals; operates chapters in Europe, Asia, and Australia. Interests include international trade, small business issues, postal rates, copyright, education, and taxation. Monitors legislation and regulations.

Media Access Project, *1707 L St. N.W., #400 20036; (202) 232-4300. Fax, (202) 466-7656. Andrew Jay Schwartzman, executive director.*

Public interest telecommunications law firm that represents the right of the public to speak and to receive information from the mass media. Interests include media ownership, access to new technologies, and the fairness doctrine.

Media Institute, *1000 Potomac St. N.W., #301 20007; (202) 298-7512. Fax, (202) 337-7092. Patrick D. Maines, president. Internet, tmi@clark.net or http://www.mediainst.org.*

Conducts conferences, files court briefs and regulatory comments, and sponsors programs on communications topics. Advocates free-speech rights for individuals, media, and corporate speakers.

Media Research Center, *113 S. West St., 2nd Floor, Alexandria, VA 22314; (703) 683-9733. Fax, (703) 683-9736. L. Brent Bozell III, chair. Internet, http://www. mediaresearch.org.*

Media-watch organization working for balanced news coverage of political issues. Records and analyzes network news programs; analyzes print media; maintains profiles of media executives and library of recordings.

National Assn. of Broadcasters, *1771 N St. N.W. 20036-2891; (202) 429-5300. Fax, (202) 429-5343. Edward O. Fritts, president. Press, (202) 429-5350. Library, (202) 429-5490. Internet, register@nab.org or http://www. nab.org.*

Membership: radio and television broadcast stations and broadcast networks holding an FCC license or construction permit; associate members include producers of equipment and programs. Assists members in areas of management, engineering, and research; interprets laws and regulations governing the broadcast media. Publishes materials about broadcasting industry. Library offers fee-based services to non-members by appointment.

National Assn. of Regulatory Utility Commissioners, *12th St. and Constitution Ave. N.W. (mailing address: P.O. Box 684, Washington, DC 20044-0684); (202) 898-2200. Fax, (202) 898-2213. Peggy Welsh, executive director. Press, (202) 898-2205. Internet, http://www.naruc.org.*

Membership: members of federal, state, municipal, and Canadian regulatory commissions that have jurisdiction over utilities and carriers. Interests include telecommunications regulation.

National Captioning Institute, *1900 Gallows Rd., Vienna, VA 22182; (703) 917-7600. Fax, (703) 917-9878. Mike Curzan, chief executive officer; Beth Mautino, chief operating officer. Main phone is voice and TDD accessible. Internet, mail@ncicap.org or http://www.ncicap.org/nci.*

Captions television programs for the deaf and hard-of-hearing on behalf of public and commercial broadcast television networks, cable network companies, syndicators, program producers, advertisers, and home video distributors. Produces and disseminates information about the national closed-captioning service.

Telecommunications for the Deaf, Inc., *8630 Fenton St., #604, Silver Spring, MD 20910; (301) 589-3786. Fax, (301) 589-3797. Claude Stout, executive director. TDD, (301) 589-3006. Internet, tdiexdir@aol.com.*

Membership: individuals, organizations, and businesses using text telephone (TTY) equipment. Provides information on TTY equipment. Interests include closed captioning for television, emergency access (911), TTY relay services, visual alerting systems, and TTY/computer conversion. Publishes a national TTY telephone directory.

Telecommunications Industry Assn., *2500 Wilson Blvd., #300, Arlington, VA 22201-3834; (703) 907-7700. Fax, (703) 907-7727. Matthew J. Flanigan, president. Press, (703) 907-7723. Internet, tia@tia.eia.org or http:// www.tiaonline.org.*

Membership: telecommunications equipment manufacturers, suppliers, and distributers. Represents members in telecommunications manufacturing issues; helps to develop standards for products; sponsors a job-matching service; cohosts trade shows worldwide. (Affiliated with the Electronic Industries Assn.)

See also National Assn. of State Utility Consumer Advocates (p. 21)

Cable Services

AGENCIES

Federal Communications Commission, *Cable Services Bureau, 2033 M St. N.W. 20554; (202) 418-7200. Fax, (202) 418-2376. Meredith J. Jones, chief. Library, (202) 418-0450. Internet, http://www.fcc.gov/Bureaus/ Cable/WWW/csb.html.*

Makes and enforces rules governing cable television and other video distribution services; promotes industry growth, competition, and availability to the public; ensures reasonable rates for consumers in areas that do not have competition in cable service.

Federal Communications Commission, *Cable Services Bureau, 2033 M St. N.W. 20554; (202) 418-7000. Fax, (202) 418-1189. John Wong, chief, Engineering and Technical Services.*

Processes applications and notifications for licensing of cable television relay service stations (CARS); registers cable television systems; develops, administers, and enforces regulation of cable television and CARS.

NONPROFIT

Alliance for Community Media, *666 11th St. N.W., #806 20001; (202) 393-2650. Fax, (202) 393-2653. Barry Forbes, executive director. Internet, alliancecm@aol.com or http://www.alliancecm.org.*

Membership: cable television companies, programming managers and producers, independent producers, cable administrators and regulators, media access centers, and others involved in community communications. Promotes local programming and participation in cable television. Interests include freedom of expression, diversity of information, and developing technologies. Monitors legislation and regulations.

Cable Telecommunications Assn., *3950 Chain Bridge Rd., Fairfax, VA (mailing address: P.O. Box 1005, Fairfax, VA 22030-1005); (703) 691-8875. Fax, (703) 691-8911. Stephen Effros, president. Internet, http://www.catanet.org.*

Membership: independent cable operating companies. Interests include cable rates, telephone company entry into cable television, regulation, and new technologies. Monitors legislation and regulations.

CTAM, *201 N. Union St., #440, Alexandria, VA 22314; (703) 549-4200. Fax, (703) 684-1167. Char Beales, president. Internet, http://www.ctam.com.*

Promotes innovation in the cable and related industries in areas of marketing, research, management, and new product development. Sponsors annual marketing conference; interests include international markets.

National Cable Television Assn., *1724 Massachusetts Ave. N.W. 20036-1969; (202) 775-3550. Fax, (202) 775-1055. Decker Anstrom, president. Information, (202) 775-3629.*

Membership: companies that operate cable television systems, cable television programmers, and manufacturers and suppliers of hardware and software for the industry. Represents the industry before federal regulatory agencies and Congress and in the courts; provides management and promotional aids and information on legal, legislative, and regulatory matters.

Enforcement, Judicial, and Legal Actions

AGENCIES

See also General Counsels box (chap. 14)

Federal Bureau of Investigation *(Justice Dept.),* **CALEA Implementation Section,** *P.O. Box 220450, Chantilly, VA 20151; (703) 814-4800. Fax, (703) 814-4720. H. Michael Warren, chief.*

Administers enforcement of the Communications Assistance for Law Enforcement Act (CALEA). Promotes cooperation between the telecommunications industry and law enforcement officials to ensure the appropriate use of code-authorized electronic surveillance.

Federal Communications Commission, *Administrative Law Judges, 2000 L St. N.W., #222 20554; (202) 418-*

2250. Fax, (202) 418-0195. Joseph Chachkin, acting chief judge.

Presides over hearings and issues initial decisions in disputes over FCC regulations and applications for licensing.

Federal Communications Commission, *Compliance and Information Bureau, 1919 M St. N.W. 20554; (202) 418-1100. Richard Lee, chief. Toll-free, (888) 225-5322. TDD, (888) 835-5322. 24-hour watch officer, (202) 632-6975. Internet, http://www.fcc.gov/cib.*

Detects violations of radio regulations by monitoring transmissions and inspecting stations; investigates complaints of radio frequency interference related to life and safety; provides radio direction finding assistance to other bureaus and agencies; pursues sanctions such as civil monetary penalties, forfeiture of property, and injunctions. Operates the National Call Center in Gettysburg, Pa.; toll-free (888) numbers handle inquiries and complaints.

Justice Dept., *Antitrust Division, 1401 H St. N.W., #8000 20530; (202) 514-5621. Fax, (202) 514-6381. Donald J. Russell, chief, Telecommunications. Toll-free, (888) 514-6381. Internet, http://www.usdoj.gov/atr/atr.htm.*

Investigates and litigates antitrust cases dealing with communications; participates in agency proceedings and rulemaking concerning communications; monitors and analyzes legislation. Oversees continuing matters concerning the breakup of AT&T.

NONPROFIT

Federal Communications Bar Assn., *1722 Eye St. N.W., #300 20006-3705; (202) 736-8640. Fax, (202) 736-8740. Paula Friedman, executive director. Internet, fcba@fcba.org or http://www.fcba.org.*

Membership: attorneys, nonattorneys, and law students in communications law who practice before the Federal Communications Commission (FCC), the courts, and state and local regulatory agencies. Cooperates with the FCC and other members of the bar on legal aspects of communications issues.

International and Satellite Communications

AGENCIES

Federal Communications Commission, *Common Carrier Bureau, 1919 M St. N.W., #500 20554; (202) 418-1500. Fax, (202) 418-2825. Richard Metzger, chief. Internet, http://www.fcc.gov/ccb.*

Develops, recommends, and administers FCC policies involving common carriers (wireline facilities that furnish interstate communications services for hire). Policy areas include long-distance and local exchange telephone companies and proposals to introduce or expand competition in telecommunications markets.

Federal Communications Commission, *International Bureau,* 2000 M St. N.W., #800 20554; (202) 418-0420. Fax, (202) 418-2818. Regina Keeney, chief. Internet, http://www.fcc.gov/ib.

Coordinates the FCC's collection and dissemination of information on communications and telecommunications policy, regulation, and market developments in other countries and the policies and regulations of international organizations. Coordinates the FCC's international policy activities; represents the FCC in international forums.

State Dept., *International Communications and Information Policy,* Main State Bldg., #4826 20520-5818; (202) 647-5832. Fax, (202) 647-5957. Vonya McCann, U.S. coordinator.

Develops and manages international communication and information policy for the State Dept. Acts as a liaison for other federal departments and agencies and the private sector in international communications issues. Trade-related telecommunications issues are handled by the Bureau of Economic and Business Affairs.

INTERNATIONAL ORGANIZATIONS

International Telecommunications Satellite Organization (INTELSAT), 3400 International Dr. N.W. 20008-3098; (202) 944-6800. Fax, (202) 944-7898. Irving Goldstein, director general. Internet, http://www.intelsat.int.

Membership: more than 140 nations. Owns and operates a global international satellite communications system.

NONPROFIT

International Assn. of Satellite Users and Suppliers, 45681 Oakbrook Court, #107, Sterling, VA 20166; (703) 759-2094. A. Fred Dassler, executive director. Library, (703) 406-2744. Internet, iasus@erols.com.

Membership: satellite users and suppliers. Provides information on the business application of satellites, new technological developments, and federal regulatory and policy actions. Assists corporations, developing countries, and consortia in efficient satellite usage. Brokers new and reconditioned telecommunications equipment; acts as a liaison between satellite users and suppliers.

Satellite Broadcasting and Communications Assn., 225 Reinekers Lane, #600, Alexandria, VA 22314; (703)

549-6990. Fax, (703) 549-7640. Charles Hewitt, president. Fax-on-demand, (888) 629-7222. Internet, http://www.sbca.com.

Membership: owners, operators, manufacturers, dealers and distributors of satellite receiving stations; software and program suppliers; and others in the home satellite industry. Promotes use of satellite earth stations for television programming and as part of the national and global information infrastructure. Monitors legislation and regulations.

Society of Satellite Professionals International, 2200 Wilson Blvd., #102-258, Arlington, VA 22201; (703) 243-8948. Fax, (703) 528-4084. LaRene Tondro, executive director. Internet, http://www.sspi.org.

Membership: professionals in satellite communications. Promotes worldwide growth of the industry; encourages professional development, information exchange, and research.

Radio and Television

See also Broadcasting (this chapter)

AGENCIES

Corporation for Public Broadcasting, 901 E St. N.W. 20004-2037; (202) 879-9600. Fax, (202) 783-1039. Robert T. Coonrod, president; , . Press, (202) 879-9687. Internet, comments@cpb.org or http://www.cpb.org.

Private corporation chartered by Congress under the Public Broadcasting Act of 1967 and funded by the federal government. Supports public broadcasting through grants for public radio and television stations; provides general support for national program production and operation; helps fund projects on U.S. and international news, culture, and history; studies emerging technologies, such as cable and satellite transmission, for possible use by public telecommunications.

Federal Communications Commission, *Compliance and Information Bureau,* 1919 M St. N.W., #734 20554-0001; (202) 418-1105. Richard Lee, chief. Toll-free, (888) 225-5322. TDD, (888) 835-5322. Internet, http://www.fcc.gov/cib.

Monitors the radio spectrum and inspects broadcast stations; ensures that U.S. radio laws and FCC rules are observed. Develops activities to inform, assist, and educate licensees; provides presentations and information. Manages the Emergency Alert System. Operates the National Call Center in Gettysburg, Pa.; toll-free (888) numbers handle inquiries and complaints.

Federal Communications Commission, *Engineering and Technology,* 2000 M St. N.W., #480 20554; (202) 418-

2470. Fax, (202) 418-1944. Richard M. Smith, chief. Internet, http://www.fcc.gov/oet.

Advises the FCC on technical and spectrum matters and assists in developing U.S. telecommunications policy. Identifies and reviews developments in telecommunications and related technologies. Studies characteristics of radio frequency spectrum. Certifies radios and other electronic equipment to meet FCC standards.

Federal Communications Commission, *Mass Media Bureau,* 1919 M St. N.W., #314 20554; (202) 418-2600. Fax, (202) 418-2828. Roy J. Stewart, chief. Internet, http://www.fcc.gov/mmb.

Licenses, regulates, and develops audio and video services in traditional broadcasting and emerging television delivery systems, including high-definition television; processes applications for licensing commercial and noncommercial radio and television broadcast equipment and facilities; handles renewals and changes of ownership; investigates public complaints.

National Endowment for the Arts *(National Foundation on the Arts and the Humanities), Creation and Presentation,* 1100 Pennsylvania Ave. N.W. 20506-0001; (202) 682-5452. Fax, (202) 682-5721. Jennifer Dowley, division coordinator. Internet, http://arts.endow.gov.

Awards grants to nonprofit organizations for film, video, and radio productions; supports arts programming broadcast nationally on public television and radio.

National Endowment for the Humanities *(National Foundation on the Arts and the Humanities), Public Programs,* 1100 Pennsylvania Ave. N.W., #426 20506; (202) 606-8278. Fax, (202) 606-8557. James Dougherty, senior program officer. Internet, info@neh.fed.us.

Awards grants for nonprofit media projects aimed at advancing knowledge of the humanities.

NONPROFIT

Assn. for Interactive Media, 1019 19th St. N.W., 10th Floor 20036; (202) 408-0008. Fax, (202) 408-0111. Andrew L. Sernovitz, chief executive officer. Internet, http://www.interactivehq.org.

Membership: companies and organizations involved in production and broadband delivery of interactive television and personal computer-based media. Informs members about changes in technology, marketing opportunities, information and product distribution channels, and international policy concerning the Internet. Sponsors the Open Internet Congress.

Assn. for Maximum Service Television, 1776 Massachusetts Ave. N.W., #310 20036; (202) 861-0344. Fax,

(202) 861-0342. Margita E. White, president. Internet, http://www.mstv.com.

Membership: commercial and educational television stations. Participates in FCC rulemaking proceedings; specializes in television engineering and other matters concerning the transmission structure of the nation's television system.

Assn. of America's Public Television Stations, 1350 Connecticut Ave. N.W., #200 20036; (202) 887-1700. Fax, (202) 293-2422. David J. Brugger, president. Internet, info@apts.org or http://www.universe.digex.net/~apts.

Membership: public television licensees. Provides information on licensees' operating characteristics, financing, and facilities; assists licensees in planning efforts. Monitors legislation and regulations.

Assn. of Independent Television Stations, 1320 19th St. N.W., #300 20036; (202) 887-1970. Fax, (202) 887-0950. James B. Hedlund, president. Internet, http://www.altv.com.

Membership: independent television stations. Monitors legislation and regulations affecting the industry. Interests include the must-carry rules, copyright laws, and television advertising and syndication issues.

Electronic Industries Assn., 2500 Wilson Blvd., #400, Arlington, VA 22201-3834; (703) 907-7500. Fax, (703) 907-7501. Peter F. McCloskey, president. Internet, http://www.eia.org.

Membership: U.S. electronics manufacturers. Interests include common distribution, government procurement, high-definition television, and home recording rights; promotes trade, competitiveness, and export expansion through the the International Business Council. Monitors legislation and regulations.

National Assn. of Broadcasters, 1771 N St. N.W. 20036-2891; (202) 429-5300. Fax, (202) 429-5343. Edward O. Fritts, president. Press, (202) 429-5350. Library, (202) 429-5490. Internet, register@nab.org or http://www.nab.org.

Membership: radio and television broadcast stations and broadcast networks holding an FCC license or construction permit; associate members include producers of equipment and programs. Interests include privatization abroad and related business opportunities. Library offers fee-based services to non-members by appointment. Monitors legislation and regulations.

National Coalition on Television Violence, 5132 Newport Ave., Bethesda, MD 20816; (301) 986-0362. Fax, (301) 656-7031. Mary Ann Banta, vice president. Internet, nctvmd@aol.com or http://www.nctvv.org.

Analyzes reports prepared by the broadcast and cable industries; monitors levels of violence in media.

National Public Radio, *635 Massachusetts Ave. N.W. 20001-3753; (202) 414-2000. Fax, (202) 414-3329. Delano Lewis, president. Press, (202) 414-2300. Audience services (tapes, transcripts, and listener inquiries), (202) 414-3232. Internet, nprlist@npr.org or http://www.npr.org.*

Membership: public radio stations nationwide. Produces and distributes news and public affairs programming, congressional hearings, speeches, cultural and dramatic presentations, and programs for specialized audiences. Provides program distribution service via satellite. Represents member stations before Congress, the FCC, and other regulatory agencies.

Public Broadcasting Service, *1320 Braddock Pl., Alexandria, VA 22314; (703) 739-5000. Fax, (703) 739-0775. Ervin Duggan, president. Internet, www@pbs.org or http://www.pbs.org.*

Membership: public television stations nationwide. Selects, schedules, promotes, and distributes national programs; provides public television stations with educational, instructional, and cultural programming; also provides news and public affairs, science and nature, fundraising, and children's programming. Assists members with technology development and fundraising.

T.V.-Free America, *1611 Connecticut Ave. N.W., #3A 20009; (202) 887-0436. Fax, (202) 518-5560. Henry Labalme, executive director. Internet, tvfa@essential.org or http://www.essential.org/orgs/tvfa.*

Promotes a voluntary and dramatic reduction in the amount of television watched by Americans. Sponsors National TV Turn-off Week.

Telephone and Telegraph

For cellular telephones, see Wireless Telecommunications

AGENCIES

Federal Communications Commission, *Common Carrier Bureau, 1919 M St. N.W., #500 20554; (202) 418-1500. Fax, (202) 418-2825. Richard Metzger, chief. Internet, http://www.fcc.gov/ccb.*

Develops, recommends, and administers FCC policies involving common carriers (wireline facilities that furnish interstate communications services for hire). Specific policy areas include long-distance and local exchange telephone companies and proposals to introduce or expand competition in telecommunications markets.

General Services Administration, *Federal Telecommunications Service, 7799 Leesburg Pike, #210 North, Falls Church, VA 22043; (703) 285-1020. Fax, (703) 285-1031. Dennis J. Fischer, commissioner. Internet, http://www.gsa.gov.*

Purchases and leases telecommunications equipment and services for the federal government. Monitors the transition from federal telecommunications service to private provider partnerships for government phones.

NONPROFIT

Assn. for Local Telecommunications Services, *888 17th St. N.W., #900 20006; (202) 969-2587. Fax, (202) 969-2581. Tricia Breckenridge, chair. Internet, http://www.alts.org.*

Seeks to open local telecommunications market to full and fair facilities-based competition. Monitors legislation and regulations.

CompTel, *1900 M St. N.W., #800 20036; (202) 296-6650. Fax, (202) 296-7585. Russell Frisby, president. Internet, http://www.comptel.org.*

Membership: providers of long-distance telecommunications services and suppliers to the industry. Analyzes domestic and international issues affecting competitive long-distance carriers, including mergers. Monitors legislation and regulations.

MultiMedia Telecommunications Assn., *2500 Wilson Blvd., #300, Arlington, VA 22201; (703) 907-7470. Fax, (703) 907-7478. William Moroney, president. Internet, info@mmta.org or http://www.mmta.org.*

Membership: manufacturers, suppliers, distributors, and users of computer and communications systems. Serves as an information source and provides members with a benefits program and legal counsel; conducts training program. Monitors legislation and regulations.

National Telephone Cooperative Assn., *2626 Pennsylvania Ave. N.W. 20037; (202) 298-2300. Fax, (202) 298-2320. Michael E. Brunner, executive vice president. Internet, frs@ntca.org or http://www.ntca.org.*

Membership: locally owned and controlled telecommunications cooperatives and companies serving rural and small-town areas. Offers educational seminars, workshops, technical assistance, and a benefits program to members. Monitors legislation and regulations.

Organization for the Protection and Advancement of Small Telephone Companies, *21 Dupont Circle N.W., #700 20036; (202) 659-5990. Fax, (202) 659-4619. John N. Rose, president. Internet, opastco@opastco.org or http://www.opastco.org.*

Membership: local exchange carriers with 50,000 or fewer access lines. Provides members with educational materials and information on regulatory, legislative, and judicial issues in the telecommunications industry. Operates Foundation for Rural Education and Development.

U.S. Telephone Assn., *1401 H St. N.W., #600 20005; (202) 326-7300. Fax, (202) 326-7333. Roy Neel, president. Internet, http://www.usta.org.*

Membership: local telephone companies and manufacturers and suppliers for these companies. Provides members with information on the industry; conducts seminars; participates in FCC regulatory proceedings.

Wireless Telecommunications

AGENCIES

Federal Communications Commission, *Wireless Telecommunications Bureau, 2025 M St. N.W., #5002 20554; (202) 418-0600. Fax, (202) 418-0787. Dan Phythyon, chief. Library, (202) 418-0450. Internet, http:// www.fcc.gov/wtb.*

Regulates wireless communications, including cellular telephone, paging, personal communications services, public safety, air and maritime navigation, and other commercial and private radio services. Assesses new uses of wireless technologies, including electronic commerce. Gettysburg office handles all licensing applications and concerns: FCC Wireless Telecommunications Bureau, Licensing Division, 1270 Fairfield Rd., Gettysburg, PA 17325; (717) 337-1212.

U.S. Secret Service *(Treasury Dept.),* **Financial Crimes,** *1800 G St. N.W., #942 20223; (202) 435-5850. Fax, (202) 435-7481. Dana Brown, special agent in charge.*

Investigates reports of cellular phone and credit fraud.

NONPROFIT

American Mobile Telecommunications Assn., *1150 18th St. N.W., #250 20036; (202) 331-7773. Fax, (202) 331-9062. Alan R. Shark, president. Internet, http:// amtausa.org.*

Membership: mobile telecommunications companies, including dispatch services. Serves as an information source on radio frequencies, licensing, new products and technology, and market conditions; offers research service of FCC records. Promotes the industry abroad through the International Mobile Telecommunications Assn. Monitors legislation and regulations.

Cellular Telecommunications Industry Assn., *1250 Connecticut Ave. N.W., #200 20036; (202) 785-0081. Fax,*

(202) 776-0540. Thomas E. Wheeler, president. Internet, http://www.wow-com.com.

Membership: system operators, equipment manufacturers, engineering firms, and others engaged in the cellular telephone and mobile communications industry. Provides information for consumers and persons with disabilities. Monitors legislation and regulations.

Council of Independent Communication Suppliers, *1110 N. Glebe Rd., #500, Arlington, VA 22201-5720; (703) 528-5115. Fax, (703) 524-1074. Cynthia Chappell, chair. Internet, info@ita-relay.com or http://www.ita-relay.com.*

Represents independent radio sales and service organizations, communications service providers, and telecommunications consultants and engineers serving the Private Land Mobile Radio Services industry. Informs members of FCC and industry activities; solicits members' views on FCC regulatory proceedings. (Affiliated with Industrial Telecommunications Assn.)

Industrial Telecommunications Assn., *1110 N. Glebe Rd., #500, Arlington, VA 22201-5720; (703) 528-5115. Fax, (703) 524-1074. Mark E. Crosby, president. Internet, info@ita-relay.com or http://www.ita-relay.com.*

FCC-certified frequency advisory committee for the Special Industrial Radio Service and Industrial/Land Transportation pools. Provides frequency coordination, licensing, research, and telecommunications engineering services to Private Land Mobile Radio Services licensees and applicants. Represents telecommunications interests of Special Industrial, Video Production, and Telephone Maintenance Radio Service licensees and informs members of FCC rule changes and industry activities.

Personal Communications Industry Assn., *500 Montgomery St., #700, Alexandria, VA 22314; (703) 739-0300. Fax, (703) 836-1608. E. B. "Jay" Kitchen Jr., president. Toll-free, (800) 759-0300. Fax-on-demand, (800) 680-7242. Internet, http://www.pcia.com.*

Membership: individuals; institutions; independent two-way radio dealers; and FCC-licensed carriers who provide the public with personal communications services, including pagers, cellular telephones, and conventional radio telephones. Provides members with information, technical assistance, and educational programs. Serves as the FCC-recognized coordinator for frequencies in the Business Radio Service. Interests include technological standards and development of international markets. Library offers fee-based services by appointment. Monitors legislation and regulations.

UTC, The Telecommunications Assn., *1140 Connecticut Ave. N.W., #1140 20036; (202) 872-0030. Fax, (202) 872-1331. Charles M. Meehan, executive director. Internet,*

utclegal@dgs.dgsys.com or http://www.dgsys.com/
~utclegal/.

Membership: electric, gas, and water utility companies and natural gas pipelines. Participates in FCC rulemaking proceedings. Interests include radio spectrum for fixed and mobile communication and technological, legislative, and regulatory developments affecting telecommunications operations of energy utilities.

Wireless Cable Assn. International, *1140 Connecticut Ave. N.W., #810 20036; (202) 452-7823. Fax, (202) 452-0041. Andrew Kreig, President. Internet, http://www. wirelesscabl.com.*

Membership: system operators, program suppliers, equipment and service providers, engineers, and others involved in delivery of subscription television programming over a terrestrial microwave platform. Develops standards; promotes technological advancement and worldwide growth of the industry. Monitors legislation and regulations.

⊞ GOVERNMENT INFORMATION

See also Access to Congressional Information (chap. 20); Internet and Related Technologies (this chapter: for list of agency Web sites); Libraries and Educational Media (chap. 6)

AGENCIES

General Services Administration, *Federal Information Center, 1800 F St. N.W. 20405 (mailing address: P.O. Box 600, Cumberland, MD 21502); Fax, (202) 501-1680. Warren Snaider, staff contact, (202) 501-1939. Toll-free, (800) 688-9889. TDD, (800) 326-2996. Internet, http:// fic.info.gov.*

Operates a toll-free hotline which provides information on all federal government agencies, programs, and services.

General Services Administration, *Federal Information Relay Service, 13221 Woodland Park Rd., 3rd Floor, Herndon, VA 20171-3022; (800) 877-8339. Carolyn Thomas, director. Information, (703) 904-2848. TDD, (800) 877-8845. Internet, http://www.gsa.gov/et/fic-firs/ firs.htm.*

Assures that the federal telecommunications system is fully accessible to deaf, hearing-impaired, and speech-impaired individuals, including federal workers. Operates 8 a.m. to 8 p.m., weekdays, Eastern time. Produces a directory of TDD/TTY services within the federal government.

National Archives and Records Administration, *8601 Adelphi Rd., #111, College Park, MD 20740-6001; (301) 713-6410. Fax, (301) 713-7141. John Carlin, archivist of the United States; Lewis J. Bellardo, deputy archivist of the United States. Press, (301) 713-7360. TDD, (202) 501-5404. Internet, inquire@nara.gov or http:// www.nara.gov.*

Identifies, preserves, and makes available federal government documents of historic value; administers regional storage centers, and archives; operates the presidential library system. Collections include photographs, graphic materials, and films; holdings include records generated by foreign governments (especially in wartime) and by international conferences, commissions, and exhibitions. (Liaison office in Washington, 7th St. and Pennsylvania Ave. N.W., 20408; 202-501-5502.)

National Archives and Records Administration, *Center for Legislative Archives, 700 Pennsylvania Ave. N.W., #8E 20408; (202) 501-5350. Fax, (202) 219-2176. Michael Gillette, director.*

Collects and maintains records of congressional committees and legislative files from 1789 to the present. Publishes inventories and guides to these records.

National Archives and Records Administration, *Electronic Records, 8601 Adelphi Rd., College Park, MD 20740-6001; (301) 713-6630. Fax, (301) 713-6911. Kenneth S. Thibodeau, director. Reference service, (301) 713-6645. Internet, cer@nara.gov.*

Preserves, maintains, and makes available electronic records of the U.S. government in all subject areas. Provides researchers with magnetic tape copies of records on a cost-recovery basis. Distributes lists of holdings.

National Archives and Records Administration, *Federal Register, 800 N. Capitol St., #700 20408; (202) 523-5230. Fax, (202) 523-6866. Frances D. McDonald, editor-in-chief. TDD, (202) 523-5229. Public Laws Update Service (PLUS), (202) 523-6641. Internet, http://www. nara.gov/nara/fedreg/fedreg.html.*

Assigns public law numbers to enacted legislation, executive orders, and proclamations; responds to inquiries on public law numbers; assists inquirers in finding presidential signing or veto messages in the *Weekly Compilation of Presidential Documents* and the *Public Papers of the Presidents* series; compiles slip laws and annual *United States Statutes at Large;* compiles indexes for finding statutory provisions. Operates Public Laws Update Service (PLUS), which provides information by telephone on new legislation. Publications available from the U.S. Government Printing Office, Washington, DC 20402; (202) 783-3238.

CHIEF INFORMATION OFFICERS FOR FEDERAL AGENCIES

DEPARTMENTS

Agriculture, Anne Reed, (202) 720-8833

Commerce, W. Scott Gould, (202) 482-4951

Defense, Arthur L. Moneyn, (703) 695-0348

  Air Force, Arthur L. Money, (703) 697-6361

  Army, Lt. Gen. William H. Campbell, (703) 697-7494

  Navy, John Douglass, (703) 602-2013

Education, Donald Rappaport, (202) 401-0085

Energy, Woody Hall, (202) 586-0166

Health and Human Services, John J. Callahan, (202) 690-6396

Housing and Urban Development, Leslie H. Graham, acting, (202) 708-0306

Interior, Daryl Y. White, (202) 208-6194

Justice, Stephen R. Colgate, (202) 514-3101

Labor, Patricia Lattimore, (202) 219-9086

State, Glen Johnson, acting, (202) 647-2226

Transportation, Michael Huerta, acting, (202) 366-1103

Treasury, Jim Flyzik, (202) 622-1200

Veterans Affairs, D. Mark Catlett, (202) 273-5589

AGENCIES

Central Intelligence Agency, John Dahms, (703) 482-8509

Environmental Protection Agency, Alvin Pesachowitz, (202) 260-4600

Federal Emergency Management Agency, G. Clay Hollister, (202) 646-3006

Federal Trade Commission, Alan Proctor, (202) 326-2204

General Accounting Office, Christopher W. Hoenig, (202) 512-6208

General Services Administration, Shereen Remez, (202) 501-1000

National Aeronautics and Space Administration, Lee Holcomb, (202) 358-1824

National Archives and Records Administration, Linda Massaro, (703) 306-1100

Nuclear Regulatory Commission, Anthony J. Galante, (301) 415-8700

Office of Management and Budget, John Koskinen, (202) 395-6190

Office of Personnel Management, Janet L. Barnes, (202) 418-3200

Securities and Exchange Commission, Michael E. Bartell, (202) 942-8800

Small Business Administration, Lawrence E. Barrett, (202) 205-6708

Social Security Administration, John R. Dyer, (410) 965-9000

National Archives and Records Administration, *Modern Records Program,* 8601 Adelphi Rd., College Park, MD 20740; (301) 713-7100. Fax, (301) 713-6850. Michael L. Miller, director. Internet, Records. Management@arch2.nara.gov.

Administers programs that establish standards, guidelines, and procedures for agency records administration. Manages training programs; inspects records management practices; monitors certain records not contained in National Archives depositories.

National Archives and Records Administration, *Presidential Libraries,* 8601 Adelphi Rd., #2200, College Park, MD 20704; (301) 713-6050. Fax, (301) 713-6045. David F. Peterson, assistant archivist. Internet, http://www.nara.gov.

Directs all programs relating to acquisition, preservation, publication, and research use of materials in presidential libraries; conducts oral history projects; publishes finding aids for research sources; provides reference service, including information from and about documentary holdings.

National Archives and Records Administration, *Regional Records Services,* 8601 Adelphi Rd., College Park, MD 20740-6001; (301) 713-7200. Fax, (301) 713-7205. Richard L. Claypoole, assistant archivist.

Stores federal records and assists agencies in microfilming records, protecting vital operating records, improving filing and classification systems, and developing disposition schedules. (See appendix for list of regional records facilities.)

National Archives and Records Administration, *Textual Reference,* 8601 Adelphi Rd., College Park, MD 20740-6001; (301) 713-7250. Fax, (301) 713-6907. Sharon Thibodeau, director.

Provides reference service for unpublished civil and military federal government records. Maintains central catalog of all library materials. Compiles comprehensive bibliographies of materials related to archival administration and records management. Permits research in American history, archival science, and records management. Maintains collections of the papers of the Conti-

PUBLICATIONS OFFICES AT FEDERAL AGENCIES

DEPARTMENTS

Agriculture, Orders, (202) 720-2791

Commerce, Orders (via NTIS), (703) 605-6000

Defense, Orders, (703) 697-5737

  Army, Orders, (703) 325-6297

Energy, Orders, (202) 586-5575

Health and Human Services, Orders, (301) 436-8500

Housing and Urban Development, Orders, (800) 767-7468; Fax orders, (202) 708-2313

Justice, Orders, (202) 514-2007

Labor, Orders, (202) 606-7828

State, Orders, (202) 647-6575; Fax-on-demand, (202) 736-7720

Transportation, Orders, (301) 322-4961; Fax orders, (301) 386-5394

Treasury, Orders, (202) 622-2960

Veterans Affairs, Orders, (202) 273-5700

AGENCIES

Census Bureau, Orders, (301) 457-4100

Commission on Civil Rights, Orders, (202) 376-8128

Consumer Product Safety Commission, Orders, (301) 504-0785

Corporation for National Service (AmeriCorps), Orders, (800) 942-2677

Energy Information Administration, Orders, (202) 586-8800

Environmental Protection Agency, Orders, (202) 260-5922

Equal Employment Opportunity Commission, Orders, (800) 669-3362

Federal Communications Commission, Orders, (202) 857-3800; Fax orders, (202) 857-3805; Fax-on-demand, (202) 418-2830

Federal Election Commission, Orders, (800) 424-9530

Federal Emergency Management Agency, Orders, (301) 497-1873

Federal Reserve System, Orders, (202) 452-3244

Federal Trade Commission, Orders, (202) 326-2222

General Accounting Office, Orders, (202) 512-6000

General Services Administration, Orders, (202) 501-1235

Government Printing Office, Orders, (202) 512-1800

International Bank for Reconstruction and Development (World Bank), Orders, (202) 473-1155

International Trade Administration
  Orders from NTIS and GPO, (202) 482-5487

National Aeronautics and Space Administration, Orders, (301) 621-0390

National Archives and Records Administration, Orders, (202) 501-5235; Toll-free, (800) 234-8861

National Endowment for the Humanities, Orders, (202) 606-8400

National Institute of Standards and Technology, Information (orders from NTIS and GPO), (301) 975-3058

National Labor Relations Board, Orders, (202) 273-1991

National Oceanic and Atmospheric Administration, Information and orders, (800) 638-8975; Fax orders, (301) 436-6829

National Park Service, Information (orders by mail only), (202) 208-4747

National Science Foundation, Orders, (301) 947-2722

National Technical Information Service,
  Military documents orders, (703) 487-4684; Other orders, (703) 605-6000

National Transportation Safety Board, Orders, (202) 314-6596

Nuclear Regulatory Commission, Orders, (202) 512-2249

Occupational Safety and Health Administration, Orders, (202) 219-4667

Office of Personnel Management, Orders, (202) 606-1915

Peace Corps, Orders, (202) 606-0062

Securities and Exchange Commission, Information, (202) 942-4040; Orders, (202) 942-4046

Smithsonian Institution, Orders: Smithsonian books, recordings, videos, (800) 669-1559; Orders: Smithsonian University Press, (800) 782-4612; Customer service, (202) 287-3738

Social Security Administration, Orders, (410) 965-4121

U.S. Fish and Wildlife Service, Orders, (703) 358-1711

U.S. Geological Survey, Orders, (800) 872-6277

U.S. Information Agency, Orders, (202) 619-4281

U.S. Institute of Peace, Book orders, (800) 868-8064; Other orders, (202) 457-1700

Women's Bureau (Labor Dept.), Orders, (202) 219-6652

nental Congress (1774-1789), U.S. State Dept. diplomatic correspondence (1789-1963), and general records of the U.S. government.

National Technical Information Service *(Commerce Dept.), 5285 Port Royal Rd., #200F, Springfield, VA 22161; (703) 605-6400. Fax, (703) 321-8547. Donald R. Johnson, director. TDD, (703) 605-6043. Sales center, (703) 605-6000; rush orders, (800) 553-6847. Internet, http://www.ntis.gov.*

Distribution center that catalogs and sells U.S. and foreign government-sponsored research, development, and scientific engineering reports and other technical analyses prepared by federal and local government agencies. Offers microfiche and computerized bibliographic search services. Online database available through commercial vendors and in machine-readable form through lease agreement.

National Technical Information Service *(Commerce Dept.), National Audiovisual Center, 5285 Port Royal Rd., Springfield, VA 22161-0001; (703) 605-6537. Fax, (703) 321-8199. George H. Ziener, director. Internet, http://www.ntis.gov.*

Sells government-produced media, including slides filmstrips, audiotapes, interactive video disks, videotapes, and multimedia kits on a wide range of subjects. Publishes catalogs of audiovisual materials produced by all agencies of the U.S. government.

CONGRESS

General Accounting Office, *Document Distribution Center, 700 4th St. N.W. (mailing address: P.O. Box 37050, Washington, DC 20013); (202) 512-6000. Fax, (202) 512-6061. Paula DeRoy, staff contact. Press, (202) 512-4800. Locator, (202) 512-3000. Internet, info@www.gao.gov.*

Provides information to the public on many federal programs. GAO publications and information about GAO publications are available upon request.

Government Printing Office, *732 N. Capitol St. N.W. 20401; (202) 512-2034. Fax, (202) 512-1347. Michael F. DiMario, public printer. Press, (202) 512-1991. Congressional documents, (202) 512-1808; general government publications, (202) 512-1800; complaints, (202) 512-2457; electronic products, (202) 512-5130. Internet, publicprinter@gpo.gov or http://www.gpo.gov.*

Prints, distributes, and sells selected publications of the U.S. Congress, government agencies, and executive departments. Makes available, for a fee, the *Monthly Catalog of U.S. Government Publications,* a comprehensive listing of all publications issued by the various depart-

ments and agencies each month. Publications are distributed to GPO Regional Depository Libraries; some titles also may be purchased at GPO bookstores in larger cities. *(See Regional Information Sources in appendix.)*

House Oversight Committee, *1309 LHOB 20515; (202) 225-8281. Fax, (202) 225-9957. Bill Thomas, R-Calif., chair; Cathy Abernathy, acting staff director. Internet, http://www.house.gov/cho.*

Jurisdiction over the printing, cost of printing, binding, and distribution of congressional publications; jurisdiction (in conjunction with the Senate Rules and Administration Committee and the Joint Committee on Printing) over the Government Printing Office, executive papers, and depository libraries; jurisdiction over federal election law.

Joint Committee on Printing, *SH-818 20510; (202) 224-5241. Fax, (202) 224-1176. Sen. John W. Warner, R-Va., chair; Eric Peterson, staff director.*

Oversees public printing, binding, and distribution of government publications; executive papers and depository libraries; and activities of the Government Printing Office (in conjunction with the House Oversight and Senate Rules and Administration committees).

Legislative Resource Center, *Resource and Reference, B-106 CHOB 20515; (202) 225-1153. Fax, (202) 226-5207. Lea Uhre, manager.*

Conducts historical research. Advises members on the disposition of their records and papers; maintains information on manuscript collections of former members; maintains biographical files on former members. Recent publications include *Biographical Directory of the United States Congress, 1774-1989: Bicentennial Edition; Guide to Research Collections of Former Members of the United States House of Representatives, 1789-1987: Bicentennial Edition; Black Americans in Congress, 1870-1989;* and *Women in Congress, 1917-1989.*

Library of Congress, *Federal Library and Information Center Committee, 701 Pennsylvania Ave. N.W., #725 20004; (202) 707-4800. Fax, (202) 707-4818. Susan Tarr, executive director. Internet, flicc@loc.gov.*

Membership: one representative from each major federal agency, one representative each from the Library of Congress and the national libraries of medicine and agriculture, and one representative from each of the major Federal Information Centers. Coordinates planning, development, operations, and activities among federal libraries.

Library of Congress, *Serial and Government Publications, 101 Independence Ave. S.E. 20540; (202) 707-5647.*

Fax, (202) 707-6128. Karen Renninger, chief. Information, (202) 707-5690.

Operates Newspaper and Periodical Reading Room; maintains library's collection of current domestic and foreign newspapers, current periodicals, and serially issued publications of federal, state, and foreign governments; has maintained full government publication depository since 1979. Responds to written or telephone requests for information on government publications.

Senate Historical Office, *SH-201 20510; (202) 224-6900. Fax, (202) 224-5329. Richard Baker, historian.*

Serves as an information clearinghouse on Senate history, traditions, and members. Collects, organizes, and distributes to the public previously unpublished Senate documents; collects and preserves photographs and pictures related to Senate history; conducts an oral history program; advises senators and Senate committees on the disposition of their noncurrent papers and records. Produces publications on the history of the Senate.

Senate Rules and Administration Committee, *SR-305 20510; (202) 224-6352. Fax, (202) 224-3036. John W. Warner, R-Va., chair; Grayson Winterling, staff director. Internet, http://www.senate.gov/~rules.*

Jurisdiction over the printing, cost of printing, binding, and distribution of congressional publications; jurisdiction (in conjunction with the House Oversight Committee and the Joint Committee on Printing) over the Government Printing Office, executive papers, and depository libraries.

Freedom of Information

AGENCIES

Each agency has rules governing public access to its documents. Grants for access are determined initially by the agency; contact the freedom of information officer of the agency involved. (See appendix for explanation of Freedom of Information Act.)

Justice Dept., *Information and Privacy, 950 Pennsylvania Ave. N.W., #570 20530; (202) 514-3642. Fax, (202) 514-1009. Daniel J. Metcalfe and Richard L. Huff, co-directors. Information, (202) 514-2000. TDD, (202) 616-5498.*

Provides federal agencies with advice and policy guidance on matters related to implementing and interpreting the Freedom of Information Act (FOIA). Litigates selected FOIA and Privacy Act cases; adjudicates administrative appeals from Justice Dept. denials of public requests for access to documents; conducts FOI training for government agencies.

National Archives and Records Administration, *Information Security Oversight, 700 Pennsylvania Ave. N.W., #5W 20408-0001; (202) 219-5250. Fax, (202) 219-5385. Steven Garfinkel, director. Internet, isoo@arch1.nara.gov.*

Oversees government policy on security classification of documents for federal agencies and industry; reviews procedures; monitors declassification programs of federal agencies.

National Archives and Records Administration, *Initial Processing/Declassification, 8601 Adelphi Rd., College Park, MD 20740; (301) 713-6600. Fax, (301) 713-7480. Jeanne Schauble, director.*

Directs the review and declassification of records and security-classified materials in the National Archives in accordance with Executive Order 12958 and the Freedom of Information Act; assists other federal archival agencies in declassifying security-classified documents in their holdings.

CONGRESS

House Government Reform and Oversight Committee, *Subcommittee on Government Management, Information, and Technology, B373 RHOB 20515; (202) 225-5147. Steve Horn, R-Calif., chair; J. Russell George, staff director. Internet, http://www.house.gov/cho.*

Jurisdiction over Freedom of Information Act.

Senate Judiciary Committee, *Subcommittee on Technology, Terrorism, and Government Information, SH-325 20510; (202) 224-6791. Fax, (202) 228-0542. Jon Kyl, R-Ariz., chair; Michelle Van Cleve, counsel. Internet, http://www.senate.gov/committee/judiciary.html.*

Jurisdiction over Freedom of Information Act.

NONPROFIT

American Civil Liberties Union, *122 Maryland Ave. N.E. 20002; (202) 544-1681. Fax, (202) 546-0738. Laura W. Murphy, director, Washington Office. Internet, http://www.aclu.org.*

Initiates test court cases and advocates legislation to guarantee constitutional rights and civil liberties. Monitors agency compliance with the Freedom of Information Act, the Privacy Act, and other access statutes. Produces publications.

American Society of Access Professionals, *1444 Eye St. N.W., #700 20005; (202) 216-9623. Fax, (202) 216-9646. Claire Shamley, executive director.*

Membership: federal employees, attorneys, journalists, and others working with or interested in access-to-information laws. Seeks to improve the administration of

FREEDOM OF INFORMATION CONTACTS

DEPARTMENTS

Agriculture, Andrea Fowler, (202) 720-8164

Commerce, Brenda Dolan, (202) 482-4115

Defense, Charlie Y. Talbott, (703) 697-1180

  Air Force, Carolyn Price, (703) 697-0269

  Army, Rosemary Christian, (703) 607-3452

  Navy, Doris M. Lama, (202) 685-6545

Education, Maria-Teresa Cueva, (202) 708-9263

Energy, Abel Lopez, (202) 586-6025

Health and Human Services, Rosario Cirrincione, (202) 690-7453

Housing and Urban Development, Charlene Anderson, (202) 708-3866

Interior, Alexandra Mallus, (202) 208-5342

Justice, Patricia D. Harris, (202) 514-1938

Labor, Miriam Miller, (202) 219-8188

State, Margaret Grafeld, (202) 647-7740

Transportation, Ann Ross, acting, (202) 366-4542

Treasury, Lana Johnson, (202) 622-0930

Veterans Affairs, Donald L. Nielson, (202) 273-8135

AGENCIES

Agency for International Development, Willette Smith, (202) 712-5027

Central Intelligence Agency, Lee S. Strickland, (703) 613-1289

Commission on Civil Rights, Emma Monreig, (202) 376-8351

Commodity Futures Trading Commission, Edward Colbert, (202) 418-5105

Consumer Product Safety Commission, Todd A. Stevenson, (301) 504-0785

Environmental Protection Agency, Jeralene B. Green, (202) 260-4048

Equal Employment Opportunity Commission, J. C. Thurmond, (202) 663-4669

Export-Import Bank, Peter Barton, (202) 565-3952

Farm Credit Administration, Deborah Buccolo, (703) 883-4020

Federal Communications Commission, Ginny Simms, (202) 418-0210

Federal Deposit Insurance Corp., Lisa Snider, (202) 898-3822

Federal Election Commission, Ron Harris, (202) 219-4155

Federal Emergency Management Agency, Sandra Jackson, (202) 646-3840

Federal Labor Relations Authority, David M. Smith, (202) 482-6620

Federal Maritime Commission, Joseph Polking, (202) 523-5725

Federal Reserve, Susan Mitchell, (202) 452-3684

Federal Trade Commission, Keith Golden, (202) 326-2410

General Services Administration, Mary Cunningham, (202) 501-2262

Legal Services Corp., JoAnn Gretch, (202) 336-8813

Merit Systems Protection Board, Michael Hoxie, (202) 653-7200

National Aeronautics and Space Administration, Patricia M. Riep-Dice, (202) 358-1764

National Archives and Records Administration, Mary Ronan, (301) 713-6025

National Credit Union Adminstration, Patricia Slye, (703) 518-6565

National Endowment for the Humanities, Nancy Weiss, (202) 606-8322

National Labor Relations Board, John W. Hornbeck, (202) 273-3847

National Mediation Board, Judy Semi, (202) 523-5996

National Science Foundation, Leslie Crawford, (703) 306-1060

National Transportation Safety Board, Melba Moye, (202) 314-6551

Nuclear Regulatory Commission, Russell Powell, (301) 415-7169

Office of Personnel Management, Bob Huley, (202) 418-3200

Peace Corps, Brian Sutherland, (202) 606-3261

Pension Benefit Guaranty Corp., Bill Fitzgerald, (202) 326-4040

Securities and Exchange Commission, Hannah R. Hall, (202) 942-4320

Selective Service, Paula Sweeney, (703) 605-4046

Small Business Administration, Beverly Linden, (202) 401-8203

Social Security Administration, Darrell Blevins, (410) 965-1727

U.S. Arms Control and Disarmament Agency, Frederick Smith Jr., (202) 647-3596

U.S. Information Agency, Lola Secora, (202) 619-5499

U.S. International Trade Commission, Donna R. Koehnke, (202) 205-2000

U.S. Postal Service, Betty Sheriff, (202) 268-2608

the Freedom of Information Act, the Privacy Act, and other access statutes.

Center for National Security Studies, *Gelman Library, 2130 H St. N.W., #701 20037; (202) 994-7060. Fax, (202) 994-7005. Kate Martin, director. Internet, cnss@gwis2.circ.gwu.edu or cnss@nicom.com.*

A project of the Fund for Peace. Specializes in the Freedom of Information Act (FOIA) as it relates to national security matters and access to government information issues in the U.S. and abroad. Affiliated with the National Security Archive. Collection open to the public by appointment.

Freedom of Information Clearinghouse, *1600 20th St. N.W. (mailing address: P.O. Box 19367, Washington, DC 20036); (202) 588-1000. Fax, (202) 588-7795. Susan Speer, director. Information, (202) 588-7790. Internet, foic@essential.org or http://www.citizen.org/.*

Arm of the Center for Study of Responsive Law; works with Public Citizen Litigation Group. Collects and disseminates information on federal, state, and foreign freedom of information laws; assists citizens, public interest groups, and the media in seeking information from the government; litigates selected cases, generally chosen for their broad effect on case law.

Radio-Television News Directors Assn., *1000 Connecticut Ave. N.W., #615 20036; (202) 659-6510. Fax, (202) 223-4007. Barbara Cochran, president. Internet, rtnda@rtnda.org or http://www.rtnda.org.*

Membership: local and network news executives in broadcasting, cable, and other electronic media. Operates the Freedom of Information Committee.

▦ INTERNET AND RELATED TECHNOLOGIES

AGENCIES

Defense Advanced Research Projects Agency *(Defense Dept.), 3701 N. Fairfax Dr., Arlington, VA 22203-1714; (703) 696-2400. Fax, (703) 696-2207. Larry Lynn, director; H. Lee Buchanan III, deputy director, (703) 696-2402. Information, (703) 696-2404. Internet, http://www.darpa.mil.*

Helps maintain U.S. technological superiority in support of national security. Conducts ongoing research to develop the World Wide Web; funds Web-related research at other organizations.

Federal Bureau of Investigation *(Justice Dept.), Financial Institution Fraud, 935 Pennsylvania Ave.*

N.W., #7373 20535; (202) 324-5594. Fax, (202) 324-5817. William Perez, chief. Press, (202) 324-3691. Internet, http://www.fbi.gov.

Investigates crimes of fraud, theft, or embezzlement within or against financial institutions. Priorities include frauds involving computers and nationally significant intrusions into computer networks.

Federal Communications Commission, *Plans and Policy, 1919 M St. N.W., #822 20554; (202) 418-2030. Fax, (202) 418-2807. Marcelino Ford-Livene, counsel, New Technology and Policy. Internet, http://www.fcc.gov/ Bureaus/OPP/welcome.html.*

Monitors developments in expansion of the global internet.

General Services Administration, *Center for Electronic Messaging Technology, 1800 F St. N.W., #G-215 20405; (202) 501-3932. Fax, (202) 501-2079. Jack L. Finley, director. Internet, jack.finley@gsa.gov or http://www. fed.gov.*

Develops and defines the electronic mail network for the federal government, including all agencies and commissions. Promotes high-quality connections between federal, state, local, and tribal governments. Standardizes e-mail addresses for persons with disabilities.

General Services Administration, *Governmentwide Information Technology Management, 1800 F St. N.W. 20405; (202) 501-0202. Fax, (202) 219-1533. Martin Wagner, director.*

Reviews agencies' information resources management and procurement of information technology.

Government E-Mail Steering Subcommittee, *200 Independence Ave. S.W., #531H 20201; (202) 690-6162. Fax, (202) 690-8715. Neil Stillman, deputy assistant secretary.*

Oversees implementation of government-wide e-mail services; coordinates proposals and assists agencies in expanding electronic mail and electronic commerce capabilities.

Information Infrastructure Task Force, *Secretariat (NIST), 108 Bureau Dr., Bldg. 101, #A-1000, Gaithersburg, MD 20899; (301) 975-2667. Fax, (301) 216-0529. Barbara Guttman, information contact. Internet, http:// www.iitf.nist.gov.*

Membership: high-level representatives of the federal agencies that play a major role in development of information and telecommunications technologies, including the National Information Infrastructure (NII). Committees advise the president and White House agencies; topics include electronic commerce, security, privacy,

WORLD WIDE WEB SITES OF FEDERAL AGENCIES

CONGRESS

General Accounting Office, http://www.gao.gov

House of Representatives, http://www.house.gov

Library of Congress, http://www.loc.gov

Senate, http://www.senate.gov

WHITE HOUSE

General Information, http://www.whitehouse.gov

DEPARTMENTS

Agriculture, http://www.usda.gov

Commerce, http://www.doc.gov

Defense, http://www.dtic.mil/defenselink

  Air Force, http://www.af.mil

  Army, http://www.army.mil

  Marine Corps, http://www.usmc.mil

  Navy, http://www.navy.mil

Education, http://www.ed.gov

Energy, http://www.doe.gov

Health and Human Services, http://www.dhhs.gov

Housing and Urban Development,
http://www.hud.gov

Interior, http://www.doi.gov

Justice, http://www.usdoj.gov

Labor, http://www.dol.gov

State, http://www.state.gov

Transportation, http://www.dot.gov

Treasury, http://www.ustreas.gov

Veterans Affairs, http://www.va.gov

AGENCIES

General Accounting Office, http://www.odci.gov/cia

Consumer Product Safety Commission,
http://www.cpsc.gov

Corporation for Public Broadcasting,
http://www.cpb.org

Drug Enforcement Administration,
http://www.usdoj.gov/dea/deahome.htm

Environmental Protection Agency,
http://www.epa.gov

Export-Import Bank, http://www.exim.gov

Federal Aviation Administration, http://www.faa.gov

Federal Bureau of Investigation, http://www.fbi.gov

Federal Communications Commission,
http://www.fcc.gov

Federal Deposit Insurance Corporation,
http://www.fdic.gov

Federal Election Commission, http://www.fec.gov

Federal Emergency Management Agency,
http://www.fema.gov

Federal Energy Regulatory Commission,
http://www.ferc.fed.us

Federal Reserve System, http://www.bog.frb.fed.us

Federal Trade Commission, http://www.ftc.gov

Food and Drug Administration, http://www.fda.gov

General Services Administration, http://www.gsa.gov

Government Printing Office, http://www.gpo.gov

Internal Revenue Service, http://www.irs.ustreas.gov

National Aeronautics and Space Administration,
http://www.nasa.gov

National Archives and Records Administration,
http://www.nara.gov

National Institute of Standards and Techology,
http://www.nist.gov

National Institutes of Health, http://www.nih.gov

National Oceanic and Atmospheric Administration,
http://www.noaa.gov

National Park Service, http://www.nps.gov

National Performance Review, http://www.npr.gov

National Railroad Passenger Corporation (Amtrak),
http://www.amtrak.com

National Science Foundation, http://www.nsf.gov

National Technical Information Services,
http://www.ntis.gov

National Transportation Safety Board,
http://www.ntsb.gov

Nuclear Regulatory Commission, http://www.nrc.gov

Occupational Safety and Health Administration,
http://www.osha.gov

Patent and Trademark Office, http://www.uspto.gov

Peace Corps, http://www.peacecorps.gov

Pension Benefit Guaranty Corporation,
http://www.pbgc.gov

Securities and Exchange Commisssion,
http://www.sec.gov

Small Business Administration, http://www.sba.gov

Smithsonian Institution, http://www.si.edu

Social Security Administration, http://www.ssa.gov

U.S. Fish and Wildlife Service, http://www.fws.gov

U.S. Geological Survey, http://www.usgs.gov

U.S. Information Agency, http://www.usia.gov

U.S. International Trade Commission,
http://www.usitc.gov

U.S. Postal Service, http://www.usps.gov

intellectual property rights, health applications, and cooperation with state, local, and foreign governments. (Secretariat hosted by National Institute of Standards and Technology.)

Justice Dept., *Computer Crime and Intellectual Property,* 1001 G St. N.W., #200 20001; (202) 514-1026. Fax, (202) 514-6113. Scott Charney, chief.

Investigates and litigates criminal and civil cases involving computers and the Internet; provides specialized technical and legal assistance to other Justice Dept. divisions; coordinates international efforts; formulates policies and proposes legislation on computer crime issues.

National Institute of Standards and Technology *(Commerce Dept.), North American ISDN Users' Forum,* c/o NIST, Bldg. 820, #445, Gaithersburg, MD 20899; (301) 975-2937. Fax, (301) 926-9675. Sara Caswell, secretariat. Internet, niuf@nist.gov or http://www. niuf.nist.gov/misc/niuf.html.

Assists government, industry, and personal users of ISDN (Integrated Services Digital Network) communications technology. Helps users participate in the development of high-speed, interoperable applications for ISDN; sponsors workshops. (Secretariat hosted by NIST Information Technology Laboratory.)

National Science Foundation, *Computer and Information Sciences and Engineering,* 4201 Wilson Blvd., Arlington, VA 22230; (703) 306-1900. Fax, (703) 306-0577. Juris Hartmanis, assistant director. Internet, http://www.cise.nsf.gov.

Directorate that promotes basic research and education in computer and information sciences and engineering; helps maintain U.S. preeminence in these fields. Coordinates NSF involvement in the High-Performance Computing and Communications (HPCC) program; develops computer resources for scholarly communication, including links with foreign research and education networks; helps set Internet policy.

National Telecommunications and Information Administration *(Commerce Dept.),* 14th St. and Constitution Ave. N.W., #4898 20230; (202) 482-1840. Fax, (202) 482-1635. Larry Irving Jr., NTIA administrator. Information, (202) 482-7002. Library, (202) 482-3999. Internet, tiiap@ntia.doc.gov or http://www.ntia.doc.gov.

Promotes private-sector development of the National Information Infrastructure (NII) and market access for U.S. firms in developing the Global Information Infrastructure (GII). Makes grants to public and nonprofit entities for innovative use of the Internet and related technologies.

Office of Management and Budget, *Information Policy and Technology,* 725 17th St. N.W., #10236 20503; (202) 395-3785. Fax, (202) 395-5167. Bruce W. McConnell, chief.

Oversees implementation and policy development under the Information Technology Reform Act of 1996 and the Paperwork Reduction Act of 1995; focuses on information technology management and substantive information policy, including records management, privacy, and computer security.

President's Commission on Critical Infrastructure Protection, *Transition Office,* P.O. Box 46258 20050-6258; (703) 696-9395. Fax, (703) 696-9411. David V. Keyes, acting director. Internet, comments@pccip.gov or http://www.pccip.gov.

Advises the president on a national stategy for protecting critical infrastructures from physical and electronic threats. Focus includes information and communications systems, banking and finance, water supplies, transportation, and government services.

CONGRESS

General Accounting Office, *Federal Management and Workforce Issues,* 441 G St. N.W. 20548; (202) 512-8676. Fax, (202) 512-4516. L. Nye Stevens, director.

Assesses the quality of the nation's major statistical databases and helps adapt the government's dissemination of information to a new technological environment.

General Accounting Office, *Information Resources Management Policies and Issues,* 441 G St. N.W. 20548; (202) 512-6406. Fax, (202) 512-6451. Christopher W. Hoenig, director.

Seeks to make the federal government more effective in its information management. Assesses practices in the public and private sectors; makes recommendations to government agencies. Interests include information security.

House Commerce Committee, *Subcommittee on Telecommunications, Trade, and Consumer Protection,* 2125 RHOB 20515; (202) 225-2927. Fax, (202) 225-1919. W. J. "Billy" Tauzin, R-La., chair; James E. Derderian, staff director. Internet, http://www.house.gov/commerce.

Jurisdiction over legislation on communications, including computer communications and the Internet.

Senate Commerce, Science, and Transportation Committee, *Subcommittee on Communications,* SH-227 20510; (202) 224-5184. Conrad Burns, R-Mont., chair; Lauren Belvin, counsel. Internet, http://www.senate. gov/~commerce.

Jurisdiction over legislation on communications, including computer communications and the Internet.

NONPROFIT

American Electronics Assn., *601 Pennsylvania Ave. N.W., North Bldg., #600 20004; (202) 682-9110. Fax, (202) 682-9111. William T. Archey, president. Internet, http://www.aeanet.org.*

Membership: companies in the software, electronics, telecommunications, and information technology industries. Interests include international trade and investment, export controls, and U.S. competitiveness internationally. Holds conferences. Monitors legislation and regulations.

Data Interchange Standards Assn., *1800 Diagonal Rd., #200, Alexandria, VA 22314-2852; (703) 548-7005. Fax, (703) 548-5738. Judy Kilpatrick, chief executive officer. Internet, http://www.disa.org.*

Supports the development and the use of electronic data interchange standards in electronic commerce. Sponsors workshops, seminars, and conferences. Helps develop international standards.

American Library Assn., *Information Technology Policy, 1301 Pennsylvania Ave. N.W., #403 20004; (202) 628-8421. Fax, (202) 628-8424. J. Andrew Magpantay, director. Toll-free, (800) 941-8478. Internet, oitp@alawash.org or http://www.ala.org/oitp.*

Provides policy analysis and development in technology and telecommunications; interests include free expression on the Internet, equitable access to new media, and treaty negotiations of the World Intellectual Property Organization.

American Society for Information Science, *8720 Georgia Ave., #501, Silver Spring, MD 20910; (301) 495-0900. Fax, (301) 495-0810. Richard Hill, executive director. Internet, asis@asis.org or http://www.asis.org.*

Membership: librarians, computer scientists, management specialists, behavioral scientists, engineers, and individuals concerned with access to information. Conducts research and educational programs.

Assn. of Research Libraries, *21 Dupont Circle N.W., #800 20036; (202) 296-2296. Fax, (202) 872-0884. Duane Webster, executive director. Internet, http://www.arl.org.*

Membership: major research libraries, mainly at universities, in the United States and Canada. Interests include computer information systems and other bibliographic tools; publishing and scholarly communication; and worldwide policy on information, copyrights, and intellectual property.

Business Software Alliance, *1150 18th St. N.W., #700 20036; (202) 872-5500. Fax, (202) 872-5501. Robert Holleyman, president. Anti-piracy hotline, (800) 688-2721. Internet, software@bsa.org or http://www.bsa.org.*

Membership: personal computer software publishing companies. Promotes growth of the software industry worldwide; helps develop electronic commerce. Operates a toll-free hotline to report software piracy; investigates claims of software theft within corporations, financial institutions, academia, state and local governments, and nonprofit organizations. Provides legal counsel and initiates litigation on behalf of members.

Capcon Library Network, *1990 M St. N.W., #200 20036; (202) 331-5771. Fax, (202) 331-5788. Dennis Reynolds, president. Internet, capcon@capcon.net or http://www.capcon.net.*

Serves as a resource to libraries and other organizations on the information technology industry. Provides Internet access and training, education programs, and bibliographic services. Sponsors workshops and product demonstrations.

Center for Democracy and Technology, *1634 Eye St. N.W., #1100 20006; (202) 637-9800. Fax, (202) 637-0968. Jerry Berman, executive director. Internet, info@cdt.org or http://www.cdt.org.*

Promotes civil liberties and democratic values in new computer and communications media, both in the United States and abroad. Interests include free speech, privacy, freedom of information, electronic commerce, and design of the information infrastructure. Monitors policy and regulations.

Computer and Communications Industry Assn., *666 11th St. N.W., #600 20001; (202) 783-0070. Fax, (202) 783-0534. Edward J. Black, president. Internet, ccia@aol. com or http://www.ccianet.org.*

Membership: manufacturers and suppliers of computer data processing and communications-related products and services. Interests include telecommunications policy, capital formation and tax policy, federal procurement policy, communications and computer industry standards, intellectual property policies, encryption, international trade, and antitrust reform.

Computer Law Assn., *3028 Javier Rd., #402, Fairfax, VA 22031-4622; (703) 560-7747. Fax, (703) 207-7028. Barbara Fieser, executive director. Internet, clanet@aol.com or http://cla.org.*

Membership: lawyers, law students, and nonattorneys concerned with the legal aspects of computers and computer communications. Sponsors programs and provides information on such issues as software protection, contracting, telecommunications, international distribution, financing, taxes, copyrights, patents, and electronic data interchange. Focus includes the Internet and year 2000 issues.

Cyberspace Policy Institute, *George Washington University School of Engineering and Applied Science, 2033 K St. N.W., #340 20052; (202) 994-5512. Fax, (202) 994-5505. Lance J. Hoffman, director. Internet, cpi@seas.gwu. edu or http://www.cpi.seas.gwu.edu.*

Conducts research on telecommunications delivery systems, management information systems, computer networks, compensation for electronic intellectual property, ethics and values among users of new media, and related cultural and geopolitical issues. Works with government and private organizations.

Electronic Messaging Assn., *1655 N. Fort Myer Dr., #500, Arlington, VA 22209; (703) 524-5550. Fax, (703) 524-5558. Kerry Stackpole, chief executive officer. Internet, info@ema.org or http://www.ema.org.*

Membership: corporations, government, academia, and organizations involved in software development, mainframe, mini-computer, LAN messaging, and network communication. Seeks to advance messaging technologies, information exchange, and electronic commerce worldwide. Sponsors annual conference.

Electronic Privacy Information Center, *666 Pennsylvania Ave. S.E., #301 20003; (202) 544-9240. Fax, (202) 547-5482. Marc Rotenberg, director. Internet, info@epic. org or http://www.epic.org.*

Public interest research center. Conducts research and conferences on domestic and international civil liberties issues, including privacy, information access, computer security, and encryption; litigates cases. Monitors legislation and regulations. (Affiliated with the Fund for Constitutional Government.)

Graphic Communications Assn., *100 Daingerfield Rd., Alexandria, VA 22314-2888; (703) 519-8160. Fax, (703) 548-2867. Norm Scharpf, president. Internet, http://www. gca.org.*

Membership: firms and customers in printing, publishing, and related industries. Helps set industry standards for electronic commerce and conducts studies on new information technologies. (Affiliated with Printing Industries of America.)

Highway 1, *601 Pennsylvania Ave. N.W.,North Bldg., #520 20004-2601; (202) 628-3900. Fax, (202) 628-3922. Kimberly Jenkins, executive director. Internet, http://www. highway1.org.*

Provides members of Congress, their staffs, other government executives, and members of the public interested in the legislative process with demonstrations, seminars, and panel discussions on new information technologies and communication tools. Teaches government officals how to use technology to communicate with constituents and operate more efficiently.

Information Industry Assn., *1625 Massachusetts Ave. N.W., #700 20036; (202) 986-0280. Fax, (202) 638-4403. Ronald G. Dunn, president. Internet, http://www. infoindustry.org.*

Membership: companies involved in creating, distributing, and using information products, services, and technologies. Helps formulate global business strategies; interests include telecommunications, government procurement, taxation, intellectual property rights, and privacy. Monitors legislation and regulations.

Information Sciences Institute, *4350 N. Fairfax Dr., #770, Arlington, VA 22203; (703) 243-9422. Fax, (703) 812-3731. Nadine Hadge, manager, Advanced Technology. Internet, http://www.isi.edu or http://www.east.isi.org.*

Conducts research in advanced computer, communications, and information processing technologies; serves as the Internet Assigned Numbers Authority (IANA). Specific projects support development of the Internet, related software, and electronic commerce. (Headquarters in Marina del Rey, Calif.; part of University of Southern California.)

Information Technology Assn. of America, *1616 N. Fort Myer Dr., #1300, Arlington, VA 22209; (703) 284-5300. Fax, (703) 525-2279. Harris N. Miller, president. Internet, http://www.itaa.org.*

Membership: organizations in the computer, communications, and data industries. Conducts research; holds seminars and workshops; interests include small business, government procurement, competitive practices, communications, software, trade, and international copyright issues. Monitors legislation and regulations.

Information Technology Industry Council, *1250 Eye St. N.W., #200 20005; (202) 737-8888. Fax, (202) 638-4922. Rhett Dawson, president. Press, (202) 626-5725. Internet, http://www.itic.org.*

Membership: providers of information technology products and services. Promotes the global competitiveness of its members and advocates free trade. Seeks to protect intellectual property and encourages the use of voluntary standards.

Institute for Global Communications, *1731 Connecticut Ave. N.W., #400 20009; (202) 588-5070. Fax,*

(202) 588-5210. Debra Floyd, director, East Coast. Internet, outreach@igc.org or http://www.igc.org.

Provides Internet tools to organizations and people working on issues of peace, justice, human rights, environmental protection, labor, and conflict resolution. (Affiliated with Assn. for Progressive Communications; headquarters in San Francisco.)

Interactive Digital Software Assn., *1130 Connecticut Ave. N.W., #710 20036; (202) 833-4372. Fax, (202) 833-4431. Douglas Lowenstein, president. Internet, info@idsa.com or http://www.idsa.com.*

Membership: publishers of interactive entertainment software. Distributes marketing statistics and information. Administers an independent rating system for the industry and a worldwide anti-piracy program. Monitors legislation and regulations.

Interactive Marketing Institute, *4640 13th St., Arlington, VA 22207-2102; (703) 528-6445. Fax, (703) 812-8157. Trey Taylor, president. Internet, igc@us.net or http://www.iglobal.com/IMI.*

Membership: corporations involved in the computer and telecommunications industries. Seeks to advance worldwide electronic commerce by conducting research, public education, and advocacy campaigns. Monitors legislation and regulations.

Interactive Services Assn., *8403 Colesville Rd., #865, Silver Spring, MD 20910; (301) 495-4955. Fax, (301) 495-4959. Jeff B. Richards, executive director. Internet, isa@isa.net or http://www.isa.net.*

Membership: advertising agencies, cable companies, consulting and research organizations, computer and terminal manufacturers, entrepreneurs, financial institutions, interactive service providers, online and gateway operators, publishers, software vendors, telecommunications companies, service bureaus and packagers, television programmers, and universities and government agencies. Promotes network-based interactive electronic services worldwide for use in homes, offices, and public locations. Library open to the public by appointment.

International Communications Industries Assn., *11242 Waples Mill Rd., #200, Fairfax, VA 22030; (703) 273-7200. Fax, (703) 278-8082. Walter Blackwell, executive director. Internet, icia@icia.org or http://www.infocomm.org.*

Membership: video, audiovisual, and microcomputer dealers; manufacturers and producers; and individuals; operates chapters in Europe, Asia, and Australia. Interests include international trade, small business issues, postal rates, copyright, education, and taxation. Monitors legislation and regulations.

International Council for Computer Communication, *P.O. Box 9745 20016; (703) 836-7787. John D. McKendree, treasurer. Internet, http://www.iccc.inter.net.*

Membership: industry, government, and academic leaders interested in computer communications issues. Promotes scientific research in and development of computer communication; encourages evaluation of applications of computer communication for educational, scientific, medical, economic, legal, cultural, and other peaceful purposes; sponsors international conferences, seminars, and workshops. (Affiliated with the International Federation for Information Processing in Vienna, Austria.)

International Telework Assn., *204 E St. N.E. 20002; (202) 547-6157. Fax, (202) 546-3289. Jack Heacock, president. Internet, http://www.telecommute.org.*

Membership: individuals, corporations, government agencies, educators, consultants, and vendors involved in telecommuting. Promotes the economic, social, and environmental benefits of telecommuting. Seeks to facilitate the development of telecommuting programs internationally.

Internet Engineering Task Force, *Secretariat, 1895 Preston White Dr., #100, Reston, VA 20191-5434; (703) 620-8990. Fax, (703) 758-5913. Steve Coya, executive director. Internet, ietf-info@ietf.org or http://www.ietf.org.*

Membership: network designers, operators, vendors, and researchers from around the world who are concerned with the evolution, smooth operation, and continuing development of the Internet. Establishes working groups to address technical concerns.

Internet Society, *12020 Sunrise Valley Dr., #210, Reston, VA 20191-3429; (703) 648-9888. Fax, (703) 648-9887. Donald M. Heath, president. Toll-free, (800) 468-9507. Internet, isoc@isoc.org or http://www.isoc.org.*

Membership: individuals, corporations, nonprofit organizations, and government agencies. Promotes development and availability of the Internet and its associated technologies and applications; promulgates international standards. Conducts research and educational programs; assists technologically developing countries in achieving Internet usage; provides information about the Internet.

Progress and Freedom Foundation, *1301 K St. N.W., #550E 20005; (202) 289-8928. Fax, (202) 289-6079. Jeffrey A. Eisenach, president. Internet, pff@aol.com or http://www.pff.org.*

Studies the impact of the digital revolution and its implications for public policy; sponsors seminars, conferences, and broadcasts.

Public Service Telecommunications Corporation,
*4900 Seminary Road, #430, Alexandria, VA 22311; (703)
998-1703. Fax, (703) 998-8480. Jack Rebman, president.
Internet, pstc@igc.org.*

Membership: educational and public service organizations. Represents the interests of members in the use of new and advanced technologies. Conducts telecommunications policy research.

Software Publishers Assn., *1730 M St. N.W., #700
20036; (202) 452-1600. Fax, (202) 223-8756. Kenneth A.
Wasch, president. Internet, http://www.spa.org.*

Membership: publishers of microcomputer software. Promotes the industry worldwide; conducts investigations and litigation to protect members' copyrights; offers contracts reference and credit information exchange services. Monitors legislation and regulations.

📠 MEDIA PROFESSIONS AND RESOURCES

AGENCIES

Federal Communications Commission, *Communications Business Opportunity,* *1919 M St. N.W., #644
20554; (202) 418-0990. Fax, (202) 418-0235. Catherine
Sandoval, director. Internet, http://www.fcc.gov/Bureaus/
OCBO/ocbo.html.*

Provides technical and legal guidance and assistance to the small, minority, and female business community in the telecommunications industry. Advises the FCC chairman on small, minority, and female business issues. Serves as liaison between federal agencies, state and local governments, and trade associations representing small, minority, and female enterprises concerning FCC policies, procedures, and rulemaking activities.

Federal Communications Commission, *Equal
Employment Opportunity,* *2025 M St. N.W. (mailing
address: 1919 M St. N.W., #7218, Washington, DC 20554);
(202) 418-1450. Fax, (202) 418-1797. Y. Paulette Laden,
chief.*

Responsible for the annual certification of cable television equal employment opportunity compliance. Oversees broadcast employment practices. Publishes annual report on employment trends in cable television and broadcast industries.

NONPROFIT

American News Women's Club, *1607 22nd St. N.W.
20008; (202) 332-6770. Fax, (202) 265-6477. Deborah
Toll, president.*

Membership: writers, reporters, photographers, cartoonists, and professionals in print and broadcast media, government and private industry, publicity, and public relations. Promotes the advancement of women in all media. Sponsors professional receptions and seminars.

Communications Workers of America, *501 3rd St.
N.W. 20001; (202) 434-1100. Fax, (202) 434-1279.
Morton Bahr, president. Internet, http://www.
cwa-union.org.*

Membership: approximately 600,000 workers in telecommunications, printing and news media, public service, cable television, electronics, and other fields. Assists members with contract negotiation and grievances; conducts training programs and workshops. Monitors legislation and regulations. (Affiliated with the AFL-CIO.)

Education and Research Institute, *800 Maryland
Ave. N.E. 20002; (202) 546-1710. Fax, (202) 546-1638.
M. Stanton Evans, chair.*

Educational organization that conducts seminars; operates the National Journalism Center to train interns in basic skills of media work.

Freedom Forum, *1101 Wilson Blvd., Arlington, VA
22209; (703) 528-0800. Fax, (703) 522-4831. Charles L.
Overby, chair. Publications fax, (703) 284-3570. Internet,
news@freedomforum.org or http://www.freedomforum.org.*

Sponsors conferences, educational activities, training, and research that promote free press, free speech, and freedom of information and that enhance the teaching and practice of journalism.

Fund for Investigative Journalism, *5120 Kenwood
Dr., Annandale, VA 22003; (703) 750-3849. Peg Lotito,
executive director. Internet, fundfij@aol.com or http://
www.fij.org.*

Provides investigative reporters with grants for articles, broadcasts, and books.

National Assn. of Black Journalists, *University of
Maryland, 3100 Taliaferro Hall, College Park, MD 20742;
(301) 405-8500. Fax, (301) 405-8555. JoAnne Lyons
Wooten, executive director. Internet, nabj@jmail.umd.edu
or http://www.nabj.org.*

Membership: African American journalists working for radio and television stations, newspapers, and magazines, and others in the field of journalism. Works to increase recognition of the achievements of minority journalists, to expand opportunities for minority students entering the field, and to promote balanced coverage of the African American community by the media. Sponsors scholarships and internship program.

MEDIA CONTACTS IN WASHINGTON

MAGAZINES

Congressional Quarterly Weekly Report, 1414 22nd St. N.W. 20037; (202) 887-8500

National Journal, 1501 M St. N.W., #300 20005; (202) 739-8400

Newsweek, 1750 Pennsylvania Ave. N.W., #1220 20006; (202) 626-2000

Time, 1050 Connecticut Ave. N.W., #850 20036; (202) 861-4000

U.S. News & World Report, 2400 N St. N.W. 20037; (202) 955-2000

NEWSPAPERS

Baltimore Sun, 1627 K St. N.W., #1100 20006; (202) 452-8250

Christian Science Monitor, 910 16th St. N.W. 20006; (202) 785-4400

Los Angeles Times, 1875 Eye St. N.W., #1100 20006; (202) 293-4650

New York Times, 1627 Eye St. N.W. 20006; (202) 862-0300

USA Today, 1000 Wilson Blvd., Arlington, VA 22229; (703) 276-3400

Wall Street Journal, 1025 Connecticut Ave. N.W. 20036; (202) 862-9200

Washington Post, 1150 15th St. N.W. 20071; (202) 334-6000

Washington Times, 3600 New York Ave. N.E. 20002; (202) 636-3000

NEWS SERVICES

Agence France-Presse, 1015 15th St. N.W., #500 20005; (202) 289-0700

Associated Press, 2021 K St. N.W. 20006; (202) 776-9400

Gannett News Service, 1000 Wilson Blvd., Arlington, VA 22229; (703) 276-5800

Knight-Ridder Newspapers, 700 National Press Bldg., 529 14th St. N.W. 20045; (202) 383-6000

Newhouse News Service, 1101 Connecticut Ave. N.W., #300 20036; (202) 383-7800

Reuters, 1333 H St. N.W. 20005; (202) 898-8300

Scripps-Howard Newspapers, 1090 Vermont Ave. N.W. 20005; (202) 408-1484

States News Service, 1333 F St. N.W., 4th Floor 20004; (202) 628-3100

United Press International, 1510 H. St. N.W. 20005; (202) 898-8000

TELEVISION/RADIO NETWORKS

ABC News, 1717 DeSales St. N.W. 20036; (202) 222-7777

Cable News Network (CNN), 820 1st St. N.E. 20002; (202) 898-7900

CBS News, 2020 M St. N.W. 20036; (202) 457-4321

C-SPAN, 400 N. Capitol St. N.W., #650 20001; (202) 737-3220

Fox News, 400 N. Capitol St. N.W., #550 20001; (202) 824-6300

Mutual/NBC Radio Network, 1755 S. Jefferson Davis Highway, Arlington, VA 22202; (703) 413-8300

National Public Radio, 635 Massachusetts Ave. N.W. 20001; (202) 414-2000

NBC News, 4001 Nebraska Ave. N.W. 20016; (202) 885-4200

Public Broadcasting Service, 1320 Braddock Place, Alexandria, VA 22314; (703) 739-5000

National Assn. of Government Communicators, *526 King St., #423, Alexandria, VA 22314; (703) 518-4369. Fax, (703) 706-9583. Elizabeth Lucas, president. Internet, info@nagc.com or http://www.nagc.com.*

Membership: federal, state, and local government communications employees. Promotes job standards for the government communications profession; monitors administrative and regulatory proposals that affect the field; provides a clearinghouse on government jobs for members.

National Assn. of Hispanic Journalists, *529 14th St. N.W. 20045; (202) 662-7145. Fax, (202) 662-7144. Anna*

Lopez, acting executive director. Internet, http://www. nahj.org.

Membership: professional journalists, educators, students, and others interested in encouraging Hispanics to study and enter the field of journalism. Promotes fair representation of Hispanics by the news media. Provides computerized job referral service; compiles and updates national directory of Hispanics in the media; sponsors national high school essay contest, journalism awards, and scholarships.

National Black Media Coalition, *11120 New Hampshire Ave., #204, Silver Spring, MD 20904; (301) 593-3600.*

Fax, (301) 593-3604. Pluria W. Marshall, chair. Internet, http://www.nbmc.org.

Advocates African American involvement in communications at local and national levels. Maintains an employment resource center. Conducts training classes; negotiates affirmative action plans with large media corporations.

National Conference of Editorial Writers, 6223 Executive Blvd., Rockville, MD 20852; (301) 984-3015. Fax, (301) 231-0026. Cora Everett, executive secretary. Internet, http://www.infi.net/ncew.

Membership: editorial writers, editors, syndicated columnists, broadcasters, students, journalism professors at accredited universities, and commentators on general circulation newspapers and television and radio stations in the United States and Canada. Sponsors critique exchange workshops. Provides critique service upon request.

National Lesbian and Gay Journalists Assn., 1718 M St. N.W., #245 20036; (202) 588-9888. Fax, (202) 588-1818. Karen-Louise Boothe, president. Internet, nlgja@aol.com or http://www.nlgja.org.

Fosters fair and accurate coverage of lesbian and gay issues. Provides professional support and networking services; sponsors conferences, seminars, and workshops.

National Press Foundation, 529 14th St. N.W. 20045; (202) 662-7350. Fax, (202) 662-1232. Bob Meyers, president. Internet, npf@aol.com.

Works to enhance the professional competence of journalists through in-career education projects. Sponsors conferences, seminars, fellowships, and awards; conducts public forums and international exchanges. Supports the National Press Club library; includes the Washington Journalism Center.

Regional Reporters Assn., 529 14th St. N.W. 20045; (202) 879-6710. Fax, (202) 879-6712. Ellen Ferguson, president.

Membership: Washington-based reporters for regional newspapers and radio and television stations. Works to improve regional correspondents' access to all branches of the federal government; encourages professional development.

Society for Technical Communication, 901 N. Stuart St., #904, Arlington, VA 22203-1854; (703) 522-4114. Fax, (703) 522-2075. William C. Stolgitis, executive director. Internet, stc@stc-va.org or http://www.stc-va.org.

Membership: writers, publishers, educators, editors, illustrators, and others involved in technical communication in the print and broadcast media. Encourages

---

CONGRESSIONAL NEWS MEDIA GALLERIES

The congressional news media galleries serve as liaisons between members of Congress and their staffs and accredited newspaper, magazine, and broadcasting correspondents. The galleries provide accredited correspondents with facilities to cover activities of Congress, and gallery staff members ensure that congressional press releases reach appropriate correspondents. Independent committees of correspondents working through the press galleries are responsible for accreditation of correspondents; see Accreditation in Washington, Legislative Branch (p. 92-93).

House Periodical Press Gallery, H304 CAP 20515; (202) 225-2941. David W. Holmes, director.

House Press Gallery, H315 CAP 20515; (202) 225-3945. Jerry Gallegos, superintendent.

House Radio and Television Gallery, H321 CAP 20515; (202) 225-5214. Tina Tate, director.

Press Photographers Gallery, S317 CAP 20510; (202) 224-6548. Jeffrey Kent, superintendent.

Senate Periodical Press Gallery, S320 CAP 20510; (202) 224-0265. Jim Talbert, superintendent.

Senate Press Gallery, S316 CAP 20510; (202) 224-0241. Robert E. Petersen Jr., superintendent.

Senate Radio and Television Gallery, S325 CAP 20510; (202) 224-6421. Larry Janezich, director.

---

research and develops training programs for technical communicators; aids educational institutions in devising curricula; awards scholarships.

Statistical Assessment Service (STATS), 2100 L St. N.W., #300 20037; (202) 223-3193. Fax, (202) 872-4014. S. Robert Lichter, president. Internet, http://www.stats.org.

Promotes accurate use of statistical and quantitative data in public policy debate. Provides journalists with analysis of current statistical disputes.

Washington Press Club Foundation, 529 14th St. N.W., #1067 20045; (202) 393-0613. Fax, (202) 783-0841. Julia D. Whiston, executive director.

Seeks to advance professionalism in journalism. Awards minority grants and scholarships. Administers an oral history of women in journalism. Sponsors annual Salute to Congress Dinner in late January to welcome Congress back into session. Maintains speakers bureau.

Women in Communications Foundation, 1244 Richie Hwy., #6, Arnold, MD 21012; (410) 544-7442. Fax,

(410) 544-4640. Pat Troy, executive director. Internet, wom@aol.com.

Membership: professionals and students in communications. Maintains job hotline for members and supports women in communications. Works for freedom of expression for all communicators.

Women's Institute for Freedom of the Press, *3306 Ross Pl. N.W. 20008-3332; (202) 966-7783. Martha Leslie Allen, director. Internet, wifponline@igc.apc.org or http:// www.igc.apc.org/wifp.*

Conducts research and publishes in areas of communications and the media that are of particular interest to women.

See also Council on Hemispheric Affairs (p. 482); Washington Center for Politics and Journalism (p. 178)

Accreditation in Washington

Most federal agencies and courts do not require special press credentials.

AGENCIES

Defense Dept., *Public Affairs, The Pentagon, #2E800 20301-1400; (703) 697-9312. Fax, (703) 695-4299. Kenneth H. Bacon, assistant secretary. Press, (703) 697-5131. National Media Pool, (703) 693-1075. Internet, http:// www.dtic.mil/defenselink.*

Grants accreditation to Washington-based media organizations to form the National Media Pool. Selected staff of accredited groups are assigned to the media pool on a rotating basis and put on alert for short-notice deployment to the site of military operations.

Foreign Press Center *(U.S. Information Agency), 529 14th St. N.W., #898 20045; (202) 724-1640. Fax, (202) 724-0007. Marjorie Ransom, director. Alternate fax, (202) 724-0122. Fax-on-demand, (202) 724-0050. Recorded information, (202) 724-1635. Internet, http://www. fpcusia.gov.*

Provides foreign journalists with access to news sources, including wire services and daily briefings from the White House, State Dept., and Pentagon. Holds live news conferences. Foreign journalists wishing to use the center must present a letter from their organization and a letter from the embassy of the country in which their paper is published.

Metropolitan Police Dept., *Police Public Information, 300 Indiana Ave. N.W., #4048 20001; (202) 727-4383. Fax, (202) 727-0437. Sgt. Joseph Gentile, director.*

Provides application forms and issues press passes required for crossing police lines within the city of Wash-

ington. Passes are issued on a yearly basis; applicants should allow four to six weeks for processing of passes.

National Park Service *(Interior Dept.), National Capital Region, 1100 Ohio Dr. S.W., #336 20242; (202) 619-7000. Fax, (202) 619-7220. Terry Carlstrom, director. Information, (202) 619-7222. Recorded information, (202) 619-7275. Permits, (202) 619-7225. Internet, http://www. nps.gov/ncro.*

Regional office that administers national parks, monuments, historic sites, and recreation areas in the Washington metropolitan area. Issues special permits required for commercial filming on public park lands. Media representatives covering public events that take place on park lands should notify the Office of Public Affairs and Tourism in advance. A White House or metropolitan police press pass is required in some circumstances.

State Dept., *Public Affairs Press Office, Main State Bldg., #2109 20520; (202) 647-2492. Fax, (202) 647-0244. James Rubin, assistant secretary.*

U.S. journalists seeking building passes must apply in person with a letter from their editor or publisher and two passport-size photographs. In addition, foreign correspondents need a letter from the embassy of the country in which their organization is based. All journalists must reside in the Washington, D.C., area and must cover the State Dept.'s daily briefing on a regular basis. Applicants should allow three months for security clearance.

White House, *Press Office, 1600 Pennsylvania Ave. N.W. 20500; (202) 456-2580. Fax, (202) 456-6210. Michael McCurry, press secretary. Fax-on-demand, (202) 395-9088. Comments and information, (202) 456-1111. Internet, http://www.whitehouse.gov.*

Journalists seeking permanent accreditation must be accredited by the House or Senate press galleries, must be residents of the Washington, D.C., area, and must be full-time employees of a news-gathering organization, expecting to cover the White House on a nearly daily basis. A journalist's editor, publisher, or employer must write to the press office requesting accreditation. Journalists wishing temporary accreditation should have their assignment desk call a day ahead to be cleared for a one-day pass. Press Office also maintains an index of journalists with permanent specialized White House accreditation. Applicants must undergo a Secret Service investigation.

CONGRESS

House Periodical Press Gallery, *H304 CAP 20515; (202) 225-2941. Craig Winneker, chair (Roll Call). Internet, periodical.press@mail.house.gov.*

Open by application to periodical correspondents whose chief occupation is gathering and reporting news for periodicals not affiliated with lobbying organizations. Accreditation with the House Gallery covers accreditation with the Senate Gallery.

Press Photographers Gallery, *Standing Committee of Press Photographers, S317 CAP 20510; (202) 224-6548. Fax, (202) 224-0280. Tim Dillon, chair (USA Today).*

Open by application to bona fide news photographers and to heads of photographic bureaus. Accreditation by the standing committee covers both the House and Senate.

Senate Press Gallery, *Standing Committee of Correspondents, S316 CAP 20510; (202) 224-0241. David Baumann, chair (CongressDaily).*

Open by application to Washington-based reporters who earn more than half their income from news services or from newspapers published at least five times a week. Accreditation with the Senate Gallery covers accreditation with the House Gallery.

Senate Radio and Television Gallery, *Executive Committee of the Radio and Television Correspondents' Galleries, S325 CAP 20510; (202) 224-6421. Fax, (202) 224-4887. Jim Mills, chair (Fox News). Internet, http://www.senate.gov/radiotv/index.htm.*

Open by application to Washington-based radio and television correspondents and technicians who earn more than half their income from or spend at least half their time in the news gathering profession. Accreditation with the Senate Gallery covers accreditation with the House Gallery.

JUDICIARY

Supreme Court of the United States, *1 1st St. N.E. 20543; (202) 479-3000. William H. Rehnquist, chief justice; Toni House, public information officer, (202) 479-3211. Library, (202) 479-3177. Internet, http://www.law.cornell.edu.*

Journalists seeking to cover the Court must be accredited by either the White House or the House or Senate press galleries. Contact the public information office to make arrangements.

Broadcasting

See also Radio and Television (this chapter)

NONPROFIT

American Federation of Television and Radio Artists, *4340 East-West Hwy., #204, Bethesda, MD 20814;* (301) 657-2560. Fax, (301) 657-4517. Patricia O'Donnell, executive director. Internet, http://www.aftra.org.

Membership: television and radio reporters, anchors, editors, staff announcers, disc jockeys, and freelancers. Labor organization that advocates a professional performing arts union. Monitors legislation and regulations.

American Women in Radio and Television, *1650 Tysons Blvd., #200, McLean, VA 22102; (703) 506-3290. Fax, (703) 506-3266. Terri Dickerson, executive director. Internet, http://www.awrt.org.*

Membership: professionals in the electronic media and full-time students in accredited colleges and universities. Promotes industry cooperation and advancement of women. Maintains foundation for educational and charitable purposes.

Broadcast Education Assn., *1771 N St. N.W. 20036-2891; (202) 429-5354. Fax, (202) 775-2981. Louisa A. Nielsen, executive director. Internet, http://www.beaweb.org.*

Membership: universities, colleges, and faculty members offering specialized training in radio and television broadcasting. Promotes improvement of curriculum and teaching methods. Fosters working relationships among academics, students, and professionals in the industry.

National Academy of Television Arts and Sciences, *9405 Russell Rd., Silver Spring, MD 20910; (301) 587-3993. Fax, (301) 587-3993. Dianne Bruno, administrator.*

Membership: professionals in television and related fields and students in communications. Works to upgrade television programming; awards scholarship to a junior, senior, or graduate student in communications. Sponsors annual Emmy Awards. (Headquarters in New York.)

National Assn. of Black-Owned Broadcasters, *1333 New Hampshire Ave. N.W., 10th Floor 20036; (202) 463-8970. Fax, (202) 429-0657. James L. Winston, executive director.*

Membership: minority owners and employees of radio and television stations and telecommunications properties. Provides members and the public with information on the broadcast industry and the FCC. Provides members with legal and advertising research facilities. Monitors legislation and regulations.

National Assn. of Broadcast Employees and Technicians, *501 3rd St. N.W., 8th Floor 20001; (202) 434-1254. Fax, (202) 434-1426. John S. Clark, president.*

Membership: approximately 10,000 commercial television and radio personnel. Helps members negotiate pay, benefits, and better working conditions; conducts training programs and workshops. Monitors legislation and regulations.

National Assn. of Broadcasters, *1771 N St. N.W. 20036-2891; (202) 429-5300. Fax, (202) 429-5343. Edward O. Fritts, president. Press, (202) 429-5350. Library, (202) 429-5490. Internet, register@nab.org or http://www. nab.org.*

Membership: radio and television broadcast stations and broadcast networks holding an FCC license or construction permit; associate members include producers of equipment and programs. Assists members in areas of management, engineering, and research; library offers fee-based services to non-members by appointment. Interests include privatization abroad and related business opportunities. Monitors legislation and regulations.

National Broadcast Assn. for Community Affairs, *1200 19th St. N.W., #300 20036-2422; (202) 857-1155. Fax, (202) 223-4579. Robert W. Armstrong, executive director. Internet, nbaca@dc.sba.com.*

Membership: professionals in electronic media and nonprofit organizations. Advocates community affairs programming in all electronic media, including radio, television, and cable.

Public Interest Video Network, *4704 Overbrook Rd., Bethesda, MD 20816; (301) 656-7244. Arlen Slobodow, executive director.*

Provides nonprofit, public interest organizations with video production services. Produces and distributes radio and television programming and video news releases to broadcast stations, cable systems, and new television outlets. Serves as consultant on distribution of public affairs programming via satellite to television and radio stations.

Radio-Television News Directors Assn., *1000 Connecticut Ave. N.W., #615 20036; (202) 659-6510. Fax, (202) 223-4007. Barbara Cochran, president. Internet, rtnda@rtnda.org or http://www.rtnda.org.*

Membership: local and network news executives in broadcasting, cable, and other electronic media. Serves as information source for members; provides advice on legislative, political, and judicial problems of electronic journalism; conducts international exchanges.

Press Freedom

CONGRESS

House Judiciary Committee, *Subcommittee on the Constitution, 362 Ford Bldg. 20515; (202) 226-7680. Fax,*

(202) 225-3746. Charles T. Canady, R-Fla., chair; Keri Folmar, counsel. Internet, http://www.house.gov/judiciary.

Jurisdiction over press shield legislation.

Senate Judiciary Committee, *Subcommittee on the Constitution, Federalism, and Property Rights, SD-164 20510; (202) 224-8081. John Ashcroft, R-Mo., chair; David Miller, chief counsel. Internet, http://www.senate.gov/ committee/judiciary.html.*

Jurisdiction over press shield legislation.

NONPROFIT

Joint Washington Media Committee, *c/o Cohn and Marks, 1920 N St. N.W., #300 20036; (202) 452-4837. Fax, (202) 293-4827. Richard M. Schmidt Jr., chair.*

Membership: representatives of media organizations. Consulting group that acts as a clearinghouse and forum for exchange of information on legislative and judicial developments affecting freedom of the press.

Reporters Committee for Freedom of the Press, *1101 Wilson Blvd., #1910, Arlington, VA 22209; (703) 807-2100. Fax, (703) 807-2109. Jane E. Kirtley, executive director. Freedom of information hotline, (800) 336-4243. Internet, rcfp@rcfp.org or http://www.rcfp.org/rcfp.*

Membership: reporters, news editors, publishers, and lawyers from the print and broadcast media. Maintains a legal defense and research fund for members of the news media involved in freedom of the press court cases; interests include freedom of speech abroad. Library open to the public by appointment.

Student Press Law Center, *1101 Wilson Blvd., #1910, Arlington, VA 22209; (703) 807-1904. Fax, (703) 807-2109. Mark Goodman, executive director. Internet, splc@splc.org or http://www.splc.org.*

Collects, analyzes, and distributes information on free expression and freedom of information rights of student journalists (print and broadcast) and on violations of those rights in high schools and colleges. Provides free legal assistance to students and faculty advisers experiencing censorship.

World Press Freedom Committee, *11690-C Sunrise Valley Dr., Reston, VA 20191; (703) 715-9811. Fax, (703) 620-6790. Marilyn J. Greene, executive director. Internet, freepress@wpfc.org.*

Worldwide organization of print and broadcast groups. Promotes freedom of the press and opposes government censorship. Conducts training programs and assists journalists in central and eastern Europe and the developing world. Participates in international conferences.

Print Media

NONPROFIT

American Press Institute, *11690 Sunrise Valley Dr., Reston, VA 20191; (703) 620-3611. Fax, (703) 620-5814. William L. Winter, president. Internet, api@apireston.org or http://www.newspaper.org/api.*

Promotes the continuing education and career development of newspaper professionals. Conducts seminars, workshops, and conferences. Programs include an intensive computerized newspaper management simulation.

American Society of Newspaper Editors, *11690B Sunrise Valley Dr., Reston, VA 20191; (703) 453-1122. Fax, (703) 453-1133. Lee Stinnett, executive director. Internet, asne@asne.org or http://www.asne.org.*

Membership: directing editors of daily newspapers. Campaigns against government secrecy; works to improve the racial mix of newsroom staff; sponsors work/training program for journalists from developing countries; serves as information clearinghouse for newsrooms of daily newspapers.

Assn. for Suppliers of Printing and Publishing Technologies, *1899 Preston White Dr., Reston, VA 22091-4367; (703) 264-7200. Fax, (703) 620-0994. Carol J. Hurlburt, director. Documents-on-demand, (800) 874-0858. Internet, npes@npes.org or http://www.npes.org.*

Trade association representing companies that manufacture and distribute equipment, supplies, systems, software and services for printing and publishing.

Assn. of American Publishers, *1718 Connecticut Ave. N.W., #700 20009-1148; (202) 232-3335. Fax, (202) 745-0694. Judith Platt, director, Communications. Internet, http://www.publishers.org.*

Membership: U.S. publishers of books, journals, tests, and software. Provides members with information on domestic and international trade and market conditions; interests include library and educational funding, educational reform, postal rates, new technology, taxes, copyright, censorship, and libel matters. Monitors legislation and regulations.

Document Management Industries Assn., *433 E. Monroe Ave., Alexandria, VA 22301-1693; (703) 836-6225. Fax, (703) 836-2241. Frank Burgess, president. Internet, http://www.dmia.org.*

Membership: manufacturers, suppliers, and distributors of business forms, labels, commercial printing, advertising specialities, electronic forms, or document products. Conducts workshops, seminars, and confer

ences; sponsors industry research. Monitors legislation and regulations.

Essential Information, *P.O. Box 19367 20036; (202) 387-8030. Fax, (202) 234-5176. John Richard, director. Internet, EI@essential.org or http://www.essential.org/EI.html.*

Provides writers and the public with information on public policy matters; awards grants to investigative reporters; sponsors conference on investigative journalism. Interests include activities of multinational corporations in developing countries.

Graphic Communications Assn., *100 Daingerfield Rd., Alexandria, VA 22314-2888; (703) 519-8160. Fax, (703) 548-2867. Norm Scharpf, president. Internet, http://www.gca.org.*

Membership: firms and customers in printing, publishing, and related industries. Assists members in production of color graphics and conducts studies on print media management methods. (Affiliated with Printing Industries of America.)

Graphic Communications International Union, *1900 L St. N.W. 20036; (202) 462-1400. Fax, (202) 331-9516. James J. Norton, president. Internet, http://www.gciu.org.*

Membership: approximately 175,000 members of the print industry, including lithographers, photoengravers, and bookbinders. Assists members with contract negotiation and grievances; conducts training programs and workshops. Monitors legislation and regulations. (Affiliated with the AFL-CIO.)

Greeting Card Assn., *1200 G St. N.W., #760 20005; (202) 393-1778. Fax, (202) 393-0336. Marianne McDermott, executive vice president. Internet, http://www.greetingcard.org.*

Membership: publishers, printers, and others interested in the greeting card industry. Monitors legislation and regulations.

International Newspaper Financial Executives, *21525 Ridgetop Circle, #200, Sterling, VA 20166; (703) 421-4060. Fax, (703) 421-4068. Robert J. Kasabian, vice president. Internet, infe@aol.com or http://www.infe.org.*

Membership: controllers and chief financial officers of newspapers. Disseminates information on financial aspects of publishing newspapers. Provides members with information on business office technology, including accounting software and spreadsheet applications. Produces publications, conducts seminars, and sponsors an annual convention.

Magazine Publishers of America, *1211 Connecticut Ave. N.W., #610 20036; (202) 296-7277. Fax, (202) 296-0343. George Gross, executive vice president, Government Affairs. Internet, http://www.magazine.org.*

Washington office represents members in all aspects of government relations in Washington and state capitals. (Headquarters in New York.)

National Newspaper Assn., *1525 Wilson Blvd., #550, Arlington, VA 22209-2434; (703) 525-7900. Fax, (703) 907-7901. Kennath Allen, president.*

Membership: community, weekly, and daily newspapers. Provides members with advisory services; informs members of legislation and regulations that affect their business. Educational arm, the National Newspaper Foundation, conducts management seminars and conferences.

National Newspaper Publishers Assn., *3200 13th St. N.W. 20010; (202) 588-8764. Fax, (202) 588-5029. Yvonne Cooper, executive director. Internet, nnpadc@nnpa.org or http://www.nnpa.org.*

Membership: newspapers owned by African Americans serving an African American audience. Assists in improving management and quality of the African American press through workshops and merit awards.

Newsletter Publishers Assn., *1501 Wilson Blvd., #509, Arlington, VA 22209; (703) 527-2333. Fax, (703) 841-0629. Patricia M. Wysocki, executive director. Internet, http://www.newsletters.org.*

Membership: newsletter publishers and specialized information services. Serves as information clearinghouse. Monitors legislation and regulations. Library open to the public.

Newspaper Assn. of America, *1921 Gallows Rd., #600, Vienna, VA 22182; (703) 902-1600. Fax, (703) 917-0636. John Sturm, president. Library, (703) 902-1692. Internet, http://www.naa.org.*

Membership: daily and weekly newspapers and other papers published in the United States, Canada, other parts of the Western Hemisphere, and Europe. Conducts research and disseminates information on newspaper publishing, including labor relations, legal matters, government relations, technical problems and innovations, telecommunications, economic and statistical data,

training programs, and public relations. Library open to the public.

Printing Industries of America, *100 Daingerfield Rd., Alexandria, VA 22314; (703) 519-8100. Fax, (703) 548-3227. Ray Roper, president. Internet, http://www.printing.org.*

Membership: printing firms and businesses that service printing industries. Represents members before Congress and regulatory agencies. Assists members with labor relations, human resources management, and other business management issues. Sponsors graphic arts competition. Monitors legislation and regulations.

Screen Printing Technical Foundation, *10015 Main St., Fairfax, VA 22031-3489; (703) 385-1335. Fax, (703) 273-0456. John M. Crawford, managing director. Internet, http://www.sgia.org.*

Provides screen printers, suppliers, manufacturers, and schools with technical support and training; conducts research on production practices and standards. Offers scholarships for college students, grants to schools and teachers, and workshops. (Affiliated with Screenprinting and Graphic Imaging Assn. International.)

Screenprinting and Graphic Imaging Assn. International, *10015 Main St., Fairfax, VA 22031-3489; (703) 385-1335. Fax, (703) 273-0456. John M. Crawford, president. Internet, http://www.sgia.org.*

Provides screen printers, graphic imagers, digital imagers, suppliers, manufacturers, and educators with technical guidebooks, training videos, managerial support, and guidelines for safety programs. Monitors legislation and regulations.

Society of National Assn. Publications, *1650 Tysons Blvd., #200, McLean, VA 22102; (703) 506-3285. Fax, (703) 506-3266. Laura Skoff, director. Internet, http://www.snaponline.org.*

Membership: publications owned or controlled by voluntary organizations. Works to develop high publishing standards, including high quality editorial and advertising content in members' publications. Compiles statistics; bestows editorial and graphics awards; monitors postal regulations.

See also The Writer's Center (p. 105)

4

Culture and Recreation

⌨ ARTS AND HUMANITIES

AGENCIES

Commission of Fine Arts, *441 F St. N.W., #312 20001-2728; (202) 504-2200. Fax, (202) 504-2195. J. Carter Brown, chair; Charles H. Atherton, secretary.*

Advises the president, congressional committees, and government agencies on designs of public buildings, parks, and statuary.

General Services Administration, *Cultural and Environmental Affairs, 1800 F St. N.W., #3341 20405; (202) 501-1811. Fax, (202) 219-7677. Constance Ramirez, director.*

Administers the Art and Historic Preservation Program, which sets aside for art projects a percentage of the estimated construction costs for new buildings or renovation costs for existing ones; manages a collection of fine arts.

General Services Administration, *Living Buildings Program, 1800 F St. N.W. 20405; (202) 501-0514. Fax, (202) 208-5912. Peter Ford, staff contact.*

Provides information on the opening of federal buildings for public use for cultural, educational, and recreational activities, including conferences, performing arts functions, and art exhibits.

John F. Kennedy Center for the Performing Arts, *20566-0001; (202) 416-8000. Fax, (202) 416-8205. James A. Johnson, chair; Lawrence J. Wilker, president, (202) 416-8010. Press, (202) 416-8448. Library, (202) 416-8780. TDD, (202) 416-8524. Performance and ticket information, (202) 467-4600; toll-free, (800) 444-1324. Internet, http://www.kennedy-center.org.*

Independent bureau of the Smithsonian Institution administered by a separate board of trustees. Sponsors educational programs; presents American and international performances in theater, music, dance, and film; sponsors the John F. Kennedy Center Education Program, which produces the annual American College Theater Festival; presents and subsidizes events for young people. Library open to the public.

National Endowment for the Arts *(National Foundation on the Arts and the Humanities), 1100 Pennsylvania Ave. N.W. 20506-0001; (202) 682-5414. Fax, (202) 682-5612. Scott Shanklin-Peterson, chair. Information, (202) 682-5400. Press, (202) 682-5570. Library, (202) 682-5485. TDD, (202) 682-5496. Internet, http://arts.endow.gov.*

Independent federal grantmaking agency. Awards grants to nonprofit arts organizations in four areas: creation and presentation; education and access; heritage

and preservation; and partnership, planning, and stabilization. Organizations must choose one of the four theme areas for submission of project proposals. Library open to the public by appointment.

National Endowment for the Arts *(National Foundation on the Arts and the Humanities), Creation and Presentation, 1100 Pennsylvania Ave. N.W. 20506-0001; (202) 682-5452. Fax, (202) 682-5721. Jennifer Dowley, coordinator. Internet, http://arts.endow.gov.*

Grantmaking theme program for the creation of new work and the presentation of new and existing works of any culture, period, or discipline.

National Endowment for the Arts *(National Foundation on the Arts and the Humanities), Education and Access, 1100 Pennsylvania Ave. N.W. 20506-0001; (202) 682-5438. Fax, (202) 682-5002. Patrice Walker Powell, coordinator. Internet, http://arts.endow.gov.*

Grantmaking theme program for projects which expand awareness and appreciation of art and art education for people of all ages.

National Endowment for the Arts *(National Foundation on the Arts and the Humanities), Heritage and Preservation, 1100 Pennsylvania Ave. N.W. 20506-0001; (202) 682-5428. Fax, (202) 682-5669. Daniel Sheehy, division coordinator. Internet, http://arts.endow.gov.*

Grantmaking theme program for projects in the arts which preserve nationally significant artistic accomplishments and works of art.

National Endowment for the Arts *(National Foundation on the Arts and the Humanities), Partnership, Planning, and Stabilization, 1100 Pennsylvania Ave. N.W. 20506-0001; (202) 682-5429. Fax, (202) 682-5613. Ed Dickey, division coordinator. Internet, http://arts. endow.gov.*

Grantmaking program for projects which focus on organizational planning, sustaining the arts, building partnerships, and developing resources. Works to increase worldwide recognition of U.S. arts; provides U.S. artists and arts organizations with information on exchanges and other international arts activities; supports international endeavors that increase public understanding of the arts, including cultural influences from abroad.

National Endowment for the Humanities *(National Foundation on the Arts and the Humanities), 1100 Pennsylvania Ave. N.W., #503 20506; (202) 606-8310. Fax, (202) 606-8588. William R. Ferris, chair; Juan E. Mestas, deputy chair, (202) 606-8273. Information, (202) 606-8400. Press, (202) 606-8446. Library, (202) 606-8244.*

TDD, (202) 606-8282. Internet, info@neh.fed.us or http:// www.neh.fed.us.

Independent federal grantmaking agency. Awards grants to individuals and institutions for research, scholarship, educational programs, and public programs (including broadcasts, museum exhibitions, lectures, and symposia) in the humanities (defined as study of archeology; history; jurisprudence; language; linguistics; literature; philosophy; comparative religion; ethics; the history, criticism, and theory of the arts; and humanistic aspects of the social sciences). Funds preservation of books, newspapers, historical documents, and photographs.

President's Committee on the Arts and the Humanities, *1100 Pennsylvania Ave. N.W., #526 20506-0001; (202) 682-5409. Fax, (202) 682-5668. Harriet Mayor Fulbright, executive director.*

Recommends to the president, the National Endowment for the Arts, and the National Endowment for the Humanities ways to promote private sector support for the arts and humanities; analyzes the effectiveness of federal support.

CONGRESS

House Appropriations Committee, *Subcommittee on Interior, B308 RHOB 20515; (202) 225-3081. Fax, (202) 225-9069. Ralph Regula, R-Ohio, chair; Deborah A. Weatherly, clerk. Internet, http://www.house.gov/ appropriations.*

Jurisdiction over legislation to appropriate funds for the Interior Dept. and government programs for the arts and the humanities, including the Smithsonian Institution, the National Foundation on the Arts and the Humanities, the Commission of Fine Arts, the Advisory Council on Historic Preservation, and the Institute of Museum and Library Services.

House Education and the Workforce Committee, *Subcommittee on Early Childhood, Youth, and Families, 2181 RHOB 20515; (202) 225-4527. Fax, (202) 225-9571. Frank Riggs, R-Calif., chair; Kevin Talley, staff director. Internet, http://www.house.gov/eeo.*

Jurisdiction over programs related to the arts and humanities, museum services, and arts and artifacts indemnity. Jurisdiction over the National Foundation on the Arts and Humanities Act.

House Government Reform and Oversight Committee, *Subcommittee on Civil Service, B371C RHOB 20515; (202) 225-6427. Fax, (202) 225-2392. John L. Mica, R-Fla., chair; George Nesterczuk, staff director. Internet, http://www.house.gov/reform.*

Jurisdiction over legislation on holidays and celebrations.

House Government Reform and Oversight Committee, *Subcommittee on Government Management, Information, and Technology, B373 RHOB 20515; (202) 225-5147. Steve Horn, R-Calif., chair; J. Russell George, staff director. Internet, http://www.house.gov/cho.*

Oversees operations of the Smithsonian Institution (jurisdiction shared with House Oversight Committee) and the National Foundation on the Arts and the Humanities.

House Oversight Committee, *1309 LHOB 20515; (202) 225-8281. Fax, (202) 225-9957. Bill Thomas, R-Calif., chair; Cathy Abernathy, acting staff director. Internet, http://www.house.gov/cho.*

Jurisdiction over legislation related to and operations of the Smithsonian Institution (jurisdiction shared with House Government Reform and Oversight Committee).

Senate Appropriations Committee, *Subcommittee on Interior, SD-131 20510; (202) 224-7233. Slade Gorton, R-Wash., chair; Bruce Evans, staff director. Internet, http:// www.senate.gov/~appropriations.*

Jurisdiction over legislation to appropriate funds for government programs for the arts and the humanities, including the Commission of Fine Arts; the National Foundation on the Arts and the Humanities; and the operations and programs of the Smithsonian Institution, the Institute of Museum and Library Services, and the Advisory Council on Historic Preservation.

Senate Judiciary Committee, *SD-224 20510; (202) 224-5225. Fax, (202) 224-9102. Orrin G. Hatch, R-Utah, chair; Manus Cooney, chief counsel. Internet, http://www. senate.gov/committee/judiciary.html.*

Jurisdiction over legislation on holidays and celebrations.

Senate Labor and Human Resources Committee, *SD-428 20510; (202) 224-5375. Fax, (202) 224-6510. James M. Jeffords, R-Vt., chair; Mark Powden, staff director. Internet, http://www.senate.gov/~labor.*

Jurisdiction over legislation on government programs for the arts and the humanities, including the National Endowment for the Arts, the National Endowment for the Humanities, and the Institute of Museum and Library Services. Jurisdiction over the Library Services and Construction Act.

Senate Rules and Administration Committee, *SR-305 20510; (202) 224-6352. Fax, (202) 224-3036. John W.*

Warner, R-Va., chair; Grayson Winterling, staff director. Internet, http://www.senate.gov/~rules.

Jurisdiction over legislation related to and operations of the Smithsonian Institution.

NONPROFIT

America the Beautiful Fund, *1511 K St. N.W., #611 20005; (202) 638-1649. Fax, (202) 638-1687. Nanine Bilski, president. Internet, http://www.charities.org.*

National service organization that promotes community self-help. Offers advisory services; grants; free seeds for civic and charitable volunteer programs; and national recognition awards to local community groups for activities that promote America's heritage, culture, environment, public parks, and human services.

American Arts Alliance, *805 15th St. N.W., #500 20005; (202) 289-1776. Fax, (202) 371-6601. Jan Denton, executive director. Internet, aaa@artswire.org.*

Membership: symphony orchestras; art museums; arts presenters; and theater, dance, and opera companies. Advocates national policies that recognize the important role played by the arts in American life.

Americans for the Arts, *1000 Vermont Ave. N.W., 12th Floor 20005; (202) 371-2830. Fax, (202) 371-0424. Robert L. Lynch, president. Internet, http://www.artsusa.org.*

Membership: groups and individuals dedicated to advancing the arts and culture in U.S. communities. Provides information on programs, activities, and administration of local arts agencies; on funding sources and guidelines; and on government policies and programs. Monitors legislation and regulations.

Aspen Institute, *1333 New Hampshire Ave. N.W., #1070 20036; (202) 736-5818. Fax, (202) 467-0790. Charles Firestone, executive vice president, Policy Program. Information, (202) 736-5800. Internet, http://www.aspeninst.org.*

Conducts seminars on Western civilization and other traditions and cultures; conducts studies and workshops on critical contemporary issues. Fields of interest include communications, energy, justice and the law, science and technology, education, international relations, social policies, rural economy, and the environment.

Assn. of Performing Arts Presenters, *1112 16th St. N.W., #400 20036; (202) 833-2787. Fax, (202) 833-1543. Tom Tomlinson, president. Internet, artpres@tmn.com or http://www.artspresenters.org.*

Connects performing artists to audiences and communities around the world. Facilitates the work of presenters, artist managers, and consultants through

continuing education, regranting programs, and legislative advocacy.

Federation of State Humanities Councils, *1600 Wilson Blvd., #902, Arlington, VA 22209; (703) 908-9700. Fax, (703) 908-9706. Gail Leftwich, president. Internet, humfed@compuserve.com or http://www.acls.org/fshc.htm.*

Membership: humanities councils from U.S. states and territories. Provides members with information; forms partnerships with other organizations and with the private sector to promote the humanities. Monitors legislation and regulations.

International Network of Performing and Visual Arts Schools, *5505 Connecticut Ave. N.W., #280 20015; (202) 966-2216. Fax, (202) 966-2283. Rod Daniel, executive director.*

Membership: schools of the arts, universities, and allied arts organizations from around the world. Supports and serves the leaders of specialized arts schools, fosters communications, and promotes development of new schools of the arts.

National Assembly of State Arts Agencies, *1029 Vermont Ave. N.W., 2nd Floor 20005; (202) 347-6352. Fax, (202) 737-0526. Jonathan Katz, executive director. Internet, nasaa@nasaa-arts.org or http://nasaa-arts.org.*

Membership: state and jurisdictional arts agencies. Provides members with information, resources, and representation. Interests include arts programs for rural and underserved populations, and the arts as a catalyst for economic development. Monitors legislation and regulations.

National Campaign for Freedom of Expression, *918 F St. N.W., #609 20004; (202) 393-2787. Fax, (202) 347-7376. Gary Schwartz, executive director. Toll-free, (800) 477-6233. Internet, http://www.artswire.org/~ncfe.*

Membership: artists, artists' organizations, and concerned individuals. Opposes censorship; promotes political empowerment of artists; seeks to increase funding for the arts. Monitors legislation and regulations.

National Humanities Alliance, *21 Dupont Circle N.W., #800 20036; (202) 296-4994. Fax, (202) 872-0884. John H. Hammer, director.*

Represents scholarly and professional humanities associations; associations of museums, libraries, and historical societies; higher education institutions; state humanities councils; and independent and university-based research centers. Promotes the interests of individuals engaged in research, writing, and teaching.

National League of American Pen Women, *1300 17th St. N.W. 20036-1973; (202) 785-1997. Elaine Waidelich, national president. Internet, http://members. aol.com/penwomen/pen.htm.*

Promotes the development of the creative talents of professional women in the fields of art, letters, and music composition. Conducts and promotes literary, educational, and charitable activities. Offers scholarships, workshops, discussion groups, and professional lectures.

Wolf Trap Foundation for the Performing Arts, *1624 Trap Rd., Vienna, VA 22182; (703) 255-1920. Fax, (703) 255-1905. Terrence D. Jones, president. Information, (703) 255-1900. Internet, http://www.wolf-trap.org.*

Established by Congress to administer Wolf Trap Farm Park for the Performing Arts. Sponsors performances in theater, music, and dance. Conducts educational programs for children, internships for college students, career-entry programs for young singers, and professional training for teachers and performers.

Education

See also Museums (this chapter)

AGENCIES

Education Dept., *Arts in Education, 400 Maryland Ave. S.W. (mailing address: 600 Independence Ave. S.W., Washington, DC 20202-6140); (202) 260-2487. Fax, (202) 205-5630. Shelton Allen, program specialist.*

Provides information on arts education programs. Awards grants to the Kennedy Center's arts and education program and to Very Special Arts, a program for the disabled.

John F. Kennedy Center for the Performing Arts, *Alliance for Arts Education Network, 20566-0001; (202) 416-8845. Fax, (202) 416-8802. Kathi Levin, director. TDD, (202) 416-8822. Internet, http://kennedy-center. org/education/kcaaen.*

Supports state alliances with operating and program grants and information. Alliances are statewide arts education organizations that provide communities with services including teacher professional development, conferences, and arts education programming.

John F. Kennedy Center for the Performing Arts, *Education, 20566-0004; (202) 416-8800. Fax, (202) 416-8802. Derek Gordon, vice president. Press, (202) 416-8448. TDD, (202) 416-8822. Internet, http://kennedy-center. org/education.*

Establishes and supports state committees to encourage arts education in schools (Kennedy Center Alliance for Arts Education Network); promotes community

partnerships between performing arts centers and school systems (Performing Arts Centers and Schools); provides teachers with professional development opportunities; offers performances for young people and families; arranges artist and company residencies in schools; sponsors the National Symphony Orchestra education program; presents lectures, demonstrations, and classes in the performing arts for the general public; offers internships in arts management and fellowships for visiting artists; and produces annually the Kennedy Center American College Theater Festival.

National Endowment for the Arts *(National Foundation on the Arts and the Humanities), Education and Access, 1100 Pennsylvania Ave. N.W. 20506-0001; (202) 682-5438. Fax, (202) 682-5002. Patrice Walker Powell, division coordinator. Internet, http://arts.endow.gov.*

Awards grants to state arts agencies and arts organizations to support arts education of students in grades pre-K through 12. Awards grants to nonprofit groups for development of community-based educational arts programs that reflect the culture of minority, inner city, rural, and tribal communities. Supports projects that create, present, or teach art. Awards grants to presenting organizations. (For grant application information, see Arts and Humanities, General.)

National Endowment for the Humanities *(National Foundation on the Arts and the Humanities), Research and Education, 1100 Pennsylvania Ave. N.W., #302 20506; (202) 606-8373. Fax, (202) 606-8394. James Herbert, director. Internet, education@neh.fed.us or http:// www.neh.fed.us.*

Advocates the improvement of education in the humanities. Projects supported include curricula and materials development and faculty training and development. Offers fellowships, stipends, seminars, and institutes for higher education faculty, school teachers, and independent scholars. Conducts research.

National Gallery of Art, *Education Resources, 6th St. and Constitution Ave. N.W. 20565; (202) 842-6273. Fax, (202) 842-6935. Ruth Perlin, head. Information, (202) 842-6273. TDD, (202) 842-6176. Order desk, (202) 842-6263. Internet, http://www.nga.gov.*

Serves as an educational arm of the gallery; lends audiovisual educational materials free of charge to schools, colleges, community groups, libraries, and individuals on a free loan basis. Answers written and telephone inquiries about European and American art.

Smithsonian Institution, *Smithsonian Associates, 1100 Jefferson Dr. S.W. MRC 701 20560; (202) 357-3030. Fax, (202) 786-2034. Mara Mayor, director. TDD, (202)*

633-9467. Internet, tsa.rap@ic.si.edu or http://www.si.edu/tsa.

National cultural and educational membership organization that offers courses and lectures for adults and young people. Presents films and offers study tours on arts-, humanities-, and science-related subjects; sponsors performances, studio arts workshops, and research.

Smithsonian Office of Education, *900 Jefferson Dr. S.W. MRC 402 20560; (202) 357-3049. Fax, (202) 357-2116. Ann Bay, director. Information, (202) 357-2425. TDD, (202) 357-1696. Internet, education@soe.si.edu.*

Serves as the Smithsonian's central education office. Provides elementary and secondary teachers with programs, publications, audiovisual materials, regional workshops, and summer courses on using museums and primary source materials as teaching tools. Publishes books and other educational materials for children.

NONPROFIT

National Art Education Assn., *1916 Association Dr., Reston, VA 20191-1590; (703) 860-8000. Fax, (703) 860-2960. Thomas A. Hatfield, executive director. Internet, http://www.naea-reston.org.*

Membership: art teachers (early childhood through university), museum staff, and manufacturers and suppliers of art materials. Issues publications on art education theory and practice, research, and current trends; offers placement service for members; provides technical assistance to art educators. Sponsors awards.

National Assn. of Schools of Art and Design, *11250 Roger Bacon Dr., #21, Reston, VA 20190; (703) 437-0700. Fax, (703) 437-6312. Samuel Hope, executive director. Internet, http://www.arts-accredit.org.*

Accrediting agency for educational programs in art and design. Provides information on art and design programs at the postsecondary level; offers professional development for executives of art and design programs.

Young Audiences, *1200 29th St. N.W., Lower Level 20007; (202) 944-2790. Fax, (202) 944-2793. Marie C. Barksdale, executive director.*

Sponsors professional musicians, actors, and dancers who present arts education programs in U.S. schools; promotes career opportunities in the performing arts. Seeks to enhance the education of students through exposure to the performing arts. Researches techniques and disseminates information on developing arts education programs.

Film, Photography, and Broadcasting

See also Media Professions and Resources (chap. 3)

AGENCIES

American Film Institute Theater *(John F. Kennedy Center for the Performing Arts), 20566-0001; (202) 828-4090. Fax, (202) 659-1970. Jean Firstenberg, director. Recorded information, (202) 785-4600. Internet, http://www.afionline.org/nft.*

Preserves and catalogs films; supports research. Shows films of historical and artistic importance. Theater open to the public. (Administrative offices and Center for Advanced Film and Television Studies located in Los Angeles.)

National Archives and Records Administration, Motion Picture, Sound, and Video, *8601 Adelphi Rd., 3rd Floor, College Park, MD 20740-6001; (301) 713-7060. Fax, (301) 713-6904. Les Waffen, acting chief. Internet, mopix@nara.gov.*

Selects and preserves audiovisual records produced or acquired by federal agencies; maintains collections from private sector, including newsreels. Research room open to the public.

National Archives and Records Administration, Still Pictures, *8601 Adelphi Rd., College Park, MD 20740-6001; (301) 713-6660. Fax, (301) 713-7436. Jim Hastings, chief. Fax-on-demand, (301) 713-6905. Internet, stillpix@nara.gov.*

Provides the public with copies of still pictures from around the world; supplies guides to these materials. Collection includes still pictures from more than 150 federal agencies.

National Endowment for the Arts *(National Foundation on the Arts and the Humanities), Creation and Presentation, 1100 Pennsylvania Ave. N.W. 20506-0001; (202) 682-5452. Fax, (202) 682-5721. Jennifer Dowley, division coordinator. Internet, http://arts.endow.gov.*

Awards grants to nonprofit organizations for film, video, and radio productions; supports film and video exhibitions and workshops. (For grant application information, see Arts and Humanities, General.)

National Endowment for the Humanities *(National Foundation on the Arts and the Humanities), Public Programs, 1100 Pennsylvania Ave. N.W., #426 20506; (202) 606-8278. Fax, (202) 606-8557. James Dougherty, senior program officer. Internet, info@neh.fed.us.*

Awards grants for nonprofit media projects aimed at advancing knowledge of the humanities.

National Technical Information Service *(Commerce Dept.), National Audiovisual Center, 5285 Port Royal Rd., Springfield, VA 22161-0001; (703) 605-6537. Fax, (703) 321-8199. George H. Ziener, director. Internet, http://www.ntis.gov.*

Serves as a clearinghouse for video cassettes, slide sets, audiotapes, interactive video disks, and multimedia kits produced by federal agencies on a wide range of subjects, including languages, health and safety, and training programs.

CONGRESS

Library of Congress, *Motion Picture, Broadcasting, and Recorded Sound, 101 Independence Ave. S.E. 20540-4690; (202) 707-5840. Fax, (202) 707-2371. David Francis, chief. Film and television reading room, (202) 707-8572. Recorded sound reference center, (202) 707-7833. Internet, http://www.loc.gov/rr/mopic.*

Collections include archives of representative motion pictures (1942 to present); historic films (1894-1915); early American films (1898-1926); German, Italian, and Japanese features, newsreels, and documentary films (1930-1945); and a selected collection of stills, newspaper reviews, and U.S. government productions. Collection also includes television programs of all types (1948 to present), recordings of radio broadcasts (1924 to present), and sound recordings (1890 to present). American Film Institute film archives are interfiled with the division's collections. Use of collections restricted to scholars and researchers. Reading room open to the public.

Library of Congress, *National Film Preservation Board, 101 Independence Ave. S.E. (mailing address: National Film Registry, Library of Congress, Washington, DC 20540); (202) 707-6240. Fax, (202) 707-6269. Winston Tabb, administrator. TDD, (202) 707-6362. Internet, http://www.loc.gov/film.*

Administers the National Film Preservation Plan. Establishes guidelines and receives nominations for the annual selection of twenty-five films of cultural, historical, or aesthetic significance; selections are entered in the National Film Registry to ensure archival preservation in their original form.

Library of Congress, *Prints and Photographs, 101 Independence Ave. S.E. 20540-4730; (202) 707-5836. Fax, (202) 707-6647. Linda L. Ayres, chief. TDD, (202) 707-9051. Reading Room, (202) 707-6394. Internet, http:// www.loc.gov.*

Maintains Library of Congress's collection of pictorial material, not in book format, totaling more than 15 million items. U.S. and international collections include artists' prints; historical prints, posters, and drawings;

photographs (chiefly documentary); political and social cartoons; and architectural plans, drawings, prints, and photographs. Reference service provided in the Prints and Photographs Reading Room. Reproductions of nonrestricted material available through the Library of Congress's Photoduplication Service; prints and photographs may be borrowed through the Exhibits Office for exhibits by qualified institutions.

NONPROFIT

Broadcast Pioneers' Library of American Broadcasting, *University of Maryland, Hornbake Library, College Park, MD 20742; (301) 405-9160. Fax, (301) 314-2634. Vacant, project curator.*

Maintains library and archives on the history of radio and television. Open to the public.

Council on International Nontheatrical Events, *1001 Connecticut Ave. N.W., #638 20036; (202) 785-1136. Fax, (202) 785-4114. Vacant, executive director. Internet, http://www.cine.org.*

Selects and enters nontheatrical films in international film festivals; holds semiannual screening competitions and annual showcase and awards ceremonies; publishes annual directory of international film and video festivals and events.

Motion Picture Assn., *1600 Eye St. N.W. 20006; (202) 293-1966. Fax, (202) 293-7674. Jack Valenti, president. Anti-piracy hotline, (800) 662-6797. Internet, http:// www.mpaa.org.*

Membership: motion picture producers and distributors. Advises state and federal governments on copyrights, censorship, cable broadcasting, and other topics; administers volunteer rating system for motion pictures; works to prevent video piracy.

Screen Actors Guild, *4340 East-West Hwy., #204, Bethesda, MD 20814; (301) 657-2560. Fax, (301) 656-3615. Patricia O'Donnell, executive director. Internet, http://www.sag.com.*

Membership: approximately 76,000 actors in television, theater, and commercials. Helps members negotiate pay, benefits, and better working conditions; conducts training programs and workshops. Monitors legislation and regulations. (Headquarters in Los Angeles.)

Language and Literature

See also Special Topics in Education (chap. 6)

AGENCIES

Center for the Advancement of Language Learning, *4040 N. Fairfax Dr., #200, Arlington, VA 22203; (703)*

312-5040. Fax, (703) 528-6746. Betty A. Kilgore, director. Internet, http://www.call.gov.

Membership: federal departments and agencies involved in foreign language training. Informs members of developments in language training techniques and technology. Holds conferences and workshops on proficiency-based language teaching and testing.

National Endowment for the Arts *(National Foundation on the Arts and the Humanities), Heritage and Preservation, 1100 Pennsylvania Ave. N.W. 20506-0001; (202) 682-5428. Fax, (202) 682-5669. Dan Sheehy, division coordinator. Internet, http://arts.endow.gov.*

Awards grants to published writers, poets, and translators of prose and poetry; awards grants to small presses and literary magazines that publish poetry and fiction. (For grant application information, see Arts and Humanities, General.)

CONGRESS

Library of Congress, *Center for the Book, 101 Independence Ave. S.E., #650 20540-4920; (202) 707-5221. Fax, (202) 707-0269. John Y. Cole, director. Internet, http://www.loc.gov/loc/cfbook.*

Seeks to broaden public appreciation of books, reading, and libraries; sponsors lectures and conferences on the educational and cultural role of the book worldwide, including the history of books and printing, television and the printed word, and the publishing and production of books; cooperates with state centers and with other organizations. Projects and programs are privately funded except for basic administrative support from the Library of Congress.

Library of Congress, *Children's Literature Center, 10 1st St. S.E. 20540-4620; (202) 707-5535. Fax, (202) 707-4632. Sybille Jagusch, chief.*

Provides reference and information services by telephone, by correspondence, and in person; maintains reference materials on all aspects of the study of children's literature, including critical reviews of current books; sponsors lectures, symposia, and exhibits. Reading room open to the public.

Library of Congress, *Poetry and Literature, 10 1st St. S.E. 20540-8910; (202) 707-5394. Fax, (202) 707-9946. Robert Pinsky, poet laureate.*

Advises the library on public literary programs and on the acquisition of literary materials. Arranges for poets to record readings of their work for the library's tape archive. The poet laureate is appointed by the Librarian of Congress on the basis of literary distinction.

NONPROFIT

Alliance Française de Washington, *2142 Wyoming Ave. N.W. 20008; (202) 234-7911. Fax, (202) 234-0125. Daniel Blondy, executive director. Internet, afwdc@worldnet.att.net or http://www.afusa.org/dc.*

Offers courses in French language and literature; presents lectures and cultural events; maintains library of French-language publications for members; offers corporate language training programs.

American Poetry and Literacy Project, *1058 Thomas Jefferson St. N.W. 20007; (202) 338-1109. Andrew Carroll, executive director.*

Donates new books of poetry to schools, libraries, hospitals, homeless shelters, nursing homes, hotels, and other public places around the country. Organizes free poetry readings open to the public.

Brazilian-American Cultural Institute, *4103 Connecticut Ave. N.W. 20008; (202) 362-8334. Fax, (202) 362-8337. José M. Neistein, executive director.*

Conducts courses in Portuguese language and Brazilian literature; sponsors art exhibitions, films, concerts, and other public presentations on Brazilian culture. Library open to the public.

Center for Applied Linguistics, *1118 22nd St. N.W. 20037; (202) 429-9292. Fax, (202) 659-5641. Donna Christian, president. Internet, webmaster@cal.org or http://www.cal.org.*

Research and technical assistance organization that serves as clearinghouse on application of linguistics to practical language problems. Interests include English as a second language, teacher training and material development, language education, language proficiency test development, bilingual education, and sociolinguistics.

English First, *8001 Forbes Pl., #102, Springfield, VA 22151; (703) 321-8818. Fax, (703) 321-8408. Jim Boulet, executive director. Internet, http://www.englishfirst.org.*

Seeks to make English the official language of the United States. Advocates policies which make English education available to all children. Monitors legislation and regulations. Opposes bilingual education and ballots.

Folger Shakespeare Library, *201 E. Capitol St. S.E. 20003-1094; (202) 544-4600. Fax, (202) 544-4623. Werner Gundersheimer, director. Information, (202) 544-7077. Internet, http://www.folger.edu.*

Administered by the trustees of Amherst College. Maintains major Shakespearean and Renaissance materials; awards fellowships for postdoctoral research; presents concerts, poetry and fiction readings, exhibits, and other public events. Offers educational programs for elementary and secondary school students and teachers.

Japan-America Society of Washington, *1020 19th St. N.W., Lower Lobby #40 20036; (202) 833-2210. Fax, (202) 833-2456. Patricia R. Kearns, executive director. Internet, jaswdc@intr.net or http://www.us-japan.org/dc.*

Assists Japanese performing artists; offers lectures and films on Japan; operates a Japanese-language school and an annual language competition for high school students; awards scholarships to college students studying in the Washington area. Maintains library for members.

Joint National Committee for Language, *1118 22nd St. N.W. 20037; (202) 466-2666. Fax, (202) 466-2892. J. David Edwards, executive director. Internet, info@languagepolicy.org or http://www.languagepolicy.org.*

Membership: translators, interpreters, and associations of language teachers (primary through postsecondary level). Supports a national policy on language study and international education. Provides forum and clearinghouse for professional language and international education associations. National Council for Languages and International Studies is the political arm.

Linguistic Society of America, *1325 18th St. N.W., #211 20036; (202) 835-1714. Fax, (202) 835-1717. Margaret W. Reynolds, executive director. Internet, lsa@lsadc.org or http://www.lsadc.org.*

Membership: individuals and institutions interested in the scientific analysis of language. Holds linguistic institutes every other year.

National Foreign Language Center *(Johns Hopkins University), 1619 Massachusetts Ave. N.W., 4th Floor 20036; (202) 667-8100. Fax, (202) 667-6907. David Maxwell, director. Internet, http://www.cais.com/nflc.*

Research and policy organization that develops new strategies to strengthen foreign language competence in the United States. Conducts research on national language needs and assists policymakers in identifying priorities, allocating resources, and designing programs. Interests include the role of foreign language in higher education, national competence in critical languages, ethnic language maintenance, and K-12 and postsecondary language programs.

PEN/Faulkner Foundation, *c/o Folger Shakespeare Library, 201 E. Capitol St. S.E. 20003-1094; (202) 544-7077. Fax, (202) 544-7520. Robert Stone, chair; Patricia Browning Griffith, president.*

Sponsors an annual juried award for American fiction. Brings authors to Washington-area public schools to teach classes. Holds readings by authors of new American fiction.

U.S. English, *1747 Pennsylvania Ave. N.W., #1100 20006; (202) 833-0100. Fax, (202) 833-0108. Mauro E. Mujica, chair of the board. Internet, http://www.usenglish.org.*

Advocates English as the official language of federal and state government.

The Writer's Center, *4508 Walsh St., Bethesda, MD 20815; (301) 654-8664. Fax, (301) 654-8667. Jane Fox, executive director. Internet, postmaster@writer.org or http://www.writer.org.*

Membership: writers, editors, graphic artists, and interested individuals. Sponsors workshops in writing and graphic arts, and a reading series of poetry, fiction, and plays. Provides access to word processing, desktop publishing, and design equipment; maintains a book gallery.

See also American Council of Teachers of Russian (p. 488); Teachers of English to Speakers of Other Languages (p. 181)

Museums

See also History and Preservation (this chapter)

AGENCIES

Anacostia Museum *(Smithsonian Institution), 1901 Fort Pl. S.E. 20020; (202) 287-3306. Fax, (202) 287-3183. Steven Newsome, director. TDD, (202) 357-1729. Recorded information, (202) 287-2060. Internet, http://www.si.edu/organiza/museums/anacost/start.htm.*

Researches, interprets, and documents the history of African Americans, placing special emphasis on the experiences of residents of Georgia, Maryland, North Carolina, South Carolina, Virginia, and the District of Columbia.

Arthur M. Sackler Gallery *(Smithsonian Institution), 1050 Independence Ave. S.W. 20560; (202) 357-2700. Fax, (202) 357-4911. Milo C. Beach, director. Press, (202) 357-4880. TDD, (202) 786-2374. Public programs, (202) 357-3200 (recording). Internet, http://www.si.edu/asia.*

Exhibits Asian and Near Eastern art drawn from collections in the U.S. and abroad; features international exhibitions and public programs. Presents films, lectures, and concerts. Library open to the public.

Federal Council on the Arts and the Humanities *(National Foundation on the Arts and the Humanities), 1100 Pennsylvania Ave. N.W. 20506; (202) 682-5574. Fax,*

MUSEUM EDUCATION PROGRAMS

Alexandria Archaeology, (703) 838-4399

American Assn. of Museums, Museum Assessment Program, (202) 289-9118

Arlington Arts Center, (703) 524-1494

Assn. of Science-Technology Centers, (202) 783-7200

B'nai B'rith Klutznick Museum, (202) 857-6583

C & O Canal, (301) 739-4200

Capital Children's Museum, (202) 675-4120

Corcoran Gallery of Art, (202) 639-1700

Daughters of the American Revolution (DAR) Museum, (202) 879-3241

Decatur House, (202) 842-0915

Dumbarton Oaks, (202) 339-6409

Federal Reserve Board, (202) 452-3686

Folger Shakespeare Library, (202) 544-7077

Gadsby's Tavern Museum, (703) 838-4242

Historical Society of Washington, D.C., (202) 785-2068

J.F.K. Center for the Performing Arts—Alliance for Arts Education, (202) 416-8800

Lyceum, (703) 838-4994

Mount Vernon, (703) 780-2000

National Arboretum, (202) 245-2726

National Archives, (202) 501-6172

National Building Museum, (202) 272-2448

National Gallery of Art, (202) 842-6246

National Museum of Women in the Arts, (202) 783-7370

Navy Museum, (202) 433-4882

Octagon Museum, (202) 638-3221

Phillips Collection, (202) 387-2151

Smithsonian Institution

  Central education office, (202) 357-3049

  Anacostia Museum, (202) 287-3369

  Arthur M. Sackler Gallery, (202) 357-4880

  Freer Gallery of Art, (202) 357-4880

  Friends of the National Zoo, (202) 673-4954

  Hirshhorn Museum and Sculpture Garden, (202) 357-3235

  National Air and Space Museum, (202) 357-1427

  National Museum of African Art, (202) 357-4600

  National Museum of American Art, (202) 357-3095

  National Museum of American History, (202) 357-3229

  National Museum of Natural History, (202) 357-2747

  National Portrait Gallery, (202) 357-2920

  Renwick Gallery, (202) 357-2531

Textile Museum, (202) 483-0981

Woodrow Wilson House, (202) 387-4062

---

(202) 682-5603. Alice M. Whelihan, indemnity administrator.

Membership: leaders of federal agencies sponsoring arts-related activities. Administers the Arts and Artifacts Indemnity Act, which helps museums reduce the costs of commercial insurance for international exhibits.

Frederick Douglass National Historic Site, *1411 W St. S.E. 20020; (202) 426-5961. Fax, (202) 426-0880. Cynthia Stith, site manager. Internet, http://www.nps.gov/fdnhs.*

Administered by the National Park Service. Museum of the life and work of abolitionist Frederick Douglass and his family. Offers tours of the home and special programs, such as documentary films, videos, and slide presentations; maintains visitor's center and bookstore.

Freer Gallery of Art *(Smithsonian Institution), 12th St. and Jefferson Dr. S.W. 20560; (202) 357-2700. Fax, (202) 357-4911. Milo C. Beach, director. Press, (202) 357-*

4880. TDD, (202) 786-2374. Public programs, (202) 357-3200 (recording). Internet, http://www.si.edu/asia.

Exhibits Asian art from the Mediterranean to Japan and late 19th and early 20th century American art from its permanent collection, including works by James McNeill Whistler. Presents films, lectures, and concerts. Library open to the public.

Hirshhorn Museum and Sculpture Garden *(Smithsonian Institution), 7th St. and Independence Ave. S.W. 20560; (202) 357-3091. Fax, (202) 786-2682. James T. Demetrion, director. Information, (202) 357-1618. Library, (202) 357-3222. TDD, (202) 357-3235. Internet, http://www.si.edu/hirshhorn.*

Preserves and exhibits contemporary American and European paintings and sculpture. Offers films, lectures, concerts, and tours of the collection.

Institute of Museum and Library Services, *1100 Pennsylvania Ave. N.W. 20506; (202) 606-8536. Fax, (202)*

606-8591. *Diane Frankel, director. Information, (202) 606-8539. TDD, (202) 606-8636. Internet, imlsinfo@imls.fed.us or http://www.imls.fed.us.*

Independent agency established by Congress to assist museums in increasing and improving their services. Awards grants for general operating support, conservation projects, and museum assessment to museums of all disciplines and budget sizes; helps fund museum associations.

National Endowment for the Arts *(National Foundation on the Arts and the Humanities), Creation and Presentation, 1100 Pennsylvania Ave. N.W. 20506-0001; (202) 682-5452. Fax, (202) 682-5721. Jennifer Dowley, division coordinator. Internet, http://arts.endow.gov.*

Awards grants to museums for installing and cataloging permanent and special collections; traveling exhibits; training museum professionals; conserving and preserving museum collections; and developing arts-related educational programs. (For grant application information, see Arts and Humanities, General.)

National Gallery of Art, *6th St. and Constitution Ave. N.W. 20565; (202) 737-4215. Fax, (202) 842-2356. Earl A. Powell III, director. Information, (202) 842-6191. TDD, (202) 842-6176. Internet, http://www.nga.gov.*

Autonomous bureau of the Smithsonian Institution administered by a separate board of trustees. Preserves and exhibits European and American paintings, sculpture, and decorative and graphic arts. Offers concerts, demonstrations, lectures, symposia, films, tours, and teachers' workshops to enhance exhibitions, the permanent collection, and related topics. Lends art to museums in all fifty states and abroad through the National Lending Service. Publishes monthly calendar of events.

National Museum of African Art *(Smithsonian Institution), 950 Independence Ave. S.W. 20560; (202) 357-4600. Fax, (202) 357-4879. Roslyn A. Walker, director, (202) 357-4858. TDD, (202) 357-4814. Internet, http://www.si.edu/nmafa.*

Collects, studies, and exhibits traditional and contemporary arts of Africa. Exhibits feature objects from the permanent collection and from private and public collections worldwide. Library and photo archive open to the public by appointment.

National Museum of American Art *(Smithsonian Institution), 8th and G Sts. N.W. 20560; (202) 357-1959. Fax, (202) 357-2528. Elizabeth Broun, director. Information, (202) 357-3176. Press, (202) 357-2247. TDD, (202) 786-2393. Internet, http://www.nmaa.si.edu.*

Exhibits and interprets American painting, sculpture, photographs, folk art, and graphic art from 18th century to present in permanent collection and temporary exhibition galleries.

National Museum of American History *(Smithsonian Institution), 14th St. and Constitution Ave. N.W. 20560; (202) 357-2510. Fax, (202) 786-2624. Spencer R. Crew, director. Information, (202) 357-3129. Library, (202) 357-2414. TDD, (202) 357-1563. Internet, viarcmx@sivm.si.edu or http://www.si.edu/organiza/museums/nmah/nmah.htm.*

Collects and exhibits objects representative of American cultural history, applied arts, industry, national and military history, and science and technology. Library open to the public by appointment.

National Museum of Health and Medicine *(Defense Dept.), Walter Reed Medical Center, Bldg. 54 South (mailing address: 6825 16th St. N.W., Washington, DC 20036-6000); (202) 782-2200. Fax, (202) 782-3573. Dr. Adrianne Noe, director.*

Collects and exhibits medical models, tools, and teaching aids. Maintains permanent exhibits on the human body, AIDS, Civil War medicine, and military contributions to medicine; collects specimens illustrating a broad range of pathological conditions. Open to the public. Study collection available for scholars by appointment.

National Museum of the American Indian *(Smithsonian Institution), 470 L'Enfant Plaza, #7102 20560; (202) 287-2523. Fax, (202) 287-2538. W. Richard West, director. Internet, http://www.si.edu/nmai.*

Established by Congress in 1989 to plan and coordinate development of the National Museum of the American Indian. The museum, scheduled to open in the year 2002, will collect, preserve, study, and exhibit American Indian languages, literature, history, art, and culture.

National Oceanic and Atmospheric Administration *(Commerce Dept.), National Weather Service Science and History Center, 1325 East-West Hwy., Silver Spring, MD 20910; (301) 713-0692. Fax, (301) 713-0662. Gloria Walker, program manager.*

Maintains and exhibits historical collection of the National Weather Service. Displays include meteorological instruments, weather satellites, photographs, and a re-creation of a 19th century weather office. Forecasting office in Sterling, Va.

National Portrait Gallery *(Smithsonian Institution), 8th and F Sts. N.W. 20560; (202) 357-2700. Fax, (202) 786-2565. Alan Fern, director. Information, (202) 357-2866. Library, (202) 357-1886. TDD, (202) 357-1729. Internet, http://www.si.edu/organiza/museums/nmah/nmah.htm.*

Exhibits paintings, photographs, sculpture, drawings, and prints of individuals who have made significant contributions to the history, development, and culture of the United States. Library open to the public.

Renwick Gallery *(Smithsonian Institution), 17th St. and Pennsylvania Ave. N.W. 20560; (202) 357-2531. Fax, (202) 786-2810. Kenneth Trapp, curator-in-charge. Information, (202) 357-2247. TDD, (202) 357-4522.*

Curatorial department of the National Museum of American Art. Exhibits late 20th century American crafts.

Smithsonian Institution, *1000 Jefferson Dr. S.W., #205 20560; (202) 357-1846. Fax, (202) 786-2515. I. Michael Heyman, secretary; Constance B. Newman, under secretary, (202) 357-3258. Information, (202) 357-2700. Library, (202) 357-2627. TDD, (202) 357-1729. Recorded daily museum highlights, (202) 357-2020. Locator, (202) 357-1300. Internet, http://www.si.edu.*

Conducts research; publishes results of studies, explorations, and investigations; maintains study and reference collections on science, culture, and history; maintains exhibitions in the arts, American history, technology, aeronautics and space exploration, and natural history. Smithsonian Institution sites in Washington, D.C., include the Anacostia Museum, Archives of American Art, Arthur M. Sackler Gallery, Arts & Industries Building, Freer Gallery of Art, Hirshhorn Museum and Sculpture Garden, National Air & Space Museum, National Museum of African Art, National Museum of American Art, National Museum of American History, National Museum of Natural History, National Portrait Gallery, National Postal Museum, National Zoological Park, S. Dillon Ripley Center, Smithsonian Institution Building, and Renwick Gallery. Supports affiliates in New York, Arizona, Florida, Maryland, Massachusetts, and Panama. Autonomous bureaus affiliated with the Smithsonian Institution include John F. Kennedy Center for the Performing Arts, National Gallery of Art, and Woodrow Wilson International Center for Scholars. Libraries open to the public by appointment.

Smithsonian Institution, *Center for Museum Studies, 900 Jefferson Dr. S.W., #2235 20560; (202) 357-3101. Fax, (202) 357-3346. Rex Ellis, director. Library, (202) 786-2271. Internet, http://www.si.edu/cms.*

Provides training, services, information, and assistance for the professional enhancement of museum personnel and institutions in the United States; sponsors museum training workshops; maintains museum reference center; offers career counseling.

Smithsonian Institution, *International Relations, 1100 Jefferson Dr. S.W., #3123, MRC 705 20560; (202)*

357-4282. Fax, (202) 786-2557. Francine C. Berkowitz, director.

Fosters the development and coordinates the international aspects of Smithsonian cultural activities; facilitates basic research in history and art and encourages international collaboration among individuals and institutions.

Smithsonian Institution, *Internship Programs and Services, 900 Jefferson Dr. S.W., #2235 MRC 427 20560; (202) 357-3102. Fax, (202) 357-3346. Elena Mayberry, coordinator. Library, (202) 786-2271. Internet, siintern@sivm.si.edu.*

Provides internship placements to undergraduate and graduate students and museum professionals. Emphasizes methods and current practices employed by museum professionals.

CONGRESS

Library of Congress, *Interpretive Programs, 101 Independence Ave. S.E. 20540-4950; (202) 707-5223. Fax, (202) 707-9063. Irene Chambers, interpretive programs officer.*

Handles exhibits within the Library of Congress; establishes and coordinates traveling exhibits; handles loans of library material.

NONPROFIT

American Assn. of Museums, *1575 Eye St. N.W., #400 20005; (202) 289-1818. Fax, (202) 289-6578. Edward H. Able Jr., president. TDD, (202) 289-8439. Internet, http://www.aam-us.org.*

Membership: individuals, institutions, museums, and museum professionals. Accredits museums; conducts educational programs; promotes international professional exchanges.

Art, Science, and Technology Institute, *2018 R St. N.W. 20009; (202) 667-6322. Fax, (202) 265-8563. Laurent Bussaut, president.*

Research and educational organization. Displays a permanent collection on the art, science, and technology of holography. Conducts research on holographic applications, laser, and photonics imaging, and new forms of expression that combine art, science, and technology.

Art Services International, *700 N. Fairfax St., #220, Alexandria, VA 22314; (703) 548-4554. Fax, (703) 548-3305. Lynn K. Rogerson, director. Internet, http://www.artservicesintl.org.*

Organizes and circulates fine arts exhibitions to museums worldwide.

Capital Children's Museum, *800 3rd St. N.E. 20002; (202) 675-4120. Fax, (202) 675-4140. Catherine Martens, president. Press, (202) 675-4183. Museum desk, (202) 675-4170. Internet, http://www.ccm.org.*

Offers exhibits that involve participation by children. Integrates art, science, the humanities, and technology through "hands-on" learning experiences. (A program of the National Learning Center.)

Corcoran Gallery of Art, *500 17th St. N.W. 20006; (202) 639-1700. Fax, (202) 639-1768. David C. Levy, director. Internet, http://www.corcoran.org or http://www. corcoran.edu.*

Exhibits paintings, sculpture, and drawings, primarily American. Collections include European art and works of local Washington artists. The affiliated Corcoran School of Art offers a BFA degree and a continuing education program. Library open to the public by appointment.

Dumbarton Oaks, *1703 32nd St. N.W. 20007; (202) 339-6410. Angeliki Laiou, director. Information, (202) 339-6400. Recorded information, (202) 339-6401. Internet, http://www.doaks.org.*

Administered by the trustees for Harvard University. Exhibits Byzantine and pre-Columbian art and artifacts; conducts advanced research and maintains publication programs and library in Byzantine and pre-Columbian studies and in landscape architecture. Gardens open to the public daily (fee charged April through October); library open to qualified scholars by advance application.

Freedom Forum Museum, *1101 Wilson Blvd., 10th Floor, Arlington, VA 22209; (703) 284-3700. Fax, (703) 284-3770. Joe Urschel, executive director. Internet, http:// www.newseum.org.*

World's only interactive museum of news. Collects items related to the history of news coverage; offers multimedia presentations and exhibits on the past, present, and future of news coverage; emphasizes the importance of the First Amendment to news coverage. (Affiliated with Freedom Forum.)

Hillwood Museum and Gardens, *4155 Linnean Ave. N.W. 20008; (202) 686-8500. Fax, (202) 966-7846. Frederick Fisher, director. TDD, (202) 363-3056. Reservations, (202) 686-5807.*

Former residence of Marjorie Merriweather Post. Maintains and exhibits collection of French and Russian decorative arts, including portraits, liturgical objects, and furniture. Gardens and museum open to the public by appointment.

Museum Services International, *1716 17th St. N.W. 20009; (202) 462-6176. Fax, (202) 462-2380. Roger Wulff, director. Internet, museplan@erols.com.*

Provides consulting services to museums around the world. Interests include museum security and value engineering (federally mandated cost analysis of architecture and construction of federal buildings, including museums).

National Building Museum, *401 F St. N.W. 20001; (202) 272-2448. Fax, (202) 272-2564. Susan Henshaw Jones, director. Press, (202) 272-3606. Internet, http:// www.nbm.org.*

Celebrates American achievements in building, architecture, urban planning, engineering, and historic preservation through educational programs, exhibitions, tours, lectures, workshops, and publications.

National Museum of Women in the Arts, *1250 New York Ave. N.W. 20005; (202) 783-5000. Fax, (202) 393-3235. Dr. Constance Battle, director. Toll-free, (800) 222-7270. Library, (202) 783-7365. Internet, http://www. nmwa.org.*

Acquires, researches, and presents the works of women artists from the Renaissance to the present. Promotes greater representation and awareness of women in the arts. Library open to the public by appointment.

Octagon Museum, *1799 New York Ave. N.W. 20006-5292; (202) 638-3221. Fax, (202) 879-7764. Eryl J. Platzer, director. TDD, (202) 638-1538. Internet, http://www. archfoundation.com.*

Federal period house open for tours; served as the executive mansion following the War of 1812. Presents temporary exhibits on architecture, decorative arts, and Washington history. Sponsors lectures, scholarly research, publications, and educational programs. (Owned by the American Architectural Foundation.)

Phillips Collection, *1600 21st St. N.W. 20009; (202) 387-2151. Fax, (202) 387-2436. Charles S. Moffett, director. Membership, (202) 387-3036; Shop, (202) 387-2151. Internet, phillipsco@aol.com.*

Maintains permanent collection of European and American paintings, primarily of the 19th and 20th centuries, and holds special exhibits from the same period. Sponsors lectures, gallery talks, and special events, including Sunday concerts (September-May). Library open to researchers and members by appointment.

Textile Museum, *2320 S St. N.W. 20008; (202) 667-0441. Fax, (202) 483-0994. Ursula E. McCracken, director.*

Exhibits historic and handmade textiles and carpets. Sponsors symposia, conferences, workshops, lectures, and an annual rug convention. Library open to the public.

Trust for Museum Exhibitions, *1424 16th St. N.W., #601 20036; (202) 745-2566. Fax, (202) 745-0103. Ann Van Devanter Townsend, president. Internet, tme@aol.com or http://www.tme.org.*

Provides lending and exhibiting institutions with traveling exhibition services, which include negotiating loans, engaging guest curators, scheduling tours, fundraising, and managing registrarial details and catalog production.

U.S. Holocaust Memorial Museum, *100 Raoul Wallenberg Pl. S.W. 20024-2150; (202) 488-0400. Fax, (202) 488-2690. Walter Reich, director. Library, (202) 488-9717. TDD, (202) 488-0406. Internet, http://www.ushmm.org.*

Works to preserve documentation about the Holocaust; encourages research; provides educational resources, including conferences, publications, and public programming. Responsible for the annual Days of Remembrance of the Victims of the Holocaust.

Woodrow Wilson House *(National Trust for Historic Preservation), 2340 S St. N.W. 20008; (202) 387-4062. Fax, (202) 483-1466. Michael T. Sheehan, director. Internet, wilsondc@worldweb.net.*

Georgian Revival home that exhibits furnishings and memorabilia from President Woodrow Wilson's political and retirement years.

See also Assn. of Science-Technology Centers (p. 207); National Geographic Society (p. 208)

Music

AGENCIES

National Archives and Records Administration, *Educational and Museum Programs, 700 Pennsylvania Ave. N.W., #G14 20408; (202) 501-5200. Fax, (202) 219-1888. Edith James, assistant archivist.*

Plans and directs activities to acquaint the public with materials of the National Archives; conducts tours, workshops, and classes; stages exhibits; produces books and pamphlets; issues teaching packets using historic documents.

National Endowment for the Arts *(National Foundation on the Arts and the Humanities), Education and Access, 1100 Pennsylvania Ave. N.W. 20506-0001; (202) 682-5438. Fax, (202) 682-5002. Patrice Walker Powell, division coordinator. Internet, http://arts.endow.gov.*

Awards grants to music professional training and career development institutions and to music perform-

ing, presenting, recording, and service organizations; awards fellowship grants to professional jazz musicians. Awards grants to professional opera and musical theater companies for regional touring and to organizations that provide services for opera and musical theater professionals. (For grant application information, see Arts and Humanities, General.)

National Museum of American History *(Smithsonian Institution), Cultural History, 12th St. and Constitution Ave. N.W. 20560; (202) 357-1707. Fax, (202) 786-2883. James Weaver, chair. Internet, http://www.si.edu/nmah.*

Handles exhibits, including construction, and audiovisual services. Presents concerts that feature jazz by regional artists and ensembles, American popular songs, and American theater music on topics related to the museum's collections and current exhibitions. The chamber music program uses a collection of historic European and American musical instruments in performances.

National Symphony Orchestra Education Program *(John F. Kennedy Center for the Performing Arts), 20566-0004; (202) 416-8820. Fax, (202) 416-8802. Carole J. Wysocki, director. TDD, (202) 416-8822. Internet, http://kennedy-center.org/nso/nsoed.html.*

Presents concerts for students, grades K-12; sponsors fellowship program for talented high school musicians and a young associates program for high school students interested in arts management and professional music careers; holds an annual soloist competition open to college and high school pianists, orchestral instrumentalists, and college vocalists; sponsors Youth Orchestra Day for area youth orchestra members selected by their conductors.

CONGRESS

Library of Congress, *Motion Picture, Broadcasting, and Recorded Sound, 101 Independence Ave. S.E. 20540-4690; (202) 707-5840. Fax, (202) 707-2371. David Francis, chief. Recorded sound reference center, (202) 707-7833. Internet, http://www.loc.gov/rr/mopic.*

Maintains library's collection of musical and vocal recordings; tapes the library's concert series and other musical events for radio broadcast; produces recordings of music and poetry for sale to the public. Collection also includes sound recordings (1890 to present). Reading room open to the public; listening and viewing by appointment.

Library of Congress, *Music Division, 101 Independence Ave. S.E. 20540-4710; (202) 707-5503. Fax, (202) 707-*

0621. *John Newsom, chief. Concert information, (202) 707-5502. Reading room, (202) 707-5507.*

Maintains and services, through the Performing Arts Reading Room, the library's collection of music manuscripts, sheet music, books, and instruments. Coordinates the library's chamber music concert series; produces radio broadcasts and, for sale to the public, recordings of concerts sponsored by the division; issues publications relating to the field of music and to division collections.

NONPROFIT

American Music Therapy Assn., *8455 Colesville Rd., #1000, Silver Spring, MD 20910; (301) 589-3300. Fax, (301) 589-5175. Andrea Farbman, executive director. Internet, info@musictherapy.org or http://www. musictherapy.org.*

Promotes the therapeutic use of music by approving degree programs and clinical training sites for therapists, setting standards for certification of music therapists, and conducting research in the music therapy field.

American Symphony Orchestra League, *1156 15th St. N.W., #800 20005-1704; (202) 776-0212. Fax, (202) 776-0224. Charles Otton, president. Internet, league@ symphony.org.*

Service and educational organization dedicated to strengthening symphony and chamber orchestras. Provides artistic, organizational, and financial leadership and service to the music directors, musicians, direct service and governance volunteers, managers, and staff of member orchestras.

Music Educators National Conference, *1806 Robert Fulton Dr., Reston, VA 20191-4348; (703) 860-4000. Fax, (703) 860-1531. John J. Mahlmann, executive director. Internet, mencser@aol.com or http://www.menc.org.*

Membership: music educators (preschool through university). Holds biennial conference. Publishes books and teaching aids for music educators.

National Assn. of Schools of Music, *11250 Roger Bacon Dr., #21, Reston, VA 20190; (703) 437-0700. Fax, (703) 437-6312. Samuel Hope, executive director.*

Accrediting agency for educational programs in music. Provides information on music education programs; offers professional development for executives of music programs.

OPERA America, *1156 15th St. N.W., #810 20005-1704; (202) 293-4466. Fax, (202) 393-0735. Marc A. Scorca, president. Internet, frontdesk@operaam.org or http:// www.operaam.org.*

Membership: professional opera companies in the United States and abroad, producing and presenting organizations, artists, and others affiliated with professional opera. Advises and assists opera companies in daily operations; encourages development of opera and musical theater; produces educational programs; implements programs to increase awareness and appreciation of opera and opera companies.

Recording Industry Assn. of America, *1330 Connecticut Ave. N.W., #300 20036; (202) 775-0101. Fax, (202) 775-7253. Jason S. Berman, chair. Internet, http:// www.riaa.com.*

Membership: creators, manufacturers, and marketers of sound recordings. Educates members about new technology in the music industry. Advocates copyright protection and opposes censorship. Works to prevent recording piracy, counterfeiting, bootlegging, and unauthorized record rental and imports. Certifies gold, platinum, and multiplatinum recordings. Publishes statistics on the recording industry.

Rhythm and Blues Foundation, *1555 Connecticut Ave. N.W., #401 20036; (202) 588-5566. Fax, (202) 588-5549. Janis Hazel, executive director. Internet, randbfdn@aol.com or http://www.rhythm-n-blues.com.*

Fosters wider recognition, financial support, and historic and cultural preservation of rhythm and blues music through various grants and programs in support of artists from the 1940s, '50s and '60s.

Washington Area Music Assn., *1690 36th St. N.W. 20007; (202) 338-1134. Fax, (703) 237-7923. Mike Schreibman, executive director. Information, (703) 237-9500. Internet, askmike@crosstownarts.com or http://www. crosstownarts.com.*

Membership: musicians, concert promoters, lawyers, recording engineers, managers, contractors, and other music industry professionals. Sponsors workshops on industry-related topics. Represents professionals from all musical genres. Serves as a liaison between the Washington-area music community and music communities nationwide.

Theater and Dance

AGENCIES

Ford's Theatre National Historic Site, *511 10th St. N.W. 20004; (202) 426-6924. Fax, (202) 426-1845. Suzanne Kelley, site manager. TDD, (202) 426-1749. Recorded ticket information, (202) 347-4833. Internet, ford's_theatre@nts.gov or http://www.nps.gov/foth.*

Administered by the National Park Service. Manages Ford's Theatre, Ford's Theatre Museum, and the Peterson House (house where Lincoln died). Presents interpretive talks, exhibits, and tours; research library open by appointment. Functions as working stage for theatrical productions.

Fund for New American Plays *(John F. Kennedy Center for the Performing Arts), 20566; (202) 416-8024. Fax, (202) 416-8025. Rebecca Foster and Max Woodward, co-managers.*

Encourages playwrights to write and nonprofit professional theaters to produce new American plays; gives playwrights financial support and provides grants to cover some expenses that exceed standard production costs. Submissions must come from the producing theater.

National Endowment for the Arts *(National Foundation on the Arts and the Humanities), Creation and Presentation, 1100 Pennsylvania Ave. N.W. 20506-0001; (202) 682-5452. Fax, (202) 682-5721. Jennifer Dowley, division coordinator. Internet, http://arts.endow.gov.*

Awards grants to dance services organizations and companies. (For grant application information, see Arts and Humanities, General.)

National Endowment for the Arts *(National Foundation on the Arts and the Humanities), Heritage and Preservation, 1100 Pennsylvania Ave. N.W. 20506-0001; (202) 682-5428. Fax, (202) 682-5669. Dan Sheehy, division coordinator. Internet, http://arts.endow.gov.*

Awards grants to professional theater companies and theater service organizations. (For grant application information, see Arts and Humanities, General.)

Smithsonian Institution, *Discovery Theater, 900 Jefferson Dr. S.W. 20560; (202) 357-1502. Fax, (202) 357-2588. Stephen Diamond, director. Reservations, (202) 357-1500.*

Presents live theatrical performances, including storytelling, dance, music, puppetry, and plays, for young people and their families.

See also John F. Kennedy Center for the Performing Arts and National Endowment for the Humanities (p. 98)

NONPROFIT

National Assn. of Schools of Dance, *11250 Roger Bacon Dr., #21, Reston, VA 22090; (703) 437-0700. Fax, (703) 437-6312. Samuel Hope, executive director.*

Accrediting agency for educational programs in dance. Provides information on dance education programs; offers professional development for executives of dance programs.

National Assn. of Schools of Theatre, *11250 Roger Bacon Dr., #21, Reston, VA 20190; (703) 437-0700. Fax, (703) 437-6312. Samuel Hope, executive director.*

Accrediting agency for educational programs in theater. Provides information on theater education programs; offers professional development for executives of theater programs.

National Conservatory of Dramatic Arts, *1556 Wisconsin Ave. N.W. 20007; (202) 333-2202. Fax, (202) 333-1753. Dennis A. Dulmage, president.*

Offers an accredited two-year program in postsecondary professional actor training and a one-year program in advanced professional training. Emphasizes both physical and mental preparedness for acting in the professional entertainment industry.

Shakespeare Theatre, *450 7th St. N.W. (mailing address: 301 E. Capitol St. S.E., Washington, DC 20003); (202) 547-3230. Fax, (202) 547-0226. Sam Sweet, managing director. TDD, (202) 638-3863. Box office, (202) 393-2700. Internet, http://www.shakespearedc.org.*

Professional resident theater that presents Shakespearean and other classical plays. Offers actor training program for youths, adults, and professional actors. Produces free outdoor summer Shakespeare plays and free Shakespeare plays for schools.

Visual Arts

See also Architecture and Design (chap. 12); Film, Photography, and Broadcasting (this chapter); Museums (this chapter)

AGENCIES

National Endowment for the Arts *(National Foundation on the Arts and the Humanities), Creation and Presentation, 1100 Pennsylvania Ave. N.W. 20506-0001; (202) 682-5452. Fax, (202) 682-5721. Jennifer Dowley, division coordinator. Internet, http://arts.endow.gov.*

Awards grants to nonprofit organizations for creative works and programs in the visual arts, including painting, sculpture, crafts, video, photography, printmaking, drawing, artists' books, and performance art. (For grant application information, see Arts and Humanities, General.)

National Endowment for the Arts *(National Foundation on the Arts and the Humanities), Heritage and Preservation, 1100 Pennsylvania Ave. N.W. 20506-0001; (202) 682-5428. Fax, (202) 682-5669. Dan Sheehy, division coordinator. Internet, http://arts.endow.gov.*

Awards grants for design arts projects in architecture; landscape architecture; urban design and planning; historic preservation; and interior, graphic, industrial, product, and costume and fashion design. (For grant application information, see Arts and Humanities, General.)

State Dept., *Art in Embassies,* Main State Bldg., #B258 20520; (202) 647-5321. Fax, (202) 647-4080. Roselyne Swig, director. Information, (202) 647-5723.

Exhibits American art in U.S. ambassadorial residences. Acquires art works from artists, collectors, galleries, and museums either as loans or as gifts.

CONGRESS

Library of Congress, *Prints and Photographs,* 101 Independence Ave. S.E. 20540-4730; (202) 707-5836. Fax, (202) 707-6647. Linda L. Ayres, chief. TDD, (202) 707-9051. Reading Room, (202) 707-6394. Internet, http://www.loc.gov.

Maintains Library of Congress's collection of pictorial material, not in book format, totaling more than 15 million items. U.S. and international collections include artists' prints; historical prints, posters, and drawings; photographs (chiefly documentary); political and social cartoons; and architectural plans, drawings, prints, and photographs. Reference service provided in the Prints and Photographs Reading Room. Reproductions of nonrestricted material available through the Library of Congress's Photoduplication Service; prints and photographs may be borrowed through the Exhibits Office for exhibits by qualified institutions.

NONPROFIT

American Institute of Architects, 1735 New York Ave. N.W. 20006; (202) 626-7310. Fax, (202) 626-7365. Mark W. Hurwitz, chief executive officer. Information, (202) 626-7300. Library, (202) 626-7492. Internet, http://www.aia.org.

Membership: registered American architects. Works to advance the standards of architectural education, training, and practice. Promotes the aesthetic, scientific, and practical efficiency of architecture, urban design, and planning; monitors international developments. Offers continuing and professional education programs; sponsors scholarships, internships, and awards. Houses archival collection, including documents and drawings of American architects and architecture. Library open to the public. Monitors legislation and regulations.

Friends of Art and Preservation in Embassies, 3600 M St. N.W., #201 20007; (202) 337-1573. Fax, (202) 337-0856. Lee Kimche McGrath, director. Internet, sapenindc@aol.com.

Foundation established to assist the State Dept.'s Office of Foreign Buildings and Art in Embassies programs. Acquires and exhibits American art and preserves high-value furnishings in U.S. embassies and other diplomatic facilities.

National Artists Equity Assn., 501 7th St. N.W. (mailing address: P.O. Box 28068, Central Station, Washington, DC 20038); (202) 628-9633. Fax, (202) 628-0034. Craig Kittner, membership manager, (703) 848-4436. Toll-free, (800) 727-6232. Internet, naea@capaccess.org.

Membership: professionals in the visual arts, including painters, sculptors, graphic artists, photographers, and potters. Interests include copyrights, health hazards of artists' materials, funding programs of the National Endowment for the Arts, artists' housing and studio space, and legislation and public policy affecting the concerns of visual artists.

National Assn. of Artists' Organizations, 918 F St. N.W., #611 20004; (202) 347-6350. Fax, (202) 347-7376. Roberto Bedoya, executive director. Internet, naao@artswire.org or http://artswire.org/Artswire/naao/index.html.

Provides technical assistance and sponsors conferences to ensure the continuation and growth of artists' organizations and publications. Monitors legislation and regulations affecting art, artists' organizations, and individual artists.

National Assn. of Schools of Art and Design, 11250 Roger Bacon Dr., #21, Reston, VA 20190; (703) 437-0700. Fax, (703) 437-6312. Samuel Hope, executive director. Internet, http://www.arts-accredit.org.

Accrediting agency for educational programs in art and design. Provides information on art and design programs at the postsecondary level; offers professional development for executives of art and design programs.

HISTORY AND PRESERVATION

See also Military History and Honors (chap. 15); Museums (this chapter)

AGENCIES

Most federal agencies have historic preservation officers who ensure that agencies protect historic buildings and other cultural resources that are on or eligible for nomination to the National Register of Historic Places, including nonfederal property that may be affected by agency activities.

Advisory Council on Historic Preservation, *1100 Pennsylvania Ave. N.W., #809 20004; (202) 606-8503. Fax, (202) 606-8672. Cathryn Buford Slater, chair; John M. Fowler, acting executive director. Internet, achp@achp.gov or http://www.achp.gov.*

Advises the president and Congress on historic preservation; reviews and comments on federal projects and programs affecting historic, architectural, archeological, and cultural resources.

Bureau of Land Management *(Interior Dept.), Cultural Heritage, Wilderness, Special Areas, and Paleontology, 1620 L St. N.W., #204 (mailing address: 1849 C St. N.W., #204-LS, Washington, DC 20240); (202) 452-0330. Fax, (202) 452-7701. Marilyn Nickels, group manager. TDD, (202) 452-0326.*

Develops bureau policy on historic preservation, archeological resource protection, consultation with Native Americans, curation of artifacts and records, heritage education, and paleontological resource management.

National Archives and Records Administration, *Advisory Committee on Preservation, 8601 Adelphi Rd., #2800, College Park, MD 20740-6001; (301) 713-6705. Fax, (301) 713-6653. Alan Calmes, preservation officer.*

Advises the archivist of the United States on preservation technology and research and on matters related to the continued preservation of records of the National Archives of the United States.

National Archives and Records Administration, *Cartographic and Architectural Branch, 8601 Adelphi Rd., #3320, College Park, MD 20740-6001; (301) 713-7030. Fax, (301) 713-7488. Robert Richardson, branch chief. TDD, (301) 713-7030. Internet, carto@arch2. nara.gov.*

Preserves and makes available historical records of federal agencies, including maps, charts, aerial photographs, architectural drawings, patents, and ships' plans. Research room open to the public. Records may be reproduced for a fee.

National Archives and Records Administration, *Preservation Programs, 8601 Adelphi Rd., #2800, College Park, MD 20740-6001; (301) 713-6705. Fax, (301) 713-6653. Maida Loescher, director. Information, (301) 713-6719.*

Responsible for conserving textual and nontextual records in the archives. Nontextual records include videotapes, sound recordings, motion pictures, still photos, preservation microfilming, and fee reproduction work. Conducts research and testing for materials purchased by and used in the archives.

National Capital Planning Commission, *801 Pennsylvania Ave. N.W., #301 20576; (202) 482-7200. Fax, (202) 482-7272. Reginald W. Griffith, executive director. Internet, http://www.ncpc.gov.*

Central planning agency for the federal government in the national capital region, which includes the District of Columbia and suburban Maryland and Virginia. Reviews and approves plans for the preservation of certain historic and environmental features in the national capital region, including the annual federal capital improvement plan.

National Endowment for the Arts *(National Foundation on the Arts and the Humanities), Heritage and Preservation, 1100 Pennsylvania Ave. N.W. 20506-0001; (202) 682-5428. Fax, (202) 682-5669. Daniel Sheehy, division coordinator. Internet, http://arts.endow.gov.*

Grantmaking theme program for projects in the arts which preserve nationally significant artistic accomplishments and works of art.

National Endowment for the Humanities *(National Foundation on the Arts and the Humanities), Preservation and Access, 1100 Pennsylvania Ave. N.W., #411 20506; (202) 606-8570. Fax, (202) 606-8639. George Farr, director. Internet, preservation@neh.fed.us or http://www. neh.fed.us.*

Sponsors preservation and access projects, the stabilization and documentation of material culture collections, and the U.S. newspaper program.

National Museum of American History *(Smithsonian Institution), Cultural History, 12th St. and Constitution Ave. N.W. 20560; (202) 357-1707. Fax, (202) 786-2883. James Weaver, chair. Internet, http://www.si. edu/nmah.*

Collects and preserves artifacts related to U.S. cultural heritage; supports research, exhibits, performances, and educational programs. Areas of focus include ethnic and religious communities; sports, recreation, and leisure; popular entertainment and mass media; business and commercial culture; musical instruments; hand tools; and educational, civic, and voluntary organizations.

National Park Service *(Interior Dept.), Cultural Resource Stewardship and Partnerships, 1849 C St. N.W., #3128 20240; (202) 208-7625. Fax, (202) 273-3237. Katherine H. Stevenson, associate director.*

Oversees preservation of federal historic sites and administration of buildings programs. Programs include the National Register of Historic Places, National Historic and National Landmark Programs, Historic American Building Survey, Historic American Engineering

Record, Archeology and Antiquities Act Program, and Technical Preservation Services. Gives grant and aid assistance and tax benefit information to properties listed in the National Register of Historic Places.

CONGRESS

House Resources Committee, *Subcommittee on National Parks and Public Lands, 814 O'Neill Bldg. 20515; (202) 226-7736. Fax, (202) 226-2301. James V. Hansen, R-Utah, chair; Allen Freemyer, staff director. Internet, http://www.house.gov/resources.*

Jurisdiction over historic preservation legislation.

Senate Energy and Natural Resources Committee, *Subcommittee on National Parks, Historic Preservation, and Recreation, SD-354 20510; (202) 224-6969. Fax, (202) 228-0459. Craig Thomas, R-Wyo., chair; Jim O'Toole, professional staff member. Internet, http://www.senate.gov/~energy.*

Jurisdiction over historic preservation legislation.

Senate Office of Conservation and Preservation, *S410 CAP 20510; (202) 224-4550. Carl Fritter, bookbinder.*

Develops and coordinates programs related to the conservation and preservation of Senate records and materials for the Secretary of the Senate.

NONPROFIT

American Historical Assn., *400 A St. S.E. 20003; (202) 544-2422. Fax, (202) 544-8307. Sandria B. Freitag, executive director. Internet, aha@theaha.org or http://chnm.gmu.edu/aha.*

Supports public access to government information; publishes original historical research, journal, bibliographies, historical directories, and job placement bulletin. Committee on Women Historians seeks to improve the status of women in the profession as well as promotes the teaching of women's history.

American Institute for Conservation of Historic and Artistic Works, *1717 K St. N.W., #301 20006; (202) 452-9545. Fax, (202) 452-9328. Elizabeth Jones, executive director. Internet, infoaic@aol.com or http://www-cpa.stanford.edu/aic.*

Membership: professional conservators, scientists, students, administrators, cultural institutions, and others. Promotes the knowledge and practice of the conservation of cultural property; supports research; and disseminates information on conservation.

American Studies Assn., *1120 19th St. N.W., #301 20036; (202) 467-4783. Fax, (202) 467-4786. John F.*

Stephens, executive director. Internet, asastaff@erols.com or http://www.georgetown.edu/crossroads.

Fosters exchange of ideas about American life; supports and assists programs for teaching American studies abroad and encourages teacher and student exchanges; awards annual prizes for contributions to American studies; provides curriculum resources.

Children of the American Revolution, *1776 D St. N.W., #227 20006; (202) 638-3153. Fax, (202) 737-3162. Phyllis P. Wathen, administrator.*

Membership: descendants, age 22 years and under, of American soldiers or patriots of the American Revolution. Conducts historical, educational, and patriotic activities; preserves places of historical interest.

Civil War Trust, *2101 Wilson Blvd., #1120, Arlington, VA 22201; (703) 516-4944. Fax, (703) 516-4947. E. Matt Andrews III, president. Internet, http://www.civilwar.org.*

Promotes the appreciation and stewardship of America's cultural and environmental heritage through the preservation of historic Civil War battlefields.

Council on America's Military Past-U.S.A., *P.O. Box 1151, Fort Myer, VA 22211-1151; (703) 912-6124. Fax, (703) 912-5666. Col. Herbert M. Hart (USMC, ret.), executive director. Toll-free, (800) 398-4693.*

Membership: historians, archeologists, curators, writers, and others interested in preservation of historic military establishments and ships.

Heritage Preservation, *3299 K St. N.W., #602 20007-4415; (202) 625-1495. Fax, (202) 625-1485. Larry Reger, president. Internet, info@heritagepreservation.org or http://www.heritagepreservation.org.*

Membership: museums, libraries, archives, historic preservation organizations, historical societies, and conservation groups. Advocates the conservation and preservation of works of art, anthropological artifacts, documents, historic objects, architecture, and natural science specimens. Programs include Save Outdoor Sculpture, which works to inventory all U.S. outdoor sculpture, and the Conservation Assessment Program, which administers grants to museums for conservation surveys of their collections.

National Conference of State Historic Preservation Officers, *444 N. Capitol St. N.W., #342 20001-1512; (202) 624-5465. Fax, (202) 624-5419. Eric Hertfelder, executive director.*

Membership: state and territorial historic preservation officers and deputy officers. Conducts research and compiles statistics on programs; monitors legislation and regulations.

National Preservation Institute, *P.O. Box 1702, Alexandria, VA 22313; (202) 393-0038. Fax, (703) 768-9350. Constance Werner-Ramirez, president. Internet, info@npi.org or http://www.npi.org.*

Provides specialized education research and technical assistance for the preservation of cultural heritage and historic environment.

National Society, Colonial Dames XVII Century, *1300 New Hampshire Ave. N.W. 20036; (202) 293-1700. Fax, (202) 466-6099. Kristina Hardin, headquarters secretary; Caroline Sheaers, staff genealogist, (202) 293-1700.*

Membership: American women who are lineal descendants of persons who rendered civil or military service and lived in America or one of the British colonies before 1701. Preserves records and shrines; encourages historical research; awards scholarships to undergraduate and graduate students and scholarships in medicine to persons of native American descent.

National Society, Daughters of the American Revolution, *1776 D St. N.W. 20006-5392; (202) 628-1776. Fax, (202) 879-3252. Dorla Dean Eaton Kemper, president general. Internet, http://www.dar.org.*

Membership: women descended from American Revolutionary War patriots. Conducts historical, educational, and patriotic activities; maintains a genealogical library, American museum, and documentary collection antedating 1830. Library open to the public (nonmembers charged fee for use).

National Society of Colonial Dames of America, *2715 Q St. N.W. 20007; (202) 337-2288. Fax, (202) 337-0348. Linda Mattingly, administrator.*

Membership: descendants of colonists in America before 1750. Conducts historical and educational activities; maintains Dumbarton House, a museum open to the public.

National Trust for Historic Preservation, *1785 Massachusetts Ave. N.W. 20036-2117; (202) 588-6000. Fax, (202) 588-6038. Richard Moe, president. Internet, http://www.nthp.org.*

Conducts seminars, workshops, and conferences on topics related to preservation, including neighborhood conservation, main street revitalization, rural conservation, and preservation law; offers financial assistance through loan and grant programs; provides advisory services; operates historic house museums, which are open to the public.

Preservation Action, *1350 Connecticut Ave. N.W., #401 20036; (202) 659-0915. Fax, (202) 659-0189. Nellie L. Longsworth, president. Internet, http://www.preservenet. cornell.edu/presaction/home.htm.*

Monitors legislation affecting historic preservation and neighborhood conservation; promotes effective management of historic preservation programs.

Society for American Archaeology, *900 2nd St. N.E., #12 20002; (202) 789-8200. Fax, (202) 789-0284. Tobi Brimsek, executive director. Internet, info@saa.org or http://www.saa.org.*

Promotes greater awareness, understanding, and research of archeology on the American continents; works to preserve and publish results of scientific data and research; serves as information clearinghouse for members.

Archives and Manuscripts

See also Film, Photography, and Broadcasting (this chapter); Music (this chapter)

AGENCIES

Assassination Records Review Board, *600 E St. N.W., 2nd Floor 20530; (202) 724-0088. Fax, (202) 724-0457. John R. Tunheim, chair.*

Identifies, secures, and reviews federal agencies' records for information on the John F. Kennedy assassination; makes records available to the public via the National Archives and Records Administration.

National Archives and Records Administration, *8601 Adelphi Rd., #111, College Park, MD 20740-6001; (301) 713-6410. Fax, (301) 713-7141. John Carlin, archivist of the United States; Lewis J. Bellardo, deputy archivist of the United States. Press, (301) 713-7360. TDD, (202) 501-5404. Internet, inquire@nara.gov or http://www.nara.gov.*

Identifies, preserves, and makes available federal government documents of historic value; administers a network of regional storage centers and archives and operates the presidential library system. Collections include photographs, graphic materials, and films; holdings include records generated by foreign governments (especially in wartime) and by international conferences, commissions, and exhibitions. (Liaison office in Washington, (202) 501-5502, 7th St. and Pennsylvania Ave. N.W., 20408.)

National Archives and Records Administration, Center for Legislative Archives, *700 Pennsylvania Ave. N.W., #8E 20408; (202) 501-5350. Fax, (202) 219-2176. Michael Gillette, director.*

Collects and maintains records of congressional committees and legislative files from 1789 to the present. Publishes inventories and guides to these records.

National Archives and Records Administration, *Presidential Libraries,* 8601 Adelphi Rd., #2200, College Park, MD 20704; (301) 713-6050. Fax, (301) 713-6045. David F. Peterson, assistant archivist. Internet, http://www.nara.gov.

Directs all programs relating to acquisition, preservation, publication, and research use of materials in presidential libraries; conducts oral history projects; publishes finding aids for research sources; provides reference service, including information from and about documentary holdings.

National Historical Publications and Records Commission (*National Archives and Records Administration*), 700 Pennsylvania Ave. N.W., #106 20408; (202) 501-5610. Fax, (202) 501-5601. Roger Bruns, acting executive director. Internet, nhprc@arch1.nara.gov.

Makes plans and recommendations and provides cost estimates for preserving and publishing documentation of U.S. history. Awards grants to government and private cultural institutions that preserve, arrange, edit, and publish documents of historical importance, including the papers of outstanding Americans.

National Museum of American History (*Smithsonian Institution*), *Archives Center,* 12th St. and Constitution Ave. N.W., #C340, MRC 601 20560; (202) 357-3270. Fax, (202) 786-2453. John A. Fleckner, chief archivist. TDD, (202) 357-1729. Internet, acnmah@sivm.si.edu.

Acquires, organizes, preserves, and makes available for research the museum's archival and documentary materials relating to American history and culture. (Three-dimensional objects and closely related documents are in the care of curatorial divisions.)

Smithsonian Institution, *Archives of American Art,* 8th and F Sts. N.W. 20560; (202) 357-2781. Fax, (202) 786-2608. Richard J. Wattenmaker, director. TDD, (202) 633-9320. Internet, aaaemref@sivm.si.edu.

Collects and preserves manuscript items, such as notebooks, sketchbooks, letters, and journals; photos of artists and works of art; tape-recorded interviews with artists, dealers, and collectors; exhibition catalogs; directories; and biographies on the history of visual arts in the United States. Library open to scholars and researchers. Reference centers that maintain microfilm copies of a selection of the Archives' collection include Boston; Detroit; New York; San Francisco; and San Marino, Calif.

CONGRESS

Legislative Resource Center, *Resources and Reference,* B-106 CHOB 20515; (202) 225-1153. Fax, (202) 226-5207. Lea Uhre, manager.

Conducts historical research. Advises members on the disposition of their records and papers; maintains information on manuscript collections of former members; maintains biographical files on former members. Recent publications include *Biographical Directory of the United States Congress, 1774-1989: Bicentennial Edition; Guide to Research Collections of Former Members of the United States House of Representatives, 1789-1987: Bicentennial Edition; Black Americans in Congress, 1870-1989;* and *Women in Congress, 1917-1989.*

Library of Congress, *Manuscript Division,* 101 Independence Ave. S.E., #LM102 20540-4780; (202) 707-5383. Fax, (202) 707-6336. James H. Hutson, chief. Reading Room, (202) 707-5387.

Maintains, describes, and provides reference service on the library's manuscript collections, including the papers of U.S. presidents and other eminent Americans. Manuscript Reading Room primarily serves serious scholars and researchers; historians and reference librarians are available for consultation.

Library of Congress, *Rare Book and Special Collections Division,* 10 1st St. S.E., #206 20540-4860; (202) 707-5434. Fax, (202) 707-4142. Mark Dimunation, chief. Reading room, (202) 707-4144.

Maintains collections of incunabula (books printed before 1501) and other early printed books; early imprints of American history and literature; illustrated books; early Spanish-American, Russian, and Bulgarian imprints; Confederate states imprints; libraries of famous personalities (including Thomas Jefferson, Woodrow Wilson, and Oliver Wendell Holmes); special format collections (miniature books, broadsides, almanacs, and pre-1870 copyright records); special interest collections; and special provenance collections. Reference assistance is provided in the Rare Book and Special Collections Reading Room.

Senate Historical Office, SH-201 20510; (202) 224-6900. Fax, (202) 224-5329. Richard Baker, historian.

Serves as an information clearinghouse on Senate history, traditions, and members. Collects, organizes, and distributes to the public previously unpublished Senate documents; collects and preserves photographs and pictures related to Senate history; conducts an oral history program; advises senators and Senate committees on the disposition of their noncurrent papers and records. Produces publications on the history of the Senate.

NONPROFIT

Council on Library and Information Resources, 1755 Massachusetts Ave. N.W., #500 20036-2188; (202)

939-4750. Fax, (202) 939-4765. Deanna B. Marcum, president. Internet, info@clir.org or http://www.clir.org.

Formed from the 1996 merger of the Commission on Preservation and Access and the Council on Library Resources. Acts on behalf of the nation's libraries, archives, and universities to develop and encourage collaborative strategies for preserving the nation's intellectual heritage and strengthening its information system.

Moorland-Spingarn Research Center *(Howard University)*, *500 Howard Pl. N.W. 20059; (202) 806-7241. Fax, (202) 806-6405. Thomas C. Battle, director. Information, (202) 806-7239. Internet, http://www.founders. howard.edu/moolrand-spingarn.*

Collects, preserves, and makes available for study numerous artifacts, books, manuscripts, newspapers, photographs, prints, recordings, and other materials documenting black history and culture in the United States, Africa, Europe, Latin America, and the Caribbean. Maintains extensive collections of black newspapers and magazines; contains the works of African American and African scholars, poets, and novelists; maintains collections on the history of Howard University.

Genealogy

AGENCIES

National Archives and Records Administration, *Educational and Museum Programs, 700 Pennsylvania Ave. N.W., #G14 20408; (202) 501-5200. Fax, (202) 219-1888. Edith James, assistant archivist.*

Co-sponsors the National Institute of Genealogical Research, a genealogical research class taught annually by National Archives staff and outside professionals; conducts workshops.

National Archives and Records Administration, *User Services Branch, 700 Pennsylvania Ave. N.W., #405 20408; (202) 501-5402. Fax, (202) 501-7154. Jo Anne Williamson, branch chief. TDD, (202) 501-5404. Internet, http://www.nara.gov.*

Assists individuals interested in researching record holdings of the National Archives, including genealogical records; issues research cards to prospective genealogical, biographical, and other researchers who present photo identification. Users must be 16. Still and motion picture research rooms located in College Park, Md.

CONGRESS

Library of Congress, *Local History and Genealogy Reading Room, 10 1st St. S.E. 20540-5554; (202) 707-5537. Fax, (202) 707-1957. Judith Reid, head. TDD, (202) 707-9958. Internet, http://www.loc.gov.*

Provides reference and referral service on topics related to local history, genealogy, and heraldry throughout the United States.

NONPROFIT

Family History Center, *Church of Jesus Christ of Latter-day Saints, 10000 Stoneybrook Dr., Kensington, MD (mailing address: P.O. Box 49, Kensington, MD 20895); (301) 587-0042. Susan Frazier, director.*

Maintains genealogical library for research. Collection includes international genealogical index, family group record archives, microfiche registers, and the Family Search Computer Program. Library open to the public.

National Genealogical Society, *4527 17th St. North, Arlington, VA 22207-2399; (703) 525-0050. Fax, (703) 525-0052. Francis J. Shane, executive director. Toll-free, (800) 473-0060. Internet, membership@ngsgenealogy.org or http://www.ngsgenealogy.org.*

Encourages study of genealogy and publication of all records that are of genealogical interest. Maintains a genealogical library for research; provides an accredited home study program; holds an annual conference. Library open to the public (closed Tuesday and Thursday; nonmembers charged fee for use).

National Society, Daughters of the American Colonists, *2205 Massachusetts Ave. N.W. 20008; (202) 667-3076. Lucretia Ottaway, president.*

Membership: women descended from men and women who gave civil or military service to the colonies prior to the Revolutionary War. Maintains library of colonial and genealogical records.

National Society, Daughters of the American Revolution, *1776 D St. N.W. 20006-5392; (202) 628-1776. Fax, (202) 879-3252. Dorla Dean Eaton Kemper, president general. Internet, http://www.dar.org.*

Membership: women descended from American Revolutionary War patriots. Maintains a genealogical library, which is open to the public (nonmembers charged fee for use).

Specific Cultures

See also Language and Literature (this chapter)

AGENCIES

Interior Dept., *Indian Arts and Crafts Board, 1849 C St. N.W. 20240-0001; (202) 208-3773. Fax, (202) 208-5196. Meredith Stanton, acting director.*

Advises Native American artisans and craft guilds; produces a source directory on arts and crafts of Native

Americans (including Eskimos and Aleuts); maintains museums of native crafts in Montana, South Dakota, and Oklahoma; provides information on Native American crafts.

National Endowment for the Arts *(National Foundation on the Arts and the Humanities), Heritage and Preservation, 1100 Pennsylvania Ave. N.W. 20506-0001; (202) 682-5428. Fax, (202) 682-5669. Dan Sheehy, division coordinator. Internet, http://arts.endow.gov.*

Seeks to preserve and enhance multicultural artistic heritage through grants for folk arts projects. (For grant application information, see Arts and Humanities, General.)

National Museum of American History *(Smithsonian Institution), History Department, 12th St. and Constitution Ave. N.W., #4601, MRC 638 20560; (202) 357-1963. Fax, (202) 633-8192. Ramunas Kondratas, acting assistant director, (202) 357-4848. Information, (202) 357-3129. Internet, http://www.si.edu/nmah.*

Conducts research, develops collections, and creates exhibits on political, community, and domestic life, based on collections of folk and popular arts, ethnic and craft objects, textiles, coins, costumes and jewelry, ceramics and glass, graphic arts, musical instruments, photographs, appliances, and machines.

Smithsonian Institution, *Center for Folklife Programs and Cultural Studies, 955 L'Enfant Plaza S.W., #2600 MRC 914 20560; (202) 287-3424. Fax, (202) 287-3699. Richard Kurin, director. Internet, cspcs.csp@ic.si.edu or http://www.si.edu/organiza/offices/folklife.*

Conducts research into traditional U.S. cultures and foreign folklife traditions; produces folkways recordings, films, monographs, and educational programs; presents annual Festival of American Folklife in Washington, D.C.

CONGRESS

Library of Congress, *American Folklife Center, 101 Independence Ave. S.E. 20540-4610; (202) 707-6590. Fax, (202) 707-2076. Alan Jabbour, director. Archive of Folk Culture, (202) 707-5510. Internet, folklife@loc.gov or http://www.loc.gov/folklife.*

Coordinates national, regional, state and local government, and private folklife activities; contracts with individuals and groups for research and field studies in American folklife and for exhibits and workshops; maintains the National Archive of Folk Culture (an ethnographic collection of American and international folklore, grass-roots oral histories, and ethnomusicology); conducts internships at the archive; sponsors summer concerts of traditional and ethnic music.

NONPROFIT

American Indian Heritage Foundation, *6051 Arlington Blvd., Falls Church, VA 22044; (703) 237-7500. Fax, (703) 532-1921. Princess Pale Moon, president. Recorded information, (202) 463-4267. Internet, http://www.indians.org/aihf.*

Promotes national and international cultural programs for Native Americans. Sponsors the National American Indian Heritage Month and the Miss Indian USA Scholarship Program; notes outstanding achievement among young native Americans; assists tribes in meeting emergency needs.

National Italian American Foundation, *1860 19th St. N.W. 20009; (202) 387-0600. Fax, (202) 387-0800. Alfred M. Rotondaro, executive director. Internet, http://www.niaf.org.*

Membership: U.S. citizens of Italian ancestry. Promotes recognition of Italian American contributions to American society. Funds cultural events, educational symposia, antidefamation programs, and scholarships. Represents the interests of Italian Americans before Congress. Serves as an umbrella organization for local Italian-American clubs throughout the United States.

National Council for the Traditional Arts, *1320 Fenwick Lane, #200, Silver Spring, MD 20910; (301) 565-0654. Fax, (301) 565-0472. Joseph T. Wilson, executive director. Internet, ncta@aol.com or http://www.ncta.com.*

Presents and provides consultation for regional and national folk festivals; offers training programs for park officials on folk culture; conducts ethnocultural surveys; coordinates exhibitions and tours of traditional folk artists with the support of the National Endowment for the Arts. Produces films and videos on traditional arts; sponsors annual national folk festival.

Washington Area

See also Museums (this chapter)

AGENCIES

National Park Service *(Interior Dept.), National Capital Region, 1100 Ohio Dr. S.W., #336 20242; (202) 619-7000. Fax, (202) 619-7220. Terry Carlstrom, director. Information, (202) 619-7222. Recorded information, (202) 619-7222; permits, (202) 619-7225. Internet, http://www.nps.gov/ncro.*

Provides visitors with information on Washington-area parks, monuments, and Civil War battlefields; offers press services for the media and processes special event applications and permits.

NATIONAL PARK SERVICE SITES IN THE CAPITAL REGION

The National Park Service administers most parks, circles, and monuments in the District of Columbia, as well as sites in nearby Maryland, Virginia, and West Virginia. For information on facilities not listed here, call (202) 619-7005; Internet, http://www.nps.gov/htdocs2/ncro/index.htm.

Antietam National Battlefield, (301) 432-5124

Arlington House, Robert E. Lee Memorial, (703) 557-0613

Catoctin Mountain Park, (301) 663-9330

C&O Canal National Historic Park, (301) 739-4200
Great Falls Area, Maryland, (301) 299-3613

Clara Barton National Historic Site, (301) 492-6245

Ford's Theatre National Historic Site, (202) 426-6924

Fort Washington Park, (301) 763-4600 (includes Piscataway Park)

Frederick Douglass National Historic Site, (202) 426-5960

Greenbelt Park, (301) 344-3948

George Washington Parkway, (703) 285-2600 (includes memorials to Theodore Roosevelt, Lyndon Johnson, and U.S. Marine Corps)
Glen Echo Park, (301) 492-6229
Great Falls Park, Virginia, (703) 285-2966

Harpers Ferry National Historic Park, (304) 535-6223

Manassas National Battlefield Park, (703) 754-1861

Mary McLeod Bethune National Historic Site, (202) 673-2402

Monocacy National Battlefield, (301) 662-3515

National Mall, (202) 426-6841 (includes presidential and war memorials and Pennsylvania Avenue National Historic Site)

Potomac Heritage National Scenic Trail, (202) 619-7222

Prince William Forest Park, (703) 221-7181

Rock Creek Park, (202) 282-1063

Thomas Stone National Historic Site, (301) 934-6027

White House, (202) 456-7041

Wolf Trap Farm Park, (703) 255-1800

White House Visitors Center, *1450 Pennsylvania Ave. N.W. 20230; (202) 208-1631. Fax, (202) 208-1643. Tom Payton, manager, President's Park. Information, (202) 456-7041. TDD, (202) 208-1636. Toll-free, (800) 717-1450.*

Administered by the National Park Service. Educates visitors about the White House through videos, exhibits, and historical artifacts. Distributes White House tour tickets daily from 7:30 a.m. to 9:00 a.m., Tuesday through Saturday, from March through Labor Day (tickets not required for the rest of the year). Tours conducted 10:00 a.m. to noon.

CONGRESS

Architect of the Capitol, *Office of the Curator, HT3 CAP 20515; (202) 228-1222. Fax, (202) 228-1893. Barbara A. Wolanin, curator. Press, (202) 228-1205. Internet, http://www.aoc.gov.*

Preserves artwork; maintains collection of drawings, photographs, and manuscripts on and about the Capitol and the House and Senate office buildings. Maintains records of the architect of the Capitol. Library open to the public.

Senate Commission on Art, *S411 CAP 20510-7102; (202) 224-2955. Fax, (202) 224-8799. Trent Lott, R-Miss., chair; Diane Skvarla, curator of the Senate. Internet, http://www.senate.gov/curator/collections.htm.*

Maintains Senate collection of paintings, sculpture, furniture, and manuscripts; presents exhibits; maintains old Senate and Supreme Court chambers.

NONPROFIT

D.C. Preservation League, *1511 K St. N.W., #738 20005; (202) 637-3275. Fax, (202) 737-1823. Sally Berk, president.*

Participates in planning, preserving, and developing buildings and sites in Washington, D.C. Programs include protection and enhancement of the city's landmarks; educational lectures, tours, and seminars; and technical assistance to neighborhood groups. Monitors legislation and regulations.

Historical Society of Washington, D.C., *1307 New Hampshire Ave. N.W. 20036; (202) 785-2068. Fax, (202) 887-5785. Barbara Franco, executive director. Internet, heurich@ibm.net.*

Maintains research collections on the District of Columbia, including photographs, manuscripts, archives, books, and prints and graphics of Washington (1790 to present); publishes *Metro D.C. History News* and *Washington History* magazine; operates a historic house museum in the Heurich mansion. Museum and library open to the public.

Martin Luther King Memorial Library, *Washingtoni-ana Division, 901 G St. N.W., #307 20001; (202) 727-1213. Fax, (202) 727-1129. Roxanna Deane, chief.*

Maintains reference collections of District of Columbia current laws and regulations, history, and culture. Collections include biographies; travel books; memoirs and diaries; family, church, government, and institutional histories; maps (1612 to present); plat books; city, telephone, and real estate directories (1822 to present); census schedules; newspapers and periodicals (including the *Washington Star* collection of clippings and photographs, 1940 to 1981); photographs of individuals and buildings; and oral history materials on local neighborhoods, ethnic groups, and businesses.

Supreme Court Historical Society, *111 2nd St. N.E. 20002; (202) 543-0400. Fax, (202) 547-7730. David T. Pride, executive director. Internet, http://www. supremecourthistory.org.*

Acquires, preserves, and displays historic items associated with the Court; conducts and publishes scholarly research. Conducts lecture programs; promotes and supports educational activities in the Court such as lectures and a summer institute for secondary school teachers.

U.S. Capitol Historical Society, *200 Maryland Ave. N.E. 20002; (202) 543-8919. Fax, (202) 544-8244. Clarence J. Brown, president. Library, (202) 543-0629. Toll-free, (800) 887-9318. Internet, uschs@uschs.org or http://www.uschs.org.*

Membership: members of Congress, individuals, and organizations interested in the preservation of the history and traditions of the U.S. Capitol. Conducts historical research; offers tours, lectures, and films; maintains information centers in the Capitol; publishes an annual historical calendar.

White House Historical Assn., *740 Jackson Pl. N.W. 20503; (202) 737-8292. Fax, (202) 789-0440. Neil W. Horstman, executive vice president. Internet, http://www. whitehousehistory.org.*

Seeks to enhance the understanding and appreciation of the White House. Publishes books on the White House, including a historical guide, a description of ceremonial events, two volumes of biographical sketches and illustrations of the presidents and first ladies, a book on White House glassware, and a book on White House paintings and sculptures. Net proceeds from book sales go toward the purchase of historic items, such as paintings and furniture, for the White House permanent collection.

⛹ RECREATION AND SPORTS

See also Parks and Recreation Areas (chap. 9)

AGENCIES

Health and Human Services Dept., *President's Council on Physical Fitness and Sports, Humphrey Bldg., #738H, 200 Indiana Ave. S.W. 20201; (202) 690-9000. Fax, (202) 690-5211. Sandra Perlmutter, executive director, (202) 690-5187.*

Provides schools, state and local governments, recreation agencies, and employers with information on designing and implementing physical fitness programs; conducts award programs for children and adults and for schools, clubs, and other institutions.

U.S. Armed Forces Sports Council, *Hoffman Bldg. #1, Room 400, 2461 Eisenhower Ave., Alexandria, VA 22331-0522; (703) 325-8871. Fax, (703) 325-2511. William G. Begel, secretariat.*

Membership: one representative from each of the four armed services. Administers and coordinates interservice, national, and international sports activities and competitions for military personnel from the intramural level to the world class athlete program.

NONPROFIT

American Alliance for Health, Physical Education, Recreation, and Dance, *1900 Association Dr., Reston, VA 20191; (703) 476-3400. Fax, (703) 476-9527. Michael Davis, executive vice president. Internet, info@aahperd.org or http://www.aahperd.org.*

Membership: teachers and others who work with school health, physical education, athletics, recreation, dance, and safety education programs (kindergarten through postsecondary levels). Member associations are American Assn. for Leisure and Recreation, National Assn. for Girls and Women in Sport, Assn. for the Advancement of Health Education, National Dance Assn., National Assn. for Sport and Physical Education, and American Assn. for Active Lifestyles and Fitness.

American Canoe Assn., *7432 Alban Station Blvd., #B-226, Springfield, VA 22150; (703) 451-0141. Fax, (703) 451-2245. Jeffrey Yeager, executive director. Internet, acadirect@aol.com or http://www.aca-paddler.org.*

Membership: individuals and organizations interested in the promotion of canoeing, kayaking, and other paddle sports. Works to preserve the nation's recreational waterways. Sponsors programs in safety education, competition, recreation, public awareness, conservation, and public policy. Monitors legislation and regulations.

American Gaming Assn., *555 13th St. N.W., #1010E 20004-1109; (202) 637-6501. Fax, (202) 637-6507. Frank J. Fahrenkopf Jr., president. Information, (202) 637-6500. Internet, http://www.americangaming.org.*

Membership: casinos, casino and gaming equipment manufacturers, and financial services companies. Compiles statistics and serves as an information clearinghouse on the gaming industry. Administers a task force to study gambling addiction, raise public awareness, and develop assistance programs. Monitors legislation and regulations.

American Hiking Society, *1422 Fenwick Lane, Silver Spring, MD 20910; (301) 565-6704. Fax, (301) 565-6714. David Lillard, president. Internet, ahsinform@aol.com or http://www.orca.org/ahs.*

Membership: individuals and clubs interested in preserving America's trail system and protecting the interests of hikers and other trail users. Sponsors research on trail construction and a trail maintenance summer program. Provides information on outdoor volunteer opportunities on public lands.

American Medical Athletic Assn., *4405 East-West Hwy., #405, Bethesda, MD 20814; (301) 913-9517. Fax, (301) 913-9520. Susan Kalish, executive director. Toll-free, (800) 776-2732. Internet, arfarun@aol.com or http://www.arfa.org.*

Membership: sports medicine and allied health professionals. Assists members in promoting physical fitness to their patients and in developing their own physical fitness programs. Promotes and reports on sports medicine research and discussion. (Affiliated with the American Running and Fitness Assn.)

American Recreation Coalition, *1225 New York Ave. N.W., #450 20005; (202) 682-9530. Fax, (202) 682-9529. Derrick A. Crandall, president. Internet, arc@funoutdoors.com or http://www.funoutdoors.com.*

Membership: organized recreationists, national and regional corporations offering recreational products and services, and recreation industry trade associations. Works to increase public and private sector activity in public recreation, land and water management, and energy policy. Provides information on innovative recreational planning.

American Resort Development Assn., *1220 L St. N.W., #500 20005; (202) 371-6700. Fax, (202) 289-8544. Cynthia A. Huheey, president. Internet, http://www.arda.org.*

Membership: U.S. and international developers, builders, financiers, marketing companies, and others involved in resort, recreational, and community develop-

ment. Serves as an information clearinghouse; monitors federal and state legislation affecting land, timeshare, and community development industries.

American Running and Fitness Assn., *4405 East-West Hwy., #405, Bethesda, MD 20814; (301) 913-9517. Fax, (301) 913-9520. Susan Kalish, executive director. Toll-free, (800) 776-2732. Internet, arfarun@aol.com or http://www.arfa.org.*

Membership: athletes, health clubs, businesses, and individuals. Promotes proper nutrition and regular exercise. Provides members with medical advice and referrals, fitness information, and assistance in developing fitness programs.

American Sportfishing Assn., *1033 N. Fairfax St., #200, Alexandria, VA 22314; (703) 519-9691. Fax, (703) 519-1872. Mike Hayden, president. Internet, amsportfish@delphi.com.*

Works to ensure healthy and sustainable fish resources, to increase participation in sport fishing, and to make its members more profitable.

Bicycle Federation of America, *1506 21st St. N.W., #200 20036; (202) 463-6622. Fax, (202) 463-6625. William C. Wilkinson III, executive director. Internet, bikefed@aol.com or http://www.bikefed.org.*

Promotes bicycle use; conducts research, planning, and training projects; develops safety education and public information materials. Works to increase public awareness of the benefits and opportunities of bicycling and walking. Manages the National Bicycle and Pedestrian Clearinghouse and the Pedestrian Federation of America.

Boat Owners Assn. of the United States, *880 S. Pickett St., Alexandria, VA 22304; (703) 461-2864. Fax, (703) 461-2845. Michael Sciulla, vice president, Government Affairs.*

Membership: owners of recreational boats. Represents boat-owner interests before the federal government; offers consumer protection and other services to members.

Disabled Sports USA, *451 Hungerford Dr., #100, Rockville, MD 20850; (301) 217-0960. Fax, (301) 217-0968. Kirk M. Bauer, executive director. TDD, (301) 217-0963. Internet, dsusa@dsusa.org or http://www.dsusa.org/~dsusa.*

Conducts sports and recreation activities and physical fitness programs for people with disabilities and their families and friends; produces videotaped exercise programs for people with physical disabilities; conducts workshops and competitions; participates in world championships.

Future Fisherman Foundation, *1033 N. Fairfax St., #200, Alexandria, VA 22314; (703) 519-9691. Fax, (703) 519-1872. Kathleen McKee, director. Internet, amsportfish@delphi.com.*

Promotes sportfishing to youth through programs such as the Aquatic Resources Education Program and the Hooked on Fishing, Not Drugs Campaign. (Affiliated with the American Sportfishing Assn.)

National Assn. for Girls and Women in Sport, *1900 Association Dr., Reston, VA 20191-1599; (703) 476-3452. Fax, (703) 476-9527. Diana Everett, executive director. Internet, nagws@aahperd.org or http://www.aahperd.org.*

Membership: students, coaches, physical education teachers, athletes, athletic directors, and trainers for girls' and women's sports programs. Seeks to increase sports opportunity for women and girls; provides information on laws relating to equality of sports funds and facilities for women; hosts training sites and rates officials; publishes sports guides; maintains speakers bureau.

National Collegiate Athletic Assn. (NCAA), *1 Dupont Circle N.W., #400 20036; (202) 293-3050. Fax, (202) 293-3075. Doris Dixon, director, Federal Relations. Internet, http://www.ncaa.org.*

Membership: senior colleges and universities, conferences, and organizations interested in the administration of intercollegiate athletics. Certifies institutions' athletic programs; compiles records and statistics; produces publications and television programs; administers youth development programs; awards student athletes with postgraduate scholarships and degree-completion grants. (Headquarters in Overland Park, Kan.)

National Football League Players Assn., *2021 L St. N.W., #600 20036; (202) 463-2200. Fax, (202) 857-0380. Gene Upshaw, executive director. Internet, http://www. nflplayers.com.*

Membership: professional football players. Represents members in matters concerning wages, hours, and working conditions. Provides assistance to charitable and community organizations. Sponsors programs and events to promote the image of professional football and its players.

National Recreation and Park Assn., *22377 Belmont Ridge Rd., Ashburn, VA 20148; (703) 858-0784. Fax, (703) 858-0794. Dean Tice, executive director. TDD, (703) 578-5559. Internet, info@nrpa.org or http://www.nrpa.org.*

Membership: park and recreation professionals and citizens interested in parks and recreation. Provides technical assistance for park and recreational programs.

Road Runners Club of America, *1150 S. Washington St., #250, Alexandria, VA 22314; (703) 836-0558. Fax,*

(703) 836-4430. Henley Gibble, executive director. Information, (703) 683-7722. Internet, execdir@rrca.org or http://www.rrca.org.

Develops and promotes road races and fitness programs, including the Children's Running Development Program. Issues guidelines on road races. Interests include safety, wheelchair participation, and baby joggers/strollers in races; facilitates communication between clubs. Supports running for people with disabilities.

Snowsports Industries America, *8377-B Greensboro Dr., McLean, VA 22102; (703) 556-9020. Fax, (703) 821-8276. David Ingemie, president. Internet, http://www. snowlink.com.*

Membership: manufacturers and distributors of ski and other outdoor sports equipment, apparel, accessories, and footwear.

Society of State Directors of Health, Physical Education, and Recreation, *9805 Hillridge Dr., Kensington, MD 20895; (301) 949-0709. Fax, (301) 949-0799. Simon A. McNeely, executive director.*

Membership: state directors, supervisors, and coordinators for physical and health education and recreation activities in state education departments, and other interested individuals. Seeks to improve school programs on comprehensive health, physical education, athletics, outdoor education, recreation, and safety.

Special Olympics International, *1325 G St. N.W., #500 20005; (202) 628-3630. Fax, (202) 824-0200. Robert Sargent Shriver Jr., chair. Internet, specialolympics@msn.com or http://www.specialolympics.org.*

Offers individuals with mental retardation opportunities for year-round sports training; sponsors athletic competition worldwide in 22 individual and team sports.

U.S. Combined Training Assn., *525 Old Waterford Rd. N.W., Leesburg, VA 20176; (703) 779-0440. Fax, (703) 779-0550. Anne Mercer, executive director. Internet, uscta4u@aol.com or http://www.hhhorse.com/uscta.*

Membership: individuals interested in combined training, an Olympic-recognized equestrian sport. Registers all national events to ensure that they meet the standards set by the American Horse Show Assn. Sponsors three-day events for members from novice to Olympic levels. Provides educational materials on competition, riding, and care of horses.

U.S. Olympic Committee, *1150 18th St. N.W., #300 20036; (202) 466-3399. Fax, (202) 466-5068. Stephen Bull, director, Government Relations. Internet, http://www.olympic-usa.org.*

Responsible for training, entering, and underwriting the full expenses for U.S. teams in the Olympic and Pan American Games. Supports the bid of U.S. cities to host the Olympic and Pan American Games; recognizes the national governing body of each sport in these games. Promotes international athletic competition. (Headquarters in Colorado Springs, Colo.)

U.S. Parachute Assn., *1440 Duke St., Alexandria, VA 22314; (703) 836-3495. Fax, (703) 836-2843. Christopher Needels, executive director. Toll-free, (800) 371-8772. Internet, uspa@uspa.org or http://www.uspa.org.*

Membership: individuals and organizations interested in skydiving. Develops safety procedures; maintains training programs; issues skydiving licenses and ratings; certifies skydiving instructors; sanctions national competitions; and documents record attempts. Offers liability insurance to members. Monitors legislation and regulations.

⛷ TRAVEL AND TOURISM

See also Americans Abroad (chap. 13); Caucuses (chap. 20)

AGENCIES

Immigration and Naturalization Service *(Justice Dept.), 425 Eye St. N.W., #7100 20536; (202) 514-1900. Fax, (202) 514-3296. Doris Meissner, commissioner. Press, (202) 514-2648. Form requests, (800) 870-3676. Internet, http://www.ins.usdoj.gov.*

Clears aliens and U.S. citizens for entry into the United States. Compiles statistics on tourists.

International Trade Administration *(Commerce Dept.), Tourism Industries, 14th St. and Constitution Ave. N.W. 20230; (202) 482-0140. Fax, (202) 482-2887. Leslie R. Doggett, deputy assistant secretary. Internet, http://tinet.ita.doc.gov.*

Fosters tourism trade development, including public-private partnerships; represents the United States in tourism-related meetings with foreign government officials. Assembles, analyzes, and disseminates data and statistics on travel and tourism.

State Dept., *Passport Services, Main State Bldg., #6811 20520; (202) 647-5366. Fax, (202) 647-0341. Kenneth Hunter, deputy assistant secretary. Passport information, (900) 225-5674. Internet, http://travel.state.gov.*

Administers passport laws and issues passports. (Most branches of the U.S. Postal Service and most U.S.

district and state courts are authorized to accept applications and payment for passports and to administer the required oath to U.S. citizens. Completed applications are sent from the post office or court to the nearest State Dept. regional passport office for processing.) Maintains a variety of records received from the Overseas Citizens Services, including consular certificates of witness to marriage and reports of birth and death. *(See Regional Information Sources in appendix.)*

CONGRESS

House Commerce Committee, *Subcommittee on Finance and Hazardous Materials, 2125 RHOB 20515; (202) 225-2927. Fax, (202) 225-1919. Michael G. Oxley, R-Ohio, chair; James E. Derderian, staff director. Internet, http://www.house.gov/commerce.*

Jurisdiction over legislation affecting tourism.

Senate Commerce, Science, and Transportation Committee, *Subcommittee on Consumer Affairs, Foreign Commerce, and Tourism, SH-425 (mailing address: SD-508, Washington, DC 20510); (202) 224-5183. Fax, (202) 228-0326. John Ashcroft, R-Mo., chair, (202) 224-6154; Kevin Sabo, senior counsel. Internet, http://www.senate.gov/~commerce.*

Jurisdiction over legislation affecting tourism.

INTERNATIONAL ORGANIZATIONS

Organization of American States, *Inter-Sectoral Unit for Tourism, 1889 F St. N.W., #300A 20006; (202) 458-3196. Fax, (202) 458-3190. Lorne T. McDonnough, director. Internet, http://www.oas.org/EN/PROG/TOURISM/home.htm.*

Responsible for matters related to tourism and its development in the hemisphere. Provides support to the Inter-American Travel Congress; works for sustainable tourism development; promotes cooperation among international, regional, and subregional tourism offices.

NONPROFIT

American Hotel and Motel Assn., *1201 New York Ave. N.W., #600 20005-3931; (202) 289-3100. Fax, (202) 289-3199. William P. Fisher, president. Library, (202) 289-3193. Internet, http://www.ahma.com.*

Provides operations, technical, educational, marketing, and communications services to members; focus includes international travel. Library open to the public by appointment. Monitors legislation and regulations.

American Society of Travel Agents, *1101 King St., #200, Alexandria, VA 22314-2944; (703) 739-2782. Fax, (703) 684-8319. Mike Spinelli, president. Consumer affairs, (703) 706-0387. Internet, http://www.astanet.com.*

Membership: representatives of the travel industry. Works to safeguard the traveling public against fraud, misrepresentation, and other unethical practices. Offers training programs for travel agents. Consumer affairs department offers help for anyone with a travel complaint against a member of the association.

Hostelling International—American Youth Hostels, *733 15th St. N.W., #840 20005; (202) 783-6161. Fax, (202) 783-6171. Richard Martyr, executive director. Internet, hiayhserv@hiayh.org or http://www.hiayh.org.*

Provides opportunities for outdoor recreation and inexpensive educational travel through hostelling. Member of the International Youth Hostel Federation.

Hotel Employees and Restaurant Employees International, *1219 28th St. N.W. 20007; (202) 393-4373. Fax, (202) 333-0468. Edward T. Hanley, president. Internet, http://www.erols.com/hereiu.*

Membership: approximately 241,000 hotel and restaurant employees. Helps members negotiate pay, benefits, and better working conditions; conducts training programs and workshops. Monitors legislation and regulations. (Affiliated with the AFL-CIO.)

International Assn. of Amusement Parks and Attractions, *1448 Duke St., Alexandria, VA 22314; (703) 836-4800. Fax, (703) 836-4801. John Graff, director. Internet, http://www.iaapa.org.*

Membership: companies from around the world in the amusement parks and attractions industry. Conducts an international exchange program for members. Monitors legislation and regulations.

International Assn. of Convention and Visitor Bureaus, *2000 L St. N.W., #702 20036-4990; (202) 296-7888. Fax, (202) 296-7889. Edward Neilsen, president. Internet, http://www.iacvb.org.*

Membership: travel- and tourism-related businesses, convention and meeting professionals, and tour operators. Encourages business travelers and tourists to visit local historic, cultural, and recreational areas; assists in meeting preparations. Monitors legislation and regulations.

National Business Travel Assn., *1650 King St., #401, Alexandria, VA 22314; (703) 684-0836. Fax, (703) 684-0263. Norman R. Sherlock, executive director. Internet, info@nbta.org or http://www.nbta.org.*

Membership: corporate travel managers. Promotes educational advancement of members and provides a forum for exchange of information on U.S. and international travel. Monitors legislation and regulations.

Passenger Vessel Assn., *1600 Wilson Blvd., #1000A, Arlington, VA 22209; (703) 807-0100. Fax, (703) 807-0103. John R. Groundwater, executive director. Internet, http://www.p-v-a.com.*

Membership: owners, operators, and suppliers for U.S. and Canadian passenger vessels; and international vessel companies. Interests include dinner and excursion boats, car and passenger ferries, overnight cruise ships, and riverboat casinos. Monitors legislation and regulations.

Travel Industry Assn. of America, *1100 New York Ave. N.W., #450 20005; (202) 408-8422. Fax, (202) 408-1255. William Norman, president. Internet, http://www.tia.org.*

Membership: business, professional, and trade associations of the travel industry and state and local associations (including official state government tourism offices) promoting tourism to a specific region or site. Encourages travel to and within the United States. (Affiliated with the Travel and Tourism Government Affairs Council.)

5

Economics and Business

GENERAL POLICY

See also Caucuses (chap. 20); Community and
Regional Development (chap. 12); International Trade
and Development (chap. 13)

AGENCIES

Census Bureau *(Commerce Dept.), Economic
Programs,* Suitland and Silver Hill Rds., Suitland, MD;
(301) 457-2112. Fax, (301) 457-3761. Frederick T.
Knickerbocker, associate director.

Compiles comprehensive statistics on the level of U.S.
economic activity and the characteristics of industrial
and business establishments at the national, state, and
local levels.

Commerce Dept., *14th St. and Constitution Ave. N.W.,
#5854 20230; (202) 482-2112. Fax, (202) 482-4576.
William M. Daley, secretary; Robert Mallett, deputy secretary, (202) 482-4625. Information, (202) 482-2000. Press,
(202) 482-4883. Library, (202) 482-5511. Internet, http://
www.doc.gov.*

Acts as principal adviser to the president on federal
policy affecting industry and commerce; promotes
national economic growth and development, competitiveness, international trade, and technological development; provides business and government with economic
statistics, research, and analysis; encourages minority
business; promotes tourism. Library reference service
staff answers questions about commerce and business.

Commerce Dept., *Business Liaison,* 14th St. and Constitution Ave. N.W., #5062 20230; (202) 482-3942. Fax,
(202) 482-4054. Cheryl Bruner, director. Information,
(202) 482-1360.

Serves as the central office for business assistance.
Handles requests for information and services as well as
complaints and suggestions from businesses; provides
businesses with a forum to comment on federal regulations; initiates meetings on policy issues with industry
groups, business organizations, trade and small-business
associations, and the corporate community.

Commerce Dept., *STAT-USA,* 14th St. and Constitution
Ave. N.W., #4880 20230; (202) 482-0434. Fax, (202) 482-
2164. Kenneth W. Rogers, director. Information, (202) 482-
1986. Internet, stat-usa@doc.gov or http://www.
stat-usa.gov.

Maintains and makes available for public use the
Economic Bulletin Board (EBB), the National Trade
Data Bank (NTDB), and STAT-USA-Internet.

Council of Economic Advisers *(Executive Office of the
President),* Old Executive Office Bldg., #314 20502; (202)

395-5042. Fax, (202) 395-6958. Janet L. Yellen, chair;
Michele Jolin, chief of staff.

Advisory body consisting of three members and supporting staff of economists. Monitors and analyzes the
economy and advises the president on economic developments, trends, and policies and on the economic
implications of other policy initiatives. Prepares the
annual *Economic Report of the President* for Congress.

Economics and Statistics Administration *(Commerce Dept.),* 14th St. and Constitution Ave. N.W., #4848
20230; (202) 482-3727. Fax, (202) 482-0432. James Price,
acting under secretary. Information, (202) 482-2235. Internet, esa@doc.gov or http://www.doc.gov/agencies/esa/
index.html.

Advises the secretary on economic policy matters,
including consumer and capital spending, inventory status, and the short- and long-term outlook in output and
unemployment. Seeks to improve economic productivity
and growth. Serves as departmental liaison with the
Council of Economic Advisers and other government
agencies concerned with economic policy. Supervises
and sets policy for the Census Bureau and the Bureau of
Economic Analysis.

Federal Reserve System, *Board of Governors,* 20th
and C Sts. N.W. 20551; (202) 452-3201. Fax, (202) 452-
3819. Alan Greenspan, chair; Alice M. Rivlin, vice chair,
(202) 452-3271. Information, (202) 452-3215. Press, (202)
452-3204. Locator, (202) 452-3000.

Sets U.S. monetary policy. Supervises the Federal
Reserve System and influences credit conditions through
the buying and selling of treasury securities in the open
market, by fixing the amount of reserves depository
institutions must maintain, and by determining discount
rates.

Federal Trade Commission, *6th St. and Pennsylvania
Ave. N.W. 20580; (202) 326-2100. Robert Pitofsky, chair;
Rosemarie Straight, executive director, (202) 326-2205.
Information, (202) 326-2000. Press, (202) 326-2180.
Library, (202) 326-2395. Chair's fax, (202) 326-2396.
Internet, http://www.ftc.gov.*

Promotes policies designed to maintain strong competitive enterprise within the U.S. economic system.
Monitors trade practices and investigates cases involving
monopoly, unfair restraints, or deceptive practices.
Enforces Truth in Lending and Fair Credit Reporting
acts. Library open to the public.

Federal Trade Commission, *Economics,* 6th St. and
Pennsylvania Ave. N.W., #268 20580; (202) 326-3419. Fax,
(202) 326-2380. Jonathan Baker, director. Internet,
http://www.ftc.gov.

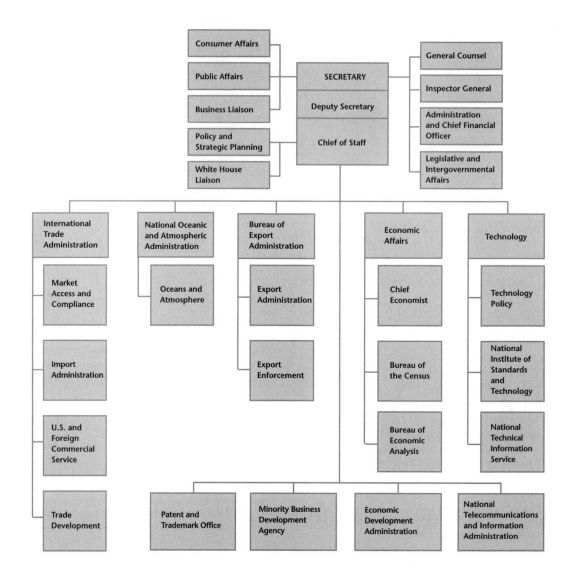

Provides economic analyses for consumer protection and antitrust investigations, cases, and rulemakings; advises the commission on the effect of government regulations on competition and consumers in various industries; develops special reports on competition, consumer protection, and regulatory issues.

National Economic Council *(Executive Office of the President), The White House 20500; (202) 456-6630. Fax, (202) 456-2223. Gene Sperling, national economic advisor.*

Comprised of cabinet members and other high-ranking executive branch officials. Coordinates domestic and international economic policymaking process to facilitate the implementation of the president's economic agenda.

National Institute of Standards and Technology *(Commerce Dept.), National Center for Standards and Certification Information, Route I-270 and Quince Orchard Rd., Bldg. 820, #164, Gaithersburg, MD 20899;*

FEDERAL TRADE COMMISSION

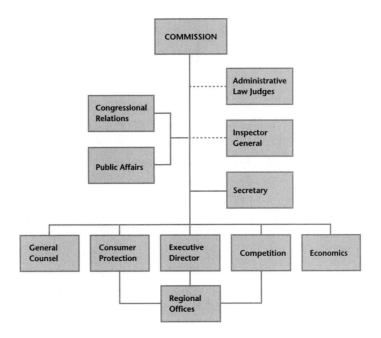

(301) 975-4040. Fax, (301) 926-1559. Joanne Overman, chief. Weekly recorded updates: GATT hotline, (301) 975-4041; EU hotline, (301) 921-4164. Internet, ncsc@nist.gov or http://www.nist.gov.

Serves as the national repository for information on voluntary industry standards and regulations for domestic and international products. Provides information on specifications, test methods, domestic and international technical regulations, codes, and recommended practices.

National Women's Business Council, 409 3rd St. S.W., #5850 20024; (202) 205-3850. Fax, (202) 205-6825. Lillian Vernon, chair; Amy Millman, executive director. Internet, http://www.womenconnect.com/nwbc.

Membership: eight women business owners, six representatives of women business organizations, and one chair appointed by the president. Independent, congressionally mandated council established by the Women's Business Ownership Act of 1988. Reviews the status of women-owned businesses nationwide and makes policy recommendations to the president and Congress. Assesses the role of the federal government in aiding and promoting women-owned businesses.

Small Business Administration, 409 3rd St. S.W. 20416; (202) 205-6605. Fax, (202) 205-6802. Aida Alvarez, administrator; Vacant, deputy administrator.

Information, (202) 205-7713. Press, (202) 205-6740. Library, (202) 205-7033. Toll-free information, (800) 827-5722. Locator, (202) 205-6600. Internet, http://www.sba.gov.

Serves as the government's principal advocate of small-business interests through financial, investment, procurement, and management assistance and counseling; evaluates effect of federal programs on and recommends policies for small business.

Treasury Dept., 1500 Pennsylvania Ave. N.W., #3330 20220; (202) 622-1100. Fax, (202) 622-0073. Robert E. Rubin, secretary; Lawrence H. Summers, deputy secretary, (202) 622-1080. Information, (202) 622-2000. Library, (202) 622-0990. Locator, (202) 622-2111. Internet, http://www.ustreas.gov.

Serves as chief financial officer of the government and adviser to the president on economic policy. Formulates and recommends domestic and international financial, economic, tax, and broad fiscal policies; manages the public debt. Library open to the public by appointment.

Treasury Dept., Economic Policy, 1500 Pennsylvania Ave. N.W., #3454 20220; (202) 622-2200. Fax, (202) 622-2633. David W. Wilcox, assistant secretary.

Assists and advises the treasury secretary in the formulation and execution of domestic and international

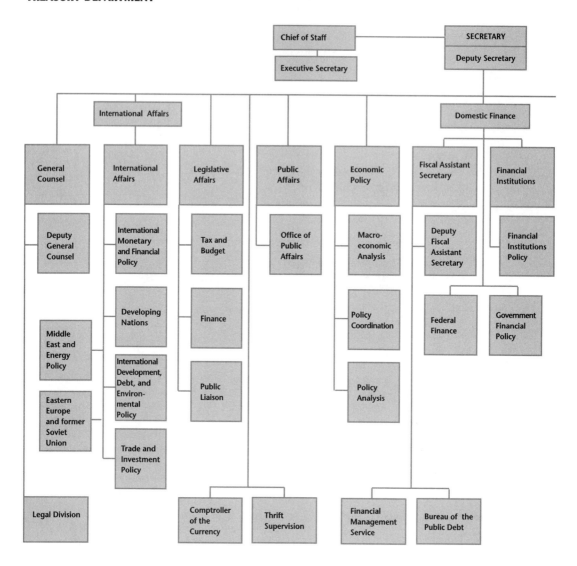

economic policies and programs; helps prepare economic forecasts for the federal budget.

Treasury Dept., *Financial Management Service, 401 14th St. S.W., #548 20227; (202) 874-7000. Fax, (202) 874-6743. Richard Gregg, commissioner. Press, (202) 874-7085. Internet, http://www.treas.gov/fms.*

Serves as the government's central financial manager, responsible for cash management and investment of government trust funds, credit administration, and debt collection. Handles central accounting for government fiscal activities; promotes sound financial management practices and increased use of automated payments, collections, accounting, and reporting systems.

Treasury Dept., *Fiscal Policy, 1500 Pennsylvania Ave. N.W., #2112 20423; (202) 622-0550. Fax, (202) 622-0962. Gerald Murphy, senior advisor.*

Administers Treasury Dept. financial operations. Supervises the Financial Management Service and the Bureau of the Public Debt.

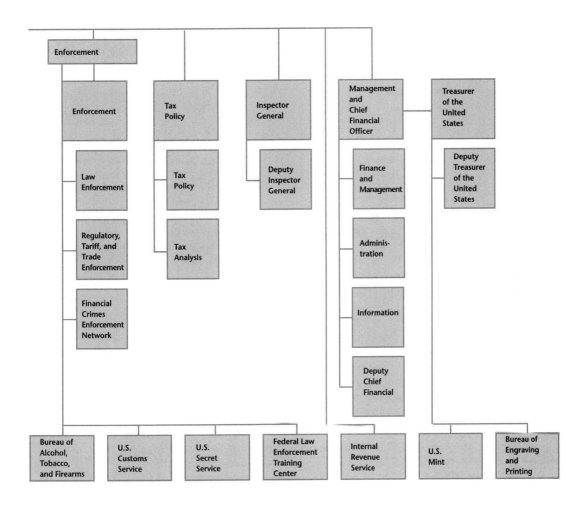

CONGRESS

General Accounting Office, *441 G St. N.W. 20548; (202) 512-5500. Fax, (202) 512-5507. James F. Hinchman, acting comptroller general. Information, (202) 512-4800. Library, (202) 512-5180. Documents, (202) 512-6000. Internet, http://www.gao.gov.*

Independent, nonpartisan agency in the legislative branch. Serves as the investigating agency for Congress; carries out legal, accounting, auditing, and claims settlement functions; makes recommendations for more effec-

tive government operations; publishes monthly lists of reports available to the public. Library open to the public by appointment.

House Appropriations Committee, *H218 CAP 20515; (202) 225-2771. Robert L. Livingston, R-La., chair; James W. Dyer, staff director. Internet, http://www.house.gov/ appropriations.*

Jurisdiction over legislation to appropriate funds for all government programs; responsible for rescissions of appropriated funds, transfers of surplus allocations, and new spending under the Congressional Budget Act. Maintains data on congressional appropriating process and government spending.

House Appropriations Committee, *Subcommittee on Commerce, Justice, State, and Judiciary, H309 Capitol 20515; (202) 225-3351. Harold Rogers, R-Ky., chair; Jim Kulikowski, staff director. Internet, http://www.house. gov/appropriations.*

Jurisdiction over legislation to appropriate funds for the Commerce Dept., the Securities and Exchange Commission, the Small Business Administration, the Competitiveness Policy Council, the Federal Trade Commission, the International Trade Commission, and the Office of the U.S. Trade Representative.

House Appropriations Committee, *Subcommittee on Treasury, Postal Service, and General Government, B307 RHOB 20515; (202) 225-5834. Fax, (202) 225-5895. Jim Kolbe, R-Ariz., chair; Michelle Mrdeza, clerk. Internet, http://www.house.gov/appropriations.*

Jurisdiction over legislation to appropriate funds for the Executive Office of the President, including the Council of Economic Advisers and the Office of Management and Budget; the Treasury Dept.; and the U.S. Tax Court.

House Banking and Financial Services Committee, *2129 RHOB 20515; (202) 225-5940. Jim Leach, R-Iowa, chair; Anthony F. Cole, staff director. Internet, http://www.house.gov/banking.*

Jurisdiction over legislation dealing with bank regulation and federal monetary policy, including the Federal Reserve System (jurisdiction shared with the House Government Reform and Oversight Committee); financial aid to commerce and industry; the measurement of economic activity; federal loan guarantees; economic development; and economic stabilization measures, including wage and price controls.

House Commerce Committee, *2125 RHOB 20515; (202) 225-2927. Fax, (202) 225-1919. Tom Bliley, R-Va., chair; James E. Derderian, staff director. Internet, commerce@mail.house.gov or http://www.house.gov/commerce.*

Jurisdiction over legislation on interstate and foreign commerce generally (some jurisdiction shared with the House International Relations Committee), including the Federal Trade Commission, and many operations of the Commerce Dept.

House Government Reform and Oversight Committee, *2157 RHOB 20515; (202) 225-5074. Fax, (202) 225-3974. Dan Burton, R-Ind., chair; Kevin Binger, staff director.*

Jurisdiction over legislation on government budget and accounting issues other than appropriations; oversight of General Accounting Office operations and of the Office of Management and Budget.

House Government Reform and Oversight Committee, *Subcommittee on National Economic Growth, Natural Resources, and Regulatory Affairs, B377 RHOB 20515; (202) 225-4407. Fax, (202) 225-2441. David M. McIntosh, R-Ind., chair; Mildred Webber, staff director. Internet, http://www.house.gov/reform.*

Oversees operations of the Commerce and Treasury departments, the Federal Reserve System, U.S. Tax Court, and other federal agencies dealing with economic and monetary affairs (jurisdiction shared with House Banking and Financial Services Committee).

House Ways and Means Committee, *1102 LHOB 20515; (202) 225-3625. Bill Archer, R-Texas, chair; Peter Singleton, chief of staff. Internet, http://www.house.gov/ ways_means.*

Jurisdiction over legislation dealing with the debt ceiling; investment policy; and taxes, including taxation of savings, interest, and dividends. Oversees the Internal Revenue Service; sets excise tax rates for the Bureau of Alcohol, Tobacco, and Firearms.

Joint Economic Committee, *SD-G01 20510; (202) 224-5171. Fax, (202) 224-0240. Rep. H. James Saxton, R-N.J., chair; Christopher Frenze, executive director. Internet, http://www.senate.gov/committee/jec.html.*

Studies and makes recommendations on economic policy, including fiscal policy; maintains data pertaining to aggregate economic activity; analyzes the president's annual economic report to Congress and communicates findings to the House and Senate.

Senate Appropriations Committee, *S128 CAP 20510; (202) 224-3471. Ted Stevens, R-Alaska, chair; Steve Cortese, staff director.*

Jurisdiction over legislation to appropriate funds for all government programs; responsible for rescissions of appropriated funds, transfers of surplus allocations, and new spending under the Congressional Budget Act. Maintains data on congressional appropriating process and government spending.

Senate Appropriations Committee, *Subcommittee on Commerce, Justice, State, and Judiciary, SR-393 20510; (202) 224-7277. Judd Gregg, R-N.H., chair, (202) 224-3324; Vas Alexopoulos, legislative assistant. Chair's fax, (202) 224-4952. Internet, http://www.senate.gov/ ~appropriations.*

Jurisdiction over legislation to appropriate funds for the Commerce Dept., the Small Business Administration, the Competitiveness Policy Council, the Federal Trade Commission, the International Trade Commission, the Securities and Exchange Commission, and the Office of the U.S. Trade Representative.

Senate Appropriations Committee, *Subcommittee on Treasury and General Government, SD-190 20510; (202) 224-7337. Ben Nighthorse Campbell, R-Colo., chair; Patricia Raymond, staff director. Internet, http://www. senate.gov/~appropriations.*

Jurisdiction over legislation to appropriate funds for the Executive Office of the President, including the Council of Economic Advisers and the Office of Management and Budget; the Treasury Dept.; and the U.S. Tax Court.

Senate Banking, Housing, and Urban Affairs Committee, *SD-534 20510; (202) 224-7391. Fax, (202) 224-5137. Alfonse M. D'Amato, R-N.Y., chair; Howard Menell, staff director. Internet, http://www.senate.gov/~banking.*

Jurisdiction over legislation dealing with bank regulation, federal monetary policy, financial aid to commerce and industry, the measurement of economic activity, federal loan guarantees, economic development, and other economic stabilization measures (including wage and price controls); oversees the Treasury Dept.; oversees the Federal Reserve System.

Senate Commerce, Science, and Transportation Committee, *SD-508 20510; (202) 224-5115. Fax, (202) 224-1259. John McCain, R-Ariz., chair; John Raidt, staff director. Internet, http://www.senate.gov/~commerce.*

Jurisdiction over legislation on interstate and foreign commerce generally, including the Federal Trade Commission, and many operations of the Commerce Dept.

Senate Finance Committee, *SD-219 20510; (202) 224-4515. Fax, (202) 224-5920. William V. Roth Jr., R-Del., chair; Lindy L. Paull, staff director. Internet, http://www. senate.gov/~finance.*

Jurisdiction over tax legislation; oversees the Internal Revenue Service and the U.S. Tax Court; sets excise tax rates for the Bureau of Alcohol, Tobacco, and Firearms.

Senate Finance Committee, *Subcommittee on Long-Term Growth, Debt, and Deficit Reduction, SD-219 20510; (202) 224-4515. Fax, (202) 224-5920. Connie Mack, R-Fla., chair; Joan Woodward, staff contact. Internet, http://www.senate.gov/~finance.*

Holds hearings on debt ceiling legislation.

Senate Finance Committee, *Subcommittee on Taxation and IRS Oversight, SD-219 20510; (202) 224-4515.*

Don Nickles, R-Okla., chair; Mark Prater, staff contact. Internet, http://www.senate.gov/~finance.

Holds hearings on legislation relating to investment policy and taxation of savings, interest, and dividends.

Senate Governmental Affairs Committee, *SD-340 20510; (202) 224-4751. Fax, (202) 224-9603. Fred Thompson, R-Tenn., chair; Hannah Sistare, staff director. Internet, http://www.senate.gov/committee/governmental_ affairs.html.*

Jurisdiction over legislation on government budget and accounting issues other than appropriations; oversight of General Accounting Office operations and of the Office of Management and Budget.

NONPROFIT

American Business Conference, *1730 K St. N.W., #1200 20006; (202) 822-9300. Fax, (202) 467-4070. Barry K. Rogstad, president. Internet, americanbc@aol.com.*

Membership: chief executive officers of midsize, high-growth companies. Seeks a public policy role for growth companies. Studies capital formation, tax policy, regulatory reform, and international trade.

American Chamber of Commerce Executives, *4232 King St., Alexandria, VA 22302; (703) 998-0072. Fax, (703) 931-5624. Paul J. Greeley Jr., president. Internet, adminacce@acce.org or http://www.acce.com.*

Membership: managers of local, state, and international chambers of commerce. Conducts, for members, educational programs and conferences on topics of interest, including economic development, management systems, and membership drives. Sponsors management councils for members.

American Council for Capital Formation, *1750 K St. N.W., #400 20006; (202) 293-5811. Fax, (202) 785-8165. Mark Bloomfield, president. Internet, http://www.accf.org.*

Advocates tax and environmental policies conducive to saving, investment, and economic growth. Affiliated with the ACCF Center for Policy Research, which conducts and funds research on capital formation topics.

American Enterprise Institute for Public Policy Research, *Economic Policy Studies, 1150 17th St. N.W. 20036; (202) 862-5884. Fax, (202) 862-7177. Marvin H. Kosters, director. Information, (202) 862-7158. Press, (202) 862-5829. Internet, http://www.aei.org.*

Research and educational organization. Interests include monetary, tax, trade, and regulatory policy and labor and social security issues.

American Management Assn., *440 1st St. N.W. 20001; (202) 347-3092. Fax, (202) 347-4549. Peter Nagrod, executive director. Internet, http://www.amanet.org.*

Membership: managers and other corporate professionals. Offers training and education programs to members. (Headquarters in New York.)

American Society of Assn. Executives, *1575 Eye St. N.W. 20005; (202) 626-2723. Fax, (202) 371-8825. R. William Taylor, president. Press, (202) 626-2798. Library, (202) 626-2746. TDD, (202) 626-2803. Internet, pr@asae.asaenet.org or http://www.asaenet.org.*

Conducts research and provides educational programs on association management, trends, and developments. Library open to the public.

Brookings Institution, *Economic Studies Program, 1775 Massachusetts Ave. N.W. 20036-2188; (202) 797-6111. Fax, (202) 797-6181. Robert E. Litan, director. Information, (202) 797-6302. Internet, http://www.brookings.org/ES/ES_HP.HTM.*

Sponsors economic research and publishes studies on domestic and international economics, worldwide economic growth and stability, public finance, urban economics, industrial organization and regulation, labor economics, social policy, and the economics of human resources.

The Business Council, *888 17th St. N.W., #506 20006; (202) 298-7650. Fax, (202) 785-0296. Philip E. Cassidy, executive director. Internet, http://www.businesscouncil.com.*

Membership: current and former chief executive officers of major corporations. Serves as a forum for business and government to exchange views and explore public policy as it affects U.S. business interests.

Business for Social Responsibility, *1612 K St. N.W., #706 20006; (202) 463-9036. Fax, (202) 463-3954. Tim Connor, director, Research and Development. Internet, http://www.bsr.org.*

Membership: large, mid-sized, and small companies. Works to define, support, and promote business practices that benefit members, their employees and communities, the economy, and the environment. Interests include global supply chains for products. (Headquarters in San Francisco.)

Business-Higher Education Forum, *1 Dupont Circle N.W., #800 20036; (202) 939-9345. Fax, (202) 833-4723. Judy Irwin, acting executive director. Internet, bhef@ace.nche.edu or http://www.acenet.edu/programs/bhef.html.*

Membership: chief executive officers of major corporations, colleges, and universities. Promotes cooperation between businesses and higher educational institutions. Interests include international economic competitive-

ness, education and training, research and development, science and technology, and global interdependence.

Business Roundtable, *1615 L St. N.W., #1100 20036; (202) 872-1260. Fax, (202) 466-3509. Samuel L. Maury, president. Internet, http://www.brtable.org.*

Membership: chief executives of the nation's largest corporations. Examines issues of concern to business, including taxation, antitrust law, international trade, employment policy, and the federal budget.

Center for the Study of Public Choice *(George Mason University), Carrow Hall, #1D3, 4400 University Dr., Fairfax, VA 22030; (703) 993-2330. Fax, (703) 993-2323. Robert D. Tollison, director. Internet, http://www.gmu.edu/departments/economics.*

Promotes research in public choice, an interdisciplinary approach to the study of the relationship between economic and political institutions. Interests include constitutional economics, public finance, federalism and local government, econometrics, and trade protection and regulation. Sponsors conferences and seminars. Library open to the public.

Citizens for a Sound Economy, *1250 H St. N.W., #700 20005; (202) 783-3870. Fax, (202) 783-4687. Paul Beckner, president. Internet, http://www.cse.org/cse.*

Citizens' advocacy group that promotes reduced taxes, free trade, and deregulation. Advocates deficit reduction through spending restraint, competitiveness in financial markets, and increased private involvement in providing public services. Encourages citizens to petition members of Congress.

Committee for Economic Development, *2000 L St. N.W., #700 20036; (202) 296-5860. Fax, (202) 223-0776. Van Doorn Ooms, senior vice president. Internet, http://www.ced.org.*

Research organization that makes recommendations on domestic and international economic policy.

Competitive Enterprise Institute, *1001 Connecticut Ave. N.W., #1250 20036; (202) 331-1010. Fax, (202) 331-0640. Fred L. Smith Jr., president. Internet, http://www.cei.org.*

Advocates free enterprise and limited government. Produces policy analyses on tax, budget, financial services, antitrust, biotechnological, and environmental issues. Monitors legislation and litigates against restrictive regulations through its Free Market Legal Program.

The Conference Board, *1113 M St. N.W. 20005; (202) 371-8126. Fax, (202) 842-3867. Meredith Whiting, senior* fellow, Government Affairs. Internet, http://www.conference-board.org.

Membership: senior executives from various industries. Researches science and technology policy, environmental affairs, corporate political activity, management-related issues, the integrated market, and European business activities. Headquarters in New York conducts research and provides economic data on business management, trends, and development.

Council for Social and Economic Studies, *1133 13th St. N.W., #C2 20005-4297; (202) 371-2700. Fax, (202) 371-1523. Roger Pearson, executive director.*

Conducts research and publishes studies on domestic and international economic, social, and political issues.

Council of State Chambers of Commerce, *c/o Committee on Taxation, 122 C St. N.W., #330 20001; (202) 484-5222. Fax, (202) 484-5229. J. William McArthur Jr., president.*

Federation of state business organizations. Conducts research on federal spending, state and local taxation, and employee relations and benefits.

Council on Competitiveness, *1401 H St. N.W., #650 20005; (202) 682-4292. Fax, (202) 682-5150. John N. Yochelson, president. Internet, http://nii.nist.gov/coc.html.*

Membership: executives from business, education, and labor. Seeks increased public awareness of economic competition.

Economic Policy Institute, *1660 L St. N.W., #1200 20036; (202) 775-8810. Fax, (202) 775-0819. Jeff Faux, president. Internet, epi@epinet.org or http://www.epinet.org.*

Research and educational organization that publishes analyses on economics, economic development, competitiveness, income distribution, industrial competitiveness, and investment. Conducts public conferences and seminars.

Ethics Resource Center, *1747 Pennsylvania Ave. N.W., #400 20006; (202) 737-2258. Fax, (202) 737-2227. Michael G. Daigneault, president. Toll-free, (800) 777-1285. Press, (202) 434-8461. Internet, http://www.ethics.org.*

Assists corporations, trade and professional associations, nonprofit groups, academic institutions, schools, and the government in developing and implementing standards of ethical conduct, and ethics training and infrastructure programs.

Financial Executives Institute, *1615 L St. N.W., #1320 20036; (202) 659-3700. Fax, (202) 857-0230. St. Clair*

Tweedie, *vice president, Government Relations. Internet, http://www.fei.org.*

Membership: senior financial executives from major companies in the United States and Canada. Provides conferences and professional development programs; publishes the *Financial Executive*. Monitors legislation and regulations affecting business.

Greater Washington Board of Trade, *1129 20th St. N.W., #200 20036; (202) 857-5900. Fax, (202) 223-2648. John Tydings, president. Internet, info@bot.org or http://www.bot.org.*

Promotes and plans economic growth for the capital region. Supports business-government partnerships, technological training, and transportation planning; promotes international trade; works to increase economic viability of the city of Washington. Monitors legislation and regulations at local, state, and federal levels.

National Assn. of Corporate Directors, *1707 L St. N.W., #560 20036; (202) 775-0509. Fax, (202) 775-4857. C. Russell Hansen, president. Internet, http://www.nacdonline.org.*

Membership: executives of closely held and public companies, outside and inside directors, and stewards of corporate governance. Serves as a clearinghouse on corporate governance and current board practices. Conducts seminars; runs executive search service; sponsors insurance program for directors and officers.

National Assn. of Manufacturers, *1331 Pennsylvania Ave. N.W. 20004; (202) 637-3000. Fax, (202) 637-3182. Jerry Jasinowski, president. Press, (202) 637-3094. Internet, http://www.nam.org.*

Represents industry views (mainly of manufacturers) to government on national and international issues. Reviews legislation, administrative rulings, and judicial decisions affecting industry. Sponsors the Human Resources Forum; operates a computer network for members and the public that provides information on legislative and other news; conducts programs on labor relations, occupational safety and health, regulatory and consumer affairs, environmental trade and technology, and other business issues.

National Assn. of State Budget Officers, *444 N. Capitol St. N.W., #642 20001-1501; (202) 624-5382. Fax, (202) 624-7745. Vacant, executive director. Internet, http://www.nasbo.org.*

Membership: state budget and financial officers. Publishes research reports on budget-related issues. (Affiliate of the National Governors' Assn.)

National Chamber Litigation Center, *1615 H St. N.W., #230 20062; (202) 463-5337. Fax, (202) 463-5346. Stephen A. Bokat, executive vice president. Internet, http:// www.uschamber.com.*

Public policy law firm of the U.S. Chamber of Commerce. Advocates business's positions in court on such issues as employment, environmental, and constitutional law. Provides businesses with legal assistance and representation in legal proceedings before federal courts and agencies.

National Cooperative Business Assn., *1401 New York Ave. N.W., #1100 20005-2146; (202) 638-6222. Fax, (202) 638-1374. Russell C. Notar, president. Internet, ncba@ ncba.org or http://www.cooperative.org.*

Alliance of cooperatives, businesses, and state cooperative associations. Supports development of cooperative businesses; promotes and develops trade among domestic and international cooperatives. Monitors legislation and regulations.

National Policy Assn., *1424 16th St. N.W., #700 20036; (202) 265-7685. Fax, (202) 797-5516. Malcolm R. Lovell Jr., president. Internet, npa@npa1.org or http://www. npa1.org.*

Research organization that conducts studies on domestic and international economic policy issues. Interests include agriculture, human resources, employment, international trade, investment and monetary policy, and U.S. economic competitiveness.

National Retail Federation, *325 7th St. N.W., #1000 20004-2802; (202) 783-7971. Fax, (202) 737-2849. Tracy Mullin, president. Internet, nrf@mcimail.com or http:// www.nrf.com.*

Membership: international, national, and state associations of retailers and major retail corporations. Concerned with federal regulatory activities and legislation that affect retailers, including tax, employment, trade, and credit issues. Provides information on retailing through seminars, conferences, and publications.

National Venture Capital Assn., *1655 N. Fort Myer Dr., #850, Arlington, VA 22209; (703) 524-2549. Fax, (703) 524-3940. Daniel T. Kingsley, executive director. Internet, http://www.nvca.org.*

Membership: venture capital organizations and individuals and corporate financiers. Promotes understanding of venture capital investment. Monitors legislation.

Private Sector Council, *1101 16th St. N.W., #300 20036-4803; (202) 822-3910. Fax, (202) 822-0638. Thomas V. Fritz, president. Internet, psci@capaccess.org.*

Membership: large corporations, private businesses, and associations, including financial and information

technology organizations. Seeks to improve government efficiency, productivity, and management through a cooperative effort of the public and private sectors.

Society of Competitive Intelligence Professionals, *1700 Diagonal Rd., #520, Alexandria, VA 22314; (703) 739-0696. Fax, (703) 739-2524. Guy Kolb, executive director. Internet, postmaster@scip.org or http://www.scip.org.*

Promotes businesses' competitiveness through a greater understanding of competitive behaviors and future strategies as well as the market dynamics in which they conduct business. Conducts seminars and conferences. Publishes the *Competitive Intelligence Review.*

U.S. Business and Industrial Council, *122 C St. N.W., #815 20001; (202) 628-2211. Fax, (202) 628-3698. Kevin L. Kearns, president. Internet, usbic@aol.com.*

Advocates energy independence, reindustrialization, and effective use of natural resources and manufacturing capacity. Current issues include business tax reduction, the liability crisis, defense and other federal spending, and the trade deficit. Media network distributes op-ed pieces to newspapers and radio stations.

U.S. Chamber of Commerce, *1615 H St. N.W. 20062-2000; (202) 659-6000. Fax, (202) 463-5836. Thomas J. Donohue, president. Press, (202) 463-5682. Publications, (800) 638-6582. Internet, http://www.uschamber.org.*

Federation of businesses, trade, and professional associations; state and local chambers of commerce; and American chambers of commerce abroad. Develops policy on legislative issues important to American business; sponsors programs on management, business confidence, small business, consumer affairs, economic policy, minority business, and tax policy; maintains a business forecast and survey center and a trade negotiation information service. Monitors legislation and regulations.

U.S. Chamber of Commerce, *Business and Government Policy, 1615 H St. N.W., #500 20062-2000; (202) 463-5500. Fax, (202) 887-3445. Vacant, director, Public Policy. Internet, http://www.uschamber.org.*

Advocates business's position on government and regulatory affairs. Monitors legislation and regulations on antitrust and corporate policy, product liability, and business-consumer relations.

U.S. Chamber of Commerce, *Economic Policy, 1615 H St. N.W. 20062-2000; (202) 463-5620. Fax, (202) 463-3174. Martin A. Regalia, chief economist. Internet, http:// www.uschamber.com.*

Represents business community's views on economic policy, including government spending, the federal budget, and tax issues. Forecasts the economy of the United States and other industrialized nations and projects the impact of major policy changes. Studies economic trends and analyzes their effect on the business community.

Coins and Currency

AGENCIES

Bureau of Engraving and Printing *(Treasury Dept.),* *14th and C Sts. S.W., #119M 20228; (202) 874-2002. Fax, (202) 874-3879. Thomas Ferguson, deputy director. Information, (202) 874-3019.*

Designs, engraves, and prints Federal Reserve notes, postage stamps, military certificates, White House invitations, presidential portraits, and special security documents for the federal government. Provides information on history, design, and engraving of currency; offers public tours; maintains reading room where materials are brought for special research (for appointment, write to the BEP's Historical Resource Center).

Bureau of Engraving and Printing *(Treasury Dept.),* *Currency Standards, 14th and C Sts. S.W. (mailing address: P.O. Box 37048, Washington, DC 20013); (202) 874-8897. Fax, (202) 874-5362. Thomas Rogers, chief. Information, (202) 874-2361. Mutilation redemption, (202) 874-2532. Unfit currency and destruction of currency, (202) 874-2771. Claims, (202) 874-2397.*

Redeems U.S. currency that has been mutilated; develops regulations and procedures for the destruction of unfit U.S. currency.

Federal Reserve System, *Board of Governors, 20th and C Sts. N.W. 20551; (202) 452-3201. Fax, (202) 452-3819. Alan Greenspan, chair. Information, (202) 452-3215. Press, (202) 452-3204.*

Influences the availability of money as part of its responsibility for monetary policy; maintains reading room for inspection of records that are available to the public.

National Museum of American History *(Smithsonian Institution), National Numismatic Collection, 14th St. and Constitution Ave. N.W. 20560; (202) 357-1798. Fax, (202) 357-4840. Elvira Clain-Stefanelli, executive director. Internet, http://www.si.edu.*

Develops and maintains collections of ancient, medieval, modern, U.S., and world coins; U.S. and world currencies; tokens; medals; orders and decorations; and primitive media of exchange. Conducts research and responds to public inquiries.

Treasury Dept., *1500 Pennsylvania Ave. N.W., #3330 20220; (202) 622-5300. Fax, (202) 622-0073. Robert E.*

Rubin, secretary. Information, (202) 622-2000. Library, (202) 622-0990. Internet, http://www.ustreas.gov.

Oversees the manufacture of U.S. coins and currency; submits to Congress final reports on the minting of coins or any changes in currency. Library open to the public by appointment.

Treasury Dept., *Financial Management Service, 401 14th St. S.W., #548 20227; (202) 874-7000. Fax, (202) 874-6743. Richard Gregg, commissioner. Press, (202) 874-7085. Internet, http://www.treas.gov/fms.*

Prepares and publishes for the president, Congress, and the public monthly, quarterly, and annual statements of government financial transactions, including reports on U.S. currency and coins in circulation.

Treasury Dept., *Treasurer of the United States, 1500 Pennsylvania Ave. N.W., #2134 20220; (202) 622-0100. Fax, (202) 622-2258. Mary Ellen Withrow, treasurer.*

Spokesperson for the Treasury Dept. in matters dealing with currency, coinage, and savings bonds. Signs currency; promotes selling and holding of savings bonds; oversees operation of the U.S. Mint and the Bureau of Engraving and Printing.

U.S. Mint *(Treasury Dept.), 633 3rd St. N.W. 20220; (202) 874-4037. Fax, (202) 874-4083. Philip N. Diehl, director. Information, (202) 874-9696.*

Manufactures and distributes all domestic coins; safeguards government's holdings of precious metals; manufactures and sells commemorative coins and medals of historic interest. Maintains an exhibit and sales area at Union Station in Washington, D.C.

CONGRESS

House Banking and Financial Services Committee, *Subcommittee on Domestic and International Monetary Policy, B304 RHOB 20515; (202) 226-0473. Fax, (202) 226-0537. Michael N. Castle, R-Del., chair; James McCormick, staff director. Internet, http://www.house.gov/ banking.*

Jurisdiction over legislation on all matters relating to coins, currency, medals, proof and mint sets, and other special coins. Oversight of the U.S. Mint and the Bureau of Engraving and Printing.

Senate Banking, Housing, and Urban Affairs Committee, *SD-534 20510; (202) 224-7391. Fax, (202) 224-5137. Alfonse M. D'Amato, R-N.Y., chair; Howard Menell, staff director. Internet, http://www.senate.gov/ ~banking.*

Jurisdiction over legislation on coins and currency, medals, proof and mint sets, and other special coins.

Oversight of the U.S. Mint and the Bureau of Engraving and Printing.

Federal Budget

See also Defense Budget (chap. 16)

AGENCIES

Federal Financing Bank *(Treasury Dept.), 1500 Pennsylvania Ave. N.W., #3054 20220; (202) 622-2470. Fax, (202) 622-0707. Charles D. Haworth, secretary; Gary H. Burner, manager.*

Coordinates federal agency borrowing by purchasing securities issued or guaranteed by federal agencies; funds its operations by borrowing from the treasury.

Office of Management and Budget *(Executive Office of the President), Old Executive Office Bldg., #252 20502; (202) 395-4840. Fax, (202) 395-3888. Franklin D. Raines, director. Press, (202) 395-7254.*

Prepares president's annual budget; works with the Council of Economic Advisers and the Treasury Dept. to develop the federal government's fiscal program; oversees administration of the budget; reviews government regulations; coordinates administration procurement and management policy.

Treasury Dept., *Bureau of the Public Debt, 999 E St. N.W. 20239; (202) 219-3300. Fax, (202) 219-3391. Van Zeck, commissioner. Information, (202) 874-4000. Press, (202) 219-3302. Savings bonds, (202) 447-1775. Internet, http://www.publicdebt.treas.gov.*

Handles public debt securities, treasury notes, and bonds; maintains all records on series EE and HH savings bonds.

Treasury Dept., *Federal Finance Policy Analysis, 1500 Pennsylvania Ave. N.W., #2034 20220; (202) 622-2680. Fax, (202) 622-0974. Norman Carleton, director.*

Analyzes and evaluates economic and financial development, problems and proposals in the areas of treasury financing, public debt management, and related economic matters. Provides analysis and technical assistance on regulatory issues involving government securities and related markets. Monitors and analyzes foreign investment in treasury securities.

Treasury Dept., *Government Financing, 1500 Pennsylvania Ave. N.W., #3040 20220; (202) 622-2460. Fax, (202) 622-0427. Charles D. Haworth, director.*

Analyzes federal credit program principles and standards, legislation, and proposals related to government borrowing, lending, and investment. Furnishes actuarial and mathematical analysis required for treasury market

financing, the Federal Financing Bank, and other government agencies. Manages the Federal Financing Bank.

Treasury Dept., *Market Finance, 1500 Pennsylvania Ave. N.W., #2209 20220; (202) 622-2630. Fax, (202) 622-0244. Jill K. Ouseley, director.*

Provides financial and economic data on government financing and public debt management. Coordinates, analyzes, and reviews government borrowing, lending, and investment activities. Monitors the volume of funds raised and supplied in the credit market. Determines interest rates for government loan programs.

CONGRESS

Congressional Budget Office, *402 Ford Bldg. 20515; (202) 226-2700. Fax, (202) 225-7509. June O'Neill, director. Information, (202) 226-2600. Internet, http://www.cbo.gov.*

Nonpartisan office that provides the House and Senate with budget-related information and analyses of alternative fiscal policies.

House Budget Committee, *309 CHOB 20515; (202) 226-7270. Fax, (202) 226-7174. John R. Kasich, R-Ohio, chair; Wayne Struble, staff director. Internet, http://www.house.gov/budget.*

Jurisdiction over congressional budget resolutions, which set levels for federal spending, revenues, deficit, and debt. Jurisdiction over reconciliation bills, which alter existing programs to meet budget goals. Oversight of Congressional Budget Office. Studies budget matters; makes available statistics pertaining to budget proposals put forward by the president and Congress.

House Judiciary Committee, *2138 RHOB 20515; (202) 225-3951. Fax, (202) 225-7682. Henry J. Hyde, R-Ill., chair; Thomas Mooney, chief counsel. Internet, http://www.house.gov/judiciary.*

Jurisdiction over legislation on proposed amendments to the Constitution, including the proposed Balanced Budget Amendment.

Senate Budget Committee, *SD-621 20510; (202) 224-0642. Fax, (202) 224-4835. Pete V. Domenici, R-N.M., chair; G. William Hoagland, staff director. Internet, http://www.senate.gov/~budget.*

Jurisdiction over congressional budget resolutions, which set levels for federal spending, revenues, deficit, and debt. Jurisdiction over reconciliation bills, which alter existing programs to meet budget goals. Oversight of the Congressional Budget Office. Studies budget matters; makes available statistics pertaining to budget proposals put forward by the president and Congress.

Senate Judiciary Committee, *SD-224 20510; (202) 224-5225. Fax, (202) 224-9102. Orrin G. Hatch, R-Utah, chair; Manus Cooney, chief counsel. Internet, http:// www.senate.gov/committee/judiciary.html.*

Jurisdiction over legislation on proposed amendments to the Constitution, including the proposed Balanced Budget Amendment.

NONPROFIT

Americans for a Balanced Budget, *101 D St. S.E. 20003; (202) 544-2601. Fax, (202) 544-2604. Tony Zagotta, president. Internet, http://www.abb.org.*

Advocacy group that seeks passage of a balanced budget amendment to the U.S. Constitution and a balanced federal budget.

Committee for a Responsible Federal Budget, *220 1/2 E St. N.E. 20002; (202) 547-4484. Fax, (202) 547-4476. Carol Cox Wait, president. Internet, crfb@aol.com.*

Educational organization that works to support and improve the congressional budget process. Seeks to increase public awareness of the dangers of federal budget deficits. Offers seminars and symposia; commissions studies and policy analyses.

Concord Coalition, *1019 19th St. N.W., #810 20036; (202) 467-6222. Fax, (202) 467-6333. Martha Phillips, executive director. Internet, http://www.concordcoalition. org.*

Bipartisan citizens' interest group that promotes tax and spending policies intended to eliminate the federal budget deficit.

Institute for Policy Studies, *National Commission for Economic Conversion and Disarmament, 733 15th St. N.W., #1020 20005; (202) 234-9382. Fax, (202) 387-7915. Miriam Pemberton, executive director. Internet, ncecd@ igc.apc.org or http://www.webcom.com/ncecd.*

Supports cutbacks in the U.S. military budget and reallocation of funds for civilian economic development. Advocates investment in civilian research and development, transportation, housing, health, education, and the environment.

OMB Watch, *1742 Connecticut Ave. N.W. 20009; (202) 234-8494. Fax, (202) 234-8584. Gary D. Bass, executive director. Internet, ombwatch@rtk.net or http://www. ombwatch.org/ombw/index.html.*

Research and advocacy organization that monitors and interprets the policies and activities of the Office of Management and Budget. Sponsors conferences and teaches the governmental decision-making process concerning accountability.

Statistics/Economic Projections

See also Federal Budget (this section)

AGENCIES

Bureau of Economic Analysis *(Commerce Dept.), 1441 L St. N.W., #6006 20230; (202) 606-9600. Fax, (202) 606-5311. J. Steven Landefeld, director. Information, (202) 606-9900. Internet, john.landefeld@bea.doc.gov or http:// www.bea.doc.gov.*

Compiles, analyzes, and publishes data on measures of aggregate U.S. economic activity, including gross national product; prices by type of expenditure; personal income and outlays; personal savings; corporate profits; leading, coincident, and lagging economic indicators; capital stock; U.S. international transactions; and foreign investment. Provides estimates of personal income and employment by industry for regions, states, metropolitan areas, and counties. Refers specific inquiries to economic specialists in the field.

Bureau of Labor Statistics *(Labor Dept.), 2 Massachusetts Ave. N.E., #2860 20212; (202) 606-5886. Fax, (202) 606-7890. Katharine G. Abraham, commissioner, (202) 606-7800. Press, (202) 606-5900. Internet, labstathelpdesk@bls.gov or http://stats.bls.gov.*

Provides statistical data on labor economics, including labor force, employment and unemployment, hours of work, wages, employee compensation, prices, living conditions, labor-management relations, productivity, technological developments, occupational safety and health, and structure and growth of the economy. Publishes reports on these statistical trends including the Consumer Price Index, Producer Price Index, and Employment and Earnings.

Census Bureau *(Commerce Dept.), Economic Programs, Suitland and Silver Hill Rds., Suitland, MD; (301) 457-2112. Fax, (301) 457-3761. Frederick T. Knickerbocker, associate director.*

Provides data and explains proper use of data on county business patterns, classification of industries and commodities, and business statistics. Compiles quarterly reports listing financial data for corporations in certain industrial sectors.

Census Bureau *(Commerce Dept.), Governments Division, Washington Plaza II, #407, Upper Marlboro, MD; (301) 457-1489. Fax, (301) 457-1423. Gordon W. Green Jr., chief.*

Provides data and explains proper use of data concerning state and local governments, employment, finance, governmental organization, and taxation.

Census Bureau *(Commerce Dept.), Manufacturing and Construction,* Suitland and Silver Hill Rds., Suitland, MD; (301) 457-4593. Fax, (301) 457-4583. Thomas L. Mesenbourg, acting chief.

Collects and distributes manufacturing, construction, and mineral industry data. Reports are organized by commodity, industry, and geographic area.

Census Bureau *(Commerce Dept.), Services Division,* Suitland and Silver Hill Rds., Suitland, MD; (301) 457-2668. Fax, (301) 457-1343. Carole A. Ambler, chief.

Provides data of five-year census programs on retail, wholesale, and service industries. Conducts periodic monthly or annual surveys for specific items within these industries.

Council of Economic Advisers *(Executive Office of the President), Statistical Office,* Old Executive Office Bldg. 20500; (202) 395-5062. Fax, (202) 395-5630. Catherine H. Furlong, senior statistician.

Compiles and reports aggregate economic data, including national income and expenditures, employment, wages, productivity, production and business activity, prices, money stock, credit, finance, government finance, corporate profits and finance, agriculture, and international statistics, including balance of payments and import-export levels by commodity and area. Data published in the *Annual Economic Report* and the monthly *Economic Indicators,* published by the congressional Joint Economic Committee.

Economic Research Service *(Agriculture Dept.),* 1800 M St. N.W. 20036; (202) 694-5000. Fax, (202) 694-5757. Susan E. Offutt, administrator. Internet, http://www.econ. ag.gov.

Analyzes the factors affecting farm production and their relationship to the environment, prices, and income; examines the outlook for various commodities. Studies include rural development and natural resources, agricultural trade and production, government policies, and foreign demand for agricultural products.

Federal Reserve System, *Monetary Affairs,* 20th and C Sts. N.W., #B3022B 20551; (202) 452-3761. Fax, (202) 452-2301. Donald L. Kohn, director.

Analyzes monetary policy and issues related to open market operations, reserve requirements, and discount policy. Reports statistics associated with monetary aggregates; issues related to the government securities market; and economic aspects of other regulatory issues closely related to monetary policy, such as banking, loans, and securities.

Federal Reserve System, *Research and Statistics,* 20th and C Sts. N.W., #B3048 20551; (202) 452-3301. Fax,

(202) 452-5296. Michael J. Prell, director. Publications, (202) 452-3245.

Publishes statistical data on business finance, real estate credit, consumer credit, industrial production, construction, and flow of funds.

Internal Revenue Service *(Treasury Dept.), Statistics of Income,* 500 N. Capitol St. N.W. (mailing address: P.O. Box 2608, Washington, DC 20013-2608); (202) 874-0700. Fax, (202) 874-0983. Daniel Skelly, director. Publications, (202) 874-0410.

Provides the public and the Treasury Dept. with statistical information on tax laws. Prepares statistical information for the Commerce Dept. to use in formulating the gross national product (GNP). Publishes *Statistics of Income,* a series available at cost to the public.

International Trade Administration *(Commerce Dept.), Trade and Economic Analysis,* 14th St. and Constitution Ave. N.W., #2815 20230; (202) 482-5145. Fax, (202) 482-4614. Jonathan C. Menes, director. Internet, http://www.ita.doc.gov/tradestats.

Monitors developments in major U.S. industrial sectors. Produces studies, including *U.S. Industrial Outlook,* which reports business planning and marketing data on more than 350 industries and projects economic trends for selected industries.

National Agricultural Statistics Service *(Agriculture Dept.),* 1400 Independence Ave. S.W., #4117S 20250; (202) 720-2707. Fax, (202) 720-9013. Donald M. Bay, administrator. Internet, nass@nass.usda.gov.

Prepares estimates and reports of production, supply, price, and other items relating to the U.S. agricultural economy. Reports include statistics on field crops, fruits and vegetables, cattle, hogs, poultry, and related products.

Office of Management and Budget *(Executive Office of the President), Statistical Policy,* New Executive Office Bldg., #10201 20503; (202) 395-3093. Fax, (202) 395-7245. Katherine K. Wallman, chief. Internet, http://www.whitehouse.gov/wh/eop/omb.

Carries out the statistical policy and coordination functions under the Paperwork Reduction Act of 1995; develops long-range plans for improving federal statistical programs; develops policy standards and guidelines for statistical data collection, classification, and publication; evaluates statistical programs and agency performance.

Securities and Exchange Commission, *Economic Analysis,* 450 5th St. N.W. 20549; (202) 942-8020. Fax, (202) 942-9657. Erik Sirri, chief economist.

Publishes data on trading volume of the stock exchanges; compiles statistics on financial reports of brokerage firms.

U.S. International Trade Commission, *Industries,* *500 E St. S.W. 20436; (202) 205-3296. Fax, (202) 205-3161. Vern Simpson, director. Press, (202) 205-1819. Internet, http://www.usitc.gov.*

Identifies, analyzes, and develops data on economic and technical matters related to the competitive position of the United States in domestic and world markets in agriculture, mining, and manufacturing.

CONGRESS

Joint Economic Committee, *SD-G01 20510; (202) 224-5171. Fax, (202) 224-0240. Rep. H. James Saxton, R-N.J., chair; Christopher Frenze, executive director. Internet, http://www.senate.gov/committee/jec.html.*

Maintains statistics on nearly all facets of economic activity; provides information to the public or refers individuals to office where information is available; provides statistics on economy pertaining to energy and environment; publishes monthly *Economic Indicators* from data supplied by the Council of Economic Advisers.

NONPROFIT

American Statistical Assn., *1429 Duke St., Alexandria, VA 22314; (703) 684-1221. Fax, (703) 684-2037. Ray Waller, executive director. Internet, asainfo@amstat.org or http://www.amstat.org.*

Membership: individuals interested in statistics and related quantitative fields. Advises government agencies on statistics and methodology in agency research; promotes development of statistical techniques for use in business, industry, finance, government, agriculture, and science.

Taxes and Tax Reform

See also Business and Tax Law (chap. 14)

AGENCIES

Bureau of Alcohol, Tobacco, and Firearms *(Treasury Dept.), Field Operations, 650 Massachusetts Ave. N.W., #8100 20226; (202) 927-7970. Fax, (202) 927-7756. Andrew L. Vita, assistant director. Information, (202) 927-7777. Press, (202) 927-9510. Internet, http://www.atf.treas.gov.*

Enforces and administers revenue laws relating to firearms, explosives, alcohol, and tobacco.

Internal Revenue Service *(Treasury Dept.), 1111 Constitution Ave. N.W. 20224; (202) 622-4115. Fax, (202)* 622-5756. Charles Rossotti, commissioner. Toll-free, (800) 829-1040. Press, (202) 622-4010. TDD, (800) 829-4059. Internet, http://www.irs.ustreas.gov/prod.

Administers and enforces internal revenue laws (except those relating to firearms, explosives, alcohol, and tobacco).

Internal Revenue Service *(Treasury Dept.), Employee Plans and Exempt Organizations, 1111 Constitution Ave. N.W., #1311 20224; (202) 622-6720. Fax, (202) 622-6873. Evelyn Petschek, assistant commissioner.*

Provides rules for the uniform interpretation and application of federal tax laws affecting tax-exempt organizations and private foundations.

Internal Revenue Service *(Treasury Dept.), Taxpayer Services, 1111 Constitution Ave. N.W. 20224; (202) 622-6860. Fax, (202) 622-8393. John Dalrymple, chief. TDD, (800) 829-4059. Forms and publications, (800) 829-3676. Recorded tax and refund information, (800) 829-4477. Tax information and notice inquiries, (800) 829-1040.*

Oversees field offices that provide information and guidance on tax matters, including group assistance in the preparation of returns and assistance to taxpayers who telephone, write, or visit IRS district offices. Arranges tax courses for groups of taxpayers through an IRS taxpayer education coordinator. Provides businesses with a tax kit, which includes tax regulations and forms. Assists foreign-based Americans and foreign nationals who pay U.S. taxes. *(See Regional Information Sources in appendix.)*

Justice Dept., *Tax Division, 950 Pennsylvania Ave. N.W., #4143 20530; (202) 514-2901. Fax, (202) 514-5479. Loretta C. Argrett, assistant attorney general. Internet, http://www.usdoj.gov/tax/tax.html.*

Acts as counsel for the Internal Revenue Service (IRS) in court litigations between the government and taxpayers (other than those handled by the IRS in the U.S. Tax Court).

Multistate Tax Commission, *444 N. Capitol St. N.W., #425 20001-1538; (202) 624-8699. Fax, (202) 624-8819. Dan R. Bucks, executive director. Internet, mtc@mtc.gov or http://www.mtc.gov.*

Membership: state governments that have enacted the Multistate Tax Compact. Promotes fair, effective, and efficient state tax systems for interstate and international commerce; works to preserve state tax sovereignty. Encourages uniform state tax laws and regulations for multistate and multinational enterprises. Maintains three regional audit offices that monitor compliance with state tax laws and encourage uniformity in taxpayer treatment. Administers program to identify businesses that do not file tax returns with states.

Treasury Dept., *Tax Policy,* 1500 Pennsylvania Ave. N.W., #1000 20220; (202) 622-0050. Fax, (202) 622-0646. *Donald Lubik, assistant secretary.*

Formulates and implements domestic and international tax policies and programs; conducts analyses of proposed tax legislation and programs; participates in international tax treaty negotiations; responsible for receipts estimates for the annual budget of the United States.

CONGRESS

Joint Committee on Taxation, 1015 LHOB 20515; (202) 225-3621. Fax, (202) 225-0832. *Rep. Bill Archer, R-Texas, chair; Kenneth J. Kies, chief of staff. Internet, http:// www.senate.gov/committee/jct.html.*

Performs staff work for House Ways and Means and Senate Finance committees on domestic and international tax matters in the Internal Revenue Code, the public debt limit, and savings bonds under the Second Liberty Bond Act. Provides those committees with general economic and budgetary analysis. Provides revenue estimates for all tax legislation.

JUDICIARY

U.S. Tax Court, 400 2nd St. N.W. 20217; (202) 606-8700. *Mary Ann Cohen, chief judge; Charles S. Casazza, clerk of the court, (202) 606-8754.*

Tries and adjudicates disputes involving income, estate, and gift taxes and personal holding company surtaxes in cases in which deficiencies have been determined by the Internal Revenue Service.

NONPROFIT

American Enterprise Institute for Public Policy Research, *Fiscal Policy Studies,* 1150 17th St. N.W. 20036; (202) 862-5800. Fax, (202) 862-7177. *Marvin H. Kosters, director. Information, (202) 862-7158. Press, (202) 862-5829. Internet, http://www.aei.org.*

Research and educational organization that conducts studies on fiscal policy, taxes, and budget issues.

Americans for Tax Reform, 1320 18th St. N.W., #200 20036; (202) 785-0266. Fax, (202) 785-0261. *Audrey Mullen, executive director. Toll-free, (888) 785-0266. Internet, amtxreform@aol.com or http://www.atr.org.*

Advocates reduction of federal and state taxes; encourages candidates for public office to pledge their opposition to income tax increases through a national pledge campaign.

Citizens for a Sound Economy, 1250 H St. N.W., #700 20005; (202) 783-3870. Fax, (202) 783-4687. *Paul Beckner, president. Internet, http://www.cse.org/cse.*

Citizens' advocacy group that promotes reduced taxes, free trade, and deregulation.

Citizens for Tax Justice, 1311 L St. N.W., #400 20005; (202) 626-3780. Fax, (202) 638-3486. *Robert S. McIntyre, director. Internet, http://www.ctj.org.*

Coalition that works for progressive taxes at the federal, state, and local levels.

Council of State Chambers of Commerce, *c/o Committee on Taxation,* 122 C St. N.W., #330 20001; (202) 484-5222. Fax, (202) 484-5229. *J. William McArthur Jr., president.*

Federation of state business organizations. Conducts research and coordinates members' interests in federal spending and state and local taxation. Represents members and affiliates on corporate state tax issues.

Federation of Tax Administrators, 444 N. Capitol St. N.W., #348 20001; (202) 624-5890. Fax, (202) 624-7888. *Harley T. Duncan, executive director. Internet, http://www.taxadmin.org.*

Membership: state tax agencies. Provides information upon written request on tax-related issues, including court decisions and legislation. Conducts research and sponsors workshops.

Institute for Research on the Economics of Taxation, 1300 19th St. N.W., #240 20036; (202) 463-1400. Fax, (202) 463-6199. *Stephen Entin, executive director. Internet, irettex@ibm.net.*

Research organization that analyzes all aspects of taxation. Conducts research on the economic effects of federal tax policies; publishes studies on domestic and international economic policy issues.

National Assn. of Manufacturers, *Taxation and Economic Policy,* 1331 Pennsylvania Ave. N.W., #600 20004; (202) 637-3073. Fax, (202) 637-3182. *Monica McGuire, director.*

Represents industry views (mainly of manufacturers) on federal tax and budget policies; conducts conferences. Monitors legislation and regulations.

National Center for Fair Competition, 8421 Frost Way, Annandale, VA 22003; (703) 280-4622. Fax, (703) 280-0942. *Kenton Pattie, president. Internet, kentonp1@aol.com.*

Membership: trade and professional associations and individual businesses. Concerned with the economic effect of commercial activity by tax-exempt and governmental entities. Supports privatization and contracting out by governmental agencies. Advocates passage of fair competition laws for state legislatures.

National Taxpayers Union, *108 N. Alfred St., 3rd Floor, Alexandria, VA 22314; (703) 683-5700. Fax, (703) 683-5722. Peter Sepp, vice president, Communications. Internet, http://www.ntu.org.*

Citizens' interest group that promotes tax and spending reduction at all levels of government. Supports constitutional amendments to balance the federal budget and limit taxes.

Tax Council, *1301 K St. N.W., #800W 20005; (202) 822-8062. Fax, (202) 414-1301. Roger J. LeMaster, executive director.*

Organization of corporations concerned with tax policy and legislation. Interests include tax rate, capital formation, capital gains, foreign source income, and capital cost recovery.

Tax Executives Institute, *1200 G St. N.W., #300 20005-3814; (202) 638-5601. Fax, (202) 638-5607. Michael J. Murphy, executive director. Internet, http://www.tei.org.*

Membership: accountants, lawyers, and other corporate and business employees dealing with tax issues. Sponsors seminars and conferences on federal, state, local, and international tax issues. Develops and monitors tax legislation, regulations, and administrative procedures.

Tax Foundation, *1250 H St. N.W., #750 20005-3908; (202) 783-2760. Fax, (202) 942-7675. J. D. Foster, executive director. Internet, http://www.taxfoundation.org.*

Membership: individuals and businesses interested in federal, state, and local fiscal matters. Conducts research and prepares reports on taxes and government expenditures.

U.S. Conference of Mayors, *1620 Eye St. N.W., 4th Floor 20006; (202) 293-7330. Fax, (202) 293-2352. J. Thomas Cochran, executive director. Internet, uscm@cais.com or http://www.usmayors.org/uscm.*

Membership: mayors of cities with populations of 30,000 or more. Monitors tax policy and legislation.

 FINANCE AND INVESTMENTS

Banking

AGENCIES

Comptroller of the Currency *(Treasury Dept.), 250 E St. S.W. 20219; (202) 874-4900. Fax, (202) 874-4950. Eugene A. Ludwig, comptroller. Information, (202) 874-5000. Press, (202) 874-5770. Library, (202) 874-4720. Internet, http://www.occ.treas.gov.*

Regulates and examines the operations of national banks; establishes guidelines for bank examinations. Library open to the public.

Comptroller of the Currency *(Treasury Dept.), Corporate Activities and Policy Analysis, 250 E St. S.W. 20219; (202) 874-5060. Fax, (202) 874-5293. Julie L. Williams, chief counsel. Press, (202) 874-5770. Library, (202) 874-4720. Internet, http://www.occ.treas.gov.*

Advises the comptroller on policy matters and programs related to bank corporate activities, and is the primary decisionmaker on national bank corporate applications, including charters, mergers, and acquisitions, conversions, and operating subsidiaries.

Federal Deposit Insurance Corp., *550 17th St. N.W. 20429; (202) 898-6974. Fax, (202) 898-3778. Andrew C. Hove Jr., acting chair; Vacant, vice chair. Toll-free, (800) 934-3342. Press, (202) 898-6993. Library, (202) 898-3631. Internet, http://www.fdic.gov.*

Insures deposits in national and state banks and savings and loans. Examines insured state banks that are not members of the Federal Reserve System.

Federal Deposit Insurance Corp., *Resolutions and Receiverships, 1776 F St. N.W. (mailing address: 550 17th St. N.W., Washington, DC 20429); (202) 898-6779. Fax, (202) 898-7024. Gail Patelunas, deputy director.*

Plans, executes, and monitors the orderly and least cost resolution of failing FDIC insured institutions. Manages remaining liability of the federal savings and loan resolution fund.

Federal Deposit Insurance Corp., *Supervision, 550 17th St. N.W. 20429; (202) 898-8510. Fax, (202) 898-3638. Nicholas J. Ketcha Jr., director.*

Serves as the federal regulator and supervisor of insured state banks that are not members of the Federal Reserve System. Conducts examinations and investigations of banks under the jurisdiction of FDIC; advises bank managers on improving policies. Administers the Bank Insurance Fund, which insures deposits in commercial banks, and the Savings Association Insurance Fund, which insures deposits in savings and loan institutions.

Federal Reserve System, *Banking Supervision and Regulation, 20th and C Sts. N.W., #3142 20551; (202) 452-2773. Fax, (202) 452-2770. Richard Spillenkothen, director. Internet, http://www.bog.frb.fed.us.*

Supervises and regulates state banks that are members of the Federal Reserve System; supervises and inspects all bank holding companies; monitors banking practices; approves bank mergers, consolidations, and other changes in bank structure.

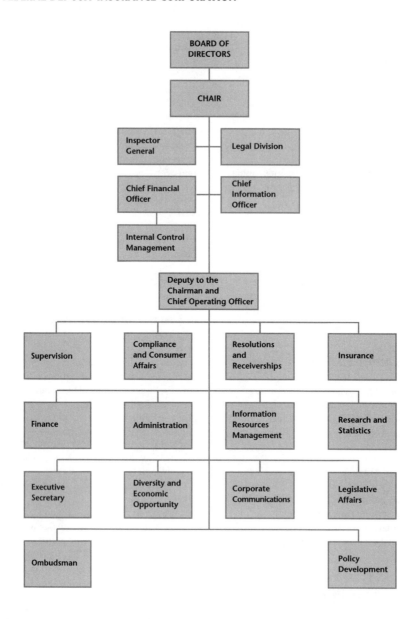

Federal Reserve System, *Board of Governors, 20th and C Sts. N.W. 20551; (202) 452-3201. Fax, (202) 452-3819. Alan Greenspan, chair. Information, (202) 452-3215. Press, (202) 452-3204. Internet, http://www.bog.frb. fed.us.*

Serves as the central bank and fiscal agent for the government. Examines Federal Reserve banks and state member banks; supervises bank holding companies. Controls wire system transfer operations and supplies currency for depository institutions. *(See Regional Information Sources in appendix.)*

Justice Dept., *Antitrust Division, 600 E St. N.W., #9500 20530; (202) 307-6122. Fax, (202) 616-8544. John F. Greaney, chief, Computers and Finance.*

FEDERAL RESERVE SYSTEM

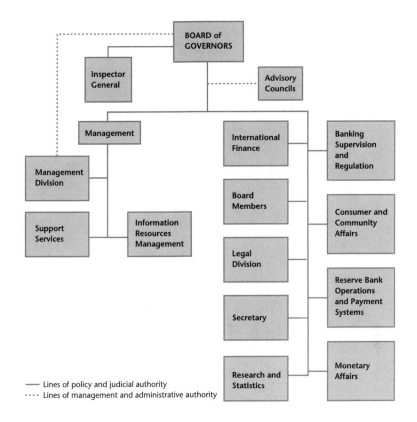

- Lines of policy and judicial authority
- - - - Lines of management and administrative authority

Investigates and litigates certain antitrust cases involving financial institutions, including banking, securities, commodities, and insurance; participates in agency proceedings and rulemaking in these areas; monitors and analyzes legislation.

National Credit Union Administration, *1775 Duke St., Alexandria, VA 22314-3428; (703) 518-6300. Fax, (703) 518-6319. Norman E. D'Amours, chair. Information, (703) 518-6330. Electronic bulletin board, (703) 518-6480. Internet, http://www@ncua.gov.*

Regulates all federally chartered credit unions; charters new credit unions; supervises and examines federal credit unions and insures their member accounts up to $100,000. Insures state-chartered credit unions that apply and are eligible. Manages the Central Liquidity Facility, which supplies emergency short-term loans to members. Conducts research on economic trends and their effect on credit unions and advises the administra-

tion's board on economic and financial policy and regulations.

Office of Management and Budget *(Executive Office of the President), Financial Institutions, New Executive Office Bldg., #9235 20503; (202) 395-7241. Fax, (202) 395-1292. Ed Brigham, chief.*

Monitors the financial condition of deposit insurance funds including the Bank Insurance Fund, the Savings Association Insurance Fund, and the Federal Savings and Loan Insurance Corp. (FSLIC) Resolution Fund. Monitors the Securities and Exchange Commission. Has limited oversight over the Federal Housing Finance Board and the Federal Home Loan Bank System.

Office of Thrift Supervision *(Treasury Dept.), 1700 G St. N.W. 20552; (202) 906-6280. Fax, (202) 898-0230. Nicolas P. Retsinas, interim director. Information, (202) 906-6000. Press, (202) 906-6913. Library, (202) 906-6470. Internet, http://www.ots.treas.gov.*

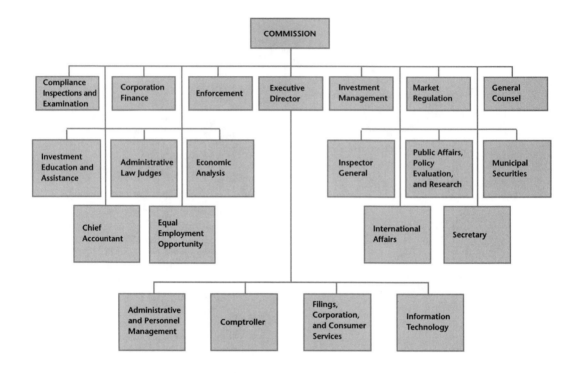

Charters, regulates, and examines the operations of savings and loan institutions. Library open to the public.

Securities and Exchange Commission, *Corporation Finance,* 450 5th St. N.W. 20549; (202) 942-2800. Fax, (202) 942-9525. Brian Lane, director. Information, (202) 942-8088.

Receives and examines disclosure statements and other information from publicly held companies, including bank holding companies.

Securities and Exchange Commission, *Economic Analysis,* 450 5th St. N.W. 20549; (202) 942-8020. Fax, (202) 942-9657. Erik Sirri, chief economist.

Provides the commission with economic analyses of proposed rule and policy changes and other information to guide the SEC in influencing capital markets. Evaluates the effect of policy and other factors on competition within the securities industry and among competing securities markets; compiles financial statistics on capital formation and the securities industry.

Treasury Dept., *Financial Institutions,* 1500 Pennsylvania Ave. N.W., #2326 20220; (202) 622-2600. Fax, (202) 622-2027. Richard S. Carnell, assistant secretary.

Advises the under secretary for domestic finance and the treasury secretary on financial institutions, banks, and thrifts.

CONGRESS

House Appropriations Committee, *Subcommittee on VA, HUD, and Independent Agencies,* H143 CAP 20515; (202) 225-3241. Jerry Lewis, R-Calif., chair; Frank Cushing, staff director. Internet, http://www.house.gov/appropriations.

Jurisdiction over legislation to appropriate funds for the Federal Deposit Insurance Corp. and the National Credit Union Administration.

House Banking and Financial Services Committee, *Subcommittee on Financial Institutions and Consumer Credit,* 2129 RHOB 20515; (202) 225-2258. Fax, (202) 225-6984. Marge Roukema, R-N.J., chair; Laurie Schaffer, staff director. Internet, http://www.house.gov/banking.

Jurisdiction over legislation regulating banking and financial institutions.

House Government Reform and Oversight Committee, *Subcommittee on National Economic Growth, Natural Resources, and Regulatory Affairs,* B377 RHOB 20515; (202) 225-4407. Fax, (202) 225-2441. David M. McIntosh, R-Ind., chair; Mildred Webber, staff director. Internet, http://www.house.gov/reform.

Oversees federal bank regulatory agencies, including the Federal Deposit Insurance Corp., National Credit Union Administration, and Export-Import Bank.

House Ways and Means Committee, *Subcommittee on Oversight,* 1136 LHOB 20515; (202) 225-7601. Fax, (202) 225-9680. Nancy L. Johnson, R-Conn., chair; William McKenney, staff director. Internet, http://www. house.gov/ways_means.

Oversees government-sponsored enterprises, including the Federal Home Loan Bank System, with regard to the financial risk posed to the federal government.

Senate Appropriations Committee, *Subcommittee on VA, HUD, and Independent Agencies,* SD-127 20510; (202) 224-7211. Christopher S. Bond, R-Mo., chair; John K. Mark, staff director. Internet, http://www.senate. gov/~appropriations.

Jurisdiction over legislation to appropriate funds for the Federal Deposit Insurance Corp. and the National Credit Union Administration.

Senate Banking, Housing, and Urban Affairs Committee, SD-534 20510; (202) 224-7391. Fax, (202) 224-5137. Alfonse M. D'Amato, R-N.Y., chair; Howard Menell, staff director. Internet, http://www.senate.gov/ ~banking.

Jurisdiction over legislation regulating banking and financial institutions. Oversees federal bank regulatory agencies, including the Federal Deposit Insurance Corp., National Credit Union Administration, and Office of Thrift Supervision; also oversees government-sponsored enterprises, including the Federal Home Loan Bank System, with regard to the financial risk posed to the federal government.

NONPROFIT

American Bankers Assn., 1120 Connecticut Ave. N.W. 20036; (202) 663-5000. Fax, (202) 663-7533. Donald G. Ogilvie, executive vice president. Information, (202) 663-5221. Library, (202) 663-5040. Internet, http://www. aba.com.

Membership: commercial banks. Operates schools to train banking personnel; conducts conferences; formu-

lates government relations policies for the banking community. Library open to the public by appointment.

American Council of State Savings Supervisors, P.O. Box 34175 20043-4175; (202) 371-0666. Fax, (703) 922-6237. Diane Homiak, executive director.

Membership: supervisors and regulators of state-chartered savings associations; associate members include state-chartered savings associations and state savings banks. Monitors legislation and regulations affecting the state-chartered thrift industry.

American Institute of Certified Public Accountants, 1455 Pennsylvania Ave. N.W., 4th Floor 20004-1081; (202) 737-6600. Fax, (202) 638-4512. John E. Hunnicutt, senior vice president. Press, (202) 434-9214. Internet, http://www.aicpa.org.

Establishes voluntary professional and ethical regulations for the profession; sponsors conferences and training workshops. Answers technical auditing and accounting questions. (Headquarters in New York.)

American League of Financial Institutions, 900 19th St. N.W., #400 20006-2105; (202) 857-5094. Fax, (202) 296-8716. Dina Nichelson, president. Internet, alfi@ acbankers.org or http://www.alfi.org.

Membership: minority-controlled community savings banks and savings associations. Helps promote small business; offers on-site technical assistance. Monitors legislative and regulatory issues.

America's Community Bankers, 900 19th St. N.W., #400 20006; (202) 857-3100. Fax, (202) 296-8716. Paul A. Schosberg, president. Press, (202) 857-3103. Internet, info@acbankers.org or http://www.acbankers.org.

Membership: insured depository institutions involved in community finance. Provides information and statistics on issues that affect the industry; sponsors conferences with international banks and savings and loan institutions. Monitors economic issues affecting savings institutions. Monitors legislation and regulations.

Assn. of Financial Services Holding Companies, 888 17th St. N.W., #312 20006; (202) 223-6575. Fax, (202) 331-3836. Patrick A. Forte, president. Internet, afshc@ ibm.net.

Defends the authority of companies to affiliate with federally insured depository institutions while remaining outside the scope of the Bank Holding Company Act.

Associated Accounting Firms International, 1000 Connecticut Ave. N.W., #1006 20036; (202) 463-7900. Fax, (202) 296-0741. Michael T. Platt, president. Internet, aafi@aafi.org or http://www.aafi.org.

Membership: medium-sized accounting firms. Helps members improve service to clients.

Associated Credit Bureaus, Inc., *1090 Vermont Ave. N.W., #200 20005-4905; (202) 371-0910. Fax, (202) 371-0134. Barry Connelly, president. Press, (202) 408-7406. Internet, acb@planetcom.com or http://www.acb-credit.com.*

Membership: credit reporting, mortgage reporting, and collection service companies. Provides information about credit rights to consumers. Monitors legislation and regulations.

Bank Marketing Assn., *1120 Connecticut Ave. N.W., 3rd Floor 20036; (202) 663-5268. Fax, (202) 828-4540. Michael J. Riley, managing director. Toll-free, (800) 433-9013. Internet, http://www.bmanet.org.*

Membership: financial institutions and firms that provide products and services to the financial industry. (Affiliate of the American Bankers Assn.)

Bankers' Assn. for Foreign Trade, *2121 K St. N.W., #701 20037; (202) 452-0952. Fax, (202) 452-0959. Mary Condeelis, executive director.*

Membership: U.S. commercial banks with major international operations; foreign banks with U.S. operations are affiliated as nonvoting members. Monitors activities that affect the operation of U.S. commercial banks.

Bankers' Roundtable, *805 15th St. N.W., #600 20005; (202) 289-4322. Fax, (202) 289-1903. Anthony T. Cluff, executive director. Internet, http://www.bankersround.org.*

Membership: bank holding companies registered with the Federal Reserve Board under the Bank Holding Company Act. Conducts research and provides information on banking and financial issues.

Conference of State Bank Supervisors, *1015 18th St. N.W., #1100 20036-5275; (202) 296-2840. Fax, (202) 296-1928. Neil Milner, president. Internet, http://www.csbsbc.org.*

Membership: state officials responsible for supervision of state-chartered banking institutions. Conducts educational programs. Monitors legislation.

Consumer Bankers Assn., *1000 Wilson Blvd., #3012, Arlington, VA 22209; (703) 276-1750. Fax, (703) 528-1290. Joe Belew, president. Press, (703) 276-3880. Internet, http://www.cbanet.org.*

Membership: federally insured financial institutions. Provides information on retail banking, including industry trends. Operates the Graduate School of Retail Bank Management to train banking personnel; sponsors conferences.

Credit Union National Assn., *805 15th St. N.W., #300 20005-2207; (202) 682-4200. Fax, (202) 682-9054. Daniel A. Mica, president. Internet, http://www.cuna.com.*

Confederation of credit unions from every state, the District of Columbia, and Puerto Rico. Represents federal and state chartered credit unions. Monitors legislation and regulations. (Headquarters in Madison, Wis.)

Electronic Funds Transfer Assn., *950 Herndon Pkwy., #390, Herndon, VA 20170; (703) 435-9800. Fax, (703) 435-7157. H. Kurt Helwig, executive director. Internet, http://www.efta.org.*

Membership: financial institutions, electronic funds transfer hardward and software providers, automatic teller machine networks, and others engaged in electronic commerce. Promotes electronic payments and commerce technologies; sponsors industry analysis. Monitors legislation and regulations.

Independent Bankers Assn. of America, *1 Thomas Circle N.W., #400 20005; (202) 659-8111. Fax, (202) 659-9216. Kenneth A. Guenther, executive vice president. Toll-free, (800) 422-8439. Internet, info@ibaa.org.*

Membership: medium-sized and smaller community banks. Interests include farm credit, deregulation, interstate banking, deposit insurance, and financial industry standards.

Mortgage Bankers Assn. of America, *1125 15th St. N.W. 20005; (202) 861-6500. Fax, (202) 861-0736. Paul Reid, executive vice president.*

Membership: institutions involved in real estate finance. Maintains School of Mortgage Banking and sponsors educational seminars; collects statistics on the industry. Library open to the public by appointment.

National Assn. of Federal Credit Unions, *3138 N. 10th St., Arlington, VA 22201; (703) 522-4770. Fax, (703) 524-1082. Kenneth L. Robinson, president. Internet, http://www.nascunet.org.*

Membership: federally chartered credit unions. Represents interests of federal credit unions before Congress and regulatory agencies and provides legislative alerts for its members. Sponsors educational meetings focusing on current financial trends, changes in legislation and regulations, and management techniques.

National Assn. of State Credit Union Supervisors, *1901 N. Moore St., #203, Arlington, VA 22209; (703) 528-8351. Fax, (703) 528-3248. Douglas Duerr, president. Internet, offices@nascus.org or http://www.nascus.org.*

Membership: state credit union supervisors, state-chartered credit unions, and credit union leagues. Interests include state regulatory systems; conducts educational programs for examiners.

National Automated Clearing House Assn., *607 Herndon Pkwy., #200, Herndon, VA 20170; (703) 834-2350. Fax, (703) 787-0996. Elliott C. McEntee, president. Internet, http://www.nacha.org.*

Membership: financial institutions involved in the ACH payment system. Establishes rules and standards for the ACH system; works for the development of technological and service innovation in electronic funds transfers; provides information for members. Sponsors workshops and seminars.

National Bankers Assn., *1513 P St. N.W. 20005; (202) 588-5432. Fax, (202) 588-5443. Samuel Foggie, president. Internet, http://www.nationalbankers.org.*

Membership: minority-owned banks and minority banking personnel. Monitors legislation and regulations affecting minority banking.

National Society of Accountants, *1010 N. Fairfax St., Alexandria, VA 22314-1574; (703) 549-6400. Fax, (703) 549-2984. Leslie Schapiro, executive vice president. Internet, http://www.nsacct.org.*

Seeks to improve the accounting profession and to enhance the status of individual practitioners. Sponsors seminars and correspondence courses on accounting, auditing, business law, and estate planning; monitors legislation and regulations affecting accountants and their small-business clients.

Treasury Management Assn., *7315 Wisconsin Ave., #600W, Bethesda, MD 20814; (301) 907-2862. Fax, (301) 907-2864. Donald E. Manger, president. Internet, http://www.tma-net.org/treasury.*

Professional association that provides forum for ideas and perspectives on the treasury management profession and its role in the business environment. Supports treasury professionals through continuing education, professional certification (Certified Cash Manager), publishing and information services, industry standards, and government relations.

Stocks, Bonds, and Securities

See also Federal Budget (this chapter)

AGENCIES

Bureau of the Public Debt *(Treasury Dept.), Savings Bonds Marketing, 999 E St. N.W., #351 20226; (202) 219-4235. Fax, (202) 208-1574. Dino DeConcini, executive director. Information, (202) 219-3302. Internet, http://www.savingsbonds.gov.*

Promotes the sale and retention of U.S. savings bonds through educational and volunteer programs; administers the payroll savings plan for savings bonds.

Federal Reserve System, *Board of Governors, 20th and C Sts. N.W. 20551; (202) 452-3201. Fax, (202) 452-3819. Alan Greenspan, chair. Information, (202) 452-3215. Press, (202) 452-3204. Internet, http://www.bog.frb.fed.us.*

Regulates amount of credit that may be extended and maintained on certain securities in order to prevent excessive use of credit for purchase or carrying of securities.

Securities and Exchange Commission, *450 5th St. N.W. 20549; (202) 942-0100. Fax, (202) 942-9646. Arthur Levitt Jr., chair; James M. McConnell, executive director, (202) 942-4300. Information, (202) 942-8090. Press, (202) 942-0020. Consumer affairs, (202) 942-7040. Locator, (202) 942-4150. Internet, http://www.sec.gov.*

Requires public disclosure of financial and other information about companies whose securities are offered for public sale, traded on exchanges, or traded over the counter; issues and enforces regulations to prevent fraud in securities markets and investigates securities frauds and violations; supervises operations of stock exchanges and activities of securities dealers, investment advisers, and investment companies; regulates purchase and sale of securities, properties, and other assets of public utility holding companies and their subsidiaries; participates in bankruptcy proceedings involving publicly held companies; has some jurisdiction over municipal securities trading. Public Reference Section, (202) 272-7450, makes available corporation reports and statements filed with SEC. The information also is available via the Web (http://www.sec.gov/edgarhp.htm). *(See Regional Information Sources in appendix.)*

Securities and Exchange Commission, *Economic Analysis, 450 5th St. N.W. 20549; (202) 942-8020. Fax, (202) 942-9657. Erik Sirri, chief economist.*

Provides the commission with economic analyses of proposed rule and policy changes and other information to guide the SEC in influencing capital markets. Evaluates the effect of policy and other factors on competition within the securities industry and among competing securities markets; compiles financial statistics on capital formation and the securities industry.

Securities and Exchange Commission, *Market Regulation, 450 5th St. N.W. 20549; (202) 942-0090. Fax, (202) 942-9643. Richard Lindsey, director. Library, (202) 942-7090.*

Oversees and regulates the operations of securities markets, brokers, dealers, and transfer agents. Promotes the establishment of a national system for clearing and settling securities transactions. Works for standards among and oversees self-regulatory organizations, such as national securities exchanges, registered clearing agencies, and the National Assn. of Securities Dealers. Facilitates the development of a national market system.

Treasury Dept., *Financial Institutions Policy, 1500 Pennsylvania Ave. N.W., #3025 20220; (202) 622-2740. Fax, (202) 622-0256. Joan Affleck-Smith, director.*

Coordinates department efforts on all legislation affecting financial institutions and the government agencies that regulate them. Develops department policy on all matters relating to agencies responsible for supervising financial institutions and financial markets.

CONGRESS

House Commerce Committee, *Subcommittee on Telecommunications, Trade, and Consumer Protection, 2125 RHOB 20515; (202) 225-2927. Fax, (202) 225-1919. W. J. "Billy" Tauzin, R-La., chair; James E. Derderian, staff director. Internet, http://www.house.gov/commerce.*

Jurisdiction over stocks, bonds, stock exchanges, over-the-counter markets, mergers and acquisitions, and securities legislation; the Federal Trade Commission, the Securities Investor Protection Corp.; and the Securities and Exchange Commission.

House Government Reform and Oversight Committee, *Subcommittee on National Economic Growth, Natural Resources, and Regulatory Affairs, B377 RHOB 20515; (202) 225-4407. Fax, (202) 225-2441. David M. McIntosh, R-Ind., chair; Mildred Webber, staff director. Internet, http://www.house.gov/reform.*

Investigates investment fraud schemes and commodities and securities fraud. Oversees operations of the Securities and Exchange Commission.

Senate Banking, Housing, and Urban Affairs Committee, *Subcommittee on Securities, SD-534 20510; (202) 224-7391. Fax, (202) 224-5137. Phil Gramm, R-Texas, chair; Wayne A. Abernathy, staff director. Internet, http://www.senate.gov/~banking.*

Jurisdiction over stocks, bonds, stock exchanges, over-the-counter markets, mergers and acquisitions, and securities legislation; the Securities Investor Protection Corp.; and the Securities and Exchange Commission.

Senate Governmental Affairs Committee, *Permanent Subcommittee on Investigations, SH-432 20510; (202) 224-3721. Fax, (202) 224-7042. Susan Collins, R-Maine, chair; Tim Shea, chief of staff. Internet, http://www.senate.gov/~gov_affairs/psi.htm.*

Investigates investment fraud schemes and commodities and securities fraud.

NONPROFIT

Assn. of Publicly Traded Companies, *1200 19th St. N.W., #300 20036; (202) 857-1114. Fax, (202) 223-4579. Brian T. Borders, president.*

Membership: companies that issue stock into public capital markets. Promotes fair and efficient capital markets and the ability to manage corporate affairs free from unnecessary government interference. Interests include taxation and accounting rules under the purview of the Financial Accounting Standards Board. Monitors legislation and regulations.

Bond Market Assn., *1445 New York Ave. N.W., 8th Floor 20005; (202) 434-8400. Fax, (202) 737-4744. Micah S. Green, executive vice president.*

Membership: banks, dealers, and brokers who underwrite, trade, and sell municipal securities, mortgage-backed securities, and government and federal agency securities. Acts as an information and education center for the public securities industry. (Headquarters in New York.)

Council of Institutional Investors, *1730 Rhode Island Ave. N.W., #512 20036; (202) 822-0800. Fax, (202) 822-0801. Sarah Teslik, executive director. Internet, http://www.ciicentral.com.*

Membership: public, union, and corporate pension funds. Studies investment issues that affect pension plan assets. Monitors legislation and regulations.

Futures Industry Assn., *2001 Pennsylvania Ave. N.W., #600 20006; (202) 466-5460. Fax, (202) 296-3184. John M. Damgard, president. Internet, http://www.fiafii.org.*

Membership: commodity futures brokerage firms and others interested in commodity futures. Serves as a forum for discussion of futures industry; provides market information and statistical data; offers educational programs; works to establish professional and ethical standards for members.

Investment Company Institute, *1401 H St. N.W., 12th Floor 20005-2148; (202) 326-5800. Fax, (202) 326-5806. Matthew P. Fink, president. Internet, http://www.ici.org.*

Membership: mutual funds and closed-end funds registered under the Investment Company Act of 1940 (including investment advisers to and underwriters of such companies) and the unit investment trust industry. Conducts research and disseminates information on issues affecting mutual funds.

Investment Program Assn., *607 14th St. N.W., #1000 20005; (202) 775-9750. Fax, (202) 331-8446. Christopher L. Davis, president.*

Membership: broker/dealer organizations and sponsors, law and accounting firms, financial planners, and partnership consultants. Works to preserve limited partnerships and real estate investment trusts as a form of investment and a source of new capital for the economy. Conducts economic research. Monitors legislation and regulations, especially those concerning tax policy.

Investor Responsibility Research Center, *1350 Connecticut Ave. N.W., #700 20036-1701; (202) 833-0700. Fax, (202) 833-3555. Scott Fenn, executive director. Internet, irrc@aol.com or http://www.irrc.org.*

Research organization that reports on and analyzes business and public policy issues affecting corporations and investors.

Municipal Securities Rulemaking Board, *1150 18th St. N.W., #400 20036; (202) 223-9347. Fax, (202) 872-0347. Christopher A. Taylor, executive director. Internet, http://www.msrb.org.*

Writes rules, subject to approval by the Securities and Exchange Commission, applicable to municipal securities brokers and dealers, in such areas as conduct, industry practices, and professional qualifications. Serves as a self-regulatory agency for the municipal securities industry.

National Assn. of Bond Lawyers, *1900 K St. N.W., #1200 20006; (202) 778-2244. Fax, (202) 955-1835. Amy K. Dunbar, director, Governmental Affairs. Internet, http://www.nabl.org.*

Membership: municipal finance lawyers. Provides members with information on laws relating to the borrowing of money by states and municipalities and to the issuance of state and local government bonds. Monitors legislation and regulations. (Headquarters in Wheaton, Ill.)

National Assn. of Real Estate Investment Trusts, *1129 20th St. N.W., #305 20036; (202) 785-8717. Fax, (202) 785-8723. Steve Wechsler, president. Internet, http://www.nareit.com.*

Membership: real estate investment trusts and corporations, partnerships, and individuals interested in real estate securities and the industry. Monitors federal and state legislation, federal taxation, securities regulation, standards and ethics, and housing and education; compiles industry statistics.

National Assn. of Securities Dealers, *1735 K St. N.W. 20006-1506; (202) 728-8000. Fax, (202) 728-8075. Frank G. Zarb, president. Member services, (301) 590-6500. Public disclosure, (800) 289-9999. Internet, http://www.nasdr.com.*

Membership: investment brokers and dealers authorized to conduct transactions of the investment banking and securities business under federal and state laws. Serves as the self-regulatory mechanism in the over-the-counter securities market.

National Investor Relations Institute, *8045 Leesburg Pike, #600, Vienna, VA 22182; (703) 506-3570. Fax, (703) 506-3571. Louis M. Thompson Jr., president. Internet, http://www.niri.org.*

Membership: executives engaged in investor relations and financial communications. Provides publications, educational training sessions, and research on investor relations for members; offers conferences and workshops; maintains job placement and referral services for its members.

New York Stock Exchange, *1800 K St. N.W., #1100 20006; (202) 293-5740. Fax, (202) 331-4158. Sheila Bair, senior vice president, Washington Office. Internet, http://www.nyse.com.*

Provides limited information on operations of the New York Stock Exchange; Washington office monitors legislation and regulations. (Headquarters in New York.)

North American Securities Administrators Assn., *10 G St. N.W., #710 20001; (202) 737-0900. Fax, (202) 783-3571. Neal Sullivan, executive director. Internet, http://www.nasaa.org.*

Membership: state, provincial, and territorial securities administrators of the United States, Canada, and Mexico. Serves as the national representative of the state agencies responsible for investor protection. Works to prevent fraud in securities markets and provides a national forum to increase the efficiency and uniformity of state regulation of capital markets. Operates the Central Registration Depository, a nationwide computer link for agent registration and transfers, in conjunction with the National Assn. of Securities Dealers. Monitors legislation and regulations.

Securities Industry Assn., *1401 Eye St. N.W., #1000 20005-2225; (202) 296-9410. Fax, (202) 296-9775. Marc E. Lackritz, president. Internet, info@sia.com or http://www.sia.com.*

Membership: investment bankers, securities underwriters, and dealers in stocks and bonds. Represents all segments of the securities industry. Monitors legislation, regulations, and international agreements. (Headquarters in New York.)

Securities Investor Protection Corp., *805 15th St. N.W., #800 20005-2207; (202) 371-8300. Fax, (202) 371-*

6728. Clifford Hudson, chair; Debbie D. Branson, vice chair. Internet, http://www.sipc.org.

Private corporation established by Congress to administer the Securities Investor Protection Act. Provides financial protection for customers of member broker-dealers that fail financially.

Tangible Assets

See also Coins and Currency (this chapter)

AGENCIES

Census Bureau *(Commerce Dept.), Manufacturing and Construction, Suitland and Silver Hill Rds., Suitland, MD; (301) 457-4680. Fax, (301) 457-2059. Patricia L. Horning, chief, Construction and Minerals.*

Collects, tabulates, and publishes statistics for the Energy Dept. concerning the domestic construction minerals industry.

Commodity Futures Trading Commission, *3 Lafayette Center, 1155 21st St. N.W. 20581; (202) 418-5030. Fax, (202) 418-5525. Brooksley Born, chair; Linda J. Ferren, executive director. Information, (202) 418-5080. Library, (202) 418-5255. Locator, (202) 418-5000. Internet, http://www.cftc.gov.*

Enforces federal statutes relating to commodity futures and options, including gold and silver futures and options. Monitors and regulates gold and silver leverage contracts, which provide for deferred delivery of the commodity and the payment of an agreed portion of the purchase price on margin.

Defense Logistics Agency *(Defense Dept.), Defense National Stockpile Center, 8725 John Jay Kingman Rd., Fort Belvoir, VA 22060-6223; (703) 767-5525. Fax, (703) 767-5538. Richard J. Connelly, administrator. Internet, http://www.dnsc.dla.mil.*

Manages the national defense stockpile of strategic and critical materials. Purchases strategic materials including beryllium and newly developed high-tech alloys. Disposes of excess materials including tin, silver, industrial diamond stones, tungsten, and vegetable tannin.

Federal Reserve System, *Accounting and Budgets, 20th and C Sts. N.W., Mail Stop 194 20551; (202) 452-3879. Fax, (202) 872-7574. Earl G. Hamilton, assistant director.*

Monitors gold certificate accounts and budgets of Federal Reserve Banks. (Gold certificate accounts are credits issued by the Treasury Dept. against gold held by the Treasury.)

U.S. Geological Survey *(Interior Dept.), Metals, 12201 Sunrise Valley Dr., MS 989, Reston, VA 20192; (703) 648-4967. Fax, (703) 648-7722. Mike McKinley, chief; Earle B. Amey, gold; Henry E. Hilliard, silver and platinum group metals; Daniel Edelstein, copper.*

Studies supply and demand of copper, precious metals (including gold, silver, and platinum group metals), and ferrous metals (iron, iron ore, steel, chromium, and nickel); collects and provides statistical data on production and consumption of precious metals; provides information on gold and silver research, production, and processing methods. (CD-ROMs may be purchased from the Government Printing Office, (202) 512-1800.)

U.S. Mint *(Treasury Dept.), 633 3rd St. N.W. 20220; (202) 874-4037. Fax, (202) 874-4083. Philip N. Diehl, director. Information, (202) 874-9696.*

Produces gold and silver coins for sale to investors.

See also Census Bureau, Foreign Trade (p. 250)

CONGRESS

House Banking and Financial Services Committee, *Subcommittee on Domestic and International Monetary Policy, B304 RHOB 20515; (202) 226-0473. Fax, (202) 226-0537. Michael N. Castle, R-Del., chair; James McCormick, staff director. Internet, http://www.house.gov/banking.*

Jurisdiction over legislation to regulate transactions in gold and precious metals.

Senate Banking, Housing, and Urban Affairs Committee, *Subcommittee on International Finance, SD-534 20510; (202) 224-7391. Fax, (202) 224-5137. Rod Grams, R-Minn., chair; Dave Berson, staff director. Internet, http://www.senate.gov/~banking.*

Jurisdiction over legislation to regulate international transactions in gold and precious metals.

NONPROFIT

Gold Institute, *1112 16th St. N.W., #240 20036; (202) 835-0185. Fax, (202) 835-0155. John Lutley, president. Internet, http://www.goldinstitute.org.*

Membership: companies that mine, refine, fabricate, or manufacture gold or gold-containing products; wholesalers of physical gold investment products; banks; and gold bullion dealers. Conducts research on new technological and industrial uses for gold. Compiles statistics by country on mine production of gold; coinage use; and the production, distribution, and use of refined gold.

Silver Institute, *1112 16th St. N.W., #240 20036; (202) 835-0185. Fax, (202) 835-0155. Paul Bateman, executive director.*

Membership: companies that mine, refine, fabricate, or manufacture silver or silver-containing products. Conducts research on new technological and industrial uses for silver. Compiles statistics by country on mine production of silver; coinage use; the production, distribution, and use of refined silver; and the conversion of refined silver into other forms, such as silverware and jewelry.

Silver Users Assn., *1730 M St. N.W., #911 20036-4505; (202) 785-3050. Fax, (202) 659-5760. Walter L. Frankland Jr., executive vice president. Internet, http://www.uschamber.org/chamber/mall/silver.*

Membership: users of silver, including the photographic industry, silversmiths, and other manufacturers. Conducts research on silver market; monitors government activities in silver; analyzes government statistics on silver consumption and production.

See also American Society of Appraisers (p. 431); Appraisal Institute (p. 431)

🏭 INDUSTRIAL PRODUCTION/ MANUFACTURING

See also Construction (chap. 12); Motor Vehicles (chap. 19)

AGENCIES

Bureau of Export Administration *(Commerce Dept.), Strategic Industries and Economic Security, 14th St. and Constitution Ave. N.W., #3876 20230; (202) 482-4506. Fax, (202) 482-5650. William Derk, acting assistant director. Information, (202) 482-2721. Internet, http://www.bxa.doc.gov.*

Assists in providing for an adequate supply of strategic and critical materials for defense activities and civilian needs, including military requirements, and other domestic energy supplies; develops plans for industry to meet national emergencies. Studies the effect of imports on national security and recommends actions.

Census Bureau *(Commerce Dept.), Manufacturing and Construction, Suitland and Silver Hill Rds., Suitland, MD; (301) 457-4593. Fax, (301) 457-4583. Thomas L. Mesenbourg, acting chief.*

Collects, tabulates, and publishes statistics concerning the domestic manufacturing industry.

Economic Development Administration *(Commerce Dept.), Trade Adjustment Assistance, 14th St. and Constitution Ave. N.W., #7315 20230; (202) 482-2127. Fax, (202) 482-0466. Tony Meyer, director.*

Assists U.S. firms in increasing their competitiveness against foreign imports. Certifies eligibility and provides domestic firms and industries adversely affected by foreign trade with technical assistance under provisions of the Trade Act of 1974. Administers twelve regional Trade Adjustment Administrative Centers which offer consulting services to eligible U.S. firms.

Economics and Statistics Administration *(Commerce Dept.), 14th St. and Constitution Ave. N.W., #4848 20230; (202) 482-3727. Fax, (202) 482-0432. James Price, acting under secretary. Information, (202) 482-2235. Internet, esa@doc.gov or http://www.doc.gov/agencies/esa/index.html.*

Advises the secretary on economic policy matters, including inventory status and the short- and long-term outlook in output. Seeks to improve economic productivity and growth. Serves as departmental liaison with the Council of Economic Advisers and other government agencies concerned with economic policy. Supervises and sets policy for the Bureau of Economic Analysis.

International Trade Administration *(Commerce Dept.), Basic Industries, 14th St. and Constitution Ave. N.W., #4043 20230; (202) 482-0614. Fax, (202) 482-5666. Michael J. Copts, deputy assistant secretary.*

Analyzes and maintains data on domestic and international industries, including metals, materials, chemicals, construction, forest products, energy, automotives, and industrial machinery; responds to government and business inquiries about materials shortages in specific industries. Analyzes supply and demand, capacity and production capability, and capital formation requirements.

Technology Administration *(Commerce Dept.), Technology Competitiveness, 14th St. and Constitution Ave. N.W., #4418 20230; (202) 482-2100. Fax, (202) 219-8667. Jon Paugh, director, (202) 482-6101. Press, (202) 482-8321. Library, (202) 482-1288. Law library, (202) 482-5517. Publications request, (202) 482-1397. Internet, http://www.ta.doc.gov.*

Encourages industrial research to promote U.S. competitiveness and economic security. Increases private access to federally developed technology by encouraging industry involvement in research conducted at federal laboratories.

CONGRESS

Senate Commerce, Science, and Transportation Committee, *Subcommittee on Manufacturing and Competitiveness,* SD-508 20510; (202) 224-5115. Fax, (202) 224-8834. *Spencer Abraham, R-Mich., chair; Gregg Willhauck, legislative counsel. Internet, http://www.senate. gov/~commerce.*

Jurisdiction over industrial policy and general manufacturing issues, including investment, innovation, job creation, deregulation, corporate subsidies, and competitiveness.

NONPROFIT

American National Standards Institute, *7315 Wisconsin Ave., #250-E, Bethesda, MD 20814; (301) 469-3360. Fax, (301) 469-3361. John Donaldson, vice president, Conformity Assessment. Customer service, (888) 267-4783. Internet, info@ansi.org or http://www.ansi.org.*

Administers and coordinates the voluntary standardization system for the U.S. private sector; maintains staff contacts for specific industries. Serves as U.S. member of the International Organization for Standardization (ISO) and hosts the U.S. National Committee of the International Electrotechnical Commission (IEC). (ANSI headquarters in New York.)

American Production and Inventory Control Society, *500 W. Annandale Rd., Falls Church, VA 22046-4274; (703) 237-8344. Fax, (703) 237-8450. Jeffry Raynes, executive director. Internet, http://www.apics.org.*

Membership: integrated resource management professionals in the manufacturing and service industries. Offers certification exams in production and inventory management and integrated resource management; provides job placement assistance; conducts workshops and symposia.

Assn. for Manufacturing Technology, *7901 Westpark Dr., McLean, VA 22102; (703) 893-2900. Fax, (703) 893-1151. Don Carlson, president. Internet, http://www. mfgtech.org.*

Supports the U.S. manufacturing industry; sponsors workshops and seminars; fosters safety and technical standards. Monitors legislation and regulations.

Business Products Industry Assn., *301 N. Fairfax St., Alexandria, VA 22314; (703) 549-9040. Fax, (703) 683-7552. Jim McGarry, president. Internet, http://www. bpia.org.*

Membership: alliances of manufacturers, wholesalers, sales representatives, and retailers of office products and furniture. Conducts conferences and training for members; studies industry performance and trends in distrib-

ution, technology, and demographics. Interests include global competitiveness.

Envelope Manufacturers Assn. of America, *300 N. Washington St., #500, Alexandria, VA 22314; (703) 739-2200. Fax, (703) 739-2209. Maynard H. Benjamin, president. Internet, http://www.envelope.org.*

Membership: envelope manufacturers and suppliers. Monitors legislation and regulations.

Flexible Packaging Assn., *1090 Vermont Ave. N.W., #500 20005-4960; (202) 842-3880. Fax, (202) 842-3841. Glenn E. Braswell, president. Internet, fpa@flexpack.org.*

Researches packaging trends and technical developments; compiles industry statistics. Monitors legislation and regulations.

Independent Lubricant Manufacturers Assn., *651 S. Washington St., Alexandria, VA 22314; (703) 684-5574. Fax, (703) 836-8503. Richard H. Ekfelt, executive director. Internet, http://www.ilma.org.*

Membership: U.S. and international companies that manufacture automotive, industrial, and metalworking lubricants; associates include suppliers and related businesses. Conducts workshops and conferences; compiles statistics. Monitors legislation and regulations.

Industrial Designers Society of America, *1142 Walker Rd., Great Falls, VA 22066-1836; (703) 759-0100. Fax, (703) 759-7679. Robert Schwartz, executive director. Internet, idsa@erols.com or http://www.idsa.org.*

Membership: designers of products, equipment, instruments, furniture, transportation, packages, exhibits, information services, and related services. Provides the Bureau of Labor Statistics and U.S. Information Agency with industry information. Monitors legislation and regulations.

Industrial Research Institute, *1550 M St. N.W., #1100 20005-1712; (202) 296-8811. Fax, (202) 776-0756. Charles F. Larson, executive director. Internet, http:// www.iriinc.org.*

Membership: companies that maintain laboratories for industrial research. Seeks to improve the process of industrial research by promoting cooperative efforts among companies, between the academic and research communities, and between industry and the government. Monitors legislation and regulations concerning technology, industry, and national competitiveness.

Institute of Packaging Professionals, *481 Carlisle Dr., Herndon, VA 20170-4823; (703) 318-8970. Fax, (703) 814-4961. William C. Pflaum, executive director. Internet, info@pkgmatters.com or http://www.packinfo-world.org.*

Represents the interests of packaging professionals. Conducts an annual packaging design competition. Publishes journals and newsletters.

International Sleep Products Assn., *333 Commerce St., Alexandria, VA 22314; (703) 683-8371. Fax, (703) 683-4503. Russell L. Abolt, executive vice president. Internet, http://www.sleepproducts.org.*

Membership: manufacturers of bedding and mattresses. Compiles statistics on the industry. (Affiliated with Sleep Products Safety Council and the Better Sleep Council.)

International Union of Electronic, Electrical, Salaried, Machine, and Furniture Workers, *1126 16th St. N.W. 20036; (202) 296-1201. Fax, (202) 785-4563. Edward L. Fire, president, (202) 785-7201. Internet, http://www.iue.org.*

Membership: approximately 125,000 workers in the field of industrial electronics and furniture and general manufacturing. Helps members negotiate pay, benefits, and better working conditions; conducts training programs and workshops. (Affiliated with the AFL-CIO.)

Manufacturers' Alliance for Productivity and Innovation, *1525 Wilson Blvd., #900, Arlington, VA 22209; (703) 841-9000. Fax, (703) 841-9514. Kenneth McLennan, president.*

Membership: companies involved in high technology industries, including electronics, telecommunications, precision instruments, computers, and the automotive and aerospace industries. Seeks to increase industrial productivity. Conducts research; organizes discussion councils. Monitors legislation and regulations.

National Assn. of Manufacturers, *1331 Pennsylvania Ave. N.W. 20004; (202) 637-3000. Fax, (202) 637-3182. Jerry Jasinowski, president. Press, (202) 637-3094. Internet, http://www.nam.org.*

Represents industry views (mainly of manufacturers) to government on national and international issues. Reviews legislation, administrative rulings, and judicial decisions affecting industry. Sponsors the Human Resources Forum; operates a computer network for members and the public that provides information on legislative and other news; conducts programs on labor relations, occupational safety and health, regulatory and consumer affairs, environmental trade and technology, and other business issues.

National Coalition for Advanced Manufacturing, *1201 New York Ave., #750 20005; (202) 216-2740. Fax, (202) 289-7618. Leo Reddy, president. Toll-free, (800) 622-*

3260. Internet, NACFAM@aol.com or http://www.nacfam. org.

Seeks a public policy environment more supportive of advanced manufacturing and industrial modernization as keys to global economic competitiveness. Advocates greater national focus on industrial base modernization, increased investment in plant and equipment, accelerated development and deployment of advanced manufacturing technology, and reform of technical education and training. (Affiliated with the Foundation for Industrial Modernization.)

National Industrial Council, *1331 Pennsylvania Ave. N.W., #600 20004-1706; (202) 637-3053. Fax, (202) 637-3182. Barry Buzby, executive director, State Associations; Mark Stuart, executive director, Employer Associations, (202) 637-3054. Internet, http://www.nam.org.*

Membership: employer associations at the regional, state, and local levels. Works to strengthen U.S. competitive enterprise system. Represents views of industry on business and economic issues; sponsors conferences and seminars. (Department of the National Assn. of Manufacturers.)

Oil, Chemical, and Atomic Workers International Union, *2722 Merrilee Dr., #250, Fairfax, VA 22031; (703) 876-9300. Fax, (703) 876-8952. Paula R. Littles, legislative director. Internet, ocaw@ocaw.org or http://www. ocaw.org.*

Membership: approximately 90,000 workers in the energy, chemical, pharmaceutical, and allied industries. Assists members with contract negotiation and grievances; conducts training programs and workshops. Monitors legislation and regulations. (Headquarters in Lakewood, Colo.; affiliated with the AFL-CIO.)

Rubber Manufacturers Assn., *1400 K St. N.W., #900 20005; (202) 682-4800. Fax, (202) 682-4854. Donald Shea, president. Toll-free, (800) 220-7622. Internet, http://www.rma.org.*

Membership: manufacturers of tires, tubes, roofing, sporting goods, and mechanical and industrial products. Interests include recycling.

U.S. Business and Industrial Council, *122 C St. N.W., #815 20001; (202) 628-2211. Fax, (202) 628-3698. Kevin L. Kearns, president. Internet, usbic@aol.com.*

Advocates energy independence, reindustrialization, and effective use of natural resources and manufacturing capacity. Current issues include business tax reduction, the liability crisis, defense and other federal spending, and the trade deficit. Media network distributes op-ed pieces to newspapers and radio stations.

Clothing and Textiles

See also Cotton (chap. 2)

AGENCIES

Federal Trade Commission, *Consumer Protection,* 6th and Pennsylvania Ave. N.W., #466H 20580; (202) 326-2996. Fax, (202) 326-3799. Elaine D. Kolish, associate director, Enforcement. Internet, http://www.ftc.gov.

Division enforces labeling acts for textile, wool, and fur fiber products; assigns product registration numbers.

International Trade Administration *(Commerce Dept.), Textiles, Apparel, and Consumer Goods Industries,* 14th St. and Constitution Ave. N.W., #3001A 20230; (202) 482-3737. Fax, (202) 482-2331. Troy H. Cribb, deputy assistant secretary.

Participates in negotiating bilateral textile and apparel import restraint agreements; responsible for textile, apparel, and consumer goods export expansion programs and reduction of nontariff barriers; provides data on economic conditions in the domestic textile, apparel, and consumer goods markets, including impact of imports.

NONPROFIT

American Apparel Manufacturers Assn., *2500 Wilson Blvd., #301, Arlington, VA 22201; (703) 524-1864. Fax, (703) 522-6741. Larry K. Martin, president. Toll-free, (800) 520-2262. Internet, http://www.americanapparel.com.*

Membership: manufacturers of apparel and allied needle-trade products. Interests include product flammability.

American Fiber Manufacturers Assn., *1150 17th St. N.W., #310 20036; (202) 296-6508. Fax, (202) 296-3052. Paul T. O'Day, president. Internet, afma@afma.org or http://www.fibersource.com.*

Membership: U.S. producers of manufactured (man-made) fibers, filaments, and yarns. Interests include international trade, education, and environmental and technical services. Monitors legislation and regulations.

American Textile Machinery Assn., *111 Park Pl., Falls Church, VA 22046; (703) 538-1789. Fax, (703) 241-5603. Harry W. Buzzerd Jr., executive vice president. Internet, http://www.webmasters.net/atma.*

Membership: U.S.-based manufacturers of textile machinery and related parts and accessories. Interests include competitiveness and expansion of foreign markets. Monitors legislation and regulations.

American Textile Manufacturers Institute, *1130 Connecticut Ave. N.W., #1200 20036-3954; (202) 862-0500. Fax, (202) 862-0570. Carlos F. J. Moore, executive vice president. Internet, http://www.atmi.org.*

Membership: U.S. companies that spin, weave, knit, or finish textiles from natural fibers, and associate members from affiliated industries. Interests include domestic and world markets. Monitors legislation and regulations.

Footwear Distributors and Retailers of America, *1319 F St. N.W., #700 20004; (202) 737-5660. Fax, (202) 638-2615. Peter T. Mangione, president. Internet, http://www.fdra.org.*

Membership: companies that operate shoe retail outlets. Provides business support and government relations to members. Interests include intellectual property rights, ocean shipping rates, trade with China, and labeling regulations.

Footwear Industries of America, *1420 K St. N.W., #600 20005; (202) 789-1420. Fax, (202) 789-4058. Fawn Evenson, president. Internet, http://www.fia.org.*

Membership: manufacturers of footwear and their suppliers, importers, and distributors. Provides members with information on the industry, including import and export data. Monitors legislation and regulations.

International Fabricare Institute, *12251 Tech Rd., Silver Spring, MD 20904; (301) 622-1900. Fax, (301) 236-9320. William E. Fisher, executive vice president. Internet, http://www.ifi.org.*

Membership: drycleaners and launderers. Conducts research and provides information on products and services. Monitors legislation and regulations.

National Cotton Council of America, *1521 New Hampshire Ave. N.W. 20036; (202) 745-7805. Fax, (202) 483-4040. John Maguire, vice president, Washington Office. Internet, http://www.cotton.org/ncc.*

Membership: all segments of the U.S. cotton industry. Formulates positions on trade policy and negotiations; seeks to improve competitiveness of U.S. exports; sponsors programs to educate the public about flammable fabrics. (Headquarters in Memphis.)

Uniform and Textile Service Assn., *1300 N. 17th St., #750, Arlington, VA 22209; (703) 247-2600. Fax, (703) 841-4750. David F. Hobson, president. Internet, info@utsa.com or http://www.utsa.com.*

Membership: companies that provide uniforms and textile products to commercial and government enterprises. Sponsors seminars and conferences; provides information on environmental policy and procedures to members. Monitors legislation and regulations.

Union of Needletrades Industrial and Textile Employees (UNITE), *888 16th St. N.W., #303 20006; (202) 347-7417. Fax, (202) 347-0708. Jay Mazur, president. Internet, unite@bellatlantic.net or http://www.unite.org.*

Membership: approximately 285,000 workers in basic apparel and textiles, millinery, shoe, laundry, retail, and related industries; and in auto parts and auto supply. Assists members with contract negotiation and grievances; conducts training programs and workshops. Monitors legislation and regulations. (Headquarters in New York; affiliated with the AFL-CIO.)

Electronics and Appliances

NONPROFIT

Consumer Electronic Manufacturers Assn., *2500 Wilson Blvd., Arlington, VA 22201-3834; (703) 907-7600. Fax, (703) 907-7601. Gary Shapiro, president. Internet, http://www.cemacity.org.*

Membership: U.S. consumer electronics manufacturers. Promotes the industry; sponsors seminars and conferences; conducts research; consults with member companies. Monitors legislation and regulations. (Affiliated with Electronic Industries Assn.)

Electronic Industries Assn., *2500 Wilson Blvd., #400, Arlington, VA 22201-3834; (703) 907-7500. Fax, (703) 907-7501. Peter F. McCloskey, president. Internet, http://www.eia.org.*

Membership: manufacturers, dealers, installers, and distributors of consumer electronics products. Provides consumer information and data on industry trends; advocates an open market. Monitors legislation and regulations.

Gas Appliance Manufacturers Assn., *1901 N. Moore St., #1100, Arlington, VA 22209; (703) 525-9565. Fax, (703) 525-0718. C. Reuben Autery, president. Internet, gamaorg@aol.com or http://www.gamanet.org.*

Membership: manufacturers of gas appliances and equipment for residential and commercial use and related industries. Advocates product improvement; provides market statistics. Monitors legislation and regulations.

National Electrical Contractors Assn., *3 Bethesda Metro Center, #1100, Bethesda, MD 20814; (301) 657-3110. Fax, (301) 215-4500. John Grau, executive vice president. Internet, http://www.necanet.org.*

Membership: electrical contractors who build and service electrical wiring, equipment, and appliances. Represents members in collective bargaining with union workers; sponsors research and educational programs.

Optoelectronics Industry Development Assn., *2010 Massachusetts Ave. N.W., #200 20036-1023; (202) 785-4426. Fax, (202) 785-4428. Fred Welsh, executive director. Internet, http://www.oida.org.*

Membership: users and suppliers of optoelectronics in North America. Promotes the global competitiveness of members; provides a forum for exchange of information; conducts workshops and conferences; sponsors research. Monitors legislation and regulations.

Steel, Metalworking, Machinery

NONPROFIT

American Boiler Manufacturers Assn., *950 N. Glebe Rd., Arlington, VA 22203; (703) 522-7350. Fax, (703) 522-2665. Russell N. Mosher, president. Internet, http://www.abma.com.*

Membership: manufacturers of boiler systems and boiler-related products, including fuel-burning systems. Interests include energy and environmental issues.

American Gear Manufacturers Assn., *1500 King St., #201, Alexandria, VA 22314; (703) 684-0211. Fax, (703) 684-0242. Joe T. Franklin, president. Internet, http://www.agma.org.*

Membership: gear manufacturers, suppliers, and industry consultants. Conducts workshops, seminars, and conferences; develops industry standards; sponsors research. Monitors legislation and regulations.

American Machine Tool Distributors Assn., *1335 Rockville Pike, #300, Rockville, MD 20852; (301) 738-1200. Fax, (301) 738-9499. Ralph Nappi, president. Toll-free, (800) 878-2683. Internet, http://www.gardnerweb.com/amtda.*

Membership: distributors of machine tools. Supports advances in manufacturing and expansion of international trade. Monitors legislation and regulations.

American Wire Producers Assn., *515 King St., #420, Alexandria, VA 22314; (703) 549-6003. Fax, (703) 684-6048. Kimberly Korbel, executive director. Internet, AWPAwire@aol.com.*

Membership: companies that produce carbon, alloy, and stainless steel wire and wire products in the United States. Interests include imports of rod, wire, and wire products and enforcement of antidumping and countervailing duty laws. Publishes survey of the domestic wire industry. Monitors legislation and regulations.

International Assn. of Bridge, Structural, Ornamental, and Reenforcing Iron Workers, *1750 New*

York Ave. N.W., #400 20006; (202) 383-4800. Fax, (202) 638-4856. Jake West, president.

Membership: approximately 82,000 iron workers. Helps members negotiate pay, benefits, and better working conditions; conducts training programs and workshops. Monitors legislation and regulations. (Affiliated with the AFL-CIO.)

International Assn. of Machinists and Aerospace Workers, *9000 Machinists Pl. 20772-2687; (301) 967-4500. Fax, (301) 967-4588. Thomas Buffenbarger, president. Internet, http://www.iamaw.org.*

Membership: machinists in more than 200 industries. Helps members negotiate pay, benefits, and better working conditions; conducts training programs and workshops. Monitors legislation and regulations. (Affiliated with the AFL-CIO, the Canadian Labour Congress, the Railway Labor Executives Assn., the International Metalworkers Federation, and the International Transport Workers' Federation.)

Machinery Dealers National Assn., *315 S. Patrick St., Alexandria, VA 22314; (703) 836-9300. Fax, (703) 836-9303. Darryl D. McEwen, executive vice president. Internet, http://www.mdna.org/mdna.html.*

Membership: companies that buy and sell used capital equipment. Establishes a code of ethics for members; publishes a buyer's guide that lists members by types of machinery they sell.

National Tooling and Machining Assn., *9300 Livingston Rd., Ft. Washington, MD 20744; (301) 248-6200. Fax, (301) 248-7104. Matthew B. Coffey, president. Internet, http://www.ntma.org.*

Membership: members of the contract precision metalworking industry, including tool, die, mold, diecasting die, and special machining companies. Assists members in developing and expanding their domestic and foreign markets. Offers training program, insurance, and legal advice; compiles statistical information. Monitors legislation and regulations.

Outdoor Power Equipment Institute, *341 S. Patrick St., Alexandria, VA 22314; (703) 549-7600. Fax, (703) 549-7604. Dennis C. Dix, president. Internet, http://opei.mow.org.*

Manufacturers of powered lawn and garden maintenance products, components and attachments, and their suppliers. Promotes safe use of outdoor power equipment; keeps statistics on the industry; fosters exchange of information. Monitors legislation and regulations.

Sheet Metal Workers' International Assn., *1750 New York Ave. N.W. 20006; (202) 783-5880. Fax, (202)*

662-0895. Arthur Moore, president. Internet, http://smwia.org.

Membership: more than 130,000 U.S. and Canadian workers in the building and construction trades, manufacturing, and the railroad and shipyard industries. Assists members with contract negotiation and grievances; conducts training programs and workshops. Monitors legislation and regulations. (Affiliated with the Sheet Metal and Air Conditioning Contractors' Assn., the AFL-CIO, and the Canadian Labour Congress.)

Specialty Steel Industry of North America, *3050 K St. N.W., #400 20007; (202) 342-8630. Fax, (202) 342-8451. David Hartquist, counsel. Toll-free, (800) 982-0355. Internet, ssina@ssina.com or http://www.ssina.com.*

Membership: manufacturers of products in stainless and other specialty steels. Establishes quality standards and manufacturing techniques; sponsors workshops; operates a hotline for technical questions.

Steel Manufacturers Assn., *1730 Rhode Island Ave. N.W., #907 20036-3101; (202) 296-1515. Fax, (202) 296-2506. Thomas A. Danjczek, president. Internet, http://www.steelnet.org.*

Membership: steel producers in North America and abroad. Helps members exchange information on technical matters; provides information on the steel industry to the public and government. Monitors legislation and regulations.

United Steelworkers of America, *1150 17th St. N.W., #300 20036; (202) 778-4384. Fax, (202) 293-5308. William Klinefelter, legislative director. Toll-free, (800) 248-8792. Internet, http://www.uswa.org.*

Membership: more than 700,000 steelworkers in the United States and Canada. Helps members negotiate pay, benefits, and better working conditions; conducts training programs and workshops. Monitors legislation and regulations. (Headquarters in Pittsburgh; affiliated with the AFL-CIO.)

▨ INSURANCE

See also Health (chap. 11); Military Personnel and Veterans (chap. 15); Pensions and Benefits (chap. 7); Real Estate (chap. 12)

AGENCIES

Federal Insurance Administration *(Federal Emergency Management Agency), 500 C St. S.W., #430 20472;*

(202) 646-2781. Fax, (202) 646-3445. Joann Howard, administrator. Internet, http://www.fema.gov.

Administers federal crime and flood insurance programs, including the National Flood Insurance Program. Makes available to eligible homeowners low-cost flood and crime insurance. Flood insurance information: (202) 731-5300; (800) 427-4661, toll-free, nationwide non-claims business; (800) 638-6831, Alaska and Hawaii; (800) 492-6605, Maryland. Crime insurance information: (202) 251-1660; (800) 638-8780, nationwide customer service.

Small Business Administration, *Disaster Assistance,* *409 3rd St. S.W., #6050 20416; (202) 205-6734. Fax, (202) 205-7728. Bernard Kulik, associate administrator. Internet, http://www.sba.gov.*

Provides victims of physical disasters with disaster and economic injury loans for homes, businesses, and personal property. Lends to individual homeowners, business concerns of all sizes, and nonprofit institutions to repair or replace damaged structures and furnishings, business machinery, equipment, and inventory.

CONGRESS

House Banking and Financial Services Committee, *Subcommittee on Housing and Community Opportunity, B303 RHOB 20515; (202) 225-6634. Rick A. Lazio, R-N.Y., chair; Joseph M. Ventrone, staff director.*

Jurisdiction over federal flood, fire, and earthquake insurance programs; oversees activities of the insurance industry pertaining to these programs.

House Commerce Committee, *Subcommittee on Finance and Hazardous Materials, 2125 RHOB 20515; (202) 225-2927. Fax, (202) 225-1919. Michael G. Oxley, R-Ohio, chair; James E. Derderian, staff director. Internet, http://www.house.gov/commerce.*

Jurisdiction over legislation on insurance, except health insurance.

Senate Banking, Housing, and Urban Affairs Committee, *Subcommittee on Housing Opportunity and Community Development, SD-534 20510; (202) 224-7391. Connie Mack, R-Fla., chair; Christopher Lord, staff director. Internet, http://www.senate.gov/~banking.*

Jurisdiction over federal flood, crime, fire, and earthquake insurance programs; oversees activities of the insurance industry pertaining to these programs.

Senate Judiciary Committee, *Subcommittee on Antitrust, Business Rights, and Competition, SD-161 20510; (202) 224-9494. Fax, (202) 228-0463. Mike*

DeWine, R-Ohio, chair; Louie DuPart, chief counsel. Internet, http://www.senate.gov/committee/judiciary.html.

Jurisdiction over legislation on insurance, except health insurance.

NONPROFIT

Alliance of American Insurers, *1211 Connecticut Ave. N.W., #400 20036; (202) 822-8811. Fax, (202) 872-1885. David M. Farmer, senior vice president, Federal Affairs. Internet, http://www.allianceai.org.*

Membership: property and casualty insurance companies. Provides educational and advisory services for members on insurance issues. (Headquarters in Schaumburg, Ill.)

American Academy of Actuaries, *1100 17th St. N.W., 7th Floor 20036; (202) 223-8196. Fax, (202) 872-1948. Wilson W. Wyatt Jr., executive director. Internet, http://www.actuary.org.*

Membership: professional actuaries practicing in the areas of life, health, liability, property, and casualty insurance; pensions; government insurance plans; and general consulting. Provides information on actuarial matters, including insurance and pensions; develops professional standards; advises public policy makers.

American Council of Life Insurance, *1001 Pennsylvania Ave. N.W., #500S 20004-2599; (202) 624-2000. Fax, (202) 624-2319. Carroll A. Campbell Jr., president. Press, (202) 624-2416. National Insurance Consumer Helpline, (800) 942-4242. Internet, http://www.acli.com.*

Membership: life insurance companies authorized to do business in the United States. Conducts research and compiles statistics at state and federal levels. Monitors legislation and regulations.

American Insurance Assn., *1130 Connecticut Ave. N.W., #1000 20036; (202) 828-7100. Fax, (202) 293-1219. Robert E. Vagley, president. Press, (202) 828-7116. Library, (202) 828-7183. Internet, http://www.aiadc.org.*

Membership: companies providing property and casualty insurance. Conducts public relations and educational activities; provides information on issues related to property and casualty insurance. Library open to the public by appointment.

American Society of Pension Actuaries, *4350 N. Fairfax Dr., #820, Arlington, VA 22203-1619; (703) 516-9300. Fax, (703) 516-9308. Brian Graff, executive director. Internet, aspa@erols.com or http://www.aspa.org.*

Membership: professional pension plan actuaries, administrators, consultants, and other benefits professionals. Sponsors educational programs to prepare actuaries and consultants for professional exams. Monitors legislation.

Assn. for Advanced Life Underwriting, *1922 F St. N.W. 20006-4387; (202) 331-6081. Fax, (202) 331-2164. David J. Stertzer, executive vice president. Internet, http://www.agents-online.com.*

Membership: specialized underwriters in the fields of estate analysis, charitable planning, business insurance, pension planning, and employee benefit plans. Monitors legislation and regulations on small-business taxes and capital formation.

Assn. of Trial Lawyers of America, *1050 31st St. N.W. 20007-4499; (202) 965-3500. Fax, (202) 342-5484. Thomas H. Henderson Jr., executive director. Internet, http://www.atlanet.org.*

Membership: attorneys, judges, law professors, and students. Interests include aspects of legal and legislative activity relating to the adversary system and trial by jury, including property and casualty insurance.

Consumer Federation of America's Insurance Group, *1424 16th St. N.W., #604 20036; (202) 387-6121. Fax, (202) 265-7989. Robert Hunter, director.*

Public interest organization that conducts research and provides consumers with information on buying insurance. Interests include auto, homeowner, renter, and life insurance. Monitors legislation and regulations.

Council of Insurance Agents and Brokers, *701 Pennsylvania Ave. N.W., #750 20004; (202) 783-4400. Fax, (202) 783-4410. Ken A. Crerar, president. Internet, ciab@ciab.com or http://www.ciab.com.*

Represents commercial property and casualty insurance agencies and brokerage firms. Members offer insurance products and risk management services to business, government, and the public.

ERISA Industry Committee, *1400 L St. N.W., #350 20005; (202) 789-1400. Fax, (202) 789-1120. Mark J. Ugoretz, president. Internet, eric@eric.org or http://www.eric.org.*

Membership: major U.S. employers. Advocates members' positions on employee retirement, health care coverage, and welfare benefit plans; promotes flexibility and cost-effectiveness in employee benefits. Monitors legislation and regulations.

General Agents and Managers Assn., *1922 F St. N.W. 20006; (202) 331-6088. Fax, (202) 785-5712. Rene Pietrangelo, managing director. Toll-free, (800) 345-2687. Internet, http://www.gamaweb.com.*

Membership: general agents and managers who provide life insurance and related financial products and services. Provides information and programs for members.

Independent Insurance Agents of America, Inc., *127 S. Peyton St., Alexandria, VA 22314; (703) 683-4422. Fax, (703) 683-7556. Jeff Yates, senior vice president. Internet, http://www.iiaa.org.*

Provides educational and advisory services; researches issues pertaining to auto, home, business, life, and health insurance; offers cooperative advertising program to members. Political action committee monitors legislation and regulations.

Insurance Information Institute, *1750 K St. N.W. 20006; (202) 833-1580. Fax, (202) 223-5779. Carolyn Gorman, vice president. Internet, mveiii@pop.erols.com or http://www.iii.org.*

Membership: property and casualty insurance companies. Monitors state and federal issues concerning insurance. Serves as a primary source for information, analysis, and referral concerning property and casualty insurance. (Headquarters in New York.)

Mortgage Insurance Companies of America, *727 15th St. N.W. 20005; (202) 393-5566. Fax, (202) 393-5557. Suzanne C. Hutchinson, executive vice president.*

Membership: companies that provide guarantee insurance on residential mortgage loans.

National Assn. of Independent Insurers, *444 N. Capitol St. N.W., #801 20001; (202) 639-0490. Fax, (202) 639-0494. John Lobert, senior vice president, Government Relations. Internet, http://www.naii.org.*

Membership: companies providing property and casualty insurance. Monitors legislation and compiles statistics; interests include auto and no-fault insurance and personal lines. (Headquarters in Des Plaines, Ill.)

National Assn. of Independent Life Brokerage Agencies, *8201 Greensboro Dr., #300, McClean, VA 22102; (703) 610-9020. Fax, (703) 610-9005. Joe Normandy, executive director. Internet, http://www.naiba.com.*

Membership: owners of independent life insurance agencies. Fosters the responsible and effective distribution of life insurance and related financial services; provides a forum for exchange of information among members. Monitors legislation and regulations.

National Assn. of Insurance Brokers, *1300 Eye St. N.W., #490E 20005; (202) 628-6700. Fax, (202) 628-6707. Carl A. Modecki, president. Internet, http://www.naib.org.*

Membership: commercial retail insurance brokerages (firms that engage in devising commercial programs for clients). Monitors legislation and regulations that affect insurance brokers, their clients, and the insurance industry.

National Assn. of Insurance Commissioners, *444 N. Capitol St. N.W., #701 20001-1512; (202) 624-7790. Fax, (202) 624-8579. Kevin Cronin, Washington counsel. Internet, http://www.naic.org.*

Membership: state insurance commissioners, directors, and supervisors. Provides members with information on computer information services, legal and market conduct, and financial services; publishes research and statistics on the insurance industry. Monitors legislation and regulations. (Headquarters in Kansas City, Mo.)

National Assn. of Life Underwriters, *1922 F St. N.W. 20006-4387; (202) 331-6000. Fax, (202) 835-9601. William V. Regan III, executive vice president. Internet, http://www.agents-online.com/NALU/NALUhome.html.*

Federation of affiliated state and local life underwriters. Provides information on life and health insurance and other financial services; sponsors education and training programs.

National Assn. of Professional Insurance Agents, *400 N. Washington St., Alexandria, VA 22314-2353; (703) 836-9340. Fax, (703) 836-1279. Douglas Culkin, executive vice president. Toll-free, (800) 742-6900. Press, (703) 518-1351. Internet, http://www.pianet.com.*

Membership: independent insurance agents and brokers. Operates schools to provide agents with basic training; offers seminars and provides educational materials. Monitors legislation and regulations.

Nonprofit Risk Management Center, *1001 Connecticut Ave. N.W., #900 20036; (202) 785-3891. Fax, (202) 833-5747. Melanie Herman, executive director. Internet, info@nonprofitrisk.org or http://www.nonprofitrisk.org.*

Assists all groups engaged in charitable service, including nonprofit organizations, government entities, and corporate volunteer programs, to improve the quality of and reduce the cost of their insurance. Provides information on insurance and risk management issues through conferences and publications.

Product Liability Alliance, *1725 K St. N.W. 20006; (202) 872-0885. Fax, (202) 296-5940. James A. Anderson Jr., vice president, Government Relations.*

Membership: manufacturers, product sellers and their insurers, and trade associations. Promotes enactment of federal product liability tort reform legislation.

Product Liability Coordinating Committee, *1001 19th St. North, #800, Arlington, VA 22209; (703) 276-*

5045. Fax, (703) 276-5166. Pat Rowland, executive director.

Membership: major corporations. Represents members' views concerning reform of national product liability legislation.

Reinsurance Assn. of America, *1301 Pennsylvania Ave. N.W., #900 20004; (202) 638-3690. Fax, (202) 638-0936. Franklin W. Nutter, president. Internet, http://www.raanet.org.*

Membership: companies writing property and casualty reinsurance. Serves as an information clearinghouse.

PATENTS, COPYRIGHTS, AND TRADEMARKS

AGENCIES

Justice Dept., *Civil Division, 1100 L St. N.W. 20005; (202) 514-7223. Fax, (202) 307-0345. Vito J. DiPietro, director, Intellectual Property.*

Represents the United States in patent, copyright, and trademark cases. Includes the defense of patent infringement suits; legal proceedings to establish government priority of invention; defense of administrative acts of the Register of Copyrights; and actions on behalf of the government involving the use of trademarks.

Patent and Trademark Office *(Commerce Dept.), 2121 Crystal Park II, #906, Arlington, VA; (703) 305-8600. Fax, (703) 305-8664. Bruce A. Lehman, commissioner. Information, (703) 308-4357. Press, (703) 305-8341. Library, (703) 308-0808. TDD, (703) 305-7785. Toll-free, (800) 786-9199. Internet, http://www.uspto.gov.*

Grants patents, registers trademarks, and provides patent and trademark information. Scientific library and search file of U.S. and foreign patents available for public use.

State Dept., *Intellectual Property and Competition, Main State Bldg., #3828 20520; (202) 647-2046. Fax, (202) 647-0892. James McGlinchey, division chief.*

Handles multilateral and bilateral policy formulation involving patents, copyrights, and trademarks, and international industrial property of U.S. nationals.

U.S. Customs Service *(Treasury Dept.), Intellectual Property Rights, 1300 Pennsylvania Ave. N.W., 3rd Floor 20229; (202) 927-2330. Fax, (202) 927-1873. John Atwood, chief.*

Responsible for Customs recordation of registered trademarks and copyrights. Enforces rules and regulations pertaining to intellectual property rights. Coordinates enforcement of International Trade Commission exclusion orders against unfairly competing goods. Determines admissibility of restricted merchandise and cultural properties. Provides support to and coordinates with international organizations and the Office of the U.S. Trade Representative.

CONGRESS

House Judiciary Committee, *Subcommittee on Courts and Intellectual Property, B351A RHOB 20515; (202) 225-5741. Fax, (202) 225-3673. Howard Coble, R-N.C., chair; Mitch Glazier, chief counsel. Internet, http://www. house.gov/judiciary.*

Jurisdiction over patent, trademark, and copyright legislation, including legislation on home audio and video taping, intellectual property rights, and financial syndication. Oversees the Patent and Trademark Office, Copyright Office, and Copyright Royalty Tribunal. (Some jurisdictions shared with House Science Committee.)

House Science Committee, *Subcommittee on Technology, 2319 RHOB 20515; (202) 225-8844. Fax, (202) 225-4438. Constance A. Morella, R-Md., chair; Richard Russell, staff director. Internet, http://www.house.gov/science.*

Jurisdiction over patent and intellectual property policies (shared with House Judiciary Committee).

Library of Congress, *Copyright Office, 101 Independence Ave. S.E., #403 20559; (202) 707-8350. Fax, (202) 707-8366. Marybeth Peters, register of copyrights. Information, (202) 707-3000. Internet, http://www.loc.gov/copyright.*

Provides information on copyright registration procedures and requirements, copyright law, and international copyrights; registers copyright claims and maintains public records of copyright registrations. Copyright record searches conducted on an hourly fee basis. Files open to public for research during weekday business hours. Does not give legal advice on copyright matters.

Senate Judiciary Committee, *SD-224 20510; (202) 224-5225. Fax, (202) 224-9102. Orrin G. Hatch, R-Utah, chair; Manus Cooney, chief counsel. Internet, http://www.senate.gov/committee/judiciary.html.*

Jurisdiction over patent, trademark, and copyright legislation, including legislation on home audio and video taping, intellectual property rights, and financial syndication.

JUDICIARY

U.S. Court of Appeals for the Federal Circuit, *717 Madison Pl. N.W. 20439; (202) 633-6556. Fax, (202) 633-6353. Haldane Robert Mayer, chief judge; Jan Horbaly, clerk, (202) 633-9613. Electronic bulletin board, (202) 633-9608 or (202) 786-6584.*

Reviews decisions of U.S. Patent and Trademark Office on applications and interferences regarding patents and trademarks; hears appeals on patent infringement cases from district courts.

NONPROFIT

American Bar Assn., *Intellectual Property Law, 740 15th St. N.W., 9th Floor 20005; (202) 662-1000. Fax, (202) 662-1032. Hayden Gregory, staff legislative consultant. Internet, http://www.abanet.org.*

Membership: attorneys practicing intellectual property law, including patent, trademark, copyright, and related unfair competition law. Promotes development and improvement of intellectual property treaties, laws, and regulations, and monitors their enforcement; conducts continuing legal education programs.

American Intellectual Property Law Assn., *2001 Jefferson Davis Hwy., #203, Arlington, VA 22202; (703) 415-0780. Fax, (703) 415-0786. Michael K. Kirk, executive director. Internet, aipla@aipla.com or http://www.aipla.com.*

Membership: lawyers practicing in the field of patents, trademarks, and copyrights (intellectual property law). Holds continuing legal education conferences.

Assn. of American Publishers, *Copyright and New Technology, 1718 Connecticut Ave. N.W., #700 20009; (202) 232-3335. Fax, (202) 745-0694. Carol A. Risher, vice president. Internet, http://www.publishers.org.*

Monitors copyright activity in government, Congress, and international forums and institutions; sponsors seminars open to the public for a fee.

Intellectual Property Owners, *1255 23rd St. N.W., #850 20037; (202) 466-2396. Fax, (202) 466-2893. Herbert C. Wamsley, executive director. Internet, http://www.ipo.org.*

Monitors legislation and conducts educational programs to protect intellectual property through patents, trademarks, copyrights, and trade secret laws.

National Assn. of Manufacturers, *Intellectual Property Subcommittee, 1331 Pennsylvania Ave. N.W., #600 20004-1790; (202) 637-3147. Fax, (202) 637-3182. David Peyton, director. Internet, http://www.nam.org.*

Develops policy and legislation on patents, copyrights, and trademarks.

National School Boards Assn., *1680 Duke St., Alexandria, VA 22314; (703) 838-6722. Fax, (703) 683-7590. Julie Underwood, general counsel. Internet, http://www. nsba.org.*

Promotes a broad interpretation of copyright law to permit legitimate scholarly use of published and musical works, videotaped programs, and materials for computer-assisted instruction.

U.S. Chamber of Commerce, *Business and Government Policy,* 1615 H St. N.W., #500 20062-2000; (202) 463-5500. Fax, (202) 887-3445. Vacant, director, Public Policy. Internet, http://www.uschamber.org.

Monitors legislation and regulations on patents, copyrights, and trademarks.

See also Council of Scientific Society Presidents (p. 594); Information Industry Assn. (p. 87); National Assn. of Plant Patent Owners (p. 603); Recording Industry Assn. of America (p. 111)

 # SALES AND SERVICES

See also Antitrust (chap. 14); Consumer Protection (chap. 1); Food and Nutrition (chap. 2)

AGENCIES

Bureau of Labor Statistics *(Labor Dept.), Prices and Living Conditions,* 2 Massachusetts Ave. N.E., #3120 20212; (202) 606-6960. Fax, (202) 606-7080. Kenneth V. Dalton, associate commissioner.

Collects, processes, analyzes, and disseminates data relating to prices and consumer expenditures; maintains the Consumer Price Index.

Census Bureau *(Commerce Dept.), Services Division,* Suitland and Silver Hill Rds., Suitland, MD; (301) 457-2668. Fax, (301) 457-1343. Carole A. Ambler, chief.

Provides data of five-year census programs on retail, wholesale, and service industries. Conducts periodic monthly or annual surveys for specific items within these industries.

Federal Trade Commission, *Consumer Protection,* 6th and Pennsylvania Ave. N.W., #466H 20580; (202) 326-3238. Fax, (202) 326-3799. Joan Z. Bernstein, director. Internet, http://www.ftc.gov.

Enforces regulations dealing with unfair or deceptive business practices in advertising, credit, marketing, and

service industries; educates consumers and businesses about these regulations; conducts investigations and litigation.

NONPROFIT

American Wholesale Marketers Assn., *1128 16th St. N.W. 20036; (202) 463-2124. Fax, (202) 463-6467. David Strachan, president. Internet, http://www.awmanet.org.*

Membership: wholesalers, manufacturers, retailers, and brokers who sell or distribute convenience products. Conducts education programs. Monitors legislation and regulations.

Assn. of Sales and Marketing Companies, *2100 Reston Pkwy., #400, Reston, VA 22091-1218; (703) 758-7790. Fax, (703) 758-7787. Robert C. Schwarze, president. Internet, info@asmc.org or http://www.asmc.org.*

Membership: sales and marketing agents and retail merchandisers of food and consumer products worldwide. Sponsors research, training, and educational programs for members and their trading partners. Monitors legislation and regulations.

Cosmetic, Toiletry, and Fragrance Assn., *1101 17th St. N.W., #300 20036; (202) 331-1770. Fax, (202) 331-1969. E. Edward Kavanaugh, president. Internet, http://www.ctfa.org.*

Membership: manufacturers and distributors of finished personal care products. Represents the industry at the local, state, and national levels. Interests include scientific research, legal issues, legislation, and regulatory policy.

Council of Better Business Bureaus, Inc., *4200 Wilson Blvd., #800, Arlington, VA 22203; (703) 276-0100. Fax, (703) 525-8277. James L. Bast, president. Internet, bbb@bbb.org or http://www.bbb.org.*

Membership: businesses and Better Business Bureaus in the United States and Canada. Promotes ethical business practices and truth in national advertising; mediates disputes between consumers and businesses.

Equipment Leasing Assn. of America, *4301 N. Fairfax Dr., #550, Arlington, VA 22203; (702) 527-8655. Fax, (703) 527-2649. Michael Fleming, chief executive officer. Internet, http://www.elaonline.com.*

Promotes the interests of the equipment leasing and finance industry; assists in the resolution of industry problems; encourages standards. Monitors legislation and regulations.

International Cemetery and Funeral Assn., *1895 Preston White Dr., #220, Reston, VA 20191; (703) 391-8400. Fax, (703) 391-8416. Linda Christenson, executive* *vice president. Toll-free, (800) 645-7700. Internet, http://www.icfa.org.*

Membership: owners and operators of cemeteries, funeral homes, mausoleums, and columbariums. Promotes the building and proper maintenance of modern interment places; promotes high ethical standards in the industry; encourages pre-arrangement of funerals.

International Council of Shopping Centers, *1033 N. Fairfax St., #404, Alexandria, VA 22314; (703) 549-7404. Fax, (703) 549-8712. Becky Sullivan, senior director, Government Relations. Internet, http://www.icsc.org.*

Membership: shopping center owners, developers, managers, retailers, contractors, and others in the industry worldwide. Provides information, including research data. Monitors legislation and regulations. (Headquarters in New York.)

International Franchise Assn., *1350 New York Ave. N.W., #900 20005; (202) 628-8000. Fax, (202) 628-0812. Don J. DeBolt, president. Internet, http://www.franchise.org.*

Membership: national and international franchisors. Sponsors seminars, workshops, trade shows, and conferences. Monitors legislation and regulations.

International Mass Retail Assn., *1700 N. Moore St., #2250, Arlington, VA 22209-1998; (703) 841-2300. Fax, (703) 841-1184. Robert J. Verdisco, president. Internet, http://www.imra.org.*

Membership: discount, specialty, home center, wholesale club, and mass retailers in the United States and abroad. Interests include industry research, trade, and government relations. Monitors legislation and regulations.

National Assn. of Convenience Stores, *1605 King St., Alexandria, VA 22314-2792; (703) 684-3600. Fax, (703) 836-4564. Kerley LeBoeuf, president. Internet, NACS1@aol.com or http://www.cstorecentral.com.*

Membership: convenience store retailers and industry suppliers. Advocates industry position on labor, tax, environment, alcohol, and food-related issues; conducts research and training programs. Monitors legislation and regulations.

National Assn. of Wholesaler-Distributors, *1725 K St. N.W., #300 20006; (202) 872-0885. Fax, (202) 785-0586. Dirk Van Dongen, president.*

Membership: wholesale distributors and trade associations. Provides members and government policymakers with research, education, and government relations information. Monitors legislation and regulations.

National Burglar and Fire Alarm Assn., *7101 Wisconsin Ave., #901, Bethesda, MD 20814-4805; (301) 907-3202. Fax, (301) 907-7897. Brad Shipp, executive director. Internet, staff@alarm.org or http://www.alarm.org.*

Promotes the electronic security industry. Conducts professional training and certification; compiles industry statistics; disseminates information to consumers regarding home security systems; sponsors seminars. Monitors legislation and regulations.

National Retail Federation, *325 7th St. N.W., #1000 20004-2802; (202) 783-7971. Fax, (202) 737-2849. Tracy Mullin, president. Internet, nrf@mcimail.com or http://www.nrf.com.*

Membership: international, national, and state associations of retailers and major retail corporations. Concerned with federal regulatory activities and legislation that affect retailers, including tax, employment, trade, and credit issues. Provides information on retailing through seminars, conferences, and publications.

Security Industry Assn., *635 Slaters Lane, #110, Alexandria, VA 22314; (703) 683-2075. Fax, (703) 683-2469. Ronald F. Spiller, executive director. Internet, http://www.siaonline.org.*

Promotes expansion and professionalism in the security industry. Sponsors trade shows, develops industry standards, supports educational programs and job training, and publishes statistical research. Serves as an information source for the media and the industry.

Service Station Dealers of America, *9420 Annapolis Rd., #307, Lanham, MD 20706; (301) 577-4956. Fax, (301) 731-0039. Tony Licata, president.*

Membership: state associations of gasoline retailers. Interests include environmental issues, retail marketing, oil allocation, imports and exports, prices, and taxation.

Society of Consumer Affairs Professionals in Business, *801 N. Fairfax St., #404, Alexandria, VA 22314-1757; (703) 519-3700. Fax, (703) 549-4886. Louis Carcia, executive director. Internet, http://www.socap.org.*

Membership: managers and supervisors who are responsible for consumer affairs, customer service, market research, and sales and marketing operations. Provides information on customer service techniques, market trends, and industry statistics; sponsors seminars and conferences. Monitors legislation and regulations.

Tradeshow Exhibitors Assn., *5501 Backlick Rd., #105, Springfield, VA 22151; (703) 941-3725. Fax, (703) 941-8275. Peter J. Mangelli, president. Internet, http://www.tsea.org.*

Membership: organizations that use exhibits as a marketing medium. Members share information on matters affecting exhibit programs.

Advertising

See also Credit Practices (chap. 1)

AGENCIES

Federal Highway Administration *(Transportation Dept.), Real Estate Services,* 400 7th St. S.W. 20590; (202) 366-0142. Fax, (202) 366-3780. *Cynthia Burbank, director.*

Administers laws concerning outdoor advertising along interstate and federally aided primary highways.

Federal Trade Commission, *Advertising Practices,* 601 Pennsylvania Ave. N.W., #S4002 20580; (202) 326-3090. Fax, (202) 326-3259. *C. Lee Peeler, associate director.*

Monitors advertising claims of products for validity; investigates allegations of deceptive advertising practices; handles complaints from consumers, public interest groups, businesses, and Congress regarding the truthfulness and fairness of advertising practices. Enforces statutes and rules preventing misrepresentations in print and broadcast advertising.

Food and Drug Administration *(Health and Human Services Dept.), Drug Marketing, Advertising, and Communications,* 5600 Fishers Lane, HFD-40, #17B-20, Rockville, MD 20857; (301) 827-2828. Fax, (301) 594-6771. *Minnie Baylor-Henry, director. Internet, http://www.fda.gov/cder.*

Monitors prescription drug advertising and labeling; investigates complaints; conducts market research on health care communications and drug issues.

NONPROFIT

American Advertising Federation, 1101 Vermont Ave. N.W., #500 20005; (202) 898-0089. Fax, (202) 898-0159. *Wallace Snyder, president. Internet, http://www.aaf.org.*

Membership: advertising companies (ad agencies, advertisers, media, and services), clubs, associations, and college chapters. A founder of the National Advertising Review Board, a self-regulatory body. Sponsors annual awards for outstanding advertising.

American Assn. of Advertising Agencies, 1899 L St. N.W., #700 20036-3891; (202) 331-7345. Fax, (202) 857-3675. *Hal Shoup, executive vice president. Internet, aaaadc@ictlink.com or http://www.commercepark.com/AAAA.*

Co-sponsors the National Advertising Review Board (a self-regulatory body), the Advertising Council, and the Media/Advertising Partnership for a Drug Free America. Monitors legislation and regulations. (Headquarters in New York.)

Assn. of National Advertisers, 700 11th St. N.W., #650 20001; (202) 626-7800. Fax, (202) 626-6161. *Daniel L. Jaffe, executive vice president.*

Co-sponsors the National Advertising Review Board, a self-regulatory body. Monitors legislation and regulations. (Headquarters in New York.)

Direct Marketing Assn., 1111 19th St. N.W., #1100 20036; (202) 955-5030. Fax, (202) 955-0085. *Patricia Faley, vice president, Ethics and Consumer Affairs. Internet, http://www.the-dma.org.*

Membership: telemarketers; users, creators, and producers of direct mail; and suppliers to the industry. Conducts research and promotes knowledge and use of direct response marketing. Handles consumer complaints about telephone and mail-order purchases. Operates a mail preference service, which removes consumer names from unwanted mailing lists, and a telephone preference service, which helps consumers handle unsolicited telephone sales calls. (Headquarters in New York.)

International Sign Assn., 707 N. Saint Asaph St., Alexandria, VA 22314; (703) 836-4012. Fax, (703) 836-8353. *Mark Lappen, president. Internet, http://www.signs.org.*

Membership: manufacturers and distributors of signs. Promotes the sign industry; conducts workshops and seminars; sponsors annual competition.

Outdoor Advertising Assn. of America, 1850 M St. N.W., #1040 20036; (202) 833-5566. Fax, (202) 833-1522. *Nancy Fletcher, president. Internet, http://www.oaaa.org.*

Membership: outdoor advertising companies, operators, suppliers, and affiliates. Serves as a clearinghouse for public service advertising campaigns. Monitors legislation and regulations.

SMALL AND DISADVANTAGED BUSINESS

AGENCIES

Agency for International Development, *Small and Disadvantaged Business Utilization/Minority Resource Center,* 1300 Pennsylvania Ave. N.W., #7.8E 20523; (202) 712-1500. Fax, (202) 216-3056. *Ivan R. Ashley, director.*

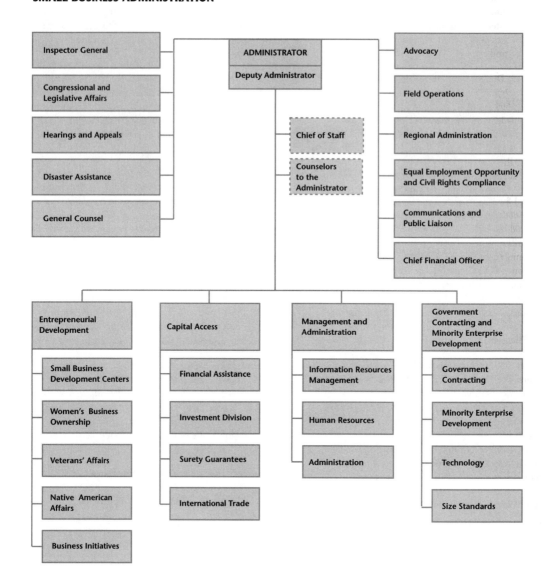

Provides information to U.S. business firms seeking export sales and technical service contracts. Devotes special attention to assisting small businesses and minority-owned firms.

Commerce Dept., *Business Liaison,* *14th St. and Constitution Ave. N.W., #5062 20230; (202) 482-3942. Fax, (202) 482-4054. Cheryl Bruner, director. Information, (202) 482-1360.*

Serves as the central office for business assistance. Handles requests for information and services as well as complaints and suggestions from businesses; provides a forum for businesses to comment on federal regulations; initiates meetings on policy issues with industry groups, business organizations, trade and small-business associations, and the corporate community.

Federal Insurance Administration *(Federal Emergency Management Agency), 500 C St. S.W., #430 20472;*

(202) 646-2781. Fax, (202) 646-3445. Joann Howard, administrator. Internet, http://www.fema.gov.

Administers federal crime and flood insurance programs. Makes available to eligible small businesses low-cost flood and crime insurance.

Food and Drug Administration *(Health and Human Services Dept.), Small Business, Scientific, and Trade Affairs, 5600 Fishers Lane, #17-45, Rockville, MD 20857; (301) 827-3430. Fax, (301) 443-5153. Beverly Corey, team leader.*

Serves as liaison between the small-business community and the FDA. Assists small businesses in complying with FDA regulatory requirements.

General Services Administration, *Enterprise Development, 1800 F St. N.W., #6029 20405; (202) 501-1021. Fax, (202) 208-5938. Dietra L. Ford, associate administrator.*

Works to increase small-business procurement of government contracts. Provides policy guidance and direction for GSA Business Service Centers, which offer advice and assistance to businesses interested in government procurement. *(See Regional Information Sources in appendix.)*

Minority Business Development Agency *(Commerce Dept.), 14th St. and Constitution Ave. N.W., #5055 20230; (202) 482-5061. Fax, (202) 501-4698. Courtland Cox, acting director. Information, (202) 482-4547.*

Coordinates federal and private programs and resources to promote minority ownership of business. Provides management, technical, and financial assistance through a consortium of minority-business development centers to minority entrepreneurs to start, expand, or manage a business. Develops and monitors national minority business programs. Reports annually on federal agencies' performance in procuring from minority-owned businesses.

National Science Foundation, *Small Business Innovative Research Program, 4201 Wilson Blvd., Arlington, VA 22230; (703) 306-1391. Fax, (703) 306-0337. Kesh Narayanan, senior adviser.*

Serves as liaison between the small-business community and NSF offices awarding grants and contracts. Administers the Small Business Innovation Research Program, which funds research proposals from small science/high technology firms and offers incentives for commercial development of NSF-funded research.

National Women's Business Council, *409 3rd St. S.W., #5850 20024; (202) 205-3850. Fax, (202) 205-6825. Lillian Vernon, chair; Amy Millman, executive director. Internet, http://www.womenconnect.com/nwbc.*

SMALL AND DISADVANTAGED BUSINESS CONTACTS AT FEDERAL AGENCIES

DEPARTMENTS

Agriculture, Sharron Harris, (202) 720-7117

Commerce, Brenda Black, (202) 482-1472

Defense, Robert L. Neal Jr., (703) 614-1151

  Air Force, Anthony J. DeLuca, (703) 697-1950

  Army, Tracey L. Pinson, (703) 695-9800

  Marines, Shelia B. D'Agostino, (703) 696-1022

  Navy, Don L. Hathaway, (202) 685-6485

Education, Viola J. Sanchez, (202) 708-9820

Energy, Corlis S. Moody, (202) 586-8383

Health and Human Services, Verl Zanders, (202) 690-7300

Housing and Urban Development, Casmir Bonkowski, (202) 708-1428

Interior, Ralph W. Rausch, (202) 208-7438

Justice, Eleanora Geary, acting director, (202) 616-0521

State, Durie N. White, (703) 875-6824

Transportation, Luz A. Hopewell, (202) 366-1930

Treasury, T. J. Garcia, (202) 622-0530

  Office of Thrift Supervision, Lawrence A. Schlosser, (202) 906-7624

Veterans Affairs, Scott F. Denniston, (202) 565-8124

AGENCIES

Agency for International Development, Ivan R. Ashley, (202) 712-1500

Consumer Product Safety Commission, John W. Barrett Jr., (301) 504-0570

Environmental Protection Agency, Jeanette L. Brown, (703) 305-7777

General Services Administration, Dietra L. Ford, (202) 501-1021

National Aeronautics and Space Administration, Ralph C. Thomas III, (202) 358-2088

Nuclear Regulatory Commission, Irene P. Little, (301) 415-7380

Social Security Administration, Wanda Eley, (410) 965-9457

Membership: eight women business owners, six representatives of women business organizations, and one chair appointed by the president. Independent, congressionally mandated council established by the Women's Business Ownership Act of 1988. Reviews the status of women-owned businesses nationwide and makes policy recommendations to the president and Congress. Assesses the role of the federal government in aiding and promoting women-owned businesses.

Securities and Exchange Commission, *Economic Analysis, 450 5th St. N.W. 20549; (202) 942-8020. Fax, (202) 942-9657. Erik Sirri, chief economist.*

Provides the commission with economic analyses of proposed rule and policy changes and other information to guide the SEC in influencing capital markets. Evaluates the effect of policy changes and other factors on competition within the securities industry and among competing securities markets; compiles financial statistics on capital formation and the securities industry.

Small Business Administration, *409 3rd St. S.W. 20416; (202) 205-6605. Fax, (202) 205-6802. Aida Alvarez, administrator. Information, (202) 205-7713. Press, (202) 205-6740. Library, (202) 205-7033. Toll-free information, (800) 827-5722. Internet, http://www.sba.gov.*

Provides small businesses with financial and management assistance; offers loans to victims of floods, natural disasters, and other catastrophes; licenses, regulates, and guarantees some financing of small-business investment companies; conducts economic and statistical research on small businesses. SBA Answer Desk is an information and referral service. District or regional offices can be contacted for specific loan information. *(See Regional Information Sources in appendix.)*

Small Business Administration, *Advocacy, 409 3rd St. S.W. 20416; (202) 205-6533. Fax, (202) 205-6928. Jere W. Glover, chief counsel. Internet, kcm@adv.sba.gov or http://www.sba.gov/ADVO.*

Acts as an advocate for small-business viewpoints in regulatory and legislative proceedings. Economic Research Office analyzes the effects of government policies on small business and documents the contributions of small business to the economy.

Small Business Administration, *Business Initiatives, 409 3rd St. S.W. 20416; (202) 205-6665. Fax, (202) 205-7416. Monika Edwards Harrison, associate administrator. Internet, http://www.sba.gov/BI.*

Provides small businesses with instruction and counseling in marketing, accounting, product analysis, production methods, research and development, and management problems.

Small Business Administration, *Capital Access, 409 3rd St. S.W. 20416; (202) 205-6657. Fax, (202) 205-7230. John Gray, associate deputy administrator. Internet, http://www.sba.gov.*

Provides financial assistance to small business; focus includes surety guarantees, investment, and international trade. Makes microloans to start-up businesses and loans to established businesses for purchase of new equipment or facilities.

Small Business Administration, *Entrepreneurial Development, 409 3rd St. S.W. 20416; (202) 205-6706. Fax, (202) 205-6903. Betsy Myers, associate administrator. Internet, http://www.sba.gov.*

Responsible for business development programs of the Small Business Development Centers and the offices of Business Initiatives, Veterans Affairs, Native American Affairs, and Women's Business Ownership.

Small Business Administration, *Financial Assistance, 409 3rd St. S.W. 20416; (202) 205-6490. Fax, (202) 205-7722. Jane Butler, acting associate administrator. Internet, http://www.sba.gov.*

Makes available guaranteed loans to aid in developing small businesses.

Small Business Administration, *Minority Enterprise Development, 409 3rd St. S.W. 20416; (202) 205-6410. Fax, (202) 205-7267. William Fisher, acting associate administrator. Internet, http://www.sba.gov/MED.*

Coordinates the services provided by private industry, banks, the SBA, and other government agencies—such as business development and management and technical assistance—to increase the number of small businesses owned by socially and economically disadvantaged Americans.

Small Business Administration, *Women's Business Ownership, 409 3rd St. S.W., 4th Floor 20416; (202) 205-6673. Fax, (202) 205-7287. Sherrye Henry, assistant administrator. Internet, http://www.sba.gov/womeninbusiness.*

Advocates for current and potential women business owners throughout the federal government and in the private sector. Provides training and counseling; offers information on national and local resources.

CONGRESS

House Government Reform and Oversight Committee, *Subcommittee on National Economic Growth, Natural Resources, and Regulatory Affairs, B377 RHOB 20515; (202) 225-4407. Fax, (202) 225-2441. David M. McIntosh, R-Ind., chair; Mildred Webber, staff director. Internet, http://www.house.gov/reform.*

Reviews regulatory process and effect of specific regulations and paperwork on the small-business community. Oversees operations of the Small Business

Administration. (Shared with House Small Business Committee.)

House Small Business Committee, *2361 RHOB 20515; (202) 225-5821. Fax, (202) 225-3587. James M. Talent, R-Mo., chair; Mark Strand, chief of staff. Internet, http://www.house.gov/smbiz.*

Jurisdiction over legislation dealing with the Small Business Administration (shared with House Government Reform and Oversight Committee). Studies and makes recommendations on problems of American small business.

House Small Business Committee, *Subcommittee on Empowerment, B363 RHOB 20515; (202) 226-2630. Fax, (202) 225-8950. Mark Souder, R-Ind., chair; Alvin S. Felzenberg, staff director. Internet, http://www.house.gov/ smbiz.*

Jurisdiction over development of economically depressed areas, including regulations and licensing policies that affect small businesses in high-risk communities.

House Small Business Committee, *Subcommittee on Government Programs and Oversight, B363 RHOB 20515; (202) 226-2630. Fax, (202) 225-8950. Roscoe G. Bartlett, R-Md., chair; Nelson Crowther, staff director.*

Jurisdiction over legislation on opportunities for women and minority-owned businesses, and federal government programs designed to assist small businesses.

House Small Business Committee, *Subcommittee on Tax, Finance, and Exports, B363 RHOB 20515; (202) 226-2630. Fax, (202) 225-8950. Donald Manzullo, R-Ill., chair; Philip D. Eskeland, staff director.*

Jurisdiction over legislation on programs affecting small-business; studies impact of tax policy on small business.

Senate Small Business Committee, *SR-428A 20510; (202) 224-5175. Fax, (202) 224-4885. Christopher S. Bond, R-Mo., chair; Louis Taylor, staff director. Internet, http://www.senate.gov/~sbc.*

Jurisdiction over and oversight of the Small Business Administration. Studies and makes recommendations on problems of American small business and on programs involving minority enterprise. Reviews regulatory process and effect of specific regulations and paperwork on the small-business community.

NONPROFIT

Latin American Management Assn., *419 New Jersey Ave. S.E. 20003-4007; (202) 546-3803. Fax, (202) 546-3807. Stephen Denlingo, executive director. Toll-free, (888) 526-2932. Toll-free, (800) 522-6623.*

Membership: Hispanic manufacturing and technical firms. Promotes Hispanic enterprise, industry, and technology throughout the United States. Supports public policy beneficial to minority businesses. Monitors legislation and regulations.

Minority Business Enterprise Legal Defense and Education Fund, *900 2nd St. N.E., #8 20002; (202) 289-1700. Fax, (202) 289-1701. Anthony W. Robinson, president.*

Acts as an advocate for the minority business community. Represents minority businesses in class action suits; conducts legal research; serves as an information clearinghouse on business and legal trends. Monitors legislation and regulations.

National Assn. of Investment Companies, *1111 14th St. N.W., #700 20005; (202) 289-4336. Fax, (202) 289-4329. Vacant, president.*

Membership: investment companies that provide minority-owned small businesses with venture capital and management guidance. Provides technical assistance; monitors legislation affecting small business.

National Assn. of Negro Business and Professional Women's Clubs, *1806 New Hampshire Ave., N.W. 20009; (202) 483-4206. Fax, (202) 462-7253. Julianne Malveaux, president. Internet, http://www.afrika.com/nanbpwc.*

Promotes opportunities for African American women in business; sponsors workshops; maintains a job bank. Monitors legislation and regulations.

National Assn. of Small Business Investment Companies, *666 11th St. N.W., #750 20001; (202) 628-5055. Fax, (202) 628-5080. Lee W. Mercer, president. Internet, http://www.nasbic.org.*

Membership: companies licensed by the Small Business Administration to provide small businesses with advisory services, equity financing, and long-term loans.

National Federation of Independent Business, *600 Maryland Ave. S.W., #700 20024; (202) 554-9000. Fax, (202) 554-0496. Jackson Faris, president. Internet, http:// www.nfibonline.com.*

Membership: independent business and professional people. Monitors public policy issues and legislation affecting small and independent businesses, including taxation, government regulation, labor-management relations, and liability insurance.

National Small Business United, *1156 15th St. N.W., #1100 20005; (202) 293-8830. Fax, (202) 872-8543. Todd McCracken, executive vice president. Internet, jpg-nsbu@ ix.netcom.com or http://www.nsbu.org.*

Membership: manufacturing, wholesale, retail, service, and other small-business firms and regional small-business organizations. Represents the interests of small business before Congress, the administration, and federal agencies. Services to members include a toll-free legislative hotline and group insurance.

Research Institute for Small and Emerging Business (RISE), *722 12th St. N.W., #208 20005; (202) 628-8382. Fax, (202) 628-8392. Mark Shultz, president. Toll-free export opportunity hotline, (800) 243-7232; in Washington, (202) 223-1104. Internet, rise@bellatlantic.net or http://www.riseb.org.*

Sponsors and conducts scientific and economic research on small-business matters. Promotes growth of small businesses. Assists small-business organizations and individuals wishing to establish small-business organizations. Serves as an information clearinghouse. Hotline assists small businesses with export-related questions.

Service Corps of Retired Executives Assn., *409 3rd St. S.W. 20024; (202) 205-6762. Fax, (202) 205-7636. W. Kenneth Yancey Jr., executive director. Toll-free, (800) 634-0245. Internet, http://www.score.org.*

Independent voluntary organization funded by the Small Business Administration through which retired, semiretired, and active business executives use

their knowledge and experience to counsel small businesses.

Small Business Legislative Council, *1156 15th St. N.W., #510 20005; (202) 639-8500. Fax, (202) 296-5333. John Satagaj, president. Internet, email@sblc.org.*

Membership: trade associations that represent small businesses in the manufacturing, wholesale, retail, service, and other sectors. Monitors and proposes legislation and regulations to benefit small businesses.

Small Business Survival Committee, *1320 18th St. N.W., #200 20036; (202) 785-0238. Fax, (202) 822-8118. Karen Kerrigan, president. Information, (202) 223-7526. Internet, rstikes@sbsc.org or http://www.sbsc.org.*

Membership: small businesses throughout the United States. Promotes small business economic growth through limited government. Acts as an educational resource for members. Monitors legislation and regulations.

U.S. Chamber of Commerce, *Small Business Center, 1615 H St. N.W. 20062-2000; (202) 463-5503. Fax, (202) 887-3445. David Voight, director.*

Seeks to enhance visibility of small business within the national chamber and the U.S. business community. Provides members with information on national small-business programs.

6

Education

⚡ GENERAL POLICY

AGENCIES

Education Dept., *600 Independence Ave. S.W. 20202; (202) 401-3000. Fax, (202) 401-0596. Richard W. Riley, secretary; Mike Smith, acting deputy secretary, (202) 401-1000. Information, (202) 401-2000. TDD, (202) 260-9137. Internet, http://www.ed.gov or ftp.ed.gov.*

Establishes education policy and acts as principal adviser to the president on education matters; administers and coordinates most federal assistance programs on education.

Education Dept., *Goals 2000: Educate America, 1250 Maryland Ave. S.W., #4000 (mailing address: 600 Independence Ave. S.W, #4000, Washington, DC 20202-6100); (202) 401-0039. Fax, (202) 205-0303. Thomas Fagan, director. Toll-free, (800) 872-5327. Press, (202) 401-1576. TDD, (800) 437-0833. Internet, http://www.ed.gov.g2k.*

Oversees strategy to attain education goals adopted by the president and the governors in 1990, including lower drop-out rate, higher math and science achievement, elimination of illiteracy, and drug-free schools.

Educational Resources Information Center (ERIC) *(Education Dept.), 2277 Research Blvd., #7A, Rockville, MD 20850-3172; (301) 519-5789. Fax, (301) 519-5760. Lynn Smarte, project director. Toll-free, (800) 538-3742. Internet, askeric@ericir.syr.edu or http://www.aspensys.com/eric.*

Coordinates a national information system comprising sixteen clearinghouses on specific subjects. Documents available in microfiche form at most university libraries. Answers queries and offers referrals to individuals on all facets of education. *For a list of clearinghouses on the Web, see box (p. 174)*

See also Domestic Policy Council (p. 328)

CONGRESS

General Accounting Office, *Health, Education, and Human Services, 441 G St. N.W. 20548; (202) 512-6806. Fax, (202) 512-5806. Richard L. Hembra, assistant comptroller general.*

Independent, nonpartisan agency in the legislative branch. Audits, analyzes, and evaluates Education Dept. programs; makes reports available to the public.

House Appropriations Committee, *Subcommittee on Labor, Health and Human Services, and Education, 2358 RHOB 20515; (202) 225-3508. John Edward Porter, R-Ill., chair; Tony McCann, staff director. Internet, http://www.house.gov/appropriations.*

Jurisdiction over legislation to appropriate funds for federal education programs (except Native American education programs), including adult education, compensatory education, and education for the disadvantaged and disabled.

House Education and the Workforce Committee, *Subcommittee on Early Childhood, Youth, and Families, 2181 RHOB 20515; (202) 225-4527. Fax, (202) 225-9571. Frank Riggs, R-Calif., chair; Kevin Talley, staff director. Internet, http://www.house.gov/eeo.*

Jurisdiction over legislation on preschool, elementary, and secondary education; adult basic education (family literacy); and overseas dependent schools.

House Education and the Workforce Committee, *Subcommittee on Postsecondary Education, Training, and Life-Long Learning, 2181 RHOB 20515; (202) 225-4527. Fax, (202) 225-9571. Howard P. "Buck" McKeon, R-Calif., chair; Kevin Talley, staff director. Internet, http://www.house.gov/eeo.*

Jurisdiction over legislation on education beyond the high school level, including training and apprenticeship programs, vocational education, rehabilitation, postsecondary student assistance, domestic volunteer programs, and library services and construction. Oversees the Robert A. Taft Institute and the U.S. Institute of Peace.

House Government Reform and Oversight Committee, *Subcommittee on Human Resources, B372 RHOB 20515; (202) 225-2548. Fax, (202) 225-2382. Christopher Shays, R-Conn., chair; Larry Halloran, staff director. Internet, http://www.house.gov/reform.*

Oversees operations of the Education Dept.

Senate Appropriations Committee, *Subcommittee on Labor, Health and Human Services, and Education, SD-184 20510; (202) 224-7230. Arlen Specter, R-Pa., chair; Craig A. Higgins, staff director. Internet, http://www.senate.gov/~appropriations/labor.*

Jurisdiction over legislation to appropriate funds for federal education programs, including adult education, compensatory education, and education for the disadvantaged and disabled.

Senate Labor and Human Resources Committee, *SD-428 20510; (202) 224-5375. Fax, (202) 224-6510. James M. Jeffords, R-Vt., chair; Mark Powden, staff director. Internet, http://www.senate.gov/~labor.*

Jurisdiction over legislation on preschool, elementary, secondary, and vocational education, including community schools, aid to private schools, the Office of Educational Research and Improvement, education tech-

EDUCATION DEPARTMENT

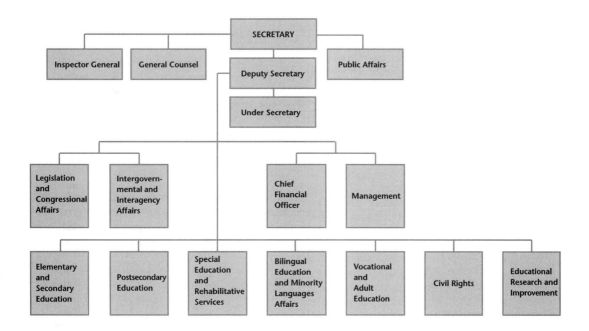

```
                              ┌─────────────┐
                              │  SECRETARY  │
                              └─────────────┘
   ┌──────────────┐  ┌──────────────┐  │  ┌──────────────┐
   │  Inspector   │  │   General    │  │  │    Public    │
   │   General    │  │   Counsel    │  │  │    Affairs   │
   └──────────────┘  └──────────────┘  │  └──────────────┘
                              ┌───────────────┐
                              │Deputy Secretary│
                              └───────────────┘
                              ┌───────────────┐
                              │Under Secretary │
                              └───────────────┘
```

| Legislation and Congressional Affairs | Intergovernmental and Interagency Affairs | | Chief Financial Officer | Management |

| Elementary and Secondary Education | Postsecondary Education | Special Education and Rehabilitative Services | Bilingual Education and Minority Languages Affairs | Vocational and Adult Education | Civil Rights | Educational Research and Improvement |

nology, and drug and alcohol abuse education; and legislation barring discrimination in preschool, elementary, secondary, and vocational education. Oversees operations of the Education Dept.

NONPROFIT

Assn. for Community Based Education, *1805 Florida Ave. N.W. 20009; (202) 462-6333. C. P. Zachariadis, executive director. Information, (202) 462-6335.*

Promotes community-based education programs, free-standing alternative colleges (independent of state or local support), and adult learning centers. Provides technical assistance to develop, expand, and improve community-based education programs.

Capital Children's Museum, *800 3rd St. N.E. 20002; (202) 675-4120. Fax, (202) 675-4140. Catherine Martens, executive director. Press, (202) 675-4183. Museum desk, (202) 675-4170. Internet, http://www.ccm.org.*

Designs, implements, and conducts studies in education. Interests include the creation and development of new educational methods, materials, and structures. Maintains the Options School.

Center for Education Reform, *1001 Connecticut Ave. N.W., #204 20036; (202) 822-9000. Fax, (202) 822-5077.*

Jeanne Allen, president. Internet, cerdc@aol.com or http://www.edreform.com.

Informs the public about innovative reforms and research in public education; distributes summaries of critical education issues.

Center for Law and Education, *1875 Connecticut Ave. N.W., #510 20009-5728; (202) 986-3000. Fax, (202) 986-6648. Paul Weckstein, co-director. Publications, (202) 462-7688. Internet, cledc@erols.com.*

Works to advance the right of all students, and low income students in particular, to a high-quality education. Interests include testing and tracking; bilingual education; discriminatory discipline; special education; special needs for Native Americans, migrants, and Hispanics; parent, community, and student participation in education; and vocational and compensatory education. (Headquarters in Boston.)

Charles F. Kettering Foundation, *444 N. Capitol St. N.W., #434 20001-1512; (202) 393-4478. Fax, (202) 393-7644. James C. Wilder, director, Washington Office. Toll-free, (800) 221-3657. Internet, http://www.kettering.org.*

Works to improve the domestic policymaking process. Supports international program focusing on unofficial, citizen-to-citizen diplomacy. Encourages

EDUCATIONAL RESOURCES INFORMATION CENTER (ERIC) CLEARINGHOUSES

ERIC, supported by the Education Dept.'s Office of Educational Research and Improvement and the National Library of Education, provides users with access to a national information system of education-related literature. Its clearinghouses collect, abstract, index, and disseminate information in sixteen subject specific categories.

Adult, Career, and Vocational Education
http://coe.ohio-state.edu/cete/ericacve/index.html

AskERIC
http://ericir.syr.edu

Assessment and Evaluation
http://ericae.net

Community College
http://www.gseis.ucla.edu/ERIC/eric.html

Counseling and Student Services
http://www.uncg.edu/~ericcas2

Disabilities and Gifted Education
http://www.cec.sped.org/ericec.htm

Educational Management
http://darkwing.uoregon.edu/~ericcem

Elementary and Early Childhood Education
http://ericps.crc.uiuc.edu/ericeece.html

Higher Education
http://www.gwu.edu/~eriche

Information and Technology
http://ericir.syr.edu/ithome

Languages and Linguistics
http://www.cal.org/ericcll

National Parent Information Network
http://npin.org

Reading, English, and Communication
http://www.indiana.edu/~eric_rec

Rural Education and Small Schools
http://aelvira.ael.org/erichp.htm

Science, Mathematics, and Environmental Education
http://www.ericse.org

Social Studies/Social Education
http://www.indiana.edu/~ssdc/eric_chess.htm

Teaching and Teacher Education
http://www.ericsp.org

Urban Education
http://eric-web.tc.columbia.edu

greater citizen involvement in formation of public policy. Interests include public education and at-risk youths. (Headquarters in Dayton, Ohio.)

Council for Advancement and Support of Education, *1308 New York Ave. N.W., 20036; (202) 328-5900. Fax, (202) 387-4973. Eustace Theodore, president. Internet, membership@ns.case.org or http://www.case.org.*

Membership: two- and four-year colleges, universities, and independent schools. Offers professional education and training programs to members; advises members on institutional advancement issues, including fundraising, alumni affairs, public relations programs, government relations, and management. Library open to the public by appointment.

Distributive Education Clubs of America, *1908 Association Dr., Reston, VA 20191-1594; (703) 860-5000. Fax, (703) 860-4013. Edward L. Davis, executive director. Internet, http://www.deca.org.*

Educational organization that helps high-school and college students develop skills in marketing, management, and entrepreneurship. Promotes business and education partnerships.

Ethics Resource Center, *1747 Pennsylvania Ave. N.W., #400 20006; (202) 737-2258. Fax, (202) 737-2227. Michael G. Daigneault, president. Toll-free, (800) 777-1285. Press, (202) 434-8461. Internet, http://www.ethics.org.*

Produces teacher training guides and video-based materials on character education for students in various grade levels; helps schools evaluate and improve programs in moral education.

Institute for Educational Leadership, *1001 Connecticut Ave. N.W., #310 20036; (202) 822-8405. Fax, (202) 872-4050. Michael Usdan, president. Internet, http://www.iel.org.*

Works with educators, human services personnel, government officials, and association executives to improve educational opportunities for youths; conducts research on education issues.

National Assn. of State Boards of Education, *1012 Cameron St., Alexandria, VA 22314; (703) 684-4000. Fax, (703) 836-2313. Brenda L. Welburn, executive director. Internet, http://www.nasbe.org.*

Membership: members of state boards of education, state board attorneys, and executives to state boards. Provides information, technical and research assistance, and training programs for members. Interests include education governance, school finance, teaching, federal legislation, at-risk youth, vocational and early childhood education, special education, and AIDS and other health education issues.

National Center on Education and the Economy,
National Alliance for Restructuring Education, 700 11th St. N.W., #750 20001; (202) 783-3668. Fax, (202) 783-3672. Mary Ann Mays, director. Internet, nareinfo@ncee. org or http://www.ncee.org.

Partnership of states, school districts, corporations, foundations, and nonprofit organizations that provides tools and technical assistance to help school systems improve student performance. Areas of focus include standards, assessments, curriculum, and instruction.

National Clearinghouse for Corporate Matching
Gifts Information, *11 Dupont Circle N.W., #400 20036-1261; (202) 328-5900. Fax, (202) 387-4973. Greg Humpert, director. Information, (202) 328-5978. Internet, matchgifts@ns.case.org.*

Provides companies and educational institutions with information on matching gift programs, in which companies match employee contributions to educational and other nonprofit institutions. Sponsored by the Council for Advancement and Support of Education.

National Community Education Assn., *3929 Old Lee Hwy., #91-A, Fairfax, VA 22030-2401; (703) 359-8973. Fax, (703) 359-0972. Starla Jewell-Kelly, executive director. Internet, ncea@ncea.com.*

Works for greater recognition of community education programs, services, and personnel. Interests include business-education partnerships to improve schools; lifelong learning; school-site child care and latchkey programs; and parental involvement in public education.

National School Public Relations Assn., *15948 Derwood Rd., Rockville, MD 20855; (301) 519-0496. Fax, (301) 519-0494. Richard D. Bagin, executive director.*

Membership: educators and individuals interested in improving communications in education. Works to improve communication between educators and the public on the needs of schools; provides educators with information on public relations and policy developments.

New American Schools Development Corp., *1000 Wilson Blvd., #2710, Arlington, VA 22209; (703) 908-9500. Fax, (703) 908-0622. John Anderson, president. Internet, postmaster@hq.nasdc.org or http://www.naschools.org.*

Promotes comprehensive school reform. Solicits and evaluates school design concepts; funds those shown to improve student performance and offers them for adoption to schools nationwide; assists communities in implementing these concepts.

Internships, Fellowships, Grants

See also Arts and Humanities (chap. 4); Postsecondary Education (this chapter); Special Topics in Education (this chapter)

AGENCIES

Harry S. Truman Scholarship Foundation, *712 Jackson Pl. N.W., 3rd Floor 20006-4901; (202) 395-4831. Fax, (202) 395-6995. Louis H. Blair, executive secretary. Internet, staff@truman.gov or http://www.truman.gov.*

Memorial to Harry S. Truman established by Congress. Provides students preparing for careers in public service with scholarships. (Candidates are nominated by their respective colleges or universities while in their third year of undergraduate study.)

National Endowment for the Arts *(National Foundation on the Arts and the Humanities), 1100 Pennsylvania Ave. N.W. 20506-0001; (202) 682-5414. Fax, (202) 682-5612. Scott Shanklin-Peterson, chair. Information, (202) 682-5400. Press, (202) 682-5570. Library, (202) 682-5485. TDD, (202) 682-5496. Internet, http://arts.endow.gov.*

Independent federal grantmaking agency. Awards grants to nonprofit arts organizations in four areas: creation and presentation; education and access; heritage and preservation; and planning and stabilization. Organizations must choose one of the four theme areas for submission of project proposals. Library open to the public by appointment.

National Endowment for the Humanities *(National Foundation on the Arts and the Humanities), 1100 Pennsylvania Ave. N.W., #503 20506; (202) 606-8310. Fax, (202) 606-8588. William R. Ferris, chair; Juan E. Mestas, deputy chair, (202) 606-8273. Information, (202) 606-8400. Press, (202) 606-8446. Library, (202) 606-8244. TDD, (202) 606-8282. Internet, info@neh.fed.us or http://www.neh.fed.us.*

Independent federal grantmaking agency. Awards grants to individuals and institutions for research, scholarship, educational programs, and public programs (including broadcasts, museum exhibitions, lectures, and symposia) in the humanities (defined as study of archeology; history; jurisprudence; language; linguistics; literature; philosophy; comparative religion; ethics; the history, criticism, and theory of the arts; and humanistic aspects of the social sciences). Funds preservation of books, newspapers, historical documents, and photographs.

National Endowment for the Humanities *(National Foundation on the Arts and the Humanities), Research and Education, 1100 Pennsylvania Ave. N.W., #302*

INTERNSHIPS IN WASHINGTON

The following are some key organizations offering internships in the Washington area. For Congressional internships, contact the individual member's office (see appendix).

Alexis de Tocqueville Institution, (703) 351-4969

American Civil Liberties Union, (202) 544-1681

American Enterprise Institute for Public Policy Research, (202) 862-5800

Amnesty International USA, (202) 544-0200

Brookings Institution, (202) 797-6096

C-SPAN, (202) 737-3220

Cato Institute, (202) 842-0200

Center for Defense Information, (202) 862-0700

Center for Policy Alternatives, (202) 387-6030

Center for Science in the Public Interest, (202) 332-9110

Center for Strategic and International Studies, (202) 775-3165

Center for Study of Responsive Law, (202) 387-8030

Central Intelligence Agency, (703) 482-0677

Children's Defense Fund, (202) 628-8787

Concord Coalition, (202) 467-6222

Conservative Caucus, (703) 938-9626

Democratic National Committee, (202) 863-8014

Empower America, (202) 452-8200

Environmental Protection Agency, (202) 260-4484

Fund for the Feminist Majority, (703) 522-2214

General Accounting Office, (202) 512-3429

The Heritage Foundation, (202) 546-4400

Institute for Policy Studies, (202) 234-9382

John F. Kennedy Center for the Performing Arts, (202) 416-8807

Joint Center for Political and Economic Studies, (202) 789-3500

Library of Congress, (202) 707-8253

National Audubon Society, (202) 861-2242

National Institutes of Health, (301) 402-2176

National Public Radio, (202) 414-2909

National Wildlife Federation, (202) 797-6800

Office of Personnel Management, (202) 606-2525

Progress & Freedom Foundation, (202) 289-8928

Public Defender Service, (800) 341-2582

Republican National Committee, (202) 863-8563

Smithsonian Institution, (202) 357-3102

State Dept., (703) 875-7490

Supreme Court of the United States, (202) 479-3374

The Urban Institute, (202) 833-7200

The White House, (202) 456-2742

20506; (202) 606-8373. Fax, (202) 606-8394. James Herbert, director. Internet, education@neh.fed.us or http://www.neh.fed.us.

Offers fellowships, stipends, seminars, and institutes for higher education faculty, school teachers, and independent scholars. Conducts research.

National Science Foundation, *Graduate Education,* 4201 Wilson Blvd., Arlington, VA 22230; (703) 306-1630. Fax, (703) 306-0468. Susan W. Duby, acting director. TDD, (703) 306-0090. Internet, http://www.nsf.gov/EHR/DGE/dge.htm.

Supports activities to strengthen the education of research scientists and engineers; promotes career development; offers pre- and postdoctoral fellowships for study and research; manages the Graduate and Minority Graduate fellowships and the Travel Awards for NATO-Advanced Study Institute.

President's Commission on White House Fellowships, *712 Jackson Pl. N.W. 20503; (202) 395-4522. Fax,*

(202) 395-6179. Jacqueline Blumenthal, director. Internet, http://www.whitehouse.gov/WH_Fellows.

Nonpartisan commission which selects White House Fellows through open competition to provide the opportunity for professionals from all sectors of national life to observe firsthand the processes of the federal government. Fellows work for one year as special assistants to Cabinet members or to principal members of the White House staff. Qualified applicants have demonstrated superior accomplishments early in their careers and have a commitment to community service.

Smithsonian Institution, *Fellowships and Grants,* 955 L'Enfant Plaza S.W., #7000 20560; (202) 287-3271. Fax, (202) 287-3691. Roberta Rubinoff, director. Internet, siofg@ofg.si.edu or http://www.si.edu/research+study.

Administers fellowships in residence that provide pre- and postdoctoral appointments for study and research at the Smithsonian Institution in history of science and technology, American and cultural history, history of art, anthropology, evolutionary and systematic biology, environmental sciences, astrophysics and astronomy, earth sciences, and tropical biology.

Woodrow Wilson International Center for Scholars, *Fellowships, 1000 Jefferson Dr. S.W., MRC 022 20560; (202) 357-2841. Fax, (202) 357-4439. Dean W. Anderson, acting director; Ann C. Sheffield, director for fellowships. Internet, http://wwics.si.edu.*

Awards fellowships to established scholars and professionals from the United States and abroad for humanities and social science research at the center. Publishes guides to scholarly research material in the Washington area.

NONPROFIT

American Assn. of University Women Educational Foundation, *1111 16th St. N.W. 20036; (202) 728-7624. Fax, (202) 463-1769. Vacant, director, Development. Internet, http://www.aauw.org.*

Awards fellowships to women who are completing doctoral or postdoctoral research and to fellows in the last year of their professional degree program. Offers fellowships to foreign women coming to the United States for one year of graduate study. Awards grants to women returning to school for postbaccalaureate education or professional development. Administers the Eleanor Roosevelt Fund, which supports a teacher sabbatical program for women who teach girls math and science in grades K-12. (Affiliate of the American Assn. of University Women.)

American Institute of Architects, *American Architectural Foundation, 1735 New York Ave. N.W. 20006; (202) 626-7500. Fax, (202) 626-7420. Norman L. Koonce, president. Library, (202) 626-7492. Internet, http://www.aafpages.org.*

Seeks to advance the quality of American architecture. Works to increase public awareness and understanding, and apply new technology to create more humane environments. Acts as liaison between the profession and the public; awards grants for architecture-oriented projects. Serves as the educational arm of the American Institute of Architects. Also operates the historic Octagon Museum.

American Political Science Assn., *Congressional Fellowship Program, 1527 New Hampshire Ave. N.W. 20036-1290; (202) 483-2512. Fax, (202) 483-2657. Jeff Biggs, administrative director. Internet, http://www.apsanet.org.*

Places political scientists, journalists, faculty of medical schools (Robert Wood Johnson Fellowships), and federal agency executives in congressional offices and committees for nine-month fellowships. Individual government agencies nominate federal executive participants.

Business and Professional Women's Foundation, *2012 Massachusetts Ave. N.W. 20036; (202) 293-1200. Fax, (202) 861-0298. Joyce Hart, president.*

Works to improve women's economic status by promoting their employment at all levels in all occupations. Provides mature women seeking training and education with scholarships and loans to increase their job skills. Awards grants for doctoral research on women's economic issues. Library open to the public. (Affiliate of Business and Professional Women U.S.A.)

Congressional Black Caucus Foundation, *1004 Pennsylvania Ave. S.E. 20003; (202) 675-6730. Fax, (202) 547-3806. Ramona Edelin, interim executive director. Internet, http://www.cbcfnet.org.*

Conducts public policy research on issues of concern to African Americans. Sponsors fellowship programs in which professionals and academic candidates work on congressional committees and subcommittees. Sponsors internship and scholarship programs.

Council for International Exchange of Scholars, *3007 Tilden St. N.W., #5L 20008-3009; (202) 686-4000. Fax, (202) 362-3442. Patti McGill Peterson, executive director. Internet, info@ciesnet.cies.org or http://www.cies.org.*

Cooperates with the U.S. Information Agency in administering Fulbright grants for university teaching and advanced research abroad. (Affiliated with the American Council of Learned Societies.)

Council on Foundations, *1828 L St. N.W., #300 20036; (202) 466-6512. Fax, (202) 785-3926. Dorothy Ridings, president. Internet, http://www.cof.org.*

Membership: independent community, family, and public and company-sponsored foundations; corporate giving programs; and foundations in other countries. Acts as clearinghouse for information on private philanthropy; sponsors conferences and workshops on effective grantmaking.

Foundation Center, *1001 Connecticut Ave. N.W., #938 20036; (202) 331-1400. Fax, (202) 331-1739. Patricia Pasqual, director, Washington Office. Internet, http://www.fdncenter.org.*

Publishes foundation guides. Serves as clearinghouse on foundations and corporate giving, nonprofit management, fundraising, and grants for individuals. Provides training and seminars on fundraising and grantwriting. Operates libraries in Atlanta, Cleveland, New York, San

Francisco, and Washington, D.C.; libraries open to the public. (Headquarters in New York.)

Fund for American Studies, *1526 18th St. N.W. 20036; (202) 986-0384. Fax, (202) 986-0390. David R. Jones, president. Toll-free, (800) 741-6964 (outside D.C. area). Internet, http://www.tfas.org.*

Educational foundation that sponsors summer institutes on comparative political and economic systems, business and government affairs, and political journalism; grants scholarships to qualified students for these study-internship programs.

National Journalism Center, *800 Maryland Ave. N.E. 20002; (202) 546-1710. Fax, (202) 546-1638. M. Stanton Evans, director.*

Sponsors 12-week internship programs in journalism; provides a stipend for living expenses; offers job placement service. Funded by the Education and Research Institute.

Washington Center, *1101 14th St. N.W., #500 20005-5601; (202) 336-7600. Fax, (202) 336-7609. William M. Burke, president. Toll-free, (800) 486-8921. Internet, info@twc.edu or http://www.twc.edu.*

Arranges congressional, agency, and public service internships for college students for credit. Fee for internship and housing assistance. Sponsors classes and lectures as part of the internship program. Scholarships and stipends available.

Washington Center for Politics and Journalism, *1901 L St. N.W., #300 (mailing address: P.O. Box 15201, Washington, DC 20003-0201); (202) 296-8455. Fax, (202) 466-7598. Terry Michael, executive director. Internet, pol-jrn@wcpj.org or http://www.wcpj.org.*

Offers internships in political journalism to undergraduate and graduate students; provides a stipend for living expenses. Sixteen-week fall and winter/spring sessions include full-time work in Washington news bureaus and seminars in campaign, governance, and interest group politics for future political reporters.

Women's Research and Education Institute, *1750 New York Ave. N.W., #350 20006; (202) 628-0444. Fax, (202) 628-0458. Betty Dooley, president. Internet, wrei@ix.netcom.com or http://www.wrei.org.*

Provides information and conducts research and policy analysis for members of Congress and other policymakers who support equity for women. Sponsors one-year fellowships for graduate students. Fellows are placed in congressional offices or on committee staffs where they work on policy issues affecting women.

Youth Policy Institute, *1333 Green Court N.W. 20005-4113; (202) 638-2144. Fax, (202) 638-2325. David L. Hackett, executive director. Internet, corpsnet@mnsinc.com.*

Seeks to involve youth in public policy decisionmaking. Partly administered and staffed by high school and college students who serve internships of 6 to 12 months; Research Center brings youths to Washington to study public policy proposals; sponsors conferences and workshops. Monitors legislation and government programs dealing with youth. Publishes a resource guide and other materials.

Professional Interests and Benefits

See also Postsecondary Education (this chapter)

NONPROFIT

Academic Collective Bargaining Information Service, *College of Professional Studies (University of the District of Columbia), 4200 Connecticut Ave. N.W., MB 5200 20008; (202) 274-7001. Fax, (202) 282-3706. Isadore Goldberg, director.*

Provides employment relations service in the field of higher education. Interests include equal employment opportunity, governance and policy issues, unionization, and collective bargaining for faculty and nonfaculty units.

American Assn. of Colleges for Teacher Education, *1 Dupont Circle N.W., #610 20036-1186; (202) 293-2450. Fax, (202) 457-8095. David G. Imig, executive director. Internet, http://www.aacte.org.*

Membership: colleges and universities with teacher education programs. Informs members of state and federal policies affecting teacher education and of professional issues such as accreditation, certification, and assessment. Collects and analyzes information on education.

American Assn. of Retired Persons, *National Retired Teachers Assn., 601 E St. N.W. 20049; (202) 434-2380. Fax, (202) 434-6406. Annette Norsman, director, Activities. Internet, aarpwrit@aol.com.*

Membership: active and retired teachers and other school personnel (elementary through postsecondary) over age 50. Provides members with information on relevant national issues. Provides state associations of retired school personnel with technical assistance.

American Assn. of School Administrators, *1801 N. Moore St., Arlington, VA 22209-9988; (703) 528-0700. Fax, (703) 841-1543. Paul D. Houston, executive director. Internet, http://www.aasa.org.*

Membership: chief school executives, administrators at district or higher level, and teachers of school administration. Promotes opportunities for minorities, women, and the disabled in educational administration and organization.

American Federation of School Administrators, *1729 21st St. N.W. 20009; (202) 986-4209. Fax, (202) 986-4211. Joe L. Greene, president. Internet, http://www.afsa.admin.org.*

Membership: approximately 12,000 school administrators, including principals, vice principals, directors, and superintendents. Helps members negotiate pay, benefits, and better working conditions; conducts training programs and workshops. Monitors legislation and regulations. (Affiliated with the AFL-CIO.)

American Federation of Teachers, *555 New Jersey Ave. N.W., 10th Floor 20001; (202) 879-4400. Fax, (202) 879-4545. Sandra Feldman, president. Internet, http://www.aft.org.*

Membership: public and private school teachers, higher education faculty, and school-related personnel. Assists members with contract negotiation and grievances; conducts training programs and workshops. Monitors legislation and regulations. (Affiliated with the AFL-CIO.)

American Political Science Assn., *1527 New Hampshire Ave. N.W. 20036; (202) 483-2512. Fax, (202) 483-2657. Catherine E. Rudder, executive director. Internet, apsa@apsa.org or http://www.apsanet.org.*

Membership: political scientists, primarily college and university professors. Works to increase public understanding of politics; provides services to facilitate and enhance research, teaching, and professional development of its members. Acts as liaison with federal agencies, Congress, and the public. Seeks to improve the status of women and minorities in the profession. Offers congressional fellowships, workshops, and awards. Provides information on political science issues.

Assn. of School Business Officials International, *11401 N. Shore Dr., Reston, VA 20190-4232; (703) 478-0405. Fax, (703) 478-0205. Don I. Tharpe, executive director. Internet, http://www.asbointl.org.*

Membership: administrators, directors, and others involved in school business management. Works to educate members on tools, techniques, and procedures of school business management. Researches, analyzes, and disseminates information; conducts workshops.

Assn. of Teacher Educators, *1900 Association Dr., Reston, VA 22091-1502; (703) 620-3110. Fax, (703) 620-*

9530. Gloria Chernay, executive director. Internet, http://www.siu.edu/departments/coe/ate.

Membership: individuals and public and private agencies involved with teacher education. Seeks to improve teacher education at all levels; conducts workshops and conferences; produces and disseminates publications.

Council of Chief State School Officers, *1 Massachusetts Ave. N.W., #700 20001-1431; (202) 408-5505. Fax, (202) 408-8072. Gordon M. Ambach, executive director. Press, (202) 336-7059. Internet, info@ccsso.org or http://www.ccsso.org.*

Membership: state superintendents and commissioners of education. Works to achieve equal education for all children and to improve ways to measure school performance; provides state education agency personnel and others with leadership, technical assistance, and training. Offers seminars, educational travel, and study programs for members.

Federal Education Assn., *1101 15th St. N.W., #1002 20005; (202) 822-7850. Fax, (202) 822-7816. Jan Mohr, president. Internet, http://www.feaonline.org.*

Membership: teachers and personnel of Defense Dept. schools for military dependents in the United States and abroad. Monitors legislation and regulations.

International Council on Education for Teaching, *2009 N. 14th St., #609, Arlington, VA 22201; (703) 525-5253. Fax, (703) 351-9381. Sandra Klassen, executive director.*

Membership: worldwide network of colleges, universities, educational groups, and individuals interested in improving education of teachers, administrators, and other education specialists. Conducts surveys, research projects, and seminars; interests include improved facilities, diversified curricula, and innovative educational methods. Maintains consulting relationship with the U.N. Educational, Scientific, and Cultural Organization (UNESCO).

International Test and Evaluation Assn., *4400 Fair Lakes Court, Fairfax, VA 22033-3899; (703) 631-6220. Fax, (703) 631-6221. R. Alan Plishker, executive director. Internet, http://www.itea.org.*

Membership: engineers, scientists, managers, and other industry, government, and academic professionals interested in testing and evaluating products and complex systems. Provides a forum for exchange of information; monitors international research.

National Assn. for Women in Education, *1325 18th St. N.W., #210 20036; (202) 659-9330. Fax, (202) 457-*

0946. Lynn Gangone, executive director. Internet, nawe@ clark.net or http://www.nawe.org.

Membership: women in educational administration, teaching, and research, mainly in higher education. Interests include career mobility for women administrators, equitable pensions, and equal educational opportunity and training.

National Assn. of Biology Teachers, *11250 Roger Bacon Dr., #19, Reston, VA 20190-5202; (703) 471-1134. Fax, (703) 435-5582. Wayne Carley, executive director. Toll-free, (800) 406-0775. Internet, NABTer@aol.com or http://www.nabt.org.*

Provides professional development opportunities through a publications program, in-service workshops, conventions, and national awards programs. Interests include teaching standards, science curriculum, and issues affecting biology education.

National Assn. of School Psychologists, *4340 East-West Hwy., #402, Bethesda, MD 20814; (301) 657-0270. Fax, (301) 657-0275. Susan Gorin, executive director. TDD, (301) 657-4155. Internet, http://www.naspweb.org.*

Advocates for the mental health and educational needs of children; encourages professional growth of members. Monitors legislation and regulations.

National Business Education Assn., *1914 Association Dr., Reston, VA 20191-1596; (703) 860-8300. Fax, (703) 620-4483. Janet M. Treichel, executive director. Internet, nbea@nbea.org or http://www.nbea.org.*

Membership: business education teachers and others interested in the field. Provides information on business education; offers teaching materials; sponsors conferences. Monitors legislation and regulations affecting business education.

National Certification Commission, *P.O. Box 15282, Chevy Chase, MD 20825-0282; (301) 588-1212. Richard C. Jaffeson, executive director. Fax-on-demand, (301) 588-1211. Internet, certusa@usa.net.*

Provides information on the development and improvement of professional certification programs.

National Council for Accreditation of Teacher Education, *2010 Massachusetts Ave. N.W., #500 20036; (202) 466-7496. Fax, (202) 296-6620. Arthur E. Wise, president. Internet, art@ncate.org or http://www. ncate.org.*

Evaluates and accredits schools, colleges, and academic departments at higher education institutions; publishes list of accredited institutions and standards for accreditation.

National Council for the Social Studies, *3501 Newark St. N.W. 20016-3167; (202) 966-7840. Fax, (202) 966-2061. Martharose F. Laffey, executive director. Internet, http://www.ncss.org.*

Membership: curriculum developers, educational administrators, state supervisors, and social studies educators, including teachers of history, political science, geography, economics, civics, psychology, sociology, and anthropology. Promotes the teaching of social studies; encourages research; sponsors publications; works with other organizations to advance social studies education.

National Council of State Education Assns., *1201 16th St. N.W., #410 20036; (202) 822-7745. Fax, (202) 822-7624. Larry Diebold, executive director.*

Membership: presidents, vice presidents, secretary-treasurers, and executive directors of state education associations. Holds meetings and training programs for officers and staff of state education associations.

National Council of Teachers of Mathematics, *1906 Association Dr., Reston, VA 20191-1593; (703) 620-9840. Fax, (703) 476-2970. Jim Rubillo, interim executive director. Internet, infocentral@nctm.org or http://www. nctm.org.*

Membership: teachers of mathematics in elementary and secondary schools and two-year colleges; university teacher education faculty; students; and other interested persons. Works for the improvement of classroom instruction at all levels. Serves as forum and information clearinghouse on issues related to mathematics education. Offers educational materials and conferences. Monitors legislation and regulations.

National Education Assn., *1201 16th St. N.W. 20036; (202) 833-4000. Fax, (202) 822-7974. Don Cameron, executive director. Internet, http://www.nea.org.*

Membership: more than 2.3 million educators from preschool to university graduate programs. Helps members negotiate pay, benefits, and better working conditions; conducts training programs and workshops. Seeks to raise awareness of the need for public education; interests include education reform, school technology, and international affairs. Monitors legislation and regulations at state and national levels.

National Foundation for the Improvement of Education, *1201 16th St. N.W., #416 20036; (202) 822-7840. Fax, (202) 822-7779. Judith Rényi, executive director. Internet, http://www.nfie.org.*

Educational and charitable organization created by the National Education Assn. Awards grants to teachers to improve teaching techniques and professional development; provides teachers with assistance to integrate computer and telecommunications technology into classroom instruction, curriculum management, and administration.

National Science Resources Center, *Smithsonian Institution, MRC 403, Arts and Industries Bldg., #1201 20560; (202) 357-4892. Fax, (202) 786-2028. Douglas M. Lapp, executive director. Internet, http://www.si.edu/nsrc.*

Sponsored by the Smithsonian Institution and the National Academy of Sciences. Works to improve science teaching in the nation's schools. Disseminates information; develops curriculum materials; seeks to increase public support for reform of science education.

National Science Teachers Assn., *1840 Wilson Blvd., Arlington, VA 22201-3000; (703) 243-7100. Fax, (703) 243-7177. Gerry Wheeler, executive director. Internet, publicinfo@nsta.org or http://www.nsta.org.*

Membership: science teachers from elementary through college levels. Seeks to improve science education; provides forum for exchange of information. Monitors legislation and regulations.

Teachers of English to Speakers of Other Languages, *1600 Cameron St., #300, Alexandria, VA 22314-2751; (703) 836-0774. Fax, (703) 836-7864. Susan Bayley, executive director. Internet, tesol@tesol.edu or http://www.tesol.edu.*

Promotes scholarship and provides information on instruction and research in the teaching of English to speakers of other languages. Offers placement service.

Research

AGENCIES

Education Dept., *Educational Research and Improvement,* *555 New Jersey Ave. N.W., #600D 20208; (202) 219-1385. Fax, (202) 219-1466. Vacant, assistant secretary. Library, (202) 219-1860. Toll-free education statistics and trends, (800) 424-1616. Internet, http://www.ed.gov/NLE.*

Gathers, analyzes, and disseminates information, statistics, and research findings on the conditions and practices of American education. Supports nationally significant model projects, including the National Assessment of Educational Progress (the Nation's Report Card), a survey of the knowledge, skills, understanding, and attitudes of 9, 13, and 17 year olds.

Education Dept., *National Center for Education Statistics,* *555 New Jersey Ave. N.W., #400 20208-5574; (202) 219-1828. Fax, (202) 219-1736. Pascal Forgione, commissioner. Information, (202) 219-5992. Toll-free information,* (800) 424-1616. Internet, ncesinfo@inet.ed.gov or http://www.ed.gov/NCES.

Gathers, analyzes, synthesizes, and disseminates qualitative and quantitative data on the characteristics and effectiveness of American education. Helps state and local education agencies improve statistical gathering and processing methods.

Education Dept., *National Institute on Student Achievement, Curriculum, and Assessment,* *555 New Jersey Ave. N.W., #510 20208-5573; (202) 219-2079. Fax, (202) 219-2135. Joseph Conaty, director.*

Supports fundamental research at every institutional level of education on topics such as the processes of teaching and learning; school organization and improvement; curriculum; and factors that contribute to excellence in education.

Education Dept., *National Library of Education,* *555 New Jersey Ave. N.W., #101 20208; (202) 219-1692. Fax, (202) 219-1696. Blane Dessy, director. Toll-free, (800) 424-1616. Internet, library@inet.ed.gov or http://www.ed.gov/NLE.*

Houses all publications produced or funded by the Education Dept., including Educational Resources Information Center (ERIC) materials. Provides information and answers questions on education statistics and research.

Education Dept., *Reform Assistance and Dissemination,* *555 New Jersey Ave. N.W., #500 20208-5572; (202) 219-2164. Fax, (202) 219-2106. Peirce A. Hammond, director.*

Seeks to identify, recognize, and disseminate information about outstanding school programs nationwide that have been effective in or have significantly improved such areas as drug prevention, vocational training, and academics. Operates the National Diffusion Network and the Blue Ribbon Schools Recognition Program.

NONPROFIT

Academy for Educational Development, *1875 Connecticut Ave. N.W., #900 20009; (202) 884-8000. Fax, (202) 884-8400. Stephen F. Moseley, president. Internet, http://www.aed.org.*

Conducts studies on domestic and international education, on a contract basis. Interests include finance; management of educational institutions; application of communications technology to health education, agricultural extension, and other development problems; exchange of information; and use of telecommunications for social services.

American Educational Research Assn., *1230 17th St. N.W. 20036; (202) 223-9485. Fax, (202) 775-1824. William J. Russell, executive officer. Internet, aera@gmu. edu or http://www.tikkun.ed.asu.edu/aera/home.html.*

Membership: educational researchers affiliated with universities and colleges, school systems, and federal and state agencies. Publishes original research in education; sponsors publication of reference works in educational research; conducts continuing education programs; studies status of women and minorities in the education field.

Council on Governmental Relations, *1200 New York Ave. N.W., #320 20005; (202) 289-6655. Fax, (202) 289-6698. Milton Goldberg, president. Internet, http://web. mit.edu/osp/www/cogr/cogr.html.*

Membership: research universities maintaining federally supported programs. Advises members and makes recommendations to government agencies regarding policies and regulations affecting university research.

Ethics and Public Policy Center, *Education and Society Program, 1015 15th St. N.W., #900 20005; (202) 682-1200. Fax, (202) 408-0632. Elliott Abrams, president. Internet, ethics@eppc.org or http://www.eppc.org.*

Conducts research and holds conferences on the role of formal education and morality in teaching facts, ideas, attitudes, and values.

National Assn. of Independent Colleges and Universities, *Research and Policy, 1025 Connecticut Ave. N.W., #700 20036; (202) 785-8866. Fax, (202) 835-0003. Frank J. Balz, vice president.*

Conducts research on national attitudes and policies concerning independent higher education; surveys student aid programs and federal tax policies affecting institutional financing; acts as a clearinghouse for state associations.

National Education Knowledge Industry Assn., *1200 19th St. N.W., #300 20036-2412; (202) 429-5101. Fax, (202) 785-3849. C. Todd Jones, executive director. Internet, http://www.nekia.org.*

Membership: regional educational laboratories and university-based educational research and development organizations. Serves as a clearinghouse for information on research conducted by members on various education issues. Formerly the Council for Educational Development and Research.

National Research Council, *Board on International Comparative Studies in Education, 2101 Constitution Ave. N.W., HA 178 20418; (202) 334-3010. Fax, (202)*

334-3584. *Patricia L. Morrison, director. Internet, http://www2.nas.edu/delhp/216a.html.*

Helps plan and implement U.S. participation in comparative international research in education. Interests include the scope of specific projects, funding, and the supply and quality of U.S. statistics for use in research.

Rand Corporation, *Education and Human Resources Program, 1333 H St. N.W., #800 20005; (202) 296-5000. Fax, (202) 296-7960. David Chu, director, Washington Research Department. Internet, http://www.rand.org.*

Research organization partially funded by federal agencies. Conducts research on education policy. (Headquarters in Santa Monica, Calif.)

See also American Institutes for Research (p. 617) and Institute for Educational Leadership (p. 174)

LIBRARIES AND EDUCATIONAL MEDIA

See also Internet and Related Technologies (chap. 3); Government Management and Oversight (chap. 10); GPO Regional Depository Libraries (appendix)

AGENCIES

Institute for Museum and Library Services, *Library Services, 1100 Pennsylvania Ave. N.W., #802 20506; (202) 606-5551. Fax, (202) 606-1077. Robert Klassen, director.*

Awards federal grants to support programs and services of public libraries. Aids research, college, and university libraries with technology applications. Promotes literacy through grants to Native American tribes and Hawaiian natives for library services and to state library agencies and local public libraries.

National Commission on Libraries and Information Science, *1110 Vermont Ave. N.W., #820 20005-3522; (202) 606-9200. Fax, (202) 606-9203. Jeanne Hurley Simon, chair; Martha Gould, vice chair. Internet, http://www.nclis.gov.*

Advises Congress and the president on national information and library policy issues; works with other agencies, the private sector, libraries, and information networks to improve access to library and information resources for all Americans, including the elderly, disadvantaged, illiterate, and geographically isolated; promotes effective local use of information generated by the federal government.

LIBRARY OF CONGRESS DIVISIONS AND PROGRAMS

African and Middle Eastern Division, (202) 707-7937

American Folklife Center, (202) 707-6590

American Memory Project, (202) 707-6233

Archive of Folk Culture, (202) 707-5510

Asian Division, (202) 707-5420

Cataloging Distribution Service, (202) 707-9797

The Center for the Book, (202) 707-5221

Children's Literature Center, (202) 707-5535

Computer Catalog Center, (202) 707-3370

Concert Office, (202) 707-5502

Copyright Office, (202) 707-3000

European Division, (202) 707-5414

Federal Library and Information Center Committee, (202) 707-4800

Folklife Reading Room, (202) 707-5510

Geography and Map Division, (202) 707-8530

Hispanic Division, (202) 707-5400

Humanities and Social Division, (202) 707-5530

Interlibrary Loans, (202) 707-5444

Interpretative Programs, (202) 707-5223

Law Library, (202) 707-5065

Law Library Reading Room, (202) 707-5079

Local History and Genealogy Reading Room, (202) 707-5537

Manuscript Division, (202) 707-5383

Mary Pickford Theater, (202) 707-5677

Microform Reading Room, (202) 707-5471

Motion Picture, Broadcasting, and Recorded Sound Division, (202) 707-5840

Music Division, (202) 707-5503

National Library Service for the Blind and Physically Handicapped, (202) 707-5104

Photoduplication Service, (202) 707-5640

Poetry and Literature Center, (202) 707-5394

Preservation Office, (202) 707-5213

Prints and Photographs Division, (202) 707-5836

Rare Book and Special Collections Division, (202) 707-5434

Science and Technology Division, (202) 707-5664

Serial and Government Publications Division, (202) 707-5647

National Endowment for the Humanities *(National Foundation on the Arts and the Humanities), Public Programs and Enterprise, 1100 Pennsylvania Ave. N.W., #426 20506; (202) 606-8271. Fax, (202) 606-8557. Thomas C. Phelps, program officer. Internet, info@neh.fed.us.*

Awards grants to libraries for projects that enhance public appreciation and understanding of the humanities through books and other resources in American library collections. Projects include conferences, exhibitions, essays, and lecture series.

CONGRESS

House Appropriations Committee, *Subcommittee on Legislative Branch, H147 CAP 20515; (202) 225-5338. James T. Walsh, R-N.Y., chair; Edward E. Lombard, staff assistant. Internet, http://www.house.gov/appropriations.*

Jurisdiction over legislation to appropriate funds for the Library of Congress, including the Congressional Research Service.

House Education and the Workforce Committee, *Subcommittee on Postsecondary Education, Training, and Life-Long Learning, 2181 RHOB 20515; (202) 225-4527. Fax, (202) 225-9571. Howard P. "Buck" McKeon, R-*

Calif., chair; Kevin Talley, staff director. Internet, http://www.house.gov/eeo.

Jurisdiction over legislation on libraries, including the Library Services and Construction Act.

House Oversight Committee, *1309 LHOB 20515; (202) 225-8281. Fax, (202) 225-9957. Bill Thomas, R-Calif., chair; Cathy Abernathy, acting staff director. Internet, http://www.house.gov/cho.*

Oversight of and jurisdiction over legislation on the Library of Congress.

Joint Committee on the Library, *SH-711 20515; (202) 225-8281. Rep. Bill Thomas, R-Calif., chair; Deborah Weiss, contact.*

Studies and makes recommendations on legislation dealing with the Library of Congress.

Library of Congress, *101 Independence Ave. S.E. 20540-1000; (202) 707-5205. Fax, (202) 707-1714. James H. Billington, librarian of Congress. Information, (202) 707-2905. Internet, http://www.loc.gov.*

Main book repository of the United States.

Library of Congress, *Center for the Book, 101 Independence Ave. S.E., #650 20540-4920; (202) 707-5221. Fax,*

LIBRARIES AT FEDERAL AGENCIES

DEPARTMENTS

Agriculture, (301) 504-6778

Commerce, (202) 482-5511

Defense, (703) 697-4301

Education, (202) 219-1692

Energy, (202) 586-9534

Interior, (202) 208-5815

Justice, (202) 514-3775

Labor, (202) 219-6992

State, (202) 647-1099

Transportation, (202) 366-0746

Treasury, (202) 622-0990

Veterans Affairs, (202) 273-6558

  Law (202) 273-6480

AGENCIES

Agency for International Development, (202) 712-4810

Commission on Civil Rights, (202) 376-8110

Commodity Futures Trading Commission, (202) 418-5255

Consumer Product Safety Commission, (301) 504-0044

Drug Enforcement Administration, (202) 307-8932

Environmental Protection Agency, (202) 260-5922

Equal Employment Opportunity Commission, (202) 663-4630

Export-Import Bank, (202) 565-3980

Farm Credit Administration, (703) 883-4296

Federal Communications Commission, (202) 418-0450

Federal Deposit Insurance Corporation, (202) 898-3631

Federal Election Commission, (202) 219-3312

Federal Emergency Management Agency, (202) 646-3771

Federal Labor Relation Authority, (202) 482-6695

Federal Maritime Commission, (202) 523-5762

Federal Reserve System, (202) 452-3332

Federal Trade Commission, (202) 326-2395

General Accounting Office

  Law (202) 512-2585

  Technical (202) 512-5180

General Services Administration, (202) 501-0788

International Bank for Reconstruction and Development (World Bank) and International Monetary Fund, (202) 623-7054

Merit Systems Protection Board, (202) 653-7132

National Aeronautics and Space Administration, (202) 358-0168

National Credit Administration, (703) 518-6540

National Endowment for the Arts, (202) 682-5485

National Endowment for the Humanities, (202) 606-8244

National Labor Relations Board, (202) 273-3720

National Library of Medicine, (301) 496-5501

National Science Foundation, (703) 306-0658

Nuclear Regulatory Commission, (301) 415-5610

Occupational Safety and Health Review Commission, (202) 606-5100, ext. 261

Office of Personnel Management, (202) 606-1381

Office of Thrift Supervision (202) 906-6470

Overseas Private Investment Corporation, (202) 336-8565

Peace Corps, (202) 606-3307

Postal Rate Commission, (202) 789-6877

Public Health Library, (301) 443-2673

Securities and Exchange Commission, (202) 942-7090

Small Business Administration

  Main Library (202) 205-7033

  Law (202) 205-6847

Smithsonian Institution, (202) 357-2139

Social Security Administration

  Main Library (410) 965-6113

  Law (410) 965-6108

U.S. Arms Control and Disarmament Agency, (202) 647-5969

U.S. International Trade Commission

  Main Library (202) 205-2630

  Law (202) 205-3287

U.S. Postal Service, (202) 268-2904

(202) 707-0269. John Y. Cole, director. Internet, http://
www.loc.gov/loc/cfbook.

Seeks to broaden public appreciation of books, reading, and libraries; sponsors lectures and conferences on
the educational and cultural role of the book worldwide,
including the history of books and printing, television
and the printed word, and the publishing and production of books; cooperates with state centers and with
other organizations. Projects and programs are privately
funded except for basic administrative support from the
Library of Congress.

Library of Congress, *Federal Library and Information
Center Committee,* 701 Pennsylvania Ave. N.W., #725
20004; (202) 707-4800. Fax, (202) 707-4818. Susan Tarr,
executive director. Internet, flicc@loc.gov.

Membership: one representative from each major
federal agency, one representative each from the Library
of Congress and the national libraries of medicine and
agriculture, and one representative from each of the
major Federal Information Centers. Coordinates planning, development, operations, and activities among federal libraries.

Library of Congress, *Preservation,* 101 Independence
Ave. S.E., #G21 20540; (202) 707-5213. Fax, (202) 707-
3434. Diane N. Kresh, director. Internet, nppo@loc.gov.

Responsible for preserving book and paper materials
in the library's collections.

Senate Appropriations Committee, *Subcommittee
on Legislative Branch,* S125 CAP 20510; (202) 224-8921.
Robert F. Bennett, R-Utah, chair; Christine Ciccone, staff
director. Internet, http://www.senate.gov/~appropriations.

Jurisdiction over legislation to appropriate funds for
the Library of Congress, including the Congressional
Research Service.

Senate Labor and Human Resources Committee,
SD-428 20510; (202) 224-5375. Fax, (202) 224-6510.
James M. Jeffords, R-Vt., chair; Mark Powden, staff direc-
tor. Internet, http://www.senate.gov/~labor.

Jurisdiction over legislation on libraries, including
the Library Services and Construction Act.

Senate Rules and Administration Committee, SR-
305 20510; (202) 224-6352. Fax, (202) 224-3036. John W.
Warner, R-Va., chair; Grayson Winterling, staff director.
Internet, http://www.senate.gov/~rules.

Oversight of and jurisdiction over legislation on the
Library of Congress.

NONPROFIT

American Library Assn., 1301 Pennsylvania Ave. N.W.,
#403 20004; (202) 628-8410. Fax, (202) 628-8419. Carol

C. Henderson, executive director, Washington Office. Internet, alawash@alawash.org or http://www.ala.org.

Educational organization of librarians, trustees, and
educators. Washington office monitors legislation and
regulations on libraries and information science. (Headquarters in Chicago.)

American Society for Information Science, 8720
Georgia Ave., #501, Silver Spring, MD 20910; (301) 495-
0900. Fax, (301) 495-0810. Richard Hill, executive director.
Internet, asis@asis.org or http://www.asis.org.

Membership: librarians, computer scientists, management specialists, behavioral scientists, engineers, and
individuals concerned with access to information. Conducts research and educational programs.

**Assn. for Educational Communications and Tech-
nology,** 1025 Vermont Ave. N.W., #820 20005; (202) 347-
7834. Fax, (202) 347-7839. Stanley D. Zenor, executive
director. Internet, aect@aect.org or http://www.aect.org.

Membership: media professionals for government
and the military, and schools and school systems
(kindergarten through postsecondary). Produces
instructional materials and publications on educational
technology such as Web-based instruction and distance
learning.

Assn. for Information and Image Management,
1100 Wayne Ave., Silver Spring, MD 20910; (301) 587-
8202. Fax, (301) 587-2711. John Mancini, president. Internet, aiim@aiim.org or http://www.aiim.org.

Membership: manufacturers and users of image-
based information systems. Works to advance the profession of information management; develops standards on
such technologies as microfilm and electronic imaging.
Library open to the public.

Assn. of Research Libraries, 21 Dupont Circle N.W.,
#800 20036; (202) 296-2296. Fax, (202) 872-0884. Duane
Webster, executive director. Internet, http://www.arl.org.

Membership: major research libraries, mainly at universities, in the United States and Canada. Interests
include development of library resources in all formats,
subjects, and languages; computer information systems
and other bibliographic tools; management of research
libraries; preservation of library materials; worldwide
information policy; and publishing and scholarly communication.

Council on Library and Information Resources,
1755 Massachusetts Ave. N.W., #500 20036-2188; (202)
939-4750. Fax, (202) 939-4765. Deanna B. Marcum, president. Internet, info@clir.org or http://www.clir.org.

Formed from the 1996 merger of the Commission on
Preservation and Access and the Council on Library

Resources. Acts on behalf of the nation's libraries, archives, and universities to develop and encourage collaborative strategies for preserving the nation's intellectual heritage and strengthening its information system.

Gallaudet University, Library, *800 Florida Ave. N.E. 20002; (202) 651-5220. Fax, (202) 651-5213. John Day, librarian. Information, (202) 651-5217. Archives, (202) 651-5209; media distribution, (202) 651-5212. Some numbers require state relay service for voice transmission.*

Maintains extensive special collection on deafness, including archival materials relating to deaf cultural history and Gallaudet University.

Information Industry Assn., *1625 Massachusetts Ave. N.W., #700 20036; (202) 986-0280. Fax, (202) 638-4403. Ronald G. Dunn, president. Internet, http://www. infoindustry.org.*

Membership: companies involved in creating, distributing, and using information products, services, and technologies. Helps formulate global business strategies; interests include telecommunications, government procurement, taxation, intellectual property rights, and privacy. Monitors legislation and regulations.

International Communications Industries Assn., *11242 Waples Mill Rd., #200, Fairfax, VA 22030; (703) 273-7200. Fax, (703) 278-8082. Walter Blackwell, executive director. Internet, icia@icia.org or http://www. infocomm.org.*

Membership: manufacturers, dealers, and specialists in educational communications products. Provides educators with information on federal funding for audiovisual, video, and computer equipment and materials; monitors trends in educational technology; conducts educational software conference on microcomputers and miniaturization.

Kidsnet, *6856 Eastern Ave. N.W., #208 20012; (202) 291-1400. Fax, (202) 882-7315. Karen W. Jaffe, executive director. Internet, kidsnet@aol.com or http://www.kidsnet.org.*

Computerized clearinghouse that provides information about audio, video, radio, multimedia, and television programming for preschool through high school. Publishes study guides for classroom use. Information available by subscription and electronically.

Society for Imaging Science and Technology, *7003 Kilworth Lane, Springfield, VA 22151; (703) 642-9090. Fax, (703) 642-9094. Calva A. Leonard, executive director. Internet, info@imaging.org or http://www.imaging.org.*

Membership: individuals and companies in fields of imaging science and technology, including photofinishing, nonimpact printing, electronic imaging, silver halide, image preservation, and hybrid imaging systems. Gathers and disseminates technical information; fosters professional development.

Special Libraries Assn., *1700 18th St. N.W. 20009-2508; (202) 234-4700. Fax, (202) 265-9317. David R. Bender, executive director. Internet, sla@sla.org or http://www. sla.org.*

Membership: librarians and information managers serving institutions that use or produce information in specialized areas, including business, engineering, law, the arts and sciences, government, museums, and universities. Sponsors professional development programs and research projects; provides a consultation service. Monitors legislation and regulations.

▨ POSTSECONDARY EDUCATION

See also Professional Interests and Benefits (this chapter); Health Professions (chap. 11); Military Education and Training (chap. 15)

AGENCIES

Education Dept., *Fund for the Improvement of Postsecondary Education, 7th and D Sts. S.W. 20202-5175; (202) 708-5750. Fax, (202) 708-6118. Charles Karelis, director. Internet, http://www.ed.gov/offices/OPE/FIPSE.*

Works to improve postsecondary education by administering grant competitions, including the Comprehensive Program for improvements in postsecondary education; the European Community/United States (ECUS) Joint Consortia for Cooperation in Higher Education and Vocational Education; the Program for North American Mobility in Higher Education; and the Disseminating Proven Reforms Program.

Education Dept., *Postsecondary Education, 7th and D Sts. S.W., #4082 20202-5100; (202) 708-5547. Fax, (202) 708-9814. David Longanecker, assistant secretary. Information, (202) 401-2000. TDD, (800) 730-8913.*

Administers federal assistance programs for public and private postsecondary institutions; provides financial support for faculty development, construction of facilities, and improvement of graduate, continuing, cooperative, and international education; awards grants and loans for financial assistance to eligible students.

CONGRESS

House Education and the Workforce Committee, *Subcommittee on Postsecondary Education, Training, and Life-Long Learning, 2181 RHOB 20515; (202) 225-*

COLLEGES AND UNIVERSITIES IN WASHINGTON

Agriculture Dept. Graduate School, 600 Maryland Ave. S.W. 20024

Switchboard: (202) 314-3307

Director: Philip Hudson, (202) 720-2077

American University, 4400 Massachusetts Ave. N.W. 20016

Switchboard: (202) 885-1000

President: Benjamin Ladner, (202) 885-2121

Catholic University, 620 Michigan Ave. N.E. 20064

Switchboard: (202) 319-5000

President: Patrick Ellis, (202) 319-5100

Columbia Union College, 7600 Flower Ave., Takoma Park, MD 20912

Switchboard: (301) 891-4000

President: Charles Scriven, (301) 891-4128

Gallaudet University, 800 Florida Ave. N.E. 20002

Switchboard: (202) 651-5000 (voice and TDD)

President: I. King Jordan, (202) 651-5005 (voice and TDD)

George Mason University, 4400 University Dr., Fairfax, VA 22030

Switchboard: (703) 993-1000

President: Alan G. Merton, (703) 993-8700

George Washington University, 2121 Eye St. N.W. 20052

Switchboard: (202) 994-1000

President: Stephen Joel Trachtenberg, (202) 994-6500

Georgetown University, 37th and O Sts. N.W. 20057

Switchboard: (202) 687-0100

President: Leo O'Donovan, (202) 687-4134

Howard University, 2400 6th St. N.W. 20059

Switchboard: (202) 806-6100

President: H. Patrick Swygert, (202) 806-2500

Marymount University, 2807 N. Glebe Rd., Arlington, VA 22207

Switchboard: (703) 522-5600

President: Eymard Gallagher, (703) 284-1598

Mount Vernon College, 2100 Foxhall Rd. N.W. 20007

Switchboard: (202) 625-0400

President: Grae Baxter, acting, (202) 625-4600

Paul H. Nitze School of Advanced International Studies (Johns Hopkins University), 1740 Massachusetts Ave. N.W. 20036

Switchboard: (202) 663-5600

Dean: Paul D. Wolfowitz, (202) 663-5624

Protestant Episcopal Theological Seminary, 3737 Seminary Rd., Alexandria, VA 22304

Switchboard: (703) 370-6600

Dean: Martha J. Horne, (703) 461-1701

Trinity College, 125 Michigan Ave. N.E. 20017

Switchboard: (202) 884-9000

President: Patricia McGuire, (202) 884-9050

University of Maryland, Rt. 1, College Park Campus, College Park, MD 20742

Switchboard: (301) 405-1000

President: William E. Kirwan, (301) 405-5803

University of the District of Columbia, 4200 Connecticut Ave. N.W. 20008

Switchboard: (202) 274-5000

President: Julius F. Nimmons Jr., acting, (202) 274-5100

4527. *Fax, (202) 225-9571. Howard P. "Buck" McKeon, R-Calif., chair; Kevin Talley, staff director. Internet, http:// www.house.gov/eeo.*

Jurisdiction over legislation on postsecondary education, including community and junior colleges, the Construction Loan Program, construction of school facilities, and financial aid, and over legislation barring discrimination in postsecondary education.

Senate Banking, Housing, and Urban Affairs Committee, *SD-534 20510; (202) 224-7391. Fax, (202) 224-5137. Alfonse M. D'Amato, R-N.Y., chair; Howard Menell, staff director. Internet, http://www.senate.gov/ ~banking.*

Oversees government-sponsored enterprises, including the Student Loan Marketing Assn. and the College Construction Loan Insurance Assn., with regard to the financial risk posed to the federal government.

Senate Labor and Human Resources Committee, *SD-428 20510; (202) 224-5375. Fax, (202) 224-6510. James M. Jeffords, R-Vt., chair; Mark Powden, staff director. Internet, http://www.senate.gov/~labor.*

Jurisdiction over legislation on postsecondary education, including community and junior colleges, the Construction Loan Program, construction of school facilities, and financial aid, and over legislation barring discrimination in postsecondary education, including the Women's Educational Equity Act of 1974 as it applies to postsecondary education.

NONPROFIT

Accuracy in Academia, *4455 Connecticut Ave. N.W., #330 20008; (202) 364-3085. Fax, (202) 364-4098. Dan Flynn, executive director. Toll-free, (800) 787-0429. Internet, cr@aim.org or http://www.aim.org.*

Investigates reports from students of inaccurate information in faculty lectures or in required reading materials that deal with only one side of controversial issues. Approaches faculty members with complaints; publicizes findings. Defends rights of professors and students to academic freedom without fear of retaliation. Interests include political discrimination and academic freedom.

ACT*American College Testing, *1 Dupont Circle N.W., #340 20036; (202) 223-2318. Fax, (202) 293-2223. Daniel Minchew, director, Washington Office. Internet, http://www.act.org.*

Administers American College Test (ACT) entrance examination for colleges and universities. Provides colleges and universities with testing, counseling, research, and student aid processing services. (Headquarters in Iowa City, Iowa.)

American Assn. for Higher Education, *1 Dupont Circle N.W., #360 20036; (202) 293-6440. Fax, (202) 293-0073. Margaret Miller, president. Internet, http://www.aahe.org.*

Membership: college and university educators, students, public officials, and others interested in postsecondary education. Evaluates issues in higher education; interests include statewide and institutional assessment, school-college collaboration, improvement of teaching and learning, and student community service. Conducts studies, conferences, and an annual convention.

American Assn. of Colleges of Pharmacy, *1426 Prince St., Alexandria, VA 22314-2841; (703) 739-2330. Fax, (703) 836-8982. Richard Penna, executive vice president. Internet, aacp@aol.com or http://www.aacp.org.*

Represents and advocates for the academic community in the profession of pharmacy. Conducts programs and activities in cooperation with other national health and higher education associations in the Washington, D.C., area.

American Assn. of Collegiate Registrars and Admissions Officers, *1 Dupont Circle N.W., #520 20036-1171; (202) 293-9161. Fax, (202) 872-8857. Wayne E. Becraft, executive director. Internet, http://www.aacrao.com.*

Membership: degree-granting postsecondary institutions, government agencies, higher education coordinating boards, private education organizations, and education-oriented businesses. Promotes higher education and contributes to the professional development of members working in admissions, enrollment management, financial aid, institutional research, records, and registration.

American Assn. of Community Colleges, *1 Dupont Circle N.W., #410 20036-1176; (202) 728-0200. Fax, (202) 223-9390. David Pierce, president. Internet, http://www.aacc.nche.edu.*

Membership: accredited, two-year community technical and junior colleges, corporate foundations, international associates, and institutional affiliates. Studies include policies for lifelong education, workforce training programs and partnerships, international curricula, enrollment trends, and cooperative programs with public schools and communities.

American Assn. of State Colleges and Universities, *1 Dupont Circle N.W., #700 20036; (202) 293-7070. Fax, (202) 296-5819. James B. Appleberry, president. Internet, http://www.aascu.nche.edu.*

Membership: presidents and chancellors of state colleges and universities. Promotes equity in education; fosters information exchange among members; interests include minority participation in higher education, student financial aid, international education programs, academic affairs, and teacher education. Monitors legislation and regulations.

American Assn. of University Professors, *1012 14th St. N.W., #500 20005; (202) 737-5900. Fax, (202) 737-5526. Mary Burgan, general secretary. Toll-free, (800) 424-2973. Internet, aaup@aaup.org or http://www.aaup.org.*

Membership: college and university faculty members. Defends faculties' academic freedom and tenure; advocates collegial governance; assists in the development of policies ensuring due process. Conducts workshops and education programs. Monitors legislation and regulations.

American Conference of Academic Deans, *1818 R St. N.W. 20009; (202) 387-3760. Fax, (202) 265-9532. Carol Schneider, president.*

Membership: academic deans of two- and four-year accredited colleges, universities, and community colleges (private and public). Fosters information exchange among members on college curricular and administrative issues.

American Council of Trustees and Alumni, *1625 K St. N.W., #310 20006-1604; (202) 467-6787. Fax, (202)*

467-6784. *Lynne V. Cheney, chair; Jerry L. Martin, president. Internet, naf@naf.org or http://www.naf.org.*

Membership: college and university alumni interested in promoting academic freedom and excellence. Seeks to help alumni direct their financial contributions to programs that will raise educational standards at their alma maters. Promotes the role of alumni in shaping higher education policies.

American Council on Education, *1 Dupont Circle N.W., #800 20036-1193; (202) 939-9300. Fax, (202) 833-4760. Stanley O. Ikenberry, president. Press, (202) 939-9365. Library, (202) 939-9405. Internet, http://www.acenet.edu.*

Membership: colleges, universities, education associations, students with disabilities, and businesses. Conducts and publishes research; maintains offices dealing with government relations, women and minorities in higher education, management of higher education institutions, adult learning and educational credentials (academic credit for nontraditional learning, especially in the armed forces), leadership development, and international education. Library open to the public by appointment.

Assn. for Supervision and Curriculum Development, *1250 N. Pitt St., Alexandria, VA 22314-1453; (703) 549-9110. Fax, (703) 299-8638. Gene R. Carter, executive director. Internet, http://www.ascd.org.*

Membership: teachers, supervisors, directors of instruction, school principals (kindergarten through secondary), university and college faculty, and individuals interested in curriculum development. Sponsors institutes and conferences. Monitors legislation and regulations affecting education.

Assn. of American Colleges and Universities, *1818 R St. N.W. 20009; (202) 387-3760. Fax, (202) 265-9532. Paula P. Brownlee, president. Internet, http://www.aacu-edu.org.*

Membership: public and private colleges, universities, and postsecondary consortia. Works to develop effective academic programs and improve undergraduate curricula and services. Seeks to encourage, enhance, and support the development of broadly based intellectual skills through the study of liberal arts and sciences.

Assn. of American Law Schools, *1201 Connecticut Ave. N.W., #800 20036; (202) 296-8851. Fax, (202) 296-8869. Carl C. Monk, executive director. Internet, http://www.aals.org.*

Membership: schools of law, subject to approval by association. Represents member organizations before federal government and private agencies; evaluates member institutions; conducts workshops on the teaching of law; assists law schools with faculty recruitment; publishes faculty placement bulletin and annual directory of law teachers.

Assn. of American Universities, *1200 New York Ave. N.W., #550 20005; (202) 408-7500. Fax, (202) 408-8184. Cornelius J. Pings, president. Internet, http://www.tulane.edu/~aau.*

Membership: public and private universities with emphasis on graduate and professional education and research. Fosters information exchange among presidents of member institutions.

Assn. of Catholic Colleges and Universities, *1 Dupont Circle N.W., #650 20036; (202) 457-0650. Fax, (202) 728-0977. Monika K. Hellwig, executive director. Internet, 105121.1321@compuserve.com.*

Membership: regionally accredited Catholic colleges and universities and individuals interested in Catholic higher education. Acts as a clearinghouse for information on Catholic institutions of higher education. (Affiliated with the National Catholic Educational Assn.)

Assn. of Community College Trustees, *1740 N St. N.W. 20036; (202) 775-4667. Fax, (202) 223-1297. Ray Taylor, president. Internet, http://www.acct.org.*

Provides members of community college governing boards with training in educational programs. Monitors federal education programs.

Assn. of Governing Boards of Universities and Colleges, *1 Dupont Circle N.W., #400 20036-1190; (202) 296-8400. Fax, (202) 223-7053. Richard T. Ingram, president. Internet, http://www.agb.org.*

Membership: presidents, boards of trustees, regents, commissions, and other groups governing colleges, universities, and institutionally related foundations. Interests include the relationship between the president and board of trustees and other subjects relating to governance. Library open to the public.

Assn. of Higher Education Facilities Officers, *1643 Prince St., Alexandria, VA 22314-2818; (703) 684-1446. Fax, (703) 549-2772. Wayne E. Leroy, executive vice president. Internet, info@appa.org or http://www.appa.org.*

Membership: professionals involved in the administration, maintenance, planning, and development of buildings and facilities used by colleges and universities. Interests include maintenance and upkeep of housing facilities. Provides information on campus energy management programs and campus accessibility for people with disabilities.

Assn. of Jesuit Colleges and Universities, *1 Dupont Circle N.W., #405 20036; (202) 862-9893. Fax, (202) 862-8523. Charles L. Currie SJ, president. Internet, blkrobe@aol.com or http://www.AJCUnet.edu.*

Membership: American Jesuit colleges and universities. Monitors government regulatory and policymaking activities affecting higher education. Publishes directory of Jesuit colleges, universities, and high schools and monthly report on the state of higher education.

Business-Higher Education Forum, *1 Dupont Circle N.W., #800 20036; (202) 939-9345. Fax, (202) 833-4723. Judy Irwin, acting executive director. Internet, bhef@ace.nche.edu or http://www.acenet.edu/programs/bhef.html.*

Membership: chief executive officers of major corporations, colleges, and universities. Promotes cooperation between businesses and higher educational institutions. Interests include international economic competitiveness, education and training, research and development, science and technology, and global interdependence.

Career College Assn., *750 1st St. N.E., #900 20002-4242; (202) 336-6700. Fax, (202) 336-6828. Omer Waddles, president. Internet, ccal@erols.com or http://www.career.org.*

Membership: private postsecondary colleges and career schools in the United States. Works to expand the accessibility of postsecondary career education and to improve the quality of education offered by member schools.

Christian College Coalition, *329 8th St. N.E. 20002; (202) 546-8713. Fax, (202) 546-8913. Robert Andringa, president. Internet, coalition@cccu.org or http://www.cccu.org.*

Membership: accredited four-year Christian liberal arts colleges. Offers faculty development conferences on faith and the academic disciplines. Coordinates annual gathering of college administrators. Sponsors internship/seminar programs for students at member colleges. Interests include religious and educational freedom.

College and University Personnel Assn., *1233 20th St. N.W., #301 20036-1250; (202) 429-0311. Fax, (202) 429-0149. Susan Jurow, executive director. Internet, http://www.cupa.org.*

Membership: college and university human resource administrators. Conducts seminars and workshops; responds to inquiries on human resource administration. Monitors legislation and regulations.

College Board, *1233 20th St. N.W., #600 20036-2304; (202) 822-5900. Fax, (202) 822-5920. John Childers, vice*

president, Communications and Government Relations. *Internet, http://www.collegeboard.org.*

Membership: colleges and universities, secondary schools, school systems, and education associations. Provides direct student support programs and professional development for educators; conducts policy analysis and research; and advocates public policy positions that support educational excellence and promote student access to higher education. Library open to the public. (Headquarters in New York.)

Council of Graduate Schools, *1 Dupont Circle N.W., #430 20036-1173; (202) 223-3791. Fax, (202) 331-7157. Jules B. LaPidus, president. Internet, http://www.cgsnet.org.*

Membership: private and public colleges and universities with significant involvement in graduate education. Produces publications and information about graduate education; provides a forum for member schools to exchange information and ideas.

Council of Independent Colleges, *1 Dupont Circle N.W., #320 20036; (202) 466-7230. Fax, (202) 466-7238. Allen P. Splete, president. Internet, cic@cic.nche.edu or http://www.cic.edu.*

Membership: private four-year liberal arts colleges. Sponsors management development institutes for college presidents and deans; conducts faculty development programs; sponsors national projects on leadership, curriculum development, and related topics. Holds workshops and produces publications.

Educational Testing Service (ETS), *1800 K St. N.W., #900 20006; (202) 659-0616. Fax, (202) 659-8075. Patricia McAllister, director, Washington Office. Internet, http://www.ets.org.*

Administers examinations for admission to educational programs and for graduate and licensing purposes; conducts instructional programs in testing, evaluation, and research in education fields. Washington office handles government and professional relations. Fee for services. (Headquarters in Princeton, N.J.)

National Assn. for College Admission Counseling, *1631 Prince St., Alexandria, VA 22314; (703) 836-2222. Fax, (703) 836-8015. Joyce Smith, executive director. Internet, http://www.nacac.com.*

Membership: high school guidance counselors, independent counselors, college and university admission officers, and financial aid officers. Assists counselors who serve students in the college admission process. Promotes and funds research on admission counseling and on the transition from high school to college. Advocates for the rights of students in the college admission process. Sponsors national college fairs and continuing education for members.

National Assn. of College and University Attorneys, *1 Dupont Circle N.W., #620 20036; (202) 833-8390. Fax, (202) 296-8379. Sheila Bell, executive director. Internet, nacua@nacua.org or http://www.nacua.org.*

Provides information on legal developments affecting postsecondary education. Operates a clearinghouse through which attorneys on campuses are able to network with their counterparts on current legal problems.

National Assn. of College and University Business Officers, *2501 M St. N.W., #400 20037; (202) 861-2500. Fax, (202) 861-2583. James E. Morley Jr., president. Internet, http://www.nacubo.org.*

Membership: chief business officers at higher education institutions. Provides members with information on financial management, federal regulations, and other subjects related to the business administration of universities and colleges; conducts workshops on issues such as student aid, institutional budgeting, and accounting.

National Assn. of Independent Colleges and Universities, *1025 Connecticut Ave. N.W., #700 20036-5405; (202) 785-8866. Fax, (202) 835-0003. David L. Warren, president.*

Membership: independent colleges and universities and related state associations. Counsels members on federal education programs and tax policy.

National Assn. of State Universities and Land-Grant Colleges, *1 Dupont Circle N.W., #710 20036-1191; (202) 778-0818. Fax, (202) 296-6456. C. Peter Magrath, president. Internet, hiebertr@nasulgc.nche.edu or http://www.nasulgc.nche.edu.*

Membership: land grant colleges and state universities. Serves as clearinghouse on issues of public higher education.

National Assn. of Student Personnel Administrators, *1875 Connecticut Ave. N.W., #418 20009-5728; (202) 265-7500. Fax, (202) 797-1157. Gwen Dungy, executive director. Internet, office@naspa.org or http://www.naspa.org.*

Membership: deans, student affairs administrators, faculty, and graduate students. Seeks to develop leadership and improve practices in student affairs administration. Initiates and supports programs and legislation to improve student affairs administration.

National Council for Resource Development, *1 Dupont Circle N.W., #410 20036-1176; (202) 822-0750.*

Fax, (202) 822-5014. Marilyn Appelson, president. Internet, http://www.slcc.edu/crd.

Membership: college presidents, administrators, fundraisers, grantwriters, and development officers at two-year colleges. Educates members on how to secure resources for their institution; conducts workshops and training programs. Monitors legislation and regulations. (Affiliated with the American Assn. of Community Colleges.)

National Council of University Research Administrators, *1 Dupont Circle N.W., #220 20036; (202) 466-3894. Fax, (202) 223-5573. Kathleen Larmett, executive director. Internet, info@ncura.edu or http://www.ncura.edu.*

Membership: individuals engaged in administering research, training, and educational programs, primarily at colleges and universities. Encourages development of effective policies and procedures in the administration of these programs.

U.S. Student Assn., *1413 K St. N.W., 9th Floor 20005; (202) 347-8772. Fax, (202) 393-5886. Sarita Gupta, president. Internet, ussa@essential.org or http://www.essential.org/ussa.*

Represents postsecondary students, student government associations, and state student lobby associations. Interests include civil rights on campus and the financing of higher education. Maintains student coalitions of women, racial, ethnic, and sexual minorities. Serves as clearinghouse for information on student problems, activities, and government; holds conferences emphasizing student lobbying techniques.

Women's College Coalition, *125 Michigan Ave. N.E. 20017; (202) 234-0443. Fax, (202) 234-0445. Jadwiga S. Sebrechts, president. Internet, http://www.academic.org.*

Membership: public and private, independent and church-related, two- and four-year women's colleges. Interests include the role of women's colleges as model institutions for educating women, gender equity issues, and retention of women in math, science, and engineering. Maintains an information clearinghouse on U.S. undergraduate women's colleges. Conducts research on gender equity issues in education and positive learning environments.

College Accreditation

Many college- or university-based and independent postsecondary education programs are accredited by member associations. See specific subject headings and associations within the chapter.

AGENCIES

Education Dept., *Accreditation and Eligibility Determination,* 7th and D Sts. S.W., #3915 20202-5244; (202) 708-7417. Fax, (202) 708-9469. Karen W. Kershenstein, division director.

Reviews accrediting agencies and state approval agencies that seek initial or renewed recognition by the secretary; provides the National Advisory Committee on Institutional Quality and Integrity with staff support.

NONPROFIT

American Academy for Liberal Education, *1015 18th St. N.W., #204 20036; (202) 452-8611. Fax, (202) 452-8620. Jeffrey Wallin, president.*

Accredits colleges and universities whose general education program in the liberal arts meets the academy's accreditation requirements. Provides support for institutions that maintain substantial liberal arts programs and which desire to raise requirements to meet AALE standards.

Council for Higher Education Accreditation, *1 Dupont Circle N.W., #510 20036-1135; (202) 995-6126. Fax, (202) 955-6129. Judith Eaton, president. Internet, chea@chea.org or http://www.chea.org.*

Advocates voluntary self regulation of colleges and universities through accreditation; coordinates research, debate, and processes that improve accreditation; mediates disputes and fosters communications among accrediting bodies and the higher education community.

Financial Aid to Students

See also Internships, Fellowships, Grants (this chapter)

AGENCIES

Education Dept., *Student Financial Assistance,* 7th and D Sts. S.W., #4004 (mailing address: 600 Independence Ave. S.W., #5102, Washington, DC 20202-5130); (202) 260-6536. Fax, (202) 708-7970. Diane Rogers, acting deputy assistant secretary. Student Aid Information Center, (800) 433-3243.

Administers federal loan, grant, and work-study programs for postsecondary education to eligible individuals. Administers the Pell Grant Program, the Perkins Loan Program, the Stafford Student Loan Program (Guaranteed Student Loan)/PLUS Program, the College Work-Study Program, the Supplemental Loans for Students (SLS), and the Supplemental Educational Opportunity Grant Program.

NONPROFIT

College Board, *1233 20th St. N.W., #600 20036-2304; (202) 822-5900. Fax, (202) 822-5920. John Childers, vice president, Communications and Government Relations. Internet, http://www.collegeboard.org.*

Membership: colleges and universities, secondary schools, school systems, and education associations. Provides direct student support programs and professional development for educators; conducts policy analysis and research; produces publications; disseminates current information on federal issues to members; and advocates public policy positions that support educational excellence and promote student access to higher education. Library open to the public. (Headquarters in New York.)

Education Finance Council, *1155 15th St. N.W., #801 20005; (202) 466-8621. Fax, (202) 466-8643. William D. Hansen, executive director. Internet, http://www.efc.org.*

Membership: nonprofit educational loan secondary market organizations. Works to maintain and expand student access to higher education through tax-exempt funding for loans.

National Assn. of Student Financial Aid Administrators, *1920 L St. N.W., #200 20036-5020; (202) 785-0453. Fax, (202) 785-1487. Dallas Martin, president. Internet, http://www.nasfa.org.*

Works to ensure adequate funding for individuals seeking postsecondary education and to ensure proper management and administration of public and private financial aid funds.

National Council of Higher Education Loan Programs, *1100 Connecticut Ave. N.W., 12th Floor 20036; (202) 822-2106. Fax, (202) 822-2142. Brett Lief, president.*

Membership: agencies and organizations involved in making, servicing, and collecting Guaranteed Student Loans. Works with the Education Dept. to develop forms and procedures for administering the Federal Family Education Loan Program. Fosters information exchange among members.

Student Loan Marketing Assn. (Sallie Mae), *1055 Thomas Jefferson St. N.W. 20007; (202) 298-2600. Fax, (202) 298-3939. Al Lord, president. Information, (202) 333-8000. Internet, http://www.salliemae.com.*

Government-sponsored private corporation. Provides funds to financial and educational institutions (such as commercial banks, colleges, and universities) that make Stafford Student Loans and other educational loans administered by the Education Dept. available to students.

PRESCHOOL, ELEMENTARY, SECONDARY EDUCATION

See also Children and Families (chap. 18); Food and Nutrition (chap. 2); Museums (chap. 4); Professional Interests and Benefits (this chapter)

AGENCIES

Education Dept., *Bilingual Education and Minority Languages Affairs,* 330 C St. S.W., #5086 20202-6510; (202) 205-5463. Fax, (202) 205-8737. Delia Pompa, director.

Administers bilingual education programs in elementary and secondary schools to help students of limited English proficiency learn the English language. The program is designed to give students of limited English proficiency better opportunities to achieve academic success and meet grade promotion and graduation requirements.

Education Dept., *Elementary and Secondary Education,* 600 Independence Ave. S.W., 4000 Portals Bldg. 20202-6100; (202) 401-0113. Fax, (202) 205-0303. Gerald Tirozzi, assistant secretary.

Administers federal assistance programs for elementary and secondary education (both public and private). Program divisions are Compensatory Education (including Chapter 1 aid for disadvantaged children); School Improvement; Migrant Education; Indian Education; Impact Aid; Goals 2000; and Safe, Drug-Free Schools.

Education Dept., *Even Start,* 600 Independence Ave. S.W. 20202-6132; (202) 260-0826. Fax, (202) 260-7764. Patricia McKee, coordinator.

Develops family-centered education projects to encourage parents of low-income families to become involved in the education of their children; helps children reach their full potential as learners and offers literacy training to parents.

Education Dept., *Impact Aid,* 600 Independence Ave. S.W. 20202-6244; (202) 260-1465. Fax, (202) 205-0088. Catherine Schagh, director. Information, (202) 260-3858.

Provides funds for elementary and secondary educational activities to school districts in federally impacted areas (where federal activities such as military bases enlarge staff and reduce taxable property).

Education Dept., *Safe and Drug-Free Schools,* 604 Portals Bldg. (mailing address: 600 Independence Ave. S.W., Washington, DC 20202-6123); (202) 260-3954. Fax, (202) 260-7767. William Modzeleski, director. Internet, http://www.ed.gov/offices/OESE/SDFS.

Develops policy for the department's drug and violence prevention initiatives for students in elementary and secondary schools and institutions of higher education. Coordinates education efforts in drug and violence prevention with those of other federal departments and agencies.

Environmental Protection Agency, *Pollution Prevention and Toxics,* 401 M St. S.W., #527 East Tower 20460; (202) 260-3810. Fax, (202) 260-0575. William Sanders, director. Information, (202) 554-1404.

Administers the Asbestos Loan and Grant Program by awarding loans and grants to needy public and private elementary and secondary schools to eliminate friable asbestos materials that pose a health threat to building occupants.

Health and Human Services Dept., *Head Start,* 330 C St. S.W., #2050 (mailing address: P.O. Box 1182, Washington, DC 20013); (202) 205-8572. Fax, (202) 260-9336. Helen Taylor, associate commissioner.

Awards grants to nonprofit organizations and local governments for operating community Head Start programs (comprehensive development programs for children, ages 3 to 5, of low-income families); manages a limited number of parent and child centers for families with children up to age 3. Conducts research and manages demonstration programs, including those under the Comprehensive Child Care Development Act of 1988; administers the Child Development Associate scholarship program, which trains individuals for careers in child development, often as Head Start teachers.

National Agricultural Library *(Agriculture Dept.),* *Food and Nutrition Information Center,* 10301 Baltimore Ave., #304, Beltsville, MD 20705-2351; (301) 504-5719. Fax, (301) 504-6409. Vacant, coordinator. Internet, fnic@nal.usda.gov or http://www.nal.usda.gov/fnic.

Serves as a resource center for school and child nutrition program personnel who need information on food service management and nutrition education. Center open to the public.

White House Commission on Presidential Scholars *(Education Dept.),* 600 Independence Ave. S.W. 20202-3500; (202) 205-0512. Fax, (202) 205-0676. Kimberly Watkins-Foote, executive director. Information, (202) 401-0961.

Honorary recognition program that selects high school seniors of outstanding achievement in academics, community service, artistic ability, and leadership to receive the Presidential Scholars Award. Scholars travel to Washington for national recognition week.

CONGRESS

House Education and the Workforce Committee, *Subcommittee on Early Childhood, Youth, and Families,* *2181 RHOB 20515; (202) 225-4527. Fax, (202) 225-9571. Frank Riggs, R-Calif., chair; Kevin Talley, staff director. Internet, http://www.house.gov/eeo.*

Jurisdiction over preschool, elementary, and secondary education legislation, including impact aid legislation and food programs for children in schools.

Senate Agriculture, Nutrition, and Forestry Committee, *Subcommittee on Research, Nutrition, and General Legislation, SR-361A 20510; (202) 224-2035. Fax, (202) 224-1725. Mitch McConnell, R-Ky., chair; David Hovermale, legislative assistant. Internet, http://www.senate.gov/~agriculture.*

Jurisdiction over legislation on food programs for children in schools.

Senate Labor and Human Resources Committee, *SD-428 20510; (202) 224-5375. Fax, (202) 224-6510. James M. Jeffords, R-Vt., chair; Mark Powden, staff director. Internet, http://www.senate.gov/~labor.*

Jurisdiction over preschool, elementary, and secondary education legislation, including impact aid legislation; and legislation barring discrimination in schools. Oversight of the Follow Through Act, which aids children in making the transition from preschool to elementary grades.

NONPROFIT

American School Food Service Assn., *1600 Duke St., 7th Floor, Alexandria, VA 22314; (703) 739-3900. Fax, (703) 739-3915. Barbara Borschow, executive director. Toll-free, (800) 877-8822. Internet, http://www.asfsa.org.*

Membership: state and local food service workers and supervisors, school cafeteria managers, nutrition educators, and others interested in school food programs and child nutrition. Sponsors National School Lunch Week.

Assn. for Childhood Education International, *17904 Georgia Ave., #215, Olney, MD 20832; (301) 570-2111. Fax, (301) 570-2212. Gerald C. Odland, executive director. Toll-free, (800) 423-3563. Internet, aceihq@aol.com or http://www.udel.edu/bateman/acei.*

Membership: educators, parents, and professionals who work with children (infancy to adolescence). Works to promote the rights, education, and well-being of children worldwide. Holds annual conference.

Assn. for Supervision and Curriculum Development, *1250 N. Pitt St., Alexandria, VA 22314-1453; (703)*

549-9110. Fax, (703) 299-8638. Gene R. Carter, executive director. Internet, http://www.ascd.org.

Membership: teachers, supervisors, directors of instruction, school principals (kindergarten through secondary), university and college faculty, and individuals interested in curriculum development. Sponsors institutes and conferences. Monitors legislation and regulations.

Council for Basic Education, *1319 F St. N.W., #900 20004-1152; (202) 347-4171. Fax, (202) 347-5047. Christopher T. Cross, president. Internet, info@c-b-e.org or http://www.c-b-e.org.*

Promotes liberal arts education in elementary and secondary schools; seeks to improve liberal arts instruction of teachers and administrators; conducts workshops, seminars, and independent summer study programs for elementary and secondary school teachers; works to establish and maintain high academic standards; serves as information clearinghouse on education issues.

Council of the Great City Schools, *1301 Pennsylvania Ave. N.W., #702 20004; (202) 393-2427. Fax, (202) 393-2400. Mike Casserly, executive director. Internet, http://www.cgcs.org.*

Membership: superintendents and school board members of large urban school districts. Provides research, legislative, and support services for members; interests include elementary and secondary education and school finance.

Home and School Institute, *MegaSkills Education Center, 1500 Massachusetts Ave. N.W. 20005; (202) 466-3633. Fax, (202) 833-1400. Dorothy Rich, president. Internet, http://www.megaskillshsi.org.*

Works to improve the quality of education for children and parents by integrating the resources of the home, the school, and the community. Develops family training curricula and materials for home use, and training programs and conferences for professionals. Interests include special, bilingual, career education; character development; and working, single, and teenage parents.

National Alliance of Business, *Education Reform, 1201 New York Ave. N.W., #700 20005-3917; (202) 289-2888. Fax, (202) 289-1303. Milton Goldberg, executive vice president. Internet, http://www.nab.com.*

Encourages business leaders, government officials, and educators to work together to upgrade the educational system. Provides information on state and local education improvement initiatives; helps build relationships between academic standards and workplace requirements.

National Assessment Governing Board, *800 N. Capitol St. N.W., #825 20002-4233; (202) 357-6938. Fax, (202) 357-6945. Roy Truby, executive director. Internet, http://www.nagb.org.*

Independent board of local, state, and federal officials, educators, and others appointed by the secretary of education and funded under the National Assessment of Educational Progress (NAEP) program. Sets policy for NAEP, a series of tests measuring achievements in U.S. schools since 1969.

National Assn. for College Admission Counseling, *1631 Prince St., Alexandria, VA 22314; (703) 836-2222. Fax, (703) 836-8015. Joyce Smith, executive director. Internet, http://www.nacac.com.*

Membership: high school guidance counselors, independent counselors, college and university admissions officers, and financial aid officers. Assists counselors who serve students in the college admission process. Promotes and funds research on admission counseling and on the transition from high school to college. Advocates for the rights of students in the college admission process. Sponsors national college fairs, continuing education for members, and an annual conference.

National Assn. for the Education of Young Children, *1509 16th St. N.W. 20036-1426; (202) 232-8777. Fax, (202) 328-1846. Marilyn M. Smith, executive director. Toll-free, (800) 424-2460. Internet, http://www.naeyc.org.*

Membership: teachers, parents, and directors of early childhood programs. Works to improve the education of and the quality of services to children from birth through age 8. Sponsors professional development opportunities for early childhood educators. Offers an accreditation program and conducts an annual conference; issues publications.

National Assn. of Elementary School Principals, *1615 Duke St., Alexandria, VA 22314-3483; (703) 684-3345. Fax, (703) 548-6021. Samuel G. Sava, executive director. Internet, naesp@naesp.org or http://www.naesp.org.*

Membership: elementary and middle school principals. Conducts workshops for members on federal and state policies and programs and on professional development. Offers assistance in contract negotiations.

National Assn. of Partners in Education, *901 N. Pitt St., #320, Alexandria, VA 22314; (703) 836-4880. Fax, (703) 836-6941. Daniel W. Merenda, president. Internet, NAPEhq@NAPEhq.org.*

Membership: teachers, administrators, volunteers, businesses, community groups, and others seeking to help students achieve academic excellence. Creates and strengthens volunteer and partnership programs. Advocates community involvement in schools.

National Assn. of Secondary School Principals, *1904 Association Dr., Reston, VA 20191-1537; (703) 860-0200. Fax, (703) 476-5432. Tom Koerner, executive director. Internet, http://www.nassp.org.*

Membership: principals and assistant principals of middle and senior high schools, both public and private, and college-level teachers of secondary education. Conducts training programs for members; serves as clearinghouse for information on secondary school administration. Student activities office provides student councils, student activity advisers, and national and junior honor societies with information on national associations.

National Congress of Parents and Teachers, *1090 Vermont Ave. N.W., #1200 20005; (202) 289-6790. Fax, (202) 289-6791. Vacant, director, Governmental Relations. Internet, http://www.pta.org.*

Membership: parent-teacher associations at the preschool, elementary, and secondary levels. Washington office represents members' interests on education, funding for education, parent involvement, child protection and safety, comprehensive health care for children, AIDS, the environment, children's television and educational technology, child care, and nutrition. (Headquarters in Chicago.)

National Head Start Assn., *1651 Prince St., Alexandria, VA 22314; (703) 739-0875. Fax, (703) 739-0878. Sarah M. Greene, chief executive officer. Internet, http://www.nhsa.org.*

Membership organization that represents Head Start children, families, and staff. Recommends strategies on issues affecting Head Start programs; provides training and professional development opportunities. Monitors legislation and regulations.

National School Boards Assn., *1680 Duke St., Alexandria, VA 22314; (703) 838-6722. Fax, (703) 683-7590. Anne Bryant, executive director. Internet, http://www.nsba.org.*

Federation of state school board associations. Interests include funding of public education, local governance, and quality of education programs. Sponsors seminars, an annual conference, and an information center. Monitors legislation and regulations. Library open to the public by appointment.

National Urban Coalition, *2120 L St. N.W., #510 20037; (202) 986-1460. Fax, (202) 986-1468. Ramona H. Edelin, president.*

Membership: urban community action groups. Operates Say Yes to a Youngster's Future, a community-based education program for low-income students in math, science, and technology. M. Carl Holman Leadership Development Institute gives students opportunities to learn from local and national leaders, including scholars, entrepreneurs, and other experts.

Reading Is Fundamental, *600 Maryland Ave. S.W., #600 20024; (202) 287-3371. Fax, (202) 287-3196. William Trueheart, president. Information, (202) 287-3220. Internet, http://www.si.edu/rif.*

Conducts programs and workshops to motivate young people to read. Provides young people with books and parents with services to encourage reading at home.

Teach for America, *1450 G St. N.W., Atrium Level 20005; (202) 393-1666. Fax, (202) 393-3612. Kaya Henderson, DC regional director. Toll-free, (800) 832-1230. Internet, tfadcw@aol.com or http://www. teachforamerica.org.*

A national teacher corps of recent college graduates from all academic majors and cultural backgrounds. Participants teach for a minimum of two years in underfunded urban and rural public schools. Promotes outstanding teaching and educational equity. Monitors legislation and regulations. (Headquarters in New York.)

Private, Parochial, and Home Schooling

AGENCIES

Education Dept., *Non-Public Education, 600 Independence Ave. S.W., #3244 20202-0122; (202) 401-1365. Fax, (202) 205-0676. Michelle L. Doyle, director.*

Acts as ombudsman for interests of teachers and students in non-public schools (elementary and secondary levels); reports to the secretary on matters relating to non-public education.

NONPROFIT

Americans United for Separation of Church and State, *1816 Jefferson Pl. N.W. 20036; (202) 466-3234. Fax, (202) 466-2587. Barry W. Lynn, executive director. Internet, americansunited@au.org or http://www.au.org.*

Citizens' interest group. Opposes federal and state aid to parochial schools; works to ensure religious neutrality in public schools; supports religious free exercise; initiates litigation; maintains speakers bureau. Monitors legislation and regulations.

Council for American Private Education, *18016 Mateny Rd., #140, Germantown, MD 20874; (301) 916-*

8460. Fax, (301) 916-8485. Joe McTighe, executive director. Internet, cape@impresso.com.

Coalition of national private school associations serving private elementary and secondary schools. Acts as a liaison between private education and government, other educational organizations, the media, and the public. Seeks greater access to private schools for all families. Monitors legislation and regulations.

Home School Legal Defense Assn., *17333 Pickwick Dr., Purcellville, VA (mailing address: P.O. Box 3000, Purcellville, VA 20134); (540) 338-5600. Fax, (540) 338-2733. Michael P. Farris, president. Internet, mailroom@hslda.org or http://www.hslda.org.*

Membership: families who practice home schooling. Provides members with legal consultation and defense. Initiates civil rights litigation on behalf of members. Monitors legislation and regulations.

Lutheran Educational Conference of North America, *1001 Connecticut Ave. N.W., #504 20036; (202) 463-6486. Fax, (202) 463-6609. Donald A. Stoike, executive director. Internet, http://www.collegeslutheran.org.*

Membership: private Lutheran-related colleges and boards of higher education. Supports federal aid to private higher education.

National Assn. of Independent Schools, *1620 L St. N.W., #1100 20036-5605; (202) 973-9700. Fax, (202) 973-9790. Jefferson G. Burnett, director, Government Relations. Press, (202) 973-9716.*

Membership: independent elementary and secondary schools in the United States and abroad. Provides statistical and educational information to members. Monitors legislation and regulations.

National Catholic Educational Assn., *1077 30th St. N.W., #100 20007-3852; (202) 337-6232. Fax, (202) 333-6706. Leonard DeFiore, president. Internet, http://www. ncea.org.*

Membership: Catholic schools (preschool through college and seminary) and school administrators. Provides consultation services to members for administration, curriculum, continuing education, religious education, campus ministry, boards of education, and union and personnel negotiations; conducts workshops; supports federal aid for private education. (Affiliated with the Assn. of Catholic Colleges and Universities.)

National Congress of Parents and Teachers, *1090 Vermont Ave. N.W., #1200 20005; (202) 289-6790. Fax, (202) 289-6791. Vacant, director, Governmental Relations. Internet, http://www.pta.org.*

Membership: parent-teacher associations at the preschool, elementary, and secondary levels. Coordinates the National Coalition for Public Education, which opposes tuition tax credits and vouchers for private education. (Headquarters in Chicago.)

National Council of Churches, *110 Maryland Ave. N.E., #108 20002; (202) 544-2350. Fax, (202) 543-1297. Albert M. Pennybacker, acting director, Washington Office. Internet, ncc-washington.parti@ecunet.org or http://www.ncccusa.org.*

Membership: Protestant, Anglican, and Eastern Orthodox churches. Opposes federal aid to private schools. (Headquarters in New York.)

National Home Education Research Institute, *12221 Van Brady Rd., Upper Marlboro, MD 20772-7924; (301) 372-2889. Fax, (301) 782-7256. Bill Lloyd, manager. Internet, http://www.nheri.org.*

Serves as an information clearinghouse for researchers, home educators, attorneys, legislators, policymakers, and the public. Conducts research on home education. Monitors legislation and regulations. (Headquarters in Salem, Ore.)

U.S. Catholic Conference, *3211 4th St. N.E. 20017; (202) 541-3130. Fax, (202) 541-3390. Thomas J. McDade, secretary for education. Press, (202) 541-3200. TDD, (202) 740-0424. Internet, http://www.nccb.uscc.org.*

Represents the Catholic church in the United States in educational matters; advises Catholic schools on federal programs; assists church organizations with religious education.

🖳 SPECIAL GROUPS IN EDUCATION

Gifted and Talented

AGENCIES

Education Dept., *Gifted and Talented Education, 555 New Jersey Ave. N.W. 20208-5572; (202) 219-2210. Fax, (202) 219-2053. Elizabeth Barnes, program analyst.*

Awards grants for developing programs for gifted and talented students, including the limited-English-speaking, economically disadvantaged, and disabled. Oversees the National Research Center, which administers grants for research and analysis of gifted and talented programs. Conducts seminars and produces publications on issues related to gifted and talented programs.

NONPROFIT

Council for Exceptional Children, *1920 Association Dr., Reston, VA 20191-1589; (703) 620-3660. Fax, (703) 264-9494. Nancy Safer, executive director. TDD, (703) 264-9446. Internet, http://www.cec.sped.org.*

Provides information on gifted and talented education nationwide; maintains clearinghouse of information on the gifted; provides lawmakers with technical assistance. Monitors legislation and regulations affecting gifted and talented education. Library open to the public.

Foundation for Exceptional Children, *1920 Association Dr., 4th Floor, Reston, VA 20191; (703) 620-1054. Fax, (703) 264-9494. Kenneth L. Collins, executive director. Internet, http://www.cec.sped.org/fd-menu.htm.*

Membership: individuals interested in meeting the needs of gifted children and children with disabilities. Provides information and assists educators and parents; works to protect the rights of exceptional children; develops education programs and faculty standards. Awards scholarships and grants.

National Assn. for Gifted Children, *1707 L St. N.W., #550 20036; (202) 785-4268. Peter D. Rosenstein, executive director. Internet, http://www.nagc.org.*

Membership: teachers, administrators, state coordinators, and parents. Works for programs for intellectually and creatively gifted children in public and private schools.

See also National Assn. of Private Schools for Exceptional Children (p. 199)

Learning and Physically Disabled

See also Social Services and Disabilities (chap. 18)

AGENCIES

Education Dept., *Special Education and Rehabilitative Services, 330 C St. S.W. 20202-2500; (202) 205-5465. Fax, (202) 205-9252. Judith Heumann, assistant secretary. Information, (202) 205-8241. TDD, (202) 205-5465.*

Administers federal assistance programs for the education and rehabilitation of people with disabilities, as provided for by the Individuals with Disabilities Education Act and the Rehabilitation Act of 1973, as amended, which are administered by the National Institute of Disability and Rehabilitation Research, the Office of Special Education Programs, and the Rehabilitation Services Administration; maintains a national information clearinghouse on people with disabilities.

Education Dept., *Special Education Programs, 330 C St. S.W. (mailing address: 600 Independence Ave. S.W.,*

Washington, DC 20202-2570); (202) 205-5507. Fax, (202) 260-0416. Thomas Hehir, director.

Responsible for special education programs and services designed to meet the needs and develop the full potential of children with disabilities. Programs include support for training of teachers and other professional personnel; grants for research; financial aid to help states initiate and improve their resources; and media services and captioned films for hearing impaired persons.

Smithsonian Institution, *Accessibility Program,* 900 Jefferson Dr. S.W., #1239 MRC 426 20560; (202) 786-2942. Fax, (202) 786-2210. Janice Majewski, coordinator. TDD, (202) 786-2414.

Coordinates Smithsonian efforts to improve accessibility of its programs and facilities to visitors and staff with disabilities. Serves as a resource for museums and individuals nationwide.

Very Special Arts, 1300 Connecticut Ave. N.W., #700 20036; (202) 628-2800. Fax, (202) 737-0725. John Kemp, chief executive officer. Toll-free, (800) 933-8721. TDD, (202) 737-0645. Internet, http://www.vsarts.org.

Initiates and supports research and program development providing arts training and demonstration for persons with disabilities. Provides technical assistance and training to Very Special Arts state organizations; acts as an information clearinghouse for arts and persons with disabilities. (Affiliated with the Kennedy Center education office.)

CONGRESS

House Education and the Workforce Committee, *Subcommittee on Early Childhood, Youth, and Families,* 2181 RHOB 20515; (202) 225-4527. Fax, (202) 225-9571. Frank Riggs, R-Calif., chair; Kevin Talley, staff director. Internet, http://www.house.gov/eeo.

Jurisdiction over legislation on special education programs including, but not limited to, alcohol and drug abuse and education of the disabled.

Library of Congress, *National Library Service for the Blind and Physically Handicapped,* 1291 Taylor St. N.W. 20542; (202) 707-5104. Fax, (202) 707-0712. Frank Kurt Cylke, director. TDD, (202) 707-0744. Reference, (202) 707-5100; outside D.C. area, (800) 424-8567. Internet, nls@loc.gov or http://lcweb.loc.gov/nls.

Administers a national program of free library services for persons with physical disabilities in cooperation with regional and subregional libraries. Produces and distributes full-length books and magazines in recorded form (disc and cassette) and in Braille. Reference section answers questions relating to blindness and physical disabilities and on library services available to persons with disabilities.

Senate Labor and Human Resources Committee, SD-428 20510; (202) 224-5375. Fax, (202) 224-6510. James M. Jeffords, R-Vt., chair; Mark Powden, staff director. Internet, http://www.senate.gov/~labor.

Jurisdiction over legislation on education of people with disabilities, including Gallaudet University and the National Technical Institute for the Deaf; jurisdiction over the Americans with Disabilities Act.

NONPROFIT

American Assn. of University Affiliated Programs for Persons with Developmental Disabilities, 8630 Fenton St., #410, Silver Spring, MD 20910; (301) 588-8252. Fax, (301) 588-2842. William E. Jones, executive director. TDD, (301) 588-3319. Internet, http://www.waisman.wisc.edu/aauap.

Network of facilities that diagnose and treat the developmentally disabled. Trains graduate students and professionals in the field; helps state and local agencies develop services. Interests include interdisciplinary training and services, early screening to prevent developmental disabilities, and development of equipment and programs to serve persons with disabilities.

Assn. for Education and Rehabilitation of the Blind and Visually Impaired, P.O. Box 22397, Alexandria, VA 22304; (703) 823-9690. Fax, (703) 823-9695. Denise Rozell, executive director. Internet, aernet@laser.net or http://www.aerbvi.org.

Membership: professionals and paraprofessionals who work with the blind and visually impaired. Provides information on services for people who are blind and visually impaired and on employment opportunities for those who work with them. Works to improve quality of education and rehabilitation services. Monitors legislation and regulations.

Council for Exceptional Children, 1920 Association Dr., Reston, VA 20191-1589; (703) 620-3660. Fax, (703) 264-9494. Nancy Safer, executive director. TDD, (703) 264-9446. Internet, http://www.cec.sped.org.

Provides information on the education of exceptional children; maintains clearinghouse of information on people with disabilities, learning disorders, and special education topics; provides lawmakers with technical assistance. Monitors legislation and regulations affecting special education. Library open to the public.

Foundation for Exceptional Children, 1920 Association Dr., 4th Floor, Reston, VA 20191; (703) 620-1054. Fax,

(703) 264-9494. Kenneth L. Collins, executive director. Internet, http://www.cec.sped.org/fd-menu.htm.

Membership: individuals interested in meeting the special needs of children with disabilities. Provides information and assists educators and parents; works to protect the rights of exceptional children; develops education programs and faculty standards. Awards scholarships and grants.

Gallaudet University, *800 Florida Ave. N.E. 20002-3695; (202) 651-5005. Fax, (202) 651-5508. I. King Jordan, president. Phone numbers are voice and TDD accessible. Internet, http://www.gallaudet.edu.*

Offers undergraduate and graduate degree programs for the deaf and hard of hearing and graduate training for teachers and other professionals who work with the deaf; conducts research; maintains outreach and regional centers and demonstration doctoral, continuing education, secondary, elementary, and preschool programs (Model Secondary School for the Deaf, Kendall Demonstration Elementary School). Sponsors the Center for Global Education, the National Information Center on Deafness, and the National Center for the Law and the Deaf.

National Assn. of Private Schools for Exceptional Children, *1522 K St. N.W., #1032 20005-1202; (202) 408-3338. Fax, (202) 408-3340. Sherry L. Kolbe, executive director. Internet, napsec@aol.com or http://www.sped-schools.com/napsec.html.*

Promotes greater opportunities for exceptional children; provides legislators and agencies with information and testimony; formulates and disseminates positions and statements on special education issues.

National Assn. of State Directors of Special Education, *1800 Diagonal Rd., #320, Alexandria, VA 22314; (703) 519-3800. Fax, (703) 519-3808. Martha J. Fields, executive director. TDD, (703) 519-7008. Internet, http://www.lrp.com.*

Membership: state education agency special education administrators, consultants, and supervisors. Coordinates and provides state education agency personnel with in-service training programs; manages federally sponsored clearinghouse on professions in special education. Monitors legislation and research developments in special education.

See also Home and School Institute (p. 194)

Minorities and Women

See also Civil Rights (chap. 1); Special Topics in Education (this chapter)

AGENCIES

Bureau of Indian Affairs *(Interior Dept.),* **Indian Education Programs,** *1849 C St. N.W., #3510 20240; (202) 208-6123. Fax, (202) 208-3312. Joann Morris, director.*

Operates schools for Native Americans, including people with disabilities. Provides special assistance to Native American pupils in public schools; aids Native American college students; sponsors adult education programs.

Commission on Civil Rights, *Civil Rights Evaluation, 624 9th St. N.W. 20425; (202) 376-8582. Fax, (202) 376-8315. Frederick Isler, assistant staff director. Library, (202) 376-8110.*

Researches federal policy on education, including desegregation. Library open to the public.

Education Dept., *Civil Rights, 330 C St. S.W., #5000 20202-1100; (202) 205-5413. Fax, (202) 205-9862. Norma Cantu, assistant secretary.*

Enforces laws prohibiting use of federal funds for education programs or activities that discriminate on the basis of race, color, sex, national origin, age, or disability; authorized to discontinue funding.

Education Dept., *Compensatory Education Programs, 1250 Maryland Ave. S.W. (mailing address: 600 Independence Ave. S.W., 4400 Portals Bldg., Washington, DC 20202-6132); (202) 260-0826. Fax, (202) 260-7764. Mary Jean LeTendre, director. Press, (202) 401-1008.*

Administers the Chapter 1 federal assistance program for education of educationally deprived children (preschool through secondary), including Native American children, homeless children, delinquents, and residents in state institutions. Administers the Even Start program. *(See Preschool, Elementary, Secondary Education.)*

Education Dept., *Indian Education Programs, 600 Independence Ave. S.W., #4300 20202-6335; (202) 260-3774. Fax, (202) 260-7779. David Beaulieu, director.*

Aids local school districts with programs for Native American students; funds schools operated by the Bureau of Indian Affairs and Native American-controlled schools and programs.

Education Dept., *Intergovernmental and Constituent Services, 600 Independence Ave. S.W., #6442 20202; (202) 401-0404. Fax, (202) 401-8607. Jennifer Davis, deputy assistant secretary.*

Acts as ombudsman for Asian-Pacific, African American, Hispanic, and women's organizations concerned with education issues. Disseminates information on government programs to organizations and educators;

reports to the secretary on interests of special populations.

Education Dept., *Migrant Education,* *1250 Maryland Ave. S.W., #4100 (mailing address: 600 Independence Ave. S.W., Washington, DC 20202-6135); (202) 260-1164. Fax, (202) 205-0089. Francisco Garcia, acting director. Internet, http://www.ed.gov/offices/oese/mep.*

Administers programs that fund education (preschool through postsecondary) for children of migrant workers.

Education Dept., *Student Services,* *1250 Maryland Ave. S.W., #600D (mailing address: 600 Independence Ave. S.W., 600D Portals Bldg., Washington, DC 20202-5249); (202) 708-4804. Fax, (202) 401-6132. Linda Byrd-Johnson, branch chief. TDD, (202) 708-4804.*

Administers programs for disadvantaged students, including Upward Bound, Talent Search, Student Support Services, the Ronald E. McNair Post-Baccalaureate Achievement Program, and educational opportunity centers; provides special programs personnel with training.

Education Dept., *White House Initiative on Historically Black Colleges and Universities,* *1250 Maryland Ave. S.W., #605 (mailing address: 600 Independence Ave. S.W., #605, Washington, DC 20202-5120); (202) 708-8667. Fax, (202) 708-7872. Catherine LeBlanc, executive director.*

Supervises and seeks to increase involvement of the private sector in historically black colleges and universities. Works to eliminate barriers to the participation of these colleges and universities in federal and private programs.

Education Dept., *Women's Educational Equity Act Program,* *1250 Maryland Ave. S.W. (mailing address: 600 Independence Ave. S.W., Washington, DC 20202-6140); (202) 260-2502. Fax, (202) 205-5630. Madeline Vaggett, program specialist.*

Administers the Women's Educational Equity Act; awards grants and contracts to individuals, higher education institutions, and public and nonprofit private organizations promoting issues related to educational equity for women; maintains liaison with national women's organizations. (Program does not offer financial aid directly to students.)

Justice Dept., *Educational Opportunity,* *601 D St. N.W., #4300 20530; (202) 514-4092. Fax, (202) 514-8337. Kenneth A. Mines, chief.*

Initiates litigation to ensure equal opportunities in public education; enforces laws dealing with civil rights in public education.

Office of Personnel Management, *Diversity,* *1900 E St. N.W., #2445 20415-0001; (202) 606-2817. Fax, (202) 606-0927. Armando E. Rodriguez, director.*

Develops and provides guidance to federal agencies on the employment of minorities and women. Administers the Federal Equal Opportunity Recruitment Program and the Disabled Veterans Affirmative Action Program.

CONGRESS

House Appropriations Committee, *Subcommittee on Interior,* *B308 RHOB 20515; (202) 225-3081. Fax, (202) 225-9069. Ralph Regula, R-Ohio, chair; Deborah A. Weatherly, clerk. Internet, http://www.house.gov/appropriations.*

Jurisdiction over legislation to appropriate funds for all native American education activities of the Education Dept. and for the Bureau of Indian Affairs.

House Education and the Workforce Committee, *2181 RHOB 20515; (202) 225-4527. Fax, (202) 225-9571. Bill Goodling, R-Pa., chair; Kevin Talley, staff director. Internet, http://www.house.gov/eeo.*

Jurisdiction over legislation pertaining to Native American education; oversight of Native American education programs (jurisdiction shared with the House Resources Committee).

House Education and the Workforce Committee, *Subcommittee on Early Childhood, Youth, and Families,* *2181 RHOB 20515; (202) 225-4527. Fax, (202) 225-9571. Frank Riggs, R-Calif., chair; Kevin Talley, staff director. Internet, http://www.house.gov/eeo.*

Jurisdiction over legislation barring discrimination in education, including the Women's Educational Equity Act of 1974.

House Education and the Workforce Committee, *Subcommittee on Postsecondary Education, Training, and Life-Long Learning,* *2181 RHOB 20515; (202) 225-4527. Fax, (202) 225-9571. Howard P. "Buck" McKeon, R-Calif., chair; Kevin Talley, staff director. Internet, http://www.house.gov/eeo.*

Jurisdiction over legislation barring discrimination in postsecondary education.

House Resources Committee, *1324 LHOB 20515-6201; (202) 225-2761. Fax, (202) 225-5929. Don Young, R-Alaska, chair; Lloyd Jones, staff director. Internet, resource@hr.house.gov or http://www.house.gov/resources.*

Jurisdiction over legislation pertaining to Native American education; oversight of Native American education programs (Jurisdiction shared with House Education and the Workforce Committee).

Senate Appropriations Committee, *Subcommittee on Interior, SD-131 20510; (202) 224-7233. Slade Gorton, R-Wash., chair; Bruce Evans, clerk. Internet, http://www. senate.gov/~appropriations.*

Jurisdiction over legislation to appropriate funds for all Native American education activities and for the Bureau of Indian Affairs.

Senate Committee on Indian Affairs, *SH-838 20510; (202) 224-2251. Fax, (202) 224-2309. Ben Nighthorse Campbell, R-Colo., chair; Gary Bohnee, staff director.*

Jurisdiction over legislation pertaining to Native American education; oversight of Native American education programs.

Senate Labor and Human Resources Committee, *SD-428 20510; (202) 224-5375. Fax, (202) 224-6510. James M. Jeffords, R-Vt., chair; Mark Powden, staff director. Internet, http://www.senate.gov/~labor.*

Jurisdiction over legislation barring discrimination in education, including the Women's Educational Equity Act of 1974.

NONPROFIT

American Assn. of University Women, *1111 16th St. N.W. 20036; (202) 785-7700. Fax, (202) 872-1425. Janice Weinman, executive director. Library, (202) 785-7763. TDD, (202) 785-7777. Internet, info@mail.aauw.org or http://www.aauw.org.*

Membership: graduates of accredited colleges, universities, and recognized foreign institutions. Interests include equity for women in education, the workplace, health care, and the family. Library open to the public by appointment.

Americans for the Restitution and Righting of Old Wrongs (ARROW), *1000 Connecticut Ave. N.W., #1204 20036; (202) 296-0685. Fax, (202) 659-4377. Hazel Elbert, executive director. Internet, arrow1949@aol.com.*

Administers scholarship program for Native Americans engaged in post-graduate study.

Aspira Assn., Inc., *1444 Eye St. N.W., #800 20005; (202) 835-3600. Fax, (202) 835-3613. Ronald Blackburn-Moreno, president. Internet, aspira1@aol.com or http://www.incacorp.com/aspira.*

Provides Latino youth with resources necessary for them to remain in school and contribute to their community. Interests include leadership development, parental involvement, and research. Monitors legislation and regulations.

Assn. of American Colleges and Universities, *1818 R St. N.W. 20009; (202) 387-3760. Fax, (202) 265-9532.*

Paula P. Brownlee, president. Internet, http://www. aacu-edu.org.

Serves as clearinghouse for information on women professionals in higher education. Interests include women's studies, women's centers, and women's leadership and professional development.

East Coast Migrant Head Start Project, *4200 Wilson Blvd., #740, Arlington, VA 22203-1800; (703) 243-7522. Fax, (703) 243-1259. Geraldine O'Brien, executive director. Internet, http://www.ecmhsp.org.*

Establishes Head Start programs for migrant children and offers training and technical assistance to established centers that enroll migrant children.

The Links, *1200 Massachusetts Ave. N.W. 20005-4501; (202) 842-8686. Fax, (202) 842-4020. Ethel Bothuel, executive director.*

Predominantly African American women's service organization that works with the educationally disadvantaged and culturally deprived; focuses on arts, services for youth, and national and international trends and services.

LULAC National Educational Service Centers, *1133 20th St. N.W., #750 20036; (202) 408-0060. Fax, (202) 408-0064. Richard Roybal, executive director. Internet, lnescdc@aol.com.*

Seeks to increase the number of minorities, especially Hispanics, attending postsecondary schools; supports legislation to increase educational opportunities for Hispanics and other minorities; provides scholarship funds and educational and career counseling. Educational arm of the League of United Latin American Citizens.

NAACP Legal Defense and Educational Fund, *1275 K St. N.W., #301 20005; (202) 682-1300. Fax, (202) 682-1312. Vacant, director, Washington Office.*

Civil rights litigation group that provides legal information about civil rights and advice on educational discrimination against women and minorities; monitors federal enforcement of civil rights laws. Not affiliated with the National Association for the Advancement of Colored People (NAACP). (Headquarters in New York.)

National Alliance of Black School Educators, *2816 Georgia Ave. N.W. 20001; (202) 483-1549. Fax, (202) 483-8323. Quentin Lawson, executive director.*

Promotes the education of African American youth and adults; seeks to raise the academic achievement level of all African American students. Sponsors workshops and conferences on major issues in education affecting African American students and educators.

National Assn. for Equal Opportunity in Higher Education, *8701 Georgia Ave., #200, Silver Spring, MD 20910; (301) 650-2440. Fax, (301) 495-3306. Henry Ponder, president.*

Membership: colleges and universities with a predominantly African American enrollment. Works for increased federal and private support for member institutions and for increased minority representation in private and governmental education agencies; serves as a clearinghouse for information on federal contracts and grants for member institutions; collects, analyzes, and publishes data on member institutions; operates internship program.

National Assn. for the Advancement of Colored People (NAACP), *1025 Vermont Ave. N.W., #1120 20005; (202) 638-2269. Fax, (202) 638-5936. Hilary Shelton, deputy director. Internet, http://www.naacp.org.*

Membership: persons interested in civil rights for all minorities. Works for equal opportunity for minorities in all areas, including education; seeks to ensure a quality desegregated education for all through litigation and legislation. (Headquarters in Baltimore.)

National Assn. of Colored Women's Clubs, *5808 16th St. N.W. 20011-2898; (202) 726-2044. Fax, (202) 726-0023. Patricia L. Fletcher, president. Internet, http://www.webspawner.com/nacwc.*

Seeks to promote education of women and youth; protect and enforce civil rights; raise the standards of the home and family living; promote interracial understanding; and enhance leadership development. Awards scholarships; conducts programs in education, social service, and philanthropy.

National Assn. of State Universities and Land Grant Colleges, *Advancement of Public Black Colleges, 1 Dupont Circle N.W., #710 20036-1191; (202) 778-0841. Fax, (202) 296-6456. Joyce Payne, director.*

Seeks to heighten awareness and visibility of public African American colleges; promotes institutional advancement. Conducts research and provides information on issues of concern; acts as a liaison with African American public colleges and universities, the federal government, and private associations. Monitors legislation and regulations.

National Council of Educational Opportunity Assns., *1025 Vermont Ave. N.W., #900 20005; (202) 347-7430. Fax, (202) 347-0786. Arnold L. Mitchem, executive director. Internet, mailbox@hq.nceoa.org or http://www.trioprograms.org.*

Represents institutions of higher learning, administrators, counselors, teachers, and others committed to

advancing equal educational opportunity in colleges and universities. Works to sustain and improve educational opportunity programs such as the federally funded TRIO program, designed to help low-income, first-generation immigrant, and physically disabled students enroll in and graduate from college.

National Council of La Raza, *1111 19th St. N.W., #1000 20036; (202) 785-1670. Fax, (202) 776-1792. Raul Yzaguirre, president. Internet, http://www.nclr.org.*

Provides research, policy analysis, and advocacy on educational status and needs of Hispanics; promotes education reform benefiting Hispanics; develops and tests community-based models for helping Hispanic students succeed in school. Interests include counseling, testing, and bilingual, vocational, preschool through postsecondary, and migrant education.

National Women's Law Center, *11 Dupont Circle N.W., #800 20036; (202) 588-5180. Fax, (202) 588-5185. Marcia Greenberger and Nancy D. Campbell, co-presidents.*

Works to expand and protect women's legal rights in education through advocacy and public education.

United Negro College Fund, *8260 Willow Oaks Corporate Dr., P.O. Box 10444, Fairfax, VA 22031-4511 (mailing address: P.O. Box 10444, Fairfax, VA 22031); (703) 205-3400. Fax, (703) 205-3575. William H. Gray III, president. Press, (703) 205-3553. Internet, http://www.uncf.org.*

Membership: private colleges and universities with historically black enrollment. Raises money for member institutions; monitors legislation and regulations.

See also Center for Law and Education (p. 173); U.S. Student Assn. and Women's College Coalition (p. 191)

SPECIAL TOPICS IN EDUCATION

See also Recreation and Sports (chap. 4); Information and Exchange Programs (chap. 13)

Bilingual and Multicultural

See also Special Groups in Education (this chapter); Language and Literature (chap. 4)

AGENCIES

Education Dept., *Bilingual Education and Minority Languages Affairs, 330 C St. S.W., #5086 20202-6510; (202) 205-5463. Fax, (202) 205-8737. Delia Pompa, director.*

Provides school districts and state education agencies with grants to establish, operate, and improve programs for people with limited English proficiency; promotes development of resources for such programs, including training for parents and education personnel. Administers assistance programs for refugee and immigrant children.

NONPROFIT

National Assn. for Bilingual Education, *1220 L St. N.W., #605 20005-4018; (202) 898-1829. Fax, (202) 789-2866. James J. Lyons, executive director. Internet, NABE@ nabe.org or http://www.nabe.org.*

Membership: educators, policy makers, paraprofessionals, publications personnel, students, researchers, and interested individuals. Works to improve educational programs for non-English-speaking students and to promote bilingualism among American students. Conducts annual conference and workshops.

National MultiCultural Institute, *3000 Connecticut Ave. N.W., #438 20008-2556; (202) 483-0700. Fax, (202) 483-5233. Elizabeth Salett, president. Internet, nmci@ nmci.org or http://www.nmci.org.*

Encourages understanding and communication among people of various backgrounds; seeks to increase awareness of different perspectives and experiences; provides multicultural training, education, and counseling programs for organizations and institutions working with diverse cultural groups.

Teachers of English to Speakers of Other Languages, *1600 Cameron St., #300, Alexandria, VA 22314-2751; (703) 836-0774. Fax, (703) 836-7864. Susan Bayley, executive director. Internet, tesol@tesol.edu or http://www. tesol.edu.*

Promotes scholarship and provides information on instruction and research in the teaching of English to speakers of other languages. Offers placement service.

See also Center for Law and Education (p. 173); Home and School Institute (p. 194); Organization of Chinese Americans (p. 10)

Citizenship Education

NONPROFIT

Close Up Foundation, *44 Canal Center Plaza, #500, Alexandria, VA 22314; (703) 706-3300. Fax, (703) 706-0000. Stephen A. Janger, president. Internet, http://www. closeup.org.*

Sponsors week-long programs on American government for high school students, teachers, older Ameri-

cans, new Americans, Native Americans, Alaskan natives, and Pacific Islanders; offers fellowships for participation in the programs; produces television series for secondary schools; conducts the national Citizen Bee, an academic social studies competition for high school students, and the Civic Achievement Award Program for elementary and junior high school students. Develops specialized programs such as the U.S.-Japan Educational Initiative; summer institutes on energy, environment, and policy choices; and Active Citizenship Today, a program that promotes community service.

Horatio Alger Assn., *99 Canal Center Plaza, Alexandria, VA 22314; (703) 684-9444. Fax, (703) 548-3822. Terrence J. Giroux, executive director. Internet, horatioaa@aol.com or http://www.horatioalger.com.*

Educates young people about the economic and personal opportunities available in the American free enterprise system. Conducts seminars on careers in public and community service; operates speakers bureau and internship program. Presents the Horatio Alger Youth Award to outstanding high school students and the Horatio Alger Award to professionals who have achieved success in their respective fields. Awards college scholarships.

League of Women Voters Education Fund, *1730 M St. N.W., #1000 20036; (202) 429-1965. Fax, (202) 429-0854. Judy Conover, executive director. Internet, http://www.lwv.org.*

Public foundation established by League of Women Voters of the United States. Promotes citizen knowledge of and involvement in representative government; conducts citizen education on current public policy issues; seeks to increase voter registration and turnout; sponsors candidate forums and debates.

National 4-H Council, *7100 Connecticut Ave., Chevy Chase, MD 20815-4999; (301) 961-2820. Fax, (301) 961-2894. Richard J. Sauer, president. Press, (301) 961-2915. Internet, http://www.fourhcouncil.edu.*

Citizenship education organization that conducts programs for youth and adult groups in Washington. Programs on American government include Wonders of Washington, Citizenship-Washington Focus, and Know America.

Presidential Classroom for Young Americans, Inc., *119 Oronoco St., Alexandria, VA 22314-2015; (703) 683-5400. Fax, (703) 548-5728. Jay D. Wickliff, executive director. Toll-free, (800) 441-6533. Internet, prezclass@aol.com or http://www.presidentialclassroom.org.*

Offers civic education programs for high school students and volunteer opportunities for college students and adults. Provides week-long series of seminars featuring representatives of each branch of government, the diplomatic community, the military, the media, private interest groups, and both major political parties.

Washington Workshops Foundation, *3222 N St. N.W., #340 20007; (202) 965-3434. Fax, (202) 965-1018. Sharon E. Sievers, president. Toll-free, (800) 368-5688. Internet, http://www.thewwf.org.*

Educational foundation that provides introductory seminars on American government and politics to junior and senior high school students; congressional seminars to secondary and postsecondary students; and seminars on diplomacy and global affairs to secondary students.

Consumer Education

For a list of federal consumer contacts, see chap. 1

AGENCIES

Agriculture Dept., *Research, Education, and Economics, 1400 Independence Ave. S.W., #217W 20250-0110; (202) 720-5923. Fax, (202) 690-2842. Eileen Kennedy, acting deputy under secretary, (202) 720-8885.*

Coordinates agricultural research, extension, and teaching programs in the food and agricultural sciences, including human nutrition, home economics, consumer services, agricultural economics, environmental quality, natural and renewable resources, forestry and range management, animal and plant production and protection, aquaculture, and the production, distribution, and utilization of food and agricultural products. Oversees the Cooperative State Research, Education, and Extension Service.

Consumer Product Safety Commission, *Information and Public Affairs, 4330 East-West Hwy., Bethesda, MD; (301) 504-0580. Fax, (301) 504-0862. Kathleen Begala, director. TDD, (800) 638-8270. Product safety hotline, (800) 638-2772. Internet, info@cpsc.gov or http://www.cpsc.gov.*

Provides information concerning consumer product safety; works with local and state governments, school systems, and private groups to develop product safety information and education programs. Toll-free hotline accepts consumer complaints on hazardous products and injuries associated with a product and offers recorded information on product recalls and CPSC safety recommendations.

Cooperative State Research, Education, and Extension Service *(Agriculture Dept.), 1400 Independence Ave. S.W., #305A 20250-2201; (202) 720-4423. Fax, (202) 720-8987. B. H. Robinson, administrator. Information,*

(202) 720-3029. TDD, (202) 690-1899. Internet, http://www.reeusda.gov.

Oversees county agents and operation of state offices that provide information on home economics, including diet and nutrition, food budgeting, food safety, home gardening, clothing care, and other consumer concerns.

Federal Trade Commission, *Consumer and Business Education, 6th St. and Pennsylvania Ave. N.W., #H403 20580; (202) 326-3268. Fax, (202) 326-3574. Carolyn Shanoff, director. TDD, (202) 326-2502. Consumer Response Center, (202) FTC-HELP.*

Develops educational material about FTC activities for consumers and businesses.

Food and Drug Administration *(Health and Human Services Dept.), Consumer Affairs, 5600 Fishers Lane, Rockville, MD 20857; (301) 827-5006. Fax, (301) 443-9767. Charles Gaylord, acting associate commissioner. Consumer inquiries, (800) 532-4440. Internet, http://www.fda.gov.*

Responds to inquiries on issues related to the FDA. Conducts consumer health education programs for specific groups, including women, the elderly, and the educationally and economically disadvantaged. Serves as liaison with national health and consumer organizations.

Food Safety and Inspection Service *(Agriculture Dept.), 1400 Independence Ave. S.W., #331E 20250; (202) 720-7025. Fax, (202) 205-0158. Thomas J. Billy, administrator. Press, (202) 720-9113. Consumer inquiries, (800) 535-4555; in Washington, (202) 720-3333. Internet, http://www.usda.gov/fsis.*

Sponsors food safety educational programs to inform the public about measures to prevent foodborne illnesses; sponsors lectures, publications, public service advertising campaigns, exhibits, and audiovisual presentations. Toll-free hotline answers food safety questions.

NONPROFIT

American Assn. of Family and Consumer Sciences, *1555 King St., Alexandria, VA 22314; (703) 706-4600. Fax, (703) 706-4663. Ann Chadwick, executive director. Internet, staff@aafcs.org or http://www.aafcs.org.*

Membership: professional home economists. Supports family and consumer sciences education; develops accrediting standards for undergraduate family and consumer science programs; trains and certifies family and consumer science professionals. Monitors legislation and regulations concerning family and consumer issues.

Future Homemakers of America, *1910 Association Dr., Reston, VA 20191-1584; (703) 476-4900. Fax, (703)*

860-2713. Alan T. Rains Jr., executive director. Internet, natlhdqtrs@fhahero.org or http://www.fhahero.org.

National student organization that helps young men and women address personal, family, work, and social issues through family and consumer sciences education. Interests include character development. Offers awards to students.

Literacy/Basic Skills

AGENCIES

AmeriCorps *(Corporation for National Service), Volunteers in Service to America (VISTA),* 1201 New York Ave. N.W., 9th Floor 20525; (202) 606-5000. Fax, (202) 565-2789. Diana London, deputy director. Volunteer recruiting information, (800) 942-2677; TDD, (800) 833-3722. Internet, http://www.cns.gov/americorps/ac_vista.html.

Assigns volunteers to local and state education departments, to public agencies, and to private, non-profit organizations that have literacy programs. Other activities include tutor recruitment and training and the organization and expansion of local literacy councils, workplace literacy programs, and intergenerational literacy programs.

Education Dept., *Adult Education and Literacy,* 330 C St. S.W., #4428 (mailing address: 600 Independence Ave. S.W., Washington, DC 20202-7240); (202) 205-8270. Fax, (202) 205-8973. Ronald S. Pugsley, director. Literacy clearinghouse, (202) 205-9996.

Provides state and local education agencies and the general public with information on establishing, expanding, improving, and operating adult education and literacy programs. Emphasizes basic and life skills attainment and high school completion. Awards grants to state education agencies for adult education and literacy programs, including grants for workplace literacy partnerships. Coordinates homeless and adult literacy programs.

Education Dept., *National Institute for Literacy,* 800 Connecticut Ave. N.W., #200 20006-2712; (202) 632-1500. Fax, (202) 632-1512. Andy Hartman, director. Internet, http://novel.nifl.gov.

Seeks to eliminate illiteracy in America by the year 2000. Operates a literacy clearinghouse and an electronic national literacy and communications system; provides private literacy groups, educational institutions, and federal, state, and local agencies working on illiteracy with assistance; awards grants and fellowships to literacy programs and individuals pursuing careers in the literacy field.

Employment and Training Administration *(Labor Dept.), Workplace Literacy,* 200 Constitution Ave. N.W., #N5637 20210; (202) 219-7674. Fax, (202) 219-5455. Jerry Gundersen, chief.

Coordinates workplace literacy projects, including technical and basic skills effectiveness training, technology training, adult education studies, and literacy surveys; sponsors, with the Education and Health and Human Services departments, the National Institute for Literacy.

CONGRESS

Library of Congress, *Center for the Book,* 101 Independence Ave. S.E., #650 20540-4920; (202) 707-5221. Fax, (202) 707-0269. John Y. Cole, director. Internet, http://www.loc.gov/loc/cfbook.

Promotes family and adult literacy; encourages the study of books and stimulates public interest in books, reading, and libraries; sponsors publication of a directory describing national organizations that administer literacy programs. Affiliated state centers sponsor projects and hold events that call attention to the importance of literacy.

NONPROFIT

AFL-CIO Human Resources Development Institute, 1101 14th St. N.W., #320 20005; (202) 638-3912. Fax, (202) 783-6536. Lynn Meyers, executive director. Internet, info@hrdi-emp.prng.org.

Provides labor unions, employers, education agencies, and community groups with technical assistance for workplace education programs focusing on adult literacy, basic skills, and job training. Interests include new technologies and workplace innovations.

American Bar Assn., *Standing Committee on Law and Literacy,* 740 15th St. N.W. 20005; (202) 662-1024. Fax, (202) 662-1032. Dick Lynch, director.

Seeks to involve lawyers in literacy programs at the local, state, and national levels; sponsors conferences on literacy and publishes a literacy program manual for state and local bars.

American Poetry and Literacy Project, 1058 Thomas Jefferson St. N.W. 20007; (202) 338-1109. Andrew Carroll, executive director.

Donates new books of poetry to schools, libraries, hospitals, homeless shelters, nursing homes, hotels, and other public places around the country. Organizes free poetry readings open to the public.

American Society for Training and Development, 1640 King St., Alexandria, VA (mailing address: P.O. Box

1443, Alexandria, VA 22313-2043); (703) 683-8100. Fax, (703) 683-8103. Curtis E. Plott, president. Internet, http://www.astd.org.

Membership: trainers and human resource developers. Publishes information on workplace literacy.

Assn. for Community Based Education, *1805 Florida Ave. N.W. 20009; (202) 462-6333. C. P. Zachariadis, executive director. Information, (202) 462-6335.*

Promotes community-based literacy programs; evaluates effectiveness of programs; conducts training program for literacy practitioners; awards minigrants to existing programs. Monitors legislation and regulations.

Barbara Bush Foundation for Family Literacy, *1112 16th St. N.W., #340 20036; (202) 955-6183. Fax, (202) 955-8084. Benita Somerfield, executive director. Internet, http://www.barbarabushfoundation.com.*

Works to break the intergenerational cycle of illiteracy. Awards grants; encourages recognition of volunteers, educators, students, and effective programs; publishes materials that document effective literacy programs.

Center for Applied Linguistics, *National Clearinghouse for ESL Literacy Education, 1118 22nd St. N.W. 20037-1214; (202) 429-9292. Fax, (202) 659-5641. Fran Keenan, assistant director. Internet, ncle@cal.org or http://www.cal.org.*

Provides information and referral service on literacy instruction for adults and out-of-school youth learning English as a second language.

General Federation of Women's Clubs, *1734 N St. N.W. 20036-2990; (202) 347-3168. Fax, (202) 835-0246. Judith Maggrett, executive director. Internet, gfwc@gfwc.org or http://www.gfwc.org.*

Nondenominational, nonpartisan international organization of women volunteers. Develops literacy projects in response to community needs; sponsors tutoring.

National Alliance of Business, *1201 New York Ave. N.W., #700 20005; (202) 289-2905. Fax, (202) 289-1303. Wesley McClendon, director, Workforce Adjustment. Press, (202) 289-2850. Internet, info@nab.com or http://www.nab.com.*

Builds business partnerships with government, labor, and education to improve the quality of the American work force. Provides technical assistance and information on workplace literacy.

Newspaper Assn. of America Foundation, *1921 Gallows Rd., #600, Vienna, VA 22182; (703) 902-1600. Fax, (703) 917-0636. Rene Gunter, manager, Educational Programs. Internet, http://www.naa.org.*

Publishes a handbook for starting newspaper literacy projects; promotes intergenerational literacy through its Family Focus program; produces a showcase of newspaper literacy projects.

Reading Is Fundamental, *600 Maryland Ave. S.W., #600 20024; (202) 287-3371. Fax, (202) 287-3196. William Trueheart, president. Information, (202) 287-3220. Internet, http://www.si.edu/rif.*

Conducts programs and workshops to motivate young people to read. Provides young people with books and parents with services to encourage reading at home.

United Way of America, *Education and Literacy Initiative, 701 N. Fairfax St., Alexandria, VA 22314-2045; (703) 836-7112. Fax, (703) 683-7840. Robbin Sorensen, director.*

Produces and distributes literacy information to local United Way chapters; conducts regional forums on literacy for state and local United Way chapters and their communities; provides communities with technical assistance, financial support, and training and scholarships for local literacy professionals.

See also Correctional Education Assn. (p. 517); Institute for Alternative Futures (p. 386)

Science and Mathematics Education

AGENCIES

Education Dept., *Eisenhower Professional Development Program, 1250 Maryland Ave. S.W. 20202 (mailing address: 600 Independence Ave. S.W., #4500 Portals Bldg., Washington, DC 20202); (202) 260-2434. Fax, (202) 205-5630. Art Cole, director, School Improvement Program.*

Administers formula grant program for states; implements the state entitlement section of the Dwight D. Eisenhower Professional Development Program, which funds programs for improving teacher education in mathematics and science, and programs for improving instruction for the underrepresented and underserved, including women, minorities, people with disabilities, individuals with limited English proficiency, and migrants.

Education Dept., *Higher Education, 1250 Maryland Ave. S.W. 20202-5251 (mailing address: 600 Independence Ave. S.W., #C80, Washington, DC 20202-5335); (202) 260-3261. Fax, (202) 401-7532. Argelia Velez-Rodriguez, senior officer, Minority Science and Engineering Improvement.*

Funds programs to improve science and engineering education in predominantly minority colleges and universities; promotes increased participation by minority students and faculty in science and engineering fields; encourages minority schools and universities to apply for grants that will generate precollege student interest in science.

National Museum of Natural History *(Smithsonian Institution), Naturalist Center, 741 Miller Dr., #G2, Leesburg, VA 20175; (703) 779-9712. Fax, (703) 779-9715. Richard H. Efthim, manager. Internet, natcenter@aol.com or http://nmnhgoph.si.edu/museum/learn.html.*

Maintains natural history research and reference library with books and more than 30,000 objects, including minerals, rocks, plants, animals, shells and corals, insects, invertebrates, micro- and macrofossil materials, and microbiological and anthropological materials. Facilities include study equipment such as microscopes, dissecting instruments, and plant presses. Operates a teachers' reference center. Library open to the public. Reservations required for groups of six or more.

National Oceanic and Atmospheric Administration *(Commerce Dept.), National Sea Grant College Program, 1315 East-West Hwy., Silver Spring, MD 20910; (301) 713-2448. Fax, (301) 713-0799. Ronald C. Baird, director.*

Provides grants, primarily to colleges and universities, for marine resource development; sponsors undergraduate and graduate education and the training of technicians at the college level.

National Science Foundation, *Education and Human Resources, 4201 Wilson Blvd., #805, Arlington, VA 22230; (703) 306-1600. Fax, (703) 306-0399. Luther S. Williams, assistant director. Internet, http://www.ehr.nsf.gov.*

Directorate that develops and supports programs to strengthen science and mathematics education. Provides fellowships and grants for graduate research and teacher education, instructional materials, and studies on the quality of existing science and mathematics programs.

National Science Foundation, *Science Resources Studies, 4201 Wilson Blvd., #965, Arlington, VA 22230; (703) 306-1780. Fax, (703) 306-0510. Jeanne E. Griffith, director. Internet, http://www.nsf.gov/sbe/srs.*

Develops and analyzes U.S. and international statistics and models on training, use, and characteristics of scientists, engineers, and technicians.

Office of Science and Technology Policy *(Executive Office of the President), Science, Old Executive Office Bldg., #436 20502; (202) 456-6130. Fax, (202) 456-6027. Arthur Bienenstock, associate director.*

Analyzes policies and advises the president on science education issues; coordinates executive office and federal agency actions related to these issues. Evaluates the effectiveness of science education programs.

NONPROFIT

American Assn. for the Advancement of Science, *Education and Human Resources Programs, 1200 New York Ave. N.W. 20005; (202) 326-6670. Fax, (202) 371-9849. Shirley M. Malcom, head. Main phone is voice and TDD accessible. Internet, http://www.aaas.org.*

Membership: scientists, scientific organizations, and others interested in science and technology education. Works to increase and provide information on the status of women, minorities, and people with disabilities in the sciences and engineering; focuses on expanding science education opportunities for women, minorities, and people with disabilities.

American Assn. of Physics Teachers, *1 Physics Ellipse, College Park, MD 20740-3845; (301) 209-3300. Fax, (301) 209-0845. Bernard V. Khoury, executive officer. Internet, aapt@acp.org or http://www.aapt.org.*

Membership: physics teachers and others interested in physics education. Seeks to advance the institutional and cultural role of physics education. Sponsors seminars and conferences; provides educational information and materials. (Affiliated with the American Institute of Physics.)

American Society for Engineering Education, *1818 N St. N.W., #600 20036; (202) 331-3500. Fax, (202) 265-8504. Frank L. Huband, executive director. Press, (202) 331-3537. Internet, http://www.asee.org.*

Membership: engineering faculty and administrators, professional engineers, government agencies, and engineering colleges, corporations, and professional societies. Conducts research, conferences, and workshops on engineering education. Monitors legislation and regulations.

Assn. of Science-Technology Centers, *1025 Vermont Ave. N.W., #500 20005-3516; (202) 783-7200. Fax, (202) 783-7207. Ellen Griffee, director, Government Relations. Internet, info@astc.org or http://www.astc.org.*

Membership: science centers and science museums. Strives to enhance the ability of its members to engage visitors in intriguing science activities and explorations of scientific phenomena. Sponsors conferences and informational exchanges on interactive exhibits, hands-on science experiences, and educational programs for children, families, and teachers.

Challenger Center for Space Science Education, *1029 N. Royal St., #300, Alexandria, VA 22314; (703) 683-*

9740. Fax, (703) 683-7546. Vance Ablott, president. Internet, http://www.challenger.org.

Educational organization designed to stimulate interest in science, math, and technology among middle school and elementary school students. Students participate in interactive mission simulations that require training and classroom preparation. Sponsors Challenger Learning Centers across the United States and Canada.

Commission on Professionals in Science and Technology, 1200 New York Ave. N.W., #390 20005; (202) 326-7080. Fax, (202) 842-1603. Catherine D. Gaddy, executive director. Internet, http://www.aaas.org/cpst.

Membership: scientific societies, corporations, academicians, and individuals. Analyzes and publishes data on scientific and engineering human resources in the United States. Interests include employment of minorities and women, salary ranges, and supply and demand of scientists and engineers.

Mathematical Assn. of America, 1529 18th St. N.W. 20036-1358; (202) 387-5200. Fax, (202) 265-2384. Marcia P. Sward, executive director. Internet, maahq@maa.org or http://www.maa.org.

Membership: mathematics professors and individuals with a professional interest in mathematics. Seeks to improve the teaching of collegiate mathematics. Conducts professional development programs.

National Assn. of Biology Teachers, 11250 Roger Bacon Dr., #19, Reston, VA 20190-5202; (703) 471-1134. Fax, (703) 435-5582. Wayne Carley, executive director. Toll-free, (800) 406-0775. Internet, NABTer@aol.com or http://www.nabt.org.

Membership: biology teachers and others interested in biology education at the elementary, secondary, and collegiate levels. Provides professional development opportunities through its publication program, summer workshops, conventions, and national award programs. Interests include teaching standards, science curriculum, and issues affecting biology education.

National Council of Teachers of Mathematics, 1906 Association Dr., Reston, VA 20191-1593; (703) 620-9840. Fax, (703) 476-2970. Jim Rubillo, interim executive director. Internet, infocentral@nctm.org or http://www.nctm.org.

Membership: teachers of mathematics in elementary and secondary schools and two-year colleges, university teacher education faculty and students, and other interested persons. Works to improve classroom instruction at all levels. Serves as forum and information clearinghouse on issues related to mathematics education. Offers

educational materials and conferences. Monitors legislation and regulations.

National Geographic Society, 1145 17th St. N.W. 20036-4688; (202) 857-7000. Fax, (202) 775-6141. Reg Murphy, president. Toll-free, (800) 647-5463. Press, (202) 857-7027. Library, (202) 857-7785. TDD, (202) 857-7198. Internet, http://www.nationalgeographic.com.

Educational and scientific organization. Publishes National Geographic, Research and Exploration, National Geographic Traveler, and World magazines; produces maps, books, and films; maintains an exhibit hall; offers film-lecture series; produces television specials. Library open to the public.

National Science Resources Center, Smithsonian Institution, MRC 403, Arts and Industries Bldg., #1201 20560; (202) 357-4892. Fax, (202) 786-2028. Douglas M. Lapp, executive director. Internet, http://www.si.edu/nsrc.

Sponsored by the Smithsonian Institution and the National Academy of Sciences. Works to improve science teaching in the nation's schools. Disseminates information; develops curriculum materials; seeks to increase public support for reform of science education. (Affiliated with the Smithsonian Institution and the National Academy of Science.)

National Science Teachers Assn., 1840 Wilson Blvd., Arlington, VA 22201-3000; (703) 243-7100. Fax, (703) 243-7177. Gerry Wheeler, executive director. Internet, publicinfo@nsta.org or http://www.nsta.org.

Membership: science teachers from elementary through college levels. Seeks to improve science education; provides forum for exchange of information. Monitors legislation and regulations.

Science Service, Inc., 1719 N St. N.W. 20036; (202) 785-2255. Fax, (202) 785-1243. Thomas Peter Bennett, president. Internet, http://www.sciserv.org.

Seeks to increase public understanding of science and to distribute scientific information. Publishes Science News; administers the Westinghouse Science Talent Search and the Intel International Science and Engineering Fair.

World Future Society, 7910 Woodmont Ave., #450, Bethesda, MD 20814; (301) 656-8274. Fax, (301) 951-0394. Edward Cornish, president. Internet, schley@tmn.com or http://www.wfs.org.

Nonpartisan scientific and educational organization interested in future social and technological developments. Publishes magazines and journals; holds annual conference.

Vocational and Adult

See also Employment and Training Programs (chap. 7)

AGENCIES

Agriculture Dept., *Graduate School,* 600 Maryland Ave. S.W., #129 20024-2520; (202) 720-2077. Fax, (202) 479-4895. Philip H. Hudson, director. Information, (202) 401-9129. Internet, pubaffairs@grad.usda.gov or http://www.grad.usda.gov.

Self-supporting educational institution that is open to the public. Offers continuing education courses for career advancement and personal fulfillment; offers training at agency locations.

Education Dept., *National Programs,* 330 C St. S.W. (mailing address: 600 Independence Ave. S.W., MES-7242, Washington, DC 20202-7242); (202) 205-9650. Fax, (202) 205-8793. Dennis Berry, director.

Awards contracts and grants on a competitive basis to individuals, state and local education agencies, institutions of higher education, and other organizations for research, demonstration, and training projects in adult and vocational education.

Education Dept., *Vocational and Adult Education,* 330 C St. S.W., #4090 (mailing address: 600 Independence Ave. S.W., Washington, DC 20202-7100); (202) 205-5451. Fax, (202) 205-8748. Patricia W. McNeil, assistant secretary.

Coordinates and recommends national policy for improving vocational and adult education. Administers grants, contracts, and technical assistance for programs in adult education, dropout prevention, literacy, and occupational training.

Education Dept., *Vocational Technical Education,* 330 C St. S.W., #4317 (mailing address: 600 Independence Ave. S.W., #4317, Washington, DC 20202-7241); (202) 205-9441. Fax, (202) 205-5522. Ronald Castaldi, acting director.

Provides state and local education agencies with information on establishment, expansion, improvement, and operation of vocational technical education programs. Awards grants to state education agencies for vocational technical education programs.

NONPROFIT

Accrediting Commission of Career Schools and Colleges of Technology, 2101 Wilson Blvd., #302, Arlington, VA 22201; (703) 247-4212. Fax, (703) 247-4533. Thomas Fischetti, executive director. Internet, http://www.accsct.org.

Serves as the national accrediting agency for private, postsecondary institutions offering occupational and vocational programs. Sponsors workshops and meetings on academic excellence and ethical practices in career education.

American Assn. for Adult and Continuing Education, 1200 19th St. N.W., #300 20036-2401; (202) 429-5131. Fax, (202) 223-4579. Drew Allbritten, executive director. Internet, http://www.albany.edu/aaace.

Membership: adult and continuing education professionals. Acts as an information clearinghouse; evaluates adult and continuing education programs; sponsors conferences, seminars, and workshops.

American Vocational Assn., 1410 King St., Alexandria, VA 22314; (703) 683-3111. Fax, (703) 683-7424. Bret D. Lovejoy, executive director. Toll-free, (800) 826-9972. Internet, http://www.avaonline.org.

Membership: teachers, students, supervisors, administrators, and others working or interested in vocational education (middle school through postgraduate). Interests include the impact of high school graduation requirements on vocational education; private sector initiatives; and improving the quality and image of vocational education. Offers conferences, workshops, and an annual convention. Monitors legislation and regulations.

Career College Assn., 750 1st St. N.E., #900 20002-4242; (202) 336-6700. Fax, (202) 336-6828. Omer Waddles, president. Internet, ccal@erols.com or http://www.career.org.

Acts as an information clearinghouse on trade and technical schools.

Distance Education and Training Council, 1601 18th St. N.W. 20009-2529; (202) 234-5100. Fax, (202) 332-1386. Michael P. Lambert, executive director. Internet, detc@detc.org or http://www.detc.org.

Membership: accredited correspondence schools. Accredits home study schools, many of which offer vocational training.

International Assn. for Continuing Education and Training, 1200 19th St. N.W., #300 20036-2401; (202) 857-1122. Fax, (202) 223-4579. Drew Allbritten, executive director. Internet, iacet@dcsba.com or http://www.iacet.org.

Membership: education and training organizations and individuals who use the Continuing Education Unit. (The C.E.U. is defined as 10 contact hours of participation in an organized continuing education program that is noncredit.) Certifies organizations which issue the

C.E.U; develops criteria and guidelines for use of the C.E.U.

International Technology Education Assn., *1914 Association Dr., Reston, VA 20191-1539; (703) 860-2100. Fax, (703) 860-0353. Kendall N. Starkweather, executive director. Internet, itea@iris.org or http://www.iteawww.org.*

Membership: technology education teachers, supervisors, teacher educators, and individuals studying to be technology education teachers. Technology education includes the curriculum areas of manufacturing, construction, communications, transportation, and energy.

National Assn. of Manufacturers, *Employment Policy, 1331 Pennsylvania Ave. N.W., 6th Floor 20004-1790; (202) 637-3133. Fax, (202) 637-3182. Sandy Boyd, director.*

Works to enhance the quality of vocational education and to increase support from the business community. Interests include opportunities for dislocated workers, legislation affecting vocational education, and the impact of high technology on the work force.

National Assn. of State Directors of Vocational/ Technical Education Consortium, *444 N. Capitol St. N.W., #830 20001; (202) 737-0303. Fax, (202) 737-1106. Kimberly Green, executive director. Internet, nasdvtec@ iris.org or http://www.iris.org/~nasdvtec.*

Membership: state vocational education agency heads, senior staff, and business, labor, and other education officials. Advocates state and national policy to strengthen vocational-technical education to create a foundation of skills for American workers and provide them with opportunities to acquire new and advanced skills.

National Institute for Work and Learning, *1875 Connecticut Ave. N.W., 9th Floor 20009-1202; (202)* 884-8186. Fax, (202) 884-8422. Ivan Charner, vice president.

Public policy research organization that seeks to improve collaboration between educational and business institutions. Conducts demonstration projects with communities throughout the country on employer-funded tuition aid, youth transition from school to work, and employee education and career development. Conducts research on education and work issues. Library open to the public. (Affiliated with the Academy for Educational Development.)

National University Continuing Education Assn., *1 Dupont Circle N.W., #615 20036; (202) 659-3130. Fax, (202) 785-0374. Kay Kohl, executive director. Internet, http://www.nucea.edu.*

Membership: higher education institutions and nonprofit organizations involved in postsecondary continuing education. Prepares statistical analyses and produces data reports for members; recognizes accomplishments in the field. Monitors legislation and regulations.

Vocational Industrial Clubs of America, *P.O. Box 3000, Leesburg, VA 20177-0300; (703) 777-8810. Fax, (703) 777-8999. Stephen Denby, executive director. Internet, http://www.vica.org.*

Membership: students, teachers, and administrators of trade, industrial, technical, and health occupations programs at public high schools, vocational schools, and two-year colleges. Promotes strong work skills, workplace ethics, understanding of free enterprise, and lifelong education.

See also American Assn. of Community Colleges (p. 188); Assn. for Community Based Education (p. 173); Correctional Education Assn. (p. 517); National Community Education Assn. (p. 175)

7 Employment and Labor

■ GENERAL POLICY

AGENCIES

Labor Dept., *200 Constitution Ave. N.W., #S2018 20210; (202) 219-8271. Fax, (202) 219-8822. Alexis Herman, secretary; Kitty Higgins, deputy secretary, (202) 219-6151. Information, (202) 219-7316. Library, (202) 219-6992. Recorded press releases, (202) 219-6899. Locator, (202) 219-5000. Internet, http://www.dol.gov.*

Promotes and develops the welfare of U.S. wage earners; administers federal labor laws; acts as principal adviser to the president on policies relating to wage earners, working conditions, and employment opportunities. Library open to the public.

Labor Dept., *Administrative Law Judges, 800 K St. N.W., #400 20001-8002; (202) 565-5341. Fax, (202) 565-5325. John Vittone, chief administrative law judge; Beverly Queen, docket clerk. Internet, http://www.oalj.dol.gov.*

Presides over formal hearings to determine violations of minimum wage requirements, overtime payments, compensation benefits, employee discrimination, grant performance, alien certification, employee protection, and health and safety regulations set forth under numerous statutes, executive orders, and regulations. With few exceptions, hearings are required to be conducted in accordance with the Administrative Procedure Act.

Labor Dept., *Administrative Review Board, 200 Constitution Ave. N.W. 20210; (202) 219-4728. Fax, (202) 219-9315. David A. O'Brien, chair.*

Issues final decisions on appeals under the Service Contract Act, the Comprehensive Employment and Training Act, the Job Training Partnership Act, the Davis-Bacon Act, the Trade Act, the Surface Transportation Assistance Act, the Energy Reorganization Act, and several environmental laws, unemployment insurance conformity proceedings, and cases brought by the Office of Federal Contract Compliance Programs.

CONGRESS

General Accounting Office, *Health, Education, and Human Services, 441 G St. N.W. 20548; (202) 512-6806. Fax, (202) 512-5806. Richard L. Hembra, assistant comptroller general.*

Independent, nonpartisan agency in the legislative branch. Audits, analyzes, and evaluates Labor Dept. programs; makes reports available to the public.

House Appropriations Committee, *Subcommittee on Labor, Health and Human Services, and Education, 2358 RHOB 20515; (202) 225-3508. John Edward Porter,*

R-Ill., chair; Tony McCann, staff director. Internet, http://www.house.gov/appropriations.

Jurisdiction over legislation to appropriate funds for the Labor Dept., the National Labor Relations Board, National Mediation Board, Federal Mediation and Conciliation Service, and other labor-related agencies.

House Education and the Workforce Committee, *2181 RHOB 20515; (202) 225-4527. Fax, (202) 225-9571. Bill Goodling, R-Pa., chair; Kevin Talley, staff director. Internet, http://www.house.gov/eeo.*

Jurisdiction over labor and employment legislation.

House Education and the Workforce Committee, *Subcommittee on Postsecondary Education, Training, and Life-Long Learning, 2181 RHOB 20515; (202) 225-4527. Fax, (202) 225-9571. Howard P. "Buck" McKeon, R-Calif., chair; Kevin Talley, staff director. Internet, http://www.house.gov/eeo.*

Jurisdiction over public and full-employment legislation.

Senate Appropriations Committee, *Subcommittee on Labor, Health and Human Services, and Education, SD-184 20510; (202) 224-7230. Arlen Specter, R-Pa., chair; Craig A. Higgins, staff director. Internet, http://www.senate.gov/~appropriations/labor.*

Jurisdiction over legislation to appropriate funds for the Labor Dept., National Labor Relations Board, National Mediation Board, Federal Mediation and Conciliation Service, and other labor-related agencies.

Senate Labor and Human Resources Committee, *Subcommittee on Employment and Training, SH-608 20510; (202) 224-2962. Mike DeWine, R-Ohio, chair; Duane Sattler, staff director. Internet, http://www.senate.gov/~labor.*

Jurisdiction over labor and employment legislation, including public and full-employment legislation.

NONPROFIT

AFL-CIO (American Federation of Labor—Congress of Industrial Organizations), *815 16th St. N.W. 20006; (202) 637-5000. John J. Sweeney, president. Internet, http://www.aflcio.org.*

Voluntary federation of national and international labor unions in the United States. Represents members before Congress and other branches of government. Each member union conducts its own contract negotiations. Library open to the public.

American Enterprise Institute for Public Policy Research, *Economic Policy Studies, 1150 17th St. N.W. 20036; (202) 862-5884. Fax, (202) 862-7177. Marvin H.*

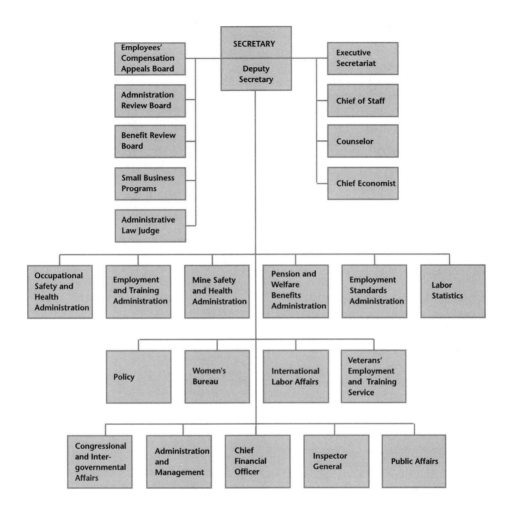

Kosters, director. Information, (202) 862-7158. Press, (202) 862-5829. Internet, http://www.aei.org.

Research and educational organization that studies trends in employment, earnings, the environment, health care, and income in the United States.

Assn. of Part-Time Professionals, 7700 Leesburg Pike, #216, Falls Church, VA 22043; (703) 734-7975. Fax, (703) 734-7405. Vacant, executive director. Internet, http://mbinet.mindbank.com/aptp.

Promotes part-time job opportunities for professional people. Maintains job referral and career counseling services; serves as an information resource center; issues publications on part-time work. Promotes a work environment responsive to individual and family needs.

Campaign for America's Future, 1101 14th St. N.W., #600 20005; (202) 371-6990. Fax, (202) 371-9669. Robert L. Borosage and Roger Hickey, co-directors. Internet, http://www.ourfuture.org.

Advocates policies to help working people. Supports improved employee benefits, including health care, child care, and paid family leave; promotes life-long education and training of workers. Seeks full employment, higher wages, and increased productivity. Monitors legislation and regulations.

Employment Policy Foundation, 1015 15th St. N.W., #1200 20005; (202) 789-8685. Fax, (202) 789-8684. Edward E. Potter, president. Internet, info@epfnet.org or http://www.epfnet.org/epf.

Research and education foundation. Seeks employment policy that facilitates U.S. economic growth; increases productivity, job creation, and job security; and raises the standard of living of the American workforce. Interests include global competitiveness.

International Telework Assn., *204 E St. N.E. 20002; (202) 547-6157. Fax, (202) 546-3289. Jack Heacock, president. Internet, http://www.telecommute.org.*

Membership: individuals, corporations, government agencies, educators, consultants, and vendors involved in telecommuting. Promotes the economic, social, and environmental benefits of telecommuting.

Labor Policy Assn., *1015 15th St. N.W., #1200 20005; (202) 789-8670. Fax, (202) 789-0064. Jeffrey C. McGuiness, president. Internet, http://www.globescope.com/lpa.*

Membership: corporate vice presidents in charge of employee relations. Promotes research in employee relations, particularly in federal employment policy and implementation. Interests include international labor issues, including immigration and child labor.

National Assn. of Personnel Services, *3133 Mount Vernon Ave., Alexandria, VA 22305; (703) 684-0180. Fax, (703) 684-0071. Dianne Callis, president. Internet, http://www.napsweb.org.*

Membership: owners and managers of private personnel services companies, including permanent and temporary service firms. Monitors legislation and regulations concerning the personnel services industry.

National Assn. of Professional Employer Organizations, *901 N. Pitt St., #150, Alexandria, VA 22314; (703) 836-0466. Fax, (703) 836-0976. Milan P. Yager, executive vice president. Internet, http://www.napeo.org/peo.*

Membership: professional employer organizations. Conducts research; sponsors seminars and conferences for members. Monitors legislation and regulations.

National Assn. of Temporary and Staffing Services, *119 S. Saint Asaph St., Alexandria, VA 22314; (703) 549-6287. Fax, (703) 549-4808. Richard Wahlquist, executive vice president. Internet, http://www.natss.org.*

Membership: companies supplying other companies with workers on a temporary basis. Monitors legislation.

Society for Human Resource Management, *1800 Duke St., Alexandria, VA 22314; (703) 548-3440. Fax, (703) 836-0367. Michael R. Losey, president. Toll-free, (800) 283-7476. TDD, (703) 548-6999. Internet, shrm@shrm.org or http://www.shrm.org.*

Membership: human resource management professionals. Monitors legislation and regulations concerning

recruitment, training, and employment practices; occupational safety and health; compensation and benefits; employee and labor relations; and equal employment opportunity. Sponsors seminars and conferences.

U.S. Chamber of Commerce, *Economic Policy, 1615 H St. N.W. 20062-2000; (202) 463-5500. Fax, (202) 463-3188. Vacant, vice president. Press, (202) 463-5682. Internet, http://www.uschamber.org.*

Monitors legislation and regulations affecting the business community, including employee benefits, health care, legal and regulatory affairs, transportation and telecommunications infrastructure, defense conversion, and equal employment opportunity.

International Issues

AGENCIES

Bureau of Labor Statistics *(Labor Dept.),* **Foreign Labor Statistics,** *2 Massachusetts Ave. N.E., #2150 20212; (202) 606-5654. Fax, (202) 606-5664. Mark Sherwood, chief. Internet, http://stats.bls.gov/flshome.htm.*

Issues statistical reports on labor force, productivity, employment, prices, and labor costs in foreign countries adjusted to U.S. concepts.

Commerce Dept., *Policy Analysis, 14th St. and Constitution Ave. N.W., #4858 20230; (202) 482-5703. Fax, (202) 482-0325. David A. Peterson, senior policy adviser.*

Responsible with the Labor Dept. and the State Dept. for U.S. government relations with the Geneva-based International Labor Organization (ILO), a tripartite agency of the United Nations that deals with worldwide labor issues.

Employment and Training Administration *(Labor Dept.),* **Trade Adjustment Assistance,** *200 Constitution Ave. N.W., #C4318 20210; (202) 219-5555. Fax, (202) 219-5753. Grant D. Beale, acting director. Internet, http://www.doleta.gov.*

Assists American workers who are totally or partially unemployed because of increased imports; offers training, job search and relocation assistance, weekly benefits at state unemployment insurance levels, and other reemployment services.

Labor Dept., *Foreign Relations, 200 Constitution Ave. N.W., #S5006 20210; (202) 219-7632. Fax, (202) 219-5613. John A. Ferch, director.*

Provides foreign governments with technical assistance in labor-related activities on a reimbursable basis. (Funding is provided by the U.S. Agency for International Development, international organizations, and foreign governments.) Participates with the State Dept. in managing the U.S. labor attaché program; conducts the U.S. International Visitors Program. Provides information on foreign labor developments, including foreign labor trends.

Labor Dept., *International Economic Affairs*, 200 Constitution Ave. N.W., #S5325 20210; (202) 219-7597. Fax, (202) 219-5071. Jorge Perez-Lopez, director.

Assists in developing U.S. foreign economic policy; examines the effect of foreign trade investment and immigration on income and job opportunities of American workers, domestic production, consumption, and the competitiveness of U.S. products.

Labor Dept., *International Labor Affairs*, 200 Constitution Ave. N.W., #S2235 20210; (202) 219-6043. Fax, (202) 219-5980. Andrew James Samet, deputy under secretary.

Assists in developing international economic policy relating to labor; helps represent the United States in multilateral and bilateral trade negotiations. Evaluates the effects of immigration policy on the wages and employment of U.S. workers.

Labor Dept., *International Organizations*, 200 Constitution Ave. N.W., #S5311 20210; (202) 219-6241. Fax, (202) 219-9074. H. Charles Spring, director.

Provides administrative support for U.S. participation in the International Labor Organization (ILO) and at the Paris-based Organization for Economic Cooperation and Development (OECD), which studies and reports on world economic issues.

Labor Dept., *U.S. International Visitors Program*, 200 Constitution Ave. N.W., #S5006 20210; (202) 219-7632. Fax, (202) 219-5613. John A. Ferch, director.

Works with the State Dept., the Agency for International Development, and other agencies in arranging visits and training programs for foreign officials interested in U.S. labor and trade unions.

President's Committee on the International Labor Organization *(Labor Dept.)*, 200 Constitution Ave. N.W., #S5311 20210; (202) 219-6241. Fax, (202) 219-9074. Alexis Herman, chair; Andrew James Samet, U.S. ILO representative, (202) 219-6043.

Advisory committee of government, employer, and worker representatives, including secretaries of State, Commerce, and Labor, the president's national security advisor, the president of the U.S. Council for International Business, and the president of the AFL-CIO. Formulates and coordinates policy on the International Labor Organization (ILO); advises the president and the secretary of labor.

State Dept., *International Labor Affairs*, Main State Bldg., #4827A 20520; (202) 647-3663. Fax, (202) 647-0431. Gare Smith, deputy assistant secretary, (202) 647-1780.

Uses bilateral and multilateral diplomacy and works with the U.S. business community to promote worker rights around the world. Concerned with issues such as child labor, freedom of expression, and freedom of association.

State Dept., *International Organization Affairs*, Main State Bldg., #5336 20520; (202) 647-4197. Fax, (202) 647-8902. Hugh Neighbour, director, Industrial and Communications Programs.

Responsible, with the Labor Dept. and the Commerce Dept., for U.S. government relations with the International Labor Organization (ILO).

CONGRESS

House Ways and Means Committee, *Subcommittee on Trade,* 1104 LHOB 20515; (202) 225-6649. Fax, (202) 226-0158. Philip M. Crane, R-Ill., chair; Thelma Askey, staff director. Internet, http://www.house.gov/ways_means.

Jurisdiction over legislation on foreign trade, including its impact on U.S. workers.

Senate Finance Committee, *Subcommittee on International Trade,* SD-219 20510; (202) 224-4515. Fax, (202) 224-5920. Charles E. Grassley, R-Iowa, chair; Grant Aldonas, staff contact. Internet, http://www.senate.gov/~finance.

Holds hearings on legislation concerning foreign trade, including its impact on U.S. workers.

INTERNATIONAL ORGANIZATIONS

International Labor Organization (ILO), *Washington Branch,* 1828 L St. N.W., #801 20036; (202) 653-7652. Fax, (202) 653-7687. Anthony G. Freeman, director. Internet, http://us.ilo.org.

Specialized agency of the United Nations. Works to improve working conditions, create employment, and promote human rights worldwide. Establishes international labor standards; conducts training and technical assistance. Washington office serves as liaison between the ILO and U.S. government, employer, and worker groups. Library open to the public by appointment. (Headquarters in Geneva.)

NONPROFIT

American Center for International Labor Solidarity, 1925 K St. N.W., #300 20006; (202) 659-6300. Fax, (202) 778-4525. Harry Kamberis, executive director. Internet, acils@acils.org.

Provides assistance to free and democratic trade unions in Latin America and the Caribbean. Provides trade union leadership courses in collective bargaining, union organization, trade integration, labor-management cooperation, union administration, and political theories. Sponsors social and community development projects; focus includes human and worker rights and the role of women in labor unions.

Institute for International Human Resources, *Society for Human Resource Management,* 1800 Duke St., Alexandria, VA 22314-3499; (703) 548-3440. Fax, (703) 836-0367. Brian Glade, vice president, International Programs. Internet, shrm@shrm.org or http://www.shrm.org/docs/iihr.html.

Provides human resources professionals with specialized, timely information on the worldwide business environment and its implications on the human resources profession.

Labor Standards and Practices

See also Equal Employment Opportunity (this chapter)

AGENCIES

Bureau of Labor Statistics *(Labor Dept.),* **Compensation and Working Conditions,** 2 Massachusetts Ave. N.E. 20212; (202) 606-6300. Fax, (202) 606-6310. Kathleen MacDonald, acting associate commissioner. Internet, labstathelpdesk@bls.gov or http://www.bls.gov.

Conducts annual area wage surveys to determine occupational pay information in individual labor markets. Conducts industry wage surveys, which provide wage and employee benefit information; presents data for selected white- and blue-collar jobs.

Employment Standards Administration *(Labor Dept.),* 200 Constitution Ave. N.W. 20210; (202) 219-6191. Fax, (202) 219-8457. Bernard Anderson, assistant secretary. Information, (202) 219-8743.

Administers and enforces employment laws and regulations. Responsibilities include ensuring compliance among federal contractors, administering benefits claims for federal employees and other workers, and protecting workers' wages and working conditions.

Employment Standards Administration *(Labor Dept.),* **Fair Labor Standards Act Enforcement,** 200 Constitution Ave. N.W., #S3516 20210; (202) 219-4907. Fax, (202) 219-5122. Daniel P. Sweeney, chief. Internet, http://www.dol.gov/dol/esa.

Issues interpretations and rulings of the Fair Labor Standards Act of 1938, as amended (Federal Minimum Wage and Overtime Pay Law).

Employment Standards Administration *(Labor Dept.),* **Federal Contract Compliance Programs,** 200 Constitution Ave. N.W., #C3325 20210; (202) 219-9475. Fax, (202) 219-6195. Shirley J. Wilcher, deputy assistant secretary.

Monitors and enforces government contractors' compliance with federal laws and regulations on equal employment opportunities and affirmative action, including employment rights of minorities, women, persons with disabilities, and disabled and Vietnam-era veterans.

Employment Standards Administration *(Labor Dept.),* **Government Contracts,** 200 Constitution Ave. N.W., #S3018 20210; (202) 219-7541. Fax, (202) 219-5122. Ethel P. Miller, team leader.

Enforces the Davis-Bacon Act, the Walsh-Healey Public Contracts Act, the Contract Work Hours and Safety Standards Act, the Service Contract Act, and other related government contract labor standards statutes.

Employment Standards Administration *(Labor Dept.),* **Planning and Analysis,** 200 Constitution Ave. N.W., #S3028 20210; (202) 219-8353. Fax, (202) 219-6833. Nancy Flynn, director.

Issues regulations and policy statements on labor standards laws, including the Fair Labor Standards Act, the Davis-Bacon Act, the Service Contract Act, the Migrant and Seasonal Agricultural Workers Protection Act, section H2A of the Immigration Reform and Control Act of 1986, the Employee Polygraph Protection Act, and the Family and Medical Leave Act.

Employment Standards Administration *(Labor Dept.),* **Special Employment,** 200 Constitution Ave. N.W., #S3510 20210; (202) 219-7640. Fax, (202) 219-5122. Arthur M. Kerschner Jr., team leader.

Authorizes subminimum wages under the Fair Labor Standards Act for certain categories of workers, including full-time students, student learners, and workers with disabilities. Administers the Fair Labor Standards Act restrictions on working at home in certain industries. Administers special minimum wage provisions applicable in Puerto Rico and American Samoa.

Employment Standards Administration *(Labor Dept.),* **Wage and Hour Division,** 200 Constitution Ave. N.W., #S3502 20210; (202) 219-8305. Fax, (202) 219-4753. John Fraser, acting administrator. Internet, http://www.dol.gov/dol/esa.

Enforces the minimum-wage and overtime provisions of the Fair Labor Standards Act.

Employment Standards Administration *(Labor Dept.),* **Wage Determinations,** 200 Constitution Ave.

N.W. 20210; (202) 219-7531. Fax, (202) 219-5771. William Gross, director; Nila Stoball, chief, Service Contract Wage Determinations, (202) 219-7568; Carl Poleskey, chief, Construction Wage Determinations, (202) 219-7455.

Issues prevailing wage determinations under the Service Contract Act of 1965 and under the Davis-Bacon Act and related acts.

CONGRESS

House Education and the Workforce Committee, Subcommittee on Workforce Protections, *2181 RHOB 20515; (202) 225-4527. Fax, (202) 225-9571. Cass Ballenger, R-N.C., chair; Kevin Talley, staff director.*

Jurisdiction over legislation on minimum wage and wage and hour standards, including the Davis-Bacon Act, the Walsh-Healey Act, and the Fair Labor Standards Act; jurisdiction over mandated benefits, including those for government contractors. Jurisdiction over legislation on job discrimination by government contractors, electronic monitoring, and polygraph testing.

Senate Labor and Human Resources Committee, Subcommittee on Employment and Training, *SH-608 20510; (202) 224-2962. Mike DeWine, R-Ohio, chair; Duane Sattler, staff director. Internet, http://www.senate. gov/~labor.*

Jurisdiction over legislation on job discrimination by government contractors, minimum wage, wage and hour standards, and mandated benefits, including those for government contractors.

Statistics and Information

AGENCIES

Bureau of Labor Statistics *(Labor Dept.),* 2 Massachusetts Ave. N.E., #2860 20212; (202) 606-5886. Fax, (202) 606-7890. Katharine G. Abraham, commissioner, (202) 606-7800. Information, (202) 606-5888. Press, (202) 606-5900. Internet, labstathelpdesk@bls.gov or http://stats. bls.gov.

Collects, analyzes, and publishes data on labor economics, including employment, unemployment, hours of work, wages, employee compensation, prices, consumer expenditures, labor-management relations, productivity, technological developments, occupational safety and health, and structure and growth of the economy. Publishes reports on these statistical trends, including the Consumer Price Index, the Producer Price Index, and Employment and Earnings.

Bureau of Labor Statistics *(Labor Dept.),* **Employment and Unemployment Statistics,** *2 Massachusetts Ave. N.E., #4945 20212; (202) 606-6400. Fax, (202) 606-*

6425. Lois Orr, associate commissioner. Internet, labstathelpdesk@bls.gov or http://www.stats.bls.gov.

Monitors employment and unemployment trends on national and local levels; compiles data on worker and industry employment and earnings.

Bureau of Labor Statistics *(Labor Dept.),* **Employment Projections,** *2 Massachusetts Ave. N.E., #2135 20212; (202) 606-5700. Fax, (202) 606-5745. Neal H. Rosenthal, associate commissioner. Internet, labstathelpdesk@bls.gov or http://stats.bls.gov/emphome. html.*

Develops economic, industrial, and demographic employment projections according to industry and occupation. Provides career guidance material.

Bureau of Labor Statistics *(Labor Dept.),* **Foreign Labor Statistics,** *2 Massachusetts Ave. N.E., #2150 20212; (202) 606-5654. Fax, (202) 606-5664. Mark Sherwood, chief. Internet, http://stats.bls.gov/flshome.htm.*

Issues statistical reports on labor force, productivity, employment, prices, and labor costs in foreign countries adjusted to U.S. concepts.

Bureau of Labor Statistics *(Labor Dept.),* **Local Area Unemployment Statistics,** *2 Massachusetts Ave. N.E., #4675 20212; (202) 606-6390. Fax, (202) 606-6459. Sharon P. Brown, chief. Information, (202) 606-6392. Internet, labstathelpdesk@bls.gov.*

Issues labor force and unemployment statistics for states, metropolitan statistical areas, cities with populations of 25,000 or more, counties, and other areas covered under federal assistance programs.

Bureau of Labor Statistics *(Labor Dept.),* **Monthly Industry Employment Statistics,** *2 Massachusetts Ave. N.E., #4860 20212; (202) 606-6528. Fax, (202) 606-6644. Patricia Getz, chief. Information, (202) 606-6555. Internet, labstathelpdesk@bls.gov or http://www.bls.gov/ceshome. html.*

Analyzes and publishes national-level employment, hour, and earnings statistics based on data submitted by the states; develops statistical information on employment, hours, and earnings by industry for the nation, states, and metropolitan statistical areas.

Bureau of Labor Statistics *(Labor Dept.),* **Productivity and Technology,** *2 Massachusetts Ave. N.E., #2150 20212; (202) 606-5600. Fax, (202) 606-5664. Edwin R. Dean, associate commissioner. TDD, (202) 606-6034.*

Develops and analyzes productivity measures for U.S. industries and total economy; adjusts productivity measures of foreign countries for comparison with U.S. standards; studies implications of technological changes on employment and occupational distribution.

Census Bureau *(Commerce Dept.), Demographic Surveys,* Suitland and Silver Hill Rds., Suitland, MD; (301) 457-3811. Fax, (301) 457-2306. Chester E. Bowie, chief.

Conducts surveys and compiles official monthly employment and unemployment statistics for the Labor Dept.'s Bureau of Labor Statistics.

Employment and Training Administration *(Labor Dept.), Unemployment Insurance Service,* 200 Constitution Ave. N.W., #S4231 20210; (202) 219-5922. Fax, (202) 219-8506. Cynthia L. Ambler, statistician, Actuarial Services.

Compiles statistics on state unemployment insurance programs. Studies unemployment issues related to benefits.

Occupational Safety and Health Administration *(Labor Dept.), Statistics,* 200 Constitution Ave. N.W., #N3507 20210; (202) 219-6463. Fax, (202) 219-5161. Joseph Dubois, director.

Compiles and provides all statistical data for OSHA, such as occupational injury and illness records, which are used in setting standards and making policy.

CONGRESS

House Education and the Workforce Committee, *Subcommittee on Employer-Employee Relations,* 2181 RHOB 20515; (202) 225-4527. Fax, (202) 225-9571. Harris W. Fawell, R-Ill., chair; Kevin Talley, staff director.

Jurisdiction over legislation on the Bureau of Labor Statistics.

Senate Labor and Human Resources Committee, *Subcommittee on Employment and Training,* SH-608 20510; (202) 224-2962. Mike DeWine, R-Ohio, chair; Duane Sattler, staff director. Internet, http://www.senate.gov/~labor.

Jurisdiction over legislation on the Bureau of Labor Statistics.

Unemployment Benefits

See also Statistics and Information (this section)

AGENCIES

Employment and Training Administration *(Labor Dept.), Trade Adjustment Assistance,* 200 Constitution Ave. N.W., #C4318 20210; (202) 219-5555. Fax, (202) 219-5753. Grant D. Beale, acting director. Internet, http://www.doleta.gov.

Assists American workers who are totally or partially unemployed because of increased imports; offers training, job search and relocation assistance, weekly benefits at state unemployment insurance levels, and other reemployment services.

Employment and Training Administration *(Labor Dept.), Unemployment Insurance Service,* 200 Constitution Ave. N.W., #S4231 20210; (202) 219-7831. Fax, (202) 219-8506. Grace Kilbane, director.

Directs and reviews the state-administered system that provides income support for unemployed workers nationwide; advises state and federal employment security agencies on wage-loss, worker dislocation, and adjustment assistance compensation programs.

CONGRESS

House Ways and Means Committee, *Subcommittee on Human Resources,* B317 RHOB 20515; (202) 225-1025. Fax, (202) 225-9480. E. Clay Shaw Jr., R-Fla., chair; Ronald Haskins, staff director. Internet, http://www.house.gov/ways_means.

Jurisdiction over unemployment benefits legislation.

Senate Finance Committee, *Subcommittee on Social Security and Family Policy,* SD-219 20510; (202) 224-4515. Fax, (202) 228-0578. John H. Chafee, R-R.I., chair; Alec Bachon, staff contact. Internet, http://www.senate.gov/~finance.

Holds hearings on unemployment benefits legislation.

NONPROFIT

Interstate Conference of Employment Security Agencies, 444 N. Capitol St. N.W., #142 20001; (202) 628-5588. Fax, (202) 783-5023. Emily DeRocco, executive director. Internet, http://www.icesa.org.

Membership: state employment security administrators. Informs members of unemployment insurance programs and legislation. Provides unemployment insurance and reemployment professionals with opportunities for networking and information exchange.

EMPLOYMENT AND TRAINING PROGRAMS

See also Civil Service (chap. 10); Equal Employment Opportunity (this chapter); Military Personnel and Veterans (chap. 15); Social Services and Disabilities (chap. 18)

AGENCIES

Employment and Training Administration *(Labor Dept.), 200 Constitution Ave. N.W., #S2307 20210; (202) 219-6050. Fax, (202) 219-6827. Ray Uhalde, acting assistant secretary. Information, (202) 219-6871. Internet, http://www.doleta.gov.*

Responsible for employment, training, and trade adjustment programs for economically disadvantaged, unemployed, and dislocated workers. Administers and directs policy for the U.S. Employment Service, the Unemployment Insurance Service, and the Office of Work-Based Learning. Administers and directs programs for Native Americans, migrants, youth, older workers, and workers with disabilities.

Employment and Training Administration *(Labor Dept.), Job Training Programs, 200 Constitution Ave. N.W., #N4459 20210; (202) 219-6236. Fax, (202) 208-5913. Theodore Mastroianni, associate assistant secretary. Information, (202) 219-6236. Internet, http://www.doleta. gov.*

Administers the Job Training Partnership Act, which provides state and local governments with funds to develop and operate employment and training programs. Oversees the Job Corps (a program for disadvantaged youth) and employment and training programs for Native Americans, migrants and seasonal workers, older workers, workers with disabilities, and economically disadvantaged workers.

Employment and Training Administration *(Labor Dept.), U.S. Employment Service, 200 Constitution Ave. N.W., #N4470 20210; (202) 219-5257. Fax, (202) 219-6643. John R. Beverly, director.*

Assists states in maintaining a system of local employment-service centers for job seekers and employers.

Employment and Training Administration *(Labor Dept.), Work-Based Learning, 200 Constitution Ave. N.W., #N4700 20210; (202) 219-6540. Fax, (202) 219-5024. Theodore Mastroianni, administrator.*

Responsible for Worker Retraining and Adjustment programs (including the Trade Adjustment Assistance Program and the Economic Dislocation and Worker Adjustment Assistance Act); examines training initiatives and technology.

National Occupational Information Coordinating Committee, *2100 M St. N.W., #156 20037; (202) 653-5665. Fax, (202) 653-2123. Juliette N. Lester, executive director. Internet, noicc@dol.gov or http://www.noicc.gov.*

Interagency group that works with the departments of Agriculture, Commerce, Defense, Education, and Labor; provides information on civilian and military occupations, educational institutions, and training programs; develops systems to provide labor market and occupational information for vocational education and employment-related program planners and administrators at the state level; supports state efforts to provide citizens with career information and guidance.

CONGRESS

House Education and the Workforce Committee, *2181 RHOB 20515; (202) 225-4527. Fax, (202) 225-9571. Bill Goodling, R-Pa., chair; Kevin Talley, staff director. Internet, http://www.house.gov/eeo.*

Jurisdiction over work incentive, education, and job training programs for youth and public assistance recipients, including the Job Opportunities and Basic Skills Training program and the Job Training Partnership Act.

House Education and the Workforce Committee, *Subcommittee on Early Childhood, Youth, and Families, 2181 RHOB 20515; (202) 225-4527. Fax, (202) 225-9571. Frank Riggs, R-Calif., chair; Kevin Talley, staff director. Internet, http://www.house.gov/eeo.*

Jurisdiction over legislation on employment training programs for elderly workers.

House Education and the Workforce Committee, *Subcommittee on Postsecondary Education, Training, and Life-Long Learning, 2181 RHOB 20515; (202) 225-4527. Fax, (202) 225-9571. Howard P. "Buck" McKeon, R-Calif., chair; Kevin Talley, staff director. Internet, http:// www.house.gov/eeo.*

Jurisdiction over employment training legislation, including legislation on apprenticeship programs, on-the-job training, dislocated workers and plant shutdowns, displaced homemakers, rural workers, and vocational rehabilitation and education for workers with disabilities. Jurisdiction over youth and young adult conservation corps programs.

House Education and the Workforce Committee, *Subcommittee on Workforce Protections, 2181 RHOB 20515; (202) 225-4527. Fax, (202) 225-9571. Cass Ballenger, R-N.C., chair; Kevin Talley, staff director.*

Jurisdiction over legislation on minimum wage and wage and hour standards, including the Davis-Bacon Act, the Walsh-Healey Act, and the Fair Labor Standards Act; jurisdiction over mandated benefits, including those for government contractors.

House Judiciary Committee, *Subcommittee on Immigration and Claims, B370B RHOB 20515; (202) 225-5727. Fax, (202) 225-3672. Lamar Smith, R-Texas, chair;*

Cordia Strom, counsel. Internet, http://www.house.gov/ judiciary.

Jurisdiction over legislation on foreign laborers once they are in the United States and on employer sanctions for not complying with the Immigration and Refugee Control Act of 1986.

Senate Finance Committee, *Subcommittee on Social Security and Family Policy, SD-219 20510; (202) 224-4515. Fax, (202) 228-0578. John H. Chafee, R-R.I., chair; Alec Bachon, staff contact. Internet, http://www.senate. gov/~finance.*

Holds hearings on legislation affecting the Job Opportunities and Basic Skills Training Program.

Senate Judiciary Committee, *Subcommittee on Immigration, SD-323 20510; (202) 224-6098. Fax, (202) 228-4506. Spencer Abraham, R-Mich., chair; Lee Lieberman Otis, chief counsel. Internet, http://www.senate.gov/ committee/judiciary.html.*

Jurisdiction over legislation on nonimmigrant foreign laborers once they are in the United States.

Senate Labor and Human Resources Committee, *Subcommittee on Aging, SH-615 20510; (202) 224-0136. Judd Gregg, R-N.H., chair; Kimberly Spalding, staff director. Internet, http://www.senate.gov/~labor.*

Jurisdiction over legislation on employment training programs for elderly workers.

Senate Labor and Human Resources Committee, *Subcommittee on Employment and Training, SH-608 20510; (202) 224-2962. Mike DeWine, R-Ohio, chair; Duane Sattler, staff director. Internet, http://www.senate. gov/~labor.*

Jurisdiction over education and job training programs for youth and public assistance recipients, including the Job Training Partnership Act and legislation on apprenticeship programs, on-the-job training, and displaced homemakers.

Senate Special Committee on Aging, *SD-G31 20510; (202) 224-5364. Fax, (202) 224-8660. Charles E. Grassley, R-Iowa, chair; Ted Totman, staff director.*

Studies and makes recommendations on legislation and federal programs affecting older Americans, including the areas of age discrimination, compensation, and unemployment; oversees Older Americans Act programs.

NONPROFIT

AFL-CIO Human Resources Development Institute, *1101 14th St. N.W., #320 20005; (202) 638-3912. Fax, (202) 783-6536. Lynn Meyers, executive director. Internet, info@hrdi-emp.prng.org.*

Provides technical assistance to labor unions, employers, education agencies, and community groups for workplace programs focusing on dislocated workers, economically disadvantaged workers, and skill upgrading. Interests include new technologies and workplace innovations.

American Labor Education Center, *2000 P St. N.W., #300 20036; (202) 828-5170. Fax, (202) 828-5173. Karen Ohmans, director. Internet, amlabor@aol.com.*

Produces materials for workers and unions. Interests include occupational health and safety, communication skills, and other labor issues.

American Society for Training and Development, *1640 King St., Alexandria, VA (mailing address: P.O. Box 1443, Alexandria, VA 22313-2043); (703) 683-8100. Fax, (703) 683-8103. Curtis E. Plott, president. Internet, http:// www.astd.org.*

Membership: trainers and human resource developers. Promotes workplace training programs and human resource development. Interests include productivity, job training and retraining, participative management, and unemployment. Holds conferences and provides information on technical and skills training.

Employee Relocation Council, *1720 N St. N.W. 20036; (202) 857-0857. Fax, (202) 467-4012. H. Cris Collie, executive vice president. Internet, http://www.erc.org.*

Membership: corporations that relocate employees and moving, real estate, and relocation management companies. Researches and recommends policies that provide a smooth transition for relocated employees and their families. Holds conferences and issues publications on employee relocation issues.

Interstate Conference of Employment Security Agencies, *444 N. Capitol St. N.W., #142 20001; (202) 628-5588. Fax, (202) 783-5023. Emily DeRocco, executive director. Internet, http://www.icesa.org.*

Membership: state employment security administrators. Informs members of federal legislation on job placement, veterans' affairs, and employment and training programs. Distributes labor market information; trains new state administrators and executive staff. Provides employment and training professionals with opportunities for networking and information exchange.

International Federation of Training and Development Organizations, *1800 Duke St., Alexandria, VA 22314; (703) 535-6011. Fax, (703) 836-0367. David A. Waugh, secretary general. Internet, iftdo@shrm.org or http://www.iftdo.org.*

Operates a worldwide network that seeks to identify, develop, and transfer knowledge skills and technology to enhance organizational growth and workplace productivity.

National Alliance of Business, *1201 New York Ave. N.W., #700 20005; (202) 289-2888. Fax, (202) 289-1303. Roberts T. Jones, president. Press, (202) 289-2850. Internet, info@nab.com or http://www.nab.com.*

Represents the interests of business in developing a quality workforce. Promotes partnerships between government and business at the federal, state, and local levels. Interests include improving public education, addressing the employment and training needs of individuals in a globally competitive economy, and easing the transition from school to the workplace.

National Assn. of Counties, *Training and Employment Program, 440 1st St. N.W., 8th Floor 20001; (202) 393-6226. Fax, (202) 737-0480. Gary Gortenberg, director. Internet, http://www.naco.org.*

Oversees, directs, and offers technical assistance to members participating in federal job training programs; informs members of related legislation. Assists county officials, private industry councils, workforce development boards, and service delivery areas in implementing workforce development systems.

National Assn. of Manufacturers, *Employment Policy, 1331 Pennsylvania Ave. N.W., 6th Floor 20004-1790; (202) 637-3133. Fax, (202) 637-3182. Sandy Boyd, director.*

Interests include opportunities for dislocated workers, striker replacement, vocational education, matters relating to the National Labor Relations Act, and the effect of high technology on the work force.

National Assn. of Private Industry Councils, *1201 New York Ave. N.W., #350 20005; (202) 289-2950. Fax, (202) 289-2846. Robert F. Knight, president. Internet, http://www.work-web.com/napic.*

Membership: private industry councils and state job training coordinating councils established under the Job Training Partnership Act of 1982. Interests include job training opportunities for unemployed, economically disadvantaged, and dislocated workers, and youth; and private sector involvement in federal employment and training policy. Provides members with technical assistance; holds conferences and seminars.

National Assn. of Workforce Development Professionals, *1620 Eye St. N.W., Lower Level 30 20006-4005; (202) 887-6120. Fax, (202) 887-8216. Cynthia A. Davis, executive director. Internet, nawp@aol.com or http://www.work-web.com/nawdp.*

Membership: professionals and policymakers in the employment and training field. Promotes professionalism, information exchange, networking, and professional growth in the work force development field.

National Center on Education and the Economy, *National Alliance for Restructuring Education, 700 11th St. N.W., #750 20001; (202) 783-3668. Fax, (202) 783-3672. Mary Ann Mays, director. Internet, nareinfo@ncee.org or http://www.ncee.org.*

Partnership of states, school districts, corporations, foundations, and nonprofit organizations that provides tools and technical assistance for school districts to improve education and training for the workplace.

National Governors' Assn., *Center for Policy Research, 444 N. Capitol St. N.W., #267 20001-1572; (202) 624-5345. Fax, (202) 624-5313. Martin Simon, director, Training and Employment Program. Press, (202) 624-5331.*

Provides information and technical assistance to members participating in federal job training programs, including programs authorized under the federal workforce development programs; informs members of related legislation. Provides technical assistance to members in areas of work and welfare programs, youth programs, employment services, dislocated workers, and dropout prevention.

National Institute for Work and Learning, *1875 Connecticut Ave. N.W., 9th Floor 20009-1202; (202) 884-8186. Fax, (202) 884-8422. Ivan Charner, vice president.*

Public policy research organization that seeks to improve collaboration between educational and business institutions. Conducts demonstration projects with communities throughout the country on employer-funded tuition aid, youth transition from school to work, employee education, and career development. Conducts research on educational and work issues. Library open to the public. (Affiliated with the Academy for Educational Development.)

U.S. Chamber of Commerce, *Center for Workforce Preparation, 1615 H St. N.W. 20062-2000; (202) 463-5525. Fax, (202) 463-5730. Michelle Griffin, executive director. Internet, http://www.uschamber.org/about/CWP/index.html.*

Works with local chambers on educational reform, human resource, and job training issues.

U.S. Conference of Mayors, *Employment and Training Council, 1620 Eye St. N.W., 4th Floor 20006; (202) 861-6724. Fax, (202) 293-2352. Joan Crigger, assistant executive director, Employment and Training.*

Offers technical assistance to members participating in federal job training programs; monitors related legislation; acts as an information clearinghouse on employment and training programs.

See also Corporation for Enterprise Development (p. 410)

Aliens

AGENCIES

Administration for Children and Families *(Health and Human Services Dept.), Refugee Resettlement, 901 D St. S.W., 6th Floor 20447; (202) 401-9246. Fax, (202) 401-5487. Lavinia Limon, director.*

Directs the Refugee Resettlement Program, which reimburses states for financial and medical assistance given to refugees; provides grants for social services, such as employment training and English instruction. Awards funds to private resettlement agencies for the provision of cash assistance to and case management of refugees.

Employment and Training Administration *(Labor Dept.), Foreign Labor Certification, 200 Constitution Ave. N.W., #N4456 20210; (202) 219-5263. Fax, (202) 208-5844. James Norris, chief, Foreign Labor Certifications.*

Sets policies and guidelines for regional offices that certify applications for alien employment in the United States; determines whether U.S. citizens are available for those jobs and whether employment of aliens will adversely affect similarly employed U.S. citizens.

Apprenticeship Programs

AGENCIES

Employment and Training Administration *(Labor Dept.), Apprenticeship and Training, 200 Constitution Ave. N.W., #N4649 20210; (202) 219-5921. Fax, (202) 219-5011. Anthony Swoope, director. Library, (202) 219-6992.*

Promotes establishment of apprenticeship programs in private industry and the public sector. Library open to the public.

Employment and Training Administration *(Labor Dept.), Federal Committee on Apprenticeship, 200 Constitution Ave. N.W., #N4649 20210; (202) 219-5943. Fax, (202) 219-5011. Anthony Swoope, director, (202) 219-5921.*

Advises the secretary of labor on the role of apprenticeship programs in employment training and on safety standards for those programs; encourages sponsors to include these standards in planning apprenticeship programs.

Dislocated Workers

AGENCIES

Employment and Training Administration *(Labor Dept.), Work-Based Learning, 200 Constitution Ave. N.W., #N4700 20210; (202) 219-6540. Fax, (202) 219-5024. Theodore Mastroianni, administrator.*

Responsible for dislocated worker retraining programs.

NONPROFIT

National Assn. of Manufacturers, *Employment Policy, 1331 Pennsylvania Ave. N.W., 6th Floor 20004-1790; (202) 637-3133. Fax, (202) 637-3182. Sandy Boyd, director.*

Interests include opportunities for dislocated workers and vocational education.

National Assn. of Private Industry Councils, *1201 New York Ave. N.W., #350 20005; (202) 289-2950. Fax, (202) 289-2846. Robert F. Knight, president. Internet, http://www.work-web.com/napic.*

Membership: private industry councils and state job training coordinating councils established under the Job Training Partnership Act of 1982. Interests include job training opportunities for dislocated workers.

National Governors' Assn., *Center for Policy Research, 444 N. Capitol St. N.W., #267 20001-1572; (202) 624-5345. Fax, (202) 624-5313. Martin Simon, director, Training and Employment Program. Press, (202) 624-5331.*

Provides technical assistance to members participating in employment and training activities for dislocated workers.

Migrant and Seasonal Farm Workers

AGENCIES

Employment and Training Administration *(Labor Dept.), Seasonal Farm Worker Programs, 200 Constitution Ave. N.W., #N4641 20210; (202) 219-5500. Fax, (202) 219-6338. Thomas M. Dowd, chief.*

Provides funds for programs that help seasonal farm workers and their families find better jobs in agriculture and other areas. Services include occupational training, education, and job development and placement.

Employment Standards Administration *(Labor Dept.), Farm Labor Programs, 200 Constitution Ave. N.W., #S3510 20210; (202) 219-7605. Fax, (202) 219-5122. Mike Hancock, chief.*

Administers and enforces the Migrant and Seasonal Agricultural Worker Protection Act, which protects migrant and seasonal agricultural workers from substandard labor practices by farm labor contractors, agricultural employers, and agricultural associations.

NONPROFIT

Assn. of Farmworker Opportunity Programs, *1611 N. Kent St., #910, Arlington, VA 22209-2111; (703) 528-4141. Fax, (703) 528-4145. Lynda D. Mull, executive director. Internet, afop@afop.org or http://www.afop.org.*

Represents state-level organizations that provide services and support to migrant and guest workers. Monitors legislation and conducts research.

Migrant Legal Action Program, *P.O. Box 53308 20009; (202) 462-7744. Fax, (202) 462-7914. Roger C. Rosenthal, executive director. Internet, hn1645@handsnet. org.*

Supports and assists local legal services, migrant education, migrant health issues, and other organizations and private attorneys with respect to issues involving the living and working conditions experienced by migrant farmworkers. Monitors legislation and regulations.

United Farm Workers of America, *c/o AFL-CIO, 815 16th St. N.W. 20006; (202) 637-5212. Fax, (202) 508-6924. Dan Hawes, manager. TDD, (202) 637-5012. Internet, http://www.ufw.org.*

Membership: approximately 50,000 farm workers. Helps members negotiate pay, benefits, and better working conditions; conducts training programs and workshops. Focus includes immigration and migrant workers. Monitors legislation and regulations. (Affiliated with the AFL-CIO.)

See also National Council of Agricultural Employers (p. 38)

Older Workers

AGENCIES

Employment and Training Administration *(Labor Dept.), Older Worker Programs, 200 Constitution Ave. N.W., #N4641 20210; (202) 219-5904. Fax, (202) 219-6338. Erich W. Larisch, chief.*

Administers the Senior Community Service Employment Program, which provides funds for part-time, community service work-training programs; the programs pay minimum wage and are operated by national sponsoring organizations and state and territorial governments. The program is aimed at economically disadvantaged persons age 55 and over.

NONPROFIT

American Assn. of Retired Persons, *Senior Community Service Employment Program, 601 E St. N.W. 20049; (202) 434-2020. Fax, (202) 434-6446. Glenn L. Northup, director. Internet, http://www.aarp.org.*

Conducts a federally funded work-experience program for economically disadvantaged older persons; places trainees in community service jobs and helps them reenter the labor force.

National Council on the Aging, *Senior Community Service Employment Program, 409 3rd St. S.W., 2nd Floor 20024; (202) 479-6631. Fax, (202) 479-6664. Donald Davis, vice president. Internet, info@ncoa.org.*

Works with the Labor Dept. under the authority of the Older Americans Act to provide workers age 55 and over with employment, community service, and training opportunities in their resident communities. Library open to the public.

National Senior Citizens Educational and Research Center, *Senior AIDES Program, 8403 Colesville Rd., #1200, Silver Spring, MD 20910-3314; (301) 578-8800. Fax, (301) 578-8999. Dorinda Fox, deputy director.*

Operates the Labor Dept.'s Senior Community Service Employment Program, which provides funds for part-time, community service work-training programs and is aimed at low-income individuals age 55 and over.

Workers with Disabilities

AGENCIES

Committee for Purchase From People Who Are Blind or Severely Disabled, *1215 Jefferson Davis Hwy., #310, Arlington, VA 22202-3461; (703) 603-7740. Fax, (703) 603-0655. Beverly L. Milkman, executive director.*

Presidentially appointed committee that determines which products and services are suitable for federal procurement from qualified nonprofit agencies employing people who are blind or have other severe disabilities; seeks to increase employment opportunities for these individuals.

Employment Standards Administration *(Labor Dept.), Special Employment, 200 Constitution Ave. N.W., #S3510 20210; (202) 219-7640. Fax, (202) 219-5122. Arthur M. Kerschner Jr., team leader.*

Administers certification of special lower minimum wage rates for workers with disabilities and impaired earning capacity; wage applies in industry, sheltered workshops, hospitals, institutions, and group homes.

Equal Employment Opportunity Commission, *Inter-agency Committee on Employees with Disabilities, 1801 L St. N.W. 20507; (202) 663-4560. Fax, (202) 663-7004. Philip Calkins, executive director. TDD, (202) 663-4593.*

Established by the Rehabilitation Act of 1973, as amended, and cochaired by the Office of Personnel Management and the EEOC. Works for increased employment of persons with disabilities, affirmative action by the federal government, and an equitable work environment for employees with mental and physical disabilities.

Office of Personnel Management, *Diversity, 1900 E St. N.W., #2445 20415-0001; (202) 606-2817. Fax, (202) 606-0927. Armando E. Rodriguez, director.*

Develops policies, programs, and procedures to promote opportunities for qualified workers with disabilities, including veterans, to obtain and advance in federal employment. Administers the Disabled Veterans Affirmative Action Program.

President's Committee on Employment of People with Disabilities, *1331 F St. N.W., #300 20004-1107; (202) 376-6200. Fax, (202) 376-6219. John Lancaster, executive director. TDD, (202) 376-6205. Internet, http://www.pcepd.gov.*

Promotes training, rehabilitation, and employment opportunities for people with disabilities.

Rehabilitation Services Administration *(Education Dept.), 330 C St. S.W. 20202-2531; (202) 205-5482. Fax, (202) 205-9874. Fredric K. Schroeder, commissioner. TDD, (202) 205-9295.*

Coordinates and directs federal services for eligible persons with physical or mental disabilities, with emphasis on programs that promote employment opportunities. Provides vocational training and job placement; supports projects with private industry; administers grants for the establishment of supported-employment programs.

NONPROFIT

Dole Foundation for Employment of People with Disabilities, *1819 H St. N.W., #340 20006-3603; (202) 457-0318. Fax, (202) 457-0473. Paul G. Hearne, president. Main phone is voice and TDD accessible.*

Provides employers, policymakers, and the public with information about employment of people with disabilities. Awards grants to nonprofit organizations that provide job training and placement programs for people with disabilities.

Inter-National Assn. of Business, Industry, and Rehabilitation, *P.O. Box 15242 20003; (202) 543-6353.*

Fax, (202) 546-2854. Charles Harles, executive director. Internet, inabir@paltech.com or http://wwww2.paltech. com/inabir.

Membership: corporations, organized labor, government agencies, rehabilitation service organizations, and other groups that work to provide competitive employment for persons with disabilities.

Mainstream, *3 Bethesda Metro Center, #830, Bethesda, MD 20814; (301) 654-2400. Fax, (301) 654-2403. Vacant, executive director. TDD, (301) 654-2400. Internet, mainstrm@aol.com.*

Seeks to bring persons with disabilities into the work force; directs a demonstration placement program in competitive employment for persons with disabilities; provides publications, videos, and employment services; holds conferences on disability issues. Library open to the public.

NISH, *2235 Cedar Lane, Vienna, VA 22182-5200; (703) 560-6800. Fax, (703) 560-9345. Daniel W. McKinnon Jr., president. TDD, (703) 560-6512.*

Assists work centers that employ people with severe disabilities in obtaining federal contracts under the Javits-Wagner-O'Day Act; supports community rehabilitation programs employing persons with severe disabilities.

Youth

AGENCIES

Employment and Training Administration *(Labor Dept.), Job Corps, 200 Constitution Ave. N.W., #N4510 20210; (202) 219-8550. Fax, (202) 219-5183. Mary Silva, director. Toll-free, (800) 733-5627. Internet, http://www. jobcorps.org.*

Administers with the Interior Dept. a national program of comprehensive job training for disadvantaged youth at residential centers.

Employment Standards Administration *(Labor Dept.), Child Labor and Special Employment Team, 200 Constitution Ave. N.W., #S3510 20210; (202) 219-7640. Fax, (202) 219-5122. Arthur M. Kerschner Jr., team leader. Press, (202) 219-8305. TDD, (202) 219-4634.*

Administers and enforces child labor and polygraph provisions of the Fair Labor Standards Act. Administers the Work Experience and Career Exploration Program aimed at reducing the number of high school dropouts.

Forest Service *(Agriculture Dept.), Youth Conservation Corps, 1621 N. Kent St., Arlington, VA (mailing address: P.O. Box 96090, Washington, DC 20090-6090);*

(703) 235-8855. Fax, (703) 235-1597. Ransom Hughes, program manager.

Administers with the National Park Service and the Fish and Wildlife Service the Youth Conservation Corps, a summer employment and training, public works program for youths ages 15 to 18. The program is conducted in national parks, in national forests, and on national wildlife refuges.

NONPROFIT

Joint Action in Community Service, *5225 Wisconsin Ave. N.W., #404 20015-2021; (202) 537-0996. Fax, (202) 363-0239. Toll free, (800) 522-7773. Harvey Wise, executive director. Internet, http://www.jacsinc.org.*

Volunteer organization that works with the Labor Dept.'s Job Corps program for disadvantaged and at-risk youths ages 16 to 24. Provides follow-up assistance to help these youths make the transition from training to jobs.

National Alliance of Business, *1201 New York Ave. N.W., #700 20005; (202) 289-2888. Fax, (202) 289-1303. Roberts T. Jones, president. Press, (202) 289-2850. Internet, info@nab.com or http://www.nab.com.*

Represents the interests of business in developing a quality workforce. Promotes partnerships between government and business at the federal, state, and local levels. Interests include improving public education, addressing the employment and training needs of individuals in a globally competitive economy, and easing the transition from school to the workplace.

National Assn. of Service and Conservation Corps, *666 11th St. N.W., #1000 20001-4542; (202) 737-6272. Fax, (202) 737-6277. Kathleen Selz, president. Internet, nascc@nascc.org or http://www.nascc.org.*

Membership: youth corps programs. Produces publications on starting and operating youth corps. Offers technical assistance to those interested in launching programs and sponsors professional development workshops. Holds annual conference. Monitors legislation and regulations.

Work, Achievement, Values, and Education (WAVE), *501 School St. S.W., #600 20024; (202) 484-0103. Fax, (202) 488-7595. Lawrence C. Brown, president. Internet, wave4kids@aol.com.*

Public service corporation that provides high school dropouts and students at risk, ages 12 to 21, with a program of education and employment services. Provides educational institutions with training and technical assistance.

EQUAL EMPLOYMENT OPPORTUNITY

See also Civil Rights (chap. 1); Military Personnel and Veterans (chap. 15)

AGENCIES

Commission on Civil Rights, *Civil Rights Evaluation, 624 9th St. N.W. 20425; (202) 376-8582. Fax, (202) 376-8315. Frederick Isler, assistant staff director. Library, (202) 376-8110.*

Researches federal policy in areas of equal employment and job discrimination; monitors the economic status of minorities and women, including their employment and earnings. Library open to the public.

Employment Standards Administration *(Labor Dept.), Federal Contract Compliance Programs, 200 Constitution Ave. N.W., #C3325 20210; (202) 219-9475. Fax, (202) 219-6195. Shirley J. Wilcher, deputy assistant secretary.*

Monitors and enforces government contractors' compliance with federal laws and regulations on equal employment opportunities and affirmative action, including employment rights of minorities, women, persons with disabilities, and disabled and Vietnam-era veterans.

Equal Employment Opportunity Commission, *1801 L St. N.W., #10006 20507; (202) 663-4001. Fax, (202) 663-4110. Paul M. Igasaki, chair; Vacant, vice chair. Information, (202) 663-4900. Library, (202) 663-4630. TDD, (202) 663-4141. Internet, http://www.eeoc.gov.*

Works to end job discrimination by private and government employers based on race, color, religion, sex, national origin, or age. Works to protect employees against reprisal for protest of employment practices alleged to be unlawful in hiring, promotion, firing, wages, and other terms and conditions of employment. Enforces Title VII of the Civil Rights Act of 1964, as amended, which includes the Pregnancy Discrimination Act; Americans with Disabilities Act; Age Discrimination in Employment Act; Equal Pay Act; and, in the federal sector, rehabilitation laws. Receives charges of discrimination; attempts conciliation or settlement; can bring court action to force compliance; has review and appeals responsibility in the federal sector.

Equal Employment Opportunity Commission, *Program Operations, 1801 L St. N.W., #8002 20507; (202) 663-4801. Fax, (202) 663-7190. Elizabeth M. Thornton, director.*

EQUAL EMPLOYMENT CONTACTS AT FEDERAL AGENCIES

DEPARTMENTS

Agriculture, Lloyd Wright, (202) 720-5212

Commerce, Kimberly Walton, acting, (202) 482-0625

Defense, William E. Leftwich III, (703) 695-0105

  Air Force, Vacant, (703) 697-4720

  Army, Luther L. Santiful, (703) 607-1976

  Marines, Howard Mathews, (703) 614-5650

  Navy, Betty Welch, (703) 695-2248

Education, James R. White, (202) 401-3560

Energy, William L. Garrett, acting, (202) 586-2218

Health and Human Services, Marcella Haynes, (202) 619-0671

Housing and Urban Development, Raymond Solecki, acting, (202) 755-0341

Interior, E. Melodee Stith, (202) 208-5693

Justice, Ted McBurrows, (202) 616-4800

Labor, Annabelle Lockhart, (202) 219-6362

State, Deidre Davis, (202) 647-9294

Transportation, Ronald A. Stroman, (202) 366-4648

Treasury, Mariam Harvey, acting, (202) 622-1160

Veterans Affairs, Gerald K. Hinch, (202) 273-5888

AGENCIES

Commission on Civil Rights, Edward A. Hailes Jr., (202) 376-7666

Commodity Futures Trading Commission, Frank Alston, (202) 418-5011

Consumer Product Safety Commission, John W. Barrett Jr., (301) 504-0570

Corporation for National Service, Nancy Voss, (202) 606-5000, ext. 309

Environmental Protection Agency, Rafael DeLeon, acting, (202) 260-4575

Equal Employment Opportunity Commission, Cynthia C. Matthews, (202) 663-7081

Export-Import Bank, Cynthia B. Wilson, (202) 565-3590

Farm Credit Administration, Eric Howard, (703) 883-4481

Federal Communications Commission, Vacant, (202) 418-0125

Federal Deposit Insurance Corporation, JoAnn Henry, (202) 416-6925

Federal Election Commission, Patricia Brown, (202) 219-6284

Federal Emergency Management Agency, Pauline Campbell, (202) 646-4122

Federal Labor Relations Authority, Dian Jamisen, (202) 482-6640

Federal Maritime Commission, Alice Blackman, (202) 523-5806

Federal Mediation and Conciliation Service, Bill Carlisle, (202) 606-5460

Federal Reserve System, Sheila Clark, (202) 452-2883

Federal Trade Commission, Barbara B. Wiggs, (202) 326-2196

General Services Administration, James Taylor, acting, (202) 501-0767

Merit Systems Protection Board, Janice E. Fritts, (202) 653-6180

National Aeronautics and Space Administration, George E. Reese, (202) 358-2167

National Credit Union Administration, Lamont R. Gibson, (703) 518-6325

National Endowment for the Humanities, Willie McGhee, (202) 606-8233

National Labor Relations Board, Barbara Gainey, (202) 273-3891

National Science Foundation, Jean Riggs, (703) 306-1020

National Transportation Safety Board, Craig Keller, (202) 314-6210

Nuclear Regulatory Commission, Irene P. Little, (301) 415-7380

Occupational Safety and Health Review Commission, William J. Gainer, (202) 606-5390

Office of Personnel Management, Alicia O. McPhie, (202) 606-2460

Peace Corps, Mabel Dobarro, (202) 606-3324

Securities and Exchange Commission, Deborah Balducchi, (202) 942-0040

Small Business Administration, Erline M. Patrick, (202) 205-6750

Smithsonian Institution, Era Marshall, (202) 287-3508

Social Security Administration, Miguel Torrado, (410) 965-1977

U.S. Arms Control and Disarmament Agency, Robert L. Nealy, (202) 647-2010

U.S. Information Agency, Delia L. Johnson, (202) 619-5157

U.S. International Trade Commission, Jackie Waters, (202) 205-2240

U.S. Postal Service, Peter L. Garwood, (202) 268-3994

Provides guidance and technical assistance to employees who suspect discrimination and to employers who are working to comply with equal employment laws.

Justice Dept., *Civil Rights,* 601 D St. N.W., #4040 20530; (202) 514-3831. Fax, (202) 514-1105. Katherine Baldwin, chief, Employment Litigation. Library, (202) 514-4098.

Investigates, negotiates, and litigates allegations of employment discrimination by public schools, universities, state and local governments, and federally funded employers; has enforcement power. Library open to the public by appointment.

Office of Personnel Management, *Diversity,* 1900 E St. N.W., #2445 20415-0001; (202) 606-2817. Fax, (202) 606-0927. Armando E. Rodriguez, director.

Responsible for government recruiting policies and guidelines; advises and assists federal agency offices in the recruitment and employment of minorities, women, veterans, and people with disabilities. Collects and maintains statistics on the federal employment of these groups. Administers the Federal Equal Opportunity Recruitment Program and the Disabled Veterans Affirmative Action Program.

CONGRESS

House Education and the Workforce Committee, *Subcommittee on Employer-Employee Relations,* 2181 RHOB 20515; (202) 225-4527. Fax, (202) 225-9571. Harris W. Fawell, R-Ill., chair; Kevin Talley, staff director.

Jurisdiction over legislation on discrimination based on race, color, religion, sex, age, or national origin in employment where public funds are involved. Oversight of federal equal opportunity, age discrimination, and equal pay laws.

House Government Reform and Oversight Committee, *Subcommittee on Human Resources,* B372 RHOB 20515; (202) 225-2548. Fax, (202) 225-2382. Christopher Shays, R-Conn., chair; Larry Halloran, staff director. Internet, http://www.house.gov/reform.

Oversees operations of the Equal Employment Opportunity Commission and other federal agencies concerned with racial and sexual discrimination in employment.

Office of Compliance, 110 2nd St. S.E., #LA-200 20540-1999; (202) 724-9250. Fax, (202) 426-1913. Constance Miller, director, Education and Training. Information, (202) 724-9260. TDD, (202) 426-1912.

Provides general information to covered employees, applicants, and former employees of the legislative branch about their equal employment rights and protections under the Congressional Accountability Act of 1995.

Senate Governmental Affairs Committee, SD-340 20510; (202) 224-4751. Fax, (202) 224-9603. Fred Thompson, R-Tenn., chair; Hannah Sistare, staff director. Internet, http://www.senate.gov/committee/governmental_affairs.html.

Jurisdiction over legislation on discrimination based on race, color, religion, sex, age, or national origin in employment where federal employees are involved.

Senate Labor and Human Resources Committee, *Subcommittee on Employment and Training,* SH-608 20510; (202) 224-2962. Mike DeWine, R-Ohio, chair; Duane Sattler, staff director. Internet, http://www.senate.gov/~labor.

Jurisdiction over legislation on discrimination based on race, color, religion, sex, age, or national origin in employment except where federal employees are involved. Oversight of federal equal pay laws and of federal agencies concerned with racial and sexual discrimination in employment. Oversees operation of the Equal Employment Opportunity Commission.

NONPROFIT

Center for Equal Opportunity, 815 15th St. N.W., #928 20005; (202) 639-0803. Fax, (202) 639-0827. Linda Chavez, president. Internet, comment@ceousa.org or http://www.ceousa.org.

Research organization concerned with issues of race, ethnicity, and assimilation; opposes racial preferences in employment and education. Monitors legislation and regulations.

Equal Employment Advisory Council, 1015 15th St. N.W., #1200 20005; (202) 789-8650. Fax, (202) 789-2291. Jeffrey A. Norris, president. TDD, (202) 789-8645. Internet, http://www.eeac.org.

Membership: principal equal employment officers and lawyers. Files amicus curiae (friend of the court) briefs; conducts research and provides information on equal employment law and policy. Monitors legislation and regulations.

NAACP Legal Defense and Educational Fund, 1275 K St. N.W., #301 20005; (202) 682-1300. Fax, (202) 682-1312. Vacant, director, Washington Office.

Civil rights litigation group that provides legal information about civil rights legislation and advice on employment discrimination against women and minorities; monitors federal enforcement of equal opportunity rights laws. Not affiliated with the National Association for the Advancement of Colored People (NAACP). (Headquarters in New York.)

National Assn. of Manufacturers, *Employment Policy, 1331 Pennsylvania Ave. N.W., 6th Floor 20004-1790; (202) 637-3133. Fax, (202) 637-3182. Sandy Boyd, director.*

Monitors Equal Employment Opportunity Commission and Office of Federal Contract Compliance programs. Studies equal employment regulations, human resources, equal rights issues, comparable worth, pregnancy disability, privacy issues, and employment and training.

National Committee on Pay Equity, *1126 16th St. N.W., #411 20036; (202) 331-7343. Fax, (202) 331-7406. Susan Bianchi-Sand, executive director. Internet, fairpay@aol.com or http://feminist.com/fairpay.htm.*

Coalition of labor, women's, and civil rights groups. Works to eliminate wage discrimination based on race and sex and to achieve equitable pay for all workers. Acts as an information clearinghouse and provides technical assistance on pay equity matters.

See also American Institutes for Research (p. 617); Lawyers' Committee for Civil Rights Under Law (p. 29); Society for Human Resource Management (p. 214); U.S. Chamber of Commerce, Domestic Policy (p. 214)

Minorities

AGENCIES

Bureau of Indian Affairs *(Interior Dept.),* **Economic Development,** *1849 C St. N.W. #4660 20240; (202) 208-5324. Fax, (202) 208-3664. Nancy Jemison, director.*

Develops policies and programs to promote the achievement of economic goals for members of federally recognized tribes who live on or near reservations. Provides job training; assists those who have completed job training programs in finding employment; provides loans and loan guarantees; enhances contracting opportunities for individuals and tribes.

Employment and Training Administration *(Labor Dept.),* **Indian and Native American Programs,** *200 Constitution Ave. N.W., #N4645 20210; (202) 219-8502. Fax, (202) 219-6338. Thomas M. Dowd, chief. Internet, dowdt@doleta.gov.*

Administers grants for training and employment-related programs to promote employment opportunity; provides unemployed, underemployed, or economically disadvantaged Native Americans and Alaskan and

Hawaiian natives with funds for training, job placement, and support services.

NONPROFIT

Coalition of Black Trade Unionists, *1625 L St. N.W. (mailing address: P.O. Box 66268, Washington, DC 20035); (202) 429-1203. Fax, (202) 429-1102. Wil Duncan, executive director.*

Monitors legislation affecting African American and other minority trade unionists. Focuses efforts on equal employment opportunity, unemployment, and voter education and registration.

Labor Council for Latin American Advancement, *888 16th St. N.W., #5330 20006; (202) 347-4223. Fax, (202) 347-5095. Oscar Sanchez, executive director. Internet, http://www.lclaa.org.*

Membership: Hispanic trade unionists. Encourages equal employment opportunity, voter registration and education, and participation in the political process. (Affiliated with the AFL-CIO.)

Mexican American Legal Defense and Educational Fund, *1518 K St. N.W., #410 20005; (202) 628-4074. Fax, (202) 393-4206. Georgina Verdugo, regional counsel, Washington Office. Internet, http://www.maldef.org.*

Provides Mexican-Americans and other Hispanics involved in class-action employment discrimination suits or complaints with legal assistance. Monitors legislation and regulations. (Headquarters in Los Angeles.)

National Assn. for the Advancement of Colored People (NAACP), *1025 Vermont Ave. N.W., #1120 20005; (202) 638-2269. Fax, (202) 638-5936. Hilary Shelton, deputy director. Internet, http://www.naacp.org.*

Membership: persons interested in civil rights for all minorities. Advises individuals with employment discrimination complaints. Seeks to eliminate job discrimination and to bring about full employment for all Americans through legislation and litigation. (Headquarters in Baltimore.)

National Assn. of Negro Business and Professional Women's Clubs, *1806 New Hampshire Ave., N.W. 20009; (202) 483-4206. Fax, (202) 462-7253. Julianne Malveaux, president. Internet, http://www.afrika.com/nanbpwc.*

Promotes opportunities for African American women in business; sponsors workshops; maintains a job bank. Monitors legislation and regulations.

National Council of La Raza, *1111 19th St. N.W., #1000 20036; (202) 785-1670. Fax, (202) 776-1792. Raul Yzaguirre, president. Internet, http://www.nclr.org.*

Provides research, policy analysis, and advocacy on Hispanic employment status and programs; provides Hispanic community-based groups with technical assistance to help develop effective employment programs with strong educational components. Works to promote understanding of Hispanic employment needs in the private sector. Interests include women in the workplace, affirmative action, equal opportunity employment, and youth employment. Monitors federal employment legislation and regulations.

National Urban League, *1111 14th St. N.W., #1001 20005-5603; (202) 898-1604. Fax, (202) 408-1965. Robert McAlpine, director, Policy and Government Relations. Internet, http://www.nul.org.*

Federation of affiliates concerned with the social welfare of African Americans and other minorities. Testifies before congressional committees and federal agencies on equal employment; studies and evaluates federal enforcement of equal employment laws and regulations. (Headquarters in New York.)

Women

AGENCIES

Agriculture Dept., *Women's Executive Leadership Program, 1400 Wilson Blvd., #1200, Arlington, VA 22209; (703) 807-0313. Fax, (703) 235-1411. Debra Eddington, director.*

Trains federally employed men and women with managerial potential for executive positions in the government. The program is geared toward GS-11 and GS-12 employees.

Labor Dept., *Women's Bureau, 200 Constitution Ave. N.W., #S3002 20210; (202) 219-6611. Fax, (202) 219-5529. Ida L. Castro, director designate. Information, (202) 219-6652. Internet, http://www.dol.gov/dol/wb/welcome.html.*

Monitors women's employment issues. Promotes employment opportunities for women; sponsors workshops, job fairs, symposia, demonstrations, and pilot projects. Offers technical assistance; conducts research and provides publications on issues that affect working women; represents working women in international forums.

Office of Personnel Management, *Federal Women's Program, 1900 E St. N.W. 20415; (202) 606-2817. Fax, (202) 606-0927. Armando E. Rodriguez, director.*

Promotes opportunities for women to obtain and advance in federal employment; assists federal agencies in the recruitment and employment of women. Collects and maintains statistics on women's employment.

NONPROFIT

Business and Professional Women U.S.A., *2012 Massachusetts Ave. N.W. 20036; (202) 293-1100. Fax, (202) 861-0298. Candace Butler, president.*

Seeks to improve the status of working women through education, legislative action, and local projects. Sponsors Business and Professional Women's Foundation, which awards grants and loans, based on need, to mature women reentering the work force or entering nontraditional fields. Sponsors publication of issues affecting working women. Library open to the public.

Federally Employed Women, *1400 Eye St. N.W., #425 20005; (202) 898-0994. Fax, (202) 898-0998. Alma Esparza, executive director. Internet, http://www.few.org.*

Membership: women and men who work for the federal government. Works to eliminate sex discrimination in government employment and to increase job opportunities for women; offers training program. Monitors legislation and regulations.

Federation of Organizations for Professional Women, *1825 Eye St. N.W., #400 20006; (202) 328-1415. Fax, (202) 429-9574. Viola Young-Horvath, executive director.*

Membership: women's organizations, women's caucuses and committees in professional associations, and people interested in equal educational and employment opportunities for women. Monitors federal programs affecting women; organizes workshops to exchange information; publishes directory of women's organizations nationwide; maintains professional women's legal fund.

Institute for Women's Policy Research, *1400 20th St. N.W., #104 20036; (202) 785-5100. Fax, (202) 833-4362. Heidi I. Hartmann, director. Internet, http://www.iwpr.org.*

Public policy research organization that focuses on women's issues, including welfare reform, family and work policies, employment and wages, and discrimination based on gender, race, or ethnicity.

National Women's Law Center, *11 Dupont Circle N.W., #800 20036; (202) 588-5180. Fax, (202) 588-5185. Marcia Greenberger and Nancy D. Campbell, co-presidents.*

Works to expand and protect women's legal rights through advocacy and public education.

Wider Opportunities for Women, *815 15th St. N.W., #916 20005; (202) 638-3143. Fax, (202) 638-4885. Lina Frescas Dobbs, executive director.*

Promotes equal employment opportunities for women through equal access to jobs and training, equal incomes, and an equitable workplace. Conducts nontraditional skills training programs; monitors public policy relating to jobs, affirmative action, vocational education, training opportunities, and welfare reform.

Women in Community Service, *1900 N. Beauregard St., #103, Alexandria, VA 22311; (703) 671-0500. Fax, (703) 671-4489. Ruth C. Herman, executive director. Toll-free, (800) 442-9427. Internet, wicsnatl@aol.com or http://www.wics.org.*

Seeks to reduce the number of women living in poverty by promoting self-reliance and economic independence. Interests include job training and welfare reform. Holds contract with Labor Dept. for outreach, support service, and job placement for the Job Corps. Sponsors the Lifeskills Program to assist at-risk women in such areas as job training and money management.

Women Work!, *1625 K St. N.W., #300 20006; (202) 467-6346. Fax, (202) 467-5366. Jill Miller and Rubie Coles, co-executive directors. Toll-free, (800) 235-2732. Internet, womenwork@worldnet.att.net or http://www. womenwork.org.*

Fosters the development of programs and services for former homemakers reentering the job market and provides information about public policy issues that affect displaced homemakers and single parents. Refers individuals to local services. Monitors legislation.

See also Assn. for Women in Science (p. 8); Business and Professional Women's Foundation (p. 177); Women's Legal Defense Fund (p. 10)

▨ LABOR-MANAGEMENT RELATIONS

See also Civil Service (chap. 10); Postal Service (chap. 10); and specific industries within each chapter

AGENCIES

Bureau of Labor Statistics *(Labor Dept.), Compensation and Working Conditions, 2 Massachusetts Ave. N.E. 20212-0001; (202) 606-6300. Fax, (202) 606-6310. Kathleen MacDonald, associate commissioner. Internet, labstathelpdesk@bls.gov or http://www.bls.gov.*

Provides data on collective bargaining agreements, wage structures, industrial relations, and work stoppages. Compiles data for *Employment Cost Index*, published quarterly.

Employment Standards Administration *(Labor Dept.), Labor-Management Standards, 200 Constitution Ave. N.W., #N5605 20210; (202) 219-6045. Fax, (202) 219-6459. John Kotch, director. Internet, http:// gatekeeper.dol.gov/dol/esa/public/olms_org.htm.*

Administers and enforces the Labor-Management Reporting and Disclosure Act of 1959 (Landrum-Griffin Act), which guarantees union members certain rights; sets rules for electing union officers, handling union funds, and using trusteeships; requires unions to file annual financial reports with the Labor Dept.

Federal Mediation and Conciliation Service, *2100 K St. N.W. 20427; (202) 606-8100. Fax, (202) 606-4251. John Calhoun Wells, director; Vella M. Traynham, deputy director. Information, (202) 606-8080. Internet, http://www.fmcs.gov.*

Assists labor and management representatives in resolving disputes in collective bargaining contract negotiation through voluntary mediation and arbitration services; awards competitive grants to joint labor-management committees; trains other federal agencies in mediating administrative disputes under the Administrative Dispute Resolution Act of 1990 and the Negotiated Rulemaking Act of 1990; provides training to unions and management in cooperative processes to improve long-term relationship.

Justice Dept., *Organized Crime and Racketeering, 1001 G St. N.W., #300 20530; (202) 514-3666. Fax, (202) 514-9837. Gerald A. Toner, assistant chief, Labor-Management Racketeering.*

Reviews and advises on prosecutions of criminal violations involving labor-management relations and internal affairs of labor unions.

National Labor Relations Board, *1099 14th St. N.W. 20570-0001; (202) 273-1790. Fax, (202) 273-4276. William B. Gould IV, chair; John J. Toner, executive secretary, (202) 273-1940. Information, (202) 273-1991. Library, (202) 273-3720. Locator, (202) 273-1000. Internet, http://www.nlrb.gov.*

Works to prevent and remedy unfair labor practices by employers and labor unions; conducts elections among employees to determine whether they wish to be represented by a labor union for collective bargaining purposes. Library open to the public.

National Mediation Board, *1301 K St. N.W., #250E 20572; (202) 523-5920. Fax, (202) 523-2179. Kenneth B. Hipp, chair; Stephen E. Crable, chief of staff, (202) 523-5012. Information, (202) 523-5335. TDD, (202) 523-8560.*

Mediates labor disputes in the railroad and airline industries; determines and certifies labor representatives for those industries.

CONGRESS

House Education and the Workforce Committee,
Subcommittee on Employer-Employee Relations, 2181 RHOB 20515; (202) 225-4527. Fax, (202) 225-9571. Harris W. Fawell, R-Ill., chair; Kevin Talley, staff director.

Jurisdiction over legislation on labor-management issues and unfair labor practices and the National Labor Relations Act.

House Government Reform and Oversight Committee, *Subcommittee on Civil Service, B371C RHOB 20515; (202) 225-6427. Fax, (202) 225-2392. John L. Mica, R-Fla., chair; George Nesterczuk, staff director. Internet, http://www.house.gov/reform.*

Jurisdiction over legislation on federal civil service labor-management issues; oversees the Federal Labor Relations Authority.

House Government Reform and Oversight Committee, *Subcommittee on Human Resources, B372 RHOB 20515; (202) 225-2548. Fax, (202) 225-2382. Christopher Shays, R-Conn., chair; Larry Halloran, staff director. Internet, http://www.house.gov/reform.*

Oversight of the Federal Mediation and Conciliation Service, the Labor Dept., and the National Labor Relations Board.

House Government Reform and Oversight Committee, *Subcommittee on National Economic Growth, Natural Resources, and Regulatory Affairs, B377 RHOB 20515; (202) 225-4407. Fax, (202) 225-2441. David M. McIntosh, R-Ind., chair; Mildred Webber, staff director. Internet, http://www.house.gov/reform.*

Oversees operations of the National Mediation Board.

Senate Governmental Affairs Committee, *Subcommittee on International Security, Proliferation, and Federal Services, SH-442 20510; (202) 224-2254. Fax, (202) 228-3796. Thad Cochran, R-Miss., chair; Mitch Kugler, staff director. Internet, http://www.senate.gov/committee/governmental_affairs.html.*

Jurisdiction over legislation on federal civil service labor-management issues, including classification, compensation, and benefits.

Senate Labor and Human Resources Committee, *Subcommittee on Employment and Training, SH-608 20510; (202) 224-2962. Mike DeWine, R-Ohio, chair; Duane Sattler, staff director. Internet, http://www.senate.gov/~labor.*

Jurisdiction over the National Labor Relations Act and over legislation on labor-management issues and unfair labor practices. Oversight of the Labor Dept., the

AFL-CIO DIVISIONS

DEPARTMENTS

Civil Rights, Richard Womack, director; (202) 637-5270

Education, Bill Fletcher, director; (202) 637-5143

Field Mobilization, Flora Whiley, (202) 637-5190

International Affairs, Barbara Shailor, director; (202) 637-5050

Legal Dept., Jonathan Hiatt, general counsel; (202) 637-5053

Legislation, Peggy Taylor, director; (202) 637-5090

Occupational Safety and Health, Peg Seminario, director; (202) 637-5366

Organizing, Richard Bensinger, director; (202) 639-6200

Political Dept., Steve Rosenthal, director; (202) 637-5102

Public Affairs, Denise Mitchell, special assistant to the president; (202) 637-5340

Public Policy, David Smith, director; (202) 637-5172

Working Women, Karen Nussbaum, director; (202) 637-5064

TRADE AND INDUSTRIAL DEPARTMENTS

Building and Construction Trades, Robert A. Georgine, president; (202) 347-1461

Food and Allied Service Trades, Jeffrey Fiedler, president; (202) 737-7200

Industrial Union, Peter diCicco, president; (202) 842-7800

Maritime Trades, Michael Sacco, president; (202) 628-6300

Metal Trades, John Meese, president; (202) 347-7255

Professional Employees, Jack Golodner, president; (202) 638-0320

Public Employees, Al Bilik, president; (202) 393-2820

Transportation Trades, Ron Carey, president; (202) 628-9262

Union Label and Service Trades, Charles E. Mercer, president; (202) 628-2131

National Mediation Board, the Federal Mediation and Conciliation Service, and the National Labor Relations Board.

NONPROFIT

Academic Collective Bargaining Information Service, *College of Professional Studies (University of the*

District of Columbia), *4200 Connecticut Ave. N.W., MB 5200 20008; (202) 274-7001. Fax, (202) 282-3706. Isadore Goldberg, director.*

Provides employment relations service in the field of higher education. Interests include equal employment opportunity, governance and policy issues, unionization, and collective bargaining for faculty and nonfaculty units.

AFL-CIO (American Federation of Labor—Congress of Industrial Organizations), *815 16th St. N.W. 20006; (202) 637-5000. John J. Sweeney, president. Internet, http://www.aflcio.org.*

Voluntary federation of national and international labor unions in the United States. Represents members before Congress and other branches of government. Each member union conducts its own contract negotiations. Library open to the public.

American Arbitration Assn., *8201 Greensboro Dr., #610, McLean, VA 22102; (703) 760-4820. Fax, (703) 760-4847. Arnold B. Crews, regional vice president. Internet, webmaster@adr.org or http://www.adr.org.*

Provides dispute resolution services worldwide, including arbitration, mediation, minitrials, and elections. (Headquarters in New York.)

American Foreign Service Assn., *2101 E St. N.W. 20037; (202) 338-4045. Fax, (202) 338-6820. Susan Reardon, executive director. Internet, afsa@afsa.org or http://www.afsa.org.*

Membership: active and retired foreign service employees of federal agencies. Represents active duty foreign service personnel in labor-management negotiations; seeks to ensure adequate resources for foreign service operations and personnel. Monitors legislation and regulations.

Coalition of Black Trade Unionists, *1625 L St. N.W. (mailing address: P.O. Box 66268, Washington, DC 20035); (202) 429-1203. Fax, (202) 429-1102. Wil Duncan, executive director.*

Monitors legislation affecting African American and other minority trade unionists. Focuses on equal employment opportunity, unemployment, and voter education and registration.

Coalition of Labor Union Women, *1126 16th St. N.W., #104 20036; (202) 466-4610. Fax, (202) 776-0537. Gloria T. Johnson, president.*

Seeks to make unions more responsive to the needs of women in the workplace; advocates affirmative action and the active participation of women in unions. Monitors legislation and regulations.

George Meany Center for Labor Studies and the George Meany Memorial Archives, *10000 New Hampshire Ave., Silver Spring, MD 20903; (301) 431-6400. Fax, (301) 434-0371. Susan Sherman, executive director. Internet, http://www.georgemeany.org.*

Educational institute that offers classes, workshops, and an undergraduate degree program to AFL-CIO-affiliated officers, representatives, and staff. Maintains the AFL-CIO archives and the Institute for the Study of Labor Organizations.

International Brotherhood of Teamsters, *25 Louisiana Ave. N.W. 20001; (202) 624-6800. Fax, (202) 624-8102. Tom Sever, acting president. Internet, http://www.teamsters.org.*

Membership: more than 1.4 million workers in the transportation and construction industries, factories, offices, hospitals, warehouses, and other workplaces. Helps members negotiate pay, benefits, and better working conditions; conducts training programs and workshops. Monitors legislation and regulations. (Affiliated with the AFL-CIO.)

Labor Council for Latin American Advancement, *888 16th St. N.W., #5330 20006; (202) 347-4223. Fax, (202) 347-5095. Oscar Sanchez, executive director. Internet, http://www.lclaa.org.*

Membership: Hispanic trade unionists. Encourages equal employment opportunity, voter registration and education, and participation in the political process. (Affiliated with the AFL-CIO.)

Laborers' International Union of North America, *905 16th St. N.W. 20006; (202) 737-8320. Fax, (202) 737-2754. Arthur A. Coia, president. Internet, http://www.laborers.org or http://www.liuna.org.*

Membership: approximately 750,000 construction workers; federal, state, and local government employees; health care professionals; mail handlers; custodial service personnel; shipbuilders; and hazardous waste handlers. Helps members negotiate pay, benefits, and better working conditions; conducts training programs and workshops. Monitors legislation and regulations. (Affiliated with the AFL-CIO.)

National Assn. of Manufacturers, *Human Resource Policy, 1331 Pennsylvania Ave. N.W., #600N 20004; (202) 637-3131. Fax, (202) 637-3182. Patrick Cleary, vice president.*

Provides information on corporate industrial relations, including collective bargaining, labor standards, international labor relations, productivity, employee benefits, health care, and other current labor issues; monitors legislation and regulations.

National Right to Work Committee, *8001 Braddock Rd., Springfield, VA 22160; (703) 321-9820. Fax, (703) 321-7342. Reed E. Larson, president. Toll-free, (800) 325-7892.*

Citizens' organization opposed to compulsory union membership. Supports right-to-work legislation.

National Right to Work Legal Defense Foundation, *8001 Braddock Rd., Springfield, VA 22160; (703) 321-8510. Fax, (703) 321-9319. Rex H. Reed, executive vice president. Internet, info@nrtw.org or http://www.nrtw.org.*

Provides free legal aid for employees in cases of compulsory union membership abuses.

Office and Professional Employees International Union, *1660 L St. N.W., #801 20036; (202) 393-4464. Fax, (202) 347-0649. Michael Goodwin, president. Internet, http://www.opeiu.org.*

Membership: 130,000 workers, including computer analysts, programmers, and data entry operators; copywriters; nurses and other health care personnel; attorneys; law enforcement officers and security guarts; accountants; secretaries; bank employees; and insurance workers and agents. Helps members negotiate pay, benefits, and better working conditions; conducts training program and workshops. Monitors legislation and regulations. (Headquarters in New York; affiliated with the AFL-CIO and the Canadian Labour Congress.)

Public Service Research Council, *527 Maple Ave. East, 3rd Floor, Vienna, VA 22180; (703) 242-3575. Fax, (703) 242-3579. David Y. Denholm, president.*

Independent, nonpartisan research and educational organization. Opposes collective bargaining, strikes, and binding arbitration in the public sector. Sponsors conferences and seminars. Library open to the public by appointment.

Service Employees International Union, *1313 L St. N.W. 20005; (202) 898-3200. Fax, (202) 898-3402. Andrew L. Stern, president. Internet, http://www.seiu.org.*

Membership: more than one million service providers, including teachers; nurses, doctors, and other health care professionals; school bus drivers; janitors; and others. Helps members negotiate pay, benefits, and better working conditions; conducts training programs and workshops. Monitors legislation and regulations. (Affiliated with the AFL-CIO.)

United Auto Workers, *1757 N St. N.W. 20036; (202) 828-8500. Fax, (202) 293-3457. Steven P. Yokich, president. Toll-free, (800) 243-8829; in Canada, (800) 387-0538. Internet, FAQs@www.uaw.org or http://www.uaw.org.*

Membership: approximately 775,000 active and 500,000 retired North America workers in aerospace, automotive, defense, manufacturing, steel, technical, and other industries. Assists members with contract negotiation and grievances; conducts training programs and workshops. Monitors legislation and regulations. (Headquarters in Detroit; affiliated with the AFL-CIO.)

United Steelworkers of America, *1150 17th St. N.W., #300 20036; (202) 778-4384. Fax, (202) 293-5308. William Klinefelter, legislative director. Toll-free, (800) 248-8792. Internet, http://www.uswa.org.*

Membership: more than 700,000 steelworkers in the United States and Canada. Helps members negotiate pay, benefits, and better working conditions; conducts training programs and workshops. Monitors legislation and regulations. (Headquarters in Pittsburgh; affiliated with the AFL-CIO.)

U.S. Chamber of Commerce, *Economic Policy, 1615 H St. N.W. 20062-2000; (202) 463-5500. Fax, (202) 463-3188. Vacant, vice president. Press, (202) 463-5682. Internet, http://www.uschamber.org.*

Monitors legislation and regulations affecting labor-management relations.

 # PENSIONS AND BENEFITS

See also Civil Service (chap. 10); Insurance (chap. 5); Social Security (chap. 18)

AGENCIES

Advisory Council on Employee Welfare and Pension Benefit Plans (ERISA Advisory Council) *(Labor Dept.), 200 Constitution Ave. N.W., #N5677 20210; (202) 219-8753. Fax, (202) 219-6531. Sharon Morrissey, executive secretary. Information, (202) 219-8776.*

Advises and makes recommendations to the secretary of labor under the Employee Retirement Income Security Act of 1974 (ERISA).

Bureau of Labor Statistics *(Labor Dept.), Compensation and Working Conditions, 2 Massachusetts Ave. N.E. 20212; (202) 606-6300. Fax, (202) 606-6310. Kathleen MacDonald, associate commissioner. Internet, labstathelpdesk@bls.gov or http://www.bls.gov.*

Provides data on pensions and related work benefits.

Federal Retirement Thrift Investment Board, *1250 H St. N.W., #400 20005; (202) 942-1600. Fax, (202) 942-1676. Roger W. Mehle, executive director.*

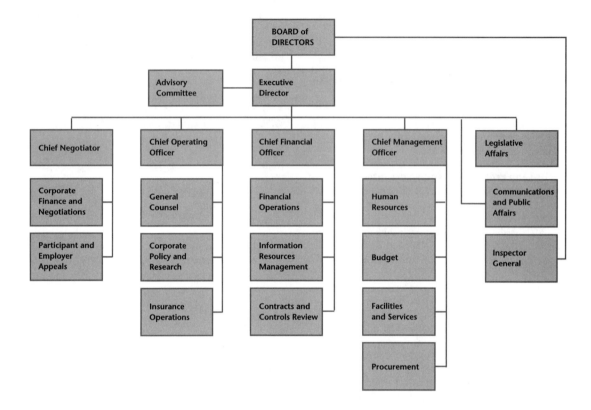

Administers the Thrift Savings Plan, a tax-deferred, defined contribution plan that permits federal employees to save for additional retirement security under a program similar to private 401(k) plans.

Internal Revenue Service *(Treasury Dept.), Employee Plans and Exempt Organizations,* 1111 Constitution Ave. N.W., #1311 20224; (202) 622-6720. Fax, (202) 622-6873. Evelyn Petschek, assistant commissioner.

Administers tax aspects of private and self-employed pension plans; determines tax-exempt status; enforces related regulations and minimum standards for funding participation and beneficiary rights under the Employee Retirement Income Security Act of 1974 (ERISA).

Joint Board for the Enrollment of Actuaries, c/o Treasury Dept. 20220; (202) 401-4091. Fax, (202) 401-6657. Robert I. Brauer, executive director.

Joint board, with members from the departments of Labor and Treasury and the Pension Benefit Guaranty Corp., established under the Employee Retirement Income Security Act of 1974 (ERISA). Promulgates regu-

lations for the enrollment of pension actuaries; examines applicants and grants certificates of enrollment; disciplines enrolled actuaries who have engaged in misconduct in the discharge of duties under ERISA.

Justice Dept., *Organized Crime and Racketeering,* 1001 G St. N.W., #300 20530; (202) 514-3666. Fax, (202) 514-9837. Gerald A. Toner, assistant chief, Labor-Management Racketeering.

Reviews and advises on prosecutions of criminal violations concerning the operation of employee benefit plans in the private sector.

Office of Personnel Management, *Retirement Information,* 1900 E St. N.W. 20415-0001; (202) 606-0500. Fax, (202) 606-0144. Gary M. Jacobs, chief. TDD, (202) 606-0551.

Provides civil servants with information and assistance on federal retirement payments.

Pension and Welfare Benefits Administration *(Labor Dept.),* 200 Constitution Ave. N.W., #S2524 20210;

(202) 219-8233. Fax, (202) 219-5526. Olena Berg, assistant secretary. Information, (202) 219-8921. Internet, http://www.dol.gov.

Administers, regulates, and enforces private employee benefit plan standards established by the Employee Retirement Income Security Act of 1974 (ERISA), with particular emphasis on fiduciary obligations; receives and maintains required reports from employee benefit plan administrators pursuant to ERISA.

Pension Benefit Guaranty Corp., *1200 K St. N.W. 20005-4026; (202) 326-4010. Fax, (202) 326-4016. David Strauss, executive director; Nell Hennessy, deputy executive director. Information, (202) 326-4000. Locator, (202) 326-4110.*

Self-financed U.S. government corporation. Insures private-sector, defined-benefit pension plans; guarantees payment of retirement benefits subject to certain limitations established in the Employee Retirement Income Security Act of 1974 (ERISA). Provides insolvent multiemployer pension plans with financial assistance to enable them to pay guaranteed retirement benefits.

See also Railroad Retirement Board (p. 681)

CONGRESS

General Accounting Office, *Health, Education, and Human Services,* 441 G St. N.W. 20548; (202) 512-6806. Fax, (202) 512-5806. Richard L. Hembra, assistant comptroller general.

Independent, nonpartisan agency in the legislative branch. Audits, analyzes, and evaluates federal agency and private sector pension programs; makes reports available to the public.

House Education and the Workforce Committee, *Subcommittee on Employer-Employee Relations,* 2181 RHOB 20515; (202) 225-4527. Fax, (202) 225-9571. Harris W. Fawell, R-Ill., chair; Kevin Talley, staff director.

Jurisdiction over pension plan, fringe benefit, and retirement income security legislation, including the Employee Retirement Income Security Act of 1974 (ERISA) and the Labor Management Reporting and Disclosure Act.

House Ways and Means Committee, *1102 LHOB 20515; (202) 225-3625. Bill Archer, R-Texas, chair; Peter Singleton, chief of staff. Internet, http://www.house.gov/ ways_means.*

Jurisdiction over legislation related to taxation of pension contributions.

House Ways and Means Committee, *Subcommittee on Oversight,* 1136 LHOB 20515; (202) 225-7601. Fax,

(202) 225-9680. Nancy L. Johnson, R-Conn., chair; William McKenney, staff director. Internet, http://www. house.gov/ways_means.

Oversees the Pension Benefit Guaranty Corp.

Senate Finance Committee, *SD-219 20510; (202) 224-4515. Fax, (202) 224-5920. William V. Roth Jr., R-Del., chair; Lindy L. Paull, staff director. Internet, http://www. senate.gov/~finance.*

Jurisdiction over legislation related to taxation of pension contributions.

Senate Finance Committee, *Subcommittee on Taxation and IRS Oversight,* SD-219 20510; (202) 224-4515. Don Nickles, R-Okla., chair; Mark Prater, staff contact. Internet, http://www.senate.gov/~finance.

Holds hearings on pension reform legislation; investigates private and self-employed pension plan problems. Oversees the Pension Benefit Guaranty Corp.

Senate Governmental Affairs Committee, *Permanent Subcommittee on Investigations,* SH-432 20510; (202) 224-3721. Fax, (202) 224-7042. Susan Collins, R-Maine, chair; Tim Shea, chief of staff. Internet, http://www. senate.gov/~gov_affairs/psi.htm.

Investigates labor racketeering, including pension and health and welfare fund frauds.

Senate Labor and Human Resources Committee, *Subcommittee on Employment and Training,* SH-608 20510; (202) 224-2962. Mike DeWine, R-Ohio, chair; Duane Sattler, staff director. Internet, http://www. senate.gov/~labor.

Jurisdiction over pension plan and retirement income security legislation and over the Labor-Management Reporting and Disclosure Act.

Senate Special Committee on Aging, *SD-G31 20510; (202) 224-5364. Fax, (202) 224-8660. Charles E. Grassley, R-Iowa, chair; Ted Totman, staff director.*

Studies and makes recommendations on private and self-employed pension plan legislation and mandatory retirement.

NONPROFIT

American Academy of Actuaries, *1100 17th St. N.W., 7th Floor 20036; (202) 223-8196. Fax, (202) 872-1948. Wilson W. Wyatt Jr., executive director. Internet, http:// www.actuary.org.*

Membership: professional actuaries practicing in areas of life, health, liability, property, and casualty insurance; pensions; government insurance plans; and general consulting. Provides information on actuarial matters, including insurance and pensions; develops professional standards; advises public policymakers.

American Assn. of Retired Persons, *601 E St. N.W. 20049; (202) 434-2277. Fax, (202) 434-2320. Horace B. Deets, executive director. Press, (202) 434-2560. Library, (202) 434-6240. TDD, (202) 434-6554. Internet, http:// www.aarp.org.*

Researches and testifies on private, federal, and other government employee pension legislation and regulations; conducts seminars; provides information on preretirement preparation. Library open to the public.

American Society of Pension Actuaries, *4350 N. Fairfax Dr., #820, Arlington, VA 22203-1619; (703) 516-9300. Fax, (703) 516-9308. Brian Graff, executive director. Internet, aspa@erols.com or http://www.aspa.org.*

Membership: professional pension plan actuaries, administrators, consultants, and other benefits professionals. Sponsors educational programs to prepare actuaries and consultants for professional exams. Monitors legislation.

Assn. of Private Pension and Welfare Plans, *1212 New York Ave. N.W., #1250 20005; (202) 289-6700. Fax, (202) 289-4582. James A. Klein, executive director. Internet, appwp@aol.com or http://www.appwp.org/appwp.*

Membership: employers, consultants, banks, and service organizations. Informs members of private pension benefits and compensation.

Center for Economic Organizing, *1522 K St. N.W., #406 20005; (202) 775-9072. Fax, (202) 775-9074. Randy Barber, director.*

Research, consulting, and training organization. Interests include the investment and control of pension funds and the role of unions and the private sector in administering these funds.

Employee Benefit Research Institute, *2121 K St. N.W., #600 20037-1896; (202) 659-0670. Fax, (202) 775-6312. Dallas L. Salisbury, president; Jack Vanderhei, research associate. Internet, http://www.ebri.org.*

Researches proposed policy changes on employee benefits. Sponsors studies on retirement income and on health, work, family, and other benefits.

Employers Council on Flexible Compensation, *927 15th St. N.W., #1000 20005; (202) 659-4300. Fax, (202) 371-1467. Kenneth E. Feltman, executive director. Internet, http://www.ecfc.org.*

Represents employers who have or are considering flexible compensation plans. Supports the preservation and expansion of employee choice in savings and pension plans. Monitors legislation and regulations.

ERISA Industry Committee, *1400 L St. N.W., #350 20005; (202) 789-1400. Fax, (202) 789-1120. Mark J.*

Ugoretz, president. Internet, eric@eric.org or http://www. eric.org.

Membership: major U.S. employers. Advocates members' positions on employee retirement, health care coverage, and welfare benefit plans; promotes flexibility and cost-effectiveness in employee benefits. Monitors legislation and regulations.

National Assn. of Manufacturers, *Employee Benefits and Compensation Committee, 1331 Pennsylvania Ave. N.W., #600 20004-1790; (202) 637-3137. Fax, (202) 637-3182. Stephen Elkins, senior associate director.*

Advises members on development of and changes in the Employee Retirement Income Security Act of 1974 (ERISA), with emphasis on employee benefits, tax policy, and single- and multiemployer pension plans. Studies the Social Security system to ensure that its long-term status remains compatible with private sector retirement plans.

National Employee Benefits Institute, *1101 Connecticut Ave. N.W., #1000 20036; (202) 737-9656. Fax, (202) 393-0796. Carlos Maxwell, director, Governmental Affairs. Toll-free, (800) 558-7258.*

Membership: large self-insured companies interested in employee benefits. Provides a forum for members and serves as a clearinghouse for information on employee benefits. Monitors legislation and regulations.

Pension Rights Center, *918 16th St. N.W., #704 20006-2902; (202) 296-3776. Fax, (202) 833-2472. Karen W. Ferguson, director. Internet, pnsn@aol.com.*

Works to preserve and expand pension rights; provides information and technical assistance on pensions.

Retirement Policy Institute, *2158 Florida Ave. N.W. 20008; (202) 483-3140. A. Haeworth Robertson, president.*

Researches and educates the public about retirement policy issues. Interests include trends, pension reform, Social Security, and policy alternatives.

Society of Professional Benefit Administrators, *2 Wisconsin Circle, #670, Chevy Chase, MD 20815-7003; (301) 718-7722. Fax, (301) 718-9440. Frederick D. Hunt Jr., president.*

Membership: independent third-party administration firms that manage outside claims and benefit plans for client employers. Monitors government compliance requirements. Interests include pensions and retirement policy and funding, health coverage, and the Employee Retirement Income Security Act of 1974 (ERISA).

United Mine Workers of America Health and Retirement Funds, *4455 Connecticut Ave. N.W. 20008; (202) 895-3700. Fax, (202) 895-3703. Russell U. Crosby, executive director.*

Labor/management trust fund that provides health and retirement benefits to coal miners. Health benefits are provided to pensioners, their dependents, and, in some cases, their survivors.

Women's Institute for Secure Retirement (WISER), *1201 Pennsylvania Ave. N.W., #619 20004; (202) 393-5452. Fax, (202) 638-1336. Cindy Hounsell, executive director. Internet, wiserwomen@aol.com.*

Provides information on women's retirement issues; conducts workshops and seminars. Monitors legislation and regulations.

See also National Council of Senior Citizens (p. 8) and National Council on the Aging (p. 223)

▨ WORKPLACE SAFETY AND HEALTH

See also Coal (chap. 8)

AGENCIES

Bureau of Labor Statistics *(Labor Dept.),* **Compensation and Working Conditions,** *2 Massachusetts Ave. N.E. 20212; (202) 606-6300. Fax, (202) 606-6310. Kathleen MacDonald, associate commissioner. Internet, labstathelpdesk@bls.gov or http://www.bls.gov.*

Compiles data on occupational safety and health.

Energy Dept., *Worker Health and Safety,* *20300 Century Blvd., Germantown, MD (mailing address: 19901 Germantown Rd. EH5 270CC, Germantown, MD 20874); (301) 903-5532. Fax, (301) 903-3189. Joseph E. Fitzgerald Jr., deputy assistant secretary.*

Develops policy and establishes standards to ensure safety and health protection in all department activities.

Federal Mine Safety and Health Review Commission, *1730 K St. N.W., #600 20006; (202) 653-5660. Fax, (202) 653-5030. Mary Lu Jordan, chair; Richard L. Baker, executive director, (202) 653-5625. Information, (202) 653-5633.*

Independent agency established by the Federal Mine Safety and Health Act of 1977. Holds fact-finding hearings and issues orders affirming, modifying, or vacating the labor secretary's enforcement actions regarding mine safety and health. Library open to the public.

Mine Safety and Health Administration *(Labor Dept.), 4015 Wilson Blvd., #622, Arlington, VA 22203; (703) 235-1385. Fax, (703) 235-4369. J. Davitt McAteer, assistant secretary. Information, (703) 235-1452. Internet, http://www.msha.gov.*

Administers and enforces the health and safety provisions of the Federal Mine Safety and Health Act of 1977.

National Institute for Occupational Safety and Health *(Centers for Disease Control and Prevention), 200 Independence Ave. S.W. 20201; (202) 401-6997. Fax, (202) 260-4464. Dr. Linda Rosenstock, director, Washington Office. Toll-free, (800) 356-4674. Press, (202) 401-3749. Internet, pubstaft@cdc.gov or http://www.cdc.gov/niosh.*

Entity within the Centers for Disease Control and Prevention in Atlanta, Ga. Supports and conducts research on occupational safety and health issues; provides technical assistance and training; develops recommendations for the Labor Dept. Operates an occupational safety and health bibliographic database (mailing address: NIOSH Clearinghouse for Occupational Safety and Health Information, 4676 Columbia Parkway, Cincinnati, OH 45226).

Occupational Safety and Health Administration *(Labor Dept.), 200 Constitution Ave. N.W., #S2315 20210; (202) 219-7162. Fax, (202) 219-6064. Charles Jeffress, assistant secretary. Information, (202) 219-8151. Internet, http://www.osha.gov.*

Sets and enforces rules and regulations for workplace safety and health. Implements the Occupational Safety and Health Act of 1970. Provides federal agencies and private industries with compliance guidance and assistance.

Occupational Safety and Health Administration *(Labor Dept.),* **Compliance Programs,** *200 Constitution Ave. N.W., #N3468 20210; (202) 219-9308. Fax, (202) 219-9187. John B. Miles, director. Internet, http://www.osha.gov.*

Interprets compliance safety standards for agency field personnel and private employees and employers.

Occupational Safety and Health Administration *(Labor Dept.),* **Construction and Engineering,** *200 Constitution Ave. N.W., #N3306 20210; (202) 219-8644. Fax, (202) 219-6599. Russell B. Swanson, director.*

Provides technical expertise to OSHA's enforcement personnel; initiates studies to determine causes of construction accidents; works with private sector to promote construction safety.

Occupational Safety and Health Administration *(Labor Dept.),* **Federal/State Operations,** *200 Constitution Ave. N.W., #N3700 20210; (202) 219-7251. Fax, (202) 219-8783. Paula White, director.*

Makes grants to nonprofit organizations under the New Directions Grant Program to assist in providing education, training, and technical assistance to meet the

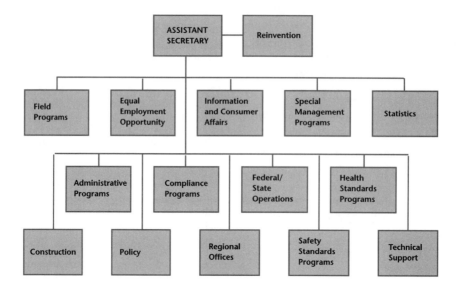

workplace safety and health needs of employers and employees; administers state enforcement and consultation programs; trains federal and private employees, OSHA and state inspectors, and state consultants.

Occupational Safety and Health Administration
(Labor Dept.), Health Standards Programs, 200 Constitution Ave. N.W., #N3718 20210; (202) 219-7075. Fax, (202) 219-7125. Adam Finkel, director. Information, (202) 219-8151.

Develops new or revised occupational health standards for toxic, hazardous, and carcinogenic substances, biological hazards, or other harmful physical agents, such as vibration, noise, and radiation.

Occupational Safety and Health Administration
(Labor Dept.), Information and Consumer Affairs, 200 Constitution Ave. N.W., #N3647 20210; (202) 219-8148. Fax, (202) 219-5986. Bonnie Friedman, director. Emergency hotline, (800) 321-OSHA. Internet, http://www. osha.gov.

Conducts public hearings on proposed workplace safety and health standards; provides information, staff assistance and support for the National Advisory Committee for Occupational Safety and Health and the Construction Advisory Committee. Advises the assistant secretary of labor for occupational safety and health on consumer affairs matters.

Occupational Safety and Health Administration
(Labor Dept.), Safety Standards, 200 Constitution Ave. N.W., #N3605 20210; (202) 219-8061. Fax, (202) 219-7477. John F. Martonik, acting director.

Develops new or revised occupational safety standards.

Occupational Safety and Health Review Commission, *1120 20th St. N.W., 9th Floor 20036-3419; (202) 606-5370. Fax, (202) 606-5050. Stuart E. Weisberg, chair; William J. Gainer, executive director, (202) 606-5380. Information, (202) 606-5398. Locator,(202) 606-5100.*

Independent executive branch agency that adjudicates disputes between private employers and the Occupational Safety and Health Administration arising under the Occupational Safety and Health Act of 1970.

CONGRESS

House Appropriations Committee, *Subcommittee on Labor, Health and Human Services, and Education, 2358 RHOB 20515; (202) 225-3508. John Edward Porter, R-Ill., chair; Tony McCann, staff director. Internet, http://www.house.gov/appropriations.*

Jurisdiction over legislation to appropriate funds for the Federal Mine Safety and Health Review Commission and the Occupational Safety and Health Review Commission.

House Education and the Workforce Committee, Subcommittee on Workforce Protections, *2181 RHOB 20515; (202) 225-4527. Fax, (202) 225-9571. Cass Ballenger, R-N.C., chair; Kevin Talley, staff director.*

Jurisdiction over legislation on workers' compensation and related wage loss; occupational safety and health; mine safety and health; youth camp safety; and migrant and agricultural labor health and safety.

House Small Business Committee, *Subcommittee on Regulatory Reform and Paperwork Reduction, B363 RHOB 20515; (202) 226-2630. Fax, (202) 225-8950. Sue W. Kelly, R-N.Y., chair; Larry McCredy, staff director. Internet, http://www.house.gov/smbiz.*

Oversees the Occupational Safety and Health Administration as it affects small business.

Senate Appropriations Committee, *Subcommittee on Labor, Health and Human Services, and Education, SD-184 20510; (202) 224-7230. Arlen Specter, R-Pa., chair; Craig A. Higgins, staff director. Internet, http://www.senate.gov/~appropriations/labor.*

Jurisdiction over legislation to appropriate funds for the Federal Mine Safety and Health Review Commission and the Occupational Safety and Health Review Commission.

Senate Labor and Human Resources Committee, Subcommittee on Public Health and Safety, *SD-422 20510; (202) 224-7139. Fax, (202) 228-5044. Bill Frist, R-Tenn., chair; Susan Ramthun, staff director. Internet, http://www.senate.gov/~labor.*

Jurisdiction over legislation on occupational safety and health, including workers' compensation and related wage loss, and on migrant and agricultural labor safety and health.

Senate Small Business Committee, *SR-428A 20510; (202) 224-5175. Fax, (202) 224-4885. Christopher S. Bond, R-Mo., chair; Louis Taylor, staff director. Internet, http://www.senate.gov/~sbc.*

Jurisdiction over the Occupational Safety and Health Administration as it affects small business.

NONPROFIT

American Industrial Health Council, *2001 Pennsylvania Ave. N.W., #760 20006; (202) 833-2131. Fax, (202) 833-2201. Gaylen M. Camera, executive director. Internet, membershipservices@aihc.org.*

Membership: chemical companies and manufacturers of pharmaceutical, petroleum, aerospace, consumer, and metal products. Monitors regulations affecting methods for assessing health risks in these industries.

American Industrial Hygiene Assn., *2700 Prosperity Ave., #250, Fairfax, VA 22031; (703) 849-8888. Fax, (703) 207-3561. O. Gordon Banks, executive director. Internet, http://www.aiha.org.*

Membership: scientists and engineers who practice industrial hygiene in government, labor, academic institutions, and independent organizations. Promotes health and safety standards in the workplace and the community; conducts research to identify potential dangers; educates workers about job-related risks; monitors safety regulations. Interests include international standards and information exchange.

Industrial Safety Equipment Assn., *1901 N. Moore St., #808, Arlington, VA 22209; (703) 525-1695. Fax, (703) 528-2148. Daniel K. Shipp, president. Internet, http://www.safetycentral.org/isea.*

Trade organization that drafts industry standards for employee personal safety and protective equipment; encourages development and use of proper equipment to deal with industrial hazards; works to influence international standards, especially in North America. Monitors legislation and regulations.

Institute for a Drug-Free Workplace, *1225 Eye St. N.W., #1000 20005; (202) 842-7400. Fax, (202) 842-0022. Mark A. de Barnardo, executive director. Internet, http://www.drugfreeworkplace.org.*

Coalition of businesses, business organizations, and individuals. Seeks to increase productivity, improve safety, and control insurance costs through detection and treatment of drug and alcohol abuse. Promotes fair and consistent implementation of drug abuse prevention programs; supports the right of employers to test for drugs. Monitors legislation and regulations.

National Assn. of Manufacturers, *Human Resources Policy, 1331 Pennsylvania Ave. N.W., #600N 20004-1790; (202) 637-3128. Fax, (202) 637-3182. Carla Sola, director.*

Conducts research, develops policy, and informs members of toxic injury compensation systems, and occupational safety and health legislation, regulations, and standards. Offers mediation service to business members.

National Safety Council, *1025 Connecticut Ave. N.W., #1200 20036; (202) 293-2270. Fax, (202) 293-0032. Jane S. Roemer, executive director, Public Policy. Internet, ehc@cais.com or http://www.nsc.org.*

Chartered by Congress. Conducts research and provides educational and informational services on occupational safety and health; promotes policies to reduce accidental deaths and injuries and preventable illnesses. Monitors legislation and regulations. (Headquarters in Itasca, Ill.)

Public Citizen, *Health Research Group, 1600 20th St. N.W. 20009; (202) 588-1000. Fax, (202) 588-7796. Dr. Sidney M. Wolfe, director. Internet, http://www.citizen.org.*

Citizens' interest group that studies and reports on occupational diseases; monitors the Occupational Safety and Health Administration and participates in OSHA enforcement proceedings.

See also National AIDS Fund (p. 388)

Workers' Compensation

AGENCIES

Bureau of Labor Statistics *(Labor Dept.), Safety, Health, and Working Conditions, 2 Massachusetts Ave. N.E., #4130 20212-0001; (202) 606-6304. Fax, (202) 606-6310. William L. Weber, acting assistant commissioner. Internet, labstathelpdesk@bls.gov.*

Compiles and publishes statistics on occupational injuries, illnesses, and fatalities.

Employment Standards Administration *(Labor Dept.), Coal Mine Workers' Compensation, 200 Constitution Ave. N.W. 20210; (202) 219-6692. Fax, (202) 219-8568. James L. DeMarce, director.*

Administers the department's black lung benefits program. Adjudicates claims, certifies benefit payments, and maintains black lung beneficiary rolls.

Employment Standards Administration *(Labor Dept.), Workers' Compensation Programs, 200 Constitution Ave. N.W., #S3524 20210; (202) 219-7503. Fax, (202) 219-4321. T. Michael Kerr, deputy assistant secretary.*

Administers three federal workers' compensation laws: the Federal Employees' Compensation Act; the Longshore and Harbor Workers' Compensation Act and extensions; and Title IV (Black Lung Benefits Act) of the Federal Coal Mine Health and Safety Act.

Labor Dept., *Benefits Review Board, 200 Constitution Ave. N.W., #N5101 20210 (mailing address: P.O. Box 37601, Washington, DC 20013-7601); (202) 565-7501. Fax, (202) 565-4137. Betty Jean Hall, chief administrative appeals judge. Internet, inquiries@brb.dol.gov.*

Reviews appeals of workers seeking benefits under the Longshore and Harbor Workers' Compensation Act and its extensions, including the District of Columbia Workers' Compensation Act, and Title IV (Black Lung Benefits Act) of the Federal Coal Mine Health and Safety Act.

Labor Dept., *Employees' Compensation Appeals Board, 200 Constition Ave. N.W., #N-2609 20210; (202) 208-1900. Fax, (202) 208-1876. Michael J. Walsh, chair.*

Reviews and determines appeals of final determinations of benefits claims made by the Office of Workers' Compensation Programs under the Federal Employees' Compensation Act.

NONPROFIT

American Insurance Assn., *1130 Connecticut Ave. N.W., #1000 20036; (202) 828-7100. Fax, (202) 293-1219. Robert E. Vagley, president. Press, (202) 828-7116. Library, (202) 828-7183.*

Membership: companies providing property and casualty insurance. Offers information on workers' compensation legislation and regulations; conducts educational activities. Library open to the public by appointment.

National Assn. of Manufacturers, *Human Resources Policy, 1331 Pennsylvania Ave. N.W., #600N 20004-1790; (202) 637-3128. Fax, (202) 637-3182. Carla Sola, director.*

Conducts research, develops policy, and informs members of workers' compensation law; provides feedback to government agencies.

8 Energy

▓ GENERAL POLICY

AGENCIES

Bureau of Land Management *(Interior Dept.), Minerals, Realty, and Resource Protection, 1849 C St. N.W., #5627 20240; (202) 208-4201. Fax, (202) 208-4800. Carson W. Culp, assistant director.*

Evaluates and classifies onshore oil, natural gas, geothermal resources, and all solid energy and mineral resources, including coal and uranium, on federal lands. Develops and administers regulations for fluid and solid mineral leasing on national lands and on the subsurface of land where fluid and solid mineral rights have been reserved for the federal government.

Economic Research Service *(Agriculture Dept.), 1800 M St. N.W. 20036; (202) 694-5000. Fax, (202) 694-5757. Susan E. Offutt, administrator. Internet, http://www.econ. ag.gov.*

Advises the Agriculture Dept. on energy-related policies and programs; coordinates energy programs and strategies for the emergency allocation of scarce fuel resources; provides the department with leadership in developing agricultural and rural components of national energy policies.

Energy Dept., *1000 Independence Ave. S.W. 20585; (202) 586-6210. Fax, (202) 586-4403. Federico F. Peña, secretary. Information, (202) 586-5575. Press, (202) 586-5806. Locator, (202) 586-5000. Internet, http://www.doe.gov.*

Decides major energy policy issues and acts as principal adviser to the president on energy matters, including trade issues, strategic reserves, and nuclear power; acts as principal spokesperson for the department.

Energy Dept., *1000 Independence Ave. S.W. 20585; (202) 586-5500. Fax, (202) 586-0148. Elizabeth Moler, deputy secretary. Press, (202) 586-5806. Internet, http://www. doe.gov.*

Manages departmental programs in energy efficiency and renewable energy, fossil energy, the Energy Information Administration, nuclear energy, civilian radioactive waste management, and the power marketing administrations.

Energy Dept., *1000 Independence Ave. S.W., #7B252 20585; (202) 586-6479. Fax, (202) 586-7210. Ernest Moniz, under secretary. Information, (202) 586-4940. Internet, http://www.doe.gov.*

Manages departmental programs in defense, environmental safety and health, and waste management (including radioactive and nuclear waste); responsible for all administration and management matters and for regulatory and information programs.

Energy Dept., *Economic Impact and Diversity, 1000 Independence Ave. S.W., #5B110 20585; (202) 586-8383. Fax, (202) 586-3075. Corlis S. Moody, director.*

Researches the effects of government energy policies on minority businesses; offers technical and financial assistance to minority businesses, educational institutions, and developmental organizations to encourage their participation in energy research, development, and conservation; acts as an information clearinghouse.

Energy Dept., *Emergency Management, 1000 Independence Ave. S.W., #GH060 20585; (202) 586-9892. Fax, (202) 586-3904. John J. Nettles Jr., director. Internet, http://www2.nn.doe.gov/nn/emerga/emerg.htm.*

Works to ensure coordinated Energy Dept. responses to energy-related emergencies. Recommends policies to mitigate the effects of energy supply crises on the United States; recommends government responses to energy emergencies.

Energy Dept., *Energy Advisory Board, 1000 Independence Ave. S.W., #8E044 20585; (202) 586-7092. Fax, (202) 586-6279. Walter Massey, chair. Internet, http://www.hr.doe.gov/seab.*

Provides the secretary with advice and long-range guidance on the department's research and development, energy, environmental, and national defense-related activities.

Energy Dept., *Nonproliferation and National Security, 1000 Independence Ave. S.W., #7A049 20585; (202) 586-0645. Fax, (202) 586-0862. Rose Gottemoeller, director. Internet, http://www.nn.doe.gov.*

Provides intelligence community with technical and analytical expertise on foreign nuclear and energy issues. Oversees programs to prevent the spread of weapons of mass destruction, to protect the U.S. nuclear deterrent, and to respond to nuclear and energy emergencies.

Energy Dept., *Policy, 1000 Independence Ave. S.W., #7C016 20585; (202) 586-5800. Fax, (202) 586-0861. Robert W. Gee, assistant secretary. Internet, http://www.doe.gov/policy.*

Serves as principal adviser to the secretary, deputy secretary, and under secretary in formulating and evaluating departmental policy. Reviews programs, budgets, regulations, and legislative proposals to ensure consistency with departmental policy.

Energy Information Administration *(Energy Dept.), 1000 Independence Ave. S.W. 20585; (202) 586-4361. Fax,*

ENERGY DEPARTMENT

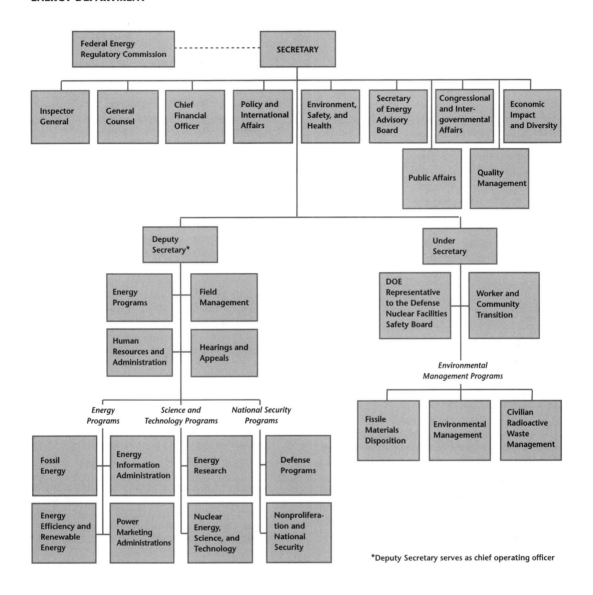

*Deputy Secretary serves as chief operating officer

(202) 586-0329. Jay Hakes, administrator. Internet, http://www.eia.doe.gov.

Collects and publishes data on all energy reserves, financial status of energy-producing companies, production, demand, consumption, and other areas; provides long- and short-term analyses of energy trends and data.

Energy Information Administration *(Energy Dept.), Energy Markets and End Use, 1000 Independence Ave.*

S.W., #2G-090 20585; (202) 586-1617. Fax, (202) 586-9753. W. Calvin Kilgore, director. Internet, infoctr@eia.doe. gov or http://www.eia.doe.gov/emeu.

Designs, develops, and maintains statistical and short-term forecasting information systems concerning consumption and other subjects that cut across energy sources. Formulates and administers financial data reporting requirements for major energy companies. Maintains survey on energy supply and use.

Energy Information Administration *(Energy Dept.),* *Integrated Analysis and Forecasting,* 1000 Independence Ave. S.W., EI-80, #2F081 20585; (202) 586-2222. Fax, (202) 586-3045. Mary J. Hutzler, director. Information, (202) 586-5000. Library, (202) 586-9534. Internet, http://www.eia.doe.gov.

Analyzes and forecasts alternative energy futures. Develops, applies, and maintains modeling systems for analyzing the interactions of demand, conversion, and supply for all energy sources and their economic and environmental impacts.

Energy Research *(Energy Dept.),* 1000 Independence Ave. S.W., #7B058 20585; (202) 586-5430. Fax, (202) 586-4120. Martha A. Krebs, director.

Advises the secretary on the department's physical science research and energy research and development programs; the use of multipurpose laboratories (except weapons laboratories); and education and training for basic and applied research activities, including fellowships for university researchers. Manages the department's high energy and nuclear physics programs and the fusion energy program. Conducts environmental and health-related research and development programs, including studies of energy-related pollutants and hazardous materials.

Environment, Safety, and Health *(Energy Dept.),* 1000 Independence Ave. S.W., #7A097 20585; (202) 586-6151. Fax, (202) 586-0956. Peter Brush, acting assistant secretary. Internet, http://www.eh.doe.gov.

Ensures that Energy Dept. programs comply with federal policies and standards designed to protect the environment and government property. Oversees health and nonnuclear safety conditions at Energy Dept. facilities.

Federal Energy Regulatory Commission *(Energy Dept.),* 888 1st St. N.E., #11A 20426; (202) 208-0000. Fax, (202) 208-0151. James J. Hoecker, chair. Information, (202) 208-0200. Press, (202) 208-1088. Dockets, (202) 208-0715. Internet, http://www.ferc.gov.

Establishes and enforces: interstate oil pipeline rates, charges, and valuations; and rates and charges for wholesale electric power transmission, sale, and interconnection. Regulates the construction and operation of interstate natural gas facilities and the interstate rates for resale and transportation of natural gas. Under the Natural Gas Wellhead Decontrol Act of 1989, all remaining commission regulation of producer sales prices for natural gas terminated on January 1, 1993. Issues licenses for nonfederal hydroelectric projects and establishes accounting rules and procedures for utilities.

Interior Dept., *Land and Minerals Management,* 1849 C St. N.W., #6628MIB 20240; (202) 208-5676. Fax, (202) 208-3144. Robert Armstrong, assistant secretary.

Directs and supervises the Bureau of Land Management, the Minerals Management Service, and the Office of Surface Mining. Supervises programs associated with land use planning, onshore and offshore minerals, surface mining reclamation and enforcement, and outer continental shelf minerals management.

National Institute of Standards and Technology *(Commerce Dept.), Technology Innovation,* Route I-270 and Quince Orchard Rd., Bldg. 820, #264, Gaithersburg, MD 20899-0001; (301) 975-5500. Fax, (301) 975-3839. George Lewett, director. Internet, innovate@enh.nist.gov.

Evaluates nonnuclear, energy-related inventions submitted by individuals and small companies and makes recommendations on their development to the Energy Dept.

Office of Management and Budget *(Executive Office of the President), Energy and Science,* New Executive Office Bldg., #8002 20503; (202) 395-3404. Fax, (202) 395-3049. Kathleen Peroff, deputy associate director.

Advises and assists the president in preparing the budget for energy programs; coordinates OMB energy policy and programs.

Office of Science and Technology Policy *(Executive Office of the President),* Old Executive Office Bldg., #424 20502; (202) 456-7116. Fax, (202) 456-6021. John H. Gibbons, director. Press, (202) 456-6018. Internet, http://www.whitehouse.gov/White_House/EOP/OSTP.

Provides the president with policy analysis on scientific and technological matters, including energy policy and technology issues; coordinates executive office and federal agency responses to these issues; evaluates the effectiveness of scientific and technological programs.

Treasury Dept., *Tax Analysis,* 1500 Pennsylvania Ave. N.W., #4217 20220; (202) 622-1782. Fax, (202) 622-2969. Geraldine Gerardi, director, Business Taxation.

Develops and provides economic analysis of business taxation policy relating to energy matters, including tax incentives for alternative energy usage and development, gasoline and automobile efficiency taxes, and tax incentives designed to encourage industrial conversion from oil to coal in industrial facilities.

See also Domestic Policy Council (p. 328)

CONGRESS

General Accounting Office, *Energy, Resources, and Science,* 441 G St. N.W., #2T23 20548; (202) 512-3841. Fax, (202) 512-6880. Victor S. Rezendes, director.

Independent, nonpartisan agency in the legislative branch that audits, analyzes, and reports on efficiency and effectiveness of federal energy and natural resource programs. Addresses government-wide science issues and the production, regulation, and consumption of all forms of energy.

House Appropriations Committee, *Subcommittee on Energy and Water Development, 2362 RHOB 20515; (202) 225-3421. Joseph M. McDade, R-Pa., chair; James Ogsbury, staff director. Internet, http://www.house.gov/ appropriations.*

Jurisdiction over legislation to appropriate funds for the Energy Dept. (except for the Economic Regulatory Administration; Energy Information Administration; strategic petroleum reserve; naval petroleum and oil shale reserves; fossil energy research and development; energy conservation; alternative fuels production; and related matters); the Nuclear Regulatory Commission, the Tennessee Valley Authority, the Federal Energy Regulatory Commission, and the federal power marketing administrations.

House Appropriations Committee, *Subcommittee on Interior, B308 RHOB 20515; (202) 225-3081. Fax, (202) 225-9069. Ralph Regula, R-Ohio, chair; Deborah A. Weatherly, clerk. Internet, http://www.house.gov/ appropriations.*

Jurisdiction over legislation to appropriate funds for the Economic Regulatory Administration; Energy Information Administration; strategic petroleum reserve and naval petroleum and oil shale reserves; clean coal technology; fossil energy research and development; energy conservation; alternate fuels production; and related matters.

House Commerce Committee, *Subcommittee on Energy and Power, 2125 RHOB 20515; (202) 225-2927. Fax, (202) 225-1919. Dan Schaefer, R-Colo., chair; James E. Derderian, staff director. Internet, http://www.house. gov/commerce.*

Jurisdiction over legislation on energy policy, regulation, conservation, exploration, production, distribution, storage, and pricing; commercialization and utilization of new technologies, including liquefied natural gas projects; and measures relating to the Energy Dept., the Federal Energy Regulatory Commission, and the regulatory function of the Economic Regulatory Administration.

House Government Reform and Oversight Committee, *Subcommittee on National Economic Growth, Natural Resources, and Regulatory Affairs, B377 RHOB 20515; (202) 225-4407. Fax, (202) 225-2441. David M. McIntosh, R-Ind., chair; Mildred Webber, staff director. Internet, http://www.house.gov/reform.*

Oversight of Energy Dept., Nuclear Regulatory Commission, and Tennessee Valley Authority.

House Resources Committee, *Subcommittee on Energy and Mineral Resources, 1626 LHOB 20515; (202) 225-9297. Fax, (202) 225-5255. Barbara Cubin, R-Wyo., chair; William Condit, staff director. Internet, http://www. house.gov/resources.*

Jurisdiction over conservation of the U.S. uranium supply, the U.S. Geological Survey (except water-related programs), mineral land laws, mining, and mineral resources on public lands.

House Resources Committee, *Subcommittee on Water and Power, 1522 LHOB 20515; (202) 225-8331. John T. Doolittle, R-Calif., chair; Robert Faber, staff director. Internet, http://www.house.gov/resources.*

Jurisdiction over water-related programs of the U.S. Geological Survey, saline water research and development, water resources research programs, and matters related to the Water Resources Planning Act.

House Science Committee, *2320 RHOB 20515; (202) 225-6371. Fax, (202) 226-0113. F. James Sensenbrenner Jr., R-Wis., chair; Todd Schultz, chief of staff. Internet, http://www.house.gov/science.*

Jurisdiction over legislation on all nonmilitary energy research and development.

House Small Business Committee, *2361 RHOB 20515; (202) 225-5821. James M. Talent, R-Mo., chair; Mark Strand, chief of staff. Internet, http://www.house. gov/smbiz.*

Studies and makes recommendations on energy allocation and marketing, and energy research and development contracts as they relate to small business.

House Ways and Means Committee, *1102 LHOB 20515; (202) 225-3625. Bill Archer, R-Texas, chair; Peter Singleton, chief of staff. Internet, http://www.house.gov/ ways_means.*

Jurisdiction over legislation on taxes, tariffs, and trade measures relating to energy.

Joint Committee on Taxation, *1015 LHOB 20515; (202) 225-3621. Fax, (202) 225-0832. Rep. Bill Archer, R-Texas, chair; Kenneth J. Kies, chief of staff. Internet, http:// www.senate.gov/committee/jct.html.*

Performs staff work for House Ways and Means and Senate Finance committees on legislation involving internal revenue, including taxation of energy producers, transporters, and consumers. Provides revenue estimates for all tax legislation.

Senate Appropriations Committee, *Subcommittee on Energy and Water Development, SD-127 20510; (202) 224-7260. Pete V. Domenici, R-N.M., chair; Alex Flint, majority clerk. Internet, http://www.senate.gov/~appropriations/energy.*

Jurisdiction over legislation to appropriate funds for the Energy Dept. (except for the Energy Regulatory Administration; Energy Information Administration; strategic petroleum reserve; fossil energy research, development, and construction; and energy conservation); the Federal Energy Regulatory Commission; the federal power marketing administrations; the Nuclear Regulatory Commission; and the Tennessee Valley Authority.

Senate Appropriations Committee, *Subcommittee on Interior, SD-131 20510; (202) 224-7233. Slade Gorton, R-Wash., chair; Bruce Evans, staff director. Internet, http://www.senate.gov/~appropriations.*

Jurisdiction over legislation to appropriate funds for the Energy Information Administration; economic regulation; strategic petroleum reserve; energy production, demonstration, and distribution; fossil energy research, development, and construction; energy conservation; civilian (nonnuclear) programs in the Energy Dept.; and related matters.

Senate Energy and Natural Resources Committee, *SD-364 20510; (202) 224-4971. Fax, (202) 224-6163. Frank H. Murkowski, R-Alaska, chair; Gregg D. Renkes, staff director. Internet, http://www.senate.gov/~energy.*

Jurisdiction over legislation on energy policy, regulation, and conservation; research and development; nonmilitary development of nuclear energy; oil and gas production and distribution (including price); energy-related aspects of deepwater ports; hydroelectric power; coal production and distribution; mining, mineral land laws, and mineral conservation; leasing and the extraction of minerals from the ocean and outer continental shelf lands; and naval petroleum reserves in Alaska. Jurisdiction over legislation on the Federal Energy Regulatory Commission. Oversees the Energy Dept., Tennessee Valley Authority, and the U.S. Geological Survey.

Senate Energy and Natural Resources Committee, *Subcommittee on Energy Research, Development, Production, and Regulation, SD-364 20510; (202) 224-6567. Fax, (202) 228-0302. Don Nickles, R-Okla., chair; David Garman, professional staff member. Internet, http://www.senate.gov/~energy.*

Jurisdiction over legislation on regulatory functions of nuclear energy; nonmilitary energy research and development; commercialization and utilization of new technologies; global climate changes; energy conservation; and liquefied natural gas projects.

Senate Finance Committee, *SD-219 20510; (202) 224-4515. Fax, (202) 224-5920. William V. Roth Jr., R-Del., chair; Lindy L. Paull, staff director. Internet, http://www.senate.gov/~finance.*

Holds hearings on legislation concerning taxes, tariffs, and trade measures relating to energy.

Senate Special Committee on Aging, *SD-G31 20510; (202) 224-5364. Fax, (202) 224-8660. Charles E. Grassley, R-Iowa, chair; Ted Totman, staff director.*

Studies and makes recommendations on the availability of energy to older people and on the adequacy of federal energy programs for the elderly.

NONPROFIT

American Assn. of Blacks in Energy, *927 15th St. N.W., #200 20005; (202) 371-9530. Fax, (202) 371-9218. Dorita M. Dixon, national project director. Internet, aabe@erols.com.*

Encourages participation of African Americans and other minorities in formulating energy policy.

American Boiler Manufacturers Assn., *950 N. Glebe Rd., Arlington, VA 22203; (703) 522-7350. Fax, (703) 522-2665. Russell N. Mosher, president. Internet, http://www.abma.com.*

Membership: manufacturers of boiler systems and boiler-related products, including fuel-burning systems. Interests include energy and environmental issues.

Consumer Energy Council of America Research Foundation, *2000 L St. N.W., #802 20036-4907; (202) 659-0404. Fax, (202) 659-0407. Ellen Berman, president. Internet, http://www.cecarf.org.*

Analyzes economic and social effects of energy policies; develops long-range conservation and load-management strategies for utilities; designs pilot programs for and conducts research on conservation initiatives. Builds consensus among public- and private-sector organizations, state and local groups, businesses, utilities, consumers, environmentalists, government agencies, and others on energy policy issues. Interests include transportation policies, transmission siting and certification, air pollution emissions trading, oil overcharge funds, and appliance rebate programs.

Federal Energy Bar Assn., *1350 Connecticut Ave. N.W., #300 20036; (202) 223-5625. Fax, (202) 833-5596. Lorna Wilson, administrator. Internet, feba@ix.netcom.com or http://www.feba.org.*

Membership: lawyers interested in federal energy law. Interests include administration of federal laws covering production, development, conservation, transmission, and economic regulation of energy.

National Assn. of Energy Service Companies, *1615 M St. N.W., #800 20036; (202) 822-0950. Fax, (202) 822-0955. Terry E. Singer, executive director. Internet, http://www.naesco.org.*

Membership: energy service companies, equipment manufacturers, affiliates of utilities, financial institutions, and governmental and other organizations involved in energy conservation and alternative energy projects. Acts as an energy information clearinghouse; sponsors conferences and seminars. Monitors legislation and regulations affecting the industry.

National Assn. of Regulatory Utility Commissioners, *12th St. and Constitution Ave. N.W. (mailing address: P.O. Box 684, Washington, DC 20044-0684); (202) 898-2200. Fax, (202) 898-2213. Peggy Welsh, executive director. Press, (202) 898-2205. Internet, http://www.naruc.org.*

Membership: members of federal, state, municipal, and Canadian regulatory commissions that have jurisdiction over utilities and carriers. Interests include electricity, natural gas, and nuclear power.

National Governors' Assn., *Natural Resources, 444 N. Capitol St. N.W., #267 20001-1512; (202) 624-5339. Fax, (202) 624-5313. Tom Curtis, staff director. Internet, http://www.nga.org.*

Develops governors' recommendations on energy and environmental issues and presents these policies to Congress and federal agencies.

Oil, Chemical, and Atomic Workers International Union, *2722 Merrilee Dr., #250, Fairfax, VA 22031; (703) 876-9300. Fax, (703) 876-8952. Paula R. Littles, legislative director. Internet, ocaw@ocaw.org or http://www.ocaw.org.*

Membership: approximately 90,000 workers in the energy, chemical, pharmaceutical, and allied industries. Assists members with contract negotiation and grievances; conducts training programs and workshops. Monitors legislation and regulations. (Headquarters in Lakewood, Colo.; affiliated with the AFL-CIO.)

Southern States Energy Board, *P.O. Box 34606 20043; (202) 667-7303. Fax, (202) 667-7313. Carolyn C. Drake, director, Washington Office. Internet, sseb@clever.net or http://www.clever.net/sseb.*

Interstate compact organization that serves as regional representative of sixteen southern states, Puerto Rico, and the Virgin Islands for energy and environmental issues. (Headquarters in Norcross, Ga.)

SRI International, *1611 N. Kent St., #700, Arlington, VA 22209; (703) 524-2053. Fax, (703) 247-8569. Jack F. Scherrer, vice president, Washington Office. Internet, http://www.sri.com.*

Research organization that conducts policy-related energy studies and scientific research. Projects include surveys of energy supply and demand; analyses of fossil fuel, solar, and nuclear energy; the environmental effects of advanced energy technology; and energy management. (Headquarters in Menlo Park, Calif.)

U.S. Chamber of Commerce, *Food, Agriculture, Energy, and Natural Resources Policy, 1615 H St. N.W. 20062-2000; (202) 463-5500. Fax, (202) 887-3445. Stew Hardy, manager. Internet, http://www.uschamber.org.*

Develops policy on all issues affecting the production, use, and conservation of energy, including transportation, energy taxes, and on- and offshore mining of energy resources.

U.S. Conference of Mayors, *Municipal Waste Management Assn., 1620 Eye St. N.W., 6th Floor 20006; (202) 293-7330. Fax, (202) 429-0422. J. Thomas Cochran, executive director.*

Membership: mayors of cities with populations of 30,000 or more. Works with Congress and the executive branch to promote urban policy on energy and environment issues; analyzes federal legislation, programs, and policies from an urban perspective.

Utility Workers Union of America, *815 16th St. N.W. 20006; (202) 347-8105. Fax, (202) 347-4872. Donald E. Wightman, president. Internet, http://www.aflcio.org/uwua.*

Membership: approximately 50,000 workers in utilities and related industries. Helps members negotiate pay, benefits, and better working conditions; conducts training programs and workshops. Monitors legislation and regulations. (Affiliated with the AFL-CIO.)

See also Federation of American Scientists (p. 567); National Academy of Sciences (p. 594); Rand Corporation (p. 496)

Energy Conservation

See also Environment and Natural Resources (chap. 9)

AGENCIES

Energy Efficiency and Renewable Energy *(Energy Dept.), 1000 Independence Ave. S.W., #6C016 20585; (202) 586-9220. Fax, (202) 586-9260. Diane W. Reicher, assistant secretary. Toll-free, (800) 363-3732. Internet, energyinfo@delphi.com or http://www.eren.doe.gov.*

Develops and manages programs to improve foreign and domestic markets for renewable energy sources including solar, biomass, wind, geothermal, and hydropower and to increase efficiency of energy use among residential, commercial, transportation, utility, and industrial users. Administers financial and technical assistance for state energy programs, weatherization for low-income households, and implementation of energy conservation measures by schools, hospitals, local governments, and public care institutions.

Energy Efficiency and Renewable Energy *(Energy Dept.), Building Technologies, 1000 Independence Ave. S.W., #EE40 20585; (202) 586-1510. Fax, (202) 586-5954. Mark Ginsberg, deputy assistant secretary.*

Supports private and government efforts to improve the energy efficiency of buildings and increase use of renewable energy sources. Conducts research to make information and energy technologies available.

Energy Efficiency and Renewable Energy *(Energy Dept.), Industrial Technologies, 1000 Independence Ave. S.W., #5F065, EE20 20585; (202) 586-9232. Fax, (202) 586-9234. Denise F. Swink, deputy assistant secretary.*

Conducts research and disseminates information to increase energy end-use efficiency, promote renewable energy use and industrial applications, and reduce the volume of industrial and municipal waste.

Energy Efficiency and Renewable Energy *(Energy Dept.), Transportation Technologies, 1000 Independence Ave. S.W., #5G086, EE30 20585; (202) 586-8027. Fax, (202) 586-1637. Thomas J. Gross, deputy assistant secretary.*

Conducts research and development programs to improve transportation energy efficiency. Programs include electric and hybrid vehicles, advanced propulsion systems, advanced materials research, and alternative fuels, including biofuels.

Energy Information Administration *(Energy Dept.), Energy Consumption, 1000 Independence Ave. S.W., #2F065 E163 20585; (202) 586-1112. Fax, (202) 586-0018. Dwight K. French, director.*

Maintains data on energy consumption in the residential, commercial, industrial, and transportation sectors. Prepares analyses on energy consumption by sector and fuel type, including the impact of conservation measures.

Housing and Urban Development Dept., *Community Viability, 451 7th St. S.W., #7240 20410; (202) 708-2894. Fax, (202) 708-3363. Richard H. Broun, director.*

Develops policies promoting energy efficiency, conservation, and renewable sources of supply in housing

and community development programs, including district heating and cooling systems and wastes-to-energy cogeneration projects.

National Institute of Standards and Technology *(Commerce Dept.), Building and Fire Research Laboratory, Route I-270 and Quince Orchard Rd., Bldg. 226, #B306, Gaithersburg, MD 20899; (301) 975-5851. Fax, (301) 975-5433. James E. Hill, chief, Building Environment. Internet, http://www.bfrl.nist.gov.*

Develops measurement techniques, test methods, and mathematical models to encourage energy conservation in large buildings. Interests include refrigeration, lighting, infiltration and ventilation, heating and air conditioning, and heat transfer in the building envelope.

CONGRESS

House Banking and Financial Services Committee, *Subcommittee on Housing and Community Opportunity, B303 RHOB 20515; (202) 225-6634. Rick A. Lazio, R-N.Y., chair; Joseph M. Ventrone, staff director.*

Jurisdiction over legislation on energy conservation measures in housing (jurisdiction shared with the House Commerce Committee).

House Commerce Committee, *Subcommittee on Energy and Power, 2125 RHOB 20515; (202) 225-2927. Fax, (202) 225-1919. Dan Schaefer, R-Colo., chair; James E. Derderian, staff director. Internet, http://www.house.gov/commerce.*

Jurisdiction over legislation on proposals to label appliances to indicate energy consumption and on emergency fuel allocation. Jurisdiction over legislation on energy conservation measures in housing (jurisdiction shared with House Banking and Financial Service Committee).

House Science Committee, *Subcommittee on Energy and Environment, 389 FHOB 20515; (202) 225-9662. Fax, (202) 266-6983. Ken Calvert, R-Calif., chair; Harlan Watson, staff director. Internet, http://www.house.gov/science.*

Jurisdiction over legislation on research and development of energy sources and over Energy Dept. basic research programs, including those in energy conservation and utilization; jurisdiction over legislation related to the Energy Dept.'s transportation energy conservation programs.

Joint Economic Committee, *SD-G01 20510; (202) 224-5171. Fax, (202) 224-0240. Rep. H. James Saxton, R-N.J., chair; Christopher Frenze, executive director. Internet, http://www.senate.gov/committee/jec.html.*

Studies and makes recommendations on the conservation and expansion of energy supplies.

Senate Banking, Housing, and Urban Affairs Committee, *Subcommittee on Housing Opportunity and Community Development, SD-534 20510; (202) 224-7391. Connie Mack, R-Fla., chair; Christopher Lord, staff director. Internet, http://www.senate.gov/~banking.*

Jurisdiction over legislation on energy conservation measures in housing.

Senate Energy and Natural Resources Committee, *Subcommittee on Energy Research, Development, Production, and Regulation, SD-364 20510; (202) 224-6567. Fax, (202) 228-0302. Don Nickles, R-Okla., chair; David Garman, professional staff member. Internet, http://www. senate.gov/~energy.*

Jurisdiction over mineral conservation and over energy conservation measures, such as emergency fuel allocation, proposals to label appliances to indicate energy consumption, gasoline rationing, and coal conversion. Jurisdiction over legislation on energy research and development, including petroleum on public lands and the U.S. uranium supply.

NONPROFIT

Alliance to Save Energy, *1200 18th St. N.W., #900 20036; (202) 857-0666. Fax, (202) 331-9588. David Nemtzow, president. Internet, http://www.ase.org.*

Coalition of government, business, consumer, and labor leaders concerned with increasing the efficiency of energy use. Advocates efficient use of energy; conducts research, demonstration projects, and public education programs.

American Council for an Energy-Efficient Economy, *1001 Connecticut Ave. N.W., #801 20036; (202) 429-8873. Fax, (202) 429-2248. Howard Geller, executive director. Internet, info@aceee.org or http://aceee.org.*

Independent research organization concerned with energy policy, technologies, and conservation. Interests include energy efficiency in buildings and appliances, improved transportation efficiency, industrial efficiency, utility issues, and conservation in developing countries.

Environmental Defense Fund, *1875 Connecticut Ave. N.W., #1016 20009-5728; (202) 387-3500. Fax, (202) 234-6049. Cheryl Pickard, office manager, Washington Office. Internet, http://www.edf.org.*

Citizens' interest group staffed by lawyers, economists, and scientists. Provides information on energy issues and advocates energy conservation measures. Interests include Antarctica and the Amazon rain forest.

Provides utilities and environmental organizations with energy conservation computer models. (Headquarters in New York.)

Friends of the Earth, *1025 Vermont Ave. N.W., #300 20005-6303; (202) 783-7400. Fax, (202) 783-0444. Brent Blackwelder, president. Internet, foe@foe.org or http:// www.foe.org.*

Citizens' interest group. Interests include nuclear energy and nuclear waste storage and cleanup; conservation and renewable energy resources; and air and water pollution, including international water projects. Specializes in federal budget and tax issues related to the environment; ozone layer and ground water protection; and World Bank and International Monetary Fund reform. Library open to the public by appointment.

International Institute for Energy Conservation, *750 1st St. N.E., #940 20002; (202) 842-3388. Fax, (202) 842-1565. Russell Sturm, president. Internet, http://www. iiec.org.*

Works with developing nations to establish sustainable growth through efficient uses of energy. Seeks to counteract air and water pollution and the threat of global warming.

National Conference of States on Building Codes and Standards, *505 Huntmar Park Dr., #210, Herndon, VA 20170; (703) 437-0100. Fax, (703) 481-3596. Robert Wible, executive director. TDD, (703) 481-2019. Internet, http://www.ncsbcs.org.*

Membership: delegates appointed by the governors of the states and territories, and individuals and organizations concerned with building standards. Prepares code reports under contract. Works with national and state organizations and governmental agencies to promote the updating and adoption of model energy conservation codes for new and existing buildings. Maintains library of national, state, and local government energy conservation codes. Library open to members.

National Insulation Assn., *99 Canal Center Plaza, #222, Alexandria, VA 22314; (703) 683-6422. Fax, (703) 549-4838. Bill Pitkin, executive vice president. Internet, niainfo@insulation.org or http://www.insulation.org.*

Membership: companies in the commercial and industrial insulation and asbestos abatement industries. Monitors legislation and regulations.

North American Insulation Manufacturers Assn., *44 Canal Center Plaza, #310, Alexandria, VA 22314; (703) 684-0084. Fax, (703) 684-0427. Kenneth D. Mentzer, president. Internet, http://www.naima.org.*

Membership: manufacturers of insulation products for use in homes, commercial buildings, and industrial facilities. Provides information on the use of insulation for thermal efficiency, sound control, and fire safety; monitors research in the industry. Monitors legislation and regulations.

Resources for the Future, *1616 P St. N.W. 20036; (202) 328-5000. Fax, (202) 939-3460. Paul Portney, president. Library, (202) 328-5089. Internet, info@rff.org or http:// www.rff.org.*

Research organization that conducts studies on economic and policy aspects of energy, conservation, and development of natural resources, including effects on the environment. Interests include hazardous waste, the Superfund, and biodiversity.

Sierra Club, *408 C St. N.E. 20002; (202) 547-1141. Fax, (202) 547-6009. Debbie Sease, legislative director. Legislative hotline, (202) 675-2394. Internet, information@ sierraclub.org or http://www.sierraclub.org.*

Citizens' interest group that promotes protection and responsible use of the Earth's ecosystems and its natural resources. Focuses on combating global warming/greenhouse effect through energy conservation, efficient use of renewable energy resources, auto efficiency, and constraints on deforestation. Monitors federal, state, and local legislation relating to the environment and natural resources. (Headquarters in San Francisco.)

Union of Concerned Scientists, *1616 P St. N.W., #310 20036; (202) 332-0900. Fax, (202) 332-0905. Alden Meyer, director, Government Relations. Internet, ucs@ucsusa.org or http://www.ucsusa.org.*

Independent group of scientists and others that advocates safe and sustainable international, national, and state energy policies. Conducts research, advocacy, and educational outreach focusing on market-based strategies for the development of renewable energy and alternative fuels, transportation policy, carbon reduction, global warning, and energy efficiency. (Headquarters in Cambridge, Mass.)

Worldwatch Institute, *1776 Massachusetts Ave. N.W., 8th Floor 20036; (202) 452-1999. Fax, (202) 296-7365. Lester R. Brown, president. Internet, worldwatch@ worldwatch.org or http://www.worldwatch.org.*

Research organization that focuses on interdisciplinary approach to solving global environmental problems. Interests include energy conservation, renewable resources, solar power, and energy use in developing countries.

International Trade and Cooperation

See also Energy Conservation (this chapter); International Affairs (chap. 13)

AGENCIES

Agency for International Development, *Center for Environment, 1300 Pennsylvania Ave. N.W., #3.08, USAID/G/ENV 20523-3800; (202) 712-1750. Fax, (202) 216-3174. David Hales, deputy assistant administrator.*

Assists with the economic growth of developing countries by providing policy, technical, and financial assistance for cost-effective, reliable, and environmentally sound energy programs. Focuses on the Global Warming Initiative, private initiatives, renewable energy, energy efficiency and conservation, technology innovation, and training officials in developing countries.

Census Bureau *(Commerce Dept.), Foreign Trade, Suitland and Silver Hill Rds., Suitland, MD (mailing address: 4700 Silver Hill Rd., Washington, DC 20233-6700); (301) 457-2203. Fax, (301) 457-2867. C. Harvey Monk Jr., chief. Trade data inquiries, (301) 457-2227. Internet, http:// www.census.gov/foreign-trade/www.*

Provides information on imports and exports of energy commodities, including coal, oil, and natural gas.

Commerce Dept., *Balance of Payments, 1441 L St. N.W., BE-58 20230; (202) 606-9545. Fax, (202) 606-5314. Christopher L. Bach, chief. Internet, http://www.stat-usa. gov.*

Provides statistics on U.S. balance of trade, including figures on energy commodities.

Energy Dept., *Emergency Management, 1000 Independence Ave. S.W., #GH060 20585; (202) 586-9892. Fax, (202) 586-3904. John J. Nettles Jr., director. Internet, http://www2.nn.doe.gov/nn/emerga/emerg.htm.*

Monitors international energy situations as they affect domestic market conditions; recommends policies on and government responses to energy emergencies; represents the United States in the International Energy Agency's emergency programs and NATO civil emergency preparedness activities.

Energy Dept., *International Energy Policy, 1000 Independence Ave. S.W., #7C034, PO-7 20585; (202) 586-6383. Fax, (202) 586-6148. David Jhirad, deputy assistant secretary.*

Monitors and evaluates energy policies of foreign nations to determine the effect on international trade; works with industry associations and the Commerce Dept. on promoting U.S. energy exports.

Energy Dept., *Policy,* *1000 Independence Ave. S.W.,* *#7C016 20585; (202) 586-5800. Fax, (202) 586-0861.* *Robert W. Lee, assistant secretary. Internet, http://www.* *doe.gov/policy.*

Advises the secretary on developing and implementing international energy policies consistent with U.S. foreign policy. Evaluates Energy Dept. programs. Represents the department in international discussions on energy matters, including the Organization for Economic Development's International Energy Ageny. Assesses world energy price and supply trends and technological developments; studies effects of international actions on U.S. energy supply.

Energy Information Administration *(Energy Dept.),* ***Energy Demand and Integration,*** *1000 Independence Ave. S.W., #2F081, EI80 20585; (202) 586-1441. Fax, (202) 586-3045. Arthur T. Andersen, director.*

Compiles, interprets, and reports international energy statistics and U.S. energy data for international energy organizations. Analyzes international energy markets; makes projections concerning world prices and trade for energy sources, including oil, natural gas, coal, and electricity; monitors world petroleum market to determine U.S. vulnerability.

Energy Research *(Energy Dept.),* *1000 Independence Ave. S.W., #7B058 20585; (202) 586-5430. Fax, (202) 586-4120. Martha A. Krebs, director.*

Coordinates energy research, science, and technology programs among producing and consuming nations; analyzes existing international research and development activities; pursues international collaboration in research and in the design, development, construction, and operation of new facilities and major scientific experiments; participates in negotiations for international cooperation activities.

Fossil Energy *(Energy Dept.),* ***Coal and Power Import and Export,*** *FE-27, 19901 Germantown Rd., Germantown, MD 20874-1290; (301) 903-4497. Fax, (301) 903-1591. Barbara McKee, director. Internet, http://www.fe.* *doe.gov/international.*

Responsible for coal and technology export and import promotion activities for the Office of Fossil Energy; assesses fossil energy markets; evaluates international research development activities.

International Trade Administration *(Commerce Dept.),* ***Energy,*** *14th St. and Constitution Ave. N.W., #4056 20230; (202) 482-1466. Fax, (202) 482-0170. Helen Burroughs, director. Internet, http://www.ita.doc.gov/oeim.*

Conducts research on the effect of federal energy policy on the business community; promotes improved

market competitiveness and participation in international trade by the basic energy fuels industries. Provides export counseling; conducts conferences and workshops.

Nuclear Energy, Science, and Technology *(Energy Dept.),* ***International Nuclear Safety,*** *1000 Independence Ave. S.W., #5A143 20585; (202) 586-7313. Fax, (202) 586-8353. Dan Geissing, associate director, International Nuclear Safety.*

Seeks to improve the safety of nuclear activities internationally and coordinates other departmental offices and government agencies in the implementation of U.S. nonproliferation policy. Promotes nuclear safety in the former Soviet Union and Eastern Europe and assists in the shutdown of plutonium production reactors. Works with other agencies to open new markets for U.S. nuclear technology.

Nuclear Regulatory Commission, *Nonproliferation, Exports, and Multilateral Relations, 11555 Rockville Pike, Rockville, MD 20852; (301) 415-2344. Fax, (301) 415-2395. Ronald D. Hauber, director.*

Coordinates application review process for exports and imports of nuclear materials, facilities, and components. Makes recommendations on licensing upon completion of review process. Conducts related policy reviews.

State Dept., *International Energy and Commodities, Main State Bldg. 20520; (202) 647-2875. Fax, (202) 647-4037. William Weingarten, director.*

Coordinates U.S. international energy policy related to commodities, including energy supply, and U.S. participation in the International Energy Agency; monitors cooperative multilateral and bilateral agreements related to energy; coordinates energy-related aspects of U.S. relations with other countries.

State Dept., *Nuclear Energy Affairs, Main State Bldg., #7828 20520; (202) 647-3310. Fax, (202) 647-0775. Richard J. K. Stratford, director.*

Coordinates and supervises international nuclear energy policy for the State Dept. Advises the secretary on policy matters relating to nonproliferation and export controls, nuclear technology and safeguards, and nuclear safety. Promotes adherence to the Nuclear Nonproliferation Treaty and other international agreements. Chairs the Subgroup on Nuclear Export Coordination, the interagency group that reviews nuclear export license applications. Enforces the Atomic Energy Act.

Treasury Dept., *International Affairs, 1500 Pennsylvania Ave. N.W., #5037 20220; (202) 622-2140. Todd Crawford, director, Middle Eastern and Central Asian Nations.*

Represents the department in the International Energy Agency, World Bank, International Monetary Fund, and other international institutions that address energy matters. Analyzes oil market and provides economic analyses of Arabian peninsular countries.

U.S. International Trade Commission, *Energy, Petroleum, Benzenoid, Chemicals, Rubber, and Plastics,* 500 E St. S.W. 20436; (202) 205-3368. Fax, (202) 205-2150. *Edmund Cappuccilli, chief.*

Advisory fact-finding agency on tariffs, commercial policy, and foreign trade matters. Analyzes data on oil, petrochemical, coal, coke, and natural gas products traded internationally; investigates effects of tariffs on certain chemical and energy imports.

U.S. Trade Representative *(Executive Office of the President),* 600 17th St. N.W., #209 20508; (202) 395-6890. Fax, (202) 395-4549. *Charlene Barshefsky, U.S. trade representative. Information, (202) 395-3230. Internet, http://www.ustr.gov.*

Serves as principal adviser to the president and primary trade negotiator on international trade policy. Develops and coordinates energy trade matters among government agencies.

CONGRESS

House International Relations Committee, *2170 RHOB 20515; (202) 225-5021. Fax, (202) 225-2035. Benjamin A. Gilman, R-N.Y., chair; Richard J. Garon Jr., chief of staff. Internet, http://www.house.gov/international_relations.*

Jurisdiction over most legislation on U.S. participation in international energy programs and legislation related to the economic aspects of trading nuclear technology and materials with foreign countries.

House Ways and Means Committee, *1102 LHOB 20515; (202) 225-3625. Bill Archer, R-Texas, chair; Peter Singleton, chief of staff. Internet, http://www.house.gov/ways_means.*

Jurisdiction over legislation on taxes, tariffs, and trade measures relating to energy, such as oil import fees.

Senate Energy and Natural Resources Committee, *SD-364 20510; (202) 224-4971. Fax, (202) 224-6163. Frank H. Murkowski, R-Alaska, chair; Gregg D. Renkes, staff director. Internet, http://www.senate.gov/~energy.*

Jurisdiction over legislation relating to U.S. participation in international energy programs (jurisdiction shared with Senate Foreign Relations Committee).

Senate Finance Committee, *SD-219 20510; (202) 224-4515. Fax, (202) 224-5920. William V. Roth Jr., R-Del.,*

chair; Lindy L. Paull, staff director. Internet, http://www.senate.gov/~finance.

Holds hearings on legislation concerning taxes, tariffs, and trade measures relating to energy, such as oil import fees.

Senate Foreign Relations Committee, *SD-450 20510; (202) 224-4651. Fax, (202) 224-0836. Jesse Helms, R-N.C., chair; James W. "Bud" Nance, staff director. Internet, http://www.senate.gov/committee/foreign.html.*

Jurisdiction over legislation related to the economic aspects of trading nuclear technology and materials. Jurisdiction over legislation relating to U.S. participation in international energy programs (jurisdiction shared with Senate Energy and Natural Resources Committee).

INTERNATIONAL ORGANIZATIONS

European Union, *Press and Public Affairs,* 2300 M St. N.W. 20037; (202) 862-9500. Fax, (202) 429-1766. *Hugo Paemen, ambassador; Soren Sondergaard, acting director. Press, (202) 862-9540. Internet, http://www.eurunion.org or http://www.europa.eu.int.*

Information and public affairs office in the United States for the European Union, which includes the European Economic Community, the European Coal and Steel Community, and the European Atomic Energy Community. Provides energy information, statistics, and documents on member countries. Library open to the public by appointment. (Headquarters in Brussels.)

International Bank for Reconstruction and Development (World Bank), *Energy, Mining, and Telecommunications,* 2121 Pennsylvania Ave., N.W. (mailing address: 1818 H St. N.W., #F5K158, Washington, DC 20433); (202) 473-4522. Fax, (202) 522-3743. *James P. Bond, director.*

Facilitates investment of capital and makes loans from its own funds for developing the energy resources of less prosperous member countries. Supports programs that promote the generation, transmission, and distribution of electric power and the discovery and development of oil, gas, and coal in developing countries, particularly by the private sector, through provision of loans and guarantees. Actively supports environmentally sustainable provision of energy in emerging economies.

International Energy Agency *(Organization for Economic Cooperation and Development),* 2001 L St. N.W., #650 20036; (202) 785-6323. Fax, (202) 785-0350. *William Danvers, head, Washington Center. Internet, http://www.oecdwash.org.*

Promotes cooperation in energy research among developed nations; assists developing countries in negotiations with energy-producing nations; prepares plans for international emergency energy allocation. Publishes statistics and analyses on most aspects of energy. Washington Center maintains reference library open to the public; offers for sale publications of the International Energy Agency. (Headquarters in Paris.)

United Nations Information Centre, *1775 K St. N.W., #400 20006; (202) 331-8670. Fax, (202) 331-9191. Joe Sills, director. Internet, http://www.un.org.*

Center for reference publications of the United Nations; publications include *World Energy Statistics, Energy Balances and Electricity Profiles,* and other statistical material on energy. Library open to the public.

NONPROFIT

Atlantic Council of the United States, *Energy and Environment Program, 910 17th St. N.W., #1000 20006; (202) 778-4962. Fax, (202) 463-7241. Eliane Lomax, associate director, Energy. Information, (202) 463-7226.*

Studies and makes policy recommendations on international energy relationships for all energy sources, including oil, natural gas, coal, synthetic fuels, and nuclear power.

U.S. Energy Assn., *1620 Eye St. N.W., #1000 20006; (202) 331-0415. Fax, (202) 331-0418. Barry K. Worthington, executive director.*

Membership: energy-related organizations, including professional, trade, and government groups. Participates in the World Energy Council (headquartered in London). Sponsors seminars and conferences on energy resources, policy management, technology, utilization, and conservation.

World Energy Efficiency Assn., *910 17th St. N.W., #1010 20006; (202) 778-4961. Fax, (202) 463-0017. Donald L. Guertin, executive director. Internet, info@weea.org or http://www.weea.org.*

Assists developing countries in accessing information on energy efficiency programs, technologies, and measures; fosters international cooperation in energy efficiency efforts.

Statistics

See also specific energy resources (this chapter)

AGENCIES

Bureau of Labor Statistics *(Labor Dept.), Industrial Prices and Price Indexes, 2 Massachusetts Ave. N.E., #3840 20212-0001; (202) 606-7720. Fax, (202) 606-7753. Kathy Klemmer, energy analyst.*

Compiles statistics on energy for the Producer Price Index; analyzes movement of prices for natural gas, petroleum, coal, and electric power in the primary commercial and industrial markets.

Energy Information Administration, *National Energy Information Center, 1000 Independence Ave. S.W., #1F048 EI-30 20585; (202) 586-8800. Fax, (202) 586-0727. Sandra Wilkins, chief. Internet, http://www.eia. doc.gov/bookshelf.html.*

Catalogs and distributes energy data; acts as a clearinghouse for statistical information on energy; makes referrals for technical information. Reading room of Energy Information Administration publications open to the public.

NONPROFIT

American Gas Assn., *Statistics, 1515 Wilson Blvd., Arlington, VA 22209; (703) 841-8647. Fax, (703) 841-8697. Chris McGill, manager. Internet, http://www. aga.com.*

Issues statistics on the gas industry, including supply and reserves.

American Petroleum Institute, *Finance, Accounting, and Statistics, 1220 L St. N.W. 20005; (202) 682-8495. Fax, (202) 962-4730. Edward H. Murphy, director. Information, (202) 682-8520. Library, (202) 682-8042.*

Provides statistics on petroleum industry, including data on exports and imports, weekly refinery operations (stock levels, output, and input), drilling activity and costs, taxation, and transportation. Publishes monthly supply-and-demand table for crude oil and weekly statistical bulletin. Collects environmental expenditure data and publishes the annual *Petroleum Industry Environmental Performance Report.* Library open to the public.

Edison Electric Institute, *Statistics, 701 Pennsylvania Ave. N.W. 20004; (202) 508-5583. Fax, (202) 508-5380. Thomas R. Daugherty, director.*

Provides statistics on electric utility operations, including the *Statistical Yearbook of the Electric Utility Industry,* which contains data on the capacity, generation, sales, and finances of the electric utility industry.

National Mining Assn., *Policy Analysis, 1130 17th St. N.W. 20036-4677; (202) 463-2654. Fax, (202) 833-9636. Constance D. Holmes, senior vice president.*

Collects, analyzes, and distributes statistics on the mining industry, including statistics on the production, transportation, and consumption of coal.

⚡ ELECTRICITY

AGENCIES

Energy Dept., *Bonneville Power Administration,* *1000 Independence Ave. S.W., #8G061 20585; (202) 586-5640. Fax, (202) 586-6762. Stephen J. Wright, vice president.*

Coordinates marketing of electric power and energy for the Bonneville Power Administration; serves as liaison between the Bonneville Power Administration and Congress. (Headquarters in Portland, Ore.)

Energy Dept., *Power Marketing Liaison Office,* *1000 Independence Ave. S.W., #8G027 20585; (202) 586-5581. Fax, (202) 586-6261. Timothy Meeks, assistant administrator.*

Serves as a liaison among the Southeastern, Southwestern, Western Area, and Alaska power administrations; other federal agencies; and Congress. Coordinates marketing of electric power from federally owned hydropower projects.

Energy Information Administration *(Energy Dept.), Coal, Nuclear, Electric, and Alternate Fuels,* *950 L'Enfant Plaza S.W. (mailing address: 1000 Independence Ave. S.W., Washington, DC 20585); (202) 426-1200. Fax, (202) 426-1278. John Geidl, director.*

Prepares analyses and forecasts on electric power supplies, including the effects of government policies and regulatory actions on capacity, consumption, finances, and rates. Publishes statistics on electric power industry.

Tennessee Valley Authority, *1 Massachusetts Ave. N.W., #300 20001; (202) 898-2999. Fax, (202) 898-2998. Vacant, administrative officer, Washington Office. Internet, http://www.tva.gov.*

Coordinates resource conservation, development, and land-use programs in the Tennessee River Valley. Supplies wholesale power to municipal and cooperative electric systems, federal installations, and some industries. (Headquarters in Knoxville, Tenn.)

CONGRESS

House Commerce Committee, *Subcommittee on Energy and Power,* *2125 RHOB 20515; (202) 225-2927. Fax, (202) 225-1919. Dan Schaefer, R-Colo., chair; James E. Derderian, staff director. Internet, http://www.house. gov/commerce.*

Jurisdiction over legislation on electric utilities regulation, energy plant siting (including nuclear facilities), and proposals to label appliances to indicate energy consumption.

House Resources Committee, *Subcommittee on Water and Power,* *1522 LHOB 20515; (202) 225-8331.*

John T. Doolittle, R-Calif., chair; Robert Faber, staff director. Internet, http://www.house.gov/resources.

Jurisdiction over legislation on the federal power administrations.

House Science Committee, *Subcommittee on Energy and Environment,* *389 FHOB 20515; (202) 225-9662. Fax, (202) 266-6983. Ken Calvert, R-Calif., chair; Harlan Watson, staff director. Internet, http://www.house.gov/science.*

Jurisdiction over legislation on electric energy research and development.

House Transportation and Infrastructure Committee, *Subcommittee on Water Resources and Environment,* *B376 RHOB 20515; (202) 225-4360. Fax, (202) 226-5435. Sherwood Boehlert, R-N.Y., chair; Ben Grumbles, counsel. Internet, http://www.house.gov/transportation.*

Jurisdiction over the Tennessee Valley Authority.

Senate Energy and Natural Resources Committee, *Subcommittee on Energy Research, Development, Production, and Regulation,* *SD-364 20510; (202) 224-6567. Fax, (202) 228-0302. Don Nickles, R-Okla., chair; David Garman, professional staff member. Internet, http://www.senate.gov/~energy.*

Jurisdiction over legislation on electric energy research and development.

Senate Energy and Natural Resources Committee, *Subcommittee on Water and Power,* *SH-312 20510; (202) 224-2564. Fax, (202) 224-6163. Jon Kyl, R-Ariz., chair; James P. Beirne, senior counsel. Internet, http://www.seante.gov/~energy.*

Jurisdiction over the federal power marketing administrations, hydroelectric power, and the impact of energy development on water resources.

Senate Environment and Public Works Committee, *Subcommittee on Clean Air, Wetlands, Private Property, and Nuclear Safety,* *SD-407 20510; (202) 224-6176. James M. Inhofe, R-Okla., chair; Chris Hessler, staff contact. Internet, http://www.senate.gov/committee/environment.html.*

Jurisdiction over Tennessee Valley Authority legislation.

NONPROFIT

Center for Energy and Economic Development, *1800 Diagonal Rd., #370, Alexandria, VA 22314; (703) 684-6292. Fax, (703) 684-6297. Stephen L. Miller, president. Internet, http://www.ceednet.com.*

Membership: coal, railroad, and electric utility companies. Educates the public and policymakers about economic, technological, and scientific research on energy resources employed in generating electricity.

Citizens for State Power, *122 S. Patrick St., Alexandria, VA 22314; (703) 739-5920. Fax, (703) 739-5924. Craig Shirley, president. Internet, csa@townhall.com or http://www.conservative.org/townhall/scripts/citizens.cgi.*

Coalition of conservative policy organizations that seeks to increase competition in the electric utility industry through federal and state deregulation.

Electric Power Supply Assn., *1401 H St. N.W., #760 20005; (202) 789-7200. Fax, (202) 789-7201. Lynne H. Church, executive director. Internet, epsaweb@mindspring.com or http://www.epsa.org.*

Membership: power generators active in U.S. and global markets, power marketers, and suppliers of goods and services to the industry. Promotes competition in the delivery of electicity to consumers.

Electricity Consumers Resource Council, *1333 H St. N.W., West Tower, 8th Floor 20005; (202) 682-1390. Fax, (202) 289-6370. John A. Anderson, executive director. Internet, alcon@alcon.org or http://www.alcon.org.*

Membership: large industrial users of electricity. Promotes development of coordinated federal, state, and local policies concerning electrical supply for industrial users; studies rate structures and their impact on consumers.

Electrification Council, *701 Pennsylvania Ave. N.W. 20004; (202) 508-5900. Fax, (202) 508-5335. Susan Mitchell, manager. Internet, http://www.eei.org/CSM/tec.*

Membership: electric utilities and independent manufacturers. Conducts training programs and provides industrial and commercial power consumers with educational materials. Interests include the efficient production, use, and management of energy. Fosters information exchange through the National Electric Industry Trade Ally Partnership.

National Electrical Contractors Assn., *3 Bethesda Metro Center, #1100, Bethesda, MD 20814; (301) 657-3110. Fax, (301) 215-4500. John Grau, executive vice president. Internet, http://www.necanet.org.*

Membership: electrical contractors who build and service electrical wiring, equipment, and appliances. Represents members in collective bargaining with union workers; sponsors research and educational programs.

National Electrical Manufacturers Assn., *1300 N. 17th St., #1847, Rosslyn, VA 22209; (703) 841-3200. Fax,*

(703) 841-3300. Malcolm O'Hagan, president. Internet, http://www.nema.org.

Membership: domestic manufacturers of electrical products. Develops and promotes use of electrical standards; compiles and analyzes industry statistics. Interests include efficient energy management, product safety and liability, occupational safety, and the environment. Monitors international trade activities, legislation, and regulations.

National Hydropower Assn., *122 C St. N.W., 4th Floor 20002; (202) 383-2530. Fax, (202) 383-2531. Linda Church Ciocci, executive director. Internet, hydroinfo@hydro.org or http://www.hydro.org.*

Membership: investor-owned utilities and municipal and independent companies that generate hydroelectric power; consulting, engineering, and law firms; and equipment suppliers and manufacturers. Focus includes regulatory relief, international marketing, and coalition building. Monitors legislation and regulations.

See also Institute of Electrical and Electronics Engineers (p. 605)

Public Utilities

AGENCIES

Federal Energy Regulatory Commission *(Energy Dept.), Electric Power Regulation, 888 1st St. N.E. 20426; (202) 208-1200. Fax, (202) 208-0960. Shelton M. Cannon, director.*

Establishes rates and power charges for electric energy transmission, sale, and interconnections. Regulates wholesale electric rates in interstate commerce.

Federal Energy Regulatory Commission *(Energy Dept.), Hydropower Licensing, 888 1st St. N.E. 20426; (202) 219-2700. Fax, (202) 219-0205. Carol L. Sampson, director.*

Issues licenses, permits, and exemptions for hydroelectric power projects. Ensures safety of licensed dams and safeguards the environment.

Rural Utilities Service *(Agriculture Dept.), 1400 Independence Ave. S.W. 20250-1500; (202) 720-9540. Fax, (202) 720-1725. Wally Beyer, administrator. Information, (202) 720-1255. Press, (202) 720-1260. Internet, http://www.usda.gov/rus.*

Makes loans and loan guarantees to rural electric utilities providing service in rural areas.

NONPROFIT

American Public Power Assn., *2301 M St. N.W. 20037; (202) 467-2900. Fax, (202) 467-2910. Alan H. Richardson,* executive director. Library, (202) 467-2957. Internet, http://www.appanet.org.

Membership: local, publicly owned electric utilities nationwide. Represents industry interests before Congress, federal agencies, and the courts; provides educational programs; collects and disseminates information; funds energy research and development projects. Library open to the public by appointment.

Edison Electric Institute, *701 Pennsylvania Ave. N.W. 20004; (202) 508-5000. Fax, (202) 508-5759. Thomas R. Kuhn, president. Information, (202) 508-5778. Internet, http://www.eei.org.*

Membership: investor-owned electric power companies and electric utility holding companies. Interests include electric utility operation and concerns, including conservation and energy management, energy analysis, resources and environment, cogeneration and renewable energy resources, nuclear power, and research. Provides information and statistics relating to electric energy; aids member companies in generating and selling electric energy; and conducts information forums. Library open to the public by appointment.

National Assn. of Regulatory Utility Commissioners, *12th St. and Constitution Ave. N.W. (mailing address: P.O. Box 684, Washington, DC 20044-0684); (202) 898-2200. Fax, (202) 898-2213. Peggy Welsh, executive director. Press, (202) 898-2205. Internet, http://www.naruc.org.*

Membership: members of federal, state, municipal, and Canadian regulatory commissions that have jurisdiction over utilities. Interests include electric utilities.

National Assn. of State Utility Consumer Advocates, *1133 15th St. N.W., #550 20005; (202) 727-3908. Fax, (202) 727-3911. Charles Acquard, executive director. Internet, nasuca@nasuca.org or http://www.nasuca.org.*

Membership: public advocate offices authorized by states to represent ratepayer interests before state and federal utility regulatory commissions. Monitors legislation and regulatory agencies with jurisdiction over electric utilities, telecommunications, natural gas, and water; conducts conferences and workshops.

National Rural Electric Cooperative Assn., *4301 Wilson Blvd., Arlington, VA 22203-1860; (703) 907-5500. Fax, (703) 907-5511. Glenn English, chief executive officer. Internet, http://www.nreca.org.*

Membership: rural electric cooperative systems and public power and utility districts. Provides members with legislative, legal, and regulatory services. Supports energy and environmental research and offers technical advice and assistance to developing countries.

Research and Development

AGENCIES

Energy Research, *(Energy Dept.), Fusion Energy, 19901 Germantown Rd., Germantown, MD 20874-1290; (301) 903-4941. Fax, (301) 903-8584. N. Anne Davies, associate director. Internet, http://wwwofe.er.doe.gov.*

Conducts research and development on fusion energy for electric power generation.

National Institute of Standards and Technology *(Commerce Dept.), Electricity, Route I-270 and Quince Orchard Rd., Gaithersburg, MD 20899; (301) 975-2400. Fax, (301) 926-3972. William Anderson, chief. Internet, http://www.eeel.nist.gov/811.*

Conducts research to characterize and define performance parameters of electrical/electronic systems, components, and materials; applies research to advance measurement instrumentation and the efficiency of electric power transmission and distribution; develops and maintains national electrical reference standards, primarily for power, energy, and related measurements, to assist in the development of new products and promote international competitiveness.

National Institute of Standards and Technology *(Commerce Dept.), Electronics and Electrical Engineering Laboratory, Route I-270 and Quince Orchard Rd., Bldg. 220, #B358, Gaithersburg, MD 20899; (301) 975-2220. Fax, (301) 975-4091. Judson French, director. Internet, eeel@nist.gov or http://www.eeel.nist.gov.*

Provides information on research, development, and applications in the fields of electrical, electronic, quantum electric, and electromagnetic materials engineering. Interests include fundamental physical constants, practical data, measurement methods, theory, standards, technology, technical services, and international trade.

NONPROFIT

Electric Power Research Institute, *2000 L St. N.W., #805 20036; (202) 872-9222. Fax, (202) 293-2697. Michael S. Delello, director, Government Relations, Washington Office. Information, (202) 293-6346. Internet, http://www.epri.com.*

Membership: investor- and municipal-owned electric utilities and rural cooperatives. Conducts research and development in power generation and delivery technologies, including fossil fuel, nuclear, and renewable energy sources used by electric utilities. Studies energy management and utilization, including conservation and environmental issues. (Headquarters in Palo Alto, Calif.)

✦ FOSSIL FUELS

See also International Trade and Cooperation (this chapter)

AGENCIES

Fossil Energy *(Energy Dept.), 1000 Independence Ave. S.W., #4G084 20585; (202) 586-6660. Fax, (202) 586-7847. Patricia Fry Godley, assistant secretary. Internet, http://www.fe.doe.gov.*

Responsible for policy and management of high-risk, long-term research and development in recovering, converting, and using fossil energy, including coal, petroleum, oil shale, and unconventional sources of natural gas. Handles the strategic petroleum reserve and the naval petroleum and oil shale reserve programs; oversees the Clean Coal Program to design and construct environmentally clean coal-burning facilities.

U.S. Geological Survey *(Interior Dept.), Energy Resources, 12201 Sunrise Valley Dr., Reston, VA (mailing address: 915 National Center, Reston, VA 20192); (703) 648-6470. Fax, (703) 648-5464. Vacant, program coordinator.*

Assesses resources, maintains fossil fuels databases, and conducts research on the quality and quantity of the nation's coal, petroleum, and natural gas resources.

CONGRESS

House Commerce Committee, *Subcommittee on Energy and Power, 2125 RHOB 20515; (202) 225-2927. Fax, (202) 225-1919. Dan Schaefer, R-Colo., chair; James E. Derderian, staff director. Internet, http://www.house.gov/commerce.*

Jurisdiction over legislation dealing with coal, oil, and natural gas, including proposed emergency presidential energy authority (such as rationing), proposals to create civilian petroleum reserves, petroleum and natural gas pricing and pipelines, natural gas imports, regulation of public utilities, energy plant siting, and low head hydro projects.

House Resources Committee, *Subcommittee on Energy and Mineral Resources, 1626 LHOB 20515; (202) 225-9297. Fax, (202) 225-5255. Barbara Cubin, R-Wyo., chair; William Condit, staff director. Internet, http://www.house.gov/resources.*

Jurisdiction over legislation on mineral land laws; mining policy; coal, oil and gas and mineral leasing on publicly owned land; and conservation and development of energy and natural resources in the ocean and outer continental shelf. Jurisdiction over oil and coal slurry pipelines (shared with House Transportation and Infrastructure Committee).

House Science Committee, *Subcommittee on Energy and Environment, 389 FHOB 20515; (202) 225-9662. Fax, (202) 266-6983. Ken Calvert, R-Calif., chair; Harlan Watson, staff director. Internet, http://www.house.gov/science.*

Jurisdiction over legislation on research and development of fossil fuel energy (including coal, petroleum, natural gas, oil shale, tar sand, and synthetic fuels such as liquefied and gasified coal) and over Energy Dept. basic research programs.

House Transportation and Infrastructure Committee, *Subcommittee on Surface Transportation, B370A RHOB 20515; (202) 225-6715. Fax, (202) 225-4623. Tom Petri, R-Wis., chair; Roger Nober, counsel. Internet, http://www.house.gov/transportation.*

Jurisdiction over legislation on oil and coal slurry pipelines. (Jursidiction shared with House Resources Committee.)

Senate Commerce, Science, and Transportation Committee, *Subcommittee on Oceans and Fisheries, SH-428 (mailing address: SD-508, Washington, DC 20510); (202) 224-8172. Fax, (202) 228-0326. Olympia J. Snowe, R-Maine, chair; Clark LeBlanc, professional staffer. Internet, http://www.senate.gov/~commerce.*

Jurisdiction over legislation on production and development of deep seabed mining and deepwater ports (jurisdiction shared with Senate Energy and Natural Resources and Senate Environment and Public Works committees).

Senate Energy and Natural Resources Committee, *Subcommittee on Energy Research, Development, Production, and Regulation, SD-364 20510; (202) 224-6567. Fax, (202) 228-0302. Don Nickles, R-Okla., chair; David Garman, professional staff member. Internet, http://www.senate.gov/~energy.*

Jurisdiction over legislation on fossil fuel research and development, including Energy Dept. programs; mining policy, including mineral leasing; and interstate aspects of production and distribution of coal, natural gas, and petroleum. Jurisdiction over deep seabed mining and deepwater ports (jurisdiction shared with Senate Commerce, Science, and Transportation and Senate Environment and Public Works committees).

Senate Environment and Public Works Committee, *Subcommittee on Drinking Water, Fisheries, and Wildlife, SD-410 20510; (202) 224-6176. Fax, (202) 224-5167. Dirk Kempthorne, R-Idaho, chair; Ann Klee, staff* contact. Internet, http://www.senate.gov/committee/ environment.html.

Jurisdiction over legislation on production and development of deep seabed mining and deepwater ports (jurisdiction shared with Senate Commerce, Science, and Transportation and Senate Energy and Natural Resources committees).

Coal

AGENCIES

Bureau of Land Management *(Interior Dept.), Solids Group, 1620 L St. N.W., #501 20240 (mailing address: 1849 C St. N.W., #LS501, Washington, DC 20240); (202) 452-0350. Fax, (202) 452-0399. Brenda Aird, group manager.*

Evaluates and classifies coal resources on federal lands; develops and administers leasing programs. Supervises coal mining operations on federal lands; oversees pre- and postlease operations, including production phases of coal development. Oversees implementation of the Mining Law of 1872 and the Mineral Materials Act of 1955.

Energy Information Administration *(Energy Dept.), Coal, Nuclear, Electric, and Alternate Fuels, 950 L'Enfant Plaza S.W. (mailing address: 1000 Independence Ave. S.W., Washington, DC 20585); (202) 426-1200. Fax, (202) 426-1278. John Geidl, director.*

Collects data, compiles statistics, and prepares analyses and forecasts on domestic coal supply, including availability, production, costs, processing, transportation, and distribution. Publishes data on the export and import of coal; makes forecasts and provides analyses on coal imports and exports.

Federal Mine Safety and Health Review Commission, *1730 K St. N.W., #600 20006; (202) 653-5660. Fax, (202) 653-5030. Mary Lu Jordan, chair; Richard L. Baker, executive director, (202) 653-5625. Information, (202) 653-5633.*

Independent agency established by the Federal Mine Safety and Health Act of 1977. Holds fact-finding hearings and issues orders affirming, modifying, or vacating the labor secretary's enforcement actions regarding mine safety and health. Library open to the public.

Fossil Energy *(Energy Dept.), Coal Fuels and Industrial Systems, 19901 Germantown Rd., Germantown, MD 20874; (301) 903-9451. Fax, (301) 903-2238. C. Lowell Miller, director.*

Fosters the development and implementation of clean coal technologies in the private sector. Monitors economic and commercial efficiency program and disseminates results. Cofunded by private industry.

Interior Dept., *Surface Mining Reclamation and Enforcement, 1951 Constitution Ave. N.W. 20240; (202) 208-4006. Fax, (202) 501-0549. Kathy Karpen, director. Information, (202) 208-2719. Internet, http://www.osmre. gov/astart3.htm.*

Administers the Surface Mining Control and Reclamation Act of 1977. Establishes and enforces national standards for the regulation and reclamation of surface coal mining and the surface effects of underground coal mining; oversees state implementation of these standards.

Mine Safety and Health Administration *(Labor Dept.), 4015 Wilson Blvd., #622, Arlington, VA 22203; (703) 235-1385. Fax, (703) 235-4369. J. Davitt McAteer, assistant secretary. Information, (703) 235-1452. Internet, http://www.msha.gov.*

Administers and enforces the health and safety provisions of the Federal Mine Safety and Health Act of 1977. Monitors underground mining and processing operations of minerals, including minerals used in construction materials; produces educational materials in engineering; and assists with rescue operations following mining accidents.

CONGRESS

House Education and the Workforce Committee, *Subcommittee on Workforce Protections, 2181 RHOB 20515; (202) 225-4527. Fax, (202) 225-9571. Cass Ballenger, R-N.C., chair; Kevin Talley, staff director.*

Jurisdiction over legislation on coal mining health and safety.

Senate Labor and Human Resources Committee, *Subcommittee on Public Health and Safety, SD-422 20510; (202) 224-7139. Fax, (202) 228-5044. Bill Frist, R-Tenn., chair; Susan Ramthun, staff director. Internet, http://www.senate.gov/~labor.*

Jurisdiction over legislation on coal mining health and safety.

NONPROFIT

American Coal Ash Assn., *2760 Eisenhower Ave., #304, Alexandria, VA 22314; (703) 317-2400. Fax, (703) 317-2409. Samuel Tyson, executive director. Internet, ACAA-USA@msn.com or http://ACAA-USA.org.*

Membership: electric utilities that use coal to produce electricity, marketers or brokers of coal ash, coal companies, and suppliers of ash-related equipment. Compiles statistics and provides information on coal ash production and utilization. Library open to the public by appointment.

American Coke and Coal Chemicals Institute, *1255 23rd St. N.W. 20037; (202) 452-1140. Fax, (202) 833-3636. Allen F. Johnson, president.*

Membership: producers of oven coke, metallurgical coal, and chemicals; coke sales agents; tar distillers; and builders of coke ovens and coke oven byproduct plants. Maintains committees on chemicals, coke, manufacturing and environment, safety and health, and traffic.

Assn. of Bituminous Contractors, *1747 Pennsylvania Ave. N.W., #1050 20006; (202) 785-4440. Fax, (202) 331-8049. William H. Howe, general counsel.*

Membership: independent and general contractors that build coal mines. Represents members before the Federal Mine Safety and Health Review Commission and in collective bargaining with the United Mine Workers of America.

Bituminous Coal Operators Assn., *918 16th St. N.W., #303 20006; (202) 783-3195. Fax, (202) 783-4862. Joseph P. Brennan, president.*

Membership: firms that mine bituminous coal. Represents members in collective bargaining with the United Mine Workers of America.

Coal Exporters Assn. of the United States, *1130 17th St. N.W. 20036; (202) 463-2639. Fax, (202) 833-9636. Moya Phelleps, executive director.*

Membership: exporters of coal. Provides information on coal exports. Monitors legislation and regulations. (Affiliate of the National Mining Assn.)

National Coal Council, *2000 N. 15th St., #500, Arlington, VA 22201; (703) 527-1191. Fax, (703) 527-1195. James F. McAvoy, executive director. Internet, natcoal@erols.com.*

Membership: individuals appointed by the secretary of energy. Represents coal producers, transporters, women and minorities in mining, and manufacturers of coal-producing equipment. Makes recommendations to the secretary on issues involving coal. Library open to the public.

National Mining Assn., *1130 17th St. N.W. 20036; (202) 463-2625. Fax, (202) 463-6152. Richard L. Lawson, president. Information, (202) 463-2623. Press, (202) 463-2651. Internet, nma@prime.planetcom.com or http://www.nma.org.*

Membership: coal producers, coal sales and transportation companies, equipment manufacturers, consulting firms, coal resource developers and exporters,

coal-burning electric utility companies, and other energy companies. Collects, analyzes, and distributes industry statistics; conducts special studies of competitive fuels, coal markets, production and consumption forecasts, and industry planning. Interests include exports, coal leasing programs, coal transportation, environmental issues, health and safety, national energy policy, slurry pipelines, and research and development, including synthetic fuels.

United Mine Workers of America, *900 15th St. N.W. 20005; (202) 842-7200. Fax, (202) 842-7227. Cecil E. Roberts, president. Internet, http://www.accessdigex.net/~miner.*

Membership: coal miners and other mining workers. Represents members in collective bargaining with industry. Conducts educational, housing, and health and safety training programs; monitors federal coal mining safety programs.

Oil and Natural Gas

AGENCIES

Energy Dept., *Regulatory Litigation,* *1000 Independence Ave. S.W., #6H045 20585; (202) 586-2909. Fax, (202) 586-3437. Steve Skubel, assistant general counsel.*

Manages and directs enforcement of federal statutes and regulations in effect before the decontrol of crude oil and petroleum product prices in January 1981; responsible for the phase-out of economic regulatory actions.

Energy Information Administration *(Energy Dept.),* **Natural Gas,** *1000 Independence Ave. S.W., #BE054 20585; (202) 586-6090. Fax, (202) 586-1076. Joan Heinkel, director. Internet, http://www.eia.doe.gov.*

Collects and publishes monthly and annual estimates of domestic crude oil, natural gas, and natural gas liquids. Performs analyses of the natural gas industry.

Energy Information Administration *(Energy Dept.),* **Oil and Gas,** *1000 Independence Ave. S.W., #2G020 20585; (202) 586-6401. Fax, (202) 586-9739. Ken Vatts, director.*

Collects, interprets, and publishes data on domestic production, use, and distribution of oil and natural gas; analyzes and projects oil and gas reserves, resources, production, capacity, and supply; surveys and monitors alternative fuel needs during emergencies; publishes statistics.

Energy Information Administration *(Energy Dept.),* **Petroleum,** *1000 Independence Ave. S.W., #2G051 20585; (202) 586-5214. Fax, (202) 586-4913. John Cook, director, (202) 586-5986. Internet, http://www.eia.doe.gov.*

Collects, compiles, interprets, and publishes data on domestic production, distribution, and prices of crude oil and refined petroleum products; analyzes and projects availability of petroleum supplies. Publishes statistics, including import and export data.

Fossil Energy *(Energy Dept.), Natural Gas and Petroleum Technology, 1000 Independence Ave. S.W., #3E028 20585; (202) 586-5600. Fax, (202) 586-6050. Guido DeHoratiis, acting director.*

Responsible for research and development programs in oil and gas exploration, production, processing, and storage; studies ways to improve efficiency of oil recovery in depleted reservoirs; coordinates and evaluates research and development among government, universities, and industrial research organizations.

Fossil Energy *(Energy Dept.), Naval Petroleum and Oil Shale Reserves, 1000 Independence Ave. S.W., #3H076 20585; (202) 586-4685. Fax, (202) 586-4446. R. Dobie Langenkamp, deputy assistant secretary.*

Develops, conserves, operates, and maintains oil shale reserves for producing oil, natural gas, and other petroleum products.

Internal Revenue Service *(Treasury Dept.), Passthrough and Special Industries, Branch 8, 1111 Constitution Ave. N.W., #5316 20224; (202) 622-3130. Fax, (202) 622-4524. Richard A. Kocak, chief.*

Administers excise tax programs, including taxes on diesel, gasoline, and special fuels. Advises district offices, internal IRS offices, and general inquirers on tax policy, rules, and regulations.

Minerals Management Service *(Interior Dept.), Engineering and Operations, 381 Elden St., Herndon, VA 20170; (703) 787-1598. Fax, (703) 787-1093. E. P. Danenberger, chief.*

Administers the Outer Continental Shelf Land Act. Supervises oil and gas operations on outer continental shelf lands; oversees lease operations including exploration, drilling, and production phases of offshore oil and gas development; administers lease provisions for offshore oil and gas.

National Oceanic and Atmospheric Administration *(Commerce Dept.), Policy and Strategic Planning, 14th St. and Constitution Ave. N.W., #6117 20230; (202) 482-5181. Fax, (202) 501-3024. Susan Fruchter, director.*

Makes recommendations to NOAA concerning environmental and ecological problems. Assesses the accuracy and coordinates the implementation of environmental impact statements for all federal projects, including offshore oil and natural gas facilities.

NONPROFIT

American Gas Assn., *1515 Wilson Blvd., Arlington, VA 22209; (703) 841-8400. Fax, (703) 841-8406. David Parker, president. Internet, http://www.aga.com.*

Membership: natural gas utilities and pipeline companies. Interests include all technical and operational aspects of the gas industry. Publishes comprehensive statistical record of gas industry; conducts national standard testing for gas appliances. Monitors legislation and regulations.

American Petroleum Institute, *1220 L St. N.W. 20005; (202) 682-8100. Fax, (202) 682-8029. Red Cavaney, president. Press, (202) 682-8120. Library, (202) 682-8042. Internet, http://www.api.org.*

Membership: producers, refiners, marketers, and transporters of oil, natural gas, and related products such as gasoline. Provides information on the industry, including data on exports and imports, taxation, transportation, weekly refinery operations (stock levels, output, and input), and drilling activity and costs; conducts research on petroleum and publishes statistical and drilling reports. Library open to the public from 1:30 to 4:30 P.M.

American Petroleum Institute, *Taxation Dept., 1220 L St. N.W., 11th Floor 20005; (202) 682-8465. Fax, (202) 682-8049. Andy Yood, director.*

Provides information on petroleum taxation.

American Public Gas Assn., *11094-D Lee Hwy., #102, Fairfax, VA 22030-5014; (703) 352-3890. Fax, (703) 352-1271. Robert S. Cave, executive director. Internet, apga@apga.org or http://www.apga.org.*

Membership: municipally owned gas distribution systems. Provides information on federal developments affecting natural gas. Promotes efficiency and works to protect the interests of public gas systems. Sponsors workshops and conferences.

Compressed Gas Assn., *1725 Jefferson Davis Hwy., #1004, Arlington, VA 22202-4102; (703) 412-0900. Fax, (703) 412-0128. Carl T. Johnson, president. Internet, http://www.cganet.com.*

Membership: all segments of the compressed gas industry, including producers and distributors of compressed and liquefied gases. Promotes and coordinates technical development and standardization of the industry. Monitors legislation and regulations.

Gas Appliance Manufacturers Assn., *1901 N. Moore St., #1100, Arlington, VA 22209; (703) 525-9565. Fax, (703) 525-0718. C. Reuben Autery, president. Internet, gamaorg@aol.com or http://www.gamanet.org.*

Membership: manufacturers of gas appliances and equipment for residential and commercial use and related industries. Advocates product improvement; provides market statistics. Monitors legislation and regulations.

Gas Research Institute, *1600 Wilson Blvd., #900, Arlington, VA 22209; (703) 526-7800. Fax, (703) 526-7805. David O. Webb, senior vice president, Policy and Regulatory Affairs.*

Membership: all segments of the natural gas industry, including producers, pipelines, and distributors. Conducts research and develops new technology for gas customers and the industry. (Headquarters in Chicago.)

Independent Liquid Terminals Assn., *1133 15th St. N.W., #650 20005; (202) 659-2301. Fax, (202) 466-4166. John Prokop, president.*

Membership: commercial operators of for-hire bulk liquid terminals and tank storage facilities, including those for crude oil and petroleum. Promotes the safe and efficient handling of various types of liquid commodities. Sponsors workshops and seminars; maintains speakers bureau; publishes directories. Monitors legislation and regulations.

Independent Petroleum Assn. of America, *1101 16th St. N.W., 2nd Floor 20036; (202) 857-4722. Fax, (202) 857-4799. Gil Thurm, president. Internet, http:// www.ipaa.org.*

Membership: independent oil and gas producers; land and royalty owners; and others with interests in domestic exploration, development, and production of oil and natural gas. Interests include leasing, prices and taxation, foreign trade, environmental restrictions, and improved recovery methods.

Independent Terminal Operators Assn., *1150 Connecticut Ave. N.W., 9th Floor 20036; (202) 828-4100. Fax, (202) 828-4130. William H. Bode, general counsel.*

Membership: independent operators of petroleum storage facilities. Interests include oil imports. Monitors legislation and regulations.

International Assn. of Drilling Contractors, *1901 L St. N.W., #702 20036; (202) 293-0670. Fax, (202) 872-0047. Brian T. Petty, senior vice president, Government Affairs. Internet, info@iadc.org or http://www.iadc.org.*

Membership: drilling contractors, oil and gas producers, and others in the industry worldwide. Promotes safe exploration and production of hydrocarbons, advances in drilling technology, and preservation of the environment. Monitors legislation and regulations. (Headquarters in Houston.)

Mid-Continent Oil and Gas Assn., *801 Pennsylvania Ave. N.W., #840 20004-2615; (202) 638-4400. Fax, (202) 638-5967. Wayne Gibbens, president.*

Membership: major and independent petroleum companies. Monitors legislation and regulations affecting the petroleum industry.

National Ocean Industries Assn., *1120 G St. N.W., #900 20005; (202) 347-6900. Fax, (202) 347-8650. Robert B. Stewart, president. Internet, noia@noia.org.*

Membership: manufacturers, producers, suppliers, and support and service companies involved in marine, offshore, and ocean work. Interests include offshore oil and gas supply and production.

National Petroleum Council, *1625 K St. N.W., #600 20006; (202) 393-6100. Fax, (202) 331-8539. Marshall W. Nichols, executive director. Internet, http://www.npc.org.*

Advisory committee to the secretary of energy on matters relating to the petroleum industry, including oil and natural gas. Publishes reports concerning technical aspects of the oil and gas industries.

National Petroleum Refiners Assn., *1899 L St. N.W., #1000 20036; (202) 457-0480. Fax, (202) 457-0486. Urvan Sternfels, president. Internet, http://www.npradc.org.*

Membership: petroleum, petrochemical, and refining companies. Interests include allocation, imports, refining technology, petrochemicals, and environmental regulations.

National Propane Gas Assn., *1101 17th St. N.W., #1004 20036; (202) 466-7200. Fax, (202) 466-7205. Richard R. Roldan, vice president, Government Relations. Internet, http://www.propanegas.com/npga.*

Membership: retail marketers, producers, wholesale distributors, appliance and equipment manufacturers, equipment fabricators, and distributors and transporters of liquefied petroleum gas. Conducts research, safety, and educational programs; provides statistics on the industry. (Headquarters in Lisle, Ill.)

Natural Gas Supply Assn., *805 15th St. N.W., #510 20005; (202) 326-9300. Fax, (202) 326-9330. Nicholas J. Bush, president. Internet, http://www.ngsa.org.*

Membership: major and independent producers of domestic natural gas. Interests include the production, consumption, marketing, and regulation of natural gas. Monitors legislation and regulations.

Natural Gas Vehicle Coalition, *1515 Wilson Blvd., #1030, Arlington, VA 22209; (703) 527-3022. Fax, (703) 527-3025. Richard R. Kolodziej, president. Internet, http:// www.ngvc.org.*

Membership: natural gas distributors; pipeline, automobile, and engine manufacturers; environmental groups; research and development organizations; and state and local government agencies. Advocates installation of compressed natural gas fuel stations and development of industry standards. Helps market new natural gas products and equipment.

Petroleum Marketers Assn. of America, *1901 N. Fort Myer Dr., #1200, Arlington, VA 22209-1604; (703) 351-8000. Fax, (703) 351-9160. Phillip R. Chisholm, executive vice president. Internet, http://www.pmaa.org.*

Membership: state and regional associations representing independent branded and nonbranded marketers of petroleum products. Provides information on all aspects of petroleum marketing. Monitors legislation and regulations.

Public Citizen, *Buyers Up, 1600 20th St. N.W. 20009; (202) 588-7780. Fax, (202) 588-7798. Garland Auton, program manager. Internet, publiccitizen@citizen.org or http://www.citizen.org/Buyersup.htm.*

Administers cooperative purchasing program for consumers of heating oil and heating and cooling services. Promotes energy conservation; helps consumers save on energy bills.

Service Station Dealers of America, *9420 Annapolis Rd., #307, Lanham, MD 20706; (301) 577-4956. Fax, (301) 731-0039. Tony Licata, president.*

Membership: state associations of gasoline retailers. Interests include environmental issues, retail marketing, oil allocation, imports and exports, prices, and taxation.

Society of Independent Gasoline Marketers of America, *11911 Freedom Dr., #590, Reston, VA 20190; (703) 709-7000. Fax, (703) 709-7007. Kenneth A. Doyle, executive vice president.*

Membership: marketers and wholesalers of brand and nonbrand gasoline. Seeks to ensure adequate supplies of gasoline at competitive prices. Monitors legislation and regulations affecting gasoline supply and price.

Pipelines

AGENCIES

Federal Energy Regulatory Commission *(Energy Dept.), Pipeline Regulation, 888 1st St. N.E. 20426; (202) 208-0700. Fax, (202) 208-0193. Kevin P. Madden, director.*

Establishes and enforces maximum rates and charges for oil and natural gas pipelines; establishes oil pipeline operating rules; issues certificates for and regulates construction, sale, and acquisition of natural gas pipeline

facilities. Ensures compliance with the Natural Gas Policy Act, the Natural Gas Act, and other statutes.

National Transportation Safety Board, *Pipeline and Hazardous Material Safety, 490 L'Enfant Plaza S.W. 20594; (202) 314-6460. Fax, (202) 314-6482. Bob Chipkevich, director.*

Investigates natural gas and petroleum pipeline accidents.

Research and Special Programs Administration *(Transportation Dept.), Hazardous Materials Safety, 400 7th St. S.W., #8422 20590; (202) 366-0656. Fax, (202) 366-5713. Alan I. Roberts, associate administrator. Internet, welisten@rspa.dot.gov or http://hazmat.dot.gov.*

Designates fuels, chemicals, and other substances as hazardous materials and regulates their transportation in interstate commerce; coordinates international standards regulations.

Research and Special Programs Administration *(Transportation Dept.), Pipeline Safety, 400 7th St. S.W., #2335 20590; (202) 366-4595. Fax, (202) 366-4566. Richard B. Felder, associate administrator. Internet, http://ops.dot.gov.*

Issues and enforces federal regulations for oil, natural gas, and petroleum products pipeline safety.

NONPROFIT

Assn. of Oil Pipe Lines, *1101 Vermont Ave. N.W., #604 20005; (202) 408-7970. Fax, (202) 408-7983. Ben Cooper, executive director. Internet, aopl@aopl.org.*

Membership: oil pipeline companies. Analyzes industry statistics. Monitors legislation and regulations.

Coal and Slurry Technology Assn., *1156 15th St. N.W., #525 20005; (202) 296-1133. Fax, (202) 223-3504. Stuart D. Serkin, executive director.*

Membership: slurry fuel producers, engineering and construction companies, utilities, equipment manufacturers and suppliers, and those planning and operating slurry systems. Seeks extension of the right of eminent domain to coal slurry pipelines; facilitates the exchange of technical information.

Interstate Natural Gas Assn. of America, *10 G St. N.E., #700 20002; (202) 626-3200. Fax, (202) 626-3239. Jerald V. Halvorsen, president.*

Membership: U.S. interstate and Canadian interprovincial natural gas pipeline companies. Commissions studies and provides information on the natural gas pipeline industry.

☢ NUCLEAR ENERGY

See also International Trade and Cooperation (this chapter); Nuclear Weapons and Power (chap. 16)

AGENCIES

Energy Information Administration *(Energy Dept.), Coal, Nuclear, Electric, and Alternate Fuels, 950 L'Enfant Plaza S.W. (mailing address: 1000 Independence Ave. S.W., Washington, DC 20585); (202) 426-1200. Fax, (202) 426-1278. John Geidl, director.*

Prepares analyses and forecasts on the availability, production, prices, processing, transportation, and distribution of nuclear energy, both domestically and internationally. Collects and publishes data concerning the uranium supply and market.

Nuclear Energy, Science, and Technology *(Energy Dept.), 1000 Independence Ave. S.W. 20585; (202) 586-6450. Fax, (202) 586-8353. Terry R. Lash, director.*

Administers nuclear fission power generation and fuel technology programs; develops and provides nuclear power sources to meet national civilian requirements. Develops, interprets and coordinates nuclear safety policy for all Energy Dept. reactors and nuclear facilities. Encourages public involvement in programs and provides information to increase public knowledge.

Nuclear Energy, Science, and Technology *(Energy Dept.), Medical, Industrial, and Reseach Isotope Supply, 19901 Germantown Rd., #B-432, NE-70, Germantown, MD 20874-1290; (301) 903-5161. Fax, (301) 903-5434. Owen W. Lowe, associate director.*

Directs all isotope production and distribution activities within the Energy Dept.; ensures a reliable supply of medical, research, and industrial isotopes consistent with customer needs.

Nuclear Energy, Science, and Technology *(Energy Dept.), Reactor Programs, 19901 Germantown Rd., #E-468, Germantown, MD 20874-1290; (301) 903-2915. Fax, (301) 903-5005. Robert G. Lange, associate director.*

Manages the design, construction, and operation of nuclear energy test facilities and Office of Energy Research reactor and supporting facilities, assuring their safe, reliable, and environmentally sound operation and cost-effective use. Helps conduct a safe industrial and radiological shutdown.

Nuclear Regulatory Commission, *11555 Rockville Pike, Rockville, MD; (301) 415-1759. Fax, (301) 415-1672. Shirley Ann Jackson, chair; Leonard J. Callan, executive*

director, *(301) 415-1700. Information, (301) 415-8200. Internet, opa@nrc.gov or http://www.nrc.gov.*

Regulates commercial uses of nuclear energy; responsibilities include licensing, inspection, and enforcement; monitors and regulates the imports and exports of nuclear material and equipment.

Tennessee Valley Authority, *1 Massachusetts Ave. N.W., #300 20001; (202) 898-2999. Fax, (202) 898-2998. Vacant, administrative officer, Washington Office. Internet, http://www.tva.gov.*

Coordinates resource conservation, development, and land-use programs in the Tennessee River Valley. Supplies wholesale power to municipal and cooperative electric systems, federal installations, and some industries; interests include nuclear power generation. (Headquarters in Knoxville, Tenn.)

CONGRESS

House Commerce Committee, *Subcommittee on Energy and Power, 2125 RHOB 20515; (202) 225-2927. Fax, (202) 225-1919. Dan Schaefer, R-Colo., chair; James E. Derderian, staff director. Internet, http://www.house.gov/commerce.*

Jurisdiction over regulation of commercial nuclear facilities and special oversight functions with respect to all laws, programs, and government activities affecting nonmilitary aspects of nuclear energy.

House Science Committee, *Subcommittee on Energy and Environment, 389 FHOB 20515; (202) 225-9662. Fax, (202) 266-6983. Ken Calvert, R-Calif., chair; Harlan Watson, staff director. Internet, http://www.house.gov/science.*

Jurisdiction over legislation and international cooperation on nuclear energy research and development. Oversight responsibilities over the uranium supply and the operation of Energy Dept. laboratories, including toxic waste cleanup.

Senate Energy and Natural Resources Committee, *SD-364 20510; (202) 224-4971. Fax, (202) 224-6163. Frank H. Murkowski, R-Alaska, chair; Gregg D. Renkes, staff director. Internet, http://www.senate.gov/~energy.*

Jurisdiction over nonmilitary and nonregulatory aspects of nuclear energy.

Senate Energy and Natural Resources Committee, *Subcommittee on Energy Research, Development, Production, and Regulation, SD-364 20510; (202) 224-6567. Fax, (202) 228-0302. Don Nickles, R-Okla., chair; David Garman, professional staff member. Internet, http://www.senate.gov/~energy.*

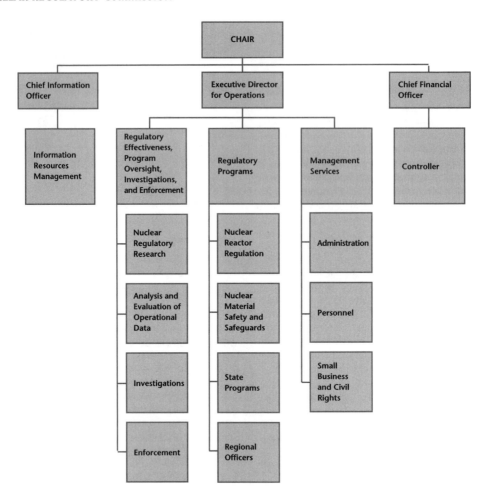

Jurisdiction over nuclear energy research and development, including uranium enrichment and nuclear fuel cycle policy.

Senate Environment and Public Works Committee, *Subcommittee on Clean Air, Wetlands, Private Property, and Nuclear Safety, SD-407 20510; (202) 224-6176. James M. Inhofe, R-Okla., chair; Chris Hessler, staff contact. Internet, http://www.senate.gov/committee/ environment.html.*

Legislative jurisdiction over nonmilitary environmental regulation and control of nuclear energy, including plant licensing and siting, radiological health and safety, security and safeguards, nuclear waste disposal,

licensing of certain nuclear exports, and liability insurance for nuclear accidents.

Senate Governmental Affairs Committee, *SD-340 20510; (202) 224-4751. Fax, (202) 224-9603. Fred Thompson, R-Tenn., chair; Hannah Sistare, staff director. Internet, http://www.senate.gov/committee/governmental_ affairs.html.*

Jurisdiction over organization and management of nuclear export policy; jurisdiction over legislation on the reform of nuclear licensing procedures, nuclear waste and spent fuel policy, physical security at nuclear installations, and nuclear proliferation.

NONPROFIT

American Physical Society, *529 14th St. N.W., #1050 20045-2001; (202) 662-8700. Fax, (202) 662-8711. Robert L. Park, director, Public Information. Internet, opa@aps. org or http://www.aps.org.*

Scientific and educational society of educators, students, scientists, and other interested citizens. Sponsors studies on issues of public concern related to physics, such as reactor safety and energy use. (Headquarters in College Park, Md.)

Nuclear Energy Institute, *1776 Eye St. N.W., #400 20006-3708; (202) 739-8000. Fax, (202) 785-4019. Joe Colvin, president. Internet, http://www.nei.org.*

Membership: utilities; industries; labor, service, and research organizations; law firms; universities; and government agencies interested in peaceful uses of nuclear energy, including the generation of electricity. Acts as a spokesperson for the nuclear power industry; provides information on licensing and plant siting, research and development, safety and security, waste disposal, and legislative and policy issues.

Nuclear Information and Resource Service, *1424 16th St. N.W., #404 20036; (202) 328-0002. Fax, (202) 462-2183. Michael Mariotte, executive director. Internet, nirsnet@igc.org or http://www.nirs.org.*

Membership: organizations and individuals concerned about nuclear energy and nuclear waste. Information clearinghouse on nuclear power plants, nuclear waste, and radiation effects. Library open to the public by appointment.

Public Citizen, *Critical Mass Energy Project, 215 Pennsylvania Ave. S.E. 20003-1155; (202) 546-4996. Fax, (202) 547-7392. Wenonah Hauter, director. Internet, cmep@ citizen.org or http://www.citizen.org/CMEP.*

Public interest group that promotes energy efficiency and renewable energy technologies; opposes nuclear energy. Interests include nuclear plant safety and energy policy issues. Library open to the public by appointment.

Safe Energy Communication Council, *1717 Massachusetts Ave. N.W., #805 20036; (202) 483-8491. Fax, (202) 234-9194. Scott Denman, executive director. Internet, seccgen@aol.com.*

Coalition of national energy, environmental, and public interest media groups that works to increase public awareness of both the ability of energy efficiency and renewable energy sources to meet an increasing share of U.S. energy needs and of the economic and environmental liabilities of nuclear power. Provides local, state, and national organizations with technical assistance through media skills training and outreach strategies.

Union of Concerned Scientists, *1616 P St. N.W., #310 20036; (202) 332-0900. Fax, (202) 332-0905. Alden Meyer, director, Government Relations. Internet, ucs@ucsusa.org or http://www.ucsusa.org.*

Independent group of scientists and others concerned with U.S. energy policy, including nuclear policy and nuclear plant safety. (Headquarters in Cambridge, Mass.)

See also Electric Power Research Institute (p. 256); National Rural Electric Cooperative Assn. (p. 256)

Licensing and Plant Siting

AGENCIES

Federal Emergency Management Agency, *Preparedness, Training, and Exercises, 500 C St. S.W. 20472; (202) 646-3487. Fax, (202) 646-4557. Kay Goss, associate director.*

Reviews off-site preparedness for commercial nuclear power facilities; evaluates emergency plans before plant licensing and submits findings to the Nuclear Regulatory Commission.

Nuclear Regulatory Commission, *Nuclear Material Safety and Safeguards, 11555 Rockville Pike, Rockville, MD; (301) 415-7800. Fax, (301) 415-5370. Carl J. Paperiello, director.*

Licenses all nuclear facilities and materials except power reactors; directs principal licensing and regulation activities for the management of nuclear waste.

Nuclear Regulatory Commission, *Nuclear Reactor Regulation, 11555 Rockville Pike, Rockville, MD; (301) 415-1270. Fax, (301) 415-8333. Samuel J. Collins, director.*

Licenses nuclear power plants and operators.

Research and Development

AGENCIES

Energy Research *(Energy Dept.), Fusion Energy, 19901 Germantown Rd., Germantown, MD 20874-1290; (301) 903-4941. Fax, (301) 903-8584. N. Anne Davies, associate director. Internet, http://wwwofe.er.doe.gov.*

Conducts research and development on fusion energy for electric power generation.

National Institute of Standards and Technology *(Commerce Dept.), Physics Laboratory, Route I-270 and Quince Orchard Rd., Bldg. 221, #B160, Gaithersburg, MD 20899; (301) 975-4200. Fax, (301) 975-3038. Katharine B. Gebbie, director. Internet, http://physics.nist.gov.*

Provides national standards for radiation measurement methods and technology. Conducts research in measurement science in the fields of electron physics; ionizing radiation dosimetry; neutron physics; and optical, ultraviolet, x-ray, gamma-ray, and infrared radiometry.

Nuclear Energy, Science, and Technology *(Energy Dept.), Space and Defense Power Systems, 19901 Germantown Rd., Germantown, MD 20874; (301) 903-3456. Fax, (301) 903-1510. Earl Wahlquist, associate director.*

Develops and produces radio isotopes power systems for space applications in support of NASA.

Nuclear Energy, Science, and Technology *(Energy Dept.), Technology and Program Planning, 1000 Independence Ave. S.W., NE-20 20585; (202) 586-6630. Fax, (202) 586-8353. William D. Magwood, associate director, Planning and Analysis.*

Responsible for uranium activities and management of fuel cycle issues. Supplies reactor fuel to university reactors; manages conversion of university reactors from highly enriched uranium fuel to low enriched fuel; supports university reactor instrumentation and equipment upgrades; provides general support to nuclear engineering programs at U.S. universities.

Nuclear Regulatory Commission, *Nuclear Regulatory Research, 11545 Rockville Pike, Rockville, MD; (301) 415-6641. Fax, (301) 415-5153. Malcolm Knapp, acting director.*

Plans, recommends, and implements nuclear regulatory research, standards development, and resolution of safety issues for nuclear power plants and other facilities regulated by the Nuclear Regulatory Commission; develops and promulgates all technical regulations.

U.S. Geological Survey *(Interior Dept.), Energy Resources, 12201 Sunrise Valley Dr., Reston, VA (mailing address: 915 National Center, Reston, VA 20192); (703) 648-6470. Fax, (703) 648-5464. Vacant, program coordinator.*

Handles exploration research on uranium, thorium, and lithium.

Safety, Security, and Waste Disposal

See also Hazardous Materials (chap. 9); International Trade and Cooperation (this chapter); Radiation Protection (chap. 9)

AGENCIES

Defense Nuclear Facilities Safety Board, *625 Indiana Ave. N.W., #700 20004; (202) 208-6400. Fax, (202) 208-6518. John T. Conway, chair. Internet, http://www.dnfsb. gov.*

Independent board created by Congress and appointed by the president to provide external oversight of Energy Dept. defense nuclear facilities and make recommendations to the secretary of energy regarding public health and safety.

Energy Dept., *Civilian Radioactive Waste Management, 1000 Independence Ave. S.W., #5A085 20585; (202) 586-6842. Fax, (202) 586-6638. Lake H. Barrett, acting director.*

Responsible for developing the waste disposal system for commercial spent nuclear fuels and some military high-level radioactive waste. Sites, licenses, constructs, and operates a permanent repository. Monitors and reports on the adequacy of congressional appropriations for the Nuclear Waste Fund to finance nuclear waste disposal through fees collected from private utility companies that generate electricity.

Energy Information Administration *(Energy Dept.), Coal, Nuclear, Electric, and Alternate Fuels, 950 L'Enfant Plaza S.W. (mailing address: 1000 Independence Ave. S.W., Washington, DC 20585); (202) 426-1200. Fax, (202) 426-1278. John Geidl, director.*

Directs collection of spent fuel data and validation of spent nuclear fuel discharge data for the Civilian Radioactive Waste Management Office.

Environment, Safety, and Health *(Energy Dept.), EH Residence, 20300 Century Blvd., Germantown, MD 20870 (mailing address: Mail Stop 270CC, #4040, Washington, DC 20585); (301) 903-3548. Fax, (301) 903-8403. Ray Hardwick, director.*

Conducts surveillances of nuclear and nonnuclear facilities.

Environment, Safety, and Health *(Energy Dept.), Environment, 1000 Independence Ave. S.W., #7A075 20585; (202) 586-5680. Fax, (202) 586-2268. Ray Berube, deputy assistant secretary.*

Establishes policies and guidance for environmental protection and compliance; provides technical assistance to departmental program and field offices in complying with environmental requirements.

Environment, Safety, and Health *(Energy Dept.), Health Studies, 19901 Germantown Rd., EH-6/27OCC, Germantown, MD 20874-1290; (301) 903-5926. Fax, (301) 903-3445. Paul J. Seligman, deputy assistant secretary.*

Evaluates and establishes standards related to radiation, industrial hygiene, and occupational medicine. Oversees epidemiologic studies.

Environment, Safety, and Health *(Energy Dept.),* *Nuclear and Facility Safety,* *1000 Independence Ave. S.W., #7A121 20878; (202) 586-2407. Fax, (202) 586-6010. Orin Pearson, deputy assistant secretary. Internet, http://tis-nt.eh.doe.gov/eh-3/sect-3.htm.*

Provides technical assistance to Energy Dept. facilities; reviews accidents, risk assessments, emergency preparedness plans, and radiological protection programs.

Environment, Safety, and Health *(Energy Dept.),* *Worker Health and Safety,* *20300 Century Blvd., Germantown, MD (mailing address: 19901 Germantown Rd. EH5 270CC, Germantown, MD 20874); (301) 903-5532. Fax, (301) 903-3189. Joseph E. Fitzgerald Jr., deputy assistant secretary.*

Develops policy and establishes standards to ensure safety and health protection in all department activities.

Environmental Management *(Energy Dept.), Environmental Restoration,* *1000 Independence Ave. S.W., #5B050 20585; (202) 586-6331. Fax, (202) 586-6523. James M. Owendoff, deputy assistant secretary.*

Manages Energy Dept. programs that treat and stabilize radioactive waste including the decontamination and decommissioning of nongovernment facilities and sites; works to develop a reliable national system for low-level waste management and techniques for treatment and immobilization of waste from former nuclear weapons complex sites.

Environmental Management *(Energy Dept.), Science and Technology,* *1000 Independence Ave. S.W., #5B014 20585; (202) 586-6382. Fax, (202) 586-6773. Gerald Boyd, deputy assistant secretary.*

Performs research, development, testing, demonstration, and evaluation for innovative, safe, and cost-effective solutions to the problems of hazardous waste and contamination of soils and groundwater.

Environmental Management *(Energy Dept.), Waste Management,* *1000 Independence Ave. S.W., #5B-040 20585; (202) 586-0370. Fax, (202) 586-0449. Mark Frei, acting deputy assistant secretary.*

Provides policy guidance for and oversees waste management operations.

Environmental Protection Agency, *Radiation and Indoor Air,* *501 3rd St. N.W. (mailing address: 401 M St. S.W., #6601J, Washington, DC 20460); (202) 564-9320. Fax, (202) 565-2043. Lawrence Weinstock, acting director.*

Establishes standards to regulate the amount of radiation discharged into the environment from uranium mining and milling projects, and other activities that result in radioactive emissions; and to ensure the safe

disposal of radioactive waste. Fields a Radiological Emergency Response Team to respond to radiological incidents.

Federal Emergency Management Agency, *500 C St. S.W. 20472; (202) 646-3923. Fax, (202) 646-3930. James Lee Witt, director. Press, (202) 646-4600. Locator, (202) 646-2500; disaster assistance, (800) 462-9029; radio network, (800) 323-5248; fax-on-demand, (202) 646-FEMA. Internet, http://www.fema.gov.*

Assists state and local governments in preparing for and responding to natural and man-made emergencies, including accidents at nuclear power facilities and accidents involving transportation of radioactive materials; provides planning guidance in the event of such accidents; operates the National Emergency Training Center. Coordinates emergency preparedness and planning for all federal agencies and departments.

National Transportation Safety Board, *Pipeline and Hazardous Material Safety,* *490 L'Enfant Plaza S.W. 20594; (202) 314-6460. Fax, (202) 314-6482. Bob Chipkevich, director.*

Investigates accidents involved in the transportation of hazardous materials.

Nuclear Regulatory Commission, *Advisory Committee on Nuclear Waste Management,* *11545 Rockville Pike, Rockville, MD; (301) 415-7360. Fax, (301) 415-5422. John T. Larkins, executive director.*

Oversees handling and disposal of high- and low-level nuclear waste, especially the disposal of high-level waste in the Yucca Mountain Repository.

Nuclear Regulatory Commission, *Advisory Committee on Reactor Safeguards,* *11545 Rockville Pike, Rockville, MD; (301) 415-7360. Fax, (301) 415-5422. John T. Larkins, executive director.*

Established by Congress to review and report on safety aspects of proposed and existing nuclear reactor facilities and the adequacy of proposed reactor safety standards; directs the Safety Research Program.

Nuclear Regulatory Commission, *Nuclear Material Safety and Safeguards,* *11555 Rockville Pike, Rockville, MD; (301) 415-7800. Fax, (301) 415-5370. Carl J. Paperiello, director.*

Develops and implements safeguards programs; directs licensing and regulation activities for the management and disposal of nuclear waste.

Nuclear Regulatory Commission, *Nuclear Reactor Regulation,* *11555 Rockville Pike, Rockville, MD; (301) 415-1270. Fax, (301) 415-8333. Samuel J. Collins, director.*

Conducts safety inspections of nuclear reactors. Regulates nuclear materials used or produced at nuclear power plants.

Nuclear Regulatory Commission, *Nuclear Regulatory Research, 11545 Rockville Pike, Rockville, MD; (301) 415-6641. Fax, (301) 415-5153. Malcolm Knapp, acting director.*

Plans, recommends, and implements resolution of safety issues for nuclear power plants and other facilities regulated by the Nuclear Regulatory Commission.

Nuclear Waste Technical Review Board, *2300 Clarendon Blvd., #1300, Arlington, VA 22201-3360; (703) 235-4473. Fax, (703) 235-4495. William D. Barnard, executive director. Internet, info@nwtrb.gov or http://www. nwtrb.gov.*

Independent board of scientists and engineers appointed by the president to review, evaluate, and report on Energy Dept. development of waste disposal systems and repositories for spent fuel and high-level radioactive waste. Oversees siting, packaging, and transportation of waste, in accordance with the Nuclear Waste Policy Act of 1987.

Research and Special Programs Administration *(Transportation Dept.), Hazardous Materials Safety, 400 7th St. S.W., #8422 20590; (202) 366-0656. Fax, (202) 366-5713. Alan I. Roberts, associate administrator. Internet, welisten@rspa.dot.gov or http://hazmat.dot.gov.*

Issues safety regulations and exemptions for the transportation of hazardous materials; works with the International Atomic Energy Agency on standards for international shipments of radioactive materials.

U.S. Geological Survey *(Interior Dept.), Earthquake Hazards, 12201 Sunrise Valley Dr., Reston, VA (mailing address: 905 National Center, Reston, VA 20192); (703) 648-6714. Fax, (703) 648-6717. John Filson, acting program coordinator.*

Monitors geologic problems relating to land use and environmental developments, including hazards to nuclear reactors; participates, at request of the Nuclear Regulatory Commission, in reviewing safety analysis reports for selected nuclear reactors.

NONPROFIT

Project on Government Oversight, *1900 L St. N.W., #314 20036-5027; (202) 466-5539. Fax, (202) 466-5596. Danielle Brian, executive director. Internet, pogo@pogo.org or http://www.pogo.org.*

Works to expose waste, fraud, abuse, and conflicts of interest in federal spending. Examines cleanup efforts at government-owned nuclear facilities to determine cost effectiveness.

See also League of Women Voters Education Fund, Natural Resources (p. 279)

▓ RENEWABLE ENERGIES/ ALTERNATIVE FUELS

AGENCIES

Energy Efficiency and Renewable Energy *(Energy Dept.), Clearinghouse (EREC), P.O. Box 3048, Merrifield, VA 22116-3048; (703) 903-0325. Fax, (703) 893-0400. Larry Goldberg, project manager. Toll-free, (800) 363-3732. TDD, (800) 273-2957. Internet, doe.erec@nciinc.com or http://www.eren.doe.gov/consumerinfo.*

Provides information on renewable energy and energy efficiency; makes referrals to other organizations for technical information on renewable energy resources.

Energy Efficiency and Renewable Energy *(Energy Dept.), Technology Utilization, 1000 Independence Ave. S.W., #5G086, EE34 20585; (202) 586-9118. Fax, (202) 586-1610. David Rodgers, director.*

Conducts research on and develops technology for alternative fuels (including methanol, ethanol, natural gas, propane, and bio-diesel) for use in heavy and light duty transportation vehicles.

Energy Efficiency and Renewable Energy *(Energy Dept.), Utility Technologies, 1000 Independence Ave. S.W., #5H021 20585; (202) 586-9275. Fax, (202) 586-1640. Allan Hoffman, acting deputy assistant secretary.*

Conducts research, development, and deployment activities to facilitate use of renewable energy resources, including solar, wind, photovoltaic, biomass, geothermal, and hydropower.

Energy Information Administration *(Energy Dept.), Coal, Nuclear, Electric, and Alternate Fuels, 950 L'Enfant Plaza S.W. (mailing address: 1000 Independence Ave. S.W., Washington, DC 20585); (202) 426-1200. Fax, (202) 426-1278. John Geidl, director.*

Prepares analyses on the availability, production, costs, processing, transportation, and distribution of uranium and alternative energy supplies, including biomass, solar, wind, waste, wood, and alcohol.

Environmental Management *(Energy Dept.), Waste Management, 1000 Independence Ave. S.W., #5B040 20585; (202) 586-0370. Fax, (202) 586-0449. Mark Frei, acting deputy assistant secretary.*

Conducts research on municipal waste conversion for use as an energy source.

CONGRESS

House Banking and Financial Services Committee, *Subcommittee on Housing and Community Opportunity, B303 RHOB 20515; (202) 225-6634. Rick A. Lazio, R-N.Y., chair; Joseph M. Ventrone, staff director.*

Jurisdiction over legislation on energy conservation measures in housing, including the Solar Bank.

House Commerce Committee, *Subcommittee on Energy and Power, 2125 RHOB 20515; (202) 225-2927. Fax, (202) 225-1919. Dan Schaefer, R-Colo., chair; James E. Derderian, staff director. Internet, http://www.house. gov/commerce.*

Jurisdiction over legislation on regulation, commercialization, and utilization of hydroelectric power, synthetic and alcohol fuels, and renewable energy resources, including wind, solar, and ocean thermal energy.

House Resources Committee, *Subcommittee on Energy and Mineral Resources, 1626 LHOB 20515; (202) 225-9297. Fax, (202) 225-5255. Barbara Cubin, R-Wyo., chair; William Condit, staff director. Internet, http://www. house.gov/resources.*

Jurisdiction over legislation concerning the development and conservation of energy and natural resources found in the ocean and the outer continental shelf. Jurisdiction over legislation affecting the use of geothermal resources.

House Resources Committee, *Subcommittee on Water and Power, 1522 LHOB 20515; (202) 225-8331. John T. Doolittle, R-Calif., chair; Robert Faber, staff director. Internet, http://www.house.gov/resources.*

Jurisdiction over legislation on irrigation and reclamation projects and electrical power marketing administrations.

House Science Committee, *Subcommittee on Energy and Environment, 389 FHOB 20515; (202) 225-9662. Fax, (202) 266-6983. Ken Calvert, R-Calif., chair; Harlan Watson, staff director. Internet, http://www.house.gov/ science.*

Jurisdiction over Energy Dept. basic research programs, including legislation on research and development of solar, wind, geothermal, and fossil fuel energy (including synthetic fuels such as liquefied and gasified coal), and other nonfossil and nonnuclear energy sources.

Senate Banking, Housing, and Urban Affairs Committee, *Subcommittee on Housing Opportunity and*

Community Development, SD-534 20510; (202) 224-7391. Connie Mack, R-Fla., chair; Christopher Lord, staff director. Internet, http://www.senate.gov/~banking.

Jurisdiction over legislation on energy conservation measures in housing, including the Solar Bank.

Senate Commerce, Science, and Transportation Committee, *Subcommittee on Oceans and Fisheries, SH-428 (mailing address: SD-508, Washington, DC 20510); (202) 224-8172. Fax, (202) 228-0326. Olympia J. Snowe, R-Maine, chair; Clark LeBlanc, professional staffer. Internet, http://www.senate.gov/~commerce.*

Studies ocean resources development and conservation. (Subcommittee does not report legislation.)

Senate Energy and Natural Resources Committee, *Subcommittee on Energy Research, Development, Production, and Regulation, SD-364 20510; (202) 224-6567. Fax, (202) 228-0302. Don Nickles, R-Okla., chair; David Garman, professional staff member. Internet, http://www. senate.gov/~energy.*

Jurisdiction over legislation on energy and nonfuel mineral resources, including hydroelectric power, irrigation and reclamation projects, power marketing administrations, and the impact of energy developments on water resources. Jurisdiction over legislation on synfuels research and development and over Energy Dept. basic research programs.

NONPROFIT

Electric Power Supply Assn., *1401 H St. N.W., #760 20005; (202) 789-7200. Fax, (202) 789-7201. Lynne Church, executive director. Internet, epsaweb@mindspring. com or http://www.epsa.org.*

Membership: companies that generate electricity, steam, and other forms of energy using a broad spectrum of fossil fuel-fired and renewable technologies.

Energy Frontiers International, *1110 N. Glebe Rd., #610, Arlington, VA 22201; (703) 276-6655. Fax, (703) 276-7662. Michael Koleda, president.*

Membership: companies interested in technologies for converting solid, liquid, and gaseous fossil fuels and biomass into other forms. Interests include coal gasification, combined cycle power generation, and liquid transportation fuels from coal, natural gas, and biomass.

Hearth Products Assn., *1601 N. Kent St., #1001, Arlington, VA 22209; (703) 522-0086. Fax, (703) 522-0548. Carter E. Keithley, president. Internet, http://www. hearthassoc.org.*

Membership: all sectors of the hearth products industry. Sponsors the Hearth Education Foundation, which provides industry training programs on the safe and efficient use of alternative fuels and appliances.

National BioEnergy Industries Assn., *122 C St. N.W., 4th Floor 20001; (202) 383-2540. Fax, (202) 383-2670. Scott Sklar, executive director. Internet, http://www.crest. org/renewables/nbia.*

Membership: landowners, foresters, harvesters, fuel transporters, processors, equipment manufacturers, and others involved in the U.S. biomass energy industry. Encourages public and private participation in the development of renewable bioenergy resources worldwide. (Affiliated with Solar Energy Industries Assn.)

National Hydrogen Assn., *1800 M St. N.W., #300 20036; (202) 223-5547. Fax, (202) 223-5537. Bob Mauro, vice president. Internet, nha@ttcorp.com or http://www. ttcorp.com/nha.*

Membership: industry, small businesses, universities, and research institutions. Promotes use of hydrogen as an energy carrier; fosters the development and application of hydrogen technologies.

U.S. Export Council for Renewable Energy, *122 C St. N.W., 4th Floor 20001; (202) 383-2550. Fax, (202) 383-2555. Vacant, president. Internet, http://www.crest.org/ renewables/usecre.*

Federation of U.S. trade associations whose members provide geothermal, hydropower, passive solar, photovoltaics, solar thermal, and wind energy. Conducts trade promotion; assists U.S. government and international agencies with renewable energy and energy effcient programs in developing countries; trains professionals to provide technical assistance.

See also Edison Electric Institute (p. 256); Electric Power Research Institute (p. 256); Public Citizen, Critical Mass Energy Project (p. 265); World Resources Institute (p. 282)

Alcohol Fuels

AGENCIES

Bureau of Alcohol, Tobacco, and Firearms *(Treasury Dept.), Wine, Beer, and Spirits Regulations, 650 Massachusetts Ave. N.W., #5000 20226; (202) 927-8230. Fax, (202) 927-8602. Richard A. Mascolo, chief.*

Develops guidelines for regional offices responsible for issuing permits for producing gasohol and other ethyl alcohol fuels, whose uses include heating and operating machinery. Writes and interprets regulations for distilleries that produce ethyl alcohol fuels.

Rural Business-Cooperative Service *(Agriculture Dept.), Business, 1400 Independence Ave. S.W., #5050*

20250-3220; (202) 720-7287. Fax, (202) 690-0097. William F. Hagy III, deputy administrator.

Makes loan guarantees to rural businesses, including those seeking to develop alcohol fuels production facilities.

NONPROFIT

American Methanol Institute, *800 Connecticut Ave. N.W., #620 20006; (202) 467-5050. Fax, (202) 331-9055. John E. Lynn, president. Internet, AmMethInst@aol.com or http://www.methanol.org.*

Membership: methanol producers and related industries. Encourages use of methanol fuels and development of chemical-derivative markets. Monitors legislation and regulations.

Renewable Fuels Assn., *1 Massachusetts Ave. N.W., #820 20001-1431; (202) 289-3835. Fax, (202) 289-7519. Eric Vaughn, president. Internet, etohrfa@erols.com or http://www.ethanolrfa.org.*

Membership: companies and state governments involved in developing the domestic ethanol industry. Distributes publications on ethanol performance.

Geothermal Energy

AGENCIES

Energy Efficiency and Renewable Energy *(Energy Dept.), Geothermal, 1000 Independence Ave. S.W., #5H072, EE-12 20585-0121; (202) 586-5340. Fax, (202) 586-8185. Allan Jelacic, acting director.*

Responsible for long-range research and technology development of geothermal energy resources.

U.S. Geological Survey *(Interior Dept.), Volcano Hazards, 12201 Sunrise Valley Dr., Reston, VA (mailing address: 905 National Center, Reston, VA 20192); (703) 648-6708. Fax, (703) 648-5483. Marianne C. Guffanti, program coordinator. Internet, http://volcanoes.usgs.gov.*

Provides staff support to the U.S. Geological Survey through programs in geothermal research and volcano hazards.

Solar, Ocean, and Wind Energy

AGENCIES

Energy Efficiency and Renewable Energy *(Energy Dept.), Photovoltaic and Wind Technology, 1000 Independence Ave. S.W., #5H095 20585; (202) 586-1721. Fax, (202) 586-8148. James Rannels, acting director.*

Researches and develops small and large wind energy conversion systems. Works to resolve environmental issues that constrain development.

Energy Efficiency and Renewable Energy *(Energy Dept.), Solar Thermal, Biomass Power, and Hydrogen Technologies, 1000 Independence Ave. S.W., #6H058 20585; (202) 586-0081. Fax, (202) 586-5127. Gary Burch, director.*

Conducts research and development on solar thermal electric power, biomass power, and hydrogen technology. Assists in the commercialization of solar technologies.

National Oceanic and Atmospheric Administration *(Commerce Dept.), Ocean and Coastal Resource Management, 1305 East-West Hwy., SSMC4, Silver Spring, MD 20910; (301) 713-3155. Fax, (301) 713-4012. Jeff Benoit, director. Internet, http://www.coasts.nos.noaa.gov.*

Responsible for scientific research on regulatory, developmental, and environmental aspects of deep seabed mining and ocean thermal energy conversion projects.

NONPROFIT

American Wind Energy Assn., *122 C St. N.W., 4th Floor 20001; (202) 383-2500. Fax, (202) 383-2505. Randall S. Swisher, executive director. Internet, awea@mcimail.com or http://www.igc.apc.org/awea.*

Membership: manufacturers, developers, operators, and distributors of wind machines; utility companies; and others interested in wind energy. Advocates wind energy as an alternative energy source; makes industry data available to the public and to federal and state legislators. Promotes export of wind energy technology.

National Ocean Industries Assn., *1120 G St. N.W., #900 20005; (202) 347-6900. Fax, (202) 347-8650. Robert B. Stewart, president. Internet, noia@noia.org.*

Membership: manufacturers, producers, suppliers, and support and service companies involved in marine, offshore, and ocean work. Interests include ocean thermal energy and new energy sources.

Passive Solar Industries Council, *1511 K St. N.W., #600 20005; (202) 628-7400. Fax, (202) 393-5043. Helen English, executive director. Internet, psicouncil@aol.com or http://www.psic.org.*

Membership: building industry associations, corporations, small businesses, and independent professionals. Provides information on the passive solar industry and related legislation, regulations, and programs. Publishes guidelines on passive solar design.

Solar Energy Industries Assn., *122 C St. N.W., 4th Floor 20001; (202) 383-2600. Fax, (202) 383-2670. Scott Sklar, director. Internet, http://www.seia.org.*

Membership: industries with interests in the production and use of solar energy. Promotes growth of U.S. and international markets; interests include photovoltaic, solar thermal power, solar hot water, and solar space heating and cooling technologies. Monitors legislation and regulations. (Affiliated with National BioEnergy Industries Assn.)

Solartherm, *1315 Apple Ave., Silver Spring, MD 20910; (301) 587-8686. Fax, (301) 587-8688. Carl Schleicher, president. Internet, mankindrf@aol.com or http://members.aol.com/mankindrf.*

Membership: scientists and scientific organizations. Conducts research and market development activities for low-cost solar energy systems and for alternative energy systems, including high-temperature solar, solid waste, ocean, and wind energy systems.

9 🏞️

Environment and Natural Resources

GENERAL POLICY

AGENCIES

Agriculture Dept., *Natural Resources and Environ-ment,* 1400 Independence Ave. S.W., #217E 20250; (202) 720-7173. Fax, (202) 720-4732. James R. Lyons, under secretary. Internet, http://www.usda.gov/agencies/agencies.htm.

Formulates and promulgates policy relating to environmental activities and management of natural resources; administers forest, conservation, and natural resource aspects of the National Environmental Policy Act. Oversees the Forest Service and the Natural Resources Conservation Service.

Council on Environmental Quality *(Executive Office of the President),* 722 Jackson Pl. N.W. 20503; (202) 456-6224. Fax, (202) 456-2710. Kathleen McGinty, chair. Internet, http://www.whitehouse.gov/CEQ.

Advises the president on environmental issues and prepares annual report on environmental quality for Congress; develops regulations for implementation of environmental impact statement law; provides information on environmental affairs.

Energy Dept., *Environment, Safety, and Health,* 1000 Independence Ave. S.W., #7A097 20585; (202) 586-6151. Fax, (202) 586-0956. Peter Brush, acting assistant secretary. Internet, http://www.eh.doe.gov.

Ensures that Energy Dept. programs comply with federal policies and standards designed to protect the environment and government property. Approves all environmental impact statements prepared by the department. Oversees health and nonnuclear safety conditions at Energy Dept. facilities.

Environmental Protection Agency, 401 M St. S.W. 20460; (202) 260-4700. Fax, (202) 260-0279. Carol Browner, administrator; Fred Hansen, deputy administrator, (202) 260-4711. Information, (202) 260-2090. Press, (202) 260-4355. Internet, http://www.epa.gov.

Administers federal environmental policies, research, and regulations; provides information on environmental subjects, including water pollution, pollution prevention, hazardous and solid waste disposal, air and noise pollution, pesticides and toxic substances, and radiation.

Environmental Protection Agency, *National Center for Environmental Assessment,* 401 M St. S.W., MC 8601 20460; (202) 260-7315. Fax, (202) 401-2492. William H. Farland, director.

Evaluates animal and human health data to define environmental health hazards and estimate risk to humans.

Environmental Protection Agency, *Policy, Planning, and Evaluation,* 401 M St. S.W., 1013 West Tower 20460; (202) 260-4332. Fax, (202) 260-0275. David Gardiner, assistant administrator.

Coordinates agency planning, policy development, and standard-setting activities.

Environmental Protection Agency, *Research and Development,* 401 M St. S.W., Mail Code 8101R 20460; (202) 564-6620. Fax, (202) 565-2431. Henry Longest, acting assistant administrator.

Develops scientific data and methods to support EPA standards and regulations; conducts exposure and risk assessments; researches applied and long-term technologies to reduce risks from pollution.

Environmental Protection Agency, *Science Advisory Board,* 401 M St. S.W., 1145 W. Tower 20460; (202) 260-4126. Fax, (202) 260-9232. Donald G. Barnes, staff director.

Coordinates nongovernment scientists and engineers who advise the administrator on scientific and technical aspects of environmental problems and issues. Evaluates EPA research projects, the technical basis of regulations and standards, and policy statements.

Housing and Urban Development Dept., *Community Viability,* 451 7th St. S.W., #7240 20410; (202) 708-2894. Fax, (202) 708-3363. Richard H. Broun, director.

Issues policies and sets standards for environmental and land-use planning and environmental management practices. Oversees HUD implementation of requirements on environment, historic preservation, archeology, flood plain management, coastal zone management, sole source aquifers, farmland protection, endangered species, airport clear zones, explosive hazards, radon, and noise.

Interior Dept., 1849 C St. N.W., #6156 20240; (202) 208-7351. Fax, (202) 208-5048. Bruce Babbitt, secretary; John Garamendi, deputy secretary. Information, (202) 208-3171. Library, (202) 208-5815. Locator, (202) 208-3100. Internet, http://www.doi.gov.

Principal U.S. conservation agency. Manages most federal land; responsible for conservation and development of mineral and water resources; responsible for conservation, development, and use of fish and wildlife resources; operates recreation programs for federal parks, refuges, and public lands; preserves and administers the nation's scenic and historic areas; reclaims arid lands in the West through irrigation; administers Native American lands and relationships with tribal governments.

Interior Dept., *Policy Analysis,* 1849 C St. N.W., #4411, Mail Stop 4426 20240; (202) 208-5978. Fax, (202) 208-4867. James Pipkin, director.

ENVIRONMENTAL PROTECTION AGENCY

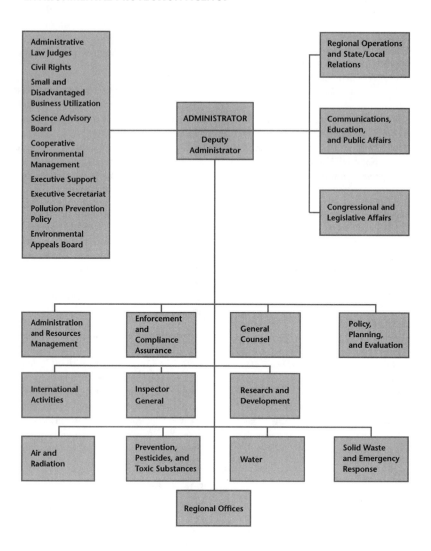

Analyzes how policies affect the department; makes recommendations and develops policy options for resolving natural resource problems.

Justice Dept., *Environment and Natural Resources,* 950 Pennsylvania Ave. N.W., #2143 20530; (202) 514-2701. Fax, (202) 514-0557. Lois J. Schiffer, assistant attorney general.

Handles civil suits involving the federal government in all areas of the environment and natural resources; handles some criminal suits involving pollution control.

National Institute of Environmental Health Sciences *(National Institutes of Health),* 9000 Rockville Pike, Bldg. 31, #B1C02, Bethesda, MD 20892 (mailing address: 31 Center Dr., MSC 2256, Bethesda, MD 20892-2256); (301) 496-3511. Fax, (301) 496-0563. Kenneth Olden, director; Chris Schonwalder, director, International Programs. Internet, http://www.niehs.nih.gov.

Conducts and supports fundamental research on the effects of chemical, biological, and physical factors in the environment on human health. Participates in international research. (Most operations located in Research Triangle Park, N.C.)

National Oceanic and Atmospheric Administration *(Commerce Dept.), 14th St. and Constitution Ave. N.W. 20230; (202) 482-3436. Fax, (202) 408-9674. D. James Baker, under secretary. Information, (202) 482-2000. Press, (202) 482-6090. Internet, http://www.noaa.gov.*

Conducts research in marine and atmospheric sciences; issues weather forecasts and warnings vital to public safety and the national economy; surveys resources of the sea; analyzes economic aspects of fisheries operations; develops and implements policies on international fisheries; provides states with grants to conserve coastal zone areas; protects marine mammals; maintains a national environmental center with data from satellite observations and other sources including meteorological, oceanic, geodetic, and seismological data centers; provides colleges and universities with grants for research, education, and marine advisory services; prepares and provides nautical and aeronautical charts and maps.

National Oceanic and Atmospheric Administration *(Commerce Dept.), National Environmental Satellite, Data, and Information Service, 4401 Suitland Rd., #2069, Suitland, MD 20746 (mailing address: 4700 Silver Hill Rd., STOP 9909, Washington, DC 20233-9909); (301) 457-5115. Fax, (301) 457-5276. Robert S. Winokur, assistant administrator. Internet, orders@ncdc.noaa.gov (National Climatic Data Center).*

Provides satellite observations of the environment by operating polar orbiting and geostationary satellites; develops satellite techniques; increases the utilization of satellite data in environmental services.

National Science and Technology Council *(Executive Office of the President), Old Executive Office Bldg., #435 20500; (202) 456-6100. Fax, (202) 456-6026. John H. Gibbons, chair. Internet, http://www.whitehouse.gov/ White_House/EOP/OSTP.*

Coordinates research and development activities and programs that involve more than one federal agency. Activities concern earth sciences, materials, forestry research, and radiation policy.

Office of Science and Technology Policy *(Executive Office of the President), Environment, Old Executive Office Bldg., #443 20502; (202) 456-6202. Fax, (202) 456-6025. Rosina Bierbaum, acting associate director.*

Provides the president with policy analysis and assistance on issues related to the environment and natural resources.

Transportation Dept., *Environmental Division, 400 7th St. S.W., #9217 20590-0001; (202) 366-4366. Fax, (202) 366-7618. Camille Mittelholtz, chief.*

Develops environmental policy and makes recommendations to the secretary; monitors Transportation Dept. implementation of environmental legislation; serves as liaison with other federal agencies and state and local governments on environmental matters related to transportation.

U.S. Geological Survey *(Interior Dept.), 12201 Sunrise Valley Dr., Reston, VA 20192; (703) 648-7411. Fax, (703) 648-4454. Thomas J. Casadevall, director. Information, (703) 648-7469. Press, (703) 648-4460. Library, (703) 648-4305. Internet, http://www.usgs.gov.*

Provides reports, maps, and databases that describe and analyze water, energy, and mineral resources; the land surface; and the underlying geological structure and dynamic processes of the earth.

CONGRESS

General Accounting Office, *Energy, Science, and Natural Resources Management Issues, 441 G St. N.W., #1842 20548; (202) 512-3841. Fax, (202) 512-8774. Victor S. Rezendes, director.*

Independent, nonpartisan agency in the legislative branch that audits, analyzes, and reports on efficiency and effectiveness of Interior Dept. programs concerned with managing natural resources.

General Accounting Office, *Environmental Protection Issues, 441 G St. N.W., #2085 20548; (202) 512-6111. Fax, (202) 512-9925. Peter F. Guerrero, director.*

Independent, nonpartisan agency in the legislative branch. Audits, analyzes, and evaluates programs of the Environmental Protection Agency; makes reports available to the public.

House Appropriations Committee, *Subcommittee on Commerce, Justice, State, and Judiciary, H309 Capitol 20515; (202) 225-3351. Harold Rogers, R-Ky., chair; Jim Kulikowski, staff director. Internet, http://www.house. gov/appropriations.*

Jurisdiction over legislation to appropriate funds for the Marine Mammal Commission and the Commerce Dept., including the National Oceanic and Atmospheric Administration.

House Appropriations Committee, *Subcommittee on Energy and Water Development, 2362 RHOB 20515; (202) 225-3421. Joseph M. McDade, R-Pa., chair; James Ogsbury, staff director. Internet, http://www.house.gov/ appropriations.*

Jurisdiction over legislation to appropriate funds for the Bureau of Reclamation in the Interior Dept., the federal power marketing administrations in the Energy

Dept., the civil programs of the Army Corps of Engineers, the Tennessee Valley Authority, and related agencies.

House Appropriations Committee, *Subcommittee on Interior,* *B308 RHOB 20515; (202) 225-3081. Fax, (202) 225-9069. Ralph Regula, R-Ohio, chair; Deborah A. Weatherly, clerk. Internet, http://www.house.gov/ appropriations.*

Jurisdiction over legislation to appropriate funds for the Interior Dept. (except the Bureau of Reclamation), the Forest Service in the Agriculture Dept., clean coal technology, fossil energy, naval petroleum and oil shale reserves, and other natural resources-related services and programs.

House Appropriations Committee, *Subcommittee on VA, HUD, and Independent Agencies,* *H143 CAP 20515; (202) 225-3241. Jerry Lewis, R-Calif., chair; Frank Cushing, staff director. Internet, http://www.house.gov/ appropriations.*

Jurisdiction over legislation to appropriate funds for the Environmental Protection Agency, Office of Environmental Policy, Council on Environmental Quality, National Science Foundation, and other environment-related services and programs.

House Commerce Committee, *Subcommittee on Finance and Hazardous Materials,* *2125 RHOB 20515; (202) 225-2927. Fax, (202) 225-1919. Michael G. Oxley, R-Ohio, chair; James E. Derderian, staff director.*

Jurisdiction over legislation on solid waste disposal, pollution, toxic substances, noise pollution control, and hazardous materials (except EPA research and development programs). Jurisdiction over the Comprehensive Environmental Response, Compensation, and Liability Act (the Superfund), the Resource Conservation and Recovery Act, and the Toxic Substances Control Act (jurisdiction shared with House Science Committee).

House Commerce Committee, *Subcommittee on Health and the Environment,* *2125 RHOB 20515; (202) 225-2927. Fax, (202) 225-1919. Michael Bilirakis, R-Fla., chair; James E. Derderian, staff director. Internet, http:// www.house.gov/commerce/health.html.*

Jurisdiction over legislation concerning environmental affairs, including global warming.

House Government Reform and Oversight Committee, *Subcommittee on National Economic Growth, Natural Resources, and Regulatory Affairs,* *B377 RHOB 20515; (202) 225-4407. Fax, (202) 225-2441. David M. McIntosh, R-Ind., chair; Mildred Webber, staff director. Internet, http://www.house.gov/reform.*

Oversight of the Interior Dept., the Environmental Protection Agency, the Office of Environmental Policy, the Nuclear Regulatory Commission, the U.S. Fish and Wildlife Service, and the Council on Environmental Quality.

House Resources Committee, *1324 LHOB 20515-6201; (202) 225-2761. Fax, (202) 225-5929. Don Young, R-Alaska, chair; Lloyd Jones, staff director. Internet, resource@hr.house.gov or http://www.house.gov/resources.*

Jurisdiction over legislation on natural resource issues, including water control.

House Resources Committee, *Subcommittee on Fisheries, Conservation, Wildlife, and Oceans,* *805 O'Neill Bldg. 20515; (202) 226-0200. Fax, (202) 225-1542. Rep. H. James Saxton, R-N.J., chair; Harry Burroughs, staff director. Internet, http://www.house.gov/resources.*

Jurisdiction over legislation on many natural resource issues, including conservation.

House Science Committee, *Subcommittee on Energy and Environment,* *389 FHOB 20515; (202) 225-9662. Fax, (202) 266-6983. Ken Calvert, R-Calif., chair; Harlan Watson, staff director. Internet, http://www.house.gov/ science.*

Jurisdiction over legislation on research and development related to natural resources, including Energy dept. environmental science activities and Environmental Protection Agency programs concerning air, water, noise, and solid waste pollution. Jurisdiction over research and development programs of the National Environmental Policy Act, the Comprehensive Environmental Response, Compensation, and Liability Act (the Superfund), the Resource Conservation and Recovery Act, and the Toxic Substances Control Act (jurisdiction shared with House Commerce Committee).

House Small Business Committee, *2361 RHOB 20515; (202) 225-5821. James M. Talent, R-Mo., chair; Mark Strand, chief of staff. Internet, http://www.house.gov/ smbiz.*

Studies and makes recommendations on environmental and pollution issues as they relate to small business.

Senate Agriculture, Nutrition, and Forestry Committee, *Subcommittee on Forestry, Conservation, and Rural Revitalization,* *SR-328A 20510; (202) 224-2035. Rick Santorum, R-Pa., chair; David French, legislative assistant. Internet, http://www.senate.gov/~agriculture.*

Jurisdiction over legislation on many natural resources issues, including conservation, forestry, and water control; oversight of the Interior Dept. and the Agriculture Dept.'s Forest Service.

Senate Appropriations Committee, *Subcommittee on Commerce, Justice, State, and Judiciary,* SR-393 20510; (202) 224-7277. Judd Gregg, R-N.H., chair, (202) 224-3324; Vas Alexopoulos, legislative assistant. Chair's fax, (202) 224-4952. Internet, http://www.senate.gov/~appropriations.

Jurisdiction over legislation to appropriate funds for the Marine Mammal Commission and the Commerce Dept., including the National Oceanic and Atmospheric Administration.

Senate Appropriations Committee, *Subcommittee on Energy and Water Development,* SD-127 20510; (202) 224-7260. Pete V. Domenici, R-N.M., chair; Alex Flint, majority clerk. Internet, http://www.senate.gov/~appropriations/energy.

Jurisdiction over legislation to appropriate funds for the Bureau of Reclamation in the Interior Dept., the federal power marketing administrations in the Energy Dept., the civil programs of the Army Corps of Engineers, the Tennessee Valley Authority, and related agencies.

Senate Appropriations Committee, *Subcommittee on Interior,* SD-131 20510; (202) 224-7233. Slade Gorton, R-Wash., chair; Bruce Evans, staff director. Internet, http://www.senate.gov/~appropriations.

Jurisdiction over legislation to appropriate funds for the Interior Dept.; the Forest Service in the Agriculture Dept.; the National Park Service; clean coal technology; fossil energy; naval petroleum and oil shale reserves; and other natural resources-related services and programs.

Senate Appropriations Committee, *Subcommittee on VA, HUD, and Independent Agencies,* SD-127 20510; (202) 224-7211. Christopher S. Bond, R-Mo., chair; John K. Mark, staff director. Internet, http://www.senate.gov/~appropriations.

Jurisdiction over legislation to appropriate funds for the Environmental Protection Agency, Office of Environmental Policy, Council on Environmental Quality, National Science Foundation, and other environment-related services and programs.

Senate Energy and Natural Resources Committee, SD-364 20510; (202) 224-4971. Fax, (202) 224-6163. Frank H. Murkowski, R-Alaska, chair; Gregg D. Renkes, staff director. Internet, http://www.senate.gov/~energy.

Jurisdiction over legislation on many aspects of natural resources, including research and development.

Senate Environment and Public Works Committee, SD-410 20510; (202) 224-6176. Fax, (202) 224-5167. John H. Chafee, R-R.I., chair; Jimmy Powell, staff director. Internet, http://www.senate.gov/committee/environment.html.

Jurisdiction over most legislation relating to environmental affairs, including global warming and Environmental Protection Agency research and development programs concerning air, water, noise, solid waste, hazardous materials, and toxic substances; jurisdiction over legislation relating to the National Environmental Policy Act, the Comprehensive Environmental Response, Compensation, and Liability Act (the Superfund), the Resource Conservation and Recovery Act, and the Toxic Substances Control Act. Oversight of the Environmental Protection Agency, the Office of Environmental Policy, the Nuclear Regulatory Commission, the U.S. Fish and Wildlife Service, the Council on Environmental Quality, and the National Science Foundation.

Senate Small Business Committee, SR-428A 20510; (202) 224-5175. Fax, (202) 224-4885. Christopher S. Bond, R-Mo., chair; Louis Taylor, staff director. Internet, http://www.senate.gov/~sbc.

Studies and makes recommendations on environmental and pollution issues as they relate to small businesses.

NONPROFIT

American Bar Assn., *Standing Committee on Environmental Law,* 740 15th St. N.W. 20005; (202) 662-1693. Fax, (202) 638-3844. Elissa Lichtenstein, director. Internet, http://www.abanet.org/publicserv/environmental.html.

Conducts domestic and international projects in environmental law and policy; coordinates environmental law activities throughout the ABA.

Americans for the Environment, 1400 16th St. N.W., #210 20036; (202) 797-6665. Fax, (202) 797-6563. Roy Morgan, president. Internet, afedc@igc.apc.org or http://www.ewg.org/pub/home/afe/homepage.htm.

Seeks to protect natural resources by influencing public policy. Encourages citizen involvement in ballot measures and the electoral process; offers training, education, and information in environmental fields and in political campaign management.

Citizens for a Sound Economy, 1250 H St. N.W., #700 20005-3908; (202) 783-3870. Fax, (202) 783-4687. Paul Beckner, executive director. Internet, http://www.csc.org/csc.

Education and research organization that seeks market-oriented solutions to environmental problems. Develops initiatives to balance environmental and economic considerations; supports private efforts to manage wildlife habitats.

Concern, *1794 Columbia Rd. N.W. 20009; (202) 328-8160. Fax, (202) 387-3378. Susan Boyd, executive director. Internet, concern@igc.org.*

Environmental education organization interested in issues such as sustainable communities, global warming, energy, agriculture, pesticides, water resources, and waste reduction.

Conservation Fund, *1800 N. Kent St., #1120, Arlington, VA 22209; (703) 525-6300. Fax, (703) 525-4610. John F. Turner, president. Internet, http://www.conservationfund. org.*

Creates partnerships with the private sector, non-profit organizations, and public agencies to promote land and water conservation.

Co-op America, *1612 K St. N.W., #600 20006; (202) 872-5307. Fax, (202) 331-8166. Alisa Gravitz, executive director. Toll-free, (800) 584-7336. Internet, info@ coopamerica.org or http://www.coopamerica.org.*

Educates consumers and businesses about social and environmental responsibility. Publishes a directory of environmentally responsible businesses, a financial planning guide for investment, and boycott information.

Earth Share, *3400 International Dr. N.W., #2K 20008; (202) 537-7100. Fax, (202) 537-7101. Kalman Stein, president. Toll-free, (800) 875-3863. Internet, info@earthshare. org or http://www.earthshare.org.*

Federation of environmental and conservation organizations. Works with government and private payroll deduction programs to solicit contributions to member organizations for environmental research, education, and community programs. Provides information on establishing environmental giving options in the workplace.

Edison Electric Institute, *701 Pennsylvania Ave. N.W. 20004; (202) 508-5000. Fax, (202) 508-5759. Thomas R. Kuhn, president. Information, (202) 508-5778. Internet, http://www.eei.org.*

Membership: investor-owned electric power companies and electric utility holding companies. Interests include electric utility operation and concerns, including conservation and energy management, energy analysis, resources and environment, cogeneration and renewable energy resources, nuclear power, and research. Library open to the public by appointment.

Environmental and Energy Study Institute, *122 C St. N.W., #700 20001-2109; (202) 628-1400. Fax, (202) 628-1825. Dick Ottinger, chair; Ken Murphy, executive director. Internet, http://www.eesi.org.*

Nonpartisan policy education and analysis group established in cooperation with the congressional Envi-

ronmental and Energy Study Conference to foster informed debate on environmental and energy issues. Interests include policies for sustainable development.

Environmental Defense Fund, *1875 Connecticut Ave. N.W., #1016 20009-5728; (202) 387-3500. Fax, (202) 234-6049. Cheryl Pickard, office manager, Washington Office. Internet, http://www.edf.org.*

Citizens' interest group staffed by lawyers, economists, and scientists. Takes legal action on environmental issues; provides information on pollution prevention, environmental health, wetlands, toxic substances, acid rain, tropical rain forests, and litigation of water pollution standards. (Headquarters in New York.)

Environmental Law Institute, *1616 P St. N.W., #200 20036; (202) 939-3800. Fax, (202) 939-3868. J. William Futrell, president. Internet, law@eli.org or http://www. eli.org.*

Research and education organization with an interdisciplinary staff of lawyers, economists, scientists, and journalists. Publishes materials on environmental issues, sponsors education and training courses, issues policy recommendations, and cosponsors conferences on environmental law.

Environmental Media Services, *1320 18th St., 5th Floor 20036; (202) 463-6670. Fax, (202) 822-4787. Arlie Schardt, director. Internet, http://www.ems.org.*

Advocates expanded and improved coverage of environmental issues in the nation's media. Conducts educational workshops.

Environmental Working Group, *1718 Connecticut Ave. N.W., #600 20009; (202) 667-6982. Fax, (202) 232-2592. Kenneth A. Cook, president. Internet, info@ewg.org or http://www.ewg.org.*

Research and advocacy organization that studies and reports on the presence of herbicides and pesticides in food and drinking water. Monitors legislation and regulations.

Friends of the Earth, *1025 Vermont Ave. N.W., #300 20005-6303; (202) 783-7400. Fax, (202) 783-0444. Brent Blackwelder, president. Internet, foe@foe.org or http:// www.foe.org.*

Citizens' interest group concerned with environmental, public health, and energy-related issues, including clean air, water, and groundwater; energy conservation; nuclear energy, waste, storage, and weapons; international water projects; transportation of hazardous wastes; global warming; and toxic substances and pesticides. Specializes in federal budget and tax issues related to the environment; ozone layer and ground water protection; and World Bank and International Monetary Fund reform. Library open to the public by appointment.

Izaak Walton League of America, *707 Conservation Lane, Gaithersburg, MD 20878-2983; (301) 548-0150. Fax, (301) 548-0146. Paul W. Hansen, executive director. Internet, general@iwla.org or http://www.iwla.org/iwla.*

Grassroots organization that promotes conservation of natural resources and the environment. Interests include air and water pollution and wildlife habitat protection. Provides information on acid rain and stream cleanup efforts at the local level.

League of Conservation Voters, *1707 L St. N.W., #750 20036; (202) 785-8683. Fax, (202) 835-0491. Debra J. Callahan, president. Internet, http://www.lcv.org.*

Works to support the environmental movement by helping elect environmentally concerned candidates to public office.

League of Women Voters Education Fund, *Natural Resources, 1730 M St. N.W., #1000 20036; (202) 429-1965. Fax, (202) 429-0854. Elizabeth Kraft, assistant director.*

Education foundation affiliated with the League of Women Voters. Promotes citizen understanding of nuclear and solid waste issues; holds regional workshops to educate community leaders on these issues.

National Assn. of Conservation Districts, *509 Capitol Court N.E. 20002-4937; (202) 547-6223. Fax, (202) 547-6450. Ernest C. Shea, chief executive officer. Internet, http://www.nacdnet.org.*

Membership: conservation districts (local subdivisions of state government). Interests include erosion and sediment control, water quality, rural development, forestry, and urban and community conservation.

National Audubon Society, *1901 Pennsylvania Ave. N.W., #1100 20006; (202) 861-2242. Fax, (202) 861-4290. Dan Beard, senior vice president, Public Policy. Internet, http://www.audubon.org.*

Citizens' interest group that promotes environmental preservation. Provides information on water resources, public lands, rangelands, forests, parks, wildlife and marine conservation, and the national wildlife refuge system. (Headquarters in New York.)

National Environmental Development Assn., *818 Connecticut Ave. N.W., 2nd Floor 20006; (202) 289-0966. Fax, (202) 289-1327. Steve Hellem, director. Internet, strat@comm.his.com.*

Membership: corporations and individuals. Provides information on balancing environmental and economic needs. Manages projects concerning clean air regulation, new federal and state environmental relationships, and international environmental advocacy.

National Environmental Trust, *1200 18th St. N.W., #500 20036; (202) 887-8800. Fax, (202) 887-8877. Phil Clapp, executive director. Internet, netinfo@envirotrust.com or http://www.envirotrust.com.*

Organization that identifies and publicizes environmental issues at the national and local levels. Interests include climate change, endangered species, hazardous chemicals, and campaign finance reform; opposes efforts to weaken environmental laws. Monitors legislation and regulations.

National Wildlife Federation, *8925 Leesburg Pike, Vienna, VA 22184; (703) 790-4000. Fax, (703) 442-7332. Mark Van Putten, president. Internet, http://www.nwf.org.*

Promotes conservation of natural resources; provides information on the environment and resource management; takes legal action on environmental issues. Laurel Ridge Conservation Education Center in Vienna, Va., provides educational materials and outdoor programs.

Natural Resources Defense Council, *1200 New York Ave. N.W., #400 20005-4709; (202) 289-6868. Fax, (202) 289-1060. Donna Wilcox, office manager. Internet, http://www.nrdc.org.*

Environmental organization staffed by lawyers and scientists who undertake litigation and research. Interests include air, water, land use, forests, toxic materials, natural resources management and conservation, preservation of endangered plant species, and ozone pollution. (Headquarters in New York.)

Nature Conservancy, *1815 N. Lynn St., Arlington, VA 22209; (703) 841-5300. Fax, (703) 841-1283. John C. Sawhill, president. Internet, http://www.tnc.org.*

Acquires land to protect endangered species and habitats; maintains international system of natural sanctuaries; operates the Heritage Program, a cooperative effort with state governments to identify and inventory threatened and endangered plants and animals.

Population-Environment Balance, *2000 P St. N.W., #210 20036; (202) 955-5700. Fax, (202) 955-6161. Maria Sepulveda, executive director. Internet, uspop@balance.org.*

Grassroots organization that advocates U.S. population stabilization to safeguard the environment.

Renew America, *1400 16th St. N.W., #710 20036; (202) 232-2252. Fax, (202) 232-2617. Anna Slafer, executive director. Internet, renewamerica@igc.org or http://www.crest.org/renew_america.*

Advances solutions to environmental problems by encouraging the replication of successful community-based initiatives.

Resources for the Future, *1616 P St. N.W. 20036; (202) 328-5000. Fax, (202) 939-3460. Paul Portney, president. Library, (202) 328-5089. Internet, info@rff.org or http:// www.rff.org.*

Engages in research and education on environmental and natural resource issues, including forestry, multiple use of public lands, costs and benefits of pollution control, endangered species, environmental risk management, energy and national security, and climate resources. Library open to the public.

Sierra Club, *408 C St. N.E. 20002; (202) 547-1141. Fax, (202) 547-6009. Debbie Sease, legislative director. Legislative hotline, (202) 675-2394. Internet, information@ sierraclub.org or http://www.sierraclub.org.*

Citizens' interest group that promotes protection of natural resources. Interests include the Clean Air Act; the Arctic National Wildlife Refuge; protection of national forests, parks, and wilderness; toxins; global warming; promotion of responsible international trade; and international development lending reform. Monitors legislation and regulations. (Headquarters in San Francisco.)

Union of Concerned Scientists, *1616 P St. N.W., #310 20036; (202) 332-0900. Fax, (202) 332-0905. Alden Meyer, director, Government Relations. Internet, ucs@ucsusa.org or http://www.ucsusa.org.*

Membership: scientists and others who advocate a comprehensive approach to resolving global environmental and resource concerns. Educates and mobilizes citizens on the linkages between resource depletion, environmental degradation, climate changes, consumption patterns, and population growth. Fosters cooperative efforts between the scientific, environmental, and religious communities through the National Religious Partnership for the Environment. (Headquarters in Cambridge, Mass.)

U.S. Chamber of Commerce, *Resources Policy, 1615 H St. N.W. 20062-2000; (202) 463-5532. Fax, (202) 887-3445. Mary E. Bernhard, senior manager, Environmental Policy. Internet, http://www.uschamber.org.*

Monitors operations of federal departments and agencies responsible for environmental programs and policies. Analyzes and evaluates legislation and regulations that affect the environment.

U.S. Public Interest Research Group (USPIRG), *218 D St. S.E. 20003; (202) 546-9707. Fax, (202) 546-2461. Gene Karpinski, executive director. Internet, uspirg@pirg. org or http://www.pirg.org.*

Coordinates grassroots efforts to advance environmental and consumer protection laws; conducts research on environmental issues, including toxic and solid waste, air and water pollution, pesticides, endangered species, forest and wildlife preservation, alternative energy sources, and energy conservation; compiles reports and disseminates information on such issues; drafts and monitors environmental laws; testifies on behalf of proposed environmental legislation.

Wilderness Society, *900 17th St. N.W. 20006; (202) 833-2300. Fax, (202) 429-3958. William H. Meadows III, president. Information, (202) 429-2650. Internet, tws@tws. org or http://www.wilderness.org.*

Promotes preservation of wilderness and the responsible management of all federal lands, including national parks and forests, wilderness areas, wildlife refuges, and land administered by the Interior Dept.'s Bureau of Land Management.

International Issues

AGENCIES

Environmental Protection Agency, *International Activities, 1300 Pennsylvania Ave. N.W., #31207 20004; (202) 564-6600. Fax, (202) 565-2407. William Nitze, assistant administrator. Internet, http://www.epa.gov.*

Coordinates the agency's work on international environmental issues and programs, including management of bilateral agreements and participation in multilateral organizations and negotiations.

International Trade Administration *(Commerce Dept.), Environmental Technologies Exports, 14th St. and Constitution Ave. N.W., 1st Floor 20230; (202) 482-5227. Fax, (202) 482-5665. Anna L. Alonzo, deputy assistant secretary. Internet, http://www.ita.doc.gov/envirotech.*

Works to facilitate and increase exports of U.S. environmental technologies, including both goods and services. Conducts market analysis, business counseling, and trade promotion.

State Dept., *Ecology and Terrestrial Conservation, Main State Bldg., #4333 20520; (202) 647-2418. Fax, (202) 736-7351. Mary E. McLeod, director.*

Represents the United States in international affairs relating to natural resources. Interests include wildlife, tropical forests, and biological diversity.

State Dept., *Environmental Policy, Main State Bldg., #4325 20520; (202) 647-9266. Fax, (202) 647-5947. Michael Metelits, director.*

Advances U.S. interests internationally regarding multilateral environmental organizations, chemical wastes and other pollutants, and bilateral and regional environmental policies.

State Dept., *Oceans and International Environmental and Scientific Affairs,* Main State Bldg., #7831 20520-7818; (202) 647-1554. Fax, (202) 647-0217. Melinda L. Kimble, acting assistant secretary.

Concerned with foreign policy as it affects natural resources and the environment, human health, the global climate, energy production, and oceans and fisheries.

U.S.-Asia Environmental Partnership, 1720 Eye St. N.W., #700 20006; (202) 835-0333. Fax, (202) 835-0366. Peter Kim, director. Internet, usasia@usaep.org or http://www.usaep.org.

Interagency program, led by the Agency for International Development (AID), which uses U.S. technology and services to help address environmental degradation and sustainable development issues in Asia and the Pacific. Focuses on pulp and paper, food processing, electroplating, petrochemical, and textile industries. (Secretariat located within the Asia and Near East Bureau at AID.)

CONGRESS

House International Relations Committee, *Subcommittee on International Economic Policy and Trade,* 702 O'Neill Bldg. 20515; (202) 225-3345. Fax, (202) 225-0432. Ileana Ros-Lehtinen, R-Fla., chair; Mauricio Tamargo, staff director. Internet, http://www.house.gov/international_relations.

Jurisdiction over legislation on international environmental agreements and policy (jurisdiction shared with Subcommittee on International Operations and Human Rights).

Senate Foreign Relations Committee, *Subcommittee on International Economic Policy, Export, and Trade Promotion,* SR-346 20510; (202) 224-4224. Fax, (202) 228-0436. Chuck Hagel, R-Neb., chair; Ken Peel, senior professional staff member. Internet, http://www.senate.gov/committee/foreign.html.

Jurisdiction over legislation on international environmental agreements and policy, including international marine affairs in the Antarctic and Arctic areas.

INTERNATIONAL ORGANIZATIONS

International Joint Commission, United States and Canada, U.S. Section, 1250 23rd St. N.W., #100 20440; (202) 736-9000. Fax, (202) 736-9015. James Chandler, secretary; Joel Fisher, environmental adviser.

Deals with disputes between the United States and Canada on transboundary water and air resources. Inves-

tigates issues upon request of the governments of the United States and Canada. Reviews applications for water resource projects. (Canadian section in Ottawa.)

Organization of American States (OAS), *Sustainable Development and Environment,* 1889 F St. N.W., #340-I 20006; (202) 458-3567. Fax, (202) 458-3560. Kirk P. Rodgers, director. Internet, http://www.oas.org/EN/PROG/prog.htm.

Provides support to OAS technical cooperation projects. Promotes integrated and sustainable development of natural resources; interests include international river basins, border areas, coastal zones, and emerging trade corridors.

World Conservation Union (IUCN), *U.S. Office,* 1400 16th St. N.W., #502 20036; (202) 797-5454. Fax, (202) 797-5461. Scott Hajost, executive director. Internet, postmaster@iucnus.org or http://www.iucn.org.

Membership: world governments, their environmental agencies, and nongovernmental organizations. Studies conservation issues from local to global levels; interests include protected areas, forests, oceans, polar regions, biodiversity, species survival, environmental law, sustainable use of resources, and the impact of trade on the environment. (Headquarters in Gland, Switzerland.)

NONPROFIT

Antarctica Project, 408 C St. N.E. 20002 (mailing address: P.O. Box 76920, Washington, DC 20013); (202) 544-0236. Fax, (202) 544-8483. Beth Clark, director. Internet, antarctica@igc.org or http://www.asoc.org.

Promotes effective implementation of the Antarctic Treaty System; works to protect the environment of the Antarctic continent. Interests include depletion of ozone in polar regions.

Conservation International, 2501 M St. N.W., #200 20037; (202) 429-5660. Fax, (202) 887-5188. Russell Mittermeier, president. Internet, http://www.conservation.org.

Works to conserve tropical rain forests through economic development; promotes exchange of debt relief for conservation programs that involve local people and organizations. Provides private groups and governments with information and technical advice on conservation efforts; supports conservation data gathering in Latin America, Africa, Asia, and the Caribbean.

Global Climate Coalition, 1275 K St. N.W., #890 20005; (202) 682-9161. Fax, (202) 638-1043. Gail McDonald, president. Internet, gcc@globalclimate.org or http://www.globalclimate.org.

Membership: business trade associations and private companies. Promotes scientific research on global climate change; analyzes economic and social impacts of policy options; produces educational materials and conducts programs.

Greenpeace USA, *1436 U St. N.W. 20009; (202) 462-1177. Fax, (202) 462-4507. Kristen Engburg, acting executive director. Internet, greenpeace.usa@wdc.greenpeace.org or http://www.greenpeace.org.*

Seeks to protect the environment through research, education, and grassroots organizing. Interests include chemical and nuclear waste dumping, solid and hazardous waste disposal, and protection of marine mammals and endangered species. Supports the establishment of Antarctica as a world park, free of industry, military presence, and nuclear power and weaponry. Monitors legislation and regulations.

World Resources Institute, *Center for International Development and Environment, 1709 New York Ave. N.W., #700 20006; (202) 638-6300. Fax, (202) 638-0036. Vacant, director. Internet, http://www.wri.org.*

International organization that conducts research on environmental concerns and studies the interrelationships of natural resources, economic growth, and human needs. Interests include forestry and land use, renewable energy, fisheries, and sustainable agriculture. Assesses environmental policies of aid agencies.

World Wildlife Fund, *1250 24th St. N.W., #400 20037; (202) 293-4800. Fax, (202) 293-9211. Kathryn S. Fuller, president. Internet, http://www.wwf.org.*

Conducts scientific research and analyzes policy on environmental and conservation issues, including pollution reduction, land use, forestry and wetlands management, parks, soil conservation, and sustainable development. Supports projects to promote biological diversity and to save endangered species and their habitats, including tropical forests in Latin America, Asia, and Africa. Awards grants and provides technical assistance to local conservation groups.

Worldwatch Institute, *1776 Massachusetts Ave. N.W., 8th Floor 20036; (202) 452-1999. Fax, (202) 296-7365. Lester R. Brown, president. Internet, worldwatch@worldwatch.org or http://www.worldwatch.org.*

Research organization that focuses on interdisciplinary approach to solving global environmental problems. Interests include natural resources and human needs, environmental threats to food production, and quality of life.

 ANIMALS AND PLANTS

See also Livestock and Poultry (chap. 2); Zoology (chap. 17)

AGENCIES

Animal and Plant Health Inspection Service *(Agriculture Dept.), Regulatory Enforcement and Animal Care, 4700 River Rd., Unit 97, Riverdale, MD 20737-1234; (301) 734-4980. Fax, (301) 734-4328. Dr. W. Ron DeHaven, acting deputy administrator. Internet, http://www.aphis.usda.gov/ac.*

Administers laws that regulate the handling, breeding, and care of animals raised for sale, used in research, transported commercially, or exhibited to the public. Conducts inspections; works to prevent neglect and inhumane treatment.

Food and Drug Administration *(Health and Human Services Dept.), Center for Veterinary Medicine, 7500 Standish Pl., Rockville, MD 20855-2764; (301) 594-1740. Fax, (301) 594-1830. Dr. Stephen F. Sundlof, director. Internet, http://www.cvm.fda.gov.*

Regulates the manufacture and marketing of drugs, food additives, feed ingredients, and devices for animals, including both livestock and pets. Conducts research; works to ensure animal health and the safety of food derived from animals.

National Institutes of Health *(Health and Human Services Dept.), Protection from Research Risks, 6100 Executive Blvd., #3B01, Rockville, MD 20892-7507; (301) 496-7005. Fax, (301) 402-2071. Gary B. Ellis, director. Animal welfare, (301) 496-7163.*

Monitors the use of animals in research to ensure that programs and procedures comply with Public Health Service and Health and Human Services Dept. regulations; conducts and develops educational programs and materials; evaluates the effectiveness of HHS policies and programs for the humane care and use of laboratory animals; helps other organizations address ethical issues in medicine and research.

National Zoological Park *(Smithsonian Institution), 3001 Connecticut Ave. N.W. 20008; (202) 673-4721. Fax, (202) 673-4607. Michael H. Robinson, director. Information, (202) 673-4821. Library, (202) 673-4771. TDD, (202) 673-4823. Recorded information, (202) 673-4800. Internet, http://usis.intnet.mu/smith/O/NA46.htm.*

Maintains a public zoo for exhibiting animals. Conducts research on animal behavior, ecology, nutrition, reproductive physiology, pathology, and veterinary medicine; operates an annex near Front Royal, Va., for the long-term propagation and study of endangered species. Houses a unit of the Smithsonian Institution library with volumes in zoology, biology, ecology, animal behavior, and veterinary medicine; makes interlibrary loans. Library open to qualified researchers by appointment.

CONGRESS

House Agriculture Committee, *Subcommittee on Department Operations, Nutrition, and Foreign Agriculture, 1430 LHOB 20515; (202) 225-0171. Fax, (202) 225-4464. Robert W. Goodlatte, R-Va., chair; Kevin Kramp, staff director. Internet, http://www.house.gov/ agriculture.*

Jurisdiction over legislation on animals used for experimentation.

House Agriculture Committee, *Subcommittee on Livestock, Dairy, and Poultry, 1301 LHOB 20515; (202) 225-0029. Fax, (202) 225-4369. Richard W. Pombo, R-Calif., chair; Chris D'Arcy, staff director. Internet, http:// www.house.gov/agriculture/livestoc.htm.*

Jurisdiction over legislation on inspection and certification of meat, livestock, and poultry and over animal welfare.

Senate Agriculture, Nutrition, and Forestry Committee, *Subcommittee on Research, Nutrition, and General Legislation, SR-361A 20510; (202) 224-2035. Fax, (202) 224-1725. Mitch McConnell, R-Ky., chair; David Hovermale, legislative assistant. Internet, http:// www.senate.gov/~agriculture.*

Jurisdiction over legislation on inspection and certification of meat, livestock, and poultry and over animal welfare.

NONPROFIT

American Herbal Products Assn., *4733 Bethesda Ave., #345, Bethesda, MD 20814; (301) 951-3204. Fax, (301) 951-3205. Jeffrey M. Morrison, president. Internet, http://www.ahpa.org.*

Membership: U.S. companies and individuals that grow, import, process, or market herbs and herbal products; and associates in education, law, media, and medicine. Supports research; promotes standardization, consumer protection, competition, and self-regulation in the industry. Monitors legislation and regulations.

American Horse Protection Assn., *1000 29th St. N.W., #T100 20007; (202) 965-0500. Fax, (202) 965-9621. Robin C. Lohnes, executive director.*

Membership: individuals, corporations, and foundations interested in protecting wild and domestic horses.

American Humane Assn., *236 Massachusetts Ave. N.E., #203 20002; (202) 543-7780. Fax, (202) 546-3266. Adele Douglass, director, Washington Office. Internet, tuam@ aol.com or http://www.amerhumane.org.*

Membership: humane societies, government agencies, and individuals. Monitors legislation and regulations to ensure the proper use of laboratory animals; assists local societies in establishing shelters and investigating cruelty cases; maintains training programs for humane society personnel; assists in public school education programs. (Headquarters in Denver.)

American Society for the Prevention of Cruelty to Animals (ASPCA), *1755 Massachusetts Ave. N.W., #418 20036; (202) 232-5020. Fax, (202) 797-8947. Nancy Blaney, director, Washington Legislative Office.*

Works for the humane treatment and protection of both domestic and wild animals. Interests include animal adoption and spaying and neutering of pets. Monitors legislation and regulations. (Headquarters in New York.)

American Veterinary Medical Assn., *1101 Vermont Ave. N.W., #710 20005-3521; (202) 789-0007. Fax, (202) 842-4360. Vacant, director, Governmental Relations. Internet, 74232.57@compuserve.com or http://www.avma.org.*

Monitors legislation and regulations affecting veterinary medicine. (Headquarters in Schaumburg, Ill.)

Americans for Medical Progress Education Foundation, *421 King St., #401, Alexandria, VA 22314-3121; (703) 836-9595. Fax, (703) 836-9594. Susan E. Paris, president. Internet, ampef@aol.com or http://www.ampef.org.*

Seeks to promote and protect animal-based medical research. Serves as a media resource by fact-checking claims of animal rights groups. Conducts public education campaign on the link between animal research and medical advances.

Animal Health Institute, *501 Wythe St., Alexandria, VA (mailing address: P.O. Box 1417-D50, Alexandria, VA 22313-1480); (703) 684-0011. Fax, (703) 684-0125. Alex Mathews, president. Internet, http://www.ahi.org.*

Membership: manufacturers of drugs and other products (including vaccines, pesticides, and vitamins) for pets and food-producing animals. Monitors legislation and regulations.

Animal Welfare Institute, *P.O. Box 3650 20007; (202) 337-2332. Fax, (202) 338-9478. Christine Stevens, president. Internet, awi@animalwelfare.com or http://www. animalwelfare.com.*

Educational group that opposes cruel treatment of animals used in research. Seeks to curtail animal experimentation and favors research methods that rely on non-animal subjects whenever possible.

Assn. of American Veterinary Medical Colleges, *1101 Vermont Ave. N.W., #710 20005-3521; (202) 371-9195. Fax, (202) 842-0773. Curt Mann, executive director. Internet, http://aavmc.org.*

Membership: U.S. and Canadian schools and colleges of veterinary medicine, departments of comparative medicine, and departments of veterinary science in agricultural colleges. Produces veterinary reports; sponsors continuing education programs.

The Fund for Animals, *8121 Georgia Ave., #301, Silver Spring, MD 20910; (301) 585-2591. Fax, (301) 585-2595. Heidi Prescott, national director. Internet, http://www.fund.org.*

Works for the humane treatment and protection of both domestic and wild animals. (Headquarters in New York.)

Humane Society of the United States, *2100 L St. N.W. 20037; (202) 452-1100. Fax, (202) 778-6132. Paul Irwin, chief executive. Internet, http://www.hsus.org.*

Citizens' interest group that seeks to reduce suffering of animals used in medical research and testing. Promotes the use of nonanimal alternatives, elimination of unnecessary testing, and refinement of procedures to minimize pain. Interests include legislation regulating the use of live animals in research and testing.

National Assn. for Biomedical Research, *818 Connecticut Ave. N.W., #303 20006; (202) 857-0540. Fax, (202) 659-1902. Frankie L. Trull, president. Internet, http://www.nabr.org.*

Membership: scientific and medical professional societies, academic institutions, and research-oriented corporations. Supports the humane use of animals in medical research, education, and product safety testing.

National Assn. of Professional Pet Sitters, *1200 G St. N.W., #760 20005; (202) 393-3317. Fax, (202) 393-0336. Maureen Crane and Anita Marsh, co-directors. Referrals, (800) 296-PETS. Internet, http://www.petsitters.org.*

Promotes in-home pet care and supports professionals engaged in the industry of pet sitting. Conducts education programs for certification, seminars, and conferences; provides referral service.

National Research Council, *Institute of Laboratory Animal Resources, 2101 Constitution Ave. N.W. 20418; (202) 334-2590. Fax, (202) 334-1687. Dr. Thomas L. Wolfle, director. Internet, ILAR@nas.edu or http://www2.nas.edu/ilarhome.*

Maintains an information center and answers inquiries concerning animal models for use in biomedical research, location of unique animal colonies, and availability of animals and genetic stocks from colonies and breeders. Develops guidelines on topics related to animal care and use in research, testing, and education; conducts conferences.

People for the Ethical Treatment of Animals (PETA), *501 Front St., Norfolk, VA 23510 (mailing address: P.O. Box 42516, Washington, DC 20015); (757) 622-7382. Fax, (757) 622-0457. Ingrid Newkirk, president. Internet, http://www.peta-online.org.*

Educational and activist group supporting animal rights. Provides information on topics including laboratory research animals, factory farming, cosmetics, and vegetarianism. Conducts workshops. Monitors legislation.

Physicians Committee for Responsible Medicine, *5100 Wisconsin Ave. N.W. (mailing address: P.O. Box 6322, Washington, DC 20015); (202) 686-2210. Fax, (202) 686-2216. Dr. Neal D. Barnard, president. Internet, pcrm@pcrm.org or http://www.pcrm.org.*

Membership: health professionals, medical students, and other individuals. Investigates alternatives to animal use in medical research experimentation, product testing, and education.

Society for Animal Protective Legislation, *P.O. Box 3719 20007; (202) 337-2334. Fax, (202) 338-9478. Christine Stevens, secretary. Internet, awi@animalwelfare.com.*

Citizens' interest group that supports legislation to ensure the proper treatment of animals.

Fish

See also Fishing/Law of the Sea (chap. 13)

AGENCIES

Atlantic States Marine Fisheries Commission, *1444 Eye St. N.W., 6th Floor 20005; (202) 289-6400. Fax, (202) 289-6051. John H. Dunnigan, executive director.*

Interstate compact commission of marine fisheries representatives from fifteen states along the Atlantic seaboard. Assists states in developing joint fisheries programs; works with other fisheries organizations and the federal government on environmental, natural resource, and conservation issues.

Interior Dept., Fish, Wildlife, and Parks, *1849 C St. N.W., #3156 20240; (202) 208-4416. Fax, (202) 208-4684. Donald Barry, acting assistant secretary.*

Responsible for programs associated with the development, conservation, and use of fish, wildlife, recreational, historical, and national park system resources. Coordinates marine environmental quality and biological resources programs with other federal agencies.

Justice Dept., *Wildlife and Marine Resources, 601 Pennsylvania Ave. N.W., #5000 20004 (mailing address: P.O. Box 7369, Ben Franklin Station, Washington, DC 20044-7369); (202) 305-0206. Fax, (202) 305-0275. Eileen Sobeck, chief.*

Supervises both civil and criminal cases under federal maritime laws and other laws protecting marine fish and mammals. Focuses on smugglers and black market dealers of protected wildlife.

National Oceanic and Atmospheric Administration *(Commerce Dept.), National Marine Fisheries Service, 1315 East-West Hwy., Silver Spring, MD 20910; (301) 713-2239. Fax, (301) 713-2258. Rolland A. Schmitten, assistant administrator. Press, (301) 713-2370. Internet, http://kingfish.ssp.nmfs.gov.*

Administers marine fishing regulations, including offshore fishing rights and international agreements; conducts marine resources research; studies use and management of these resources; administers the Magnuson Fishery Conservation and Management Act; manages and protects marine resources, especially endangered species and marine mammals, within the exclusive economic zone.

U.S. Fish and Wildlife Service *(Interior Dept.), 1849 C St. N.W., #3256 20240; (202) 208-4717. Fax, (202) 208-6965. Jamie R. Clark, director. Information, (202) 208-5634. Internet, http://www.fws.gov.*

Meets federal mandates concerning inland sport fisheries and fishery research activities and improves fish resources through responsible management of fish habitats; provides conservation education and information programs on fish.

U.S. Fish and Wildlife Service, *(Interior Dept.), Fish and Wildlife Ecological Services, 1849 C St. N.W., #3242 20240; (202) 208-4646. Fax, (202) 208-6916. Garry Jackson, assistant director. Internet, http://www.fws.gov.*

Monitors federal policy on fish and wildlife. Reviews all federal and federally licensed projects to determine environmental effect on fish and wildlife; responsible for maintaining the endangered species list and for protecting and restoring species to healthy numbers.

U.S. Fish and Wildlife Service, *(Interior Dept.), Fisheries, 1849 C St. N.W., #3245 20240; (202) 208-6394. Fax, (202) 208-4674. Gary B. Edwards, assistant director. Internet, http://www.fws.gov.*

Develops, manages, and protects interstate and international fisheries, including fisheries of the Great Lakes, fisheries on federal lands, aquatic ecosystems, endangered species of fish, and anadromous species. Administers the National Fish Hatchery System and the National Fish and Wildlife Resource Management Offices.

U.S. Geological Survey *(Interior Dept.), Biological Resources, 12201 Sunrise Valley Dr., Reston, VA 20192; (703) 648-4050. Fax, (703) 648-4042. Dennis B. Fenn, chief biologist. Internet, http://www.nbs.gov.*

Performs research in support of biological resource management. Monitors and reports on the status of the nation's biotic resources, including fish resources. Conducts research on fish diseases, nutrition, and culture techniques; studies ecology of the Great Lakes and the effects of pesticides and herbicides on fish.

CONGRESS

House Resources Committee, *Subcommittee on Fisheries, Conservation, Wildlife, and Oceans, 805 O'Neill Bldg. 20515; (202) 226-0200. Fax, (202) 225-1542. H. James Saxton, R-N.J., chair; Harry Burroughs, staff director. Internet, http://www.house.gov/resources.*

Jurisdiction over legislation on fish and fish hatcheries, fisheries promotion, the Magnuson-Stevens Fishery Conservation and Management Act, fisheries research, aquaculture, and seafood safety.

Senate Commerce, Science, and Transportation Committee, *Subcommittee on Oceans and Fisheries, SH-428 (mailing address: SD-508, Washington, DC 20510); (202) 224-8172. Fax, (202) 228-0326. Olympia J. Snowe, R-Maine, chair; Clark LeBlanc, professional staffer. Internet, http://www.senate.gov/~commerce.*

Studies all aspects of fish and fish hatcheries, including the Magnuson Fishery Conservation and Management Act, fisheries research, aquaculture, and seafood safety. (Subcommittee does not report legislation.)

NONPROFIT

American Fisheries Society, *5410 Grosvenor Lane, #110, Bethesda, MD 20814-2199; (301) 897-8616. Fax, (301) 897-8096. Paul Brouha, executive director. Internet, http://www.fisheries.org.*

Membership: biologists and other scientists interested in fisheries. Promotes the fisheries profession, the advancement of fisheries science, and conservation of renewable aquatic resources. Monitors legislation and regulations.

Center for Marine Conservation, *1725 DeSales St. N.W., #600 20036; (202) 429-5609. Fax, (202) 872-0619.*

Roger E. McManus, president. Internet, http://www.cmc-ocean.org.

Works to prevent the overexploitation of living marine resources, including fisheries, and to restore depleted marine wildlife populations.

International Assn. of Fish and Wildlife Agencies, *444 N. Capitol St. N.W., #544 20001; (202) 624-7890. Fax, (202) 624-7891. R. Max Peterson, executive vice president. Internet, fwa@sso.org.*

Membership: federal, state, and provincial fish and wildlife management agencies in the United States, Canada, and Mexico. Encourages balanced fish and wildlife resource management.

National Fisheries Institute, *1901 N. Fort Myer Dr., #700, Arlington, VA 22209; (703) 524-8880. Fax, (703) 524-4619. Dick Gutting, executive vice president. Internet, office@nfi.org or http://www.nfi.org.*

Membership: vessel owners and distributors, processors, wholesalers, importers, traders, and brokers of fish and shellfish. Monitors legislation and regulations on fisheries.

National Food Processors Assn., *1401 New York Ave. N.W., #400 20005; (202) 639-5900. Fax, (202) 639-5932. John R. Cady, president. Press, (202) 639-5919.*

Membership: manufacturers and suppliers of processed and packaged food, drinks, and juice. Serves as industry liaison between seafood processors and the federal government.

Trout Unlimited, *1500 Wilson Blvd., #310, Arlington, VA 22209-2404; (703) 522-0200. Fax, (703) 284-9400. Charles Gauvin, president. Internet, http://www.tu.org.*

Membership: individuals interested in the protection and enhancement of cold-water fish and their habitat. Sponsors research projects with federal and state fisheries agencies; maintains programs for water quality surveillance and cleanup of streams and lakes.

U.S. Tuna Foundation, *1101 17th St. N.W., #609 20036; (202) 857-0610. Fax, (202) 331-9686. David G. Burney, executive director.*

Membership: tuna processors, vessel owners, and fishermen's unions. Interests include fishing legislation and government relations.

Wildlife and Marine Mammals

AGENCIES

Animal and Plant Health Inspection Service *(Agriculture Dept.),* **Wildlife Services,** *1400 Independence Ave. S.W., #1624S 20250-3402; (202) 720-2054. Fax, (202)*

690-0053. Bobby R. Acord, deputy administrator. Internet, http://www.aphis.usda.gov/ws.

Works to minimize damage caused by wildlife to crops and livestock, natural resources, and human health and safety. Removes or eliminates predators and nuisance birds; interests include aviation safety and coexistence of people and wildlife in suburban areas. Oversees the National Wildlife Research Center, located in Denver, Colo.

Forest Service *(Agriculture Dept.),* **Wildlife, Fisheries, and Rare Plants,** *1400 Independence Ave. S.W. (mailing address: P.O. Box 96090, Washington, DC 20090-6090); (202) 205-1205. Fax, (202) 205-1599. Harv Forgren, acting director. Internet, http://www.fs.fed.us.*

Provides national policy direction and management for fish, endangered species, wildlife, and rare plants programs on lands managed by the Forest Service.

Interior Dept., Fish, Wildlife, and Parks, *1849 C St. N.W., #3156 20240; (202) 208-4416. Fax, (202) 208-4684. Donald Barry, acting assistant secretary.*

Responsible for programs associated with the development, conservation, and use of fish, wildlife, recreational, historical, and national park system resources. Coordinates marine environmental quality and biological resources programs with other federal agencies.

Interior Dept., North American Wetlands Conservation Council, *4401 N. Fairfax Dr., #110, Arlington, VA 22203; (703) 358-1784. Fax, (703) 358-2282. David A. Smith, coordinator. Internet, r9arw_nawwo@mail.fws.gov or http://www.fws.gov.*

Membership: government and private-sector conservation experts. Works to protect, restore, and manage wetlands and other habitats for migratory birds and other animals and to maintain migratory bird and waterfowl populations.

Justice Dept., Wildlife and Marine Resources, *601 Pennsylvania Ave. N.W., #5000 20004 (mailing address: P.O. Box 7369, Ben Franklin Station, Washington, DC 20044-7369); (202) 305-0206. Fax, (202) 305-0275. Eileen Sobeck, chief.*

Responsible for criminal enforcement and civil litigation under federal fish and wildlife conservation statutes, including protection of wildlife, fish, and plant resources within U.S. jurisdiction; monitors interstate and foreign commerce of these resources.

Marine Mammal Commission, *4340 East-West Hwy., #905, Bethesda, MD 20814; (301) 504-0087. Fax, (301) 504-0099. John R. Twiss Jr., executive director; Robert J. Hofman, scientific program director.*

Established by Congress to ensure protection and conservation of marine mammals; conducts research and makes recommendations on federal programs that affect marine mammals.

National Oceanic and Atmospheric Administration *(Commerce Dept.), Protected Resources, 1315 East-West Hwy., #13342, Silver Spring, MD 20910; (301) 713-2332. Fax, (301) 713-0376. Hilda Diaz-Soltero, director.*

Provides guidance on the conservation and protection of marine mammals and endangered species and on the conservation and restoration of their habitats. Develops national guidelines and policies for relevant research programs; prepares and reviews management and recovery plans and environmental impact analyses.

U.S. Fish and Wildlife Service *(Interior Dept.), 1849 C St. N.W., #3256 20240; (202) 208-4717. Fax, (202) 208-6965. Jamie R. Clark, director. Information, (202) 208-5634. Internet, http://www.fws.gov.*

Maintains and improves wildlife resources through responsible management of migratory birds, waterfowl, and endangered wildlife; habitat preservation; administration of the National Wildlife Refuge System; enforcement of federal wildlife laws; and research, including migratory bird and waterfowl studies.

U.S. Fish and Wildlife Service, *(Interior Dept.), Fish and Wildlife Ecological Services, 1849 C St. N.W., #3242 20240; (202) 208-4646. Fax, (202) 208-6916. Gerry Jackson, assistant director. Internet, http://www.fws.gov.*

Monitors federal policy on fish and wildlife. Reviews all federal and federally licensed projects to determine environmental effect on fish and wildlife; responsible for maintaining the endangered species list and for protecting and restoring species to healthy numbers.

U.S. Fish and Wildlife Service, *(Interior Dept.), Migratory Bird Conservation Commission, 4401 N. Fairfax Dr., #622, Arlington, VA 22203; (703) 358-1713. Fax, (703) 358-2223. Jeffery M. Donahoe, secretary. Internet, http://www.fws.gov.*

Established by the Migratory Bird Conservation Act of 1929. Decides which areas to purchase for use as migratory bird refuges.

U.S. Fish and Wildlife Service, *(Interior Dept.), North American Waterfowl and Wetlands, 4401 N. Fairfax Dr., #110, Arlington, VA 22203; (703) 358-1784. Fax, (703) 358-2282. Byron Kenneth Williams, executive director. Internet, r9arw_nawwo@mail.fws.gov.*

Coordinates U.S. activities with Canada and Mexico to protect waterfowl habitats, restore waterfowl populations, and set research priorities under the North American Waterfowl Management Plan.

U.S. Fish and Wildlife Service, *(Interior Dept.), Refuges and Wildlife, 1849 C St. N.W., #3251 20240; (202) 208-5333. Fax, (202) 208-3082. Nita Fuller, assistant director. Internet, http://www.fws.gov.*

Determines policy for the management of wildlife, including migratory birds; administers hunting regulations and establishes hunting seasons for migratory birds; marks and bands waterfowl; manages the National Wildlife Refuge System; enforces federal wildlife regulations for hunting and importing wildlife; manages land acquisition for wildlife refuges; and oversees the federal duck stamp program, which generates revenue for wetlands acquisition.

U.S. Geological Survey *(Interior Dept.), Biological Resources, 12201 Sunrise Valley Dr., Reston, VA 20192; (703) 648-4050. Fax, (703) 648-4042. Dennis B. Fenn, chief biologist. Internet, http://www.nbs.gov.*

Performs research in support of biological resource management. Monitors and reports on the status of the nation's biotic resources. Conducts research on fish and wildlife, including the effects of disease and environmental contaminants on wildlife populations. Studies endangered and other species.

CONGRESS

House Government Reform and Oversight Committee, *Subcommittee on National Economic Growth, Natural Resources, and Regulatory Affairs, B377 RHOB 20515; (202) 225-4407. Fax, (202) 225-2441. David M. McIntosh, R-Ind., chair; Mildred Webber, staff director. Internet, http://www.house.gov/reform.*

Oversight of the U.S. Fish and Wildlife Service.

House Resources Committee, *Subcommittee on Fisheries, Conservation, Wildlife, and Oceans, 805 O'Neill Bldg. 20515; (202) 226-0200. Fax, (202) 225-1542. H. James Saxton, R-N.J., chair; Harry Burroughs, staff director. Internet, http://www.house.gov/resources.*

Jurisdiction over legislation on fisheries and wildlife, habitat preservation and research programs, endangered species and marine mammal protection, wildlife refuges, estuarine protection, wetlands conservation, and biological diversity. General oversight of the U.S. Fish and Wildlife Service, the National Marine Fisheries Service, the Office of Environmental Policy, and the Marine Mammal Commission, and certain programs of the National Oceanic and Atmospheric Administration.

Senate Environment and Public Works Committee, *Subcommittee on Drinking Water, Fisheries, and Wildlife, SD-410 20510; (202) 224-6176. Fax, (202) 224-5167. Dirk Kempthorne, R-Idaho, chair; Ann Klee, staff* contact. Internet, http://www.senate.gov/committee/environment.html.

Jurisdiction over legislation on fisheries and wildlife, habitat preservation and research programs, endangered species and marine mammal protection, wildlife refuges, estuarine protection, wetlands conservation, and biological diversity; oversight of the U.S. Fish and Wildlife Service, the Office of Environmental Policy, and the Marine Mammal Commission.

NONPROFIT

Animal Welfare Institute, *P.O. Box 3650 20007; (202) 337-2332. Fax, (202) 338-9478. Christine Stevens, president. Internet, awi@animalwelfare.com or http://www.animalwelfare.com.*

Educational group that opposes steel jaw animal traps and supports the protection of marine mammals. Interests include preservation of endangered species, reform of cruel methods of raising food animals, and humane treatment of laboratory animals.

Center for Marine Conservation, *1725 DeSales St. N.W., #600 20036; (202) 429-5609. Fax, (202) 872-0619. Roger E. McManus, president. Internet, http://www.cmc-ocean.org.*

Works to conserve the diversity and abundance of life in the oceans and coastal areas, to prevent the overexploitation of living marine resources and the degradation of marine ecosystems, and to restore depleted marine wildlife populations and their ecosystems.

Defenders of Wildlife, *1101 14th St. N.W., #1400 20005; (202) 682-9400. Fax, (202) 682-1331. Rodger Schlickeisen, president. Internet, http://www.defenders.org.*

Advocacy group that works to protect wild animals and plants in their natural communities. Interests include endangered species and biodiversity. Monitors legislation and regulations.

Ducks Unlimited, *1709 New York Ave. N.W., #202 20006; (202) 347-1530. Fax, (202) 347-1533. Scott Sutherland, director, Governmental Affairs. Internet, http://www.ducks.org.*

Works to restore populations of North American waterfowl by restoring, enhancing, and protecting habitat in the United States, Canada, and Mexico. Monitors legislation and regulations. (Headquarters in Memphis, Tenn.)

Greenpeace USA, *1436 U St. N.W. 20009; (202) 462-1177. Fax, (202) 462-4507. Kristen Engburg, acting executive director. Internet, greenpeace.usa@wdc.greenpeace.org or http://www.greenpeace.org.*

Seeks to protect the environment through research, education, and grassroots organizing. Works to stop commercial slaughter of whales, seals, and dolphins; to preserve marine habitats; and to establish Antarctica as a world park, free of industry, military presence, and nuclear power and weaponry. Monitors legislation and regulations.

Humane Society of the United States, *2100 L St. N.W. 20037; (202) 452-1100. Fax, (202) 778-6132. Paul Irwin, chief executive. Internet, http://www.hsus.org.*

Works for the humane treatment and protection of animals. Interests include protecting endangered wildlife and marine mammals and their habitats and ending inhumane or cruel conditions in zoos.

International Assn. of Fish and Wildlife Agencies, *444 N. Capitol St. N.W., #544 20001; (202) 624-7890. Fax, (202) 624-7891. R. Max Peterson, executive vice president. Internet, fwa@sso.org.*

Membership: federal, state, and provincial fish and wildlife management agencies in the United States, Canada, and Mexico. Encourages balanced fish and wildlife resource management.

National Fish and Wildlife Foundation, *1120 Connecticut Ave. N.W., #900 20036; (202) 857-0166. Fax, (202) 857-0162. Amos S. Eno, executive director. Internet, http://www.nfwf.org.*

Forges partnerships between the public and private sectors in support of conservation activities that identify the root causes of environmental problems.

National Wildlife Federation, *8925 Leesburg Pike, Vienna, VA 22184; (703) 790-4000. Fax, (703) 442-7332. Mark Van Putten, president. Internet, http://www.nwf.org.*

Educational organization that promotes preservation of natural resources; provides information on wildlife.

National Wildlife Refuge Assn., *1000 Thomas Jefferson St. N.W. #311 20007; (202) 298-8095. Fax, (202) 298-8155. William Ashe, president. Internet, nwra@refugenet.org or http://www.refugenet.org.*

Works to improve management and protection of the Refuge System by providing information to administrators, Congress, and the public. Advocates adequate funding and improved policy guidance for the Refuge System; assists individual refuges with particular needs.

Nature Conservancy, *1815 N. Lynn St., Arlington, VA 22209; (703) 841-5300. Fax, (703) 841-1283. John C. Sawhill, president. Internet, http://www.tnc.org.*

Acquires land to protect endangered species and habitats; maintains international system of natural sanctuaries; operates the Heritage Program, a cooperative effort with state governments to identify and inventory threatened and endangered plants and animals.

Wildlife Habitat Council, *1010 Wayne Ave., #920, Silver Spring, MD 20910; (301) 588-8994. Fax, (301) 588-4629. William Howard, president. Internet, whc@wildlifehc.org or http://www.wildlifehc.org/wildlifehc.*

Membership: corporations, conservation groups, and individuals. Supports use of underdeveloped private lands for the benefit of wildlife, fish, and plant life. Provides technical assistance and educational programs; fosters information sharing among members.

Wildlife Management Institute, *1101 14th St. N.W., #801 20005; (202) 371-1808. Fax, (202) 408-5059. Rollin D. Sparrowe, president. Internet, wmihq@aol.com or http://www.wildlifemgt.org/wmi.*

Research and consulting organization that provides technical services and information on natural resources, particularly on wildlife management. Interests include threatened and endangered species, nongame and hunted wildlife, waterfowl, large land mammals, and predators.

Wildlife Society, *5410 Grosvenor Lane, Bethesda, MD 20814-2197; (301) 897-9770. Fax, (301) 530-2471. Harry E. Hodgdon, executive director. Internet, tws@wildlife.org or http://www.wildlife.org/wildlife.*

Membership: wildlife biologists and resource management specialists. Provides information on management techniques; sponsors conferences; maintains list of job opportunities for members.

World Wildlife Fund, *1250 24th St. N.W., #400 20037; (202) 293-4800. Fax, (202) 293-9211. Kathryn S. Fuller, president. Internet, http://www.wwf.org.*

International conservation organization that supports and conducts scientific research and conservation projects to promote biological diversity and to save endangered species and their habitats. Awards grants for habitat protection.

See also National Audubon Society (p. 279)

 # POLLUTION AND TOXINS

See also Energy (chap. 8); Environmental and Earth Sciences (chap. 17)

AGENCIES
Environmental Protection Agency, *Enforcement and Compliance Assurance, 1200 Pennsylvania Ave. N.W.*

20460; (202) 564-2440. Fax, (202) 501-3842. Steven A. Herman, assistant administrator.

Principal adviser to the administrator on enforcement of standards for air, water, toxic substances and pesticides, hazardous and solid waste management, radiation, and emergency preparedness programs. Investigates criminal and civil violations of environmental standards; oversees federal facilities' environmental compliance and site cleanup; serves as EPA's liaison office for federal agency compliance with the National Environmental Policy Act; manages environmental review of other agencies' projects and activities and coordinates EPA native American environmental programs.

Justice Dept., *Environmental Crimes, 601 Pennsylvania Ave. N.W., #6101 (mailing address: P.O. Box 23985, Washington, DC 20026-3985); (202) 305-0322. Fax, (202) 305-0397. Steven P. Solow, chief.*

Conducts criminal enforcement actions on behalf of the United States for all environmental protection statutes, including air, water, pesticides, hazardous wastes, wetland matters investigated by the Environmental Protection Agency, and other criminal environmental enforcement.

Justice Dept., *Environmental Defense, 601 D St. N.W., #8000 20004 (mailing address: P.O. Box 23986, Washington, DC 20026-3986); (202) 514-2219. Fax, (202) 514-6685. Letitia J. Grishaw, chief.*

Conducts litigation on air, water, noise, pesticides, solid waste, toxic substances, Superfund, and wetlands in cooperation with the Environmental Protection Agency; represents the EPA in suits involving judicial review of EPA actions; represents the U.S. Army Corps of Engineers in cases involving dredge-and-fill activity in navigable waters and adjacent wetlands; represents the Coast Guard in oil and hazardous spill cases; defends all federal agencies in environmental litigation.

Justice Dept., *Environmental Enforcement, 1425 New York Ave. N.W., 13th Floor 20005 (mailing address: P.O. Box 7611, Ben Franklin Station, Washington, DC 20044-7611); (202) 514-1604. Fax, (202) 514-0097. Joel M. Gross, chief.*

Conducts civil enforcement actions on behalf of the United States for all environmental protection statutes, including air, water, pesticides, hazardous waste, wetland matters investigated by the Environmental Protection Agency, and other civil environmental enforcement.

See also Domestic Policy Council (p. 328)

NONPROFIT

American Academy of Environmental Engineers, *130 Holiday Court, #100, Annapolis, MD 21401; (410) 266-3311. Fax, (410) 266-7653. William C. Anderson, executive director. Direct dial from Washington, (301) 261-8958. Internet, aaee@ea.net or http://www. enviro-engrs.org.*

Membership: state-licensed environmental engineers who have passed examinations in environmental engineering specialties, including general environment, air pollution control, solid waste management, hazardous waste management, industrial hygiene, radiation protection, water supply, and wastewater.

Environmental Industry Assns., *4301 Connecticut Ave. N.W., #300 20008; (202) 244-4700. Fax, (202) 966-4818. Bruce Parker, president. Internet, http://www.envasns.org.*

Membership: trade associations from the waste services and environmental technology industries. Represents the National Solid Waste Management Assn., the Hazardous Waste Management Assn., and the Waste Equipment Technology Assn.

See also America the Beautiful Fund (p. 104); Earth Share (p. 26); National Governors' Assn., Natural Resources (p. 247); Zero Population Growth (p. 393)

Air Pollution

AGENCIES

Environmental Protection Agency, *Air and Radiation, 401 M St. S.W., West Tower, MC 6101 20460; (202) 260-7400. Fax, (202) 260-5155. Richard Wilson, acting assistant administrator. Docket and Information Center, (202) 260-7548; fax, (202) 260-4400.*

Administers air quality standards and planning programs of the Clean Air Act Amendment of 1990; operates the Air and Radiation Docket and Information Center. Supervises the Office of Air Quality Planning and Standards in Durham, N.C., which develops air quality standards and provides information on air pollution control issues, including industrial air pollution. Administers the Air Pollution Technical Information Center in Research Triangle Park, N.C., which collects and provides technical literature on air pollution.

Environmental Protection Agency, *Atmospheric Programs, 501 3rd St. N.W. 20001 (mailing address: 401 M St. N.W., MC 6201J, Washington, DC 20460); (202) 564-9140. Fax, (202) 565-2147. Paul Stolpman, director.*

Responsible for acid rain and stratospheric ozone programs; examines strategies for preventing atmospheric pollution and mitigating climate change.

Environmental Protection Agency, *Manufacturing, Energy, and Transportation, 1200 Pennsylvania Ave. N.W., 7th Floor 20044 (mailing address: 401 M St. S.W., MC 2223A, Washington, DC 20460); (202) 564-2300. Fax, (202) 564-0050. John B. Rasnic, director.*

Administers Clean Air Act provisions for extraction of fuels and minerals; electric and gas utilities; petroleum refining; transport operations; and manufacturing of textiles, wood and paper products, steel and construction materials, transportation equipment, and electronics. Maintains data on the compliance status of various sources.

Environmental Protection Agency, *Mobile Sources, 401 M St. S.W., MC 6401 20460; (202) 260-7645. Fax, (202) 260-3730. Margo T. Oge, director.*

Handles Clean Air Act provisions for mobile sources, including motor vehicle air pollution control programs. Ann Arbor, Mich., office handles aircraft emission standards.

Environmental Protection Agency, *Radiation and Indoor Air, 501 3rd St. N.W. (mailing address: 401 M St. S.W., #6601J, Washington, DC 20460); (202) 564-9320. Fax, (202) 565-2043. Lawrence Weinstock, acting director.*

Administers indoor air quality control programs, including those regulating radon and environmental tobacco smoke; trains building managers in sound operation practices to promote indoor air quality.

Federal Aviation Administration *(Transportation Dept.), Environment and Energy, 800 Independence Ave. S.W., #900W 20591; (202) 267-3576. Fax, (202) 267-5594. James Erickson, director.*

Enforces government standards for aircraft emissions; conducts research on ozone depletion and high-altitude aircraft.

U.S. Geological Survey *(Interior Dept.), Energy Resources, 12201 Sunrise Valley Dr., Reston, VA (mailing address: 915 National Center, Reston, VA 20192); (703) 648-6470. Fax, (703) 648-5464. Vacant, program coordinator.*

Conducts research to determine radon levels present in certain geographic areas and to measure the likelihood of radon occurrence.

CONGRESS

House Commerce Committee, *Subcommittee on Health and the Environment, 2125 RHOB 20515; (202) 225-2927. Fax, (202) 225-1919. Michael Bilirakis, R-Fla., chair; James E. Derderian, staff director. Internet, http://www.house.gov/commerce/health.html.*

Jurisdiction over legislation on indoor and outdoor air pollution, including the Clean Air Act.

Senate Environment and Public Works Committee, Subcommittee on Clean Air, Wetlands, Private Property, and Nuclear Safety, *SD-407 20510; (202) 224-6176. James M. Inhofe, R-Okla., chair; Chris Hessler, staff contact. Internet, http://www.senate.gov/committee/environment.html.*

Jurisdiction over legislation on indoor and outdoor air pollution, including the Clean Air Act.

NONPROFIT

Alliance for Responsible Atmospheric Policy, *2111 Wilson Blvd., #850, Arlington, VA 22201; (703) 243-0344. Fax, (703) 243-2874. David Stirpe, executive director.*

Coalition of users and producers of chlorofluorocarbons (CFCs). Seeks further study of the ozone depletion theory.

Asbestos Information Assn./North America, *1745 Jefferson Davis Hwy., #406, Arlington, VA 22202; (703) 412-1150. Fax, (703) 412-1152. B. J. Pigg, president.*

Membership: firms that manufacture, sell, and use products containing asbestos fiber and those that mine, mill, and sell asbestos. Provides information on asbestos and health and on industry efforts to eliminate problems associated with asbestos dust; serves as liaison between the industry and federal and state governments.

Assn. of Local Air Pollution Control Officials, *444 N. Capitol St. N.W., #307 20001; (202) 624-7864. Fax, (202) 624-7863. S. William Becker, executive director. Internet, http://www.4cleanair.org.*

Membership: local representatives of air pollution control programs nationwide that are responsible for implementing provisions of the Clean Air Act. Disseminates policy and technical information; analyzes air pollution issues; conducts seminars, workshops, and conferences. Monitors legislation and regulations.

Center for Auto Safety, *2001 S St. N.W., #410 20009; (202) 328-7700. Clarence M. Ditlow III, executive director. Internet, http://www.essential.org/orgs/cas.*

Public interest organization that conducts research on air pollution caused by auto emissions; monitors fuel economy regulations.

Center for Clean Air Policy, *750 1st St. N.W., #1140 20002; (202) 408-9260. Fax, (202) 408-8896. Ned Helme, executive director. Internet, general@ccap.org.*

Membership: governors, corporations, environmentalists, and academicians. Analyzes economic and environmental effects of air pollution and related environmental problems. Serves as a liaison among government, corporate, community, and environmental groups.

Climate Institute, *120 Maryland Ave. N.E. 20002; (202) 547-0104. Fax, (202) 547-0111. John C. Topping Jr., president. Internet, climateinst@igc.apc.org or http://www.climate.org.*

Educates the public and policymakers on climate change (greenhouse effect, or global warming) and on the depletion of the ozone layer. Develops strategies on mitigating climate change in developing countries.

Environmental Defense Fund, *1875 Connecticut Ave. N.W., #1016 20009-5728; (202) 387-3500. Fax, (202) 234-6049. Cheryl Pickard, office manager, Washington Office. Internet, http://www.edf.org.*

Citizens' interest group staffed by lawyers, economists, and scientists. Conducts research and provides information on pollution prevention, environmental health, and protection of the Amazon rain forest and the ozone layer. (Headquarters in New York.)

Manufacturers of Emission Controls Assn., *1660 L St. N.W., #1100 20036; (202) 296-4797. Fax, (202) 331-1388. Bruce I. Bertelsen, executive director. Internet, http://www.meca.org.*

Membership: manufacturers of motor vehicle and stationary source emission control equipment. Provides information on emission technology and industry capabilities.

State and Territorial Air Pollution Program Administrators, *444 N. Capitol St. N.W., #307 20001; (202) 624-7864. Fax, (202) 624-7863. S. William Becker, executive director. Internet, http://www.4cleanair.org.*

Membership: state and territorial air quality officials responsible for implementing programs established under the Clean Air Act. Disseminates policy and technical information and analyzes air quality issues; conducts seminars, workshops, and conferences. Monitors legislation and regulations.

See also American Council for an Energy-Efficient Economy (p. 249)

Hazardous Materials

See also Fertilizer and Pesticides (chap. 2); Water Pollution (this section)

AGENCIES

Agency for Toxic Substances and Disease Registry (Health and Human Services Dept.), *200 Independence*

Ave. S.W., #719B 20201; (202) 690-7536. Fax, (202) 690-6985. Andrea A. Wargo, associate administrator. Internet, http://www.atsdr1.atsdr.cdc.gov:8080/atsdrhome.html.

Works with federal, state, and local agencies to minimize or eliminate adverse effects of exposure to toxic substances at spill and waste disposal sites; maintains a registry of persons exposed to hazardous substances and of diseases and illnesses resulting from exposure to hazardous or toxic substances; maintains inventory of hazardous substances; maintains registry of sites closed or restricted because of contamination by hazardous material. (Headquarters in Atlanta.)

Defense Dept., *Environmental Security,* 3400 Defense Pentagon, #3E792 20301-3400; (703) 695-6639. Fax, (703) 693-7011. Sherri W. Goodman, deputy under secretary. Internet, http://www.acq.osd.mil/ens.

Integrates environmental, safety, and occupational health considerations into U.S. defense and economic policies. Works to ensure responsible performance in defense operations, to maintain quality installations, to reduce the costs of complying with environmental laws, and to clean up past contamination.

Environmental Protection Agency, *Chemical Control,* 401 M St. S.W., MC 7405 20460; (202) 260-3749. Fax, (202) 260-8168. Charlie M. Auer, director.

Selects and implements control measures for new and existing chemicals that present a risk to human health and the environment. Oversees and manages regulatory evaluation and decision-making processes. Evaluates alternative remedial control measures under the Toxic Substances Control Act and makes recommendations concerning the existence of unreasonable risk from exposure to chemicals. Develops generic and chemical-specific rules for new chemicals.

Environmental Protection Agency, *Chemical Emergency Preparedness and Prevention,* 401 M St. S.W., Southeast 393, MC 5101 20460; (202) 260-8600. Fax, (202) 260-7906. Jim Makris, director. Toll-free hotline, (800) 535-0202.

Develops and administers chemical emergency preparedness and prevention programs; reviews effectiveness of programs; prepares community right-to-know regulations. Provides guidance materials, technical assistance, and training. Implements the preparedness and community right-to-know provisions of the Superfund Amendments and Reauthorization Act of 1986.

Environmental Protection Agency, *Enforcement and Compliance Assurance,* 1200 Pennsylvania Ave. N.W. 20460; (202) 564-2440. Fax, (202) 501-3842. Steven A. Herman, assistant administrator.

Enforces laws that protect public health and the environment from hazardous materials, pesticides, and toxic substances.

Environmental Protection Agency, *Pollution Prevention and Toxics,* 401 M St. S.W., #527 East Tower 20460; (202) 260-3810. Fax, (202) 260-0575. William Sanders, director. Information, (202) 554-1404.

Assesses the health and environmental hazards of existing chemical substances and mixtures; collects information on chemical use, exposure, and effects; maintains inventory of existing chemical substances; reviews new chemicals and regulates the manufacture, distribution, use, and disposal of harmful chemicals.

Environmental Protection Agency, *Prevention, Pesticides, and Toxic Substances,* 401 M St. S.W., MC 7101 20460; (202) 260-2902. Fax, (202) 260-1847. Dr. Lynn R. Goldman, assistant administrator. Pollution prevention and toxic substances control, (202) 260-3810.

Studies and makes recommendations for regulating chemical substances under the Toxic Substances Control Act; compiles list of chemical substances subject to the act; registers, controls, and regulates use of pesticides and toxic substances.

Environmental Protection Agency, *Solid Waste and Emergency Response,* 401 M St. S.W., #5101, SE 360 20460; (202) 260-4610. Fax, (202) 260-3527. Timothy Fields Jr., acting assistant administrator. Superfund/ Resource conservation and recovery hotline, (800) 424-9346 or (703) 412-9810. TDD, (800) 553-7672 or (703) 412-3323.

Administers and enforces the Superfund Act; manages the handling, cleanup, and disposal of hazardous wastes.

Housing and Urban Development Dept., *Lead Hazard Control,* 490 L'Enfant Plaza East S.W., #3202 (mailing address: 451 7th St. S.W., #B-133, Washington, DC 20410); (202) 755-1785. Fax, (202) 755-1000. David E. Jacobs, director. Community Outreach, (202) 755-1785, ext. 114. Internet, http://www.hud.gov/lea/leahome.html.

Advises HUD offices, other agencies, health authorities, and the housing industry on lead poisoning prevention. Develops regulations for lead-based paint; conducts research; makes grants to state and local governments for hazard reduction and inspection of housing.

Justice Dept., *Environmental Enforcement,* 1425 New York Ave. N.W., 13th Floor 20005 (mailing address: P.O. Box 7611, Ben Franklin Station, Washington, DC 20044-7611); (202) 514-1604. Fax, (202) 514-0097. Joel M. Gross, chief.

Represents the United States in civil cases under environmental laws that involve the handling, storage, treatment, transportation, and disposal of hazardous waste. Recovers federal money spent to clean up hazardous waste sites or sues defendants to clean up sites under Superfund.

National Response Center *(Transportation Dept.),* *2100 2nd St. S.W., #2611 20593; (202) 267-2675. Fax, (202) 267-2165. Cmdr. Syed Qadir, chief. Toll-free hotline, (800) 424-8802. Internet, http://www.nrc.uscg.mil.*

Maintains 24-hour hotline for reporting oil spills or hazardous materials accidents. Notifies appropriate federal officials to reduce the effects of accidents.

National Transportation Safety Board, *Pipeline and Hazardous Material Safety, 490 L'Enfant Plaza S.W. 20594; (202) 314-6460. Fax, (202) 314-6482. Bob Chipkevich, director.*

Investigates natural gas and liquid pipeline accidents and other accidents involving the transportation of hazardous materials.

Research and Special Programs Administration *(Transportation Dept.), 400 7th St. S.W., #8410 20590; (202) 366-4433. Fax, (202) 366-3666. Kelley Coyner, acting administrator. Internet, http://www.rspa.dot.gov.*

Coordinates research and development programs to improve safety of transportation systems; focus includes hazardous materials shipments, pipeline safety, and preparedness for transportation emergencies.

Research and Special Programs Administration *(Transportation Dept.), Hazardous Materials Safety, 400 7th St. S.W., #8422 20590; (202) 366-0656. Fax, (202) 366-5713. Alan I. Roberts, associate administrator. Internet, welisten@rspa.dot.gov or http://hazmat.dot.gov.*

Issues safety regulations and exemptions for the transportation of hazardous materials.

Research and Special Programs Administration *(Transportation Dept.), Pipeline Safety, 400 7th St. S.W., #2335 20590; (202) 366-4595. Fax, (202) 366-4566. Richard B. Felder, associate administrator. Internet, http://ops.dot.gov.*

Issues and enforces federal regulations for hazardous liquids pipeline safety.

State Dept., *Environmental Policy, Main State Bldg., #4325 20520; (202) 647-9266. Fax, (202) 647-5947. Michael Metelits, director.*

Advances U.S. interests internationally regarding multilateral environmental organizations, chemical wastes and other pollutants, and bilateral and regional environmental policies.

CONGRESS

House Commerce Committee, *Subcommittee on Finance and Hazardous Materials, 2125 RHOB 20515; (202) 225-2927. Fax, (202) 225-1919. Michael G. Oxley, R-Ohio, chair; James E. Derderian, staff director. Internet, http://www.house.gov/commerce.*

Jurisdiction over legislation on pollution; toxic substances, including the Toxic Substances Control Act; hazardous substances, including the Comprehensive Environmental Response, Compensation, and Liability Act (the Superfund); and other hazardous materials programs (jurisdiction shared with House Science and House Transportation and Infrastructure committees).

House Science Committee, *Subcommittee on Energy and Environment, 389 FHOB 20515; (202) 225-9662. Fax, (202) 266-6983. Ken Calvert, R-Calif., chair; Harlan Watson, staff director. Internet, http://www.house.gov/science.*

Jurisdiction over legislation and environmental research and development on pollution; toxic substances, including the Toxic Substances Control Act; and the Comprehensive Environmental Response, Compensation, and Liability Act (the Superfund) (jurisdiction shared with House Commerce and House Transportation and Infrastructure committees).

House Transportation and Infrastructure Committee, *Subcommittee on Water Resources and Environment, B376 RHOB 20515; (202) 225-4360. Fax, (202) 226-5435. Sherwood Boehlert, R-N.Y., chair; Ben Grumbles, counsel. Internet, http://www.house.gov/transportation.*

Shares jurisdiction over the Comprehensive Environmental Response, Compensation, and Liability Act (the Superfund) with the House Commerce and House Science committees.

Senate Environment and Public Works Committee, *Subcommittee on Superfund, Waste Control, and Risk Assessment, SD-410 20510; (202) 224-6176. Fax, (202) 224-5167. Robert C. Smith, R-N.H., chair; Tom Gibson, staff contact. Internet, http://www.senate.gov/committee/environment.html.*

Jurisdiction over legislation on pollution; environmental research and development; pesticides; and toxic substances, including the Toxic Substances Control Act. Oversight of the Comprehensive Environmental Response, Compensation, and Liability Act (the Superfund) and of hazardous materials programs.

NONPROFIT

Center For Health, Environment, and Justice, *150 S. Washington St., #300, Falls Church, VA (mailing address:*

P.O. Box 6806, Falls Church, VA 22040); (703) 237-2249. Fax, (703) 237-8389. Lois Marie Gibbs, executive director. Internet, cchw@essential.org or http://www.essential.org/cchw.

Provides citizens' groups, individuals, and municipalities with support and information on solid and hazardous waste. Sponsors workshops, speakers bureau, leadership development conference, and convention. Operates a toxicity data bank on environmental and health effects of common chemical compounds; maintains a registry of technical experts to assist in solid and hazardous waste problems; gathers information on polluting corporations.

Chemical Specialties Manufacturers Assn., 1913 Eye St. N.W. 20006; (202) 872-8110. Fax, (202) 872-8114. Ralph Engel, president. Internet, info@csma.org or http://www.csma.org.

Membership: manufacturers, marketers, packagers, and suppliers in the chemical specialties industry. Specialties include cleaning compounds and detergents, insecticides, disinfectants, automotive and industrial products, polishes and floor finishes, and aerosol products. Monitors scientific developments; conducts surveys and research; provides chemical safety information and consumer education programs; sponsors National Poison Prevention Week and Aerosol Education Bureau. Monitors legislation and regulations.

Chlorine Institute, Inc., 2001 L St. N.W., #506 20036; (202) 775-2790. Fax, (202) 223-7225. Robert G. Smerko, president. Internet, http://www.cl2.com.

Safety, health, and environmental protection center of the chlor-alkali (chlorine, caustic soda, caustic potash, and hydrogen chloride) industry. Interests include employee health and safety, resource conservation and pollution abatement, control of chlorine emergencies, product specifications, and public and community relations. Publishes technical pamphlets and drawings.

Clean Sites, 901 N. Washington St., #604, Alexandria, VA 22314; (703) 683-8522. Fax, (703) 548-8773. Edwin H. Clark II, president. Information, (703) 739-1200. Internet, cleansites@aol.com or http://www.cleansites.org.

Works to accelerate hazardous waste cleanup. Helps involved parties and governments reach legal settlements, divide cleanup costs among responsible parties, and manage cleanup activities. Provides financial services in collecting and disbursing cleanup funds. Conducts research on waste cleanup.

Environmental Technology Council, 734 15th St. N.W., #720 20005; (202) 783-0870. Fax, (202) 737-2038.

David Case, executive director. Internet, http://www.etc.org.

Membership: environmental service firms. Interests include the recycling, detoxification, and disposal of hazardous and industrial waste and cleanup of contaminated industrial sites; works to encourage permanent and technology-based solutions to environmental problems. Provides the public with information.

Greenpeace USA, 1436 U St. N.W. 20009; (202) 462-1177. Fax, (202) 462-4507. Kristen Engburg, acting executive director. Internet, greenpeace.usa@wdc.greenpeace.org or http://www.greenpeace.org.

Seeks to protect the environment through research, education, and grassroots organizing. Works to prevent careless disposal and incineration of hazardous waste; encourages the development of methods to reduce production of hazardous waste. Monitors legislation and regulations.

Hazardous Materials Advisory Council, 1101 Vermont Ave. N.W., #301 20005; (202) 289-4550. Fax, (202) 289-4074. Jonathan Collom, president. Internet, staff_hmac@radix.net or http://www.hmac.org.

Membership: shippers, carriers, container manufacturers, and emergency response and spill cleanup companies. Promotes safety in the domestic and international transportation of hazardous materials. Provides information and educational services; sponsors conferences, workshops, and seminars. Advocates uniform hazardous materials regulations.

International Assn. of Heat and Frost Insulators and Asbestos, 1776 Massachusetts Ave. N.W., #301 20036-1989; (202) 785-2388. Fax, (202) 429-0568. William G. Bernard, president.

Membership: approximately 18,000 workers in insulation industries. Helps members negotiate pay, benefits, and better working conditions; conducts training programs and workshops. Monitors legislation and regulations. (Affiliated with the AFL-CIO.)

National Insulation Assn., 99 Canal Center Plaza, #222, Alexandria, VA 22314; (703) 683-6422. Fax, (703) 549-4838. Bill Pitkin, executive vice president. Internet, niainfo@insulation.org or http://www.insulation.org.

Membership: companies in the commercial and industrial insulation and asbestos abatement industries. Monitors legislation and regulations.

Rachel Carson Council, 8940 Jones Mill Rd., Chevy Chase, MD 20815; (301) 652-1877. Fax, (301) 951-7179. Diana Post, executive director. Internet, rccouncil@aol.com or http://members.aol.com/rccouncil/ourpage/rcc_page.htm.

Disseminates information on the toxicity of chemical contaminants and pesticides and their effects on human health and the environment. Library open to the public by appointment.

See also Chemical Specialties Manufacturers Assn. (p. 294); League of Women Voters Education Fund, Natural Resources (p. 279)

Radiation Protection

See also Nuclear Energy (chap. 8)

AGENCIES

Armed Forces Radiobiology Research Institute *(Defense Dept.), National Naval Medical Center, 8901 Wisconsin Ave., Bethesda, MD 20889-5603; (301) 295-1210. Fax, (301) 295-4967. Col. Robert Eng (MSUSA), director. Internet, http://www.afrri.usuhs.mil.*

Serves as the principal ionizing radiation radiobiology research laboratory under the jurisdiction of the Uniformed Services University of the Health Sciences. Participates in international conferences and projects. Library open to the public.

Energy Dept., *Nuclear and Facility Safety, 1000 Independence Ave. S.W., #7A121 20878; (202) 586-2407. Fax, (202) 586-6010. Orin Pearson, deputy assistant secretary. Internet, http://tis-nt.eh.doe.gov/eh-3/sect-3.htm.*

Reviews radiological protection standards and programs at Energy Dept. facilities; provides the department with technical assistance in the area of nuclear and facility safety. Investigates potential violations of safety rules.

Environmental Protection Agency, *Radiation and Indoor Air, 501 3rd St. N.W. (mailing address: 401 M St. S.W., #6601J, Washington, DC 20460); (202) 564-9320. Fax, (202) 565-2043. Lawrence Weinstock, acting director.*

Establishes standards to regulate the amount of radiation discharged into the environment from uranium mining and milling projects and other activities that result in radioactive emissions; and to ensure safe disposal of radioactive waste. Fields a Radiological Emergency Response Team. Administers the nationwide Environmental Radiation Ambient Monitoring System (ERAMS), which analyzes environmental radioactive contamination.

Food and Drug Administration *(Health and Human Services Dept.), Center for Devices and Radiological Health, 9200 Corporate Blvd., #100, Rockville, MD 20850; (301) 443-4690. Fax, (301) 594-1320. Dr. D. Bruce Burlington, director. Internet, http://www.fda.gov/cdrh.*

Administers national programs to control exposure to radiation; establishes standards for emissions from consumer and medical products; conducts factory inspections. Accredits and certifies mammography facilities and personnel; provides physicians and consumers with guidelines on radiation-emitting products. Conducts research, training, and educational programs. Library open to the public.

NONPROFIT

Institute for Science and International Security, *236 Massachusetts Ave. N.E., #500 20002; (202) 547-3633. Fax, (202) 547-3634. David Albright, president. Internet, 73744.3675@compuserve.com.*

Analyzes scientific and policy issues affecting national and international security, including the problems of war, regional and global arms races, the spread of nuclear weapons, and the environmental, health, and safety hazards of nuclear weapons production.

NAHB Research Center, *Radon Research and Indoor Air Quality, 400 Prince George's Blvd., Upper Marlboro, MD 20774; (301) 249-4000. Fax, (301) 249-0305. Tom Kenney, director, Laboratory Services. Internet, http://www.nahbrc.org.*

Develops site evaluation and radon prevention techniques; monitors development of indoor air quality related to codes and standards; measures indoor radon levels and other indoor pollutants. Conducts infiltration measurements. (Affiliated with the National Assn. of Home Builders.)

National Council on Radiation Protection and Measurements, *7910 Woodmont Ave., #800, Bethesda, MD 20814; (301) 657-2652. Fax, (301) 907-8768. William M. Beckner, executive director. Toll-free, (800) 229-2652. Internet, http://www.ncrp.com.*

Corporation chartered by Congress that collects and analyzes information and provides recommendations on radiation protection and measurement. Studies radiation emissions from household items and from office and medical equipment. Holds annual conference; publishes reports on radiation protection and measurement.

See also American College of Radiology (p. 372); Public Citizen, Health Research Group (p. 355)

Recycling and Solid Waste

AGENCIES

Environmental Protection Agency, *Solid Waste and Emergency Response, 401 M St. S.W., #5101, SE 360 20460; (202) 260-4610. Fax, (202) 260-3527. Timothy Fields Jr., acting assistant administrator. Superfund/*

Resource conservation and recovery hotline, (800) 424-9346; in Washington, (703) 412-9810. TDD, (800) 553-7672; in Washington, (703) 412-3323.

Administers and enforces the Resource Conservation and Recovery Act.

CONGRESS

House Commerce Committee, *Subcommittee on Finance and Hazardous Materials, 2125 RHOB 20515; (202) 225-2927. Fax, (202) 225-1919. Michael G. Oxley, R-Ohio, chair; James E. Derderian, staff director. Internet, http://www.house.gov/commerce.*

Jurisdiction over legislation on solid waste disposal, including the Resource Conservation and Recovery Act. (Jurisdiction shared with House Science and House Transportation and Infrastructure committees.)

House Science Committee, *Subcommittee on Energy and Environment, 389 FHOB 20515; (202) 225-9662. Fax, (202) 266-6983. Ken Calvert, R-Calif., chair; Harlan Watson, staff director. Internet, http://www.house.gov/science.*

Jurisdiction over legislation and research and development on solid waste disposal, including the Resource Conservation and Recovery Act. (Jurisdiction shared with House Commerce and House Transportation and Infrastructure committees.)

House Transportation and Infrastructure Committee, *Subcommittee on Water Resources and Environment, B376 RHOB 20515; (202) 225-4360. Fax, (202) 226-5435. Sherwood Boehlert, R-N.Y., chair; Ben Grumbles, counsel. Internet, http://www.house.gov/transportation.*

Shares jurisdiction over the Comprehensive Environmental Response, Compensation, and Liability Act (the Superfund) with the House Commerce and House Science committees.

Senate Environment and Public Works Committee, *Subcommittee on Superfund, Waste Control, and Risk Assessment, SD-410 20510; (202) 224-6176. Fax, (202) 224-5167. Robert C. Smith, R-N.H., chair; Tom Gibson, staff contact. Internet, http://www.senate.gov/committee/environment.html.*

Jurisdiction over research and development and legislation on solid waste disposal, including the Resource Conservation and Recovery Act.

NONPROFIT

American Plastics Council, *1801 K St. N.W., #701L 20006; (202) 974-5400. Fax, (202) 296-7119. Red Cavaney, president. Internet, http://www.plasticsresource.com.*

Seeks to increase plastics recycling; conducts research on disposal of plastic products; sponsors research on waste-handling methods, incineration, and degradation; supports programs that test alternative waste management technologies. Monitors legislation and regulations. (Affiliated with the Society of the Plastics Industry.)

Alliance of Foam Packaging Recyclers, *2424 Priest Bridge Dr., #19, Crofton, MD 21114; (410) 451-8340. Fax, (410) 451-8343. Betsy DeCampos, executive director. Toll-free, (800) 944-8448. Internet, http://www.epspackaging.org.*

Membership: companies that recycle foam packaging material. Coordinates national network of collection centers for postconsumer foam packaging products; helps to establish new collection centers.

Assn. of State and Territorial Solid Waste Management Officials, *444 N. Capitol St. N.W., #315 20001; (202) 624-5828. Fax, (202) 624-7875. Thomas Kennedy, executive director. Internet, swmtrina@sso.org or http://www.astswmo.org.*

Membership: state and territorial solid waste management officials. Works with the Environmental Protection Agency to develop policy on solid and hazardous waste.

Container Recycling Institute, *1911 Fort Myer Dr., #900, Arlington, VA 22209; (202) 797-6839. Fax, (202) 797-5437. Pat Franklin, executive director. Internet, cri@igc.org or http://www.igc.apc/cri.*

Studies alternatives for reducing container and packaging waste; researches container and packaging reuse and recycling options; serves as an information clearinghouse.

Environmental Industry Assns., *4301 Connecticut Ave. N.W., #300 20008; (202) 244-4700. Fax, (202) 966-4818. Bruce Parker, president. Internet, http://www.envasns.org.*

Membership: organizations engaged in refuse collection, processing, and disposal. Provides information on solid and hazardous waste management and waste equipment; sponsors workshops.

Flexible Packaging Assn., *1090 Vermont Ave. N.W., #500 20005-4960; (202) 842-3880. Fax, (202) 842-3841. Glenn E. Braswell, president. Internet, fpa@flexpack.org.*

Coordinates environmental programs on reducing solid waste for schools and the public.

Foodservice and Packaging Institute, *1550 Wilson Blvd., #701, Arlington, VA 22209; (703) 527-7505. Fax, (703) 527-7512. Richard B. Norment, president. Internet, http://www.fpi.org.*

Membership: manufacturers, suppliers, and distributors of disposable products used in food service, packaging, and consumer products. Promotes the use of disposables for commercial and home use; sponsors research on recycling and composting technology. Monitors environmental legislation.

Glass Packaging Institute, *1627 K St. N.W., #800 20006; (202) 887-4850. Fax, (202) 785-5377. Joseph Cattaneo, executive vice president. Internet, http://www. gpi.org.*

Membership: manufacturers of glass containers and their suppliers. Promotes industry policies to protect the environment, conserve natural resources, and reduce energy consumption; conducts research; monitors legislation affecting the industry. Interests include glass recycling.

Institute for Local Self-Reliance, *2425 18th St. N.W. 20009-2096; (202) 232-4108. Fax, (202) 332-0463. Neil Seldman, president. Internet, ilsr@igc.apc.org or http:// www.ilsr.org.*

Conducts research and provides technical assistance on environmentally sound economic development for government, small businesses, and community organizations. Advocates the development of a materials policy at local, state, and regional levels to reduce per capita consumption of raw materials and to shift from dependence on fossil fuels to reliance on renewable resources.

Institute of Scrap Recycling Industries, Inc., *1325 G St. N.W., #1000 20005; (202) 737-1770. Fax, (202) 626-0900. Robin Wiener, executive director. Internet, http:// www.isri.org.*

Represents processors, brokers, and consumers of scrap paper, glass, plastic, textiles, rubber, and ferrous and nonferrous metals.

Integrated Waste Services Assn., *1401 H St. N.W., #220 20005; (202) 467-6240. Fax, (202) 467-6225. Maria Zannes, president. Internet, iwsa@ix.netcom.com or http:// www.wte.org.*

Membership: companies that design, build, and operate resource recovery facilities. Promotes integrated solutions to municipal solid waste management issues. Encourages the use of waste-to-energy technology.

National Assn. of Chemical Recyclers, *1900 M St. N.W., #750 20036; (202) 296-1725. Fax, (202) 296-2530. Chris Goebel, executive director. Internet, http://www.nacr. org.*

Membership: commercial chemical recyclers and others interested in the industry. Promotes the recovery and reuse of spent solvent as an alternative to waste disposal.

Seeks to educate members on the safest and most efficient methods of recycling. Sponsors seminars and conferences. Monitors legislation and regulations.

National Recycling Coalition, *1727 King St., #105, Alexandria, VA 22314; (703) 683-9025. Fax, (703) 683-9026. William M. Ferretti, executive director.*

Membership: public officials; community recycling groups; local, state, and national agencies; environmentalists; waste haulers; solid waste disposal consultants; and private recycling companies. Encourages recycling to reduce waste, preserve resources, and promote economic development.

Polystyrene Packaging Council, *1801 K St. N.W., #600K 20006; (202) 974-5321. Fax, (202) 296-7354. Michael Levy, executive director. Internet, http://www. polystyrene.org.*

Membership: manufacturers and suppliers of polystyrene foam products. Promotes effective use and recycling of polystyrene; studies and reports on solid waste disposal issues, including waste-to-energy incineration and use of landfills. Serves as an information clearinghouse. Monitors legislation and regulations.

Shippers of Recycled Textiles, *7910 Woodmont Ave., #1130, Bethesda, MD 20814; (301) 656-1077. Fax, (301) 656-1079. Bernard D. Brill, executive vice president. Internet, smartasn@erols.com or http://www.smartasn.org.*

Membership: organizations and individuals involved in shipping and distributing recycled textiles and other textile products. Publishes statistics on the amount of waste material recycled. (Affiliated with the Secondary Materials and Recycled Textiles Assn.)

Solid Waste Assn. of North America, *1100 Wayne Ave., #700, Silver Spring, MD (mailing address: P.O. Box 7219, Silver Spring, MD 20907); (301) 585-2898. Fax, (301) 589-7068. John Skinner, executive director. Internet, swana@millkern.com or http://www.swana.org.*

Membership: government officials who manage municipal solid waste programs. Interests include waste reduction, collection, recycling, combustion, and disposal. Conducts training and certification programs. Operates solid waste information clearinghouse. Monitors legislation and regulsations.

U.S. Conference of Mayors, *Municipal Waste Management Assn., 1620 Eye St. N.W., 6th Floor 20006; (202) 293-7330. Fax, (202) 429-0422. David Gatton, managing director.*

Organization of local governments and private companies involved in planning and developing solid waste management programs, including pollution prevention, waste-to-energy, and recycling. Assists communities with financing, environmental assessments, and associated policy implementation.

See also Automotive Recyclers Assn. (p. 677)

Water Pollution

See also Water Resources (this chapter)

AGENCIES

Environmental Protection Agency, *Ground and Drinking Water, 401 M St. S.W., 1209 East Tower, MC 4601 20460; (202) 260-5508. Fax, (202) 260-4383. Cynthia Dougherty, director. Toll-free hotline, (800) 426-4791.*

Develops standards for the quality of drinking water supply systems; regulates underground injection of waste and protection of groundwater wellhead areas under the Safe Drinking Water Act; provides information on public water supply systems.

Environmental Protection Agency, *Municipal Support, 401 M St. S.W., 2606 Northeast Mall, MC 4204 20460; (202) 260-5859. Fax, (202) 260-1827. Michael J. Quigley, director.*

Directs programs to assist in the design and construction of municipal sewage systems; develops programs to ensure efficient operation and maintenance of municipal wastewater treatment facilities; implements programs for prevention of water pollution.

Environmental Protection Agency, *Science and Technology, 401 M St. S.W., MC4301 811 East Tower 20460; (202) 260-5400. Fax, (202) 260-5394. Tudor T. Davies, director.*

Develops and coordinates water pollution control programs for the Environmental Protection Agency; monitors water quality nationwide and maintains a data collection system; assists state and regional agencies in establishing water quality standards and planning local water resources management; develops guidelines for industrial wastewater discharge.

Environmental Protection Agency, *Wastewater Management, 401 M St. S.W., MC 4201, 2607 North Mall East 20460; (202) 260-5850. Fax, (202) 260-1040. Michael B. Cook, director.*

Oversees the issuance of water permits. Responsible for the Pretreatment Program regulating industrial discharges to local sewage treatment. Oversees the State Revolving Funds Program, which provides assistance for the construction of wastewater treatment plants.

National Drinking Water Advisory Council, *401 M St. S.W., MC 4601, 1209 East Tower 20460; (202) 260-*

2285. Fax, (202) 260-4383. Charlene Shaw, officer. Internet, http://www.epa.gov/OGWDW.

Advises the EPA administrator on activities, functions, and policies relating to implementation of the Safe Drinking Water Act.

National Oceanic and Atmospheric Administration *(Commerce Dept.), Ocean Resources, Conservation, and Assessment, 1305 East-West Hwy., Silver Spring, MD 20910; (301) 713-2989. Fax, (301) 713-4389. Charles N. Ehler, director. Internet, http://www-orca.nos.noaa.gov.*

Provides information on damage to marine ecosystems caused by pollution. Provides information on spill trajectory projections and chemical hazard analyses. Researches trends of toxic contamination on U.S. coastal regions.

U.S. Coast Guard *(Transportation Dept.), National Pollution Funds Center, 4200 Wilson Blvd., #1000, Arlington, VA 22203; (703) 235-4700. Fax, (703) 235-4840. Daniel F. Sheehan, director. Internet, http://www. uscg.mil/hq/npfc/npfc.htm.*

Certifies the financial responsibility of vessels and companies involved in oil exploration and transportation in U.S. waters and on the outer continental shelf; manages the Oil Spill Liability Trust Fund under the Oil Pollution Act of 1990.

U.S. Coast Guard *(Transportation Dept.), Response, 2100 2nd St. S.W., #2100 20593; (202) 267-0518. Fax, (202) 267-4085. Capt. Larry L. Hereth, chief. Internet, http://www.uscg.mil/hq/g-m/nmc/responce/Default.htm.*

Oversees cleanup operations after spills of oil and other hazardous substances in U.S. waters, on the outer continental shelf, and in international waters. Reviews coastal zone management and enforces international standards for pollution prevention and response.

CONGRESS

House Commerce Committee, *Subcommittee on Health and the Environment, 2125 RHOB 20515; (202) 225-2927. Fax, (202) 225-1919. Michael Bilirakis, R-Fla., chair; James E. Derderian, staff director. Internet, http:// www.house.gov/commerce/health.html.*

Jurisdiction over legislation on drinking water purity, including the Safe Drinking Water Act.

House Resources Committee, *Subcommittee on Fisheries, Conservation, Wildlife, and Oceans, 805 O'Neill Bldg. 20515; (202) 226-0200. Fax, (202) 225-1542. Rep. H. James Saxton, R-N.J., chair; Harry Burroughs, staff director. Internet, http://www.house.gov/resources.*

Jurisdiction over legislation concerning coastal marine pollution, including the Magnuson-Stevens Fishery Conservation and Management Act, and elements of the Clean Water Act and the National Environmental Policy Act.

House Transportation and Infrastructure Committee, *Subcommittee on Coast Guard and Maritime Transportation, 507 Ford Bldg. 20515; (202) 226-3552. Fax, (202) 226-2524. Wayne T. Gilchrest, R-Md., chair; Rebecca Dye, counsel. Internet, http://www.house.gov/ transportation.*

Jurisdiction over legislation on ocean dumping, oil spills and financial responsibility requirements, and marine pollution control and abatement. (Jurisdiction shared with the Subcommittee on Water Resources and Environment.)

House Transportation and Infrastructure Committee, *Subcommittee on Water Resources and Environment, B376 RHOB 20515; (202) 225-4360. Fax, (202) 226-5435. Sherwood Boehlert, R-N.Y., chair; Ben Grumbles, counsel. Internet, http://www.house.gov/ transportation.*

Jurisdiction over most legislation on water pollution, including the Clean Water Act. Shares jurisdiction on oil spills and financial responsibility requirements with the Subcommittee on Coast Guard and Maritime Transportation.

Senate Environment and Public Works Committee, *Subcommittee on Drinking Water, Fisheries, and Wildlife, SD-410 20510; (202) 224-6176. Fax, (202) 224-5167. Dirk Kempthorne, R-Idaho, chair; Ann Klee, staff contact. Internet, http://www.senate.gov/committee/ environment.html.*

Jurisdiction over legislation on ocean dumping and ocean pollution research; drinking water purity; water pollution; oil spill laws and financial responsibility requirements; and marine pollution control and abatement; jurisdiction over the Clean Water Act, National Environmental Policy Act, Safe Drinking Water Act, and Ocean Dumping Act.

NONPROFIT

Alliance for Environmental Technology, *1250 24th St. N.W., #300 20037; (202) 835-1688. Fax, (202) 835-1601. Douglas C. Pryke, executive director. Internet, http://www.aet.org.*

Membership: U.S. and Canadian chemical manufacturers and forest products companies. Seeks to improve environmental performance of the pulp and paper industry, particularly in waste water; supports use of chlorine dioxide to prevent pollution. Monitors legislation and regulations.

Assn. of State and Interstate Water Pollution Control Administors, *750 1st St. N.E., #910 20002; (202) 898-0905. Fax, (202) 898-0929. Roberta Haley Savage, executive director. Internet, http://www.asiwpca.org.*

Membership: administrators of state water pollution agencies and related associations. Represents the states' concerns on implementation, funding, and reauthorization of the Clean Water Act. Monitors legislation and regulations.

Center for Marine Conservation, *1725 DeSales St. N.W., #600 20036; (202) 429-5609. Fax, (202) 872-0619. Roger E. McManus, president. Internet, http://www. cmc-ocean.org.*

Protects the health of oceans and seas. Advocates policies that restrict discharge of pollutants harmful to marine ecosystems.

Clean Water Action, *4455 Connecticut Ave. N.W., #A300 20008; (202) 895-0420. Fax, (202) 895-0438. David R. Zwick, president. Internet, cwa@essential.org or http:// www.essential.org/cwa.*

Citizens' organization interested in clean, safe, and affordable water. Works to influence public policy through education, technical assistance, and grassroots organizing. Interests include toxins and pollution, drinking water, water conservation, sewage treatment, pesticides, mass burn incineration, bay and estuary protection, and consumer water issues. Monitors legislation and regulations.

League of Women Voters Education Fund, *Natural Resources, 1730 M St. N.W., #1000 20036; (202) 429-1965. Fax, (202) 429-0854. Elizabeth Kraft, assistant director.*

Education foundation affiliated with the League of Women Voters. Conducts a national project concerning community drinking water systems and groundwater. Sponsors research and develops educational materials on water issues; helps local leagues manage demonstration programs.

Water Environment Federation, *601 Wythe St., Alexandria, VA 22314-1994; (703) 684-2400. Fax, (703) 684-2492. Quincalee Brown, executive director. Internet, http://www.wef.org.*

Membership: civil and environmental engineers, wastewater treatment plant operators, scientists, government officials, and others concerned with water quality. Works to preserve and improve water quality worldwide. Provides the public wth technical information and educational materials. Monitors legislation and regulations.

◼ RESOURCES MANAGEMENT

See also Energy (chap. 8)

AGENCIES

Bureau of Land Management *(Interior Dept.),* *Renewable Resources and Planning,* 1849 C St. N.W., #5650 20240; (202) 208-4896. Fax, (202) 208-5010. *Maitland Sharpe, assistant director.*

Develops and implements natural resource programs for renewable resources use and protection, including management of forested land, rangeland, wild horses and burros, wildlife habitats, endangered species, soil and water quality, rights of way, recreation, and cultural programs.

Interior Dept., 1849 C St. N.W., #6156 20240; (202) 208-7351. Fax, (202) 208-5048. *Bruce Babbitt, secretary; John Garamendi, deputy secretary. Information,* (202) 208-3171. *Library,* (202) 208-5815. *Locator,* (202) 208-3100. *Internet, http://www.doi.gov.*

Manages most federal land through its component agencies; responsible for conservation and development of mineral, water, and fish and wildlife resources; operates recreation programs for federal parks, refuges, and public lands; preserves and administers the scenic and historic areas; administers Native American lands and relationships with tribal governments.

Tennessee Valley Authority, 1 Massachusetts Ave. N.W., #300 20001; (202) 898-2999. Fax, (202) 898-2998. *Vacant, administrative officer, Washington Office. Internet, http://www.tva.gov.*

Coordinates resource conservation, development, and land-use programs in the Tennessee River Valley. Activities include forestry and wildlife development. (Headquarters in Knoxville, Tenn.)

NONPROFIT

National Assn. of Conservation Districts, 509 Capitol Court N.E. 20002-4937; (202) 547-6223. Fax, (202) 547-6450. *Ernest C. Shea, chief executive officer. Internet, http://www.nacdnet.org.*

Membership: conservation districts (local subdivisions of state government). Develops policies and works to promote the conservation of water, land, forests, and other natural resources. Interests include erosion and sediment control, water quality, rural development, and urban and community conservation.

Renewable Natural Resources Foundation, 5430 Grosvenor Lane, Bethesda, MD 20814-2193; (301) 493-9101. Fax, (301) 493-6148. *Robert D. Day, executive director. Internet, rnrf@aol.com or http://members.aol.com/rnrf.*

Consortium of professional, scientific, and education organizations working to advance scientific and public education in renewable natural resources. Encourages the application of sound scientific practices to resource management and conservation. Fosters interdisciplinary cooperation among its member organizations.

U.S. Chamber of Commerce, *Food, Agriculture, Energy, and Natural Resources Policy,* 1615 H St. N.W. 20062-2000; (202) 463-5500. Fax, (202) 887-3445. *Stew Hardy, manager. Internet, http://www.uschamber.org.*

Develops policy on all issues affecting the production, use, and conservation of natural resources, including fuel and nonfuel minerals, timber, water, public lands, on- and offshore energy, wetlands, and endangered species.

Wildlife Management Institute, 1101 14th St. N.W., #801 20005; (202) 371-1808. Fax, (202) 408-5059. *Rollin D. Sparrowe, president. Internet, wmihq@aol.com or http://www.wildlifemgt.org/wmi.*

Research and consulting organization that provides technical services and information about natural resources. Interests include forests, rangelands, and land, water, and wildlife resources.

See also Rand Corporation (p. 496)

Forests and Rangelands

AGENCIES

Forest Service *(Agriculture Dept.),* 201 14th St. S.W., #4NW (mailing address: P.O. Box 96090, Washington, DC 20090-6090); (202) 205-1661. Fax, (202) 205-1765. *Mike Dombeck, chief. Internet, http://www.fs.fed.us.*

Manages national forests and grasslands for outdoor recreation and sustained yield of renewable natural resources, including timber, water, forage, fish, and wildlife. Cooperates with state and private foresters; conducts forestry research.

Forest Service, *International Programs,* 201 14th St. S.W. (mailing address: P.O. Box 96090, Washington, DC 20090-6090); (202) 205-1650. Fax, (202) 205-1603. *Valdis Mezainis, director. Internet, http://www.fs.fed.us/global/welcome1.html.*

Responsible for the Forest Service's involvement in international forest conservation efforts. Analyzes international resource issues; promotes information exchange; provides planning and technical assistance.

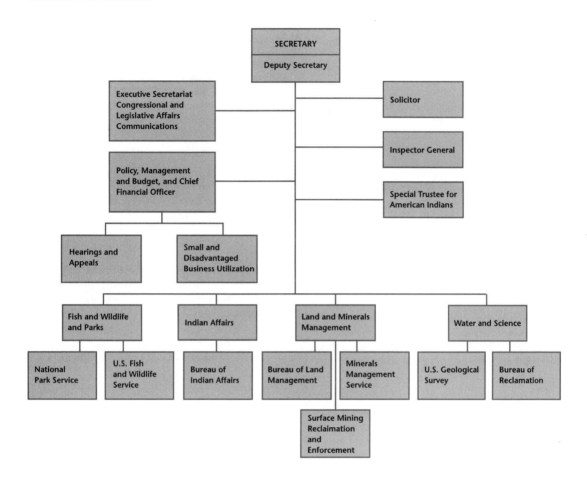

Interests include tropical forests and sustainable forest management.

Forest Service, *National Forest System, 201 14th St. S.W., #3NW (mailing address: P.O. Box 96090, Washington, DC 20090-6090); (202) 205-1523. Fax, (202) 205-1758. Robert Joslin, deputy chief. Internet, http://www.fs.fed.us.*

Manages 191 million acres of forests and rangelands. Products and services from these lands include timber, water, forage, wildlife, minerals, and recreation.

Forest Service, *Research, 201 14th St. S.W. (mailing address: P.O. Box 96090, Washington, DC 20090-6090); (202) 205-1665. Fax, (202) 205-1530. Robert Lewis Jr., deputy chief. Internet, http://www.fs.fed.us.*

Conducts biological, physical, and economic research related to forestry, including studies on harvesting methods, acid deposition, international forestry, the effects of global climate changes on forests, and forest products. Provides information on the establishment, improvement, and growth of trees, grasses, and other forest vegetation. Works to protect forest resources from fire, insects, diseases, and animal pests. Examines the effect of forest use activities on water quality, soil erosion, and sediment production. Conducts continuous forest survey and analyzes outlook for future supply and demand.

Forest Service, *State and Private Forestry, 1400 Independence Ave. S.W. (mailing address: P.O. Box 96090, Washington, DC 20090-6090); (202) 205-1657. Fax, (202) 205-1174. Phil Janik, deputy chief. Internet, http://www.fs.fed.us.*

Assists state and private forest owners with the protection and management of 574 million acres of forest and associated watershed lands. Assistance includes fire control, protecting forests from insects and diseases, land-use planning, developing multiple-use management, and improving practices in harvesting, processing, and marketing of forest products.

Forest Service, Youth Conservation Corps, *1621 N. Kent St., Arlington, VA (mailing address: P.O. Box 96090, Washington, DC 20090-6090); (703) 235-8855. Fax, (703) 235-1597. Ransom Hughes, program manager.*

Administers, with the National Park Service and the Fish and Wildlife Service, the Youth Conservation Corps, a summer employment and training, public works program for youths ages 15 to 18. The program is conducted in national parks, in national forests, and on national wildlife refuges.

CONGRESS

House Agriculture Committee, *Subcommittee on Forestry, Resource Conservation, and Research,* *1336 LHOB 20515; (202) 225-2342. Larry Combest, R-Texas, chair; Russell Laird, staff director. Internet, http://www.house.gov/agriculture.*

Jurisdiction over legislation on forestry, in general, and forest reserves acquired from state and local governments or private sources. Oversight of Forest Service.

House Resources Committee, *1324 LHOB 20515-6201; (202) 225-2761. Fax, (202) 225-5929. Don Young, R-Alaska, chair; Lloyd Jones, staff director. Internet, resource@hr.house.gov or http://www.house.gov/resources.*

Jurisdiction over legislation on forest reserves and public lands in Alaska.

House Resources Committee, *Subcommittee on Forests and Forest Health,* *1337 LHOB 20515; (202) 225-0691. Helen Chenoweth, R-Idaho, chair; William M. Simmons, staff director. Internet, resource@hr.house.gov or http://www.house.gov/resources.*

Jurisdiction over legislation on public forest lands (except in Alaska), including issues of forestry, wilderness preservation, water rights, national trails and rivers, and recreation.

House Resources Committee, *Subcommittee on National Parks and Public Lands,* *814 O'Neill Bldg. 20515; (202) 226-7736. Fax, (202) 226-2301. James V. Hansen, R-Utah, chair; Allen Freemyer, staff director. Internet, http://www.house.gov/resources.*

Jurisdiction over legislation on public lands (except lands in Alaska and forests), the national park system, the establishment of wildlife refuges on public lands, and the Bureau of Land Management.

Senate Agriculture, Nutrition, and Forestry Committee, *Subcommittee on Forestry, Conservation, and Rural Revitalization,* *SR-328A 20510; (202) 224-2035. Rick Santorum, R-Pa., chair; David French, legislative assistant. Internet, http://www.senate.gov/~agriculture.*

Jurisdiction over legislation on forestry in general and forest reserves acquired from state, local, or private sources.

Senate Energy and Natural Resources Committee, *Subcommittee on Forests and Public Land Management,* *SD-306 20510; (202) 224-6170. Fax, (202) 228-0539. Larry E. Craig, R-Idaho, chair; Mark Rey, professional staff member. Internet, http://www.senate.gov/~energy.*

Jurisdiction over legislation on forest reserves, public lands, the national forest system, the establishment of wildlife refuges on public lands, and the Bureau of Land Management.

NONPROFIT

American Forest and Paper Assn., *1111 19th St. N.W., #800 20036; (202) 463-2700. Fax, (202) 463-2785. Jo Cooper, vice president, Regulatory Affairs. Internet, http://www.afandpa.org.*

Membership: manufacturers of wood and specialty products and related associations. Interests include tax, housing, environmental, international trade, natural resources, and land-use issues that affect the wood products industry.

American Forests, *910 17th St. N.W., #600 20006 (mailing address: P.O. Box 2000, Washington, DC 20013-2000); (202) 955-4500. Fax, (202) 955-4588. Deborah Gangloff, executive vice president. Internet, http://www.amfor.org.*

Citizens' interest group that promotes protection and responsible management of forests and natural resources. Provides information on conservation, public land policy, urban forestry, and timber management. Runs an international tree planting campaign to help mitigate global warming.

American Hardwood Export Council, *1111 19th St. N.W., #800 20036; (202) 463-2720. Fax, (202) 463-2787. Tracy Himmel Isham, executive director. Internet, http://www.ahec.org.*

Trade association of companies and associations that export hardwood products. Aids members in developing and expanding export capabilities in new and existing markets.

American Pulpwood Assn., *600 Jefferson Plaza, #350, Rockville, MD 20852; (301) 838-9385. Fax, (301) 838-9481. Richard Lewis, president. Internet, http://www.apulpa.org.*

Membership: logging contractors, pulpwood dealers, suppliers, and consumers. Administers programs to improve the productivity, safety, and efficiency of pulpwood harvesting and transport; provides information on new equipment, tools, and methods; works to ensure continued access to the timberland base. Monitors legislation and regulations.

American Wood Preservers Institute, *2750 Prosperity Ave. #550, Fairfax, VA 22031-4312; (703) 204-0500. Fax, (703) 204-4610. Vacant, president. Internet, http://www.awpi.org.*

Membership: wood preservers, including manufacturers, formulators of wood preservatives, and wood treating companies. Acts as a liaison between the industry and federal agencies, including the Environmental Protection Agency. Sponsors annual environmental seminar and legislative conference. Monitors legislation and regulations.

International Wood Products Assn., *4214 King St., Alexandria, VA 22302; (703) 820-6696. Fax, (703) 820-8550. Wendy Baer, executive vice president. Internet, info@ihpa.org or http://www.ihpa.org.*

Membership: companies that handle imported wood products. Encourages environmentally responsible forest management and international trade in wood products. Sponsors research and environmental education on tropical forestry. (Affiliated with the Tropical Forest Foundation.)

National Assn. of State Foresters, *444 N. Capitol St. N.W., #540 20001; (202) 624-5415. Fax, (202) 624-5407. Bill Imbergamo, executive director. Internet, nasf@sso.org or http://sso.org/nasf/nasf.html.*

Membership: directors of state forestry agencies from all states, the District of Columbia, and U.S. territories. Members manage and protect over two thirds of the nation's forests, as well as assist private landowners in managing their forests. Monitors legislation and regulations.

National Forest Foundation, *1099 14th St. N.W., #5600W 20005; (202) 273-4754. Fax, (202) 219-6585. Terry Austin, acting president.*

Established by Congress to support the U.S. Forest Service in its management of public lands. Promotes research and multiple-use, cooperative forestry. Interests include conservation, preservation, recreation, wildlife, and environmental education.

National Lumber and Building Material Dealers Assn., *666 Pennsylvania Ave. S.E., #302A 20003; (202) 547-2230. Fax, (202) 547-7640. Gary W. Donnelly, president. Internet, nlbmda@nlbmda.org or http://www.nlbmda.org.*

Membership: federated associations of retailers in the lumber and building material industries. Monitors legislation and regulations that affect the lumber industry.

Save America's Forests, *4 Library Court S.E. 20003; (202) 544-9219. Carl Ross, executive director. Internet, http://www.saveamericasforests.org.*

Coalition of environmental and public interest groups, businesses, and individuals. Advocates recycling and comprehensive nationwide laws to prevent deforestation and to protect forest ecosystems.

Society of American Foresters, *5400 Grosvenor Lane, Bethesda, MD 20814-2198; (301) 897-8720. Fax, (301) 897-3690. William H. Banzhaf, executive vice president. Internet, http://www.safnet.org.*

Association of forestry professionals. Provides technical information on forestry; accredits forestry programs in universities and colleges.

See also Alliance for Environmental Technology (p. 299); International Center (p. 442)

Land Resources and Rights

See also Rural Areas (chap. 12); Soil and Watershed Conservation (chap. 2)

AGENCIES

Bureau of Land Management *(Interior Dept.), 1849 C St. N.W., #5660 20240; (202) 208-3801. Fax, (202) 208-5242. Patrick Shea, director. Internet, http://www.blm.gov.*

Manages public lands and federally owned mineral resources, including oil, gas, and coal. Resources managed and leased include wildlife habitats, timber, minerals, open space, wilderness areas, forage, and recreational resources. Surveys federal lands and maintains public land records.

Bureau of Land Management *(Interior Dept.), Lands and Realty, 1620 L St. N.W. (mailing address: 1849 C St. N.W., MC 1000LS, Washington, DC 20240); (202) 452-7780. Fax, (202) 452-7708. Ray Brady, manager. Internet, http://www.blm.gov.*

Oversees use, acquisition, and disposal of public lands. Conducts the Public Lands Survey; authorizes rights-of-way on public lands, including roads and power lines.

Bureau of Reclamation *(Interior Dept.), 1849 C St. N.W., #7060 20240; (202) 208-4157. Fax, (202) 208-3484. Eluid Martinez, commissioner. Information, (202) 208-4215. Internet, http://www.usbr.gov.*

Responsible for acquisition, administration, management, and disposal of lands in seventeen western states associated with bureau water resource development projects.

Interior Dept., *Board of Land Appeals, 4015 Wilson Blvd., #1007A, Arlington, VA 22203; (703) 235-3750. Fax, (703) 235-8349. James L. Byrnes, chief administrative judge.*

Adjunct office of the interior secretary that decides appeals from decisions rendered by the Bureau of Land Management, the Minerals Management Service, the Office of Surface Mining, and the Bureau of Indian Affairs concerning the use and disposition of public lands; issues final decisions concerning the Surface Mining Control and Reclamation Act of 1977.

Interior Dept., *Land and Minerals Management, 1849 C St. N.W., #6628MIB 20240; (202) 208-5676. Fax, (202) 208-3144. Robert Armstrong, assistant secretary.*

Directs and supervises the Bureau of Land Management, the Minerals Management Service, and the Office of Surface Mining. Supervises programs associated with land use planning, onshore and offshore minerals, surface mining reclamation and enforcement, and outer continental shelf minerals management.

Interior Dept., *North American Wetlands Conservation Council, 4401 N. Fairfax Dr., #110, Arlington, VA 22203; (703) 358-1784. Fax, (703) 358-2282. David A. Smith, coordinator. Internet, r9arw_nawwo@mail.fws.gov or http://www.fws.gov.*

Membership: government and private-sector conservation experts. Works to protect, restore, and manage wetlands and other habitats for migratory birds and other animals and to maintain migratory bird and waterfowl populations.

Interior Dept., *Surface Mining Reclamation and Enforcement, 1951 Constitution Ave. N.W. 20240; (202) 208-4006. Fax, (202) 501-0549. Kathy Karpen, director. Information, (202) 208-2719. Internet, http://www.osmre.gov/astart3.htm.*

Regulates surface mining of coal and surface effects of underground coal mining. Responsible for reclamation of abandoned coal mine lands.

Natural Resources Conservation Service *(Agriculture Dept.), 1400 Independence Ave. S.W. (mailing address: P.O. Box 2890, Washington, DC 20013-2890); (202) 720-4525. Fax, (202) 720-7690. Pearlie Reed, chief. Information, (202) 720-3210. Internet, http://www.ncg.nrcs.usda.gov.*

Responsible for soil and water conservation programs, including watershed protection, flood prevention, river basin surveys, and resource conservation and development. Provides landowners, operators, state and local units of government, and community groups with technical assistance in carrying out local programs.

Tennessee Valley Authority, *1 Massachusetts Ave. N.W., #300 20001; (202) 898-2999. Fax, (202) 898-2998. Vacant, administrative officer, Washington Office. Internet, http://www.tva.gov.*

Coordinates resource conservation, development, and land-use programs in the Tennessee River Valley. Provides information on land usage in the region. (Headquarters in Knoxville, Tenn.)

U.S. Geological Survey *(Interior Dept.), Critical Ecosystems, National Center M.S. 918, Reston, VA 22092; (703) 648-6895. Fax, (703) 648-6683. Sarah Gerould, program coordinator.*

Provides hydrologic, geologic, geochemical, cartographic, and ecological information to assist land and resource managers in restoring critical ecosystems in south Florida, the San Francisco Bay, and the Chesapeake Bay areas.

CONGRESS

House Resources Committee, *Subcommittee on Energy and Mineral Resources, 1626 LHOB 20515; (202) 225-9297. Fax, (202) 225-5255. Barbara Cubin, R-Wyo., chair; William Condit, staff director. Internet, http://www.house.gov/resources.*

Jurisdiction over legislation on land use planning, including surface mining and development of public lands.

House Resources Committee, *Subcommittee on National Parks and Public Lands, 814 O'Neill Bldg. 20515; (202) 226-7736. Fax, (202) 226-2301. James V. Hansen, R-Utah, chair; Allen Freemyer, staff director. Internet, http://www.house.gov/resources.*

Jurisdiction over legislation on public lands (except in Alaska), the land and water conservation fund, and the Bureau of Land Management.

Senate Energy and Natural Resources Committee, *Subcommittee on Energy Research, Development, Production, and Regulation, SD-364 20510; (202) 224-6567.*

Fax, (202) 228-0302. Don Nickles, R-Okla., chair; David Garman, professional staff member. Internet, http://www.senate.gov/~energy.

Jurisdiction over legislation on land use planning, including surface mining; coal production, distribution, and utilization; and coal severance tax.

Senate Energy and Natural Resources Committee, Subcommittee on Forests and Public Land Management, SD-306 20510; (202) 224-6170. Fax, (202) 228-0539. Larry E. Craig, R-Idaho, chair; Mark Rey, professional staff member. Internet, http://www.senate.gov/~energy.

Jurisdiction over legislation on public lands, the land and water conservation fund, the Bureau of Land Management, and the Alaska National Interest Lands Conservation Act.

Senate Environment and Public Works Committee, Subcommittee on Clean Air, Wetlands, Private Property, and Nuclear Safety, SD-407 20510; (202) 224-6176. James M. Inhofe, R-Okla., chair; Chris Hessler, staff contact. Internet, http://www.senate.gov/committee/environment.html.

Jurisdiction over legislation on wetlands.

NONPROFIT

American Geological Institute, 4220 King St., Alexandria, VA 22302; (703) 379-2480. Fax, (703) 379-7563. Marcus E. Milling, executive director. Internet, http://www.agiweb.org.

Membership: earth science societies and associations. Maintains computerized database of the world's geoscience literature (available to the public for a fee).

American Resort Development Assn., 1220 L St. N.W., #500 20005; (202) 371-6700. Fax, (202) 289-8544. Cynthia A. Huheey, president. Internet, http://www.arda.org.

Membership: U.S. and international developers, builders, financiers, marketing companies, and others involved in resort, recreational, and community development. Serves as an information clearinghouse; monitors federal and state legislation affecting land, timeshare, and community development industries.

Defenders of Property Rights, 1350 Connecticut Ave. N.W., #410 20036; (202) 822-6770. Fax, (202) 822-6774. Nancie Marzulla, president; Roger Marzulla, chair. Internet, http://www.defendersprorights.org.

Advocates private property rights. Works to ensure that federal and state governments compensate property owners for property seizures and for effects on property value due to government regulations. Conducts litigation on behalf of property owners.

Land Trust Alliance, 1319 F St. N.W., #501 20004-1106; (202) 638-4725. Fax, (202) 638-4730. Jean Hocker, president. Internet, http://www.lta.org.

Membership: organizations and individuals who work to conserve land resources. Serves as a forum for the exchange of information; conducts research and public education programs. Monitors legislation and regulations.

National Assn. of Conservation Districts, 509 Capitol Court N.E. 20002-4937; (202) 547-6223. Fax, (202) 547-6450. Ernest C. Shea, chief executive officer. Internet, http://www.nacdnet.org.

Membership: conservation districts (local subdivisions of state government). Works to promote the conservation of land, forests, and other natural resources. Interests include erosion and sediment control; water quality; forestry, water, flood plain, and range management; rural development; and urban and community conservation.

Public Lands Council, 1301 Pennsylvania Ave. N.W., #300 20004-1701; (202) 347-5355. Fax, (202) 737-4086. Lance Kotschwar, executive director. Internet, http:/www.cowtown.org.

Membership: cattle and sheep ranchers who hold permits and leases to graze livestock on public lands.

Scenic America, 801 Pennsylvania Ave. S.E., #300 20003; (202) 833-4300. Fax, (202) 833-4304. Meg Maguire, president. Internet, http://www.transact.org/sa/scenic.htm.

Membership: national, state, and local groups concerned with land-use control, growth management, and landscape protection. Works to enhance the scenic quality of America's communities and countryside. Provides information and technical assistance on scenic byways, tree preservation, economics of aesthetic regulation, billboard and sign control, scenic areas preservation, and growth management.

See also National Cattlemen's Beef Assn. (p. 66)

Metals and Minerals

AGENCIES

Bureau of Land Management *(Interior Dept.), Minerals, Realty, and Resource Protection,* 1849 C St. N.W., #5627 20240; (202) 208-4201. Fax, (202) 208-4800. Carson W. Culp, assistant director.

Evaluates and classifies onshore oil, natural gas, geothermal resources, and all solid energy and mineral resources, including coal and uranium on federal lands. Develops and administers regulations for fluid and solid mineral leasing on national lands and on the subsurface of land where fluid and solid mineral rights have been reserved for the federal government.

Federal Emergency Management Agency, *Resources Preparedness and Capabilities, 500 C St. S.W., #633 20472; (202) 646-3544. Fax, (202) 646-3397. Thomas R. McQuillan, director.*

Supports the enhancement and availability of a mineral resources base to respond to national emergencies; administers the Defense Production Act; promotes inter- and intra-agency development of mineral resource mobilization plans and policies.

Interior Dept., *Board of Land Appeals, 4015 Wilson Blvd., #1007A, Arlington, VA 22203; (703) 235-3750. Fax, (703) 235-8349. James L. Byrnes, chief administrative judge.*

Adjunct office of the interior secretary that decides appeals from decisions rendered by the Bureau of Land Management, the Minerals Management Service, the Office of Surface Mining, and the Bureau of Indian Affairs concerning the use and disposition of public minerals; issues final decisions concerning the Surface Mining Reclamation Control Act of 1977.

Interior Dept., *Land and Minerals Management, 1849 C St. N.W., #6628MIB 20240; (202) 208-5676. Fax, (202) 208-3144. Robert Armstrong, assistant secretary.*

Directs and supervises the Bureau of Land Management, the Minerals Management Service, and the Office of Surface Mining. Supervises programs associated with land-use planning, onshore and offshore minerals, surface mining reclamation and enforcement, and outer continental shelf minerals management.

Interior Dept., *Water and Science, 1849 C St. N.W., #6657, Mail Stop 6640 20240; (202) 208-3186. Fax, (202) 371-2815. Patricia J. Beneke, assistant secretary.*

Administers departmental water, scientific, and research activities. Directs and supervises the Bureau of Reclamation and the U.S. Geological Survey.

Minerals Management Service *(Interior Dept.), 1849 C St. N.W., MS 4230 20240; (202) 208-3500. Fax, (202) 208-7242. Cynthia L. Quarterman, director. Internet, http://www.mms.gov.*

Collects and accounts for revenues from onshore and offshore minerals production; disburses royalties to the federal government and Native American groups; oversees development of offshore resources, especially oil and natural gas.

Minerals Management Service, *Engineering and Operations, 381 Elden St., Herndon, VA 20170; (703) 787-1598. Fax, (703) 787-1093. E. P. Danenberger, chief.*

Oversees postlease operations, including exploration, drilling, and production phases of oil and gas development. Ensures compliance with environmental statutes and regulations.

Minerals Management Service, *Royalty Management Program, 1849 C St. N.W., #4245, Mail Stop 4230 20240; (202) 208-3512. Fax, (202) 208-3982. R. Dale Fazio, chief, Washington Royalty Office. Internet, http://www.mms.gov.*

Collects and manages royalties on minerals produced on federal and Native American lands. (Headquarters and accounting center in Denver.)

State Dept., *International Energy and Commodities Policy, Main State Bldg., #3529 20520; (202) 647-2871. Fax, (202) 647-8758. Stephen Muller, chief.*

Handles foreign policy aspects of minerals, international commodity arrangements, and national defense stockpile policy, including deep seabed mining and Antarctic mineral development.

U.S. Geological Survey *(Interior Dept.), Mineral Resource Program, 12201 Sunrise Valley Dr., MS 913, Reston, VA 20192; (703) 648-6100. Fax, (703) 648-6057. Vacant, program coordinator.*

Coordinates mineral resource activities for the Geological Survey, including geochemical and geophysical instrumentation and application research.

CONGRESS

House Resources Committee, *Subcommittee on Energy and Mineral Resources, 1626 LHOB 20515; (202) 225-9297. Fax, (202) 225-5255. Barbara Cubin, R-Wyo., chair; William Condit, staff director. Internet, http://www.house.gov/resources.*

Jurisdiction over legislation on metallic and nonmetallic minerals; oversight and legislative jurisdiction over the Minerals Management Service, mineral aspects of the Office of Surface Mining, mineral leasing of the Bureau of Land Management, and offshore hardrock mineral development programs.

Senate Energy and Natural Resources Committee, *Subcommittee on Energy Research, Development, Production, and Regulation, SD-364 20510; (202) 224-6567. Fax, (202) 228-0302. Don Nickles, R-Okla., chair; David Garman, professional staff member. Internet, http://www.senate.gov/~energy.*

Jurisdiction over legislation on metallic and nonmetallic minerals, including mineral supply and leasing;

oversight and legislative jurisdiction over the Minerals Management Service and offshore hardrock mineral development programs.

Senate Energy and Natural Resources Committee, Subcommittee on Forests and Public Land Management, *SD-306 20510; (202) 224-6170. Fax, (202) 228-0539. Larry E. Craig, R-Idaho, chair; Mark Rey, professional staff member. Internet, http://www.senate. gov/~energy.*

Jurisdiction over legislation on the Bureau of Land Management.

NONPROFIT

Aluminum Assn., *900 19th St. N.W., #300 20006; (202) 862-5100. Fax, (202) 862-5164. J. Stephen Larkin, president. Internet, http://www.aluminum.org.*

Represents the aluminum industry. Develops voluntary standards and technical data; compiles statistics concerning the industry.

American Iron and Steel Institute, *1101 17th St. N.W., 13th Floor 20036-4700; (202) 452-7100. Fax, (202) 463-6573. Andrew G. Sharkey III, president. Internet, http://www.steel.org.*

Represents the iron and steel industry. Publishes statistics on iron and steel production; promotes the use of steel; conducts research. Monitors legislation and regulations.

American Zinc Assn., *1112 16th St. N.W., #240 20036; (202) 835-0164. Fax, (202) 835-0155. George F. Vary, executive director. Internet, http://www.zinc.org.*

Provides information on zinc. Monitors legislation and regulations.

Mineralogical Society of America, *1015 18th St. N.W., #601 20036; (202) 775-4344. Fax, (202) 775-0018. Bruce Watson, president. Internet, http://www.minsocam. org.*

Membership: mineralogists, petrologists, crystallographers, geochemists, educators, students, and others interested in mineralogy. Conducts research; sponsors educational programs; promotes industrial application of mineral studies.

National Mining Assn., *1130 17th St. N.W. 20036; (202) 463-2625. Fax, (202) 463-6152. Richard L. Lawson, president. Information, (202) 463-2623. Press, (202) 463-2651. Internet, nma@prime.planetcom.com or http://www. nma.org.*

Membership: domestic producers of coal and industrial-agricultural minerals and metals; manufacturers of mining equipment; engineering and consulting

firms; and financial institutions. Interests include mine leasing programs, mine health and safety, research and development, public lands, and minerals availability. Monitors legislation and regulations.

Salt Institute, *700 N. Fairfax St., #600, Alexandria, VA 22314; (703) 549-4648. Fax, (703) 548-2194. Richard L. Hanneman, president. Internet, info@saltinstitute.org or http://www.saltinsitute.org.*

Membership: North American salt companies and overseas companies that produce dry salt for use in food, animal feed, highway deicing, water softening, and chemicals. Sponsors education and training projects with the Bureau of Mines and the Food and Drug Administration. Monitors legislation and regulations.

Native American Trust Resources

See also Civil Rights (chap. 1)

AGENCIES

Bureau of Indian Affairs *(Interior Dept.),* **Trust Responsibilities,** *1849 C St. N.W., #4511, Mail Stop 4513 20240; (202) 208-5831. Fax, (202) 219-1255. Terrance Virden, director.*

Assists in developing and managing bureau programs involving Native American trust resources (agriculture, minerals, forestry, wildlife, water, transportation, irrigation, environmental services, and real property management).

Interior Dept., *Office of the Solicitor, 1849 C St. N.W., #6458, Mail Stop 6456 20240; (202) 208-3401. Fax, (202) 219-1791. Derril Jordan, associate solicitor, Indian Affairs.*

Advises the Bureau of Indian Affairs and the secretary of interior on all legal matters, including its trust responsibilities toward Native Americans and their natural resources.

Justice Dept., *Indian Resources, 601 Pennsylvania Ave. N.W., #6702 (mailing address: P.O. Box 44378 L'Enfant Plaza, Washington, DC 20004); (202) 305-0259. Fax, (202) 305-0271. James J. Clear, chief.*

Represents the United States in suits, including trust violations, brought by individual Native Americans and Native American tribes against the government. Also represents the Unites States as trustee for native Americans in court actions involving protection of Native American land and resources.

Minerals Management Service *(Interior Dept.),* **Royalty Management Program,** *1849 C St. N.W., #4245, Mail Stop 4230 20240; (202) 208-3512. Fax, (202) 208-3982. R. Dale Fazio, chief, Washington Royalty Office. Internet, http://www.mms.gov.*

Collects and manages royalties on minerals produced on federal and native American lands. (Headquarters and accounting center in Denver.)

CONGRESS

House Resources Committee, *1324 LHOB 20515-6201; (202) 225-2761. Fax, (202) 225-5929. Don Young, R-Alaska, chair; Lloyd Jones, staff director. Internet, resource@hr.house.gov or http://www.house.gov/resources.*

Jurisdiction over Native American legislation, including land management and trust responsibilities and claims against the United States.

Senate Committee on Indian Affairs, *SH-838 20510; (202) 224-2251. Fax, (202) 224-2309. Ben Nighthorse Campbell, R-Colo., chair; Gary Bohnee, staff director.*

Jurisdiction over Native American legislation, including land management and trust responsibilities and claims against the United States.

NONPROFIT

Native American Rights Fund, *1712 N St. N.W. 20036; (202) 785-4166. Fax, (202) 822-0068. Robert M. Peregoy, acting attorney, Washington Office.*

Provides Native Americans and Alaskan natives with legal assistance in land claims, water rights, hunting, and other areas. (Headquarters in Boulder.)

See also Rural Coalition (p. 38)

Ocean Resources

See also Fishing/Law of the Sea (chap. 13); Oceanography (chap. 17)

AGENCIES

National Oceanic and Atmospheric Administration *(Commerce Dept.), Commissioned Corps, 1315 East-West Hwy., 12th Floor, Silver Spring, MD 20910-3282; (301) 713-1045. Fax, (301) 713-1541. Rear Adm. William L. Stubblefield, director. Recruiting, (301) 713-3470. Internet, http://www.noaa.gov/nchome.*

Uniformed service of the Commerce Dept. that operates and manages NOAA's fleet of hydrographic, oceanographic, and fisheries research ships and aircraft. Supports NOAA's scientific programs.

National Oceanic and Atmospheric Administration *(Commerce Dept.), National Environmental Satellite, Data, and Information Service, 4401 Suitland Rd., #2069, Suitland, MD 20746 (mailing address: 4700 Silver Hill Rd., STOP 9909, Washington, DC 20233-9909); (301) 457-5115. Fax, (301) 457-5276. Robert S. Winokur, assis-*

tant administrator. Internet, orders@ncdc.noaa.gov (National Climatic Data Center).

Disseminates worldwide environmental data through a system of meteorological, oceanographic, geophysical, and solar-terrestrial data centers.

National Oceanic and Atmospheric Administration *(Commerce Dept.), National Sea Grant College Program, 1315 East-West Hwy., Silver Spring, MD 20910; (301) 713-2448. Fax, (301) 713-0799. Ronald C. Baird, director.*

Provides institutions with grants for marine research, education, and advisory services; provides marine environmental information.

National Oceanic and Atmospheric Administration *(Commerce Dept.), Ocean and Coastal Resource Management, 1305 East-West Hwy., SSMC4, Silver Spring, MD 20910; (301) 713-3155. Fax, (301) 713-4012. Jeff Benoit, director. Internet, http://www.coasts.nos.noaa.gov.*

Administers the Coastal Zone Management Act, the National Estuarine Research Reserve System, the National Marine Sanctuary Program, the Deep Seabed Hard Mineral Resources Act, and the Ocean Thermal Energy Conversion Act to carry out NOAA's goals for preservation, conservation, and restoration management of the ocean and coastal environment.

National Oceanic and Atmospheric Administration *(Commerce Dept.), Ocean Resources, Conservation, and Assessment, 1305 East-West Hwy., Silver Spring, MD 20910; (301) 713-2989. Fax, (301) 713-4389. Charles N. Ehler, director. Internet, http://www-orca.nos.noaa.gov.*

Conducts national studies and develops policies on ocean management and use along the U.S. coastline and the exclusive economic zone.

National Oceanic and Atmospheric Administration *(Commerce Dept.), Sanctuaries and Reserves, 1305 East-West Hwy., 11th Floor, Silver Spring, MD 20910; (301) 713-3125. Fax, (301) 713-0404. Stephanie Thornton, chief.*

Administers the National Marine Sanctuary program, which seeks to protect the ecology and the recreational and cultural resources of marine and Great Lakes waters. Administers the National Estuarine Research Reserve System, which helps to acquire, develop, and operate estuarine areas as natural field laboratories for research and education.

CONGRESS

House Resources Committee, *Subcommittee on Fisheries, Conservation, Wildlife, and Oceans, 805 O'Neill*

Bldg. 20515; (202) 226-0200. Fax, (202) 225-1542. Rep. H. James Saxton, R-N.J., chair; Harry Burroughs, staff director. Internet, http://www.house.gov/resources.

Jurisdiction over legislation concerning research on ocean life and the National Environmental Policy Act as it applies to ocean resources. Jurisdiction over ocean environment and charting, ocean engineering, coastal barriers, coastal zone management, Law of the Sea, Sea Grant programs and extension services, and all matters relating to the protection of coastal and marine environments.

Senate Commerce, Science, and Transportation Committee, SD-508 20510; (202) 224-5115. Fax, (202) 224-1259. John McCain, R-Ariz., chair; John Raidt, staff director. Internet, http://www.senate.gov/~commerce.

Jurisdiction over legislation concerning research on ocean life, the National Environmental Policy Act as it applies to ocean resources, deep seabed mining, ocean environment and charting, coastal zone management, Law of the Sea, Sea Grant programs and extension services, and commerce and transportation aspects of outer continental shelf lands.

Senate Commerce, Science, and Transportation Committee, *Subcommittee on Oceans and Fisheries,* SH-428 (mailing address: SD-508, Washington, DC 20510); (202) 224-8172. Fax, (202) 228-0326. Olympia J. Snowe, R-Maine, chair; Clark LeBlanc, professional staffer. Internet, http://www.senate.gov/~commerce.

Studies all aspects of ocean policy including marine science funding and the outer continental shelf. Studies issues involving marine research, coastal zone management, ocean environment, and the Law of the Sea. Studies deep seabed mining, ocean charting, and the National Environmental Policy Act as it applies to ocean resources. (Subcommittee does not report legislation.)

NONPROFIT

Coastal States Organization, 444 N. Capitol St. N.W., #322 20001; (202) 508-3860. Fax, (202) 508-3843. Anthony MacDonald, executive director. Internet, cso@sso. org or http://www.sso.org/cso.

Nonpartisan organization that represents governors of U.S. coastal states, territories, and commonwealths on management of coastal, Great Lakes, and marine resources. Interests include ocean dumping, coastal pollution, wetlands preservation and restoration, national oceans policy, and the outer continental shelf. Gathers and analyzes data to assess state coastal needs; sponsors and participates in conferences and workshops.

Marine Technology Society, 1828 L St. N.W., #906 20036-5104; (202) 775-5966. Fax, (202) 429-9417. Martin J. Finerty Jr., executive director. Internet, mtsadmin@ erols.com or http://www.cms.udel.edu/mts.

Membership: scientists, engineers, technologists, and others interested in marine science and technology. Provides information on marine science, technology, and education.

National Ocean Industries Assn., 1120 G St. N.W., #900 20005; (202) 347-6900. Fax, (202) 347-8650. Robert B. Stewart, president. Internet, noia@noia.org.

Membership: manufacturers, producers, suppliers, and support and service companies involved in marine, offshore, and ocean work. Interests include offshore oil and gas supply and production, deep-sea mining, ocean thermal energy, and new energy sources.

Outer Continental Shelf

AGENCIES

Minerals Management Service *(Interior Dept.), Offshore Minerals Management,* 1849 C St. N.W., #4227, Mail Stop 4230 20240; (202) 208-3530. Fax, (202) 208-6048. Carlitta V. Kallaur, associate director. Internet, http://www.mms.gov.

Administers the Outer Continental Shelf Lands Act. Evaluates, classifies, and supervises oil, gas, and other mineral reserves and operations on outer continental shelf lands; manages the submerged lands of the outer continental shelf.

Minerals Management Service *(Interior Dept.), Resources and Environmental Management,* 381 Elden St., Herndon, VA 20170; (703) 787-1211. Fax, (703) 787-1209. Thomas A. Readinger, deputy associate director. Internet, http://www.mms.gov.

Oversees prelease operations; administers offshore oil and gas leasing.

U.S. Geological Survey *(Interior Dept.), Marine and Coastal Geologic Surveys,* 12201 Sunrise Valley Dr., Reston, VA (mailing address: 915B National Center, Reston, VA 20192); (703) 648-6511. Fax, (703) 648-5464. S. Jeffress Williams, program coordinator.

Handles resource assessment, exploration research, and marine geologic and environmental studies on the U.S. outer continental shelf.

CONGRESS

House Resources Committee, *Subcommittee on Energy and Mineral Resources,* 1626 LHOB 20515; (202) 225-9297. Fax, (202) 225-5255. Barbara Cubin, R-Wyo., chair; William Condit, staff director. Internet, http://www. house.gov/resources.

Jurisdiction over legislation on leasing and development of the outer continental shelf under the Outer Continental Shelf Lands Act.

Senate Commerce, Science, and Transportation Committee, *Subcommittee on Oceans and Fisheries,* SH-428 (mailing address: SD-508, Washington, DC 20510); (202) 224-8172. Fax, (202) 228-0326. Olympia J. Snowe, R-Maine, chair; Clark LeBlanc, professional staffer. Internet, http://www.senate.gov/~commerce.

Studies outer continental shelf matters related to coastal zone management, marine research, and ocean environment. (Jurisdiction shared with the Senate Energy and Natural Resouces and the Senate Environmental and Public Works committees.)

Senate Energy and Natural Resources Committee, SD-364 20510; (202) 224-4971. Fax, (202) 224-6163. Frank H. Murkowski, R-Alaska, chair; Gregg D. Renkes, staff director. Internet, http://www.senate.gov/~energy.

Jurisdiction over legislation on ocean environment and coastal zone matters, including leasing and development of the outer continental shelf under the Outer Continental Shelf Lands Act; and on the environmental impact of offshore drilling on the outer continental shelf (jurisdiction shared with Senate Commerce, Science, and Transportation and Senate Environment and Public Works committees).

Senate Environment and Public Works Committee, *Subcommittee on Drinking Water, Fisheries, and Wildlife,* SD-410 20510; (202) 224-6176. Fax, (202) 224-5167. Dirk Kempthorne, R-Idaho, chair; Ann Klee, staff contact. Internet, http://www.senate.gov/committee/environment.html.

Jurisdiction over legislation on the environmental impact of offshore drilling on the outer continental shelf. (Jurisdiction shared with Senate Commerce, Science, and Transportation and Senate Energy and Natural Resources committees.)

Parks and Recreation Areas

See also History and Preservation (chap. 4); Recreation and Sports (chap. 4)

AGENCIES

Bureau of Land Management (Interior Dept.), *Cultural Heritage, Wilderness, Special Areas, and Paleontology,* 1620 L St. N.W., #204 (mailing address: 1849 C St. N.W., #204-LS, Washington, DC 20240); (202) 452-0330. Fax, (202) 452-7701. Marilyn Nickels, group manager. TDD, (202) 452-0326.

Identifies and manages cultural heritage and recreation programs on public lands.

Bureau of Reclamation (Interior Dept.), 1849 C St. N.W., #7060 20240; (202) 208-4157. Fax, (202) 208-3484. Eluid Martinez, commissioner. Information, (202) 208-4215. Internet, http://www.usbr.gov.

Responsible for acquisition, administration, management, and disposal of lands in seventeen western states associated with bureau water resource development projects. Provides overall policy guidance for land use, including agreements with public agencies for outdoor recreation, fish and wildlife enhancement, and land use authorizations such as leases, licenses, permits, and rights of way.

Forest Service (Agriculture Dept.), *Recreation Management,* 1400 Independence Ave. S.W. (mailing address: P.O. Box 96090, Washington, DC 20090-6090); (202) 205-1706. Fax, (202) 205-1145. Steven Deitemeyer, acting director. Internet, http://www.fs.fed.us.

Develops policy and sets guidelines on administering national forests and grasslands for recreational purposes. (The Forest Service administers some of the lands designated as national recreation areas.)

Interior Dept., *Fish, Wildlife, and Parks,* 1849 C St. N.W., #3156 20240; (202) 208-4416. Fax, (202) 208-4684. Donald Barry, acting assistant secretary.

Responsible for programs associated with the development, conservation, and use of fish, wildlife, recreational, historical, and national park system resources. Coordinates marine environmental quality and biological resources programs with other federal agencies.

Interior Dept., *National Park Service Policy,* 1849 C St. N.W., #2414 20240; (202) 208-7456. Fax, (202) 219-8835. Loran G. Fraser, chief.

Researches and develops management policy on matters relating to the National Park Service; makes recommendations on the historical significance of national trails and landmarks.

National Park Service (Interior Dept.), 1849 C St. N.W., #3316 20240 (mailing address: P.O. Box 37127, Washington, DC 20013-7127); (202) 208-4621. Fax, (202) 208-7889. Robert Stanton, director. Press, (202) 208-6843. Washington area activities, (202) 619-7275 (recording). Internet, http://www.nps.gov.

Administers national parks, monuments, historic sites, and recreation areas. Oversees coordination, planning, and financing of public outdoor recreation programs at all levels of government. Conducts recreation research surveys; administers financial assistance program to states for planning and development of outdoor recreation programs. (Some lands designated as national recreation areas are not under NPS jurisdiction.)

Tennessee Valley Authority, *1 Massachusetts Ave. N.W., #300 20001; (202) 898-2999. Fax, (202) 898-2998. Vacant, administrative officer, Washington Office. Internet, http://www.tva.gov.*

Operates Land Between the Lakes, a national recreation and environmental education area located in western Kentucky and Tennessee. (TVA headquarters in Knoxville, Tenn.)

U.S. Fish and Wildlife Service, *Refuges and Wildlife, 1849 C St. N.W., #3251 20240; (202) 208-5333. Fax, (202) 208-3082. Nita Fuller, assistant director. Internet, http://www.fws.gov.*

Manages the National Wildlife Refuge System. Most refuges are open to public use; activities include bird and wildlife watching, fishing, hunting, and environmental education.

CONGRESS

House Resources Committee, *Subcommittee on Forests and Forest Health, 1337 LHOB 20515; (202) 225-0691. Helen Chenoweth, R-Idaho, chair; William M. Simmons, staff director. Internet, resource@hr.house.gov or http://www.house.gov/resources.*

Jurisdiction over legislation on public forest lands (except in Alaska), including issues of wilderness preservation, national trails and rivers, and recreation.

House Resources Committee, *Subcommittee on National Parks and Public Lands, 814 O'Neill Bldg. 20515; (202) 226-7736. Fax, (202) 226-2301. James V. Hansen, R-Utah, chair; Allen Freemyer, staff director. Internet, http://www.house.gov/resources.*

Jurisdiction over legislation on the national park system, the Bureau of Land Management, and related parks and recreation.

Senate Energy and Natural Resources Committee, *Subcommittee on National Parks, Historic Preservation, and Recreation, SD-354 20510; (202) 224-6969. Fax, (202) 228-0459. Craig Thomas, R-Wyo., chair; Jim O'Toole, professional staff member. Internet, http://www.senate.gov/~energy.*

Jurisdiction over legislation on national parks, recreation areas, wilderness areas, trails, wild and scenic rivers, historic sites, and military parks and battlefields.

NONPROFIT

American Hiking Society, *1422 Fenwick Lane, Silver Spring, MD 20910; (301) 565-6704. Fax, (301) 565-6714.*

David Lillard, president. Internet, ahsinform@aol.com or http://www.orca.org/ahs.

Membership: individuals and clubs interested in preserving America's trail system and protecting the interests of trail users. Provides information on outdoor volunteer opportunities on public lands.

American Recreation Coalition, *1225 New York Ave. N.W., #450 20005; (202) 682-9530. Fax, (202) 682-9529. Derrick A. Crandall, president. Internet, arc@funoutdoors.com or http://www.funoutdoors.com.*

Membership: organized recreationists, national and regional corporations offering recreational products and services, and recreation industry trade associations. Works to increase public and private sector activity in public recreation, land and water management, and energy policy. Provides information on innovative recreational planning.

National Park Foundation, *1101 17th St. N.W., #1102 20036-4704; (202) 785-4500. Fax, (202) 785-3539. James D. Maddy, president. Internet, http://www.nationalparks.org.*

Chartered by Congress and chaired by the interior secretary. Encourages private-sector support of the national park system; provides grants and sponsors educational and cultural activities.

National Parks and Conservation Assn., *1776 Massachusetts Ave. N.W., #200 20036-6404; (202) 223-6722. Fax, (202) 659-0650. Tom Kiernan, president. Toll-free, (800) 628-7275. Internet, http://www.npca.org.*

Citizens' interest group that seeks to protect national parks and other park system areas.

National Recreation and Park Assn., *22377 Belmont Ridge Rd., Ashburn, VA 20148; (703) 858-0784. Fax, (703) 858-0794. Dean Tice, executive director. TDD, (703) 578-5559. Internet, info@nrpa.org or http://www.nrpa.org.*

Membership: park and recreation professionals and interested citizens. Provides technical assistance for park and recreational programs.

Rails-to-Trails Conservancy, *1100 17th St. N.W., 10th Floor 20036; (202) 331-9696. Fax, (202) 331-9680. David G. Burwell, president. Internet, rtrails@transact.org or http://www.railtrails.org.*

Promotes the conversion of abandoned railroad corridors into hiking and biking trails for public use. Provides public education programs and technical and legal assistance. Publishes trail guides. Monitors legislation and regulations.

Scenic America, *801 Pennsylvania Ave. S.E., #300 20003; (202) 833-4300. Fax, (202) 833-4304. Meg Maguire, president. Internet, http://www.transact.org/sa/scenic.htm.*

Membership: national, state, and local groups concerned with land-use control, growth management, and landscape protection. Works to enhance the scenic quality of America's communities and countryside. Provides information and technical assistance on scenic byways, tree preservation, economics of aesthetic regulation, billboard and sign control, scenic areas preservation, and growth management.

Student Conservation Assn., *1800 N. Kent St., #1260, Arlington, VA 22209; (703) 524-2441. Fax, (703) 524-2451. Reginald Hagood, national director. Internet, http://www.sca-inc.org.*

Educational organization that provides youth and adults with opportunities for training and work experience in natural resource management and conservation. Volunteers serve in national parks, forests, wildlife refuges, and other public lands. (Headquarters in Charlestown, N.H.)

World Wildlife Fund, *1250 24th St. N.W., #400 20037; (202) 293-4800. Fax, (202) 293-9211. Kathryn S. Fuller, president. Internet, http://www.wwf.org.*

International conservation organization that provides funds and technical assistance for establishing and maintaining parks.

Water Resources

See also Rural Areas (chap. 2); Soil and Watershed Conservation (chap. 2); Water Pollution (this chapter)

AGENCIES

Army Corps of Engineers *(Defense Dept.),* *20 Massachusetts Ave. N.W. 20314-1000; (202) 761-0001. Fax, (202) 761-4463. Lt. Gen. Joe N. Ballard (USACE), chief of engineers. Internet, http://www.usace.army.mil.*

Provides local governments with disaster relief, flood control, navigation, and hydroelectric power services.

Bureau of Reclamation *(Interior Dept.),* *1849 C St. N.W., #7659 20240; (202) 208-4157. Fax, (202) 208-3484. Eluid Martinez, commissioner. Information, (202) 208-4215. Internet, http://www.usbr.gov.*

Administers federal programs for water and power resource development and management in seventeen western states; oversees municipal and industrial water supply, hydroelectric power generation, irrigation, flood control, water quality improvement, river regulation, fish and wildlife enhancement, and outdoor recreation.

Delaware River Basin Commission, *1010 Massachusetts Ave. N.W., #100 20001; (202) 343-5761. Fax, (202) 343-1013. Vincent P. D'Anna, U.S. commissioner.*

Federal-interstate commission. Oversees projects to develop the Delaware River Basin that include regulation and development of ground and surface water supplies for municipal, industrial, and agricultural uses; development of hydropower; abatement of stream pollution; flood damage reduction; and protection of fish and wildlife.

Environmental Protection Agency, *Wetlands Protection,* *499 S. Capitol St. S.W. (mailing address: 401 M St. S.W., #4502-F, Washington, DC 20460); (202) 260-7791. Fax, (202) 260-2356. John W. Meagher, director.*

Manages dredge-and-fill program under section 404 of the Clean Water Act. Coordinates federal policies affecting wetlands. Promotes public awareness of wetland preservation and management. Encourages the development of stronger wetland programs at the state level.

Interstate Commission on the Potomac River Basin, *6110 Executive Blvd., #300, Rockville, MD 20852; (301) 984-1908. Fax, (301) 984-5841. Robert Bolle, acting executive director.*

Nonregulatory interstate compact commission established by Congress to control and reduce water pollution and to restore and protect living resources in the Potomac River and its tributaries. Monitors water quality; assists metropolitan water utilities; seeks innovative methods to solve water supply and land resource problems. Provides information and educational materials on the Potomac River basin.

Office of Management and Budget *(Executive Office of the President),* *Water and Power,* *New Executive Office Bldg., #8002 20503; (202) 395-4590. Fax, (202) 395-4817. Rick Mertens, chief.*

Reviews all plans and budgets related to federal or federally assisted water power and related land resource projects.

Rural Utilities Service *(Agriculture Dept.),* *1400 Independence Ave. S.W. 20250-1500; (202) 720-9540. Fax, (202) 720-1725. Wally Beyer, administrator. Information, (202) 720-1255. Press, (202) 720-1260. Internet, http://www.usda.gov/rus.*

Makes loans and provides technical assistance for development, repair, and replacement of water and waste disposal systems in rural areas.

Smithsonian Environmental Research Center *(Smithsonian Institution),* *647 Contees Wharf Rd., Edgewater, MD (mailing address: P.O. Box 28, Edgewater, MD 21037); (410) 798-4424. Fax, (301) 261-7954. Ross Simons, acting director. Internet, http://www.serc.si.edu.*

Studies the interaction of the Rhode River with its watershed, the effect of human activities on the system, and the long-term effects of water quality on the plant and animal population.

Susquehanna River Basin Commission, *1010 Massachusetts Ave. N.W., #100 20001; (202) 343-4091. Fax, (202) 343-1013. Kenneth J. Cole, U.S. commissioner.*

Federal-interstate compact commission that manages water and water-related resources to develop the Susquehanna River basin. Regulates and develops ground and surface water supplies for municipal, industrial, and agricultural uses; works to reduce stream pollution and flood damage, and to protect fish and wildlife.

Tennessee Valley Authority, *1 Massachusetts Ave. N.W., #300 20001; (202) 898-2999. Fax, (202) 898-2998. Vacant, administrative officer, Washington Office. Internet, http://www.tva.gov.*

Coordinates resource conservation, development, and land-use programs in the Tennessee River Valley. Operates the river control system; projects include flood control, navigation development, and multiple-use reservoirs. (Headquarters in Knoxville, Tenn.)

U.S. Geological Survey *(Interior Dept.),* **National Water Information Center,** *12201 Sunrise Valley Dr., MS 440, Reston, VA 20192; (703) 648-5699. Fax, (703) 648-5644. Lewis V. Wade, assistant chief hydrologist, Water Information. Toll-free, (800) 426-9000. Internet, http://water.usgs.gov/public/wrd005.html.*

Referral service for governmental and private water resources organizations. Assists in identifying, locating, and acquiring data on water resources. Information available through cooperating organizations and assistance centers.

U.S. Geological Survey *(Interior Dept.),* **Water Resources,** *12201 Sunrise Valley Dr., Reston, VA 20192; (703) 648-5215. Fax, (703) 648-5295. Robert M. Hirsch, chief hydrologist. Internet, http://www.usgs.gov.*

Administers the Water Resources Research Act of 1990. Assesses the quantity and quality of surface and groundwater resources; collects, analyzes, and disseminates data on water use and the effect of human activity and natural phenomena on hydrologic systems. Provides federal agencies, state and local governments, international organizations, and foreign governments with scientific and technical assistance.

CONGRESS

House Agriculture Committee, *Subcommittee on Forestry, Resource Conservation, and Research, 1336 LHOB 20515; (202) 225-2342. Larry Combest, R-Texas,*

chair; Russell Laird, staff director. Internet, http://www.house.gov/agriculture.

Jurisdiction over legislation on small watershed programs, including stream channelization.

House Commerce Committee, *Subcommittee on Energy and Power, 2125 RHOB 20515; (202) 225-2927. Fax, (202) 225-1919. Dan Schaefer, R-Colo., chair; James E. Derderian, staff director. Internet, http://www.house.gov/commerce.*

Jurisdiction over legislation on hydroelectric power and ocean thermal energy resource commercialization, utilization, and conversion.

House Resources Committee, *Subcommittee on Water and Power, 1522 LHOB 20515; (202) 225-8331. John T. Doolittle, R-Calif., chair; Robert Faber, staff director. Internet, http://www.house.gov/resources.*

Jurisdiction over legislation on water rights, including federally reserved water rights on public lands; irrigation and reclamation projects; compacts relating to use and apportionment of interstate water resources; and power marketing administrations.

House Science Committee, *Subcommittee on Energy and Environment, 389 FHOB 20515; (202) 225-9662. Fax, (202) 266-6983. Ken Calvert, R-Calif., chair; Harlan Watson, staff director. Internet, http://www.house.gov/science.*

Jurisdiction over water resources research legislation.

House Transportation and Infrastructure Committee, *Subcommittee on Water Resources and Environment, B376 RHOB 20515; (202) 225-4360. Fax, (202) 226-5435. Sherwood Boehlert, R-N.Y., chair; Ben Grumbles, counsel. Internet, http://www.house.gov/transportation.*

Jurisdiction over legislation on water resources; watershed and flood control programs; U.S. Army Corps of Engineers water resources projects; wetlands protection; navigation and river basin programs; small watershed programs within the Agriculture Dept.; groundwater programs; construction, operation, and maintenance of harbors and inland waterways; and hydroelectric power.

Senate Agriculture, Nutrition, and Forestry Committee, *Subcommittee on Forestry, Conservation, and Rural Revitalization, SR-328A 20510; (202) 224-2035. Rick Santorum, R-Pa., chair; David French, legislative assistant. Internet, http://www.senate.gov/~agriculture.*

Jurisdiction over legislation on small watershed programs, including stream channelization, and on flood control programs that involve structures of less than 4,000 acre-feet in storage capacity.

Senate Energy and Natural Resources Committee, *Subcommittee on Water and Power,* SH-312 20510; (202) 224-2564. Fax, (202) 224-6163. Jon Kyl, R-Ariz., chair; James P. Bierne, senior counsel. Internet, http://www.senate.gov/~energy.

Jurisdiction over legislation on hydroelectric power; irrigation and reclamation projects; water rights, including federally reserved water rights on public lands; compacts relating to use and apportionment of interstate water resources; and power marketing administrations.

Senate Environment and Public Works Committee, *Subcommittee on Drinking Water, Fisheries, and Wildlife,* SD-410 20510; (202) 224-6176. Fax, (202) 224-5167. Dirk Kempthorne, R-Idaho, chair; Ann Klee, staff contact. Internet, http://www.senate.gov/committee/environment.html.

Jurisdiction over water resources and water resources research legislation; watershed and flood control programs; U.S. Army Corps of Engineers water resources projects; navigation and river basin programs; small watershed programs of the Natural Resources Conservation Service; wetlands protection and groundwater programs; and construction, operation, and maintenance of harbors.

NONPROFIT

American Rivers, *1025 Vermont Ave. N.W., #720 20005; (202) 547-6900. Fax, (202) 342-9240. Rebecca Wodder, president. Internet, http://www.amrivers.org.*

Works to preserve the nation's river system and to control river development and dam and canal construction.

American Water Resources Assn., *950 Herndon Pkwy., #300, Herndon, VA 20170; (703) 904-1225. Fax, (703) 904-1228. Kenneth D. Reid, executive vice president. Internet, awrahq@aol.com or http://www.awra.org/~awra.*

Collects and provides information on all aspects of water resources. Interests include research and education on planning, managing, and developing water resources.

American Water Works Assn., *1401 New York Ave. N.W., #640 20005; (202) 628-8303. Fax, (202) 628-2846. John H. Sullivan, deputy executive director, Washington Office. Internet, http://www.awwa.org.*

Membership: municipal water utilities, manufacturers of equipment for water industries, water treatment companies, and individuals. Provides information on drinking water treatment; publishes voluntary standards for the water industry. (Headquarters in Denver.)

Assn. of State Drinking Water Administrators, *1120 Connecticut Ave. N.W., #1060 20036; (202) 293-7655. Fax, (202) 293-7656. Vanessa Leiby, executive director. Internet, asdwa@erols.com or http://www.asdwa.org.*

Membership: state officials responsible for the drinking water supply and enforcement of safety standards. Monitors legislation and regulations.

Environmental Defense Fund, *1875 Connecticut Ave. N.W., #1016 20009-5728; (202) 387-3500. Fax, (202) 234-6049. Cheryl Pickard, office manager, Washington Office. Internet, http://www.edf.org.*

Citizens' interest group staffed by lawyers, economists, and scientists. Takes legal action on environmental issues; provides information on pollution prevention, environmental health, water resources, and water marketing. (Headquarters in New York.)

Irrigation Assn., *8260 Willow Oaks Corporate Dr., #120, Fairfax, VA 22031; (703) 573-3551. Fax, (703) 573-1913. Thomas Kimmell, executive director. Internet, http://www.irrigation.org.*

Membership: companies and individuals involved in irrigation, drainage, and erosion control worldwide. Seeks to improve the products and practices used to manage water resources; interests include economic development and environmental enhancement.

Izaak Walton League of America, *707 Conservation Lane, Gaithersburg, MD 20878-2983; (301) 548-0150. Fax, (301) 548-0146. Paul W. Hansen, executive director. Internet, general@iwla.org or http://www.igc.apc.org/iwla.*

Grassroots organization that promotes conservation of natural resources and the environment. Coordinates a citizen action program to monitor and improve the condition of local streams.

National Assn. of Conservation Districts, *509 Capitol Court N.E. 20002-4937; (202) 547-6223. Fax, (202) 547-6450. Ernest C. Shea, chief executive officer. Internet, http://www.nacdnet.org.*

Membership: conservation districts (local subdivisions of state government). Develops national policies and works to promote the conservation of water resources. Interests include erosion and sediment control and control of nonpoint source pollution.

National Assn. of Flood and Stormwater Management Agencies, *1401 Eye St. N.W., #900 20005; (202) 218-4122. Fax, (202) 842-0621. Susan Gilson, executive director.*

Membership: state, county, and local governments concerned with management of water resources. Monitors legislation and regulations.

National Assn. of Regulatory Utility Commission-ers, *12th St. and Constitution Ave. N.W. (mailing address: P.O. Box 684, Washington, DC 20044-0684); (202) 898-2200. Fax, (202) 898-2213. Peggy Welsh, executive director. Press, (202) 898-2205. Internet, http://www.naruc.org.*

Membership: members of federal, state, municipal, and Canadian regulatory commissions that have jurisdiction over utilities. Interests include water.

National Assn. of Water Companies, *1725 K St. N.W., #1212 20006; (202) 833-8383. Fax, (202) 331-7442. Peter L. Cook, executive director. Internet, http://www.nawc.org.*

Membership: privately owned, regulated water companies. Provides members with information on legislative and regulatory issues and other subjects.

National Rural Community Assistance Program, *602 S. King St., #402, Leesburg, VA 20175; (703) 771-8636. Fax, (703) 771-8753. Kathleen Stanley, executive director. Internet, http://www.rcap.org.*

Federally funded organization that conducts program to improve water delivery and disposal of waste water for rural residents, particularly low-income families.

National Utility Contractors Assn., *4301 N. Fairfax Dr., #360, Arlington, VA 22203-1627; (703) 358-9300. Fax, (703) 358-9307. William G. Harley, executive vice president. Internet, http://www.nuca.com.*

Membership: contractors who perform water, sewer, and other underground utility construction. Sponsors conferences; conducts surveys. Monitors public works legislation and regulations.

National Water Resources Assn., *3800 N. Fairfax Dr., #4, Arlington, VA 22203; (703) 524-1544. Fax, (703) 524-1548. Thomas F. Donnelly, executive vice president. Internet, http://www.nwra.org.*

Membership: conservation and irrigation districts, municipalities, and others interested in water resources. Works for the development and maintenance of water resource projects in the western reclamation states. Represents interests of members before Congress and regulatory agencies.

River Network, *4000 Albemarle St. N.W., #303 20016; (202) 364-2550. Fax, (202) 364-2520. Pat Munoz, program manager. Internet, rivernet2@aol.com or http://www.rivernetwork.org.*

Acquires and conserves watersheds of rivers used for drinking water supply, floodplain management, fish and wildlife habitats, and recreation. Works to build and support citizen watershed councils. (Headquarters in Portland, Ore.)

See also Irrigation Assn. (p. 314)

10 🏛

Government Personnel and Services

🏛 CENSUS/POPULATION DATA

The Census Bureau publishes a pamphlet, "Telephone Contacts for Data Users," that lists key Census Bureau personnel and their fields of specialty. Copies may be obtained from the Census Bureau, Data User Services Division, User Training Branch, Washington, DC 20233; (301) 457-2822. For a specific inquiry about computer data, call (301) 457-4100.

AGENCIES

Census Bureau *(Commerce Dept.),* Suitland and Silver Hill Rds., Suitland, MD; (301) 457-2135. Fax, (301) 457-3761. James F. Holmes, acting director. Information, (301) 457-2800. Press, (301) 457-3030. Library, (301) 457-2511. Internet, http://www.census.gov.

Conducts surveys and censuses (including the decennial census of population and housing); collects and analyzes demographic, social, economic, housing, agricultural, and foreign trade data and data on governments; publishes statistics for use by Congress, business, state and local governments, planners, and the public. Library open to the public.

Census Bureau, *Decennial Census,* Suitland and Silver Hill Rds., Suitland, MD; (301) 457-3946. Fax, (301) 457-3024. John Thompson, associate director.

Provides data from the 1990 decennial census (including general plans and procedures); economic, demographic, and population statistics; and information on trends.

Census Bureau, *Demographic Surveys,* Suitland and Silver Hill Rds., Suitland, MD; (301) 457-3811. Fax, (301) 457-2306. Chester E. Bowie, chief.

Provides and explains proper use of data on consumer spending, crime, employment and unemployment, income, and housing. Conducts surveys on various subjects, including population, prisoners, health, and travel.

Census Bureau, *Housing and Household Economic Statistics,* 4700 Silver Hill Rd., Suitland, MD 20746-8500; (301) 457-3234. Fax, (301) 457-3248. Daniel H. Weinberg, chief.

Develops statistical programs for the decennial census and for other surveys on housing, income, poverty, and the labor force. Collects and explains the proper use of economic, social, and demographic data. Responsible for the technical planning, analysis, and publication of data from current surveys, including the decennial census, the American Housing Survey, Current Population Survey, and Survey of Income and Program Participation.

Census Bureau, *Population,* Suitland and Silver Hill Rds., Suitland, MD; (301) 457-2071. Fax, (301) 457-2644. John F. Long, chief.

Prepares population estimates and projections for national, state, and local areas and congressional districts. Provides data on demographic and social statistics in the following areas: families and households, marital status and living arrangements, farm population, migration and mobility, population distribution, ancestry, fertility, child care, race and ethnicity, language patterns, school enrollment, educational attainment, and voting.

CONGRESS

House Appropriations Committee, *Subcommittee on Commerce, Justice, State, and Judiciary,* H309 Capitol 20515; (202) 225-3351. Harold Rogers, R-Ky., chair; Jim Kulikowski, staff director. Internet, http://www.house.gov/appropriations.

Jurisdiction over legislation to appropriate funds for the Commerce Dept., including the Census Bureau.

House Government Reform and Oversight Committee, *Subcommittee on Civil Service,* B371C RHOB 20515; (202) 225-6427. Fax, (202) 225-2392. John L. Mica, R-Fla., chair; George Nesterczuk, staff director. Internet, http://www.house.gov/reform.

Jurisdiction over census legislation and statistics collection, demography, and population issues; oversight of the Census Bureau.

Senate Appropriations Committee, *Subcommittee on Commerce, Justice, State, and Judiciary,* SR-393 20510; (202) 224-7277. Judd Gregg, R-N.H., chair, (202) 224-3324; Vas Alexopoulos, legislative assistant. Chair's fax, (202) 224-4952. Internet, http://www.senate.gov/~appropriations.

Jurisdiction over legislation to appropriate funds for the Commerce Dept., including the Census Bureau.

Senate Governmental Affairs Committee, SD-340 20510; (202) 224-4751. Fax, (202) 224-9603. Fred Thompson, R-Tenn., chair; Hannah Sistare, staff director. Internet, http://www.senate.gov/committee/governmental_affairs.html.

Jurisdiction over census legislation and statistics collection, demography, and population issues; oversight of the Census Bureau.

NONPROFIT

Population Assn. of America, 721 Ellsworth Dr., #303, Silver Spring, MD 20910; (301) 565-6710. Fax, (301) 565-7850. Stephanie Dudley, executive administrator. Internet, info@popassoc.org or http://www.popassoc.org.

Membership: university, government, and industry researchers in demography. Holds annual technical sessions to present papers on population issues and statistics.

Population Reference Bureau, *1875 Connecticut Ave. N.W., #520 20009-5728; (202) 483-1100. Fax, (202) 328-3937. Peter J. Donaldson, president. Internet, http://www.prb.org.*

Educational organization engaged in information dissemination, training, and policy analysis on U.S. population trends and issues. Interests include international development and family planning programs, the environment, and U.S. social and economic policy. Library open to the public.

🏛 CIVIL SERVICE

See also Government Management and Oversight (this chapter)

AGENCIES

National Archives and Records Administration, *Information Security Oversight, 700 Pennsylvania Ave. N.W., #5W 20408-0001; (202) 219-5250. Fax, (202) 219-5385. Steven Garfinkel, director. Internet, isoo@arch1.nara.gov.*

Oversees the security classification system throughout the executive branch; reports to the president on implementation of the security classification system. Develops and disseminates security education materials. Oversees the Classified Information Nondisclosure Agreement, which bars federal employees from disclosing classified and sensitive government information.

Office of Personnel Management, *1900 E St. N.W. 20415; (202) 606-1000. Fax, (202) 606-2573. Janice Lachance, director; Vacant, deputy director. Information, (202) 606-1800. Library, (202) 606-1381. TDD, (202) 606-2118. Locator, (202) 606-2424; job information, (202) 606-2525. Internet, http://www.usajobs.opm.gov.*

Administers civil service rules and regulations; sets policy for personnel management, labor-management relations, work force effectiveness, and employment within the executive branch; manages federal personnel activities, including recruitment, pay comparability, and benefit programs. Library open to the public.

Office of Personnel Management, *Compensation Administration, 1900 E St. N.W., 20415; (202) 606-2880. Fax, (202) 606-4264. Donald J. Winstead, assistant director.*

Responsible for policy development and administration of compensation systems for almost two million federal civilian white-collar and blue-collar employees.

Office of Personnel Management, *Merit Systems Oversight and Effectiveness, 1900 E St. N.W., #7470 20415-0001; (202) 606-1575. Fax, (202) 606-1798. Carol J. Okin, associate director.*

Monitors federal agencies' personnel practices and ensures that they abide by the Merit Systems Principles.

Office of Personnel Management, *Statistical Analysis and Services, 1900 E St. N.W., #7439 20415; (202) 606-2850. Fax, (202) 606-1719. Andrew Klugh, acting assistant director.*

Produces information for the Office of Personnel Management, Congress, and the public on statistical aspects of the federal civilian work force, including trends in composition, grade levels, minority employment, sizes of agencies, and salaries.

Office of Personnel Management, *Workforce Compensation and Performance Service, 1900 E St. N.W., #7508 20415-0001; (202) 606-2800. Fax, (202) 606-1443. Henry Romero, associate director.*

Works to improve personnel management within agencies by developing and implementing policy on white- and blue-collar pay systems, incentive awards, labor-management relations, employee benefits, and information systems.

CONGRESS

House Appropriations Committee, *Subcommittee on Treasury, Postal Service, and General Government, B307 RHOB 20515; (202) 225-5834. Fax, (202) 225-5895. Jim Kolbe, R-Ariz., chair; Michelle Mrdeza, clerk. Internet, http://www.house.gov/appropriations.*

Jurisdiction over legislation to appropriate funds for the Office of Personnel Management and the Merit Systems Protection Board.

House Education and the Workforce Committee, *Subcommittee on Workforce Protections, 2181 RHOB 20515; (202) 225-4527. Fax, (202) 225-9571. Cass Ballenger, R-N.C., chair; Kevin Talley, staff director.*

Jurisdiction over legislation on federal employees' compensation.

House Government Reform and Oversight Committee, *Subcommittee on Civil Service, B371C RHOB 20515; (202) 225-6427. Fax, (202) 225-2392. John L. Mica, R-Fla., chair; George Nesterczuk, staff director. Internet, http://www.house.gov/reform.*

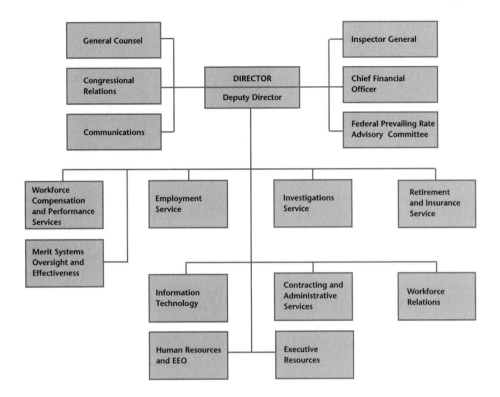

Jurisdiction over legislation on civil service labor-management issues, job classifications, hiring and recruiting, pay and compensation, benefits, retirement, rights of privacy, and code of ethics; and legislation related to the Hatch Act, which deals with the political activity of civil service employees. Oversight of the Senior Executive Service and intergovernmental personnel programs. Studies the effects of reorganization of agencies on federal employees.

House Government Reform and Oversight Committee, *Subcommittee on Human Resources, B372 RHOB 20515; (202) 225-2548. Fax, (202) 225-2382. Christopher Shays, R-Conn., chair; Larry Halloran, staff director. Internet, http://www.house.gov/reform.*

Oversight of the Office of Personnel Management and the Merit Systems Protection Board.

Senate Appropriations Committee, *Subcommittee on Treasury and General Government, SD-190 20510; (202) 224-7337. Ben Nighthorse Campbell, R-Colo., chair;*

Patricia Raymond, staff director. Internet, http://www. senate.gov/~appropriations.

Jurisdiction over legislation to appropriate funds for the Office of Personnel Management and the Merit Systems Protection Board.

Senate Governmental Affairs Committee, *SD-340 20510; (202) 224-4751. Fax, (202) 224-9603. Fred Thompson, R-Tenn., chair; Hannah Sistare, staff director. Internet, http://www.senate.gov/committee/governmental_affairs.html.*

Jurisdiction over legislation on civil service labor-management issues; hiring, recruiting, and job classifications; compensation, including pay allowances and benefits; code of ethics; rights of privacy; intergovernmental personnel programs; effects of reorganization; leave and retirement; and legislation related to the Hatch Act, which deals with the political activity of civil service employees. Oversight of the Senior Executive Service, the Office of Personnel Management, and the Merit Systems Protection Board.

PERSONNEL OFFICES AT FEDERAL AGENCIES

DEPARTMENTS

Agriculture, (202) 720-3327

Commerce, recording, (202) 482-5138

Defense (civilian), (703) 696-2720

  Air Force (civilian), (703) 697-3127

  Army (civilian), (202) 761-5179

  Navy (civilian), (703) 695-8784

  Defense Logistics Agency, (703) 767-7150

Education, (202) 401-0553
vacancies, (202) 401-0559

Energy, recording, (202) 586-4333

Health and Human Services, (301) 504 3301

  Food and Drug Administration, (301) 827-4070

  Health Resources and Services Administration,
recording, (301) 443-1230

  National Institutes of Health, recording,
(301) 496-2403

  Public Health and Science, (202) 205-4859

  **Substance Abuse and Mental Health
Services Administration,** (301) 443-5407
recording, (301) 443-2282

Housing and Urban Development, (202) 708-0408
recording, (202) 708-3203

Interior, recording, (800) 336-4562

Justice, (202) 514-6877

Labor, recording, (202) 219-6646

State, (202) 647-7252
civil service recording, (202) 647-7284
foreign service recording, (703) 875-7490

Transportation, (202) 366-9392
recording, (202) 366-9391
toll-free, (800) 525-2878

Treasury, recording, (202) 622-1029

Veterans Affairs, (202) 273-4901

AGENCIES

Administrative Office of the U. S. Courts,
recording, (202) 273-2760

Commodity Futures Trading Commission,
(202) 418-5010

Consumer Product Safety Commission,
(301) 504-0100

Corporation for National Service, (202) 606-5000,
ext. 330

Environmental Protection Agency, recording,
(202) 260-3267

Equal Employment Opportunity Commission,
(202) 663-4337

Export-Import Bank, (202) 565-3300

Farm Credit Administration, recording,
(703) 883-4139

Federal Communications Commission, (202) 418-0130
recording, (202) 418-0101

Federal Deposit Insurance Corporation,
(202) 942-3311

Federal Election Commission, (202) 219-4290

Federal Emergency Management Agency,
(202) 646-4040

Federal Labor Relations Authority, (202) 482-6660

Federal Mediation and Conciliation Service, (202)
606-5460

Federal Reserve Board, (202) 452-3880

Federal Trade Commission, recording, (202) 326-2020

General Accounting Office, (202) 512-4500
recording, (202) 512-6092

General Services Administration, (202) 501-0398

Government Printing Office, (202) 512-1200

Merit Systems Protection Board, (202) 653-5916

National Aeronautics and Space Administration,
(202) 358-1560

National Archives and Records Administration,
(301) 713-6760

National Credit Union Administration,
(703) 518-6510

National Endowment for the Arts, (202) 682-5405

National Endowment for the Humanities,
(202) 606-8415

National Labor Relations Board, (202) 273-3980

National Mediation Board, (202) 523-5950

National Science Foundation, (703) 306-1182

National Transportation Safety Board, (202) 314-6230

Nuclear Regulatory Commission, (301) 415-7400

Office of Personnel Management, recording,
(202) 606-2424

Securities and Exchange Commission,
recording, (202) 942-4150

Small Business Administration, (202) 205-6780

Smithsonian Institution, (202) 287-3100
recording, (202) 287-3102

Social Security Administration, (410) 965-3318

U.S. Arms Control and Disarmament Agency,
(202) 647-2034

U.S. Information Agency, (202) 619-4617
recording, (202) 619-4539

U.S. International Trade Commission, (202) 205-2651

U.S. Postal Service, (202) 268-3646

NONPROFIT

American Council of the Blind Government Employees, *1155 15th St. N.W., #720 20005; (202) 467-5081. Fax, (202) 467-5085. Sharon Keeran, president. Toll-free, (800) 424-8666. Internet, http://www.acb.org.*

Membership: federal, state, and local government employees and retirees who are blind or visually impaired and other interested persons. Seeks to improve government employment opportunities for visually disabled persons. Offers technical assistance. (Affiliated with American Council of the Blind.)

American Federation of Government Employees, *80 F St. N.W. 20001; (202) 737-8700. Fax, (202) 639-6490. Bobby L. Harnage, President. Membership, (202) 639-6411. Internet, http://www.afge.org.*

Membership: approximately 700,000 federal government employees. Provides legal services to members; assists members with contract negotiations and grievancies. Monitors legislation and regulations. (Affiliated with the AFL-CIO.)

Blacks in Government, *1820 11th St. N.W. 20001-5015; (202) 667-3280. Fax, (202) 667-3705. Oscar Eason Jr., president. Internet, http://www.bignet.org.*

Advocacy organization for public employees. Promotes equal opportunity and career advancement for African American government employees; provides career development information; seeks to eliminate racism in the federal work force; sponsors programs, business meetings, and social gatherings; represents interests of African American government workers to Congress and the executive branch; promotes voter education and registration.

Council for Excellence in Government, *1301 K St. N.W., #450 West 20005; (202) 728-0418. Fax, (202) 728-0422. Patricia G. McGinnis, president. Internet, http://www.exceogov.org.*

Membership: business and professional leaders with previous executive-level government experience. Works to improve public-sector performance by strengthening federal leadership and management and seeks to build a public understanding of and confidence in government.

Federal Managers Assn., *1641 Prince St., Alexandria, VA 22314; (703) 683-8700. Fax, (703) 683-8707. Frances Webb, chief operating officer. Internet, fma@ix.netcom.com.*

Seeks to improve the effectiveness of federal supervisors and managers and the operations of the federal government.

Federally Employed Women, *1400 Eye St. N.W., #425 20005; (202) 898-0994. Fax, (202) 898-0998. Alma Esparza, executive director. Internet, http://www.few.org.*

Membership: women and men who work for the federal government. Works to eliminate sex discrimination in government employment and to increase job opportunities for women; offers training programs. Monitors legislation and regulations.

Professional Managers Assn., *P.O. Box 45070, L'Enfant Plaza Station 20026-5070; (202) 401-6737. Fax, (202) 401-4277. Ray Woolner, president. Internet, pmaoffice@aol.com.*

Membership: midlevel career federal managers. Conducts research on management practices in the federal government; works to improve the working atmosphere, pay and benefits, and public image of government employees; provides educational materials.

Public Employees Roundtable, *901 D St. N.W., #131 (mailing address: P.O. Box 44801, Washington, DC 20026-4801); (202) 401-4344. Fax, (202) 401-4433. Nicholas Nolan, director of operations. Internet, permail@patriot.net or http://www.patriot.net/users/permail.*

Membership: professional and managerial associations representing a wide range of public employees at all levels. Sponsors conferences, celebrations, and publicity events to educate the public about the contributions of public employees. Sponsors annual scholarship program for college students pursuing a public service career.

Senior Executives Assn., *P.O. Box 44808 20026; (202) 927-7000. Carol A. Bonosaro, president. Internet, http://www.seniorexecs.com.*

Professional association representing Senior Executive Service members and other federal career executives. Sponsors professional education. Interests include management improvement. Monitors legislation and regulations.

See also American Foreign Service Assn. (p. 332)

Dismissals and Disputes

AGENCIES

Merit Systems Protection Board, *1120 Vermont Ave. N.W. 20419; (202) 653-7101. Fax, (202) 653-7130. Ben Erdreich, chair; Beth Slazet, vice chair, (202) 653-7105. Information, (202) 653-7200. TDD, (202) 653-8896. Locator, (202) 653-5916. Internet, http://www.mspb.gov.*

Independent quasi-judicial agency that handles hearings and appeals involving federal employees; protects the integrity of federal merit systems and ensures adequate protection for employees against abuses by agency management. Library open to the public.

Merit Systems Protection Board, *Appeals Counsel, 1120 Vermont Ave. N.W. 20419; (202) 653-8888. Fax, (202) 653-2260. Stephen E. Alpern, director.*

Analyzes and processes petitions for review of appeals decisions from the regional offices; prepares opinions and orders for board consideration; analyzes and processes cases that are reopened and prepares proposed dispositions.

Merit Systems Protection Board, *Policy and Evaluations,* 1120 Vermont Ave. N.W. 20419; (202) 653-7208. Fax, (202) 653-7211. John M. Palguta, director. Internet, pe@mspb.gov or http://www.mspb.gov.

Conducts studies on the civil service and other executive branch merit systems; reports to the president and Congress on whether federal employees are adequately protected against political abuses and prohibited personnel practices. Conducts annual oversight review of the Office of Personnel Management.

Merit Systems Protection Board, *Washington Regional Office,* 5203 Leesburg Pike, #1109, Falls Church, VA 22041; (703) 756-6250. Fax, (703) 756-7112. P. J. Winzer, director.

Hears and decides appeals of adverse personnel actions (such as removals, suspensions for more than 14 days, and reductions in grade or pay), retirement, and performance-related actions for federal civilian employees who work in the Washington area or in overseas areas not covered by other board regional offices. Federal civilian employees who work outside Washington should contact the Merit Systems Protection Board regional office in their area. *(See Regional Information Sources in appendix.)*

Office of Personnel Management, 1900 E St. N.W., #7353 20415-0001; (202) 606-1700. Fax, (202) 606-0082. Lorraine Lewis, general counsel.

Represents the federal government before the Merit Systems Protection Board, other administrative tribunals, and the courts.

Office of Special Counsel, 1730 M St. N.W., #300 20036-4505; (202) 653-7122. Fax, (202) 653-5151. Elaine D. Kaplan, special counsel. Information, (202) 653-7188. Issues relating to the Hatch Act, (800) 854-2824. Internet, http://www.access.gpo.gov/osc.

Investigates allegations of prohibited personnel practices, including reprisals against whistleblowers (federal employees who disclose waste, fraud, inefficiency, and wrongdoing by supervisors of federal departments and agencies). Initiates necessary corrective or disciplinary action. Enforces the Hatch Act.

JUDICIARY

U.S. Court of Appeals for the Federal Circuit, 717 Madison Pl. N.W. 20439; (202) 633-6556. Fax, (202) 633-

6353. Haldane Robert Mayer, chief judge; Jan Horbaly, clerk, (202) 633-9613. Electronic bulletin board, (202) 633-9608 or (202) 786-6584.

Reviews decisions of the Merit Systems Protection Board.

Hiring, Recruitment, and Training

AGENCIES

The Career America Connection in Washington, (202) 606-2700, the U.S. government's official employment service, provides the public with information on applications for civil service jobs. This automated service is available twenty-four hours a day. See also list of personnel offices under Civil Service, General.

Office of Personnel Management, *Classification,* 1900 E St. N.W., #6H31 20415; (202) 606-2950. Fax, (202) 606-4891. Vacant, assistant director.

Develops job classification standards for agencies within the federal government.

Office of Personnel Management, *Diversity,* 1900 E St. N.W., #2445 20415-0001; (202) 606-2817. Fax, (202) 606-0927. Armando E. Rodriguez, director.

Develops policies and guidelines for government recruiting programs, including diversity employment efforts related to women, minorities, persons with disabilities, and veterans. Collects and maintains statistics on the federal employment of these groups. Administers the Federal Equal Opportunity Recruitment Program and the Disabled Veterans Affirmative Action Program.

Office of Personnel Management, *Employment Service,* 1900 E St. N.W., #6F08 20415; (202) 606-0800. Fax, (202) 606-1637. Mary Lou Lindholm, associate director.

Develops civil service tests for most federal jobs through GS-15; develops qualification standards and governmentwide staffing policies; administers special programs to find jobs for displaced federal employees, minorities, veterans, women, youth, and persons with disabilities; administers the Administrative Law Judges program, federal recruitment efforts, and special personnel programs.

Office of Personnel Management, *Executive Resources,* 1900 E St. N.W., #6484 20415; (202) 606-1610. Fax, (202) 606-2126. K. Joyce Edwards, assistant director.

Responsible for training and curriculum development programs for government executives and supervisors. Administers executive personnel systems, including those for the Senior Executive Service (SES) and personnel in executive positions not in SES. Oversees the Federal Executive Institute.

Office of Personnel Management, *Federal Investigations,* 1900 E St. N.W., #5516 20415; (202) 606-1042. Fax, (202) 606-2390. Richard Ferris, associate director, Investigations.

Initiates and conducts investigations of new federal employees; determines whether applicants and appointees are suitable for positions other than those involving national security.

Office of Personnel Management, *Personnel Mobility Program,* 1900 E St. N.W., #7463 20415; (202) 606-1181. Fax, (202) 606-3577. Tony Ryan, program head.

Implements temporary personnel exchanges between federal agencies and nonfederal entities including state and local governments, institutions of higher education, and other organizations.

Labor-Management Relations

See also Labor-Management Relations (chap. 7)

AGENCIES

Federal Labor Relations Authority, 607 14th St. N.W., #410 20424-0001; (202) 482-6500. Fax, (202) 482-6635. Phyllis N. Segal, chair; Solly J. Thomas Jr., executive director, (202) 482-6560. Internet, http://www.access.gpo.gov/flra.

Oversees the federal labor-management relations program; administers the law that protects the right of federal employees to organize, bargain collectively, and participate through labor organizations of their own choosing.

Federal Service Impasses Panel *(Federal Labor Relations Authority),* 607 14th St. N.W., #220 20424-1000; (202) 482-6670. Fax, (202) 482-6674. Betty Bolden, chair; H. Joseph Schimansky, executive director.

Assists in resolving contract negotiation impasses between federal agencies and labor organizations representing federal employees.

Office of Personnel Management, 1900 E St. N.W., #7353 20415-0001; (202) 606-1700. Fax, (202) 606-0082. Lorraine Lewis, general counsel.

Advises the government on law and legal policy relating to federal labor-management relations; represents the government before the Merit Systems Protection Board.

Office of Personnel Management, *Center for Partnership, Labor-Management Relations,* 1900 E St. N.W.,

#7H28 20415; (202) 606-2930. Fax, (202) 606-2613. Rose Gwin, director.

Provides government agencies and unions with information and advice on employee- and labor-management relations.

Office of Personnel Management, *National Partnership Council,* 1900 E St. N.W. 20415-0001; (202) 606-2930. Fax, (202) 606-2613. Michael Cushing, director, Center for Partnership, Labor-Management Relations; James B. King, chair, (202) 606-1000.

Membership: officials of executive departments, government agencies, federal labor unions, the Federal Managers Assn., and the Senior Executives' Assn. Advises the president on labor-management relations in the executive branch. (Affiliated with the National Partnership Clearinghouse.)

NONPROFIT

National Alliance of Postal and Federal Employees, 1628 11th St. N.W. 20001; (202) 939-6325. Fax, (202) 939-6389. James M. McGee, president. Internet, http://www.napfe.com.

Membership: approximately 70,000 postal and federal employees. Helps members negotiate pay, benefits, and better working conditions; conducts training programs and workshops. Monitors legislation and regulations.

National Assn. of Government Employees, 317 S. Patrick St., Alexandria, VA 22314; (703) 519-0300. Fax, (703) 519-0311. Susanne Pooler, regional director. Internet, http://www.nage.org.

Membership: approximately 200,000 federal government employees. Helps members negotiate pay, benefits, and better working conditions; conducts training programs and workshops. Monitors legislation and regulations. (Headquarters in Quincy, Mass.; affiliated with the AFL-CIO.)

National Federation of Federal Employees, 1016 16th St. N.W., #300 20036; (202) 862-4400. Fax, (202) 862-4432. James Cunningham, national president.

Membership: approximately 52,000 federal government employees. Helps members negotiate pay, benefits, and better working conditions; conducts training programs and workshops. Monitors legislation and regulations.

National Treasury Employees Union, 901 E St. N.W., #600 20004; (202) 783-4444. Fax, (202) 783-4085. Robert M. Tobias, president. Internet, http://www.nteu.org.

Membership: approximately 150,000 employees from the Treasury Dept. and eighteen other federal agencies.

Helps members negotiate pay, benefits, and better working conditions; conducts training programs and workshops. Monitors legislation and regulations.

Public Service Research Council, *527 Maple Ave. East, 3rd Floor, Vienna, VA 22180; (703) 242-3575. Fax, (703) 242-3579. David Y. Denholm, president.*

Independent, nonpartisan research and educational organization. Opposes collective bargaining, strikes, and binding arbitration in the public sector. Sponsors conferences and seminars. Library open to the public by appointment.

Pay and Employee Benefits

AGENCIES

Bureau of Labor Statistics *(Labor Dept.),* **Survey, Data Analysis, and Publications,** *2 Massachusetts Ave. N.E., #4175 20212; (202) 606-6225. Fax, (202) 606-6647. Jordan N. Pfuntner, chief. Information, (202) 606-6220. Internet, ocltinfo@bls.gov.*

Develops occupational pay surveys on area and national industries; analyzes, distributes, and disseminates information.

Labor Dept., *Federal Employees' Compensation, 200 Constitution Ave. N.W., #S3229 20210; (202) 219-7552. Fax, (202) 219-7260. Thomas Markey, director. Internet, http://www.dol.gov/dol/esa/owcp.htm.*

Administers the Federal Employees Compensation Act, which provides workers' compensation for federal employees and others.

Office of Personnel Management, *Compensation Administration, 1900 E St. N.W., #7H31 20415; (202) 606-2858. Fax, (202) 606-0824. Jerome Mikowicz, chief.*

Authorizes pay incentives for staffing and makes allowances for uniforms, employee relocation, hazardous duty, and commutes to remote workplaces.

Office of Personnel Management, *Employee Health Services, 1900 E St. N.W. 20415; (202) 606-1740. Fax, (202) 606-0967. Marjorie Marks, chief, Work and Family Programs and Employee Relations.*

Sets policy and guides federal agencies in establishing and maintaining programs on alcohol and drug abuse, drug-free workplaces, AIDS issues, workplace violence, and fitness programs.

Office of Personnel Management, *Federal Prevailing Rate Advisory Committee, 1900 E St. N.W., #5559 20415; (202) 606-1500. Fax, (202) 606-5104. Phyllis Foley, acting chair.*

Advises OPM on pay systems for federal blue-collar workers.

Office of Personnel Management, *Insurance Programs, 1900 E St. N.W., #3400 20415; (202) 606-0770. Fax, (202) 606-0767. Frank D. Titus, assistant director.*

Administers group life insurance for federal employees and retirees; negotiates rates and benefits with health insurance carriers; settles disputed claims.

Office of Personnel Management, *Performance Management and Incentive Awards, 1900 E St. N.W., #7412 20415; (202) 606-2720. Fax, (202) 606-2395. Doris A. Hausser, chief.*

Performance Management division sets policy and implements the performance appraisal and pay-for-performance system for all federal employees. Consults with agencies to help them develop their own systems; reviews and approves agencies' plans before implementation. Sets policy for performance appraisal and awards for federal employees. Incentive Awards division provides agencies with technical assistance and guidance on the Federal Incentive Awards Program and other awards programs that recognize achievements of federal workers.

Office of Personnel Management, *Retirement and Insurance Service, 1900 E St. N.W., #4A10 20415-0001; (202) 606-0600. Fax, (202) 606-2711. William E. Flynn III, associate director.*

Develops and interprets federal policy and regulations on retirement benefits.

Office of Personnel Management, *Retirement Information, 1900 E St. N.W. 20415-0001; (202) 606-0500. Fax, (202) 606-0144. Gary M. Jacobs, chief. TDD, (202) 606-0551.*

Responds to telephone inquiries on retirement law and health and life insurance; handles reports of annuitants' deaths; conducts interviews on individual cases; makes appropriate referrals.

Office of Personnel Management, *Retirement Programs, 1900 E St. N.W., #3305 20415; (202) 606-0300. Fax, (202) 606-1998. Sydney M. Conley, assistant director.*

Administers the civil service and federal employees' retirement systems; responsible for monthly annuity payments and other benefits; organizes and maintains retirement records; distributes information on retirement and on insurance programs for annuitants.

Office of Personnel Management, *Salary and Wage Systems, 1900 E St. N.W., #7H31 20415; (202) 606-2838. Fax, (202) 606-4264. Ruth M. O'Donnell, chief.*

Responsible for the annual pay adjustment review process and for local adjustment allowances (locality pay) for federal white-collar workers. Works jointly with the Office of Management and Budget and the Labor Dept. to aid the director of OPM in the role of "pay agent" for the president. Report available to the public after presidential consideration. Adminsters the federal wage system that establishes pay scales for federal blue-collar employees. Responds to inquiries on federal blue-collar pay rates and pay administration matters.

NONPROFIT

National Assn. of Retired Federal Employees, *606 N. Washington St., Alexandria, VA 22314; (703) 838-7760. Fax, (703) 838-7782. Charles R. Jackson, president. Member relations, (800) 456-8410. Internet, narfehq@aol.com.*

Works to preserve the integrity of the civil service retirement system. Provides members with information about benefits for retired federal employees and for survivors of deceased federal employees. Monitors legislation and regulations.

National Committee on Public Employee Pension Systems, *1221 Connecticut Ave. N.W., 4th Floor 20036; (202) 293-3960. Fax, (202) 293-7614. Hastings Keith and Ralph Wood, co-chairs. Internet, http://www.peps.inter.net.*

Seeks reform of pension policies for public employees, particularly at the federal level. Goals include placing caps on cost of living adjustments for pension plans and redefining early retirement and disability to bring them in line with private sector standards.

Political Activity and the Hatch Act

Enacted in 1939 and revised in 1993, the Hatch Act limits the political activities of most federal employees and most District of Columbia government employees. Its provisions do not extend to employees of the executive office of the president, to individuals who are appointed by the president and confirmed by the Senate, or to members of the armed forces, whose conduct is governed by separate Defense Dept. rules. The Hatch Act prohibits federal employees from participating in political activity while on duty, including wearing a campaign button. While off duty, most federal employees may hold office in a political party, participate in campaigns and rallies, publicly endorse candidates, and raise political funds from within their agency's political action committee. However, they may not run for partisan elective offices or solicit contributions from the public. Stricter provisions on off-duty political activity apply to employees in certain sensitive agencies, including the Federal Election Commission, Federal Bureau of Investigation, Secret Service, the intelligence agencies, the Criminal Division of the Justice Dept., and others.

AGENCIES

Office of Special Counsel, *1730 M St. N.W., #300 20036-4505; (202) 653-9001. Fax, (202) 653-5161. Karen*

Dalheim, director, Congressional Affairs. Internet, http://www.access.gpo.gov/osc.

Interprets federal laws, including the Hatch Act, concerning political activities allowed by certain federal employees; investigates allegations of Hatch Act violations and conducts prosecutions.

NONPROFIT

American Civil Liberties Union, *National Capital Area, 1400 20th St. N.W. 20036; (202) 457-0800. Fax, (202) 452-1868. Fritz Mulhauser, coordinator, Litigation Screening Committee.*

Civil liberties organization that advises and represents in court proceedings selected civil service employees charged with illegal political activity. Supports broader opportunities for political participation by federal employees. Maintains public education programs.

🏛 FEDERAL CONTRACTS AND PROCUREMENT

See also Government Managment and Oversight (this chapter); Labor Standards and Practices (chap. 7); Procurement, Acquisition, and Logistics (chap. 16)

AGENCIES

Agencies and departments have their own contracting offices to deal with firms, organizations, and individuals seeking to sell goods and services to the government. Government solicitations for bids on goods and services are published in Commerce Business Daily *issued by the Commerce Dept., Publishing Division, (202) 482-0632. See also list of procurement officers (this section).*

Committee for Purchase From People Who Are Blind or Severely Disabled, *1215 Jefferson Davis Hwy., #310, Arlington, VA 22202; (703) 603-7740. Fax, (703) 603-0655. Beverly L. Milkman, executive director.*

Presidentially appointed committee. Determines which products and services are suitable for federal procurement from qualified nonprofit agencies that employ people who are blind or have other severe disabilities; seeks to increase employment opportunities for these individuals.

Comptroller of the Currency *(Treasury Dept.), Outreach Program, 250 E St. S.W. 20219; (202) 874-5040. Fax, (202) 874-5625. Anthony Cooch, program specialist.*

Ensures that businesses owned and controlled by minorities, women, and individuals with disabilities are given the opportunity to participate in contracts with the Comptroller of the Currency.

PROCUREMENT OFFICERS FOR FEDERAL AGENCIES

DEPARTMENTS

Agriculture, Russ Ashworth, (202) 720-9448

Commerce, Howard Price, (202) 482-4185

Defense, Eleanor R. Spector, (703) 695-7145

Education, Glenn Perry, (202) 708-5514

Energy, Richard H. Hopf, (202) 586-8613

Health and Human Services, Debra Peters, (202) 690-8457

Housing and Urban Development, Craig Durkin, (202) 708-1290

Interior, Paul Denett, (202) 208-3668

Justice, James W. Johnston, (202) 307-2000

Labor, Daniel P. Murphy, (202) 219-4631

State, Betsy Murphy, (703) 875-6037

Transportation, Dom Telet, (202) 366-4953

Treasury, Annelie Kuhn, acting, (202) 622-0540

Veterans Affairs, David Derr, (202) 273-6047

AGENCIES

Consumer Product Safety Commission, Robert Frost, (301) 504-0444

Corporation for National Service, Simon Woodward, (202) 606-5000

Export-Import Bank, Daniel A. Garcia, (202) 565-3335

Farm Credit Administration, Jim Judge, (703) 883-4135

Federal Communications Commission, Sonna B. Stampone, (202) 418-0930

Federal Deposit Insurance Corporation, Rodney Cartwright, (202) 942-3680

Federal Maritime Commission, Michael Kilby, (202) 523-5900

Federal Mediation and Conciliation Service, Sam Baumgardner, (202) 606-8111

Federal Reserve System, Mike Kelly, (202) 452-3296

Federal Trade Commission, Julius Justice, (202) 326-2275

General Services Administration, Ida M. Ustad, (202) 501-1043

National Aeronautics and Space Administration, Deidre Lee, (202) 358-2090

National Labor Relations Board, Paula M. Roy, (202) 273-4210

National Mediation Board, Jan Smith, (202) 523-5950

National Science Foundation, Veronica Bankins, (202) (703) 306-1122

Nuclear Regulatory Commission, Timothy F. Hagan, (301) 415-6732

Office of Personnel Management, Alfred Chatterton, (202) 606-2240

Securities and Exchange Commission, Linda Sudhoff, (202) 942-4990

Social Security Administration, James Fornataro, (410) 965-9459

Small Business Administration, Lucille Brooks, (202) 205-6622

U.S. Arms Control and Disarmament Agency, Nancy Aderholdt, (202) 647-8666

U.S. International Trade Commission, Michael Boling, (202) 205-2730

U.S. Postal Service, A. Keith Strange, (202) 268-4040

General Services Administration, *Acquisition Policy, 1800 F St. N.W., #4040 20405; (202) 501-1043. Fax, (202) 501-1986. Ida M. Ustad, deputy associate administrator.*

Develops and implements federal government acquisition policies and procedures; conducts preaward and postaward contract reviews; administers federal acquisition regulations for civilian agencies; suspends and debars contractors for unsatisfactory performance; coordinates and promotes career management and training programs for government contracting personnel.

General Services Administration, *Enterprise Development, 1800 F St. N.W., #6029 20405; (202) 501-1021. Fax, (202) 208-5938. Dietra L. Ford, associate administrator.*

Works to increase small-business procurement of government contracts. Provides policy guidance and direction for GSA Business Service Centers, which give advice and assistance to businesses interested in government procurement. *(See Regional Information Sources in appendix.)*

General Services Administration, *Governmentwide Information Systems, 7th and D Sts. S.W., #5652 20407; (202) 401-1529. Fax, (202) 401-1546. Robert Brown, director.*

Makes available quarterly information about government procurement contracts over $25,000; collects and disseminates data on the amount of business that companies do with each federal department and agency.

General Services Administration, *Governmentwide Policy,* *1800 F St. N.W., #5240 20405; (202) 501-8880. Fax, (202) 501-8898. G. Martin Wagner, associate administrator. Internet, http://www.policyworks.gov.*

Coordinates GSA policymaking activities; promotes collaboration between government and the private sector in developing policy and management techniques; works to integrate acquisition, management, and disposal of government property.

Minority Business Development Agency *(Commerce Dept.), 14th St. and Constitution Ave. N.W., #5055 20230; (202) 482-5061. Fax, (202) 501-4698. Courtland Cox, director.*

Assists minority business owners in obtaining federal loans and contract awards; produces an annual report on federal agencies' performance in procuring from minority-owned businesses.

Office of Management and Budget *(Executive Office of the President), Federal Procurement Policy, Old Executive Office Bldg., #352 20503; (202) 395-5802. Fax, (202) 395-3242. Allan Brown, acting administrator.*

Coordinates government procurement policies, regulations, and procedures. Responsible for cost accounting rules governing federal contractors and subcontractors.

CONGRESS

General Accounting Office, *Procurement Law Division, 441 G St. N.W. 20548; (202) 512-6071. Fax, (202) 512-9749. Anthony Gamboa, senior associate general counsel.*

Considers and rules on the proposed or actual award of a government contract upon receipt of a written protest.

House Government Reform and Oversight Committee, *Subcommittee on Government Management, Information, and Technology, B373 RHOB 20515; (202) 225-5174. Fax, (202) 225-3974. Steve Horn, R-Calif., chair; J. Russell George, staff director. Internet, http://www.house.gov/cho.*

Jurisdiction over legislation on the federal procurement system; oversees rules and regulations concerning government procurement.

House Small Business Committee, *Subcommittee on Tax, Finance, and Exports, B363 RHOB 20515; (202) 226-2630. Fax, (202) 225-8950. Donald Manzullo, R-Ill., chair; Philip D. Eskeland, staff director.*

Jurisdiction over legislation on programs affecting small business and the federal procurement system; oversees rules and regulations concerning government procurement.

Senate Governmental Affairs Committee, *Subcommittee on Oversight of Government Management, Restructuring, and the District of Columbia, SH-604 20510; (202) 224-3682. Fax, (202) 224-3328. Sam Brownback, R-Kan., chair; Michael Rubin, acting staff director. Internet, http://www.senate.gov/committee/ governmental_affairs.html.*

Jurisdiction over legislation on the federal procurement system; oversees rules and regulations concerning government procurement.

Senate Small Business Committee, *SR-428A 20510; (202) 224-5175. Fax, (202) 224-4885. Christopher S. Bond, R-Mo., chair; Louis Taylor, staff director. Internet, http://www.senate.gov/~sbc.*

Studies and makes recommendations on legislation concerning government procurement as it affects small business.

NONPROFIT

Some nongovernmental groups provide members with information about government contracts. Contact representative group for information.

Coalition for Government Procurement, *1990 M St. N.W., #400 20036; (202) 331-0975. Fax, (202) 822-9788. Larry Allen, executive director. Internet, coalgovpro@aol. com or http://www.usassociations.com/cgp.*

Alliance of business firms that sell to the federal government. Seeks equal opportunities for businesses to sell to the government; monitors practices of the General Services Administration and government procurement legislation and regulations.

Contract Services Assn., *1200 G St. N.W., #750 20005; (202) 347-0600. Fax, (202) 347-0608. Gary Engebretson, president. Internet, http://www.csa-dc.org.*

Membership: companies that, under contract, provide federal, state, and local governments and other agencies with various technical and support services (particularly in defense, space, transportation, environment, energy, and health care). Analyzes the process by which the government awards contracts to private firms. Monitors legislation and regulations.

National Contract Management Assn., *1912 Woodford Rd., Vienna, VA 22182; (703) 448-9231. Fax, (703) 448-0939. Jim Goggins, executive vice president. Toll-free, (800) 344-8096. Internet, http://www.ncma.org.*

Membership: individuals concerned with administering, procuring, negotiating, and managing government contracts and subcontracts. Sponsors Certified Professional Contracts Manager Program and various educational and professional programs.

National Institute of Governmental Purchasing, *11800 Sunrise Valley Dr., #1050, Reston, VA 22091; (703) 715-9400. Fax, (703) 715-9897. James E. Brinkman, executive vice president. Toll-free, (800) 367-6447. Internet, http://www.nigp.org.*

Membership: governmental purchasing departments, agencies, and organizations at the federal, state, and local levels in the United States and Canada. Provides public procurement officers with technical assistance and information, training seminars, and professional certification.

Professional Services Council, *8607 Westwood Center Dr., #204, Vienna, VA 22182; (703) 883-2030. Fax, (703) 883-2035. Bert M. Concklin, president. Internet, http://www.govcon.com.*

Membership: associations and firms that provide local, state, federal, and international governments with professional and technical services. Promotes reform of the procurement system; seeks to improve the compilation of data and statistics about the professional and technical services industry.

See also National Industries for the Blind (p. 645)

🏛 GOVERNMENT MANAGEMENT AND OVERSIGHT

See also Civil Service (this chapter); Government Information (chap. 3)

AGENCIES

Domestic Policy Council *(Executive Office of the President),* *The White House 20502; (202) 456-2216. Fax, (202) 456-7028. Bruce Reed, assistant to the president for domestic policy.*

Comprises cabinet officials and staff members. Coordinates the domestic policymaking process to facilitate the implementation of the president's domestic agenda in such areas as agriculture, education, energy, environment, health, housing, labor, and veterans affairs.

Federal Bureau of Investigation *(Justice Dept.), Personnel,* *935 Pennsylvania Ave. N.W., #6012 20535; (202) 324-3515. Fax, (202) 324-1091. James A. Oppy, assistant director. Information, (202) 324-2727.*

Performs background investigations of presidential appointees.

General Services Administration, *1800 F St. N.W., #6137 20405; (202) 501-0800. David J. Barram, administrator; Thurman M. Davis Sr., deputy administrator, (202)*

501-1226. Information, (202) 708-5082. Press, (202) 501-1231. Library, (202) 501-0788. TDD, (202) 708-9300. Internet, http://www.gsa.gov.

Establishes policies for managing federal government property, including construction and operation of buildings and procurement and distribution of supplies and equipment; manages transportation and telecommunications. Manages disposal of surplus federal property.

General Services Administration, *Acquisition Policy,* *1800 F St. N.W., #4040 20405; (202) 501-1043. Fax, (202) 501-1986. Ida M. Ustad, deputy associate administrator.*

Develops and implements federal government acquisition policies and procedures; conducts preaward and postaward contract reviews; administers federal acquisition regulations for civilian agencies; suspends and debars contractors for unsatisfactory performance; coordinates and promotes governmentwide career management and training programs for contracting personnel.

General Services Administration, *Board of Contract Appeals,* *1800 F St. N.W., #7022 20405; (202) 501-0585. Fax, (202) 501-0664. Stephen M. Daniels, chair. For filings, (202) 501-0116.*

Resolves disputes arising out of contracts with the General Services Administration, the Treasury Dept., the Education Dept., the Commerce Dept., and other independent agencies.

General Services Administration, *Federal Information Center,* *1800 F St. N.W. 20405; Fax, (202) 501-1680. Warren Snaider, contracting officer's technical representative, (202) 501-1939. Toll-free, (800) 688-9889. TDD, (800) 326-2996. Internet, http://fic.info.gov.*

Responds to inquiries about federal programs and services. Gives information or locates particular agencies or persons best suited to help with specific concerns.

General Services Administration, *Governmentwide Policy,* *1800 F St. N.W., #5240 20405; (202) 501-8880. Fax, (202) 501-8898. G. Martin Wagner, associate administrator. Internet, http://www.policyworks.gov.*

Coordinates GSA policymaking activities; promotes collaboration between government and the private sector in developing policy and management techniques; works to integrate acquisition, management, and disposal of government property.

General Services Administration, *National Capital Region,* *7th and D Sts. S.W., #7022 20407; (202) 708-9100. Fax, (202) 708-9966. Nelson B. Alcalde, regional administrator.*

Provides federal agencies with space, supplies, telecommunications, transportation, data processing,

EXECUTIVE OFFICE OF THE PRESIDENT

BILL CLINTON, president

1600 Pennsylvania Ave. N.W. 20500

Phone: (202) 456-1414

Internet, president@whitehouse.gov or http://www.whitehouse.gov

Erskine Bowles, chief of staff, (202) 456-6797

John Podesta, deputy chief of staff, (202) 456-2459

Sylvia M. Mathews, deputy chief of staff, (202) 456-1960

Carol Parmelee, executive assistant to the chief of staff, (202) 456-6797

Thomas F. "Mack" McLarty III, senior counselor to the president, (202) 456-2000

Cabinet Affairs, Thurgood Marshall Jr., cabinet secretary, (202) 456-2572

Counsel to the President, Charles F. C. Ruff, (202) 456-2632

Domestic Policy Council, Bruce Reed, assistant, (202) 456-2216

Elena Kagan, deputy assistant, (202) 456-5584

Intergovernmental Affairs, Mickey Ibarra, director, (202) 456-7060

Legislative Affairs, Larry Stein, assistant, (202) 456-2230

House Liaison, Alphonso Maldon and Chuck Brain, deputy assistants, (202) 456-6620

Senate Liaison, Janet Murguia, deputy assistant, (202) 456-6493

Management and Administration, Virginia M. Apuzzo, assistant, (202) 456-2861

National Economic Council, Gene Sperling, assistant, (202) 456-2620

Oval Office Operations, Nancy Hernreich, director, (202) 456-6610

Political Affairs, Craig T. Smith, director, (202) 456-1125

Presidential Correspondence, Daniel Burkhardt, director, (202) 456-7610

Presidential Personnel, Robert J. Nash, director, (202) 456-6676

President's Commission on White House Fellowships, Jackie Blumenthal, director, (202) 395-4522

President's Committee on the Arts and Humanities, Harriet Mayor Fulbright, executive director, (202) 682-5409

President's Foreign Intelligence Advisory Board, Warren Rudman, chair, (202) 456-2352

Press Office, Michael McCurry, press secretary, (202) 456-2673

Media Affairs, Amy Weiss Tobe, deputy press secretary, (202) 456-2987

News Analysis, Mark Kitchens and Jason Schecter, coordinators, (202) 456-7150

Public Liaison, Maria Echaveste, director, (202) 456-2930

Scheduling and Advance, Stephanie Streett, director, (202) 456-7560

Staff Secretary, Todd Stern, assistant, (202) 456-2702

Strategic Planning and Communications, Ann Lewis, assistant, (202) 456-2640

Research, Ann Walker, director, (202) 456-7845

White House Military Office, Alan P. Sullivan, director, (202) 456-2150

OFFICE OF THE VICE PRESIDENT

ALBERT GORE JR., vice president

Old Executive Office Bldg.

17th St. and Pennsylvania Ave. N.W. 20501

Phone: (202) 456-2326

Internet: vice-president@whitehouse.gov

Ron Klain, chief of staff, (202) 456-6605

Larry Haas, director of communications, (202) 456-7035

OFFICE OF THE FIRST LADY

HILLARY RODHAM CLINTON, first lady

1600 Pennsylvania Ave. N.W. 20500

Phone: (202) 456-6266

Internet: first.lady@whitehouse.gov

Melanne Verveer, chief of staff, (202) 456-6266

Marsha Berry, director of communications, (202) 456-2960

and construction services; has equal status with regional offices. (*See Regional Information Sources in appendix.*)

General Services Administration, *Public Buildings Service, 1800 F St. N.W., #6344 20405; (202) 501-1100. Fax, (202) 219-2310. Robert A. Peck, commissioner.*

Manages and disposes of federal real estate. Administers the construction, maintenance, and operation of buildings owned or leased by the federal government.

National Archives and Records Administration, *Federal Register, 800 N. Capitol St., #700 20408; (202)*

GENERAL ACCOUNTING OFFICE

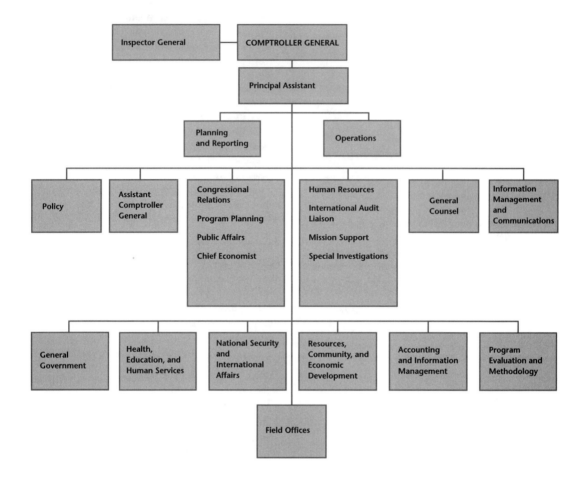

523-5230. Fax, (202) 523-6866. Frances D. McDonald, editor-in-chief. TDD, (202) 523-5229. Public Laws Update Service (PLUS), (202) 523-6641. Internet, http://www. nara.gov/nara/fedreg/fedreg.html.

Assigns public law numbers to enacted legislation, executive orders, and proclamations; responds to inquiries on public law numbers; assists inquirers in finding presidential signing or veto messages in the *Weekly Compilation of Presidential Documents* and the *Public Papers of the Presidents* series; compiles slip laws and annual *United States Statutes at Large;* compiles indexes for finding statutory provisions. Operates Public Laws Update Service (PLUS), which provides information by telephone on new legislation. Publications available from the U.S. Government Printing Office, Washington, DC 20402; (202) 783-3238.

Office of Administration *(Executive Office of the President),* 725 17th St. N.W., #5001 20503; (202) 395-7235. Fax, (202) 456-7921. Ada L. Posey, director. Internet, http://www.whitehouse.gov/WH/EOP/html/other/OA.html.

Provides administrative support services to the Executive Office of the President, including personnel and financial management, data processing, library services, and general office operations.

Office of Management and Budget *(Executive Office of the President), Federal Procurement Policy,* Old Executive Office Bldg., #352 20503; (202) 395-5802. Fax, (202) 395-3242. Allan Brown, acting administrator. Information, (202) 395-3501.

Coordinates government procurement policies, regulations, and procedures. Responsible for cost accounting rules governing federal contractors and subcontractors.

Office of Management and Budget *(Executive Office of the President), Information and Regulatory Affairs,* Old Executive Office Bldg., #350 20503; (202) 395-4852. Fax, (202) 395-3047. Don Arbuckle, acting administrator.

Oversees development of federal regulatory programs. Supervises agency information management activities in accordance with the Paperwork Reduction Act of 1980, as amended; reviews agency analyses of the effect of government regulatory activities on the U.S. economy.

Office of Management and Budget *(Executive Office of the President), Personnel, Postal, EXOP,* 725 17th St. N.W., #7236 20503; (202) 395-5017. Fax, (202) 395-5738. Lisa Fairhall, chief.

Examines, evaluates, and suggests improvements for agencies and programs within the Office of Personnel Management, the U.S. Postal Service, and the Executive Office of the President.

Office of Management and Budget *(Executive Office of the President), Treasury,* New Executive Office Bldg., #9236 20503; (202) 395-6156. Fax, (202) 395-6825. Harry Meyers, chief.

Examines, evaluates, and suggests improvements for agencies and programs within the Treasury Dept. (including the Internal Revenue Service and the Customs Dept.), and the District of Columbia government.

Regulatory Information Service Center *(General Services Administration),* 1800 F St. N.W., #3033 20405; (202) 482-7350. Fax, (202) 482-7360. Mark G. Schoenberg, executive director. Information, (202) 482-7340. Internet, http://www.risc.gsa.gov.

Provides the president, Congress, and the public with information on federal regulatory policies; recommends ways to make regulatory information more accessible to government officials and the public.

See also GSA Business Service Centers in Regional Information Sources (appendix)

CONGRESS

General Accounting Office, 441 G St. N.W. 20548; (202) 512-5500. Fax, (202) 512-5507. James F. Hinchman, acting comptroller general. Information, (202) 512-4800. Library, (202) 512-5180. Documents, (202) 512-6000. Internet, http://www.gao.gov.

Independent, nonpartisan agency in the legislative branch. Serves as the investigating agency for Congress; carries out legal, accounting, auditing, and claims settlement functions; makes recommendations for more effective government operations; publishes monthly lists of reports available to the public. Library open to the public by appointment.

House Appropriations Committee, *Subcommittee on Treasury, Postal Service, and General Government,* B307 RHOB 20515; (202) 225-5834. Fax, (202) 225-5895. Jim Kolbe, R-Ariz., chair; Michelle Mrdeza, clerk. Internet, http://www.house.gov/appropriations.

Jurisdiction over legislation to appropriate funds for the Office of Management and Budget, the General Services Administration (except the Consumer Information Center), the National Archives and Records Administration, and the Executive Office of the President.

House Government Reform and Oversight Committee, 2157 RHOB 20515; (202) 225-5074. Fax, (202) 225-3974. Dan Burton, R-Ind., chair; Kevin Binger, staff director.

Jurisdiction over legislation on all procurement practices. Also examines the efficiency of government operations, including federal regulations and program management.

House Government Reform and Oversight Committee, *Subcommittee on Government Management, Information, and Technology,* B373 RHOB 20515; (202) 225-5147. Steve Horn, R-Calif., chair; J. Russell George, staff director. Internet, http://www.house.gov/cho.

Jurisdiction over legislation concerning the efficiency and management of government operations and activities; oversight responsibilities for operations of the White House, the Executive Office of the President, and the Office of Management and Budget. Jurisdiction over legislation for the General Services Administration and General Accounting Office.

Senate Appropriations Committee, *Subcommittee on Treasury and General Government,* SD-190 20510; (202) 224-7337. Ben Nighthorse Campbell, R-Colo., chair; Patricia Raymond, staff director. Internet, http://www. senate.gov/~appropriations.

Jurisdiction over legislation to appropriate funds for the General Services Administration (except the Consumer Information Center), National Archives and Records Administration, and Executive Office of the President.

Senate Environment and Public Works Committee, *Subcommittee on Transportation and Infrastructure,* SD-410 20510; (202) 224-6176. John W. Warner, R-Va., chair; Dan Corbett, staff contact.

Oversight of the public buildings service of the General Services Administration.

FINANCIAL OFFICERS FOR FEDERAL AGENCIES

DEPARTMENTS

Agriculture, Erwin David, (202) 720-5539

Commerce, W. Scott Gould, (202) 482-4951

Defense, William T. Lynn, (703) 695-3237

  Air Force, Robert F. Hale, (703) 693-6457

  Army, Helen T. McCoy, (703) 697-8121

  Navy, Debra P. Christie, (703) 697-2325

Education, Don Rappaport, (202) 401-0085

Energy, Michael L. Telson, (202) 586-4171

Health and Human Services, John Callahan, (202) 690-6396

Housing and Urban Development, Richard F. Keevey, (202) 708-1946

Interior, John Berry, (202) 208-4203

Justice, Steven Colgate, (202) 514-1843

Labor, Kenneth Bresnahan, acting, (202) 219-6891

State, Richard L. Greene, (202) 647-7490

Transportation, David Kleinberg, (202) 366-9192

Treasury

  Comptroller of the Currency, Eugene A. Ludwig, (202) 874-4900

Veterans Affairs, D. Mark Catlett, (202) 273-5589

AGENCIES

Advisory Council on Historic Preservation, Carol McLain, (202) 606-8503

Agency for International Development, Donald K. Charney, (202) 712-1890

Central Intelligence Agency, Mary Sturtevant, (703) 482-4456

Commission on Civil Rights, George Harbison, (202) 376-8356

Commodity Futures Trading Commission, Madge Bolinger, (202) 418-5190

Consumer Product Safety Commission, Edward E. Quist, (301) 504-0029

Corporation for National Service, Donna Cunningham, (202) 606-5000

Corporation for Public Broadcasting, Rita Jankovich, acting, (202) 879-9795

Environmental Protection Agency, Michael W. S. Ryan, (202) 260-9674

Equal Employment Opportunity Commission, Cassie Billingsly, (202) 663-4200

Export-Import Bank, James K. Hess, (202) 565-3240

Farm Credit Administration, Donald P. Clark, (703) 883-4200

Federal Bureau of Investigation, Wade B. Houk, (202) 324-1345

Federal Communications Commission, Linda King Friedman, (202) 418-1970

Federal Deposit Insurance Corporation, Paul Sachtleben, (202) 416-6900

Federal Election Commission, Richard Pullen, (202) 219-3570

Federal Emergency Management Agency, Gary D. Johnson, (202) 646-3545

Federal Energy Regulatory Commission, Christie McGue, (202) 208-0300

Federal Home Loan Mortgage Corporation, John Gibbons, (703) 903-4200

Federal Labor Relations Authority, Kevin K. Copper, (202) 482-6640

Federal Maritime Commission, Sandra Kusumoto, (202) 523-5770

Federal Mediation and Conciliation Service, Fran Leonard, (202) 606-3661

Senate Governmental Affairs Committee, *Subcommittee on Oversight of Government Management, Restructuring, and the District of Columbia, SH-604 20510; (202) 224-3682. Fax, (202) 224-3328. Sam Brownback, R-Kan., chair; Michael Rubin, acting staff director. Internet, http://www.senate.gov/committee/governmental_affairs.html.*

Jurisdiction over legislation for the General Services Administration and the National Archives and Records Administration; government procurement and legislation to reduce the volume of federal paperwork; and the improvement of federal information management. Oversight responsibilities for operations of the White House and the Office of Management and Budget. Jurisdiction over the Ethics and Government Act of 1978. Examines the efficiency of government operations, including federal regulations and program management.

Ethics in Government

See also Political Activity and the Hatch Act (this chapter)

FINANCIAL OFFICERS FOR FEDERAL AGENCIES (continued)

Federal National Mortgage Association, Timothy Howard, (202) 752-7140

Federal Reserve System, Stephen J. Clark, (202) 452-3553

Federal Trade Commission, Richard Arnold, (202) 326-2314

General Accounting Office, James F. Hinchman, (202) 512-5500

General Services Administration, Thomas Bloom, (202) 501-1721

International Bank for Reconstruction and Development (World Bank), Jules W. Muis, (202) 458-1674

John F. Kennedy Center for the Performing Arts, Clifton B. Jeter, (202) 416-8602

Merit Systems Protection Board, Robert Lawsher, (202) 653-5805

National Academy of Sciences, Archie Turner, (202) 334-3110

National Aeronautics and Space Administration, Arnold G. Holz, (202) 358-2262

National Archives and Records Administration, David M. Millane, (301) 713-6810

National Credit Union Administration, Dennis Wayands, (703) 518-6571

National Endowment for the Arts, Aaron Fineman, (202) 682-5767

National Endowment for the Humanities, Eric Murchison, (202) 606-8428

National Labor Relations Board, Karl Rohrbaugh, (202) 273-4230

National Mediation Board, June D. W. King, (202) 523-5402

National Railroad Passenger Corporation (Amtrak), Alfred F. Altschul, (202) 906-4800

National Science Foundation, Joseph L. Kull, (703) 306-1201

National Transportation Safety Board, Craig Keller, (202) 314-6210

Nuclear Regulatory Commission, Jesse L. Funchez, (301) 415-7501

Occupational Safety and Health Review Commission, Al Milion, (202) 606-5390

Office of Management and Budget, G. Edward DeSeve, (202) 395-3585

Office of Personnel Management, J. Gilbert Seaux, (202) 606-5076

Overseas Private Investment Corporation, Mildred O. Callear, (202) 336-8450

Peace Corps, Lana Hurdle, (202) 606-3960

Pension Benefit Guaranty Corporation, N. Anthony Calhoun, (202) 326-4170

Postal Rate Commission, Margaret P. Crenshaw, (202) 789-6840

Securities and Exchange Commission, Margaret Carpenter, (202) 942-0340

Small Business Administration, John Larry Wilson, (202) 205-6449

Smithsonian Institution, Rick Johnson, (202) 287-3275

Social Security Administration, Dale W. Sopper, (410) 965-2910

United States Arms Control and Disarmament Agency, William Amoroso, (202) 647-1921

United States Information Agency, Stanley Silverman, (202) 619-4315

United States International Trade Commission, Queen E. Cox, (202) 205-2678

United States Postal Service, Michael J. Riley, (202) 268-2454

AGENCIES

Office of Government Ethics, *1201 New York Ave. N.W., #500 20005-3917; (202) 208-8000. Fax, (202) 208-8037. Stephen D. Potts, director; Gary Davis, deputy director. Internet, http://www.usoge.gov.*

Administers executive branch policies relating to financial disclosure, employee conduct, and conflict-of-interest laws.

Office of Special Counsel, *1730 M St. N.W., #300 20036-4505; (202) 653-7122. Fax, (202) 653-5151.*

Vacant, special counsel. Information, (202) 653-7188. Issues relating to the Hatch Act, (800) 854-2824. Internet, http://www.access.gpo.gov/osc.

Investigates allegations of prohibited personnel practices and prosecutes individuals who violate civil service regulations. Receives and refers federal employee disclosures of waste, fraud, inefficiency, mismanagement, and other violations in the federal government. Enforces the Hatch Act.

See also Inspectors General list (this section)

INSPECTORS GENERAL FOR FEDERAL AGENCIES

Departmental and agency inspectors general are responsible for identifying and reporting program fraud and abuse, criminal activity, and unethical conduct in the federal government. In the legislative branch the General Accounting Office also has fraud and abuse hotlines: (800) 424-5454; (202) 512-7470 in Washington.

DEPARTMENTS

Agriculture, Roger C. Viadero, (202) 720-8001
Hotline, (800) 424-9121; (202) 690-1622 in Washington

Commerce, Johnnie Frazier, acting, (202) 482-4661
Hotline, (800) 424-5197; (202) 482-2495 in Washington

Defense, Eleanor Hill, (703) 604-8300
Hotline, (800) 424-9098; (703) 604-8555 in Washington

Education, Thomas R. Bloom, (202) 205-5439
Hotline, (800) 647-8733; (202) 205-5770 in Washington

Energy, Gregory H. Friedman, (202) 586-4393
Hotline, (800) 541-1625; (202) 586-4073 in Washington

Health and Human Services, June Gibbs Brown, (202) 619-3148
Hotline, (800) 447-8477

Housing and Urban Development, Susan Gaffney, (202) 708-0430
Hotline, (800) 347-3735; (202) 708-4200 in Washington

Interior, Robert Williams, acting, (202) 208-5745
Hotline, (202) 208-5317

Justice, Michael R. Bromwich, (202) 514-3435
Hotline, (800) 869-4499

Labor, Charles C. Masten, (202) 219-7296
Hotline, (800) 347-3756; (202) 219-5227 in Washington

State, Jacquelyn Williams-Bridgers, (202) 647-9450
Hotline, (202) 647-3320

Transportation, Kenneth Mead, (202) 366-1959
Hotline, (800) 424-9071; (202) 366-1461 in Washington

Treasury, Valerie Lau, (202) 622-1090
Hotline, (800) 359-3898

Veterans Affairs, Richard Griffin, (202) 565-8620
Hotline, (800) 488-8244

AGENCIES

Agency for International Development, Jeffrey Rush Jr., (202) 712-1150
Hotline, (800) 230-6539

Central Intelligence Agency, Frederick P. Hitz, (703) 874-2553

Environmental Protection Agency, Nikki Tinsley, acting, (202) 260-3137
Hotline, (202) 260-5629

Federal Deposit Insurance Corporation, Gaston Gianni, (202) 416-2532
Hotline, (800) 964-3342

Federal Emergency Management Agency, George Opfer, (202) 646-3910
Hotline, (800) 323-8603

General Services Administration, William Barton, (202) 501-0450
Hotline, (800) 424-5210; (202) 501-1780 in Washington

Merit Systems Protection Board, Hotline, (202) 653-7054

National Aeronautics and Space Administration, Roberta L. Gross, (202) 358-1220
Hotline, (800) 424-9183; (202) 535-8134 in Washington

National Science Foundation, Linda Sundro, (703) 306-2100

Nuclear Regulatory Commission, Hubert Bell, (301) 415-5930
Hotline, (800) 233-3497

Office of Personnel Management, Patrick E. McFarland, (202) 606-1200
Hotline, (202) 606-2423

Small Business Administration, James F. Hoobler, (202) 205-7151
Hotline, (800) 767-0385

Social Security Administration, David C. Williams, (410) 966-8385
Hotline, (800) 269-0271

U.S. Postal Service, Carla Corcoran, (202) 268-4267
Hotline, (800) 654-8896; (202) 484-5480 in Washington

CONGRESS

House Appropriations Committee, *Subcommittee on Treasury, Postal Service, and General Government,* B307 RHOB 20515; (202) 225-5834. Fax, (202) 225-5895. Jim Kolbe, R-Ariz., chair; Michelle Mrdeza, clerk. Internet, http://www.house.gov/appropriations.

Jurisdiction over legislation to appropriate funds for the Office of Government Ethics.

House Government Reform and Oversight Committee, *Subcommittee on Civil Service,* B371C RHOB 20515; (202) 225-6427. Fax, (202) 225-2392. John L. Mica, R-Fla., chair; George Nesterczuk, staff director. Internet, http://www.house.gov/reform.

Jurisdiction over legislation on civil service issues, including code of ethics.

House Government Reform and Oversight Committee, *Subcommittee on Government Management, Information, and Technology,* B373 RHOB 20515; (202) 225-5074. Fax, (202) 225-3974. Steve Horn, R-Calif., chair; J. Russell George, staff director. Internet, http://www.house.gov/cho.

Oversight of the Office of Government Ethics.

Senate Appropriations Committee, *Subcommittee on Treasury and General Government,* SD-190 20510; (202) 224-7337. Ben Nighthorse Campbell, R-Colo., chair; Patricia Raymond, staff director. Internet, http://www.senate.gov/~appropriations.

Jurisdiction over legislation to appropriate funds for the Office of Government Ethics.

Senate Governmental Affairs Committee, SD-340 20510; (202) 224-4751. Fax, (202) 224-9603. Fred Thompson, R-Tenn., chair; Hannah Sistare, staff director. Internet, http://www.senate.gov/committee/governmental_affairs.html.

Jurisdiction over legislation on civil service issues, including code of ethics and right to privacy. Oversight of the Office of Government Ethics.

NONPROFIT

Center for Public Integrity, 1634 Eye St., #902 20006; (202) 783-3900. Fax, (202) 783-3906. Charles Lewis, executive director. Internet, contact@publicintegrity.org or http://www.publicintegrity.org.

Educational foundation supported by corporations, labor unions, foundations, and individuals. Publishes comprehensive reports concerning ethics-related issues.

Council for Citizens Against Government Waste, 1301 Connecticut Ave. N.W., #400 20036; (202) 467-5300.

Fax, (202) 467-4253. Thomas A. Schatz, president. Toll-free, (800) 232-6479. Internet, http://www.cagw.org.

Nonpartisan organization that seeks to eliminate waste, mismanagement, and inefficiency in the federal government. Monitors legislation and regulations.

Fund for Constitutional Government, 122 Maryland Ave. N.E., 3rd Floor 20002; (202) 546-3799. Fax, (202) 543-3156. Anne B. Zill, president. Internet, funcongov@aol.com.

Seeks to expose and correct corruption in the federal government and private sector through research and public education. Sponsors the Electronic Privacy Information Center, the Government Accountability Project, and the Project on Government Oversight.

Government Accountability Project, 1612 K St. N.W., #400 20006; (202) 408-0034. Fax, (202) 408-9855. Louis Clark, executive director. Internet, gap1@erols.com or http://www.whistleblower.org/gap.

Membership: federal employees, union members, professionals, and interested citizens. Provides legal and strategic counsel to public and private employees who seek to expose corporate and government actions that are illegal, wasteful, or repressive; aids such employees in personnel action taken against them; assists grassroots organizations investigating corporate wrongdoing, government inaction, or corruption.

Project on Government Oversight, 1900 L St. N.W., #314 20036-5027; (202) 466-5539. Fax, (202) 466-5596. Danielle Brian, executive director. Internet, pogo@pogo.org or http://www.pogo.org.

Public interest organization that works to expose waste, fraud, abuse, and conflicts of interest in all aspects of federal spending.

Executive Reorganization

AGENCIES

National Partnership for Reinventing Government, 750 17th St. N.W., #200 20006; (202) 632-0150. Fax, (202) 632-0390. Bob Stone, project manager. Internet, rego.news@npr.gsa.gov or http://www.npr.gov.

Initiated by Vice President Al Gore; formerly the National Performance Review. Assesses the operation and functions of government in an attempt to make it more efficient. Assists federal agencies in evaluating their missions, simplifying the bureaucratic process, and reforming the regulatory system. Staffed by workers from federal agencies.

Office of Management and Budget, *President's Management Council,* Old Executive Office Bldg., #260

20503; (202) 395-6190. Fax, (202) 395-5730. John Koski-nen, chair.

Membership: chief operating officers of federal government departments and agencies. Responsible for implementing the management improvement initiatives of the administration. Develops and oversees improved governmentwide management and administrative systems; formulates long-range plans to promote these systems; works to resolve interagency management problems and to implement reforms.

Office of Personnel Management, *National Partnership Council,* 1900 E St. N.W. 20415-0001; (202) 606-2903. Fax, (202) 606-2613. Michael Cushing, director, Center for Partnership and Labor; James B. King, chair, (202) 606-1000.

Membership: officials of executive departments, government agencies, federal labor unions, the Federal Managers' Assn., and the Senior Executives' Assn. Advises the president on labor-management relations in the executive branch. (Affiliated with the National Partnership Clearinghouse.)

CONGRESS

General Accounting Office, *Federal Management and Workforce Issues,* 441 G St. N.W. 20548; (202) 512-8676. Fax, (202) 512-4516. L. Nye Stevens, director.

Assesses the effectiveness of the National Performance Review efforts, implementation of the Government Performance and Results Act, and opportunities to introduce market-based incentives and reorganization into federal personnel management.

General Accounting Office, *Information Resources Management Policies and Issues,* 441 G St. N.W. 20548; (202) 512-6406. Fax, (202) 512-6451. Christopher W. Hoenig, director.

Seeks to make the federal government more effective in its information management. Assesses practices in the public and private sectors; makes recommendations to government agencies. Interests include information security.

House Government Reform and Oversight Committee, *Subcommittee on Civil Service,* B371C RHOB 20515; (202) 225-6427. Fax, (202) 225-2392. John L. Mica, R-Fla., chair; George Nesterczuk, staff director. Internet, http://www.house.gov/reform.

Studies the effect of reorganization of agencies on federal employees.

House Government Reform and Oversight Committee, *Subcommittee on Government Management,*

Information, and Technology, B373 RHOB 20515; (202) 225-5147. Steve Horn, R-Calif., chair; J. Russell George, staff director. Internet, http://www.house.gov/cho.

Jurisdiction over executive and legislative reorganization legislation.

Senate Governmental Affairs Committee, SD-340 20510; (202) 224-4751. Fax, (202) 224-9603. Fred Thompson, R-Tenn., chair; Hannah Sistare, staff director. Internet, http://www.senate.gov/committee/governmental_affairs.html.

Jurisdiction over executive and legislative reorganization legislation; studies the effect of reorganization of agencies on federal employees.

NONPROFIT

Alliance for Redesigning Government, 1120 G St. N.W., #850 20005-3801; (202) 347-3190. Fax, (202) 347-3252. Gail Christopher, director. Internet, http://www.alliance.napawsh.org.

Advocates a smaller, more efficient, and more effective government. Serves as an information clearinghouse; sponsors projects that seek innovation in government. (Affiliated with the National Academy of Public Administration.)

Brookings Institution, *Center for Public Management,* 1775 Massachusetts Ave. N.W. 20036; (202) 797-6081. Fax, (202) 797-6144. Donald F. Kettl, director. Internet, http://www.brookings.org/gs/cpm/cpm_hp.HTM.

Conducts research on public management and critical problems of federal, state, and local governance; offers training programs in leadership and management for government executives.

Council for Excellence in Government, 1301 K St. N.W., #450 West 20005; (202) 728-0418. Fax, (202) 728-0422. Patricia G. McGinnis, president. Internet, http://www.exceogov.org.

Membership: business and professional leaders with previous executive-level government experience. Works to improve public-sector performance by strengthening federal leadership and management; seeks to build a public understanding of and confidence in government.

Federal Managers Assn., 1641 Prince St., Alexandria, VA 22314; (703) 683-8700. Fax, (703) 683-8707. Frances Webb, chief operating officer. Internet, fma@ix.netcom.com.

Seeks to improve the effectiveness of federal supervisors and managers and the operations of the federal government.

Private Sector Council, *1101 16th St. N.W., #300 20036-4803; (202) 822-3910. Fax, (202) 822-0638. Thomas V. Fritz, president. Internet, psci@capaccess.org.*

Membership: large corporations, private businesses, and associations, including financial and information technology organizations. Seeks to improve government efficiency, productivity, and management through a cooperative effort of the public and private sectors.

Federal Buildings

AGENCIES

General Services Administration, *Business Performance, 1800 F St. N.W., #4340 20405; (202) 501-0971. Fax, (202) 501-3296. Kevin Kampschroer, assistant commissioner.*

Oversees safety programs for federal buildings, employees, and visitors to federal buildings.

General Services Administration, *Federal Protective Service, 1800 F St. N.W., #2341 20405; (202) 501-0907. Fax, (202) 208-5866. Clarence Edwards, assistant commissioner.*

Oversees security and law enforcement programs for federal buildings, employees, and visitors to federal buildings.

General Services Administration, *Public Buildings Service, 1800 F St. N.W., #6344 20405; (202) 501-1100. Fax, (202) 219-2310. Robert A. Peck, commissioner.*

Administers the construction, maintenance, and operation of buildings owned or leased by the federal government.

Supplies and Transportation

AGENCIES

General Services Administration, *Federal Acquisition Institute, 1800 F St. N.W. 20405; (202) 501-0964. Fax, (202) 501-3341. Michael F. Miller, director. Internet, http://www.gsa.gov/staff.*

Fosters development of a professional acquisition workforce governmentwide; collects and analyzes acquisition workforce data; helps agencies identify and recruit candidates for the acquisitions field; develops instructional materials; evaluates training and career development programs.

General Services Administration, *Federal Supply Service, 1941 Jefferson Davis Hwy., Arlington, VA 22202; (703) 305-6667. Fax, (703) 305-5500. Frank P. Pugliese Jr., commissioner. Internet, http://www.fss.gsa.gov.*

Responsible for providing federal agencies with common-use goods and nonpersonal services and for pro-

curement and supply, transportation and travel management, and disposal of surplus personal property.

General Services Administration, *Transportation and Property Management, 1941 Jefferson Davis Hwy., #815, Arlington, VA 22202; (703) 305-7660. Fax, (703) 305-6905. Allan Zaic, assistant commissioner.*

Manages governmentwide programs and activities relating to the use of excess personal property (except Automated Data Processing [ADP] equipment); provides transportation, travel, aircraft, mail, relocation, and vehicle fleet services. Produces *Federal Travel Regulations* and *Federal Travel Directory.*

🏛 POSTAL SERVICE

AGENCIES

U.S. Postal Service, *475 L'Enfant Plaza S.W. 20260-0001; (202) 268-2000. Fax, (202) 268-4860. Tirso del Junco, chair; William J. Henderson, postmaster general, (202) 268-2500. Press, (202) 268-2156. Library, (202) 268-2904. Locator, (202) 268-2020. Internet, http://www.usps.gov.*

Offers postal service throughout the country as an independent establishment of the executive branch. Library open to the public.

U.S. Postal Service, *Inspection Service, 475 L'Enfant Plaza S.W., #3100 20260; (202) 268-4267. Fax, (202) 268-4563. Kenneth J. Hunter, chief postal inspector. Fraud and abuse hotline, (888) 877-7644.*

Investigates criminal violations of postal laws, such as theft of mail or posted valuables, assaults on postal employees, organized crime in postal-related matters, and prohibited mailings. Conducts internal audits; investigates postal activities to determine effectiveness of procedures; monitors compliance of individual post offices with postal regulations; functions as the inspector general for the postal service.

CONGRESS

House Appropriations Committee, *Subcommittee on Treasury, Postal Service, and General Government, B307 RHOB 20515; (202) 225-5834. Fax, (202) 225-5895. Jim Kolbe, R-Ariz., chair; Michelle Mrdeza, clerk. Internet, http://www.house.gov/appropriations.*

Jurisdiction over legislation to appropriate funds for the U.S. Postal Service and the Postal Rate Commission.

House Government Reform and Oversight Committee, *Subcommittee on the Postal Service, B349C RHOB 20515; (202) 225-3741. Fax, (202) 225-2544. John*

M. McHugh, R-N.Y., chair; Robert Taub, staff director. Internet, http://www.house.gov/reform.

Jurisdiction over postal service legislation; oversight of the U.S. Postal Service and the Postal Rate Commission. Analyzes the impact on federal jobs of the use of mail consultants and contractors by government agencies.

Senate Appropriations Committee, *Subcommittee on Treasury and General Government,* SD-190 20510; (202) 224-7337. Ben Nighthorse Campbell, R-Colo., chair; Patricia Raymond, staff director. Internet, http://www. senate.gov/~appropriations.

Jurisdiction over legislation to appropriate funds for the U.S. Postal Service and the Postal Rate Commission.

Senate Governmental Affairs Committee, *Permanent Subcommittee on Investigations,* SH-432 20510; (202) 224-3721. Fax, (202) 224-7042. Susan Collins, R-Maine, chair; Tim Shea, chief of staff. Internet, http://www. senate.gov/~gov_affairs/psi.htm.

Investigates postal fraud.

Senate Governmental Affairs Committee, *Subcommittee on International Security, Proliferation, and Federal Services,* SH-442 20510; (202) 224-2254. Fax, (202) 228-3796. Thad Cochran, R-Miss., chair; Mitch Kugler, staff director. Internet, http://www.senate.gov/ committee/governmental_affairs.html.

Jurisdiction over postal service legislation, including legislation on postal service consumer protection, labor relations, automation of postal facilities, postal fraud, mail rates, and classifications for the postal service and philately; postal finances and expenditures; and mail transportation and military mail. Oversight of the U.S. Postal Service and the Postal Rate Commission. Analyzes the impact on federal jobs of the use of mail consultants and contractors by government agencies.

Consumer Services

AGENCIES

U.S. Postal Service, *Consumer Affairs,* 475 L'Enfant Plaza S.W. 20260-2200; (202) 268-2284. Fax, (202) 268-2304. Michael Shinay, vice president. TDD, (202) 268-2310.

Handles consumer complaints; oversees investigations into consumer problems; intercedes in local areas when problems are not adequately resolved; provides information on specific products and services; represents consumers' viewpoint before postal management bodies; initiates projects to improve postal service.

U.S. Postal Service, *Consumer Protection,* 475 L'Enfant Plaza S.W., #6249 20260-1127; (202) 268-3081. Fax, (202) 268-5287. Jennifer Y. Angelo, chief counsel.

Initiates civil administrative proceedings to stop mail delivery that solicits money by lottery or misrepresentation; enforces statutes designed to prevent receipt of unwanted sexual material.

U.S. Postal Service, *Customer Relations,* 475 L'Enfant Plaza S.W. #5014 20260-1400; (202) 268-2222. Fax, (202) 268-3428. John R. Wargo, vice president.

Analyzes, develops, and markets postal products and services, primarily to commercial customers; oversees regional marketing and communications; acts as liaison with major customer groups such as Mailers' Technical Advisory Committee; manages the National and Regional Postal Forums. *(See Regional Information Sources in appendix.)*

U.S. Postal Service, *Enforcement Law,* 475 L'Enfant Plaza S.W. 20260-1148; (202) 268-3076. Fax, (202) 268-5287. George C. Davis, chief counsel.

Reviews and processes cases falling under the Program Fraud Civil Remedies Act of 1986.

U.S. Postal Service, *Stamp Distribution,* 475 L'Enfant Plaza S.W., #4474E 20260-2436; (202) 268-2325. Fax, (202) 268-3710. Lawrence L. Lum, manager.

Distributes postage stamps and postal stationery; develops inventory controls.

Employee and Labor Relations

AGENCIES

U.S. Postal Service, *Diversity Development,* 475 L'Enfant Plaza S.W., #3821 20260-5600; (202) 268-6566. Fax, (202) 268-6573. Robert F. Harris, vice president.

Responsible for policy and planning with regard to affirmative action hiring and supplier/vendor selection.

U.S. Postal Service, *Human Resources,* 475 L'Enfant Plaza S.W., #9100 20260-5000; (202) 268-3783. Fax, (202) 268-3074. Yvonne D. Maguire, vice president.

Drafts and implements employment policies and practices, safety and health guidelines, training and development programs, and compensation guidelines.

U.S. Postal Service, *Labor Relations,* 475 L'Enfant Plaza S.W., #9021 20260-4100; (202) 268-3816. Fax, (202) 268-3074. Jack Potter, vice president.

Handles collective bargaining and contract administration for the U.S. Postal Service and processes complaints regarding equal employment opportunity.

U.S. Postal Service, *Personnel Operations Support,* *475 L'Enfant Plaza S.W., #1813 20260-4261; (202) 268-4255. Fax, (202) 268-6195. Janet Qualters, manager.*

Matches needs of U.S. Postal Service with career goals and job preferences of its executive employees.

NONPROFIT

American Postal Workers Union, *1300 L St. N.W. 20005; (202) 842-4200. Fax, (202) 842-4297. Moe Biller, president. Internet, http://www.apwu.org.*

Membership: approximately 366,000 postal employees, including clerks, motor vehicle operators, special delivery messengers, and other employees. Assists members with contract negotiation and grievances; conducts training programs and workshops. Monitors legislation and regulations. (Affiliated with the Postal, Telegraph, and Telephone International and the AFL-CIO.)

National Alliance of Postal and Federal Employees, *1628 11th St. N.W. 20001; (202) 939-6325. Fax, (202) 939-6389. James M. McGee, president. Internet, http://www.napfe.com.*

Membership: approximately 70,000 postal and federal employees. Helps members negotiate pay, benefits, and better working conditions; conducts training programs and workshops. Monitors legislation and regulations.

National Assn. of Letter Carriers, *100 Indiana Ave. N.W. 20001; (202) 393-4695. Fax, (202) 737-1540. Vincent R. Sombrotto, president. Internet, nalinf@access.digex.net or http://www.nacl.org.*

Membership: approximately 315,000 city letter carriers working for, or retired from, the U.S. Postal Service. Assists members with contract negotiation and grievances; conducts training programs and workshops. Monitors legislation and regulations. (Affiliated with the AFL-CIO and the Postal, Telegraph, and Telephone International.)

National Assn. of Postal Supervisors, *1727 King St., #400, Alexandria, VA 22314-2753; (703) 836-9660. Fax, (703) 836-9665. Vincent Palladino, president. Internet, http://www.naps.org.*

Membership: present and former postal supervisors. Cooperates with other postal management associations, unions, and the U.S. Postal Service to improve the efficiency of the postal service; promotes favorable working conditions and broader career opportunities for all postal employees; provides members with information on current functions and legislative issues of the postal service.

National Assn. of Postmasters of the United States, *8 Herbert St., Alexandria, VA 22305-2600; (703) 683-9027. Fax, (703) 683-6820. Ed Baer, executive director. Internet, napus@erols.com or http://www.napus.org.*

Membership: present and former postmasters of the United States. Promotes quality mail service and favorable relations between the postal service and the public; works with other postal groups and levels of management in the interest of postal matters and the welfare of its members.

National League of Postmasters, *1023 N. Royal St., Alexandria, VA 22314; (703) 548-5922. Fax, (703) 836-8937. William P. Brennan, president. Toll-free, (800) 524-4771.*

Membership: state and area postmaster associations. Promotes effective postal management; sponsors insurance plans for members; operates a 24-hour help line, which makes confidential referrals for those experiencing stress. Monitors legislation and regulations.

National Rural Letter Carriers' Assn., *1630 Duke St., 4th Floor, Alexandria, VA 22314-5545; (703) 684-5545. Fax, (703) 548-8735. Steven R. Smith, president. Internet, http://www.nrlca.org.*

Membership: approximately 97,000 rural letter carriers working for, or retired from, the U.S. Postal Service. Seeks to improve rural mail delivery. Helps members negotiate pay, benefits, and better working conditions; conducts training programs and workshops. Monitors legislation and regulations.

National Star Route Mail Contractors Assn., *324 E. Capitol St. 20003-3897; (202) 543-1661. Fax, (202) 543-8863. John V. Maraney, executive director.*

Membership: contractors for highway mail transport and selected rural route deliverers. Acts as liaison between contractors and the U.S. Postal Service, the Transportation Dept., and the Labor Dept. concerning contracts, wages, and other issues. Monitors legislation and regulations.

Mail Rates and Classification

AGENCIES

Postal Rate Commission, *1333 H St. N.W., #300 20268-0001; (202) 789-6800. Fax, (202) 789-6886. Ed Gleiman, chair; George Haley, vice chair, (202) 789-6868.*

Submits recommendations to the governors of the U.S. Postal Service concerning proposed changes in postage rates, fees, and mail classifications; issues advisory opinions on proposed changes in postal services; studies and submits recommendations on public complaints concerning postal rates and nationwide service. Reviews appeals of post office closings.

U.S. Postal Service, *Business Mail Acceptance, 475 L'Enfant Plaza S.W., #6801 20260-6808; (202) 268-5174. Fax, (202) 268-4404. Anita Bizzotto, manager.*

Implements policies on and answers customer inquiries about domestic mail classification matters.

U.S. Postal Service, *Mail Preparation and Standards, 475 L'Enfant Plaza S.W., #6801 20260-2401; (202) 268-6249. Fax, (202) 268-4336. Michelle Denny, manager.*

Issues policy statements on domestic mail classification matters. Ensures the accuracy of policies developed by the Postal Rate Commission with respect to domestic mail classification schedules.

U.S. Postal Service, *Marketing, 475 L'Enfant Plaza S.W., #5141 20260-2406; (202) 268-2650. Fax, (202) 268-4801. Annette Wilderson, pricing manager.*

Sets prices for postal service product lines using competitive pricing methods.

NONPROFIT

Advertising Mail Marketing Assn., *1333 F St. N.W., #710 20004-1108; (202) 347-0055. Fax, (202) 347-0789. Gene A. Del Polito, president. Recorded postal information, (202) 347-0799; electronic bulletin board service, (202) 347-5128. Internet, http://www.amma.org.*

Membership: companies and organizations interested in advertising (third-class) mail. Provides members with information about postal policy, postal rates, and legislation regarding postal regulations.

Alliance of Nonprofit Mailers, *1211 Connecticut Ave. N.W., #620 20036-2701; (202) 462-5132. Fax, (202) 462-0423. Neal Denton, executive director.*

Works to maintain reasonable mail rates for nonprofit organizations. Represents member organizations before Congress, the U.S. Postal Service, the Postal Rate Commission, and the courts on nonprofit postal rate and mail classification issues.

Direct Marketing Assn., *1101 17th St. N.W., #1100 20036; (202) 955-5030. Fax, (202) 955-0085. Jerry Cerasale, senior vice president, Government Affairs. Internet, http://www.the-dma.org.*

Membership: telemarketers; users, creators, and producers of direct mail; and suppliers to the industry. Serves as liaison between members and the U.S. Postal Service. Monitors federal legislation and regulations concerning postal rates. (Headquarters in New York.)

Mail Advertising Service Assn., *1421 Prince St., Alexandria, VA 22314-2806; (703) 836-9200. Fax, (703)*

548-8204. David A. Weaver, president. Internet, http://www.masa.org.

Membership: U.S. and foreign letter and printing shops that engage in direct mail advertising. Serves as a clearinghouse for members on improving methods of using the mail for advertising.

National Federation of Nonprofits, *815 15th St. N.W., #822 20005-2201; (202) 628-4380. Fax, (202) 628-4383. Lee M. Cassidy, executive director. Internet, nfndc@aol.com.*

Membership: educational, cultural, fraternal, religious, and scientific organizations that mail nonprofit second-, third-, or fourth-class mail. Serves as liaison between members and the U.S. Postal Service; represents nonprofit members' interests on the Mailers' Technical Advisory Committee. Monitors legislation and regulations.

Parcel Shippers Assn., *1211 Connecticut Ave. N.W., #610 20036; (202) 296-3690. Fax, (202) 296-0343. James V. Jellison, executive vice president.*

Voluntary organization of business firms concerned with the shipment of small parcels. Works to improve parcel post rates and service; represents members before the Postal Rate Commission in matters regarding parcel post rates. Monitors legislation and regulations.

Stamps/Postal History

AGENCIES

National Postal Museum *(Smithsonian Institution), Smithsonian Institution, 2 Massachusetts Ave. N.E., MRC 570 20560; (202) 633-9360. Fax, (202) 633-9393. James H. Bruns, director.*

Exhibits postal history and philatelic collections; provides information on world postal history and philatelic history.

U.S. Postal Service, *Citizens' Stamp Advisory Committee, 475 L'Enfant Plaza S.W., #4474 East Bldg. 20260-2437; (202) 268-2312. Fax, (202) 268-2714. James C. Tolbert Jr., manager, Stamp Development.*

Reviews stamp subject nominations. Develops the annual Stamp Program and makes subject and design recommendations to the Postmaster General.

U.S. Postal Service, *Stamp Acquisition, 475 L'Enfant Plaza S.W., #4474 E 20260-2436; (202) 268-2321. Fax, (202) 268-3710. Kathryn Caggiano, manager.*

Manufactures postage stamps and postal stationery.

U.S. Postal Service, *Stamp Development, 475 L'Enfant Plaza S.W. 20260-2437; (202) 268-2312. Fax, (202) 268-2714. James C. Tolbert Jr., manager.*

Manages the stamp selection function; develops the basic stamp pre-production design; manages relationship with philatelic community.

🏛 PUBLIC ADMINISTRATION

AGENCIES

Office of Management and Budget, *President's Management Council, Old Executive Office Bldg., #260 20503; (202) 395-6190. Fax, (202) 395-5730. John Koskinen, chair.*

Membership: chief operating officers of federal government departments and agencies. Responsible for implementing the management improvement initiatives of the administration. Develops and oversees improved governmentwide management and administrative systems; formulates long-range plans to promote these systems; works to resolve interagency management problems and to implement reforms.

President's Commission on White House Fellowships, *712 Jackson Pl. N.W. 20503; (202) 395-4522. Fax, (202) 395-6179. Jacqueline Blumenthal, director. Internet, http://www.whitehouse.gov/WH_Fellows.*

Nonpartisan commission which provides professionals from all sectors of national life with the opportunity to observe firsthand the processes of the federal government. Fellows work for one year as special assistants to Cabinet members or to principal members of the White House staff. Qualified applicants have demonstrated superior accomplishments early in their careers and have a commitment to community service.

CONGRESS

House Government Reform and Oversight Committee, *Subcommittee on Government Management, Information, and Technology, B373 RHOB 20515; (202) 225-5074. Fax, (202) 225-3974. Steve Horn, R-Calif., chair; J. Russell George, staff director. Internet, http://www.house.gov/cho.*

Jurisdiction over legislation on all procurement practices. Also examines the efficiency of government operations, including federal regulations and program management.

House Government Reform and Oversight Committee, *Subcommittee on National Economic Growth, Natural Resources, and Regulatory Affairs, B377 RHOB 20515; (202) 225-4407. Fax, (202) 225-2441. David M. McIntosh, R-Ind., chair; Mildred Webber, staff director. Internet, http://www.house.gov/reform.*

Jurisdiction over legislation involving the efficiency and management of government operations, including federal paperwork reduction.

House Standards of Official Conduct Committee, *HT-2 CAP 20515; (202) 225-7103. Fax, (202) 225-7392. James V. Hansen, R-Utah, chair; Theodore J. Van Der Meid, chief counsel.*

Jurisdiction over the Ethics in Government Act of 1978.

Senate Governmental Affairs Committee, *Subcommittee on Oversight of Government Management, Restructuring, and the District of Columbia, SH-604 20510; (202) 224-3682. Fax, (202) 224-3328. Sam Brownback, R-Kan., chair; Michael Rubin, acting staff director. Internet, http://www.senate.gov/committee/ governmental_affairs.html.*

Jurisdiction over the Ethics in Government Act of 1978 and over legislation on all procurement practices. Examines the efficiency of government operations, including federal regulations and program management.

Senate Judiciary Committee, *Subcommittee on Administrative Oversight and the Courts, SH-308 20510; (202) 224-6736. Charles E. Grassley, R-Iowa, chair; Kolan L. Davis, chief counsel. Internet, http://www. senate.gov/committee/judiciary.html.*

Oversees operations of the Administrative Conference of the United States; jurisdiction over administrative practices and procedures.

NONPROFIT

American Society for Public Administration, *1120 G St. N.W., #700 20005; (202) 393-7878. Fax, (202) 638-4952. Mary Hamilton, executive director. Internet, http:// www.aspanet.org.*

Membership: government administrators, public officials, educators, researchers, and others interested in public administration. Presents awards to distinguished professionals in the field; sponsors workshops and conferences; disseminates information about public administration. Promotes high ethical standards for public service.

Assn. of Government Accountants, *2200 Mount Vernon Ave., Alexandria, VA 22301; (703) 684-6931. Fax, (703) 548-9367. Charles Culkin, executive director. Internet, http://www.agacgfm.org.*

Membership: individuals engaged in government accounting, auditing, budgeting, and information systems.

Federally Employed Women, *1400 Eye St. N.W., #425 20005; (202) 898-0994. Fax, (202) 898-0998. Alma Esparza, executive director. Internet, http://www.few.org.*

Membership: women and men who work for the federal government. Works to eliminate sex discrimination in government employment and to increase job opportunities for women; offers training programs. Monitors legislation and regulations.

International City/County Management Assn., *777 N. Capitol St. N.E., #500 20001; (202) 962-3610. Fax, (202) 962-3500. William H. Hansell Jr., executive director. Library, (202) 962-3654. Internet, http://www.icma.org.*

Membership: city and county managers, council of government directors, and municipal administrators. Sponsors a professional development institute that offers courses and workshops in municipal administration; maintains an information service on local government management practices. Library open to the public by appointment.

International Personnel Management Assn., *1617 Duke St., Alexandria, VA 22314; (703) 549-7100. Fax, (703) 684-0948. Neil Reichenberg, executive director. Internet, ipma@ipma.hr.org or http://www.ipma.hr.org.*

Membership: personnel professionals from federal, state, and local governments. Provides information on training procedures, management techniques, and legislative developments on the federal, state, and local levels.

National Academy of Public Administration, *1120 G St. N.W., #850 20005-3801; (202) 347-3190. Fax, (202) 393-0993. R. Scott Fosler, president. Internet, napa@tmn.com or http://www.napawash.org.*

Membership: scholars and administrators in public management. Offers assistance to federal, state, and local government agencies, public officials, foreign governments, foundations, and corporations on problems related to public administration.

National Assn. of Schools of Public Affairs and Administration, *1120 G St. N.W., #730 20005; (202) 628-8965. Fax, (202) 626-4978. Michael Brintnall, executive director. Internet, naspaa@naspaa.org or http://www. unomaha.edu/~wwpa/nashome.html.*

Membership: universities and government agencies interested in the advancement of education, research, and training in public management. Serves as a clearinghouse for information on public administration and public affairs programs in colleges and universities. Accredits masters degree programs.

National Women's Political Caucus, *1211 Connecticut Ave. N.W., #425 20036; (202) 785-1100. Fax, (202) 785-*

3605. Heather Herndon, deputy political director. Internet, mailnwpc@aol.com or http://www.feminist.com/nwpc.htm.

Seeks to increase the number of women in policy-making positions in federal, state, and local government. Identifies, recruits, trains, and supports women candidates for public office. Monitors agencies and provides names of qualified women for high- and midlevel appointments.

Women in Government Relations, Inc., *1029 Vermont Ave. N.W., #510 20005-3527; (202) 347-5432. Fax, (202) 347-5434. Maryann Leisher, administrative director. Internet, wgr@earthlink.net.*

Membership: professionals in business, trade associations, and government whose jobs involve governmental relations at the federal, state, or local level. Serves as a forum for exchange of information among its members.

🏛 STATE AND LOCAL GOVERNMENT

See also Community and Regional Development (chap. 12); State Officials list (appendix)

AGENCIES

Census Bureau *(Commerce Dept.),* **Governments Division,** *Washington Plaza II, #407, Upper Marlboro, MD; (301) 457-1489. Fax, (301) 457-1423. Gordon W. Green Jr., chief.*

Compiles annual *Federal Expenditures by State* (available to the public), which provides information on overall federal grants-in-aid expenditures to state and local governments; collects data on finances, employment, and structure of the public sector; and serves as national clearinghouse on state and local audit reports. Computer data obtainable from Data User Services, (301) 457-4100.

District of Columbia Tax Revision Commission, *1755 Massachusetts Ave. N.W., #550 20036; (202) 518-7275. Fax, (202) 466-7967. Robert D. Ebel, chair. Internet, taxrevis@erols.com or http://www.dctrc.org.*

An ad-hoc, nonpartisan commission. Reviews the present D.C. tax system; recommends changes to the mayor and D.C. council to stimulate economic development.

Executive Office of the President, *Intergovernmental Affairs, White House 20502; (202) 456-7060. Fax, (202) 456-6220. Mickey Ibarra, director.*

Serves as liaison with state and local governments; provides information on administration programs and policies.

General Services Administration, *Federal Domestic Assistance Catalog Staff, 300 7th St. S.W., #101 20405; (202) 708-5126. Fax, (202) 401-8233. Robert Brown, director.*

Operates computerized Federal Assistance Programs Retrieval System, which helps state and local governments locate programs with the greatest funding potential to meet their developmental needs. Pepares *Catalog of Federal Domestic Assistance* (published annually in June and updated in December), which lists all types of federal aid and explains types of assistance, eligibility requirements, application process, and suggestions for writing proposals. Copies may be ordered from the Superintendent of Documents, U.S. Government Printing Office, Washington, D.C. 20402; (202) 512-1800. Also available on CD-ROM and floppy diskettes.

Housing and Urban Development Dept., *Policy Development and Research, 451 7th St. S.W., #8100 20410-6000; (202) 708-1600. Fax, (202) 619-8000. Vacant, assistant secretary. Internet, http://www.huduser.html.*

Assesses urban economic development and the fiscal capacity of state and local governments.

Multistate Tax Commission, *444 N. Capitol St. N.W., #425 20001-1538; (202) 624-8699. Fax, (202) 624-8819. Dan R. Bucks, executive director. Internet, mtc@mtc.gov or http://www.mtc.gov.*

Membership: state governments that have enacted the Multistate Tax Compact. Promotes fair, effective, and efficient state tax systems for interstate and international commerce; works to preserve state tax sovereignty. Encourages uniform state tax laws and regulations for multistate and multinational enterprises. Maintains three regional audit offices that monitor compliance with state tax laws and encourage uniformity in taxpayer treatment. Administers program to identify businesses that do not file tax returns with states.

Office of Management and Budget *(Executive Office of the President), Federal Financial Management, New Executive Office Bldg., #6025 20503; (202) 395-3585. Fax, (202) 395-3047. G. Edward DeSeve, controller.*

Facilitates exchange of information on financial management standards, techniques, and processes among officers of state and local governments.

CONGRESS

General Accounting Office, *Health, Education, and Human Services, 441 G St. N.W. 20548; (202) 512-6806. Fax, (202) 512-5806. Richard L. Hembra, assistant comptroller general.*

Independent, nonpartisan agency in the legislative branch. Responsible for intergovernmental relations

---

LOCAL GOVERNMENT IN THE WASHINGTON AREA

DISTRICT OF COLUMBIA

Executive Office of the Mayor
Marion Barry Jr., mayor
441 4th St. N.W., #1100 20001; (202) 727-2980;
   fax, (202) 727-6561
http://ci.washington.dc.us

**Financial Responsibility and Management
   Assistance Authority (D.C. Control Board)**
Andrew Brimmer, chair
1 Thomas Circle, #900 20005; (202) 504-3400;
   fax, (202) 504-3431
http://www.dcfra.gov

MARYLAND

Montgomery County
Douglas M. Duncan, county executive
101 Monroe St., Rockville, MD 20850; (301)
   217-2500; fax, (301) 217-2517
http://www.co.mo.md.us

Prince George's County
Wayne K. Curry, county executive
14741 Gov. Oden Bowie Dr., Upper Marlboro, MD
   20772, (301) 952-4131; fax, (301) 952-3784
http://www.co.pg.md.us

VIRGINIA

City of Alexandria
Kerry J. Donley, mayor
301 King St., City Hall, Alexandria, VA 22314; (703)
   838-4500; fax, (703) 838-6433
http://ci.alexandria.va.us

Arlington County
Christopher Zimmerman, board chair
2100 Clarendon Blvd., #300, Arlington, VA 22201;
   (703) 228-3130; fax, (703) 228-7430
http://co.arlington.va.us

Fairfax County
Robert J. O'Neill Jr., county executive
1200 Government Center Pkwy., #552, Fairfax, VA
   22035; (703) 324-2531; fax, (703) 824-3956
http://www.co.fairfax.va.us

City of Falls Church
H. Alan Brangman, mayor
300 Park Ave., Falls Church, VA 22046; (703) 241-
   5014; fax, (703) 241-5146
http://ci.falls-church.va.us

---

activities. Reviews the effects of federal grants and regulations on state and local governments; works to reduce intergovernmental conflicts and costs; seeks to improve the allocation and targeting of federal funds to state and local governments through changes in federal funding formulas.

House Appropriations Committee, *Subcommittee on the District of Columbia,* H147 CAP 20515; (202) 225-5338. Fax, (202) 225-8044. Charles H. Taylor, R-N.C., chair; Americo S. Miconi, staff assistant. Internet, http://www.house.gov/appropriations.

Jurisdiction over legislation to appropriate funds for the District of Columbia.

House Government Reform and Oversight Committee, *Subcommittee on Human Resources,* B372 RHOB 20515; (202) 225-2548. Fax, (202) 225-2382. Christopher Shays, R-Conn., chair; Larry Halloran, staff director. Internet, http://www.house.gov/reform.

Jurisdiction over legislation dealing with the interrelationship among federal, state, and local governments.

House Government Reform and Oversight Committee, *Subcommittee on the District of Columbia,* B-349A 20515; (202) 225-6751. Thomas M. Davis III, R-Va., chair; Ronald P. Hamm, staff director.

Jurisdiction over all measures relating to the municipal affairs of the District of Columbia, other than appropriations.

Senate Appropriations Committee, *Subcommittee on the District of Columbia,* S128 CAP 20510; (202) 224-1526. Lauch Faircloth, R-N.C., chair; Mary Beth Nethercutt, clerk. Internet, http://www.senate.gov/~appropriations.

Jurisdiction over legislation to appropriate funds for the District of Columbia and St. Elizabeth's Hospital.

Senate Finance Committee, SD-219 20510; (202) 224-4515. Fax, (202) 224-5920. William V. Roth Jr., R-Del., chair; Lindy L. Paull, staff director. Internet, http://www.senate.gov/~finance.

Jurisdiction over legislation dealing with the interrelationship among federal, state, and local governments, including revenue sharing legislation (jurisdiction shared with Senate Governmental Affairs Committee).

Senate Governmental Affairs Committee, SD-340 20510; (202) 224-4751. Fax, (202) 224-9603. Fred Thompson, R-Tenn., chair; Hannah Sistare, staff director. Internet, http://www.senate.gov/committee/governmental_affairs.html.

Jurisdiction over legislation dealing with the interrelationship between federal, state, and local governments, including revenue sharing legislation (jurisdiction shared with Senate Finance Committee).

Senate Governmental Affairs Committee, *Subcommittee on Oversight of Government Management, Restructuring, and the District of Columbia,* SH-604 20510; (202) 224-3682. Fax, (202) 224-3328. Sam Brownback, R-Kan., chair; Michael Rubin, acting staff director. Internet, http://www.senate.gov/committee/governmental_affairs.html.

Jurisdiction over all measures relating to the municipal affairs of the District of Columbia, other than appropriations.

NONPROFIT

Academy for State and Local Government, 444 N. Capitol St. N.W., #345 20001; (202) 434-4850. Fax, (202) 434-4851. Dawn Hatzer, coordinator.

Offers technical assistance, training, and research to the Council of State Governments, International City/County Management Assn., National Assn. of Counties, National Conference of State Legislatures, National Governors' Assn., National League of Cities, and U.S. Conference of Mayors. Promotes cooperation among federal, state, and local governments; the private sector; and researchers. Interests include tax policy, finance, and state and local relations. Works to improve state and local litigation in the Supreme Court. Promotes the exchange of information from overseas with state and local officials.

American Legislative Exchange Council, 910 17th St. N.W., 5th Floor 20006; (202) 466-3800. Fax, (202) 466-3801. Duane Parde, executive director. Internet, http://www.alec.org.

Bipartisan educational and research organization for state legislators. Conducts research and provides information and model state legislation on public policy issues. Supports the development of state policies to limit government, expand free markets, promote economic growth, and preserve individual liberty.

Center for Policy Alternatives, 1875 Connecticut Ave. N.W., #710 20009-5728; (202) 387-6030. Fax, (202) 986-2539. Linda Tarr-Whelan, president. Internet, info@cfpa.org or http://www.cfpa.org.

Clearinghouse and research center that assists state and local officials in developing policy initiatives. Interests include state and local economic development and tax reform, toxic chemicals and environmental problems, governmental reform, health policy, voter registration, and women's rights issues; provides technical assistance.

Coalition of Northeastern Governors (CONEG), *Policy Research Center, Inc.,* 400 N. Capitol St. N.W., #382 20001; (202) 624-8450. Fax, (202) 624-8463. Anne D. Stubbs, executive director.

Membership: governors of nine northeastern states (Conn., Maine, Mass., N.H., N.J., N.Y., Pa., R.I., and Vt.). Addresses common issues of concern such as energy, economic development, transportation, and the environment; serves as an information clearinghouse and liaison among member states and with the federal government.

Council of Governors Policy Advisors, *400 N. Capitol St. N.W., #390 20001; (202) 624-5386. Fax, (202) 624-7846. Richard J. Gross, executive director. Internet, cgpa@sso.org.*

Membership: chiefs of staff, policy directors, agency heads, and other top policy advisers. Provides a forum to share ideas on policy development and to debate issues; conducts policy research; provides members with management training and technical assistance. Interests include state policies for economic development, human investment, capital planning and budgeting, agricultural and rural development, and telecommunications. Affiliated with the National Governors Assn. Formerly known as the Council of State Planning Agencies. (Note: at press time in April 1998 this organization had recently disbanded.)

Council of State Governments, *444 N. Capitol St. N.W., #401 20001; (202) 624-5460. Fax, (202) 624-5452. Vacant, director, Washington Office. Internet, info@csg.org or http://www.csg.org.*

Membership: governing bodies of states, commonwealths, and territories. Promotes interstate, federal-state, and state-local cooperation; interests include education, transportation, human services, housing, natural resources, and economic development. Provides services to affiliates and associated organizations, including the National Assn. of State Treasurers, National Assn. of Secretaries of State, National Assn. of Government Labor Officials, and other state administrative organizations in specific fields. Monitors legislation and executive policy. (Headquarters in Lexington, Ky.)

Government Finance Officers Assn., *1750 K St. N.W., #650 20006; (202) 429-2750. Fax, (202) 429-2755. Betsy Dotson, director, Federal Liaison Center. Internet, federalliaison@gfoa.org or http://www.gfoa.org.*

Membership: state and local government finance managers. Offers training and publications in public financial management. Conducts research in public fiscal management, design and financing of government programs, and formulation and analysis of government fiscal policy. (Headquarters in Chicago.)

International Municipal Lawyers Assn., *1110 Vermont Ave. N.W., #200 20005; (202) 466-5424. Fax, (202)*

785-0152. Henry W. Underhill Jr., general counsel. Internet, imladc@aol.com.

Membership: chief legal officers of cities and municipalities. Acts as a research service for members in all areas of municipal law; participates in litigation of municipal and constitutional law issues.

Municipal Treasurers' Assn. of the United States and Canada, *1229 19th St. N.W., 4th Floor 20036; (202) 833-1017. Fax, (202) 833-0375. Stacey Crane, executive director.*

Provides continuing education and certification programs. Monitors legislation and regulations.

National Assn. of Bond Lawyers, *1900 K St. N.W., #1200 20006; (202) 778-2244. Fax, (202) 955-1835. Amy K. Dunbar, director, Governmental Affairs. Internet, http://www.nabl.org.*

Membership: municipal finance lawyers. Provides members with information on laws relating to the borrowing of money by states and municipalities and to the issuance of state and local government bonds. Monitors legislation and regulations. (Headquarters in Wheaton, Ill.)

National Assn. of Counties, *440 1st St. N.W., 8th Floor 20001-2080; (202) 942-4230. Fax, (202) 393-2630. Larry Naake, executive director. Press, (202) 942-4222. Internet, http://www.naco.org.*

Membership: county officials. Conducts research, provides information, and offers technical assistance on issues affecting counties. Monitors legislation and regulations.

National Assn. of Regional Councils, *1700 K St. N.W., #1300 20006; (202) 457-0710. Fax, (202) 296-9352. William Dodge, executive director.*

Membership: regional councils of local governments. Works to improve local governments' ability to deal with common public needs, address regional issues, and reduce public expense. Interests include housing, urban and rural planning, transportation, the environment, workforce development, economic development, and aging.

National Assn. of State Budget Officers, *444 N. Capitol St. N.W., #642 20001-1501; (202) 624-5382. Fax, (202) 624-7745. Gloria Timmer; executive director. Internet, http://www.nasbo.org.*

Membership: state budget and financial officers. Publishes research reports on state budget-related issues. (Affiliate of the National Governors' Assn.)

National Assn. of Towns and Townships, *444 N. Capitol St. N.W., #294 20001; (202) 624-3550. Fax, (202)*

624-3554. *Thomas Halicki, executive director. Internet, natat@sso.org or http://www.natat.org.*

Membership: towns, townships, other small communities, and others interested in supporting small town government. Provides local government officials from small jurisdictions with technical assistance, educational services, and public policy support; conducts research and coordinates training for local government officials nationwide; holds annual conferences.

National Black Caucus of State Legislators, *444 N. Capitol St. N.W., #622 20001; (202) 624-5457. Fax, (202) 508-3826. Ivan Lanier, executive director.*

Membership: African American state legislators. Promotes effective leadership among African American state legislators; serves as an information network and clearinghouse for members.

National Conference of State Legislatures, *444 N. Capitol St. N.W., #515 20001; (202) 624-5400. Fax, (202) 737-1069. Carl Tubbesing, director, Washington Office. Internet, http://www.ncsl.org.*

Coordinates and represents state legislatures at the federal level; conducts research, produces videos, and publishes reports in areas of interest to state legislatures; conducts an information exchange program on intergovernmental relations; sponsors seminars for state legislators and their staffs. Monitors legislation and regulations. (Headquarters in Denver.)

National Governors' Assn., *444 N. Capitol St. N.W., #267 20001; (202) 624-5300. Fax, (202) 624-5313. Raymond C. Scheppach, executive director. Press, (202) 624-5364. Internet, http://www.nga.org.*

Membership: governors of states, commonwealths, and territories. Provides members with policy and technical assistance. Makes policy recommendations to Congress and the president in community and economic development; education; international trade and foreign relations; energy and the environment; health care and welfare reform; agriculture; transportation, commerce, and technology; communications; criminal justice; public safety; and workforce development.

National League of Cities, *1301 Pennsylvania Ave. N.W., #550 20004-1763; (202) 626-3000. Fax, (202) 626-3043. Donald J. Borut, executive director. Information, (202) 626-3120. Press, (202) 626-3158. Internet, http://www.nlc.org.*

Membership: cities and state municipal leagues. Provides city leaders with training, technical assistance, and publications; investigates needs of local governments in implementing federal programs that affect cities. Holds

annual conference; conducts research; sponsors awards. (Affiliates include National Black Caucus of Local Elected Officials.)

Public Risk Management Assn., *1815 N. Fort Myer Dr., #1020, Arlington, VA 22209; (703) 528-7701. Fax, (703) 528-7966. Dennis Kirschbaum, executive director. Internet, info@primacentral.org or http://www.primacentral.org.*

Membership: state and local government risk management practitioners, including benefits and insurance managers. Develops and teaches cost-effective management techniques for handling public liability issues; promotes professional development of its members. Gathers and disseminates information about risk management to the public and private sectors.

Public Technology, *1301 Pennsylvania Ave. N.W., #800 20004; (202) 626-2400. Fax, (202) 626-2498. Costis Toregas, president. Press, (202) 626-2412. Library, (202) 626-2456. Toll-free, (800) 852-4934. Internet, press@pti.nw.dc.us or http://pti.nw.dc.us.*

Cooperative research, development, and technology-transfer organization of cities and counties in North America. Assists local governments in increasing efficiency, reducing costs, improving services, and developing public enterprise programs to help local officials create revenues and serve citizens. Participates in international conferences.

Southern Governors' Assn., *444 N. Capitol St. N.W., #200 20001; (202) 624-5897. Fax, (202) 624-7797. Elizabeth G. Schneider, executive director. Internet, sga@sso.org or http://www.southerngovernors.org.*

Membership: governors of seventeen southern states and the territories of Puerto Rico and the Virgin Islands. Provides a regional, bipartisan forum for governors to help formulate and implement national policy; works to enhance the region's competitiveness nationally and internationally.

U.S. Conference of Mayors, *1620 Eye St. N.W., 4th Floor 20006; (202) 293-7330. Fax, (202) 293-2352. J. Thomas Cochran, executive director. Internet, uscm@cais.com or http://www.usmayors.org/uscm.*

Membership: mayors of cities with populations of 30,000 or more. Promotes city-federal cooperation; publishes reports and conducts meetings on federal programs, policies, and initiatives that affect urban and suburban interests. Serves as a clearinghouse for information on urban and suburban problems.

Western Governors' Assn., *400 N. Capitol St. N.W., #388 20001; (202) 624-5402. Fax, (202) 624-7707. Richard Bechtel, director. Internet, http://www.westgov.org.*

Independent, nonpartisan organization of governors from eighteen western states, two Pacific territories, and one commonwealth. Identifies and addresses key policy and governance issues in natural resources, the environment, human services, economic development, international relations, and public management. (Headquarters in Denver.)

Women In Government, *2600 Virginia Ave. N.W., #709 20037; (202) 333-0825. Fax, (202) 333-0875. Joy N. Newton, executive director.*

Membership: women serving in state legislatures. Acts as a forum for discussion of women in politics; sponsors seminars; conducts educational research.

See also Coastal States Organization (p. 309); Multistate Tax Commission (p. 141); National Assn. of State Development Agencies (p. 408)

11 Health

⊞ GENERAL POLICY

See also Food and Nutrition (chap. 2); Recreation and Sports (chap. 4); Caucuses (chap. 20)

AGENCIES

Agency for Health Care Policy and Research
(Health and Human Services Dept.), 2101 E. Jefferson St., #600, Rockville, MD 20852; (301) 594-6662. Fax, (301) 594-2168. John M. Eisenberg, administrator. TDD, (888) 586-6340. Internet, http://www.ahcpr.gov.

Works to enhance the quality, appropriateness, and effectiveness of health care services and to improve access to services. Promotes improvements in clinical practices and in organizing, financing, and delivering health care services. Conducts and supports research, demonstration projects, evaluations, and training; disseminates information on a wide range of activities.

Centers for Disease Control and Prevention *(Health and Human Services Dept.), 200 Independence Ave. S.W., #746-G 20201; (202) 690-8598. Fax, (202) 690-7519. Donald E. Shriber, associate director, Washington Office. Internet, http://www.cdc.gov.*

Surveys national and international disease trends, epidemics, and environmental health problems; administers block grants to states for preventive health services; promotes national health education program; administers foreign quarantine program and occupational safety and health programs; assists state and local health departments and programs with control of sexually transmitted diseases, treatment of tuberculosis, childhood immunization, and health promotion regarding chronic diseases and injury. (Headquarters in Atlanta: 1600 Clifton Rd. N.E. 30333. Public inquiries, (404) 639-3534.)

Food and Drug Administration *(Health and Human Services Dept.), 5600 Fishers Lane, Rockville, MD 20857; (301) 827-2410. Fax, (301) 443-3100. Michael Friedman, deputy commissioner. Information, (301) 443-3170. Press, (301) 827-6242. Internet, http://www.fda.gov.*

Conducts research and develops standards on the composition, quality, and safety of drugs, cosmetics, medical devices, radiation-emitting products, foods, food additives, and infant formulas; develops labeling and packaging standards; conducts inspections of manufacturers; issues orders to companies to recall and/or cease selling or producing hazardous products; enforces rulings and recommends action to Justice Dept. when necessary. Library open to the public.

Food and Drug Administration *(Health and Human Services Dept.), International Affairs, 5600 Fishers Lane, Rockville, MD 20857; (301) 827-4480. Fax, (301) 443-0235. Walter Batts, director. Internet, oia@bangate.fda.gov or http://www.fda.gov/opacom/morechoices/oia.html.*

Serves as the principal FDA liaison with foreign counterpart agencies, international organizations, and U.S. government agencies on international issues. Coordinates agency involvement in international trade, harmonization, and technical assistance; administers programs for foreign scientists and other international visitors.

Food and Drug Administration *(Health and Human Services Dept.), Regulatory Affairs, 5600 Fishers Lane, #1490, Rockville, MD 20857; (301) 827-3101. Fax, (301) 443-6591. Ronald G. Chesemore, associate commissioner. Internet, http://www.fda.gov.*

Directs and coordinates the FDA's compliance activities; manages field offices; advises FDA commissioner on domestic and international regulatory policies.

Health and Human Services Dept., *National Committee on Vital and Health Statistics, 6525 Belcrest Rd., #1100, Hyattsville, MD 20782; (301) 436-7050. Fax, (301) 436-4233. Marjorie S. Greenberg, executive secretary. Internet, http://aspe.os.dhhs.gov/ncvhs.*

Advises the secretary on health problem statistics; works with agencies and committees of other nations on health problems of mutual concern.

Health and Human Services Dept., *Planning and Evaluation, 200 Independence Ave. S.W., #415S 20201; (202) 690-7858. Fax, (202) 690-7383. Dr. Margaret A. Hamburg, acting assistant secretary. Internet, http://aspe.os.dhhs.gov.*

Provides policy advice and makes recommendations to the secretary on the full range of department planning, including Medicare, Medicaid, health care services, human resources, health care facilities development and financing, biomedical research, and health care planning.

Health Resources and Services Administration
(Health and Human Services Dept.), 5600 Fishers Lane, #1405, Rockville, MD 20857; (301) 443-2216. Fax, (301) 443-1246. Dr. Claude Earl Fox, administrator. Information, (301) 443-3376. Press, (301) 443-2086.

Administers federal health services programs related to access, quality, equity, and cost of health care. Supports state and community efforts to deliver care to underserved areas and groups with special health needs.

Health Resources and Services Administration
(Health and Human Services Dept.), Rural Health

HEALTH AND HUMAN SERVICES DEPARTMENT

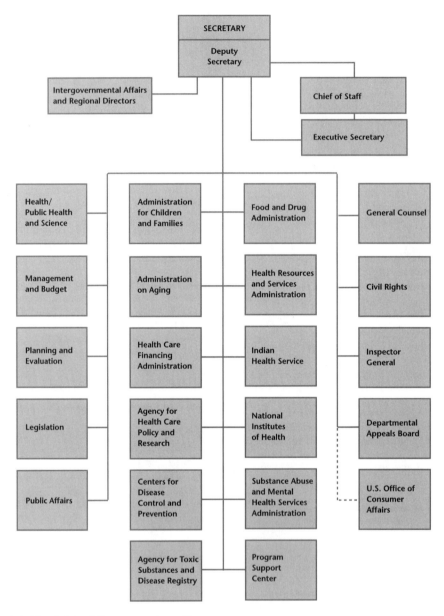

- - - - Located administratively in HHS but reports to the president.

Policy, 5600 Fishers Lane, #905, Rockville, MD 20857; (301) 443-0835. Fax, (301) 443-2803. Dena Puskin, acting director. Internet, http://www.nal.usda.gov/ric/richs/ orhp.htm.

Works with federal agencies, states, and the private sector to develop solutions to health care problems in rural communities. Administers grants to rural communities and supports rural health services research. Studies the effects of Medicare and Medicaid programs on rural access to health care. Oversees the joint working group on telemedicine. Provides the National Advisory Committee on Rural Health with staff support.

National Center for Health Statistics *(Centers for Disease Control and Prevention), 6525 Belcrest Rd., #1140, Hyattsville, MD 20782; (301) 436-7016. Fax, (301) 436-5202. Edward J. Sondik, director. Information, (301) 436-8500. Press, (301) 436-7551. Internet, http://www.cdc. gov/nchswww/nchshome.htm.*

Compiles, analyzes, and disseminates national statistics on population health characteristics, health facilities and human resources, health costs and expenditures, and health hazards.

National Clearinghouse for Primary Care Information *(Health and Human Services Dept.), 2070 Chain Bridge Rd., #450, Vienna, VA 22182; (703) 821-8955. Fax, (703) 821-2098. Judy A. Cramer, project director.*

Supports the planning, development, and delivery of ambulatory health care to urban and rural areas in need of medical personnel and services; gives information to health care providers, administrators, and other interested persons.

National Institute for Occupational Safety and Health *(Centers for Disease Control and Prevention), 200 Independence Ave. S.W. 20201; (202) 401-6997. Fax, (202) 260-4464. Dr. Linda Rosenstock, director, Washington Office. Toll-free, (800) 356-4674. Press, (202) 401-3749. Internet, pubstaff@cdc.gov or http://www.cdc. gov/niosh.*

Entity within the Centers for Disease Control and Prevention in Atlanta. Supports and conducts research on occupational safety and health issues; provides technical assistance and training; develops recommendations for the Labor Dept. Operates an occupational safety and health bibliographic database (mailing address: NIOSH Clearinghouse for Occupational Safety and Health Information, 4676 Columbia Pkwy., Cincinnati, OH 45226).

National Institutes of Health *(Health and Human Services Dept.), 1 Center Dr., Bldg. 1, #126, Bethesda, MD 20892-0148; (301) 496-2433. Fax, (301) 402-2700. Harold Varmus, director. Press, (301) 496-4461. Internet, http://www.nih.gov.*

Supports and conducts biomedical research into the causes and prevention of diseases and furnishes information to health professionals and the public. Comprises research institutes *(see Health Topics: Research and Advocacy, this chapter)*, and other components (the National Library of Medicine, the Warren Grant Magnuson Clinical Center, the National Center for Research Resources,

the John E. Fogarty International Center, the Division of Research Grants, and the Division of Computer Research and Technology). All institutes are located in Bethesda except the National Institute of Environmental Health Sciences, P.O. Box 12233, Research Triangle Park, NC 27709.

Public Health and Science *(Health and Human Services Dept.), 200 Independence Ave. S.W., #716G 20201; (202) 690-7694. Fax, (202) 690-6960. Dr. David Satcher, assistant secretary for health. Internet, http://www.osophs. dhhs.gov.*

Directs activities of the Public Health Service. Serves as the secretary's principal adviser on health concerns; exercises specialized responsibilities in various health areas, including population affairs and international health.

Public Health and Science *(Health and Human Services Dept.), Disease Prevention and Health Promotion, 200 Independence Ave. S.W., #738G 20201; (202) 401-6295. Fax, (202) 205-9478. Susanne Stoiber, acting deputy assistant secretary for health. Toll-free, (800) 336-4797. Internet, http://odphp.osophs.dhhs.gov.*

Develops national policies for disease prevention, clinical preventive services, and health promotion; assists the private sector and agencies with disease prevention, clinical preventive services, and health promotion activities.

Public Health and Science *(Health and Human Services Dept.), National Health Information Center, 5640 Nicholson Lane, Rockville, MD (mailing address: P.O. Box 1133, Washington, DC 20013-1133); (301) 565-4167. Fax, (301) 984-4256. Jill Herzog, project director. Toll-free, (800) 336-4797. Internet, nhicinfo@health.org or http:// nhic-nt.health.org.*

A project of the office of Disease Prevention and Health Promotion; provides referrals on health topics and resources.

Public Health and Science *(Health and Human Services Dept.), Surgeon General, 5600 Fishers Lane, #18-66, Rockville, MD 20857; (301) 443-4000. Fax, (301) 443-3574. Dr. David Satcher, surgeon general. Press, (301) 443-6496.*

Advises the public on health issues such as smoking, AIDS, immunization, diet, nutrition, disease prevention, and general health issues. Oversees activities of all members of the Public Health Service Commissioned Corps.

CONGRESS

General Accounting Office, *Health, Education, and Human Services, 441 G St. N.W. 20548; (202) 512-6806.*

Fax, (202) 512-5806. Richard L. Hembra, assistant comptroller general.

Independent, nonpartisan agency in the legislative branch. Audits all federal government health programs, including those administered by the departments of Defense, Health and Human Services, and Veterans Affairs.

House Appropriations Committee, *Subcommittee on Agriculture, Rural Development, FDA, and Related Agencies, 2362 RHOB 20515; (202) 225-2638. Joe Skeen, R-N.M., chair; Timothy K. Sanders, staff director. Internet, http://www.house.gov/appropriations.*

Jurisdiction over legislation to appropriate funds for the Food and Drug Administration, Food Safety and Inspection Service, and Food and Consumer Service.

House Appropriations Committee, *Subcommittee on Labor, Health and Human Services, and Education, 2358 RHOB 20515; (202) 225-3508. John Edward Porter, R-Ill., chair; Tony McCann, staff director. Internet, http://www.house.gov/appropriations.*

Jurisdiction over legislation to appropriate funds for health agencies in the Health and Human Services Dept. (excluding the Food and Drug Administration and Native American health and health facilities construction activities); the National Commission on Acquired Immune Deficiency Syndrome; and the National Council on Disability.

House Commerce Committee, *Subcommittee on Health and the Environment, 2125 RHOB 20515; (202) 225-2927. Fax, (202) 225-1919. Michael Bilirakis, R-Fla., chair; James E. Derderian, staff director. Internet, http://www.house.gov/commerce/health.html.*

Jurisdiction over most health legislation, including Medicaid, national health insurance proposals (jurisdiction shared with the House Ways and Means Committee), public health and quarantine, alcohol abuse, drug abuse including medical and psychological rehabilitation programs for drug abusers, dental health, medical devices, long-term and nursing home care, orphan drugs, preventive health and emergency medical care, family planning, population research, mental health, and prenatal, maternal, and child health care. Oversight of the Food and Drug Administration.

House Government Reform and Oversight Committee, *Subcommittee on Human Resources, B372 RHOB 20515; (202) 225-2548. Fax, (202) 225-2382. Christopher Shays, R-Conn., chair; Larry Halloran, staff director. Internet, http://www.house.gov/reform.*

Oversees operations of the Health and Human Services Dept.

House Ways and Means Committee, *Subcommittee on Health, 1136 LHOB 20515; (202) 225-3943. Fax, (202) 226-1765. Bill Thomas, R-Calif., chair; Chip Kahn, staff director. Internet, http://www.house.gov/ways_means.*

Jurisdiction over legislation dealing with health care research and delivery programs supported by tax revenues, including Medicare, and proposals to establish a national health insurance system (jurisdiction shared with the House Commerce Committee).

Senate Appropriations Committee, *Subcommittee on Agriculture, Rural Development, and Related Agencies, SD-136 20510; (202) 224-5270. Fax, (202) 224-9450. Thad Cochran, R-Miss., chair; Rebecca M. Davies, clerk. Internet, http://www.senate.gov/committee/appropriations.html.*

Jurisdiction over legislation to appropriate funds for the Food and Drug Administration; Food Safety and Inspection Service, and the Food and Consumer Service (of the Agriculture Dept.); and other health-related services and programs.

Senate Appropriations Committee, *Subcommittee on Labor, Health and Human Services, and Education, SD-184 20510; (202) 224-7230. Arlen Specter, R-Pa., chair; Craig A. Higgins, staff director. Internet, http://www.senate.gov/~appropriations/labor.*

Jurisdiction over legislation to appropriate funds for health agencies in the Health and Human Services Dept. (excluding the Food and Drug Administration and Native American health programs).

Senate Finance Committee, *SD-219 20510; (202) 224-4515. Fax, (202) 224-5920. William V. Roth Jr., R-Del., chair; Lindy L. Paull, staff director. Internet, http://www.senate.gov/~finance.*

Jurisdiction over health programs supported by tax revenues, including Medicaid and Medicare.

Senate Judiciary Committee, *SD-224 20510; (202) 224-5225. Fax, (202) 224-9102. Orrin G. Hatch, R-Utah, chair; Manus Cooney, chief counsel. Internet, http://www.senate.gov/committee/judiciary.html.*

Jurisdiction over legislation on drug abuse, which includes regulatory aspects of federal drug abuse programs and criminal justice system rehabilitation programs for juvenile drug abusers.

Senate Labor and Human Resources Committee, *SD-428 20510; (202) 224-5375. Fax, (202) 224-6510. James M. Jeffords, R-Vt., chair; Mark Powden, staff director. Internet, http://www.senate.gov/~labor.*

Jurisdiction over most health legislation, including insurance, dental health, emergency medical care, mental health, medical devices, public health and quarantine, family planning, population research, prenatal, and some maternal and child health care legislation, including the dangers of lead-based paint and sudden infant death syndrome. Jurisdiction over legislation on radiation hazards of consumer products and machines used in industry. Jurisdiction over alcohol and drug abuse legislation. Oversees operations of the Health and Human Services Dept.

INTERNATIONAL ORGANIZATIONS

International Bank for Reconstruction and Development (World Bank), *Human Development, 1750 Pennsylvania Ave. N.W., #S9035 (mailing address: 1818 H St. N.W., #S9035, Washington, DC 20433); (202) 473-8729. Fax, (202) 522-3235. David de Ferranti, vice president. Internet, http://www.worldbank.org/html/hcovp/hdd/ contents.html.*

Provides developing member countries with loans to help improve citizens' primary health care and nutrition and to help slow population growth through family planning.

Pan American Health Organization, *525 23rd St. N.W. 20037; (202) 974-3000. Fax, (202) 974-3663. Dr. George A. Alleyne, director. Information, (202) 974-3458. Library, (202) 974-3305. Internet, http://www.paho.org.*

Regional office for the Americas of the World Health Organization, headquartered in Geneva, Switzerland. Works to extend health services to underserved populations of its member countries and to control or eradicate communicable diseases; promotes cooperation among governments to solve public health problems. Library open to the public by appointment.

World Federation of Public Health Assns., *1015 15th St. N.W. 20005; (202) 789-5696. Fax, (202) 789-5661. Diane Kuntz, secretary.*

International health organization composed of national public health associations whose membership includes health professionals and laypersons interested in improving community health. Sponsors triennial international congress.

NONPROFIT

American Assn. for World Health, *1825 K St. N.W., #1208 20006; (202) 466-5883. Fax, (202) 466-5896. Richard L. Wittenberg, president. Internet, http://www. aawhworldhealth.org.*

Works to inform Americans about world health problems and increase American support for organizations dealing with these problems. Distributes educational materials; sponsors World Health Day, World

No-Tobacco Day, and World AIDS Day. Association board serves as the U.S. Committee for the World Health Organization and the Pan American Health Organization.

American Clinical Laboratory Assn., *1250 H St. N.W., #880 20005; (202) 637-9466. Fax, (202) 637-2050. Dr. David N. Sundwall, president.*

Membership: laboratories and laboratory service companies. Advocates laws and regulations that recognize the role of laboratory services in cost-effective health care. Works to ensure the confidentiality of patient test results. Provides education, information, and research materials to members.

American Industrial Health Council, *2001 Pennsylvania Ave. N.W., #760 20006; (202) 833-2131. Fax, (202) 833-2201. Gaylen M. Camera, executive director. Internet, membershipservices@aiha.org.*

Coalition of industrial firms and trade associations concerned about potential health effects associated with industrial and commercial activities. Advocates using scientific information to evaluate and assess health risks; promotes the development and use of scientifically valid risk assessment data by regulatory agencies. Provides information on health hazards of toxic substances, genetic testing, and causes of cancer and birth defects.

American Public Health Assn., *1015 15th St. N.W., #300 20005; (202) 789-5600. Fax, (202) 789-5661. Dr. Mohammad Akhter, executive director. Internet, http:// www.apha.org.*

Membership: health care professionals, educators, environmentalists, social workers, industrial hygienists, and individuals. Interests include all aspects of health care and education. Establishes standards for scientific procedures in public health; conducts research on the causes and origin of communicable diseases. Produces data on the number of women and minority workers in public health and on their health status.

Assn. of State and Territorial Health Officials, *1275 K St. N.W., #800 20002; (202) 371-9090. Fax, (202) 371-9797. Cheryl Beversdorf, executive vice president. Internet, http://www.astho.org.*

Membership: executive officers of state and territorial health departments. Serves as legislative review agency and information source for members.

Brookings Institution, *Economic Studies Program, 1775 Massachusetts Ave. N.W. 20036-2188; (202) 797-6111. Fax, (202) 797-6181. Robert E. Litan, director. Information, (202) 797-6302. Internet, http://www.brookings. org/ES/ES_HP.HTM.*

Studies federal health care issues and health programs, including Medicare, Medicaid, and long-term care.

Center for Patient Advocacy, *1350 Beverly Rd., #108, McLean, VA 22101; (703) 748-0400. Fax, (703) 748-0402. Terre McFillan Hall, executive director. Toll-free, (800) 846-7444. Internet, patientadv@aol.com or http://www. patientadvocacy.org.*

Supports the right of patients to receive state-of-the-art medical care in a timely manner. Monitors the Food and Drug Administration's regulation of drugs and medical devices. Works to preserve the doctor-patient relationship and establish universal clinical practice guidelines. Monitors legislation and regulations.

Grantmakers in Health, *1100 Connecticut Ave. N.W., 12th Floor 20036; (202) 452-8331. Fax, (202) 452-8340. Lauren LeRoy, president. Internet, http://www.gih.org.*

Seeks to increase the capacity of private sector grantmakers to enhance public health. Fosters information exchange among grantmakers. Publications include a bulletin on current news in health and human services and the *Directory of Health Philanthropy.* (Headquarters in New York.)

Health Education Foundation, *2600 Virginia Ave. N.W., #502 20037; (202) 338-3501. Fax, (202) 965-6520. Dr. Morris Chafetz, president.*

Develops health information programs. Promotes responsible drinking behavior.

Healthcare Leadership Council, *900 17th St. N.W., #600 20006; (202) 452-8700. Fax, (202) 296-9561. Pamela G. Bailey, president. Internet, http://www.hlc.org.*

Membership: health care leaders who examine major health issues, including access and affordability. Works to implement new public policies.

Institute for Health Care Research and Policy, *2233 Wisconsin Ave. N.W., #525 20007; (202) 687-0880. Fax, (202) 687-3110. James Reuter, director.*

Research branch of Georgetown University School of Medicine. Interests include quality of care, cost effectiveness, outcomes research, structure and impact of managed care, and access to care.

Intergovernmental Health Policy Project, *444 N. Capitol St. N.W., #515 20001; (202) 624-8698. Fax, (202) 737-1069. Richard Merritt, director.*

Researches state health laws and programs. Provides health policymakers, administrators, and others with information on state health programs and policies. (Affiliated with the National Conference of State Legislatures.)

National Assn. of Counties, *Health,* *440 1st St. N.W., 8th Floor 20001-2028; (202) 393-6226. Fax, (202) 942-4281. Thomas L. Joseph, associate legislative director. Internet, http://www.naco.org.*

Promotes federal understanding of county government's role in providing, funding, and overseeing health care services at the local level. Interests include indigent health care, Medicaid and Medicare, prevention of and services for HIV infection and AIDS, long-term care, mental health, maternal and child health, and traditional public health programs conducted by local health departments.

National Assn. of County and City Health Officials, *440 1st St. N.W., #450 20001; (202) 783-5550. Fax, (202) 783-1583. Thomas L. Milne, executive director. Internet, http://www.naccho.org.*

Represents local health departments. Promotes partnership among local, state, and federal health agencies. Works to improve the capacity of local health departments to assess health needs, develop public health policies, and ensure delivery of community services. Submits health policy proposals to the federal government.

National Council for International Health, *1701 K St. N.W., #600 20006; (202) 833-5900. Fax, (202) 833-0075. Zuheir Al-Faqih, president. Internet, ncih@ncih.org or http://www.ncih.org.*

Seeks to strengthen U.S. participation in international health activities, especially in developing countries. Serves as an information clearinghouse for the international health community. Promotes cooperation among private and public organizations involved in international health activities. Provides policy analysis and public education. Holds the annual International Health Conference. Sponsors career services program and international health seminars.

National Governors' Assn., *Health Policy Studies,* *444 N. Capitol St. N.W., #267 20001; (202) 624-5319. Fax, (202) 624-5313. Randy Desoma, director. Information, (202) 624-5300. Internet, http://www.nga.org.*

Provides technical assistance regarding the Title 21 Program, state oversight of managed care, public/private efforts to improve health care quality, and long term care services.

National Health Council, *1730 M St. N.W., #500 20036-4505; (202) 785-3913. Fax, (202) 785-5923. Myrl Weinberg, president. Internet, http://www.healthanswers. com.*

Membership: voluntary health agencies, associations, and business, insurance, and government groups interested in health. Conducts research on health and health-related issues; serves as an information clearinghouse on health careers. Monitors legislation and regulations.

National Health Policy Forum, *2021 K St. N.W., #800 20006; (202) 872-1390. Fax, (202) 862-9837. Judith Miller Jones, director.*

Nonpartisan policy analysis and research organization that provides state agencies and congressional staff with information on financing and delivery of health care services. Affiliated with George Washington University.

Partnership for Prevention, *1233 20th St. N.W., #200 20036; (202) 833-0009. Fax, (202) 833-0113. Jordan Richland, president.*

Seeks to make prevention a priority in national health policy and practice. Coordinates the prevention-oriented efforts of federal health agencies, corporations, states, and other nonprofit organizations in order to achieve the Healthy People 2000 national prevention goals.

Public Citizen, *Health Research Group, 1600 20th St. N.W. 20009; (202) 588-1000. Fax, (202) 588-7796. Dr. Sidney M. Wolfe, director. Internet, http://www.citizen.org.*

Citizens' interest group that conducts policy-oriented research on health care issues. Interests include hospital quality and costs, doctors' fees, physician discipline and malpractice, state administration of Medicare programs, workplace safety and health, unnecessary surgery, comprehensive health planning, dangerous drugs, carcinogens, and medical devices. Favors a single-payer (Canadian-style), comprehensive health program.

Rand Corporation, *Health Program, 1333 H St. N.W., #800 20005; (202) 296-5000. Fax, (202) 296-7960. David Chu, director, Washington Research Department. Internet, http://www.rand.org.*

Research organization that assesses health issues, including alternative reimbursement schemes for health care. Monitors national and international trends. (Headquarters in Santa Monica, Calif.)

Regulatory Affairs Professionals Society, *12300 Twinbrook Pkwy., #350, Rockville, MD 20852; (301) 770-2920. Fax, (301) 770-2924. Sherry Keramidas, executive director. Internet, raps@raps.org or http://www.raps.org.*

Membership: regulatory professionals in the pharmaceutical, medical device, biologic, biotechnicology, and related industries. Fosters cooperation among health care regulatory professionals; sponsors seminars. Monitors legislation and regulations.

Robert Wood Johnson Foundation, *Center for Studying Health System Change, 600 Maryland Ave. S.W., #550*

20024-2512; (202) 484-5261. Fax, (202) 484-9258. Paul B. Ginsburg, director. Internet, http://www.hschange.com.

Studies change in the health care system; conducts and monitors research; disseminates information to researchers, health care professionals, and national, state, and local policymakers. Sponsors workshops and conferences. (Foundation headquarters in Princeton, N.J.)

Health Insurance/Managed Care

See also Insurance (chap. 5); Medicaid and Medicare (this chapter)

AGENCIES

Health Care Financing Administration *(Health and Human Services Dept.), Health Plans and Providers, 7500 Security Blvd., S3-02-01, Baltimore, MD 21244-1850; (410) 786-4165. Fax, (410) 786-5010. Kathy Buto, acting director. Internet, http://www.hcfa.gov.*

Sets national policies for federally qualified health maintenance organizations (HMOs) and competitive medical plans; monitors HMO compliance with federal regulations. Administers and promotes prepaid health plan participation in Medicare and Medicaid programs.

CONGRESS

Congressional Budget Office, *Health and Human Resources, 418A Ford Bldg. 20515; (202) 226-2669. Fax, (202) 225-3149. Joseph Antos, assistant director.*

Analyzes program and budget issues in the areas of health, education, employment and training, housing, and social services. Examines the potential impacts on the private sector of proposed federal mandates in those areas.

House Commerce Committee, *Subcommittee on Health and the Environment, 2125 RHOB 20515; (202) 225-2927. Fax, (202) 225-1919. Michael Bilirakis, R-Fla., chair; James E. Derderian, staff director. Internet, http://www.house.gov/commerce/health.html.*

Jurisdiction over national health insurance proposals (jurisdiction shared with the House Ways and Means Committee) and legislation on malpractice insurance, Medicaid, and health maintenance organizations.

House Ways and Means Committee, *Subcommittee on Health, 1136 LHOB 20515; (202) 225-3943. Fax, (202) 226-1765. Bill Thomas, R-Calif., chair; Chip Kahn, staff director. Internet, http://www.house.gov/ways_means.*

Jurisdiction over national health insurance proposals (jurisdiction shared with the House Commerce Committee) and legislation on health insurance supported by tax revenues, including Medicare.

Senate Finance Committee, *Subcommittee on Health Care,* *SD-219 20510; (202) 224-4515. Phil Gramm, R-Texas, chair; Julie James, staff contact. Internet, http://www.senate.gov/~finance.*

Holds hearings on national health insurance proposals (jurisdiction shared with the Senate Labor and Human Resources Committee) and on legislation on health insurance and Medicaid for low-income individuals.

Senate Labor and Human Resources Committee, *SD-428 20510; (202) 224-5375. Fax, (202) 224-6510. James M. Jeffords, R-Vt., chair; Mark Powden, staff director. Internet, http://www.senate.gov/~labor.*

Jurisdiction over national health insurance proposals (jurisdiction shared with the Senate Finance Committee) and legislation on malpractice insurance and health maintenance organizations.

NONPROFIT

Alliance for Health Reform, *1900 L St. N.W., #512 20036; (202) 466-5626. Fax, (202) 466-6525. Edward Howard, executive vice president. Internet, http://www.allhealth.org.*

Nonpartisan organization that advocates health care reform, including cost containment and universal coverage. Sponsors conferences and seminars for journalists, business leaders, policymakers, and the public.

American Assn. of Health Plans, *1129 20th St. N.W., #600 20036; (202) 778-3200. Fax, (202) 331-7487. Karen Ignagni, president. Press, (202) 778-3274. Internet, http://www.aahp.org.*

Membership: managed health care plans and organizations. Provides legal counsel and conducts educational programs. Conducts research and analysis of managed care issues; produces publications. Monitors legislation and regulations.

American Medical Assn., *1101 Vermont Ave. N.W., 12th Floor 20005; (202) 789-7400. Fax, (202) 789-7485. Lee Stillwell, president, Government Affairs. Internet, http://www.ama-assn.org.*

Membership: physicians, residents, and medical students. Provides information on health care. Monitors legislation and regulations. (Headquarters in Chicago.)

Blue Cross and Blue Shield Assn., *1310 G St. N.W. 20005; (202) 626-4780. Fax, (202) 626-4833. Patrick G. Hays, president. Internet, http://www.bluecares.com.*

Membership: Blue Cross and Blue Shield insurance plans which operate autonomously at the local level. Certifies member plans; acts as consultant to plans in

evaluating new medical technologies and contracting with doctors and hospitals. Operates a national telecommunications network to collect, analyze, and disseminate data. (Headquarters in Chicago.)

Council for Affordable Health Insurance, *112 S. West St., Alexandria, VA 22314; (703) 836-6200. Fax, (703) 836-6550. David Lack, executive director. Internet, cahi@concentric.net or http://www.worldweb.net/~cahi.*

Membership: small and mid-size insurance companies that favor free-market health care financing reform. Promotes reform measures, including establishment of medical savings accounts, tax equity, limited rating bands (rates that vary with age, physical condition, or geography), universal access, medical price disclosure prior to treatment, and caps on malpractice awards. Serves as a liaison with businesses, provider organizations, and public interest groups. Monitors legislation and regulations.

Employee Benefit Research Institute, *2121 K St. N.W., #600 20037-1896; (202) 659-0670. Fax, (202) 775-6312. Dallas L. Salisbury, president; Jack Vanderhei, research associate. Internet, http://www.ebri.org.*

Conducts research on health insurance coverage, health care utilization, and health care cost containment; studies health care delivery and financing alternatives, including long-term care, flexible benefits, and retiree health financing options.

Employers Council on Flexible Compensation, *927 15th St. N.W., #1000 20005; (202) 659-4300. Fax, (202) 371-1467. Kenneth E. Feltman, executive director. Internet, http://www.ecfc.org.*

Represents employers who have or are considering flexible compensation plans. Supports the preservation and expansion of employee choice in health insurance coverage. Monitors legislation and regulations.

Health Insurance Assn. of America, *555 13th St. N.W., #600E 20004; (202) 824-1600. Fax, (202) 824-1722. Willis D. Gradison Jr., president. Internet, http://www.hiaa.org.*

Membership: health insurance companies that write and sell health insurance policies. Promotes effective management of health care expenditures; provides statistical information on health insurance issues. Monitors legislation and regulations.

Managed Health Care Assn., *1401 Eye St. N.W., #900 20005; (202) 218-4121. Fax, (202) 842-0621. Pamela Kalen, executive director.*

Organization of public- and private-sector employers that promotes the expansion and improvement of managed health care. Provides health care management professionals with education and training. Supports innovation in the design and operation of managed care programs. Provides a forum for information exchange among employers, managed care organizations, and health care providers. Serves as a technical resource on managed health care systems.

National Academy of Social Insurance, *1776 Massachusetts Ave. N.W., #615 20036-1904; (202) 452-8097. Fax, (202) 452-8111. Pamela J. Larson, executive vice president. Internet, nasi@nasi.org or http://www.nasi.org.*

Promotes research and education on Social Security, health care financing, and related public and private programs; assesses social insurance programs and their relationship to other programs; supports research and leadership development. Acts as a clearinghouse for social insurance information.

National Assn. of Health Underwriters, *1000 Connecticut Ave. N.W., #810 20036; (202) 223-5533. Fax, (202) 785-2274. Kevin Corcoran, executive vice president. Internet, nahu@nahu.org or http://www.nahu.org.*

Promotes the health insurance industry; certifies health underwriters; conducts advanced health insurance underwriting and research seminars at universities; maintains a speakers bureau.

National Assn. of Manufacturers, *Employee Benefits, 1331 Pennsylvania Ave. N.W. 20004; (202) 637-3040. Fax, (202) 637-3182. Sharon Canner, vice president, Entitlement Policy.*

Interests include health care, employee benefits, cost containment, mandated benefits, Medicare, and other federal programs that affect employers.

National Health Care Anti-Fraud Assn., *1255 23rd St. N.W., #850 20037-1174; (202) 659-5955. Fax, (202) 833-3636. William J. Mahon, executive director. Internet, http://www.nhcaa.org.*

Membership: health insurance companies and regulatory and law enforcement agencies. Members work to identify, investigate, and prosecute individuals defrauding health care reimbursement systems.

Society of Professional Benefit Administrators, *2 Wisconsin Circle, #670, Chevy Chase, MD 20815-7003; (301) 718-7722. Fax, (301) 718-9440. Frederick D. Hunt Jr., president.*

Membership: independent third-party administration firms that manage employee benefit plans for client employers. Interests include health care and insurance legislation and regulations, revision of Medicare programs, and health care cost containment. Monitors

industry trends, government compliance requirements, and developments in health care financing.

Washington Business Group on Health, *777 N. Capitol St. N.W., #800 20002; (202) 408-9320. Fax, (202) 408-9332. Mary Jane England, president. TDD, (202) 408-9333. Internet, http://www.wbgh.com.*

Membership: large corporations with an interest in health. Monitors health care legislation and regulations of interest to large corporations. Interests include reimbursement policies, Medicare, retiree medical cost, hospital cost containment, health planning, and corporate health education.

Hospitals

AGENCIES

Health Care Financing Administration *(Health and Human Services Dept.), Disabled and Elderly Health Programs, 7500 Security Blvd., S2-14-27, Baltimore, MD 21244; (410) 786-6763. Fax, (410) 786-9004. Robert A. Streimer, director.*

Enforces health care and safety standards for hospitals, nursing homes, and other long-term care facilities; clinical and other laboratories; clinics; and other health care facilities.

Health Resources and Services Administration *(Health and Human Services Dept.), Health Resources Development, 5600 Fishers Lane, Parklawn Bldg., #705, Rockville, MD 20857; (301) 443-1993. Fax, (301) 443-9645. William H. Aspden Jr., deputy associate administrator.*

Reviews applications for hospital mortgage insurance; monitors repayment of insured mortgages and direct and guaranteed loans; publishes guidelines for constructing and equipping health facilities; directs efforts to improve their operational effectiveness and efficiency. Plans, directs, coordinates, and monitors activities relating to emergency medical services and trauma system planning and implementation.

See also National Clearinghouse for Primary Care Information (p. 351)

CONGRESS

House Banking and Financial Services Committee, *Subcommittee on Capital Markets, Securities, and Government-Sponsored Enterprises, 2129 RHOB 20515; (202) 226-0469. Fax, (202) 225-3692. Richard H. Baker, R-La., chair; Greg Wierzynski, staff director. Internet, http://www.house.gov/banking.*

Oversees government-sponsored enterprises, including the College Construction Loan Insurance Assn.

(Connie Lee), with regard to the financial risk posed to the federal government. Connie Lee insures loans for teaching hospitals.

House Commerce Committee, *Subcommittee on Health and the Environment, 2125 RHOB 20515; (202) 225-2927. Fax, (202) 225-1919. Michael Bilirakis, R-Fla., chair; James E. Derderian, staff director. Internet, http://www.house.gov/commerce/health.html.*

Jurisdiction over legislation on health planning, health facilities construction, and government-run health care facilities, including Public Health Service hospitals.

Senate Banking, Housing, and Urban Affairs Committee, *SD-534 20510; (202) 224-7391. Fax, (202) 224-5137. Alfonse M. D'Amato, R-N.Y., chair; Howard Menell, staff director. Internet, http://www.senate.gov/~banking.*

Oversees government-sponsored enterprises, including the College Construction Loan Insurance Assn. (Connie Lee), with regard to the financial risk posed to the federal government. Connie Lee insures loans for teaching hospitals.

Senate Labor and Human Resources Committee, *SD-428 20510; (202) 224-5375. Fax, (202) 224-6510. James M. Jeffords, R-Vt., chair; Mark Powden, staff director. Internet, http://www.senate.gov/~labor.*

Jurisdiction over legislation on health planning, health facilities construction, and government-run health care facilities, including Public Health Service hospitals.

NONPROFIT

Air Care Alliance, *P.O. Box 1940, Manassas, VA 20108-0804; (703) 361-1191. Fax, (703) 361-1792. Ed Boyer, executive vice president. Toll-free, (800) 296-1217. Internet, http://www.angelflightfla.org/aircareall.org/acahome.html.*

Coordinates the efforts of national and regional volunteer pilot associations; seeks to save lives by providing safe air transportation to health care facilities. (Affiliated with Mercy Air Flights.)

American Hospital Assn., *325 7th St. N.W. 20004; (202) 638-1100. Fax, (202) 626-2345. Richard J. Davidson, president. Internet, http://www.aha.org.*

Membership: hospitals, other inpatient care facilities, outpatient centers, Blue Cross plans, areawide planning agencies, regional medical programs, hospital schools of nursing, and individuals. Conducts research and education projects in such areas as provision of comprehensive care, hospital economics, hospital facilities and design, and community relations; participates with other health care associations in establishing hospital care standards. Monitors legislation and regulations.

Assn. of Academic Health Centers, *1400 16th St. N.W., #720 20036; (202) 265-9600. Fax, (202) 265-7514. Dr. Roger J. Bulger, president. Internet, http://www.ahcnet.org.*

Membership: academic health centers (composed of a medical school, a teaching hospital, and at least one other health professional school or program). Participates in studies and public debates on health professionals' training and education, patient care, and biomedical research.

Federation of American Health Systems, *1111 19th St. N.W., #402 20036; (202) 833-3090. Fax, (202) 861-0063. Thomas A. Scully, president. Internet, http://www.fahs.com.*

Membership: investor-owned, for-profit hospitals and health care systems. Interests include health care reform, cost containment, and Medicare and Medicaid reforms. Maintains speakers bureau; compiles statistics on investor-owned hospitals. Monitors legislation and regulations.

National Assn. of Children's Hospitals and Related Institutions, *401 Wythe St., Alexandria, VA 22314; (703) 684-1355. Fax, (703) 684-1589. Lawrence A. McAndrews, president.*

Advocates and promotes education and research on child health care related to children's hospitals; compiles statistics and provides information on pediatric hospitalizations.

National Assn. of Public Hospitals, *1212 New York Ave. N.W., #800 20005; (202) 408-0223. Fax, (202) 408-0235. Larry S. Gage, president. Internet, naph@naph.org or http://www.naph.org.*

Membership: city and county public hospitals, state universities, and hospital districts and authorities. Works to improve and expand health care in hospitals; interests include Medicaid patients and vulnerable populations, including AIDS patients, the homeless, the mentally ill, and non-English-speaking patients. Holds annual regional meetings. Monitors legislation and regulations.

See also American Osteopathic Healthcare Assn. (p. 366); Assn. for Healthcare Philanthropy (p. 367)

Medicaid and Medicare

See also Health Insurance/Managed Care (this chapter); Health Services for Special Groups, Elderly (this chapter); Social Security (chap. 18)

AGENCIES

Health Care Financing Administration *(Health and Human Services Dept.), 200 Independence Ave. S.W.,*

#314G 20201; (202) 690-6726. Fax, (202) 690-6262. Nancy-Ann Min DeParle, administrator. Information, (202) 690-6105. Internet, http://www.hcfa.gov.

Administers Medicare (a health insurance program for persons with disabilities or age 65 or older, who are eligible to participate) and Medicaid (a health insurance program for persons judged unable to pay for health services).

Health Care Financing Administration *(Health and Human Services Dept.), Clinical Standards and Quality, 7500 Security Blvd., S2-11-7, Baltimore, MD 21244; (410) 786-6842. Fax, (410) 786-6857. Jeff Kang, director.*

Develops, establishes, and enforces standards that regulate the quality of care of hospitals and other health care facilities under Medicare and Medicaid programs. Administers operations of survey and peer review organizations that enforce health care standards, primarily for institutional care. Oversees clinical laboratory improvement programs and end stage renal disease networks. Monitors providers' and suppliers' compliance with standards.

Health Care Financing Administration *(Health and Human Services Dept.), Disabled and Elderly Health Programs, 7500 Security Blvd., S2-14-27, Baltimore, MD 21244; (410) 786-6763. Fax, (410) 786-9004. Robert A. Streimer, director.*

Certifies facilities that participate in federal Medicare and Medicaid programs. Determines whether facilities meet federal health and safety standards required for participation in such programs.

Health Care Financing Administration *(Health and Human Services Dept.), Health Plans and Providers, 7500 Security Blvd., C5-02-17, Baltimore, MD 21244; (410) 786-5674. Fax, (410) 786-0594. Kathy Buto, acting director.*

Issues regulations and guidelines for administration of the Medicare program.

Health Care Financing Administration *(Health and Human Services Dept.), Information Services, 7500 Security Blvd., N3-15-06, Baltimore, MD 21244-1850; (410) 786-1800. Fax, (410) 786-1810. Gary Christoph, director.*

Serves as primary federal statistical office for disseminating economic data on Medicare.

Health Care Financing Administration *(Health and Human Services Dept.), Medicaid, 7500 Security Blvd., #C52223, Baltimore, MD 21244; (410) 786-3230. Fax, (410) 786-0025. Judith D. Moore, deputy director.*

Administers and monitors Medicaid programs to ensure program quality and financial integrity; promotes beneficiary awareness and access to services.

Health Care Financing Administration *(Health and Human Services Dept.), Medicare Contractor Management, 7500 Security Blvd., S2-01-23, Baltimore, MD 21244; (410) 786-8050. Fax, (410) 786-1978. Gary Kavanagh, acting director.*

Manages the contractual framework for the Medicare program; establishes and enforces performance standards for contractors who process and pay Medicare claims.

Health Resources and Services Administration *(Health and Human Services Dept.), Rural Health Policy, 5600 Fishers Lane, #905, Rockville, MD 20857; (301) 443-0835. Fax, (301) 443-2803. Dena Puskin, acting director. Internet, http://www.nal.usda.gov/ric/richs/orhp.htm.*

Studies the effects of Medicare and Medicaid programs on rural access to health care.

NONPROFIT

Blue Cross and Blue Shield Assn., *1310 G St. N.W. 20005; (202) 626-4780. Fax, (202) 626-4833. Patrick G. Hays, president. Internet, http://www.bluecares.com.*

Acts as the primary contractor for the federal government in administration of Medicare Part A, which covers hospitalization and institutional care for persons with disabilities and persons age 65 or older. (Headquarters in Chicago.)

Federation of American Health Systems, *1111 19th St. N.W., #402 20036; (202) 833-3090. Fax, (202) 861-0063. Thomas A. Scully, president. Internet, http://www.fahs.com.*

Membership: investor-owned, for-profit hospitals and health care systems. Studies Medicaid and Medicare reforms. Maintains speakers bureau; compiles statistics on investor-owned hospitals. Monitors legislation and regulations.

National Committee to Preserve Social Security and Medicare, *10 G St. N.E., #600 20002; (202) 216-0420. Fax, (202) 216-0451. Martha McSteen, president. Internet, http://www.ncpssm.org.*

Educational and advocacy organization that focuses on Social Security and Medicare programs and on related income security and health issues. Interests include retirement income protection, health care reform, and the quality of life of seniors. Monitors legislation and regulations.

See also American Assn. of Retired Persons, Health and Long Term Care (p. 378)

Medical Devices and Technology

See also Health Services for Special Groups (this chapter); Labeling and Packaging (chap. 1)

AGENCIES

Food and Drug Administration *(Health and Human Services Dept.), Center for Devices and Radiological Health, 9200 Corporate Blvd., #100, Rockville, MD 20850; (301) 443-4690. Fax, (301) 594-1320. Dr. D. Bruce Burlington, director. International Reference System, (301) 827-3993. Internet, http://www.fda.gov/cdrh.*

Evaluates safety, efficacy, and labeling of medical devices; classifies devices; establishes performance standards; assists in legal actions concerning medical devices; coordinates research and testing; conducts training and educational programs. Maintains an international reference system, to facilitate trade in devices. Library open to the public.

Food and Drug Administration *(Health and Human Services Dept.), Small Manufacturers Assistance, 1350 Piccard Dr., HFZ-220, Rockville, MD 20850; (301) 443-6597. Fax, (301) 443-8818. John F. Stigi, director. Toll-free, (800) 638-2041. Fax-on-demand, (800) 899-0381.*

Serves as liaison between small-business manufacturers of medical devices and the FDA. Assists manufacturers in complying with FDA regulatory requirements; sponsors seminars.

NONPROFIT

American Institute of Ultrasound in Medicine, *14750 Sweitzer Ln., #100, Laurel, MD 20707-5906; (301) 498-4100. Fax, (301) 498-4450. Frederick Kremkau, president. Internet, admin@aium.org or http://www.aium.org.*

Membership: medical professionals who use ultrasound technology in their practices. Promotes multidisciplinary research and education in the field of diagnostic ultrasound through conventions and educational programs. Monitors international research.

American Medical Informatics Assn., *4915 St. Elmo Ave., #401, Bethesda, MD 20814; (301) 657-1291. Fax, (301) 657-1296. Dennis Reynolds, executive director. Document-on-Request, (800) 819-2334. Internet, mail@mail.amia.org or http://www.amia.org.*

Provides information on medical systems and use of computers in the health care field. Promotes use of computers and information systems in patient care; conducts and promotes research on medical technology; encourages development of universal standards, terminology, and coding systems. Participates in the International

Medical Informatics Assn., which is headquartered in Geneva.

American Orthotic and Prosthetic Assn., *1650 King St., #500, Alexandria, VA 22314; (703) 836-7116. Fax, (703) 836-0838. Charles Unger, president. Internet, http://www.theaopa.org.*

Membership: companies that manufacture or supply artificial limbs and braces. Provides information on the profession.

American Roentgen Ray Society, *1891 Preston White Dr., Reston, VA 20191; (703) 648-8992. Fax, (703) 264-8863. Paul R. Fullagar, executive director. Internet, http://www.arrs.org.*

Membership: physicians and researchers in radiology and allied sciences. Publishes research; conducts conferences; presents scholarships and awards.

Health Industry Distributors Assn., *66 Canal Center, #520, Alexandria, VA 22314-1591; (703) 549-4432. Fax, (703) 549-6495. S. Wayne Kay, president.*

Membership: medical products distributors and home health care providers. Administers educational programs and conducts training seminars. Monitors legislation and regulations.

Health Industry Manufacturers Assn., *1200 G St. N.W., #400 20005; (202) 783-8700. Fax, (202) 783-8750. Alan H. Magazine, president. Internet, http://www.himanet.com.*

Membership: manufacturers of medical devices, diagnostic products, and health care information systems. Interests include safe and effective medical devices; conducts educational seminars. Monitors legislation, regulations, and international issues.

National Assn. for Medical Equipment Services, *625 Slaters Lane, #200, Alexandria, VA 22314; (703) 836-6263. Fax, (703) 836-6730. William D. Coughlan, president. Internet, http://www.names.org.*

Membership: home medical equipment suppliers, manufacturers, and state associations. Promotes legislative and regulatory policy that improves access to quality home medical equipment.

Optical Society of America, *2010 Massachusetts Ave. N.W. 20036; (202) 223-8130. Fax, (202) 223-1096. Vacant, executive director. Internet, http://www.osa.org.*

Membership: researchers, educators, manufacturers, students, and others interested in optics and photonics worldwide. Promotes research and information exchange; conducts conferences. Interests include use of optics in medical imaging and surgery.

Program for Appropriate Technology in Health,
1990 M St. N.W., #700 20036; (202) 822-0033. Fax, (202) 457-1466. Ann Wilson, director. Internet, info@path-dc.org or http://www.path.org.

Seeks to improve the safety and availability of health products and technologies worldwide, particularly in developing countries. Interests include reproductive health, immunization, maternal-child health, AIDS, and nutrition. (Headquarters in Seattle.)

See also Center for Patient Advocacy (p. 354); Johns Hopkins University Applied Physics Laboratory (p. 386); Public Citizen, Health Research Group (p. 355)

Nursing Homes and Hospices

See also Health Services for Special Groups, Elderly (this chapter)

AGENCIES

Health Care Financing Administration *(Health and Human Services Dept.), Disabled and Elderly Health Programs, 7500 Security Blvd., S2-14-27, Baltimore, MD 21244; (410) 786-6763. Fax, (410) 786-9004. Robert A. Streimer, director.*

Enforces health care and safety standards for hospitals, nursing homes, and other long-term care facilities; clinical and other laboratories; clinics; and other health care facilities.

Health Care Financing Administration *(Health and Human Services Dept.), Outcomes and Improvements, 7500 Security Blvd., S2-14-17, Baltimore, MD 21244-1850; (410) 786-6807. Fax, (410) 786-6730. Helene Fredeking, director.*

Monitors compliance of nursing homes, psychiatric hospitals, and long-term and intermediate care facilities with government standards. Focus includes quality of care, environmental conditions, and participation in Medicaid and Medicare programs. Coordinates health care programs for the mentally retarded.

NONPROFIT

American College of Health Care Administrators,
325 S. Patrick St., Alexandria, VA 22314-3571; (703) 549-5822. Fax, (703) 739-7901. Karen Tucker, executive vice president. Internet, http://www.achca.org.

Membership: administrators of long-term health care organizations and facilities, including home health care programs, hospices, daycare centers for the elderly, nursing and hospital facilities, retirement communities, and mental health care centers. Conducts research on statistical characteristics of nursing home and other medical administrators; conducts seminars; offers education courses; provides certification for administrators. Library open to the public by appointment.

American Health Care Assn., *1201 L St. N.W. 20005; (202) 842-4444. Fax, (202) 842-3860. Paul R. Willging, executive vice president. Information, (202) 898-2839. Library, (202) 898-2839. Publication orders, (800) 321-0343. Internet, http://www.ahca.org.*

Federation of associations representing assisted living nursing facilities and subacute care providers. Sponsors and provides educational programs and materials. Library open to the public by appointment.

Assisted Living Facilities Assn. of America, *10300 Eaton Pl., Fairfax, VA 22031; (703) 691-8100. Fax, (703) 691-8106. Karen Wayne, executive director.*

Promotes the development of standards and increased awareness for the assisted living industry. Provides members with information on policy, funding access, and quality of care. Interests include funding alternatives to make assisted living available to all who need it. Monitors legislation and regulations.

Hospice Foundation of America, *2001 S St. N.W., #300 20009; (202) 638-5419. Fax, (202) 638-5312. Lisa McGahey, vice president for programs. Toll-free, (800) 854-3402 (Miami Beach). Internet, hospicefdn@charitiesusa.com or http://www.hospicefoundation.org.*

Promotes hospice care for terminally ill people. Disseminates information; conducts education and training; awards small grants. (Headquarters in Miami Beach, Fla.)

National Assn. for Homecare, *228 7th St. S.E. 20003; (202) 547-7424. Fax, (202) 547-3540. Val J. Halamandaris, president. Internet, http://www.nahc.org.*

Promotes high-quality hospice, home care, and other community services for those with chronic health problems or life-threatening illness. Conducts research and provides information on related issues. Works to educate the public concerning health and social policy matters. Oversees the National HomeCaring Council, which provides training, education, accreditation, and certification in the field. Monitors legislation and regulations.

National Citizens' Coalition for Nursing Home Reform, *1424 16th St. N.W., #202 20036-2211; (202) 332-2275. Fax, (202) 332-2949. Sarah Burger, acting executive director.*

Seeks to improve the long-term care system and quality of life for residents in nursing homes and other facilities for the elderly; coordinates the Campaign for Quality Care. Promotes citizen participation in all aspects of nursing homes; acts as clearinghouse for nursing home advocacy.

National Hospice Organization, *1901 N. Moore St., #901, Arlington, VA 22209; (703) 243-5900. Fax, (703) 525-5762. Karen Davie, president. Toll-free information and referral helpline, (800) 658-8898. Internet, http:// www.nho.org.*

Membership: institutions and individuals providing hospice care and other interested organizations and individuals. Promotes supportive care for the terminally ill and their families; sets hospice program standards; provides information on hospices. Monitors legislation and regulations.

See also American Assn. of Homes and Services for the Aging (p. 378)

Pharmaceuticals

See also Labeling and Packaging (chap. 1); Health Topics: Research and Advocacy, Substance Abuse (this chapter)

AGENCIES

Food and Drug Administration *(Health and Human Services Dept.), Center for Drug Evaluation and Research, 5600 Fishers Lane, Woodmont II, #6027, Rockville, MD 20857; (301) 594-5400. Fax, (301) 594-6197. Dr. Janet Woodcock, director. Information, (301) 827-4573. Press, (301) 827-6242.*

Reviews and approves applications to investigate and market new drugs; monitors prescription drug advertising; works to harmonize drug approval internationally.

Food and Drug Administration *(Health and Human Services Dept.), Generic Drugs, 7500 Standish Pl., Rockville, MD 20855; (301) 827-5845. Fax, (301) 594-0183. Douglas Sporn, director.*

Oversees generic drug review process to ensure the safety and effectiveness of approved drugs.

Food and Drug Administration *(Health and Human Services Dept.), Health Affairs, 5600 Fishers Lane, Parklawn Bldg., #1536, Rockville, MD 20857; (301) 827-6630. Fax, (301) 443-1309. Dr. Stuart Nightingale, associate commissioner.*

Serves as liaison between FDA and health professionals for medical and scientific information and policy issues; coordinates agency's international activities on importing and exporting pharmaceuticals. Interests include food and drug patents.

Public Health and Science *(Health and Human Services Dept.), Orphan Products Board, 5600 Fishers Lane,*

#8-73, Rockville, MD 20857; (301) 827-3666. Fax, (301) 443-4915. Dr. Robert Steeves, executive secretary.

Promotes the development of drugs, devices, and alternative medical food therapies for rare diseases or conditions. Coordinates activities on the development of orphan drugs among federal agencies, manufacturers, and organizations representing patients.

NONPROFIT

American Assn. of Colleges of Pharmacy, *1426 Prince St., Alexandria, VA 22314-2841; (703) 739-2330. Fax, (703) 836-8982. Richard Penna, executive vice president. Internet, aacp@aol.com or http://www.aacp.org.*

Represents and advocates for pharmacists in the academic community. Conducts programs and activities in cooperation with other national health and higher education associations.

American Assn. of Pharmaceutical Scientists, *1650 King St., #200, Alexandria, VA 22314-2747; (703) 548-3000. Fax, (703) 684-7349. Amy Miller, public relations. Internet, http://www.aaps.org.*

Membership: pharmaceutical scientists from biomedical, biotechnological, and health care fields. Promotes pharmaceutical sciences as an industry; represents scientific interests within academia and public and private institutions. Monitors legislation and regulations.

American Pharmaceutical Assn., *2215 Constitution Ave. N.W. 20037; (202) 628-4410. Fax, (202) 783-2351. Dr. John A. Gans, executive vice president. Toll-free, (800) 237-2742. Library, (202) 429-7524. Internet, http://www. aphanet.org.*

Membership: practicing pharmacists, pharmaceutical scientists, and pharmacy students. Promotes professional education and training; publishes scientific journals and handbook on nonprescription drugs; monitors international research. Library open to the public by appointment.

American Society for Pharmacology and Experimental Therapeutics, *9650 Rockville Pike, Bethesda, MD 20814-3995; (301) 530-7060. Fax, (301) 530-7061. Dr. Christine Carrico, executive officer. Internet, aspetinfo@aspet.faseb.org or http://www.faseb.org/aspet.*

Membership: researchers and teachers involved in basic and clinical pharmacology in the United States and Canada.

American Society of Health-System Pharmacists, *7272 Wisconsin Ave., Bethesda, MD 20814; (301) 657-3000. Fax, (301) 657-1251. Henri Manasse, chief executive officer. Internet, http://www.ashp.com.*

FOOD AND DRUG ADMINISTRATION

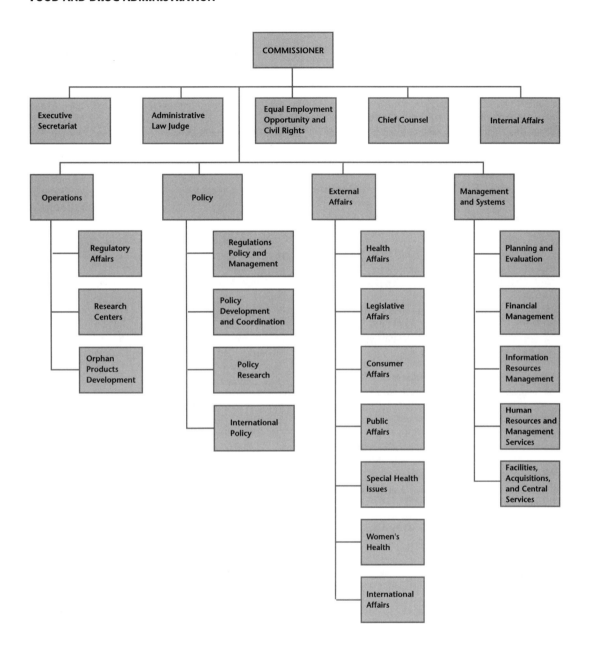

Membership: pharmacists who practice in organized health care settings such as hospitals, health maintenance organizations, and long-term care facilities. Provides publishing and educational programs designed to help members improve pharmaceutical services; accredits pharmacy residency and pharmacy technician training programs. Monitors legislation and regulations.

Drug Policy Foundation, *4455 Connecticut Ave. N.W., #B500 20008-2302; (202) 537-5005. Fax, (202) 537-3007.*

Cher Horosko, director. Internet, dpf@dpf.org or http://www.dpf.org.

Seeks to broaden debate on drug policy to include consideration of legalizing prescriptions for heroin and marijuana in treatment of cancer and other serious diseases. Studies drug policy in other countries. Monitors legislation and regulations.

Food and Drug Law Institute, *1000 Vermont Ave. N.W., #200 20005-4903; (202) 371-1420. Fax, (202) 371-0649. John Villforth, president. Internet, comments@fdli.org or http://www.fdli.org.*

Membership: providers of products and services to the food, drug, medical device, and cosmetics industries, including major food and drug companies; and lawyers working in food and drug law. Arranges conferences on technological and legal developments in the industry; sponsors law courses, fellowships, and legal writing. Library open to the public.

Generic Pharmaceutical Industry Assn., *1620 Eye St. N.W., #800 20006; (202) 833-9070. Fax, (202) 833-9612. Alice E. Till, president.*

Represents the generic pharmaceutical industry in legislative, regulatory, scientific, and health care policy matters. Attempts to increase availability and public awareness of generic medicines.

National Assn. of Chain Drug Stores, *413 N. Lee St., Alexandria, VA (mailing address: P.O. Box 1417-D49, Alexandria, VA 22313); (703) 549-3001. Fax, (703) 836-4869. Ronald L. Ziegler, president. Internet, http://www.nacds.org.*

Membership: chain drug retailers; associate members include manufacturers, suppliers, publishers, and advertising agencies. Provides information on the pharmacy profession, community pharmacy practice, and retail prescription drug economics.

National Community Pharmacists Assn., *205 Daingerfield Rd., Alexandria, VA 22314; (703) 683-8200. Fax, (703) 683-3619. Calvin Anthony, executive vice president. Internet, http://www.ncpanet.org.*

Membership: independent drug store owners and pharmacists working in retail drugstores. Interests include drug regulation and national health insurance. Provides consumer information on such issues as prescription drugs, poison control, and mail order drug fraud.

National Council on Patient Information and Education, *666 11th St. N.W., #810 20001; (202) 347-6711. Fax, (202) 638-0773. W. Ray Bullman, executive director.*

Membership: organizations of health care professionals, pharmaceutical manufacturers, federal agencies, voluntary health organizations, and consumer groups. Works to increase information available to patients about prescription medicines; conducts educational programs; distributes public service announcements for television and radio.

National Pharmaceutical Council, *1894 Preston White Dr., Reston, VA 20191-5433; (703) 620-6390. Fax, (703) 476-0904. Karen Williams, president. Internet, main@npcnow.com.*

Membership: pharmaceutical manufacturers that research and produce trade-name prescription medication and other pharmaceutical products. Provides information on the quality and cost-effectiveness of pharmaceutical products and the economics of drug programs.

National Wholesale Druggists' Assn., *1821 Michael Faraday Dr., #400, Reston, VA (mailing address: P.O. Box 2219, Reston, VA 20195-0219); (703) 787-0000. Fax, (703) 787-6930. Ronald J. Streck, president. Internet, http://www.nwda.org.*

Membership: full-service drug wholesalers. Works to improve relations among supplier and customer industries; serves as a forum on major industry issues; researches and disseminates information on management practices for drug wholesalers. Monitors legislation and regulations.

Nonprescription Drug Manufacturers Assn., *1150 Connecticut Ave. N.W. 20036; (202) 429-9260. Fax, (202) 223-6835. James D. Cope, president.*

Membership: manufacturers and distributors of nonprescription medicines; associate members include suppliers, advertising agencies, and research and testing laboratories. Promotes the role of self-medication in health care. Monitors legislation and regulations.

Parenteral Drug Assn., *7500 Old Georgetown Rd., #620, Bethesda, MD 20814; (301) 986-0293. Fax, (301) 986-0296. Edmund M. Fry, president. Internet, http://www.pda.org.*

Educates pharmaceutical professionals on parenteral and sterile-product technologies. Promotes pharmaceutical research. Serves as a liaison with pharmaceutical manufacturers, suppliers, users, academics, and government regulatory officials.

Pharmaceutical Care Management Assn., *2300 9th St. South, #210, Arlington, VA 22204; (703) 920-8480. Fax, (703) 920-8491. Delbert D. Konnor, president.*

Membership: companies providing home-delivered pharmaceutical services. Monitors standards for drug delivery; promotes legislation, research, education, and practice standards that foster quality, affordable pharmaceutical care.

Pharmaceutical Research and Manufacturers of America, *1100 15th St. N.W., #900 20005; (202) 835-3400. Fax, (202) 835-3414. Alan F. Holmer, president. Internet, http://www.phrma.org.*

Membership: companies that discover, develop, and manufacture prescription drugs. Provides consumer information on drug abuse, the safe and effective use of prescription medicines, and developments in important areas, including AIDS. Provides pharmaceutical industry statistics.

U.S. Pharmacopeial Convention, *12601 Twinbrook Pkwy., Rockville, MD 20852; (301) 881-0666. Fax, (301) 816-8299. Jerome A. Halperin, executive director. Internet, http://www.usp.org.*

Establishes and revises standards for drug strength, quality, purity, packaging, labeling, and storage. Publishes drug use information, official drug quality standards, patient education materials, and consumer drug references. Interests include international standards.

See also Animal Health Institute (p.65); Center for Patient Advocacy (p. 354); Institute for Alternative Futures (p. 386)

HEALTH PROFESSIONS

AGENCIES

Health Care Financing Administration *(Health and Human Services Dept.), Clinical Standards and Quality, 7500 Security Blvd., S2-11-07, Baltimore, MD 21244; (410) 786-6842. Fax, (410) 786-6857. Jeff Kang, director.*

Oversees professional review and other medical review programs; establishes guidelines; prepares issue papers relating to legal aspects of professional review and quality assurance.

Health Resources and Services Administration *(Health and Human Services Dept.), Health Education Assistance Loan Branch, 5600 Fishers Lane, #8-37 Parklawn Bldg., Rockville, MD 20857; (301) 443-1540. Fax, (301) 594-6911. Stephen J. Boehlert, associate division director.*

Administers federal program of insured loans to graduate students in medicine, osteopathy, dentistry, veterinary medicine, optometry, podiatry, public health, pharmacy, clinical psychology, chiropractics, and health

administration under the Health Professions Education Assistance Act of 1976.

Health Resources and Services Administration *(Health and Human Services Dept.), Health Professions, 5600 Fishers Lane, #805, Rockville, MD 20857; (301) 443-5794. Fax, (301) 443-2111. Dr. Neil H. Sampson, acting associate administrator; Ciriaco Gonzales, director, Disadvantaged Assistance. Internet, http://www.hrsa.dhhs.gov/bhpr.*

Promotes primary care and public health education and practice. Advocates recruitment of health care professionals, including nursing and allied health professionals, for underserved populations. Administers categorical training programs, scholarship and loan programs, and minority and disadvantaged assistance programs. Oversees national practitioner data bank and vaccine injury compensation program.

Health Resources and Services Administration *(Health and Human Services Dept.), Health Services Corps Scholarship Program, 4350 East-West Hwy., 10th Floor, Bethesda, MD 20814; (301) 594-4410. Fax, (301) 594-4985. Dr. Marilyn Gaston, director. Toll-free applications and information hotlines, (800) 638-0824 and (800) 783-1547.*

Administers service-obligated scholarship and loan repayment programs that support students in medical and health professional schools.

Health Resources and Services Administration *(Health and Human Services Dept.), National Health Service Corps, 4350 East-West Hwy., 8th Floor, Bethesda, MD 20814; (301) 594-4130. Fax, (301) 594-4076. Dr. Donald L. Weaver, director.*

Supplies communities experiencing a shortage of health care personnel with doctors and other medical professionals.

Health Resources and Services Administration *(Health and Human Services Dept.), National Practitioners Data Bank, 5600 Fishers Lane, Parklawn Bldg., #8A-55, Rockville, MD 20857; (301) 443-2300. Fax, (301) 443-6725. Thomas C. Croft, director, Quality Assurance. Toll-free, (800) 767-6732.*

Provides information on reports of malpractice payments, adverse state licensure, clinical privileges, and society membership actions (only to eligible state licensing boards, hospitals, and other health care entities) about physicians, dentists, and other licensed health care practitioners.

National Institutes of Health *(Health and Human Services Dept.), Minority Biomedical Research Support*

Program, *45 Center Dr., Bldg. 45, #2AS.37, Bethesda, MD 20892; (301) 594-3900. Fax, (301) 480-2753. Dr. Clifton A. Poodry, director.*

Awards grants to eligible minority universities and colleges to support biomedical research by minority students and faculty; funds development of research facilities.

Program Support Center *(Health and Human Services Dept.), Commissioned Personnel, 5600 Fishers Lane, #4A15, Rockville, MD 20857; (301) 594-3000. Fax, (301) 594-2711. Capt. Michael Davidson (CC), director.*

Administers the Public Health Service Commissioned Corps, which helps health professionals become commissioned officers with the same benefits offered in the other uniformed services.

See also National Clearinghouse for Primary Care Information (p. 351)

CONGRESS

House Commerce Committee, *Subcommittee on Health and the Environment, 2125 RHOB 20515; (202) 225-2927. Fax, (202) 225-1919. Michael Bilirakis, R-Fla., chair; James E. Derderian, staff director. Internet, http://www.house.gov/commerce/health.html.*

Jurisdiction over legislation on the education, training, and distribution of health professionals.

House Ways and Means Committee, *Subcommittee on Health, 1136 LHOB 20515; (202) 225-3943. Fax, (202) 226-1765. Bill Thomas, R-Calif., chair; Chip Kahn, staff director. Internet, http://www.house.gov/ways_means.*

Jurisdiction over Professional Standards Review Organizations legislation.

Senate Labor and Human Resources Committee, *Subcommittee on Public Health and Safety, SD-422 20510; (202) 224-7139. Fax, (202) 228-5044. Bill Frist, R-Tenn., chair; Susan Ramthun, staff director. Internet, http://www.senate.gov/~labor.*

Jurisdiction over legislation on the education, training, and distribution of health professionals and over Professional Standards Review Organizations legislation.

NONPROFIT

American Assn. for Health Education, *1900 Association Dr., Reston, VA 20191; (703) 476-3437. Fax, (703) 476-6638. Becky J. Smith, executive director. Internet, aahe@aahperd.org or http://www.aahperd.org/aahe/aahe.html.*

Membership: health educators and allied health professionals in community and volunteer health agencies, educational institutions, and businesses. Develops health education programs; monitors legislation.

American Assn. of Colleges of Pharmacy, *1426 Prince St., Alexandria, VA 22314-2841; (703) 739-2330. Fax, (703) 836-8982. Richard Penna, executive vice president. Internet, aacp@aol.com or http://www.aacp.org.*

Membership: teachers and administrators representing colleges of pharmacy accredited by the American Council on Pharmaceutical Education. Sponsors educational programs; conducts research; provides career information; helps administer the Pharmacy College Admissions Test.

American Assn. of Healthcare Consultants, *11208 Waples Mill Rd., #109, Fairfax, VA 22030; (703) 691-2242. Fax, (703) 691-2247. Vaughan A. Smith, president. Internet, consultahc@aol.com or http://www.aahc.net.*

Membership organization that develops credentials and standards for consulting services in all aspects of health planning and management; supports continuing education and training of health care professionals. Enforces code of professional ethics.

American College of Health Care Administrators, *325 S. Patrick St., Alexandria, VA 22314-3571; (703) 549-5822. Fax, (703) 739-7901. Karen Tucker, executive vice president. Internet, http://www.achca.org.*

Membership: administrators of long-term health care organizations and facilities, including home health care programs, hospices, daycare centers for the elderly, nursing and hospital facilities, retirement communities, and mental health care centers. Conducts research on statistical characteristics of nursing home and other medical administrators; conducts seminars; offers education courses; provides certification for administrators. Library open to the public by appointment.

American Medical Group Assn., *1422 Duke St., Alexandria, VA 22314-3430; (703) 838-0033. Fax, (703) 548-1890. Donald W. Fisher, chief executive officer. Internet, http://www.amga.org.*

Membership: medical and dental group practices. Compiles statistics on group practice; sponsors a foundation for research and education programs.

American Osteopathic Healthcare Assn., *5550 Friendship Blvd., #300, Chevy Chase, MD 20815; (301) 968-2642. Fax, (301) 968-4995. David Kushner, president. Internet, http://www.aoha.org.*

Conducts educational programs on management techniques for executives of member hospitals. Monitors legislation and regulations.

American Society of Consultant Pharmacists, *1321 Duke St., 4th Floor, Alexandria, VA 22314-3563; (703) 739-1300. Fax, (703) 739-1321. R. Tim Webster, executive director. Internet, http://www.ascp.com.*

Membership: dispensing and clinical pharmacists who provide services to long-term care facilities. Makes grants and conducts research in the science and practice of consultant pharmacy. Monitors legislation and regulations.

American Speech-Language-Hearing Assn., *10801 Rockville Pike, Rockville, MD 20852; (301) 897-5700. Fax, (301) 571-0457. Frederick T. Spahr, executive director. Press, (301) 897-0156. TDD, (301) 897-0157. Toll-free hotline (except Alaska, Hawaii, and Maryland), (800) 498-2071 (voice and TDD accessible). Internet, http://www.asha.org.*

Membership: specialists in speech-language pathology and audiology. Sponsors professional education programs; acts as accrediting agent for graduate college programs and for public clinical education programs in speech-language pathology and audiology. Advocates the rights of the communicatively disabled; provides information on speech, hearing, and language problems. Provides referrals to speech-language pathologists and audiologists.

Assn. for Healthcare Philanthropy, *313 Park Ave., #400, Falls Church, VA 22046; (703) 532-6243. Fax, (703) 532-7170. William C. McGinly, president. Internet, http://www.go-ahp.org.*

Membership: hospital and health care executives who manage fundraising activities.

Assn. of Hispanic Serving Health Professions Schools, *900 Jefferson Dr. S.W., #1239 20560; (202) 887-1986. Fax, (202) 887-1968. Vacant, executive director. Internet, NAHSHPS@msn.com.*

Seeks to increase representation of Hispanics in all health care professions. Monitors legislation and regulations.

Assn. of Reproductive Health Professionals, *2401 Pennsylvania Ave. N.W., #350 20037-1718; (202) 466-3825. Fax, (202) 466-3826. Wayne Shields, president. Internet, http://www.arhp.org.*

Membership: obstetricians, gynecologists, other physicians, researchers, clinicians, educators, and others. Educates health professionals and the public on reproductive health issues, including family planning, contraception, HIV/AIDS, other sexually transmitted diseases, abortion, menopause, infertility, and cancer prevention and detection.

Assn. of Schools of Allied Health Professions, *1730 M St. N.W., #500 20036; (202) 293-4848. Fax, (202) 293-4852. Thomas Elwood, executive director. Internet, ashp1@asahp.org.*

Membership: two- and four-year colleges and academic health science centers with allied health professional training programs; administrators, educators, and practitioners; and professional societies. Serves as information resource; works with the Health and Human Services Dept. to conduct surveys of allied health education programs. Interests include health promotion and disease prevention, ethics in health care, and the participation of women and persons with disabilities in allied health. Monitors legislation and regulations.

Assn. of Schools of Public Health, *1660 L St. N.W., #204 20036; (202) 296-1099. Fax, (202) 296-1252. Michael K. Gemmell, executive director. Internet, http://www.asph.org.*

Membership: accredited graduate schools of public health. Promotes improved education and training of professional public health personnel; interests include international health. Library open to the public.

Assn. of State and Territorial Health Officials, *1275 K St. N.W., #800 20002; (202) 371-9090. Fax, (202) 371-9797. Cheryl Beversdorf, executive vice president. Internet, http://www.astho.org.*

Membership: executive officers of state and territorial health departments. Serves as legislative review agency and information source for members.

Assn. of Teachers of Preventive Medicine, *1660 L St. N.W., #208 20036; (202) 463-0550. Fax, (202) 463-0555. Barbara J. Calkins, executive director. Internet, http://www.atpm.org/atpm.htm.*

Membership: medical educators, practitioners, administrators, students, and health care agencies. Works to advance education in preventive medicine; interests include public health, international health, clinical prevention, and aerospace and occupational medicine. Promotes collaborative research and programs; fosters information exchange.

Assn. of University Programs in Health Administration, *1110 Vermont Ave. N.W., #220 20005; (202) 822-8550. Fax, (202) 822-8555. Henry A. Fernandez, president. Internet, http://www.aupha.org.*

Membership: colleges and universities with programs in health administration. Offers consultation services to health administration programs; maintains task forces on undergraduate education, ethics, epidemiology, AIDS, health law, health facilities, long-term care, international development, institutional research, information management, quality improvement, and technology assessment.

Council on Education for Public Health, *1015 15th St. N.W., #402 20005; (202) 789-1050. Fax, (202) 789-1895. Patricia P. Evans, executive director.*

Accredits schools of public health and graduate programs in community health education and community health preventive medicine. Works to strengthen public health programs through consultation, research, and other services.

Federation of Nurses and Health Professionals, *555 New Jersey Ave. N.W. 20001; (202) 879-4491. Fax, (202) 879-4597. Sandra Feldman, president. Internet, http://www.aft.org/fnhp/main.htm.*

Membership: nurses and other technical health care workers. Assists members with contract negotiation and grievances; conducts training programs and workshops. Monitors legislation and regulations. (Division of the American Federation of Teachers.)

Healthcare Financial Management Assn., *1050 17th St. N.W., #700 20036-5503; (202) 296-2920. Fax, (202) 223-9771. Elizabeth Propp, vice president. Toll-free, (800) 252-4362. Internet, http://www.hfma.org.*

Membership: health care financial management specialists. Offers educational programs; provides information on financial management of health care. (Headquarters in Westchester, Ill.)

National Assn. of County and City Health Officials, *440 1st St. N.W., #450 20001; (202) 783-5550. Fax, (202) 783-1583. Thomas L. Milne, executive director. Internet, http://www.naccho.org.*

Membership: city, county, and district health officers. Provides members with information on national, state, and local health developments. Works to develop the technical competence, managerial capacity, and leadership potential of local public health officials.

National Assn. of Healthcare Access Management, *1200 19th St. N.W., #300 20036-2401; (202) 857-1125. Fax, (202) 857-1115. Sherry Meyers, executive director.*

Promotes professional growth and recognition of health care patient access managers; provides instructional videotapes; sponsors educational programs.

National Center for Homeopathy, *801 N. Fairfax St., #306, Alexandria, VA 22314; (703) 548-7790. Fax, (703) 548-7792. Sharon Stevenson, executive director. Internet, http://www.homeopathic.org.*

Educational organization for professionals, groups, associations, and individuals interested in homeopathy and homeotherapeutics. Promotes health through home-

opathy; conducts education programs; holds annual conference.

National Health Lawyers Assn., *1120 Connecticut Ave. N.W., #950 20036; (202) 833-1100. Fax, (202) 833-1105. Nancy Wynstra, president. Internet, http://www.nhla-aaha.org.*

Membership: corporate, institutional, and government lawyers interested in the health field; law students; and health professionals. Serves as an information clearinghouse on health law; sponsors health law educational programs and seminars.

National Organization for Competency Assurance, *1200 19th St. N.W., #300 20036-2401; (202) 857-1165. Fax, (202) 223-4579. Bonnie Aubin, executive director. Internet, http://www.noca.org.*

Membership: certifying agencies and other groups that issue credentials to health professionals. Promotes public understanding of competency assurance certification programs for health professions and occupations. oversees commission that establishes certification program standards. Monitors regulations.

> *See also Assn. of Academic Health Centers (p. 358); Health Volunteers Overseas (p. 446)*

Chiropractors

NONPROFIT

American Chiropractic Assn., *1701 Clarendon Blvd., Arlington, VA 22209; (703) 276-8800. Fax, (703) 243-2593. Garret F. Cuneo, executive vice president. Internet, http://www.amerchiro.org/aca.*

Promotes professional growth and recognition for chiropractors. Interests include health care coverage, sports injuries, physical fitness, internal disorders, and orthopedics. Supports foundation for chiropractic education and research. Monitors legislation and regulations.

International Chiropractors Assn., *1110 N. Glebe Rd., Arlington, VA 22201; (703) 528-5000. Fax, (703) 528-5023. Ronald Hendrickson, executive director. Internet, http://www.chiropractic.org.*

Membership: chiropractors, students, and educators. Seeks to increase public awareness of chiropractic. Supports research on health issues; administers scholarship program; monitors legislation and regulations.

Dental Care

AGENCIES

Health Resources and Services Administration *(Health and Human Services Dept.), Associated, Den-*

tal, and Public Health Professions, 5600 Fishers Lane, #8-101, Rockville, MD 20857; (301) 443-6853. Fax, (301) 443-1164. J. Henry Montes, director.

Funds and conducts research on dental employment, education, and delivery systems. Areas of study include geographic distribution of dentists, women and minorities in dentistry, curriculum development, and dental health care delivery.

National Institute of Dental Research *(National Institutes of Health),* 31 Center Dr., MSC-2290, #2C39, Bethesda, MD 20892-2290; (301) 496-3571. Fax, (301) 402-2185. Dr. Harold C. Slavkin, director. Information, (301) 496-4261. Internet, http://www.nidr.nih.gov.

Conducts and funds research on the causes, prevention, and treatment of oral diseases and conditions.

NONPROFIT

American Assn. of Dental Schools, 1625 Massachusetts Ave. N.W., #600 20036-2212; (202) 667-9433. Fax, (202) 667-0642. Dr. Richard Valachovic, executive director. Internet, http://www.aads.jhu.edu.

Membership: individuals interested in dental education; undergraduate and graduate schools of dentistry; hospital dental education programs; and allied dental education programs in the United States, Canada, and Puerto Rico. Provides information on dental teaching and research and on admission requirements of U.S. and Canadian dental schools; publishes a directory of dental educators.

American College of Dentists, 839 Quince Orchard Rd., Suite J, Gaithersburg, MD 20878; (301) 977-3223. Fax, (301) 977-3330. Stephen Ralls, executive director. Internet, info@acdentist.org.

Honorary society of dentists. Fellows are elected based on their contributions to education, research, dentistry, and community and civic organizations. Interests include ethics, professionalism, and dentistry in health care.

American Dental Assn., 1111 14th St. N.W., #1100 20005; (202) 898-2400. Fax, (202) 898-2437. Vacant, director, Government Relations. Internet, http://www.ada.org.

Conducts research; provides dental education materials; compiles statistics on dentistry and dental care. Monitors legislation and regulations. (Headquarters in Chicago.)

American Dental Trade Assn., 4222 King St. West, Alexandria, VA 22302-1597; (703) 379-7755. Fax, (703) 931-9429. Nikolaj M. Petrovic, president.

Membership: dental laboratories and distributors and manufacturers of dental equipment and supplies. Collects and disseminates statistical and management information; conducts studies, programs, and projects of interest to the industry; acts as liaison with government agencies.

International Assn. for Dental Research, 1619 Duke St., Alexandria, VA 22314-3406; (703) 548-0066. Fax, (703) 548-1883. Dr. Eli Schwartz, executive director. Internet, research@iadr.com or http://www.iadr.com.

Membership: professionals engaged in dental research worldwide. Conducts annual convention, conferences, and symposia.

National Assn. of Dental Laboratories, 8201 Greensboro Rd., #300, Maclean, VA 22102; (703) 610-9035. Fax, (703) 610-9005. Audrey Calormino, acting executive director. Internet, nadl@erols.com or http://www.nadl.org.

Membership: dental laboratories, industry manufacturers and suppliers, and schools of dental technology. Interests include certification, improving education in dental technology, and content of alloys used in dentistry. Monitors state and federal legislation.

National Dental Assn., 5506 Connecticut Ave. N.W., #24 20015; (202) 244-7555. Fax, (202) 244-5992. Robert S. Johns, executive director.

Promotes the interests of African American and other minority dentists through educational programs and federal legislation and programs.

Medical Researchers

NONPROFIT

American Assn. for Clinical Chemistry, Inc., 2101 L St. N.W., #202 20037-1526; (202) 857-0717. Fax, (202) 887-5093. Richard G. Flaherty, executive vice president. Internet, http://www.aacc.org.

International society of chemists, physicians, and other scientists specializing in clinical chemistry. Provides educational and professional development services; presents awards for outstanding achievement. Monitors legislation and regulations.

American Assn. of Immunologists, 9650 Rockville Pike, Bethesda, MD 20814-3994; (301) 530-7178. Fax, (301) 571-1816. M. M. Hogan, executive director. Internet, infoaai@aai.faseb.org or http://www.scienceXchange.com/aai.

Membership: scientists working in virology, bacteriology, biochemistry, genetics, and related disciplines. Conducts training courses and workshops; compiles statistics.

American Society for Clinical Laboratory Science, *7910 Woodmont Ave., #530, Bethesda, MD 20814-3015; (301) 657-2768. Fax, (301) 657-2909. Elissa Passiment, executive director. Internet, http://www.ascls.org.*

Membership: laboratory technologists. Conducts continuing education programs for medical technologists and laboratory workers. Monitors legislation and regulations.

American Society of Clinical Pathologists, *1225 New York Ave. N.W., #250 20005; (202) 347-4450. Fax, (202) 347-4453. Robin E. Stombler, director, Washington Office. Toll-free, (800) 621-4142. Internet, http://www.ascp.org.*

Membership: pathologists, residents, and other physicians; clinical scientists; registered certified medical technologists; and technicians. Promotes continuing education, educational standards, and research in pathology. Monitors legislation, regulations, and international research. (Headquarters in Chicago.)

Assn. of State and Territorial Public Health Laboratory Directors, *1211 Connecticut Ave. N.W., #608 20036; (202) 822-5227. Fax, (202) 887-5098. Michael Sheels, president. Internet, http://www.astphld.org.*

Membership: state and territorial public health laboratory directors. Administers the National Laboratory Training Network which assesses, develops, and delivers continuing education for laboratory practitioners. Implements international training and assistance programs for developing nations. Acts as a liaison to the Centers for Disease Control.

Society of Toxicology, *1767 Business Center Dr., #302, Reston, VA 20190; (703) 438-3115. Fax, (703) 438-3113. Shawn Lamb, executive director. Internet, sothq@toxicology.org or http://www.toxicology.org.*

Membership: scientists from academic institutions, government, and industry worldwide who work in toxicology. Promotes professional development, exchange of information, public health, and protection of the environment.

See also American Roentgen Ray Society (p. 360)

Nurses and Physician Assistants

AGENCIES

National Institute of Nursing Research *(National Institutes of Health), 31 Center Dr., Bldg. 31, #5B03, Bethesda, MD 20892-2178; (301) 496-8230. Fax, (301) 480-4969. Dr. Patricia A. Grady, director. Information, (301) 496-0207.*

Provides grants and awards for nursing research and research training. Programs include research in health

promotion and disease prevention, acute and chronic illness, and delivery of nursing care.

NONPROFIT

American Academy of Physician Assistants, *950 N. Washington St., Alexandria, VA 22314; (703) 836-2272. Fax, (703) 684-1924. Stephen C. Crane, executive vice president. Internet, aapa@aapa.org or http://www.aapa.org.*

Membership: physician assistants. Sponsors continuing medical education programs for recertification of physician assistants; offers malpractice insurance; Interests include federal support for physician assistants' education programs; health issues related to underserved populations, Medicare coverage of physician assistants' services, and state laws regulating practice. Maintains speakers bureau. Monitors legislation and regulations.

American Assn. of Colleges of Nursing, *1 Dupont Circle N.W., #530 20036; (202) 463-6930. Fax, (202) 785-8320. Geraldine Bednash, executive director. Internet, http://www.aacn.nche.edu.*

Promotes quality baccalaureate and graduate nursing education; works to secure federal support of nursing education, nursing research, and student financial assistance; operates databank providing information on enrollments, graduations, salaries, and other conditions in nursing higher education.

American College of Nurse-Midwives, *818 Connecticut Ave. N.W., #900 20006; (202) 728-9860. Fax, (202) 728-9897. Deanne Williams, chief operating officer. Press, (202) 728-9875. Internet, info@acnm.org or http://www.midwife.org.*

Membership: certified nurse-midwives who preside at deliveries. Interests include preventive health care for women.

American Nurses Assn., *600 Maryland Ave. S.W., #100W 20024-2571; (202) 651-7000. Fax, (202) 651-7001. Argene Carswell, acting executive director. Internet, http://www.ana.org.*

Membership: registered nurses. Sponsors the American Nurses Foundation. Monitors legislation and regulations.

Federation of Nurses and Health Professionals, *555 New Jersey Ave. N.W. 20001; (202) 879-4491. Fax, (202) 879-4597. Sandra Feldman, president. Internet, http://www.aft.org/fnhp/main.htm.*

Membership: nurses and other technical health care workers. Assists members with contract negotiation and grievances; conducts training programs and workshops. Monitors legislation and regulations. (Division of the American Federation of Teachers.)

Physical and Occupational Therapy

See also Health Services for Special Groups (this chapter)

NONPROFIT

American Occupational Therapy Assn., *4720 Montgomery Lane, Bethesda, MD (mailing address: P.O. Box 31220, Bethesda, MD 20824-1220); (301) 652-2682. Fax, (301) 652-7711. Jeanette Bair, executive director. TDD, (800) 377-8555. Internet, http://www.aota.org.*

Membership: registered occupational therapists, certified occupational therapy assistants, and students. Associate members include businesses and organizations supportive of occupational therapy. Accredits colleges and universities and certifies therapists.

American Physical Therapy Assn., *1111 N. Fairfax St., Alexandria, VA 22314-1488; (703) 684-2782. Fax, (703) 684-7343. Francis Mallon, executive vice president. Toll-free, (800) 999-2782. TDD, (703) 683-6748. Internet, svcctr@apta.org or http://www.apta.org.*

Membership: physical therapists, assistants, and students. Establishes professional standards and accredits physical therapy programs; seeks to improve physical therapy education, practice, and research.

Physicians

For veterinary medicine, see Animals and Plants (chap. 9)

NONPROFIT

American Academy of Family Physicians, *2021 Massachusetts Ave. N.W. 20036; (202) 232-9033. Fax, (202) 232-9044. Rosemarie Sweeney, vice president. Internet, http://www.aafp.org.*

Membership: family physicians, family practice residents, and medical students. Sponsors continuing medical education programs; promotes family practice residency programs. Monitors legislation and regulations. (Headquarters in Kansas City, Mo.)

American Academy of Otolaryngology-Head and Neck Surgery, Inc., *1 Prince St., Alexandria, VA 22314; (703) 836-4444. Fax, (703) 683-5100. Dr. Michael Maves, executive vice president. Press, (703) 519-1560. TDD, (703) 519-1585. Internet, http://www.entnet.org.*

Coordinates research in ear, nose, and throat disorders and head and neck surgery; provides continuing education. Related interests include allergies, plastic and reconstructive surgery, and medical problems resulting from the use of tobacco. Monitors legislation and regulations.

American Assn. of Colleges of Osteopathic Medicine, *5550 Friendship Blvd., #310, Chevy Chase, MD 20815; (301) 968-4100. Fax, (301) 968-4101. Dr. Douglas L. Wood, president. Internet, http://www.aacom.org.*

Administers a centralized application service for osteopathic medical colleges; supports increase in the number of minority and economically disadvantaged students in osteopathic colleges; maintains an information database; sponsors recruitment and retention programs. Monitors legislation and regulations.

American Assn. of Colleges of Podiatric Medicine, *1350 Piccard Dr., #322, Rockville, MD 20850-4307; (301) 990-7400. Fax, (301) 990-2807. Anthony J. McNevin, president. Toll-free, (800) 922-9266. Internet, http://www.aacpm.org.*

Membership: schools of podiatric medicine and affiliate teaching hospitals in the United States. Serves as an information clearinghouse on podiatric medical education; conducts research and policy analysis; administers centralized admissions program to colleges of podiatric medicine and to graduate residency programs; advises on establishing new colleges of podiatric medicine.

American College of Cardiology, *9111 Old Georgetown Rd., Bethesda, MD 20814-1699; (301) 897-5400. Fax, (301) 897-9745. David J. Field, executive vice president. Internet, http://www.acc.org.*

Membership: physicians, surgeons, and scientists specializing in cardiovascular health care. Sponsors programs in continuing medical education; collaborates with national and international cardiovascular organizations. Library open to the public.

American College of Emergency Physicians, *1111 19th St. N.W., #650 20036; (202) 728-0610. Fax, (202) 728-0617. John Scott, director, Government Affairs. Internet, http://www.acep.org.*

Monitors legislation affecting emergency medicine and practitioners. Interests include Medicare and Medicaid legislation and regulations, graduate medical education, indigent care, prehospital care, drunk driving, public health, tax policy, domestic violence, and the ban on assault weapons. (Headquarters in Dallas.)

American College of Nuclear Physicians, *4400 Jenifer St. N.W. 20015; (202) 244-7904. Fax, (202) 244-7355. Peter Anas, executive director. Internet, http://www.acnp.com.*

Fosters professional standards among nuclear physicians; works to ensure the proper and safe practice of nuclear medicine at a reasonable cost; seeks to advance and improve the science of nuclear medicine.

American College of Obstetricians and Gynecologists, *409 12th St. S.W. 20024 (mailing address: P.O. Box 96920, Washington, DC 20090-6920); (202) 638-5577. Fax, (202) 484-5107. Dr. Ralph Hale, executive director. Press, (202) 484-3321. Internet, http://www.acog.org.*

Membership: medical specialists in obstetrics and gynecology. Monitors legislation, regulations, and international research on maternal and child health care.

American College of Osteopathic Surgeons, *123 N. Henry St., Alexandria, VA 22314-2903; (703) 684-0416. Fax, (703) 684-3280. Guy D. Beaumont, executive director.*

Membership: osteopathic surgeons in disciplines of orthopedics, neurosurgery, thoracic surgery, cardiovascular surgery, urology, plastic surgery, and general surgery. Offers members continuing education programs.

American College of Physicians, *700 13th St. N.W., #250 20005-3960; (202) 393-1650. Fax, (202) 783-1347. Howard B. Shapiro, vice president, Public Policy. Toll-free, (800) 523-1546. Internet, http://www.acponline.org.*

Membership: U.S., Canadian, and Latin American internists, nonsurgical specialists, and physicians-in-training. Supports research and continuing education; examines health issues and recommends policies to deal with them. Monitors legislation, regulations, and international research. (Headquarters in Philadelphia.)

American College of Preventive Medicine, *1660 L St. N.W., #206 20036; (202) 466-2044. Fax, (202) 466-2662. Hazel K. Keimowitz, executive director. Internet, http://www.acpm.org.*

Membership: physicians in general preventive medicine, public health, international health, occupational medicine, and aerospace medicine. Provides educational opportunities; advocates public policies consistent with scientific principles of the discipline; supports the investigation and analysis of issues relevant to the field.

American College of Radiology, *1891 Preston White Dr., Reston, VA 20191; (703) 648-8900. Fax, (703) 648-9176. John J. Curry, executive director. Internet, info@acr.org or http://www.acr.org.*

Membership: certified radiologists in the United States and Canada. Develops programs in radiation protection, technologist training, practice standards, and health care insurance; maintains a placement service for radiologists; participates in international conferences.

American College of Surgeons, *1640 Wisconsin Ave. N.W. 20007; (202) 337-2701. Fax, (202) 337-4271. Cynthia A. Brown, manager, Washington Office. Internet, http://www.facs.org.*

Monitors legislation and regulations concerning surgery; conducts continuing education programs and sponsors scholarships for graduate medical education. Interests include hospital cancer programs, trauma care, hospital accreditation, and international research. (Headquarters in Chicago.)

American Health Quality Assn., *1140 Connecticut Ave. N.W., #1050 20036; (202) 331-5790. Fax, (202) 833-2047. Josef Reum, director. Internet, http://www.ahqa.org.*

Seeks to improve physicians' ability to assess the quality of medical care services; assists in developing methods to monitor the appropriateness of medical care. Monitors legislation.

American Medical Assn., *1101 Vermont Ave. N.W., 12th Floor 20005; (202) 789-7400. Fax, (202) 789-7485. Lee Stillwell, president, Government Affairs. Internet, http://www.ama-assn.org.*

Membership: physicians, residents, and medical students. Provides information on the medical profession and health care; cooperates in setting standards for medical schools and hospital intern and residency training programs; offers physician placement service and counseling on management practices; provides continuing medical education. Interests include international research and peer review. Monitors legislation and regulations. (Headquarters in Chicago.)

American Medical Women's Assn., *801 N. Fairfax St., #400, Alexandria, VA 22314; (703) 838-0500. Fax, (703) 549-3864. Eileen McGrath, executive director. Internet, amwaleg@aol.com or http://www.amwa-doc.org.*

Membership: female physicians, interns, residents, and medical students. Promotes continuing education; evaluates manufacturers' research on products for women's health; provides student educational loans. Monitors legislation and regulations.

American Osteopathic Assn., *1090 Vermont Ave. N.W., #510 20005; (202) 414-0140. Fax, (202) 544-3525. Wayne Powell, director, Washington Office. Toll-free, (800) 962-9008. Internet, http://www.am-osteo-assn.org.*

Membership: osteopathic physicians. Promotes general health and education; accredits osteopathic educational institutions. Monitors legislation and regulations. (Headquarters in Chicago.)

American Podiatric Medical Assn., *9312 Old Georgetown Rd., Bethesda, MD 20814-1698; (301) 571-9200. Fax, (301) 530-2752. Dr. Glenn Gastwirth, acting executive director. Internet, http://www.apma.org.*

Membership: podiatrists. Accredits colleges of podiatric medicine and podiatric residency programs. Interests include the status of podiatrists in the military, federally supported financial assistance for podiatric students, and national health care initiatives.

American Psychiatric Assn., *1400 K St. N.W. 20005; (202) 682-6000. Fax, (202) 682-6850. Dr. Steven Mirin, medical director. Press, (202) 682-6142. Library, (202) 682-6080. Internet, apa@psych.org or http://www.psych.org.*

Membership: psychiatrists. Promotes availability of high-quality psychiatric care; provides the public with information; assists state and local agencies; conducts educational programs for professionals and students in the field. Library open to the public by appointment.

American Society of Addiction Medicine, *4601 N. Park Ave., Upper Arcade, #101, Chevy Chase, MD 20815; (301) 656-3920. Fax, (301) 656-3815. James F. Callahan, executive vice president. Internet, email@asam.org or http://www.asam.org.*

Membership: physicians and medical students. Supports the study and provision of effective treatment and care for people with alcohol and drug dependencies; educates physicians; administers certification program in addiction medicine. Monitors legislation and regulations.

American Society of Internal Medicine, *2011 Pennsylvania Ave. N.W., #800 20006; (202) 835-2746. Fax, (202) 835-0443. Dr. Alan R. Nelson, executive vice president. Internet, http://www.asim.org.*

Federation of societies representing internists nationwide. Concerned with the social, economic, and political factors affecting the delivery of medical care.

American Society of Nuclear Cardiology, *9111 Old Georgetown Rd., Bethesda, MD 20814-1699; (301) 493-2360. Fax, (301) 493-2376. William D. Nelligan, executive director. Internet, http://www.asnc.org.*

Membership: physicians and scientists engaged in nuclear cardiology practice or research. Provides professional education programs; establishes standards and guidelines for training and practice; promotes research worldwide. Monitors user-licensing requirements of the Nuclear Regulatory Commission.

Assn. for Hospital Medical Education, *1200 19th St. N.W., #300 20036-2401; (202) 857-1196. Fax, (202) 223-4579. Dennis Smeage, executive director. Internet, http://www.ahme.med.edu.*

Membership: physicians and others engaged in graduate and continuing medical education at community teaching hospitals. Conducts graduate and continuing education programs.

Assn. of American Medical Colleges, *2450 N St. N.W. 20037; (202) 828-0400. Fax, (202) 828-1125. Dr. Jordan J.*

Cohen, president. Internet, http://www.aamc.org.

Membership: U.S. schools of medicine, councils of deans, teaching hospitals, academic societies, medical students, and residents. Administers Medical College Admissions Test.

Assn. of Professors of Medicine, *2501 M St. N.W., #550 20037; (202) 861-7700. Fax, (202) 861-9731. Tod Ibrahim, executive director. Internet, apm@im.org or http://www.im.org.*

Membership: chairs of internal medicine departments at all U.S medical schools and several affiliated teaching hospitals.

Clerkship Directors in Internal Medicine, *1200 19th St., #300 20036-2422; (202) 857-1158. Fax, (202) 223-4579. Tod Ibrahim, executive director. Internet, apm1cdim@aol.com.*

Membership: directors of third-year internal medicine clerkships at U.S. medical schools.

College of American Pathologists, *1350 Eye St. N.W., #590 20005-3305; (202) 371-6617. Fax, (202) 371-0028. Jayne A. Hart-Chamber, vice president. Toll-free, (800) 392-9994. Internet, http://www.cap.org.*

Membership: physicians who are board certified in clinical or anatomic pathology. Accredits laboratories and provides them with proficiency testing programs; promotes the practice of pathology and laboratory medicine worldwide. (Headquarters in Northfield, Ill.)

International Council of Societies of Pathology, *7001 Georgia St., Chevy Chase, MD 20815; (202) 782-2759. Fax, (202) 782-3056. Dr. F. K. Mostofi, secretary-treasurer.*

Seeks to develop and maintain international cooperative research and education programs in pathology. Assists the World Health Organization and other international organizations in the delivery of medical care.

National Medical Assn., *1012 10th St. N.W. 20001; (202) 347-1895. Fax, (202) 842-3293. Dr. Nathaniel Murdock, president.*

Membership: minority physicians. Supports increased participation of minorities in the health professions, especially medicine.

Vision Care

See also Blind and Visually Impaired (chap. 18)

AGENCIES

National Eye Institute *(National Institutes of Health), 31 Center Dr., MSC-2510, #6A03, Bethesda, MD 20892-2510; (301) 496-2234. Fax, (301) 496-9970. Dr. Carl*

Kupfer, director; Terrence Gillen, assistant director, International Program Activities, (301) 496-4876. Information, (301) 496-5248. Internet, http://www.nei.nih.gov.

Conducts and funds research on the eye and visual disorders. Participates in international research.

NONPROFIT

American Academy of Ophthalmology, *1101 Vermont Ave. N.W., #700 20005-3570; (202) 737-6662. Fax, (202) 737-7061. Kathy G. Cohen, director. Internet, http://www.eyenet.org.*

Membership: eye physicians and surgeons. Provides information on eye diseases. Monitors legislation, regulations, and international research. (Headquarters in San Francisco.)

American Academy of Optometry, *6110 Executive Blvd., #506, Rockville, MD 20852; (301) 984-1441. Fax, (301) 984-4737. Lois Schoenbrun, executive director. Internet, http://www.aaopt.org.*

Membership: optometrists and students of optometry. Conducts research and continuing education; participates in international meetings; interests include primary care optometry, contact lenses, low vision, and diseases of the eye.

American Board of Opticianry, *10341 Democracy Lane, Fairfax, VA 22030; (703) 691-8356. Fax, (703) 691-3929. Vacant, executive director. Information, (703) 715-6435. Internet, aboncle@opticians.org.*

Establishes standards for opticians who dispense eyeglasses. Administers professional exams and awards certification; maintains registry of certified eyeglass dispensers. Adopts and enforces continuing education requirements; assists state licensing boards; approves educational offerings for recertification requirements.

American Optometric Assn., *1505 Prince St., Alexandria, VA 22314; (703) 739-9200. Fax, (703) 739-9497. Vacant, director, Washington Office. Internet, http://www.aoanet.org/aoanet.*

Membership: optometrists and optometry students. Monitors legislation and regulations and acts as liaison with international optometric groups and government optometrists; conducts continuing education programs for optometrists and provides information on eye care. (Headquarters in St. Louis.)

Assn. for Research in Vision and Ophthalmology, *9650 Rockville Pike, Bethesda, MD 20814-3998; (301) 571-1844. Fax, (301) 571-8311. Joanne Angle, executive director. Internet, admin@arvo.org or http://www.faseb.org/arvo.*

Promotes eye and vision research; issues awards for significant research and administers research grant program.

Assn. of Schools and Colleges of Optometry, *6110 Executive Blvd., #510, Rockville, MD 20852; (301) 231-5944. Fax, (301) 770-1828. Martin A. Wall, executive director. Internet, admini@opted.org or http://www.opted.org.*

Membership: U.S. and Puerto Rican optometry schools and colleges, and foreign affiliates. Provides information about the Optometry College Admissions Test to students. Monitors legislation and regulations.

Contact Lens Society of America, *441 Carlisle Dr., Reston, VA 20170; (703) 437-5100. Fax, (703) 437-0727. Tina M. Schott, executive director. Internet, clfa@huskynet.com or http://www.onlinenet.com/clsa.*

Membership: contact lens professionals. Conducts courses and continuing education seminars for contact lens fitters and technicians.

Eye Bank Assn. of America, *1001 Connecticut Ave. N.W., #601 20036-5504; (202) 775-4999. Fax, (202) 429-6036. Patricia Aiken-O'Neill, president. Internet, sightebaa@aol.com or http://www.restoresight.org.*

Membership: eye banks in Canada, England, Saudi Arabia, and the United States. Sets and enforces medical standards for eye banking; seeks to increase donations to eye, tissue, and organ banks; conducts training and certification programs for eye bank technicians; compiles statistics.

International Eye Foundation, *7801 Norfolk Ave., Bethesda, MD 20814; (301) 986-1830. Fax, (301) 986-1876. Victoria M. Sheffield, executive director. Internet, ief@iefusa.org.*

Operates eye health care and blindness prevention programs in developing countries. Sends volunteer surgeons and public health specialists to provide care; trains paramedical and public health personnel in developing countries in various aspects of public eye health care. Implements programs to control vitamin A deficiency and onchocerciasis (river blindness). Provides technology transfer and ophthalmic equipment and medicines.

Optical Laboratories Assn., *P.O. Box 2000, Merrifield, VA 22116-2000; (703) 359-2830. Fax, (703) 359-2834. Robert Dziuban, executive vice president. Internet, http://www.ola-labs.org.*

Membership: optical laboratories. Promotes the eyeware industry; sponsors conferences. Monitors legislation and regulations.

Opticians Assn. of America, *10341 Democracy Lane, Fairfax, VA 22030; (703) 691-8355. Fax, (703) 691-3929. David Digby, executive director. Internet, oaa@opticians. org or http://www.oaa.org.*

Membership: independent retail optical firms, optical corporations, state societies of opticians, and individual optical dispensers. Conducts education programs for members. Monitors legislation and regulations.

Vision Council of America, *1655 N. Fort Myer Dr., #200, Rosslyn, VA 22209; (703) 243-1508. Fax, (703) 243-1537. Susan Burton, executive director. Internet, http:// www.visionsite.org.*

Sponsors trade shows and public relations programs for the ophthalmic industry. Educates the public on developments in the optical industry.

See also AARP Andrus Foundation (p. 378)

✚ HEALTH SERVICES FOR SPECIAL GROUPS

AGENCIES

Administration for Children and Families *(Health and Human Services Dept.), 901 D St. S.W. (mailing address: 370 L'Enfant Promenade S.W., Washington, DC 20447); (202) 401-9200. Fax, (202) 401-5770. Olivia A. Golden, assistant secretary. Information, (202) 401-9215. Internet, http://www.acf.dhhs.gov.*

Administers and funds programs for Native Americans, children, youth, families, and those with developmental disabilities. Responsible for Social Services Block Grants to the states. Provides agencies with technical assistance; administers Head Start program; funds the National Runaway Switchboard, (800) 621-400, the Domestic Violence Hotline, (800) 799-7233, and programs for abused children.

Health Care Financing Administration *(Health and Human Services Dept.), Outcomes and Improvement, 7500 Security Blvd., S2-14-17, Baltimore, MD 21244-1850; (410) 786-6807. Fax, (410) 786-6730. Helene Fredeking, director.*

Monitors compliance of nursing homes, psychiatric hospitals, and long-term and intermediate care facilities with government standards. Focus includes quality of care, environmental conditions, and participation in Medicaid and Medicare programs. Coordinates health care programs for the mentally retarded.

Health Resources and Services Administration *(Health and Human Services Dept.), Community and*

Migrant Health, *4350 East-West Hwy., 7th Floor, Bethesda, MD 20814; (301) 594-4300. Fax, (301) 594-4983. Richard C. Bohrer, director.*

Awards grants to public and nonprofit migrant, community, and health care centers to provide direct health care services in areas that are medically underserved. Administers National Migrant Health Advisory Council.

Health Resources and Services Administration *(Health and Human Services Dept.), Health Resources Development, 5600 Fishers Lane, Parklawn Bldg., #705, Rockville, MD 20857; (301) 443-1993. Fax, (301) 443-9645. William H. Aspden Jr., deputy associate administrator.*

Administers programs that provide communities with grants for the delivery of health care services to persons infected with the HIV virus; supports health facilities for uncompensated care, construction grants, and loans; provides grants to organ procurement transplantation programs; plans, directs, coordinates, and monitors activities relating to emergency medical services and trauma system planning and implementation.

Health Resources and Services Administration *(Health and Human Services Dept.), Immigration Health Services, 425 Eye St. N.W., #3008 20536; (202) 514-3339. Fax, (202) 514-0095. Gene Migliaccio, director.*

Division of the Bureau of Primary Health Care. Works to improve the health of new immigrants and detained aliens in the United States; promotes increased access to comprehensive primary and preventive health care.

Health Resources and Services Administration *(Health and Human Services Dept.), Primary Health Care, 4350 East-West Hwy., #11-10, Bethesda, MD 20814; (301) 594-4110. Fax, (301) 594-4072. Dr. Marilyn H. Gaston, director.*

Advocates accessible primary health care for underserved communities and individuals. Promotes partnerships in public and private health care delivery communities. Researches and analyzes effectiveness of community based systems of care.

Health Resources and Services Administration *(Health and Human Services Dept.), Special Populations, 4350 East-West Hwy., West Towers Bldg., 9th Floor, Bethesda, MD 20814; (301) 594-4420. Fax, (301) 594-4989. Nathan Stinson, director.*

Awards grants to community-based organizations to provide primary health care services to special populations, including HIV-infected persons, women considered to be at risk, homeless individuals, substance abusers, elderly people, and native Hawaiian and Pacific Basin residents. Focus includes Alzheimer's disease.

Indian Health Service *(Health and Human Services Dept.), 5600 Fishers Lane, #6-05 Parklawn Bldg., Rockville, MD 20857; (301) 443-1083. Fax, (301) 443-4794. Dr. Michael H. Trujillo, director. Information, (301) 443-3593. Internet, http://www.tucson.ihs.gov.*

Operates hospitals and health centers that provide Native Americans and Alaska natives with preventive and remedial health care. Provides or improves sanitation and water supply systems in native American communities.

National Institute of Child Health and Human Development *(National Institutes of Health), National Center for Medical Rehabilitation Research, 6100 Executive Blvd., Bldg. 6100E, #2A-03, Bethesda, MD 20892-7510; (301) 402-2242. Fax, (301) 402-0832. Dr. Marcus Fuhrer, director. TDD, (301) 402-2554. Internet, http://silk.nih.gov/silk/NCMRR.*

Conducts and supports research to develop improved technologies, techniques, and prosthetic and orthotic devices for people with disabilities; promotes medical rehabilitation training.

National Institute on Deafness and Other Communication Disorders *(National Institutes of Health), 31 Center Dr., MSC-2320, #3C02, Bethesda, MD 20892-2320; (301) 402-0900. Fax, (301) 402-1590. Dr. James F. Battey Jr., director. Information, (301) 496-7243. TDD, (301) 496-6596. Internet, http://www.nih.gov/nidcd.*

Conducts and supports research and research training and disseminates information on hearing disorders and other communication processes, including diseases that affect hearing, balance, smell, taste, voice, speech, and language. Monitors international research.

Public Health and Science *(Health and Human Services Dept.), Minority Health, 5515 Security Lane, #1000 Rockwall II Bldg., Rockville, MD 20852; (301) 443-5084. Fax, (301) 594-0767. Clay E. Simpson Jr., deputy assistant secretary. Toll-free, (800) 444-6472. Internet, http://www.os.dhhs.gov/progorg/ophs/omh.*

Oversees the implementation of the secretary's Task Force on Black and Minority Health and legislative mandates; develops programs to meet the health care needs of minorities; awards grants to coalitions of minority community organizations and to minority AIDS education and prevention projects.

Rehabilitation Services Administration *(Education Dept.), 330 C St. S.W. 20202-2531; (202) 205-5482. Fax, (202) 205-9874. Fredric K. Schroeder, commissioner. TDD, (202) 205-9295.*

Allocates funds to state agencies and nonprofit organizations for programs serving eligible physically and mentally disabled persons; services provided by these funds include medical and psychological treatment as well as establishment of supported-employment and independent-living programs.

CONGRESS

House Commerce Committee, *Subcommittee on Health and the Environment, 2125 RHOB 20515; (202) 225-2927. Fax, (202) 225-1919. Michael Bilirakis, R-Fla., chair; James E. Derderian, staff director. Internet, http://www.house.gov/commerce/health.html.*

Jurisdiction over legislation on the mentally retarded, migrant health care, the disabled, long-term and nursing home programs, health care for the poor (including Medicaid and national health insurance proposals), and medical research on aging. (Jurisdiction over Native American health care shared with House Resources Committee.)

House Education and the Workforce Committee, *Subcommittee on Early Childhood, Youth, and Families, 2181 RHOB 20515; (202) 225-4527. Fax, (202) 225-9571. Frank Riggs, R-Calif., chair; Kevin Talley, staff director. Internet, http://www.house.gov/eeo.*

Jurisdiction over legislation on general programs for the elderly, including health and nutrition programs.

House Education and the Workforce Committee, *Subcommittee on Workforce Protections, 2181 RHOB 20515; (202) 225-4527. Fax, (202) 225-9571. Cass Ballenger, R-N.C., chair; Kevin Talley, staff director.*

Jurisdiction over workers' health and safety legislation, including migrant and agricultural labor matters.

House Resources Committee, *1324 LHOB 20515-6201; (202) 225-2761. Fax, (202) 225-5929. Don Young, R-Alaska, chair; Lloyd Jones, staff director. Internet, resource@hr.house.gov or http://www.house.gov/resources.*

Jurisdiction over legislation pertaining to Native American health care and special services; oversight of Native American health care programs. (Jurisdiction shared with House Commerce Committee.)

Senate Committee on Indian Affairs, *SH-838 20510; (202) 224-2251. Fax, (202) 224-2309. Ben Nighthorse Campbell, R-Colo., chair; Gary Bohnee, staff director.*

Jurisdiction over legislation pertaining to Native American health care; oversight of Native American health care programs.

Senate Finance Committee, *Subcommittee on Health Care, SD-219 20510; (202) 224-4515. Phil Gramm, R-*

Texas, chair; Julie James, staff contact. Internet, http://www.senate.gov/~finance.

Holds hearings on health legislation for low-income individuals, including Medicaid and national health insurance proposals.

Senate Labor and Human Resources Committee, SD-428 20510; (202) 224-5375. Fax, (202) 224-6510. James M. Jeffords, R-Vt., chair; Mark Powden, staff director. Internet, http://www.senate.gov/~labor.

Jurisdiction over legislation on migrant health care, health care for the poor and elderly (excluding Medicaid and Medicare), health care for individuals with physical and developmental disabilities, government-run health care facilities, and medical research on aging.

Senate Special Committee on Aging, SD-G31 20510; (202) 224-5364. Fax, (202) 224-8660. Charles E. Grassley, R-Iowa, chair; Ted Totman, staff director.

Studies and makes recommendations on the overall health problems of the elderly, including quality and cost of long-term care, and on access to and quality of health care for minority elderly; oversight of federally funded programs for the elderly, including Medicare, Medicaid, and programs concerning day-to-day care.

NONPROFIT

Americans for the Restitution and Righting of Old Wrongs (ARROW), 1000 Connecticut Ave. N.W., #1204 20036; (202) 296-0685. Fax, (202) 659-4377. Hazel Elbert, executive director. Internet, arrow1949@aol.com.

Recruits physicians and nurses to volunteer their services on reservation health care facilities; maintains personnel bank of volunteers. Works to prevent drug, alcohol, and child abuse.

Brain Injury Assn., 105 N. Alfred St., Alexandria, VA 22314; (703) 236-6000. Fax, (703) 236-6001. George Zitnay, president. Family helpline, (800) 444-6443.

Works to improve the quality of life for persons with traumatic brain injuries and for their families. Promotes the prevention of head injuries through public awareness and education programs. Offers state-level support services for individuals and their families. Monitors legislation and regulations.

Catholic Health Assn. of the United States, 1875 Eye St. N.W., #1000 20006; (202) 296-3993. Fax, (202) 296-3997. Michael Place, president. Internet, http://www.chausa.org.

Concerned with the health care needs of the poor and disadvantaged. Promotes health care reform, including universal insurance coverage, and more cost-effective, affordable health care.

Center on Disability and Health, 1522 K St. N.W., #800 20005; (202) 842-4408. Fax, (202) 842-2402. Bob Griss, director. Internet, bgrisscdh@aol.com.

Promotes changes in the financing and delivery of health care to meet the needs of persons with disabilities and other chronic health conditions. Conducts research; provides technical assistance to disability groups and agencies. Monitors legislation and regulations.

Farm Worker Health Services, Inc., 1234 Massachusetts Ave. N.W., C-1017 20005-4526; (202) 347-7377. Fax, (202) 347-6385. Vacant, executive director. Internet, farmwlths@aol.com.

Funded by the Health and Human Services Dept. Assigns health professionals and allied health care personnel to health facilities along the East Coast. Assists migrants in addressing health and social needs and familiarizes providers with migrants' special health care needs.

National Assn. of Community Health Centers, 1330 New Hampshire Ave. N.W., #122 20036; (202) 659-8008. Fax, (202) 659-8519. Thomas Van Coverden, president.

Membership: community health centers, migrant and homeless health programs, and other community health care programs. Provides the medically underserved with health services; seeks to ensure the continued development of community health care programs through policy analysis, research, technical assistance, publications, education, and training.

National Coalition of Hispanic Health and Human Services Organizations, 1501 16th St. N.W. 20036; (202) 387-5000. Fax, (202) 797-4353. Jane L. Delgado, president.

Assists agencies and groups serving the Hispanic community in general health care and in targeting health and psychosocial problems; provides information, technical assistance, health care provider training, and policy analysis; coordinates and supports research. Interests include mental health, chronic diseases, substance abuse, maternal and child health, youth issues, juvenile delinquency, and access to care.

National Easter Seal Society, 700 13th St. N.W. 20005; (202) 347-3066. Fax, (202) 737-7914. Joseph D. Romer, executive vice president. TDD, (202) 347-7385. Internet, http://www.seals.com.

Federation of state and local groups with programs that help people with disabilities achieve independence. Washington office monitors legislation and regulations. Affiliates assist individuals with a broad range of disabilities, including muscular dystrophy, cerebral palsy, stroke, speech and hearing loss, blindness, amputation, and learning disabilities. Services include physical, occupational, vocational, and speech therapy; speech, hearing, physical, and vocational evaluation; psychological testing and counseling; personal and family counseling; and special education programs. (Headquarters in Chicago.)

National Health Law Program, *1101 14th St. N.W., #405 20005; (202) 289-7661. Fax, (202) 289-7724. Lawrence Lavin, director. Internet, nhelp@healthlaw.org or http://www.healthlaw.org.*

Organization of lawyers representing the economically disadvantaged, minorities, and the elderly in issues concerning federal, state, and local health care programs. Offers technical assistance and training for health law specialists. (Headquarters in Los Angeles.)

Spina Bifida Assn. of America, *4590 MacArthur Blvd. N.W., #250 20007-4226; (202) 944-3285. Fax, (202) 944-3295. Lawrence Pencak, executive director. Toll-free, (800) 621-3141. Internet, sbaa@sbaa.org or http://www.sbaa.org.*

Membership: individuals with spina bifida, their supporters, and concerned professionals. Offers educational programs and support services; acts as a clearinghouse; provides referrals. Serves as U.S. member of the International Federation for Hydrocephalus and Spina Bifida, which is headquartered in Geneva. Monitors legislation and regulations.

Elderly

See also Medicaid and Medicare (this chapter); Nursing Homes and Hospices (this chapter); Senior Citizens (chap. 1); Social Services and Disabilities (chap. 18)

AGENCIES

National Institute on Aging *(National Institutes of Health), 31 Center Dr., MSC-2292, #5C35, Bethesda, MD 20892-2292; (301) 496-9265. Fax, (301) 496-2525. Dr. Richard J. Hodes, director; Leslie Stenull, director, International Activities, (301) 496-0767. Information, (301) 496-1752. Internet, http://www.nih.gov/nia.*

Conducts and funds research; disseminates information on the biological, medical, behavioral, and social aspects of aging and the common problems of the elderly

NONPROFIT

AARP Andrus Foundation, *601 E St. N.W. 20049; (202) 434-6200. Fax, (202) 434-6458. Margaret Dixon, chair.*

Awards grants for applied research projects in gerontology. Disseminates research findings to professionals, policymakers, the media, and the public. Interests

include vision loss, arthritis, breast cancer, mental health, and the effects of life-prolonging medical technology. (Affiliated with American Assn. of Retired Persons.)

Alliance for Aging Research, *2021 K St. N.W., #305 20006; (202) 293-2856. Fax, (202) 785-8574. Daniel Perry, executive director. Internet, agecom@aol.com.*

Membership: senior corporate and foundation executives, science leaders, and congressional representatives. Promotes scientific research on aging and the problems of the elderly.

Alzheimer's Assn., *1319 F St. N.W., #710 20004-1106; (202) 393-7737. Fax, (202) 393-2109. Stephen R. McConnell, senior vice president, Public Policy. Toll-free, (800) 272-3900. Internet, http://www.alz.org.*

Offers family support services and educates the public about Alzheimer's disease, a neurological disorder mainly affecting the brain tissue in older adults. Promotes research and long-term care protection. Monitors legislation and regulations. (Headquarters in Chicago.)

American Assn. of Homes and Services for the Aging, *901 E St. N.W., #500 20004; (202) 783-2242. Fax, (202) 783-2255. Michael F. Rodgers, senior vice president, Policy and Governmental Affairs. Internet, http://www. aahsa.org.*

Membership: nonprofit homes, housing, and health-related facilities for the elderly sponsored by religious, fraternal, labor, private, and governmental organizations. Conducts research on long-term care for the elderly; sponsors institutes and workshops on accreditation, financing, and institutional life. Monitors legislation and regulations.

American Assn. of Retired Persons, *Health and Long Term Care, 601 E St. N.W., #A5 20049; (202) 434-2230. Fax, (202) 434-7683. Edna Kane Williams, manager. Internet, http://www.aarp.org.*

Promotes good health habits among older persons and encourages effective use of the health care system through educational and voluntary programs. Assists older adults in making health care decisions.

Gerontological Society of America, *1275 K St. N.W., #350 20005-4006; (202) 842-1275. Fax, (202) 842-1150. Lisa Gargano, executive director. Internet, geron@geron.org or http://www.geron.org.*

Scientific organization of researchers, educators, and professionals in the field of aging. Promotes the study of aging and the application of research to public policy; interests include international aging and migration.

National Assn. for Homecare, *228 7th St. S.E. 20003; (202) 547-7424. Fax, (202) 547-3540. Val J. Halaman-daris, president. Internet, http://www.nahc.org.*

Membership: home care professionals and parapro-fessionals. Advocates the rights of the elderly, infirm, and terminally ill to remain independent in their own homes as long as possible. Monitors legislation and regulations.

National Citizens' Coalition for Nursing Home Reform, *1424 16th St. N.W., #202 20036-2211; (202) 332-2275. Fax, (202) 332-2949. Sarah Burger, acting exec-utive director.*

Seeks to improve the long-term care system and qual-ity of life for residents in nursing homes and other facili-ties for the elderly; coordinates the Campaign for Quality Care. Promotes citizen participation in all aspects of nursing homes; acts as clearinghouse for nursing home advocacy.

National Council of Senior Citizens, *8403 Colesville Rd., #1200, Silver Spring, MD 20910-3314; (301) 578-8800. Fax, (301) 578-8999. Steve Protulis, executive direc-tor. Internet, http://www.ncscinc.org.*

Supports expansion of Medicare, improved health programs, national health care, and reduced cost of drugs. Nursing Home Information Service provides information on nursing home standards and regulations.

National Council on the Aging, *409 3rd St. S.W., 2nd Floor 20024; (202) 479-1200. Fax, (202) 479-0735. James Firman, president. Information, (202) 479-6653. Press, (202) 479-6610. Library, (202) 479-6669. TDD, (202) 479-6674. Internet, info@ncoa.org or http://www.ncoa.org.*

Promotes the physical, mental, and emotional health of older persons and studies adult daycare and commu-nity-based long-term care. Monitors legislation and reg-ulations. Library open to the public.

National Hispanic Council on Aging, *2713 Ontario Rd. N.W. 20009; (202) 265-1288. Fax, (202) 745-2522. Marta Sotomayor, president. Internet, nhcoa@worldnet. att.net or http://www.incacorp.com/nhcoa.*

Membership: senior citizens, health care workers, professionals in the field of aging, and others in the United States and Puerto Rico who are interested in top-ics related to Hispanics and aging.

National Osteoporosis Foundation, *1150 17th St. N.W., #500 20036; (202) 223-2226. Fax, (202) 223-2237. Sandra C. Raymond, executive director. Toll-free, (800) 223-9994. Internet, http://www.nof.org.*

Seeks to reduce osteoporosis through educational programs, research, and patient advocacy.

National State Long Term Care Ombudsman Resource Center, *1424 16th St. N.W., #202 20036-2211; (202) 332-2275. Fax, (202) 332-2949. Jacquelyn Koenig, director.*

Provides technical assistance, management guidance, policy analysis, and program development information in behalf of state and substate ombudsman programs. (Affiliate of the National Citizens' Coalition for Nursing Home Reform.)

United Seniors Health Cooperative, *1331 H St. N.W., #500 20005-4706; (202) 393-6222. Fax, (202) 783-0588. Eric Shulman, acting president. Internet, http://www. ushc-online.org.*

Provides members with health care information and health insurance counseling. Operates the Cooperative Caring Network designed to help older people remain independent in their homes. Publishes on health issues affecting older Americans.

Prenatal, Maternal, and Child Health Care

See also Children and Families (chap. 18)

AGENCIES

Centers for Disease Control and Prevention *(Health and Human Services Dept.), 200 Independence Ave. S.W., #746-G 20201; (202) 690-8598. Fax, (202) 690-7519. Donald E. Shriber, associate director, Washington Office. Internet, http://www.cdc.gov.*

Conducts research and assists state and local health agencies that receive grants for the control of childhood diseases preventable by immunization. (Headquarters in Atlanta: 1600 Clifton Rd. N.E. 30333. Public inquiries, (404) 639-3534.)

Health Care Financing Administration *(Health and Human Services Dept.), Medicaid, 7500 Security Blvd., #C52223, Baltimore, MD 21244; (410) 786-3230. Fax, (410) 786-0025. Judith D. Moore, deputy director.*

Develops health care policies and programs for needy children under Medicaid; works with the Public Health Service and other related agencies to coordinate the department's child health resources.

Health Resources and Services Administration *(Health and Human Services Dept.), Maternal and Child Health, 5600 Fishers Lane, #18-05, Rockville, MD 20857; (301) 443-2170. Fax, (301) 443-1797. Dr. Audrey H. Nora, director. Internet, http:.//www.os.dhhs.gov/hrsa/ mchb.*

Administers block grants to states for mothers and children and for children with special health needs;

awards funding for research training, genetic disease testing, counseling and information dissemination, hemophilia diagnostic and treatment centers, and demonstration projects to improve the health of mothers and children. Interests also include pediatric AIDS health care and emergency medical services for children.

Health Resources and Services Administration *(Health and Human Services Dept.), National Maternal and Child Health Clearinghouse, 2070 Chain Bridge Rd., #450, Vienna, VA 22182; (703) 821-8955. Fax, (703) 821-2098. Linda Cramer, project director. Internet, http://www.circsol.com/mch.*

Disseminates information on various aspects of maternal and child health and genetics.

Health Resources and Services Administration *(Health and Human Services Dept.), National Sudden Infant Death Syndrome Resource Center, 2070 Chain Bridge Rd., #450, Vienna, VA 22182; (703) 821-8955. Fax, (703) 821-2098. Olivia Cowdrill, director.*

A component of the National Maternal and Child Health Clearinghouse. Provides information about sudden infant death syndrome (SIDS), apnea, and related issues; makes referrals to local SIDS programs and parent support groups. Publishes educational information about SIDS.

Health Resources and Services Administration *(Health and Human Services Dept.), National Vaccine Injury Compensation Program, 5600 Fishers Lane, Parklawn Bldg., #8A-35, Rockville, MD 20857; (301) 443-6593. Fax, (301) 443-8196. Thomas E. Balbier Jr., director. Toll-free hotline, (800) 338-2382. Internet, http://www.hrsa.dhhs.gov/bhpr/vicp/new.htm.*

Provides no-fault compensation to individuals injured by certain childhood vaccines (diphtheria and tetanus toxoids and pertussis vaccine; measles, mumps, and rubella vaccine; and oral polio and inactivated polio vaccine).

National Institute of Child Health and Human Development *(National Institutes of Health), Center Drive, Bldg. 31, MSC-2425, Bethesda, MD 20892-2425; (301) 496-3454. Fax, (301) 402-1104. Dr. Duane F. Alexander, director; Antonia Novella, special representative to UNICEF, (301) 496-0186. Information, (301) 496-5133. Internet, http://www.nih.gov/nichd.*

Conducts research and research training on biological and behavioral human development. Studies reproduction and population studies, perinatal biology and infant mortality, congenital defects, nutrition, human learning and behavior, medical rehabilitation, and mental retardation. Interests include UNICEF and other international organizations.

National Institute of Child Health and Human Development *(National Institutes of Health), Center for Research for Mothers and Children, 6100 Executive Blvd., #4B05, Bethesda, MD 20892-7510 (mailing address: 9000 Rockville Pike, #4B05, MSC-7510, Bethesda, MD 20892-7510); (301) 496-5097. Fax, (301) 480-7773. Dr. Sumner J. Yaffe, director.*

Supports biomedical and behavioral science research and training for maternal and child health care. Areas of study include fetal development, maternal-infant health problems, HIV-related diseases in childbearing women, roles of nutrients and hormones in child growth, developmental disabilities, and behavioral development.

Public Health and Science *(Health and Human Services Dept.), Adolescent Pregnancy Programs, 4350 East-West Hwy., #200, Bethesda, MD 20814; (301) 594-4004. Fax, (301) 594-5981. Patrick J. Sheeran, acting director. Internet, http://www.dhhs.gov/progorg/opa/oapp.html.*

Awards, administers, and evaluates research and demonstration grants through the Adolescent Family Life Program, which funds community health care and pregnancy prevention programs. Administers a program that provides pregnant adolescents and children of teenage parents with comprehensive health education and social services, and a program that focuses on sexual abstinence. Interests include adolescent sexual behavior, adoption, and early childbearing.

NONPROFIT

Advocates for Youth, *1025 Vermont Ave. N.W., #200 20005; (202) 347-5700. Fax, (202) 347-2263. James Wagoner, executive director. Internet, info@advocatesforyouth.org or http://www.advocatesforyouth.org.*

Seeks to reduce the incidence of unintended teenage pregnancy and AIDS through public education, training and technical assistance, research, and media programs.

Alan Guttmacher Institute, *1120 Connecticut Ave. N.W., #460 20036-3902; (202) 296-4012. Fax, (202) 223-5756. Cory L. Richards, vice president, Public Policy. Internet, info@agi-usa.org or http://www.agi-usa.org.*

Conducts research, policy analysis, and public education in reproductive health issues, including maternal and child health. (Headquarters in New York.)

Alliance to End Childhood Lead Poisoning, *227 Massachusetts Ave. N.E., #200 20002; (202) 543-1147. Fax, (202) 543-4466. Don Ryan, executive director. Internet, aeclp@aeclp.org or http://www.aeclp.org.*

Works to increase awareness of childhood lead poisoning and to develop and implement prevention programs.

American Academy of Child and Adolescent Psychiatry, *3615 Wisconsin Ave. N.W. 20016; (202) 966-7300. Fax, (202) 966-2891. Virginia Q. Anthony, executive director. Internet, http://www.aacap.org.*

Membership: psychiatrists working with children and adolescents. Sponsors annual meeting and review for medical board examinations; provides information on child abuse, youth suicide, and drug abuse; monitors international research and U.S. legislation concerning mentally ill children.

American Academy of Pediatrics, *601 13th St. N.W., #400N 20005; (202) 347-8600. Fax, (202) 393-6137. Jackie Noyes, director. Toll-free, (800) 336-5475. Internet, kids1st@aap.org or http://www.aap.org.*

Advocates for maternal and child health legislation and regulations. Interests include increased access and coverage for persons under age 21, immunizations, injury prevention, environmental hazards, child abuse, emergency medical services, biomedical research, Medicaid, disabilities, pediatric AIDS, substance abuse, and nutrition. (Headquarters in Elk Grove Village, Ill.)

American Assn. of Children's Residential Centers, *440 1st St. N.W., 3rd Floor 20001; (202) 628-1816. Fax, (202) 638-4004. Jeff Kramer, executive director. Internet, aacrc@dc.net.*

Membership: mental health out-of-home agencies and individuals interested in clinical practice in residential care for children with emotional disturbance. Represents interests of children with emotional disturbance and their families before the government; holds conferences; provides information on residential treatment.

American College of Nurse-Midwives, *818 Connecticut Ave. N.W., #900 20006; (202) 728-9860. Fax, (202) 728-9897. Deanne Williams, chief operating officer. Press, (202) 728-9875. Internet, info@acnm.org or http://www.midwife.org.*

Membership: certified nurse-midwives who preside at deliveries. Interests include preventive health care for women.

American College of Obstetricians and Gynecologists, *409 12th St. S.W. 20024 (mailing address: P.O. Box 96920, Washington, DC 20090-6920); (202) 638-5577. Fax, (202) 484-5107. Dr. Ralph Hale, executive director. Press, (202) 484-3321. Internet, http://www.acog.org.*

Membership: medical specialists in obstetrics and gynecology. Monitors legislation, regulations, and international research on maternal and child health care.

Children's Defense Fund, *25 E St. N.W. 20001; (202) 628-8787. Fax, (202) 662-3510. Marian Wright Edelman, president. Internet, http://www.childrensdefense.org.*

Advocacy group concerned with programs for children and youth. Assesses adequacy of the Early and Periodic Screening, Diagnosis, and Treatment Program for Medicaid-eligible children. Promotes adequate prenatal care for adolescent and lower-income women; works to prevent adolescent pregnancy.

Human Growth Foundation, *7777 Leesburg Pike, #202S, Falls Church, VA 22043; (703) 883-1773. Fax, (703) 883-1776. Kimberly Frye, executive director. Toll-free, (800) 451-6434. Internet, hgfound@erols.com and http://www.genetic.org/hgf.*

Promotes research into growth and growth disorders; provides those affected by growth disorders and their families with education and support; encourages exchange of information with the medical profession. Sponsors Human Growth Month and national conferences; awards research grants.

Lamaze International, *1200 19th St. N.W., #300 20036-2401; (202) 857-1128. Fax, (202) 223-4579. Linda Harmon, executive director. Toll-free, (800) 368-4404. Internet, lamaze@dc.sba.com or http://www.lamaze-childbirth.com.*

Membership: supporters of the Lamaze method of childbirth, including parents, physicians, childbirth educators, and other health professionals. Trains and certifies Lamaze educators. Provides referral service for parents seeking Lamaze classes.

March of Dimes Birth Defects Foundation, *1901 L St. N.W., #260 20036; (202) 659-1800. Fax, (202) 296-2964. Marina Weiss, director, Policy and Government Affairs. Internet, http://www.modimes.org.*

Works to prevent birth defects, low birth weight, and infant mortality. Awards grants for research and provides funds for treatment of birth defects. Medical services grantees provide prenatal counseling. Monitors legislation and regulations. (Headquarters in White Plains, N.Y.)

National Assn. of Children's Hospitals and Related Institutions, *401 Wythe St., Alexandria, VA 22314; (703) 684-1355. Fax, (703) 684-1589. Lawrence A. McAndrews, president.*

Advocates and promotes education and research on child health care related to children's hospitals; compiles statistics and provides information on pediatric hospitalizations.

National Center for Education in Maternal and Child Health, *2000 15th St. North, #701, Arlington, VA 22201; (703) 524-7802. Fax, (703) 524-9335. Dr. Rochelle Mayer, director. Internet, info@ncemch.org or http://www.ncemch.org.*

Collects and disseminates information about maternal and child health to health professionals and the general public. Carries out special projects for the U.S. Maternal and Child Health Bureau. Library open to the public by appointment. (Affiliated with Georgetown University.)

National Consortium for Child Mental Health Services, *3615 Wisconsin Ave. N.W. 20016; (202) 966-7300. Fax, (202) 966-2891. Virginia Q. Anthony, executive director.*

Membership: organizations interested in developing mental health services for children. Fosters information exchange; advises local, state, and federal agencies that develop children's mental health services. (Affiliated with American Academy of Child and Adolescent Psychiatry.)

National Organization on Adolescent Pregnancy, Parenting, and Prevention, *1319 F St. N.W., #400 20004; (202) 783-5770. Fax, (202) 783-5775. Patricia Canessa, president. Internet, noappp@erols.com or http://www.noappp.org.*

Membership: health and social work professionals, community and state leaders, and individuals. Promotes services to prevent and resolve problems associated with adolescent sexuality, pregnancy, and parenting. Helps to develop stable and supportive family relationships through program support and evaluation. Monitors legislation and regulations.

National Organization on Fetal Alcohol Syndrome, *1819 H St. N.W., #750 20006; (202) 785-4585. Fax, (202) 466-6456. Lance Friedsam, president. Toll-free, (800) 666-6327. Internet, nofas@erols.com or http://www.nofas.org.*

Works to eradicate alcohol-related birth defects through public education, conferences, medical school curricula, and partnerships with federal programs interested in fetal alcohol syndrome.

Zero to Three/National Center for Infants, Toddlers, and Families, *734 15th St. N.W., 10th Floor 20005; (202) 638-1144. Fax, (202) 638-0851. Matthew Melmed, executive director. Publications, (800) 899-4301.*

Works to improve infant health, mental health, and development. Sponsors training programs for professionals; offers fellowships. Provides private and government organizations with information on infant development issues.

See also Assn. of Reproductive Health Professionals (p. 367); Cystic Fibrosis Foundation (p. 394); Program for Appropriate Technology in Health (p. 361)

⊞ HEALTH TOPICS: RESEARCH AND ADVOCACY

See also Animals and Plants (chap. 9); General Policy: Medical Devices and Technology (this chapter); Mental Health (this chapter)

For research on aging, see Health Services for Special Groups, Elderly (this chapter)

AGENCIES

Armed Forces Institute of Pathology *(Defense Dept.), 14th St. and Alaska Ave. N.W. 20306-6000; (202) 782-2100. Fax, (202) 782-9376. Col. Michael J. Dickerson (USAF), director. Internet, http://www.afip.mil.*

Maintains a central laboratory of pathology for consultation and diagnosis of pathologic tissue for the Defense Dept., other federal agencies, and civilian pathologists. Conducts research and provides instruction in advanced pathology and related subjects.

Armed Forces Radiobiology Research Institute *(Defense Dept.), National Naval Medical Center, 8901 Wisconsin Ave., Bethesda, MD 20889-5603; (301) 295-1210. Fax, (301) 295-4967. Col. Robert Eng (MSUSA), director. Internet, http://www.afrri.usuhs.mil.*

Serves as the principal ionizing radiation radiobiology research laboratory under the jurisdiction of the Uniformed Services University of the Health Sciences. Participates in international conferences and projects. Library open to the public.

Environment, Safety, and Health *(Energy Dept.), Health Studies, 19901 Germantown Rd., EH-6/27OCC, Germantown, MD 20874-1290; (301) 903-5926. Fax, (301) 903-3445. Paul J. Seligman, deputy assistant secretary.*

Manages the federal program that addresses the potential health effects of electric and magnetic fields. Oversees the epidemiologic studies programs, the international health studies programs, and the occupational medicine and medical surveillance programs of the Energy Dept.

Fogarty International Center *(National Institutes of Health), 9000 Rockville Pike, Bldg. 31, #B2C02, Bethesda, MD 20892-2220; (301) 496-1415. Fax, (301) 402-2173. Philip E. Schambra, director. Internet, http://www.nih.gov/fic.*

Coordinates international epidemiologic research on chronic and infectious diseases. Disseminates information on biomedical research in the United States and abroad; studies international health issues. Directs John

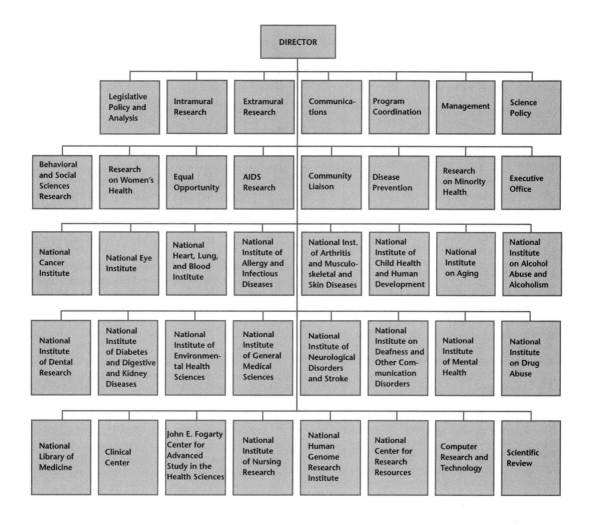

E. Fogarty International Center/World Health Organization programs in biomedical research and training.

Health Resources and Services Administration

(Health and Human Services Dept.), Transplantation, 5600 Fishers Lane, #7-29, Rockville, MD 20857; (301) 443-7577. Fax, (301) 594-6095. John L. Nelson, acting director. Internet, rdean@hrsa.dhhs.gov.

Implements provisions of the National Organ Transplant Act. Provides information on federal, state, and private programs involved in transplantation; supports a national computerized network for organ procurement and matching; maintains information on transplant recipients; awards grants to organ procurement organizations. Administers the National Marrow Donor Program, which maintains a registry of potential unrelated bone marrow donors.

National Heart, Lung, and Blood Institute

(National Institutes of Health), 9000 Rockville Pike, Bldg. 31, #5A52, Bethesda, MD 20892; (301) 496-5166. Fax, (301) 402-0818. Dr. Claude Lenfant, director; Dr. Ruth Hegyeli, associate director, international programs, (301) 496-5375. Internet, http://www.nhlbi.nih.gov.

Collects and disseminates information on diseases of the heart, lung, and blood, on sleep disorders, and on transfusion medicine, with an emphasis on disease prevention. Conducts educational programs for scientists and clinicians; participates in international research.

National Institute of Diabetes and Digestive and Kidney Diseases *(National Institutes of Health), 9000 Rockville Pike, Bldg. 31, #9A52, Bethesda, MD 20892; (301) 496-5877. Fax, (301) 402-2125. Dr. Phillip Gorden, director.*

Conducts and supports research on kidney, urologic, hematologic, digestive, metabolic, and endocrine diseases, as well as on diabetes and nutrition. Provides health information to the public; participates in international research.

National Institute of General Medical Sciences *(National Institutes of Health), 45 Center Dr., MSC-6200, #2AN12B, Bethesda, MD 20892-6200; (301) 594-2172. Fax, (301) 402-0156. Marvin Cassman, director. Internet, http://www.nih.gov/nigms.*

Supports basic biomedical research and training that are not targeted to specific diseases; focus includes cell biology, genetics, pharmacology, and systemic response to trauma and anesthesia.

National Institutes of Health *(Health and Human Services Dept.), 1 Center Dr., Bldg. 1, #126, Bethesda, MD 20892-0148; (301) 496-2433. Fax, (301) 402-2700. Harold Varmus, director. Press, (301) 496-4461. Internet, http://www.nih.gov.*

Supports and conducts biomedical research on the causes and prevention of diseases; furnishes health professionals and the public with information.

National Institutes of Health *(Health and Human Services Dept.), Center for Information Technology, 9000 Rockville Pike, Bldg. 12A, #3033, Bethesda, MD 20892-5654; (301) 496-5703. Fax, (301) 402-1754. Emmett Ward, acting director. Information, (301) 496-6203. Internet, http://www.nih.gov/dcrt.html.*

Responsible for incorporating computers into biomedical research and administrative procedures of NIH. Serves as the primary scientific and technological resource for NIH in the areas of high performance computing, database applications, mathematics, statistics, laboratory automation, engineering, computer science and technology, telecommunications, and information resources management.

National Institutes of Health *(Health and Human Services Dept.), Minority Biomedical Research Support Program, 45 Center Dr., Bldg. 45, #2AS.37, Bethesda, MD 20892; (301) 594-3900. Fax, (301) 480-2753. Dr. Clifton A. Poodry, director.*

Awards grants to eligible minority universities and colleges to support biomedical research by minority students and faculty; funds development of research facilities.

National Institutes of Health *(Health and Human Services Dept.), National Center for Research Resources, 31 South Drive, MSC-2128, Bldg. 31, #3B11, Bethesda, MD 20892-5662; (301) 496-5793. Fax, (301) 402-0006. Dr. Judith L. Vaitukaitis, director. Internet, http://www.ncrr.nih.gov.*

Discovers, develops, and provides biomedical researchers with access to critical research technologies and resources, including sophisticated instrumentation, models of human disease, and clinical research environments.

National Institutes of Health *(Health and Human Services Dept.), Protection from Research Risks, 6100 Executive Blvd., #3B01, Rockville, MD 20892-7507; (301) 496-7005. Fax, (301) 402-2071. Gary B. Ellis, director. Human subjects, (301) 496-7041. Animal welfare, (301) 496-7163.*

Monitors the use of humans and animals in research to ensure that programs and procedures comply with Public Health Service and Health and Human Services Dept. regulations; conducts and develops educational programs for the protection of human subjects and the humane care and use of laboratory animals; helps other organizations address ethical issues in medicine and research.

National Institutes of Health *(Health and Human Services Dept.), Research Grants, 6701 Rockledge Dr., MSC-7776, Rockledge II Bldg., #3109, Bethesda, MD 20892-7776; (301) 435-1114. Fax, (301) 480-3965. Dr. Elvera Ehrenfeld, director. Information, (301) 435-0714.*

Conducts scientific merit review of research grant and fellowship applications submitted to NIH. Assists in formulating grant and award policies. Compiles, stores, and analyzes information on operating grant programs. Disseminates information on obtaining research grants.

National Institutes of Health *(Health and Human Services Dept.), Research on Minority Health, 1 Center Dr., Bldg. 1, #260, Bethesda, MD 20892-0164; (301) 402-1366. Fax, (301) 402-2517. Dr. John Ruffin, associate director.*

Coordinates the development of NIH policies and objectives related to minority health research and research training programs. Encourages minorities to work in the biomedical research field.

National Library of Medicine *(National Institutes of Health), 8600 Rockville Pike, Bethesda, MD 20894; (301) 496-6221. Fax, (301) 496-4450. Dr. Donald A. B. Lindberg, director. Internet, http://www.nlm.nih.gov.*

Offers medical library services and computer-based reference service to the public, health professionals, libraries in medical schools and hospitals, and research institutions; operates a toxicology information service for the scientific community, industry, and federal agencies; assists medical libraries through the National Network of Libraries of Medicines with research in medical library science. Assists in the improvement of basic library resources.

National Library of Medicine (*National Institutes of Health*), *International Programs, 8600 Rockville Pike, Bldg. 38, #2S20, Bethesda, MD 20894; (301) 496-2311. Fax, (301) 496-4450. Elliot R. Siegel, director.*

Facilitates worldwide use of the library's medical databases, through agreements with individual nations, international organizations, and commercial vendors. Helps the library acquire and share international biomedical literature; promotes international collaboration in creating new databases. Conducts programs for international visitors.

Naval Medical Research Institute (*Defense Dept.*), *8901 Wisconsin Ave., Bethesda, MD 20889-5607; (301) 295-0021. Fax, (301) 295-2720. Capt. Thomas J. Contreares Jr., commanding officer. Internet, http://131.158. 70.70.*

Performs basic and applied biomedical research in areas of military importance, including infectious diseases, hyperbaric medicine, wound repair enhancement, environmental stress, and immunobiology. Provides support to field laboratories and naval hospitals; monitors research internationally.

Walter Reed Army Institute of Research (*Defense Dept.*), *6825 16th St. N.W., #1103 20307-5100; (202) 782-3551. Fax, (202) 782-3114. Col. Martin H. Crumrine, director. Internet, http://wrair-www.army.mil.*

Provides research, education, and training in support of the Defense Dept.'s health care system. Interests include biochemistry, biometrics, communicable diseases, pathology, surgery, veterinary medicine, and defense against biological and chemical agents.

Warren Grant Magnuson Clinical Center (*National Institutes of Health*), *9000 Rockville Pike, Bldg. 10, #2C146, Bethesda, MD 20892; (301) 496-4114. Fax, (301) 402-0244. Dr. John I. Gallin, director. Information, (301) 496-2351. Internet, http://www.cc.nih.gov.*

Serves as a clinical research center for the NIH; patients are referred by physicians throughout the United States and overseas.

CONGRESS

House Commerce Committee, *Subcommittee on Health and the Environment, 2125 RHOB 20515; (202)* 225-2927. Fax, (202) 225-1919. Michael Bilirakis, R-Fla., chair; James E. Derderian, staff director. Internet, http://www.house.gov/commerce/health.html.

Jurisdiction over legislation on health research, the treatment of cancer, AIDS, medical research on human subjects, and developmental disabilities (including epilepsy, cerebral palsy, autism, and mental retardation).

House Science Committee, *Subcommittee on Basic Research, B374 RHOB 20515; (202) 225-7858. Fax, (202) 225-7815. Vacant, chair; Steve Eule, staff director. Press, (202) 225-0584. Internet, http://www.house.gov/science.*

Jurisdiction over legislation on research and development involving health, nutrition, and medical programs.

Senate Labor and Human Resources Committee, *Subcommittee on Public Health and Safety, SD-422 20510; (202) 224-7139. Fax, (202) 228-5044. Bill Frist, R-Tenn., chair; Susan Ramthun, staff director. Internet, http://www.senate.gov/~labor.*

Jurisdiction over legislation on health research and health professions education. Oversight of public health programs, including the National Institutes of Health, Centers for Disease Control and Prevention, Agency for Health Care Policy and Research, and Substance Abuse and Mental Health Services Administration. Oversight of the Occupational Safety and Health Administration.

NONPROFIT

American Physiological Society, *9650 Rockville Pike, Bethesda, MD 20814-3991; (301) 530-7105. Fax, (301) 571-8305. Dr. Martin Frank, executive director. Internet, info@aps.faseb.org or http://www.faseb.org/aps.*

Researches how the body and its organ systems function. Promotes scientific research, education, and dissemination of information; monitors international research. Offers travel fellowships for scientific meetings; encourages minority participation in physiological research. Works to establish standards for the humane care and use of laboratory animals.

American Trauma Society, *8903 Presidential Pkwy., #512, Upper Marlboro, MD 20772-2656; (301) 420-4189. Fax, (301) 420-0617. Harry Teter, executive director. Internet, http://www.amtrauma.org.*

Seeks to prevent trauma and improve its treatment. Coodinates programs aimed at reducing the incidence and severity of trauma; sponsors research. Monitors legislation and regulations.

Assn. for Health Services Research, *1130 Connecticut Ave. N.W., #700 20036; (202) 223-2477. Fax, (202) 835-8972. Michael Stafford, chief executive officer. Internet, http://www.ahsr.org.*

Membership: universities, private research organizations, professional associations, consulting firms, advocacy organizations, insurers, managed care companies, health care systems, and pharmaceutical companies. Serves as an information clearinghouse on health services research; works to increase public and private funding for research. Monitors legislation and regulations.

Center for Patient Advocacy, *1350 Beverly Rd., #108, McLean, VA 22101; (703) 748-0400. Fax, (703) 748-0402. Terre McFillan Hall, executive director. Toll-free, (800) 846-7444. Internet, patientadv@aol.com or http://www. patientadvocacy.org.*

Supports the right of patients to receive state-of-the-art medical care in a timely manner. Monitors the Food and Drug Administration's regulation of drugs and medical devices. Works to preserve the doctor-patient relationship and establish universal clinical practice guidelines. Monitors legislation and regulations.

Howard Hughes Medical Institute, *4000 Jones Bridge Rd., Chevy Chase, MD 20815-6789; (301) 215-8500. Fax, (301) 215-8663. Dr. Purnell W. Choppin, president. Internet, http://www.hhmi.org.*

Conducts biomedical research programs in major academic medical centers and universities. Areas of research include cell biology, genetics, immunology, neuroscience, and structural biology. Maintains a grants program in science education, including postgraduate, graduate, undergraduate, and precollege levels.

Impotence World Assn., *10400 Little Patuxent Pkwy., #485, Columbia, MD 21044-3502; (410) 715-9605. Fax, (410) 715-9609. Victoria Tate, acting executive director. Toll-free, (800) 669-1603.*

Represents impotent men and their partners, physicians who treat impotence, and the industry that develops products for treatment. Provides members with medical referrals and educational materials. Sponsors national support group, Impotence Anonymous; maintains toll-free help line.

Institute for Alternative Futures, *100 N. Pitt St., #235, Alexandria, VA 22314-3108; (703) 684-5880. Fax, (703) 684-0640. Clem Bezold, executive director. Internet, futurist@altfutures.com or http://www.altfutures.com.*

Research and educational organization that explores the implications of scientific developments. Works with state and local governments, Congress, and associations; conducts seminars. Interests include pharmaceutical research, health care, telecommunications, artificial intelligence, and the environment.

Institute of Medicine, *2101 Constitution Ave. N.W. 20418; (202) 334-3300. Fax, (202) 334-2158. Kenneth I.*

Shine, president. Information, (202) 334-2169. Press, (202) 334-2138. Library, (202) 334-2125. Internet, http://www2. nas.edu/iom.

Independent research organization chartered by the National Academy of Sciences. Conducts studies of policy issues related to health and medicine and issues position statements; interests include international health. National Academy of Sciences library open to the public by appointment.

Johns Hopkins University Applied Physics Laboratory, *Johns Hopkins Rd., Laurel, MD 20723-6099; (240) 228-5000. Fax, (240) 228-1093. Dr. G. L. Smith, director. Information, (240) 228-5021. Internet, http://www. jhuapl.edu.*

Organization that, with affiliated medical centers, conducts research and develops engineering-related biomedical programs and high technology systems to improve medical care.

National Chronic Pain Outreach Assn., *P.O. Box 274, Millboro, VA 24460; (540) 997-5004. Fax, (540) 997-1305. Michael Troyer, executive director. Internet, NCPOA1@ aol.com.*

Works to improve the lives of people with chronic pain. Serves as a clearinghouse for information on pain management; educates the public and health care professionals; helps develop support groups by providing publications and tapes.

National Sleep Foundation, *729 15th St. N.W., 4th Floor 20005; (202) 347-3471. Fax, (202) 347-3472. William McLin, executive director. Internet, natsleep@ erols.com or http://www.sleepfoundation.org.*

Promotes research to understand sleep disorders, including insomnia, sleep apnea, and narcolepsy. Works to prevent sleep-related accidents, especially those that involve driving.

Research!America, *908 King St., #400E, Alexandria, VA 22314; (703) 739-2577. Fax, (703) 739-2372. Mary Woolley, president. Toll-free, (800) 366-2873. Internet, http://www.researchamerica.org.*

Membership: academic and professional societies, voluntary health organizations, corporations, and individuals interested in promoting medical research. Provides information on the benefits of medical research and seeks to increase funding for research.

SRI International, *1611 N. Kent St., #700, Arlington, VA 22209; (703) 524-2053. Fax, (703) 247-8569. Jack F. Scherrer, vice president, Washington Office. Internet, http://www.sri.com.*

Research and consulting organization. Conducts studies on biotechnology, genetic engineering, drug metabolism, cancer, toxicology, disease control systems, and other areas of basic and applied research; monitors international research. (Headquarters in Menlo Park, Calif.)

Undersea and Hyperbaric Medical Society, *10531 Metropolitan Ave., Kensington, MD 20895-2627; (301) 942-2980. Fax, (301) 942-7804. Leon J. Greenbaum Jr., executive director. Internet, uhms@uhms.net or http:// www.uhms.org.*

Works internationally to advance undersea and hyperbaric medicine and its supporting sciences. Studies the effect of greater than normal atmospheric pressure on the human body. Serves as a forum for information exchange on scientific issues.

See also American Institutes for Research (p. 617); American Roentgen Ray Society (p. 360)

AIDS and HIV

See also Blood and Bone Marrow (this chapter)

AGENCIES

Centers for Disease Control and Prevention *(Health and Human Services Dept.), 200 Independence Ave. S.W., #746-G 20201; (202) 690-8598. Fax, (202) 690-7519. Donald E. Shriber, associate director, Washington Office. Internet, http://www.cdc.gov.*

Conducts research to prevent and control acquired immune deficiency syndrome (AIDS); promotes public awareness through guidelines for health care workers, educational packets for schools, and monthly reports on incidences of AIDS. (Headquarters in Atlanta: 1600 Clifton Rd. N.E. 30333. Public inquiries, (404) 639-3534.)

Food and Drug Administration *(Health and Human Services Dept.), Center for Biologics Evaluation and Research, 1401 Rockville Pike, #200 North, Rockville, MD 20852-1448; (301) 827-0548. Fax, (301) 827-0440. Kathryn C. Zoon, director; Elaine C. Esber, associate director, Medical and International Affairs, (301) 827-0641. Press, (301) 827-2000. Internet, http://www.access.gpo.gov.*

Develops testing standards for vaccines, blood supply, and blood products and derivatives to prevent transmission of the human immunodeficiency virus (HIV); regulates biological therapeutics; helps formulate international standards. Serves as the focus for AIDS activities within the FDA.

Food and Drug Administration *(Health and Human Services Dept.), Center for Drug Evaluation and Research, 5600 Fishers Lane, Woodmont II, #6027, Rockville, MD 20857; (301) 594-5400. Fax, (301) 594-*

6197. Dr. Janet Woodcock, director. Information, (301) 827-4573. Press, (301) 827-6242.

Approves new drugs for AIDS and AIDS-related diseases. Reviews and approves applications to investigate and market new drugs; works to harmonize drug approval internationally.

Health Resources and Services Administration *(Health and Human Services Dept.), AIDS Program, 5600 Fishers Lane, #705, Rockville, MD 20857; (301) 443-1993. Fax, (301) 443-9645. Joseph O'Neill, associate administrator.*

Administers grants to support health care programs for AIDS patients, including those that reimburse low-income patients for drug expenses. Provides patients with AIDS and HIV-related disorders with ambulatory and community-based care. Conducts AIDS/HIV education and training activities for health professionals.

National Institute of Allergy and Infectious Diseases *(National Institutes of Health), AIDS, 6003 Executive Blvd., Solar Bldg., #2A18, Rockville, MD 20852; (301) 496-0545. Fax, (301) 402-1505. Dr. John Killen, director. Information, (301) 496-5717. Toll-free hotline, (800) 342-2437. Internet, http://www.niaid.nih.gov/ research/daids.htm.*

Primary institute at NIH for AIDS research. Conducts a network of AIDS clinical trials and preclinical drug development research. Supports epidemiological studies and research into AIDS vaccines. Studies the pathogenesis of HIV infection.

Office of National AIDS Policy *(Executive Office of the President), 808 17th St. N.W., #820 20006; (202) 632-1090. Fax, (202) 632-1096. Sandy Thurman, director.*

Advises the president and formulates policy on matters related to AIDS and AIDS treatment.

Public Health and Science *(Health and Human Services Dept.), HIV/AIDS Policy, 200 Independence Ave. S.W., #736E 20201; (202) 690-5560. Fax, (202) 690-7560. Dr. Eric Goosby, director.*

Coordinates national AIDS policy, sets priorities, recommends funding, and helps implement all Public Health Service HIV programs. Monitors progress of prevention and control programs; serves as a liaison with governmental and private organizations.

Public Health and Science *(Health and Human Services Dept.), Minority Health, 5515 Security Lane, #1000 Rockwall II Bldg., Rockville, MD 20852; (301) 443-5084. Fax, (301) 594-0767. Clay E. Simpson Jr., deputy assistant secretary. Toll-free, (800) 444-6472. Internet, http://www. os.dhhs.gov/progorg/ophs/omh.*

Awards grants to minority AIDS education and prevention projects to administer health promotion, education, and disease prevention programs.

Walter Reed Army Institute of Research *(Defense Dept.), Combined Military Diagnostic Retrovirology Service, 1600 E. Gude Dr., Rockville, MD 20850-5318; (301) 295-6414. Fax, (301) 309-8346. Dr. Debi Birx, director.*

Conducts and funds AIDS research for the military's retrovirus program; oversees AIDS testing for Defense Dept. personnel.

Warren Grant Magnuson Clinical Center *(National Institutes of Health), Transfusion Medicine, 10 Center Dr., MSC-1184, Bldg. 10, #1C711, Bethesda, MD 20892-1184; (301) 496-9702. Fax, (301) 594-1981. Dr. Harvey Klein, chief. Information, (301) 496-4506.*

Supplies blood and blood components for patient care and research. Conducts research on diseases transmissible by blood, primarily AIDS.

See also National Museum of Health and Medicine (p. 107)

NONPROFIT

AIDS Action Council, *1875 Connecticut Ave. N.W., #700 20009; (202) 986-1300. Fax, (202) 986-1345. Daniel Zingale, executive director. Internet, aidsaction@ aidsaction.org or http://www.aidsaction.org.*

Promotes and monitors legislation on AIDS research and education and on related public policy issues.

AIDS National Interfaith Network, *1400 Eye St. N.W., #1220 20005; (202) 842-0010. Fax, (202) 842-3323. Ken South, executive director.*

Coordinates national network of faith-based, AIDS-specific ministries. Maintains a database on the HIV/AIDS activites of religious organizations. Educates AIDS service organizations, the religious community, and the general public about AIDS and AIDS ministries.

AIDS Policy Center for Children, Youth, and Families, *918 16th St. N.W., #201 20006; (202) 785-3564. Fax, (202) 785-3579. David C. Harvey, executive director. Internet, apccyf@aol.com or http://www.aidspolicycenter.org.*

Conducts research and disseminates information on health care and HIV issues. Develops and promotes policy aimed at improving the health and welfare of children, youth, and families affected by HIV.

American Foundation for AIDS Research (AmFAR), *1828 L St. N.W., #802 20036; (202) 331-8600. Fax, (202) 331-8606. Jane Silver, director, Public Policy. Toll-free, (800) 392-2327. Internet, http://www.amfar.org.*

Supports funding for basic biomedical and clinical AIDS research; promotes AIDS prevention education worldwide; advocates effective AIDS-related public policy. Monitors legislation, regulations, and international research. (Headquarters in New York.)

American Red Cross, *National Headquarters, 430 17th St. N.W., 2nd Floor 20006-2401; (202) 737-8300. Fax, (202) 783-3432. Elizabeth Dole, president. Internet, http://www.redcross.org.*

Humanitarian relief and health education organization chartered by Congress. Conducts public education campaigns on AIDS. (Public inquiries, 8111 Gatehouse Rd., Falls Church, VA 22042; (703) 206-7090; fax (703) 206-7749.)

Human Rights Campaign, *1101 14th St. N.W., #200 20005; (202) 628-4160. Fax, (202) 347-5323. Elizabeth Birch, executive director. Internet, hrc@hrc.org or http://www.hrc.org.*

Promotes legislation to fund AIDS research.

National AIDS Fund, *1400 Eye St. N.W., #1220 20005; (202) 408-4848. Fax, (202) 408-1818. B. J. Stiles, president. Internet, http://www.aidsfund.org.*

Provides grants to support state HIV/AIDS programs. Assists public health agencies in developing new models of community-based care and prevention. Supports community leadership with financial, program, and technical assistance. Administers the Workplace Resource Center, which works with businesses to create AIDS policies, guidelines, and education programs.

National Assn. of People with AIDS, *1413 K St. N.W. 20005; (202) 898-0414. Fax, (202) 898-0435. Cornelius Baker, executive director. Fax on demand, (202) 789-2222. MedExpress Pharmacy drug information and delivery service, (800) 808-8060. Internet, http://www.thecure.org.*

Membership: people with AIDS or HIV disease. Provides persons infected by AIDS or HIV disease with information and social service referrals; contributes to educational campaigns about AIDS; maintains speakers bureau.

National Minority AIDS Council, *1931 13th St. N.W. 20009; (202) 483-6622. Fax, (202) 483-1135. Paul A. Kawata, executive director. Internet, http://www.nmac.org.*

Works to encourage leadership within minority communities responding to the HIV/AIDS epidemic; provides community-based AIDS programs with technical assistance. Disseminates information on AIDS, especially information on the impact of the disease on minority communities. Monitors legislation and regulations.

See also National Foundation for Infectious Diseases (p. 375)

Arthritis

AGENCIES

National Arthritis and Musculoskeletal and Skin Diseases Information Clearinghouse *(National Institutes of Health),* *1 AMS Circle, Bethesda, MD 20892; (301) 495-4484. Fax, (301) 587-4352. Mary Flum, senior information specialist. TDD, (301) 565-2966. Internet, http://www.nih.gov/niams.*

Provides physicians and the public with educational materials related to rheumatic, musculoskeletal, and skin diseases.

National Institute of Arthritis and Musculoskeletal and Skin Diseases *(National Institutes of Health),* *31 Center Dr., MSC-2350, #4C32, Bethesda, MD 20892-2350; (301) 496-4353. Fax, (301) 480-6069. Dr. Stephen I. Katz, director. Information, (301) 496-8188. Internet, http://www.nih.gov/niams.*

Conducts and funds research on arthritis and other rheumatic and bone diseases and musculoskeletal disorders. Funds national arthritis centers.

Blood and Bone Marrow

In this chapter, see also AIDS and HIV; Genetic Disorders; Heart Disease, Strokes

AGENCIES

Health Resources and Services Administration *(Health and Human Services Dept.), Transplantation,* *5600 Fishers Lane, #7-29, Rockville, MD 20857; (301) 443-7577. Fax, (301) 594-6095. John L. Nelson, acting director. Internet, rdean@hrsa.dhhs.gov.*

Administers the National Marrow Donor Program, which maintains a registry of potential unrelated bone marrow donors.

National Heart, Lung, and Blood Institute *(National Institutes of Health), Blood Diseases and Resources,* *6701 Rockledge Dr., MSC-7950, Bethesda, MD 20892-7950; (301) 435-0080. Fax, (301) 480-0867. Dr. Clarice D. Reid, director.*

Administers and conducts research and training programs to improve the diagnosis, prevention, and treatment of blood diseases and related disorders. Works to ensure the efficient and safe use and adequate supply of high-quality blood and blood products.

National Heart, Lung, and Blood Institute *(National Institutes of Health), Bone Marrow Transplantation,* *6701 Rockledge Dr., MSC-7950, Bethesda, MD 20892-7950; (301) 435-0065. Fax, (301) 435-0867. Dr. Paul R. McCurdy, director, Blood Resources Program.*

Promotes and supports research on bone marrow and stem cell transplantation technology and on transplantation procedure-related complications.

National Heart, Lung, and Blood Institute *(National Institutes of Health), Information Center,* *P.O. Box 30105, Bethesda, MD 20824-0105; (301) 251-1222. Fax, (301) 251-1223. Margot Raphael, manager. Press, (301) 496-4236. Internet, http://www.nhlbi.nih.gov/nhlbi/infcntr/infocent.htm.*

Acquires, maintains, and disseminates information on cholesterol and high blood pressure. Provides reference and referral services. Library open to the public.

National Institute of Diabetes and Digestive and Kidney Diseases *(National Institutes of Health), Hematology,* *45 Center Dr., Natcher Bldg., #6AS-13C, Bethesda, MD 20892-6600; (301) 594-7717. Fax, (301) 480-3510. David G. Badman, director.*

Supports basic research on and clinical studies of the states of blood cell formation, mobilization, and release. Interests include anemia associated with chronic diseases, iron and white blood cell metabolism, and genetic control of hemoglobin.

Warren Grant Magnuson Clinical Center *(National Institutes of Health), Transfusion Medicine,* *10 Center Dr., MSC-1184, Bldg. 10, #1C711, Bethesda, MD 20892-1184; (301) 496-9702. Fax, (301) 594-1981. Dr. Harvey Klein, chief. Information, (301) 496-4506.*

Supplies blood and blood components for research and patient care. Provides training programs and conducts research in the preparation and transfusion of blood and blood products. Research topics include hepatitis, automated cell separation, immunohematology, and AIDS transmittal through transfusions.

NONPROFIT

American Assn. of Blood Banks, *8101 Glenbrook Rd., Bethesda, MD 20814-2749; (301) 907-6977. Fax, (301) 907-6895. Karen Shoos-Lipton, executive officer. Internet, http://www.aabb.org.*

Membership: physicians, nurses, technologists, and administrators in the blood banking field. Inspects and accredits blood bank and transfusion services; sponsors certification exam for blood bank personnel; sponsors, with the College of American Pathologists, hepatitis and AIDS testing programs.

American Red Cross, *National Headquarters, 430 17th St. N.W., 2nd Floor 20006; (202) 737-8300. Fax, (202)*

783-3432. Elizabeth Dole, president. Internet, http://www. redcross.org.

Humanitarian relief and health education organization chartered by Congress; provides services in the United States and internationally. Collects blood and maintains blood centers; conducts research; operates the national bone marrow registry and a rare-donor registry, including a joint sickle cell anemia program with the NAACP; operates transfusion alternative program. Conducts training programs in nursing and first aid; trains volunteers. Serves as U.S. member of the International Federation of Red Cross and Red Crescent Societies. (Public inquiries, 8111 Gatehouse Rd., Falls Church, VA 22042; (703) 206-7090; fax (703) 206-7749.)

Cancer

See also Nursing Homes and Hospices (this chapter)

AGENCIES

National Cancer Institute *(National Institutes of Health),* 31 Center Dr., MSC-2590, #11A48, Bethesda, MD 20892; (301) 496-5615. Fax, (301) 402-0338. Dr. Richard D. Klausner, director; Federico Welsch, associate director, International Affairs, (301) 496-4761. Information, (301) 496-5583. Press, (301) 496-6641. Internet, http://www.nci.nih.gov.

Conducts and funds research on the causes, diagnosis, treatment, prevention, control, and biology of cancer and the rehabilitation of cancer patients; administers the National Cancer Program; coordinates international research activities. Sponsors regional and national cancer information services.

National Cancer Institute *(National Institutes of Health), Cancer Prevention,* 31 Center Dr., MSC-2580, #10A52, Bethesda, MD 20892-2580; (301) 496-6616. Fax, (301) 496-9931. Dr. Peter Greenwald, acting director.

Funds projects for innovative and effective approaches to preventing and controlling cancer. Coordinates support for establishing multidisciplinary cancer care and clinical research activities in community hospitals. Supports cancer research training, clinical and continuing education, and career development.

National Cancer Institute *(National Institutes of Health), International Cancer Information Center,* 9030 Old Georgetown Rd., #100, Bethesda, MD 20892; (301) 496-9096. Fax, (301) 480-8105. Susan Molloy Hubbard, director. Internet, http://www.icic.nci.nih.gov.

Collects and disseminates scientific information on cancer biology, etiology, screening, prevention, treatment, and supportive care. Evaluates and develops new media formats for cancer information.

National Cancer Institute *(National Institutes of Health), Organ Systems Coordinating Branch,* 6130 Executive Blvd., #512, Rockville, MD 20892; (301) 496-8528. Fax, (301) 402-5319. Andrew Chiarodo, chief.

Encourages the study of cancers in solid tumors. Encourages multidisciplinary research linking laboratory and clinical medicine.

President's Cancer Panel, *c/o National Cancer Institute,* 31 Center Dr., #4A48 MSC-2473, Bethesda, MD 20892-2473; (301) 496-1148. Fax, (301) 402-1508. Dr. Maureen O. Wilson, executive secretary.

Presidentially appointed committee that monitors and evaluates the National Cancer Program; reports to the president and Congress.

NONPROFIT

American Cancer Society, 701 Pennsylvania Ave. S.E., #650 20004; (202) 661-5700. Fax, (202) 661-5750. Susan Polan, director, Governmental Relations. Toll-free, (800) 227-2345. Internet, http://www.cancer.org.

Supports medical research, education for health care professionals, and public information programs on cancer. Monitors legislation. (Headquarters in Atlanta.)

American Institute for Cancer Research, 1759 R St. N.W. 20009; (202) 328-7744. Fax, (202) 328-7226. Marilyn Gentry, executive director. Toll-free, (800) 843-8114. Internet, http://www.aicr.org.

Funds cancer research in areas of diet and nutrition; sponsors education programs. Library open to the public by appointment.

American Society for Therapeutic Radiology and Oncology, 1891 Preston White Dr., Reston, VA 20191; (703) 716-7588. Fax, (703) 476-8167. Dr. Larry Kun, president. Internet, http://www.astro.org.

Seeks to advance the practice of radiation oncology; disseminates data on scientific research; sponsors workshops and conferences. Monitors legislation and regulations.

American Society of Clinical Oncology, 225 Reinekers Lane, #650, Alexandria, VA 22314; (703) 299-0150. Fax, (703) 299-1044. Dr. John Durant, executive vice president. Internet, http://www.asco.org.

Membership: physicians and scientists specializing in cancer prevention, treatment, education, and research. Promotes exchange of information in clinical research and patient care relating to all stages of cancer.

Assn. of Community Cancer Centers, 11600 Nebel St., #201, Rockville, MD 20852; (301) 984-9496. Fax, (301) 770-1949. Lee E. Mortenson, executive director. Internet, http://www.assoc-cancer-ctrs.org.

Membership: individuals from community hospitals involved in multidisciplinary cancer programs, including physicians, administrators, nurses, medical directors, pharmacists, and other members of the cancer care team.

Candlelighters Childhood Cancer Foundation, *7910 Woodmont Ave., #460, Bethesda, MD 20814; (301) 657-8401. Fax, (301) 718-2686. Laura Lee Liebermann, executive director. Toll-free, (800) 366-2223. Internet, info@candlelighters.org or http://www.candlelighters.org.*

Membership: families of children with cancer, survivors of childhood cancer, and health and education professionals. Serves as an information and educational network; sponsors self-help groups for parents of children and adolescents with cancer; operates Ombudsman Program for employment and insurance problems. Monitors legislation and regulations.

Leukemia Society of America, *2900 Eisenhower Ave., #419, Alexandria, VA 22314; (703) 960-1100. Fax, (703) 960-0920. David M. Timko, executive director. Toll-free, (800) 955-4572. Internet, http://www.leukemia.org.*

Seeks to expand knowledge of leukemia and allied diseases. Conducts leukemia research; provides research scholarships and fellowships; maintains speakers bureau. Local chapters provide leukemia patients with financial assistance, counseling, and referrals. (Headquarters in New York.)

National Breast Cancer Coalition, *1707 L St. N.W., #1060 20036; (202) 296-7477. Fax, (202) 265-6854. Fran Visco, president. Internet, http://www.natlbcc.org.*

Membership: organizations, local coalitions, and individuals. Advocates increased funding for research to prevent and treat breast cancer; promotes better access to screening and care; conducts training for breast cancer activists.

National Coalition for Cancer Survivorship, *1010 Wayne Ave., #505, Silver Spring, MD 20910; (301) 650-8868. Fax, (301) 565-9670. Ellen Stovall, executive director. Internet, http://www.cansearch.org/cansearch/cansearch.htm.*

Membership: survivors of cancer (newly diagnosed to long-term), their families and friends, health care providers, and support organizations. Disseminates information about living with cancer; works to reduce cancer-based discrimination in employment and insurance; operates Cansearch, a guide to cancer resources on the Internet.

See also AARP Andrus Foundation (p. 378); Drug Policy Foundation (p. 363)

Diabetes, Digestive Diseases

AGENCIES

National Diabetes Information Clearinghouse *(National Institutes of Health), 1 Information Way, Bethesda, MD 20892-3560; (301) 654-3327. Fax, (301) 907-8906. Ellen Schwab, senior information specialist. Internet, http://www.niddk.nih.gov.*

Provides health professionals and the public with information on the symptoms, causes, treatments, and general nature of diabetes.

National Digestive Diseases Information Clearinghouse *(National Institutes of Health), 2 Information Way, Bethesda, MD 20892-3570; (301) 654-3810. Fax, (301) 907-8906. Kelly Collins, senior information specialist. Internet, http://www.niddk.nih.gov.*

Provides health professionals and the public with information on the symptoms, causes, treatments, and general nature of digestive ailments.

National Institute of Diabetes and Digestive and Kidney Diseases *(National Institutes of Health), Diabetes, Endocrinology, and Metabolic Diseases, 31 Center Dr., MSC-2560, #9A16, Bethesda, MD 20892-2560; (301) 496-7348. Fax, (301) 480-6792. Dr. Richard Eastman, director.*

Awards grants and contracts to support basic and clinical research of diabetes mellitus and its complications.

National Institute of Diabetes and Digestive and Kidney Diseases *(National Institutes of Health), Digestive Diseases and Nutrition, 31 Center Dr., MSC-2560, #9A23, Bethesda, MD 20892-2560; (301) 496-1333. Fax, (301) 496-2830. Dr. Jay H. Hoofnagle, director.*

Awards grants and contracts to support basic and clinical research on digestive diseases.

NONPROFIT

American Diabetes Assn., *1660 Duke St., Alexandria, VA 22314-3427; (703) 549-1500. Fax, (703) 836-7439. John H. Graham IV, chief executive officer. Toll-free, (800) 232-3472. Internet, http://www.diabetes.org.*

Conducts and funds research on diabetes; monitors international research. Provides local affiliates with education, information, and referral services.

American Gastroenterological Assn., *7910 Woodmont Ave., 7th Floor, Bethesda, MD 20814; (301) 654-2055. Fax, (301) 654-5927. Robert Greenberg, executive vice president. Internet, http://www.gastro.org.*

Membership: gastroenterology clinicians, scientists, health care professionals, and educators. Sponsors scientific research on digestive diseases; disseminates information on new methods of prevention and treatment. Monitors legislation and regulations. (Affiliated with the American Digestive Health Foundation.)

Endocrine Society, *4350 East West Hwy., #500, Bethesda, MD 20814-0200; (301) 941-0200. Fax, (301) 941-0259. Scott Hunt, executive director. Internet, http://www.endo-society.org.*

Membership: scientists, doctors, health care educators, clinicians, nurses, and others interested in endocrine glands and their disorders. Promotes endocrinology research and clincial practice; sponsors seminars and conferences; gives awards and travel grants.

Juvenile Diabetes Foundation, *1400 Eye St. N.W., #500 20005; (202) 371-9746. Fax, (202) 371-2760. William T. Schmidt, director, Governmental Relations. Toll-free, (800) 533-1868. Internet, http://www.jdfcure.com.*

Conducts research, education, and public awareness programs aimed at improving the lives of people with diabetes and finding a cure for diabetes. Monitors legislation and regulations. (Headquarters in New York.)

Family Planning and Population

See also Abortion and Reproductive Issues (chap. 14); Census/Population Data (chap. 10); Prenatal, Maternal, and Child Health Care (this chapter)

AGENCIES

Agency for International Development, *Population, 1300 Pennsylvania Ave. N.W., 3rd Floor 20723-3600; (202) 712-0540. Fax, (202) 216-3046. Elizabeth S. Maguire, director. Internet, http://www.info.usaid.gov/pop_health/.*

Division of the Center for Population, Health, and Nutrition. Supports family planning and reproductive health programs; conducts research.

Census Bureau *(Commerce Dept.),* **Fertility and Family Statistics,** *4700 Silver Hill Rd., #2351/3, Suitland, MD; (301) 457-2416. Fax, (301) 457-2481. Martin O'Connell, chief.*

Provides data and statistics on fertility and family composition. Conducts census and survey research on the number of children, households and living arrangements, and current child spacing patterns of women in the United States, especially working mothers. Conducts studies on child care.

National Institute of Child Health and Human Development *(National Institutes of Health),* **Center for Population Research,** *6100 Executive Blvd., Rockville, MD 20852; (301) 496-1101. Fax, (301) 496-0962. Dr. Florence P. Haseltine, director.*

Supports biomedical research on reproductive processes influencing human fertility and infertility; develops methods for regulating fertility; evaluates the safety and effectiveness of contraceptive methods; conducts research on the reproductive motivation of individuals and the causes and consequences of population change.

Public Health and Science *(Health and Human Services Dept.),* **Population Affairs,** *4350 East-West Hwy., #200, Bethesda, MD 20814; (301) 594-4000. Fax, (301) 594-5980. Tom Kring, acting deputy assistant secretary. Internet, http://www.osophs.dhhs.gov.*

Responsible for planning, monitoring, and evaluating population research, voluntary family planning, and adolescent family life programs.

Public Health and Science *(Health and Human Services Dept.),* **Population Affairs Clearinghouse,** *P.O. Box 30686, Bethesda, MD 20824-0686; (301) 654-6190. Fax, (301) 215-7731. Mark Edwards, project manager. Internet, http://www.dhhs.gov/progorg/opa.*

Federally contracted program that collects and disseminates information on family planning and related topics, including adoption and adolescent abstinence.

INTERNATIONAL ORGANIZATIONS

International Bank for Reconstruction and Development (World Bank), *Human Development, 1750 Pennsylvania Ave. N.W., #S9035 (mailing address: 1818 H St. N.W., #S9035, Washington, DC 20433); (202) 473-8729. Fax, (202) 522-3235. David de Ferranti, vice president. Internet, http://www.worldbank.org/html/hcovp/hdd/contents.html.*

Provides member countries with loans and technical advice for family planning projects designed to slow population growth. (Works in conjunction with regional World Bank offices.)

NONPROFIT

Advocates for Youth, *1025 Vermont Ave. N.W., #200 20005; (202) 347-5700. Fax, (202) 347-2263. James Wagoner, executive director. Internet, info@advocatesforyouth.org or http://www.advocatesforyouth.org.*

Seeks to reduce the incidence of unintended teenage pregnancy and AIDS through public education, training and technical assistance, research, and media programs.

Alan Guttmacher Institute, *1120 Connecticut Ave. N.W., #460 20036-3902; (202) 296-4012. Fax, (202) 223-5756. Cory L. Richards, vice president, Public Policy. Internet, info@agi-usa.org or http://www.agi-usa.org.*

Conducts research, policy analysis, and public education in reproductive health, fertility regulation, population, and related areas of U.S. and international health and social policy. (Headquarters in New York.)

National Abortion Federation, *1755 Massachusetts Ave. N.W., #600 20036; (202) 667-5881. Fax, (202) 667-5890. Vicki Saporta, executive director. Toll-free, (800) 772-9100. Internet, http://www.prochoice.org.*

Federation of facilities providing abortion services. Offers information on medical, legal, and social aspects of abortion; sets quality standards for abortion care. Conducts training workshops and seminars. Monitors legislation and regulations.

National Family Planning and Reproductive Health Assn., *122 C St. N.W., #380 20001; (202) 628-3535. Fax, (202) 737-2690. Judith DeSarno, president. Recording, (202) 452-5978. Internet, http://www.nfprha.org.*

Membership: health professionals and others interested in family planning and reproductive health. Operates a network for information, referral, research, policy analysis, and training designed to improve and expand the delivery of family planning services and reproductive health care.

Planned Parenthood Federation of America, *1120 Connecticut Ave. N.W., #461 20036; (202) 785-3351. Fax, (202) 293-4349. Rosann Wisman, acting vice president, Public Policy. Internet, http://www.plannedparenthood.org.*

Educational, research, and medical services organization. Washington office conducts research and monitors legislation on fertility-related health topics, including abortion, reproductive health, contraception, family planning, and international population control. (Headquarters in New York accredits affiliated local centers, which offer medical services, birth control, and family planning information.)

Population Action International, *1120 19th St. N.W., #550 20036; (202) 659-1833. Fax, (202) 293-1795. Patricia McGrath, vice president. Internet, pai@popact.org or http://www.populationaction.org.*

Promotes population stabilization through public education and universal access to voluntary family planning. Library open to the public by appointment.

Population-Environment Balance, *2000 P St. N.W., #210 20036; (202) 955-5700. Fax, (202) 955-6161. Maria Sepulveda, executive director. Internet, uspop@balance.org.*

Grassroots organization that advocates U.S. population stabilization to safeguard the environment.

Population Institute, *107 2nd St. N.E. 20002; (202) 544-3300. Fax, (202) 544-0068. Werner Fornos, president. Internet, web@populationinstitute.org or http://www. populationinstitute.org.*

Encourages leaders of developing nations to balance population growth through resource management; works with leaders of industrial nations to help achieve a balance between population and natural resources.

Population Reference Bureau, *1875 Connecticut Ave. N.W., #520 20009-5728; (202) 483-1100. Fax, (202) 328-3937. Peter J. Donaldson, president. Internet, http://www. prb.org.*

Educational organization engaged in information dissemination, training, and policy analysis on U.S. population trends and issues. Interests include family planning and international development programs, the environment, and U.S. social and economic policy. Library open to the public.

Zero Population Growth, *1400 16th St. N.W., #320 20036; (202) 332-2200. Fax, (202) 332-2302. Tim Klein, director, Communications. Internet, zpg@igc.apc.org or http://www.zpg.org.*

Membership: persons interested in sustainable world populations. Promotes the expansion of domestic and international family planning programs; supports a voluntary population stabilization policy and women's access to abortion and family planning services; works to protect the earth's resources and environment.

See also Assn. of Reproductive Health Professionals (p. 367); Program for Appropriate Technology in Health (p. 361)

Genetic Disorders

See also Biotechnology (chap. 17)

AGENCIES

Health Resources and Services Administration *(Health and Human Services Dept.), Genetic Services, 5600 Fishers Lane, #18A20, Rockville, MD 20857; (301) 443-1080. Fax, (301) 443-8604. Dr. Michele Puryear, chief.*

Awards funds, including demonstration grants, to develop or enhance regional, local, and state genetic screening, diagnostic, counseling, and follow-up programs; assists states in their newborn screening programs. Supports comprehensive care for individuals and families with Cooley's anemia, and those with sickle cell anemia identified through newborn screening. Supports educational programs.

National Heart, Lung, and Blood Institute *(National Institutes of Health), Sickle Cell Disease, 6701 Rockledge Dr., 10th Floor, Bethesda, MD 20892-7950; (301) 435-0055. Fax, (301) 480-0868. Helena Mishoe, director, Blood Disease Program.*

Supports research into the diagnosis and treatment of sickle cell anemia and continuing education programs for professionals and the public.

National Human Genome Research Institute
(National Institutes of Health), 31 Center Dr., MSC-2152, #4B09, Bethesda, MD 20892-2152; (301) 496-0844. Fax, (301) 402-0837. Dr. Francis S. Collins, director. Information, (301) 402-0911. Internet, http://www.nhgri. nih.gov.

Responsible, with the Energy Dept., for U.S. involvement in the international Human Genome Project, which seeks to map all genes in human DNA, as well as those of model organisms. Works to improve techniques for cloning, storing, and handling DNA and to enhance data processing and analysis; promotes exchange of information.

National Institute of Allergy and Infectious Diseases *(National Institutes of Health), Allergy, Immunology, and Transplantation, 6003 Executive Blvd., Rockville, MD 20852 (mailing address: 9000 Rockville Pike, Solar Bldg., #4A18, Bethesda, MD 20892-7640); (301) 496-1886. Fax, (301) 402-2571. Dr. Daniel Rothrosen, acting director. Information, (301) 496-5717. Internet, http://www.niaid.nih.gov/research/Dait.htm.*

Focuses on the immune system as it functions to maintain health and as it malfunctions to produce disease; interests include allergies, asthma, immune deficiencies (other than AIDS), transplantation of organs and tissue, and genetics. Monitors international research.

National Institute of Diabetes and Digestive and Kidney Diseases *(National Institutes of Health), Hematology, 45 Center Dr., Natcher Bldg., #6AS-13C, Bethesda, MD 20892-6600; (301) 594-7717. Fax, (301) 480-3510. David G. Badman, director.*

Supports basic and clinical studies of the states of blood cell formation, mobilization, and release. Interests include genetic control of hemoglobin.

National Institute of General Medical Sciences *(National Institutes of Health), Genetics and Developmental Biology, 45 Center Dr., MSC-6200, #2AS19H, Bethesda, MD 20892-6200; (301) 594-0943. Fax, (301) 480-2228. Judith H. Greenberg, director. Internet, http://www.nih.gov/nigms/about_nigms/gdb.html.*

Supports research and research training in genetics.

National Institutes of Health *(Health and Human Services Dept.), Recombinant DNA Activities, 6000 Executive Blvd., #302, MSC 7010, Bethesda, MD 20892-7010; (301) 496-9838. Fax, (301) 496-9839. Deborah Knorr, acting director. Internet, http://www.nih.gov/od/orda.*

Reviews requests submitted to NIH involving recombinant DNA technology and implements research guidelines.

NONPROFIT

Center for Sickle Cell Disease *(Howard University), 2121 Georgia Ave. N.W. 20059; (202) 806-7930. Fax, (202) 806-4517. Dr. Oswaldo Castro, director.*

Screens and tests for sickle cell disease; conducts research; promotes public education and community involvement; provides counseling and patient care.

Cystic Fibrosis Foundation, *6931 Arlington Rd., Bethesda, MD 20814; (301) 951-4422. Fax, (301) 951-6378. Robert J. Beall, president. Toll-free, (800) 344-4823. Internet, info@cff.org or http://www.cff.org.*

Conducts research on cystic fibrosis, an inherited genetic disease affecting the respiratory and digestive systems. Provides funding for care centers; publishes and disseminates information on the disease.

Genetics Society of America, *9650 Rockville Pike, Bethesda, MD 20814; (301) 571-1825. Fax, (301) 530-7079. Elaine Strass, executive director. Internet, society@ genetics.faseb.org or http://www.faseb.org/genetics.*

Encourages professional cooperation among persons working in genetics and related sciences; participates in international conferences.

Kennedy Institute of Ethics *(Georgetown University), 1437 37th St. N.W. 20057; (202) 687-8099. Fax, (202) 687-8089. Dr. Leroy Walters, director. Library, (800) 633-3849; in Washington, (202) 687-3885. Internet, http:// guweb.georgetown.edu/kennedy.*

Sponsors research on medical ethics, including legal and ethical definitions of death, allocation of scarce health resources, and recombinant DNA and human gene therapy. Supplies National Library of Medicine with online database on bioethics; publishes annual bibliography. Library open to the public by appointment.

March of Dimes Birth Defects Foundation, *1901 L St. N.W., #260 20036; (202) 659-1800. Fax, (202) 296-2964. Marina Weiss, director, Policy and Government Affairs. Internet, http://www.modimes.org.*

Works to prevent and treat birth defects. Awards grants for research and provides funds for treatment of birth defects. Monitors legislation and regulations. (Headquarters in White Plains, N.Y.)

See also American Assn. of Immunologists (p. 369); Howard Hughes Medical Institute (p. 386); SRI International (p. 386)

Heart Disease, Strokes

AGENCIES

National Heart, Lung, and Blood Institute *(National Institutes of Health), Heart and Vascular Diseases, 6701 Rockledge Dr., #9160, Bethesda, MD 20892-7940; (301) 435-0466. Fax, (301) 480-1336. Dr. Michael J. Horan, director.*

Conducts and funds research on the prevention, causes, and treatment of heart and vascular diseases.

National Heart, Lung, and Blood Institute *(National Institutes of Health), Information Center, P.O. Box 30105, Bethesda, MD 20824-0105; (301) 251-1222. Fax, (301) 251-1223. Margot Raphael, manager. Press, (301) 496-4236. Internet, http://www.nhlbi.nih. gov/nhlbi/infcntr/infocent.htm.*

Acquires, maintains, and disseminates information on cholesterol, high blood pressure, heart attack awareness, and asthma to the public and health professionals. Provides reference and referral services. Library open to the public.

National Institute of Neurological Disorders and Stroke *(National Institutes of Health), 31 Center Dr., MSC-2540, #8A52, Bethesda, MD 20892-2540; (301) 496-9746. Fax, (301) 496-0296. Dr. Audrey S. Penn, acting director. Information, (301) 496-5751. Internet, http://www.ninds.nih.gov.*

Conducts and funds stroke research. Monitors international research.

NONPROFIT

American Heart Assn., *1150 Connecticut Ave. N.W., #810 20036; (202) 785-7900. Fax, (202) 785-7950. Diane Canova, vice president. Toll-free, (800) 242-1793. Internet, http://www.americanheart.org.*

Membership: physicians, scientists, and other interested individuals. Supports cardiovascular research, treatment, and community service programs that provide information about heart disease and stroke; participates in international conferences and research. Monitors legislation and regulations. (Headquarters in Dallas.)

Citizens for Public Action on Blood Pressure and Cholesterol, Inc., *P.O. Box 30374, Bethesda, MD 20824; (301) 770-1711. Fax, (301) 770-1713. Gerald J. Wilson, executive director.*

Works to ensure public health resources for cholesterol and blood pressure education, screening, and treatment; prepares patient and professional educational materials and programs. Monitors legislation and regula-

tions on heart disease research, programs, and services available through the public health system.

Infectious Diseases, Allergies

AGENCIES

National Institute of Allergy and Infectious Diseases *(National Institutes of Health), 31 Center Dr., MSC-2520, #7A03, Bethesda, MD 20892-2520; (301) 496-2263. Fax, (301) 496-4409. Dr. Anthony S. Fauci, director. Information, (301) 496-5717. Internet, niaidoc@flash. niaid.nih.gov or http://www.niaid.nih.gov.*

Conducts and funds research on infectious diseases, allergies, and other immunological disorders. Participates in international research, especially on AIDS and HIV.

NONPROFIT

Allergy and Asthma Network/Mothers of Asthmatics, Inc., *3554 Chain Bridge Rd., #200, Fairfax, VA 22030; (703) 385-4403. Fax, (703) 352-4354. Nancy Sander, president. Toll-free, (800) 878-4403. Internet, aanma@aol.com or http://www.podi.com/health/aanma.*

Membership: families dealing with asthma and allergies. Promotes research; provides information on treatments and therapies, new products, support groups, and coping techniques.

Asthma and Allergy Foundation of America, *1125 15th St. N.W., #502 20005; (202) 466-7643. Fax, (202) 466-8940. Mary Worstell, executive director. Toll-free, (800) 727-8462. Internet, info@aafa.org or http://www.aafa.org.*

Provides information on asthma and allergies; maintains specialists referral service and speakers bureau; conducts self-management program for asthmatic children and their parents; awards research grants; provides school and occupational nurses, teachers, and others with in-service training.

National Foundation for Infectious Diseases, *4733 Bethesda Ave., #750, Bethesda, MD 20814; (301) 656-0003. Fax, (301) 907-0878. Len Novick, executive director. Internet, http://www.medscape.com/NFID.*

Raises, receives, maintains, and disburses funds to support research on infectious diseases; educates the public and health professionals about infectious diseases; conducts prevention programs, including an annual adult immunization awareness campaign; coordinates activities for the National Coalition for Adult Immunization. Monitors international research.

Kidney Disease

AGENCIES

Health Care Financing Administration *(Health and Human Services Dept.), Chronic Care Management,* 7500 Security Blvd., C5-05-27, Baltimore, MD 21244-1850; (410) 786-4533. Fax, (410) 786-0594. Lana K. Price, director. Information, (410) 786-4567.

Administers coverage policy for Medicare persons with chronic kidney failure. Coordinates coverage under new treatment methods.

National Institute of Allergy and Infectious Diseases *(National Institutes of Health), Allergy, Immunology, and Transplantation,* 6003 Executive Blvd., Rockville, MD 20852 (mailing address: 9000 Rockville Pike, Solar Bldg., #4A18, Bethesda, MD 20892-7640); (301) 496-1886. Fax, (301) 402-2571. Dr. Daniel Rothrosen, acting director. Information, (301) 496-5717. Internet, http://www.niaid.nih.gov/research/Dait.htm.

Focuses on the immune system as it functions to maintain health and as it malfunctions to produce disease; interests include allergies, asthma, immune deficiencies (other than AIDS), transplantation of organs and tissue, and genetics. Monitors international research.

National Institute of Diabetes and Digestive and Kidney Diseases *(National Institutes of Health), Kidney, Urologic, and Hematological Diseases,* 45 Center Dr., MSC-6600, Natcher Bldg., #6AS-19, Bethesda, MD 20892-6600; (301) 594-7717. Fax, (301) 480-3510. Dr. Gladys H. Hirschman, director, Chronic Renal Disease. Information, (301) 496-3583.

Funds research on the prevention, diagnosis, and treatment of renal disorders. Conducts research and reviews grant proposals concerning maintenance therapy for persons with chronic renal disease.

National Institute of Diabetes and Digestive and Kidney Diseases *(National Institutes of Health), National Kidney and Urologic Diseases Information Clearinghouse,* 3 Information Way, Bethesda, MD 20892-3580; (301) 654-4415. Fax, (301) 907-8906. Sue Pitman, senior information specialist. Internet, http://www.niddk.nih.gov.

Supplies health care providers and the public with information on the symptoms, causes, treatments, and general nature of kidney and urologic diseases.

NONPROFIT

American Kidney Fund, 6110 Executive Blvd., #1010, Rockville, MD 20852; (301) 881-3052. Fax, (301) 881-0898. Vacant, executive director. Toll-free, (800) 638-8299.

Voluntary health organization that gives financial assistance to kidney disease victims. Disseminates public service announcements and public education materials; sponsors research grants and conferences for professionals; promotes organ donation for transplantation.

National Kidney Foundation, 1911 N. Fort Myer Dr., #801, Arlington, VA 22209; (703) 522-8544. Fax, (703) 522-8586. Troy Zimmerman, director, Government Relations. Toll-free, (800) 889-9559. Internet, http://www.kidney.org.

Supports funding for kidney dialysis and other forms of treatment for kidney disease; provides information on detection and screening of kidney diseases. Monitors legislation, regulations, and international research. (Headquarters in New York.)

Lung Diseases

AGENCIES

National Heart, Lung, and Blood Institute *(National Institutes of Health), Information Center,* P.O. Box 30105, Bethesda, MD 20824-0105; (301) 251-1222. Fax, (301) 251-1223. Margot Raphael, manager. Press, (301) 496-4236. Internet, http://www.nhlbi.nih.gov/nhlbi/infcntr/infocent.htm.

Acquires, maintains, and disseminates information on asthma and other lung ailments. Provides reference and referral services. Library open to the public.

National Heart, Lung, and Blood Institute *(National Institutes of Health), Lung Diseases,* 6701 Rockledge Dr., #10018, Bethesda, MD 20892; (301) 435-0233. Fax, (301) 480-3547. Suzanne S. Hurd, director. Information, (301) 251-1222. Press, (301) 496-4236. Internet, http://www.nhlbi.nih.gov/nhlbi/nhlbi.htm.

Plans and directs research and training programs in lung diseases including research on causes, treatments, prevention, and health education.

NONPROFIT

American Assn. for Respiratory Care, 1225 King St., 2nd Floor, Alexandria, VA 22314; (703) 548-8538. Fax, (703) 548-8499. Cheryl West, director, Government Affairs, (703) 548-8506. Internet, info@aarc.org or http://www.aarc.org.

Membership: respiratory care practitioners in hospitals and home care; educators; and managers of respiratory and cardiopulmonary services. Monitors legislation and regulations. (Headquarters in Dallas.)

American Lung Assn., 1726 M St. N.W., #902 20036-4502; (202) 785-3355. Fax, (202) 452-1805. Fran

Du Melle, director, Washington Office. Internet, http://www.lungusa.org.

Fights lung disease through research, educational programs, and public awareness campaigns. Interests include antismoking campaigns, lung-related biomedical research, air pollution, school health education, and all lung diseases, including tuberculosis and occupational lung diseases. Participates in international research. (Headquarters in New York.)

Cystic Fibrosis Foundation, *6931 Arlington Rd., Bethesda, MD 20814; (301) 951-4422. Fax, (301) 951-6378. Robert J. Beall, president. Toll-free, (800) 344-4823. Internet, info@cff.org or http://www.cff.org.*

Conducts research on cystic fibrosis, an inherited genetic disease affecting the respiratory and digestive systems. Provides funding for care centers; publishes and disseminates information on the disease.

Neurological and Muscular Disorders

AGENCIES

National Institute of Neurological Disorders and Stroke *(National Institutes of Health), 31 Center Dr., MSC-2540, #8A52, Bethesda, MD 20892-2540; (301) 496-9746. Fax, (301) 496-0296. Dr. Audrey S. Penn, acting director. Information, (301) 496-5751. Internet, http://www.ninds.nih.gov.*

Conducts and funds research on neurological diseases. Monitors international research.

NONPROFIT

Alzheimer's Assn., *1319 F St. N.W., #710 20004-1106; (202) 393-7737. Fax, (202) 393-2109. Stephen R. McConnell, senior vice president, Public Policy. Toll-free, (800) 272-3900. Internet, http://www.alz.org.*

Offers family support services and educates the public about Alzheimer's disease, a neurological disorder mainly affecting the brain tissue in older adults. Promotes research and long-term care protection. Monitors legislation and regulations. (Headquarters in Chicago.)

Epilepsy Foundation of America, *4351 Garden City Dr., Landover, MD 20785; (301) 459-3700. Fax, (301) 577-2684. Paulette V. Maehara, chief executive officer. Toll-free, (800) 332-1000. Library, (800) 332-4050. Internet, postmaster@efa.org or http://www.efa.org.*

Promotes research and treatment of epilepsy; disseminates information and educational materials. Affiliates provide direct services for people with epilepsy and make referrals when necessary. Makes grants for epilepsy research. Library open to the public by appointment.

Foundation for the Advancement of Chiropractic Tenets and Science, *1110 N. Glebe Rd., Arlington, VA 22201; (703) 528-5000. Fax, (703) 528-5023. Ronald Hendrickson, executive director. Internet, http://www.chiropractic.org.*

Offers financial aid for education and research programs in colleges and independent institutions; studies chiropractic services in the United States. (Affiliate of the International Chiropractors Assn.)

International Rett Syndrome Assn., *9121 Piscataway Rd., #2B, Clinton, MD 20735; (301) 856-3334. Fax, (301) 856-3336. Kathy Hunter, president. Toll-free, (800) 818-7388. Internet, irsa@paltech.com or http://www2.paltech.com/irsa/irsa.htm.*

Provides information and support to families of children with Rett syndrome, a severe neurological disorder causing mental and physical disabilities. Promotes research on causes and treatment.

National Coalition for Research in Neurological Disorders, *1250 24th St. N.W., #300 20037; (202) 293-5453. Fax, (202) 466-0585. Morgan Downey, executive director. Internet, http://www.brainnet.org/ncr.htm.*

Coalition of voluntary agencies, physicians, and scientists. Works to increase federal funding for neurological disorder research; conducts educational programs.

National Foundation for Brain Research, *1250 24th St. N.W., #300 20037; (202) 293-5453. Fax, (202) 466-0585. Lawrence S. Hoffheimer, executive director. Internet, http://www.brainnet.org/nfbr.htm.*

Membership: professional societies, voluntary organizations, and businesses that support research into neurological and addictive brain disorders, including Alzheimer's disease, obsessive-compulsive behavior, dyslexia, drug addiction and alcoholism, stroke, Tay-Sachs disease, and depression. Sponsors programs that heighten public and professional awareness of brain disorders. Serves as a liaison with government agencies, medical and scientific societies, volunteer health organizations, and industry.

National Multiple Sclerosis Society, *2021 K St. N.W., #715 20006; (202) 296-9891. Fax, (202) 296-3425. Jeanne Oates Angulo, president, Washington Office. Internet, http://www.dcw.nmss.org.*

Seeks to advance medical knowledge of multiple sclerosis, a disease of the central nervous system; disseminates information worldwide. Patient services include individual and family counseling, exercise programs, equipment loans, medical and social service referrals, transportation assistance, back-to-work training programs, and in-service training seminars for nurses, homemakers, and physical and occupational therapists. (Headquarters in New York.)

Neurofibromatosis, Inc., *8855 Annapolis Rd., #110, Lanham, MD 20706-2924; (301) 577-8984. Fax, (301) 577-0016. Michael Flamingo, president. Toll-free, (800) 942-6825. Internet, nfinc1@oal.com or http://www. nfinc.org.*

Provides information and assistance to health care professionals, individuals and families affected by neurofibromatosis and related disorders. Promotes research; maintains a database of resources; markes referrals to physicians, service providers, and peer counselors.

Society for Neuroscience, *11 Dupont Circle N.W., #500 20036; (202) 462-6688. Fax, (202) 234-9770. Lorne Mendell, president. Internet, http://www.sfn.org.*

Membership: scientists and physicians worldwide who research the brain, spinal cord, and nervous system. Interests include the molecular and cellular levels of the nervous system; systems within the brain, such as vision and hearing; and behavior produced by the brain. Promotes education in the neurosciences and the application of research to treat nervous system disorders.

United Cerebral Palsy Assns., *1660 L St. N.W., #700 20036; (202) 776-0406. Fax, (202) 776-0414. Vacant, executive director. Toll-free, (800) 872-5827. Main phone is voice and TDD accessible. Internet, http://www.ucpa.org.*

National network of state and local affiliates that assists individuals with cerebral palsy and other developmental disabilities and their families. Provides parent education, early intervention, employment services, family support and respite programs, therapy, assistive technology, and vocational training. Promotes research on cerebral palsy; supports the use of assistive technology and community-based living arrangements for persons with cerebral palsy and other developmental disabilities.

See also National Easter Seal Society (p. 377)

Skin Disorders

AGENCIES

National Institute of Arthritis and Musculoskeletal and Skin Diseases *(National Institutes of Health), 31 Center Dr., MSC-2350, #4C32, Bethesda, MD 20892-2350; (301) 496-4353. Fax, (301) 480-6069. Dr. Stephen I. Katz, director. Information, (301) 496-8188. Internet, http://www.nih.gov/niams.*

Supports research on the causes and treatment of skin diseases, including psoriasis, eczema, and acne.

NONPROFIT

American Academy of Facial Plastic and Reconstructive Surgery, *310 S. Henry St., Alexandria, VA 22314; (703) 299-9291. Fax, (703) 299-8895. Stephen C. Duffy, executive vice president. Toll-free information and physician referral, (800) 332-3223. Internet, aafprs@aol. com or http://www.facial-plastic-surgery.org.*

Promotes research and study in the field. Helps train residents in facial plastic and reconstructive surgery; offers continuing medical education. Sponsors scientific and medical meetings, international symposia, fellowship training program, seminars, and workshops. Provides videotapes on facial plastic and reconstructive surgery.

Substance Abuse

See also Tobacco (chap. 1); Drug Control (chap. 14)

AGENCIES

Education Dept., *Safe and Drug-Free Schools, 604 Portals Bldg. (mailing address: 600 Independence Ave. S.W., Washington, DC 20202-6123); (202) 260-3954. Fax, (202) 260-7767. William Modzeleski, director. Internet, http://www.ed.gov/offices/OESE/SDFS.*

Develops policy for the department's drug and violence prevention initiatives for students in elementary and secondary schools and institutions of higher education. Coordinates education efforts in drug and violence prevention with those of other federal departments and agencies.

Food and Drug Administration *(Health and Human Services Dept.), Health Affairs, 5600 Fishers Lane, Parklawn Bldg., #1536, Rockville, MD 20857; (301) 827-6630. Fax, (301) 443-1309. Dr. Stuart Nightingale, associate commissioner.*

Coordinates interagency reviews of international control of abusive drugs.

Health Resources and Services Administration *(Health and Human Services Dept.), Special Populations, 4350 East-West Hwy., West Towers Bldg., 9th Floor, Bethesda, MD 20814; (301) 594-4420. Fax, (301) 594-4989. Nathan Stinson, director.*

Funds a program that links primary care and substance abuse treatment.

National Institute on Alcohol Abuse and Alcoholism *(National Institutes of Health), 6000 Executive Blvd., Willco Bldg., #400, MSC 7003, Bethesda, MD 20892-7003; (301) 443-3885. Fax, (301) 443-7043. Dr. Enoch Gordis, director. Information, (301) 443-3860. Internet, http://www.niaaa.nih.gov.*

Supports basic and applied research on preventing and treating alcoholism and alcohol-related problems; conducts research and disseminates findings on alcohol abuse and alcoholism. Participates in international research.

National Institute on Drug Abuse *(National Institutes of Health), 5600 Fishers Lane, #10-05, Rockville, MD 20857; (301) 443-6480. Fax, (301) 443-9127. Alan I. Leshner, director. Information, (301) 443-1124. Press, (301) 443-6245. Toll-free, (800) 843-4971. Internet, http:// www.nida.nih.gov.*

Conducts and sponsors research on the prevention, effects, and treatment of drug abuse. Operates toll-free hotline for employers trying to eradicate drug abuse in the workplace. Monitors international policy and research.

Office of National Drug Control Policy *(Executive Office of the President), 750 17th St. N.W. (mailing address: Old Executive Office Bldg., Washington, DC 20503); (202) 395-6700. Fax, (202) 395-6708. Barry McCaffrey, director. Internet, http://www. whitehousedrugpolicy.gov.*

Establishes policies and oversees the implementation of a national drug control strategy; recommends changes to reduce demand for and supply of illegal drugs; advises the National Security Council on drug control policy.

Office of Personnel Management, *Employee Health Services, 1900 E St. N.W. 20415; (202) 606-1740. Fax, (202) 606-0967. Marjorie Marks, chief, Work and Family Programs and Employee Relations.*

Sets policy and guides federal agencies in establishing and maintaining alcohol and drug abuse programs and drug-free workplaces.

Substance Abuse and Mental Health Services Administration *(Health and Human Services Dept.), 5600 Fishers Lane, #12-105, Rockville, MD 20857; (301) 443-4795. Fax, (301) 443-0284. Nelba Chavez, administrator. Information, (301) 443-8956. Internet, http://www. samhsa.gov.*

Coordinates activities of the Center for Substance Abuse Treatment, Center for Mental Health Services, and Center for Substance Abuse Prevention, which sponsors the National Clearinghouse for Alcohol and Drug Information.

Substance Abuse and Mental Health Services Administration *(Health and Human Services Dept.), Center for Substance Abuse Prevention, 5515 Security Lane, Rockwall 2, Rockville, MD 20857; (301) 443-0365. Fax, (301) 443-5447. Carol Kumpher, acting director; John*

Noble, clearinghouse director, (301) 468-2600. Toll-free, (800) 729-6686. TDD, (800) 487-4889. Internet, http:// www.health.org.

Promotes strategies to prevent alcohol and drug abuse. Operates the National Clearinghouse for Alcohol and Drug Information, which provides information, publications, and grant applications for programs to prevent substance abuse. (Clearinghouse address: P.O. Box 2345, Rockville, MD 29847.)

Substance Abuse and Mental Health Services Administration *(Health and Human Services Dept.), Center for Substance Abuse Treatment, 5600 Fishers Lane, Rockwall 2, #615, Rockville, MD 20857; (301) 443-2467. Fax, (301) 443-8751. Camille Barry, acting director. Information, (301) 443-5052. Treatment referral, literature, and reports: (800) 662-4357; (800) 662-9832 (Spanish-language); (800) 228-0427 (hearing-impaired).*

Develops and supports policies and programs that improve and expand treatment services for alcoholics and drug addicts. Administers grants that support private and public addiction prevention and treatment services. Conducts research on and evaluates alcohol treatment programs and other drug treatment programs and delivery systems.

INTERNATIONAL ORGANIZATIONS

International Commission for the Prevention of Alcoholism and Drug Dependency, *12501 Old Columbia Pike, Silver Spring, MD 20904; (301) 680-6719. Fax, (301) 680-6090. Thomas R. Neslund, executive director. Internet, 74617.2242@compuserve.com or http:// www.adventist.org/ICPA.*

Membership: health officials, physicians, educators, clergy, and judges worldwide. Promotes scientific research on prevention of alcohol and drug dependencies; provides information about medical effects of alcohol and drugs; conducts world congresses.

NONPROFIT

American Society of Addiction Medicine, *4601 N. Park Ave., Upper Arcade, #101, Chevy Chase, MD 20815; (301) 656-3920. Fax, (301) 656-3815. James F. Callahan, executive vice president. Internet, email@asam.org or http://www.asam.org.*

Membership: physicians and medical students. Supports the study and provision of effective treatment and care for people with alcohol and drug dependencies; educates physicians; administers certification program in addiction medicine. Monitors legislation and regulations.

Employee Assistance Professionals Assn., *2101 Wilson Blvd., #500, Arlington, VA 22201; (703) 522-6272. Fax,*

(703) 522-4585. *Sylvia Straub, chief operating officer. Internet, eapamain@aol.com or http://www. eap-association.com.*

Represents professionals in the workplace who assist employees and their family members with personal and behavioral problems, including health, marital, family, financial, alcohol, drug, legal, emotional, stress, or other personal problems that adversely affect employee job performance and productivity.

National Assn. of Alcoholism and Drug Abuse Counselors, *1911 N. Fort Myer Dr., #900, Arlington, VA 22209; (703) 741-7686. Fax, (703) 741-7698. Linda P. Kaplan, executive director. Toll-free, (800) 548-0497. Internet, naadac@internetmci.com or http://www.naadac.org.*

Provides information on drug dependency treatment, research, and resources. Works with private groups and federal agencies concerned with treating and preventing alcoholism and drug abuse; certifies addiction counselors; holds workshops and conferences for treatment professionals.

National Assn. of State Alcohol and Drug Abuse Directors, *808 17th St. N.W., #410 20006; (202) 293-0090. Fax, (202) 293-1250. John S. Gustafson, executive director.*

Membership: state alcohol and drug abuse agencies. Provides information on alcohol and other drug abuse treatment and prevention services and resources; contracts with federal and state agencies to design and conduct research on alcohol and drug abuse programs.

National Council on Alcoholism and Drug Dependence, *1511 K St. N.W. 20005; (202) 737-8122. Fax, (202) 628-4731. Sarah Kayson, director, Public Policy. Internet, http://www.ncadd.org.*

Membership: local affiliates and individuals interested in alcoholism, other drug dependencies, and their related problems. Monitors legislation and regulations. Affiliates offer information and referral services. (Headquarters in New York.)

Therapeutic Communities of America, *1611 Connecticut Ave. N.W. #4B 20009; (202) 296-3503. Fax, (202) 518-5475. Linda R. Wolf Jones, executive director. Internet, http://www.tcanet.org.*

Membership: substance abuse treatment and rehabilitation agencies. Provides policy analysis and educates the public on substance abuse and treatment issues. Promotes the interests of therapeutic communities, their clients, and staffs. Monitors legislation and regulations.

See also National Organization on Fetal Alcohol Syndrome (p. 382)

Women's Health

AGENCIES

National Institutes of Health *(Health and Human Services Dept.), Research on Women's Health,* 9000 *Rockville Pike, Bldg. 1, #201, Bethesda, MD 20892-0161; (301) 402-1770. Fax, (301) 402-1798. Dr. Vivian W. Pinn, director. Internet, http://ohrm.od.nih.gov/orwh/index.html.*

Establishes NIH goals and policies for research related to women's health; supports expansion of research on diseases, conditions, and disorders that affect women; monitors appropriate numerical participation of women in clinical research; advocates recruitment and advancement of women in biomedical careers.

Public Health and Science *(Health and Human Services Dept.), Women's Health,* 200 *Independence Ave. S.W., #712E 20201; (202) 690-7650. Fax, (202) 401-4005. Dr. Wanda K. Jones, deputy assistant secretary.*

Coordinates HHS activities in women's health research and medical care, including professional education and advancement of women; works with other agencies and organizations; participates in international conferences. Oversees the National Women's Health Information Center; interests include breast cancer.

NONPROFIT

American Medical Women's Assn., *801 N. Fairfax St., #400, Alexandria, VA 22314; (703) 838-0500. Fax, (703) 549-3864. Eileen McGrath, executive director. Internet, amwaleg@aol.com or http://www.amwa-doc.org.*

Membership: female physicians, interns, residents, and medical students. Promotes continuing education; evaluates manufacturers' research on products for women's health; provides student educational loans. Monitors legislation and regulations that affect women's health.

Institute for Women's Policy Research, *1400 20th St. N.W., #104 20036; (202) 785-5100. Fax, (202) 833-4362. Heidi I. Hartmann, director. Internet, http://www.iwpr.org.*

Public policy research organization that focuses on women's issues, including health care and comprehensive family and medical leave programs.

National Women's Health Network, *514 10th St. N.W., #400 20004; (202) 347-1140. Fax, (202) 347-1168. Cynthia Pearson, executive director.*

Acts as an information clearinghouse on women's health issues; monitors federal health policies and legislation. Interests include older women's health issues, contraception, breast cancer, abortion, unsafe drugs, and AIDS.

Society for the Advancement of Women's Health Research, *1828 L St. N.W., #625 20036; (202) 223-7009. Fax, (202) 833-3472. Phyllis Greenberger, executive director. Internet, http://www.womens-health.org.*

Promotes public and private funding for women's health research and changes in public policies affecting women's health. Seeks to advance women as leaders in the health professions and to inform policymakers, educators, and the public of research outcomes. Sponsors meetings; produces reports and educational videotapes.

See also Assn. of Reproductive Health Professionals (p. 367); National Breast Cancer Coalition (p. 391)

✠ MENTAL HEALTH

AGENCIES

National Institute of Mental Health *(National Institutes of Health), 5600 Fishers Lane, #17-99, Rockville, MD 20857; (301) 443-3673. Fax, (301) 443-2578. Dr. Steven E. Hyman, director. Information, (301) 443-4513. Press, (301) 443-4536. TDD, (301) 443-4229. Internet, http://www.nimh.nih.gov.*

Conducts research on the cause, diagnosis, treatment, and prevention of mental disorders; provides information on mental health problems and programs.

National Institute of Mental Health *(National Institutes of Health), Basic and Clinical Neuroscience Research, 5600 Fishers Lane, #11-103, Rockville, MD 20857; (301) 443-3563. Fax, (301) 443-1731. Stephen H. Koslow, director.*

Directs, plans, and supports programs of basic and clinical neuroscience research, genetics and therapeutics research, research training, resource development, and research dissemination to further understand the treatment and prevention of brain disorders. Interests include: behavioral and integrative neuroscience; molecular and cellular neuroscience; genetics; and preclinical and clinical therapeutics. Analyzes national needs and research opportunities.

National Institute of Mental Health *(National Institutes of Health), Depression, Awareness, Recognition, and Treatment (DART), 5600 Fishers Lane, #10-85, Rockville, MD 20857; (301) 443-4140. Fax, (301) 443-4045. Isabel Davidoff, director. Publication orders, (800) 421-4211.*

Educates the public and health professionals about depression and its treatment; develops workplace educational programs for managers, employees, and health program directors; produces and disseminates materials.

National Institute of Mental Health *(National Institutes of Health), Prevention, 5600 Fishers Lane, #9C-25, Rockville, MD 20857; (301) 443-3533. Fax, (301) 443-8022. Juan Ramos, director.*

Promotes research programs concerning the prevention of mental disorders and the promotion of mental health. Interests includes: AIDS, international activities, and mental health training.

National Institute of Mental Health *(National Institutes of Health), Special Populations, 5600 Fishers Lane, #17C-14, Rockville, MD 20857; (301) 443-2847. Fax, (301) 443-8552. Delores Parron, associate director.*

Sets research policy on women and racial and ethnic minorities. Administers the minority institutions programs, which support research on and research training for minorities in the mental health field.

Substance Abuse and Mental Health Services Administration *(Health and Human Services Dept.), 5600 Fishers Lane, #12-105, Rockville, MD 20857; (301) 443-4795. Fax, (301) 443-0284. Nelba Chavez, administrator. Information, (301) 443-8956. Internet, http://www.samhsa.gov.*

Coordinates activities of the Center for Substance Abuse Treatment, Center for Mental Health Services, and Center for Substance Abuse Prevention, which sponsors the National Clearinghouse for Alcohol and Drug Information.

Substance Abuse and Mental Health Services Administration *(Health and Human Services Dept.), Center for Mental Health Services, 5600 Fishers Lane, #15-99, Rockville, MD 20857; (301) 443-0001. Fax, (301) 443-1563. Dr. Bernard S. Arons, director. Information, (301) 443-2792. TDD, (301) 443-9006.*

Works with federal agencies, state, and local governments to demonstrate, evaluate, and disseminate service delivery models to treat mental illness, promote mental health, and prevent the developing or worsening of mental illness.

NONPROFIT

American Academy of Child and Adolescent Psychiatry, *3615 Wisconsin Ave. N.W. 20016; (202) 966-7300. Fax, (202) 966-2891. Virginia Q. Anthony, executive director. Internet, http://www.aacap.org.*

Membership: psychiatrists working with children and adolescents. Sponsors annual meeting and review for medical board examinations; provides information on child abuse, youth suicide, and drug abuse; monitors international research and U.S. legislation concerning mentally ill children.

American Assn. of Pastoral Counselors, *9504A Lee Hwy., Fairfax, VA 22301-2303; (703) 385-6967. Fax, (703) 352-7725. C. Roy Woodruff, executive director. Internet, info@aapc.org or http://www.metanoia.org/aapc.*

Membership: mental health professionals with training in both religion and the behavioral sciences. Nonsectarian organization that accedits pastoral counseling centers, certifies pastoral counselors, and approves training programs.

American Assn. of Suicidology, *4201 Connecticut Ave. N.W., #310 20008; (202) 237-2280. Fax, (202) 237-2282. Dr. Alan Berman, executive director. Internet, Berm101@ ix.nctcom.comv or http://www.cyberpsych.org.*

Membership: educators, researchers, suicide prevention centers, school districts, volunteers, and survivors affected by suicide. Works to understand and prevent suicide; serves as an information clearinghouse.

American Bar Assn., *Commission on Mental and Physical Disability Law, 740 15th St. N.W. 20005; (202) 662-1570. Fax, (202) 662-1032. John Parry, director. Internet, http://www.abanet.org/disability/home.html.*

Serves as a clearinghouse for information on mental and physical disability law and offers legal research services.

American Counseling Assn., *5999 Stevenson Ave., Alexandria, VA 22304; (703) 823-9800. Fax, (703) 823-0252. John L. Jaco, executive director. Toll-free, (800) 347-6647. Internet, http://www.counseling.org.*

Membership: professional counselors and counselor educators. Provides members with leadership training, continuing education programs, and advocacy services; develops professional and ethical standards for the counseling profession; accredits counselor education programs. Monitors legislation and regulations. Library open to the public.

American Mental Health Counselors Assn., *801 N. Fairfax St., #304, Alexandria, VA 22314; (703) 548-6002. Fax, (703) 548-4775. Beth Powell, director, Public Policy and Legislation.*

Membership: professional counselors and graduate students in the mental health field. Sponsors leadership training and continuing education programs for members; serves as a liaison between counselors and clients. Monitors legislation and regulations. (Affiliated with the American Counseling Assn.)

American Psychiatric Assn., *1400 K St. N.W. 20005; (202) 682-6000. Fax, (202) 682-6850. Dr. Steven Mirin, medical director. Press, (202) 682-6142. Library, (202) 682-6080. Internet, apa@psych.org or http://www.psych.org.*

Membership: psychiatrists. Promotes availability of high-quality psychiatric care; provides the public with information; assists state and local agencies; conducts educational programs for professionals and students in the field. Library open to the public by appointment.

American Psychological Assn., *750 1st St. N.E. 20002-4242; (202) 336-5500. Fax, (202) 336-6069. Raymond D. Fowler, executive vice president. Library, (202) 336-5640. TDD, (202) 336-6123. Internet, http://www.apa.org.*

Membership: professional psychologists, educators, and behavioral research scientists. Supports research, training, and professional services; works toward improving the qualifications, training programs, and competence of psychologists; monitors international research and U.S. legislation on mental health.

Anxiety Disorders Assn. of America, *11900 Parklawn Dr., #100, Rockville, MD 20852; (301) 231-9350. Fax, (301) 231-7392. Ivy Farber, administrative director. Internet, http://www.adaa.org.*

Membership: people with phobias and anxiety disorders, their support persons, and mental health professionals. Provides self-help groups with technical and networking support; encourages research and treatment for anxiety disorders.

Assn. of Black Psychologists, *821 Kennedy St. N.W. (mailing address: P.O. Box 55999, Washington, DC 20040-5999); (202) 722-0808. Fax, (202) 722-5941. Dr. Dana Dennard, president. Internet, http://www.abpsi.org.*

Membership: psychologists and psychology students. Develops policies to foster mental health in the African American community.

Bazelon Center for Mental Health Law, *1101 15th St. N.W., #1212 20005; (202) 467-5730. Fax, (202) 223-0409. Robert Berstein, director. TDD, (202) 467-4232. Internet, hn1660@handsnet.org or http://www.bazelon.org.*

Public interest law firm. Conducts test case litigation to defend rights of persons with mental disabilities. Provides legal support for legal services offices, protection and advocacy agencies, and private attorneys. Monitors legislation and regulations.

International Assn. of Psychosocial Rehabilitation Services, *10025 Gov. Warfield Pkwy., #301, Columbia, MD 21044-3357; (410) 730-7190. Fax, (410) 730-5965. Ruth A. Hughes, chief executive officer. TDD, (410) 730-1723. Internet, iapsrs33@aol.com.*

Membership: agencies, mental health practitioners, policymakers, family groups, and consumer organizations. Supports the community adjustment of persons with psychiatric disabilities; promotes the role of rehabilitation in mental health systems; opposes discrimination basied on mental disability.

National Alliance for the Mentally Ill, *200 N. Glebe Rd., #1015, Arlington, VA 22203-3754; (703) 524-7600. Fax, (703) 524-9094. Laurie M. Flynn, executive director. Helpline, (800) 950-6264. Internet, offc@aol.com or http://www.nami.org.*

Membership: mentally ill individuals and their families and friends. Works to eradicate mental illness and improve the lives of those affected by brain diseases; sponsors public education and research. Monitors legislation and regulations.

National Assn. of Psychiatric Health Systems, *1317 F St. N.W., #301 20004-1105; (202) 393-6700. Fax, (202) 783-6041. Mark Covall, executive director. Internet, http://www.naphs.org.*

Membership: organizations that deliver and finance clinical treatment and prevention programs for people with mental and substance abuse disorders. Promotes members' interests and industry standards.

National Assn. of State Mental Health Program Directors, *66 Canal Center Plaza, #302, Alexandria, VA 22314-1591; (703) 739-9333. Fax, (703) 548-9517. Robert W. Glover, executive director. Internet, http://www.nasmhpd.org.*

Membership: officials in charge of state mental health agencies. Compiles data on state mental health programs. Fosters collaboration among menbers; provides technical assistance and consultation. Interests include aging, human resources, and children. Maintains research institute.

National Community Mental Healthcare Council, *12300 Twinbrook Pkwy., Rockville, MD 20852; (301) 984-6200. Fax, (301) 881-7159. Charles G. Ray, chief executive officer. Internet, http://www.nccbh.org.*

Membership: community mental health agencies and state community mental health associations. Conducts research on community mental health activities; provides information, technical assistance, and referrals. Operates a job bank; publishes a membership directory and newsletters. Monitors legislation and regulations affecting community mental health facilities.

National Consortium for Child Mental Health Services, *3615 Wisconsin Ave. N.W. 20016; (202) 966-7300. Fax, (202) 966-2891. Virginia Q. Anthony, executive director.*

Membership: organizations interested in developing mental health services for children. Fosters information exchange; advises local, state, and federal agencies that develop children's mental health services. (Affiliated with American Academy of Child and Adolescent Psychiatry.)

National Mental Health Assn., *1021 Prince St., Alexandria, VA 22314-2971; (703) 684-7722. Fax, (703) 684-5968. Michael Faenza, president. Toll-free, (800) 969-6642. Internet, http://www.nmha.org.*

Citizens' interest group. Encourages research on mental illness; helps to establish community mental health centers; visits hospitals and other mental health facilities to ensure quality care; participates in litigation supporting patients' rights; produces educational materials including films. Serves as clearinghouse for mental health issues.

12 Housing and Development

GENERAL POLICY

AGENCIES

Economic Development Administration *(Commerce Dept.),* *14th St. and Constitution Ave. N.W., #7800 20230; (202) 482-5081. Fax, (202) 273-4781. Phillip A. Singerman, assistant secretary. Information, (202) 482-5112. Internet, http://www.doc.gov/eda.*

Advises the commerce secretary on domestic economic development. Administers development assistance programs that provide financial and technical aid to economically distressed areas to stimulate economic growth and create jobs. Awards public works and technical assistance grants to public institutions, nonprofit organizations, and Native American tribes; assists state and local governments with economic adjustment problems caused by long-term or sudden economic dislocation.

General Services Administration, *Federal Domestic Assistance Catalog Staff, 300 7th St. S.W., #101 20405; (202) 708-5126. Fax, (202) 401-8233. Robert Brown, director.*

Maintains computerized Federal Assistance Programs Retrieval System, which helps state and local governments locate programs with the greatest funding potential to meet their developmental needs. Prepares the *Catalog of Federal Domestic Assistance,* which lists all types of assistance, eligibility requirements, application procedure, and suggestions for writing proposals. Copies may be ordered from the Superintendent of Documents, U.S. Government Printing Office, Washington, DC. 20402; (202) 512-1800. Also available on CD-ROM and floppy diskettes.

Housing and Urban Development Dept., *451 7th St. S.W., #10000 20410; (202) 708-0417. Fax, (202) 619-8365. Andrew M. Cuomo, secretary; Vacant, deputy secretary. Information, (202) 708-0980. Press, (202) 708-0685. Library, (202) 708-3180. TDD, (202) 708-1455. Internet, http://www.hud.gov.*

Responsible for federal programs concerned with housing needs, fair housing opportunity, and improving and developing the nation's urban and rural communities. Administers mortgage insurance, rent subsidy, preservation, rehabilitation, and antidiscrimination in housing programs. Advises the president on federal policy and makes legislative recommendations on housing and community development issues.

Housing and Urban Development Dept., *HUD USER, P.O. Box 6091, Rockville, MD 20849; (301) 519-5154. Fax, (301) 519-5767. Tony Cain, director. Toll-free,*

(800) 245-2691. Internet, huduser@aspensys.com or http://www.huduser.org.

Research information service and clearinghouse for HUD research reports. Provides information on past and current HUD research; maintains HUD USER, an in-house database. Performs custom search requests for a nominal fee; blueprints available upon request. Some documents available on-line.

Housing and Urban Development Dept., *Policy Development and Research, 451 7th St. S.W., #8100 20410-6000; (202) 708-1600. Fax, (202) 619-8000. Vacant, assistant secretary. Internet, http://www.huduser.html.*

Studies ways to improve the effectiveness and equity of HUD programs; analyzes housing and urban issues, including national housing goals, the operation of housing financial markets, the management of housing assistance programs, and statistics on federal and housing insurance programs; conducts the American Housing Survey; develops policy recommendations to improve federal housing programs. Works to increase the affordability of rehabilitated and newly constructed housing through technological and regulatory improvements.

Housing and Urban Development Dept., *Program Evaluation, 451 7th St. S.W., #8140 20410; (202) 708-0574. Fax, (202) 708-5873. Kevin J. Neary, director.*

Conducts research, program evaluations, and demonstrations for all HUD housing, community development, and fair housing and equal opportunity programs.

Office of Management and Budget, *Housing, New Executive Office Bldg., #9226 20503; (202) 395-4610. Fax, (202) 395-1307. F. Stevens Redburn, chief.*

Assists and advises the OMB director in budget preparation, reorganizations, and evaluations of Housing and Urban Development Dept. housing programs.

CONGRESS

House Appropriations Committee, *Subcommittee on VA, HUD, and Independent Agencies, H143 CAP 20515; (202) 225-3241. Jerry Lewis, R-Calif., chair; Frank Cushing, staff director. Internet, http://www.house.gov/appropriations.*

Jurisdiction over legislation to appropriate funds for all programs of the Housing and Urban Development Dept., the Federal Emergency Management Agency, the National Credit Union Administration, and the Neighborhood Reinvestment Corporation.

House Banking and Financial Services Committee, *Subcommittee on Housing and Community Opportu-*

HOUSING AND URBAN DEVELOPMENT DEPARTMENT

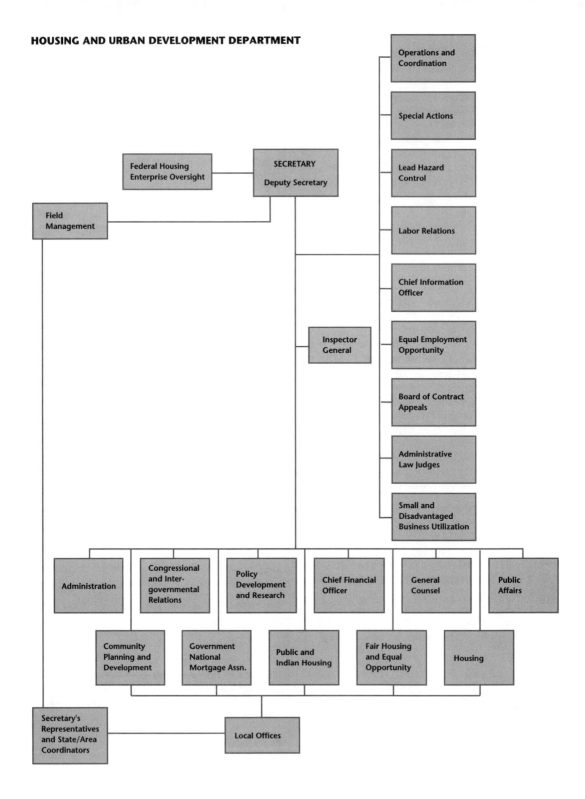

nity, B303 RHOB 20515; (202) 225-6634. Rick A. Lazio, R-N.Y., chair; Joseph M. Ventrone, staff director.

Jurisdiction over all housing legislation, including construction standards and materials, condominiums and cooperatives, home ownership aid, manufactured homes, single and multifamily housing, and rural housing; oversees the Rural Housing Service in the Agriculture Dept. and other housing-related services and programs.

House Government Reform and Oversight Committee, *Subcommittee on Human Resources,* B372 RHOB 20515; (202) 225-2548. Fax, (202) 225-2382. Christopher Shays, R-Conn., chair; Larry Halloran, staff director. Internet, http://www.house.gov/reform.

Oversight of the Housing and Urban Development Dept.

House Small Business Committee, *Subcommittee on Empowerment,* B363 RHOB 20515; (202) 226-2630. Fax, (202) 225-8950. Mark Souder, R-Ind., chair; Alvin S. Felzenberg, staff director. Internet, http://www.house.gov/smbiz.

Jurisdiction over development of economically depressed areas, including regulations and licensing policies that affect small businesses in high-risk communities.

Senate Appropriations Committee, *Subcommittee on VA, HUD, and Independent Agencies,* SD-127 20510; (202) 224-7211. Christopher S. Bond, R-Mo., chair; John K. Mark, staff director. Internet, http://www.senate.gov/~appropriations.

Jurisdiction over legislation to appropriate funds for all programs of the Housing and Urban Development Dept., the Federal Emergency Management Agency, the National Credit Union Administration, the Neighborhood Reinvestment Corporation, and the National Institute of Building Sciences.

Senate Banking, Housing, and Urban Affairs Committee, *Subcommittee on Financial Institutions and Regulatory Relief,* SD-534 20510; (202) 224-7391. Lauch Faircloth, R-N.C., chair; Jim Hyland, staff director. Internet, http://www.senate.gov/~banking.

Jurisdiction over legislation on economic stabilization and growth, including regulatory relief issues and barriers to development in rural areas.

Senate Banking, Housing, and Urban Affairs Committee, *Subcommittee on Housing Opportunity and Community Development,* SD-534 20510; (202) 224-7391. Connie Mack, R-Fla., chair; Christopher Lord, staff director. Internet, http://www.senate.gov/~banking.

Jurisdiction over legislation concerning housing issues, including rural housing, construction standards and materials, condominiums and cooperatives, home ownership aid, manufactured homes, and single and multifamily housing. Oversees the Housing and Urban Development Dept. and housing programs in the Agriculture Dept.

Senate Small Business Committee, SR-428A 20510; (202) 224-5175. Fax, (202) 224-4885. Christopher S. Bond, R-Mo., chair; Louis Taylor, staff director. Internet, http://www.senate.gov/~sbc.

Jurisdiction over small and disadvantaged business and related economic development.

NONPROFIT

Center for Housing Policy, 815 15th St. N.W., #538 20005; (202) 393-5772. Fax, (202) 393-5656. Robert J. Reid, executive director. Internet, chp@nhc.org.

Researches and develops fundamentals of housing policy. Seeks to create new policies which integrate housing into overall social and economic goals. Sponsors educational forums. (Affiliated with the National Housing Conference.)

Housing and Development Law Institute, 630 Eye St. N.W., 20001; (202) 289-3400. Fax, (202) 289-3401. William F. Maher, executive director.

Assists public agencies that administer assisted housing and community development programs in addressing common legal concerns and problems; publishes legal periodicals concerning affordable housing issues; conducts seminars on legal issues and practices in the housing and community development field. (Affiliated with the National Assn. of Housing and Redevelopment Officials.)

Institute for Local Self-Reliance, 2425 18th St. N.W. 20009-2096; (202) 232-4108. Fax, (202) 332-0463. Neil Seldman, president. Internet, ilsr@igc.apc.org or http://www.ilsr.org.

Conducts research and provides technical assistance on environmentally sound economic development for government, small businesses, and community organizations.

National Assn. of Housing and Redevelopment Officials, 630 Eye St. N.W. 20001; (202) 289-3500. Fax, (202) 289-8181. Richard Y. Nelson Jr., executive director. Internet, http://www.nahro.org.

Membership: housing, community, and urban development practitioners and organizations, and state and local government agencies and personnel. Works with federal government agencies to improve community development and housing programs; conducts training programs.

National Assn. of State Development Agencies, *750 1st St. N.E., #710 20002-4241; (202) 898-1302. Fax, (202) 898-1312. Miles Friedman, executive director. Internet, http://www.ids.net/nasda.*

Membership: directors of state economic development agencies. Provides economic development consulting service; sponsors conferences and seminars. Interests include financing techniques, job training programs, aid to small business, and state-local coordination strategies.

National Development Council, *3921 Albemarle St. N.W. 20016; (202) 364-9641. Fax, (202) 364-9648. Nelson R. Bregon, director. Internet, ndccvg@aol.com.*

Seeks to increase economic development in low-income communities. Assists small businesses in finding long-term financing for expansion; works to increase employment opportunities. (Headquarters in New York.)

Statistics

AGENCIES

Census Bureau *(Commerce Dept.), Governments Division, Washington Plaza II, #407, Upper Marlboro, MD; (301) 457-1489. Fax, (301) 457-1423. Gordon W. Green Jr., chief.*

Compiles the annual *Federal Expenditures by State,* which provides information on federal domestic spending, federal grants programs, and federal aid to states.

Census Bureau *(Commerce Dept.), Housing and Household Economic Statistics, 4700 Silver Hill Rd., Suitland, MD 20746-8500; (301) 457-3234. Fax, (301) 457-3248. Daniel H. Weinberg, chief.*

Publishes decennial census of housing and the American Housing Survey, which describe housing inventory characteristics. Also publishes a quarterly survey of market absorption. Survey on housing vacancy is available on the Internet.

Census Bureau *(Commerce Dept.), Manufacturing and Construction, Suitland and Silver Hill Rds., Suitland, MD; (301) 457-4593. Fax, (301) 457-4583. Thomas L. Mesenbourg, acting chief.*

Publishes statistics on the value of construction put in place; housing starts, sales, and completions; building permits; price index of single-family homes sold; characteristics of new housing; and expeditures for residential improvements. Conducts a census of construction industries every five years.

Housing and Urban Development Dept., *Economic Affairs, 451 7th St. S.W., #8204 20410; (202) 708-3080. Fax, (202) 619-8000. Frederick J. Eggers, deputy assistant secretary.*

Directs research in public finance and urban economic development; assembles data on housing markets; conducts annual housing surveys; analyzes financial instruments used in housing.

International Trade Administration *(Commerce Dept.), Basic Industries, 14th St. and Constitution Ave. N.W., #4043 20230; (202) 482-0614. Fax, (202) 482-5666. Michael J. Copts, deputy assistant secretary.*

Analyzes and maintains data on international construction and engineering. Monitors production costs, prices, financial and labor conditions, technological changes, distribution, markets, trade patterns, and other aspects of these industries. Promotes international trade, develops competitive assessments, and assists engineering and construction companies in obtaining overseas construction projects.

Office of Thrift Supervision *(Treasury Dept.), Financial Reporting, 1700 G St. N.W. 20552; (202) 906-6720. Fax, (202) 906-5735. Patrick Berbakos, director.*

Provides housing and mortgage statistics, including terms and rates of conventional home mortgages, and asset and liability information for thrift institutions insured by the Savings Association Insurance Fund.

📠 COMMUNITY AND REGIONAL DEVELOPMENT

AGENCIES

Administration for Children and Families *(Health and Human Services Dept.), Community Services, 901 D St. S.W. (mailing address: 370 L'Enfant Promenade S.W., Washington, DC 20447); (202) 401-9333. Fax, (202) 401-4694. Donald Sykes, director.*

Administers the Community Services Block Grant and Discretionary Grant programs.

Administration for Native Americans *(Health and Human Services Dept.), 200 Independence Ave. S.W., #348F 20201; (202) 690-7776. Fax, (202) 690-7441. Gary N. Kimble, commissioner.*

Awards grants for locally determined social and economic development strategies; promotes Native American economic and social self-sufficiency; funds Native American and native Hawaiian organizations. Commissioner chairs the Intradepartmental Council on Indian

Affairs, which coordinates Native American-related programs.

Army Corps of Engineers *(Defense Dept.),* *20 Massachusetts Ave. N.W. 20314-1000; (202) 761-0001. Fax, (202) 761-4463. Lt. Gen. Joe N. Ballard (USACE), chief of engineers. Internet, http://www.usace.army.mil.*

Provides local governments with disaster relief, flood control, navigation, and hydroelectric power services.

Defense Dept., *Base Closure and Community Reinvestment,* *400 Army-Navy Dr., #200, Arlington, VA 22202-2884; (703) 604-6020. Fax, (703) 604-5843. Paul J. Dempsey, director; Helene O'Connor, acting director, Economic Adjustment, (703) 604-5948.*

Civilian office that helps community officials develop strategies and coordinate plans to alleviate the economic effect of major defense program changes, including base closings, reductions in forces, and contract cutbacks. Assists communities where defense activities are being expanded. Serves as the staff for the Economic Adjustment Committee, an interagency group that coordinates federal defense economic adjustment activities.

Housing and Urban Development Dept., *Block Grant Assistance,* *451 7th St. S.W., #7286 20410; (202) 708-3587. Fax, (202) 401-2044. Richard Kennedy, director. Press, (202) 708-0685.*

Develops regulations and procedures for the Community Development Block Grant Program and the Section 108 Loan Guarantee Program. Manages close-out functions of the Urban Renewal Program.

Housing and Urban Development Dept., *Community Planning and Development,* *451 7th St. S.W., #7100 20410; (202) 708-2690. Fax, (202) 708-3336. Saul Ramirez Jr., assistant secretary. Information, (202) 708-0980.*

Provides cities and states with community and economic development and housing assistance, including community development block grants. Encourages public-private partnerships in urban development and private sector initiatives. Oversees enterprise zone development program.

Housing and Urban Development Dept., *Community Viability,* *451 7th St. S.W., #7240 20410; (202) 708-2894. Fax, (202) 708-3363. Richard H. Broun, director.*

Issues policies and sets standards for environmental and land-use planning and for environmental management practices. Develops policies promoting energy efficiency, conservation, and renewable sources of supply in housing and community development programs, including district heating and cooling systems and wastes-to-energy cogeneration projects.

Housing and Urban Development Dept., *Executive Services,* *451 7th St. S.W., #7208 20410; (202) 708-1283. Fax, (202) 708-5446. John Simmons, acting director.*

Conducts policy analyses and evaluations of community planning and development programs, including the Community Development Block Grant Program, the Empowerment Zones/Enterprise Communities Program, and the McKinney Act programs.

Housing and Urban Development Dept., *Field Management,* *451 7th St. S.W., #7152 20410; (202) 708-2565. Fax, (202) 401-9681. Nadeb O. Bynum, director.*

Acts as liaison and coordinates all activities between the Office of Community Planning and Development and regional and field offices; evaluates the performance of regional and field offices. *(See Regional Information Sources in appendix.)*

Housing and Urban Development Dept., *State and Small Cities,* *451 7th St. S.W., #7184 20410; (202) 708-1322. Fax, (202) 708-3363. Steve Johnson, director.*

Provides states with grants for distribution to small cities and counties with fewer than 50,000 persons that are not entitled to community development block grants; insular areas also are eligible. Funds support community development programs in low- and moderate-income communities and communities with urgent needs.

Housing and Urban Development Dept., *Technical Assistance,* *451 7th St. S.W., #7216 20410; (202) 708-3176. Fax, (202) 708-3363. Donna Abbenante, director.*

Develops program policies and designs and implements technical assistance plans for state and local governments for use in community planning and development programs.

Interagency Empowerment Zone/Enterprise Community Task Force, *300 7th St. N.W., #701 20024; (202) 619-7980. Fax, (202) 401-7420. Rick Wetherill, director. TDD, (202) 720-7807. Toll-free, (800) 645-4712. Internet, http://www.ezec.gov.*

Provides information about federal empowerment zones and enterprise communities in economically distressed urban and rural areas.

CONGRESS

House Banking and Financial Services Committee, *Subcommittee on Housing and Community Opportunity,* *B303 RHOB 20515; (202) 225-6634. Rick A. Lazio, R-N.Y., chair; Joseph M. Ventrone, staff director.*

Jurisdiction over all community development legislation; urban planning, design, and research; urban redevelopment and relocation; and community development training and fellowships. Jurisdiction over Urban Development Action Grants and enterprise zones. Oversees the Housing and Urban Development Dept. and housing programs in the Agriculture Dept.

House Transportation and Infrastructure Committee, *Subcommittee on Public Buildings and Economic Development, 586 Ford Bldg. 20515; (202) 225-3014. Fax, (202) 226-1898. Jay C. Kim, R-Calif., chair; Richard C. Barnett, staff director. Internet, http://www.house.gov/ transportation.*

Jurisdiction over legislation on development of economically depressed areas, including Appalachia, and legislation designed to create jobs, often with public works and water resource development projects; jurisdiction over the Economic Development Administration.

Senate Banking, Housing, and Urban Affairs Committee, *Subcommittee on Housing Opportunity and Community Development, SD-534 20510; (202) 224-7391. Connie Mack, R-Fla., chair; Christopher Lord, staff director. Internet, http://www.senate.gov/~banking.*

Jurisdiction over community development legislation (including Urban Development Action Grants and enterprise zones); federal insurance (including flood insurance); urban planning, design, and research; and urban redevelopment and relocation. Oversees the Housing and Urban Development Dept. and housing programs in the Agriculture Dept.

Senate Environment and Public Works Committee, *Subcommittee on Superfund, Waste Control, and Risk Assessment, SD-410 20510; (202) 224-6176. Fax, (202) 224-5167. Robert C. Smith, R-N.H., chair; Tom Gibson, staff contact. Internet, http://www.senate.gov/committee/ environment.html.*

Jurisdiction over legislation on development of economically depressed areas, including Appalachia, and over legislation designed to create jobs, often with public works and water resource development projects; jurisdiction over the Economic Development Administration.

Senate Finance Committee, *SD-219 20510; (202) 224-4515. Fax, (202) 224-5920. William V. Roth Jr., R-Del., chair; Lindy L. Paull, staff director. Internet, http://www. senate.gov/~finance.*

Jurisdiction over revenue sharing legislation (jurisdiction shared with Senate Governmental Affairs Committee).

Senate Governmental Affairs Committee, *SD-340 20510; (202) 224-4751. Fax, (202) 224-9603. Fred Thompson, R-Tenn., chair; Hannah Sistare, staff director. Internet, http://www.senate.gov/committee/governmental_ affairs.html.*

Jurisdiction over revenue sharing legislation (jurisdiction shared with Senate Finance Committee).

NONPROFIT

American Planning Assn., *1776 Massachusetts Ave. N.W., #400 20036-1904; (202) 872-0611. Fax, (202) 872-0643. Frank So, executive director. Internet, http://www. planning.org.*

Membership: professional planners and others interested in urban and rural planning. Serves as a clearinghouse for planners. Sponsors professional development workshops conducted by the American Institute of Certified Planners. Prepares studies and technical reports; conducts seminars and conferences.

American Resort Development Assn., *1220 L St. N.W., #500 20005; (202) 371-6700. Fax, (202) 289-8544. Cynthia A. Huheey, president. Internet, http://www. arda.org.*

Membership: U.S. and international developers, builders, financiers, marketing companies, and others involved in resort, recreational, and community development. Serves as an information clearinghouse; monitors federal and state legislation affecting land, timeshare, and community development industries.

Center for Community Change, *1000 Wisconsin Ave. N.W. 20007; (202) 342-0519. Fax, (202) 342-1132. Pablo Eisenberg, executive director.*

Provides community-based organizations serving minorities and the economically disadvantaged with technical assistance. Areas of assistance include community development block grants, housing, economic and resource development, rural development projects, and program planning.

Community Information Exchange, *1029 Vermont Ave. N.W., #710 20005; (202) 628-2981. Fax, (202) 783-1485. Kathleen M. Desmond, president. Internet, cie@ comminfoexch.org or http://www.comminfoexch.org.*

Serves community-based nonprofit organizations and other groups interested in revitalizing low-income communities. Provides technical information on affordable housing and on economic and community development. Database of case examples, funding sources, referrals to experts, publications, and sample documents available by subscription; staff-assisted searches also available.

Corporation for Enterprise Development, *777 N. Capitol St. N.E., #410 20002; (202) 408-9788. Fax, (202)*

408-9793. Brian Dabson, president. Internet, cfed@cfed.org or http://www.cfed.org.

Research and consulting organization that promotes economic self-sufficiency among low-income people through enterprise development, including microbusinesses to generate self-employment for the unemployed. Provides technical assistance and policy analysis to state and local governments and community organizations.

Council of State Community Development Agencies, *444 N. Capitol St. N.W., #224 20001; (202) 624-3630. Fax, (202) 624-3639. John M. Sidor, executive director. Internet, http://www.sso.org/coscda.*

Membership: directors and staff of state community development agencies. Promotes common interests among the states, including community and economic development, housing, homelessness, infrastructure, and state and local planning.

International Institute of Site Planning, *715 G St. S.E. 20003; (202) 546-2322. Fax, (202) 546-2722. Beatriz de W. Coffin, director.*

Directs research and provides information on site planning development and design of sites and buildings; conducts study/travel programs.

Land Trust Alliance, *1319 F St. N.W., #501 20004-1106; (202) 638-4725. Fax, (202) 638-4730. Jean Hocker, president. Internet, http://www.lta.org.*

Membership: organizations and individuals who work to conserve land resources. Serves as a forum for the exchange of information; conducts research and public education programs. Monitors legislation and regulations.

Local Initiatives Support Corp., *1825 K St. N.W., #1100 20006; (202) 785-2908. Fax, (202) 835-8931. Michael Tierney, senior vice president. Internet, http://www.liscnet.org.*

Provides community development corporations with financial and technical assistance to build affordable housing and revitalize distressed neighborhoods. (Headquarters in New York.)

National Assn. of Conservation Districts, *509 Capitol Court N.E. 20002-4937; (202) 547-6223. Fax, (202) 547-6450. Ernest C. Shea, chief executive officer. Internet, http://www.nacdnet.org.*

Membership: conservation districts (local subdivisions of state government). Works to promote the conservation of land, forests, and other natural resources. Interests include erosion and sediment control; water quality; forestry, water, flood plain, and range management; rural development; and urban and community conservation.

National Assn. of Counties, *Community and Economic Development, 440 1st St. N.W., 8th Floor 20001; (202) 393-6226. Fax, (202) 393-2630. Haron N. Battle, associate legislative director, (202) 942-4204. Information, (202) 393-6226. Internet, http://www.naco.org.*

Membership: county governments. Conducts research and provides information on community development block grants, assisted low-income housing, and other housing and economic development programs. Monitors legislation and regulations.

National Assn. of Development Organizations, *444 N. Capitol St. N.W., #630 20001; (202) 624-7806. Fax, (202) 624-8813. Aliceann Wohlbruck, executive director. Internet, nado@sso.org or http://www.nado.org.*

Membership: organizations interested in regional, local, and rural economic development. Provides information on federal, state, and local development programs and revolving loan funds; sponsors conferences and seminars.

National Assn. of Regional Councils, *1700 K St. N.W., #1300 20006; (202) 457-0710. Fax, (202) 296-9352. William Dodge, executive director.*

Membership: regional councils of local governments. Works with member local governments to encourage areawide economic growth and cooperation between public and private sectors, with emphasis on community development.

National Community Development Assn., *522 21st St. N.W., #120 20006; (202) 293-7587. Fax, (202) 887-5546. John A. Sasso, executive secretary. Internet, ncda@ncdaonline.org or http://www.ncdaonline.org.*

Membership: local governments that administer federally supported community and economic development, housing, and human service programs.

National Congress for Community Economic Development, *11 Dupont Circle, #325 20036; (202) 234-5009. Fax, (202) 234-4510. Roy Priest, president. Internet, http://www.ncced.org.*

Membership: organizations engaged in revitalizing economically distressed communities. Services include advocacy, fundraising and technical assistance, information and referrals, conferences, and training. Conducts research and compiles statistics on industry issues and trends. Library open to the public.

National Trust for Historic Preservation, *1785 Massachusetts Ave. N.W. 20036-2117; (202) 588-6000. Fax, (202) 588-6038. Richard Moe, president. Internet, http://www.nthp.org.*

Conducts seminars, workshops, and conferences on topics related to preservation, including neighborhood conservation, main street revitalization, rural conservation, and preservation law; offers financial assistance through loan and grant programs; provides advisory services; operates historic house museums, which are open to the public.

Partners for Livable Communities, *1429 21st St. N.W., 2nd Floor 20036; (202) 887-5990. Fax, (202) 466-4845. Robert H. McNulty, president. Internet, partners@ livable.com or http://www.livable.com.*

Promotes working partnerships among public, private, and governmental sectors to improve the quality of life and economic development at local and regional levels. Conducts conferences and workshops; maintains referral clearinghouse.

Scenic America, *801 Pennsylvania Ave. S.E., #300 20003; (202) 833-4300. Fax, (202) 833-4304. Meg Maguire, president. Internet, http://www.transact.org/sa/scenic.htm.*

Membership: national, state, and local groups concerned with land-use control, growth management, and landscape protection. Works to enhance the scenic quality of America's communities and countryside. Provides information and technical assistance on scenic byways, tree preservation, economics of aesthetic regulation, billboard and sign control, scenic areas preservation, and growth management.

Rural Areas

AGENCIES

Agriculture Dept., *Rural Development, 1400 Independence Ave. S.W., #206W 20250; (202) 720-4581. Fax, (202) 720-2080. Jill Long Thompson, under secretary. Internet, http://www.rurdev.usda.gov.*

Acts as chief adviser to the secretary on agricultural credit and related matters; coordinates rural development policies and programs throughout the federal government; supervises the Rural Utilities Service, Rural Housing Service, and Rural Business-Cooperative Service.

Farm Service Agency *(Agriculture Dept.), Farm Credit Programs, 1400 Independence Ave. S.W. 20250; (202) 720-4671. Fax, (202) 690-3573. Caroline B. Cooksie, deputy administrator. Internet, http://www.fsa.usda.gov.*

Supports rural development through farm program loans, including real estate, farm production, and emergency loans.

Rural Business-Cooperative Service *(Agriculture Dept.), 1400 Independence Ave. S.W. 20250; (202) 690-4730. Fax, (202) 690-4737. Dayton J. Watkins, administra-*

tor. Information, (202) 720-6903. Internet, http://www. rurdev.usda.gov/rbs/index.html.

Promotes rural economic development by financing community facilities and assisting community businesses.

Rural Housing Service *(Agriculture Dept.), 1400 Independence Ave. S.W., #5014 20250; (202) 690-1533. Fax, (202) 690-0500. Jan E. Shadburn, acting administrator. Information, (202) 720-4323. Internet, http://www.rurdev. usda.gov/rhs/index.html.*

Offers financial assistance to apartment dwellers and homeowners in rural areas; provides funds to construct or improve community facilities.

Rural Utilities Service *(Agriculture Dept.), 1400 Independence Ave. S.W. 20250-1500; (202) 720-9540. Fax, (202) 720-1725. Wally Beyer, administrator. Information, (202) 720-1255. Press, (202) 720-1260. Internet, http:// www.usda.gov/rus.*

Makes loans and loan guarantees to rural electric and telephone utilities providing service in rural areas. Administers the Rural Telephone Bank, which provides supplemental financing from federal sources. Makes loans for economic development and creation of jobs in rural areas, for water and waste disposal, and for distance learning and telemedicine.

CONGRESS

House Agriculture Committee, *Subcommittee on Forestry, Resource Conservation, and Research, 1336 LHOB 20515; (202) 225-2342. Larry Combest, R-Texas, chair; Russell Laird, staff director. Internet, http://www. house.gov/agriculture.*

Jurisdiction over legislation on rural development.

Senate Agriculture, Nutrition, and Forestry Committee, *Subcommittee on Forestry, Conservation, and Rural Revitalization, SR-328A 20510; (202) 224-2035. Rick Santorum, R-Pa., chair; David French, legislative assistant. Internet, http://www.senate.gov/~agriculture.*

Jurisdiction over legislation on rural development.

NONPROFIT

Farm Credit Council, *50 F St. N.W., #900 20001; 202) 626-8710. Fax, (202) 626-8718. William R. Weber, president.*

Represents the Farm Credit System, a national financial cooperative that makes loans to agricultural producers, rural homebuyers, farmer cooperatives, and rural utilities. Finances the export of U.S. agricultural commodities.

Housing Assistance Council, *1025 Vermont Ave. N.W., #606 20005-3516; (202) 842-8600. Fax, (202) 347-3441. Moises Loza, executive director. Toll-free, (800) 989-4422. Internet, hn0143@handsnet.org.*

Operates in rural areas and in cities of fewer than 25,000 citizens. Advises low-income and minority groups seeking federal assistance for improving rural housing and community facilities; studies and makes recommendations for state and local housing policies; makes low-interest loans for housing programs for low-income and minority groups living in rural areas, including Native Americans and farm workers.

Irrigation Assn., *8260 Willow Oaks Corporate Dr., #120, Fairfax, VA 22031; (703) 573-3551. Fax, (703) 573-1913. Thomas Kimmell, executive director. Internet, http://www. irrigation.org.*

Membership: companies and individuals involved in irrigation, drainage, and erosion control worldwide. Seeks to improve the products and practices used to manage water resources; interests include economic development and environmental enhancement.

National Cooperative Business Assn., *1401 New York Ave. N.W., #1100 20005-2146; (202) 638-6222. Fax, (202) 638-1374. Russell C. Notar, president. Internet, ncba@ ncba.org or http://www.cooperative.org.*

Alliance of cooperatives, businesses, and state cooperative associations. Provides information about starting and managing agricultural cooperatives in the United States and in developing nations. Monitors legislation and regulations.

National Council of Farmer Cooperatives, *50 F St. N.W., #900 20001; (202) 626-8700. Fax, (202) 626-8722. David Graves, president. Internet, info@ncfc.org or http:// www.access.digex.net/~ncfc/members.*

Membership: cooperative businesses owned and operated by farmers. Encourages research on agricultural cooperatives; provides statistics and analyzes trends. Monitors legislation and regulations on agricultural trade, transportation, energy, and tax issues.

National Rural Community Assistance Program, *602 S. King St., #402, Leesburg, VA 20175; (703) 771-8636. Fax, (703) 771-8753. Kathleen Stanley, executive director. Internet, http://www.rcap.org.*

Federally funded organization that conducts program to improve water delivery and disposal of waste water for rural residents, particularly low-income families.

National Rural Electric Cooperative Assn., *4301 Wilson Blvd., Arlington, VA 22203-1860; (703) 907-5500. Fax, (703) 907-5511. Glenn English, chief executive officer. Internet, http://www.nreca.org.*

Membership: rural electric cooperative systems and public power and utility districts. Provides members with legislative, legal, and regulatory services.

National Telephone Cooperative Assn., *2626 Pennsylvania Ave. N.W. 20037; (202) 298-2300. Fax, (202) 298-2320. Michael E. Brunner, executive vice president. Internet, frs@ntca.org or http://www.ntca.org.*

Membership: locally owned and controlled telecommunications cooperatives and companies serving rural and small-town areas. Offers educational seminars, workshops, technical assistance, and a benefits program to members. Monitors legislation and regulations.

Rural Coalition, *110 Maryland Ave. N.E., #101 20002; (202) 544-9611. Fax, (202) 544-9613. Lorette Picciano, executive director. Internet, ruralco@aol.com or http:// www2.cibola.net/~sinfront/rcpage/html.*

Alliance of organizations that develop public policies benefiting rural communities. Collaborates with community-based groups on agriculture and rural development issues, including health and the environment, minority farmers, farmworkers, Native Americans' rights, and rural community development. Provides rural groups with technical assistance.

Specific Regions

AGENCIES

Appalachian Regional Commission, *1666 Connecticut Ave. N.W., #600 20235; (202) 884-7660. Fax, (202) 884-7691. Jesse White, federal co-chair; Thomas Hunter, executive director, (202) 884-7700. Information, (202) 884-7773. Press, (202) 884-7770. Internet, http://www. arc.gov.*

Federal-state-local partnership for economic development of the region including West Virginia and parts of Alabama, Georgia, Kentucky, Maryland, Mississippi, New York, North Carolina, Ohio, Pennsylvania, South Carolina, Tennessee, and Virginia. Plans and provides technical and financial assistance and coordinates federal and state efforts for economic development of Appalachia.

Bureau of Reclamation *(Interior Dept.), 1849 C St. N.W., #7659 20240; (202) 208-4157. Fax, (202) 208-3484. Eluid Martinez, commissioner. Information, (202) 208-4215. Internet, http://www.usbr.gov.*

Administers federal programs for water and power resource development and management in seventeen western states; oversees municipal and industrial water supply, hydroelectric power generation, irrigation, flood control, water quality improvement, river regulation, fish and wildlife enhancement, and outdoor recreation.

Delaware River Basin Commission, *1010 Massachusetts Ave. N.W., #100 20001; (202) 343-5761. Fax, (202) 343-1013. Vincent P. D'Anna, U.S. commissioner.*

Federal-interstate commission. Oversees projects to develop the Delaware River Basin that include regulation and development of ground and surface water supplies for municipal, industrial, and agricultural uses; development of hydropower; abatement of stream pollution; flood damage reduction; and protection of fish and wildlife.

Interstate Commission on the Potomac River Basin, *6110 Executive Blvd., #300, Rockville, MD 20852; (301) 984-1908. Fax, (301) 984-5841. Robert Bolle, acting executive director.*

Nonregulatory interstate compact commission established by Congress to control and reduce water pollution and to restore and protect living resources in the Potomac River and its tributaries. Monitors water quality; assists metropolitan water utilities; seeks innovative methods to solve water supply and land resource problems. Provides information and educational materials on the Potomac River basin.

National Capital Planning Commission, *801 Pennsylvania Ave. N.W., #301 20576; (202) 482-7200. Fax, (202) 482-7272. Reginald W. Griffith, executive director. Internet, http://www.ncpc.gov.*

Central planning agency for the federal government in the national capital region, which includes the District of Columbia and suburban Maryland and Virginia. Reviews and approves plans for the physical growth and development of the national capital area, using environmental, historic, and land-use criteria.

Susquehanna River Basin Commission, *1010 Massachusetts Ave. N.W., #100 20001; (202) 343-4091. Fax, (202) 343-1013. Kenneth J. Cole, U.S. commissioner.*

Federal-interstate compact commission that manages water and water-related resources to develop the Susquehanna River basin. Regulates and develops ground and surface water supplies for municipal, industrial, and agricultural uses; works to reduce stream pollution and flood damage, and to protect fish and wildlife.

Tennessee Valley Authority, *1 Massachusetts Ave. N.W., #300 20001; (202) 898-2999. Fax, (202) 898-2998. Vacant, administrative officer, Washington Office. Internet, http://www.tva.gov.*

Coordinates resource conservation, development, and land-use programs in the Tennessee River Valley. Supplies wholesale power to municipal and cooperative electric systems, federal installations, and some industries. (Headquarters in Knoxville, Tenn.)

NONPROFIT

Greater Washington Board of Trade, *1129 20th St. N.W., #200 20036; (202) 857-5900. Fax, (202) 223-2648. John Tydings, president. Internet, info@bot.org or http://www.bot.org.*

Promotes and plans economic growth for the capital region. Supports business-government partnerships, technological training, and transportation planning; promotes international trade; works to increase economic viability of the city of Washington. Monitors legislation and regulations at local, state, and federal levels.

New England Council, *331 Constitution Ave. N.E. 20002; (202) 547-0048. Fax, (202) 547-9149. Jack Looney, vice president, Government Relations.*

Provides information on business and economic issues concerning New England; serves as liaison between the New England congressional delegations and business community. (Headquarters in Boston.)

Northeast-Midwest Institute, *218 D St. S.E. 20003; (202) 544-5200. Fax, (202) 544-0043. Dick Munson, executive director. Internet, http://www.nemw.org.*

Public policy research organization that promotes the economic vitality of the northeast and midwest regions. Interests include distribution of federal funding to regions, economic development, human resources, energy, and natural resources.

Urban Areas

AGENCIES

Housing and Urban Development Dept., *Affordable Housing, 451 7th St. S.W., #7164 20410; (202) 708-2685. Fax, (202) 708-1744. Marshall Dodge, acting director.*

Coordinates with cities to convey publicly owned, abandoned property to low-income families in exchange for their commitment to repair, occupy, and maintain property.

Housing and Urban Development Dept., *Economic Development, 451 7th St. S.W., #7136 20410; (202) 708-2290. Fax, (202) 708-7543. Michael T. Savage, director. Internet, http://www.ezec.gov.*

Manages economic development programs, including Urban Development Action Grants, Empowerment Zones/Enterprise Communities, and YOUTHBUILD. Encourages private-public partnerships for development through neighborhood development corporations. Formulates policies and legislative proposals on economic development.

Neighborhood Reinvestment Corp., *1325 G St. N.W., #800 20005; (202) 376-2400. Fax, (202) 376-2600. George Knight, executive director. Internet, http://www.nw.org.*

Chartered by Congress to assist localities in developing and operating local neighborhood-based programs designed to reverse decline in urban residential neighborhoods and rural communities. Oversees the National NeighborWorks Network, an association of local nonprofit organizations concerned with urban and rural development.

NONPROFIT

International Downtown Assn., *910 17th St. N.W., #210 20006; (202) 293-4505. Fax, (202) 293-4509. Elizabeth Jackson, president. Internet, question@ida-downtown. org or http://www.ida-downtown.org.*

Membership: organizations, corporations, public agencies, and individuals interested in the development and management of city downtown areas. Supports cooperative efforts between the public and private sectors to revitalize downtowns and adjacent neighborhoods; provides members with information, technical assistance, and advice; administers the Downtown Development Foundation.

Milton S. Eisenhower Foundation, *1660 L St. N.W., #200 20036; (202) 429-0440. Fax, (202) 452-0169. Lynn A. Curtis, president. Internet, tmsef@tnt.org.*

Strives to help inner city communities combat violence by supporting programs with proven records of success. Provides funding, technical assistance, evaluation, and supervision to communities wishing to replicate successful programs.

National Assn. for the Advancement of Colored People (NAACP), *1025 Vermont Ave. N.W., #1120 20005; (202) 638-2269. Fax, (202) 638-5936. Hilary Shelton, deputy director. Internet, http://www.naacp.org.*

Membership: persons interested in civil rights for all minorities. Works to eliminate discrimination in housing and urban affairs. Interests include programs for urban redevelopment, urban homesteading, and low-income housing. Supports programs that make affordable rental housing available to minorities and that maintain African American ownership of urban and rural land. (Headquarters in Baltimore.)

National Assn. of Neighborhoods, *1651 Fuller St. N.W. 20009; (202) 332-7766. Fax, (202) 332-2314. Ricardo C. Byrd, executive director. Internet, http://www. consumermortgage.org.*

Federation of neighborhood groups that provides technical assistance to local governments, neighborhood

groups, and businesses. Seeks to increase influence of grassroots groups on decisions affecting neighborhoods; sponsors training workshops promoting neighborhood awareness.

National Center for Neighborhood Enterprise, *1424 16th St. N.W., #300 20036; (202) 518-6500. Fax, (202) 588-0314. Robert L. Woodson Sr., chair. Internet, http:// www.ncne.com.*

Public policy research and demonstration organization. Interests include economic development, education, family preservation, and crime prevention. Attempts to identify model neighborhood-based economic and social development projects. Gives technical assistance to enterprises undertaking neighborhood development.

National Center for Urban Ethnic Affairs, *P.O. Box 20, Cardinal Station 20064; (202) 319-5128. Fax, (202) 319-6289. John A. Kromkowski, president. Information, (202) 232-3600.*

Educational and research organization that preserves and revitalizes urban neighborhoods through community organization and development; provides technical support and encourages interethnic and interracial cooperation, particularly between recent and older immigrants.

National Council for Urban Economic Development, *1730 K St. N.W., #700 20006; (202) 223-4735. Fax, (202) 223-4745. Jeffrey Finkle, executive director. Internet, nail@urbandevelopment.com or http://www. cued.org.*

Membership: public economic development directors, chamber of commerce staff, utility executives, academicians, and others who design and implement development programs. Provides information to members on job creation, attraction, and retention.

National League of Cities, *1301 Pennsylvania Ave. N.W., #550 20004-1763; (202) 626-3000. Fax, (202) 626-3043. Donald J. Borut, executive director. Information, (202) 626-3120. Press, (202) 626-3158. Internet, http:// www.nlc.org.*

Membership: cities and state municipal leagues. Aids city leaders in developing programs; investigates needs of local governments in implementing federal community development programs.

National Neighborhood Coalition, *1875 Connecticut Ave. N.W., #410 20009; (202) 986-2096. Fax, (202) 986-1941. Betty Weiff, executive director. Internet, http://www. comminfoexch.org/nnc.htm.*

Membership: national and regional organizations that have neighborhood-based affiliates, provide technical assistance to neighborhood groups, or conduct research on issues affecting neighborhoods. Monitors national programs and policies that affect inner-city neighborhoods; conducts monthly information forums.

National Urban League, *1111 14th St. N.W., #1001 20005-5603; (202) 898-1604. Fax, (202) 408-1965. Robert McAlpine, director, Policy and Government Relations. Internet, http://www.nul.org.*

Federation of affiliates concerned with the social welfare of African Americans and other minorities. Operates a job bank. Conducts legislative and policy analysis on housing and urban affairs. (Headquarters in New York.)

Urban Institute, *Center for Public Finance and Housing, 2100 M St. N.W., #500 20037; (202) 833-7200. Fax, (202) 728-0232. G. Thomas Kingsley, director. Internet, http://www.urban.org.*

Research organization that deals with urban problems. Researches federal, state, and local policies; focus includes community development block grants, neighborhood rehabilitation programs, and housing issues. Conducts economic research on the infrastructure of urban areas.

Urban Land Institute, *1025 Thomas Jefferson St. N.W., #500W 20007; (202) 624-7000. Fax, (202) 624-7140. Richard Rosan, executive vice president. Toll-free, (800) 321-5011. Library, (202) 624-7116. Internet, http://www. uli.org.*

Membership: land developers, planners, state and federal agencies, financial institutions, home builders, consultants, and realtors. Provides information on land-use planning, development, and management; sends teams to communities to examine land-use and development problems; monitors trends in new community development. Library open to the public by appointment for a fee.

U.S. Conference of Mayors, *1620 Eye St. N.W., 4th Floor 20006; (202) 293-7330. Fax, (202) 293-2352. J. Thomas Cochran, executive director. Internet, uscm@ cais.com or http://www.usmayors.org/uscm.*

Membership: mayors of cities with populations of 30,000 or more. Promotes city-federal cooperation; publishes reports and conducts meetings on federal programs, policies, and initiatives that affect urban and suburban interests. Serves as a clearinghouse for information on urban and suburban problems. Holds annual conference.

CONSTRUCTION

See also Government Management and Oversight (chap. 10); Military Installations (chap. 16); Transportation (chap. 19)

AGENCIES

Census Bureau *(Commerce Dept.),* **Manufacturing and Construction,** *Suitland and Silver Hill Rds., Suitland, MD; (301) 457-4593. Fax, (301) 457-4583. Thomas L. Mesenbourg, acting chief.*

Publishes statistics on the value of construction put in place; housing starts, sales, and completions; building permits; price index of single-family homes sold; characteristics of new housing; and expenditures for residential improvements. Conducts a census of construction industries every five years.

General Services Administration, *Public Buildings Service, 1800 F St. N.W., #6344 20405; (202) 501-1100. Fax, (202) 219-2310. Robert A. Peck, commissioner.*

Manages and disposes of federal real estate. Administers the construction, maintenance, and operation of buildings owned or leased by the federal government.

International Trade Administration *(Commerce Dept.),* **Basic Industries,** *14th St. and Constitution Ave. N.W., #4043 20230; (202) 482-0614. Fax, (202) 482-5666. Michael J. Copts, deputy assistant secretary.*

Analyzes and maintains data on international construction and engineering. Monitors production costs, prices, financial and labor conditions, technological changes, distribution, markets, trade patterns, and other aspects of these industries. Promotes international trade, develops competitive assessments, and assists engineering and construction companies in obtaining overseas construction projects.

NONPROFIT

American Public Works Assn., *1301 Pennsylvania Ave. N.W., #501 20004; (202) 393-2792. Fax, (202) 737-9153. William J. Bertera, executive director. Internet, apwadc@ us.net.*

Membership: engineers, architects, and others who maintain and manage public works facilities and services. Conducts research and promotes exchange of information on infrastructure issues. (Headquarters in Kansas City.)

American Subcontractors Assn., *1004 Duke St., Alexandria, VA 22314-3588; (703) 684-3450. Fax, (703)*

836-3482. *Colette Nelson, executive vice president. Internet, asaoffice@aol.com or http://www.asaonline.com.*

Membership: construction subcontractors, specialty contractors, and their suppliers. Addresses business, contract, and payment issues affecting all subcontractors. Interests include procurement laws, payment practices, and lien laws. Monitors legislation and regulations.

Associated Builders and Contractors, *1300 N. 17th St., Rosslyn, VA 22209; (703) 812-2000. Fax, (703) 812-8202. Charlie Hawkins, executive vice president. Internet, http://www.abc.org.*

Membership: construction contractors engaged primarily in nonresidential construction, subcontractors, and suppliers. Sponsors apprenticeship, safety, and training programs. Provides labor relations information; compiles statistics. Monitors legislation and regulations.

Associated General Contractors of America, *1957 E St. N.W. 20006-5194; (202) 393-2040. Fax, (202) 347-4004. Stephen Sandherr, executive vice president. Internet, http://www.agc.org.*

Membership: general contractors engaged primarily in nonresidential construction; subcontractors; suppliers; accounting, insurance and bonding, and law firms. Conducts training programs, conferences, seminars, and market development activities for members. Produces position papers on construction issues. Monitors legislation and regulations.

Associated Landscape Contractors of America, *150 Elden St., #270, Herndon, VA 20170; (703) 736-9666. Fax, (703) 736-9668. Debra H. Holder, executive director. Internet, http://www.alca.org.*

Represents the interior and exterior landscape contracting industry. Monitors legislation and regulations.

Construction Management Assn. of America, *7918 Jones Branch Dr., McLean, VA 22102; (703) 356-2622. Fax, (703) 356-6388. Karl F. Borgstrom, executive vice president. Internet, cmaa@access.digex.net or http://www.access.digex.net/~cmaa.*

Promotes the development of construction management as a profession through publications, education, a certification program, and an information network. Serves as an advocate for construction management in the legislative, executive, and judicial branches of government.

Construction Specifications Institute, *601 Madison St., #400, Alexandria, VA 22314; (703) 684-0300. Fax, (703) 684-0465. Gregory Balestrero, executive director. Toll-free, (800) 689-2900. Internet, http://www.csinet.org.*

Membership: architects, engineers, contractors, and others in the construction industry. Promotes construction technology; maintains speakers bureau; publishes reference materials to help individuals prepare construction documents; sponsors certification programs for construction specifiers and manufacturing representatives.

Mechanical Contractors Assn. of America, *1385 Piccard Dr., Rockville, MD 20850; (301) 869-5800. Fax, (301) 990-9690. John R. Gentille, executive vice president. Internet, http://www.mcaa.org.*

Membership: mechanical contractors and members of related professions. Seeks to improve building standards and codes. Provides information, publications, and training programs; conducts seminars and annual convention. Monitors legislation and regulations.

National Assn. of Home Builders, *1201 15th St. N.W. 20005; (202) 822-0200. Fax, (202) 861-2131. Kent W. Colton, executive vice president. Press, (202) 822-0253. Internet, http://www.nahb.com.*

Membership: contractors, builders, architects, engineers, mortgage lenders, and others interested in home building and commercial real estate construction. Participates in updating and developing building codes and standards; offers technical information. Library open to the public.

National Assn. of Minority Contractors, *666 11th St. N.W., #520 20001; (202) 347-8259. Fax, (202) 628-1876. Samuel A. Carradine Jr., executive director.*

Membership: minority businesses and related firms, associations, and individuals serving those businesses in the construction industry. Advises members on commercial and government business; develops resources for technical assistance and training; provides bid information on government contracts.

National Assn. of Plumbing-Heating-Cooling Contractors, *180 S. Washington St., Falls Church, VA (mailing address: P.O. Box 6808, Falls Church, VA 22040); (703) 237-8100. Fax, (703) 237-7442. Allen Inlow, chief executive officer. Toll-free, (800) 533-7694. Internet, http:// www.naphcc.org.*

Provides education, training, and research for plumbing, heating, and cooling contractors and their employees. Offers career information, internships, and scholarship programs for business and engineering students to encourage careers in the mechanical/electrical contracting field.

National Assn. of the Remodeling Industry, *4900 Seminary Rd., #320, Alexandria, VA 22311; (703) 575-1100. Fax, (703) 575-1121. William C. Carmichael, execu-*

tive vice president. Toll-free, (800) 440-6274. Internet, http://www.nari.org.

Membership: remodeling contractors, manufacturers, wholesalers, distributors, lenders, and utilities. Sponsors educational programs on construction products and techniques; provides information on industry statistics and small-business practices; publishes consumer information. Monitors legislation and regulations.

National Constructors Assn., *1730 M St. N.W., #503 20036; (202) 466-8880. Fax, (202) 466-7512. Nicholas A. Fiore, president.*

Membership: designers and builders of oil refineries, chemical plants, steel mills, power plants, and other industrial facilities. Interests include governmental energy policies, regulations, worker safety and health, and labor relations.

National Electrical Contractors Assn., *3 Bethesda Metro Center, #1100, Bethesda, MD 20814; (301) 657-3110. Fax, (301) 215-4500. John Grau, executive vice president. Internet, http://www.necanet.org.*

Membership: electrical contractors who build and service electrical wiring, equipment, and appliances. Represents members in collective bargaining with union workers; sponsors research and educational programs.

National Utility Contractors Assn., *4301 N. Fairfax Dr., #360, Arlington, VA 22203-1627; (703) 358-9300. Fax, (703) 358-9307. William G. Harley, executive vice president. Internet, http://www.nuca.com.*

Membership: contractors who perform water, sewer, and other underground utility construction. Sponsors conferences; conducts surveys. Monitors public works legislation and regulations.

Rebuild America Coalition, *c/o American Public Works Assn., 1301 Pennsylvania Ave. N.W., #501 20004; (202) 347-7254. Fax, (202) 737-9153. William J. Bertera, executive director. Internet, http://www.rebuildamerica.org.*

Coalition of public and private organizations concerned with maintaining the infrastructure of the United States. Advocates government encouragement of innovative technology, financing, and public-private partnerships to build and rebuild public facilities.

Sheet Metal and Air Conditioning Contractors National Assn., *4201 Lafayette Center Dr., Chantilly, VA 20151; (703) 803-2980. Fax, (703) 803-3732. John W. Sroka, executive vice president. Internet, http://www.smacna.org.*

Membership: sheet metal and air conditioning contractors. Provides information on standards and installation and fabrication methods. Operates the National

Environmental Balancing Bureau with the Mechanical Contractors Assn. of America.

Society for Marketing Professional Services, *99 Canal Center Plaza, #250, Alexandria, VA 22314-1588; (703) 549-6117. Fax, (703) 549-2498. Bonnie Shelton, executive director. Toll-free, (800) 292-7677. Internet, http://www.smps.org.*

Membership: individuals who provide professional services to the building industry. Assists individuals who market services in the areas of architecture, engineering, planning, interior design, landscape architecture, and construction management. Provides seminars, workshops, and publications for members. Maintains job banks.

Women Construction Owners and Executives USA, *4849 Connecticut Ave. N.W., #702 20008-5838; (202) 636-4822. Linda Ferlaak, national administrator. Toll-free, (800) 788-3548. Internet, wcoeusa@aol.com or http://www.wcoeusa.org.*

Supports the interests of women in the construction industry. Sponsors education programs, speakers' bureau, and national conferences. Monitors legislation and regulation.

Architecture and Design

AGENCIES

General Services Administration, *Cultural and Environmental Affairs, 1800 F St. N.W., #3341 20405; (202) 501-1811. Fax, (202) 219-7677. Constance Ramirez, director.*

Administers the Art and Historic Preservation Program, which sets aside for art projects a percentage of the estimated construction costs for new buildings or renovation costs for existing ones; manages a collection of fine arts.

National Endowment for the Arts *(National Foundation on the Arts and the Humanities), Heritage and Preservation, 1100 Pennsylvania Ave. N.W. 20506-0001; (202) 682-5428. Fax, (202) 682-5669. Dan Sheehy, division coordinator. Internet, http://arts.endow.gov.*

Awards grants for design arts projects in architecture; landscape architecture; urban design and planning; historic preservation; and interior, graphic, industrial, product, and costume and fashion design.

NONPROFIT

American Design Drafting Assn., *P.O. Box 799, Rockville, MD 20848-0799; (301) 460-6875. Fax, (301) 460-8591. Rachel H. Howard, executive director. Internet, national@adda.org or http://www.adda.org.*

Membership: designers, drafters, educators, and managers working in industry, government, and education. Promotes professional growth and advancement; sponsors certification program for school curriculum and individual drafters.

American Institute of Architects, *1735 New York Ave. N.W. 20006; (202) 626-7310. Fax, (202) 626-7365. Mark W. Hurwitz, chief executive officer. Information, (202) 626-7300. Library, (202) 626-7492. Internet, http://www. aia.org.*

Membership: registered American architects. Works to advance the standards of architectural education, training, and practice. Promotes the aesthetic, scientific, and practical efficiency of architecture, urban design, and planning; monitors international developments. Offers continuing and professional education programs; sponsors scholarships, internships, and awards. Houses archival collection, including documents and drawings of American architects and architecture. Library open to the public. Monitors legislation and regulations.

American Nursery and Landscape Assn., *1250 Eye St. N.W., #500 20005; (202) 789-2900. Fax, (202) 789-1893. Warren Quinn, administrator. Internet, http://www. anla.org.*

Serves as an information clearinghouse on the technical aspects of nursery and landscape business and design.

American Society of Interior Designers, *608 Massachusetts Ave. N.E. 20002-6006; (202) 546-3480. Fax, (202) 546-3240. Robert Angle, executive director. Internet, network@asid.noli.com.*

Offers certified professional development courses addressing the technical, professional, and business needs of designers; bestows annual scholarships, fellowships, and awards; supports licensing efforts at the state level.

American Society of Landscape Architects, *636 Eye St. N.W. 20001; (202) 898-2444. Fax, (202) 898-1185. Peter Kirsch, executive vice president. Internet, http://www. asla.org.*

Advises government agencies on land-use policy and environmental matters. Accredits university-level programs in landscape architecture; conducts professional education seminars for members.

Assn. of Collegiate Schools of Architecture, *1735 New York Ave. N.W. 20006; (202) 785-2324. Fax, (202) 628-0448. G. Martin Moeller Jr., executive director. Internet, http://www.acsa-arch.org.*

Conducts workshops and seminars for architecture school faculty; presents awards for student and faculty

excellence in architecture; publishes directory of architecture schools in North America.

Industrial Designers Society of America, *1142 Walker Rd., Great Falls, VA 22066-1836; (703) 759-0100. Fax, (703) 759-7679. Robert Schwartz, executive director. Internet, idsa@erols.com or http://www.idsa.org.*

Membership: designers of products, equipment, instruments, furniture, transportation, packages, exhibits, information services, and related services. Provides the Bureau of Labor Statistics and U.S. Information Agency with industry information. Monitors legislation and regulations.

Landscape Architecture Foundation, *4401 Connecticut Ave. N.W., #500 20008-2369; (202) 686-8306. Fax, (202) 686-1001. James Dalton, executive director. Internet, http://www.asla.org.*

Conducts research and provides educational and scientific information on landscape architecture and related fields. Awards scholarships and fellowships in landscape architecture.

National Architectural Accrediting Board, *1735 New York Ave. N.W. 20006; (202) 783-2007. Fax, (202) 783-2822. John Maudlin-Jeronimo, executive director. Internet, ArchBd@aol.com or http://www.naab.org.*

Accredits Bachelor and Master of Architecture degree programs.

National Assn. of Schools of Art and Design, *11250 Roger Bacon Dr., #21, Reston, VA 20190; (703) 437-0700. Fax, (703) 437-6312. Samuel Hope, executive director. Internet, http://www.arts-accredit.org.*

Accrediting agency for educational programs in art and design. Provides information on art and design programs at the postsecondary level; offers professional development for executives of art and design programs.

National Council of Architectural Registration Boards, *1735 New York Ave. N.W., #700 20006; (202) 783-6500. Fax, (202) 783-0290. Lenore M. Lucey, executive vice president. Internet, http://www.ncarb.org.*

Membership: state architectural licensing boards. Develops examination used in U.S. states and territories for licensing architects; certifies architects.

Codes, Standards, and Research

AGENCIES

Architectural and Transportation Barriers Compliance Board (Access Board), *1331 F St. N.W., #1000 20004-1111; (202) 272-5434. Fax, (202) 272-5447. Lawrence W. Roffee, executive director. TDD, (202) 272-*

5449. Toll-free technical assistance, (800) 872-2253. Internet, http://www.access-board.gov.

Enforces standards requiring that buildings and telecommunications and transportation systems be accessible to persons with disabilities; provides technical assistance and information on designing these facilities; sets accessibility guidelines for the Americans with Disabilities Act and the Telecommunications Act of 1996.

Environmental Protection Agency, *Radiation and Indoor Air, 501 3rd St. N.W. (mailing address: 401 M St. S.W., #6601J, Washington, DC 20460); (202) 564-9320. Fax, (202) 565-2043. Lawrence Weinstock, acting director.*

Establishes standards for measuring radon; develops model building codes for state and local governments; provides states and building contractors with technical assistance and training on radon detection and mitigation.

Federal Housing Administration *(Housing and Urban Development Dept.), Manufactured Housing and Standards, 451 7th St., S.W. #9152 20410; (202) 708-6409. Fax, (202) 708-4213. Marion F. Conell, director. Consumer complaints, (800) 927-2891. Internet, http://www.hud.gov/fha/mhs/mhshome.html.*

Establishes and maintains standards for selection of new materials and methods of construction; evaluates technical suitability of products and materials; develops uniform, preemptive, and mandatory national standards for manufactured housing; enforces standards through design review and quality control inspection of factories; administers a national consumer protection program.

Housing and Urban Development Dept., *Affordable Housing Research and Technology, 451 7th St. S.W., #8132 20410; (202) 708-4370. Fax, (202) 708-5873. David Engel, director.*

Studies regulatory barriers to housing, such as land development and building zones. Conducts building technology research on radon, other environmental hazards, and energy efficiency. Reviews and assesses changes in building codes and standards. Conducts demonstrations on innovative building construction techniques.

Housing and Urban Development Dept., *Lead Hazard Control, 490 L'Enfant Plaza East S.W., #3202 (mailing address: 451 7th St. S.W., #B-133, Washington, DC 20410); (202) 755-1785. Fax, (202) 755-1000. David E. Jacobs, director. Community Outreach, (202) 755-1785, ext. 114. Internet, http://www.hud.gov/lea/leahome.html.*

Advises HUD offices, other agencies, health authorities, and the housing industry on lead poisoning prevention. Develops regulations for lead-based paint; conducts research; makes grants to state and local governments for hazard reduction and inspection of housing.

National Institute of Building Sciences, *1090 Vermont Ave. N.W., #700 20005; (202) 289-7800. Fax, (202) 289-1092. David A. Harris, president. Internet, nibs@nibs.org or http:/www.nibs.org.*

Public-private partnership authorized by Congress to improve the regulation of building construction, facilitate the safe introduction of innovative building technology, and disseminate performance criteria and other technical information.

National Institute of Standards and Technology *(Commerce Dept.), Building and Fire Research Laboratory, Route I-270 and Quince Orchard Rd., Gaithersburg, MD 20899; (301) 975-5900. Fax, (301) 975-4032. Richard N. Wright, director. Library, (301) 975-6859. Internet, http://www.bfrl.nist.gov.*

Performs analytical, laboratory, and field research in the area of building technology and its applications for building usefulness, safety, and economy; produces performance criteria and evaluation, test, and measurement methods for building owners, occupants, designers, manufacturers, builders, and federal, state, and local regulatory authorities.

Occupational Safety and Health Administration *(Labor Dept.), Safety Standards, 200 Constitution Ave. N.W., #N3605 20210; (202) 219-8061. Fax, (202) 219-7477. John F. Martonik, acting director.*

Administers regulations for fire safety standards; sponsors programs for maritime, fire protection, construction, mechanical, and electrical industries.

U.S. Fire Administration *(Federal Emergency Management Agency), 16825 S. Seton Ave., Emmitsburg, MD 21727; (301) 447-1018. Fax, (301) 447-1270. Carrye B. Brown, administrator. Internet, http://www.usfa.fema.gov.*

Conducts research and collects, analyzes, and disseminates data on combustion, fire prevention, firefighter safety, and the management of fire prevention organizations; studies and develops arson prevention programs and fire prevention codes; maintains the National Fire Data System.

NONPROFIT

Air Conditioning and Refrigeration Institute, *4301 N. Fairfax Dr., #425, Arlington, VA 22203; (703) 524-8800. Fax, (703) 528-3816. Vacant, director, Legislative and Regulatory Affairs. Internet, ari@dgsys.com or http://www.ari.org.*

Represents manufacturers of central air conditioning and commercial refrigeration equipment. Develops product performance rating standards and administers programs to verify manufacturers' certified ratings.

American Society of Civil Engineers, *1801 Alexander Bell Dr., Reston, VA 20191-4400; (703) 295-6000. Fax, (703) 295-6333. James E. Davis, executive director. Internet, http://www.asce.org.*

Membership: professionals and students in civil engineering. Develops and produces consensus standards for construction documents and building codes. Maintains the Civil Engineering Research Foundation, which focuses national attention and resources on the research needs of the civil engineering profession. Participates in international conferences.

American Society of Heating, Refrigerating, and Air Conditioning Engineers, *1828 L St. N.W., #906 20036; (202) 833-1830. Fax, (202) 833-0118. J. E. Cox, director, Government Affairs. Internet, http://www. ashrae.org.*

Membership: engineers for the heating and cooling industry in the United States and abroad, including students. Sponsors research, meetings, and educational activities. Develops industry standards; publishes technical data. Monitors legislation and regulations.

Center for Auto Safety, *2001 S St. N.W., #410 20009; (202) 328-7700. Clarence M. Ditlow III, executive director. Internet, http://www.essential.org/orgs/cas.*

Monitors Federal Trade Commission warranty regulations and HUD implementation of federal safety and construction standards for manufactured mobile homes.

Council of American Building Officials, *5203 Leesburg Pike, Falls Church, VA 22041; (703) 931-4533. Fax, (703) 379-1546. Richard P. Kuchnicki, chief executive officer. Internet, http://www.cabo.org.*

Seeks to ensure consistency among model codes; encourages uniformity in administration of building regulations; maintains a one- and two-family dwelling code, a model energy code, and manufactured home construction and safety standards; provides review board for the American National Standards Institute disabled accessibility standards.

NAHB Research Center, *400 Prince George's Blvd., Upper Marlboro, MD 20774; (301) 249-4000. Fax, (301) 249-0305. Liza K. Bowles, president. Internet, http://www. nahbrc.org.*

Conducts contract research and product labeling and certification for U.S. industry, government, and trade associations related to home building and light commer-

cial industrial building. Interests include energy conservation, new technologies, international research, public health issues, affordable housing, special needs housing for the elderly and persons with disabilities, building codes and standards, land development, and environmental issues. (Affiliated with the National Assn. of Home Builders.)

National Conference of States on Building Codes and Standards, *505 Huntmar Park Dr., #210, Herndon, VA 20170; (703) 437-0100. Fax, (703) 481-3596. Robert Wible, executive director. TDD, (703) 481-2019.*

Membership: individuals and organizations concerned with building standards. Works with HUD to ensure that manufactured housing conforms to HUD standards and codes; assists states in improving their building codes, standards, and regulations; promotes local, state, and interstate cooperation.

National Fire Protection Assn., *1110 N. Glebe Rd., #560, Arlington, VA 22201; (703) 516-4346. Fax, (703) 516-4350. Anthony R. O'Neill, vice president, Government Affairs. Internet, wdc@nfpa.org.*

Membership: individuals and organizations interested in fire protection. Develops and updates fire protection codes and standards; sponsors technical assistance programs; collects fire data statistics. Monitors legislation and regulations. (Headquarters in Quincy, Mass.)

National Spa and Pool Institute, *2111 Eisenhower Ave., Alexandria, VA 22314-4698; (703) 838-0083. Fax, (703) 549-0493. Roger Galvin, chief executive officer. Internet, http://www.POOLSPAWORLD.com.*

Membership: manufacturers, dealers, and distributors of pools, spas, and hot tubs. Promotes the industry; compiles statistics; establishes construction standards for pools and spas. Monitors legislation and regulations.

Materials and Labor

See also Codes, Standards, and Research (this section); Employment and Labor (chap. 7)

NONPROFIT

American Forest and Paper Assn., *1111 19th St. N.W., #800 20036; (202) 463-2700. Fax, (202) 463-2785. Bob Glowinski, staff contact. Internet, http://www. afandpa.org.*

Membership: manufacturers of wood and specialty products and related associations. Interests include tax, housing, environmental, international trade, natural resources, and land-use issues that affect the wood and paper products industry.

American Portland Cement Alliance, *1225 Eye St. N.W., #300 20005; (202) 408-9494. Fax, (202) 408-0877. Richard C. Creighton, president.*

Membership: producers of portland cement. Monitors legislation and regulations.

Architectural Woodwork Institute, *1952 Isaac Newton Square West, Reston, VA 20190; (703) 733-0600. Fax, (703) 733-0584. Judith B. Durham, executive vice president. Internet, http://www.awinet.org.*

Promotes the use of architectural woodworking; establishes industry standards; conducts seminars and workshops; certifies professionals in the industry. Monitors legislation and regulations.

Asbestos Information Assn./North America, *1745 Jefferson Davis Hwy., #406, Arlington, VA 22202; (703) 412-1150. Fax, (703) 412-1152. B. J. Pigg, president.*

Membership: firms that manufacture, sell, and use products containing asbestos fiber and those that mine, mill, and sell asbestos. Provides information on asbestos and health and on industry efforts to eliminate problems associated with asbestos dust; serves as liaison between the industry and federal and state governments.

Asphalt Roofing Manufacturers Assn., *4041 Powder Mill Rd., #404, Calverton, MD 20705; (301) 348-2002. Fax, (301) 348-2020. Richard D. Snyder, executive vice president.*

Membership: manufacturers of bitumen-based roofing products. Assists in developing local building codes and standards for asphalt roofing products. Provides technical information; supports research. Monitors legislation and regulations.

Assn. of the Wall and Ceiling Industries, *307 East Annandale Rd., #200, Falls Church, VA 22042; (703) 534-8300. Fax, (703) 534-8307. Steven A. Etkin, executive vice president. Internet, http://www.awci.org.*

Membership: contractors and suppliers working in the wall and ceiling industries. Sponsors conferences and seminars. Monitors legislation and regulations.

Brick Institute of America, *11490 Commerce Park Dr., #300, Reston, VA 20191-1525; (703) 620-0010. Fax, (703) 620-3928. Nelson J. Cooney, president. Internet, http://www.bia.org.*

Membership: manufacturers of clay brick. Provides technical expertise and assistance; promotes bricklaying vocational education programs; maintains collection of technical publications on brick masonry construction. Monitors legislation and regulations.

Building Systems Councils of the National Assn. of Home Builders, *1201 15th St. N.W. 20005-2800; (202)*

822-0576. Fax, (202) 861-2141. Barbara K. Martin, executive director.

Membership: manufacturers and suppliers of home building products and services. Represents all segments of the industry. Assists in developing National Assn. of Home Builders policies regarding building codes, legislation, and government regulations affecting manufacturers of model code complying, factory-built housing; sponsors educational programs; conducts plant tours of member operations.

Composite Panel Assn., *18928 Premiere Court, Gaithersburg, MD 20879; (301) 670-0604. Fax, (301) 840-1252. Rich Margosian, president. Internet, pbmdf@pbmdf.com or http://www.pbmdf.com.*

Membership: manufacturers of particleboard and medium-density fiberboard. Promotes use of these materials; conducts industry education through the PB-MDF Institute. Monitors legislation and regulations.

Door and Hardware Institute, *14170 Newbrook Dr., Chantilly, VA 20151-2232; (703) 222-2010. Fax, (703) 222-2410. Jerry Heppes, executive director. Internet, http://www.dhi.org.*

Membership: companies and individuals that manufacture or distribute doors and related fittings. Promotes the industry. Interests include building security, life safety and exit devices, and compliance with the Americans with Disabilities Act. Monitors legislation and regulations.

Gypsum Assn., *810 1st St. N.E., #510 20002; (202) 289-5440. Fax, (202) 289-3707. Jerry A. Walker, executive director. Internet, http://www.gypsum.org.*

Membership: manufacturers of gypsum wallboard and plaster. Assists members, code officials, builders, designers, and others with technical problems and building code questions; publishes Fire Resistance Design Manual referenced by major building codes; conducts safety programs for member companies. Monitors legislation and regulations.

Hardwood, Plywood, and Veneer Assn., *1825 Michael Faraday Dr., Reston, VA 20190-5350 (mailing address: P.O. Box 2789, Reston, VA 20195-0789); (703) 435-2900. Fax, (703) 435-2537. E. T. Altman, president. Internet, http://www.hpva.org.*

Membership: distributors, wholesalers, suppliers, and sales agents of plywood, veener, and laminated wood floor. Disseminates business information; sponsors workshops and seminars; conducts research.

International Assn. of Bridge, Structural, Ornamental, and Reenforcing Iron Workers, *1750 New*

York Ave. N.W., #400 20006; (202) 383-4800. Fax, (202) 638-4856. Jake West, president.

Membership: approximately 82,000 iron workers. Helps members negotiate pay, benefits, and better working conditions; conducts training programs and workshops. Monitors legislation and regulations. (Affiliated with the AFL-CIO.)

International Assn. of Heat and Frost Insulators and Asbestos, *1776 Massachusetts Ave. N.W., #301 20036-1989; (202) 785-2388. Fax, (202) 429-0568. William G. Bernard, president.*

Membership: approximately 18,000 workers in insulation industries. Helps members negotiate pay, benefits, and better working conditions; conducts training programs and workshops. Monitors legislation and regulations. (Affiliated with the AFL-CIO.)

International Brotherhood of Boilermakers, Iron Ship Builders, Blacksmiths, Forgers, and Helpers, *2722 Merrilee Dr., #360, Fairfax, VA 22031; (703) 560-1493. Fax, (703) 560-2584. Andy Abbott, director, Legislative Affairs. Internet, http://www.boilermakers.org.*

Membership: approximately 80,000 workers in construction, repair, maintenance, manufacturing, and related industries in the United States and Canada. Helps members negotiate pay, benefits, and better working conditions; conducts training programs and workshops. Monitors legislation and regulations. (Headquarters in Kansas City, Kan.; affiliated with the AFL-CIO.)

International Brotherhood of Electrical Workers, *1125 15th St. N.W. 20005; (202) 833-7000. Fax, (202) 728-6057. John J. Barry, president. Library, (202) 467-6313. Internet, IBEWnet@compuserve.com or http://ourworld.compuserve.com/homepages/ibewnet.*

Helps members negotiate pay, benefits, and better working conditions; conducts training programs and workshops. Monitors legislation and regulations. (Affiliated with the AFL-CIO.)

International Brotherhood of Painters and Allied Trades, *1750 New York Ave. N.W., 8th Floor 20006; (202) 637-0700. Fax, (202) 637-0771. A. L. "Mike" Monroe, president. Internet, http://www.ibpat.net or http://www.ibpat.org.*

Membership: more than 130,000 painters, paint makers, drywall finishers, decorators, carpet and soft tile layers, scenic artists, and workers in allied trades. Helps members negotiate pay, benefits, and better working conditions; conducts training programs and workshops. Monitors legislation and regulations. (Affiliated with the AFL-CIO.)

International Brotherhood of Teamsters, *25 Louisiana Ave. N.W. 20001; (202) 624-6800. Fax, (202) 624-8102. Tom Sever, acting president. Internet, http://www.teamsters.org.*

Membership: more than 1.4 million workers in the transportation and construction industries, factories, offices, hospitals, warehouses, and other workplaces. Helps members negotiate pay, benefits, and better working conditions; conducts training programs and workshops. Monitors legislation and regulations. (Affiliated with the AFL-CIO.)

International Union of Bricklayers and Allied Craftworkers, *815 15th St. N.W. 20005; (202) 783-3788. Fax, (202) 393-0219. John T. Joyce, president. Internet, http://www.bacweb.org.*

Membership: bricklayers, stonemasons, and other skilled craftworkers in the building industry. Helps members negotiate pay, benefits, and better working conditions; conducts training programs and workshops. Monitors legislation and regulations. (Affiliated with the AFL-CIO and the International Masonry Institute.)

International Union of Operating Engineers, *1125 17th St. N.W. 20036; (202) 429-9100. Fax, (202) 778-2616. Frank Hanley, president. Internet, http://www.iuoe.org.*

Membership: approximately 400,000 operating enginners, including heavy equipment operators, mechanics, and surveyors in the construction industry, and stationary engineers, including operations and building maintenance staff. Helps members negotiate pay, benefits, and better working conditions; conducts training programs and workshops. Monitors legislation and regulations. (Affiliated with the AFL-CIO.)

Kitchen Cabinet Manufacturers Assn., *1899 Preston White Dr., Reston, VA 20191-5435; (703) 264-1690. Fax, (703) 620-6530. C. Richard Titus, executive vice president. Internet, http://www.kcna.org.*

Represents cabinet manufacturers and suppliers to the industry. Provides government relations, management statistics, marketing information, and plant tours. Administers cabinet testing and certification programs.

National Assn. of Brick Distributors, *11490 Commerce Park Dr., #300, Reston, VA 20191; (703) 620-0010. Fax, (703) 620-3928. Vacant, executive director. Internet, http://www.brickvalue.org.*

Membership: brick and clay product distributors and manufacturers. Serves as sales and marketing arm of the brick industry; holds annual convention and trade exhibit; conducts educational seminars.

National Concrete Masonry Assn., *2302 Horse Pen Rd., Herndon, VA 20171; (703) 713-1900. Fax, (703) 713-1910. Chris Stinebert, president. Internet, http://www.ncma.org.*

Membership: producers of concrete masonry and suppliers of related goods and services. Conducts research; provides members with technical, marketing, government relations, and communications assistance.

National Glass Assn., *8200 Greensboro Dr., #302, McLean, VA 22102-3881; (703) 442-4890. Fax, (703) 442-0630. Brenda Stempson, executive director. Internet, nga@glass.org or http://www.glass.org.*

Membership: glassmaking companies and individuals in the industry. Conducts conferences; provides information on industry codes. Interests include glass for automobiles. Monitors legislation and regulations.

National Insulation Assn., *99 Canal Center Plaza, #222, Alexandria, VA 22314; (703) 683-6422. Fax, (703) 549-4838. Bill Pitkin, executive vice president. Internet, niainfo@insulation.org or http://www.insulation.org.*

Membership: companies in the commercial and industrial insulation and asbestos abatement industries. Monitors legislation and regulations.

National Lumber and Building Material Dealers Assn., *666 Pennsylvania Ave. S.E., #302A 20003; (202) 547-2230. Fax, (202) 547-7640. Gary W. Donnelly, president. Internet, nlbmda@nlbmda.org or http://www.nlbmda.org.*

Membership: federated associations of retailers in the lumber and building material industries. Monitors legislation and regulations.

National Paint and Coatings Assn., *1500 Rhode Island Ave. N.W. 20005; (202) 462-6272. Fax, (202) 462-8549. J. Andrew Doyle, president. Internet, npca@paint.org or http://www.paint.org.*

Membership: paint and coatings manufacturers, raw materials suppliers, and distributors. Provides educational and public outreach programs for the industry; interests include health, safety, and the environment. Monitor legislation and regulations.

North American Insulation Manufacturers Assn., *44 Canal Center Plaza, #310, Alexandria, VA 22314; (703) 684-0084. Fax, (703) 684-0427. Kenneth D. Mentzer, president. Internet, http://www.naima.org.*

Membership: manufacturers of insulation products for use in homes, commercial buildings, and industrial facilities. Provides information on the use of insulation for thermal efficiency, sound control, and fire safety; monitors research in the industry. Monitors legislation and regulations.

Operative Plasterers' and Cement Masons' International Assn. of the United States and Canada, *14405 Laurel Pl., #300, Laurel, MD 20707; (301) 470-4200. Fax, (301) 470-2502. John Dougherty, president.*

Membership: approximately 58,000 concrete masons and terrazzo workers. Helps members negotiate pay, benefits, and better working conditions; conducts training programs and workshops. Monitors legislation and regulations. (Affiliated with the AFL-CIO.)

Painting and Decorating Contractors of America, *3913 Old Lee Hwy., #33B, Fairfax, VA 22030; (703) 359-0826. Fax, (703) 359-2576. L. E. Travis III, president. Internet, http://www.pdca.com.*

Promotes the painting and decorating industry; sponsors workshops and seminars. Monitors legislation and regulations.

Roof Coatings Manufacturers Assn., *4041 Powder Mill Rd., #404, Calverton, MD 20705; (301) 348-2002. Fax, (301) 348-2020. Russell K. Snyder, executive vice president.*

Represents the manufacturers of cold-applied protective roof coatings, cements, and systems, and the suppliers of products, equipment, and services to and for the roof coating manufacturing industry.

Sheet Metal Workers' International Assn., *1750 New York Ave. N.W. 20006; (202) 783-5880. Fax, (202) 662-0895. Arthur Moore, president. Internet, http://smwia.org.*

Membership: more than 130,000 U.S. and Canadian workers in the building and construction trades, manufacturing, and the railroad and shipyard industries. Assists members with contract negotiation and grievances; conducts training programs and workshops. Monitors legislation and regulations. (Affiliated with the Sheet Metal and Air Conditioning Contractors' Assn., the AFL-CIO, and the Canadian Labour Congress.)

United Assn. of Journeymen and Apprentices of the Plumbing and Pipe Fitting Industry of the United States and Canada, *901 Massachusetts Ave. N.W. 20001; (202) 628-5823. Fax, (202) 628-5024. Martin J. Maddaloni, president. Internet, http://www.ua.org.*

Membership: approximately 290,000 workers who fabricate, install, and service piping systems. Assists members with contract negotiation and grievances; sponsors training programs, apprenticeships, and workshops. Monitors legislation and regulations. (Affiliated with the AFL-CIO and the Canadian Federation of Labour.)

United Brotherhood of Carpenters and Joiners of America, *101 Constitution Ave. N.W. 20001; (202) 546-*

6206. Fax, (202) 543-5724. Douglas J. McCarron, president.

Membership: approximately 500,000 carpenters and joiners. Helps members negotiate pay, benefits, and better working conditions; conducts training programs and workshops. Monitors legislation and regulations. (Affiliated with the AFL-CIO.)

United Union of Roofers, Waterproofers, and Allied Workers, *1660 L St. N.W., #800 20036; (202) 463-7663. Fax, (202) 463-6906. Earl Kruse, president.*

Membership: approximately 25,000 roofers, waterproofers, and allied workers. Helps members negotiate pay, benefits, and better working conditions; conducts training programs and workshops. Monitor legislation and regulations. (Affiliated with the AFL-CIO.)

Utility Workers Union of America, *815 16th St. N.W. 20006; (202) 347-8105. Fax, (202) 347-4872. Donald E. Wightman, president. Internet, http://www.aflcio.org/uwua.*

Membership: approximately 50,000 workers in utilities and related industries. Helps members negotiate pay, benefits, and better working conditions; conducts training programs and workshops. Monitors legislation and regulations. (Affiliated with the AFL-CIO.)

▦ HOUSING

See also Homelessness (chap. 18); Statistics (this chapter)

AGENCIES

Federal Housing Administration *(Housing and Urban Development Dept.), Insured Single Family Housing, 451 7th St. S.W., #9162 20410; (202) 708-3046. Fax, (202) 708-2582. John J. Coonts, director.*

Offers a mortgage insurance program for new and existing single-family dwellings (one to four units), including certain cooperatives and condominiums.

Federal Housing Administration *(Housing and Urban Development Dept.), Multifamily Housing Development, 451 7th St. S.W., #6134 20410; (202) 708-3000. Fax, (202) 708-3104. Willie Spearmon, director.*

Establishes procedures for the development of housing under the multifamily mortgage insurance programs. Administers the mortgage insurance programs for rental, cooperative, and condominium housing.

Federal Housing Administration *(Housing and Urban Development Dept.), Multifamily Housing Programs, 451 7th St. S.W., #6106 20410; (202) 708-2495. Fax, (202) 708-2583. Charles W. Wehrwein, acting deputy assistant secretary.*

Determines risk and administers programs associated with government-insured mortgage programs, architectural procedures, and land development programs for multifamily housing. Administers the Rural Rental Housing Program and the development of congregate housing facilities which provide affordable housing, adequate space for meals, and supportive services.

Federal Housing Administration *(Housing and Urban Development Dept.), Single Family Housing, 451 7th St. S.W., #9282 20410; (202) 708-3175. Fax, (202) 708-2582. Emelda P. Johnson, deputy assistant secretary.*

Determines risk and administers programs associated with government-insured mortgage programs, architectural procedures, land development programs, and interstate land sales for single family housing. Administers requirements to obtain and maintain federal government approval of mortgages.

Housing and Urban Development Dept., *Entitlement Communities, 451 7th St. S.W., #7282 20410; (202) 708-1577. Fax, (202) 401-2044. Deirdre Macguire-Zinni, director.*

Provides entitled cities and counties with block grants to provide housing and economic opportunity for low- and moderate-income people.

Housing and Urban Development Dept., *Housing— Federal Housing Commissioner, 451 7th St. S.W., #9100 20410; (202) 708-3600. Fax, (202) 708-2580. Nicolas P. Retsinas, assistant secretary. Internet, http://www.hud.gov/ fha/fhahome.html.*

Administers housing programs including the production, financing, and management of housing; directs preservation and rehabilitation of the housing stock; manages regulatory programs.

Rural Housing Service *(Agriculture Dept.), 1400 Independence Ave. S.W., #5014 20250; (202) 690-1533. Fax, (202) 690-0500. Jan E. Shadburn, acting administrator. Information, (202) 720-4323. Internet, http://www.rurdev. usda.gov/rhs/index.html.*

Offers financial assistance to apartment dwellers and homeowners in rural areas.

Rural Housing Service *(Agriculture Dept.), Housing Programs, 1400 Independence Ave. S.W., #5013 20250; (202) 720-5177. Fax, (202) 690-3025. Ronnie O. Tharrington, deputy administrator. Press, (202) 720-6903.*

Makes loans and grants in rural communities (population under 20,000) to low-income borrowers, including the elderly and persons with disabilities, for buying, building, or improving single-family houses. Makes grants to communities for rehabilitating single-family homes or rental units.

CONGRESS

House Banking and Financial Services Committee, *Subcommittee on Housing and Community Opportunity, B303 RHOB 20515; (202) 225-6634. Rick A. Lazio, R-N.Y., chair; Joseph M. Ventrone, staff director.*

Jurisdiction over all housing legislation, including housing allowances, housing for the elderly and persons with disabilities, public housing, and subsidized housing.

House Judiciary Committee, *Subcommittee on the Constitution, 362 Ford Bldg. 20515; (202) 226-7680. Fax, (202) 225-3746. Charles T. Canady, R-Fla., chair; Keri Folmar, counsel. Internet, http://www.house.gov/judiciary.*

Jurisdiction over fair housing legislation pertaining to discrimination against minorities.

Senate Banking, Housing, and Urban Affairs Committee, *Subcommittee on Housing Opportunity and Community Development, SD-534 20510; (202) 224-7391. Connie Mack, R-Fla., chair; Christopher Lord, staff director. Internet, http://www.senate.gov/~banking.*

Jurisdiction over all housing legislation, including housing allowances, housing for the elderly and persons with disabilities, public housing, and subsidized housing.

Senate Judiciary Committee, *Subcommittee on the Constitution, Federalism, and Property Rights, SD-164 20510; (202) 224-8081. John Ashcroft, R-Mo., chair; David Miller, chief counsel. Internet, http://www.senate.gov/committee/judiciary.html.*

Jurisdiction over fair housing legislation, including legislation pertaining to discrimination against minorities.

Senate Special Committee on Aging, *SD-G31 20510; (202) 224-5364. Fax, (202) 224-8660. Charles E. Grassley, R-Iowa, chair; Ted Totman, staff director.*

Studies and makes recommendations on housing access for the elderly.

NONPROFIT

Center for Housing Policy, *815 15th St. N.W., #538 20005; (202) 393-5772. Fax, (202) 393-5656. Robert J. Reid, executive director. Internet, chp@nhc.org.*

Researches and develops fundamentals of housing policy. Seeks to create new policies which integrate housing into overall social and economic goals. Sponsors educational forums. (Affiliated with the National Housing Conference.)

Enterprise Foundation, *10227 Wincopin Circle, #500, Columbia, MD 21044; (410) 964-1230. Fax, (410) 964-1918. Ed Quinn, senior vice president. Internet, http://www.enterprisefoundation.org.*

Works with local groups to help provide decent, affordable housing for low-income individuals and families.

Habitat for Humanity International, *1511 K St. N.W., #605 20005; (202) 628-9171. Fax, (202) 628-9169. Thomas L. Jones, managing director. Internet, public_info@habitat.org or http://www.habitat.org.*

Ecumenical housing ministry that, with the help of volunteers, donors, and its own affiliate offices, builds affordable homes worldwide for low-income persons. (Headquarters in Americus, Ga.)

Housing Assistance Council, *1025 Vermont Ave. N.W., #606 20005-3516; (202) 842-8600. Fax, (202) 347-3441. Moises Loza, executive director. Toll-free, (800) 989-4422. Internet, hn0143@handsnet.org.*

Operates in rural areas and in cities of fewer than 25,000 citizens. Advises low-income and minority groups seeking federal assistance for improving rural housing and community facilities; studies and makes recommendations for state and local housing policies; makes low-interest loans for housing programs for low-income and minority groups living in rural areas, including Native Americans and farm workers.

National Housing and Rehabilitation Assn., *1726 18th St. N.W. 20009-2525; (202) 328-9171. Fax, (202) 265-4435. Peter H. Bell, executive director. Internet, http://www.housingonline.com.*

Membership: development firms and organizations and city, state, and local agencies concerned with affordable multifamily housing. Monitors government policies affecting multifamily development and rehabilitation.

National Housing Conference, *815 15th St. N.W., #538 20005; (202) 393-5772. Fax, (202) 393-5656. Robert J. Reid, executive director. Internet, nhc@nhc.org.*

Membership: state and local housing officials, community development specialists, builders, bankers, lawyers, civic leaders, tenants, architects and planners, labor and religious groups, and national housing and housing-related organizations. Mobilizes public support for community development and affordable housing programs; conducts educational sessions.

National Leased Housing Assn., *1300 19th St. N.W., #410 20036; (202) 785-8888. Fax, (202) 785-2008. Denise Muha, executive director. Internet, hudnlha@worldweb.net.*

Membership: public and private organizations and individuals concerned with multifamily, government-assisted housing programs. Conducts training seminars. Monitors legislation and regulations.

National Low Income Housing Coalition, *1012 14th St. N.W., #610 20005; (202) 662-1530. Fax, (202) 393-1973. Helen Dunlap, president. Internet, http://www. nlihc.org.*

Membership: individuals and organizations interested in low-income housing. Works for decent, affordable housing and freedom of housing choice for low-income citizens. Provides information and technical assistance through the Low Income Housing Information Service. Monitors legislation.

National Rural Housing Coalition, *601 Pennsylvania Ave. N.W., #850 20004; (202) 393-5229. Fax, (202) 393-3034. Robert A. Rapoza, legislative director.*

Advocates improved housing for low-income rural families; works to increase public awareness of rural housing problems; monitors legislation.

Fair Housing/Special Groups

AGENCIES

Bureau of Indian Affairs *(Interior Dept.),* **Housing Assistance,** *1849 C St. N.W., #4603 20240; (202) 208-3667. Fax, (202) 208-2648. June Henkel, chief.*

Administers one-time grant program that assists federally recognized tribes in renovating and improving existing housing and in constructing new housing; advises tribes about assistance available through other programs.

Federal Housing Administration *(Housing and Urban Development Dept.),* **Multifamily Housing Management,** *451 7th St. S.W., #6160 20410; (202) 708-3730. Fax, (202) 401-5978. Frank Malone, acting director.*

Administers rental assistance, moderate rehabilitation, and housing programs for the elderly and people with disabilities. Manages grants for housing for the elderly and the disabled under Sections 202 and 811 of the Housing Act of 1959.

Housing and Urban Development Dept., *Fair Housing and Equal Opportunity,* *451 7th St. S.W., #5100 20410; (202) 708-4252. Fax, (202) 708-4483. Eva M. Plaza, assistant secretary. Housing discrimination hotline, (800) 669-9777.*

Monitors compliance with legislation requiring equal opportunities in housing for minorities, persons with disabilities, and families with children. Monitors compli-

ance with construction codes to accommodate people with disabilities in multifamily dwellings. Hotline answers inquiries about housing discrimination.

Housing and Urban Development Dept., **FHIP/FHAP Support,** *451 7th St. S.W., #5216 20410; (202) 708-0455. Fax, (202) 708-6211. Ivy Davis, director.*

Awards grants to public and private organizations and to state and local agencies. Funds projects work to educate the public about fair housing rights; programs are designed to prevent or eliminate discriminatory housing practices. Administers the Fair Housing Initiative and the Fair Housing Assistance Programs (FHIP/FHAP).

Housing and Urban Development Dept., *Native American Programs,* *490 L'Enfant Plaza, #8204 (mailing address: 451 7th St. S.W., #B133, Washington, DC 20410); (202) 755-0032. Fax, (202) 755-0182. Jacqueline Johnson, deputy assistant secretary.*

Works through tribal and state housing authorities to assess housing needs; directs Native Americans to HUD programs; provides Native American housing authorities with financial and technical assistance for developing low-income projects in Native American areas.

Justice Dept., *Civil Rights,* *601 D St. N.W., #4040 20530; (202) 514-2151. Fax, (202) 514-0293. Bill Lann Lee, acting assistant attorney general. Information, (202) 514-2007. Library, (202) 514-4098. TDD, (800) 514-0383.*

Enforces federal civil rights laws prohibiting discrimination on the basis of race, color, religion, sex, disability, age, or national origin in housing, public accommodations and facilities, and credit and federally assisted programs.

Office of Thrift Supervision *(Treasury Dept.),* **Consumer Programs,** *1700 G St. N.W., 6th Floor 20552; (202) 906-6237. Fax, (202) 906-6326. Gilda Morse, manager. Consumer complaints, (800) 842-6929.*

Handles complaints of discrimination against minorities and women by savings and loan associations; assists minority-owned or minority-controlled savings and loan institutions.

Rural Development *(Agriculture Dept.),* **Civil Rights,** *1400 Independence Ave. S.W. (mailing address: AG Box 0703, Washington, DC 20250-0703); (202) 690-9800. Fax, (202) 690-9803. Cheryl Prejean Greaux, director.*

Enforces compliance with laws prohibiting discrimination in credit transactions on the basis of sex, marital status, race, color, religion, age, or disability. Ensures equal opportunity in granting Rural Economic and Community Development housing, farm ownership, and operating loans, and a variety of community and business program loans.

NONPROFIT

American Assn. of Homes and Services for the Aging, *901 E St. N.W., #500 20004-2037; (202) 783-2242. Fax, (202) 783-2255. Michael F. Rodgers, senior vice president, Policy and Governmental Affairs. Internet, http:// www.aahsa.org.*

Membership: nonprofit nursing homes, housing, and health-related facilities for the elderly. Provides research and technical assistance on housing and long-term care for the elderly; conducts certification program for retirement housing professionals. Operates a capital formation program to procure financing for new housing facilities for the elderly. Monitors legislation and regulations.

American Assn. of Retired Persons, *Consumer Issues, 601 E St. N.W. 20049; (202) 434-6030. Fax, (202) 434-6466. Jane King, manager. Library, (202) 434-6240. Internet, aarpwrit@aol.com or http://www.aarp.org.*

Offers consultation and information services to organizations and consumers interested in housing for older persons. Supports affordable and appropriate housing for older Americans, including shared housing, continuing care, and home equity conversion. Library open to the public.

Assn. of Community Organizations for Reform Now (ACORN), *739 8th St. S.E. 20003; (202) 547-2500. Fax, (202) 546-2483. Melanie Marcus, head, Washington Office. Internet, dcnatacorn@igc.apc.org.*

Works to advance the interests of minority and low-income families through community organizing and action. Interests include jobs, living wages, housing, welfare reform, and community reinvestment. (Headquartered in New Orleans.)

B'nai B'rith International, *Senior Citizens Housing Committee, 1640 Rhode Island Ave. N.W. 20036-3278; (202) 857-6581. Fax, (202) 857-0980. Mark D. Olshan, director. Internet, seniors@bnaibrith.org or http:// bnaibrith.org.*

Works with local groups to sponsor federally assisted housing for independent low-income senior citizens and persons with disabilities, regardless of race or religion.

Center for Community Change, *1000 Wisconsin Ave. N.W. 20007; (202) 342-0519. Fax, (202) 342-1132. Pablo Eisenberg, executive director.*

Provides community-based organizations serving minorities and the economically disadvantaged with technical assistance. Areas of assistance include community development block grants, housing, economic and resource development, rural development projects, and program planning.

National American Indian Housing Council, *900 2nd St. N.E., #007 20002; (202) 789-1754. Fax, (202) 789-1758. Christopher Boesen, executive director. Internet, http://www.naihc.indian.com.*

Membership: Native American housing authorities. Clearinghouse for information on Native American housing issues; works for safe and sanitary dwellings for Native American and Alaska native communities; monitors HUD policies and housing legislation; provides members with training and technical assistance in managing housing assistance programs.

National Assn. for the Advancement of Colored People (NAACP), *1025 Vermont Ave. N.W., #1120 20005; (202) 638-2269. Fax, (202) 638-5936. Hilary Shelton, deputy director. Internet, http://www.naacp.org.*

Membership: persons interested in civil rights for all minorities. Works to eliminate discrimination in housing and urban affairs. Supports programs that make affordable rental housing available to minorities and that maintain African American ownership of land. (Headquarters in Baltimore.)

National Assn. of Real Estate Brokers, *1629 K St. N.W., #602 20006; (202) 785-4477. Fax, (202) 785-1244. H. Bernie Jackson, president. Internet, http://www.nareb3. com.*

Membership: minority real estate brokers, appraisers, contractors, property managers, and salespersons. Works to prevent discrimination in housing policies and practices; conducts regional seminars on federal policy, legislation, and regulations; advises members on procedures for procuring federal contracts.

National Council of La Raza, *1111 19th St. N.W., #1000 20036; (202) 785-1670. Fax, (202) 776-1792. Raul Yzaguirre, president. Internet, http://www.nclr.org.*

Helps Hispanic community-based groups obtain funds, develop and build low-income housing and community facilities, and develop and finance community economic development projects; conducts research and provides policy analysis on the housing status and needs of Hispanics; monitors legislation on fair housing and government funding for low-income housing.

National Council on the Aging, *409 3rd St. S.W., 2nd Floor 20024; (202) 479-1200. Fax, (202) 479-0735. James Firman, president. Information, (202) 479-6653. Press, (202) 479-6610. Library, (202) 479-6669. TDD, (202) 479-6674. Internet, info@ncoa.org or http://www.ncoa.org.*

Serves as an information clearinghouse on aging. Works to ensure quality housing for older persons. Monitors legislation and regulations. Library open to the public.

Public and Subsidized Housing

AGENCIES

Housing and Urban Development Dept., *Public and Assisted Housing*, *451 7th St. S.W., #4204 20410; (202) 708-1380. Fax, (202) 401-9135. Maryann Russ, deputy assistant secretary.*

Establishes policies and procedures for low-income public housing and rental assistance programs, including special needs for the elderly and disabled, standards for rental and occupancy, utilities and maintenance engineering, and financial management.

Housing and Urban Development Dept., *Public Housing Investment*, *451 7th St. S.W., #4138 20410; (202) 401-8812. Fax, (202) 401-2730. Elinor R. Bacon, deputy assistant secretary.*

Establishes development policies and procedures for low-income housing programs, including criteria for site approval and construction standards; oversees administration of the Comprehensive Improvement Assistance Program for modernizing existing public housing.

Public and Indian Housing *(Housing and Urban Development Dept.)*, *Rental Assistance, 451 7th St. S.W., #4220 20410; (202) 708-0477. Fax, (202) 401-7974. Gerald Benoit, director.*

Administers certificate and housing voucher programs authorized by Section 8 of the Housing Act of 1937, as amended. Provides rental subsidies to lower income families living in housing that was formerly substandard but has been upgraded through the Moderate Rehabilitation Program.

NONPROFIT

Public Housing Authorities Directors Assn., *511 Capitol Court N.E., #200 20002-4937; (202) 546-5445. Fax, (202) 546-2280. Timothy G. Kaiser, executive director. Internet, advnews@worldweb.net or http://www.phada. org/house.*

Membership: executive directors of public housing authorities. Serves as liaison between members and the Housing and Urban Development Dept. and Congress; conducts educational seminars and conferences. Monitors legislation and regulations.

Urban Institute, *Center for Public Finance and Housing*, *2100 M St. N.W., #500 20037; (202) 833-7200. Fax,*

(202) 728-0232. G. Thomas Kingsley, director. Internet, http://www.urban.org.

Research organization that deals with urban problems. Researches housing policy problems, including housing management, public housing programs, finance, and rent control.

REAL ESTATE

See also Government Management and Oversight (chap. 10); Military Installations (chap. 16); Statistics (this chapter)

AGENCIES

Federal Highway Administration *(Transportation Dept.)*, *Real Estate Services, 400 7th St. S.W. 20590; (202) 366-0142. Fax, (202) 366-3780. Cynthia Burbank, director.*

Funds and oversees acquisition of land by states for federally assisted highways; provides financial assistance to relocate people and businesses forced to move by highway construction; cooperates in administering program for the use of air rights in connection with federally aided highways; administers Highway Beautification Act to control billboards and junkyards along interstate and federally aided primary highways.

Federal Insurance Administration *(Federal Emergency Management Agency)*, *500 C St. S.W., #430 20472; (202) 646-2781. Fax, (202) 646-3445. Joann Howard, administrator. Internet, http://www.fema.gov.*

Administers federal crime and flood insurance programs, including the National Flood Insurance Program. Makes available to eligible homeowners low-cost flood and crime insurance. Flood insurance information: (202) 731-5300; (800) 427-4661, toll-free, nationwide nonclaims business; (800) 638-6831, Alaska and Hawaii; (800) 492-6605, Maryland. Crime insurance information: (202) 251-1660; (800) 638-8780, nationwide customer service.

General Services Administration, *Public Buildings Service*, *1800 F St. N.W., #6344 20405; (202) 501-1100. Fax, (202) 219-2310. Robert A. Peck, commissioner.*

Manages and disposes of federal real estate. Administers the construction, maintenance, and operation of buildings owned or leased by the federal government.

Housing and Urban Development Dept., *Interstate Land Sales/RESPA (Real Estate Settlement Procedure Act)*, *451 7th St. S.W., #9146 20410; (202) 708-0502. Fax, (202) 708-4559. Rebecca J. Holtz, director.*

Administers the Interstate Land Sales Full Disclosure Act, which requires land developers who sell undeveloped land through interstate commerce or the mails to disclose required information about the land to the purchaser prior to signing a sales contract and to file information with the federal government.

Housing and Urban Development Dept., *Relocation and Real Estate, 451 7th St. S.W., #7168 20410; (202) 708-1367. Fax, (202) 708-1744. Marcia Dodge, acting director.*

Administers the Uniform Relocation Assistance and Real Property Acquisition Policies Act of 1970, as amended, and other laws requiring that relocation assistance be given to persons displaced by federally assisted housing and community development programs.

Small Business Administration, *Disaster Assistance, 409 3rd St. S.W., #6050 20416; (202) 205-6734. Fax, (202) 205-7728. Bernard Kulik, associate administrator. Internet, http://www.sba.gov.*

Provides victims of physical disasters with disaster and economic injury loans for homes, businesses, and personal property. Lends to individual homeowners, business concerns of all sizes, and nonprofit institutions to repair or replace damaged structures and furnishings, business machinery, equipment, and inventory.

CONGRESS

House Banking and Financial Services Committee, *Subcommittee on Financial Institutions and Consumer Credit, 2129 RHOB 20515; (202) 225-2258. Fax, (202) 225-6984. Marge Roukema, R-N.J., chair; Laurie Schaffer, staff director. Internet, http://www.house.gov/banking.*

Jurisdiction over legislation on federal financial regulatory agencies and authorized activities of federally chartered and supervised financial institutions.

House Banking and Financial Services Committee, *Subcommittee on Housing and Community Opportunity, B303 RHOB 20515; (202) 225-6634. Rick A. Lazio, R-N.Y., chair; Joseph M. Ventrone, staff director.*

Jurisdiction over mortgage banking legislation, including mortgage insurance, secondary mortgage markets, and mortgage credit (except programs administered by the Veterans Affairs Dept.). Jurisdiction over federal insurance, including flood insurance.

House Ways and Means Committee, *Subcommittee on Oversight, 1136 LHOB 20515; (202) 225-7601. Fax, (202) 225-9680. Nancy L. Johnson, R-Conn., chair; William McKenney, staff director. Internet, http://www.house.gov/ways_means.*

Oversees government-sponsored enterprises, including the Federal Home Loan Mortgage Corp. and the Federal National Mortgage Assn., with regard to the financial risk posed to the federal government.

Senate Banking, Housing, and Urban Affairs Committee, *SD-534 20510; (202) 224-7391. Fax, (202) 224-5137. Alfonse M. D'Amato, R-N.Y., chair; Howard Menell, staff director. Internet, http://www.senate.gov/~banking.*

Jurisdiction over legislation on federal financial regulatory agencies and authorized activities of federally chartered and supervised financial institutions. Oversees government-sponsored enterprises, including the Federal Home Loan Mortgage Corp. and the Federal National Mortgage Assn.

Senate Banking, Housing, and Urban Affairs Committee, *Subcommittee on Housing Opportunity and Community Development, SD-534 20510; (202) 224-7391. Connie Mack, R-Fla., chair; Christopher Lord, staff director. Internet, http://www.senate.gov/~banking.*

Jurisdiction over legislation on mortgage insurance and secondary mortgage markets. Jurisdiction over federal insurance, including flood insurance.

NONPROFIT

American Homeowners Foundation, *6776 Little Falls Rd., Arlington, VA 22213; (703) 536-7776. Bruce Hahn, vice president. Internet, http://homes.inresco.com/Bcorgs_ahf.html.*

Conducts research and compiles statistics on home ownership; sponsors seminars and workshops; publishes model contracts.

American Land Title Assn., *1828 L St. N.W., #705 20036; (202) 296-3671. Fax, (202) 223-5843. James R. Maher, executive vice president. Internet, http://www.alta.org.*

Membership: land title insurance underwriting companies, abstracters, and title insurance agents. Searches, reviews, and insures land titles to protect real estate investors, including home buyers and mortgage lenders; provides industry information. Monitors legislation and regulations.

American Resort Development Assn., *1220 L St. N.W., #500 20005; (202) 371-6700. Fax, (202) 289-8544. Cynthia A. Huheey, president. Internet, http://www.arda.org.*

Membership: U.S. and international developers, builders, financiers, marketing companies, and others involved in resort, recreational, and community development. Serves as an information clearinghouse; monitors federal and state legislation.

American Society of Appraisers, *555 Herndon Pkwy., #125, Herndon, VA (mailing address: P.O. Box 17265, Washington, DC 20041); (703) 478-2228. Fax, (703) 742-8471. Edwin W. Baker, executive director. Toll-free, (800) 272-8258. Internet, webmaster@apo.com or http://www.apo.com.*

Membership: accredited appraisers of real property, including land, houses, and commercial buildings; businesses; machinery and equipment; yachts; aircraft; public utilities; personal property, including antiques, fine art, residential contents, gems, and jewelry. Affiliate members include students and professionals interested in appraising. Provides technical information; accredits appraisers; provides consumer information program.

Appraisal Foundation, *1029 Vermont Ave. N.W., #900 20005; (202) 347-7722. Fax, (202) 347-7727. David S. Bunton, executive vice president. Internet, http://www.appraisalfoundation.org.*

Seeks to ensure that appraisers are qualified to offer their services by promoting uniform appraisal standards and establishing education, experience, and examination requirements.

Appraisal Institute, *2600 Virginia Ave. N.W., #200 20037; (202) 296-4447. Fax, (202) 296-9464. Donald E. Kelly, vice president, Governmental Affairs. Internet, http://www.appraisalinstitute.org.*

Provides Congress, regulatory agencies, and the executive branch with information on appraisal matters. (Headquarters in Chicago.)

Assn. of Foreign Investors in U.S. Real Estate, *700 13th St. N.W., #950 20005; (202) 434-4510. Fax, (202) 434-4509. James A. Fetgatter, chief executive. Internet, chane@afire.org.*

Represents foreign institutions that are interested in the laws, regulations, and economic trends affecting the U.S. real estate market. Informs the public and the government of the contributions foreign investment makes to the U.S. economy. Examines current issues and organizes seminars for members.

International Real Estate Federation, *American Chapter, 2030 Clarendon Blvd., #400, Arlington, VA 22201-2911; (703) 524-4279. Fax, (703) 528-2392. Robert Hatcher, president. Internet, http://www.fiabci-usa.com.*

Membership: real estate professionals in the fields of appraisal, brokerage, counseling, development, financing, and property management. Sponsors seminars, workshops, and conferences. (International headquarters in Paris.)

Investment Program Assn., *607 14th St. N.W., #1000 20005; (202) 775-9750. Fax, (202) 331-8446. Christopher L. Davis, president.*

Represents the partnership industry, public and private investments that employ partnerships, Real Estate Investment Trusts (REIT), limited liability companies, and other direct investment programs. Conducts conferences and seminars.

Manufactured Housing Institute, *2101 Wilson Blvd., #610, Arlington, VA 22201; (703) 558-0400. Fax, (703) 558-0401. Richard Ernst, president. Internet, http://www.mfghome.org.*

Represents park owners, financial lenders, and builders, suppliers, and retailers of manufactured homes. Provides information on manufactured home construction standards, finance, site development, property management, and marketing.

National Assn. of Home Builders, *1201 15th St. N.W. 20005; (202) 822-0200. Fax, (202) 861-2131. Kent W. Colton, executive vice president. Press, (202) 822-0253. Internet, http://www.nahb.com.*

Membership: contractors, builders, architects, engineers, mortgage lenders, and others interested in home building and commercial real estate construction. Offers educational programs and information on housing policy and mortgage finance in the United States. Library open to the public.

National Assn. of Real Estate Brokers, *1629 K St. N.W., #602 20006; (202) 785-4477. Fax, (202) 785-1244. H. Bernie Jackson, president. Internet, http://www.nareb3.com.*

Membership: minority real estate brokers, appraisers, contractors, property managers, and salespersons. Works to prevent discrimination in housing policies and practices; conducts regional seminars on federal policy, legislation, and regulations; advises members on procedures for procuring federal contracts.

National Assn. of Real Estate Investment Trusts, *1129 20th St. N.W., #305 20036; (202) 785-8717. Fax, (202) 785-8723. Steve Wechsler, president. Internet, http://www.nareit.com.*

Membership: real estate investment trusts and corporations, partnerships, and individuals interested in real estate securities and the industry. Monitors federal and state legislation, federal taxation, securities regulation, standards and ethics, and housing and education; compiles industry statistics.

National Assn. of Realtors, *700 11th St. N.W. 20001-4507; (202) 383-1238. Fax, (202) 383-7850. Stephen*

Driesler, senior vice president, Government Affairs. Internet, http://www.realtor.com.

Sets standards of ethics for the real estate business; promotes education, research, and exchange of information. Monitors legislation and regulations. (Headquarters in Chicago.)

National Home Buyers and Home Owners Assn., 1050 17th St. N.W., #1100 20036; (202) 659-6500. Fax, (202) 293-2608. Benny L. Kass, general counsel.

Promotes consumer interests in housing, including condominiums; publishes a homebuyer's checklist in English and Spanish.

National Realty Committee, 1420 New York Ave. N.W., #1100 20005-2159; (202) 639-8400. Fax, (202) 639-8442. Jeffrey D. DeBoer, president. Internet, email@nrc.org.

Membership: real estate owners, advisers, builders, investors, lenders, and managers. Serves as forum for public policy issues including taxes, the environment, capital, credit, and investments.

Society of Industrial and Office Realtors, 700 11th St. N.W., #510 20001-4511; (202) 737-1150. Fax, (202) 737-8796. Pam Hinton, senior executive vice president. Internet, sior@sior.com or http://www.sior.com.

Membership: commerical and industrial real estate brokers worldwide. Certifies brokers; sponsors seminars and conferences; mediates and arbitrates business disputes; sponsors a speakers bureau. (Affiliated with the National Assn. of Realtors.)

Mortgages and Finance

AGENCIES

Federal Agricultural Mortgage Corp. (Farmer Mac), 919 18th St. N.W., #200 20006-5503; (202) 872-7700. Fax, (202) 872-7713. Thomas R. Clark, vice president. Internet, http://www.farmermac.com.

Private corporation chartered by Congress to provide a secondary mortgage market for farm and rural housing loans. Guarantees principal and interest repayment on securities backed by farm and rural housing loans.

Federal Home Loan Mortgage Corp. (Freddie Mac), 8200 Jones Branch Dr., McLean, VA 22102; (703) 903-2701. Fax, (703) 903-3495. David W. Glenn, president; Leland C. Brendsel, chair, (703) 903-3001. Information, (703) 903-2000. Press, (703) 903-2411. Internet, http://www.fhlmc.com.

Chartered by Congress to increase the flow of funds for residential mortgages by buying conforming mortgages and selling mortgage securities to major investors.

Federal Housing Administration (Housing and Urban Development Dept.), **Insured Single Family Housing,** 451 7th St. S.W., #9162 20410; (202) 708-3046. Fax, (202) 708-2582. John J. Coonts, director.

Establishes acceptable financial risks for the operation of government-insured mortgage programs for single-family properties (one to four units); monitors and oversees HUD-approved local counseling agencies for Federal Housing Administration programs.

Federal Housing Administration (Housing and Urban Development Dept.), **Multifamily Housing Development,** 451 7th St. S.W., #6134 20410; (202) 708-3000. Fax, (202) 708-3104. Willie Spearmon, director.

Establishes procedures for the development of housing under the multifamily mortgage insurance programs. Administers the mortgage insurance programs for rental, cooperative, and condominium housing.

Federal Housing Administration (Housing and Urban Development Dept.), **Title I Insurance,** 451 7th St. S.W., #9272 20410; (202) 708-6396. Fax, (202) 401-8951. Maurice Gulledge, director.

Administers programs for insuring approved lending institutions against loss on manufactured home and property improvement loans.

Federal Housing Enterprise Oversight (Housing and Urban Development Dept.), 1700 G St. N.W., 4th Floor 20552-0100; (202) 414-3800. Fax, (202) 414-3823. Mark Kinsey, acting deputy director.

Works to ensure the financial soundness of the Federal National Mortgage Assn. (Fannie Mae) and the Federal Home Loan Mortgage Corp. (Freddie Mac).

Federal Housing Finance Board, 1777 F St. N.W. 20006; (202) 408-2587. Fax, (202) 408-1435. Bruce A. Morrison, chair; Rita I. Fair, managing director, (202) 408-2890. Information, (202) 408-2500. Press, (202) 408-2986. TDD, (202) 408-2579. Public reading room, (202) 408-2969. Internet, http://www.fhfb.gov.

Regulates and supervises the credit and financing operations of the twelve Federal Home Loan Banks, which provide a flexible credit reserve for member institutions engaged in home mortgage lending. Member institutions of the Federal Home Loan Banks include savings and loans, savings banks, commercial banks, credit unions, insurance companies, and other financial intermediaries.

Federal National Mortgage Assn. (Fannie Mae), 3900 Wisconsin Ave. N.W. 20016; (202) 752-7000. Fax, (202) 752-3616. James A. Johnson, chair; Lawrence M. Small, president, (202) 752-7790. Toll-free, (800) 732-

6643. Press, (202) 752-7928. Library, (202) 752-7750. TDD, (202) 752-1324. Internet, http://www.fanniemae. com.

Congressionally chartered, shareholder-owned corporation. Makes mortgage funds available by buying conventional and government-insured mortgages in the secondary mortgage market; raises capital through sale of short- and long-term obligations, mortgages, and stock; issues and guarantees mortgage-backed securities. Library open to the public by appointment.

Government National Mortgage Assn. (Ginnie Mae) *(Housing and Urban Development Dept.),* 451 7th St. S.W., #6100 20410; (202) 708-0926. Fax, (202) 708-0490. Kevin Chavers, president.

Supports government housing objectives by establishing secondary markets for residential mortgages. Serves as a vehicle for channeling funds from the securities markets into the mortgage market through mortgage-backed securities programs and helps to increase the supply of credit available for housing. Guarantees privately issued securities backed by Federal Housing Administration, Veterans Affairs Dept., and Farmers Home Administration mortgages.

Housing and Urban Development Dept., *Housing— Federal Housing Commissioner,* 451 7th St. S.W., #9100 20410; (202) 708-3600. Fax, (202) 708-2580. Nicolas P. Retsinas, assistant secretary. Internet, http://www.hud.gov/ fha/fhahome.html.

Administers all Federal Housing Administration (FHA) mortgage insurance programs; approves and monitors all lending institutions that conduct business with HUD.

Office of Thrift Supervision *(Treasury Dept.),* 1700 G St. N.W. 20552; (202) 906-6280. Fax, (202) 898-0230. Nicolas P. Retsinas, interim director. Information, (202) 906-6000. Press, (202) 906-6913. Library, (202) 906-6470. Mortgage rates recording, 906-6988. Internet, http://www. ots.treas.gov.

Charters, regulates, and examines the operations of savings and loan institutions; focus includes mortgage rates. Library open to the public.

NONPROFIT

American League of Financial Institutions, 900 19th St. N.W., #400 20006-2105; (202) 857-5094. Fax, (202) 296-8716. Dina Nichelson, president. Internet, alfi@ acbankers.org or http://www.alfi.org.

Membership: minority-controlled community savings associations and savings banks. Offers on-site technical assistance to resolve problems in operations.

Encourages financing of low- and moderate-income housing and promotes community reinvestment activities. Monitors legislative and regulatory issues.

America's Community Bankers, 900 19th St. N.W., #400 20006; (202) 857-3100. Fax, (202) 296-8716. Paul A. Schosberg, president. Press, (202) 857-3103. Internet, info@ acbankers.org or http://www.acbankers.org.

Membership: insured depository institutions involved in community finance. Provides information on issues that affect the industry. Monitors economic issues affecting savings institutions; publishes homebuyers survey. Monitors legislation and regulations.

Assn. of Local Housing Finance Agencies, 1200 19th St. N.W., #300 20036-2401; (202) 857-1197. Fax, (202) 223-4579. John C. Murphy, executive director. Internet, http://www.cais.net/alhfa.

Membership: professionals of city and county government that finance affordable housing. Provides professional development programs in new housing finance and other areas. Monitors legislation and regulations.

Mortgage Bankers Assn. of America, 1125 15th St. N.W. 20005; (202) 861-6500. Fax, (202) 861-0736. Paul Reid, executive vice president.

Membership: institutions involved in real estate finance. Maintains School of Mortgage Banking; collects statistics on the industry. Conducts seminars and workshops in specialized areas of mortgage finance. Monitors legislation and regulations. Library open to the public by appointment.

Mortgage Insurance Companies of America, 727 15th St. N.W. 20005; (202) 393-5566. Fax, (202) 393-5557. Suzanne C. Hutchinson, executive vice president.

Membership: companies that provide guarantee insurance on residential, high-ratio mortgage loans. Insures members against loss from default on low down payment home mortgages and provides coverage that acts as a credit enhancement on mortgage securities.

National Assn. of Affordable Housing Lenders, 1200 19th St. N.W., #300 20036; (202) 429-5150. Fax, (202) 857-1111. Vacant, executive director. Internet, naahl@dc.sba.com.

Membership: lenders who specialize in providing financing for affordable housing and community development, including regulated financial institutions, insurance companies, mortgage banking companies, loan funds, and federal agencies. Serves as an information clearinghouse; provides education, training, and direct technical assistance. Monitors legislation and regulations.

National Assn. of Mortgage Brokers, *8201 Greensboro Dr., #300, McLean, VA 22102; (703) 610-9009. Fax, (703) 610-9005. Brian J. Kinsella, executive vice president. Internet, http://www.namb.org.*

Membership: mortgage brokers. Seeks to improve the mortgage broker industry. Offers educational programs to members. Provides referrals. Monitors legislation and regulations.

National Council of State Housing Agencies, *444 N. Capitol St. N.W., #438 20001; (202) 624-7710. Fax, (202) 624-5899. John McEvoy, executive director. Internet, http://www.ncsha.org.*

Membership: state housing finance agencies. Promotes greater opportunities for lower-income people to rent or buy affordable housing.

Property Management

AGENCIES

Bureau of Land Management *(Interior Dept.),* **Lands and Realty,** *1620 L St. N.W. (mailing address: 1849 C St. N.W., MC 1000LS, Washington, DC 20240); (202) 452-7780. Fax, (202) 452-7708. Ray Brady, manager. Internet, http://www.blm.gov.*

Oversees use, acquisition, and disposal of public lands. Conducts the Public Lands Survey; authorizes rights-of-way on public lands, including roads and power lines.

Federal Housing Administration *(Housing and Urban Development Dept.),* **Administrative Support,** *451 7th St. S.W., #9128 20410; (202) 708-0820. Fax, (202) 708-3716. Theodore A. Ford, director.*

Develops policies and procedures for procurement contracting related to the rehabilitation, repair, rental, maintenance, management, demolition, and sale of acquired multifamily and single-family properties and properties under the federal surplus land program. Provides housing program offices with reconditioning and contracting services.

Federal Housing Administration *(Housing and Urban Development Dept.),* **Multifamily Housing Management,** *451 7th St. S.W., #6160 20410; (202) 708-3730. Fax, (202) 401-5978. Frank Malone, acting director.*

Services mortgages developed under HUD's multifamily mortgage insurance programs, including the Community Disposal Program; reviews management of multifamily housing projects and administers project-based subsidy programs; advises state housing agencies that administer multifamily projects.

NONPROFIT

Building Owners and Managers Assn. International, *1201 New York Ave. N.W., #300 20005; (202) 408-2662. Fax, (202) 371-0181. Vacant, executive vice president. Internet, http://www.boma.org.*

Membership: office building owners and managers. Reviews changes in model codes and building standards; conducts seminars and workshops on building operation and maintenance issues; sponsors educational and training programs. Monitors legislation and regulations.

Building Service Contractors Assn. International, *10201 Lee Hwy., #225, Fairfax, VA 22030; (703) 359-7090. Fax, (703) 352-0493. Carol A. Dean, executive vice president. Internet, http://www.bscai.org.*

Membership: building service contractors. Promotes industry practices that are professional and environmentally responsive.

Community Associations Institute, *1630 Duke St., Alexandria, VA 22314; (703) 548-8600. Fax, (703) 684-1581. Barbara Byrd, executive vice president. Fax-on-demand, (703) 836-6904. Internet, http://www.caionline.org.*

Membership: homeowner associations, builders, lenders, owners, managers, realtors, insurance companies, and public officials. Provides members with information on creating, financing, and maintaining common facilities and services in condominiums and other planned developments.

Cooperative Housing Foundation, *8300 Colesville Rd., #420, Silver Spring, MD 20910; (301) 587-4700. Fax, (301) 587-2626. Michael Doyle, president. Internet, west@chfhq.com or http://www.chfhq.org.*

Works under contract with the Agency for International Development, United Nations, and World Bank to strengthen government housing departments abroad. Develops and strengthens nonprofit technical service organizations; conducts training workshops; assists tenant groups in converting units into cooperatives; conducts research.

NAIOP, National Assn. of Industrial and Office Properties, *2201 Cooperative Way, 3rd Floor, Herndon, VA 20171; (703) 904-7100. Fax, (703) 904-7942. Thomas J. Bisacquino, executive vice president. Internet, http://www.naiop.org.*

Membership: developers, planners, designers, builders, financiers, and managers of industrial and office properties. Provides research and continuing education programs. Monitors legislation and regulations on capital gains, real estate taxes, impact fees, growth management, environmental issues, and hazardous waste liability.

National Apartment Assn., *201 N. Union St., #200, Alexandria, VA 22314; (703) 518-6141. Fax, (703) 518-6191. Jerry Molique, president. Internet, http://www. naahq.org.*

Membership: state and local associations of owners, managers, investors, developers, and builders of apartment houses or other rental properties; conducts educational and professional certification programs. Monitors legislation and regulations.

National Assn. of Home Builders, *1201 15th St. N.W. 20005; (202) 822-0200. Fax, (202) 861-2131. Kent W. Colton, executive vice president. Press, (202) 822-0253. Internet, http://www.nahb.com.*

Membership: contractors, builders, architects, engineers, mortgage lenders, and others interested in home building and commercial real estate construction. Offers a Registered Apartment Managers certification program; provides educational programs and information on apartment construction and management, condominiums and cooperatives, multifamily rehabilitation, and low-income and federally assisted housing. Library open to the public.

National Assn. of Housing and Redevelopment Officials, *630 Eye St. N.W. 20001; (202) 289-3500. Fax, (202) 289-8181. Richard Y. Nelson Jr., executive director. Internet, http://www.nahro.org.*

Membership: housing, community, and urban development practitioners and organizations, and state and local government agencies and personnel. Conducts studies and provides training and certification in the operation and management of rental housing; develops performance standards for low-income rental housing operations.

National Assn. of Housing Cooperatives, *1614 King St., Alexandria, VA 22314; (703) 549-5201. Fax, (703) 549-5204. Herbert J. Cooper-Levy, executive director. Internet, http://www.coophousing.org.*

Membership: housing cooperative professionals, developers, and members. Promotes housing cooperatives; sets standards; provides technical assistance in all phases of cooperative housing; sponsors educational programs and on-site training; monitors legislation; maintains an information clearinghouse on housing cooperatives.

National Center for Housing Management, *1010 Massachusetts Ave. N.W., 4th Floor 20001; (202) 872-1717. Fax, (202) 789-1179. W. Glenn Stevens, president. Internet, http://www.nchm.org.*

Private corporation created by executive order to meet housing management and training needs. Conducts research, demonstrations, and educational and training programs in all types of multifamily housing management. Develops and implements certification systems for housing management programs.

National Cooperative Business Assn., *1401 New York Ave. N.W., #1100 20005-2146; (202) 638-6222. Fax, (202) 638-1374. Russell C. Notar, president. Internet, ncba@ ncba.org or http://www.cooperative.org.*

Alliance of cooperatives, businesses, and state cooperative associations. Provides information about starting and managing housing cooperatives. Monitors legislation and regulations.

National Multi Housing Council, *1850 M St. N.W., #540 20036; (202) 659-3381. Fax, (202) 775-0112. Jonathan L. Kempner, president. Internet, http://www. nmhc.org.*

Membership: owners, financiers, managers, and developers of multifamily housing. Advocates policies and programs at the federal, state, and local levels to increase the supply and quality of multifamily units in the United States; serves as a clearinghouse on rent control, condominium conversion, taxes, fair housing, housing for seniors, and environmental issues.

Property Management Assn., *7900 Wisconsin Ave., #204, Bethesda, MD 20814; (301) 657-9200. Fax, (301) 907-9326. Thomas E. Cohn, executive vice president. Internet, http://www.pma-dc.org.*

Membership: property managers and firms that offer products and services needed in the property management field. Promotes information exchange on property management practices.

13 🌍

International Affairs

GENERAL POLICY

See also Military Aid and Peacekeeping (chap. 16)

AGENCIES

Defense Dept., *International Security Affairs,* The Pentagon, #4E838 20301-2400; (703) 695-4351. Fax, (703) 697-7230. Franklin D. Kramer, assistant secretary.

Advises the secretary and recommends policies on regional security issues (except those involving countries of the former Soviet Union).

National Security Council *(Executive Office of the President),* The White House 20504; (202) 456-9471. Fax, (202) 456-9460. Samuel R. "Sandy" Berger, assistant to the president for national security affairs. Press, (202) 456-9271. Internet, http://www.whitehouse.gov.

Advises the president on matters relating to national security; collects information on foreign policy and defense issues; coordinates the national security, defense, and intelligence functions of departments such as State and Defense.

Office of Science and Technology Policy *(Executive Office of the President),* **National Security and International Affairs,** Old Executive Office Bldg., #494 20502; (202) 456-2894. Fax, (202) 456-6028. Kerri-Ann Jones, associate director.

Supports and advises the president on national security policy, international science matters, and other science policy areas. Coordinates international science and technology issues at the interagency level.

President's Foreign Intelligence Advisory Board *(Executive Office of the President),* Old Executive Office Bldg., #340 20502; (202) 456-2352. Fax, (202) 395-3403. Warren Rudman, chair; Randy Deitering, acting executive director.

Members appointed by the president. Assesses the quality, quantity, and adequacy of foreign intelligence collection and of counterintelligence activities by all government agencies; advises the president on matters concerning intelligence and national security.

State Dept., Main State Bldg., 2201 C St. N.W. 20520; (202) 647-5291. Fax, (202) 647-6434. Madeleine K. Albright, secretary; Strobe Talbott, deputy secretary, (202) 647-9640. Information, (202) 647-4000. Press, (202) 647-2492. Internet, http://www.state.gov.

Directs and coordinates U.S. foreign relations and interdepartmental activities of the U.S. government overseas.

State Dept., *Consular Affairs,* Main State Bldg., #6811 20520-4818; (202) 647-9576. Fax, (202) 647-0341. Mary A. Ryan, assistant secretary. Information, (202) 647-1488. Passport services, (202) 647-0518. Assistance to U.S. citizens overseas, (202) 647-5225. Internet, http://www.travel.state.gov.

Issues passports to U.S. citizens and visas to immigrants and nonimmigrants seeking to enter the United States. Provides protection, assistance, and documentation for American citizens abroad.

State Dept., *Global Affairs,* Main State Bldg., #7250 20520; (202) 647-6240. Fax, (202) 647-0753. Vacant, under secretary. Internet, global_state@juno.com.

Advises the secretary on international issues. Divisions include Democracy, Human Rights, and Labor; International Narcotics and Law Enforcement Affairs; Oceans and International Environmental and Scientific Affairs; and Population, Refugees, and Migration.

State Dept., *Intelligence and Research,* Main State Bldg., #6531 20520-6531; (202) 647-9177. Fax, (202) 736-4688. Phyllis E. Oakley, assistant secretary.

Coordinates foreign-policy-related research, analysis, and intelligence programs for the State Dept. and other federal agencies.

State Dept., *International Conferences,* Main State Bldg., #1517 20520-6319; (202) 647-6875. Fax, (202) 647-1301. Frank R. Provyn, managing director.

Coordinates U.S. participation in international conferences.

State Dept., *International Organization Affairs,* Main State Bldg., #6323 20520-6319; (202) 647-9600. Fax, (202) 736-4116. Princeton N. Lyman, assistant secretary. Press, (202) 647-6400.

Coordinates and develops policy guidelines for U.S. participation in the United Nations and in other international organizations and conferences.

State Dept., *Management,* Main State Bldg., #7207 20520; (202) 647-1500. Fax, (202) 647-0168. Bonnie R. Cohen, under secretary.

Serves as principal adviser to the secretary on management matters, including budgetary, administrative, and personnel policies of the department and the Foreign Service.

State Dept., *Policy Planning Staff,* Main State Bldg., #7311 20520; (202) 647-2372. Fax, (202) 647-4147. Gregory Craig, director.

Advises the secretary and other State Dept. officials on foreign policy matters.

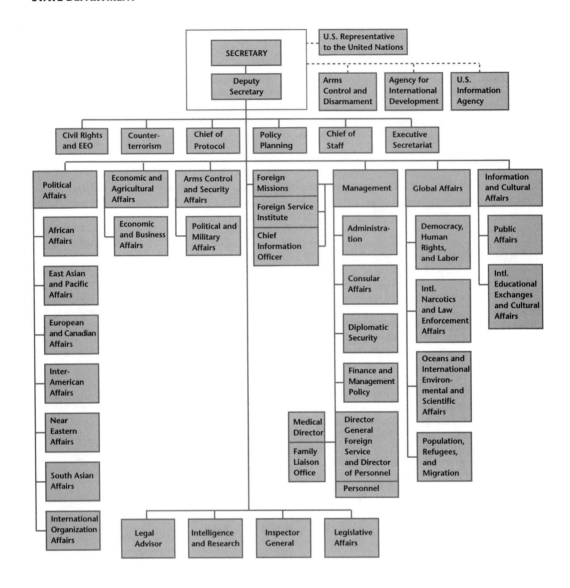

State Dept., *Political Affairs,* Main State Bldg., #7240 20520; (202) 647-2471. Fax, (202) 647-4780. Thomas R. Pickering, under secretary.

Assists in the formulation and conduct of foreign policy and in the overall direction of the department; coordinates interdepartmental activities of the U.S. government abroad.

U.S. Institute of Peace, 1550 M St. N.W., #700 20005-1708; (202) 457-1700. Fax, (202) 429-6063. Chester Crocker, chair; Richard H. Solomon, president. TDD, (202) 457-1719. Internet, http://www.usip.org.

Independent organization created and funded by Congress to promote the peaceful resolution of international conflict through negotiation and mediation. Provides federal agencies and individuals with training, research programs, and information; awards grants to institutions and individuals; and provides fellowships to scholars from the United States and abroad. Library open to the public by appointment.

CONGRESS

General Accounting Office, *National Security and International Affairs, 441 G St. N.W., #4035 20548; (202) 512-2800. Fax, (202) 512-7686. Henry L. Hinton, assistant comptroller general.*

Independent, nonpartisan agency in the legislative branch. Audits, analyzes, and evaluates international programs; makes unclassified reports available to the public.

House Appropriations Committee, *Subcommittee on Commerce, Justice, State, and Judiciary, H309 Capitol 20515; (202) 225-3351. Harold Rogers, R-Ky., chair; Jim Kulikowski, staff director. Internet, http://www.house.gov/ appropriations.*

Jurisdiction over legislation to appropriate funds for the State Dept. (except migration and refugee assistance), the U.S. Arms Control and Disarmament Agency, the Foreign Claims Settlement Commission, the U.S. Information Agency, the Commission on Security and Cooperation in Europe, and the Japan-United States Friendship Commission.

House Appropriations Committee, *Subcommittee on Foreign Operations, Export Financing, and Related Programs, H150 Capitol 20515; (202) 225-2041. Sonny Callahan, R-Ala., chair; Charles O. Flickner, staff director. Internet, http://www.house.gov/appropriations.*

Jurisdiction over legislation to appropriate funds for foreign operations, including migration, refugee, economic, and military assistance programs of the State Dept.; the Export-Import Bank; the International Bank for Reconstruction and Development (World Bank); the Inter-American Development Bank; the International Monetary Fund; the Agency for International Development; the Peace Corps; and related international organizations.

House Government Reform and Oversight Committee, *Subcommittee on National Security, International Affairs, and Criminal Justice, B373 RHOB 20515; (202) 225-2577. Fax, (202) 225-1154. Dennis Hastert, R-Ill., chair; Robert Charles, staff director. Internet, http:// www.house.gov/reform.*

Oversees operations of the State Dept., the Peace Corps, the Agency for International Development, and other agencies concerned with foreign affairs.

House International Relations Committee, *2170 RHOB 20515; (202) 225-5021. Fax, (202) 225-2035. Benjamin A. Gilman, R-N.Y., chair; Richard J. Garon Jr., chief of staff. Internet, http://www.house.gov/international_ relations.*

Jurisdiction over legislation on and operations of the State Dept., U.S. foreign embassies, and the U.S. Infor-

mation Agency. Jurisdiction over authorization of budget for the Agency for International Development and the Arms Control and Disarmament Agency, and U.S. contributions to the United Nations and other international organizations. Oversight of State and Defense department operations regarding arms transfers, export licenses, sales, administration of security assistance, and foreign military training and advisory programs.

Library of Congress, *Serial and Government Publications, 101 Independence Ave. S.E. 20540; (202) 707-5647. Fax, (202) 707-6128. Karen Renninger, chief. Information, (202) 707-5690.*

Collects and maintains information on governmental and nongovernmental organizations that are internationally based, financed, and sponsored. Responds to written or telephone requests to provide information on the history, structure, operation, and activities of these organizations. Some book material available for interlibrary loan through the Library of Congress Loan Division.

Senate Appropriations Committee, *Subcommittee on Commerce, Justice, State, and Judiciary, SR-393 20510; (202) 224-7277. Judd Gregg, R-N.H., chair, (202) 224-3324; Vas Alexopoulos, legislative assistant. Chair's fax, (202) 224-4952. Internet, http://www.senate.gov/ ~appropriations.*

Jurisdiction over legislation to appropriate funds for the State Dept. (except counterterrorism, migration and refugee assistance, and international narcotics control), the U.S. Arms Control and Disarmament Agency, the Foreign Claims Settlement Commission, the U.S. Information Agency, and other foreign policy and aid-related services and programs.

Senate Appropriations Committee, *Subcommittee on Foreign Operations, SD-142 20510; (202) 224-2104. Fax, (202) 228-1323. Mitch McConnell, R-Ky., chair; Robin Cleveland, staff director. Internet, http://www. senate.gov/~appropriations.*

Jurisdiction over legislation to appropriate funds for foreign operations, including migration, refugee, development, economic, and military assistance programs of the State Dept.

Senate Foreign Relations Committee, *SD-450 20510; (202) 224-4651. Fax, (202) 224-0836. Jesse Helms, R-N.C., chair; James W. "Bud" Nance, staff director. Internet, http://www.senate.gov/committee/foreign.html.*

Jurisdiction over legislation on foreign affairs, including economic and military assistance programs. Oversight responsibilities for operations of the State Dept., the Foreign Service, U.S. participation in the United

Nations, the Agency for International Development, and other agencies concerned with foreign affairs.

Senate Foreign Relations Committee, *Subcommittee on Western Hemisphere, Peace Corps, Narcotics, and Terrorism, SD-450 20510; (202) 224-4651. Fax, (202) 224-0836. Paul Coverdell, R-Ga., chair; Roger Noriega, senior professional staff member. Internet, http://www. senate.gov/committee/foreign.html.*

Jurisdiction over foreign affairs legislation dealing with the Americas; oversight of all matters of the Peace Corps and the U.S. delegation to the Organization of American States.

INTERNATIONAL ORGANIZATIONS

European Union, *Press and Public Affairs, 2300 M St. N.W. 20037; (202) 862-9500. Fax, (202) 429-1766. Hugo Paemen, ambassador; Soren Sondergaard, acting director. Press, (202) 862-9540. Internet, http://www.eurunion.org or http://www.europa.eu.int.*

Information and public affairs office in the United States for the European Union, which includes the European Economic Community, the European Coal and Steel Community, and the European Atomic Energy Community. Member countries are Austria, Belgium, Denmark, Finland, France, Germany, Great Britain, Greece, Ireland, Italy, Luxembourg, the Netherlands, Portugal, Spain, and Sweden. Provides social policy data on the European Union and provides statistics and documents on member countries, including those related to energy, economics, development and cooperation, commerce, agriculture, industry, and technology. Library open to the public by appointment. (Headquarters in Brussels.)

International Bank for Reconstruction and Development (World Bank), *1818 H St. N.W. 20433; (202) 477-1234. Fax, (202) 522-3433. James D. Wolfensohn, president. Press, (202) 473-6599. Publications, (202) 473-1155. Internet, http://www.worldbank.org.*

International development institution funded by membership subscriptions and borrowings on private capital markets. Encourages the flow of public and private foreign investment into developing countries through loans and technical assistance. Finances foreign economic development projects in agriculture, environmental protection, education, public utilities, telecommunications, water supply, sewerage, public health, and other areas.

International Monetary Fund (IMF), *700 19th St. N.W. 20431; (202) 623-7759. Fax, (202) 623-4661. Karin Lissakers, U.S. executive director. Information, (202) 623-*

7000. Press, (202) 623-7300. Library, (202) 623-7054. Internet, http://www.imf.org.

Intergovernmental organization that maintains funds, contributed and available for use by members, to promote world trade and aid members with temporary balance-of-payments problems.

Organization for Economic Cooperation and Development (OECD), *2001 L St. N.W., #650 20036; (202) 785-6323. Fax, (202) 785-0350. William Danvers, head, Washington Center. Internet, http://www.oecdwash. org.*

Membership: twenty five nations including Australia, Canada, Japan, Mexico, New Zealand, the United States, and Western European nations. Serves as a forum for members to exchange information and attempt to coordinate their economic policies. Washington Center maintains reference library open to the public. (Headquarters in Paris.)

Organization of American States (OAS), *17th St. and Constitution Ave. N.W. 20006 (mailing address: 1889 F St. N.W., Washington, DC 20006); (202) 458-3000. Fax, (202) 458-3967. Cesar Gaviria, secretary general. Information, (202) 458-3760. Library, (202) 458-6037. Internet, http:// www.oas.org.*

Membership: the United States, Canada, and all independent Latin American and Caribbean countries. Funded by quotas paid by member states and by contributions to special multilateral funds. Works to promote democracy, eliminate poverty, and resolve disputes among member nations. Provides member states with technical and advisory services in cultural, educational, scientific, social, and economic areas. Library open to the public.

United Nations Information Centre, *1775 K St. N.W., #400 20006; (202) 331-8670. Fax, (202) 331-9191. Joe Sills, director. Internet, http://www.un.org.*

Lead United Nations office in Washington. Center for reference publications of the U.N. Library, open to the public, includes all official U.N. records and publications.

NONPROFIT

American Enterprise Institute for Public Policy Research, *Foreign and Defense Policy Studies, 1150 17th St. N.W. 20036; (202) 862-5814. Fax, (202) 862-7177. Jeane Kirkpatrick, director. Information, (202) 862-6158. Press, (202) 862-5829.*

Research and educational organization that conducts conferences, seminars, and debates, and sponsors research on international affairs.

American Peace Society, *1319 18th St. N.W. 20036; (202) 296-6261. Fax, (202) 296-5149. Jeane Kirkpatrick, president.*

Conducts research and publishes journals dealing with international problems.

Assn. on Third World Affairs, *1629 K St. N.W., #802 20006; (202) 331-8455. Fax, (202) 785-3607. Lorna Hahn, executive director.*

Membership: individuals and groups interested in developing nations. Promotes research projects; arranges lectures and conferences; sponsors student interns.

Assn. to Unite the Democracies, *1506 Pennsylvania Ave. S.E. 20003-3116; (202) 544-5150. Fax, (202) 544-3742. Tom Hudgens, president. Toll-free, (800) 288-6483. Internet, atunite@aol.com or http://www.atunite.org.*

Educational organization that promotes and conducts research on unity among the industrial democracies, including the United States, Japan, western European countries, and new and emerging democracies in the former Soviet bloc. Advocates a federation of these states.

Atlantic Council of the United States, *910 17th St. N.W., 10th Floor 20006; (202) 463-7226. Fax, (202) 463-7241. David C. Acheson, president. Internet, info@acgate.acus.org.*

Conducts studies and makes policy recommendations on American foreign security and international economic policies in the Atlantic and Pacific communities; sponsors conferences and educational exchanges.

Brookings Institution, *Foreign Policy Studies, 1775 Massachusetts Ave. N.W. 20036-2188; (202) 797-6400. Fax, (202) 797-6004. Richard Haass, director. Information, (202) 797-6000. Press, (202) 797-6105. Publications, (202) 797-6258. Internet, http://www.brook.edu.*

Conducts studies on foreign policy, national security, regional affairs, and international policies on energy, economics, and trade.

Carnegie Endowment for International Peace, *1779 Massachusetts Ave. N.W. 20036; (202) 483-7600. Fax, (202) 483-1840. Jessica T. Matthews, president. Internet, carnegie@ceip.org or http://www.ceip.org.*

Conducts research on international affairs and American foreign policy. Program activities cover a broad range of military, political, and economic issues; sponsors panel discussions. (Affiliate office in Moscow.)

Center for Democracy, *1101 15th St. N.W., #505 20005-5002; (202) 429-9141. Fax, (202) 293-1768. Allen Weinstein, president. Internet, centdemo@aol.com.*

Nonpartisan organization that works to promote the democratic process and strengthen democratic institutions in the United States and worldwide. Monitors elections and provides democratizing governments with technical and informational assistance.

Center for Strategic and International Studies, *1800 K St. N.W. 20006; (202) 887-0200. Fax, (202) 775-3199. David M. Abshire, president. Information, (202) 775-3176. Publications, (202) 775-3119. Internet, http://www.csis.org.*

Independent bipartisan research institute that studies international and domestic policy issues. Interests include science and technology, international business and economics, political-military affairs, arms control, international communications, fiscal policy, and health care reform.

Center of Concern, *3700 13th St. N.E. 20017; (202) 635-2757. Fax, (202) 832-9494. James Hug, executive director. Internet, coc@igc.apc.org or http://www.coc.org/coc.*

Independent, interdisciplinary organization that conducts social analysis, theological reflection, policy advocacy, and public education on issues of international justice and peace.

Charles F. Kettering Foundation, *444 N. Capitol St. N.W., #434 20001-1512; (202) 393-4478. Fax, (202) 393-7644. James C. Wilder, director, Washington Office. Toll-free, (800) 221-3657. Internet, http://www.kettering.org.*

Works to improve the domestic policymaking process. Supports international program focusing on unofficial, citizen-to-citizen diplomacy. Encourages greater citizen involvement in formation of public policy. Interests include public education and at-risk youths. (Headquarters in Dayton, Ohio.)

Citizens Network for Foreign Affairs, *1111 19th St. N.W., #900 20036; (202) 296-3920. Fax, (202) 296-3948. John H. Costello, president. Internet, http://www.cnfa.com.*

Public policy and education organization that works to involve Americans in the foreign policy process. Advocates a more collaborative partnership between the public and private sectors to promote global economic growth.

Council on Foreign Relations, *1779 Massachusetts Ave. N.W. 20036; (202) 518-3400. Fax, (202) 986-2984. Paula J. Dobriansky, director. Internet, http://www.foreignrelations.org.*

Promotes understanding of U.S. foreign policy and international affairs. Awards research grants through its International Affairs Fellowship Program. (Headquarters in New York.)

Eisenhower World Affairs Institute, *1620 Eye St. N.W., #703 20006; (202) 223-6710. Fax, (202) 452-1837. Jane L. Kratovil, executive director.*

Sponsors public policy and educational programs for future leaders designed to improve understanding of the presidency and world affairs.

Friends Committee on National Legislation, *245 2nd St. N.E. 20002-5795; (202) 547-6000. Fax, (202) 547-6019. Joe Volk, executive secretary. Recorded information, (202) 547-4343. Internet, fcnl@igc.apc.org or http://www. fas.org/pub/gen/fcnl.*

Seeks to broaden public interest and affect legislation and policy concerning regional and global institutions, peace processes, international development, and the work of the United Nations. Affiliated with the Religious Society of Friends (Quakers).

Institute for Policy Studies, *733 15th St. N.W., #1020 20005; (202) 234-9382. Fax, (202) 387-7915. John Cavanagh, director. Internet, http://www.igc.org/ifps.*

Research and educational organization. Interests include foreign policy, the U.S. military-industrial complex, international development, human rights, and national security.

International Center, *731 8th St. S.E. 20003; (202) 547-3800. Fax, (202) 546-4784. Lindsay Mattison, executive director. Internet, ic-nfp@clark.net or http://www. internationalcenter.org.*

Research organization concerned with U.S. foreign policy. Sponsored U.S. delegation to more than twenty countries. Current projects include: Commission on U.S.-Russian Relations, New Forests Project, U.S.-Vietnam Trade Council, U.S.-Mongolia Business Council, Russian Information and Business Center, U.S.-Bulgaria Council, and the Cuban American Alliance Education Fund.

International Republican Institute, *1212 New York Ave. N.W., 9th Floor 20005-3987; (202) 408-9450. Fax, (202) 408-9462. Lorne Craner, president. Internet, iri@iri. org or http://www.iri.org.*

Created under the National Endowment for Democracy Act. Fosters democratic self-rule through closer ties and cooperative programs with political parties and other nongovernmental institutions overseas.

National Democratic Institute for International Affairs, *1717 Massachusetts Ave. N.W., #503 20036; (202) 328-3136. Fax, (202) 939-3166. Kenneth Wollack, president. Internet, demos@ndi.org or http://www.ndi.org.*

Conducts nonpartisan international programs to help maintain and strengthen democratic institutions

worldwide. Focuses on party building, governance, and electoral systems.

National Endowment for Democracy, *1101 15th St. N.W., #700 20005; (202) 293-9072. Fax, (202) 223-6042. Carl Gershman, president; Barbara Haig, program director. Internet, http://www.ned.org.*

Grantmaking organization that receives funding from Congress. Awards grants to private organizations involved in democratic development abroad, including the areas of democratic political processes; pluralism; and education, culture, and communications.

National Peace Foundation, *1835 K St. N.W., #610 20006; (202) 223-1770. Fax, (202) 223-1718. Stephen P. Strickland, president. Toll-free, (800) 237-3223. Internet, http://www.nationalpeace.org.*

Supports conflict resolution education and the U.S. Institute of Peace. Holds conferences and provides information on peace education and managing and resolving conflict.

National Security Archive, *Gelman Library, 2130 H St. N.W., #701 20037; (202) 994-7000. Fax, (202) 994-7005. Thomas Blanton, executive director. Internet, nsarchiv@ gwis2.circ.gwu.edu or http://www.seas.gwu.edu/nsarchive.*

Research institute and library that provides information on U.S. foreign policy and national security affairs. Maintains collection of declassified and unclassified national security documents. Archive open to the public by appointment.

Paul H. Nitze School of Advanced International Studies, *1740 Massachusetts Ave. N.W. 20036; (202) 663-5624. Fax, (202) 663-5621. Paul D. Wolfowitz, dean. Information, (202) 663-5600. Press, (202) 663-5626.*

Offers graduate programs in international relations and public policy. Sponsors the Johns Hopkins Foreign Policy Institute, and centers for Canadian, Brazilian, East Asian, and Sino-American studies.

Potomac Foundation, *U.S. Global Strategy Program, 1311 Dolley Madison Blvd., #2A, McLean, VA 22101; (703) 506-1790. Fax, (703) 506-8085. Dan McDonald, president.*

Advocates development of long-term, global policies to promote national security, economic well-being, and international stability. Interests include economic, political, social, and military changes in Asia, the Pacific basin, the Caribbean, and Latin America; reform in South Africa; international terrorism; and international economic competition.

United Nations Assn. of the USA, *1779 Massachusetts Ave. N.W., #610 20036; (202) 462-3446. Fax, (202) 462-*

3448. Steven A. Dimoff, vice president. Internet, unadc@unausa.org or http://www.unausa.org.

Research and educational organization focusing on international institutions, multilateral diplomacy, U.S. foreign policy, and international economics. Coordinates Model United Nations program for high school and university students. Monitors legislation and regulations. (Headquarters in New York.)

U.S. Catholic Conference, *International Justice and Peace,* 3211 4th St. N.E. 20017; (202) 541-3199. Fax, (202) 541-3339. Vacant, director. Internet, http://www.mtn.org/justice/sdwp.htm.

Works with the U.S. State Dept., foreign government offices, and international organizations on issues of peace, justice, and human rights.

Women in International Security, *University of Maryland, CISSM, SPA, 4133F Van Munching Hall, College Park, MD 20742; (301) 405-7612. Fax, (301) 403-8107. Peggy Knudson, executive director. Internet, http://www.puaf.umd.edu/WIIS.*

Seeks to advance women in the field of international studies. Maintains a database of women foreign and defense policy specialists worldwide; organizes conferences in Europe, the former Soviet Union, and Asia; disseminates information on jobs, internships, and fellowships for women in international affairs.

Women's Foreign Policy Group, *1875 Connecticut Ave. N.W., #720 20009-5728; (202) 884-8597. Fax, (202) 884-8499. Patricia Ellis, executive director. Internet, wfpg@aed.org.*

Promotes the leadership of women in international affairs professions. Conducts policy programs, mentoring, and research.

World Federalist Assn., *418 7th St. S.E. 20003; (202) 546-3950. Fax, (202) 546-3749. Tim Barner, executive director. Toll-free, (800) 923-0123. Internet, http://www.wfa.org.*

Sponsors projects and conducts research related to international affairs; seeks to broaden public support for world order organizations and a restructured United Nations.

Diplomats and Foreign Agents

See also Americans Abroad (this chapter); Foreign Embassies, U.S. Ambassadors, and Country Desk Officers (appendix)

AGENCIES

For information on the annual foreign service exam, contact FSO Exam, State Dept., P.O. Box 12226, Arlington,

VA 22219; (703) 875-7490. Exam information is also available via the Internet at http://www.state.gov/www/careers/rexamcontents.html.

Foreign Service Institute *(State Dept.),* 4000 Arlington Blvd., Arlington, VA 22204-1500; (703) 302-6703. Fax, (703) 302-7461. Ruth A. Davis, director. Student messages and course information, (703) 302-7143.

Provides training for U.S. government personnel involved in foreign affairs agencies, including employees of the State Dept., the Agency for International Development, the U.S. Information Agency, the Defense Dept., and other agencies.

Justice Dept., *Foreign Agents Registration Unit,* 1400 New York Ave. N.W. 20530; (202) 514-1216. Fax, (202) 514-2836. Marshall Williams, chief. Internet, http://www.usdoj.gov/criminal/fara.

Receives and maintains the registrations of agents representing foreign countries, companies, organizations, and individuals. Compiles semi-annual report on foreign agent registrations. Foreign agent registration files are open for public inspection.

State Dept., *Career Development and Assignments,* Main State Bldg., #2328 (mailing address: PER/CDA, Washington, DC 20520-2810); (202) 647-1692. Fax, (202) 647-0277. James A. Williams, director.

Coordinates programs related to the professional development of American members of the Foreign Service, including career development and assignment counseling programs; training; and presidential appointments and resignations.

State Dept., *Diplomatic Security Bureau,* Main State Bldg., #6316 20520; (202) 647-6290. Fax, (202) 647-0953. Eric J. Boswell, assistant secretary.

Provides a secure environment for conducting American diplomacy and promoting American interests abroad and in the United States.

State Dept., *Family Liaison,* Main State Bldg., #1212A 20520-7512; (202) 647-1076. Fax, (202) 647-1670. F. Kendall Montgomery, director. Internet, http://www.state.gov/www/flo.

Provides support for U.S. foreign affairs personnel and their families in Washington, D.C. and abroad. Maintains liaison offices that give support services to the U.S. foreign affairs community overseas. Services include dependent employment assistance and continuing education programs; educational assistance for families with children; and information on adoption and separation, regulations, allowance, and finances. Assists families in emergencies.

State Dept., *Foreign Missions, Main State Bldg., #2238 20520-7207; (202) 647-3416. Fax, (202) 647-1919. Vacant, director; Thomas E. Burns Jr., deputy director.*

Regulates the benefits, privileges, and immunities granted to foreign missions and their personnel in the United States on the basis of the treatment accorded U.S. missions abroad and considerations of national security and public safety.

State Dept., *Foreign Service, Main State Bldg., #6218 20520; (202) 647-9898. Fax, (202) 647-5080. Edward W. Gnehm Jr., director general.*

Administers the Foreign Service.

State Dept., *Medical Services, 2401 E St. N.W., #209 20522-0102; (202) 663-1611. Fax, (202) 663-1613. Dr. Cedric E. Dumont, medical director.*

Operates a worldwide primary health care system for American citizen employees, and eligible dependents, of the U.S. government residing abroad. Conducts physicial examinations of Foreign Service officers and candidates; provides clinical services; assists with medical evacuation of patients overseas.

State Dept., *Protocol, Main State Bldg., #1238 20520; (202) 647-4543. Fax, (202) 647-3980. Mary Mel French, chief. Press, (202) 647-1685.*

Serves as principal adviser to the president, vice president, the secretary, and other high-ranking government officials on matters of diplomatic procedure governed by law or international customs and practice.

CONGRESS

House International Relations Committee, *Subcommittee on International Operations and Human Rights, B-358 RHOB 20515; (202) 225-5748. Fax, (202) 225-7485. Christopher H. Smith, R-N.J., chair; Grover Joseph Rees, staff director. Internet, http://www.house.gov/ international_relations.*

Jurisdiction over legislation on the foreign service, the United Nations, other international organizations, and educational and cultural exchange programs. Oversight of the U.S. Information Agency.

Senate Foreign Relations Committee, *Subcommittee on International Operations, SD-450 20510; (202) 224-4651. Fax, (202) 224-0836. Rod Grams, R-Minn., chair; Chris Walker, senior professional staff member. Internet, http://www.senate.gov/committee/foreign.html.*

Jurisdiction over legislation on the foreign service, the United Nations, other international organizations and conferences, and educational and cultural exchange programs. Oversight of the U.S. Information Agency.

NONPROFIT

American Foreign Service Assn., *2101 E St. N.W. 20037; (202) 338-4045. Fax, (202) 338-6820. Susan Reardon, executive director. Internet, afsa@afsa.org or http:// www.afsa.org.*

Membership: active and retired foreign service employees of the State Dept., Agency for International Development, Foreign Commercial Service, Foreign Agricultural Service, and the U.S. Information Agency. Offers scholarship program; maintains club for members; represents active duty foreign service personnel in labor-management negotiations. Seeks to ensure adequate resources for foreign service operations and personnel. Interests include business-government collaboration and international trade. Monitors legislation and regulations.

Council of American Ambassadors, *888 17th St. N.W., #901 20006; (202) 296-3757. Fax, (202) 296-0926. Ogden Reid, president; Carolyn M. Gretzinger, executive director. Internet, council@his.com or http://www.his.com/ ~council.*

Membership: U.S. ambassadors. Seeks to advance the understanding of the American ambassador's role in serving U.S. interests abroad; assists in the ambassadorial selection process.

Institute for the Study of Diplomacy *(Georgetown University), 801 Intercultural Center, 37th and O Sts. N.W. 20057; (202) 687-6279. Fax, (202) 687-8312. Casimir A. Yost, director. Internet, http://www.georgetown. edu/sfs/programs/isd.*

Part of the Edmund A. Walsh School of Foreign Service. Focuses on the practical implementation of foreign policy objectives; draws on academic research and the concrete experience of diplomats and other members of the foreign service.

Humanitarian Aid

See also Development Assistance (this chapter); Emergency Preparedness (chap. 16); World Food Assistance (chap. 2)

AGENCIES

Administration for Children and Families *(Health and Human Services Dept.), Refugee Resettlement, 901 D St. S.W., 6th Floor 20447; (202) 401-9246. Fax, (202) 401-5487. Lavinia Limon, director.*

Directs a domestic resettlement program for refugees; reimburses states for costs incurred in giving refugees monetary and medical assistance; awards funds to private resettlement agencies for providing refugees with monetary assistance and case management; provides states and nonprofit agencies with grants for social services such as English and employment training.

Agency for International Development, *Center for Population, Health, and Nutrition,* *1300 Pennsylvania Ave. N.W., GPHN/POP 20523-3600; (202) 712-5407. Fax, (202) 216-3046. Duff Gillespie, deputy assistant director. Internet, http://www.info.usaid.gov/pop_health.*

Participates in global efforts to stabilize world population growth and support women's reproductive rights. Focus includes family planning; reproductive health care; infant, child, and maternal health; and prevention of sexually transmitted diseases, especially AIDS. Conducts demographic and health surveys; educates girls and women.

Agency for International Development, *Humanitarian Response Bureau,* *1300 Pennsylvania Ave. N.W., #8.06 20523; (202) 712-0770. Fax, (202) 216-3397. Leonard Rogers, acting assistant administrator.*

Manages U.S. foreign disaster assistance, U.S. government food aid programs, grants to private voluntary and cooperative development organizations, and American sponsored schools and hospitals around the world. Manages U.S. government relief efforts in Somalia.

Agency for International Development, *U.S. Foreign Disaster Assistance,* *1300 Pennsylvania Ave. N.W., #8.06 20523; (202) 712-0400. Fax, (202) 216-3707. William Garvelink, deputy director.*

Division of the Humanitarian Response Bureau. Administers disaster relief and preparedness assistance to foreign countries. Aids displaced persons in disaster situations and helps other countries manage natural and man-made disasters.

Defense Dept., *Peacekeeping and Humanitarian Assistance,* *The Pentagon, #4B680, ODASD (PK-HA) 20301-2500; (703) 614-0446. Fax, (703) 614-0442. James A. Schear, deputy assistant secretary.*

Develops policy and plans for department provision of humanitarian assistance, refugee affairs, U.S. international information programs, and international peacekeeping and peace enforcement activities. Develops policy related to creating, identifying, training, exercising, and committing military forces for peacekeeping and peace enforcement activities.

Public Health and Science *(Health and Human Services Dept.),* *International and Refugee Health,* *5600 Fishers Lane, Rockville, MD 20857; (301) 443-1774. Fax, (301) 443-6288. Linda A. Vogel, director. Internet, http://www.os.dhhs.gov/progorg/ophs.*

Represents the Health and Human Services Dept. before other governments, U.S. government agencies, international organizations, and the private sector on international and refugee health issues. Promotes international cooperation; provides health-related humanitarian and developmental assistance; facilitates cooperation by Public Health and Science with the Agency for International Development; provides leadership for bilateral programs with select countries.

State Dept., *Population, Refugees, and Migration,* *Main State Bldg., #5824 20520-5824; (202) 647-7360. Fax, (202) 647-8162. Julia. V. Taft, assistant secretary. Information, (202) 663-1026.*

Develops and implements policies and programs on international refugee matters, including repatriation and resettlement programs; funds and monitors overseas relief, assistance, and repatriation programs; manages refugee admission to the United States.

CONGRESS

House International Relations Committee, *2170 RHOB 20515; (202) 225-5021. Fax, (202) 225-2035. Benjamin A. Gilman, R-N.Y., chair; Richard J. Garon Jr., chief of staff. Internet, http://www.house.gov/international_relations.*

Jurisdiction over international disaster assistance legislation, including the Foreign Assistance Act.

House Judiciary Committee, *Subcommittee on Immigration and Claims,* *B370B RHOB 20515; (202) 225-5727. Fax, (202) 225-3672. Lamar Smith, R-Texas, chair; Cordia Strom, counsel. Internet, http://www.house.gov/judiciary.*

Jurisdiction over legislation on immigration, refugees, and repatriated Americans; oversight of private immigration relief bills.

Senate Foreign Relations Committee, *SD-450 20510; (202) 224-4651. Fax, (202) 224-0836. Jesse Helms, R-N.C., chair; James W. "Bud" Nance, staff director. Internet, http://www.senate.gov/committee/foreign.html.*

Jurisdiction over international disaster assistance legislation, including the International Emergency Economic Powers Act.

Senate Judiciary Committee, *Subcommittee on Immigration,* *SD-323 20510; (202) 224-6098. Fax, (202) 228-4506. Spencer Abraham, R-Mich., chair; Lee Lieberman Otis, chief counsel. Internet, http://www.senate.gov/committee/judiciary.html.*

Jurisdiction over legislation on refugees, repatriated Americans, immigration, and naturalization. Oversight of private immigration relief bills.

INTERNATIONAL ORGANIZATIONS

International Organization for Migration, *1750 K St. N.W., #1110 20006; (202) 862-1826. Fax, (202) 862-1879. Hans-Petter Boe, chief of mission. Internet, srowashington@iom.int or http://www.iom.int.*

Nonpartisan organization that plans and operates refugee resettlement, national migration, and emergency relief programs at the request of its member governments. Recruits skilled professionals for developing countries. (Headquarters in Geneva.)

Pan American Health Organization, *525 23rd St. N.W. 20037; (202) 974-3200. Fax, (202) 974-3663. Dr. George A. Alleyne, director. Information, (202) 974-3458. Library, (202) 974-3305. Internet, http://www.paho.org.*

Regional office for the Americas of the World Health Organization, headquartered in Geneva, Switzerland. Works to extend health services to underserved populations in member countries and to control or eradicate communicable diseases; promotes cooperation among governments to solve public health problems. Library open to the public by appointment.

United Nations High Commissioner for Refugees, *1775 K St. N.W., #300 20006-1502; (202) 296-5191. Fax, (202) 296-5660. Annewillem Bijleveld, Washington representative. Internet, usawa@unhcr.ch or http://www.unhcr.ch.*

Works with governments and voluntary organizations to protect and assist refugees worldwide. Promotes long-term alternatives to refugee camps, including voluntary repatriation, local integration, and resettlement overseas. (Headquarters in Geneva.)

U.S. Committee for the United Nations Children's Fund, *1775 K St. N.W., #360 20006; (202) 296-4242. Fax, (202) 296-4060. Martin S. Rendon, vice president, Public Policy and Advocacy. Toll-free, (800) 367-5437. Internet, http://www.unicefusa.org.*

Serves as information reference service on UNICEF; advocates policies to advance the well-being of the world's children. Interests include international humanitarian assistance, U.S. voluntarism, child survival, and international health. (Headquarters in New York.)

See also Pan American Development Foundation (p. 483)

NONPROFIT

American Red Cross, *National Headquarters, 430 17th St. N.W., 2nd Floor 20006; (202) 737-8300. Fax, (202) 783-3432. Elizabeth Dole, president. Internet, http://www.redcross.org.*

Service organization chartered by Congress to provide domestic and international disaster relief and to act as a medium of communication between the U.S. armed forces and their families in time of war. Coordinates the distribution of supplies, funds, and technical assistance for relief in major foreign disasters through the International Federation of Red Cross and Red Crescent Societies and the International Committee of the Red Cross, both headquartered in Geneva. (Public inquiries, 8111 Gatehouse Rd., Falls Church, VA 22042; (703) 206-7090; fax (703) 206-7749.)

Central American Refugee Center, *1459 Columbia Rd. N.W. 20009; (202) 328-9799. Fax, (202) 328-0023. Saul Solorzano, executive director. Internet, carecendc2@aol.com.*

Human rights organization that seeks recognition of refugees' rights, including the right not to be deported. Provides legal representation for refugees seeking asylum; encourages church congregations to assist refugees in applying for political asylum. Interests include community education, documentation of human rights abuses, and social services. Operates Clinica del Pueblo, a medical clinic in Washington, D.C.

Christian Children's Fund, *1400 16th St. N.W., #420 20036; (202) 462-2161. Fax, (202) 462-0601. Betty Meyer, director, Washington Liaison Office. Internet, http://www.christianchildrensfund.org.*

Nonsectarian humanitarian organization that promotes improved child welfare standards and services worldwide by supporting long-term sustainable development. Provides children in emergency situations brought on by war, natural disaster, and other circumstances with education, medical care, food, clothing, and shelter. Provides aid to children of all backgrounds. (Headquarters in Richmond, Va.)

Church World Service, *110 Maryland Ave. N.E. 20002; (202) 543-6336. Fax, (202) 546-6232. Carol Capps, director, Development Policy. Internet, cwslwr@igc.apc.org.*

International relief, refugee, and development agency of the National Council of Churches. Provides food and medical assistance in drought- and famine-stricken areas; disaster relief services in the United States; and development assistance in developing countries. Monitors legislation and regulations. (Headquarters in New York.)

Health Volunteers Overseas, *1001 Connecticut Ave. N.W., #725 20036 (mailing address: Washington Station, P.O. Box 65157, Washington, DC 20035-5157); (202) 296-0928. Fax, (202) 296-8018. Nancy Kelly, executive director. Internet, hvo@aol.com or http://www.concentric.net/~hvousa.*

Operates training programs in developing countries for health professionals who wish to teach low-cost health care delivery practices.

Holy Childhood Assn., *1720 Massachusetts Ave. N.W. 20036; (202) 775-8637. Fax, (202) 429-2987. Francis W. Wright, national director.*

Religious education and relief organization that provides educational materials to teach American children about underprivileged children in foreign countries. Provides financial aid for programs and facilities that benefit underprivileged children abroad under age 14.

International Rescue Committee, *Washington office, 1612 K St. N.W., #700 20006; (202) 822-0043. Fax, (202) 822-0089. Sheppie Abramowitz, vice president, Government Relations. Internet, http://www.intrescom.org.*

Provides worldwide emergency aid, resettlement services, and educational support for refugees; recruits volunteers. (Headquarters in New York.)

Jesuit Refugee Service/USA, *1616 P St. N.W., #400 20036-1405; (202) 462-5200. Fax, (202) 462-7009. Richard Ryscavage SJ, national coordinator. Internet, jesuitusa@igc.apc.org or http://www.jesuit.org/refugee.*

U.S. Jesuit organization that aids refugees in Africa, Southeast Asia, Central America, and Mexico. Provides information on refugee problems; places individual Jesuits, sisters, and lay people in refugee work abroad. Monitors refugee- and immigration-related legislation. (International headquarters in Rome.)

Lutheran World Relief, *110 Maryland Ave. N.E. 20002; (202) 543-6336. Fax, (202) 546-6232. Carol Capps, director, Development Policy. Internet, cwslwr@igc.apc.org.*

Provides food to drought- and famine-stricken areas; relief services to refugees and victims of natural disasters; and development assistance to promote reforestation, long-term medical care, improved food supplies, and increased availability of water. Monitors legislation and regulations. (Headquarters in New York.)

Program for Appropriate Technology in Health, *1990 M St. N.W., #700 20036; (202) 822-0033. Fax, (202) 457-1466. Ann Wilson, director. Internet, info@path-dc.org or http://www.path.org.*

Seeks to improve the safety and availability of health products and technologies worldwide, particularly in developing countries. Interests include reproductive health, immunization, maternal-child health, AIDS, and nutrition. (Headquarters in Seattle.)

Refugee Policy Group, *1424 16th St. N.W. 20036; (202) 387-3015. Fax, (202) 667-5034. Dennis Gallagher, executive director. Internet, refugeePG@worldnet.att.net.*

Conducts policy analyses and research on domestic and international refugee issues; sponsors symposia. Library open to the public by appointment.

Refugee Voices, *1717 Massachusetts Ave. N.W., #701 20036; (202) 347-3507. Fax, (202) 347-3418. Barbara Karl, director. Toll-free, (800) 688-7338. Internet, rv@ irsa-uscr.org.*

Advocates on behalf of refugees; produces radio programs to educate Americans about the plight of refugees; coordinates information network. Monitors legislation and regulations. (Affiliated with U.S. Committee for Refugees.)

Southeast Asia Resource Action Center, *1628 16th St. N.W., 3rd Floor 20009; (202) 667-4690. Fax, (202) 667-6449. Vacant, executive director. Internet, searacdc@ aol.com or http://www.searac.org.*

Assists Southeast Asians in the United States with resettlement. Advocates for refugee rights. Interests include education, citizenship development, Indochinese self-help organizations, and economic development.

U.S. Catholic Conference, *Migration and Refugee Services, 3211 4th St. N.E. 20017; (202) 541-3352. Fax, (202) 541-3399. Mark Franken, executive director.*

Provides refugees and immigrants with resettlement services and legal counseling; operates training programs for volunteers and professionals; develops and implements USCC policy on migration, immigration, and refugee issues.

U.S. Committee for Refugees, *1717 Massachusetts Ave. N.W., #701 20036; (202) 347-3507. Fax, (202) 347-3418. Roger P. Winter, director. Internet, irsa@irsa-uscr.org.*

Public information and educational organization that monitors the world refugee situation and informs the public about refugee issues. Interests include human rights abuses. Publishes position papers and an annual survey. (Affiliated with Refugee Voices.)

World Mercy Fund, *P.O. Box 227, Waterford, VA 20197; (540) 882-4425. Fax, (540) 882-3226. Patrick Leonard, president.*

Provides the developing world with medical, educational, agricultural, and other forms of aid.

World Vision, *220 Eye St. N.E., #270 20002; (202) 547-3743. Fax, (202) 547-4834. Andrew Natsios, executive director. Internet, http://www.worldvision.org.*

Provides children and families around the world with aid, including emergency disaster relief; helps impoverished communities become self-sustaining through agriculture, health care, community organization, food programming, nutritional training, income generation and credit, and other development projects. (Headquarters in Seattle.)

Information and Exchange Programs

See also International Programs (chap. 17); Language and Literature (chap. 4); Regional Affairs (this chapter)

AGENCIES

Broadcasting Board of Governors *(U.S. Information Agency), 330 Independence Ave. S.W., #3360 20547; (202) 401-3736. Fax, (202) 401-6605. David W. Burke, chair; Kathleen Harrington, chief of staff.*

Established by Congress to direct and supervise all U.S. government nonmilitary international broadcasting, including Voice of America, Radio and TV Marti, Worldnet Television, Radio Free Europe/Radio Liberty, and Radio Free Asia. Assesses the quality and effectiveness of broadcasts with regard to U.S. foreign policy objectives; reports annually to the president and to Congress.

U.S. Advisory Commission on Public Diplomacy *(U.S. Information Agency), 301 4th St. S.W., #600 20547; (202) 619-4457. Fax, (202) 619-5489. Bruce Gregory, staff director. Internet, ac@usia.gov or http://www.usia.gov.*

Provides bipartisan oversight and assessment of the international information broadcasting, cultural, and educational exchange programs of the U.S. government. Reports to the president, the secretary of state, the USIA director, and Congress.

U.S. Information Agency, *301 4th St. S.W. 20547; (202) 619-4742. Fax, (202) 619-6705. Joseph Duffey, director; Penn Kemble, deputy director, (202) 619-5747. Press, (202) 619-4355. Locator, (202) 619-5576 or (202) 619-4700. Internet, http://www.usia.gov.*

Independent agency responsible for international information, education, and exchange programs designed to promote understanding of American society and culture and U.S. foreign policy. Oversees more than 200 posts in 147 foreign countries.

U.S. Information Agency, *Educational and Cultural Affairs, 301 4th St. S.W., #849 20547; (202) 619-4597. Fax, (202) 619-5068. John P. Loiello, associate director. Internet, http://www.usia.gov.*

Administers Fulbright-Hays scholarship exchange program for U.S. and foreign scholars, university and college faculty, and graduate students; arranges intensive short-term study and observation visits for foreign leaders and professionals who meet and consult with Americans active in their fields; awards grants to private organizations that administer international exchange

programs; conducts international exchange programs for youth; distributes American literature and presents American cultural activities (music, art, and drama), news, and editorial material overseas.

USDA Graduate School *(Agriculture Dept.), International Institute for Training and Education, 600 Maryland Ave. S.W. 20024; (202) 401-9279. Fax, (202) 401-9133. Jack Hogan, director. Internet, http://www.grad. usda.gov/International/iitehome.html.*

Offers professional training and educational services to employees of foreign governments, international organizations, nongovernmental agencies, and employees of U.S. agencies engaged in international activities. Areas of concentration include governance and democratization, international conflict resolution, privatization, environmental management, and management skills and systems development. Conducts courses in Washington, D.C., and San Francisco and educational and cultural exchanges with other countries.

Voice of America *(U.S. Information Agency), 330 Independence Ave. S.W., #3300 20547; (202) 619-3375. Fax, (202) 619-0085. Evelyn S. Lieberman, director. Information, (202) 619-2538. Locator, (202) 619-4700.*

Official radio broadcast service of the U.S. Information Agency. Offers overseas broadcasts of news, editorials, and features dealing with developments in American foreign and domestic affairs. Operates African, East Asian and Pacific, European, Eurasian, Latin American republics, North African, and Near East and South Asian affairs offices, as well as the World English program.

NONPROFIT

Alliance for International Educational and Cultural Exchange, *1828 L St. N.W., #901 20036; (202) 293-6141. Fax, (202) 293-6144. Michael McCarry, executive director. Internet, info@alliance-exchange.org.*

Promotes public policies that support the growth of international exchange between the United States and other countries. Provides professional representation, resource materials, publications, and public policy research for those involved in international exchanges.

American Bar Assn., *International Legal Exchange Program, 1700 Pennsylvania Ave. N.W., #620 20006; (202) 393-7122. Fax, (202) 347-9015. Edison W. Dick, executive director. Internet, ilexewd@aol.com or http://www.abanet.org/intlaw/ilex.html.*

Organizes the exchange of lawyers between the United States and other countries and arranges short-term placements for foreign lawyers with law firms nationwide. Coordinates briefing trips for U.S. lawyers overseas.

American Council of Young Political Leaders, *1612 K St. N.W., #300 20006; (202) 857-0999. Fax, (202) 857-0027. Winston McGregor, executive director. Internet, acypl@erols.com or http://www.acypl.org.*

Bipartisan political education organization that promotes understanding of foreign policy between state and local leaders and their counterparts abroad. Sponsors conferences and political study tours for U.S. and foreign political leaders between the ages of 25 and 41.

Business-Higher Education Forum, *1 Dupont Circle N.W., #800 20036; (202) 939-9345. Fax, (202) 833-4723. Judy Irwin, acting executive director. Internet, bhef@ace.nche.edu or http://www.acenet.edu/programs/bhef.html.*

Membership: chief executive officers of major corporations, colleges, and universities. Promotes the development of industry-university alliances around the world. Provides countries in central and eastern Europe with technical assistance in enterprise development, management training, market economics, education, and infrastructure development.

Center for Intercultural Education and Development, *3307 M St. N.W., #302 (mailing address: P.O. Box 579400, Georgetown University, Washington, DC 20057); (202) 298-0200. Fax, (202) 338-0608. Julio Giulietti SJ, director. Internet, http://www.georgetown.edu/CIED.*

Designs and administers programs aimed at improving the quality of life of economically disadvantaged people; provides technical education, job training, leadership skill development, and business management training; runs programs in Central America, the Caribbean, Central Europe, and Southeast Asia.

Council for International Exchange of Scholars, *3007 Tilden St. N.W., #5L 20008-3009; (202) 686-4000. Fax, (202) 362-3442. Patti McGill Peterson, executive director. Internet, info@ciesnet.cies.org or http://www.cies.org.*

Cooperates with the U.S. Information Agency in administering Fulbright grants for university teaching and advanced research abroad. (Affiliated with the American Council of Learned Societies.)

Delphi International, *1828 L St. N.W., #900 20036; (202) 898-0950. Fax, (202) 842-0885. Nalini Shetty, president. Internet, postmaster@delphi-int.org or http://www.delphi-int.org.*

Assists public and private organizations engaged in international cooperation and business. Works with governments and private counterparts to support foreign professional exchanges. Develops technical training programs and educational curricula for foreign visitors. Provides technical expertise, management support, travel, and business development services.

English-Speaking Union, *15 Dupont Circle, 4th Floor 20036; (202) 234-4602. Fax, (202) 234-4639. Diana Nicholson, executive director. Internet, esu.wdc@erols.com.*

International educational and cultural organization that promotes cultural exchange programs with countries in which English is a major language; offers free English conversational tutoring to persons for whom English is a second language; sponsors scholarships for studies in English-speaking countries; sponsors annual Shakespeare competition among D.C. schools. (Headquarters in New York.)

Foreign Services Research Institute, *2718 Unicorn Lane N.W. (mailing address: P.O. Box 6317, Washington, DC 20015-0317); (202) 362-1588. John E. Whiteford Boyle, president.*

Provides information on American culture to embassies, foreign business firms, and foreign educational establishments. Advises on placement of foreign students; maintains library on U.S. educational and cultural data. Represents the International Academy of Independent Scholars, which aids retired scholars in research, library access, and travel, and the Essentialist Philosophical Society.

Institute of International Education, *1400 K St. N.W., 6th Floor 20005-2403; (202) 898-0600. Fax, (202) 326-7696. Jeanne Thum, administrative officer. Internet, http://www.iie.org.*

Educational exchange, technical assistance, and training organization that arranges professional programs for international visitors; conducts training courses in energy, environment, journalism, human resource development, educational policy and administration, and business-related fields; provides developing countries with short- and long-term technical assistance in human resource development; arranges professional training and support for staff of human rights organizations; sponsors fellowships and applied internships for midcareer professionals from developing countries; implements contracts and cooperative agreements for organizations, including the U.S. Information Agency, Agency for International Development, philanthropic foundations, multilateral banks, and other organizations. (Headquarters in New York.)

International Research and Exchange Board (IREX), *1616 H St. N.W. 20006; (202) 628-8188. Fax, (202) 628-8189. Daniel C. Matuszewski, president. Internet, irex@irex.org or http://www.irex.org.*

Administers academic exchanges between the United States and Russia, the new independent states, central and eastern Europe, Mongolia, and China. Exchange efforts include professional training, institution building, technical assistance, and policy development.

Meridian International Center, *1630 Crescent Pl. N.W. 20009; (202) 667-6800. Fax, (202) 667-1475. Walter L. Cutler, president. Information, (202) 667-6670. Internet, meridian@meridian.org or http://www.meridian.org.*

Conducts international educational and cultural programs; provides foreign visitors and diplomats in the United States with services, including cultural orientation, seminars, and language assistance. Offers world affairs programs and international exhibitions for Americans.

NAFSA: Assn. of International Educators, *1875 Connecticut Ave. N.W., #1000 20009-5728; (202) 462-4811. Fax, (202) 667-3419. Marlene Johnson, executive director. Press, (202) 939-3106. Publications, (800) 836-4994. Internet, inbox@nafsa.org or http://www.nafsa.org.*

Membership: individuals, educational institutions, and others interested in international educational exchange. Seeks to increase awareness of and support for international education in colleges and universities, government, and the community. Provides information on evaluating exchange programs; assists members in complying with federal regulations affecting foreign students and scholars; administers grant programs with an international education focus.

Radio Free Europe/Radio Liberty, Inc., *1201 Connecticut Ave. N.W. 20036-2605; (202) 457-6900. Fax, (202) 457-6992. Jane Lester, corporate secretary. Information, (202) 457-6914. Press, (202) 457-6935. Internet, http://www.rferl.org.*

Independent radio broadcast service funded by federal grants to promote and support democracy. Radio Free Europe broadcasts programs to Bulgaria, the Czech Republic, Estonia, Latvia, Lithuania, Poland, Romania, and Slovakia; programming includes entertainment, news, and specials on political developments in eastern Europe. Radio Liberty broadcasts similar programming to the former Soviet Union. Research materials available to the public by appointment. (Headquarters in Prague.)

Town Affiliation Assn. of the U.S., Inc., *Sister Cities International, 120 S. Payne St., Alexandria, VA 22314; (703) 836-3535. Fax, (703) 836-4815. Juanita Crabb, executive director. Internet, info@sister-cities.org or http://www.sister-cities.org.*

Assists U.S. and foreign cities in establishing formal city-to-city affiliations, including exchanges of people, ideas, and materials; serves as program coordinator and information clearinghouse; sponsors youth programs and scholarships.

World Learning, Inc., *1015 15th St. N.W., #750 20005; (202) 408-5380. Fax, (202) 408-5397. Robert Chase, vice president, Projects in International Development and Training. School for International Training, (800) 451-4465. Summer Abroad, (800) 345-2929. Incoming Hosts and Volunteers, (800) 327-4678. Internet, http://www.worldlearning.org.*

Educational and training organization that administers exchange programs for U.S. and foreign students. Washington office manages development assistance and training grants and contracts for the United Nations, U.S. government agencies, and other donors. Other projects include subgrants to and training for local nongovernmental organizations (particularly in management, project implementation, democratic institution-building, health, and environmental issues) and selected refugee training services. Administers aupair program for American and foreign young people. (Headquarters in Brattleboro, Vt.)

Youth for Understanding, *3501 Newark St. N.W. 20016; (202) 966-6800. Fax, (202) 895-1104. Steve Johnson, president. Toll-free, (800) 424-3691. Internet, info@mail.yfu.org or http://www.yfu.org.*

Educational organization that administers cross-cultural exchange programs for secondary school students. Administers scholarship programs that sponsor student exchanges, including the Congress-Bundestag Scholarship Program.

🏛 IMMIGRATION AND NATURALIZATION

AGENCIES

Administration for Children and Families *(Health and Human Services Dept.), Refugee Resettlement, 901 D St. S.W., 6th Floor 20447; (202) 401-9246. Fax, (202) 401-5487. Lavinia Limon, director.*

Directs a domestic resettlement program for refugees; reimburses states for financial and medical assistance given to refugees; awards funds to private resettlement agencies for providing refugees with cash assistance and case management; provides grants to states and nonprofit agencies for social services, such as employment training and English instruction.

Immigration and Naturalization Service *(Justice Dept.), 425 Eye St. N.W., #7100 20536; (202) 514-1900. Fax, (202) 514-3296. Doris Meissner, commissioner. Press, (202) 514-2648. Form requests, (800) 870-3676. Internet, http://www.ins.usdoj.gov.*

Administers and enforces immigration and naturalization laws relating to the admission, exclusion, deportation, and naturalization of aliens; responsible for preventing illegal entry into the United States; investigates, apprehends, and deports illegal aliens; oversees Border Patrol enforcement activities. Field offices provide aliens with information on application for asylum and U.S. citizenship. *(See Regional Information Sources in appendix.)*

Justice Dept., *950 Pennsylvania Ave. N.W. 20530; (202) 514-2001. Fax, (202) 514-4371. Janet Reno, attorney general. Information, (202) 514-2000. Internet, http://www. usdoj.gov.*

Administers immigration and naturalization laws. Justice Dept. encompasses the Immigration and Naturalization Service, Board of Immigration Appeals, and the Foreign Claims Settlement Commission of the United States.

Justice Dept., *Civil Division, 950 Pennsylvania Ave. N.W., #3143 20530; (202) 514-3301. Fax, (202) 514-8071. Frank W. Hunger, assistant attorney general; Robert L. Bombaugh, immigration litigation director, (202) 616-4900. Internet, http://www.usdoj.gov/civil/civil.html.*

Handles most civil litigation arising under immigration and nationality laws.

Justice Dept., *Executive Office for Immigration Review, 5107 Leesburg Pike, #2400, Falls Church, VA 22041; (703) 305-0169. Fax, (703) 305-0470. Anthony C. Moscato, director.*

Quasi-judicial body separate from the Immigration and Naturalization Service. Interprets immigration laws; conducts hearings and hears appeals on immigration issues.

Justice Dept., *Special Investigations, 1001 G St. N.W., #1000 20530; (202) 616-2492. Fax, (202) 616-2491. Eli M. Rosenbaum, director.*

Identifies Nazi war criminals who illegally entered the United States after World War II. Handles legal action to ensure denaturalization and/or deportation.

Labor Dept., *International Economic Affairs, 200 Constitution Ave. N.W., #S5325 20210; (202) 219-7597. Fax, (202) 219-5071. Jorge Perez-Lopez, director.*

Assists in developing U.S. immigration policy.

State Dept., *Visa Services, 2401 E St. N.W., SA-1 #L-703 20522-0106; (202) 663-1155. Fax, (202) 663-1247. Nancy Sambaiew, deputy assistant secretary. Information, (202) 663-1291. Internet, http://travel.state.gov.*

Supervises visa issuance system, which is administered by U.S. consular offices abroad.

CONGRESS

House Judiciary Committee, *Subcommittee on Immigration and Claims, B370B RHOB 20515; (202) 225-5727. Fax, (202) 225-3672. Lamar Smith, R-Texas, chair; Cordia Strom, counsel. Internet, http://www.house.gov/ judiciary.*

Jurisdiction over immigration and naturalization legislation.

Senate Judiciary Committee, *Subcommittee on Immigration, SD-323 20510; (202) 224-6098. Fax, (202) 228-4506. Spencer Abraham, R-Mich., chair; Lee Lieberman Otis, chief counsel. Internet, http://www.senate.gov/ committee/judiciary.html.*

Jurisdiction over legislation on refugees, immigration, and naturalization. Oversight of the Immigration and Naturalization Service, the U.S. Board of Immigration Appeals, international migration and refugee laws and policies, and private immigration relief bills.

INTERNATIONAL ORGANIZATIONS

International Organization for Migration, *1750 K St. N.W., #1110 20006; (202) 862-1826. Fax, (202) 862-1879. Hans-Petter Boe, chief of mission. Internet, srowashington@iom.int or http://www.iom.int.*

Nonpartisan organization that plans and operates refugee resettlement, national migration, and humanitarian assistance programs at the request of its member governments. Recruits skilled professionals for developing countries. (Headquarters in Geneva.)

NONPROFIT

Alexis de Tocqueville Institution, *American Immigration Institute, 1611 N. Kent St., #901, Arlington, VA 22209; (703) 351-4969. Fax, (703) 351-0090. Merrick Carey, president. Internet, alexisde@aol.com or http:// www.schoolreport.com/adti.*

Works to increase public understanding of the cultural and economic benefits associated with legal immigration. Supports pro-immigration policy reform.

American Immigration Lawyers Assn., *1400 Eye St. N.W., #1200 20005; (202) 371-9377. Fax, (202) 371-9449. Jeanne Butterfield, executive director. Internet, http://www. aila.org.*

Bar association for attorneys interested in immigration law. Provides information and continuing education programs on immigration law and policy; offers workshops and conferences. Monitors legislation and regulations.

Center for Immigration Studies, *1522 K St. N.W., #820 20005-1202; (202) 466-8185. Fax, (202) 466-8076. Mark Krikorian, executive director. Internet, center@cis.org or http://www.cis.org/cis.*

Nonpartisan organization that conducts research and policy analysis of the economic, social, demographic, and environmental impact of immigration on the United States. Sponsors symposiums.

Federation for American Immigration Reform, *1666 Connecticut Ave. N.W., #400 20009; (202) 328-7004. Fax, (202) 387-3447. Daniel A. Stein, executive director. Internet, fair@fairus.org or http://www.fairus.org.*

Organization of individuals interested in immigration reform. Monitors immigration laws and policies.

Immigration and Refugees Services of America, *1717 Massachusetts Ave. N.W. 20036; (202) 347-3507. Fax, (202) 347-3418. Roger P. Winter, executive director. Internet, irsa@irsa-uscr.org.*

Helps immigrants and refugees adjust to American society; assists in resettling recently arrived immigrants and refugees; offers information, counseling services, and temporary living accommodations through its member agencies nationwide; issues publications on immigration law, refugees, and refugee resettlement. Operates U.S. Committee for Refugees, which collects and disseminates information on refugee issues in the United States and abroad. Monitors legislation and regulations.

Lutheran Immigration and Refugee Service, *122 C St. N.W., #125 20001-2172; (202) 783-7509. Fax, (202) 783-7502. Philip G. Anderson, Washington representative. Internet, lirswdc@aol.com or http://www.lirs.org.*

Provides refugees in the United States with resettlement assistance, follow-up services, and immigration counseling. Funds local projects that provide social and legal services to all refugees, including undocumented persons. (Headquarters in New York.)

National Council of La Raza, *1111 19th St. N.W., #1000 20036; (202) 785-1670. Fax, (202) 776-1792. Raul Yzaguirre, president. Internet, http://www.nclr.org.*

Provides research, policy analysis, and advocacy relating to immigration policy and programs. Monitors federal legislation on immigration, legalization, employer sanctions, employment discrimination, and eligibility of immigrants for federal benefit programs. Assists community-based groups involved in immigration and education services and educates employers about immigration laws.

U.S. Catholic Conference, *Migration and Refugee Services, 3211 4th St. N.E. 20017; (202) 541-3352. Fax, (202) 541-3399. Mark Franken, executive director.*

Provides refugees and immigrants with resettlement services and legal counseling; operates training programs for volunteers and professionals; develops and implements USCC policy on migration, immigration, and refugee issues.

See also Institute for Public Representation (p. 70); National Center for Urban Ethnic Affairs (p. 415)

✈ INTERNATIONAL LAW AND AGREEMENTS

See also Intelligence and Counterterrorism (chap. 16)

AGENCIES

Commission on Security and Cooperation in Europe *(Helsinki Commission), 234 Ford Bldg. 20515; (202) 225-1901. Fax, (202) 226-4199. Sen. Alfonse M. D'Amato, R-N.Y., and Rep. Christopher H. Smith, R-N.J., co-chairs; Michael Hathaway, staff director. Internet, http://www.house.gov/csce.*

Independent agency created by Congress. Membership includes individuals from the executive and legislative branches. Monitors and encourages compliance with the Helsinki Accords, a series of agreements with provisions on security, economic, environmental, human rights, and humanitarian issues; conducts hearings; serves as an information clearinghouse for issues in eastern and western Europe, Canada, and the United States relating to the Helsinki Accords.

Federal Bureau of Investigation *(Justice Dept.), International Relations, 935 Pennsylvania Ave. N.W., #7443 20535; (202) 324-5904. Fax, (202) 324-5229. J. Michael di Pretoro, deputy assistant director.*

Supports FBI involvement in international investigations; oversees liaison offices in U.S. embassies abroad. Maintains contacts with other federal agencies; Interpol; foreign police and security officers based in Washington, D.C.; and national law enforcement associations.

Securities and Exchange Commission, *International Affairs, 450 5th St. N.W., Mail Stop 11-4 20549; (202) 942-2770. Fax, (202) 942-9524. Marisa Lago, director.*

Serves as liaison with enforcement and diplomatic officials abroad; seeks to enhance international cooperation in enforcement activities for the securities market; obtains evidence from abroad relating to investigations and litigation. Develops agreements with foreign countries to assist commission enforcement and regulatory efforts.

State Dept., *International Claims and Investment Disputes,* 2430 E St. N.W., #203 20037-2800; (202) 776-8360. Fax, (202) 776-8389. Ronald J. Bettauer, assistant legal adviser.

Handles claims by foreign governments and their nationals against the U.S. government, as well as claims against the State Dept. for negligence under the Federal Tort Claims Act. Administers the Iranian claims program and negotiates agreements with other foreign governments on claims settlements.

State Dept., *Law Enforcement and Intelligence Affairs,* Main State Bldg., #5419 20520; (202) 647-7324. Fax, (202) 647-4802. Samuel Witten, assistant legal adviser.

Negotiates extradition treaties, legal assistance treaties in criminal matters, and other agreements relating to international criminal matters.

State Dept., *Legal Adviser,* Main State Bldg., #6423 20520-6310; (202) 647-9598. Fax, (202) 647-1037. David R. Andrews, legal adviser.

Provides the department with legal advice on international problems; participates in international negotiations; represents the U.S. government in international litigation and in international conferences related to legal issues.

State Dept., *Political-Military Affairs,* Main State Bldg., #7325 20520; (202) 647-9022. Fax, (202) 736-4779. Eric D. Newsom, acting assistant secretary.

Negotiates U.S. military base and operating rights overseas; acts as liaison between the Defense Dept. and State Dept.; controls military travel to sensitive or restricted areas abroad; arranges diplomatic clearance for overflights and ship visits.

State Dept., *Treaty Affairs,* Main State Bldg., #5420 20520; (202) 647-1345. Fax, (202) 736-7541. Robert E. Dalton, assistant legal adviser.

Provides legal advice on treaties and other international agreements, including constitutional questions, drafting, negotiation, and interpretation of treaties and accords; maintains records of treaties and executive agreements.

Technology Administration *(Commerce Dept.),* **International Technology Policy,** 14th St. and Constitution Ave. N.W., #4411 20230; (202) 482-1287. Fax, (202) 219-3310. Phyllis Yoshida, acting director.

Provides information on foreign research and development; coordinates, on behalf of the Commerce Dept., negotiation of international science and technology agreements.

Transportation Dept., *International Aviation,* 400 7th St. S.W., #6402 20590; (202) 366-2423. Fax, (202) 366-3694. Paul L. Gretch, director.

Responsible for international aviation regulation and negotiations, including fares, tariffs, and foreign licenses; represents the United States at international aviation meetings.

Treasury Dept., *International Tax Affairs,* 1500 Pennsylvania Ave. N.W., #1334 20220; (202) 622-2986. Fax, (202) 622-0605. Joseph Guttentag, deputy assistant secretary.

Provides other agencies with technical assistance in international tax matters; negotiates international tax treaties; formulates domestic legislative proposals and reviews tax rules and regulations.

CONGRESS

House International Relations Committee, 2170 RHOB 20515; (202) 225-5021. Fax, (202) 225-2035. Benjamin A. Gilman, R-N.Y., chair; Richard J. Garon Jr., chief of staff. Internet, http://www.house.gov/international_relations.

Jurisdiction over legislation on international law enforcement, including narcotics control; boundaries; international terrorism (jurisdiction shared with House Judiciary Committee); international human rights, including implementation of the Universal Declaration of Human Rights; executive agreements; regional security agreements; protection of Americans abroad, including the Foreign Airports Security Act; embassy security; and United Nations Organizations.

House Judiciary Committee, *Subcommittee on Immigration and Claims,* B370B RHOB 20515; (202) 225-5727. Fax, (202) 225-3672. Lamar Smith, R-Texas, chair; Cordia Strom, counsel. Internet, http://www.house.gov/judiciary.

Jurisdiction over legislation on treaties, conventions, and international agreements; diplomatic immunity; foreign sovereign immunity; and admission and resettlement of refugees.

Senate Foreign Relations Committee, SD-450 20510; (202) 224-4651. Fax, (202) 224-0836. Jesse Helms, R-N.C., chair; James W. "Bud" Nance, staff director. Internet, http://www.senate.gov/committee/foreign.html.

Jurisdiction over legislation on human rights; international boundaries; regional security; executive agreements; international narcotics control; embassy security; international terrorism (jurisdiction shared with Senate Judiciary Committee); and exchange of prisoners with Canada and Mexico.

Senate Foreign Relations Committee, *Subcommittee on International Operations,* SD-450 20510; (202) 224-4651. Fax, (202) 224-0836. Rod Grams, R-Minn., chair; Chris Walker, senior professional staff member. Internet, http://www.senate.gov/committee/foreign.html.

Jurisdiction over legislation dealing with international terrorism; protection of Americans abroad, including the Foreign Airports Security Act; the international flow of illegal drugs; and the United Nations.

Senate Governmental Affairs Committee, *Permanent Subcommittee on Investigations,* SH-432 20510; (202) 224-3721. Fax, (202) 224-7042. Susan Collins, R-Maine, chair; Tim Shea, chief of staff. Internet, http://www.senate.gov/~gov_affairs/psi.htm.

Investigates international narcotics trafficking.

INTERNATIONAL ORGANIZATIONS

INTERPOL *(Justice Dept.),* 600 E St. N.W. (mailing address: U.S. Justice Dept., Washington, DC 20530); (202) 616-9000. Fax, (202) 616-8400. John J. Imhoff, chief. Internet, http://www.usdoj.gov/usncb.

U.S. national central bureau for INTERPOL; acts in international investigations on behalf of U.S. police; coordinates the exchange of investigative information dealing with common law crimes, including drug trafficking, counterfeiting, missing persons, and terrorism; assists with extradition processes. Coordinates law enforcement requests for investigative assistance in the United States and abroad. Serves as liaison between foreign and U.S. law enforcement agencies at federal, state, and local levels. (Headquarters in Lyons, France.)

NONPROFIT

American Arbitration Assn., 8201 Greensboro Dr., #610, McLean, VA 22102; (703) 760-4820. Fax, (703) 760-4847. Arnold B. Crews, regional vice president. Internet, webmaster@adr.org or http://www.adr.org.

Provides dispute resolution services and information. Administers certain international arbitration and mediation systems. (Headquarters in New York.)

American Bar Assn., *International Law and Practice,* 740 15th St. N.W. 20005; (202) 662-1660. Fax, (202) 662-1669. Fletcher Hall, director. Internet, http://www.abanet.org/intlaw/home.html.

Monitors domestic and international policy developments that affect the practice of public and private international law. Conducts seminars and provides information for members.

American Bar Assn., *Standing Committee on World Order Under Law,* 740 15th St. N.W. 20005; (202) 662-1000. Fax, (202) 662-1032. Patricia Hanrahan, director.

Examines legal issues relating to international peace and security, human rights, peaceful resolution of international conflicts, and the United Nations; develops model treaties; makes policy recommendations.

American Society of International Law, 2223 Massachusetts Ave. N.W. 20008; (202) 939-6000. Fax, (202) 797-7133. Charlotte Ku, executive director. Internet, http://www.asil.org.

Membership: lawyers, political scientists, economists, government officials, and students. Conducts research and study programs on international law; sponsors the International Law Students Assn. Library open to the public.

Antarctica Project, 408 C St. N.E. 20002 (mailing address: P.O. Box 76920, Washington, DC 20013); (202) 544-0236. Fax, (202) 544-8483. Beth Clark, director. Internet, antarctica@igc.org or http://www.asoc.org.

Promotes effective implementation of the Antarctic Treaty System; works to protect the environment of the Antarctic continent. Interests include depletion of ozone in polar regions.

Inter-American Bar Assn., 1211 Connecticut Ave. N.W., #202 20036; (202) 393-1217. Fax, (202) 393-1241. Louis Ferrand, secretary general. Internet, iaba@iaba.org or http://www.iaba.org.

Membership: lawyers and bar associations in the Western Hemisphere with associate members in Europe and Asia. Works to promote uniformity of national and international laws; holds conferences; makes recommendations to national governments and organizations. Library open to the public.

World Jurist Assn., 1000 Connecticut Ave. N.W., #202 20036-5302; (202) 466-5428. Fax, (202) 452-8540. Margaret M. Henneberry, executive vice president.

Membership: lawyers, law professors, judges, law students, and nonlegal professionals worldwide. Conducts research; promotes world peace through adherence to international law; holds biennial world conferences. (Affiliates, at same address, include World Assn. of Judges, World Assn. of Law Professors, and World Assn. of Lawyers.)

Americans Abroad

See also Diplomats and Foreign Agents (this chapter); Travel and Tourism (chap. 4)

AGENCIES

Administration for Children and Families *(Health and Human Services Dept.), Repatriate Program,* 901 D St. S.W., 6th Floor 20447; (202) 401-9246. Fax, (202) 401-5487. Lavinia Limon, director.

Administers and operates a repatriation program available to State Dept.-certified U.S. citizens returning from foreign countries because of destitution, illness, or emergencies. Reimburses state and local governments for transportation from port of entry; food, shelter, and clothing; and medical care, including hospitalization.

Foreign Claims Settlement Commission of the United States *(Justice Dept.), 600 E St. N.W., #6002 20579; (202) 616-6975. Fax, (202) 616-6993. Delissa A. Ridgway, chair; Judith H. Lock, administrative officer, (202) 616-6988.*

Processes claims by U.S. nationals against foreign governments for property losses sustained.

State Dept., *American Citizens Services and Crisis Management, Main State Bldg., #4811 20520-4818; (202) 647-9019. Fax, (202) 647-6201. Georgia A. Rogers, director. Recorded consular information, (202) 647-5225.*

Handles matters involving protective services for Americans abroad, including arrests, assistance in death cases, financial assistance, medical emergencies, welfare and whereabouts inquiries, travel warnings and consular information, nationality and citizenship determination, document issuance, judicial and notarial services, estates, property claims, third-country representation, and disaster assistance.

State Dept., *Children's Issues, Main State Bldg., #4811 20520-4800; (202) 647-2688. Fax, (202) 647-2835. Ray Clore, director. Recorded consular information, (202) 736-7000. Fax-on-demand, (202) 647-3000.*

Assists with consular aspects of children's services and fulfills U.S. treaty obligations relating to the abduction of children. Advises foreign service posts on international parental child abduction and transnational adoption.

State Dept., *International Claims and Investment Disputes, 2430 E St. N.W., #203 20037-2800; (202) 776-8360. Fax, (202) 776-8389. Ronald J. Bettauer, assistant legal adviser.*

Handles claims by U.S. government and citizens against foreign governments; handles claims by owners of U.S. flag vessels for reimbursements of fines, fees, licenses, and other direct payments for illegal seizures by foreign governments in international waters under the Fishermen's Protective Act.

State Dept., *Passport Services, Main State Bldg., #6811 20520; (202) 647-5366. Fax, (202) 647-0341. Kenneth Hunter, deputy assistant secretary. Passport information, (900) 225-5674. Internet, http://travel.state.gov.*

Administers passport laws and issues passports. (Most branches of the U.S. Postal Service and most U.S.

district and state courts are authorized to accept applications and payment for passports and to administer the required oath to U.S. citizens. Completed applications are sent from the post office or court to the nearest State Dept. regional passport office for processing.) Maintains a variety of records received from the Overseas Citizens Services, including consular certificates of witness to marriage and reports of birth and death. *(See Regional Information Sources in appendix.)*

State Dept., *Policy Review and Interagency Liaison, Main State Bldg., #4817 20520-4818; (202) 647-3666. Fax, (202) 647-0103. Ed Betancourt, acting director. Recorded consular information, (202) 647-5225.*

Offers guidance concerning the administration and enforcement of laws on citizenship and on the appropriate documentation of Americans traveling and residing abroad; gives advice on legislative matters, including implementation of new laws, and on treaties and agreements; reconsiders the acquisition and loss of U.S. citizenship in complex cases; and administers the overseas federal benefits program.

Boundaries

AGENCIES

Saint Lawrence Seaway Development Corp. *(Transportation Dept.), 400 7th St. S.W., #5424 20590; (202) 366-0118. Fax, (202) 366-7147. David G. Sanders, acting administrator. Information, (202) 366-0091. Internet, http://www.dot.gov/slsdc.*

Operates and maintains the Saint Lawrence Seaway within U.S. territorial limits; conducts development programs and coordinates activities with its Canadian counterpart.

State Dept., *Mexican Affairs, Main State Bldg., #4258 20520-6258; (202) 647-9894. Fax, (202) 647-5752. M. Elizabeth Swope, coordinator, Border Affairs. Internet, http://www.state.gov/www/regions/ara/mexico.html.*

Acts as liaison between the State Dept. and the U.S. section of the International Boundary and Water Commission, United States and Mexico (based in El Paso, Texas), in international boundary and water matters as defined by binational treaties and agreements.

INTERNATIONAL ORGANIZATIONS

International Boundary Commission, United States and Canada, *U.S. Section, 1250 23rd St. N.W., #100 20037; (202) 736-9100. Fax, (202) 736-9015. Thomas Baldini, commissioner.*

Defines and maintains the demarcation of the international boundary line between the United States and Canada. (Canadian section in Ottawa.)

International Joint Commission, United States and Canada, U.S. Section, *1250 23rd St. N.W., #100 20440; (202) 736-9000. Fax, (202) 736-9015. James Chandler, secretary.*

Handles disputes concerning the use of boundary waters; negotiates questions dealing with the rights, obligations, and interests of the United States and Canada along the border; establishes procedures for the adjustment and settlement of questions. (Canadian section in Ottawa.)

Extradition

AGENCIES

Justice Dept., Enforcement Operations, *P.O. Box 7600, Ben Franklin Station 20044-7600; (202) 514-3684. Fax, (202) 514-5143. Frederick D. Hess, director.*

Implements prisoner transfer treaties with foreign countries.

Justice Dept., International Affairs, *1400 New York Ave. N.W., #5100 (mailing address: P.O. Box 27330, Washington, DC 20038); (202) 514-0000. Fax, (202) 514-0080. Frances Fragos Townsend, director.*

Performs investigations necessary for extradition of fugitives from the United States and other nations. Handles U.S. and foreign government requests for legal assistance, including documentary evidence.

State Dept., Law Enforcement and Intelligence Affairs, *Main State Bldg., #5419 20520; (202) 647-7324. Fax, (202) 647-4802. Samuel Witten, assistant legal adviser.*

Negotiates and approves extradition of fugitives between the United States and other nations.

NONPROFIT

Center for National Security Studies, *Gelman Library, 2130 H St. N.W., #701 20037; (202) 994-7060. Fax, (202) 994-7005. Kate Martin, director. Internet, cnss@gwis2.circ.gwu.edu or cnss@nicom.com.*

A project of the Fund for Peace. Monitors and conducts research on extradition, intelligence, national security, and civil liberties.

Fishing/Law of the Sea

AGENCIES

National Oceanic and Atmospheric Administration (Commerce Dept.), National Marine Fisheries Service, *1315 East-West Hwy., Silver Spring, MD 20910; (301) 713-2239. Fax, (301) 713-2258. Rolland A. Schmitten, assistant administrator. Press, (301) 713-2370. Internet, http://kingfish.ssp.nmfs.gov.*

Administers marine fishing regulations, including offshore fishing rights and international agreements.

State Dept., Oceans, Science, and Technology, *Main State Bldg., #5806 20520-7831; (202) 647-2396. Fax, (202) 647-0217. Mary Beth West, deputy assistant secretary.*

Coordinates U.S. negotiations concerning international fishing and oceans issues. Handles both foreign fleets fishing in U.S. waters and U.S. fleets fishing in foreign waters or the open seas.

CONGRESS

House International Relations Committee, *2170 RHOB 20515; (202) 225-5021. Fax, (202) 225-2035. Benjamin A. Gilman, R-N.Y., chair; Richard J. Garon Jr., chief of staff. Internet, http://www.house.gov/international_relations.*

Jurisdiction over legislation concerning international fisheries agreements and Law of the Sea. (Jurisdiction shared with House Resources and House Transportation and Infrastructure committees.)

House Resources Committee, Subcommittee on Fisheries, Conservation, Wildlife, and Oceans, *805 O'Neill Bldg. 20515; (202) 226-0200. Fax, (202) 225-1542. Rep. H. James Saxton, R-N.J., chair; Harry Burroughs, staff director. Internet, http://www.house.gov/resources.*

Jurisdiction over legislation concerning international fisheries agreements and the U.N. Convention on the Law of the Sea. (Jurisdiction shared with House International Relations and House Transportation and Infrastructure committees.)

House Transportation and Infrastructure Committee, Subcommittee on Coast Guard and Maritime Transportation, *507 Ford Bldg. 20515; (202) 226-3552. Fax, (202) 226-2524. Wayne T. Gilchrest, R-Md., chair; Rebecca Dye, counsel. Internet, http://www.house.gov/transportation.*

Jurisdiction over legislation concerning Law of the Sea, including laws and treaties on marine pollution control and abatement. (Jurisdiction shared with House International Relations and House Resources committees.)

Senate Commerce, Science, and Transportation Committee, Subcommittee on Oceans and Fisheries, *SH-428 (mailing address: SD-508, Washington, DC 20510); (202) 224-8172. Fax, (202) 228-0326. Olympia J. Snowe, R-Maine, chair; Clark LeBlanc, professional staffer. Internet, http://www.senate.gov/~commerce.*

Studies issues concerning international fishing laws and Law of the Sea (jurisdiction shared with Senate Foreign Relations Committee). (Subcommittee does not report legislation.)

Senate Foreign Relations Committee, *SD-450 20510; (202) 224-4651. Jesse Helms, R-N.C., chair; James W. "Bud" Nance, staff director. Internet, http://www.senate. gov/committee/foreign.html.*

Oversight of Law of the Sea matters (jurisdiction shared with Senate Commerce, Science, and Transportation Committee).

NONPROFIT

U.S. Tuna Foundation, *1101 17th St. N.W., #609 20036; (202) 857-0610. Fax, (202) 331-9686. David G. Burney, executive director.*

Membership: tuna processors, vessel owners, and fishermen's unions. Provides members with information and research on the tuna industry; offers advice on fisheries to the U.S. delegation to the United Nations Law of the Sea Conference and to other U.S. delegations.

Human Rights

See also Humanitarian Aid (this chapter); Regional Affairs (this chapter)

AGENCIES

Commission on Security and Cooperation in Europe *(Helsinki Commission), 234 Ford Bldg. 20515; (202) 225-1901. Fax, (202) 226-4199. Sen. Alfonse M. D'Amato, R-N.Y. and Rep. Christopher H. Smith, R-N.J., co-chairs; Michael Hathaway, staff director. Internet, http://www.house.gov/csce.*

Independent agency created by Congress. Membership includes individuals from the executive and legislative branches. Monitors and encourages compliance with the human rights provisions of the Helsinki Accords; conducts hearings; serves as an information clearinghouse for human rights issues in eastern and western Europe, Canada, and the United States relating to the Helsinki Accords.

State Dept., *Democracy, Human Rights, and Labor, Main State Bldg., #7802 20520-7812; (202) 647-2126. Fax, (202) 647-5283. John Shattuck, assistant secretary.*

Implements U.S. policies relating to human rights; prepares annual review of human rights worldwide; provides the Immigration and Naturalization Service with advisory opinions regarding asylum petitions.

State Dept., *International Women's Issues, Main State Bldg., #2906 20520; (202) 647-5440. Fax, (202) 647-5337. Theresa Loar, senior coordinator. Internet, http://www. state.gov/www/global/women.*

Works to promote the human rights of women within U.S. foreign policy. Participates in international

organizations and conferences; advises other U.S. agencies; disseminates information. Reports to under secretary for global affairs.

NONPROFIT

Amnesty International USA, *304 Pennsylvania Ave. S.E. 20003; (202) 544-0200. Fax, (202) 546-7142. Stephen Rickard, director, Washington Office. Internet, http://www. amnesty-usa.org.*

International organization that works for the release of men and women imprisoned anywhere in the world for their beliefs, political affiliation, color, ethnic origin, sex, language, or religion, provided they have neither used nor advocated violence. Opposes torture and the death penalty; urges fair and prompt trials for all political prisoners. Library open to the public. (U.S. headquarters in New York.)

Center for Human Rights and Humanitarian Law, *4801 Massachusetts Ave. N.W., #310 20016-8084; (202) 274-4180. Fax, (202) 274-4130. Robert Guitteau, executive director. Internet, http://www.wcl.american.edu/pub/ humright/home.htm.*

Seeks to promote human rights and humanitarian law. Establishes training programs for judges, lawyers, and law schools; assists emerging democracies and other nations in developing laws and institutions that protect human rights; organizes conferences with public and private institutions.

Human Rights Watch, *1522 K St. N.W., #910 20005; (202) 371-6592. Fax, (202) 371-0124. Allyson Collins, associate director. Internet, hrwdc@hrw.org or http://www. hrw.org.*

International, nonpartisan human rights organization that monitors human rights violations worldwide. Subdivided into five regional concentrations—Africa, Americas, Asia, Helsinki (Europe), and Middle East. Coordinates thematic projects on women's rights, arms sales, and prisons. Sponsors fact-finding missions to various countries; publicizes violations and encourages international protests; maintains file on human rights violations. (Headquarters in New York.)

International Assn. of Official Human Rights Agencies, *444 N. Capitol St. N.W., #408 20001; (202) 624-5410. Fax, (202) 624-8185. Linda Burnette, office manager. Internet, http://www.fairhousing.com/iaohra.*

Works with government and human rights agencies worldwide to identify needs common to civil rights enforcement. Offers management training for human rights executives and civil rights workshops for criminal justice agencies; develops training programs in investigative techniques, settlement and conciliation, and legal theory. Serves as an information clearinghouse on human rights laws and enforcement.

International Human Rights Law Group, *1200 18th St. N.W., #602 20036; (202) 822-4600. Fax, (202) 822-4606. Gay McDougall, executive director. Internet, ihrlg@aol.com.*

Public interest law center concerned with promoting and protecting international human rights. Conducts educational programs and conferences; provides information and legal assistance regarding human rights violations; monitors the electoral and judicial process in several countries.

Lawyers Committee for Human Rights, *499 S. Capitol St. S.W., #508 20003; (202) 547-5692. Fax, (202) 543-5999. Elisa Massimino, director. Internet, wdc@lchr.org or http://www.lchr.org.*

Promotes human rights as guaranteed by the International Bill of Human Rights. Mobilizes the legal community to protect the rule of law. (Headquarters in New York.)

Robert F. Kennedy Memorial, *Center for Human Rights, 1367 Connecticut Ave. N.W., #200 20036; (202) 463-7575. Fax, (202) 463-6606. James Silk, executive director. Internet, hrcenter@rfkmemorial.org or http://www.rfkmemorial.org.*

Works to increase awareness of human rights issues among policymakers and the public; initiates programs to ensure international laws protecting human rights are enforced; investigates and publishes reports on tortures, disappearances, extrajudicial executions, and other abuses. Presents annual human rights award.

Narcotics Trafficking

See also Drug Control (chap. 14)

AGENCIES

Defense Dept., *Counter-Narcotics, The Pentagon, #2B913 20318-3000; (703) 695-1476. Fax, (703) 695-1727. Capt. Dennis J. Van Buskirk (USN), chief.*

Responsible for countering the importation of narcotics into the United States.

Defense Dept., *Drug Enforcement Policy and Support, The Pentagon 20301-1510; (703) 695-7996. Fax, (703) 693-7588. Robert J. Newberry, acting deputy assistant secretary.*

Coordinates and monitors Defense Dept. support of civilian drug law enforcement agencies and interagency efforts to detect and monitor the maritime and aerial transit of illegal drugs into the United States. Represents the secretary on drug control matters outside the department.

Drug Enforcement Administration *(Justice Dept.), 700 Army-Navy Dr., Arlington, VA; (202) 307-8000. Fax, (202) 307-7335. Thomas A. Constantine, administrator. Information, (202) 307-7977. Locator, (202) 307-1000. Internet, http://www.usdoj.gov/dea.*

Assists foreign narcotics agents; cooperates with the State Dept., embassies, the Agency for International Development, and international organizations to strengthen narcotics law enforcement and to reduce supply and demand in developing countries; trains and advises narcotics enforcement officers in developing nations.

State Dept., *International Narcotics and Law Enforcement, Main State Bldg., #7333 20520-7512; (202) 647-8464. Fax, (202) 736-4885. Randy Beers, acting assistant secretary.*

Coordinates international drug control activities, including policy development, diplomatic initiatives, bilateral and multilateral assistance for crop control, interdiction and related enforcement activities in producer and transit nations, development assistance, technical assistance for demand reduction, and training for foreign personnel in narcotics enforcement and related procedures.

U.S. Coast Guard *(Transportation Dept.), Operational Law Enforcement, 2100 2nd St. S.W., #3110 20593-0001; (202) 267-1155. Fax, (202) 267-4082. Capt. Anthony S. Tangeman, chief.*

Enforces or assists in the enforcement of federal laws and treaties and other international agreements to which the United States is party, on, over, and under the high seas and waters subject to the jurisdiction of the United States; conducts investigations into suspected violations of such laws and international agreements, including drug smuggling and trafficking.

🌐 INTERNATIONAL TRADE AND DEVELOPMENT

See also Economics and Business (chap. 5); Regional Affairs (this chapter)

AGENCIES

Advisory Committee for Trade Policy and Negotiations *(Executive Office of the President), 600 17th St.*

N.W., #100 20508; (202) 395-6120. Fax, (202) 395-3692. Pate Feltz, director, Public Liaison. Internet, http://www.ustr.gov.

Serves as chief private sector advisory committee for the president, U.S. trade representative, and Congress on all matters concerning U.S. trade policy. Interests include the North American Free Trade Agreement (NAFTA) and the World Trade Organization (WTO).

Agency for International Development, *Center for Trade and Investment Services, 515 22nd St. N.W., #100 20523-0229; (202) 663-2660. Fax, (202) 663-2670. Ken Rogers, contract manager. Toll-free, (800) 872-4348. Internet, ctis@usaid.gov or http://www.info.usaid.gov/business/ctis.*

Provides business information to U.S. and developing country firms, U.S. and foreign government agencies, international organizations, and nonprofit groups. Serves as an information clearinghouse on AID programs and on the economies of developing countries.

Bureau of Export Administration *(Commerce Dept.), 14th St. and Constitution Ave. N.W., #3898 20230; (202) 482-1427. Fax, (202) 482-2387. William Alan Reinsch, under secretary. Information, (202) 482-2721. Export licensing information, (202) 482-4811. Internet, http://www.bxa.doc.gov.*

Administers Export Administration Act; coordinates export administration programs of federal departments and agencies; maintains control lists and performs export licensing for the purposes of national security, foreign policy, and short supply. Monitors impact of foreign boycotts on the United States; ensures availability of goods and services essential to industrial performance on contracts for national defense. Assesses availability of foreign products and technology to maintain control lists and licensing.

Census Bureau *(Commerce Dept.), Foreign Trade, Suitland and Silver Hill Rds., Suitland, MD (mailing address: 4700 Silver Hill Rd., Washington, DC 20233-6700); (301) 457-2203. Fax, (301) 457-2867. C. Harvey Monk Jr., chief. Trade data inquiries, (301) 457-2227. Internet, http://www.census.gov/foreign-trade/www.*

Provides data on all aspects of foreign trade in commodities.

Commerce Dept., *International Investment, 1441 L St. N.W., #7005 20230; (202) 606-9807. Fax, (202) 606-5318. David Belli, chief. Information, (202) 606-9900. Internet, http://www.stat-usa.gov.*

Compiles statistics under the International Investment and Trade in Services Act for an ongoing study of foreign direct investment in the United States and direct investment abroad by the United States.

Economic Development Administration *(Commerce Dept.), Trade Adjustment Assistance, 14th St. and Constitution Ave. N.W., #7315 20230; (202) 482-2127. Fax, (202) 482-0466. Tony Meyer, director.*

Assists U.S. firms in increasing their competitiveness against foreign imports. Certifies eligibility and provides domestic firms and industries adversely affected by foreign trade with technical assistance under provisions of the Trade Act of 1974. Administers twelve regional Trade Adjustment Administrative Centers which offer consulting services to eligible U.S. firms.

Export-Import Bank of the United States, *811 Vermont Ave. N.W. 20571; (202) 565-3500. Fax, (202) 565-3505. James A. Harmon, chair; Jackie M. Clegg, vice chair. Information, (202) 565-3310. Press, (202) 565-3200. TDD, (202) 565-3377. Toll-free hotline, (800) 565-3946; in Washington, D.C., (202) 565-3900. Internet, http://www.exim.gov.*

Independent agency of the U.S. government. Aids in financing exports of U.S. goods and services; offers direct credit to borrowers outside the United States; guarantees export loans made by commercial lenders, working capital guarantees, and export credit insurance; conducts an intermediary loan program. Hotline advises businesses in using U.S. government export programs.

Federal Trade Commission, *Competition, 6th St. and Pennsylvania Ave. N.W., #H380 20580; (202) 326-2390. Fax, (202) 326-3384. Debra A. Valentine, assistant director, International Antitrust.*

Enforces antitrust laws and investigates possible violations involving international cases; seeks voluntary compliance and pursues civil judicial remedies; reviews premerger filings; coordinates activities with Antitrust Division of the Justice Dept.

Foreign Trade Zones Board *(Commerce Dept.), 14th St. and Constitution Ave. N.W., #3716 20230; (202) 482-2862. Fax, (202) 482-0002. Dennis Puccinelli, acting executive secretary. Internet, http://www.ita.doc.gov/import_admin/records.*

Authorizes public and private corporations to establish foreign trade zones to which foreign and domestic goods can be brought without being subject to customs duties.

International Trade Administration *(Commerce Dept.), 14th St. and Constitution Ave. N.W., #3850 20230; (202) 482-2867. Fax, (202) 482-4821. David Aaron, under secretary. Information, (202) 482-3808. Press, (202) 482-3809. Publications, (202) 482-5487. Trade information, (800) 872-8723. Internet, http://www.ita.doc.gov.*

Serves as the focal point of operational responsibilities in nonagricultural world trade. Participates in for-

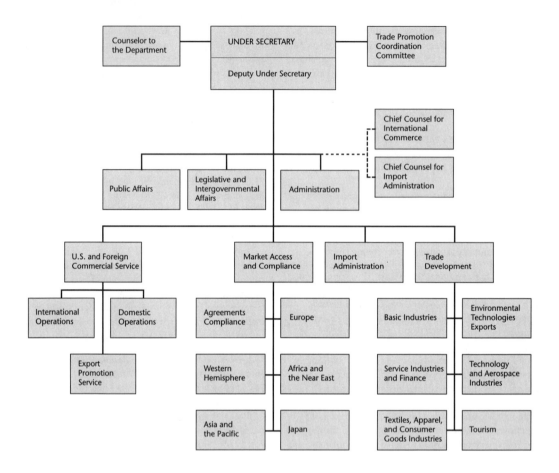

mulating international trade policy and implements programs to promote world trade and strengthen the international trade and investment position of the United States. Library open to the public.

International Trade Administration (*Commerce Dept.*), *Export Promotion Services,* 14th St. and Constitution Ave. N.W., #2810 20230; (202) 482-6220. Fax, (202) 482-2526. Mary Fran Kirchner, deputy assistant secretary. Internet, http://www.ita.doc.gov.

Promotes and directs programs to expand exports abroad; manages overseas trade missions; conducts trade fair certification programs. Participates in trade fairs and technology seminars to introduce American products abroad. Provides the business community with sales and trade information through an automated system, which allows a direct connection between U.S. and overseas offices.

International Trade Administration (*Commerce Dept.*), *Import Administration,* 14th St. and Constitution Ave. N.W., #3099B 20230; (202) 482-1780. Fax, (202) 482-0947. Robert LaRussa, assistant secretary.

Enforces antidumping and countervailing duty statutes if foreign goods are subsidized or sold at less than fair market value. Evaluates and processes applications by U.S. international air- and seaport communities seeking to establish limited duty-free zones. Administers the Statutory Import Program, which governs specific tariff schedules and imports and determines whether property left abroad by U.S. agencies may be imported back into the United States.

International Trade Administration (*Commerce Dept.*), *Market Access and Compliance,* 14th St. and Constitution Ave. N.W., #3868A 20230; (202) 482-3022.

Fax, (202) 482-5444. Franklin J. Vargo, acting assistant secretary. Internet, http://www.ita.doc.gov.

Develops and implements trade and investment policies affecting countries, regions, or international organizations to improve U.S. market access abroad. Provides information and analyses of foreign business and economic conditions to the U.S. private sector; monitors consultation and renegotiation of the MTN (Multilateral Trade Negotiations) affecting specific areas; represents the United States in many other trade negotiations.

International Trade Administration *(Commerce Dept.), NAFTA Office, 14th St. and Constitution Ave. N.W., #3022 20230; (202) 482-0393. Fax, (202) 482-5865. Juliet Bender, director. Fax-on-demand, (202) 482-4464. Internet, http://www.itaiep.doc.gov/nafta/nafta2.htm.*

Coordinates Commerce Dept. activities regarding NAFTA (North American Free Trade Agreement). Maintains, with Latin America office of International Trade Administration, a fax-on-demand system for information on NAFTA and on doing business in Latin America and the Caribbean, including Haiti.

International Trade Administration *(Commerce Dept.), Trade and Economic Analysis, 14th St. and Constitution Ave. N.W., #2815 20230; (202) 482-5145. Fax, (202) 482-4614. Jonathan C. Menes, director. Internet, http://www.ita.doc.gov/tradestats.*

Monitors and analyzes U.S. international trade and competitive performance, foreign direct investment in the United States, and international economic factors affecting U.S. trade; identifies future trends and problems. Annual reports include *U.S. Industrial Outlook,* and *Foreign Direct Investment in the United States: Transactions.* Foreign Trade Reference Room open to the public.

International Trade Administration *(Commerce Dept.), Trade Development, 14th St. and Constitution Ave. N.W., #3832 20230; (202) 482-1461. Fax, (202) 482-5697. Ellis Mottur, acting assistant secretary. Internet, http://www.ita.doc.gov.*

Seeks to strengthen the international competitiveness of U.S. businesses; coordinates export promotion programs and trade missions; compiles and analyzes trade data. Divisions focus on basic industries; service industries and finance; technology and aerospace; textiles, apparel, and consumer goods; tourism; and environmental technologies exports.

International Trade Administration *(Commerce Dept.), Trade Information Center, 14th St. and Constitution Ave. N.W., #7424 20230; (202) 482-0543. Fax, (202) 482-4473. Wendy Smith, director. Toll-free, (800) 872-*

8723. TDD, (800) 833-8723. Internet, tic@ita.doc.gov or http://www.ita.doc.gov.

Counsels U.S. business firms on programs and services provided by the agencies that are members of the Trade Promotion Coordinating Committee to facilitate exports. Agencies include the Agriculture and Commerce departments, Export-Import Bank, OPIC, and AID. *(See Regional Information Sources in appendix.)*

International Trade Administration *(Commerce Dept.), U.S. and Foreign Commercial Service, 14th St. and Constitution Ave. N.W., #3802 20230; (202) 482-5777. Fax, (202) 482-5013. Marjory E. Searing, acting director general. Internet, http://www.ita.doc.gov.*

Promotes the export of U.S. goods and services; protects and advocates U.S. business interests abroad; provides counseling and information on overseas markets, international contacts, and trade promotion.

Justice Dept., *Antitrust Division, 601 D St. N.W., #10024 20530; (202) 514-2464. Fax, (202) 514-4508. Charles S. Stark, chief, Foreign Commerce.*

Acts as the division's liaison with foreign governments and international organizations including the European Union. Works with the State Dept. to exchange information with foreign governments concerning investigations involving foreign corporations and nationals.

National Institute of Standards and Technology *(Commerce Dept.), Technical Standards Activities, Bldg. 820, #164, Gaithersburg, MD 20899; (301) 975-4029. Fax, (301) 963-2871. Samuel Chappell, chief. GATT hotline, (301) 975-4041. National Center for Standards and Certification Information, (301) 975-4040. Internet, http://ts.nist.gov/ts/htdocs/210/215/215.htm.*

Compiles information on proposed foreign technical regulations. Provides recorded information on selected international trade regulation matters from the World Trade Organization secretariat in Switzerland. Maintains National Center for Standards and Certification Information to provide U.S. exporters with information on product standards in foreign countries.

Overseas Private Investment Corp., *1100 New York Ave. N.W. 20527; (202) 336-8400. Fax, (202) 408-9859. George Muñoz; president. Information, (202) 336-8799. Press, (202) 336-8680. Internet, http://www.opic.gov.*

Provides assistance through political risk insurance, direct loans, and loan guarantees to qualified U.S. private investors to support their investments in less developed countries. Offers preinvestment information and counseling. Provides insurance against the risks of inconvertibility of local currency; expropriation; and war, revolution, insurrection, or civil strife.

President's Export Council *(Commerce Dept.),* 14th St. and Constitution Ave. N.W., #2015B 20230; (202) 482-1124. Fax, (202) 482-4452. Sylvia L. Prosak, director.

Advises the president on all aspects of export trade including export controls, promotion, and expansion.

Small Business Administration, *International Trade,* 409 3rd St. S.W., 8th Floor 20416; (202) 205-6720. Fax, (202) 205-7272. Eileen Cassidy, acting assistant administrator. Internet, http://www.sba.gov/oit.

Offers instruction, assistance, and information on exporting through counseling and conferences. Helps businesses gain access to export financing through loan guarantee programs.

State Dept., *Coordinator for Business Affairs,* Main State Bldg., #2318 20520; (202) 647-1625. Fax, (202) 647-3953. Marshal Adair, acting senior coordinator. Internet, http://www.state.gov/www/about_state/business/index.html.

Serves as primary contact in the State Dept. for U.S. businesses. Coordinates efforts to facilitate U.S. business interests abroad, ensures that U.S. business interests are given sufficient consideration in foreign policy, and provides assistance to firms with problems overseas (such as claims and trade complaints). Works with agencies in the Trade Promotion Coordinating Committee to better integrate assistance to U.S. business overseas.

State Dept., *Economic and Business Affairs,* Main State Bldg., #6828 20520; (202) 647-7971. Fax, (202) 647-5713. Alan P. Larson, assistant secretary.

Formulates and implements policies related to U.S. economic relations with foreign countries, including international business practices, trade, finance, investment, development, natural resources, energy, and transportation.

State Dept., *Economic, Business, and Agricultural Affairs,* Main State Bldg., #7256 20520; (202) 647-7575. Fax, (202) 647-9763. Stuart E. Eizenstat, under secretary.

Advises the secretary on formulation and conduct of foreign economic policies and programs, including international monetary and financial affairs, trade, telecommunications, energy, agriculture, commodities, investments, and international transportation issues. Coordinates economic summit meetings.

State Dept., *Economic Sanctions Policy,* Main State Bldg., #3329 20520; (202) 647-5673. Fax, (202) 647-4064. David R. Moran, director.

Develops and implements U.S. foreign policy sanctions of embargo and terrorist listed countries. Coordinates U.S. participation in multilateral strategic trade control and revisions related to the export of strategically

critical high-technology goods. Cooperates with the Commerce, Defense, and Treasury departments regarding export controls.

State Dept., *Investment Affairs,* Main State Bldg., #3336 20520; (202) 736-4247. Fax, (202) 647-0320. Wesley Scholz, director.

Develops U.S. investment policy. Makes policy recommendations regarding multinational enterprises and the expropriation of and compensation for U.S. property overseas. Negotiates bilateral and multilateral investment agreements.

State Dept., *Trade Policy and Programs,* Main State Bldg., #3831A, EB/TPP 20520; (202) 647-2532. Fax, (202) 647-1537. David Marchick, deputy assistant secretary.

Develops and administers policies and programs on international trade, including trade negotiations and agreements, import relief, unfair trade practices, trade relations with developing countries, export development, and export controls (including controls imposed for national security or foreign policy purposes).

Trade Promotion Coordinating Committee, 14th St. and Constitution Ave. N.W., #3051 20230; (202) 482-5455. Fax, (202) 482-4137. William M. Daley, chair; Jeri Jensen-Moran, director.

Coordinates all export promotion and export financing activities of the U.S. government. Comprises representatives from the departments of Commerce, State, Treasury, Defense, Interior, Agriculture, Labor, Transportation, and Energy, OMB, U.S. Trade Representative, Council of Economic Advisers, EPA, Small Business Administration, AID, Export-Import Bank, Overseas Private Investment Corporation, U.S. Trade and Development Agency, and U.S. Information Agency.

Treasury Dept., *Foreign Assets Control,* 1500 Pennsylvania Ave. N.W., Annex Bldg., 2nd Floor 20220; (202) 622-2510. Fax, (202) 622-1657. R. Richard Newcomb, director. Internet, http://www.ustreas.gov/treasury/services/ac/ffac.html.

Has authority under the revised Trading with the Enemy Act, the International Emergency Economic Powers Act, and the United Nations Participation Act to control financial and commercial dealings with certain countries and their foreign nationals in times of war or emergencies. Regulations involving foreign assets control and commercial transactions currently apply in varying degrees to Cuba, Iran, Iraq, Libya, North Korea, and Angola.

Treasury Dept., *International Investment,* 1500 Pennsylvania Ave. N.W., #1136 20220; (202) 622-1860. Fax, (202) 622-0391. Gay Sills Hoar, director.

Advises senior department officials on direct foreign investment.

Treasury Dept., *International Trade*, *1500 Pennsylvania Ave. N.W., #4436 20220; (202) 622-2110. Fax, (202) 622-1731. T. Whittier Warthin, director. Information, (202) 622-2000. Press, (202) 622-2960.*

Formulates Treasury Dept. foreign trade policies and coordinates them with other agencies.

U.S. Customs Service *(Treasury Dept.), 1300 Pennsylvania Ave. N.W., #4.4A 20229; (202) 927-1000. Fax, (202) 927-1390. Samuel H. Banks, acting commissioner. Press, (202) 927-1770. Library, (202) 927-1350. Internet, http://www.customs.ustreas.gov.*

Assesses and collects duties and taxes on imported merchandise; processes persons and baggage entering the United States; collects import and export data for international trade statistics; controls export carriers and goods to prevent fraud and smuggling. Library open to the public.

U.S. Customs Service *(Treasury Dept.), Trade Compliance, 1300 Pennsylvania Ave. N.W., #5.2A 20229; (202) 927-0300. Fax, (202) 927-1096. Philip Metzger, director. Internet, http://www.customs.ustreas.gov.*

Enforces compliance with all commercial import requirements; collects import statistics; assesses and collects countervailing and antidumping duties after determinations have been made by the Commerce Dept. in conjunction with the U.S. International Trade Commission.

U.S. International Trade Commission, *500 E St. S.W. 20436; (202) 205-2000. Fax, (202) 205-2338. Marcia E. Miller, chair, (202) 205-2021; Lynn M. Bragg, vice chair, (202) 205-2250. Press, (202) 205-1819. Internet, http://www.usitc.gov.*

Provides Congress, the president, and government agencies with technical information and advice on trade and tariff matters; helps develop uniform statistics on imports, exports, and domestic production. Assists in antidumping and countervailing duty investigations; directs actions against certain unfair trade practices, such as intellectual property infringement; works to establish an international harmonized commodity code. Library open to the public.

U.S. Trade and Development Agency, *1621 N. Kent St., #300, Rosslyn, VA 22209; (703) 875-4357. Fax, (703) 875-4009. J. Joseph Grandmaison, director; Nancy D. Frame, deputy director. Internet, info@tda.gov, http://www.tda.gov.*

Assists U.S. companies exporting to developing and middle income countries. Provides technical assistance

and identifies commercial opportunities in these countries.

U.S. Trade Representative *(Executive Office of the President), 600 17th St. N.W., #209 20508; (202) 395-6890. Fax, (202) 395-4549. Charlene Barshefsky, U.S. trade representative. Information, (202) 395-3230. Internet, http://www.ustr.gov.*

Serves as principal adviser to the president and primary trade negotiator on international trade policy. Develops and coordinates U.S. trade policy including commodity and direct investment matters; import remedies; East-West trade policy; U.S. export expansion policy; and the implementation of MTN (Multilateral Trade Negotiations) agreements. Conducts international trade negotiations and represents the United States in World Trade Organization (WTO) matters.

U.S. Trade Representative *(Executive Office of the President), Investment and Services Policy Advisory Committee, 600 17th St. N.W., #100 20508; (202) 395-6120. Fax, (202) 395-3692. William Daley Jr., liaison. Internet, http://www.ustr.gov.*

Advises the U.S. trade representative on direct investment and service industry issues relating to international trade. Focus includes operations of multinational enterprise, international investment agreements, and planning of future bilateral and multilateral negotiations. Analyzes the effect of international trade policies on manufacturing, labor, agriculture, and service industries.

CONGRESS

House Appropriations Committee, *Subcommittee on Commerce, Justice, State, and Judiciary, H309 Capitol 20515; (202) 225-3351. Harold Rogers, R-Ky., chair; Jim Kulikowski, staff director. Internet, http://www.house.gov/appropriations.*

Jurisdiction over legislation to appropriate funds for the Commerce Dept., the Office of the U.S. Trade Representative, and the International Trade Commission.

House Commerce Committee, *Subcommittee on Telecommunications, Trade, and Consumer Protection, 2125 RHOB 20515; (202) 225-2927. Fax, (202) 225-1919. W. J. "Billy" Tauzin, R-La., chair; James E. Derderian, staff director. Internet, http://www.house.gov/commerce.*

Jurisdiction over legislation on foreign investment in the United States (jurisdiction shared with House International Relations Committee).

House Government Reform and Oversight Committee, *Subcommittee on National Economic Growth, Natural Resources, and Regulatory Affairs, B377 RHOB 20515; (202) 225-4407. Fax, (202) 225-2441. David M.*

McIntosh, R-Ind., chair; Mildred Webber, staff director. Internet, http://www.house.gov/reform.

Jurisdiction over operations of the Export-Import Bank, Overseas Private Investment Corp., U.S. International Trade Commission, and the Office of the U.S. Trade Representative. (Some jurisdictions shared with House International Relations Committee.)

House International Relations Committee, *Subcommittee on International Economic Policy and Trade,* 702 O'Neill Bldg. 20515; (202) 225-3345. Fax, (202) 225-0432. Ileana Ros-Lehtinen, R-Fla., chair; Mauricio Tamargo, staff director. Internet, http://www.house.gov/international_relations.

Jurisdiction over legislation on foreign investment in the United States (shares jurisdiction with House Commerce Committee) and foreign trade, including activities of U.S. firms abroad, the Export Administration Act, the International Emergency Economic Powers Act, the Overseas Private Investment Corp., and the revised Trading with the Enemy Act, which authorizes trade restrictions. Oversees the Export-Import Bank of the United States, international financial and monetary institutions, and customs. (Some jurisdictions shared with House Government Reform and Oversight Committee.)

House Small Business Committee, *Subcommittee on Tax, Finance, and Exports,* B363 RHOB 20515; (202) 226-2630. Fax, (202) 225-8950. Donald Manzullo, R-Ill., chair; Philip D. Eskeland, staff director.

Jurisdiction over legislation on export expansion as it relates to the small-business community.

House Ways and Means Committee, *Subcommittee on Oversight,* 1136 LHOB 20515; (202) 225-7601. Fax, (202) 225-9680. Nancy L. Johnson, R-Conn., chair; William McKenney, staff director. Internet, http://www.house.gov/ways_means.

Oversees the U.S. Customs Service.

House Ways and Means Committee, *Subcommittee on Trade,* 1104 LHOB 20515; (202) 225-6649. Fax, (202) 226-0158. Philip M. Crane, R-Ill., chair; Thelma Askey, staff director. Internet, http://www.house.gov/ways_means.

Jurisdiction over legislation on tariffs, trade, and customs. Authorizes budgets for the U.S. Customs Service, U.S. International Trade Commission, and the Office of the U.S. Trade Representative.

Joint Economic Committee, SD-G01 20510; (202) 224-5171. Fax, (202) 224-0240. Rep. H. James Saxton, R-N.J., chair; Chris Firenze, executive director. Internet, http://www.senate.gov/committee/jec.html.

Studies and makes recommendations on international economic policy and programs, trade, and foreign investment policy; monitors economic policy in foreign countries.

Senate Appropriations Committee, *Subcommittee on Commerce, Justice, State, and Judiciary,* SR-393 20510; (202) 224-7277. Judd Gregg, R-N.H., chair, (202) 224-3324; Vas Alexopoulos, legislative assistant. Chair's fax, (202) 224-4952. Internet, http://www.senate.gov/~appropriations.

Jurisdiction over legislation to appropriate funds for the Commerce Dept., the Office of the U.S. Trade Representative, International Trade Commission, and other international economics-related agencies, services, and programs.

Senate Banking, Housing, and Urban Affairs Committee, *Subcommittee on International Finance,* SD-534 20510; (202) 224-7391. Fax, (202) 224-5137. Rod Grams, R-Minn., chair; Dave Berson, staff director. Internet, http://www.senate.gov/~banking.

Jurisdiction over legislation on international monetary and exchange rate policies, international capital flows, foreign investments in the United States, export control, foreign trade promotion, the Export-Import Bank, the Export Administration Act, and the revised Trading with the Enemy Act, which authorizes trade restrictions (some jurisdictions shared with Senate Finance and Foreign Relations committees).

Senate Finance Committee, *Subcommittee on International Trade,* SD-219 20510; (202) 224-4515. Fax, (202) 224-5920. Charles E. Grassley, R-Iowa, chair; Grant Aldonas, staff contact. Internet, http://www.senate.gov/~finance.

Holds hearings on tariff and trade legislation; oversees the U.S. Customs Service.

Senate Foreign Relations Committee, *Subcommittee on International Economic Policy, Export, and Trade Promotion,* SR-346 20510; (202) 224-4224. Fax, (202) 228-0436. Chuck Hagel, R-Neb., chair; Ken Peel, senior professional staff member. Internet, http://www.senate.gov/committee/foreign.html.

Jurisdiction over legislation to encourage foreign trade and to protect American business interests abroad. Jurisdiction over legislation affecting multinational corporations; balance of payments; the African Development Bank; the World Bank; the Asian Development Bank; the Inter-American Development Bank; the Overseas Private Investment Corp.; the Trade Development Agency; the International Monetary Fund, the Export-Import Bank, and other international monetary organizations; international economic and monetary policy as it relates to U.S. foreign policy (jurisdiction shared with the Senate Finance and Senate Banking, Housing, and Urban Affairs committees).

Senate Small Business Committee, *SR-428A 20510; (202) 224-5175. Fax, (202) 224-4885. Christopher S. Bond, R-Mo., chair; Louis Taylor, staff director. Internet, http://www.senate.gov/~sbc.*

Jurisdiction over legislation on export expansion as it relates to the small-business community.

JUDICIARY

U.S. Court of Appeals for the Federal Circuit, *717 Madison Pl. N.W. 20439; (202) 633-6556. Fax, (202) 633-6353. Haldane Robert Mayer, chief judge; Jan Horbaly, clerk, (202) 633-9613. Electronic bulletin board, (202) 633-9608 or (202) 786-6584.*

Reviews decisions of U.S. Court of International Trade (located in New York) on classifications of and duties on imported merchandise; settles legal questions about unfair practices in import trade (such as antidumping cases) found by the U.S. International Trade Commission and on import duties found by the Commerce Dept.

INTERNATIONAL ORGANIZATIONS

European Union, *Press and Public Affairs, 2300 M St. N.W. 20037; (202) 862-9500. Fax, (202) 429-1766. Hugo Paemen, ambassador; Soren Sondergaard, acting director. Press, (202) 862-9540. Internet, http://www.eurunion.org or http://www.europa.eu.int.*

Information and public affairs office in the United States for the European Union, which includes the European Economic Community, the European Coal and Steel Community, and the European Atomic Energy Community. Provides commercial policy data on the European Union and provides information and documents on member countries, including economic, development and cooperation, industry, and technology data. Library open to the public by appointment. (Headquarters in Brussels.)

Food and Agriculture Organization of the United Nations, *Liaison Office for North America, 2175 K St. N.W., #300 20437; (202) 653-2400. Fax, (202) 653-5760. Charles H. Riemenschneider, director. Library, (202) 653-2402. Internet, http://www.fao.org.*

Serves as the main forum of the international community on world food, agriculture, fisheries, and forestry problems; provides developing nations with technical assistance to improve and increase agricultural productivity. Library open to the public by appointment. (International headquarters in Rome.)

Inter-American Development Bank, *1300 New York Ave. N.W. 20577; (202) 623-1100. Fax, (202) 623-1799. Enrique V. Iglesias, president; Vacant, U.S. executive director, (202) 623-1031. Information, (202) 623-1000. Press, (202) 623-1371. Library, (202) 623-3211. Internet, http://www.iadb.org.*

Promotes, through loans and technical assistance, the investment of public and private capital in member countries for social and economic development purposes. Facilitates economic integration of the Latin American region. Library open to the public by appointment.

International Bank for Reconstruction and Development (World Bank), *1818 H St. N.W. 20433; (202) 477-1234. Fax, (202) 522-3433. James D. Wolfensohn, president; Jan Piercy, U.S. executive director, (202) 458-0110. Press, (202) 473-6599. Publications, (202) 473-1155. Internet, http://www.worldbank.org.*

International development institution funded by membership subscriptions and borrowings on private capital markets. Encourages the flow of public and private foreign investment into developing countries through loans and technical assistance; collects data on selected economic indicators, world trade, and external public debt. Finances economic development projects in agriculture, environmental protection, education, public utilities, telecommunications, water supply, sewerage, public health, and other areas.

International Centre for Settlement of Investment Disputes, *1818 H St. N.W. 20433; (202) 458-1601. Fax, (202) 477-5828. Ibrahim F. I. Shihata, secretary general. Information, (202) 477-1234. Internet, http://www.worldbank.org/html/extdr/glance.html.*

World Bank affiliate that handles the conciliation and arbitration of investment disputes between contracting states and foreign investors.

International Development Assn., *1818 H St. N.W. 20433; (202) 477-1234. Fax, (202) 522-2632. James D. Wolfensohn, president. Press, (202) 473-1782. Internet, http://www.worldbank.org.*

Affiliate of the World Bank funded by membership contributions and transfers of funds from the World Bank. Extends interest-free credits to poorest member countries for high-priority development projects.

International Monetary Fund (IMF), *Statistics, 1825 Eye St. N.W. (mailing address: 700 19th St. N.W., Washington, DC 20431); (202) 623-6180. Fax, (202) 623-6220. Carol S. Carson, director. Publications, (202) 623-7430.*

Publishes monthly *International Financial Statistics (IFS),* which includes comprehensive financial data for most countries, and *Direction of Trade Statistics,* a quarterly publication, which includes the distribution of exports and imports for 152 countries. Annual statistical publications include the *Balance of Payments Statistics Yearbook, Direction of Trade Statistics Yearbook,* the *Government Finance Statistics Yearbook,* and the *International Financial Statistics Yearbook.* Subscriptions available to the public. IFS also is available on CD-ROM.

Organization for Economic Cooperation and Development (OECD), *2001 L St. N.W., #650 20036; (202) 785-6323. Fax, (202) 785-0350. William Danvers, head, Washington Center. Internet, http://www.oecdwash. org.*

Membership: twenty five nations including Australia, Canada, Japan, Mexico, New Zealand, the United States, and Western European nations. Funded by membership contributions. Serves as a forum for members to exchange information and coordinate their economic policies; compiles statistics. Washington Center sells OECD publications and software; maintains reference library that is open to the public. (Headquarters in Paris.)

United Nations Information Centre, *1775 K St. N.W., #400 20006; (202) 331-8670. Fax, (202) 331-9191. Joe Sills, director. Internet, http://www.un.org.*

Lead United Nations office in Washington. Center for reference publications of the U.N.; publications include statistical compilations on international trade and development, national accounts, growth of world industry, and demographic statistics. Library open to the public.

NONPROFIT

American League for Exports and Security Assistance, *122 C St. N.W., #310 20001; (202) 783-0051. Fax, (202) 737-4727. Toby Roth Jr., executive vice president. Internet, alesa@erols.com.*

Membership: defense related and high-technology companies. Supports government policies which promote the export of defense related goods consistent with U.S. security interests.

Assn. of Foreign Investors in U.S. Real Estate, *700 13th St. N.W., #950 20005; (202) 434-4510. Fax, (202) 434-4509. James A. Fetgatter, chief executive. Internet, chane@afire.org.*

Represents foreign institutions that are interested in the laws, regulations, and economic trends affecting the U.S. real estate market. Informs the public and the government of the contributions foreign investment makes to the U.S. economy. Examines current issues and organizes seminars for members.

Assn. of Women in International Trade, Inc., *P.O. Box 65962 20035; (202) 785-9842. Mary Alexander, president, (202) 223-2575. Internet, http://www.embassy. org/wiit.*

Membership: women and men from all sectors concerned with international trade, including import-export firms, government, corporations, and nonprofit organizations. Provides members with opportunities for professional development. Maintains job bank.

Business Alliance for International Economic Development, *601 13th St. N.W., #900-S 20005; (202) 783-5588. Fax, (202) 783-5595. Terrence L. Bracy, executive director. Internet, http://www.milcom.com/alliance.*

Studies the relation between foreign economic assistance and the expansion of U.S. exports and jobs. Supports proper implementation of foreign aid by the U.S. government and multilateral development banks.

Center for International Private Enterprise, *1615 H St. N.W., #207 20062-2000; (202) 463-5901. Fax, (202) 887-3447. Willard Workman, vice president. Internet, cipe@cipe.org or http://www.cipe.org.*

Works to strengthen private voluntary business organizations worldwide and to promote participation in the formation of public policy. Cooperates with local, national, regional, and multilateral institutions promoting private enterprise. (Affiliate of the U.S. Chamber of Commerce.)

Coalition for Employment Through Exports, *1100 Connecticut Ave. N.W., #910 20036-4101; (202) 296-6107. Fax, (202) 296-9709. Edmund B. Rice, executive director.*

Alliance of governors and representatives of business and organized labor. Works to ensure adequate lending authority for the Export-Import Bank and other trade finance facilities as well as aggressive export financing policies for the United States.

Consumers for World Trade, *2000 L St. N.W., #200 20036; (202) 785-4835. Fax, (202) 416-1734. Doreen L. Brown, president.*

Consumer organization that advocates open and competitive trade policies. Represents consumer views in the formulation of foreign trade policy.

Economic Strategy Institute, *1401 H St. N.W., #750 20005; (202) 289-1288. Fax, (202) 289-1319. Clyde V. Prestowitz Jr., president. Internet, esidc@aol.com or http://www.econstrat.com/econstrat.*

Works to increase U.S. economic competitiveness through research on domestic and international economic policies, industrial and technological developments, and global security issues. Testifies before Congress and government agencies.

Emergency Committee for American Trade,
1211 Connecticut Ave. N.W., #801 20036; (202) 659-5147. Fax, (202) 659-1347. Calman J. Cohen, president.

Membership: U.S. corporations and banks interested in international trade and investment. Supports open trade and opposes restrictions on U.S. exports and imports.

Federation of International Trade Assns.,
1851 Alexander Bell Dr., Reston, VA 22091; (703) 620-1588. Fax, (703) 391-0159. Nelson T. Joyner, chair. Toll-free fax, (800) 926-FITA. Internet, FITA@mcimail.com or http://www.fita.org.

Membership: local, regional, and national trade associations throughout the United States that have an international mission. Works to increase U.S. exports.

G7 Council, *1133 Connecticut Ave. N.W., #901 20036; (202) 223-0774. Fax, (202) 861-0790. Josef Neusser and Manuel Johnson, co-chairs.*

Membership: international economic policy experts and business leaders, including former G7 officials. Advocates promoting the international economy over national economies. Promotes cooperation and coordination among the G7 countries and other industrial nations.

Institute for International Economics, *11 Dupont Circle N.W., 6th Floor 20036; (202) 328-9000. Fax, (202) 328-5432. C. Fred Bergsten, director. Internet, http://www. iie.com.*

Conducts studies and makes policy recommendations on international monetary affairs, trade, investment, energy, exchange rates, commodities, and North-South and East-West economic relations.

International Management and Development Institute, *1615 L St. N.W., #900 20036; (202) 337-1022. Fax, (202) 337-6678. Don Bonker, president. Internet, imdimail@aol.com.*

Educational organization that works to improve government-business understanding and international economic and trade cooperation worldwide through policy seminars and research on international economic and trade issues.

International Trade Commission Trial Lawyers Assn., *601 13th St. N.W. 20005; (202) 626-6361. Fax, (202) 783-2331. Judith Oken, executive director. Internet, admin@itctla.org or http://www.itctla.org.*

Disseminates information relating to practice before the U.S. International Trade Commission. Monitors and comments on proposed legislation on trade and intellectual property issues.

National Assn. of Manufacturers, *Economic Policy, 1331 Pennsylvania Ave. N.W., #600 20004-1790; (202) 637-3144. Fax, (202) 637-3182. Howard Lewis III, vice president.*

Represents manufacturing business interests on international economic issues, including trade and technology, international investment and financial affairs, and multinational corporations.

National Assn. of State Development Agencies, *750 1st St. N.E., #710 20002-4241; (202) 898-1302. Fax, (202) 898-1312. Miles Friedman, executive director. Internet, http://www.ids.net/nasda.*

Membership: directors of state economic development agencies. Assists member agencies in encouraging direct capital investment by foreign firms intending to manufacture goods in the United States. Aids in development of export promotion strategies.

National Customs Brokers and Forwarders Assn. of America, *1200 18th St. N.W., #901 20036; (202) 466-0222. Fax, (202) 466-0226. Eric Scharf, executive vice president. Internet, staff@ncbfaa.org or http://www. ncbfaa.org.*

Membership: customs brokers and freight forwarders in the United States. Fosters information exchange within the industry. Monitors legislation and regulations.

National Foreign Trade Council, *1625 K St. N.W., #1090 20006; (202) 887-0278. Fax, (202) 452-8160. Frank D. Kittredge, president.*

Membership: U.S. companies engaged in international trade and investment. Advocates open international trading, export expansion, and policies to assist U.S. companies competing in international markets. Provides members with information on international trade topics. Sponsors seminars and conferences.

National Policy Assn., *1424 16th St. N.W., #700 20036; (202) 265-7685. Fax, (202) 797-5516. Malcolm R. Lovell Jr., president. Internet, npa@npa1.org or http://www. npa1.org.*

Research organization that conducts studies and makes policy recommendations on international economic issues, including international trade, investment, monetary policy, and U.S. economic competitiveness.

Overseas Development Council, *1875 Connecticut Ave. N.W., #1012 20009-5728; (202) 234-8701. Fax, (202) 745-0067. John W. Sewell, president. Internet, http://www. odc.org.*

Research and educational organization that encourages review of U.S. policy toward developing nations by the business community, educators, policymakers, specialists, the public, and the media. Library open to the public by appointment.

United States Council for International Business, *1015 15th St. N.W., #975 20005-2605; (202) 371-1316. Fax, (202) 371-8249. Timothy Deal, senior vice president. Internet, http://www.uscib.org.*

Membership: multinational corporations, service companies, law firms, and business associations. Represents U.S. business positions before intergovernmental bodies, foreign governments, and business communities. Promotes an open system of world trade, finance, and investment. (Headquarters in New York.)

U.S. Chamber of Commerce, *International Policy, 1615 H St. N.W., #207 20062-2000; (202) 463-5455. Fax, (202) 463-3114. Willard Workman, vice president. Information, (202) 463-5460. Internet, ipolicy@uschamber.com.*

Provides liaison with network of American chambers of commerce abroad; administers multilateral business councils; responsible for international economic policy development; informs members of developments in international affairs, business economics, and trade; sponsors seminars and conferences.

Washington International Trade Assn., *2025 Eye St. N.W., #822 20006; (202) 293-4193. Fax, (202) 293-4194. Pam Slater, executive director. Internet, http://www.wita.org.*

Membership: trade professionals. Conducts programs and provides forums to discuss international trade issues; works to expand exports. Monitors legislation and regulations.

See also Atlantic Council of the United States (p. 253)

Development Assistance

See also Humanitarian Aid (this chapter); World Food Assistance (chap. 2)

AGENCIES

Agency for International Development, *1300 Pennsylvania Ave. N.W., #609-010 20523; (202) 712-4040. Fax, (202) 216-3237. J. Brian Atwood, administrator. Information, (202) 712-4300. Press, (202) 712-4320. Internet, http://www.info.usaid.gov.*

Provides developing countries and the nations of central and eastern Europe with economic assistance and disaster relief. Assists with transnational problems. Promotes free markets and economic growth, sound envi-

ronmental policies, and natural resource management. Maintains economic, social, and demographic data for the developing countries of Africa, Central and South America, Asia, and the Near East.

Agency for International Development, *Center for Human Capacity Development, 1300 Pennsylvania Ave. N.W., #3.09-091 20523-3901; (202) 712-4273. Fax, (202) 716-3229. Emily Vargas-Baron, director.*

Administers the AID Participant Training Program, which provides students and midcareer professionals from developing countries with academic and technical training; the Entrepreneur International Initiative, a short-term training/trade program that matches developing country entrepreneurs with American counterparts to familiarize them with American goods, services, and technology; and the Girls' and Women's Education Initiative, which promotes women's literacy in developing countries by increasing girls' attendance and completion of primary school.

Agency for International Development, *Global Programs, Field Support, and Research Bureau, 1300 Pennsylvania Ave. N.W., #3.09 20523-3901; (202) 712-1479. Fax, (202) 216-3235. Sally Shelton, assistant administrator.*

Administers grants to research and educational institutions for development of foreign assistance programs. Divisions focus on economic growth (including business, agriculture, microenterprise development, and insititutional reform); the environment (including energy use); population, health, and nutrition; democracy and governance; human capacity development (including education and training); and women in development.

Foreign Agricultural Service *(Agriculture Dept.), 1400 Independence Ave. S.W., #5071 20250-1000; (202) 720-5691. Fax, (202) 690-2159. Christopher E. Goldthwait, general sales manager. Information, (202) 720-7115. TDD, (202) 690-4879. Internet, http://www.fas.usda.gov.*

Administers the U.S. foreign food aid program with the Agency for International Development. Responsible for Title I of the Food for Peace program, the Food for Progress program, and the Section 416(b) program, which provides developing countries with surplus commodities.

Peace Corps, *1990 K St. N.W. 20526; (202) 606-3970. Fax, (202) 606-4458. Mark D. Gearan, director; Charles R. Baquet III, deputy director. Press, (202) 606-3010. Locator, (202) 606-3886. Toll-free, (800) 424-8580. Internet, http://www.peacecorps.gov.*

Promotes world peace and mutual understanding between the United States and developing nations. Administers volunteer programs in developing nations to provide assistance in education, the environment, health, small business development, agriculture, and urban development.

State Dept., *Development Finance, Main State Bldg., #3425 20520-5820; (202) 647-9426. Fax, (202) 647-5585. Joyce Rabens, director.*

Provides liaison between the International Bank for Reconstruction and Development (World Bank), regional development banks, and the U.S. Export-Import Bank to facilitate U.S. assistance to developing nations. Helps to formulate State Dept. and U.S. government positions on multilateral lending.

Treasury Dept., *Multilateral Development Banks, 1500 Pennsylvania Ave. N.W., #5400 20220; (202) 622-1231. Fax, (202) 622-1228. Joe Eichenberger, director. Information, (202) 622-1810.*

Provides support for U.S. participation in multilateral development banks: the World Bank Group, the Inter-American Development Bank, the African Development Bank/Fund, the Asian Development Bank, and the European Bank for Reconstruction and Development.

U.S. International Development Cooperation Agency, *Main State Bldg., 320 21st St. N.W. 20523; (202) 647-8578. Fax, (202) 647-1770. J. Brian Atwood, director. Information, (202) 647-4000. Press, (202) 647-4274.*

Independent agency that includes the Agency for International Development (AID) and the Overseas Private Investment Corporation (OPIC). Formulates U.S. international policies affecting developing nations; coordinates U.S.-supported bilateral and multilateral development assistance activities; responsible for development aspects of U.S. participation in international organizations, including United Nations development programs; shares with the Treasury Dept. responsibility for U.S. participation in multilateral development banks such as the World Bank; shares with the Agriculture Dept. responsibility for the Food for Peace program.

INTERNATIONAL ORGANIZATIONS

United Nations Development Programme, *1775 K St. N.W., #420 20006; (202) 331-9130. Fax, (202) 331-9363. Roy D. Morey, director, Washington Office. Internet, http://www.undp.org.*

Funded by voluntary contributions from member nations and by nonmember recipient nations. Administers and coordinates technical assistance programs provided through the United Nations system. Seeks to increase economic and social development in developing nations. (Headquarters in New York.)

NONPROFIT

Academy for Educational Development, *1875 Connecticut Ave. N.W., #900 20009; (202) 884-8000. Fax, (202) 884-8400. Monica Ruiz-Casares, research associate. Internet, http://www.aed.org.*

Distributes information on basic education programs in developing countries and on education-related issues.

Adventist Development and Relief Agency International, *12501 Old Columbia Pike, Silver Spring, MD 20904; (301) 680-6380. Fax, (301) 680-6370. Ralph S. Watts Jr., president. Toll-free, (800) 424-2372. Press, (301) 680-6340. Library, (301) 680-5127.*

Worldwide humanitarian agency of the Seventh-day Adventist church. Works to alleviate poverty in developing countries and responds to disasters. Sponsors activities that improve health, foster economic and social well-being, and build self-reliance. Library open to the public by appointment.

Alliance for Communities in Action, *P.O. Box 30154, Bethesda, MD 20824-0154; (301) 229-7707. Fax, (301) 229-0457. Richard Schopfer, executive director.*

Collaborates with local and international development organizations to promote self-help projects for small Latin American communities and small-business projects for skilled workers. Provides funding, technical assistance, and supplies for health, housing, food production, and water projects. Promotes microenterprise development projects.

Ashoka: Innovators for the Public, *1700 N. Moore St., #1920, Arlington, VA 22209; (703) 527-8300. Fax, (703) 527-8383. William Drayton, president. Internet, info@ashoka.org or http://www.ashoka.org.*

Supports fellowships for individuals with ideas for social change in developing nations. Provides fellows with research support, organizational networking, legal counseling, and business consulting. Seeks to educate the public about the developing world and the work of its fellows.

Assn. for the Advancement of Policy, Research, and Development in the Third World, *1730 K St. N.W., #304 20006; (202) 296-0947. Fax, (202) 331-3759. Mekki Mtewa, executive director.*

Serves as a forum for the exchange of scientific and technological information to aid developing countries; conducts research; sponsors workshops, seminars, and an annual conference on international development.

CARE, *1625 K St. N.W., #200 20006; (202) 223-2277. Fax, (202) 296-8695. Marianne Leach, executive director. Internet, info@care.org or http://www.care.org.*

Assists the developing world's poor through emergency assistance and community self-help programs that focus on sustainable development, agriculture, agroforestry, water and sanitation, health, family planning, and income generation. (U.S. headquarters in Atlanta; international headquarters in Brussels.)

Center for Intercultural Education and Development, *3307 M St. N.W., #302 (mailing address: P.O. Box 579400, Georgetown University, Washington, DC 20057); (202) 298-0200. Fax, (202) 338-0608. Julio Giulietti SJ, director. Internet, http://www.georgetown.edu/CIED.*

Designs and administers programs aimed at improving the quality of life of economically disadvantaged people; provides technical education, job training, leadership skill development, and business management training; runs programs in Central America, the Caribbean, Central Europe, and Southeast Asia.

Citizens Democracy Corps, *1400 Eye St. N.W., #1125 20005; (202) 872-0933. Fax, (202) 872-0923. Michael Levett, president. Internet, info@cdc.org or http://www.cdc.org.*

Mobilizes volunteers in the U.S. private sector to assist in the development of market economies and democratic societies in central and eastern Europe and in the newly independent states. Through the Business Entrepreneur Program, American volunteers assist private and privatizing businesses and public and nonprofit institutions that support business development.

Cooperative Housing Foundation, *8300 Colesville Rd., #420, Silver Spring, MD 20910; (301) 587-4700. Fax, (301) 587-2626. Michael Doyle, president. Internet, west@chfhq.com or http://www.chfhq.org.*

Works under contract with the Agency for International Development, United Nations, and World Bank to strengthen local government housing departments abroad.

Development Group for Alternative Policies, *927 15th St. N.W., 4th Floor 20005; (202) 898-1566. Fax, (202) 898-1612. Douglas Hellinger, executive director. Internet, dgap@igc.apc.org or http://www.igc.apc.org/dgap.*

Works with grassroots organizations in developing countries to promote changes in international economic policies to benefit the poor.

InterAction, *1717 Massachusetts Ave. N.W., #801 20036; (202) 667-8227. Fax, (202) 667-8236. Jim Moody, president. Internet, ia@interaction.org or http://www.interaction.org.*

Provides a forum for exchange of information among private U.S. voluntary agencies on development assistance issues, including food aid and other relief services, migration, and refugee affairs. Monitors legislation and regulations.

International Center for Research on Women, *1717 Massachusetts Ave. N.W., #302 20036; (202) 797-0007. Fax, (202) 797-0020. Geeta Rao Jupta, president. Internet, icrw@igc.apc.org or http://www.icrw.org.*

Seeks to advance women's rights and opportunities. Promotes social and economic development with participation of women; provides technical assistance on women's productive and reproductive roles; advocates with governments and agencies.

International Voluntary Services, *1901 Pennsylvania Ave. N.W., #501 20006; (202) 387-5533. Fax, (202) 466-5669. Donald B. Peterson, chief operating officer. Internet, ivs@pacthq.org.*

Provides developing countries with volunteers and technical assistance in the areas of health, agriculture, small business, and community and rural development.

National Peace Corps Assn., *1900 L St. N.W., #205 20036; (202) 293-7728. Fax, (202) 293-7554. Charles F. Dambach, president. Internet, http://www.rpcv.org.*

Membership: returned Peace Corps volunteers, staff, and interested individuals. Promotes a global perspective in the United States; seeks to educate the public about the developing world; supports Peace Corps programs; maintains network of returned volunteers.

New TransCentury Foundation, *1901 N. Fort Myer Dr., #1017, Arlington, VA 22209; (703) 351-5500. Fax, (703) 351-5510. Lisa Wiggins, president. Internet, transcentury@compuserve.com.*

International development research and consulting organization. Provides developing countries with technical assistance. Interests include agriculture, health, labor and migration, refugee resettlement, credit entrepreneurship (loans to entrepreneurs to start businesses), and assistance to private voluntary and nongovernmental organizations.

Partners for Livable Communities, *1429 21st St. N.W., 2nd Floor 20036; (202) 887-5990. Fax, (202) 466-4845. Robert H. McNulty, president. Internet, partners@livable.com or http://www.livable.com.*

Provides technical assistance, support services, and information to assist communities in creating better living environments. Works in the Caribbean area, South America, and Europe on public/private partnerships and resource development to improve living environments. Conducts conferences and workshops; maintains referral clearinghouse.

Pax World Service, *1111 16th St. N.W., #120 20036; (202) 293-7290. Fax, (202) 293-7023. Larry Ekin, president. Internet, info@paxworld.org or http://www.paxworld.org.*

Initiates and supports community-based sustainable development projects. Supports educational activities and facilitates citizen diplomacy through people-to-people tours, a program that allows individuals to develop a better understanding of the culture and diverse viewpoints of people living in regions of conflict.

Planning Assistance, *1832 Jefferson Pl. N.W. 20036; (202) 466-3290. Fax, (202) 466-3293. Robert Learmonth, executive director. Internet, planasst@igc.apc.org.*

Provides managerial assistance to governmental and nongovernmental organizations seeking to create, expand, or improve their social and economic development programs. Focuses on development in Africa, Asia, and Latin America.

Salvation Army World Service Office, *615 Slaters Lane, P.O. Box 269, Alexandria, VA 22313; (703) 684-5528. Fax, (703) 684-5536. Harden White, executive director.*

Works in Russia and the new independent states, Latin America, the Caribbean, Africa, Asia, and the South Pacific to provide technical assistance in support of local Salvation Army programs of health services (including HIV/AIDs), community development, education, institutional development, and relief and reconstruction assistance. (International headquarters in London.)

United Way International, *701 N. Fairfax St., Alexandria, VA 22314-2045; (703) 519-0092. Fax, (703) 519-0097. Robert Beggan, president.*

Membership: independent United Way organizations in other countries. Provides United Way fundraising campaigns with technical assistance; trains volunteers and professionals; operates an information exchange for affiliated organizations.

Volunteers in Overseas Cooperative Assistance, *50 F St. N.W., #1075 20001; (202) 383-4961. Fax, (202) 783-7204. Michael Deegan, president.*

Recruits professionals for voluntary, short-term technical assistance to cooperatives, environmental groups, and agricultural enterprises, upon request, in developing countries and emerging democracies.

Volunteers in Technical Assistance, *1600 Wilson Blvd., #500, Arlington, VA (mailing address: P.O. Box 12438, Arlington, VA 22209); (703) 276-1800. Fax, (703) 243-1865. Henry R. Norman, president. Internet, vita@vita.org or http://www.vita.org.*

Provides individuals and groups in developing countries with information and technical resources aimed at fostering self-sufficiency. Assistance includes needs assessment and program development support; consulting services; information systems and training; communications; and management of long-term field projects.

Finance/Monetary Affairs

AGENCIES

Commerce Dept., *Balance of Payments, 1441 L St. N.W., BE-58 20230; (202) 606-9545. Fax, (202) 606-5314. Christopher L. Bach, chief. Internet, http://www.stat-usa.gov.*

Compiles, analyzes, and publishes quarterly U.S. balance-of-payments figures.

Federal Reserve System, *International Finance, 20th and C Sts. N.W., #B1242C 20551; (202) 452-3614. Fax, (202) 452-6424. Edwin M. Truman, staff director.*

Provides the Federal Reserve's board of governors with economic analyses of international developments. Compiles data on balance of payments, international trade, and exchange rates.

State Dept., *International Finance and Development, Main State Bldg., #3336 20520; (202) 647-9496. Fax, (202) 647-0320. Barbara J. Griffiths, deputy assistant secretary.*

Formulates and implements policies related to multinational investment and insurance; activities of the World Bank and regional banks in the financial development of various countries; bilateral aid; international monetary reform; international antitrust cases; and international debt, banking, and taxation.

State Dept., *Monetary Affairs, Main State Bldg., #3425 20520; (202) 647-9497. Fax, (202) 647-7453. Robert Deutsch, director.*

Formulates balance-of-payments and debt rescheduling policies. Monitors balance-of-payments developments in other countries.

Treasury Dept., *Foreign Exchange Operations, 1500 Pennsylvania Ave. N.W., #2409 20220; (202) 622-2650. Fax, (202) 622-2021. Timothy Dulaney, director.*

Monitors foreign exchange market developments; manages the Exchange Stabilization Fund to counter disruptive market conditions and to provide developing countries with bridge loans.

Treasury Dept., *International Affairs, 1500 Pennsylvania Ave. N.W., #3432 20220; (202) 622-1270. Fax, (202) 622-0417. David A. Lipton, under secretary.*

Coordinates and implements U.S. international economic policy in cooperation with other government agencies. Works to improve the structure and stabilizing operations of the international monetary and investment system; monitors developments in international gold and foreign exchange operations; coordinates policies and programs of development lending institutions; coordinates Treasury Dept. participation in direct and portfolio investment by foreigners in the United States; studies international monetary, economic, and financial issues; analyzes data on international transactions.

Treasury Dept., *Trade Finance, 1500 Pennsylvania Ave. N.W., #4448 20220; (202) 622-1739. Fax, (202) 622-0967. Steven F. Tvardek, director.*

Reviews lending policies of the Export-Import Bank, the Commodity Credit Corp., and the Defense Dept.'s foreign military sales program. Serves as U.S. representative to the Export Credits Group, a committee of the Organization for Economic Cooperation and Development, and negotiates international arrangements for export credits.

CONGRESS

House Banking and Financial Services Committee, *Subcommittee on Domestic and International Monetary Policy, B304 RHOB 20515; (202) 226-0473. Fax, (202) 226-0537. Michael N. Castle, R-Del., chair; James McCormick, staff director. Internet, http://www.house.gov/banking.*

Jurisdiction over legislation on international monetary policy, international capital flows, and foreign investment in the United States as they affect domestic monetary policy and the economy; exchange rates; the African, Asian, European, and Inter-American Development Banks; the World Bank; legislation on international trade, investment, and monetary policy and export expansion matters related to the International Monetary Fund and the Export-Import Bank.

Senate Banking, Housing, and Urban Affairs Committee, *Subcommittee on International Finance, SD-534 20510; (202) 224-7391. Fax, (202) 224-5137. Rod Grams, R-Minn., chair; Dave Berson, staff director. Internet, http://www.senate.gov/~banking.*

Jurisdiction over legislation on international monetary and exchange rate policies, international capital flows, foreign investments in the United States, export control, foreign trade promotion, the Export-Import Bank, the Export Administration Act, and the revised Trading with the Enemy Act, which authorizes trade restrictions (some jurisdictions shared with Senate Finance and Foreign Relations committees).

Senate Finance Committee, *SD-219 20510; (202) 224-4515. Fax, (202) 224-5920. William V. Roth Jr., R-Del., chair; Lindy L. Paull, staff director. Internet, http://www.senate.gov/~finance.*

Jurisdiction over legislation on international monetary matters (shares jurisdiction with the Senate Foreign Relations and Banking, Housing, and Urban Affairs committees).

Senate Foreign Relations Committee, *Subcommittee on International Economic Policy, Export, and Trade Promotion, SR-346 20510; (202) 224-4224. Fax, (202) 228-0436. Chuck Hagel, R-Neb., chair; Ken Peel, senior professional staff member. Internet, http://www.senate.gov/committee/foreign.html.*

Jurisdiction over legislation to encourage foreign trade and to protect American business interests abroad. Jurisdiction over legislation affecting multinational corporations; balance of payments; international monetary organizations; and international economic and monetary policy as it relates to U.S. foreign policy (jurisdiction shared with the Senate Finance and Senate Banking, Housing, and Urban Affairs committees).

INTERNATIONAL ORGANIZATIONS

International Finance Corp., *2121 Pennsylvania Ave. N.W. (mailing address: 1818 H St. N.W., Washington, DC 20433); (202) 477-1234. Fax, (202) 477-6391. James D. Wolfensohn, president; Jannik Lindbaek, executive vice president, (202) 473-0381. Internet, http://www.ifc.org.*

Promotes private enterprise in developing countries through direct investments in projects that establish new businesses or expand, modify, or diversify existing businesses; provides its own financing or recruits financing from other sources. Gives developing countries technical assistance in capital market development, privatization, corporate restructuring, and foreign investment. Affiliated with the World Bank.

International Monetary Fund (IMF), *700 19th St. N.W. 20431; (202) 623-7759. Fax, (202) 623-4661. Karin Lissakers, U.S. executive director. Information, (202) 623-7000. Press, (202) 623-7300. Library, (202) 623-7054. Internet, http://www.imf.org.*

Intergovernmental organization that maintains funds, contributed by and available for use by members, to promote world trade and aid members with temporary balance-of-payments problems.

Multilateral Investment Guarantee Agency, *1818 H St. N.W., #U12001 20433; (202) 473-6138. Fax, (202) 522-2620. Akira Iida, executive vice president. Internet, http://www.miga.org.*

World Bank affiliate that seeks to encourage foreign investment in developing countries. Provides guarantees against losses due to currency transfer, expropriation, war, civil disturbance, and breach of contract. Advises member developing countries on means of improving their attractiveness to foreign investors. Membership open to World Bank member countries and Switzerland.

NONPROFIT

Bankers' Assn. for Foreign Trade, *2121 K St. N.W., #701 20037; (202) 452-0952. Fax, (202) 452-0959. Mary Condeelis, executive director.*

Membership: U.S. commercial banks with major international operations; foreign banks with U.S. operations are nonvoting members. Monitors activities that affect the operation of U.S. commercial banks.

Bretton Woods Committee, *1990 M St. N.W., #450 20036; (202) 331-1616. Fax, (202) 785-9423. James C. Orr, executive director. Internet, http://www.brettonwoods.org.*

Works to increase public understanding of the World Bank, the original development institutions, and the International Monetary Fund.

Institute of International Finance, *2000 Pennsylvania Ave. N.W., #8500 20006-1812; (202) 857-3600. Fax, (202) 775-1430. Charles Dallara, managing director. Press, (202) 331-8183. Internet, http://www.iif.com.*

Membership: international commercial banks, multinational corporations, and official lending agencies. Promotes better understanding of international lending transactions. Analyzes information to help members evaluate credit risks of public and private borrowers in developing and middle-income countries. Examines factors affecting the future of international lending.

🌍 REGIONAL AFFAIRS

See also Foreign Embassies, U.S. Ambassadors, and Country Desk Officers (appendix); Language and Literature (chap. 4)

Africa

For North Africa, see Near East and South Asia

AGENCIES

African Development Foundation, *1400 Eye St. N.W., 10th Floor 20005; (202) 673-3916. Fax, (202) 673-3810. William R. Ford, president. Internet, http://www.adf.gov.*

Established by Congress to work with and fund organizations and individuals involved in development projects at the local level in Africa. Gives preference to projects involving extensive participation by local Africans.

Agency for International Development, Africa Bureau, *1300 Pennsylvania Ave. N.W., #4.08C 20523-0073; (202) 712-0500. Fax, (202) 216-3008. Carol A. Peasley, acting assistant administrator.*

Advises AID administrator on U.S. policy toward developing countries in Africa.

State Dept., Bureau of African Affairs, *Main State Bldg., #6234A 20520; (202) 647-2530. Fax, (202) 647-6301. Susan E. Rice, assistant secretary. Press, (202) 647-7373.*

Advises the secretary on U.S. policy toward Sub-Saharan Africa. Directors, assigned to different regions in Africa, aid the assistant secretary.

State Dept., Central African Affairs, *Main State Bldg., #4246 20520-2902; (202) 647-2080. Fax, (202) 647-1726. Marc Baas, director.*

Includes Burundi, Cameroon, Central African Republic, Chad, Congo, Equatorial Guinea, Gabon, Rwanda, Sao Tome and Principe, and Zaire.

State Dept., East African Affairs, *Main State Bldg., #5240 20520; (202) 647-9742. Fax, (202) 647-0810. David Dunn, director.*

Includes Comoros, Djibouti, Eritrea, Ethiopia, Kenya, Madagascar, Mauritius, Seychelles, Somalia, Sudan, Tanzania, Uganda, and Indian Ocean Territory.

State Dept., Southern African Affairs, *Main State Bldg., #4238 20520; (202) 647-9836. Fax, (202) 647-5007. John W. Blaney, director.*

Includes Angola, Botswana, Lesotho, Malawi, Mozambique, Namibia, South Africa, Swaziland, Zambia, and Zimbabwe.

State Dept., West African Affairs, *Main State Bldg., #4250 20520; (202) 647-3406. Fax, (202) 647-4855. Howard Jeter, director.*

Includes Benin, Burkina Faso, Cape Verde, Côte D'Ivoire, Gambia, Ghana, Guinea, Guinea-Bissau, Liberia, Mali, Mauritania, Niger, Nigeria, Senegal, Sierra Leone, Togo, and Western Sahara.

U.S. Information Agency, African Affairs, *301 4th St. S.W., #716 20547; (202) 619-4894. Fax, (202) 619-5925. Marilyn Hulbert, director.*

Administers USIA programs throughout Sub-Saharan Africa in support of U.S. policies. Manages U.S. information service offices in individual African countries that conduct cultural and educational exchange programs through lectures, radio broadcasts, films, television, and other media outlets. Advises the president, Congress, and federal agencies on U.S. policies toward African nations.

CONGRESS

House International Relations Committee, *Subcommittee on Africa,* *705 O'Neill Bldg. 20515; (202) 226-7812. Fax, (202) 225-7491. Ed Royce, R-Calif., chair; Thomas Sheehy, staff director. Internet, http://www.house. gov/international_relations.*

Jurisdiction over foreign affairs legislation dealing with Africa, except Egypt. Concurrent jurisdiction over matters assigned to the functional House International Relations subcommittees insofar as they affect the region.

Library of Congress, *African and Middle Eastern Division,* *110 2nd St. S.E., #220 20540; (202) 707-7937. Fax, (202) 252-3180. Beverly Gray, chief.*

Maintains collections of African, Near Eastern, and Hebraic material. Prepares bibliographies and special studies relating to Africa and the Middle East. Reference service and reading rooms available to the public.

Senate Foreign Relations Committee, *Subcommittee on African Affairs,* *SD-450 20510; (202) 224-4651. Fax, (202) 224-0836. John Ashcroft, R-Mo., chair, (202) 224-6154; James Odom, Legislative Assistant. Internet, http:// www.senate.gov/committee/foreign.html.*

Jurisdiction over foreign affairs legislation dealing with Africa, with the exception of countries bordering on the Mediterranean Sea from Egypt to Morocco.

INTERNATIONAL ORGANIZATIONS

International Bank for Reconstruction and Development (World Bank), *Africa,* *1818 H St. N.W., #J5097 20433; (202) 458-2858. Fax, (202) 477-0380. Callisto E. Madavo, vice president, (202) 458-2856; Jean-Louis Sarbib, vice president, (202) 473-4946. Information, (202) 473-4619.*

Encourages public and private foreign investment in the countries of Sub-Saharan Africa through loans, loan guarantees, and technical assistance. Finances economic development projects in agriculture, environmental protection, education, public utilities, telecommunications, water supply, sewerage treatment, public health, and other areas.

NONPROFIT

African-American Institute, *1625 Massachusetts Ave. N.W., #400 20036; (202) 667-5636. Fax, (202) 265-6332. Jerry L. Drew, director, Washington Office.*

Arranges U.S. itineraries for African visitors sponsored by the U.S. Information Agency (USIA). Sponsors policy studies program to educate Congress on African issues. Promotes trade and investment in Africa. (Headquarters in New York.)

Africare, *440 R St. N.W. 20001; (202) 462-3614. Fax, (202) 387-1034. C. Payne Lucas, president.*

Seeks to improve the quality of life in rural Africa through development of water resources, increased food production, and delivery of health care and other services. Resource center open to the public by appointment.

American African Affairs Assn., *1001 Connecticut Ave. N.W., #1135 20036; (202) 223-5110. J. A. Parker, co-chair.*

Educational organization that provides information on African states. Interests include world communism and the role of the United States in development.

TransAfrica, *1744 R St. N.W. 20009-2410; (202) 797-2301. Fax, (202) 797-2382. Randall Robinson, president. Internet, transforum@igc.org or http://www. transafricaforum.org.*

Focuses on U.S. foreign policy toward African nations, the Caribbean, and peoples of African descent. Provides members with information on foreign policy issues; conducts educational training programs for minority students considering careers in international affairs; operates the Arthur R. Ashe Jr. Foreign Policy Library.

U.S.-Africa Chamber of Commerce, *1899 L St. N.W., 5th Floor 20036; (202) 331-7053. Fax, (202) 331-1809. Elias W. Belayneh, president.*

Membership: U.S. and overseas based businesses, trade associations, universities, foundations, and individuals interested in trade and investment between the United States and Africa. Promotes the development of free enterprise and economic, commercial, and financial relations.

Washington Office on Africa, *110 Maryland Ave. N.E. 20002; (202) 546-7961. Fax, (202) 546-1545. Pearl Alice Marsh, executive director. Internet, apic@africapolicy.org or http://www.africapolicy.org.*

Monitors legislation and executive actions concerning Africa; issues action alerts. Library open to the public by appointment. (Affiliated with the African Policy Center).

East Asia and the Pacific

See also Russia and New Independent States

AGENCIES

Agency for International Development, *Asia and Near East Bureau,* 1300 Pennsylvania Ave., #4.09-034 20523; (202) 712-0200. Fax, (202) 216-3386. Kelly Kammerer, acting assistant administrator.

Advises AID administrator on U.S. economic development policy in Asia, the Pacific, and the Near East.

Defense Dept., *Asian and Pacific Affairs,* The Pentagon, #4C839 20301-2400; (703) 695-4175. Fax, (703) 695-8222. Kurt M. Campbell, deputy assistant secretary.

Advises the assistant secretary for international security affairs on matters dealing with Asia and the Pacific.

Japan-United States Friendship Commission, 1120 Vermont Ave. N.W., #925 20005; (202) 275-7712. Fax, (202) 275-7413. Eric J. Gangloff, executive director. Internet, jusfc@compuserve.com or http://www2.dgsys.com/~jusfc.

Independent agency established by Congress that makes grants and administers funds and programs promoting educational and cultural exchanges between Japan and the United States. Consults with public and private organizations in both countries.

State Dept., *Bureau of East Asian and Pacific Affairs,* Main State Bldg., #4313A 20520-6205; (202) 647-9596. Fax, (202) 647-7350. Stanley Roth, assistant secretary. Press, (202) 647-2538.

Advises the secretary on U.S. policy toward East Asian and Pacific countries. Directors, assigned to specific countries within the bureau, aid the assistant secretary.

State Dept., *Australia, New Zealand, and Pacific Island Affairs,* Main State Bldg., #4209 20520; (202) 647-9690. Fax, (202) 647-0118. Suzanne Butcher, director.

State Dept., *Burma, Cambodia, Laos, Thailand, and Vietnam Affairs,* Main State Bldg., #5206 20520-6310; (202) 647-3132. Fax, (202) 647-3069. Marie Huhtala, director.

State Dept., *Chinese and Mongolian Affairs,* Main State Bldg., #4318 20520; (202) 647-6300. Fax, (202) 647-6820. Howard Lange, director.

State Dept., *Japanese Affairs,* Main State Bldg., #4206 20520; (202) 647-2913. Fax, (202) 647-4402. Robert Reis, director.

State Dept., *Korean Affairs,* Main State Bldg., #5313 20520; (202) 647-7717. Fax, (202) 647-7388. Mark Minton, director, (202) 647-8890.

State Dept., *Philippines, Indonesia, Malaysia, Brunei, and Singapore Affairs,* Main State Bldg., #5210 20520; (202) 647-3276. Fax, (202) 736-4559. Douglas Hartwick, director.

State Dept., *Taiwan Coordination Staff,* Main State Bldg., #4312 20520; (202) 647-7711. Fax, (202) 647-0076. Sylvia G. Stanfield, director.

U.S. Information Agency, *East Asia and Pacific Affairs,* 301 4th St. S.W., #766 20547; (202) 619-4829. Fax, (202) 619-6684. William Maurer, director.

Administers USIA programs throughout the East Asian and Pacific region in support of U.S. policies. Conducts informational and educational exchange programs. Advises the president, Congress, and federal agencies on U.S. public affairs policy toward nations in East Asia and the Pacific.

CONGRESS

House International Relations Committee, *Subcommittee on Asia and the Pacific,* B-359 RHOB 20515; (202) 226-7825. Fax, (202) 226-7829. Doug Bereuter, R-Neb., chair; Michael Ennis, staff director. Internet, http://www.house.gov/international_relations.

Jurisdiction over foreign affairs legislation dealing with East Asia and the Pacific, the Near East, and South Asia, from Afghanistan to the Far East. Concurrent jurisdiction over matters assigned to the functional House International Relations subcommittees insofar as they affect the region.

Library of Congress, *Asian Division,* 110 2nd St. S.E., #LJ149 20540-4740; (202) 707-5420. Fax, (202) 707-1724. Mya Thanda Poe, chief.

Maintains collections of Chinese, Korean, Japanese, Southeast Asian, and South Asian material covering all subjects except law, technical agriculture, and clinical medicine. Reference service is provided in the Asian Reading Room.

Senate Foreign Relations Committee, *Subcommittee on East Asian and Pacific Affairs,* SD-450 20510; (202) 224-4651. Fax, (202) 224-0836. Craig Thomas, R-Wyo., chair; Ellen Bork, senior professional staff member. Internet, http://www.senate.gov/committee/foreign.html.

Jurisdiction over foreign affairs legislation dealing with East Asia and the Pacific, including the mainland of Asia from China and Korea to Burma, Japan, the Philippines, Malaysia, Indonesia, Australia and New Zealand, Oceania, and the South Pacific islands.

INTERNATIONAL ORGANIZATIONS

International Bank for Reconstruction and Development (World Bank), *East Asia and Pacific, 1818 H St. N.W., MC9-123 20433; (202) 458-2008. Fax, (202) 477-0169. Jean-Michel Severino, vice president.*

Encourages public and private investment in the countries of East Asia and the Pacific through loans, loan guarantees, and technical assistance. Finances economic development projects in agriculture, environmental protection, education, public utilities, telecommunications, water supply, sewerage, public health, and other areas.

NONPROFIT

American Institute in Taiwan, *1700 N. Moore St., #1700, Arlington, VA 22209; (703) 525-8474. Fax, (703) 841-1385. Barbara Schrage, deputy director. Internet, http://www.ait.org.tw.*

Chartered by Congress to coordinate commercial, cultural, and other activities between the people of the United States and Taiwan. Represents U.S. interests and maintains offices in Taiwan.

Asia Foundation, *1779 Massachusetts Ave. N.W., #815 20036; (202) 588-9420. Fax, (202) 588-9409. Nancy Yuan, director. Internet, http://www.asiafoundation.org.*

Provides grants and technical assistance in Asia and the Pacific islands (except the Middle East). Seeks to strengthen legislatures, legal and judicial systems, market economies, the media, and nongovernmental organizations. (Headquarters in San Francisco.)

Asia Pacific Center for Justice and Peace, *110 Maryland Ave. N.E., Box #70 20002; (202) 543-1094. Fax, (202) 546-5103. Miriam A. Young, director. Internet, apcjp@igc. apc.org or http://www.apcjp.org.*

Nonprofit organization that supports justice and peace throughout Asia and the Pacific. Focuses on the policies of the U.S. government, corporations, international institutions, and religious bodies as they impact Asia and the Pacific. Monitors countries and issues; sponsors public education forums; supports people-to-people relationships.

Asia Society, *1800 K St. N.W., #1102 20006; (202) 833-2742. Fax, (202) 833-0189. Judith Sloan, director, Washington Office. Internet, http://www.asiasociety.org.*

Membership: individuals interested in Asia and the Pacific (excluding the Middle East). Sponsors seminars and lectures on political, economic, and cultural issues. (Headquarters in New York.)

Heritage Foundation, *Asian Studies Center, 214 Massachusetts Ave. N.E. 20002; (202) 608-6081. Fax, (202) 675-1779. Jim Przystup, director.*

Conducts research and provides information on U.S. policies in Asia and the Pacific. Interests include economic and security issues in the Asia Pacific region. Hosts speakers and visiting foreign policy delegations; sponsors conferences.

Japan-America Society of Washington, *1020 19th St. N.W., Lower Lobby #40 20036; (202) 833-2210. Fax, (202) 833-2456. Patricia R. Kearns, executive director. Internet, jaswdc@intr.net or http://www.us-japan.org/dc.*

Conducts programs on U.S.-Japan trade, politics, and economic issues. Cultural programs include lectures, films, a Japanese-language school, scholarships, and assistance to Japanese performing artists. Maintains library for members.

Japan Economic Institute of America, *1000 Connecticut Ave. N.W., #211 20036; (202) 296-5633. Fax, (202) 296-8333. Arthur J. Alexander, president. Internet, jei@jei. org or http://www.jei.org.*

Research organization supported by Japan's Ministry of Foreign Affairs. Publishes current information on the Japanese economy and U.S.-Japan economic relations. Library open to the public.

Japan Information Access Project, *2000 P St. N.W., #620 20036; (202) 822-6040. Fax, (202) 822-6044. Mindy Kotler, director. Internet, access@nmjc.org or http://www.nmjc.org/jiap.*

Membership organization that works to strengthen international understanding of Japanese science, technology, management, and business information. Teaches professionals how to access, use, and evaluate Japanese information for research and planning. Studies Japanese and Western science, technology, management, and trade issues.

Japan Productivity Center for Socio-Economic Development, *1001 Connecticut Ave. N.W., #425 20036; (202) 955-5663. Fax, (202) 955-6125. Daisaku Harada, director, U.S. Office. Internet, jpc@cais.com.*

Promotes education and exchange of information between Japanese and American businesspeople by coordinating overseas meetings and visits for participating countries. (Headquarters in Tokyo.)

Pacific Economic Cooperation Council (U.S.-PECC), *1112 16th St. N.W., #520 20036; (202) 293-3995. Fax, (202) 293-1402. Mark Borthwick, executive director. Internet, uspecc@erols.com or http://www.pecc.org.*

Membership: business, government, and research representatives from twenty two Asia-Pacific economies. Works on practical government and business policy issues to increase trade, investment, and economic development in the region. Serves as one of three observer organizations to the government forum on Asia Pacific Economic Cooperation (APEC).

Taipei Economic and Cultural Representative Office, *4201 Wisconsin Ave. N.W. 20016; (202) 895-1800. Fax, (202) 966-0825. Stephen Chen, representative. Press, (202) 662-7562.*

Represents political, economic, and cultural interests of the government of the Republic of China (Taiwan) in the United States; handles former embassy functions.

U.S.-Asia Institute, *232 E. Capitol St. N.E. 20003; (202) 544-3181. Fax, (202) 543-1748. Joji Konoshima, president.*

Organization of individuals interested in Asia. Encourages communication among political and business leaders in the United States and Asia. Interests include foreign policy, international trade, Asian and American cultures, education, and employment. Conducts research and sponsors conferences and workshops in cooperation with the State Dept. to promote greater understanding between the United States and Asian nations. Conducts programs that take congressional staff members to Singapore, Japan, Indonesia, Malaysia, and China.

U.S.-China Business Council, *1818 N St. N.W., #200 20036-2406; (202) 429-0340. Fax, (202) 775-2476. Robert A. Kapp, president. Internet, http;//www.uschina.org.*

Member-supported organization that represents U.S. companies engaged in business relations with the People's Republic of China. Participates in U.S. policy issues relating to China and other international trade. Publishes research reports. (Maintains offices in Beijing, Shanghai, and Hong Kong.)

Europe and Canada

(Includes the Baltic states)

AGENCIES

Agency for International Development, *Europe and the New Independent States Bureau, 1300 Pennsylvania Ave. N.W., #5.06 20523-5600; (202) 712-5123. Fax, (202) 216-5057. Donald Pressly, acting assistant administrator.*

Advises AID administrator on U.S. economic development policy in Europe and the new independent states.

Defense Dept., *European and NATO Affairs, The Pentagon, #4D800 20301-2400; (703) 697-7207. Fax, (703)*

697-5992. Brig. Gen. Thomas K. Longstreth, deputy assistant secretary.

Advises the assistant secretary for international security affairs on matters dealing with Europe and NATO (North Atlantic Treaty Organization).

International Trade Administration *(Commerce Dept.), Central and Eastern Europe Business Information Center, 14th St. and Constitution Ave. N.W., #2325 20230; (202) 482-2645. Fax, (202) 501-0787. Jay Burgess, director. Flash fax, (202) 482-5745. Internet, ceebic@usita. gov or http://www.mac.doc.gov/eebic/ceebic.html.*

Provides information on trade and investment in central and eastern Europe. Disseminates information on potential trade partners, regulations and incentives, and trade promotion; encourages private enterprise in the region.

State Dept., *Bureau of European and Canadian Affairs, Main State Bldg., #6226 20520; (202) 647-9626. Fax, (202) 647-0967. Marc Grossman, assistant secretary. Information, (202) 647-6925.*

Advises the secretary on U.S. policy toward European countries and Canada. Directors, assigned to specific countries within the bureau, aid the assistant secretary.

State Dept., *Canadian Affairs, Main State Bldg., #4511 20520; (202) 647-2170. Fax, (202) 647-4088. Eric A. Kunsman, director.*

State Dept., *European Security and Political Affairs, Main State Bldg., #6227 20520; (202) 647-1626. Fax, (202) 647-1369. Barbaro Owens-Kirkpatrick, director.*

Coordinates and advises, with the Defense Dept. and other agencies, the U.S. mission to the North Atlantic Treaty Organization and the U.S. delegation to the Organization on Security and Cooperation in Europe regarding political, military, and arms control matters.

State Dept., *European Union and Regional Affairs, Main State Bldg., #6519 20520-6511; (202) 647-3932. Fax, (202) 647-9959. William Primosch, director.*

Handles all matters concerning the European Union, the Council of Europe, and the Organization for Economic Cooperation and Development, with emphasis on trade issues. Monitors export controls and economic activities for the North Atlantic Treaty Organization and the Conference on Security and Cooperation in Europe.

State Dept., *German, Austrian, and Swiss Affairs, Main State Bldg., #4228 20520; (202) 647-1484. Fax, (202) 647-5117. Ruth Van Heusen, director.*

Includes Austria, Germany, Liechtenstein, and Switzerland.

State Dept., *Nordic and Baltic Affairs,* *Main State Bldg., #5229 20520; (202) 647-5669. Fax, (202) 736-4170. Gillian Milovanic, director.*

Includes Denmark, Estonia, Finland, Iceland, Latvia, Lithuania, Norway, and Sweden.

State Dept., *North Central European Affairs,* *Main State Bldg., #5220 20520; (202) 647-4136. Fax, (202) 736-4853. Jonathan B. Rickert, director.*

Includes Czech Republic, Hungary, Poland, Romania, Slovakia, and Slovenia.

State Dept., *South Central European Affairs,* *Main State Bldg., #5221 20520; (202) 647-0608. Fax, (202) 647-0555. James W. Swigert, director.*

Includes Albania, Bosnia-Herzegovina, Bulgaria, Croatia, Macedonia, Montenegro, and Serbia.

State Dept., *Southern European Affairs,* *Main State Bldg., #5511 20520; (202) 647-6112. Fax, (202) 647-5087. Stephen D. Mull, director.*

Includes Cyprus, Greece, and Turkey.

State Dept., *United Kingdom, Benelux, and Ireland Affairs,* *Main State Bldg., #4513 20520; (202) 647-5687. Fax, (202) 647-3463. Randolph M. Bell, director.*

Includes Belgium, Bermuda, Ireland, Luxembourg, the Netherlands, and the United Kingdom.

State Dept., *Western European Affairs,* *Main State Bldg., #5226 20520-6511; (202) 647-3072. Fax, (202) 647-3459. Shirley Barnes, director.*

Includes France, Italy, Malta, Monaco, Portugal, San Marino, Spain, and the Vatican.

U.S. Information Agency, *East European and NIS Affairs,* *301 4th St. S.W., #868 20547; (202) 619-4563. Fax, (202) 401-6893. Robert E. McCarthy, director.*

Administers USIA programs in eastern Europe and in the newly independent states in support of U.S. policies. Manages U.S. information service offices in individual countries that conduct cultural and educational exchange programs through lectures, radio broadcasts, films, and television. Advises the president, Congress, and federal agencies on U.S. policies toward eastern Europe and the newly independent states.

U.S. Information Agency, *West European and Canadian Affairs,* *301 4th St. S.W., #751 20547; (202) 619-6565. Fax, (202) 619-6821. Charles Miller Crouch, director.*

Administers USIA programs in Canada and western Europe in support of U.S. policies. Manages U.S. information service offices in individual countries that con-

duct cultural and educational exchange programs through lectures, radio broadcasts, films, and television. Advises the president, Congress, and federal agencies on U.S. policies toward western Europe and Canada.

CONGRESS

House International Relations Committee, *2170 RHOB 20515; (202) 225-5021. Fax, (202) 225-2035. Benjamin A. Gilman, R-N.Y., chair; Richard J. Garon Jr., chief of staff. Internet, http://www.house.gov/international_relations.*

Jurisdiction over foreign affairs legislation dealing with Europe. Concurrent jurisdiction over matters assigned to the functional House International Relations subcommittees insofar as they affect the region.

House International Relations Committee, *Subcommittee on the Western Hemisphere,* *2401A RHOB 20515; (202) 226-7820. Fax, (202) 226-2722. Elton Gallegly, R-Calif., chair; Vince Morelli, staff director. Internet, http://www.house.gov/international_relations.*

Jurisdiction over foreign affairs legislation dealing with Canada.

Library of Congress, *European Division,* *101 Independence Ave. S.E. 20540-4830; (202) 707-5414. Fax, (202) 707-8482. John Van Oudenaren, chief. Reference desk, (202) 707-4515. Internet, http://lcweb.loc.gov/rreuropean.*

Provides reference service on the library's European collections (except collections on Spain, Portugal, and the British Isles). Prepares bibliographies and special studies relating to European countries, including the former Soviet Union. Maintains current unbound Slavic language periodicals and newspapers, which are available at the European Reference Desk.

Senate Foreign Relations Committee, *Subcommittee on European Affairs,* *SD-450 20510; (202) 224-4651. Fax, (202) 224-0836. Gordon H. Smith, R-Ore., chair; Steve Biegun, senior professional staff member. Internet, http://www.senate.gov/committee/foreign.html.*

Jurisdiction over foreign affairs legislation dealing with Europe (including Greece and Turkey), the United Kingdom, Greenland, Iceland, the former Soviet Union, and the North Polar region.

Senate Foreign Relations Committee, *Subcommittee on Western Hemisphere, Peace Corps, Narcotics, and Terrorism,* *SD-450 20510; (202) 224-4651. Fax, (202) 224-0836. Paul Coverdell, R-Ga., chair; Roger Noriega, senior professional staff member. Internet, http://www.senate.gov/committee/foreign.html.*

Jurisdiction over foreign affairs legislation dealing with Canada.

INTERNATIONAL ORGANIZATIONS

European Union, *Press and Public Affairs, 2300 M St. N.W. 20037; (202) 862-9500. Fax, (202) 429-1766. Hugo Paemen, ambassador; Soren Sondergaard, acting director. Press, (202) 862-9540. Internet, http://www.eurunion.org or http://www.europa.eu.int.*

Information and public affairs office in the United States for the European Union, which includes the European Economic Community, the European Coal and Steel Community, and the European Atomic Energy Community. Provides social policy data on the European Union and provides statistics and documents on member countries, including those related to energy, economics, development and cooperation, commerce, agriculture, industry, and technology. Library open to the public by appointment. (Headquarters in Brussels.)

International Bank for Reconstruction and Development (World Bank), *Europe and Central Asia, 600 19th St. N.W. (mailing address: 1818 H St. N.W., Washington, DC 20433); (202) 458-0602. Fax, (202) 477-1942. Johannes Linn, vice president.*

Encourages public and private foreign investment in the countries of eastern Europe through loans, loan guarantees, and technical assistance. Finances economic development projects in agriculture, environmental protection, education, energy, public utilities, telecommunications, water supply, sewerage, public health, and other areas.

NONPROFIT

American Bar Assn., *Central and East European Law Initiative, 740 15th St. N.W., 8th Floor 20005-1009; (202) 662-1950. Fax, (202) 662-1597. Mark Ellis, executive director. Internet, ceeli@abanet.org or http://www.abanet. org/ceeli.*

Promotes the rule of law and specific legal reforms in the emerging democracies of central and eastern Europe, Russia, and the new independent states; recruits volunteer legal professionals from the United States and western Europe. Interests include civil, criminal, commercial, and environmental law; judicial restructuring; bar development; and legal education and research.

American Hellenic Institute, *1220 16th St. N.W. 20036; (202) 785-8430. Fax, (202) 785-5178. Eugene Rossides, general counsel. Internet, info@ahiworld.com or http://www.ahiworld.com.*

Works to strengthen trade and commerce between Greece and Cyprus and the United States and within the American Hellenic community.

Balkan Institute, *P.O. Box 27974 20038-7974; (202) 737-1414. Fax, (202) 737-1940. Stephen W. Walker and James R. Hooper, co-directors. Internet, bi@balkaninstitute.org or http://www.balkaninstitute.org.*

Seeks to heighten public awareness of the war in Bosnia-Herzegovina. Provides other organizations with information and educational materials. Helps deliver humanitarian aid to those in need. (Affiliated with Action Council for Peace in the Balkans.)

British-American Business Assn., *P.O. Box 17482 20041; (202) 293-0010. Fax, (202) 296-3332. Christopher G. Nicholson, president. Internet, http://www.baba-dc.org.*

Membership: organizations dedicated to the development of business relations between the United Kingdom and the United States.

British American Security Information Center (BASIC), *1900 L St. N.W., #401 20036; (202) 785-1266. Fax, (202) 387-6298. Daniel T. Plesch, director. Internet, http://www.basicint.org.*

Research organization that analyzes international security policy in Europe and North America. Promotes public awareness of defense and disarmament issues. Monitors and reports on the activities of Congress and the departments of State and Defense.

European-American Business Council, *1333 H St. N.W., #630 20005; (202) 347-9292. Fax, (202) 628-5498. Willard M. Berry, president. Internet, eabc@eabc.org or http://www.eabc.org.*

Membership: American companies with operations in Europe and European companies with operations in the United States. Works for free and fair trade and investment between the United States and the European Union.

French-American Chamber of Commerce, *918 16th St. N.W., #406 20006; (202) 775-0256. Fax, (202) 785-4604. Susan Shillinglaw, executive director. Internet, faccwdc@aol.com.*

Membership: small and large enterprises based in France and the United States. Promotes trade and investment between the U.S. and France. Provides seminars and various cultural events.

German American Business Council, *1413 K St. N.W., #1400 20005; (202) 371-0555. Fax, (202) 408-9369. Leo G. B. Welt, executive director.*

Promotes trade, investment, and business relationships between the United States and Germany. Provides seminars and opportunities for members to meet with industry leaders and government officials.

German Marshall Fund of the United States, *11 Dupont Circle N.W. 20036; (202) 745-3950. Fax, (202)*

265-1662. *Craig Kennedy, president. Internet, info@ gmfus.org.*

U.S. foundation funded by the Federal Republic of Germany as a memorial to the Marshall Plan. Seeks to strengthen U.S.-European relations; explores changing U.S.-European economic roles; supports reform in central and eastern Europe; builds environmental partnerships; promotes contacts between individuals with similar responsibilities in different countries; awards grants; offers fellowships.

Irish American Unity Conference, *529 14th St. N.W., #837 20045; (202) 662-8830. Fax, (202) 662-8831. Andrew L. Somers, president. Toll-free, (800) 947-4282. Internet, iauc@iauc.org or http://www.iauc.org.*

Nationwide organization that encourages nonviolent means of resolving conflict in Northern Ireland. Conducts symposia and provides information on Northern Ireland. Monitors legislation and regulations.

Irish National Caucus, *413 E. Capitol St. S.E. 20003-3810; (202) 544-0568. Fax, (202) 543-2491. Sean McManus, president. Internet, inc@knight-hub.com or http://www.knight-hub.com/inc.*

Educational organization concerned with protecting human rights in Northern Ireland. Seeks to end anti-Catholic discrimination in Northern Ireland through implementation of the McBride principles, initiated in 1984. Advocates nonviolence. Monitors legislation and regulations.

Joint Baltic American National Committee, *400 Hurley Ave., Rockville, MD 20850; (301) 340-1954. Fax, (301) 309-1406. Algis Rimas, chair. Internet, jbanc@jbanc. org or http://www.jbanc.org.*

Washington representative of the Estonian, Latvian, and Lithuanian American communities in the United States; acts as a representative on issues affecting the Baltic states.

National Federation of Croatian Americans, *1329 Connecticut Ave. N.W. 20036; (202) 331-2830. Fax, (202) 331-0050. Edward Yambrusic, acting president. Internet, NFCAhdq@aol.com.*

Membership: Croatian American organizations. Promotes independence, democracy, human rights, and a free-market economy in Croatia and Bosnia-Herzegovina. Supports equal rights in these countries regardless of ethnicity or religious beliefs.

Latin America and the Caribbean

AGENCIES

Agency for International Development, *Latin America and the Caribbean Bureau, 1300 Pennsylvania*

Ave. N.W., #5.8-A 20523-5900; (202) 712-4800. Fax, (202) 216-3012. Mark L. Schneider, assistant administrator.

Advises AID administrator on U.S. policy toward developing Latin American and Caribbean countries. Designs and implements assistance programs for developing nations.

Defense Dept., *Inter-American Affairs, The Pentagon, #4C800 20301-2400; (703) 697-5884. Fax, (703) 695-8404. Maria Fernandez-Greczmiel, deputy assistant secretary.*

Advises the assistant secretary for international security affairs on inter-American matters; aids in the development of U.S. policy toward Latin America.

Inter-American Foundation, *901 N. Stuart St., 10th Floor, Arlington, VA 22203; (703) 841-3811. Fax, (703) 841-0973. George A. Evans, president. Information, (703) 841-3800. Internet, http://www.iaf.gov.*

Supports small-scale Latin American and Caribbean social and economic development efforts through grassroots development programs, grants, and fellowships.

International Trade Administration *(Commerce Dept.), NAFTA Office, 14th St. and Constitution Ave. N.W., #3022 20230; (202) 482-0393. Fax, (202) 482-5865. Juliet Bender, director. Fax-on-demand, (202) 482-4464. Internet, http://www.itaiep.doc.gov/nafta/nafta2.htm.*

Coordinates Commerce Dept. activities regarding NAFTA (North American Free Trade Agreement). Maintains, with Latin America office of International Trade Administration, a fax-on-demand system for information on NAFTA and on doing business in Latin America and the Caribbean, including Haiti.

Panama Canal Commission, *1825 Eye St. N.W., #1050 20006-5402; (202) 634-6441. Fax, (202) 634-6439. John A. Mills, secretary. Internet, http://www.pananet.com/ pancanal.*

Independent federal agency that manages, operates, and maintains the Panama Canal and its complementary works, installations, and equipment; provides for the orderly transit of vessels through the canal.

State Dept., *Bureau of Inter-American Affairs, Main State Bldg., #6263 20520-6258; (202) 647-5780. Fax, (202) 647-0791. Jeffrey Davidow, assistant secretary. Information, (202) 647-4726.*

Advises the secretary on U.S. policy toward Latin American and Caribbean countries. Directors, assigned to specific countries within the bureau, aid the assistant secretary.

State Dept., *Andean Affairs, Main State Bldg., #5906 20520-6258; (202) 647-1715. Fax, (202) 647-2628. David Passage, director.*

Includes Bolivia, Colombia, Ecuador, Peru, and Venezuela.

State Dept., *Brazilian, Southern Cone Affairs,* Main State Bldg., #5911 20520-6258; (202) 647-2407. Fax, (202) 736-4475. David F. Rogus, director.

Includes Argentina, Brazil, Chile, Paraguay, and Uruguay.

State Dept., *Caribbean Affairs,* Main State Bldg., #4908 20520-6258; (202) 647-2620. Fax, (202) 647-4477. Peter Reams, director.

Includes Anguilla, Antigua and Barbuda, Aruba, Bahamas, Barbados, British Virgin Islands, Cayman Islands, Dominica, Dominican Republic, Grenada, Guyana, Haiti, Jamaica, Martinique, Montserrat, Netherlands Antilles, St. Kitts and Nevis, St. Lucia, St. Vincent and the Grenadines, Suriname, Trinidad and Tobago, and Turks and Caicos Islands.

State Dept., *Central American Affairs,* Main State Bldg., #4915 20520-6258; (202) 647-4010. Fax, (202) 647-2597. Donald F. McConville, director.

Includes Belize, Costa Rica, El Salvador, Guatemala, Honduras, Nicaragua, and Panama.

State Dept., *Cuban Affairs,* Main State Bldg., #3234 20520-3234; (202) 647-9272. Fax, (202) 736-4476. Michael Ranneberger, director.

State Dept., *Mexican Affairs,* Main State Bldg., #4258 20520-6258; (202) 647-9894. Fax, (202) 647-5752. John Leonard, director. Internet, http://www.state.gov/www/regions/ara/mexico.html.

State Dept., *U.S. Mission to the Organization of American States,* Main State Bldg., #6494 20520-6258; (202) 647-9376. Fax, (202) 647-0911. Victor Marrero, U.S. permanent representative. Press, (202) 647-9378.

Formulates U.S. policy and represents U.S. interests at the Organization of American States (OAS).

U.S. Information Agency, *Inter-American Affairs,* 301 4th St. S.W., #750 20547; (202) 619-4860. Fax, (202) 619-5172. Linda Jewell, director.

Administers USIA programs throughout Central and South America and the Caribbean in support of U.S. policies. Manages U.S. information service offices in individual countries that conduct cultural and educational exchange programs through lectures, radio broadcasts, films, television, and other media outlets. Advises the president, Congress, and federal agencies on U.S. policies toward Latin America.

CONGRESS

House International Relations Committee, *Subcommittee on the Western Hemisphere,* 2401A RHOB 20515; (202) 226-7820. Fax, (202) 226-2722. Elton Gallegly, R-Calif., chair; Vince Morelli, staff director. Internet, http://www.house.gov/international_relations.

Jurisdiction over foreign affairs legislation dealing with Latin America, the Caribbean, Mexico, and Canada. Concurrent jurisdiction over matters assigned to the functional House International Relations subcommittees insofar as they affect the region.

Library of Congress, *Hispanic Division,* 101 Independence Ave. S.E., #LJ-240 20540-4850; (202) 707-5400. Fax, (202) 707-2005. Georgette Dorn, chief. Reference staff and reading room, (202) 707-5397. Internet, http://lcweb.loc.gov/rr/hispanic.

Reading room staff (in the Hispanic Division Room) orients researchers and scholars in the area of Iberian, Latin American, Caribbean, and U.S. Latino studies. Primary and secondary source materials are available in the library's general collections for the study of all periods, from pre-Columbian to the present. All major subject areas are represented with emphasis on history, literature, and the social sciences; the "Archive of Hispanic Literature on Tape" is available in the reading room.

Senate Foreign Relations Committee, *Subcommittee on Western Hemisphere, Peace Corps, Narcotics, and Terrorism,* SD-450 20510; (202) 224-4651. Fax, (202) 224-0836. Paul Coverdell, R-Ga., chair; Roger Noriega, senior professional staff member. Internet, http://www.senate.gov/committee/foreign.html.

Jurisdiction over foreign affairs legislation dealing with Latin America, the Caribbean, Mexico, and Canada; oversight of all matters of the Peace Corps and the U.S. delegation to the Organization of American States.

INTERNATIONAL ORGANIZATIONS

Inter-American Development Bank, *1300 New York Ave. N.W. 20577; (202) 623-1100. Fax, (202) 623-1799. Enrique V. Iglesias, president; Vacant, U.S. executive director. Information, (202) 623-1000. Press, (202) 623-1371. Library, (202) 623-3211. Internet, http://www.iadb.org.*

Promotes, through loans and technical assistance, the investment of public and private capital in member countries for social and economic development purposes. Facilitates economic integration of the Latin American region. Library open to the public by appointment.

International Bank for Reconstruction and Development (World Bank), *Latin America and the*

Caribbean, *1850 Eye St. N.W. (mailing address: 1818 H St. N.W., Washington, DC 20433); (202) 458-2332. Fax, (202) 676-9271. Shahid Javed Burki, vice president.*

Encourages public and private foreign investment in the countries of Latin America and the Caribbean through loans, loan guarantees, and technical assistance. Finances economic development projects in agriculture, environmental protection, education, public utilities, telecommunications, water supply, sewerage, public health, and other areas.

Organization of American States (OAS), *17th St. and Constitution Ave. N.W. 20006 (mailing address: 1889 F St. N.W., Washington, DC 20006); (202) 458-3000. Fax, (202) 458-3967. Cesar Gaviria, secretary general. Information, (202) 458-3760. Library, (202) 458-6037. Internet, http://www.oas.org.*

Membership: the United States, Canada, and all independent Latin American and Caribbean countries. Funded by quotas paid by member states and by contributions to special multilateral funds. Works to promote democracy, eliminate poverty, and resolve disputes among member nations. Provides member states with technical and advisory services in cultural, educational, scientific, social, and economic areas. Library open to the public.

United Nations Economic Commission for Latin America and the Caribbean, *1825 K St. N.W., #1120 20006; (202) 955-5613. Fax, (202) 296-0826. Isaac Cohen, director. Internet, eclac@tmn.com or http://www.eclac.org.*

Membership: Latin American and some industrially developed Western nations. Seeks to strengthen economic relations between countries both within and outside Latin America through research and analysis of socioeconomic problems, training programs, and advisory services to member governments. (Headquarters in Santiago, Chile.)

NONPROFIT

Caribbean/Latin American Action, *1818 N St. N.W., #500 20036; (202) 466-7464. Fax, (202) 822-0075. Antonio Colorado, executive director. Internet, info@claa.org or http://www.claa.org.*

Promotes trade and investment in Caribbean Basin countries; encourages democratic public policy in member countries and works to strengthen private initiatives.

Center for International Policy, *1755 Massachusetts Ave. N.W., #312 20036; (202) 232-3317. Fax, (202) 232-3440. William Goodfellow, director. Internet, http://www.ciponline.org.*

Research and educational organization concerned with peace and security in the Western Hemisphere. Spe-

cial projects include U.S. intelligence policy, and U.S. policy towards Cuba and Haiti. Publishes the *International Policy Report.*

Council of the Americas/Americas Society, Inc., *1310 G St. N.W., #690 20005; (202) 639-0724. Fax, (202) 639-0794. William Price, managing director. Internet, http://www.counciloftheamericas.org.*

Membership: businesses with interests and investments in Latin America. Seeks to expand the role of private enterprise in development of the region. (Headquarters in New York.)

Council on Hemispheric Affairs, *1444 Eye St. N.W., #211 20005; (202) 393-3322. Fax, (202) 216-9193. Laurence R. Birns, director. Internet, coha@coha.org or http://www.coha.org.*

Seeks to expand interest in inter-American relations and increase press coverage of Latin America and Canada. Monitors U.S., Latin American, and Canadian relations, with emphasis on human rights, trade, growth of democratic institutions, freedom of the press, and hemispheric economic and political developments; provides educational materials and analyzes issues. Issues annual survey on human rights and freedom of the press.

Cuban American National Foundation, *1000 Thomas Jefferson St. N.W., #505 20007; (202) 265-2822. Fax, (202) 338-0308. Jose Cardenas, director, Washington Office. Internet, canfnet@icanect.net or http://www.canfnet.org.*

Conducts research and provides information on Cuba; supports the establishment of a democratic government in Cuba. Library open to the public by appointment. (Headquarters in Miami.)

Guatemala Human Rights Commission/USA, *3321 12th St. N.E. 20017-4008; (202) 529-6599. Fax, (202) 526-4611. Alice Zachmann, coordinator. Internet, ghrc@igc.apc.org.*

Provides information and collects and makes available reports on human rights violations in Guatemala; publishes a bimonthly report of documented cases of specific abuses and a quarterly bulletin of human rights news and analysis. Takes on special projects to further sensitize the public and the international community to human rights abuses in Guatemala.

Inter-American Dialogue, *1211 Connecticut Ave. N.W., #510 20036-2701; (202) 822-9002. Fax, (202) 822-9553. Peter Hakim, president. Internet, iad@iadialog.org or http://www.iadialog.org.*

Serves as a forum for communication and exchange among leaders of the Americas. Provides analyses and policy recommendations on issues of hemispheric concern. Interests include economic integration and the strengthening of democracy in Latin America. Sponsors conferences and seminars.

Network in Solidarity with the People of Guatemala, *1830 Connecticut Ave. N.W. 20009; (202) 223-6474. Fax, (202) 223-8221. Lael Parish, executive director. Internet, nisgua@igc.apc.org or http://www.scruz. net/~goyo/nisgua/home.html.*

Membership: organizations interested in promoting social justice and human rights in Central America. Opposes U.S. intervention in Central America; seeks to inform the public about human rights and U.S. policy in Guatemala.

Pan American Development Foundation, *2600 16th St. N.W. 20009-4202; (202) 458-3969. Fax, (202) 458-6316. John Davison, acting executive director.*

Works with the public and private sectors to improve the quality of life throughout the Caribbean and Latin America. Associated with the Organization of American States (OAS).

Partners of the Americas, *1424 K St. N.W., #700 20005; (202) 628-3300. Fax, (202) 628-3306. William S. Reese, president. Internet, http://www.partners.net.*

Membership: individuals in the United States, Latin America, and the Caribbean. Sponsors technical assistance projects and exchanges between the United States, Latin America, and the Caribbean; supports self-help projects in agriculture, public health, education, and democratic participation.

Religious Task Force on Central America and Mexico, *3053 4th St. N.E. 20017; (202) 529-0441. Margaret Swedish, director. Internet, rtfca@igc.org.*

Network of religious-based organizations and individuals concerned about Central America and Mexico. Provides information and promotes human rights and social justice in the region.

U.S.-Mexico Chamber of Commerce, *1726 M St. N.W., #704 20036; (202) 296-5198. Fax, (202) 728-0768. Albert C. Zapanta, president. Internet, http://www.usmcoc.org.*

Promotes trade and investment between the United States and Mexico. Provides members with information and expertise on conducting business between the two countries. Serves as a clearinghouse for information.

Washington Office on Latin America, *400 C St. N.E. 20002; (202) 544-8045. Fax, (202) 546-5288. George Vickers, director. Internet, wola@wola.org or http://www.wola.org.*

Acts as a liaison between government policymakers and groups concerned with human rights and U.S. policy

in Latin America. Disseminates information. Monitors legislation.

Near East and South Asia

(Includes North Africa)

AGENCIES

Agency for International Development, *Asia and Near East Bureau, 1300 Pennsylvania Ave. N.W., #4.09-034 20523; (202) 712-0200. Fax, (202) 216-3386. Kelly Kammerer, acting assistant administrator.*

Advises AID administrator on U.S. economic development policy in Asia and the Near East.

Defense Dept., *Near East and South Asia Affairs, The Pentagon, #4D765 20301; (703) 697-5146. Fax, (703) 693-6795. Alina Romanowski, deputy assistant secretary.*

Advises the assistant secretary for international security affairs on matters dealing with the Near East and South Asia.

State Dept., *Bureau of Near Eastern Affairs, Main State Bldg., #6241 20520-6243; (202) 647-7209. Fax, (202) 736-4462. Martin Indyk, assistant secretary. Information, (202) 647-5150.*

Advises the secretary on U.S. policy toward countries of the Near East and North Africa. Directors, assigned to specific countries within the bureau, aid the assistant secretary.

State Dept., *Bureau of South Asian Affairs, Main State Bldg., #6254 20520-6258; (202) 736-4325. Fax, (202) 736-4333. Karl F. Inderfurth, assistant secretary. Information, (202) 736-4255.*

Advises the secretary on U.S. policy toward South Asian countries. Directors, assigned to specific countries within the bureau, aid the assistant secretary.

State Dept., *Arabian Peninsula Affairs, Main State Bldg., #4224 20520-6243; (202) 647-6184. Fax, (202) 736-4459. John Craig, director.*

Includes Bahrain, Kuwait, Oman, Qatar, Saudi Arabia, United Arab Emirates, and Yemen.

State Dept., *Egyptian and North African Affairs, Main State Bldg., #5250A 20520-6243; (202) 647-2300. Fax, (202) 736-4460. Ronald Schlicher, director.*

Includes Algeria, Egypt, Libya, Morocco, and Tunisia.

State Dept., *India, Nepal, and Sri Lanka Affairs, Main State Bldg., #5251 20520-6243; (202) 647-2141. Fax, (202) 736-4463. Steve Mann, director.*

Includes Bhutan and Maldives.

State Dept., *Israel and Arab-Israeli Affairs,* Main State Bldg., #6251 20520; (202) 647-3672. Fax, (202) 736-4461. David Satterfield, director.

State Dept., *Lebanon, Jordan, Palestine, and Syria Affairs,* Main State Bldg., #6250 20520-6243; (202) 647-2670. Fax, (202) 647-0989. Elizabeth McKune, director.

State Dept., *Northern Gulf Affairs,* Main State Bldg., #4515 20520; (202) 647-5692. Fax, (202) 736-4464. Ann Korky, director.

Includes Iran and Iraq.

State Dept., *Pakistan, Afghanistan, and Bangladesh Affairs,* Main State Bldg., #5247 20520-6258; (202) 647-7593. Fax, (202) 647-3001. Michael E. Malanowsky, director.

U.S. Information Agency, *North Africa, Near East, and South Asian Affairs,* 301 4th St. S.W., #866 20547; (202) 619-5526. Fax, (202) 619-5605. David P. Good, director.

Administers USIA programs throughout North Africa, the Near East, and South Asia in support of U.S. policies. Manages U.S. information services offices in individual countries that conduct cultural and educational exchange programs through lectures, radio broadcasts, films, television, and other media outlets. Advises the president, Congress, and federal agencies on U.S. policies toward North Africa, the Near East, and South Asia.

CONGRESS

House International Relations Committee, *Subcommittee on Asia and the Pacific,* B-359 RHOB 20515; (202) 226-7825. Fax, (202) 226-7829. Doug Bereuter, R-Neb., chair; Michael Ennis, staff director. Internet, http://www.house.gov/international_relations.

Jurisdiction over foreign affairs legislation dealing with East Asia and the Pacific, the Near East, and South Asia, from Afghanistan to the Far East. Concurrent jurisdiction over matters assigned to the functional House International Relations subcommittees insofar as they affect the region.

Library of Congress, *African and Middle Eastern Division,* 110 2nd St. S.E., #220 20540; (202) 707-7937. Fax, (202) 252-3180. Beverly Gray, chief.

Maintains collections of African, Near Eastern, and Hebraic material. Prepares bibliographies and special studies relating to Africa and the Middle East. Reference service and reading rooms available to the public.

Library of Congress, *Asian Division,* 110 2nd St. S.E., #LJ149 20540-4740; (202) 707-5420. Fax, (202) 707-1724. Mya Thanda Poe, chief.

Maintains collections of Chinese, Korean, Japanese, Southeast Asian, and South Asian material covering all subjects except law, technical agriculture, and clinical medicine. Reference service is provided in the Asian Reading Room.

Senate Foreign Relations Committee, *Subcommittee on Near Eastern and South Asian Affairs,* SD-450 20510; (202) 224-4651. Fax, (202) 224-0836. Sam Brownback, R-Kan., chair; Danielle Pletka, senior professional staff member. Internet, http://www.senate.gov/committee/foreign.html.

Jurisdiction over foreign affairs legislation dealing with the Near East and South Asia, including the Arab states and Israel, Bhutan, Bangladesh, India, Pakistan, Afghanistan, Nepal, Sri Lanka, and across North Africa from Egypt to Morocco.

INTERNATIONAL ORGANIZATIONS

International Bank for Reconstruction and Development (World Bank), *Middle East and North Africa,* 600 19th St. N.W. (mailing address: 1818 H St. N.W., #H7605, Washington, DC 20433); (202) 473-2776. Fax, (202) 477-0810. Kemal Dervis, vice president.

Encourages public and private foreign investment in the countries of the Middle East and North Africa through loans, loan guarantees, and technical assistance. Finances economic development projects in agriculture, education, public utilities, telecommunications, water supply, sewerage, and other areas.

International Bank for Reconstruction and Development (World Bank), *South Asia,* 1818 H St. N.W., MC10-123 20433; (202) 458-0600. Fax, (202) 522-3707. Mieko Nishimizu, vice president.

Encourages public and private foreign investment in the countries of South Asia through loans, loan guarantees, and technical assistance. Finances economic development projects in agriculture, environmental protection, education, public utilities, telecommunications, water supply, sewerage, public health, and other areas.

League of Arab States, 1100 17th St. N.W., #602 20036; (202) 265-3210. Fax, (202) 331-1525. Khalid M. Abdalla, director, Washington Office.

Intergovernmental organization of Arab states. Seeks to improve Arab-American relations and provide greater understanding of Arab culture and involvement in world affairs. Maintains the Arab Information Center. (Headquarters in Cairo.)

NONPROFIT

American Israel Public Affairs Committee, *440 1st St. N.W., #600 20001; (202) 639-5200. Fax, (202) 347-4889. Howard Kohr, executive director. Internet, help@aipac.org or http://www.aipac.org.*

Works to maintain and improve relations between the United States and Israel.

American Jewish Congress, *2027 Massachusetts Ave. N.W. 20036; (202) 332-4001. Fax, (202) 387-3434. David Harris, Washington representative. Internet, washrep@ajcongress.org or http://www.ajcongress.org.*

National Jewish organization that advocates the maintenance and improvement of U.S.-Israeli relations through legislation, public education, and joint economic ventures. Interests include the Arab boycott of Israel and foreign investment in the United States. (Headquarters in New York.)

American Kurdish Information Network, *2623 Connecticut Ave. N.W., #1 20008-1522; (202) 483-6444. Fax, (202) 483-6476. Kani Xulam, director. Internet, akin@kurdish.org or http://www.kurdistan.org.*

Membership: Americans of Kurdish origin, recent Kurdish immigrants and refugees, and others. Collects and disseminates information about the Kurds, an ethnic group living in parts of Turkey, Iran, Iraq, and Syria. Monitors human rights abuses against Kurds; promotes self-determination in Kurdish homelands; fosters Kurdish American friendship and understanding.

American Near East Refugee Aid, *1522 K St. N.W., #202 20005-1270; (202) 347-2558. Fax, (202) 682-1637. Peter Gubser, president. Internet, anera@mail.anera.org or http://www.anera.org.*

Assists Palestinian and Lebanese grassroots organizations in providing their communities with health and welfare services, employment, and educational opportunities. Provides relief in response to civilian emergencies. (Field offices in Jerusalem and Gaza.)

AMIDEAST, *1730 M St. N.W., #1100 20036; (202) 776-9600. Fax, (202) 776-7000. William Rugh, president. Internet, http://www.amideast.org.*

Promotes understanding and cooperation between Americans and the people of the Middle East and North Africa through education, information, and development programs. Produces educational material to help improve teaching about the Arab world in American schools and colleges.

Asia Foundation, *1779 Massachusetts Ave. N.W., #815 20036; (202) 588-9420. Fax, (202) 588-9409. Nancy Yuan, director. Internet, http://www.asiafoundation.org.*

Provides grants and technical assistance in Asia and the Pacific islands (except the Middle East). Seeks to strengthen legislatures, legal and judicial systems, market economies, the media, and nongovernmental organizations. (Headquarters in San Francisco.)

Asia Society, *1800 K St. N.W., #1102 20006; (202) 833-2742. Fax, (202) 833-0189. Judith Sloan, director, Washington Office. Internet, http://www.asiasociety.org.*

Membership: individuals interested in Asia and the Pacific (excluding the Middle East). Sponsors seminars and lectures on political, economic, and cultural issues. (Headquarters in New York.)

Center for Contemporary Arab Studies *(Georgetown University), 241 Intercultural Center 20057-1020; (202) 687-5793. Fax, (202) 687-7001. Barbara Stowasser, director. Internet, http://www.georgetown.edu/sfs/programs/ccas.*

Sponsors lecture series, seminars, and conferences. Conducts a community outreach program which assists secondary school teachers in the development of instructional materials on the Middle East; promotes the study of the Arabic language in area schools.

Council on American-Islamic Relations, *1050 17th St. N.W., #490 20036; (202) 659-2247. Fax, (202) 659-2254. Nihad Awad, executive director. Internet, cair1@ix.netcom.com or http://www.cair-net.org.*

Promotes an Islamic perspective on issues of importance to the American public. Seeks to empower the Muslim community in America through political and social activism.

Foundation for Middle East Peace, *1763 N St. N.W. 20036; (202) 835-3650. Fax, (202) 835-3651. Lucius D. Battle, president. Internet, http://www.fmep.org.*

Educational organization that seeks to promote understanding and resolution of the Israeli-Palestinian conflict. Publishes a bimonthly report, *Israeli Settlement in the Occupied Territories;* provides media with information.

Institute for Palestine Studies, *3501 M St. N.W. 20007; (202) 342-3990. Fax, (202) 342-3927. Philip Mattar, executive director. Internet, jps@cais.com or http://www.cais.net/ipsjps.*

Scholarly research institute that specializes in the history and development of the Palestine problem, the Arab-Israeli conflict, and their peaceful resolution. (Headquarters in Beirut, Lebanon.)

Kashmiri-American Council, *733 15th St. N.W., #1100 20005; (202) 628-6789. Fax, (202) 393-0062. Ghulam*

Nabi Fai, executive director. Internet, http://www.erols.com/gfai.

Promotes self-determination for Jammu and Kashmir, a region claimed by both India and Pakistan; monitors human rights violations in the region; fosters unity and social interaction among people of Kashmiri ancestry, regardless of religious or political affiliations.

Middle East Institute, *1761 N St. N.W. 20036-2882; (202) 785-1141. Fax, (202) 331-8861. Roscoe Suddarth, president. Library, (202) 785-0183. Language Dept., (202) 785-2710. Internet, mei@mideasti.org or http://www.mideasti.org/mei.*

Membership: individuals interested in the Middle East. Seeks to broaden knowledge of the Middle East through research, conferences and seminars, language classes, lectures, and exhibits. Library open to the public.

Middle East Policy Council, *1730 M St. N.W., #512 20036-4505; (202) 296-6767. Fax, (202) 296-5791. Chas. W. Freeman Jr., president. Internet, general@mepc.org or http://www.mepc.org.*

Encourages public discussion and understanding of issues affecting U.S. policy in the Middle East. Sponsors conferences for the policy community; conducts workshops for high school teachers nationwide.

Middle East Research and Information Project, *1500 Massachusetts Ave. N.W., #119 20005; (202) 223-3677. Fax, (202) 223-3604. Judy Barselou, executive director. Internet, merip@igc.org or http://www.merip.org.*

Works to educate the public about the contemporary Middle East. Focuses on U.S. policy in the region and issues of human rights and social justice.

National Assn. of Arab-Americans, *1212 New York Ave. N.W., #230 20005-3987; (202) 842-1840. Fax, (202) 842-1614. Khalil Jahshan, president. Internet, naaainc@erols.com or http://www.naaa.net.*

Organization of Americans of Arab descent or heritage. Acts as a representative on political issues for its membership; sponsors Mid-East Policy and Research Center.

National Council on U.S.-Arab Relations, *1140 Connecticut Ave. N.W., #1210 20036; (202) 293-0801. Fax, (202) 293-0903. John Duke Anthony, president. Internet, info@ncusar.org or http://www.ncusar.org.*

Educational organization that works to improve mutual understanding between the United States and the Arab world. Serves as a clearinghouse on Arab issues and maintains speakers bureau. Coordinates trips for U.S. professionals and congressional delegations to the Arab world.

National U.S.-Arab Chamber of Commerce, *1100 New York Ave. N.W., #550, E. Tower 20005; (202) 289-5920. Fax, (202) 289-5938. Richard Holmes, president. Internet, http://www.nusacc.com.*

Promotes trade between the United States and the Arab world. Offers members informational publications, research and certification services, and opportunities to meet with international delegations.

New Israel Fund, *1625 K St. N.W., #500 20006; (202) 223-3333. Fax, (202) 659-2789. Norman Rosenberg, executive director. Internet, info@nif.org or http://www.nif.org.*

International philanthropic partnership of North Americans, Israelis, and Europeans. Supports activities that defend civil and human rights, promote Jewish-Arab equality and coexistence, advances the status of women, nurtures tolerance, bridges social and economic gaps, encourages government accountability, and assists citizen efforts to protect the environment. Makes grants and provides capacity-building assistance to Israeli public interest groups; trains civil rights and environmental lawyers.

United Palestinian Appeal, *2100 M St. N.W., #409 20037; (202) 659-5007. Fax, (202) 296-0224. Makboula Yasin, financial officer. Internet, upa@cais.com or http://www.cais.net/upa.*

Charitable organization dedicated to improving the quality of life for Palestinians in the Middle East, particularly those in the West Bank, the Gaza Strip, and refugee camps. Provides funding for community development projects, health care, education, children's services, and emergency relief. Funded by private donations from individuals and foundations in the United States and Arab world.

Washington Institute for Near East Policy, *1828 L St. N.W., #1050 20036; (202) 452-0650. Fax, (202) 223-5364. Robert Satloff, executive director. Internet, info@washingtoninstitute.org or http://www.washingtoninstitute.org.*

Research and educational organization that seeks to improve the effectiveness of American policy in the Near East by promoting debate among policymakers, journalists, and scholars.

Russia and New Independent States

For the Baltic states, see Europe and Canada

AGENCIES

Agency for International Development, *Europe and the New Independent States Bureau, 1300 Pennsylvania Ave. N.W., #5.06 20523-5600; (202) 712-5123. Fax, (202) 216-5057. Donald Pressly, acting assistant administrator.*

Advises AID administrator on U.S. economic development policy in Europe and the new independent states.

Kennan Institute for Advanced Russian Studies, *370 L'Enfant Promenade S.W., #704 20024-2518; (202) 287-3400. Fax, (202) 287-3772. Blair A. Ruble, director. Internet, http://wwics.si.edu/PROGRAMS/REGION/ KENNAN/kennan.htm.*

Offers residential research scholarships to academic scholars and to specialists from government, media, and the private sector for studies to improve American knowledge about Russia and the former Soviet Union. Sponsors lectures; publishes reports; promotes dialogue between academic specialists and policymakers. (Affiliated with the Woodrow Wilson International Center for Scholars.)

State Dept., *Ambassadors-at-Large (NIS), Main State Bldg., #7531 20520-7512; (202) 647-3112. Fax, (202) 647-2699. Stephen R. Sestanovich, ambassador-at-large.*

Handles relations with Russia and other countries of the former Soviet Union, except the Baltic states; assists other agencies in dealings with the new independent states. Directors, assigned to specific countries, aid the ambassadors-at-large.

State Dept., *Caucasus and Central Eurasian Security Affairs, Main State Bldg., #4217 20520-7512; (202) 647-9370. Fax, (202) 736-4710. Stephen Young, Director.*

Includes Armenia, Azerbaijan, and Georgia.

State Dept., *Russian Affairs, Main State Bldg., #4223 20520-7512; (202) 647-9806. Fax, (202) 647-3506. George Krol, director.*

State Dept., *Western Slavic and Moldovan Affairs, Main State Bldg., #4225 20520-7512; (202) 647-8671. Fax, (202) 647-3506. Jack D. Segal, director.*

Includes Belarus, Moldova, and Ukraine.

U.S. Information Agency, *East European and NIS Affairs, 301 4th St. S.W., #868 20547; (202) 619-4563. Fax, (202) 401-6893. Robert E. McCarthy, director.*

Administers USIA programs in eastern Europe and the new independent states in support of U.S. policies. Manages U.S. information service offices in individual countries that conduct cultural and educational exchange programs through lectures, radio broadcasts, films, and television. Advises the president, Congress, and federal agencies on U.S. policies toward eastern Europe and the new independent states.

CONGRESS

House International Relations Committee, *2170 RHOB 20515; (202) 225-5021. Fax, (202) 225-2035. Benjamin A. Gilman, R-N.Y., chair; Richard J. Garon Jr., chief of staff. Internet, http://www.house.gov/international_ relations.*

Jurisdiction over legislation dealing with Russia and the new independent states. Concurrent jurisdiction over matters assigned to the functional House International Relations subcommittees insofar as they affect the region.

Library of Congress, *European Division, 101 Independence Ave. S.E. 20540-4830; (202) 707-5414. Fax, (202) 707-8482. John Van Oudenaren, chief. Reference desk, (202) 707-4515. Internet, http://lcweb.loc.gov/rreuropean.*

Provides reference service on the library's European collections (except collections on Spain, Portugal, and the British Isles). Prepares bibliographies and special studies relating to European countries, including Russia and the new independent states. Maintains current unbound Slavic language periodicals and newspapers, which are available at the European Reference Desk.

Senate Foreign Relations Committee, *SD-450 20510; (202) 224-4651. Fax, (202) 224-0836. Jesse Helms, R-N.C., chair; James W. "Bud" Nance, staff director. Internet, http://www.senate.gov/committee/foreign.html.*

Jurisdiction over legislation dealing with Russia and the new independent states. Concurrent jurisdiction over matters assigned to the functional Senate Foreign Relations subcommittees insofar as they affect the region.

INTERNATIONAL ORGANIZATIONS

International Bank for Reconstruction and Development (World Bank), *Europe and Central Asia, 600 19th St. N.W. (mailing address: 1818 H St. N.W., Washington, DC 20433); (202) 458-0602. Fax, (202) 477-1942. Johannes Linn, vice president.*

Encourages public and private foreign investment in eastern Europe and central Asia, including the former Soviet Union, through loans, loan guarantees, and technical assistance. Finances economic development projects in agriculture, environmental protection, education, energy, public utilities, telecommunications, water supply, sewerage, public health, and other areas.

NONPROFIT

American Bar Assn., *Central and East European Law Initiative, 740 15th St. N.W., 8th Floor 20005-1009; (202) 662-1950. Fax, (202) 662-1597. Mark Ellis, executive director. Internet, ceeli@abanet.org or http://www.abanet.org/ceeli.*

Promotes the rule of law and specific legal reforms in the emerging democracies of central and eastern Europe, Russia, and the new independent states; recruits volunteer legal professionals from the United States and west-ern Europe. Interests include civil, criminal, commercial, and environmental law; judicial restructuring; bar development; and legal education and research.

American Council of Teachers of Russian, *1776 Massachusetts Ave. N.W., #700 20036; (202) 833-7522. Fax, (202) 833-7523. Lisa Choate, assistant director. Internet, general@actr.org or http://www.actr.org.*

Conducts educational exchanges for high school, university, and graduate school students as well as scholars with the countries of the former Soviet Union and Eastern Europe. Assists the countries of the former Soviet Union in implementing education reforms, advises them on academic testing, and provides them with language instruction materials. Supports a network of U.S. educators who study Russian language and the countries of the former Soviet Union.

Armenian Assembly of America, *122 C St. N.W., #350 20001; (202) 393-3434. Fax, (202) 638-4904. Ross Vartian, executive director. Internet, http://www.aaainc.org.*

Promotes public understanding and awareness of Armenian issues; advances research and data collection and disseminates information on the Armenian people; advocates greater Armenian American participation in the American democratic process; works to alleviate human suffering of Armenians.

Eurasia Foundation, *1527 New Hampshire Ave. N.W. 20036; (202) 234-7370. Fax, (202) 234-7377. Charles Williams Maynes, president. Internet, eurasia@eurasia.org or http://www.eurasia.org.*

Grantmaking organization that funds programs that build democratic and free market institutions in the new independent states. Interests include economic and governmental reform, development of the nonprofit sector, and projects in media and communications.

Free Congress Research and Education Foundation, *717 2nd St. N.E. 20002-4368; (202) 546-3004. Fax, (202) 543-8425. Paul M. Weyrich, president. Internet, net@fcref.org or http://www.fcref.org.*

Public policy research and education foundation. Through the Krieble Institute, provides citizens of the former Soviet bloc with training in democratic processes and free enterprise.

Institute for European, Russian, and Eurasian Studies *(George Washington University), 2013 G St. N.W., #401 20052; (202) 994-6340. Fax, (202) 994-5436. James R. Millar, director.*

Studies and researches European, Russian, and Eurasian affairs. Sino-Soviet Information Center open to the public.

National Conference on Soviet Jewry, *1640 Rhode Island Ave. N.W., #501 20036; (202) 898-2500. Fax, (202) 898-0822. Mark B. Levin, executive director. Internet, ncsj@erols.com.*

Membership: national Jewish organizations and local federations. Coordinates efforts by members to aid Jews in the former Soviet Union, including Jewish families attempting to emigrate.

Ukrainian National Information Service, *214 Massachusetts Ave. N.E., #225 20002; (202) 547-0018. Fax, (202) 543-5502. Michael Sawkiw, director. Internet, unis@ucca.org.*

Information bureau of the Ukrainian Congress Committee of America in New York. Provides information and monitors U.S. policy on Ukraine and the Ukrainian community in the United States and abroad. (Headquarters in New York.)

U.S.-Russia Business Council, *1701 Pennsylvania Ave. N.W., #650 20006; (202) 739-9180. Fax, (202) 659-5920. Eugene K. Lawson, president. Press, (202) 739-9184.*

Membership: U.S. companies involved in trade and investment in Russia. Promotes commercial ties between the United States and Russia.

U.S. Territories and Associated States

AGENCIES

Interior Dept., *Insular Affairs, 1849 C St. N.W., #4311, Mail Drop 4328 20240; (202) 208-4736. Fax, (202) 501-7759. Allen P. Stayman, director.*

Promotes economic, social, and political development of U.S. territories (Guam, American Samoa, the Virgin Islands, and the Commonwealth of the Northern Mariana Islands). Supervises federal programs for the freely associated states (Federated States of Micronesia, Republic of the Marshall Islands, and Republic of Palau).

CONGRESS

American Samoa's Delegate to Congress, *2422 RHOB 20515; (202) 225-8577. Fax, (202) 225-8757. Eni F. H. Faleomavaega, D-Am. Samoa, delegate.*

Represents American Samoa in Congress.

Guam's Delegate to Congress, *424 CHOB 20515; (202) 225-1188. Fax, (202) 226-0341. Robert A. Underwood, D-Guam, delegate.*

Represents Guam in Congress.

House Appropriations Committee, *Subcommittee on Interior, B308 RHOB 20515; (202) 225-3081. Fax, (202) 225-9069. Ralph Regula, R-Ohio, chair; Deborah A.*

Weatherly, clerk. Internet, http://www.house.gov/
appropriations.

Jurisdiction over legislation to appropriate funds for
territorial affairs.

House Resources Committee, *1324 LHOB 20515-*
6201; (202) 225-2761. Fax, (202) 225-5929. Don Young,
R-Alaska, chair; Lloyd Jones, staff director. Internet,
resource@hr.house.gov or http://www.house.gov/resources.

Jurisdiction, oversight, and investigative authority
over activities, policies, and programs for U.S. territories
(Guam, American Samoa, Puerto Rico, the Northern
Mariana Islands, and the Virgin Islands) and for the
freely associated states (Federated States of Micronesia,
Republic of the Marshall Islands, Republic of Palau).

Puerto Rican Resident Commissioner, *2443 RHOB*
20515; (202) 225-2615. Fax, (202) 225-2154. Carlos
Romero-Barceló, D-Puerto Rico, resident commissioner.

Represents the Commonwealth of Puerto Rico in
Congress.

Senate Appropriations Committee, *Subcommittee*
on Interior, SD-131 20510; (202) 224-7233. Slade Gorton,
R-Wash., chair; Bruce Evans, staff director. Internet, http://
www.senate.gov/~appropriations.

Jurisdiction over legislation to appropriate funds for
territorial and Pacific island affairs.

Senate Energy and Natural Resources Committee,
SD-364 20510; (202) 224-4971. Fax, (202) 224-6163.
Frank H. Murkowski, R-Alaska, chair; Gregg D. Renkes,
staff director. Internet, http://www.senate.gov/~energy.

Jurisdiction, oversight, and investigative authority
over activities, policies, and programs for U.S. territories
(Guam, American Samoa, Puerto Rico, the Northern
Mariana Islands, and the Virgin Islands) and for the
freely associated states (Federated States of Micronesia,
Republic of the Marshall Islands, and Republic of
Palau).

Virgin Islands Delegate to Congress, *1711 LHOB*
20515; (202) 225-1790. Fax, (202) 225-5517. Donna M.
Christian-Green, D-Virgin Is., delegate.

Represents the Virgin Islands in Congress.

NONPROFIT

Puerto Rico Federal Affairs Administration, *1100*
17th St. N.W., #800 20036; (202) 778-0710. Fax, (202)
778-0721. Xavier Romeu, director. Press, (202) 778-0289.
Internet, http://www.prfaa-govpr.org.

Represents the governor and the government of the
Commonwealth of Puerto Rico before Congress and the
executive branch; conducts research; serves as official
press information center for the Commonwealth of
Puerto Rico. Monitors legislation and regulations.

U.S. Virgin Islands Department of Tourism, *444 N.*
Capitol St. N.W., #298 20001; (202) 624-3590. Fax, (202)
624-3594. Nicholas Berry, regional manager. Internet,
http://www.usvi.net.

Provides information about the U.S. Virgin Islands;
promotes tourism. (Headquarters in St. Thomas.)

14 ⚖

Law and
Justice

GENERAL POLICY

See also Public Interest Law (chap. 1)

AGENCIES

Executive Office for U.S. Attorneys *(Justice Dept.),* *950 Pennsylvania Ave. N.W., #2241 20530; (202) 514-2121. Fax, (202) 616-2278. Donna A. Bucella, director. Information, (202) 514-1020. Internet, http://www.usdoj.gov/usao/eousa.*

Provides the offices of U.S. attorneys with technical assistance and supervision in areas of legal counsel, personnel, and training. Publishes the *U.S. Attorneys' Manual.* Administers the Attorney General's Advocacy Institute, which conducts workshops and seminars to develop the litigation skills of the department's attorneys in criminal and civil trials. Develops and implements Justice Dept. procedures and policy for collecting criminal fines.

Justice Dept., *950 Pennsylvania Ave. N.W., #5111 20530; (202) 514-2001. Fax, (202) 514-4371. Janet Reno, attorney general; Eric H. Holder Jr., deputy attorney general, (202) 514-2101. Information, (202) 514-2000. Internet, http://www.usdoj.gov.*

Investigates and prosecutes violations of federal laws; represents the government in federal cases and interprets laws under which other departments act. Supervises federal corrections system; administers immigration and naturalization laws. Justice Dept. organization includes divisions on antitrust, civil law, civil rights, criminal law, environment and natural resources, and tax, as well as the Federal Bureau of Investigation, Federal Bureau of Prisons, Office of Legal Counsel, Office of Policy Development, Office of Professional Responsibility, U.S. Parole Commission, Immigration and Naturalization Service, Board of Immigration Appeals, Executive Office for Immigration Review, Drug Enforcement Administration, Foreign Claims Settlement Commission of the United States, Office of Justice Programs, U.S. Marshals Service, and U.S. Trustees.

Justice Dept., *Policy Development, 950 Pennsylvania Ave. N.W., #4234 20530; (202) 514-4601. Fax, (202) 514-2424. Eleanor Dean Acheson, assistant attorney general.*

Studies, develops, and coordinates Justice Dept. policy. Drafts and reviews legislative proposals. Oversees implementation of the Freedom of Information and Privacy acts.

Justice Dept., *Professional Responsibility, 950 Pennsylvania Ave. N.W., #4304 20530; (202) 514-3365. Fax, (202) 514-4371. Richard M. Rogers, acting counsel.*

Receives and reviews allegations of misconduct by Justice Dept. employees; refers cases that warrant further review to appropriate investigative agency or unit; makes recommendations to the attorney general for action on certain misconduct cases.

Justice Dept., *Solicitor General, 950 Pennsylvania Ave. N.W., #5143 20530; (202) 514-2201. Fax, (202) 514-9769. Seth P. Waxman, solicitor general. TDD, (800) 514-3883. Information on pending cases, (202) 514-2218. Internet, http://www.usdoj.gov/osg.*

Represents the federal government before the Supreme Court of the United States.

Office of Justice Programs *(Justice Dept.), 1810 7th St. N.W. 20531; (202) 307-5933. Fax, (202) 514-7805. Laurie Robinson, assistant attorney general. Internet, http://www.ojp.usdoj.gov.*

Sets program policy, provides staff support, and coordinates administration for the National Institute of Justice, which conducts research on criminal justice; the Bureau of Justice Statistics, which gathers and evaluates national crime data; the Office for Victims of Crime, which funds state victim compensation and assistance programs; the Office of Juvenile Justice and Delinquency Prevention, which administers federal juvenile delinquency programs; and the Bureau of Justice Assistance, which provides funds for anticrime programs.

State Justice Institute, *1650 King St., #600, Alexandria, VA 22314; (703) 684-6100. Fax, (703) 684-7618. David I. Tevelin, executive director. Internet, http://www.clark.net/pub/sji/.*

Quasi-governmental corporation established by Congress. Awards grants to state courts and to state agencies working to improve judicial administration in the state courts. Interests include judicial education, court technology, victim assistance, prevention of violence against women, and federal-state relations.

CONGRESS

General Accounting Office, *General Government, 441 G St. N.W., #2A38 20548; (202) 512-8777. Fax, (202) 512-8692. Norman Rabkin, director. Documents, (202) 512-6000.*

Independent, nonpartisan agency in the legislative branch. Audits, analyzes, and evaluates federal administration of justice programs and activities; makes some reports available to the public.

House Appropriations Committee, *Subcommittee on Commerce, Justice, State, and Judiciary, H309 Capitol 20515; (202) 225-3351. Harold Rogers, R-Ky., chair; Jim*

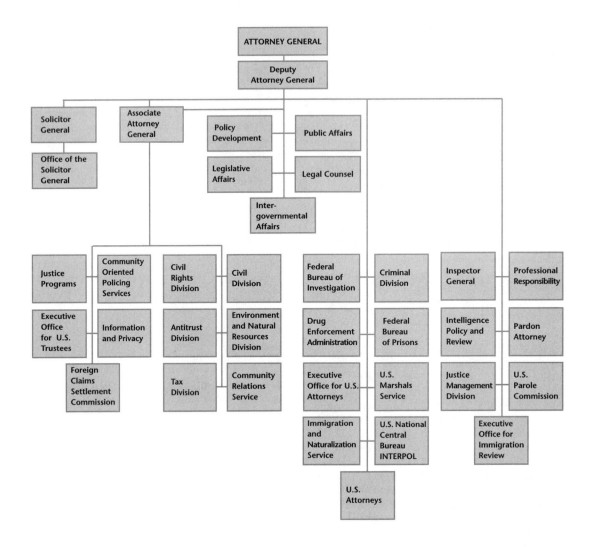

Jurisdiction over legislation to appropriate funds for the Justice Dept., the federal judiciary, the Legal Services Corp., the State Justice Institute, juvenile justice and delinquency prevention, district courts, and other judicial-related services and programs.

House Government Reform and Oversight Committee, *Subcommittee on National Security, International Affairs, and Criminal Justice, B373 RHOB 20515; (202) 225-2577. Fax, (202) 225-1154. Dennis Hastert,*

R-Ill., chair; Robert Charles, staff director. Internet, http://www.house.gov/reform.

Oversees operations of the Justice Dept., the federal judiciary (except the U.S. Tax Court), the Legal Services Corp., and the State Justice Institute.

House Judiciary Committee, *2138 RHOB 20515; (202) 225-3951. Fax, (202) 225-7682. Henry J. Hyde, R-Ill., chair; Thomas Mooney, chief counsel. Internet, http://www.house.gov/judiciary.*

Jurisdiction over legislation on judicial proceedings, constitutional amendments, civil liberties, ethics in government, federal judiciary, federal corrections system, interstate compacts, patents, copyrights and trademarks, bankruptcy, mutiny, espionage and counterfeiting, immigration and naturalization, revision and codification of the statutes of the United States, internal security, local courts in the territories and possessions, protection of trade and commerce against unlawful restraints and monopolies, legislation relating to claims against the United States, and state and territorial boundary lines.

House Judiciary Committee, *Subcommittee on Courts and Intellectual Property, B351A RHOB 20515; (202) 225-5741. Fax, (202) 225-3673. Howard Coble, R-N.C., chair; Mitch Glazier, chief counsel. Internet, http://www. house.gov/judiciary.*

Jurisdiction over legislation on court admistration and management and over rules of civil judicial procedure. Oversees the Administrative Office of the U.S. Courts.

Senate Appropriations Committee, *Subcommittee on Commerce, Justice, State, and Judiciary, SR-393 20510; (202) 224-7277. Judd Gregg, R-N.H., chair, (202) 224-3324; Vas Alexopoulos, legislative assistant. Chair's fax, (202) 224-4952. Internet, http://www.senate.gov/ ~appropriations.*

Jurisdiction over legislation to appropriate funds for the Justice Dept., the federal judiciary, the Legal Services Corp., the State Justice Institute, juvenile justice and delinquency prevention, district courts, and other judicial-related services and programs.

Senate Judiciary Committee, *SD-224 20510; (202) 224-5225. Fax, (202) 224-9102. Orrin G. Hatch, R-Utah, chair; Manus Cooney, chief counsel. Internet, http://www. senate.gov/committee/judiciary.html.*

Jurisdiction over legislation on judicial proceedings, constitutional amendments, civil liberties, ethics in government, federal judiciary, federal corrections system, interstate compacts, government information, patents, copyrights and trademarks, bankruptcy, mutiny, espionage and counterfeiting, immigration and naturalization, revision and codification of the statutes of the United States, internal security, local courts in the territories and possessions, protection of trade and commerce against unlawful restraints and monopolies, legislation relating to claims against the United States, and state and territorial boundary lines. Oversees operations of the Justice Dept., the federal judiciary (except the U.S. Tax Court), the Legal Services Corp., and the State Justice Institute.

Senate Judiciary Committee, *Subcommittee on Administrative Oversight and the Courts, SH-308*

20510; (202) 224-6736. Charles E. Grassley, R-Iowa, chair; Kolan L. Davis, chief counsel. Internet, http://www.senate. gov/committee/judiciary.html.

Jurisdiction over legislation on court administration and management and over rules of civil judicial procedure.

JUDICIARY

Administrative Office of the U.S. Courts, *1 Columbus Circle N.E., #7-100 20544; (202) 273-3000. Fax, (202) 273-2349. L. Ralph Mecham, director. Information, (202) 273-0107. Library, (202) 273-1888. Internet, http://www. uscourts.gov.*

Supervises all nonjudicial, administrative matters of the federal court system, except the Supreme Court. Examines dockets of the courts; prepares statistical data and reports on the business of the courts. Provides the Judicial Conference of the United States with staff assistance; drafts legislative proposals relating to the federal court system. Supervises offices of federal magistrates and federal public defenders.

Federal Judicial Center, *1 Columbus Circle N.E. 20002; (202) 273-4000. Fax, (202) 273-4019. Rya Zobel, director. Press, (202) 273-4153. Internet, http://www.fjc.gov.*

Conducts research on the operations of the federal court system; develops and conducts continuing education and training programs for judges and judicial personnel; and makes recommendations to improve the administration of the courts.

Judicial Conference of the United States, *1 Columbus Circle N.E., #7-425 20544; (202) 273-1140. Fax, (202) 273-1145. William H. Rehnquist, chief justice of the United States, chair; L. Ralph Mecham, secretary. Internet, http:// www.uscourts.gov.*

Serves as the policymaking and governing body for the administration of the federal judicial system; advises Congress on the creation of new federal judgeships. Interests include international judicial relations.

Supreme Court of the United States, *1 1st St. N.E. 20543; (202) 479-3000. William H. Rehnquist, chief justice; William K. Suter, clerk, (202) 479-3011. Library, (202) 479-3177. Supreme Court opinions and information, (202) 479-3211. Internet, http://www.law.cornell.edu/ lii.table.html.*

Highest appellate court in the federal judicial system. Interprets the U.S. Constitution, federal legislation, and treaties. Provides information on new cases filed, the status of pending cases, and admissions to the Supreme Court Bar. Library open to Supreme Court bar members only. *(For complete list of justices, see box in this section.)*

GENERAL COUNSELS FOR FEDERAL AGENCIES

DEPARTMENTS

Agriculture, Bonnie Luken, acting, (202) 720-3351

Commerce, Andrew J. Pincus, (202) 482-4772

Defense, Judith A. Miller, (703) 695-3341

  Air Force, Sheila Cheston, (703) 697-0941

  Army, William T. Coleman III, (703) 697-9235

  Navy, Steven Honigman, (703) 614-1994

Education, Jamie Studley, acting, (202) 401-6000

Energy, Eric J. Fygi, acting, (202) 586-5281

Health and Human Services, Harriet S. Rabb, (202) 690-7741

Housing and Urban Development, Gail Lester, acting, (202) 708-2244

Interior, John Leshy, (202) 208-4423

Justice, Dawn Johnson, acting, (202) 514-2041

Labor, Marvin Krislov, (202) 219-7675

State, David R. Andrews, (202) 647-9598

Transportation, Nancy E. McFadden, (202) 366-4702

Treasury, Edward S. Knight, (202) 622-0287

Veterans Affairs Robert E. Coy, acting, (202) 273-6660

AGENCIES

Advisory Council on Historic Preservation, John M. Fowler, (202) 606-8503

Agency for International Development, Singleton McAllister, (202) 712-4476

Central Intelligence Agency, Robert M. McNamara, Jr., (703) 482-1951

Commission on Civil Rights, Stephanie Moore, (202) 376-8351

Commodity Futures Trading Commission, Daniel R. Waldman, (202) 418-5120

Consumer Product Safety Commission, Jeffrey S. Bromme, (301) 504-0980

Corporation for National Service, Ken Klothen, acting, (202) 606-5000

Environmental Protection Agency, Jonathan Z. Cannon, (202) 260-8040

Equal Employment Opportunity Commission, Clifford Gregory Stewart, (202) 663-4702

Export-Import Bank, Kenneth Hansen, (202) 565-3430

Farm Credit Administration, Jean Noonan, (703) 883-4020

Federal Communications Commission, Christopher J. Wright, (202) 418-1700

Federal Deposit Insurance Corporation, William F. Kroener III, (202) 898-3680

Federal Election Commission, Lawrence M. Noble, (202) 219-3690

Federal Emergency Management Agency, Ernest Abbott, (202) 646-4105

Federal Energy Regulatory Commission, Douglas W. Smith, (202) 208-1000

Federal Labor Relations Authority, Joseph Swerdzewski, (202) 482-6600

Federal Maritime Commission, Thomas Tanebianco, (202) 523-5740

NONPROFIT

Alliance for Justice, *2000 P St. N.W., #712 20036; (202) 822-6070. Fax, (202) 822-6068. Nan Aron, president. Internet, alliance@afj.org or http://www.afj.org.*

Membership: public interest lawyers and advocacy, environmental, civil rights, and consumer organizations. Promotes reform of the legal system to ensure access to the courts; monitors selection of federal judges; works to preserve the rights of nonprofit organizations to advocate on behalf of their constituents.

American Bar Assn., *Washington Office, 740 15th St. N.W. 20005; (202) 662-1000. Fax, (202) 662-1032. Robert D. Evans, director. Information, (202) 662-1010. Library, (202) 662-1011. TDD, (202) 662-1012. Internet, http://www.abanet.org.*

Comprised of the Public Service Division, the Government and Public Sector Division, International Law and Practice Section, Criminal Justice Section, Taxation Section, Individual Rights and Responsibilities Section, Dispute Resolution Section, and others. Acts as a clearinghouse for the association's legislative activities and communicates the status of important bills and regulations to state and local bar associations and to all sections concerned with major governmental activities that affect the legal profession. (Headquarters in Chicago.)

American Tort Reform Assn., *1850 M St. N.W., #1095 20036; (202) 682-1163. Fax, (202) 682-1022. Sherman Joyce, president. Internet, http://www.atra.org.*

Membership: businesses, associations, trade groups, professional societies, and individuals interested in

GENERAL COUNSELS FOR FEDERAL AGENCIES (continued)

Federal Mediation and Conciliation Service, Elizabeth Watson, (202) 606-5443

Federal Reserve System, J. Virgil Mattingly Jr., (202) 452-3430

Federal Trade Commission, Debra A. Valentine, (202) 326-2480

General Services Administration, Emily C. Hewitt, 501-2200

International Bank for Reconstruction and Development (World Bank), Ibrahim F. I. Shihata, (202) 458-1601

Merit Systems Protection Board, Mary L. Jennings, (202) 653-7171

National Aeronautics and Space Administration, Edward A. Frankle, (202) 358-2450

National Credit Union Administration, Robert M. Fenner, (703) 518-6540

National Endowment for the Arts, Karen Christensen, (202) 682-5654

National Endowment for Humanities, Michael S. Shapiro, (202) 606-8322

National Labor Relations Board, Fred Feinstein, (202) 273-3700

National Mediation Board, Ronald M. Etters, (202) 523-5944

National Railroad Passenger Corporation (Amtrak), Sarah Duggin, (202) 906-3402

National Science Foundation, Lawrence Rudolph, (703) 306-1060

National Transportation Safety Board, Daniel D. Campbell, (202) 314-6080

Nuclear Regulatory Commission, Karen D. Cyr, (301) 415-1743

Occupational Safety and Health Review Commission, Earl R. Ohman Jr., (202) 606-5410

Office of Personnel Management, Lorraine Lewis, (202) 606-1700

Overseas Private Investment Corporation, Charles D. Toy, (202) 336-8410

Peace Corps, Nancy Hendry, (202) 606-3114

Pension Benefit Guaranty Corporation, James Keightley, (202) 326-4020

Postal Rate Commission, Stephen Sharfman, (202) 789-6820

Securities and Exchange Commission, Richard H. Walker, (202) 942-0900

Small Business Administration, John T. Spotila, (202) 205-6642

Smithsonian Institution, John E. Huerta, (202) 357-2583

Social Security Administration, Arthur Fried, (410) 965-0600

U.S. Arms Control and Disarmament Agency, Mary Elizabeth Hoinkes (202) 647-3596

U.S. Information Agency, Les Jin, (202) 619-4979

U.S. International Trade Commission, Lyn M. Schlitt, (202) 205-3061

U.S. Postal Service, Mary S. Elcano, (202) 268-2950

---

reforming the civil justice system in the United States. Develops model state legislation and position papers on tort reform. Works with state coalitions in support of tort reform legislation.

Assn. of Trial Lawyers of America, *1050 31st St. N.W. 20007-4499; (202) 965-3500. Fax, (202) 625-7312. Thomas H. Henderson Jr., executive director.*

Membership: attorneys, judges, law professors, and students. Works to strengthen the civil justice system and the right to trial by jury. Interests include victims' rights, property and casualty insurance, revisions of federal rules of evidence, criminal code, jurisdictions of courts, juries, and consumer law.

Center for Study of Responsive Law, *1530 P St. N.W. (mailing address: P.O. Box 19367, Washington, DC 20036);*

(202) 387-8030. Fax, (202) 234-5176. John Richard, administrator. Internet, http://www.csrl.org.

Consumer interest clearinghouse. Conducts research and holds conferences on public interest law. Interests include white-collar crime, the environment, occupational health and safety, the postal system, banking deregulation, insurance, freedom of information policy, and broadcast issues.

Center for the Community Interest, *919 18th St. N.W., #800 20006; (202) 785-7844. Fax, (202) 785-4370. Roger Conner, executive director.*

Community interest group that focuses on crime and quality-of-life issues. Advocates balance between individual rights and responsibility. Interests include drug prevention and anti-violence programs; conducts research and litigates cases. (Operates office in New York.)

Federal Bar Assn., *1815 H St. N.W., #408 20006; (202) 638-0252. Fax, (202) 775-0295. Michael E. Campiglia, executive director. Internet, fba@fedbar.org or http://www.fedbar.org.*

Membership: attorneys employed by the federal government or practicing before federal courts or agencies. Conducts research and programs in fields including tax, Native American, antitrust, immigration, and international law; concerns include professional ethics, legal education (primarily continuing education), and legal services.

Help Abolish Legal Tyranny—An Organization of Americans for Legal Reform, *1612 K St. N.W., #510 20006; (202) 887-8255. Fax, (202) 887-9699. James C. Turner, executive director. Internet, http://www.halt.org.*

Public interest organization concerned with legal reform. Conducts research on alternative dispute resolution programs for delivery of legal services, including arbitration, legal clinics, and mediation services; provides educational and self-help manuals on the use of the legal system. Operates The Law Store, a legal document preparation service created to research, test, and promote innovative techniques for improving access to legal services for the average citizen.

Lawyers for Civil Justice, *2100 M St. N.W., #305 20037; (202) 429-0045. Fax, (202) 429-6982. Barry Bauman, executive director.*

Membership: defense trial lawyers and corporate and insurance attorneys. Interests include tort reform, litigation cost containment, and tort and product liability. Monitors legislation and regulations affecting the civil justice system.

National Assn. for the Advancement of Colored People (NAACP), *1025 Vermont Ave. N.W., #1120 20005; (202) 638-2269. Fax, (202) 638-5936. Hilary Shelton, deputy director. Internet, http://www.naacp.org.*

Membership: persons interested in civil rights for all minorities. Seeks, through litigation, to end discrimination in all areas, including discriminatory practices in the administration of justice. Studies and recommends policy on court administration and jury selection. Maintains branch offices in many state and federal prisons. (Headquarters in Baltimore.)

National Bar Assn., *1225 11th St. N.W. 20001-4217; (202) 842-3900. Fax, (202) 289-6170. John Crump, executive director. Internet, http://www.nationalbar.org.*

Membership: primarily minority attorneys, legal professionals, judges, and law students. Interests include legal education and improvement of the judicial process. Sponsors legal education seminars in all states that require continuing legal education for lawyers.

National Center for State Courts, *1700 N. Moore St., #1710, Arlington, VA 22209; (703) 841-0200. Fax, (703) 841-0206. Thomas A. Henderson, executive director, Government Relations. Internet, http://ncsc.dni.us.*

Works to improve state court systems through research, technical assistance, and training programs. Monitors legislation affecting court systems; interests include habeas corpus and state-federal jurisdiction. Serves as secretariat for several state court organizations, including the Conference of Chief Justices, Conference of State Court Administrators, and American Judges Assn. (Headquarters in Williamsburg, Va.)

National Legal Center for the Public Interest, *1000 16th St. N.W., #500 20036; (202) 296-1683. Fax, (202) 293-2118. Ernest B. Hueter, president.*

Public interest law center and information clearinghouse. Studies judicial issues and the impact of the legal system on the private sector; sponsors seminars; does not litigate cases.

Rand Corporation, *1333 H St. N.W., #800 20005; (202) 296-5000. Fax, (202) 296-7960. David Chu, director, Washington Research Dept. Internet, http://www.rand.org.*

Analyzes current problems of the American civil and criminal justice systems and evaluates recent and pending changes and reforms. (Headquarters in Santa Monica, Calif.)

U.S. Chamber of Commerce, *Business and Government Policy, 1615 H St. N.W., #500 20062-2000; (202) 463-5500. Fax, (202) 887-3445. Randy Johnson, vice president, labor policy. Internet, http://www.uschamber.org.*

Federation of individuals, firms, corporations, trade and professional associations, and local, state, and regional chambers of commerce. Monitors legislation and regulations in administrative law, antitrust policy, civil justice reform, and product liability reform.

Washington Legal Foundation, *2009 Massachusetts Ave. N.W. 20036; (202) 588-0302. Fax, (202) 588-0371. Daniel J. Popeo, general counsel. Internet, http://www.wlf.org.*

Public interest law and policy center. Interests include constitutional law, government regulation, media law, and criminal justice; litigates on behalf of small businesses, members of Congress, and victims of violent crimes who bring civil suits against their attackers.

Women's Bar Assn., *1815 15th St. N.W., #1815 20005; (202) 639-8880. Fax, (202) 639-8889. Jacqueline Pumpaly, executive director. Internet, http://www.wbadc.org.*

Membership: women and men who are judges, attorneys in the public and private sectors, law students, and lawyers at home who remain professionally active. Promotes appointment of members to positions in government and legislative policies that assist women in the workplace.

World Jurist Assn., *1000 Connecticut Ave. N.W., #202 20036-5302; (202) 466-5428. Fax, (202) 452-8540. Margaret M. Henneberry, executive vice president.*

Membership: lawyers, law professors, judges, law students, and nonlegal professionals worldwide. Conducts research; promotes world peace through adherence to international law; holds biennial world conferences. (Affiliates, at same address, include World Assn. of Judges, World Assn. of Law Professors, and World Assn. of Lawyers.)

See also Product Liability Alliance (p. 161)

Dispute Resolution

AGENCIES

Justice Dept., *Alternative Dispute Resolution, 950 Pennsylvania Ave. N.W., #5240 20530; (202) 616-9471. Fax, (202) 616-9570. Peter R. Steenland Jr., senior counsel.*

Division of the office of the associate attorney general. Coordinates Justice Dept. activities related to alternative dispute resolution.

NONPROFIT

American Arbitration Assn., *8201 Greensboro Dr., #610, McLean, VA 22102; (703) 760-4820. Fax, (703) 760-4847. Arnold B. Crews, regional vice president. Internet, webmaster@adr.org or http://www.adr.org.*

Provides dispute resolution services worldwide, including arbitration, mediation, minitrials, and elections. (Headquarters in New York.)

American Bar Assn., *Dispute Resolution, 740 15th St. N.W. 20005; (202) 662-1680. Fax, (202) 662-1683. Jack Hanna, director. Internet, http://www.abanet.org.*

Acts as a clearinghouse on dispute resolution; supports methods for resolving disputes other than litigation; provides technical assistance.

Center for Dispute Settlement, *1666 Connecticut Ave. N.W., #500 20009; (202) 265-9572. Fax, (202) 328-9162. Linda R. Singer, executive director.*

Designs, implements, and evaluates alternative and nonjudicial methods of dispute resolution; mediates disputes; provides training in dispute resolution.

Council of Better Business Bureaus, Inc., *Alternative Dispute Resolution, 4200 Wilson Blvd., #800, Arlington, VA 22203; (703) 247-9361. Fax, (703) 276-0634. Charles I. Underhill, senior vice president. Internet, bbb@bbb.org or http://www.bbb.org/complaints.*

Administers mediation and arbitration programs through Better Business Bureaus nationwide to assist in resolving disputes between businesses and consumers. Assists with unresolved disputes between car owners and automobile manufacturers. Maintains pools of certified arbitrators nationwide. Provides mediation training.

Help Abolish Legal Tyranny—An Organization of Americans for Legal Reform, *1612 K St. N.W., #510 20006; (202) 887-8255. Fax, (202) 887-9699. James C. Turner, executive director. Internet, http://www.halt.org.*

Public interest organization concerned with legal reform. Conducts research on alternative dispute resolution programs for delivery of legal services, including arbitration, legal clinics, and mediation services; provides educational and self-help manuals on the use of the legal system. Operates The Law Store, a legal document preparation service created to research, test, and promote innovative techniques for improving access to legal services for the average citizen.

National Institute for Dispute Resolution, *1726 M St. N.W., #500 20036-4502; (202) 466-4764. Fax, (202) 466-4769. Margery F. Baker, president. Internet, nidr@nidr.org or http://www.nidr.org.*

Promotes the development of fair, effective, and efficient conflict resolution processes; fosters the use of such processes and programs in new arenas locally, nationally, and internationally; stimulates innovative approaches to the resolution of future conflict. Provides information and technical assistance regarding the use of dispute resolution processes. Develops approaches to youth conflict and alternatives to violence.

Judicial Appointments

AGENCIES

Justice Dept., *Policy Development, 950 Pennsylvania Ave. N.W., #4234 20530; (202) 514-4601. Fax, (202) 514-2424. Eleanor Dean Acheson, assistant attorney general. Internet, http://www.usdoj.gov.*

Investigates and processes prospective candidates for presidential appointment (subject to Senate confirmation) to the federal judiciary.

CONGRESS

House Judiciary Committee, *Subcommittee on Courts and Intellectual Property, B351A RHOB 20515; (202) 225-5741. Fax, (202) 225-3673. Howard Coble, R-N.C., chair; Mitch Glazier, chief counsel. Internet, http://www.house.gov/judiciary.*

SUPREME COURT JUSTICES

CHIEF JUSTICE

William H. Rehnquist

Appointed Associate Justice by President Nixon, sworn in Jan. 7, 1972; appointed Chief Justice by President Reagan, sworn in Sept. 26, 1986.

ASSOCIATE JUSTICES

in order of appointment

John Paul Stevens

Appointed by President Ford, sworn in Dec. 17, 1975.

Sandra Day O'Connor

Appointed by President Reagan, sworn in Sept. 25, 1981.

Antonin Scalia

Appointed by President Reagan, sworn in Aug. 17, 1982.

Anthony M. Kennedy

Appointed by President Reagan, sworn in Feb. 18, 1988.

David H. Souter

Appointed by President Bush, sworn in Oct. 9, 1990.

Clarence Thomas

Appointed by President Bush, sworn in Oct. 23, 1991.

Ruth Bader Ginsburg

Appointed by President Clinton, sworn in Aug. 19, 1993.

Stephen G. Breyer

Appointed by President Clinton, sworn in Aug. 3, 1994.

Jurisdiction over legislation on federal judicial appointments, which includes legislation to create new federal judgeships; conducts hearings on presidential appointees to federal judgeships, including Supreme Court nominees.

Senate Judiciary Committee, *SD-224 20510; (202) 224-5225. Fax, (202) 224-9102. Orrin G. Hatch, R-Utah, chair; Manus Cooney, chief counsel. Internet, http://www. senate.gov/committee/judiciary.html.*

Jurisdiction over legislation on federal judicial appointments, which includes legislation to create new federal judgeships; conducts hearings on presidential appointees to federal judgeships, including Supreme Court nominees.

JUDICIARY

Administrative Office of the U.S. Courts, *1 Columbus Circle N.E., #7-100 20544; (202) 273-3000. Fax, (202) 273-2349. L. Ralph Mecham, director. Information, (202) 273-0107. Library, (202) 273-1888. Internet, http://www. uscourts.gov.*

Supervises all administrative matters of the federal court system, except the Supreme Court. Transmits to Congress the recommendations of the Judicial Conference of the United States concerning creation of federal judgeships and other legislative proposals.

Judicial Conference of the United States, *1 Columbus Circle N.E., #7-425 20544; (202) 273-1140. Fax, (202) 273-1145. William H. Rehnquist, chief justice of the United States, chair; L. Ralph Mecham, secretary. Internet, http:// www.uscourts.gov.*

Policymaking and governing body of the federal judicial system. Advises Congress on the creation of federal judgeships.

NONPROFIT

Alliance for Justice, *Judicial Selection Project, 2000 P St. N.W., #712 20036; (202) 822-6070. Fax, (202) 822-6068. Stephan Kline, director. Internet, alliance@afj.org or http://www.afj.org.*

Monitors candidates for vacancies in the federal judiciary; independently reviews nominees' records; maintains statistics on the judiciary.

BUSINESS AND TAX LAW

See also Economics and Business (chap. 5)

Antitrust

AGENCIES

Antitrust Division *(Justice Dept.), 950 Pennsylvania Ave. N.W., #3109 20530; (202) 514-2401. Fax, (202) 616-2645. Joel I. Klein, assistant attorney general. Internet, http://www.usdoj.gov/atr.*

Enforces antitrust laws to prevent monopolies and unlawful restraint of trade; has civil and criminal jurisdiction; coordinates activities with Bureau of Competition of the Federal Trade Commission.

Antitrust Division *(Justice Dept.), Computers and Finance, 600 E St. N.W., #9500 20530; (202) 307-6122. Fax, (202) 616-8544. John F. Greaney, chief.*

Investigates and litigates certain antitrust cases involving either communications industries or financial institutions, including banking, securities, commodity futures, and insurance firms; participates in agency proceedings and rulemaking in these areas.

Antitrust Division *(Justice Dept.), Documents*, 325 7th St. N.W., #215 20530; (202) 514-2481. Fax, (202) 514-3763. Janie Ingalls, chief.

Maintains files and handles requests for information on federal civil and criminal antitrust cases; provides the president and Congress with copies of statutory reports prepared by the division; issues opinion letters on whether certain business activity violates antitrust laws.

Antitrust Division *(Justice Dept.), Professions and Intellectual Property*, 325 7th St. N.W., 4th Floor 20530; (202) 307-5799. Fax, (202) 514-1517. Gail Kursh, chief.

Litigates certain antitrust cases involving health care and professional services, professional associations, sports and labor groups, and the motion picture, publishing, newspaper, and pharmaceutical industries. Handles certain violations of antitrust laws that involve patents, copyrights, and trademarks.

Antitrust Division *(Justice Dept.), Transportation, Energy, and Agriculture*, 325 7th St. N.W., #500 20530; (202) 307-6351. Fax, (202) 307-2784. Roger Phones, chief.

Enforces antitrust laws in the airline, railroad, motor carrier, barge line, ocean carrier, and energy industries; litigates antitrust cases pertaining to agriculture and related commodities.

Comptroller of the Currency *(Treasury Dept.)*, 250 E St. S.W. 20219; (202) 874-4900. Fax, (202) 874-4950. Eugene A. Ludwig, comptroller. Information, (202) 874-5000. Press, (202) 874-5770. Library, (202) 874-4720. Internet, http://www.occ.treas.gov.

Regulates and examines operations of national banks; establishes guidelines for bank examinations; handles mergers of national banks with regard to antitrust law. Library open to the public.

Federal Communications Commission, *Common Carrier Bureau*, 1919 M St. N.W., #500 20554; (202) 418-1500. Fax, (202) 418-2825. Richard Metzger, chief. Internet, http://www.fcc.gov/ccb.

Regulates mergers involving common carriers (wireline facilities that furnish interstate communications services).

Federal Deposit Insurance Corp., *Supervision*, 550 17th St. N.W. 20429; (202) 898-8510. Fax, (202) 898-3638. Nicholas J. Ketcha Jr., director.

Studies and analyzes applications for mergers, consolidations, acquisitions, and assumption transactions between insured banks.

Federal Energy Regulatory Commission *(Energy Dept.)*, 888 1st St. N.E., #11A 20426; (202) 208-0000. Fax, (202) 208-0151. James J. Hoecker, chair. Information, (202) 208-0200. Press, (202) 208-1088. Dockets, (202) 208-0715. Internet, http://www.ferc.gov.

Regulates mergers, consolidations, and acquisitions of electric utilities; regulates the acquisition of interstate natural gas pipeline facilities.

Federal Maritime Commission, 800 N. Capitol St. N.W., #1046 20573; (202) 523-5725. Fax, (202) 523-0014. Harold J. Creel Jr., chair; Edward P. Walsh, managing director, (202) 523-5800. Library, (202) 523-5762. TDD, (202) 343-3679. Internet, http://www.fmc.gov.

Regulates foreign and domestic ocean shipping of the United States; reviews agreements (on rates, schedules, and other matters) filed by common carriers for compliance with antitrust laws and grants antitrust immunity. Library open to the public.

Federal Reserve System, *Banking Supervision and Regulation*, 20th and C Sts. N.W., #M3142 20551; (202) 452-2773. Fax, (202) 452-2770. Richard Spillenkothen, director. Internet, http://www.bog.frb.fed.us.

Approves bank mergers, consolidations, and other alterations in bank structure.

Federal Trade Commission, *Competition*, 6th St. and Pennsylvania Ave. N.W., #H374 20580; (202) 326-2932. Fax, (202) 326-2884. William J. Baer, director. Information, (202) 326-2178.

Enforces antitrust laws and investigates possible violations, including international cases; seeks voluntary compliance and pursues civil judicial remedies; reviews premerger filings; coordinates activities with Antitrust Division of the Justice Dept.

Surface Transportation Board *(Transportation Dept.)*, 1925 K St. N.W. 20423-0001; (202) 565-1500. Fax, (202) 565-9004. Linda J. Morgan, chair; Gus A. Owen, vice chair. Internet, http://www.stb.dot.gov.

Regulates rail rate disputes, railroad consolidations, rail line construction proposals, line abandonments, rail car service, and motor carrier undercharge cases.

CONGRESS

House Banking and Financial Services Committee, *Subcommittee on Financial Institutions and Consumer Credit*, 2129 RHOB 20515; (202) 225-2258. Fax, (202) 225-6984. Marge Roukema, R-N.J., chair; Laurie Schaffer, staff director. Internet, http://www.house.gov/banking.

Jurisdiction over legislation on mergers, acquisitions, consolidations, and conversions of financial institutions.

House Judiciary Committee, *2138 RHOB 20515; (202) 225-3951. Fax, (202) 225-7682. Henry J. Hyde, R-Ill., chair; Thomas Mooney, chief counsel. Internet, http://www.house.gov/judiciary.*

Jurisdiction over legislation affecting anticompetitive and monopolistic practices and over Justice Dept. antitrust enforcement policies. Oversight of the Sherman Act and the Clayton Act.

House Small Business Committee, *Subcommittee on Regulatory Reform and Paperwork Reduction, B363 RHOB 20515; (202) 226-2630. Fax, (202) 225-8950. Sue W. Kelly, R-N.Y., chair; Larry McCredy, staff director. Internet, http://www.house.gov/smbiz.*

Jurisdiction over legislation on all antitrust matters relating to small business; investigates anticompetitive and monopolistic practices.

Senate Judiciary Committee, *Subcommittee on Antitrust, Business Rights, and Competition, SD-161 20510; (202) 224-9494. Fax, (202) 228-0463. Mike DeWine, R-Ohio, chair; Louie DuPart, chief counsel. Internet, http://www.senate.gov/committee/judiciary. html.*

Jurisdiction over legislation affecting anticompetitive and monopolistic practices and over Justice Dept. antitrust enforcement polices. Oversight of the Sherman Act and the Clayton Act.

Senate Small Business Committee, *SR-428A 20510; (202) 224-5175. Fax, (202) 224-4885. Christopher S. Bond, R-Mo., chair; Louis Taylor, staff director. Internet, http://www.senate.gov/~sbc.*

Investigates antitrust matters relating to small business; investigates anticompetitive and monopolistic practices.

NONPROFIT

American Corporate Counsel Assn., *1225 Connecticut Ave. N.W., #302 20036; (202) 296-4522. Fax, (202) 331-7454. Frederick J. Krebs, president. Internet, http://www.acca.com.*

Membership: practicing attorneys in corporate law departments. Provides information on corporate law issues, including securities, health and safety, the environment, intellectual property, litigation, international legal affairs, pro bono work, and labor benefits. Monitors legislation and regulations, with primary focus on issues affecting in-house attorneys' ability to practice law.

Business Roundtable, *1615 L St. N.W., #1100 20036-5610; (202) 872-1260. Fax, (202) 466-3509. Samuel L. Maury, president. Internet, http://www.brtable.org.*

Membership: chief executives of the nation's largest corporations. Examines issues of concern to business, including antitrust law.

See also American Bar Assn. (p. 494); Federal Bar Assn. (p. 496); Federal Communications Bar Assn. (p. 72); National Chamber Litigation Center (p. 136); U.S. Chamber of Commerce, Economic Policy (p. 136)

Bankruptcy

AGENCIES

Executive Office for U.S. Trustees *(Justice Dept.), 901 E St. N.W., #700 20530; (202) 307-1391. Fax, (202) 307-0672. Joseph Patchan, director. Internet, http://www.usdoj.gov/ust.*

Handles the administration and oversight of bankruptcy and liquidation cases filed under the Bankruptcy Reform Act. Provides individual U.S. trustee offices with administrative and management support.

Justice Dept., *Policy Development, 950 Pennsylvania Ave. N.W., #4234 20530; (202) 514-4601. Fax, (202) 514-2424. Eleanor Dean Acheson, assistant attorney general.*

Studies and develops policy for improvement of the criminal and civil justice systems, including bankruptcy reform policy.

CONGRESS

House Judiciary Committee, *Subcommittee on Commercial and Administrative Law, B353 RHOB 20515; (202) 225-2825. Fax, (202) 225-4299. George W. Gekas, R-Pa., chair; Ray Smietanka, counsel.*

Jurisdiction over bankruptcy legislation. Oversees the bankruptcy court.

Senate Judiciary Committee, *Subcommittee on Administrative Oversight and the Courts, SH-308 20510; (202) 224-6736. Charles E. Grassley, R-Iowa, chair; Kolan L. Davis, chief counsel. Internet, http://www.senate.gov/committee/judiciary.html.*

Jurisdiction over bankruptcy legislation.

JUDICIARY

Administrative Office of the U.S. Courts, *Bankruptcy Judges Division, 1 Columbus Circle N.E., #4-250 20544; (202) 273-1900. Fax, (202) 273-1917. Francis F. Szczebak, chief.*

Provides administrative assistance and support in the operation of the U.S. Bankruptcy Court.

NONPROFIT

American Bankruptcy Institute, *44 Canal Center Plaza, #404, Alexandria, VA 22314-1592; (703) 739-0800. Fax, (703) 739-1060. Samuel Gerdano, executive director. Internet, http://www.abiworld.org.*

Membership: lawyers; federal and state legislators; and representatives of accounting and financial services firms, lending institutions, credit organizations, and consumer groups. Provides information and educational services on insolvency, reorganization, and bankruptcy issues; sponsors conferences, seminars, and workshops.

Tax Violations

See also Taxes and Tax Reform (chap. 5)

AGENCIES

Internal Revenue Service *(Treasury Dept.), Field Service, 1111 Constitution Ave. N.W., #4050 20224; (202) 622-7800. Fax, (202) 622-6889. Deborah Butler, assistant chief counsel.*

Oversees field office litigation of civil cases that involve underpayment of taxes when the taxpayer chooses to challenge the determinations of the Internal Revenue Service (IRS) in the U.S. Tax Court, or when the taxpayer chooses to pay the amount in question and sue the IRS for a refund. Reviews briefs and defense letters prepared by field offices for tax cases; prepares tax litigation advice memoranda; formulates litigation strategy. Makes recommendations concerning appeal and certiorari. Litigates insurance and declaratory judgment cases in the U.S. Tax Court.

Justice Dept., *Tax Division, 950 Pennsylvania Ave. N.W., #4143 20530; (202) 514-2901. Fax, (202) 514-5479. Loretta C. Argrett, assistant attorney general. Internet, http://www.usdoj.gov/tax/tax.html.*

Authorizes prosecution of all criminal cases involving tax violations investigated and developed by the Internal Revenue Service (IRS); represents IRS in civil litigation except in U.S. Tax Court proceedings; represents other agencies, including the departments of Defense and Interior, in cases with state or local tax authorities.

CONGRESS

House Ways and Means Committee, *1102 LHOB 20515; (202) 225-3625. Bill Archer, R-Texas, chair; Phillip D. Moseley, chief of staff. Internet, http://www.house.gov/ways_means.*

Jurisdiction over legislation concerning changes in enforcement of tax laws.

Senate Finance Committee, *Subcommittee on Taxation and IRS Oversight, SD-219 20510; (202) 224-4515. Don Nickles, R-Okla., chair; Mark Prater, staff contact. Internet, http://www.senate.gov/~finance.*

Holds hearings on legislation concerning changes in enforcement of tax laws.

JUDICIARY

U.S. Tax Court, *400 2nd St. N.W. 20217; (202) 606-8700. Mary Ann Cohen, chief judge; Charles S. Casazza, clerk of the court, (202) 606-8754.*

Tries and adjudicates disputes involving income, estate, and gift taxes and personal holding company surtaxes in cases in which deficiencies have been determined by the Internal Revenue Service.

NONPROFIT

American Bar Assn., *Taxation Section, 740 15th St. N.W. 20005; (202) 662-8670. Fax, (202) 662-8682. Christine A. Brunswick, director.*

Studies and recommends policies on taxation; provides information on tax issues; sponsors continuing legal education programs; monitors tax laws and legislation.

▣ CONSTITUTIONAL LAW AND CIVIL LIBERTIES

See also Public Interest Law (chap. 1)

AGENCIES

Commission on Civil Rights, *624 9th St. N.W., #700 20425; (202) 376-7700. Fax, (202) 376-7672. Mary Frances Berry, chair. Press, (202) 376-8364. Library, (202) 376-8110. TDD, (202) 376-8116. Complaints, (800) 552-6843; in Washington, (202) 376-8582. Internet, http://www.usccp.gov.*

Assesses federal laws and policies of government agencies and reviews legal developments to determine the nature and extent of denial of equal protection on the basis of race, color, religion, sex, national origin, age, or disability; investigates complaints of denials of voting rights. Library open to the public.

Education Dept., *Civil Rights, 330 C St. S.W., #5000 20202-1100; (202) 205-5413. Fax, (202) 205-9862. Norma Cantu, assistant secretary.*

Enforces laws prohibiting use of federal funds for education programs or activities that discriminate on the basis of race, color, sex, national origin, age, or disability; authorized to discontinue funding.

Health and Human Services Dept., *Civil Rights,* *200 Independence Ave. S.W., #522A 20201; (202) 619-0403. Fax, (202) 619-3818. Dennis Hayashi, director. Information, (202) 619-0585. TDD, (800) 537-7697. Toll-free hotline, (800) 368-1019. Internet, http://www.os.dhhs.gov/ progorg/ocr/ocrhmpg.html.*

Administers and enforces laws prohibiting discrimination on the basis of sex, race, color, religion, national origin, age, or disability in health care and social services programs funded by the department; authorized to discontinue funding.

Justice Dept., *Civil Rights,* *601 D St. N.W., #4040 20530; (202) 514-2151. Fax, (202) 514-0293. Bill Lann Lee, acting assistant attorney general. Information, (202) 514-2007. Library, (202) 514-4098. TDD, (800) 514-0383. Internet, http://www.usdoj.gov/crt.*

Enforces federal civil rights laws prohibiting discrimination on the basis of race, color, religion, sex, disability, age, or national origin in voting, education, employment, credit, housing, public accommodations and facilities, and federally assisted programs.

Justice Dept., *Legal Counsel,* *950 Pennsylvania Ave. N.W., #3266 20530; (202) 514-2041. Fax, (202) 514-0539. Dawn Johnson, acting assistant attorney general.*

Advises the attorney general, the president, and executive agencies on questions regarding constitutional law.

Justice Dept., *Redress Administration,* *1425 New York Ave., #5062 20005; (202) 219-6900. Fax, (202) 219-9314. Joanne Chiedi, administrator. Information, (202) 514-4224. TDD, (202) 219-4710.*

Administers redress payments to Japanese-Americans interned in the United States during World War II.

Labor Dept., *Civil Rights,* *200 Constitution Ave. N.W., #N4123 20210; (202) 219-8927. Fax, (202) 219-5658. Annabelle Lockhart, director. TDD, (202) 219-7773.*

Resolves complaints of discrimination on the basis of race, color, religion, sex, national origin, age, or disability in programs funded by the department.

CONGRESS

House Government Reform and Oversight Committee, *Subcommittee on National Security, International Affairs, and Criminal Justice,* *B373 RHOB 20515; (202) 225-2577. Fax, (202) 225-1154. Dennis Hastert, R-Ill., chair; Robert Charles, staff director. Internet, http:// www.house.gov/reform.*

Oversees operations of the Commission on Civil Rights.

House Judiciary Committee, *2138 RHOB 20515; (202) 225-3951. Fax, (202) 225-7682. Henry J. Hyde, R-Ill., chair; Thomas Mooney, chief counsel. Internet, http://www.house.gov/judiciary.*

Jurisdiction over legislation on proposed amendments to the Constitution; subcommittee jurisdiction determined by subject of proposed amendment.

House Judiciary Committee, *Subcommittee on the Constitution,* *362 Ford Bldg. 20515; (202) 226-7680. Fax, (202) 225-3746. Charles T. Canady, R-Fla., chair; Keri Folmar, counsel. Internet, http://www.house.gov/judiciary.*

Jurisdiction over legislation dealing with civil rights enforcement, civil liberties, and constitutional issues. Oversees the Justice Dept.'s Civil Rights Division and the Commission on Civil Rights.

Senate Judiciary Committee, *Subcommittee on the Constitution, Federalism, and Property Rights,* *SD-164 20510; (202) 224-8081. John Ashcroft, R-Mo., chair; David Miller, chief counsel. Internet, http://www.senate.gov/ committee/judiciary.html.*

Jurisdiction over legislation on proposed amendments to the Constitution, civil rights enforcement, the Voting Rights Act and affirmative action, civil liberties (including the First Amendment, excluding computers), constitutional issues involving criminal law, habeas corpus, the death penalty, and the exclusionary rule; oversees operations of the Commission on Civil Rights.

JUDICIARY

Supreme Court of the United States, *1 1st St. N.E. 20543; (202) 479-3000. William H. Rehnquist, chief justice; William K. Suter, clerk, (202) 479-3011. Library, (202) 479-3037. Opinions and information, (202) 479-3211. Internet, http://www.law.cornell.edu/lii.table.html.*

Highest appellate court in the federal judicial system. Interprets the U.S. Constitution, federal legislation, and treaties. Provides information on new cases filed, the status of pending cases, and admissions to the Supreme Court Bar.

NONPROFIT

American Civil Liberties Union (ACLU), *122 Maryland Ave. N.E. 20002; (202) 544-1681. Fax, (202) 546-0738. Laura W. Murphy, director, Washington Office. Internet, http://www.aclu.org.*

Initiates test court cases and advocates legislation to guarantee constitutional rights and civil liberties. Focuses on First Amendment rights, minority and women's rights, gay and lesbian rights, and privacy;

supports legalized abortion, opposes government-sponsored school prayer and legislative restrictions on television content. Washington office monitors legislative and regulatory activities and public policy. Library open to the public by appointment. (Headquarters in New York maintains docket of cases.)

Center for Individual Rights, *1233 20th St. N.W., #300 20036; (202) 833-8400. Fax, (202) 833-8410. Michael S. Greve, executive director. Internet, cir@wdn.com or http://www.wdn.com/cir.*

Public interest law firm that supports reform of the civil justice system on the basis of private rights and individual responsibility. Interests include economic regulation, freedom of speech, and libel law.

Ethics and Public Policy Center, *Law and Society Program, 1015 15th St. N.W., #900 20005; (202) 682-1200. Fax, (202) 408-0632. Elliott Abrams, president. Internet, ethics@eppc.org.*

Examines current issues of jurisprudence, especially those relating to constitutional interpretation.

Institute for Justice, *1717 Pennsylvania Ave. N.W., #200 20006; (202) 955-1300. Fax, (202) 955-1329. Chip Mellor, president. Internet, general@instituteforjustice.org or http://www.instituteforjustice.org.*

Sponsors seminars to train law students, grassroots activists, and practicing lawyers in applying advocacy strategies in public interest litigation. Seeks to protect from arbitrary government interference free speech, private property rights, parental school choice, and economic liberty. Litigates cases.

Legal Affairs Council, *3554 Chain Bridge Rd., #301, Fairfax, VA 22030; (703) 591-7767. Fax, (703) 273-4514. Richard A. Delgaudio, president.*

Provides conservative activists with financial and legal assistance for court challenges of alleged violations of human and civil rights, especially First Amendment rights.

NAACP Legal Defense and Educational Fund, *1275 K St. N.W., #301 20005; (202) 682-1300. Fax, (202) 682-1312. Vacant, director, Washington Office.*

Civil rights litigation group that provides legal information on civil rights issues, including employment, housing, and educational discrimination; monitors federal enforcement of civil rights laws. Not affiliated with the National Assn. for the Advancement of Colored People (NAACP). (Headquarters in New York.)

National Assn. for the Advancement of Colored People (NAACP), *1025 Vermont Ave. N.W., #1120*

20005; (202) 638-2269. Fax, (202) 638-5936. Hilary Shelton, deputy director. Internet, http://www.naacp.org.

Membership: persons interested in civil rights for all minorities. Works for the political, educational, social, and economic equality of minorities through legal, legislative, and direct action, and educational programs. (Headquarters in Baltimore.)

National Organization for Women (NOW), *1000 16th St. N.W., #700 20036; (202) 331-0066. Fax, (202) 785-8576. Patricia Ireland, president. TDD, (202) 331-9002. Internet, now@now.org or http://www.now.org.*

Membership: women and men interested in civil rights for women. Works to end discrimination based on gender, to preserve abortion rights, and to pass an equal rights amendment to the Constitution.

See also Lawyers' Committee for Civil Rights Under Law (p. 29)

Abortion and Reproductive Issues

See also Family Planning and Population (chap. 11)

CONGRESS

House Judiciary Committee, *Subcommittee on the Constitution, 362 Ford Bldg. 20515; (202) 226-7680. Fax, (202) 225-3746. Charles T. Canady, R-Fla., chair; Keri Folmar, counsel. Internet, http://www.house.gov/judiciary.*

Jurisdiction over proposed abortion amendments to the Constitution.

Senate Judiciary Committee, *Subcommittee on the Constitution, Federalism, and Property Rights, SD-164 20510; (202) 224-8081. John Ashcroft, R-Mo., chair; David Miller, chief counsel. Internet, http://www.senate.gov/committee/judiciary.html.*

Jurisdiction over proposed abortion amendments to the Constitution.

NONPROFIT

Assn. of Reproductive Health Professionals, *2401 Pennsylvania Ave. N.W., #350 20037-1718; (202) 466-3825. Fax, (202) 466-3826. Wayne Shields, president. Internet, http://www.arhp.org.*

Membership: obstetricians, gynecologists, other physicians, researchers, clinicians, educators, and others. Educates health professionals and the public on reproductive health issues, including family planning, contraception, HIV/AIDS, other sexually transmitted diseases, abortion, menopause, infertility, and cancer prevention and detection.

Catholics for a Free Choice, *1436 U St. N.W., #301 20009-3997; (202) 986-6093. Fax, (202) 332-7995. Frances Kissling, president. Internet, cffc@igc.apc.org.*

Works to change church positions and public policies that limit individual freedom, particularly those related to sexuality and reproduction. Provides the public, policymakers, and groups working for change with information and analysis.

Feminists for Life of America, *733 15th St. N.W., #1100 20005; (202) 737-3352. Fax, (202) 737-0414. Rosemary Oelrich Bottcher, president. Internet, http://www.serve.com/fem4life.*

Membership: women and men who advocate classical feminism, including its pro-life position. Opposes abortion, euthanasia, and capital punishment; seeks to redress economic and social conditions that cause women to choose abortion.

Human Life International, *4 Family Life, Front Royal, VA 22630; (540) 635-7884. Fax, (540) 636-7363. Richard Welch, president. Internet, hli@hli.org or http://www.hli.org.*

Educational organization that opposes abortion, sterilization, infanticide, euthanasia, and contraception.

March for Life, *P.O. Box 90300 20090; (202) 543-3377. Fax, (202) 543-8202. Nellie J. Gray, president.*

Membership: individuals and organizations that support government action prohibiting abortion. Sponsors annual march in Washington each January 22. Monitors legislation and regulations.

National Abortion and Reproductive Rights Action League (NARAL), *1156 15th St. N.W., 7th Floor 20005; (202) 973-3000. Fax, (202) 973-3099. Kate Michelman, president. Press, (202) 973-3032. Internet, http://www.naral.org.*

Membership: persons favoring legalized abortion. Promotes grassroots support of political candidates in favor of legalized abortion.

National Abortion Federation, *1755 Massachusetts Ave. N.W., #600 20036; (202) 667-5881. Fax, (202) 667-5890. Vicki Saporta, executive director. Internet, http://www.prochoice.org.*

Membership: abortion providers. Seeks to preserve and enhance the quality and accessibility of abortion care.

National Committee for a Human Life Amendment, *1511 K St. N.W., #335 20005; (202) 393-0703. Fax, (202) 347-1383. Michael A. Taylor, executive director.*

Supports legislation and a constitutional amendment prohibiting abortion.

National Conference of Catholic Bishops/United States Catholic Conference, *Secretariat for Pro-Life Activities,* *3211 4th St. N.E. 20017-1194; (202) 541-3070. Fax, (202) 541-3054. Gail Quinn, executive director.*

Provides information on the position of the Roman Catholic Church on abortion; monitors legislation on abortion and related issues; provides alternatives to abortion through Catholic charities.

National Right to Life Committee, *419 7th St. N.W. 20004; (202) 626-8800. Fax, (202) 737-9189. David N. O'Steen, executive director. Internet, nrlc@nrlc.org or http://www.nrlc.org.*

Association of fifty state right-to-life organizations. Opposes abortion, infanticide, and euthanasia; supports legislation prohibiting abortion except when the life of the mother is endangered. Operates an information clearinghouse and speakers bureau. Monitors legislation and regulations.

National Women's Health Network, *514 10th St. N.W., #400 20004; (202) 347-1140. Fax, (202) 347-1168. Cynthia Pearson, executive director.*

Advocacy organization interested in women's health. Seeks to preserve legalized abortion; monitors legislation and regulations; testifies before Congress.

National Women's Political Caucus, *1211 Connecticut Ave. N.W., #425 20036; (202) 785-1100. Fax, (202) 785-3605. Anita Perez Ferguson, president. Toll-free, (800) 729-6972. Internet, mailnwpc@aol.com or http://www.feminist.com/nwpc.htm.*

Advocacy group that seeks greater involvement of women in politics. Supports legalized abortion.

Operation Rescue, *2020 Pennsylvania Ave. N.W. 20006; (202) 546-0054. Gary McCullough, director, Press Relations. Internet, oprescue@aol.com.*

Advocates active stand against abortion. Seeks repeal of the Freedom of Access to Clinic Entrances law. Monitors legislation and regulations. (Headquarters in Dallas.)

Religious Coalition for Reproductive Choice, *1025 Vermont Ave. N.W., #1130 20005; (202) 628-7700. Fax, (202) 628-7716. Carlton Wadsworth Veazey, executive director. Internet, info@rcrc.org or http://www.rcrc.org.*

Coalition of religious groups favoring legalized abortion. Opposes constitutional amendments and federal and state legislation restricting access to abortion services.

Voters for Choice, *2604 Connecticut Ave. N.W., 2nd Floor (mailing address: P.O. Box 53301, Washington, DC*

20009-9301); (202) 588-5200. Fax, (202) 588-0600. Julie Burton, executive director. Internet, vfc@ibm.net.

Independent, nonpartisan political committee that supports candidates favoring legalized abortion. Provides candidates at all levels of government with campaign strategy information; opposes constitutional amendments and legislation restricting abortion.

See also American Civil Liberties Union (p. 502); National Council of Catholic Women (p. 33); National Organization for Women (p. 503)

Claims Against the Government

AGENCIES

Justice Dept., *Civil Division,* 950 Pennsylvania Ave. N.W., #3143 20530; (202) 514-3301. Fax, (202) 514-8071. Frank W. Hunger, assistant attorney general. Information, (202) 514-2007. Internet, http://www.usdoj.gov/civil/civil. html.

Represents the United States in the U.S. Court of Federal Claims, except in cases involving taxes, lands, or Native American claims.

Justice Dept., *Environment and Natural Resources,* 950 Pennsylvania Ave. N.W., #2143 20530; (202) 514-2701. Fax, (202) 514-0557. Lois J. Schiffer, assistant attorney general. Internet, http://www.usdoj.gov/enrd.

Represents the United States in the U.S. Court of Federal Claims in cases arising from acquisition of property or related matters.

Justice Dept., *Tax Division,* 950 Pennsylvania Ave. N.W., #4143 20530; (202) 514-2901. Fax, (202) 514-5479. Loretta C. Argrett, assistant attorney general. Internet, http://www.usdoj.gov/tax/tax.html.

Represents the United States and its officers in all civil and criminal litigation arising under the internal revenue laws, other than proceedings in the United States Tax Court.

State Dept., *International Claims and Investment Disputes,* 2430 E St. N.W., #203 20037-2800; (202) 776-8360. Fax, (202) 776-8389. Ronald J. Bettauer, assistant legal adviser.

Handles claims by the U.S. government and citizens against foreign governments; claims by foreign governments and their nationals against the U.S. government; claims against the State Dept. for negligence (in the United States or abroad) under the Federal Tort Claims Act; and claims by owners of U.S. flag vessels for reimbursement of fines, fees, licenses, and other direct payments for illegal seizures by foreign governments in

international waters under the Fishermen's Protective Act. Negotiates agreements with foreign governments on claims settlements.

CONGRESS

House Judiciary Committee, *Subcommittee on Immigration and Claims,* B370B RHOB 20515; (202) 225-5727. Fax, (202) 225-3672. Lamar Smith, R-Texas, chair; Cordia Strom, counsel. Internet, http://www.house.gov/judiciary.

Jurisdiction over legislation related to claims against the United States.

Senate Judiciary Committee, SD-224 20510; (202) 224-5225. Fax, (202) 224-9102. Orrin G. Hatch, R-Utah, chair; Manus Cooney, chief counsel. Internet, http://www.senate.gov/committee/judiciary.html.

Jurisdiction over legislation related to claims against the United States.

JUDICIARY

U.S. Court of Federal Claims, 717 Madison Pl. N.W. 20005; (202) 219-9668. Fax, (202) 219-9630. Loren A. Smith, chief judge; David A. Lampen, clerk, (202) 219-9657.

Renders judgment on any nontort claims for monetary damages against the United States founded upon the Constitution, statutes, government regulations, and government contracts. Examples include compensation for taking of property, claims arising under construction and supply contracts, certain patent cases, and cases involving the refund of federal taxes. Hears cases involving Native American claims.

Interstate Compacts

CONGRESS

House Judiciary Committee, *Subcommittee on Commercial and Administrative Law,* B353 RHOB 20515; (202) 225-2825. Fax, (202) 225-4299. George W. Gekas, R-Pa., chair; Ray Smietanka, counsel.

Jurisdiction over all interstate compacts, including hazardous waste transportation, water rights, and boundaries. (Congressional approval of interstate compacts is required by the Constitution.)

Senate Judiciary Committee, *Subcommittee on Antitrust, Business Rights, and Competition,* SD-161 20510; (202) 224-9494. Fax, (202) 228-0463. Mike DeWine, R-Ohio, chair; Louie DuPart, chief counsel. Internet, http://www.senate.gov/committee/judiciary.html.

Jurisdiction over interstate compacts dealing with such matters as hazardous waste transportation, water rights, and boundaries. (Congressional approval of interstate compacts is required by the Constitution.)

Religious Freedom

See also Private, Parochial, and Home Schooling (chap. 6); Religion and Ethics (chap. 1)

CONGRESS

House Judiciary Committee, *Subcommittee on the Constitution, 362 Ford Bldg. 20515; (202) 226-7680. Fax, (202) 225-3746. Charles T. Canady, R-Fla., chair; Keri Folmar, counsel. Internet, http://www.house.gov/judiciary.*

Jurisdiction over proposed constitutional amendments; oversight of the First Amendment right to religious freedom.

Senate Judiciary Committee, *Subcommittee on the Constitution, Federalism, and Property Rights, SD-164 20510; (202) 224-8081. John Ashcroft, R-Mo., chair; David Miller, chief counsel. Internet, http://www.senate.gov/committee/judiciary.html.*

Jurisdiction over proposed constitutional amendments; oversight of the First Amendment right to religious freedom.

NONPROFIT

American Jewish Congress, *2027 Massachusetts Ave. N.W. 20036; (202) 332-4001. Fax, (202) 387-3434. David Harris, Washington representative. Internet, washrep@ajcongress.org or http://www.ajcongress.org.*

Advocacy organization that seeks to uphold civil and constitutional rights. Litigates cases involving prayer in public schools, tuition tax credits, equal access, and religious symbols on public property. (Headquarters in New York.)

Americans for Religious Liberty, *P.O. Box 6656, Silver Spring, MD 20916; (301) 598-2447. Fax, (301) 438-8424. Edd Doerr, executive director. Internet, arlinc@erols.com.*

Educational organization concerned with issues involving the separation of church and state. Opposes government-sponsored school prayer and tax support for religious institutions; supports religious neutrality in public education; defends abortion rights. Provides legal services in litigation cases. Maintains speakers bureau.

Americans United for Separation of Church and State, *1816 Jefferson Pl. N.W. 20036; (202) 466-3234. Fax, (202) 466-2587. Barry W. Lynn, executive director. Internet, americansunited@au.org or http://www.au.org.*

Citizens' interest group that opposes government-sponsored prayer in public schools and tax aid for parochial schools.

Christian Legal Society, *4208 Evergreen Lane, #222, Annandale, VA 22003; (703) 642-1070. Fax, (703) 642-1075. Samuel B. Casey, executive director. Internet, cls@clsnet.com or http://www.clsnet.com.*

Membership: attorneys, judges, law professors, and law students. Seeks to create and mobilize a national network of Christians to advocate justice and religious freedom.

Council on Religious Freedom, *4545 42nd St. N.W., #201 20016; (202) 363-8098. Fax, (202) 363-0304. Lee Boothby, vice president.*

Seeks to preserve principles of religious liberty through litigation and educational programs. Opposes prayer in public schools.

International Religious Liberty Assn., *12501 Old Columbia Pike, Silver Spring, MD 20904-6600; (301) 680-6680. Fax, (301) 680-6695. John Graz, secretary general.*

Seeks to preserve and expand religious liberty and freedom of conscience; advocates separation of church and state; sponsors international and domestic meetings and congresses.

National Assn. of Evangelicals, *1023 15th St. N.W., #500 20005; (202) 789-1011. Fax, (202) 842-0392. Rich Cizik, policy analyst. Internet, oga@nae.net or http://www.nae.net.*

Membership: evangelical churches, organizations (including schools), and individuals. Supports religious freedom. Monitors legislation and regulations. (Headquarters in Wheaton, Ill.)

National Council of Churches, *110 Maryland Ave. N.E., #108 20002; (202) 544-2350. Fax, (202) 543-1297. Albert M. Pennybacker, acting director, Washington Office. Internet, ncc-washington.parti@ecunet.org or http://www.ncccusa.org.*

Membership: Protestant, Anglican, and Orthodox churches. Opposes government-sponsored prayer in public schools. Provides information on the school prayer issue. (Headquarters in New York.)

Rutherford Institute, *733 15th St. N.W., #410 20005; (202) 393-7008. Fax, (202) 393-7010. Jim Cox, director, Public Policy. Internet, http://www.rutherford.org.*

International legal and educational organization; works to defend religious liberties for people of all faiths. Conducts litigation; sponsors internships and research programs for law students. Interests include religious freedom overseas, parental rights, and home schooling. (Headquarters in Charlottesville, Va.)

See also American Civil Liberties Union (p. 502)

Separation of Powers

CONGRESS

House Government Reform and Oversight Committee, *Subcommittee on Human Resources, B372 RHOB 20515; (202) 225-2548. Fax, (202) 225-2382. Christopher Shays, R-Conn., chair; Larry Halloran, staff director. Internet, http://www.house.gov/reform.*

Jurisdiction over legislation on some aspects of executive privilege and separation of powers (jurisdiction over separation of powers shared with House Judiciary Committee).

House Judiciary Committee, *2138 RHOB 20515; (202) 225-3951. Fax, (202) 225-7682. Henry J. Hyde, R-Ill., chair; Thomas Mooney, chief counsel. Internet, http://www.house.gov/judiciary.*

Jurisdiction over legislation dealing with separation of powers and presidential succession (jurisdiction over separation of powers shared with House Government Reform and Oversight Committee).

Senate Judiciary Committee, *Subcommittee on the Constitution, Federalism, and Property Rights, SD-164 20510; (202) 224-8081. John Ashcroft, R-Mo., chair; David Miller, chief counsel. Internet, http://www.senate.gov/committee/judiciary.html.*

Jurisdiction over legislation on separation of powers, presidential succession, and some aspects of executive privilege.

NONPROFIT

Public Citizen Litigation Group, *1600 20th St. N.W. 20009; (202) 588-7721. Fax, (202) 588-7795. David Vladeck, director. Internet, http://www.citizen.org.*

Conducts litigation for Public Citizen, a citizens' interest group, in cases involving separation of powers; represents individuals and groups with similar interests.

 # CRIMINAL LAW

AGENCIES

Criminal Division *(Justice Dept.), 950 Pennsylvania Ave. N.W., #2107 20530; (202) 514-2601. Fax, (202) 514-9412. John C. Keeney, acting assistant attorney general. Internet, http://www.usdoj.gov/criminal.*

Enforces all federal criminal laws except those specifically assigned to the antitrust, civil rights, environment and natural resources, and tax divisions of the Justice Dept. Supervises and directs U.S. attorneys in the field on criminal matters and litigation; supervises international extradition proceedings. Coordinates federal enforcement efforts against white-collar crime, fraud, and child pornography; handles civil actions under customs, liquor, narcotics, gambling, and firearms laws; coordinates enforcement activities against organized crime. Directs the National Asset Forfeiture Program for seizing the proceeds of criminal activity. Investigates and prosecutes criminal offenses involving public integrity and subversive activities, including treason, espionage, and sedition; Nazi war crimes; and related criminal offenses. Handles all civil cases relating to internal security and counsels federal departments and agencies regarding internal security matters. Drafts responses on proposed and pending criminal law legislation.

Criminal Division *(Justice Dept.), Enforcement Operations, P.O. Box 7600 Ben Franklin Station 20044-7600; (202) 514-3684. Fax, (202) 514-5143. Frederick D. Hess, director.*

Coordinates federal witness security and victim compensation programs; selects individuals to enter the programs.

Federal Bureau of Investigation *(Justice Dept.), 935 Pennsylvania Ave. N.W. 20535; (202) 324-3444. Fax, (202) 324-4705. Louis J. Freeh, director. Information, (202) 324-3691. Internet, http://www.fbi.gov.*

Investigates all violations of federal criminal laws except those assigned specifically to other federal agencies. Exceptions include alcohol, counterfeiting, tobacco, and customs violations (departments of Treasury and Commerce); postal violations (U.S. Postal Service); and illegal entry of aliens (Justice Dept.'s Immigration and Naturalization Service). Services provided to other law enforcement agencies include fingerprint identification, laboratory services, police training, and the National Crime Information Center (communications network among FBI, state, and local police agencies).

Office of Justice Programs *(Justice Dept.), National Institute of Justice, 810 7th St. N.W. 20531; (202) 307-2942. Fax, (202) 307-6394. Jeremy Travis, director. Internet, http://www.ncjrs.org/nijhome.htm.*

Conducts research on all aspects of criminal justice, including crime prevention, enforcement, adjudication, and corrections; evaluates programs; develops model programs using new techniques. Serves as an affiliated institute of the United Nations Crime Prevention and

Criminal Justice Programme (UNCPCJ); studies transnational issues, especially within the Western Hemisphere. Maintains the National Criminal Justice Reference Service, which provides information on criminal justice research: (800) 851-3420; in Maryland, (301) 251-5500; Internet, http://www.ncjrs.org.

Office of Justice Programs *(Justice Dept.), Victims of Crime, 810 7th St. N.W., 8th Floor 20531; (202) 307-5983. Fax, (202) 514-6383. Reginald Robinson, director. Internet, http://www.ojp.usdoj.gov/ovc.*

Provides funds to state victim compensation and assistance programs, including counseling for victims of rape, child abuse, and spouse abuse; supports victim assistance programs for Native Americans. Operations are financed by the crime victims fund, which is financed by federal criminal fines, penalties, and bond forfeitures. Provides information on victim and witness services.

CONGRESS

House Commerce Committee, *Subcommittee on Health and the Environment, 2125 RHOB 20515; (202) 225-2927. Fax, (202) 225-1919. Michael Bilirakis, R-Fla., chair; James E. Derderian, staff director. Internet, http://www.house.gov/commerce/health.html.*

Jurisdiction over legislation on drug abuse and rehabilitation of drug abusers, including narcotics addicts who have had contact (arrest or conviction) with the federal criminal justice system.

House Education and the Workforce Committee, *Subcommittee on Early Childhood, Youth, and Families, 2181 RHOB 20515; (202) 225-4527. Fax, (202) 225-9571. Frank Riggs, R-Calif., chair; Kevin Talley, staff director. Internet, http://www.house.gov/eeo.*

Jurisdiction over legislation on juvenile justice and related issues, including the role of children in the courts (jurisdiction shared with House Judiciary Committee). Oversight of the Juvenile Justice and Delinquency Prevention Act, the Runaway Youth Act, and juvenile justice programs administered by the Office of Justice Programs.

House Government Reform and Oversight Committee, *Subcommittee on the Postal Service, B349C RHOB 20515; (202) 225-3741. Fax, (202) 225-2544. John M. McHugh, R-N.Y., chair; Robert Taub, staff director. Internet, http://www.house.gov/reform.*

Jurisdiction over legislation on postal fraud.

House Judiciary Committee, *2138 RHOB 20515; (202) 225-3951. Fax, (202) 225-7682. Henry J. Hyde, R-Ill., chair; Thomas Mooney, chief counsel. Internet, http://www.house.gov/judiciary.*

Jurisdiction over internal security legislation.

House Judiciary Committee, *Subcommittee on Crime, 207 CHOB 20515; (202) 225-3926. Fax, (202) 225-3737. Bill McCollum, R-Fla., chair; Paul J. McNulty, chief counsel. Internet, http://www.house.gov/judiciary.*

Responsible for all aspects of criminal law and procedure, and revision of the U.S. criminal code (jurisdiction over juvenile justice and the role of children in the courts shared with House Education and the Workforce Committee). Oversees federal law enforcement agencies, including the Federal Bureau of Investigation (shares intelligence operations jurisdiction with the House Select Committee on Intelligence); the Drug Enforcement Administration; the Bureau of Alcohol, Tobacco, and Firearms; the Federal Bureau of Prisons; the U.S. Parole Commission; the U.S. Marshals Service, and the Secret Service. Jurisdiction over legislation concerning the Criminal Division of the Justice Dept.

House Select Committee on Intelligence, *H405 CAP 20515; (202) 225-4121. Fax, (202) 225-1991. Porter J. Goss, R-Fla., chair; John I. Millis, staff director.*

Jurisdiction over legislation on control of domestic terrorism; oversight of the intelligence operations of the Federal Bureau of Investigation (jurisdiction shared with House Judiciary Committee).

Senate Foreign Relations Committee, *Subcommittee on International Operations, SD-450 20510; (202) 224-4651. Fax, (202) 224-0836. Rod Grams, R-Minn., chair; Chris Walker, senior professional staff member. Internet, http://www.senate.gov/committee/foreign.html.*

Jurisdiction over legislation dealing with the international flow of illegal drugs.

Senate Governmental Affairs Committee, *SD-340 20510; (202) 224-4751. Fax, (202) 224-9603. Fred Thompson, R-Tenn., chair; Hannah Sistare, staff director. Internet, http://www.senate.gov/committee/governmental_affairs.html.*

Oversight of Bureau of Alcohol, Tobacco, and Firearms.

Senate Governmental Affairs Committee, *Permanent Subcommittee on Investigations, SH-432 20510; (202) 224-3721. Fax, (202) 224-7042. Susan Collins, R-Maine, chair; Tim Shea, chief of staff. Internet, http://www.senate.gov/~gov_affairs/psi.htm.*

Investigates organized criminal activity, national and international narcotics trafficking, postal fraud, prison crime, child pornography, government contracts fraud, insurance fraud, entitlement fraud, fraud involving the use of computers, and securities theft and fraud. Investigates federal arson prevention and control activities.

Senate Judiciary Committee, *SD-224 20510; (202) 224-5225. Fax, (202) 224-9102. Orrin G. Hatch, R-Utah, chair; Manus Cooney, chief counsel. Internet, http://www. senate.gov/committee/judiciary.html.*

Responsible for all aspects of criminal law and procedure and revision of the U.S. criminal code. Jurisdiction over legislation on internal security, speedy trials and pretrial procedures, grand juries, federal trial juries, federal corrections institutions (including prisoner health care), sentences, parole, pardons, the U.S. Parole Commission, and capital punishment. Jurisdiction over legislation dealing with organized crime, including the Racketeer Influenced and Corrupt Organizations Act (RICO); judicial ethics; gun control; control of domestic terrorism; some aspects of narcotics abuse, including control, enforcement, and criminal penalties; regulation of trade; and import-export control.

Senate Judiciary Committee, *Subcommittee on Youth Violence, SD-518 20510; (202) 224-7572. Fax, (202) 228-0545. Jeff Sessions, R-Ala., chair; Kristi Lee, chief counsel. Internet, http://www.senate.gov/committee/judiciary.html.*

Jurisdiction over legislation on juvenile justice and related issues, including the role of children in the courts. Oversight of the Juvenile Justice and Delinquency Prevention Act, the Runaway and Homeless Youth Act, and juvenile justice programs administered by the Office of Justice Programs.

Senate Labor and Human Resources Committee, *SD-428 20510; (202) 224-5375. Fax, (202) 224-6510. James M. Jeffords, R-Vt., chair; Mark Powden, staff director. Internet, http://www.senate.gov/~labor.*

Jurisdiction over legislation on drug abuse and rehabilitation of drug abusers, including narcotics addicts who have had contact (arrest or conviction) with the federal criminal justice system.

Senate Select Committee on Intelligence, *SH-211 20510; (202) 224-1700. Richard C. Shelby, R-Ala., chair; Taylor Lawrence, staff director. Internet, http://www. senate.gov/committee/intelligence.html.*

Studies, makes recommendations, and proposes legislation on intelligence agencies' activities, policies, and funds; oversees the Central Intelligence Agency, National Security Agency, Defense Intelligence Agency, the intelligence activities of the Federal Bureau of Investigation, and other intelligence operations of the U.S. government to ensure conformity with the U.S. Constitution and laws; authorizes appropriations for the intelligence community. Oversight of directives and procedures governing intelligence activities affecting the rights of Americans abroad.

INTERNATIONAL ORGANIZATIONS

INTERPOL *(Justice Dept.), 600 E St. N.W. (mailing address: U.S. Justice Dept., Washington, DC 20530); (202) 616-9000. Fax, (202) 616-8400. John J. Imhoff, chief. Internet, http://www.usdoj.gov/usncb.*

U.S. national central bureau for INTERPOL; participates in international investigations on behalf of U.S. police; coordinates the exchange of investigative information on crimes, including drug trafficking, counterfeiting, missing persons, and terrorism. Coordinates law enforcement requests for investigative assistance in the United States and abroad. Assists with extradition processes. Serves as liaison between foreign and U.S. law enforcement agencies at federal, state, and local levels. (Headquarters in Lyons, France.)

NONPROFIT

American Bar Assn., *Criminal Justice, 740 15th St. N.W. 20005; (202) 662-1500. Fax, (202) 662-1501. Thomas C. Smith, director. Internet, http://www.abanet.org.*

Responsible for all matters pertaining to criminal law and procedure for the association. Studies and makes recommendations on all facets of the criminal and juvenile justice system, including sentencing, juries, pretrial procedures, grand juries, white-collar crime, and the Racketeer Influenced and Corrupt Organizations Act (RICO). (Headquarters in Chicago.)

American Prosecutors Research Institute, *99 Canal Center Plaza, #510, Alexandria, VA 22314; (703) 549-4253. Fax, (703) 836-3195. Jennifer Panagopoulos, deputy director. Internet, apri.ndaa@aspensys.com or http://www. ndaa-apri.org.*

Conducts research, provides information, and analyzes policies related to improvements in criminal prosecution. (Affiliated with the National District Attorneys' Assn.)

Institute of Criminal Law and Procedure, *Georgetown University Law Center, 600 New Jersey Ave. N.W. 20001; (202) 662-9070. Fax, (202) 662-9444. Samuel Dash, director.*

Contract research organization affiliated with Georgetown University Law Center. Conducts research on the criminal justice system, including plea bargaining and police-prosecutor relations.

Justice Policy Institute, *2208 Martin Luther King Jr. Ave. S.E. 20020; (202) 678-2843. Fax, (202) 678-9321. Vincent Schiraldi, director.*

Research, advocacy, and policy development organization. Analyzes current and emerging criminal justice problems; works to develop new initiatives; educates the public about criminal justice issues. Interests include new prison construction, alternatives to incarceration, and curfew laws.

National Assn. of Attorneys General, *750 1st St. N.E., #1100 20002; (202) 326-6053. Fax, (202) 408-7014. Christine Milliken, executive director. Press, (202) 326-6047.*

Membership: attorneys general of the states, territories, and commonwealths. Fosters interstate cooperation on legal and law enforcement issues, conducts policy research and analysis, and facilitates communication between members and all levels of government. *(For list of attorneys general, see Governors and Other State Officials in appendix.)*

National Assn. of Crime Victim Compensation Boards, *P.O. Box 16003, Alexandria, VA 22302-8003; (703) 370-2996. Fax, (703) 370-2996. Dan Eddy, executive director.*

Provides state compensation agencies with training and technical assistance. Provides public information on victim compensation.

National Assn. of Criminal Defense Lawyers, *1025 Connecticut Ave. N.W., #901 20036; (202) 872-8600. Fax, (202) 872-8690. Stuart M. Statler, executive director. Internet, http://www.criminaljustice.org.*

Membership: criminal defense attorneys. Provides members with continuing legal education programs, a brief bank, an ethics hotline, and specialized assistance in areas such as DNA and Section 8300 cash reporting requirements. Offers free legal assistance to members who are harassed, charged with contempt, or receive a bar grievance for providing ethical but aggressive representation. Interests include eliminating mandatory minimum sentencing, reforming the FBI laboratories, opposing the death penalty, and minimizing the effect on civil liberties of the war on drugs. Monitors legislation and regulations.

National Crime Prevention Council, *1700 K St. N.W., 2nd Floor 20006-3817; (202) 466-6272. Fax, (202) 296-1356. John A. Calhoun, executive director. Internet, http://www.weprevent.org.*

Educates public on crime prevention through media campaigns, supporting materials, and training workshops; sponsors McGruff public service campaign; runs demonstration programs in schools.

National District Attorneys' Assn., *99 Canal Center Plaza, #510, Alexandria, VA 22314; (703) 549-9222. Fax, (703) 836-3195. Newman Flanagan, executive director.*

Sponsors conferences and workshops on criminal justice; provides information on district attorneys, crimi-

nal justice, the courts, child abuse, environmental crime, and national traffic laws.

National Organization for Victim Assistance, *1757 Park Rd. N.W. 20010; (202) 232-6682. Fax, (202) 462-2255. Marlene A. Young, executive director. Toll-free information hotline, (800) 879-6682; (202) 232-6682 in Washington area. Internet, nova@digex.net or http://www.access.digex.net/~nova.*

Membership: persons involved with victim and witness assistance programs, criminal justice professionals, researchers, crime victims, and others interested in victims' rights. Monitors legislation; provides victims and victim support programs with technical assistance, referrals, and program support; provides information on victims' rights.

National Victim Center, *2111 Wilson Blvd., #300, Arlington, VA 22201; (703) 276-2880. Fax, (703) 276-2889. Susan Herman, executive director. Internet, http://www.nvc.org.*

Works with victims' groups and criminal justice agencies to protect the rights of crime victims through state and federal statutes and policies. Promotes greater responsiveness to crime victims through training and education; provides research and technical assistance in the development of victim-related legislation.

See also Assn. of Trial Lawyers of America (p. 495); Federal Bar Assn. (p. 496)

Child Abuse, Domestic Violence, and Sexual Assault

See also Children and Families (chap. 18)

AGENCIES

Administration for Children, Youth, and Families *(Health and Human Services Dept.), Family and Youth Services, 330 C St. S.W. (mailing address: P.O. Box 1182, Washington, DC 20013); (202) 205-8102. Fax, (202) 260-9333. Terry Lewis, associate commissioner.*

Administers federal discretionary grant programs for projects serving runaway and homeless youth and for projects that deter youth involvement in gangs. Provides youth service agencies with training and technical assistance. Monitors federal policies, programs, and legislation. Supports research on youth development issues, including gangs, runaways, and homeless youth. Operates national clearinghouse on families and youth.

Criminal Division *(Justice Dept.), Child Exploitation and Obscenity Section, 1331 F St. N.W., #637 20014; (202) 514-5780. Fax, (202) 514-1793. Terry Lord, chief.*

Enforces federal obscenity and child pornography laws; prosecutes cases involving violations of these laws. Maintains collection of briefs, pleadings, and other material for use by federal, state, and local prosecutors.

Office of Justice Programs *(Justice Dept.), National Institute of Justice,* 810 7th St. N.W. 20531; (202) 307-2942. Fax, (202) 307-6394. Jeremy Travis, director. Internet, http://www.ncjrs.org/nijhome.htm.

Conducts research on all aspects of criminal justice, including AIDS issues for law enforcement officials. Studies on rape and domestic violence available from the National Criminal Justice Reference Service: (800) 851-3420; in Maryland, (301) 251-5500; Internet, http://www.ncjrs.org.

Office of Justice Programs *(Justice Dept.), Violence Against Women,* 10th and Constitution Ave. N.W., #5302 20530; (202) 616-8894. Fax, (202) 307-3911. Bonnie Campbell, director. Internet, http://www.usdoj.gov/vawo.

Seeks more effective policies and services to combat domestic violence, sexual assault, stalking, and other crimes against women. Helps administer grants to states to fund shelters, crisis centers, and hotlines, and to hire law enforcement officers, prosecutors, and counselors specializing in cases of sexual violence and other violent crimes against women.

NONPROFIT

American Bar Assn., *Center on Children and the Law,* 740 15th St. N.W., 9th Floor 20005; (202) 662-1720. Fax, (202) 662-1755. Howard Davidson, director. Internet, ctrchildlaw@abanet.org or http://www.abanet.org.

Provides child welfare community with training and technical assistance. Interests include child abuse and neglect, adoption, foster care, and medical neglect.

National Center for Prosecution of Child Abuse, 99 Canal Center Plaza, #510, Alexandria, VA 22314; (703) 739-0321. Fax, (703) 549-6259. Daniel Armagh, director. Internet, http://www.ndaa-apri.org.

Provides prosecutors involved in child abuse cases with training and information. Monitors legislation concerning child abuse.

Rape, Abuse, and Incest National Network (RAINN), 635-B Pennsylvania Ave. S.E. 20003; (202) 544-1034. Fax, (202) 544-1401. Debbie Andrews, executive director. Toll-free, (800) 656-HOPE. Internet, rainnmail@aol.com or http://www.rainn.org.

Publicizes the issue of sexual assault and the availability of local counseling services for rape and incest

survivors. RAINN's 24-hour sexual assault hotline provides free counseling services through a national network of rape crisis centers.

See also Center for Women Policy Studies (p. 9)

Drug Control

See also Narcotics Trafficking (chap. 13); Substance Abuse (chap. 11)

AGENCIES

Criminal Division *(Justice Dept.), Narcotic and Dangerous Drugs,* 1400 New York Ave. N.W., #1100 20530; (202) 514-0917. Fax, (202) 514-6112. Theresa Van Vliet, chief.

Investigates and prosecutes participants in criminal syndicates involved in the large-scale importation, manufacture, shipment, or distribution of illegal narcotics and other dangerous drugs. Trains agents and prosecutors in the techniques of major drug litigation.

Defense Dept., *Drug Enforcement Policy and Support,* The Pentagon 20301-1510; (703) 695-7996. Fax, (703) 693-7588. Robert J. Newberry, acting deputy assistant secretary.

Advises the secretary on Defense Dept. policies and programs in support of federal counternarcotics operations and the implementation of the president's National Drug Control Policy.

Drug Enforcement Administration *(Justice Dept.),* 700 Army-Navy Dr., Arlington, VA; (202) 307-8000. Fax, (202) 307-7335. Thomas A. Constantine, administrator. Information, (202) 307-7977. Locator, (202) 307-1000. Internet, http://www.usdoj.gov/dea.

Enforces federal laws and statutes relating to narcotics and other dangerous drugs, including addictive drugs, depressants, stimulants, and hallucinogens; manages the National Narcotics Intelligence System in cooperation with federal, state, and local officials; investigates violations and regulates legal trade in narcotics and dangerous drugs. Provides school and community officials with drug abuse policy guidelines. Provides information on drugs and drug abuse.

Federal Bureau of Investigation *(Justice Dept.),* 935 Pennsylvania Ave. N.W. 20535; (202) 324-3444. Fax, (202) 324-4705. Louis J. Freeh, director. Information, (202) 324-3691. Internet, http://www.fbi.gov.

Shares responsibility with the Drug Enforcement Administration for investigating violations of federal criminal drug laws; investigates organized crime involvement with illegal narcotics trafficking.

Food and Drug Administration *(Health and Human Services Dept.), Center for Drug Evaluation and Research,* 5600 Fishers Lane, Woodmont II, #6027, Rockville, MD 20857; (301) 594-5400. Fax, (301) 594-6197. Dr. Janet Woodcock, director. Information, (301) 827-4573. Press, (301) 827-6242.

Makes recommendations to the Justice Dept.'s Drug Enforcement Administration on narcotics and dangerous drugs to be controlled.

Interior Dept., *Managing Risk and Public Safety,* 1849 C St. N.W., #7358 20240-4108; (202) 208-4108. Fax, (202) 208-5078. L. Michael Kaas, director.

Administers drug and law enforcement programs for the Interior Dept., including programs in national parks, ranges, and fish and wildlife refuges. Cooperates with local law enforcement agencies, state park rangers, and other drug enforcement agencies.

Office of Justice Programs *(Justice Dept.), Justice Assistance,* 810 7th St. N.W., 4th Floor 20531; (202) 514-6278. Fax, (202) 305-1367. Nancy E. Gist, director. Internet, http://www.ojp.usdoj.gov/BJA.

Awards grants and provides eligible state and local governments with training and technical assistance to enforce laws relating to narcotics and other dangerous drugs.

Office of National Drug Control Policy *(Executive Office of the President),* 750 17th St. N.W. (mailing address: Old Executive Office Bldg., Washington, DC 20500); (202) 395-6700. Fax, (202) 395-6708. Barry McCaffrey, director. Internet, http://www.whitehouse.gov/WH/EOP/ondcp/html/ondcp.html.

Establishes policies and oversees the implementation of a national drug control strategy; recommends changes to reduce demand for and supply of illegal drugs; advises the National Security Council on drug control policy.

U.S. Coast Guard *(Transportation Dept.), Operational Law Enforcement,* 2100 2nd St. S.W., #3110 20593-0001; (202) 267-1155. Fax, (202) 267-4082. Capt. Anthony S. Tangeman, chief.

Combats smuggling of narcotics and other dangerous drugs into the United States via the Atlantic and Pacific oceans and the Gulf of Mexico; works with U.S. Customs Service on drug law enforcement; interdicts illegal migrants; enforces fisheries.

U.S. Customs Service *(Treasury Dept.), Investigations,* 1300 Pennsylvania Ave. N.W., #6.5E 20229; (202) 927-1600. Fax, (202) 927-1948. Bonni G. Tischler, assistant commissioner. Information, (202) 927-1770. Internet, http://www.customs.ustreas.gov.

Interdicts and seizes contraband, including narcotics and other dangerous drugs smuggled into the United States. To report information on drug smuggling, call (800) 232-5378.

NONPROFIT

American Prosecutors Research Institute, *National Drug Prosecution Center,* 99 Canal Center Plaza, #510, Alexandria, VA 22314; (703) 549-6790. Fax, (703) 836-3195. Jennifer Panagopoulos, chief administrator. Internet, apri.ndaa@aspensys.com.

Trains prosecutors to investigate and prosecute drug cases; develops legislation to revise drug laws. Established by a grant from the Justice Dept. (Affiliated with the National District Attorneys' Assn.)

Common Sense for Drug Policy, 3619 Tallwood Terr., Falls Church, VA 22041; (703) 354-5694. Fax, (703) 354-5695. Kevin B. Zeese, president. Internet, http://www.drugsense.org.

Provides technical assistance, fundraising, and public relations advice to groups that promote health-based strategies of drug control. Seeks to encourage development of an effective drug policy and to reduce drug-related harms, including spread of AIDS and other diseases, crime and violence, and social dysfunction; focus includes international drug policy.

Drug Policy Foundation, 4455 Connecticut Ave. N.W., #B500 20008-2302; (202) 537-5005. Fax, (202) 537-3007. Cher Horosko, director. Internet, dpf@dpf.org or http://www.dpf.org.

Supports reform of current drug control policy. Advocates medical treatment to control drug abuse; opposes random drug testing. Sponsors the International Network of Cities Drug Policy, which focuses on drug issues in urban settings worldwide.

Marijuana Policy Project, P.O. Box 77492 20013; (202) 462-5747. Fax, (202) 232-0442. Robert D. Kampia, director, Government Relations. Internet, mpp@mpp.org or http://www.mpp.org.

Promotes reform of marijuana policies and regulations. Opposes the prohibition of responsible growing and use of marijuana by adults. Interests include allowing doctors to prescribe marijuana to seriously ill patients and reforming federal sentencing policies.

National Assn. of Chiefs of Police, 1000 Connecticut Ave. N.W., #9 20036; (202) 293-9088. George Vuilleumier, president. Internet, http://www.aphf.org.

Conducts research and provides organizations interested in reducing drug demand with information, programs, and training. Administers Going Straight, a campaign that works to create drug-free schools. (Headquarters in Miami.)

National Assn. of State Alcohol and Drug Abuse Directors, *808 17th St. N.W., #410 20006; (202) 293-0090. Fax, (202) 293-1250. John S. Gustafson, executive director.*

Provides information on drug abuse treatment and prevention; contracts with federal and state agencies for design of programs to fight drug abuse.

National Organization for the Reform of Marijuana Laws (NORML), *1001 Connecticut Ave. N.W., #710 20036; (202) 483-5500. Fax, (202) 483-0057. Keith Stroup, executive director. Internet, natlnorml@aol.com or http://www.norml.org.*

Works to reform federal, state, and local marijuana laws and policies. Educates the public and conducts litigation on behalf of marijuana consumers. Monitors legislation and regulations.

Rand Corporation, *Drug Policy Research Center, 1333 H St. N.W., #800 20005-4707; (202) 296-5000. Fax, (202) 296-7960. Barbara Williams, senior adviser. Internet, http://www.rand.org/centers/dprc.*

Studies and analyzes the nation's drug problems and policies; interests include international policy, trafficking, and interdiction. Provides policymakers with information. (Headquarters in Santa Monica, Calif.)

Gun Control

AGENCIES

Bureau of Alcohol, Tobacco, and Firearms *(Treasury Dept.), Field Operations, 650 Massachusetts Ave. N.W., #8100 20226; (202) 927-7970. Fax, (202) 927-7756. Andrew L. Vita, assistant director. Information, (202) 927-7777. Press, (202) 927-9510. Internet, http://www.atf.treas.gov.*

Enforces and administers laws to eliminate illegal possession and use of firearms. Investigates criminal violations and regulates legal trade, including imports and exports. To report thefts, losses, or discoveries of explosive materials, call (800) 800-3855.

NONPROFIT

Center to Prevent Handgun Violence, *1225 Eye St. N.W., #1100 20005; (202) 289-7319. Fax, (202) 408-1851. Sarah Brady, chair.*

Educational, research, and legal action organization that seeks to allay handgun violence, especially among children, through gun control legislation. (Affiliated with Handgun Control, Inc.)

Citizens Committee for the Right to Keep and Bear Arms, *600 Pennsylvania Ave. S.E., #205 20003; (202) 543-3363. Fax, (202) 546-2462. John M. Snyder, director, Publications and Public Affairs.*

Concerned with rights of gun owners. Maintains National Advisory Council, comprising members of Congress and other distinguished Americans, which provides advice on issues concerning the right to keep and bear arms. (Headquarters in Bellevue, Wash.)

Coalition to Stop Gun Violence, *1000 16th St. N.W., #603 20036; (202) 530-0340. Fax, (202) 530-0331. Michael K. Beard, president. Internet, noguns@aol.com or http://www.gunfree.org.*

Membership: organizations and individuals seeking to ban handguns. Provides national, state, and local groups operating handgun education programs with materials; engages in research and field work to support legislation to ban or control handguns.

Educational Fund to End Handgun Violence, *1000 16th St. N.W., #603 20036; (202) 530-5888. Fax, (202) 530-0331. Joshua Horwitz, executive director. Internet, edfund@aol.com.*

Works to reduce handgun violence through education; assists schools and organizations in establishing antiviolence programs; maintains a firearms litigation clearinghouse.

Gun Owners of America, *8001 Forbes Pl., #102, Springfield, VA 22151; (703) 321-8585. Fax, (703) 321-8408. Lawrence D. Pratt, executive director. Internet, http://www.gunowners.org.*

Seeks to preserve the right to bear arms and to protect the rights of law-abiding gun owners. Administers foundation that provides gun owners with legal assistance in suits against the federal government. Monitors legislation, regulations, and international agreements.

Handgun Control, Inc., *1225 Eye St. N.W., #1100 20005; (202) 898-0792. Fax, (202) 371-9615. Robert Walker, president. Internet, http://www.handguncontrol.org.*

Public interest organization that works for handgun control legislation and serves as an information clearinghouse.

National Rifle Assn. of America, *11250 Waples Mill Rd., Fairfax, VA 22030; (703) 267-1000. Fax, (703) 267-3976. Wayne La Pierre Jr., executive vice president. Press, (703) 267-3820. Internet, http://www.nra.org.*

Membership: target shooters, hunters, gun collectors, gunsmiths, police officers, and others interested in firearms. Promotes shooting sports and recreational shooting and safety; studies and makes recommendations on firearms laws. Opposes gun control legislation.

Juvenile Justice

See also Children and Families (chap. 18)

AGENCIES

Education Dept., *Compensatory Education Programs,* *1250 Maryland Ave. S.W., #4400 (mailing address: 600 Independence Ave. S.W., 4400 Portals Bldg., Washington, DC 20202-6132); (202) 260-0826. Fax, (202) 260-7764. Mary Jean LeTendre, director. Press, (202) 401-1008.*

Funds state and local institutions responsible for providing neglected or delinquent children with free public education.

Office of Justice Programs *(Justice Dept.), Juvenile Justice and Delinquency Prevention, 810 7th St. N.W., 8th Floor 20531; (202) 307-5911. Fax, (202) 307-2093. Shay Bilchik, administrator. Technical information, (202) 307-0751. Clearinghouse, (800) 638-8736. Internet, http:// www.ncjrs.org/ojjhome.htm.*

Administers most federal programs related to prevention and treatment of juvenile delinquency, missing and exploited children, and research and evaluation of juvenile justice system; coordinates youth programs of the departments of Agriculture, Education, Housing and Urban Development, Interior, and Labor, and of the Substance Abuse and Mental Health Services Administration, including the Center for Studies of Crime and Delinquency. Operates the Juvenile Justice Clearinghouse.

NONPROFIT

Coalition for Juvenile Justice, *1211 Connecticut Ave. N.W., #414 20036; (202) 467-0864. Fax, (202) 887-0738. David Doi, executive director. Internet, juvjustice@aol.com.*

Represents state juvenile justice advisory groups. Promotes the improvement of the juvenile justice system and the prevention of juvenile delinquency.

Robert F. Kennedy Memorial, *National Youth Project, 1367 Connecticut Ave. N.W. 20036; (202) 463-7575. Fax, (202) 463-6606. Brodrick Clarke, director. Internet, info@rfcmemorial.org or http://rfkmemorial.org.*

Develops new approaches to the problems of drug and alcohol addiction, crime and violence, school failures, and family disorder. Programs include: The Pico Aliso Gang Prevention/Intervention Program, The RFK Fellows Program, and The D.C. Juvenile Justice Program.

Organized Crime

AGENCIES

Criminal Division *(Justice Dept.), Narcotic and Dangerous Drugs, 1400 New York Ave. N.W., #1100 20530;*

(202) 514-0917. Fax, (202) 514-6112. Theresa Van Vliet, chief.

Investigates and prosecutes participants in criminal syndicates involved in the large-scale importation, manufacture, shipment, or distribution of illegal narcotics and other dangerous drugs. Trains agents and prosecutors in the techniques of major drug litigation.

Justice Dept. *(Justice Dept.), Organized Crime and Racketeering, 1001 G St. N.W. 20530; (202) 514-3594. Fax, (202) 305-1448. Vacant, chief.*

Enforces federal criminal laws when subjects under investigation are alleged racketeers or part of syndicated criminal operations; coordinates efforts of federal, state, and local law enforcement agencies against organized crime, including emerging international groups. Cases include infiltration of legitimate businesses and labor unions, public corruption, labor-management racketeering, and violence that disrupts the criminal justice process.

Other Violations

See also Campaigning (chap. 20)

AGENCIES

Bureau of Alcohol, Tobacco, and Firearms *(Treasury Dept.), Field Operations, 650 Massachusetts Ave. N.W., #8100 20226; (202) 927-7970. Fax, (202) 927-7756. Andrew L. Vita, assistant director. Information, (202) 927-7777. Press, (202) 927-9510. Internet, http://www.atf. treas.gov.*

Enforces and administers laws relating to alcohol (beer, wine, and distilled spirits), tobacco, firearms, arson, explosives, and destructive devices; investigates criminal violations and regulates legal trade. To report thefts, losses, or discoveries of explosive materials, call (800) 800-3855.

Criminal Division *(Justice Dept.), Asset Forfeiture and Money Laundering, 1400 New York Ave. N.W., #10100 20005; (202) 514-1758. Fax, (202) 616-1344. Gerald E. McDowell, chief.*

Investigates and prosecutes money-laundering offenses involving illegal transfer of funds within the United States and from the United States to other countries. Oversees and coordinates legislative policy proposals. Advises U.S. attorney's offices in multi-district money laundering prosecutions. Represents Justice Dept. in international anti-money laundering initiatives.

Criminal Division *(Justice Dept.), Fraud, 1400 New York Ave. N.W., #2100 20530; (202) 514-0640. Fax, (202) 514-6118. Mary C. Spearing, chief. Internet, http://www. usdoj.gov/criminal/fraud.*

Administers federal enforcement activities related to fraud and white-collar crime. Focuses on frauds against government programs, transnational and multidistrict fraud, and cases involving the security and commodity exchanges, banking practices, and consumer victimization.

Criminal Division *(Justice Dept.), Terrorism and Violent Crime,* 601 D St. N.W., #6500 20530; (202) 514-0849. Fax, (202) 514-8714. James S. Reynolds, chief.

Investigates and prosecutes incidents of international terrorism involving U.S. interests, domestic violent crime, firearms, and explosives violations. Provides legal advice on federal statutes relating to murder, assault, kidnapping, threats, robbery, weapons and explosives control, malicious destruction of property, and aircraft and sea piracy.

Federal Bureau of Investigation *(Justice Dept.), Economic Crimes,* 935 Pennsylvania Ave. N.W., #7373 20535; (202) 324-6056. Fax, (202) 324-8072. John Kingston, chief. Press, (202) 324-3691.

Investigates crimes of fraud, theft, or embezzlement within or against the national or international financial community, excluding frauds against financial institutions. Priorities include money laundering, copyright infringement, insurance, securities and commodities, bankruptcy, and telemarketing.

U.S. Customs Service *(Treasury Dept.), Investigations,* 1300 Pennsylvania Ave. N.W., #6.5E 20229; (202) 927-1600. Fax, (202) 927-1948. Bonni G. Tischler, assistant commissioner. Information, (202) 927-1770. Internet, http://www.customs.ustreas.gov.

Combats smuggling and the unreported transportation of funds in excess of $10,000; enforces statutes relating to the processing and regulation of people, carriers, cargo, and mail into and out of the United States. Investigates counterfeiting, child pornography, and commercial fraud cases.

U.S. Postal Service, *Inspection Service,* 475 L'Enfant Plaza S.W., #3100 20260; (202) 268-4267. Fax, (202) 268-4563. Kenneth J. Hunter, chief postal inspector. Fraud and abuse hotline, (888) 877-7644.

Protects mail, postal funds, and property from violations of postal laws, such as mail fraud or distribution of obscene materials.

U.S. Secret Service *(Treasury Dept.),* 1800 G St. N.W. 20223; (202) 435-5700. Fax, (202) 435-5246. Lewis C. Merletti, director. Information, (202) 435-5708. Internet, http://www.treas.gov/usss/main.html.

Enforces and administers counterfeiting and forgery laws. Investigates electronic fund transfer, credit card,

and other types of access fraud, and threats against the president, vice president, and foreign heads of state visiting the United States.

Sentencing and Corrections

AGENCIES

Federal Bureau of Prisons *(Justice Dept.),* 320 1st St. N.W. 20534; (202) 307-6300. Fax, (202) 514-6878. Kathleen M. Hawk Sawyer, director. Information, (202) 307-3198. Inmate locator service, (202) 307-3126. Internet, http://www.bop.gov.

Supervises operations of federal correctional institutions and community treatment facilities, and commitment and management of federal inmates; oversees contracts with local institutions for confinement and support of federal inmates. Regional offices are responsible for administration; central office in Washington coordinates operations and issues standards and policy guidelines. Central office includes Federal Prison Industries, a government corporation providing prison-manufactured goods and services for sale to federal agencies, and the National Institute of Corrections, an information and technical assistance center on state and local corrections programs. *(See Regional Information Sources in appendix.)*

Federal Bureau of Prisons *(Justice Dept.), Health Services,* 320 1st St. N.W., #1054 20534; (202) 307-3055. Fax, (202) 307-0826. Dr. Kenneth P. Moritsugu, medical director.

Administers health care and treatment programs for inmates in federal institutions.

Federal Bureau of Prisons *(Justice Dept.), Industries, Education, and Vocational Training—UNICOR,* 400 1st St. N.W. (mailing address: 320 1st St. N.W., Washington, DC 20534); (202) 305-3500. Fax, (202) 305-7340. Steve Schwalb, chief operating officer. Internet, http://www.unicor.gov.

Administers program whereby inmates in federal prisons produce goods and services that are sold to the federal government.

Federal Bureau of Prisons *(Justice Dept.), National Institute of Corrections,* 320 1st St. N.W. 20534; (202) 307-3106. Fax, (202) 307-3361. Morris L. Thigpen, director.

Awards grants and offers technical assistance and training for upgrading state and local corrections systems through staff development, research, and evaluation of correctional operations and programs. Acts as a clearinghouse on correctional information.

Justice Dept., *Pardon Attorney, 500 1st St. N.W., #400 20530; (202) 616-6070. Fax, (202) 616-6069. Roger C. Adams, acting pardon attorney. Internet, http://www. usdoj.gov/offices/opa.html.*

Receives and reviews petitions to the president for all forms of executive clemency, including pardons and sentence reductions; initiates investigations and prepares the deputy attorney general's recommendations to the president on petitions.

Office of Justice Programs *(Justice Dept.), Justice Assistance, 810 7th St. N.W., 4th Floor 20531; (202) 514-6278. Fax, (202) 305-1367. Nancy E. Gist, director. Internet, http://www.ojp.usdoj.gov/BJA.*

Provides states and communities with funds and technical assistance for corrections demonstration projects.

Office of Justice Programs *(Justice Dept.), National Institute of Justice, 810 7th St. N.W. 20531; (202) 307-2942. Fax, (202) 307-6394. Jeremy Travis, director. Internet, http://www.ncjrs.org/nijhome.htm.*

Division of the Office of Justice Programs. Conducts research on all aspects of criminal justice, including crime prevention, enforcement, adjudication, and corrections. Maintains the National Criminal Justice Reference Service, which provides information on corrections research: (800) 851-3420; in Maryland, (301) 251-5500; Internet, http://www.ncjrs.org.

U.S. Parole Commission *(Justice Dept.), 5550 Friendship Blvd., #420, Chevy Chase, MD 20815-7286; (301) 492-5990. Fax, (301) 492-5307. Michael Gaines, chair. Chair's fax, (301) 492-5010. Internet, http://www. usdoj.gov/uspc.*

Makes release decisions for all federal prisoners serving sentences of more than one year including military prisoners; jurisdiction over paroled federal prisoners and over other prisoners on mandatory release under the "good time" statutes. U.S. probation officers supervise parolees and mandatory releases. *(See Regional Information Sources in appendix.)*

U.S. Sentencing Commission, *1 Columbus Circle N.E., #2-500 South Lobby 20002-8002; (202) 273-4500. Fax, (202) 273-4529. Richard C. Conaboy, chair. Internet, http://www.ussc.gov.*

Establishes sentencing guidelines and policy for all federal courts, including guidelines prescribing the appropriate form and severity of punishment for those convicted of federal crimes. Provides training and research on sentencing-related issues. Serves as an information resource for Congress, criminal justice practitioners, and the public.

JUDICIARY

Administrative Office of the U.S. Courts, *1 Columbus Circle N.E., #7-100 20544; (202) 273-3000. Fax, (202) 273-2349. L. Ralph Mecham, director. Information, (202) 273-0107. Library, (202) 273-1888. Internet, http://www. uscourts.gov.*

Supervises all administrative matters of the federal court system, except the Supreme Court; collects statistical data on business of the courts.

Administrative Office of the U.S. Courts, *Federal Corrections and Supervision, 1 Columbus Circle N.E., #4-300 20544; (202) 273-1610. Fax, (202) 273-1603. Eunice R. Holt Jones, chief.*

Supervises federal probation and pretrial services officers, subject to primary control by the respective district courts in which they serve. Responsible for general oversight of field offices; tests new probation programs such as probation teams and deferred prosecution.

NONPROFIT

American Bar Assn., *Criminal Justice, 740 15th St. N.W. 20005; (202) 662-1500. Fax, (202) 662-1501. Thomas C. Smith, director. Internet, http://www.abanet.org.*

Studies and makes recommendations on all aspects of the correctional system, including overcrowding in prisons and the privatization of prisons and correctional institutions. (Headquarters in Chicago.)

American Civil Liberties Union Foundation, *National Prison Project, 1875 Connecticut Ave. N.W., #410 20009-5728; (202) 234-4830. Fax, (202) 234-4890. Elizabeth Alexander, executive director. Internet, http:// www.npp.org.*

Litigates on behalf of prisoners through class action suits. Seeks to improve prison conditions and the penal system; serves as resource center for prisoners' rights; operates an AIDS education project.

American Correctional Assn., *4380 Forbes Blvd., Lanham, MD 20706; (301) 918-1800. Fax, (301) 918-1900. James A. Gondles Jr., executive director. Internet, http:// www.corrections.com/aca.*

Membership: corrections administrators and staff in juvenile and adult institutions, community corrections facilities, and jails; affiliates include state and regional corrections associations in the United States and Canada. Conducts and publishes research; provides state and local governments with technical assistance. Interests include correctional standards and accreditation programs. Library open to the public.

Amnesty International USA, *304 Pennsylvania Ave. S.E. 20003; (202) 544-0200. Fax, (202) 546-7142. Stephen*

Rickard, director, Washington Office. Internet, http://www.amnesty-usa.org.

International organization that opposes retention or reinstitution of the death penalty; advocates humane treatment of all prisoners. (U.S. headquarters in New York.)

Correctional Education Assn., *4380 Forbes Blvd., Lanham, MD 20706; (301) 918-1915. Fax, (301) 918-1900. Stephen J. Steurer, executive director.*

Membership: educators and administrators who work with students in correctional settings. Provides members with information and technical assistance to improve quality of educational programs and services offered in correctional settings. Interests include postsecondary and vocational education, special education, jail education, and libraries and literacy.

Families Against Mandatory Minimums, *1612 K St. N.W., #1400 20006; (202) 822-6700. Fax, (202) 822-6704. Julie Stewart, president. Internet, famm@famm.org or http://www.famm.org.*

Seeks to repeal statutory mandatory minimum prison sentences. Works to increase public awareness of inequity of mandatory minimum sentences through grassroots efforts and media outreach programs.

NAACP Legal Defense and Educational Fund, *1275 K St. N.W., #301 20005; (202) 682-1300. Fax, (202) 682-1312. Vacant, director, Washington Office.*

Civil rights litigation group that supports abolition of capital punishment; assists attorneys representing prisoners on death row; focuses public attention on race discrimination in the application of the death penalty. Not affiliated with the National Assn. for the Advancement of Colored People (NAACP). (Headquarters in New York.)

National Center on Institutions and Alternatives, *1325 Mt. Vernon Ave., Alexandria, VA 22205; (703) 684-0373. Fax, (703) 684-6037. Jerome G. Miller, president. Internet, ncia@igc.apc.org or http://www.ncianet.org/ncia.*

Seeks to reduce incarceration as primary form of punishment imposed by criminal justice system; advocates use of extended community service, work-release, and halfway house programs; provides defense attorneys and courts with specific recommendations for sentencing and parole.

National Coalition to Abolish the Death Penalty, *1436 U St. N.W., #104 20009; (202) 387-3890. Fax, (202) 387-5590. Steven Hawkins, executive director. Internet, info@ncadp.org or http://www.ncadp.org.*

Membership: organizations and individuals opposed to the death penalty. Maintains collection of death penalty research. Provides training, resources, and conferences. Works with families of murder victims; tracks execution dates. Monitors legislation and regulations.

Prison Fellowship Ministries, *1856 Old Reston Ave., Reston, VA (mailing address: P.O. Box 17500, Washington, DC 20041-0500); (703) 478-0100. Fax, (703) 478-0452. Thomas C. Pratt, president. Internet, http://www.pfm.org.*

Religious organization that ministers to prisoners and ex-prisoners, victims, and the families involved. Offers counseling, seminars, and postrelease support for readjustment; works to increase the fairness and effectiveness of the criminal justice system.

Sentencing Project, *918 F St. N.W., #501 20004; (202) 628-0871. Fax, (202) 628-1091. Malcolm Young, executive director. Internet, http://www.sentencingproject.org.*

Develops and promotes sentencing programs that reduce reliance on incarceration; provides technical assistance to sentencing programs; compares domestic and international rates of incarceration; publishes research and information on criminal justice policy.

See also Episcopal Peace Fellowship (p. 32); National Legal Aid and Defender Assn. (p. 29); National Sheriffs' Assn. (p. 519)

LAW ENFORCEMENT

See also Criminal Law (this chapter); Legal Professions and Resources (this chapter)

AGENCIES

Criminal Division *(Justice Dept.), Computer Crime and Intellectual Property, 1001 G St. N.W., #200 20001; (202) 514-1026. Fax, (202) 514-6113. Scott Charney, chief. Internet, http://www.usdoj.gov/criminal/cybercrime.*

Investigates and litigates criminal and civil cases involving computers and the Internet; provides specialized technical and legal assistance to other Justice Dept. divisions; coordinates international efforts; formulates policies and proposes legislation on computer crime issues.

Federal Law Enforcement Training Center *(Treasury Dept.), 650 Massachusetts Ave. N.W., #3100 20026; (202) 927-8940. Fax, (202) 927-8782. John C. Dooher, associate director. Internet, 104702.2035@compuserve.com or http://www.ustreas.gov/treasury/bureaus/fletc.*

Trains federal law enforcement personnel from seventy agencies, excluding the Federal Bureau of Investigation and the Drug Enforcement Administration. (Headquarters in Glynco, Ga.)

National Institute of Standards and Technology *(Commerce Dept.), Law Enforcement Standards, Route I-270 and Quince Orchard Rd., Bldg. 225, #A323, Gaithersburg, MD 20899; (301) 975-2757. Fax, (301) 948-0978. Kathleen Higgins, director. Internet, oles@nist.gov.*

Answers inquiries and makes referrals concerning the application of science and technology to the criminal justice community; maintains information on standards and current research; prepares reports and formulates standards for the National Institute of Justice, the Federal Bureau of Investigation, and the National Highway Traffic Safety Administration.

Office of Justice Programs *(Justice Dept.), Justice Assistance, 810 7th St. N.W., 4th Floor 20531; (202) 514-6278. Fax, (202) 305-1367. Nancy E. Gist, director. Internet, http://www.ojp.usdoj.gov/BJA.*

Provides funds to eligible state and local governments and to nonprofit organizations for criminal justice programs, primarily those that combat drug trafficking and other drug-related crime.

Treasury Dept., *Financial Crimes Enforcement Network, 2070 Chain Bridge Rd., #200, Vienna, VA 22182; (703) 905-3591. Fax, (703) 905-3690. William Baity, acting director. Internet, http://www.ustreas.gov/treasury/bureaus/fincen.*

Administers information network to aid federal, state, local, and foreign law enforcement agencies in the detection, investigation, and prosecution of money-laundering operations and other financial crimes.

U.S. Marshals Service *(Justice Dept.), 600 Army-Navy Dr., #1200, Arlington, VA 22202-4210; (202) 307-9001. Fax, (703) 557-9788. Eduardo Gonzalez, director. Information, (202) 307-9065. TDD, (202) 307-9525.*

Provides the federal judiciary system and the attorney general with support services, including court and witness security, prisoner custody and transportation, prisoner support, maintenance and disposal of seized and forfeited property, and special operations. Administers the Federal Witness Protection program. Apprehends fugitives, including those wanted by foreign nations and believed to be in the United States; oversees the return of fugitives apprehended abroad and wanted by U.S. law enforcement.

CONGRESS

House Judiciary Committee, *Subcommittee on the Constitution, 362 Ford Bldg. 20515; (202) 226-7680. Fax,*

(202) 225-3746. Charles T. Canady, R-Fla., chair; Keri Folmar, counsel. Internet, http://www.house.gov/judiciary.

Jurisdiction over legislation dealing with the use, collection, evaluation, and release of criminal justice data. Oversight of legislation on information policy, electronic privacy, computer security, and trade and licensing.

House Judiciary Committee, *Subcommittee on Crime, 207 CHOB 20515; (202) 225-3926. Fax, (202) 225-3737. Bill McCollum, R-Fla., chair; Paul J. McNulty, chief counsel. Internet, http://www.house.gov/judiciary.*

Jurisdiction over legislation related to Office of Justice Programs and the Criminal Division at the Justice Dept. Oversees federal assistance to state and local law enforcement; the Federal Bureau of Investigation; the Drug Enforcement Administration; the Bureau of Alcohol, Tobacco, and Firearms; the U.S. Marshals Service; and the Secret Service.

Senate Judiciary Committee, *SD-224 20510; (202) 224-5225. Fax, (202) 224-9102. Orrin G. Hatch, R-Utah, chair; Manus Cooney, chief counsel. Internet, http://www.senate.gov/committee/judiciary.html.*

Jurisdiction over legislation related to Office of Justice Programs, which includes the Bureau of Justice Assistance, Bureau of Justice Statistics, National Institute of Justice, Office of Juvenile Justice and Delinquency Prevention, and the Office for Victims of Crime.

Senate Judiciary Committee, *Subcommittee on Technology, Terrorism, and Government Information, SH-325 20510; (202) 224-6791. Fax, (202) 228-0542. Jon Kyl, R-Ariz., chair; Michelle Van Cleve, counsel. Internet, http://www.senate.gov/committee/judiciary.html.*

Jurisdiction over legislation dealing with the use, collection, evaluation, and release of criminal justice data. Oversight of legislation on information policy, electronic privacy, computer security, and trade and licensing.

NONPROFIT

American Federation of Police, *1000 Connecticut Ave. N.W., #9 20036; (202) 293-9088. Donna Shepherd, director, Washington Office.*

Membership: governmental and private law enforcement officers. Provides members with insurance benefits and training programs. (Headquarters in Miami.)

International Assn. of Chiefs of Police, *515 N. Washington St., Alexandria, VA 22314-2357; (703) 836-6767. Fax, (703) 836-4543. Daniel N. Rosenblatt, executive director. Internet, http://www.amdahl.com/ext/iacp.*

Membership: foreign and U.S. police executives and administrators. Consults and conducts research on all aspects of police activity; conducts training programs and develops educational aids; conducts public education programs.

International Assn. of Law Enforcement Planners, *1000 Connecticut Ave. N.W., #9 20036; (202) 857-8485. Chris Stockard, president. Internet, http://www.dps. state.ak.us/ialep/index.html.*

Membership: individuals from around the world who work in planning and research for criminal justice agencies. Serves as a forum for exchange of information on issues, techniques, and innovations for advancing criminal cases. Holds conferences; publishes newsletter and membership directory.

International Union of Police Assns., *1421 Prince St., #330, Alexandria, VA 22314; (703) 549-7473. Fax, (703) 683-9048. Sam Cabral, president. Internet, http://www.sddi.com/iupa.*

Membership: about 80,000 law enforcement officers and personnel. Helps members negotiate pay, benefits, and better working conditions; conducts training programs and workshops; offers legal services to members. Monitors legislation and regulations. (Affiliated with the AFL-CIO.)

Law Enforcement Alliance of America, *7700 Leesburg Pike, #421, Falls Church, VA 22043; (703) 847-2677. Fax, (703) 556-6485. Jim Fotis, executive director. Internet, lawalliance@aol.com.*

Membership: law enforcement professionals, citizens, and victims of crime. Advocacy group on law and order issues.

National Assn. of Chiefs of Police, *1000 Connecticut Ave. N.W., #9 20036; (202) 293-9088. George Vuilleumier, president. Internet, http://www.aphf.org.*

Membership: U.S. chiefs of police and supervisory command rank officers. Conducts educational and in-service training programs; conducts research. (Headquarters in Miami.)

National Black Police Assn., *3251 Mt. Pleasant St. N.W., 2nd Floor 20010-2103; (202) 986-2070. Fax, (202) 986-0410. Ronald Hampton, executive director. Internet, nbpanatofc@worldnet.att.net.*

Membership: local, state, and regional African American police associations. Works to improve the relationship between police departments and minorities; to evaluate the effect of criminal justice policies and programs on the minority community; to recruit minority police officers; to eliminate police corruption, brutality, and racial discrimination; and to educate and train police officers.

National Criminal Justice Assn., *444 N. Capitol St. N.W., #618 20001; (202) 624-1440. Fax, (202) 508-3859. Kabell Cropper, executive director. Internet, http://www.sso.org/ncja.*

Membership: criminal justice organizations and professionals. Provides members and interested individuals with technical assistance and information.

National Law Enforcement Council, *888 16th St. N.W., #700 20006; (202) 835-8020. Fax, (202) 835-8136. Donald Baldwin, executive director.*

Membership: national law enforcement organizations. Fosters information exchange and explores the effects of public policy on law enforcement.

National Organization of Black Law Enforcement Executives, *4609 Pine Crest Office Park Dr., Suite F, Alexandria, VA 22312; (703) 658-1529. Fax, (703) 658-9479. Robert Stuart, executive director.*

Membership: minority police chiefs and senior law enforcement executives. Works to increase community involvement in the criminal justice system and to enhance the role of minorities in law enforcement. Provides urban police departments with assistance in police operations, community relations, and devising strategies to combat urban and hate crimes.

National Sheriffs' Assn., *1450 Duke St., Alexandria, VA 22314; (703) 836-7827. Fax, (703) 683-6541. Aldine N. Moser Jr., executive director. Toll-free, (800) 424-7827. Internet, http://www.sheriffs.org.*

Membership: sheriffs and other municipal, state, and federal law enforcement officers. Conducts research and training programs for members in law enforcement, court procedures, and corrections.

Police Executive Research Forum, *1120 Connecticut Ave. N.W., #930 20036; (202) 466-7820. Fax, (202) 466-7826. Chuck Wexler, executive director. Internet, http://www.PoliceForum.org.*

Membership: law enforcement executives from moderate to large police departments. Conducts research on law enforcement issues and methods of disseminating criminal justice and law enforcement information.

Police Foundation, *1201 Connecticut Ave. N.W., #200 20036; (202) 833-1460. Fax, (202) 659-9149. Hubert Williams, president.*

Research and education foundation that conducts studies to improve police procedures; provides technical assistance for innovative law enforcement strategies, including community-oriented policing. Houses the National Center for the Study of Police and Civil Disorder.

⬛ LEGAL PROFESSIONS AND RESOURCES

See also Criminal Law (this chapter); Public Interest Law (chap. 1)

AGENCIES

Executive Office for U.S. Attorneys *(Justice Dept.),* *Legal Education and Continuing Professional Growth,* *600 E St. N.W., #7600 20530; (202) 616-6700. Fax, (202) 616-6476. Michael Bailie, director. Internet, http://www. usdoj.gov/usao/eousa/ole.html.*

Designs and implements continuing legal education programs for attorneys in all executive branch agencies. Attorney General's Advocacy Institute trains Justice Dept. lawyers, including those who work for U.S. Attorney offices nationwide. Legal Education Institute provides attorneys in other agencies with advocacy training.

NONPROFIT

American Bar Assn., *International Law and Practice,* *740 15th St. N.W. 20005; (202) 662-1660. Fax, (202) 662-1669. Fletcher Hall, director. Internet, http://www.abanet. org/intlaw/home.html.*

Monitors domestic and international policy developments that affect the practice of public and private international law. Conducts seminars and provides information for members.

American Blind Lawyers Assn., *1155 15th St. N.W., #720 20005; (202) 467-5081. Fax, (202) 467-5085. Gary Austin, president.*

Membership: blind lawyers and law students. Provides members with legal information; acts as an information clearinghouse on legal materials available in Braille, in large print, on computer disc, and on tape. (Affiliated with American Council of the Blind.)

American Inns of Court Foundation, *127 S. Peyton St., #201, Alexandria, VA 22314; (703) 684-3590. Fax, (703) 684-3607. Don Stumbaugh, executive director. Internet, http://www.innsofcourt.org.*

Promotes professionalism, ethics, civility, and legal skills of judges, lawyers, academicians, and law students in order to improve the quality and efficiency of the justice system.

Americans for the Restitution and Righting of Old Wrongs (ARROW), *National American Indian Court Clerks Assn., 1000 Connecticut Ave. N.W., #1204 20036; (202) 296-0685. Fax, (202) 639-4377. Hazel Elbert, executive director. Internet, arrow1949@aol.com.*

Helps train nonlawyer Native American court clerks, administrators, law enforcement officers, and social workers to improve the tribal system of law, order, and justice; publishes training materials for tribal court officers. Provides program and financial management support for training of Native American court officers.

Assn. of American Law Schools, *1201 Connecticut Ave. N.W., #800 20036; (202) 296-8851. Fax, (202) 296-8869. Carl C. Monk, executive director. Internet, http:// www.aals.org.*

Membership: schools of law, subject to approval by association. Represents member organizations before federal government and private agencies; evaluates member institutions; conducts workshops on the teaching of law; assists law schools with faculty recruitment; publishes faculty placement bulletin and annual directory of law teachers.

Friends of the Jessup, *2223 Massachusetts Ave. N.W. 20008-2864; (202) 939-6030. Fax, (202) 265-0386. Jonathan Clark Green, chair.*

Membership: supporters and former participants of the Philip C. Jessup International Law Moot Court Competition. Raises funds for the competition, helps to organize and support teams from disadvantaged countries, and conducts educational programs for competition participants. (Affiliated with the International Law Students Assn.)

Hispanic National Bar Fund, *P.O. Box 66105 20035; (202) 293-1507. Fax, (202) 293-1508. Loretta Gutierrez Nestor, executive director. Internet, hnba@aol.com.*

Membership: Hispanic American attorneys, judges, professors, and law students. Seeks to increase professional opportunities in law for Hispanic Americans and to increase Hispanic American representation in law school. (Affiliated with National Hispanic Leadership Agenda and the American Bar Assn.)

International Law Institute, *1615 New Hampshire Ave. N.W. 20009-2520; (202) 483-3036. Fax, (202) 483-3029. Stuart Kerr, executive director. Internet, http://www. ili.org.*

Performs scholarly research, offers training programs, and provides technical assistance in the area of international law.

International Law Students Assn., *2223 Massachusetts Ave. N.W. 20008-2864; (202) 939-6030. Fax, (202) 265-0386. Yvette Roozenbeck, executive director. Internet, ilsa@access.digex.net or http://www.kentlaw.edu/ilsa.*

Promotes the study and understanding of international law and related issues. Encourages communicaton and cooperation among law students and lawyers internationally; works to expand opportunities for learning about legal systems worldwide.

International Trade Commission Trial Lawyers Assn., *601 13th St. N.W. 20005; (202) 626-6361. Fax, (202) 783-2331. Judith Oken, executive director. Internet, admin@itctla.org or http://www.itctla.org.*

Disseminates information relating to practice before the U.S. International Trade Commission. Monitors and comments on proposed legislation on trade and intellectual property issues.

National Consumer Law Center, *1629 K St. N.W., #600 20006; (202) 986-6060. Fax, (202) 463-9462. Margot Saunders, managing attorney.*

Provides lawyers funded by the Legal Services Corp. with research and assistance; provides lawyers with training in consumer and energy law. (Headquarters in Boston.)

National Court Reporters Assn., *8224 Old Courthouse Rd., Vienna, VA 22182; (703) 556-6272. Fax, (703) 556-6291. Brian E. Cartier, executive director. TDD, (703) 556-6289. Internet, http://www.ncraonline.org.*

Membership organization that certifies and offers continuing education for court reporters. Acts as a clearinghouse on technology and information for and about court reporters.

National Health Lawyers Assn., *1120 Connecticut Ave. N.W., #950 20036; (202) 833-1100. Fax, (202) 833-1105. Nancy Wynstra, president. Internet, http://www. nhla-aaha.org.*

Membership: corporate, institutional, and government lawyers interested in the health field; law students; and health professionals. Serves as an information clearinghouse on health law; sponsors health law educational programs and seminars.

Street Law Inc., *918 16th St. N.W., #602 20006; (202) 293-0088. Fax, (202) 293-0089. Maureen Meyer, director. TDD, (202) 546-7591.*

Educational organization that promotes public understanding of the law and the legal system, particularly through citizen participation. Provides information, curriculum materials, training, and technical assistance to public and private school systems at elementary and secondary levels, law schools, departments of corrections, local juvenile justice systems, bar associations, community groups, and state and local governments interested in establishing law-related education programs, including mediation.

See also American Civil Liberties Union (p. 502); National Law Center on Homelessness and Poverty (p. 648); National Women's Law Center (p. 202); Public Law Education Institute (p. 526); Trial Lawyers for Public Justice (p. 17)

Data and Research

AGENCIES

Office of Justice Programs *(Justice Dept.),* **Bureau of Justice Statistics,** *810 7th St. N.W., #2400 20001; (202) 307-0765. Fax, (202) 307-5846. Jan Chaiken, director. Internet, http://www.ojp.usdoj.gov/vjs.*

Collects, evaluates, publishes, and provides statistics on criminal justice. Data available from the National Criminal Justice Reference Service, P.O. Box 6000, Rockville, Md. 20857; toll-free, (800) 732-3277; in Maryland, (301) 251-5500.

Office of Justice Programs *(Justice Dept.),* **National Institute of Justice,** *810 7th St. N.W. 20531; (202) 307-2942. Fax, (202) 307-6394. Jeremy Travis, director. Internet, http://www.ncjrs.org/nijhome.htm.*

Division of the Office of Justice Programs. Conducts research on all aspects of criminal justice, including crime prevention, enforcement, adjudication, and corrections; evaluates programs; develops model programs using new techniques. Serves as an affiliated institute of the United Nations Crime Prevention and Criminal Justice Programme (UNCPCJ); studies transnational issues. Maintains the National Criminal Justice Reference Service, which provides information on criminal justice, including activities of the Office of National Drug Control Policy and law enforcement in Latin America: (800) 851-3420 or (301) 251-5500; Internet, http://www.ncjrs.org.

CONGRESS

Library of Congress, *Law Library, 101 Independence Ave. S.E., #LM201 20540; (202) 707-5065. Fax, (202) 707-1820. Rubens Medina, law librarian. Reading room, (202) 707-5080.*

Maintains collections of foreign, international, and comparative law organized jurisdictionally by country; covers all legal systems—common, civil, Roman, canon, religious, and ancient and medieval law. Services include a public reading room; a microtext facility, with readers and printers for microfilm and microfiche; and foreign law/rare book reading areas. Staff of legal specialists is competent in approximately forty languages; does not provide advice on legal matters.

JUDICIARY

Administrative Office of the U.S. Courts, *1 Colum-*
bus Circle N.E., #7-100 20544; (202) 273-3000. Fax, (202)
273-2349. L. Ralph Mecham, director. Information, (202)
273-0107. Library, (202) 273-1888. Internet, http://www.
uscourts.gov.

Supervises all administrative matters of the federal
court system, except the Supreme Court; prepares statistical data and reports on the business of the courts,
including reports on juror utilization, caseloads of federal, public, and community defenders, and types of
cases adjudicated.

Administrative Office of the U.S. Courts, *Statistics,*
1 Columbus Circle N.E., #2-250 20544; (202) 273-2240.
Fax, (202) 273-2247. Steven R. Schlesinger, chief. Press,
(202) 273-1120.

Compiles information and statistics from civil, criminal, appeals, and bankruptcy cases. Publishes statistical
reports on court management; juror utilization; federal
offenders; equal access to justice; the Financial Privacy
Act; caseloads of federal, public, and community defenders; and types of cases adjudicated.

Supreme Court of the United States, *Library, 1 1st*
N.E. 20543; (202) 479-3037. Fax, (202) 479-3477. Shelley
L. Dowling, librarian.

Maintains collection of Supreme Court documents
dating from the mid-1800s. Records, briefs, and depository documents available for public use.

See also Federal Judicial Center (p. 493)

NONPROFIT

Justice Research and Statistics Assn., *777 N. Capitol*
St. N.E., #801 20002; (202) 842-9330. Fax, (202) 842-
9329. Joan C. Weiss, executive director. Internet,
cjinfo@jrsa.org or http://www.jrsainfo.org.

Provides information on the collection, analysis, dissemination, and use of data concerning crime and criminal justice at the state level; serves as liaison between the
Justice Dept. Bureau of Justice Statistics and the states;
develops standards for states on the collection, analysis,
and use of statistics. Offers courses in criminal justice
software and in research and evaluation methodologies
through the National Computer Center.

15

Military Personnel and Veterans

■ GENERAL POLICY

AGENCIES

Air Force Dept. *(Defense Dept.), Force Management and Personnel,* The Pentagon, #5E977 20330-1660; (703) 614-4752. Fax, (703) 693-4244. Ruby B. DeMesme, deputy assistant secretary.

Civilian office that coordinates military and civilian personnel policies of the Air Force Dept. Focus includes pay; health care; education and training; commissaries, PXs, and service clubs; recruitment; retirement; and veterans affairs.

Air Force Dept. *(Defense Dept.), Personnel,* The Pentagon, #4E194 20330-1040; (703) 697-6088. Fax, (703) 614-5436. Lt. Gen. Michael D. McGinty, deputy chief of staff. Toll-free casualty assistance, (800) 433-0048.

Military office that coordinates military personnel policies of the Air Force Dept.

Army Dept. *(Defense Dept.), Manpower and Reserve Affairs,* The Pentagon 20310-0111; (703) 697-9253. Fax, (703) 614-5975. Jason Spiegel, acting assistant secretary.

Civilian office that reviews policies and programs for Army personnel and reserves; makes recommendations to the secretary of the Army.

Army Dept. *(Defense Dept.), Military Personnel Management and Equal Opportunity Policy,* 111 Army Pentagon 20310-0111; (703) 697-2631. Fax, (703) 614-5975. John P. McLaurin III, deputy assistant secretary.

Civilian office that coordinates military personnel policies of the Army. Focus includes pay; health care; equal opportunity; drug and alcohol abuse; recruitment; retirement; and commissaries, PXs, and service clubs.

Army Dept. *(Defense Dept.), Personnel,* The Pentagon, #2E736 20310-0300; (703) 695-6003. Fax, (703) 614-1211. Lt. Gen. Fredrick E. Vollrath, deputy chief of staff.

Military office that coordinates military personnel policies of the Army Dept.

Army Dept. *(Defense Dept.), U.S. Army Service Center for the Armed Forces,* The Pentagon, #1B866 20310-6604; (703) 695-5643. Fax, (202) 697-9756. Lacy E. Saunders, director.

Assists Defense Dept. personnel (military, civilian, retirees, and dependents) with travel requests, movement of household goods, and processing of passports; provides support for the Armed Forces Hostess Assn. and for the chaplain's office. Operates the Pentagon library and motorpool and the Pentagon Athletic Center.

Defense Dept., Equal Opportunity Policy, The Pentagon, #3A272 20301-4000; (703) 695-0105. Fax, (703) 697-7534. William E. Leftwich III, deputy assistant secretary.

Develops military equal opportunity policy and civilian equal employment opportunity policy for the Defense Dept.

Defense Dept., Military Personnel Policy, The Pentagon, #3E767 20301-4000; (703) 697-4166. Fax, (703) 614-7046. Lt. Gen. Normand Lezy (USAF), deputy assistant secretary.

Military office that coordinates military personnel policies of the Defense Dept. and reviews military personnel policies of the individual services.

Defense Dept., Personnel and Readiness, The Pentagon, #3E764 20301-4000; (703) 695-5254. Fax, (703) 693-0171. Rudy de Leon, under secretary.

Coordinates civilian and military personnel policies of the Defense Dept. and reviews personnel policies of the individual services. Handles equal opportunity policies; serves as focal point for all readiness issues.

Defense Dept., Public Communication, The Pentagon, #1E757 20301-1000; (703) 697-5737. Fax, (703) 695-1149. Harold Heilsnis, director.

Responds to public inquiries on Defense Dept. personnel, including those listed as missing in action.

Navy Dept. *(Defense Dept.), Manpower,* The Pentagon, #4E792 20350-1000; (703) 695-4350. Fax, (703) 614-4103. Karen S. Heath, principal deputy assistant secretary.

Civilian office that coordinates military personnel policies of the Navy and the Marine Corps. Focus includes pay, health care, education and training, family services, recruitment, retirement, and veterans affairs.

Navy Dept. *(Defense Dept.), Military Personnel Policy and Career Progression,* Navy Annex, #1825, Arlington, VA; (703) 614-5571. Fax, (703) 614-5595. Rear Adm. John Foley, assistant chief.

Military office that coordinates naval personnel policies, including promotions, professional development, and compensation, for officers and enlisted personnel.

Navy Dept. *(Defense Dept.), Naval Personnel,* Navy Annex, #2, Arlington, VA; (703) 614-2000. Fax, (703) 614-8321. Vice Adm. Dan Oliver, chief.

Military office that coordinates Navy Dept.'s military personnel policies of the Navy Dept.

Selective Service System, 1515 Wilson Blvd., Arlington, VA 22209-2425; (703) 605-4010. Fax, (703) 605-4006. Gil Coronado, director; Willie L. Blanding Jr., executive director. Locator, (703) 605-4000. Internet, http://www.sss.gov.

Supplies the armed forces with manpower when authorized; registers male citizens of the United States ages 18 to 25. In an emergency, would institute a draft and would provide alternative service assignments to men classified as conscientious objectors.

U.S. Coast Guard *(Transportation Dept.), Human Resources, 2100 2nd St. S.W. 20593-0001; (202) 267-0905. Fax, (202) 267-4205. Rear Adm. Fred L. Ames, chief. Internet, http://www.uscg.mil/hq/g-w/hrhome.htm.*

Responsible for hiring, recruiting, and training all military and nonmilitary Coast Guard personnel.

CONGRESS

House National Security Committee, *Subcommittee on Military Personnel, 2340 RHOB 20515; (202) 225-7560. Fax, (202) 226-0789. Steve Buyer, R-Ind., chair; John Chapla, professional staff member. Internet, http://www.house.gov/nsc.*

Jurisdiction over legislation on military personnel, including drug and alcohol abuse, equal opportunity, banking and insurance, family services, medical care and benefits, pay and compensation, recruitment, military reserve strength, and retirement benefits. Jurisdiction over legislation on civilian personnel of the armed forces.

Senate Armed Services Committee, *Subcommittee on Personnel, SR-228 20510; (202) 224-3871. Fax, (202) 228-3781. Dirk Kempthorne, R-Idaho, chair; Charles S. Abell, professional staff member.*

Jurisdiction over legislation on military personnel, including drug and alcohol abuse, equal opportunity, banking and insurance, family services, medical care and benefits, Americans missing in action (MIAs), education of overseas dependents, pay and compensation, recruitment, military reserve strength, and retirement benefits. Jurisdiction over legislation on civilian personnel of the armed forces.

NONPROFIT

Air Force Assn., *1501 Lee Hwy., Arlington, VA 22209-1198; (703) 247-5800. Fax, (703) 247-5853. Gen. John A. Shaud (USAF, ret.), executive director. Press, (703) 247-5850. Library, (703) 247-5829. Internet, http://www.afa.org.*

Membership: civilians and active, reserve, retired, and cadet personnel of the Air Force. Informs members and the public of developments in the aerospace field; monitors legislation and Defense Dept. policies. Library on aviation history open to the public by appointment.

Air Force Sergeants Assn., *5211 Auth Rd., Suitland, MD 20746; (301) 899-3500. Fax, (301) 899-8136. James D. Staton, executive director.*

Membership: active duty, reserve, National Guard, and retired enlisted Air Force personnel. Monitors defense policies and legislation on issues such as the proposed phasing out of federal subsidies for medical and retirement benefits and commissaries.

Assn. of the United States Army, *2425 Wilson Blvd., Arlington, VA 22201; (703) 841-4300. Fax, (703) 525-9039. Gen. Gordon Sullivan (USA, ret.), president. Internet, http://www.ausa.org.*

Membership: civilians and active and retired members of the armed forces. Conducts symposia on defense issues and researches topics that affect the military.

Fleet Reserve Assn., *125 N. West St., Alexandria, VA 22314-2754; (703) 683-1400. Fax, (703) 549-6610. Charles L. Calkins, national executive secretary. Toll-free, (800) 372-1924. Internet, news-fra@fra.org or http://www.fra.org.*

Membership: active duty, reserve, and retired Navy, Marine Corps, and Coast Guard personnel. Works to safeguard the compensation, benefits, and entitlements of Sea Services personnel. Recognized by the Veterans Affairs Dept. to assist veterans and widows of veterans with benefit claims.

Marine Corps League, *8626 Lee Hwy., Fairfax, VA (mailing address: P.O. Box 3070, Merrifield, VA 22116); (703) 207-9588. Fax, (703) 207-0047. William "Brooks" Corley Jr., executive director. Internet, mcl@mcleague.org or http://www.mcleague.org.*

Membership: active duty, retired, and reserve Marine Corps groups. Promotes the interests of the Marine Corps and works to preserve its traditions; assists veterans and their survivors. Monitors legislation and regulations.

Military Order of the World Wars, *435 N. Lee St., Alexandria, VA 22314; (703) 683-4911. Fax, (703) 683-4501. Maj. Gen. George G. Kundahl (USA, ret.), chief of staff. Internet, mowwhq@aol.com or http://www.moww.org.*

Membership: retired and active duty commissioned officers, warrant officers, and flight officers. Supports a strong national defense; supports patriotic education in schools; presents awards to outstanding Reserve Officers Training Corps (ROTC) cadets.

National Assn. for Uniformed Services, *5535 Hempstead Way, Springfield, VA 22151-4094; (703) 750-1342. Fax, (703) 354-4380. James C. Pennington, president. Toll-free, (800) 842-3451. Internet, http://www.naus.org.*

Membership: active, reserve, and retired officers and enlisted personnel of all uniformed services and their families and survivors. Supports legislation that benefits military personnel and veterans. (Affiliated with the Society of Military Widows.)

National Interreligious Service Board for Conscientious Objectors, *1830 Connecticut Ave. N.W. 20009; (202) 483-2220. Fax, (202) 483-1246. Raymond Toney, executive director. Internet, nisbco@igc.apc.org or http://www.nonviolence.org/nisbco.*

Seeks to defend and extend the rights of conscientious objectors. Provides information and advocacy about the military draft and national service. Offers counseling and information to military personnel seeking discharge or transfer to noncombatant positions within the military.

Navy League of the United States, *2300 Wilson Blvd., Arlington, VA 22201; (703) 528-1775. Fax, (703) 528-2333. Charles L. Robinson, executive director. Internet, mail@navyleague.org or http://www.navyleague.org.*

Membership: retired and reserve military personnel and civilians interested in the U.S. Navy, Marine Corps, Coast Guard, and Merchant Marine. Distributes literature, provides speakers, and conducts seminars to promote interests of the sea services; monitors legislation.

Non-Commissioned Officers Assn., *225 N. Washington St., Alexandria, VA 22314; (703) 549-0311. Fax, (703) 549-0245. Charles R. Jackson, president.*

Congressionally chartered fraternal organization of active and retired enlisted military personnel. Sponsors job fairs to assist members in finding employment. (Headquarters in San Antonio.)

Public Law Education Institute, *454 New Jersey Ave. S.E. 20003; (202) 544-8646. Thomas Alder, president.*

Conducts research and serves as an information clearinghouse on military law, the draft, selective service, veterans' affairs, and tort law related to military affairs.

United Service Organizations (USO), *901 M St. S.E., Bldg. #198 20374-5096; (202) 610-5700. Fax, (202) 610-5701. Carl E. Mundy Jr., president, World USO.*

Voluntary civilian organization chartered by Congress. Provides military personnel and their families in the United States and overseas with social, educational, and recreational programs.

U.S. Army Warrant Officers Assn., *462 Herndon Pkwy., #207, Herndon, VA 20170; (703) 742-7727. Fax, (703) 742-7728. Raymond Bell, executive vice president. Internet, usawoa@erols.com or http://www.penfed.org/woa/home.htm.*

Membership: active duty, reserve, and retired Army warrant officers. Monitors and makes recommendations to Defense Dept., Army Dept., and Congress on policies and programs affecting Army warrant officers.

◫ DEFENSE PERSONNEL

See also Military Installations (chap. 16)

Chaplains

AGENCIES

Air Force Dept. *(Defense Dept.), Chief of Chaplains, Boiling Air Force Base, 112 Luke Ave. 20332-9050; (202) 767-4577. Fax, (202) 404-7841. Maj. Gen. William J. Dendinger, chief.*

Oversees chaplains and religious services with the Air Force; maintains liaison with religious denominations.

Armed Forces Chaplain Board *(Defense Dept.), 4000 Defense Pentagon, #3D322 20301-4000; (703) 697-9015. Fax, (703) 697-8256. Maj. Gen. William J. Dendinger (USAF), chair; Capt. M. R. Ferguson (USN), executive director.*

Membership: chiefs and deputy chiefs of chaplains of the armed services; works to coordinate religious policies and services among the military branches.

Army Dept. *(Defense Dept.), Chief of Chaplains, 2700 Army Pentagon, #1E416 20310-2700; (703) 695-1133. Fax, (703) 695-9834. Maj. Gen. Donald W. Shea, chief.*

Oversees chaplains and religious services within the Army; maintains liaison with religious denominations.

Marine Corps *(Defense Dept.), Chaplain, The Pentagon, #3026, FB2 20380-1775; (703) 614-5630. Fax, (703) 614-4491. Capt. G. W. Pucciarelli (USN), chaplain.*

Oversees chaplains and religious services within the Marine Corps; maintains liason with religious denominations.

National Guard Bureau *(Defense Dept.), Air National Guard, 3500 Fetchet Ave., Andrews AFB, MD 20762; (301) 836-8435. Fax, (301) 836-8922. Col. John B. Ellington Jr., chief chaplain.*

Oversees chaplains and religious services within the Air National Guard; maintains liaison with religious denominations.

National Guard Bureau *(Defense Dept.), Army National Guard, 111 S. George Mason Dr., Arlington, VA 22204-1382; (703) 607-7072. Fax, (703) 607-8621. Col. Donald W. Hill, chief chaplain.*

Oversees chaplains and religious services with the Army National Guard; maintains liaison with religious denominations; serves as policy leader for chaplains.

Navy Dept. *(Defense Dept.), Chief of Chaplains,* N097, 2 Navy Annex, #G837 20370-0400; (703) 614-4043. Fax, (703) 614-4725. Rear Adm. A. Byron Holderby, chief.

Oversees chaplains and religious services within the Navy; maintains liaison with religious denominations.

NONPROFIT

Military Chaplains Assn. of the United States of America, *P.O. Box 42660 20015-0660; (202) 574-2423. David E. White, executive director. Internet, http://www. wrldnet.net/~mca/index.htm.*

Membership: chaplains of all faiths in all branches of the armed services and chaplains of veterans affairs. Sponsors workshops and conventions; coordinates a speakers' bureau.

National Conference on Ministry to the Armed Forces, *4141 N. Henderson Rd., Arlington, VA 22203; (703) 276-7905. Fax, (703) 276-7906. Clifford T. Weathers, coordinator.*

Offers support to the Armed Forces Chaplains Board and the chief of chaplains of each service; disseminates information on matters affecting service personnel welfare.

Civilian Employees

AGENCIES

Air Force Dept. *(Defense Dept.), Civilian Personnel and Personnel Plans,* Headquarters USAF/DPC, The Pentagon 20330-1040; (703) 695-2141. Fax, (703) 695-6049. Sandra Grese, director.

Implements and evaluates Air Force civilian personnel policies; serves as the principal adviser to the Air Force personnel director on civilian personnel matters and programs.

Air Force Dept. *(Defense Dept.), Civilian Policy,* The Pentagon 20330-1040; (703) 695-7381. Fax, (703) 695-6049. Richard Wheat, chief.

Civilian office that monitors and reviews Air Force equal employment opportunity programs and policies, benefits and entitlements, civilian pay, career programs, and external and internal placement of staff.

Army Dept. *(Defense Dept.), Civilian Personnel,* The Pentagon 20310-0300; (703) 695-4237. Fax, (703) 693-3513. Carol Ashby Smith, director.

Develops and reviews Army civilian personnel policies and advises the secretary of the Army on civilian personnel matters.

Army Dept. *(Defense Dept.), Equal Employment Opportunity Agency,* Crystal Mall 4, #207, 1941 Jefferson Davis Hwy., Arlington, VA 22202; (703) 607-1978. Fax, (703) 607-2042. Luther L. Santiful, director. Main phone is voice and TDD accessible.

Civilian office that administers equal employment opportunity programs and policies for civilian employees of the Army.

Defense Dept., *Civilian Assistance and Re-Employment (CARE),* 1400 Key Blvd., B-200, Arlington, VA 22209-5144; (703) 696-1798. Fax, (703) 696-5416. Charles Rogers, chief.

Manages transition programs for Defense Dept. civilians, including placement, early retirement, and transition assistance programs.

Marine Corps *(Defense Dept.), Civilian Personnel,* Navy Annex, #4331, Arlington, VA (mailing address: Headquarters, U.S. Marine Corps, Code MPO-30, Washington, DC 20380-1775); (703) 614-5624. Fax, (703) 614-8506. Frank T. Catenaccio, head; Howard Mathews, deputy equal employment opportunities officer, (703) 614-5650.

Develops and implements personnel and equal employment opportunity programs for civilian employees of the Marine Corps.

Navy Dept. *(Defense Dept.), Civilian Personnel Policy/Equal Employment Opportunity,* The Pentagon, #4E789 20350-1000; (703) 695-2248. Fax, (703) 614-4103. Betty S. Welch, deputy assistant secretary.

Civilian office that develops and reviews Navy and Marine Corps civilian personnel and equal opportunity programs and policies.

U.S. Coast Guard *(Transportation Dept.), Civil Rights,* 2100 2nd St. S.W., #2400 20593-0001; (202) 267-0040. Fax, (202) 267-4282. Marcia H. Coates, acting director, Internal Programs.

Administers the Affirmative Employment Program relating to civilian Coast Guard positions; processes complaints.

Equal Opportunity

AGENCIES

Air Force Dept. *(Defense Dept.), Social Actions,* 1040 Air Force Pentagon, #5C238 20330-1040; (703) 614-8488. Fax, (703) 695-4083. Lt. Col. Terry Hankerson, chief.

Military office that develops and administers Air Force equal opportunity programs and policies.

Army Dept. *(Defense Dept.), Equal Opportunity Programs,* The Pentagon 20310-0300; (703) 697-3106. Fax, (703) 695-8657. Lt. Col. John Westwood, chief, Leadership Division.

Military office that develops and administers equal opportunity programs and policies for the Army.

Defense Dept., *Military Equal Opportunity,* The Pentagon, #3A272 20301-4000; (703) 697-6381. Fax, (703) 697-7534. Col. Robert Brady (USAF), director.

Receives civil rights complaints from military personnel and assists in seeking corrective action.

Defense Dept., *Military Personnel Policy—Defense Advisory Committee on Women in the Services,* The Pentagon, #3D769 20301-4000; (703) 697-2122. Fax, (703) 614-6233. Capt. Barbara Brehm (USN), military director.

Advises the secretary of defense and provides the public with information on matters relating to women and men in the military, including recruitment and retention.

Marine Corps *(Defense Dept.),* Equal Opportunity, Commandant of the Marine Corps, 2 Naval Annex, #2229 20380-1775; (703) 693-2565. Fax, (703) 693-2566. Lt. Col. Anthony L. Jackson, head.

Military office that develops, monitors, and administers Marine Corps equal opportunity programs.

Navy Dept. *(Defense Dept.),* Equal Opportunity, Navy Annex, Arlington, VA; (703) 614-2007. Fax, (703) 697-1803. Cmdr. Ron Evan, director.

Military office that develops and administers Navy equal opportunity programs and policies.

U.S. Coast Guard *(Transportation Dept.),* Civil Rights, 2100 2nd St. S.W. 20593-0001; (202) 267-0034. Fax, (202) 267-4282. Mark Fiebrandt, acting chief, Military Equal Opportunity.

Administers equal opportunity regulations for Coast Guard military personnel.

NONPROFIT

Human Rights Campaign, 1101 14th St. N.W., #200 20005; (202) 628-4160. Fax, (202) 347-5323. Elizabeth Birch, executive director. Internet, hrc@hrc.org or http://www.hrc.org.

Promotes legislation affirming the rights of lesbians and gays. Focus includes discrimination in the military.

Minerva Center, 20 Granada Rd., Pasadena, MD 21122-2708; (410) 437-5379. Linda Grant De Pauw, director. Internet, http://www.minervacenter.com.

Encourages the study of women in the military. Focus includes current U.S. servicewomen; women veterans; women, war, and military abroad; and the preservation of artifacts, oral history, and first-hand accounts of women's experience in military service.

Servicemembers Legal Defense Network, *P.O. Box 65301 20035-5301; (202) 328-3244. Fax, (202) 797-1635. Michelle M. Benecke and C. Dixon Osburn, co-directors. Internet, sldn@sldn.org or http://www.sldn.org.*

Provides legal assistance to individuals affected by the military's policy on gays and lesbians. Monitors legislation and regulations.

Women Military Aviators, *P.O. Box 46819 20050-6819; (301) 627-0965. Eileen Isola, president, (618) 257-0843.*

Membership: women graduates of military pilot training programs as well as any aircrew members. Seeks to encourage the advancement of women military aviators and to preserve their historic achievements.

Family Services

AGENCIES

Air Force Dept. *(Defense Dept.),* Family Matters, The Pentagon, Headquarters USAF/DPCH 20330-1040; (703) 697-4720. Fax, (703) 695-4083. Col. Wanda Wood, chief.

Military office that monitors and reviews services provided to Air Force families and civilian employees with family concerns; oversees family support centers.

Air Force Dept. *(Defense Dept.),* Personnel, The Pentagon, #4E194 20330-1040; (703) 697-6088. Fax, (703) 614-5436. Lt. Gen. Michael D. McGinty, deputy chief of staff. Toll-free casualty assistance, (800) 433-0048.

Military office that responds to inquiries concerning deceased Air Force personnel and their beneficiaries; refers inquiries to the Military Personnel Center at Randolph Air Force Base in San Antonio, Texas.

Army Dept. *(Defense Dept.),* Casualty Operations, 2461 Eisenhower Ave., #920, Alexandria, VA 22331-0481; (703) 325-7990. Fax, (703) 325-0134. Lt. Col. Gene Samanka, chief.

Verifies beneficiaries of deceased Army personnel for benefits distribution.

Army Dept. *(Defense Dept.),* Community and Family Support Center, 4700 King St., Alexandria, VA 22302; (703) 681-7469. Fax, (703) 681-7446. Brig. Gen. Evan R. Gaddis, commanding general.

Military office that directs operations of Army recreation, community service, child development, and youth activity centers. Handles dependent education in conjunction with the Defense Dept.

Defense Dept., *Dependents Education Activity,* 4040 N. Fairfax Dr., Arlington, VA 22203-1635; (703) 696-4247. Fax, (703) 696-8918. Lillian Gonzalez, director.

Civilian office that maintains school system for dependents of all military personnel and eligible civilians in the U.S. and abroad; advises the secretary of defense on overseas education matters; supervises selection of teachers in schools for military dependents.

Defense Dept., *Quality of Life,* The Pentagon, #3B916 20301-4000; (703) 697-7191. Fax, (703) 695-1977. Jane Burke, director.

Coordinates policies of the individual services relating to the families of military personnel.

Marine Corps *(Defense Dept.), Casualty Section,* 3033 Wilson Blvd., Arlington, VA (mailing address: Headquarters, U.S. Marine Corps, 2 Navy Annex, Code MHP-10, Washington, DC 20380-1775); (703) 696-2069. Fax, (703) 696-2072. Maj. M. L. Ward, head.

Confirms beneficiaries of deceased Marine Corps personnel for benefits distribution.

Marine Corps *(Defense Dept.), Family Programs,* 3033 Wilson Blvd., Arlington, VA (mailing address: Headquarters, U.S. Marine Corps, Code MHF, Washington, DC 20380-1775); (703) 696-1187. Fax, (703) 696-1143. Lt. Col. Patrick Dunckhorst, head.

Sponsors family service centers located on major Marine Corps installations. Oversees the administration of policies affecting the quality of life of Marine Corps military families. Administers relocation assistance programs.

Navy Dept. *(Defense Dept.), Casualty Assistance and Retired Activities,* Navy Annex, #1720, Arlington, VA 20370; (703) 697-2171. Fax, (703) 614-3345. Cmdr. Jonie Parker, director.

Confirms beneficiaries of deceased Navy personnel for benefits distribution; oversees retired activities for the Navy.

Navy Dept. *(Defense Dept.), Force Support and Families,* The Pentagon 20350-1000; (703) 697-2427. Fax, (703) 693-4957. Buster Tate, staff director.

Civilian office that oversees the administration of all policies affecting the quality of life of families of Navy military personnel.

Navy Dept. *(Defense Dept.), Personal Readiness and Community Support,* Navy Annex, #1070, Arlington, VA 20370; (703) 614-4259. Fax, (703) 614-3193. Rear Adm. James Hinkle, assistant chief.

Oversees Navy family service centers; provides naval personnel and families being sent overseas with information and support; addresses problems of abuse and sexual assault within families; helps Navy spouses find employment; facilitates communication between Navy families and Navy officials. Assists in relocating Navy families during transition from military to civilian life.

U.S. Coast Guard *(Transportation Dept.), Individual and Family Support,* 2100 2nd St. S.W., #6400 20593-0001; (202) 267-6727. Fax, (202) 267-4862. Capt. Walter Hanson, chief.

Offers broad array of human services to individuals in the Coast Guard and their families, including child care, elderly care, educational services, domestic violence counseling, and health care.

CONGRESS

House Education and the Workforce Committee, *Subcommittee on Early Childhood, Youth, and Families,* 2181 RHOB 20515; (202) 225-4527. Fax, (202) 225-9571. Frank Riggs, R-Calif., chair; James M. "Jay" Eagen III, staff director.

Jurisdiction over legislation concerning overseas and domestic military dependents' education programs (jurisdiction shared with House National Security Committee).

House National Security Committee, *Subcommittee on Military Readiness,* 2117 RHOB 20515; (202) 226-1036. Fax, (202) 225-7102. Herbert H. Bateman, R-Va., chair; Peter Steffes, professional staff member. Internet, http://www.house.gov/nsc.

Jurisdiction over legislation on education of overseas military dependents (jurisdiction shared with House Education and Labor Committee).

Senate Armed Services Committee, *Subcommittee on Personnel,* SR-228 20510; (202) 224-3871. Fax, (202) 228-3781. Dirk Kempthorne, R-Idaho, chair; Charles S. Abell, professional staff member.

Jurisdiction over legislation concerning military dependents' education programs.

NONPROFIT

Air Force Aid Society, 1745 Jefferson Davis Hwy., #202, Arlington, VA 22202; (703) 607-3072. Fax, (703) 607-3024. Gen. Robert T. Marsh (USAF, ret.), director.

Membership: Air Force active duty, reserve, and retired military personnel and their dependents. Provides active duty and retired Air Force military personnel with personal emergency loans for basic needs, travel, or dependents' health expenses; assists families of active, deceased, or retired Air Force personnel with postsecondary education, loans, and grants.

American Red Cross, *Armed Forces Emergency Services,* 8111 Gatehouse Rd., Falls Church, VA 22042; (703)

206-7481. Fax, (703) 206-8533. Sue Richter, vice president. Internet, http://www.crossnet.org.

Provides emergency services for active duty armed forces personnel and their families, including reporting and communications, financial assistance, information and referral, and counseling.

American Red Cross, *Emergency Communications,* *8111 Gatehouse Rd., Falls Church, VA 22042; (703) 206-7550. Fax, (703) 206-6181. Rick Davis, manager.*

Contacts military personnel in family emergencies; provides military personnel with verification of family situations for emergency leave applications.

Armed Forces Hostess Assn., *The Pentagon 20310-6604; (703) 697-3180. Fax, (703) 693-9510. Gail Taylor, president.*

Volunteer office staffed by wives of military personnel of all services. Serves as an information clearinghouse for military and civilian Defense Dept. families; maintains information on military bases in the United States and abroad; issues information handbook for families in the Washington area.

Army Distaff Foundation, *6200 Oregon Ave. N.W. 20015; (202) 541-0105. Fax, (202) 364-2856. Maj. Gen. Calvert P. Benedict (USA, ret.), executive director. Toll-free, (800) 541-4255.*

A nonprofit continuing care retirement community for career military officers and their families. Provides retirement housing and health care services.

EXPOSE, Ex-partners of Servicemen (Women) for Equality, *P.O. Box 11191, Alexandria, VA 22312; (703) 941-5844. Fax, (703) 212-6951. Kathleen Rogers, director.*

Membership: former spouses of military personnel, both officers and enlisted, and other interested parties. Seeks federal laws to restore to ex-spouses benefits lost through divorce, including retirement pay; survivors' benefits; and medical, commissary, and exchange benefits. Provides information concerning related federal laws and regulations. Serves as an information clearinghouse.

Federal Education Assn., *1101 15th St. N.W., #1002 20005; (202) 822-7850. Fax, (202) 822-7816. Jan Mohr, president. Internet, http://www.feaonline.org.*

Membership: teachers and personnel of Defense Dept. schools for military dependents in the United States and abroad. Helps members negotiate pay, benefits, and better working conditions. Monitors legislation and regulations. (Affliated with the National Education Assn.)

National Military Family Assn., *6000 Stevenson Ave., #304, Alexandria, VA 22304-3526; (703) 823-6632. Fax,*

(703) 751-4857. Col. James Mutter (USMC, Ret.), president. Internet, families@nmfa.org or http://www.nmfa.org.

Membership: active duty and retired military, National Guard, and reserve personnel of all U.S. uniformed services, their families, and interested individuals. Works to improve the quality of life for military families.

Navy-Marine Corps Relief Society, *801 N. Randolph St., #1228, Arlington, VA 22203-1978; (703) 696-4904. Fax, (703) 696-0144. Adm. Jerome L. Johnson (USN, ret.), president. Internet, http://www.navy.mil/homepages/nmcrs.*

Assists active and retired Navy and Marine Corps personnel and their families in times of need. Disburses interest-free loans and grants. Provides educational scholarships and loans, visiting nurse services, thrift shops, food lockers, budget counseling, and volunteer training.

Navy Wifeline Assn., *Washington Navy Yard, Bldg. 172, 901 M St. S.E. 20374-5067; (202) 433-2333. Fax, (202) 433-2622. Patricia Marfiak, chair. Internet, WIFELINE@ aol.com.*

Offers support services to spouses of Navy, Marine Corps, and Coast Guard personnel; disseminates information on all aspects of military life; fosters sense of community among naval personnel and their families.

Financial Services

AGENCIES

Air Force Dept. *(Defense Dept.),* **Financial Management,** *The Pentagon 20330-1130; (703) 697-1974. Fax, (703) 693-1996. Robert F. Hale, comptroller.*

Advises the secretary of the Air Force on policies relating to financial services for military and civilian personnel.

Defense Dept., *Accounting Policy,* *The Pentagon, #3A882 20301-1100; (703) 695-7000. Fax, (703) 697-4608. De Ritchie, director.*

Develops policy for banks and credit unions on military installations for all service branches.

CONGRESS

House Banking and Financial Services Committee, *Subcommittee on Financial Institutions and Consumer Credit,* *2129 RHOB 20515; (202) 225-2258. Fax, (202) 225-6984. Marge Roukema, R-N.J., chair; Laurie Schaffer, staff director. Internet, http://www.house.gov/banking.*

Jurisdiction over legislation regulating banking and credit unions on military bases (jurisdiction shared with Subcommittee on General Oversight and Investigations).

House Banking and Financial Services Committee, Subcommittee on General Oversight and Investigations, *212 O'Neill Bldg. 20515; (202) 226-3280. Spencer Bachus, R-Ala., chair; Jim Clinger, staff director.*

Oversight of banking and credit unions on military bases (jurisdiction shared with Subcommittee on Financial Institutions and Consumer Credit).

Senate Banking, Housing, and Urban Affairs Committee, *SD-534 20510; (202) 224-7391. Fax, (202) 224-5137. Alfonse M. D'Amato, R-N.Y., chair; Howard Menell, staff director. Internet, http://www.senate.gov/~banking.*

Oversees and has jurisdiction over legislation regulating banking and credit unions on military bases.

NONPROFIT

Armed Forces Benefit Assn., *909 N. Washington St., Alexandria, VA 22314; (703) 549-4455. Fax, (703) 548-6497. C. C. Blanton, president. Internet, http://www.afba.com.*

Membership: active and retired personnel of the uniformed services, federal civilian employees, and dependents. Offers low-cost health and life insurance and financial, banking, and investment services worldwide.

Army and Air Force Mutual Aid Assn., *102 Sheridan Ave., Fort Myer, VA 22211-1336; (703) 522-3060. Fax, (703) 522-1336. Bradley J. Snyder, president. Toll-free, (800) 336-4538. Internet, info@aafmaa.com or http://www.aafmaa.com.*

Private service organization that offers member and family insurance services to active duty and reserve Army and Air Force officers, warrant officers, noncommissioned officers, and retired officers under age 66.

Defense Credit Union Council, *805 15th St. N.W., #300 20005; (202) 682-5993. Fax, (202) 682-9054. David C. Lundahl, president. Internet, dcuc@meteor.org or http://www.dcuc.org.*

Trade association of credit unions serving the Defense Dept.'s military and civilian personnel. Works with the National Credit Union Administration to solve problems concerning the operation of credit unions for the military community; maintains liaison with the Defense Dept.

Health Care

AGENCIES

Air Force Dept. *(Defense Dept.), Managed Care, 110 Luke Ave., #400, Bolling Air Force Base 20332-7050; (202) 767-5066. Fax, (202) 404-7366. Col. Debra Cerha, chief.*

Military office that develops and administers medical benefits and entitlement programs for Air Force military personnel. Oversees modernization of Air Force medical facilities.

Air Force Dept. *(Defense Dept.), Surgeon General, 110 Luke Ave., Bldg. 5681, #400, Bolling Air Force Base 20336; (202) 767-4444. Fax, (202) 404-6208. Lt. Gen. Charles H. Roadman Jr., acting surgeon general.*

Directs the provision of medical and dental services for Air Force personnel and their dependents.

Army Dept. *(Defense Dept.), Health Services, 5109 Leesburg Pike, Falls Church, VA 22041-3258; (703) 681-3119. Fax, (703) 681-3163. Col. Francis O'Donnell, senior medical officer.*

Military office that administers medical benefits programs for Army military personnel; answers inquiries regarding eligibility and formulates clinical policy.

Army Dept. *(Defense Dept.), Personnel Readiness, The Pentagon 20310-0300; (703) 614-7701. Fax, (703) 223-0212. Lt. Col. Joan Grewe, chief.*

Military office that develops Army policies on HIV-positive Army personnel, suicide prevention, and general health promotion. Develops policies for combating alcohol and drug abuse; monitors and evaluates programs of the major Army commands.

Army Dept. *(Defense Dept.), Surgeon General, 5109 Leesburg Pike, #672, Falls Church, VA 22041-3258; (703) 681-3000. Fax, (703) 681-3167. Lt. Gen. Ronald R. Blanck, surgeon general. Information, (703) 681-8020. Internet, http://www.armymedicine.army.mil.*

Directs the provision of medical and dental services for Army personnel and their dependents.

Defense Dept., *Health Affairs, The Pentagon 20301-1200; (703) 697-2111. Fax, (703) 614-3537. Gary Christopherson, acting assistant secretary.*

Administers the medical benefits programs for active duty and retired military personnel and dependents in the Defense Dept.; develops policies relating to medical programs.

Defense Dept., *Health Affairs, The Pentagon 20301-1200; (703) 695-7117. Fax, (703) 693-2548. Dr. John F. Mazzuchi, deputy assistant secretary, Clinical Program Policy.*

Reviews and directs drug and alcohol abuse identification, education, prevention, treatment, and rehabilitation programs within the Defense Dept.

Marine Corps *(Defense Dept.), Drug, Alcohol, and Health Affairs, Marine Corps Headquarters, Code MHH 20380-1775; (703) 696-1174. Fax, (703) 696-1186. James H. McHugh, head.*

Military office that directs Marine Corps health care and drug and alcohol abuse policies and programs.

Naval Medical Research Institute *(Defense Dept.),* *8901 Wisconsin Ave., Bethesda, MD 20889-5607; (301) 295-0021. Fax, (301) 295-2720. Capt. Thomas J. Contreares Jr., commanding officer. Internet, http://131.158. 70.70.*

Performs basic and applied biomedical research in areas of military importance, including infectious diseases, hyperbaric medicine, wound repair enhancement, environmental stress, and immunobiology. Provides support to field laboratories and naval hospitals; monitors research internationally.

Navy Dept. *(Defense Dept.), Drug and Alcohol Program,* Navy Annex, Arlington, VA (mailing address: Code 602, #1812, Washington, DC 20370-5000); (703) 614-8008. Fax, (703) 697-4466. Capt. Richard Tanga, director. Internet, http://www.nprdc.navy.mil/navdweb.

Military office that develops and administers Navy drug and alcohol abuse programs.

Navy Dept. *(Defense Dept.), Health Affairs,* The Pentagon, #5D825 20350-1000; (703) 693-0238. Fax, (703) 693-4959. Cmdr. Kelly McConville, director.

Reviews medical programs for Navy and Marine Corps military personnel and develops and reviews policies relating to these programs.

Navy Dept. *(Defense Dept.), Patient Administration,* 23rd and E Sts. N.W. 20372-5300; (202) 762-3152. Fax, (202) 762-3743. Lt. Bob Rahal, head.

Military office that assists in the development of eligibility policy for medical benefits programs for Navy and Marine Corps military personnel. Interprets and oversees the implementation of Navy health care policy.

Navy Dept. *(Defense Dept.), Surgeon General,* 23rd and E Sts. N.W., #1112 20372-5120; (202) 762-3701. Fax, (202) 762-3714. Vice Adm. Harold M. Koenig, surgeon general.

Directs the provision of medical and dental services for Navy and Marine Corps personnel and their dependents; oversees the Navy's Bureau of Medicine and Surgery.

U.S. Coast Guard *(Transportation Dept.), Health and Safety,* 2100 2nd St. S.W., G-WK 20593-0001; (202) 267-1098. Fax, (202) 267-4512. Rear Adm. Joyce M. Johnson, chief.

Oversees all health and safety aspects of the Coast Guard, including the operation of medical and dental clinics, sick bays on ships, and mess halls and galleys.

Investigates Coast Guard accidents, such as the grounding of ships and downing of aircraft.

Walter Reed Army Institute of Research *(Defense Dept.),* 6825 16th St. N.W., #1103 20307-5100; (202) 782-3551. Fax, (202) 782-3114. Col. Martin H. Crumrine, director. Internet, http://wrair-www.army.mil.

Provides research, education, and training in support of the Defense Dept.'s health care system. Interests include biochemistry, biometrics, communicable diseases, pathology, surgery, veterinary medicine, and defense against biological and chemical agents.

NONPROFIT

Assn. of Military Surgeons of the United States, *9320 Old Georgetown Rd., Bethesda, MD 20814; (301) 897-8800. Fax, (301) 530-5446. Rear Adm. Frederic G. Stanford (USN, ret.), executive director. Internet, http://www.amsus.org.*

Membership: health professionals, including nurses, dentists, pharmacists, and physicians, who work or have worked for the U.S. Public Health Service, the VA, or the Army, Navy, or Air Force, and students. Works to improve all phases of federal health services.

Commissioned Officers Assn. of the U.S. Public Health Service, *8201 Corporate Dr., #560, Landover, MD 20785; (301) 731-9080. Fax, (301) 731-9084. Michael W. Lord, executive director. Internet, membercoa@aol.com or http://www.coausphs.org.*

Membership: commissioned officers of the U.S. Public Health Service. Supports expansion of federal health care facilities, including military facilities.

Missing in Action/Prisoners of War

AGENCIES

Air Force Dept. *(Defense Dept.), Personnel,* The Pentagon, #4E194 20330-1040; (703) 697-6088. Fax, (703) 614-5436. Lt. Gen. Michael D. McGinty, deputy chief of staff. Toll-free casualty assistance, (800) 433-0048.

Military office that responds to inquiries about missing in action (MIA) personnel for the Air Force; refers inquiries to the Military Personnel Center at Randolph Air Force Base in San Antonio, Texas.

Army Dept. *(Defense Dept.), Repatriation and Family Affairs,* 2461 Eisenhower Ave., Alexandria, VA 22331-0482; (703) 325-5305. Fax, (703) 325-1808. Lt. Col. Rosemary Salak, chief, POWs and MIAs.

Military office that responds to inquiries about prisoner of war (POW) and missing in action (MIA) personnel for the Army and distributes information about Army POWs and MIAs to the next of kin.

Defense Dept., *Prisoners of War and Missing Personnel,* *1745 Jefferson Davis Hwy., #800, Arlington, VA 22202; (703) 602-2102. Fax, (703) 602-1890. J. Alan Liotta, acting deputy assistant secretary.*

Civilian office responsible for policy matters relating to prisoners of war and missing personnel issues. Represents the Defense Dept. before Congress, the media, veterans organizations, and prisoner of war and missing personnel families.

Defense Dept., *Public Communication,* *The Pentagon, #1E757 20301-1000; (703) 697-5737. Fax, (703) 695-1149. Harold Heilsnis, director.*

Responds to public inquiries on Defense Dept. personnel, including those listed as missing in action.

Marine Corps *(Defense Dept.),* ***Casualty Section,*** *3033 Wilson Blvd., Arlington, VA (mailing address: Marine Corps Headquarters, 2 Navy Annex, Code MHP-10, Washington, DC 20380-1775); (703) 696-2069. Fax, (703) 696-2072. Maj. M. L. Ward, head.*

Military office that responds to inquiries about missing in action (MIA) personnel for the Marine Corps and distributes information about Marine Corps MIAs to the next of kin.

Navy Dept. *(Defense Dept.),* ***Naval Personnel,*** *Navy Annex, #2, Arlington, VA; (703) 614-2000. Fax, (703) 614-8321. Vice Adm. Dan Oliver, chief, Navy Personnel.*

Military office that responds to inquiries about missing in action (MIA) personnel for the Navy and distributes information about Navy MIAs.

State Dept., *Burma, Cambodia, Laos, Thailand, and Vietnam Affairs,* *Main State Bldg., #5206 20520-6310; (202) 647-3132. Fax, (202) 647-3069. Dennis Hunter, director.*

Handles issues related to Americans missing in action in Indochina; serves as liaison with Congress, international organizations, and foreign governments on developments in these countries.

CONGRESS

House National Security Committee, *Subcommittee on Military Personnel,* *2340 RHOB 20515; (202) 225-7560. Fax, (202) 226-0789. Steve Buyer, R-Ind., chair; John Chapla, professional staff member. Internet, http://www. house.gov/nsc.*

Jurisdiction over legislation on Americans missing in action (MIAs).

Senate Armed Services Committee, *Subcommittee on Personnel,* *SR-228 20510; (202) 224-3871. Fax, (202) 228-3781. Dirk Kempthorne, R-Idaho, chair; Charles S. Abell, professional staff member.*

Jurisdiction over legislation on Americans missing in action (MIAs).

NONPROFIT

American Defense Institute, *Pride In America,* *1055 N. Fairfax St., #200, Alexandria, VA 22314; (703) 519-7000. Fax, (703) 519-8627. Capt. Eugene B. McDaniel (USN, ret.), president. Internet, rdt2@americandefinst.org.*

Nonpartisan organization that seeks to educate young Americans on matters of national security and foreign policy, including POW/MIA issues.

National League of Families of American Prisoners and Missing in Southeast Asia, *1001 Connecticut Ave. N.W., #919 20036; (202) 223-6846. Fax, (202) 785-9410. Ann Mills Griffiths, executive director. Recording, (202) 659-0133. Internet, powmiafam@aol.com or http://www. pow-miafamilies.org.*

Membership: family members of MIAs and POWs and returned POWs of the Vietnam War. Works for the release of all prisoners of war, an accounting of the missing, and repatriation of the remains of those who have died serving their country in Southeast Asia. Works to raise public awareness of these issues; maintains regional and state coordinators; sponsors an annual recognition day.

Pay and Compensation

AGENCIES

Air Force Dept. *(Defense Dept.),* ***Military Compensation,*** *The Pentagon, #4C236 20330-1040; (703) 695-1111. Fax, (703) 697-8453. Col. Steve Tindell, chief.*

Military office that develops and administers Air Force military personnel pay and compensation policies.

Army Dept. *(Defense Dept.),* ***Military Compensation and Entitlements,*** *The Pentagon, #2D677 20310-0300; (703) 695-5645. Fax, (703) 693-1832. Lt. Col. Curtis Crutchfield, chief.*

Military office that develops and administers Army military personnel pay and compensation policies.

Defense Dept., *Compensation,* *The Pentagon, #2B279 20301-4000; (703) 695-3176. Fax, (703) 697-8725. Capt. Elliot Bloxom (USN), director.*

Coordinates military pay and compensation policies with the individual service branches and advises the secretary of defense on compensation policy.

Marine Corps *(Defense Dept.), Manpower Policy,* Navy Annex, Arlington, VA (mailing address: Headquarters, U.S. Marine Corps, Washington, DC 20380); (703) 614-3440. Fax, (703) 614-8506. Maj. Joe Terry, compensation/incentive officer.

Military office that develops and administers Marine Corps personnel pay and compensation policies.

Navy Dept. *(Defense Dept.), Military Compensation and Policy Coordination,* Navy Annex, Arlington, VA; (703) 614-2053. Fax, (703) 695-3311. Capt. Peter Cornell, director.

Military office that develops and administers Navy military pay, compensation, and personnel policies.

Recruitment

AGENCIES

Air Force Dept. *(Defense Dept.), Accession Policy,* The Pentagon, #4E161 20330-1040; (703) 697-2388. Fax, (703) 614-1436. Lt. Col. Paula Dickinson, chief.

Military office that coordinates Air Force recruiting activities with the recruitment service at Randolph Air Force Base in San Antonio, Texas.

Army Dept. *(Defense Dept.), Army Career and Alumni Program,* 2461 Eisenhower Ave., Alexandria, VA 22331-0476; (703) 325-3591. Fax, (703) 325-8092. Paula T. Davis, chief. Toll-free, (800) 445-2049.

Military office that provides Army military personnel with information concerning transition benefits.

Army Dept. *(Defense Dept.), Enlisted Accessions,* 300 Army Pentagon 20310-0300; (703) 697-6744. Fax, (703) 695-0183. Col. Patrick Snapp, chief.

Military office that develops policies and administers Army recruitment programs.

Defense Dept., *Accession Policy,* The Pentagon, #2B271 20301-4000; (703) 695-5525. Fax, (703) 614-9272. Wayne S. Sellman, director.

Civilian office that develops Defense Dept. recruiting programs and policies, including advertising, market research, and enlistment standards. Coordinates with the individual services on recruitment of military personnel.

Marine Corps *(Defense Dept.), Recruiting Command,* 2 Navy Annex 20380-1775; (703) 614-2508. Fax, (703) 697-4171. Maj. Gen. Jack W. Klimp, commanding general.

Military office that administers and develops policies for Marine Corps officer and enlisted recruitment programs.

Navy Dept. *(Defense Dept.), Navy Recruiting Command,* 801 N. Randolph St., Arlington, VA 22203; (703)

696-4181. Fax, (703) 696-8957. Rear Adm. B. E. McGann, commander.

Military office that administers Navy recruitment programs.

Retirement

See also Veterans (this chapter)

AGENCIES

Air Force Dept. *(Defense Dept.), Separation and Retirement Policy,* The Pentagon, #4E173 20330-1040; (703) 697-9012. Fax, (703) 227-0903. Lt. Col. David Aldrich, chief.

Military office that coordinates Air Force officer and enlisted separation and retirement matters with the Air Force Personnel Center at Randolph Air Force Base, San Antonio, Texas.

Army Dept. *(Defense Dept.), Retirement Services,* 200 Stovall St., #3N33, Alexandria, VA 22332; (703) 325-9158. Fax, (703) 325-8947. Gary F. Smith, chief. Toll-free, (800) 336-4909.

Military office that administers retirement programs for Army military personnel.

Defense Dept., *Compensation,* The Pentagon, #2B279 20301-4000; (703) 695-3176. Fax, (703) 697-8725. Capt. Elliot Bloxom (USN), director.

Develops retirement policies and reviews administration of retirement programs for all Defense Dept. military personnel.

Marine Corps *(Defense Dept.), Retired Activities,* 2 Navy Annex, Arlington, VA (mailing address: Headquarters, U.S. Marine Corps, Code MMSR-6, Washington, DC 20380-1775); (703) 614-1901. Fax, (703) 614-4400. Shirley Stadtmueller, head.

Military office that administers retirement programs and benefits for Marine Corps retirees.

Marine Corps *(Defense Dept.), Separation and Retirement,* Navy Annex, Arlington, VA (mailing address: Headquarters, U.S. Marine Corps, Code MMSR, Washington, DC 20380-1775); (703) 614-1735. Fax, (703) 614-4400. James P. Rathbun, head.

Military office that processes Marine Corps military personnel retirements but does not administer benefits.

Navy Dept. *(Defense Dept.), Retired Activities,* Navy Annex, Arlington, VA (mailing address: PERS 622, Washington, DC 20370-6220); (703) 614-3197. Fax, (703) 614-3345. June Herrin, head.

Military office that administers retirement programs and benefits for Navy military personnel.

Navy Dept. *(Defense Dept.)*, **Retirements Branch,** *Navy Annex, Arlington, VA (mailing address: Bureau of Naval Personnel, PERS 272/822, Washington, DC 20370-5000); (703) 614-2690. Fax, (703) 695-9902. Robert Lewis, deputy director.*

Military office that processes Navy military personnel retirements but does not administer benefits.

U.S. Soldiers' and Airmen's Home, *3700 N. Capitol St. N.W. 20317; (202) 722-3226. Fax, (202) 722-9087. Maj. Gen. Donald C. Hilbert (USA, ret.), director. Information, (202) 722-3556.*

Gives domiciliary and medical care to retirees and members of the armed services or career service personnel unable to earn a livelihood. (U.S. Naval Home in Gulfport, Miss., also serves all branches of the armed services.)

NONPROFIT

Army Distaff Foundation, *6200 Oregon Ave. N.W. 20015; (202) 541-0105. Fax, (202) 364-2856. Maj. Gen. Calvert P. Benedict (USA, ret.), executive director. Toll-free, (800) 541-4255.*

A nonprofit continuing care retirement community for career military officers and their families. Provides retirement housing and health care services.

⚑ MILITARY EDUCATION AND TRAINING

AGENCIES

Air Force Dept. *(Defense Dept.)*, **Air Force Academy Admissions Liaison,** *HQ USAFA/OL-C The Pentagon 20330-1040; (703) 695-4005. Fax, (703) 695-7999. Karen Parker, chief.*

Military office that receives congressional nominations for the Air Force Academy; counsels congressional offices on candidate selection.

Air Force Dept. *(Defense Dept.)*, **Force Management and Personnel,** *The Pentagon, #5E977 20330-1660; (703) 614-4752. Fax, (703) 693-4244. Ruby B. DeMesme, deputy assistant secretary.*

Civilian office that monitors and reviews education policies of the U.S. Air Force Academy at Colorado Springs and officer candidates' training and Reserve Officers Training Corps (ROTC) programs for the Air Force. Advises the secretary of the Air Force on education matters, including graduate education, voluntary education programs, and flight, specialized, and recruit training.

Air Force Dept. *(Defense Dept.)*, **Personnel Programs, Education, and Training,** *The Pentagon, #4E144 20330-1040; (703) 695-6770. Fax, (703) 614-8523. Maj. Gen. Susan Pamerleau, director.*

Supervises operations and policies of all professional military education, including continuing education programs. Oversees operations and policies of Air Force service schools, including technical training for newly enlisted Air Force personnel.

Army Dept. *(Defense Dept.)*, **Education,** *2461 Eisenhower Ave., Attn.: TAPC-PDE #922, Alexandria, VA 22331-0472; (703) 325-9800. Fax, (703) 325-7476. Dian Stoskopf, chief.*

Military office that manages the operations and policies of voluntary education programs for active Army personnel. Administers the tuition assistance program and basic army special skills program.

Army Dept. *(Defense Dept.)*, **Military Personnel Management,** *The Pentagon 20310-0300; (703) 695-2497. Fax, (703) 693-5980. Maj. Gen. Arthur T. Dean, director.*

Military office that supervises operations and policies of the U.S. Military Academy and officer candidates' training and Reserve Officers Training Corps (ROTC) programs. Advises the chief of staff of the Army on academy and education matters.

Army Dept. *(Defense Dept.)*, **Training Operations,** *The Pentagon 20310-0450; (703) 614-8198. Fax, (703) 697-0936. Col. Paul Trahan, chief.*

Military office that runs civilian and military training readiness programs; monitors and reviews operations and policies of Army service schools and advises the chief of staff of the Army on education matters; administers certain service schools and serves as an information source for others.

Army Dept. *(Defense Dept.)*, **West Point Liaison,** *200 Stovall St., Attn.: TAPC-OPD-CM, Alexandria, VA 22332-0413; (703) 325-7414. Fax, (703) 325-6073. Jorja L. Graves, chief.*

Military office that receives congressional nominations for West Point; counsels congressional offices on candidate selection.

Civil Air Patrol, *National Capital Wing, Bolling Air Force Base, 222 Luke Ave., #2 20332-5114; (202) 767-5689. Fax, (202) 767-5695. Col. Roland Butler, wing commander.*

Official auxiliary of the U.S. Air Force. Sponsors a cadet training and education program for junior and senior high school age students. Cadets who have earned the Civil Air Patrol's Mitchell Award are eligible to enter the Air Force at an advanced pay grade. Conducts an aerospace education program for adults. (Headquarters at Maxwell Air Force Base, Ala.)

Defense Dept., *Accession Policy, The Pentagon, #2B271 20301-4000; (703) 695-5525. Fax, (703) 614-9272. Wayne S. Sellman, director.*

Reviews and develops education policies of the service academies, service schools, graduate and voluntary education programs, education programs for active duty personnel, tuition assistance programs, and officer candidates' training and Reserve Officers Training Corps (ROTC) programs for the Defense Dept. Advises the secretary of defense on education matters.

Defense Dept., *Readiness and Training, The Pentagon, #1C757 20301-4000; (703) 695-2618. Fax, (703) 693-7382. Michael Parmentier, director.*

Develops, reviews, and analyzes legislation, policies, plans, programs, resource levels, and budgets for the training of military personnel and military units.

Defense Systems Management College *(Defense Dept.), 9820 Belvoir Rd., #G38, Fort Belvoir, VA 22060-5565; (703) 805-3360. Fax, (703) 805-2639. Rear Adm. Leonard Vincent (USN), commandant. Registrar, (703) 805-2227. Internet, http://www.dsmc.dsm.mil.*

Academic institution that offers courses to military and civilian personnel who specialize in acquisition and procurement. Conducts research to support and improve management of defense systems acquisition programs.

Industrial College of the Armed Forces *(Defense Dept.), Fort Lesley J. McNair, 408 4th Ave., Bldg. #59 20319-5062; (202) 685-4333. Fax, (202) 685-4175. Maj. Gen. John S. Cowings (USA), commandant, (202) 475-1838. Internet, http://www.ndu.edu.*

Division of National Defense University. Offers professional level courses for senior military officers and senior civilian government officials. Academic program focuses on management of national resources, mobilization, and industrial preparedness.

Marine Corps *(Defense Dept.), Training and Education, 1019 Elliot Rd., U.S. Marine Corps, Code MCCDC (C46), Quantico, VA 22134-5027; (703) 784-3730. Fax, (703) 784-3724. Brig. Gen. K. T. Holcomb, director.*

Military office that develops and implements training and education programs for regular and reserve personnel and units.

National Defense University *(Defense Dept.), Fort Lesley J. McNair, 4th and P Sts. S.W. 20319-6000; (202) 685-3922. Fax, (202) 685-3931. Lt. Gen. Richard Chilcoat (USAF), president. Press, (202) 685-3938. Internet, http://www.ndu.edu.*

Specialized university sponsored by the Joint Chiefs of Staff to prepare individuals for senior executive duties in the national security establishment. Offers master of science degrees in national resource strategy and national security strategy, as well as nondegree programs and courses.

National War College *(Defense Dept.), Fort Lesley J. McNair, Bldg. #61 20319-5078; (202) 685-4342. Fax, (202) 685-3993. Rear Adm. Thomas F. Marfiak (USN), commandant. Information, (202) 685-4312.*

Division of National Defense University. Offers professional level courses for senior military officers and senior civilian government officials. Academic program focuses on the formulation and implementation of national security policy and military strategy.

Navy Dept. *(Defense Dept.), Manpower, The Pentagon, #4E792 20350-1000; (703) 695-4350. Fax, (703) 614-4103. Karen S. Heath, principal deputy assistant secretary.*

Civilian office that reviews policies of the U.S. Naval Academy, Navy and Marine Corps service schools, and officer candidates' training and Reserve Officer Training Corps (ROTC) programs. Advises the secretary of the Navy on education matters, including voluntary education programs.

Navy Dept. *(Defense Dept.), Naval Training, The Pentagon 20350-2000; (703) 697-4071. Fax, (703) 693-6480. Vice Adm. Patricia Tracey, director.*

Develops and implements naval training policies. Oversees Navy service college and graduate school programs. Administers training programs for Naval Reserve Officer Training Corps, Naval Junior ROTC, and officer and enlisted personnel.

Uniformed Services University of the Health Sciences *(Defense Dept.), 4301 Jones Bridge Rd., Bethesda, MD 20814-4799; (301) 295-3013. Fax, (301) 295-1960. Dr. James A. Zimble, president. Information, (301) 295-3166. Registrar, (301) 295-3101. Internet, http://www.usuhs.mil.*

Fully accredited four-year medical school under the auspices of the Defense Dept. Awards doctorates and master's degrees in health- and science-related fields. The Graduate School of Nursing awards a masters of science (nursing).

U.S. Coast Guard *(Transportation Dept.), Human Resources, 2100 2nd St. S.W. 20593-0001; (202) 267-0905. Fax, (202) 267-4205. Rear Adm. Fred L. Ames, chief. Internet, http://www.uscg.mil/hq/g-w/hrhome.htm.*

Responsible for hiring, recruiting, and training all military and nonmilitary Coast Guard personnel.

U.S. Naval Academy *(Defense Dept.)*, *106 Maryland Ave., Annapolis, MD 21402-5023; (410) 293-1000. Fax, (410) 293-2303. Adm. Charles R. Larson, superintendent, (410) 293-1500; Edward C. Wallace, director, Candidate Guidance, (410) 293-4336. Press, (410) 293-2293. Visitors information, (410) 263-6933. Candidate guidance, (800) 638-9156. Internet, navy@nadn.navy.mil or http://www. usna.navy.mil.*

Provides undergraduate education for young men and women who have been nominated by members of their state's congressional delegation, or, in some cases, the president or vice president of the United States. Graduates receive bachelor of science degrees and are commissioned as either an ensign in the U.S. Navy or a second lieutenant in the U.S. Marine Corps.

CONGRESS

House National Security Committee, *Subcommittee on Military Personnel,* *2340 RHOB 20515; (202) 225-7560. Fax, (202) 226-0789. Steve Buyer, R-Ind., chair; John Chapla, professional staff member. Internet, http://www. house.gov/nsc.*

Jurisdiction over legislation on precommissioning programs and on military service academies and schools.

Senate Armed Services Committee, *Subcommittee on Personnel,* *SR-228 20510; (202) 224-3871. Fax, (202) 228-3781. Dirk Kempthorne, R-Idaho, chair; Charles S. Abell, professional staff member.*

Jurisdiction over legislation on precommissioning programs and on military service academies and schools.

NONPROFIT

Assn. of Military Colleges and Schools of the U.S., *9429 Garden Ct., Potomac, MD 20854; (301) 765-0695. Fax, (301) 983-0583. Lewis Sorley (USA, ret.), executive director. Internet, http://www.amcsus.org.*

Membership: nonfederal military colleges, junior colleges, and secondary schools that emphasize character development, leadership, and knowledge. Interests include: Reserve Officers Training Corps (ROTC); publishes a newsletter; sponsors an annual meeting and outreach activities.

George and Carol Olmsted Foundation, *1515 N. Courthouse Rd., #305, Arlington, VA 22201; (703) 527-9070. Barbara S. Schimpff, executive vice president.*

Administers grants for military academies and scholarship programs for selected officers of the armed forces.

Military Order of the World Wars, *435 N. Lee St., Alexandria, VA 22314; (703) 683-4911. Fax, (703) 683-4501. Maj. Gen. George G. Kundahl (USA, ret.), chief of*

staff. *Internet, mowwhq@aol.com or http://www. moww.org.*

Membership: retired and active duty commissioned officers, warrant officers, and flight officers. Presents awards to outstanding Reserve Officers Training Corps (ROTC) cadets; gives awards to Boy Scouts and Girl Scouts; conducts youth leadership conferences.

Navy League of the United States, *2300 Wilson Blvd., Arlington, VA 22201; (703) 528-1775. Fax, (703) 528-2333. Charles L. Robinson, executive director. Internet, mail@navyleague.org or http://www.navyleague.org.*

Sponsors Naval Sea Cadet Corps and Navy League Sea Cadet Corps for young people ages 11 through 18 years. Graduates are eligible to enter the Navy at advanced pay grades.

Servicemembers Opportunity Colleges, *1 Dupont Circle N.W., #680 20036-1117; (202) 667-0079. Fax, (202) 667-0622. Steve F. Kime, director. Toll-free, (800) 368-5622. Internet, socmail@aascu.nche.edu.*

Partnership of higher education associations, educational institutions, the Defense Dept., and the military services. Offers credit courses and degree programs to military personnel and their families stationed in the United States and around the world.

🎖 MILITARY GRIEVANCES AND DISCIPLINE

AGENCIES

Air Force Dept. *(Defense Dept.)*, *Air Force Personnel Council,* *1535 Command Dr., EE Wing, Andrews AFB, MD 20762-7002; (301) 981-5739. Fax, (301) 981-9282. Col. Cheryl Harris, director.*

Military office that administers boards that review appeal cases. Administers the Air Force Board of Review, Disability Review Board, Clemency and Parole Board, Discharge Review Board, Decorations Board, Personnel Board, and the Physical Disability Appeal Board.

Air Force Dept. *(Defense Dept.)*, *Air Force Review Boards,* *1535 Command Dr., #E302, Andrews AFB, MD 20762-7002; (301) 981-3137. Fax, (301) 981-3136. Joe G. Lineberger, director.*

Civilian office that responds to complaints from Air Force military personnel and assists in seeking corrective action.

Air Force Dept. *(Defense Dept.)*, *Inquiries Directorate,* *The Pentagon 20330-1140; (703) 614-6321. Fax, (703) 614-6461. Col. Robert Rhodes, chief.*

Military office that handles complaints and requests for assistance from civilians and Air Force and other military personnel.

Army Dept. *(Defense Dept.), Army Council of Review Boards,* 1941 Jefferson Davis Hwy., Arlington, VA 22202-4508; (703) 607-1607. Fax, (703) 607-2036. Col. William E. Mathews, director.

Military office that administers boards that review appeal cases. Administers the Ad Hoc Review Board, Army Grade Determination Board, Disability Rating Review Board, Discharge Review Board, Elimination Review Board, Security Review Board, and Physical Disability Appeal Board.

Army Dept. *(Defense Dept.), Military Personnel Management and Equal Opportunity Policy,* 111 Army Pentagon 20310-0111; (703) 697-2631. Fax, (703) 614-5975. John P. McLaurin III, deputy assistant secretary.

Civilian office that receives complaints from Army military personnel and assists in seeking corrective action.

Defense Dept., *Legal Policy,* The Pentagon, #4C763 20301-4000; (703) 697-3387. Fax, (703) 693-6708. Col. Paul Black (USAF), director.

Coordinates policy for the discharge review boards of the armed services.

Defense Dept., *Military Equal Opportunity,* The Pentagon, #3A272 20301-4000; (703) 697-6381. Fax, (703) 697-7534. Col. Robert Brady (USAF), director.

Receives civil rights complaints from military personnel and assists in seeking corrective action.

Marine Corps *(Defense Dept.), Inspection,* Navy Annex, Arlington, VA (mailing address: Headquarters, U.S. Marine Corps, Code IG, Washington, DC 20380-1775); (703) 614-1698. Fax, (703) 697-6690. Brig. Gen. Stephen Cheney, inspector general.

Military office that investigates issues complaints from Marine Corps personnel and assists in seeking corrective action.

Navy Dept. *(Defense Dept.), Management Support,* Navy Annex, Arlington, VA (mailing address: 2 Navy Annex, PERS-3, Washington, DC 20370); (703) 614-2820. Fax, (703) 693-6905. Capt. John B. Frank Jr., assistant chief.

Military office that handles complaints and requests for assistance from Navy military personnel and members of Congress.

Navy Dept. *(Defense Dept.), Manpower and Reserve Affairs,* The Pentagon 20350-1000; (703) 697-2179. Fax, (703) 614-4103. Bernard D. Rostker, assistant secretary.

Civilian office that receives complaints from Navy and Marine Corps military personnel and assists in seeking corrective action.

Navy Dept. *(Defense Dept.), Naval Council of Personnel Boards,* 901 M St. S.E., Bldg. 36 20374-5023; (202) 685-6408. Fax, (202) 685-6610. Capt. Jacob L. Johnson, director.

Military office that administers boards that review appeal cases for the Navy and the Marine Corps. Composed of the Physical Evaluation Boards, the Naval Discharge Review Board, and the Naval Clemency and Parole Board.

CONGRESS

House National Security Committee, *Subcommittee on Military Personnel,* 2340 RHOB 20515; (202) 225-7560. Fax, (202) 226-0789. Steve Buyer, R-Ind., chair; John Chapla, professional staff member. Internet, http://www.house.gov/nsc.

Jurisdiction over legislation on military personnel matters, including courts martial and appeals and military grievance procedures.

Senate Armed Services Committee, *Subcommittee on Personnel,* SR-228 20510; (202) 224-3871. Fax, (202) 228-3781. Dirk Kempthorne, R-Idaho, chair; Charles S. Abell, professional staff member.

Jurisdiction over legislation on military personnel matters, including courts martial and appeals and military grievance procedures.

NONPROFIT

National Institute of Military Justice, *c/o Feldesman, Tucker,* 2001 L St. N.W., #300 20036; (202) 466-8960. Eugene R. Fidell, president. Internet, efidell@feldesmantucker.com.

Advances the administration of military justice within the U.S. armed services; fosters improved public understanding of the military justice system.

National Interreligious Service Board for Conscientious Objectors, 1830 Connecticut Ave. N.W. 20009; (202) 483-2220. Fax, (202) 483-1246. Raymond Toney, executive director. Internet, nisbco@igc.apc.org or http://www.nonviolence.org/nisbco.

Seeks to defend and extend the rights of conscientious objectors. Provides information and advocacy about the military draft and national service. Offers counseling and information to military personnel seeking discharge or transfer to noncombatant positions within the military.

Servicemembers Legal Defense Network, P.O. Box 65301 20035-5301; (202) 328-3244. Fax, (202) 797-1635.

Michelle M. Benecke and C. Dixon Osburn, co-directors. Internet, sldn@sldn.org or http://www.sldn.org.

Provides legal assistance to individuals affected by the military's policy on gays and lesbians. Monitors legislation and regulations.

Correction of Military Records

AGENCIES

Air Force Dept. *(Defense Dept.), Board for the Correction of Military Records,* 1535 Command Dr., EE Wing, 3rd Floor, Andrews AFB, MD 20762-7002; (301) 981-5380. Fax, (301) 981-9207. Mack Burton, executive director.

Civilian board that reviews appeals for corrections to Air Force personnel records and makes recommendations to the secretary of the Air Force.

Army Dept. *(Defense Dept.), Board for the Correction of Military Records,* 1941 Jefferson Davis Hwy., 2nd Floor, Arlington, VA 22202-4508; (703) 607-1611. Fax, (703) 602-0935. Karl F. Schneider, acting director.

Civilian board that reviews appeals for corrections to Army personnel records and makes recommendations to the secretary of the Army.

Defense Dept., *Legal Policy,* The Pentagon, #4C763 20301-4000; (703) 697-3387. Fax, (703) 693-6708. Col. Paul Black (USAF), director.

Coordinates policy for armed services boards charged with correcting military records.

Navy Dept. *(Defense Dept.), Board for Correction of Naval Records,* Navy Annex, Arlington, VA; (703) 614-1402. Fax, (703) 614-9857. W. Dean Pfeiffer, executive director.

Civilian board that reviews appeals for corrections to Navy and Marine Corps personnel records and makes recommendations to the secretary of the Navy.

U.S. Coast Guard *(Transportation Dept.), Board for Correction of Military Records,* 400 7th St. S.W. 20590; (202) 366-9335. Fax, (202) 366-7152. Robert H. Joost, chair.

Civilian board that reviews appeals for corrections to Coast Guard personnel records and makes recommendations to the general counsel of the Transportation Dept.

Legal Proceedings

AGENCIES

Air Force Dept. *(Defense Dept.), Air Force Personnel Council,* 1535 Command Dr., EE Wing, Andrews AFB, MD 20762-7002; (301) 981-5739. Fax, (301) 981-9282. Col. Cheryl Harris, director.

Military office that administers review boards, including the Clemency and Parole Board, which in turn reviews cases of military prisoners and makes recommendations to the secretary of the Air Force.

Air Force Dept. *(Defense Dept.), Judge Advocate General,* The Pentagon 20330-1420; (703) 614-5732. Fax, (703) 614-8894. Maj. Gen. Bryan G. Hawley, judge advocate general.

Military office that prosecutes and defends Air Force personnel during military legal proceedings. Gives legal advice and assistance to Air Force staff.

Army Dept. *(Defense Dept.), Army Clemency and Parole Board,* Crystal Mall 4, 1941 Jefferson Davis Hwy., Arlington, VA 22202-4508; (703) 607-1504. Fax, (703) 607-2047. James E. Vick, chair.

Civilian and military board that reviews cases of military prisoners and makes recommendations to the secretary of the Army; reviews suspension of less-than-honorable discharges and restoration of prisoners to active duty or parole.

Army Dept. *(Defense Dept.), Judge Advocate General,* The Pentagon 20310-2200; (703) 697-5151. Fax, (703) 695-8370. Maj. Gen. Walter B. Hussman, judge advocate general.

Military office that prosecutes and defends Army personnel during military legal proceedings. Serves as an administrative office for military appeals court, which hears legal proceedings involving Army personnel.

Defense Dept., *U.S. Court of Appeals for the Armed Forces,* 450 E St. N.W. 20442-0001; (202) 761-1448. Fax, (202) 761-4672. Thomas F. Granahan, clerk of the court. Library, (202) 761-1466.

Serves as the appellate court for cases involving dishonorable or bad conduct discharges, confinement of a year or more, and the death penalty, and for cases certified to the court by the judge advocate general of an armed service. Less serious cases are reviewed by the individual armed services. Library open to the public.

Navy Dept. *(Defense Dept.), Judge Advocate General,* 200 Stovall St., Alexandria, VA 22332-2400; (703) 614-7420. Fax, (703) 697-4610. Rear Adm. John D. Hutson, judge advocate general.

Military office that administers legal proceedings involving Navy and Marine personnel.

Navy Dept. *(Defense Dept.), Naval Clemency and Parole Board,* 901 M St. S.E., Bldg. 36 20374-5023; (202) 685-6455. Fax, (202) 685-6629. Lt. Col. Geoffrey P. Lyon (USMC), executive secretary.

Military board that reviews cases of Navy and Marine Corps prisoners and makes recommendations to the secretary of the Navy.

NONPROFIT

Judge Advocates Assn., *1815 H St. N.W., #408 20006; (202) 628-0979. Fax, (202) 775-0295. Michael E. Campiglia, administrator. Internet, fedbar@access.digex. net or http://www.access.digex.net/~fedbar.*

Membership: active duty, reserve, and retired military lawyers; civilian lawyers practicing in the military law field; and members of the U.S. Court of Appeals for the Armed Forces. Informs members of developments and proposed changes in military law.

Public Law Education Institute, *454 New Jersey Ave. S.E. 20003; (202) 544-8646. Thomas Alder, president.*

Conducts research and serves as an information clearinghouse on military law, the draft, selective service, veterans' affairs, and tort law related to military affairs.

Military Police and Corrections

AGENCIES

Air Force Dept. *(Defense Dept.),* **Military Personnel Policy,** *The Pentagon 20330-1040; (703) 695-9886. Fax, (703) 695-8011. Lt. Col. Steve Waszck, chief, Quality Force and Personal Affairs.*

Military office that develops Air Force policies intended to reduce unauthorized absence and desertion.

Army Dept. *(Defense Dept.),* **Security Force Protection and Law Enforcement,** *400 Army Pentagon, DAMO-ODL, #BF758 20310-0400; (703) 614-1061. Col. Robert W. Neubert, chief.*

Develops policies and supports military police and corrections programs in all branches of the U.S. military. Operates the Military Police Management Information System (MPMIS), which automates incident reporting and tracks information on facilities, staff, and inmates, including enemy prisoners of war.

Army Dept. *(Defense Dept.),* **Security Force Protection and Law Enforcement,** *4401 Ford Ave., #225, Alexandria, VA 22302-1432; (703) 681-6880. Fax, (703) 681-6081. Jeff Porter, federal liaison officer.*

Military office that develops Army policies and responds to inquiries relating to deserters.

Defense Dept., *Legal Policy, The Pentagon, #4C763 20301-4000; (703) 697-3387. Fax, (703) 693-6708. Col. Paul Black (USAF), director.*

Coordinates and reviews Defense Dept. policies and programs relating to deserters.

Marine Corps *(Defense Dept.),* **Corrections,** *Marine Corps Headquarters, Code MHC, Arlington, VA 22214-5000; (703) 696-1064. Fax, (703) 696-2080. CWO5 Tim Purcell, head.*

Military office that develops Marine Corps policies and responds to inquiries relating to deserters. Oversees Marine Corps brigs (correctional facilities).

Navy Dept. *(Defense Dept.),* **Corrections and Programs,** *Navy Annex, #2803, Columbia Pike and Southgate Rd., Arlington, VA 20370; (703) 614-2794. Fax, (202) 614-4009. Capt. William Peck, director.*

Military office that develops Navy policies on corrections and deserters. Responds to inquiries relating to deserters; operates correctional facilities.

MILITARY HISTORY AND HONORS

AGENCIES

Air Force Dept. *(Defense Dept.),* **Air Force History,** *Bolling Air Force Base, 500 Duncan Ave., #94 20332-1111; (202) 404-2167. Fax, (202) 404-2270. Richard P. Hallion, historian.*

Publishes histories, studies, monographs, and reference works; directs worldwide Air Force History Program and provides guidance to the Air Force Historical Research Agency at Maxwell Air Force Base in Alabama; supports Air Force Air Staff agencies and responds to inquiries from the public and the U.S. government. Library open to the public.

Army Dept. *(Defense Dept.),* **Center of Military History,** *1099 14th St. N.W. 20005-3402; (202) 761-5420. Fax, (202) 761-5390. Brig. Gen. John W. Mountcastle, chief. Information, (202) 761-5421. Library, (202) 761-5416. Internet, http://www.army.mil/cmh-pg.*

Publishes the official history of the Army. Provides information on Army history; coordinates Army museum system and art program. Works with Army school system to ensure that history is included in curriculum. Sponsors professional appointments, fellowships, and awards.

Army Dept. *(Defense Dept.),* **Institute of Heraldry,** *9325 Gunston Rd., Bldg. 1466, #S-112, Fort Belvoir, VA 22060-5579; (703) 806-4968. Fax, (703) 806-4964. Thomas B. Proffitt, acting director. Information, (703) 806-4971.*

Furnishes heraldic services to the Armed Forces and other U.S. government agencies, including the Executive Office of the President. Responsible for research, design, development, and standardization of official symbolic items, including seals, decorations, medals, insignias, badges, flags, and other items awarded to or authorized for official wear or display by government personnel and agencies. Limited research and information services on these items are provided to the general public.

Defense Dept., _Historical Office,_ _The Pentagon, #5C328 20301-1950; (703) 697-4216. Fax, (703) 697-9763. Alfred Goldberg, historian._

Collects, compiles, and publishes documents and data on the history of Defense Dept. and the office of the secretary; coordinates historical activities of the Defense Dept. and prepares special studies at the request of the secretary.

Defense Dept., _Joint History Office,_ _The Pentagon, #1B707 20318-9999; (703) 695-2114. Fax, (703) 614-6243. Brig. Gen. David A. Armstrong (USA, ret.), director._

Provides historical support services to the Joint Chiefs of Staff, including research; writes the official history of the Joint Chiefs.

Marine Corps _(Defense Dept.),_ **Historical Center,** _Washington Navy Yard S.E. 20374-5040; (202) 433-2273. Fax, (202) 433-7265. Col. Michael F. Monigan (USMC), director. Information, (202) 433-3534. Library, (202) 433-3447. Reference, (202) 433-3483._

Maintains official Marine Corps archives; writes official histories of the corps for government agencies and the public; answers inquiries about Marine Corps history; maintains museum; conducts prearranged tours of the historical center and museum. Library open to the public.

National Archives and Records Administration, _Textual Reference,_ _8601 Adelphi Rd., College Park, MD 20740-6001; (301) 713-7250. Fax, (301) 713-6907. Sharon Thibodeau, director._

Contains Army records from the Revolutionary War to the Vietnam War, Navy records from the Revolutionary War to the Korean War, and Air Force records from 1947 to 1954. Handles records captured from enemy powers at the end of World War II and a small collection of records captured from the Vietnamese. Conducts research in response to specific inquiries; makes records available for reproduction or examination in research room.

National Museum of American History _(Smithsonian Institution),_ **Armed Forces History Collections,** _14th St. and Constitution Ave. N.W., NMAH-4011, MRC 620_ _20560; (202) 357-1883. Fax, (202) 357-1853. Jennifer Locke, assistant chair. Internet, http://www.si.edu/organiza/museums/nmah/csr/cadht.htm._

Maintains collections relating to the history of the U.S. armed forces and the American flag; includes manuscripts, documents, correspondence, uniforms, ordnance material of European and American origin, and other personal memorabilia of armed forces personnel of all ranks.

National Museum of Health and Medicine _(Defense Dept.),_ _Walter Reed Medical Center, Bldg. 54 South (mailing address: 6825 16th St. N.W., Washington, DC 20036-6000); (202) 782-2200. Fax, (202) 782-3573. Dr. Adrianne Noe, director._

Maintains exhibits related to pathology and the history of medicine, particularly military medicine during the Civil War. Open to the public. Study collection available for scholars by appointment.

National Park Service _(Interior Dept.),_ _1849 C St. N.W., #3316 20240; (202) 208-4621. Fax, (202) 208-7889. Robert Stanton, director. Press, (202) 208-6843. Washington area activities, (202) 619-7275 (recording). Internet, http://www.nps.gov._

Administers national parks, monuments, historic sites, and recreation areas. Responsible for national battlefields, selected historic forts, and other sites associated with U.S. military history.

Navy Dept. _(Defense Dept.),_ **Naval Historical Center,** _Washington Navy Yard, Bldg. 57 901 M St., S.E. 20374-5060; (202) 433-2210. Fax, (202) 433-3593. William S. Dudley, director. Library, (202) 433-4132. Museum, (202) 433-4882; Art Gallery, (202) 433-3815; Archives, (202) 433-3171. Internet, http://www.history.navy.mil._

Produces publications on naval history. Maintains historical files on Navy ships, operations, shore installations, and aviation. Collects Navy art, artifacts, and photographs. Library and archives open to the public.

U.S. Coast Guard _(Transportation Dept.),_ **Historian,** _2100 2nd St. S.W. 20593-0001; (202) 267-2596. Fax, (202) 267-4309. Robert Browning, chief historian._

Collects and maintains Coast Guard historical materials, including service artifacts, documents, photographs, and books. Publishes historical inserts in the _Coast Guard_ magazine. Archives are available to the public by appointment only.

NONPROFIT

Aerospace Education Foundation, _1501 Lee Hwy., Arlington, VA 22209; (703) 247-5839. Fax, (703) 247-_

5853. Darryl Hayes, managing director. Toll-free, (800) 727-3337. Internet, aefstaff@aef.org or http://www.aef.org.

Promotes knowledge of U.S. military and civilian aerospace development and history. Sponsors educational symposia and scholarships for enlisted personnel and officers on active duty or in the National Guard and Reserves. (Affiliated with the Air Force Assn.)

Air Force Historical Foundation, 1535 Command Dr., #A-122, Andrews AFB, MD 20762; (301) 981-4728. Fax, (301) 981-3574. Lt. Col. Maynard Binge (USAF, ret.), acting executive director.

Membership: individuals interested in the history of the U.S. Air Force and U.S. air power. Awards scholarships to Air Force Reserve Officers' Training Corps graduates for master's and doctoral level training in fields related to Air Force needs. Bestows grants and awards on Air Force Academy and Air War College students and to other active duty personnel. Funds research and publishes books on aviation and Air Force history.

Council on America's Military Past-U.S.A., P.O. Box 1151, Fort Myer, VA 22211-1151; (703) 912-6124. Fax, (703) 912-5666. Col. Herbert M. Hart (USMC, ret.), executive director. Toll-free, (800) 398-4693.

Membership: historians, archeologists, curators, writers, and others interested in military history and preservation of historic military establishments and ships.

National Museum of American Jewish Military History, 1811 R St. N.W. 20009; (202) 265-6280. Fax, (202) 234-5662. Ed Blatt, president. Internet, http://www.pemfed.org/jwv/home.htm.

Collects, preserves, and displays memorabilia of Jewish men and women in the military; conducts research; sponsors seminars; provides information on the history of Jewish participation in the U.S. armed forces.

Naval Historical Foundation, Washington Navy Yard S.E. 20374; (202) 678-4333. Fax, (202) 889-3565. James L. Holloway III, president.

Collects private documents and artifacts relating to naval history; maintains collection on deposit with the Library of Congress for public reference.

Cemeteries and Memorials

AGENCIES

American Battle Monuments Commission, 2300 Clarendon Blvd., #500, Arlington, VA 22201; (703) 696-6900. Fax, (703) 696-6666. Maj. Gen. John Herrling (USA, ret.), secretary.

Maintains military cemeteries and memorials on foreign soil and certain memorials in the United States; provides next of kin with grave site and related information.

Army Dept. *(Defense Dept.), Arlington National Cemetery,* , Arlington, VA 22211; (703) 697-2131. Fax, (703) 614-6339. Vicki Tanner, chief, Interment Services.

Arranges interment services and provides eligibility information for burials at Arlington National Cemetery.

Veterans Affairs Dept., National Cemetery System, 810 Vermont Ave. N.W., #400 20420; (202) 273-5145. Fax, (202) 273-6696. Jerry W. Bowen, director.

Administers VA national cemeteries; furnishes markers and headstones for deceased veterans; administers state grants to establish, expand, and improve veterans' cemeteries. Provides presidential memorial certificates to next of kin.

CONGRESS

House Appropriations Committee, Subcommittee on VA, HUD, and Independent Agencies, H143 CAP 20515; (202) 225-3241. Jerry Lewis, R-Calif., chair; Frank Cushing, staff director. Internet, http://www.house.gov/appropriations.

Jurisdiction over legislation to appropriate funds for the American Battle Monuments Commission and for cemeterial expenses for the Army Dept., including Arlington National Cemetery.

Senate Appropriations Committee, Subcommittee on VA, HUD, and Independent Agencies, SD-127 20510; (202) 224-7211. Christopher S. Bond, R-Mo., chair; John K. Mark, staff director. Internet, http://www.senate.gov/~appropriations.

Jurisdiction over legislation to appropriate funds for the American Battle Monuments Commission and for cemeterial expenses for the Army Dept., including Arlington National Cemetery.

Senate Veterans' Affairs Committee, SR-412 20510; (202) 224-9126. Fax, (202) 224-9475. Arlen Specter, R-Pa., chair; Charles C. Battaglia, staff director.

Jurisdiction over legislation on national cemeteries, including Arlington National Cemetery.

NONPROFIT

Air Force Memorial Foundation, 1501 Lee Hwy., #101, Arlington, VA 22209-1198; (703) 247-5808. Fax, (703) 247-5819. Gen. Robert D. Springer (USAF, ret.), executive director. Internet, http://www.airforcememorial.org.

Plans to design and construct an Air Force Memorial to honor the achievements of men and women who have served in the U.S. Air Force, or its predecessors, such as the Army Air Forces.

Black Revolutionary War Patriots Foundation, *1612 K St. N.W., #1104 20006-2802; (202) 452-1776. Fax, (202) 728-0770. Wayne Smith, president. Internet, http://www.blackpatriots.org.*

Private corporation authorized by Congress to fund and build a national memorial to honor black patriots who served in the militia or provided civilian assistance during the American Revolution.

No Greater Love, *1750 New York Ave. N.W. 20006; (202) 783-4665. Fax, (202) 783-1168. Carmella LaSpada, chief executive officer. Internet, http://www.ngl.org.*

Provides programs of remembrance, friendship, and care for families of Americans killed in war or by acts of terrorism.

U.S. Navy Memorial Foundation, *701 Pennsylvania Ave. N.W., #123 20004-2608; (202) 737-2300. Fax, (202) 737-2308. Rear Adm. Henry C. McKinney (USN, ret.), president. Toll-free, (800) 821-8892. Internet, ahoy@lonesailor.org or http://www.lonesailor.org.*

Educational foundation authorized by Congress. Focuses on American naval history; built and supports the Navy memorial to honor those who serve or have served in the naval services.

Women in Military Service for America Memorial Foundation, *5510 Columbia Pike, #302, Arlington, VA (mailing address: Dept. 560, Washington, DC 20042-0560); (703) 533-1155. Fax, (703) 931-4208. Brig. Gen. Wilma L. Vaught (USAF, ret.), president. Toll-free, (800) 222-2294. Internet, wimsa@aol.com or http://www.wimsa.org.*

Authorized by Congress to create, support, and build the national memorial to honor women who serve or have served in the U.S. armed forces from the revolutionary war to the present.

Ceremonies/Military Bands

AGENCIES

Air Force Dept. *(Defense Dept.), Air Force Band, Bolling Air Force Base, 201 McCord St. 20332-0203; (202) 767-5255. Fax, (202) 767-0686. Col. Lowell E. Graham, commander. Internet, http://www.bolling.af.mil/band/band.htm.*

Supports the Air Force by providing musical services for official military ceremonies and community events.

Air Force Dept. *(Defense Dept.), Bands and Music, 1690 Air Force Pentagon, #4A120 20330-1690; (703) 695-*

0019. Fax, (703) 693-1523. Vacant, chief. Internet, http://www.af.mil/band/home.htm.

Disseminates information to the public regarding various Air Force bands; coordinates their schedules and performances.

Army Dept. *(Defense Dept.), Army Band, Attn: ANAB, Bldg. 400, 204 Lee Ave., Fort Myer, VA 22211-1199; (703) 696-3647. Fax, (703) 696-3904. Col. L.B. Shelburne, commander. Internet, http://www.army.mil/armyband.*

Supports the Army by providing musical services for official military ceremonies and community events.

Army Dept. *(Defense Dept.), Army Field Band, 4700 Cooper Ave., Fort Meade, MD 20755-5330; (301) 677-6231. Fax, (301) 677-6533. Col. Jack H. Grogan Jr., commander. Internet, http://www.mdw.army.mil/fband/usafb.htm.*

Supports the Army by providing musical services for official military ceremonies and community events. Sponsors vocal and instrumental clinics for high school and college students.

Army Dept. *(Defense Dept.), Ceremonies and Special Events, Fort Lesley J. McNair, 103 3rd Ave. S.W. 20319-5058; (202) 685-2994. Fax, (202) 685-3379. Capt. Darryl Suggs, special events coordinator.*

Coordinates and schedules public ceremonies and special events, including appearances of all armed forces bands and honor guards.

Army Dept. *(Defense Dept.), Ceremonies and Special Events, Fort Lesley J. McNair, 4th and P Sts. S.W. 20319-5050; (202) 685-2983. Fax, (202) 685-3379. Thomas L. Groppel, director.*

Responsible for ceremonies at the Tomb of the Unknown Soldier in Arlington National Cemetery; arranges for military ceremonies at civilian cemeteries in the military district of Washington and surrounding area.

Defense Dept., *Community Relations, The Pentagon 20301-1400; (703) 697-7385. Fax, (703) 697-2577. Michael Byers, civilian public affairs officer, (703) 695-2113; William Harris, military public affairs officer.*

Provides armed forces bands with policy guidance for related public events.

Marine Corps *(Defense Dept.), Marine Band, 8th and Eye Sts. S.E. 20390; (202) 433-4044. Lt. Col. T.W. Foley, director. Internet, http://www.marineband.hqmc.usmc.mil.*

Supports the Marines by providing musical services for official military ceremonies and community events.

Navy Dept. *(Defense Dept.), Navy Band,* Washington Navy Yard, Bldg. 105 901 M St. S.E. 20374-5054; (202) 433-3366. Fax, (202) 433-4108. Lt. Cmdr. John R. Pastin, officer in charge. Internet, http://www.navy.mil/homepages/bupers/navyband/index.htm.

Supports the Navy by providing musical services for official military ceremonies and community events.

U.S. Naval Academy *(Defense Dept.), Band,* c/o U.S. Naval Academy, 101 Buchanan Rd., Annapolis, MD 21402-5080; (410) 293-1253. Cmdr. Ralph M. Gambone, director. Concert information, (410) 293-0263. Internet, http://www.nadn.navy.mil/USNABand.

The Navy's oldest continuing musical organization. Supports the Navy by providing musical services for official military ceremonies and community events.

U.S. Naval Academy *(Defense Dept.), Drum and Bugle Corps,* c/o U.S. Naval Academy, Stop 3A, Annapolis, MD 21402; (410) 293-4508. Jeff Weir, civilian director. Internet, drumbug@nadn.navy.mil or http://www.usna.navy.mil/USNADB.

The oldest drum and bugle corps in existence in the United States. Plays for Brigade of Midshipmen at sporting events, pep rallies, parades, and daily formations. Supports the Navy by providing musical services for official military ceremonies and community events.

🎖 RESERVES AND NATIONAL GUARD

AGENCIES

Air Force Dept. *(Defense Dept.), Air Force Reserve,* The Pentagon 20330-1150; (703) 695-9225. Fax, (703) 695-8959. Maj. Gen. Robert A. McIntosh, chief. Information, (703) 697-1761.

Military office that coordinates and directs Air Force Reserve matters (excluding the Air National Guard).

Air Force Dept. *(Defense Dept.), Reserve Affairs,* The Pentagon 20330-1660; (703) 697-6375. Fax, (703) 695-2701. Bryan E. Sharratt, deputy assistant secretary.

Civilian office that reviews and monitors Air Force Reserve, Air National Guard, counterdrug, and Civil Air Patrol policies.

Army Dept. *(Defense Dept.), Army Reserve,* The Pentagon 20310-2400; (703) 697-1784. Fax, (703) 697-1891. Maj. Gen. Max Baratz, chief. Information, (703) 696-3962.

Military office that coordinates and directs Army Reserve matters (excluding the Army National Guard).

Army Dept. *(Defense Dept.), Reserve Affairs, Mobilization, Readiness, and Training,* The Pentagon 20310-0111; (703) 697-0919. Fax, (703) 614-5975. Col. Wendell Long, assistant deputy.

Oversees training, military preparedness, and mobilization for all active and reserve members of the Army.

Defense Dept., *Reserve Affairs,* The Pentagon 20301-1500; (703) 697-6631. Fax, (703) 693-5371. Deborah Lee, assistant secretary.

Civilian office that addresses national guard and reserve component issues.

Marine Corps *(Defense Dept.), Reserve Affairs,* Navy Annex, Arlington, VA (mailing address: Headquarters, U.S. Marine Corps, Washington, DC 20380-1775); (703) 614-1161. Fax, (703) 697-8160. Brig. Gen. David M. Mize, assistant deputy chief of staff.

Military office that coordinates and directs Marine Corps Reserve matters.

National Guard Bureau *(Defense Dept.),* 2500 Army Pentagon, #2E394 20310-2500; (703) 695-6987. Fax, (703) 693-3422. Lt. Gen. Edward D. Baca (USA), chief. Information, (703) 695-0241. Internet, http://www.ngb.dtic.mil.

Military office that oversees and coordinates activities of the Air National Guard and Army National Guard.

National Guard Bureau *(Defense Dept.), Air National Guard,* The Pentagon, NGB/CF 20310-2500; (703) 693-4750. Fax, (703) 697-7587. Gen. Paul Weaver, director. Information, (703) 693-3369.

Military office that coordinates and directs Air National Guard matters.

National Guard Bureau *(Defense Dept.), Air National Guard,* 3500 Fetchet Ave., Andrews AFB, MD 20762; (301) 836-8435. Fax, (301) 836-8922. Col. John B. Ellington Jr., chief chaplain.

Oversees chaplains and religious services within the Air National Guard; maintains liaison with religious denominations.

National Guard Bureau *(Defense Dept.), Army National Guard,* The Pentagon 20310-2500; (703) 697-5559. Fax, (703) 607-7088. Maj. Gen. William A. Navas Jr., director. Information, (703) 695-0421.

Military office that coordinates and directs Army National Guard matters.

National Guard Bureau *(Defense Dept.), Army National Guard,* 111 S. George Mason Dr., Arlington, VA 22204-1382; (703) 607-7072. Fax, (703) 607-8621. Col. Donald W. Hill, chief chaplain.

Oversees chaplains and religious services with the Army National Guard; maintains liaison with religious denominations; policy leader for chaplain core.

Navy Dept. *(Defense Dept.), Naval Reserve, The Pentagon, CNO-NO95 20350-2000; (703) 695-5353. Fax, (703) 695-3357. Rear Adm. G. Dennis Vaughn, director. Information, (703) 601-1806.*

Military office that coordinates and directs Naval Reserve matters.

Navy Dept. *(Defense Dept.), Reserve Affairs, The Pentagon 20350-1000; (703) 614-5410. Fax, (703) 614-4103. Vacant, deputy assistant secretary.*

Civilian office that reviews Navy and Marine Corps Reserve policies.

U.S. Coast Guard *(Transportation Dept.), Reserve and Training, 2100 2nd St. S.W. 20593-0001; (202) 267-2350. Fax, (202) 267-4243. Rear Adm. Thomas J. Barrett, director.*

Oversees and ensures Coast Guard readiness to perform its peacetime mission and its wartime role. Responsible for training all reserve forces.

NONPROFIT

Adjutants General Assn. of the United States, *1 Massachusetts Ave. N.W. 20001-1431; (202) 789-0031. Fax, (202) 682-9358. Maj. Gen. Ronald Harrison, president; Capt. Pam Kane, director of communications.*

Organization of the adjutants general of the National Guard. Works to promote a strong national defense and National Guard with the Congress, governors, and Defense Dept.

Assn. of Civilian Technicians, *12510-B Lake Ridge Dr., Lake Ridge, VA 22192-2354; (703) 690-1330. Fax, (703) 494-0961. John T. Hunter, president.*

Membership: federal civil service employees of the National Guard. Represents members before federal agencies and Congress.

Enlisted Assn. of the National Guard of the United States, *1219 Prince St., Alexandria, VA 22314; (703) 519-3846. Fax, (703) 519-3849. Master Sgt. Michael P. Cline, executive director. Toll-free, (800) 234-3264. Internet, natloffc@eangus.org or http://www.eangus.org.*

Membership: active and retired enlisted members and veterans of the National Guard. Promotes a strong national defense and National Guard. Sponsors scholarships, conducts seminars, and provides information concerning members and their families.

Marine Corps Reserve Officers Assn., *110 N. Royal St., #406, Alexandria, VA 22314-3234; (703) 548-7607.*

Fax, (703) 519-8779. Col. Joseph Vowell (USMC, ret.), acting executive director. Toll-free, (800) 927-6270.

Membership: active and retired Marine Corps Reserve officers. Promotes the interests of the Marine Corps and the Marine Corps Reserve.

National Guard Assn. of the United States, *1 Massachusetts Ave. N.W. 20001-1431; (202) 789-0031. Fax, (202) 682-9358. Maj. Gen. Edward J. Philbin (USANG, ret.), executive director. Internet, ngaus@ngaus.org or http://www.ngaus.org.*

Membership: active duty and retired officers of the National Guard. Works to promote a strong national defense and to maintain a strong, ready National Guard.

Naval Reserve Assn., *1619 King St., Alexandria, VA 22314; (703) 548-5800. Fax, (703) 683-3647. Rear Adm. Thomas F. Hall (USN, ret.), executive director. Internet, http://www.navy-reserve.org.*

Membership: active duty, inactive, and retired Navy and Naval Reserve officers. Supports and promotes U.S. military and naval policies, particularly the interests of the Navy and Naval Reserve. Offers education programs for naval reservists and potential naval commissioned officers. Provides the public with information on national security issues. Assists members with Naval Reserve careers, military retirement, and veterans' benefits.

Reserve Officers Assn. of the United States, *1 Constitution Ave. N.E. 20002-5655; (202) 479-2200. Fax, (202) 479-0416. Maj. Gen. Roger W. Sandler (USA, ret.), executive director. Toll-free, (800) 809-9448. Internet, http://www.roa.org.*

Membership: active and inactive commissioned officers of all uniformed services. Supports continuation of a reserve force to enhance national security.

🎖 VETERANS

AGENCIES

Center for Women Veterans *(Veterans Affairs Dept.), 810 Vermont Ave. N.W. 20420; (202) 273-6193. Fax, (202) 273-7092. Joan A. Furey, director. Internet, http://www.va.gov/womenvet/CenWomVet.htm.*

Advices the secretary and promotes research on matters related to women veterans; seeks to assure that women veterans receive benefits and services on par with men.

Defense Special Weapons Agency *(Defense Dept.), Nuclear Test Personnel Review Program, 6801 Telegraph Rd., Alexandria, VA 22310-3398; (703) 325-2407. Fax,*

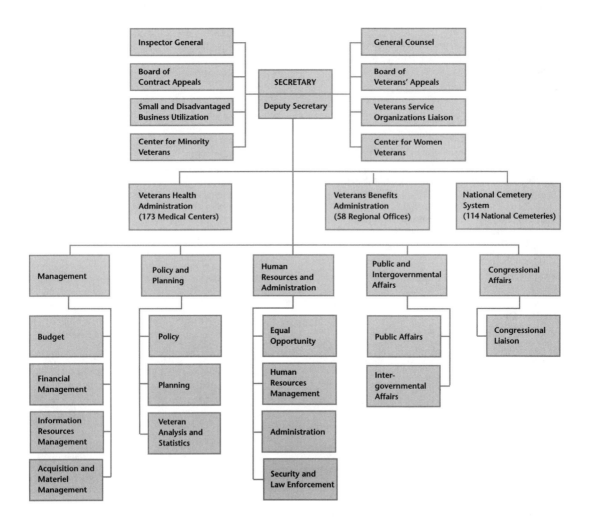

(703) 325-2951. *D. Michael Schaeffer, program manager. Information, (703) 325-7095. Veterans hotline, (800) 462-3683.*

Manages database of participants in U.S. atmospheric nuclear tests and in the post-war occupation of Hiroshima and Nagasaki, Japan; provides participation information to veterans, their families, and government organizations representing their interests.

U.S. Soldiers' and Airmen's Home, *3700 N. Capitol St. N.W. 20317; (202) 722-3226. Fax, (202) 722-9087. Maj. Gen. Donald C. Hilbert (USA, ret.), director. Information, (202) 722-3556.*

Gives domiciliary and medical care to retirees and members of the armed services or career service person-

nel unable to earn a livelihood. (U.S. Naval Home in Gulfport, Miss., also serves all branches of the armed services.)

Veterans Affairs Dept., *810 Vermont Ave. N.W. 20420; (202) 273-4800. Fax, (202) 273-4877. Togo D. West Jr., acting secretary; Hershel W. Gober, deputy secretary, (202) 273-4817. Information, (202) 273-5700. Locator, (202) 273-5400. Internet, http://www.va.gov.*

Administers programs benefiting veterans, including disability compensation, pensions, education, home loans, insurance, vocational rehabilitation, medical care at veterans' hospitals and outpatient facilities, and burial benefits.

Veterans Affairs Dept., *Compensation and Pension Service,* 810 Vermont Ave. N.W., Mail Code 21 20420; (202) 273-7203. Fax, (202) 275-1728. Kristine A. Moffitt, director.

Administers disability payments; handles claims for burial and plot allowances by veterans' survivors. Provides information on and assistance with benefits legislated by Congress for veterans of active military, naval, or air service.

Veterans Affairs Dept., *National Cemetery System,* 810 Vermont Ave. N.W., #400 20420; (202) 273-5145. Fax, (202) 273-6696. Jerry W. Bowen, director.

Administers VA national cemeteries; furnishes markers and headstones for deceased veterans; administers state grants to establish, expand, and improve veterans' cemeteries. Provides presidential memorial certificates to next of kin.

Veterans Affairs Dept., *National Center for Veteran Analysis and Statistics,* 810 Vermont Ave. N.W. 20420; (202) 273-5081. Fax, (202) 273-5991. H. David Burge Jr., director.

Serves as the single, departmentwide repository, clearinghouse, and publication source for veterans' demogaphic and statistical information.

Veterans Affairs Dept., *Policy and Planning,* 810 Vermont Ave. N.W. 20420; (202) 273-5033. Fax, (202) 273-5993. Dennis M. Duffy, assistant secretary.

Develops policy and provides policymakers with analytical reports on improving services to veterans and their families.

Veterans Benefits Administration *(Veterans Affairs Dept.),* 810 Vermont Ave. N.W. 20420; (202) 273-6761. Fax, (202) 275-3591. Joseph Thompson, under secretary. Information, (202) 418-4343. Toll-free insurance hotline, (800) 669-8477. Internet, http://www.va.gov.

Administers nonmedical benefits programs for veterans and their dependents and survivors. Benefits include veterans' compensation and pensions, survivors' benefits, education and rehabilitation assistance, home loan benefits, insurance coverage, and burials. (Directs benefits delivery nationwide through regional offices and veterans' insurance offices in Philadelphia and St. Paul.)

CONGRESS

General Accounting Office, *Health, Education, and Human Services,* 441 G St. N.W. 20548; (202) 512-6806. Fax, (202) 512-5806. Richard L. Hembra, assistant comptroller general.

Independent, nonpartisan agency in the legislative branch that audits, analyzes, and evaluates Veterans Affairs Dept. programs; makes reports available to the public.

House Appropriations Committee, *Subcommittee on VA, HUD, and Independent Agencies,* H143 CAP 20515; (202) 225-3241. Jerry Lewis, R-Calif., chair; Frank Cushing, staff director. Internet, http://www.house.gov/appropriations.

Jurisdiction over legislation to appropriate funds for the Veterans Affairs Dept., the Board of Veterans Appeals, the U.S. Court of Veterans Appeals, and other veterans' programs.

House Government Reform and Oversight Committee, *Subcommittee on Human Resources,* B372 RHOB 20515; (202) 225-2548. Fax, (202) 225-2382. Christopher Shays, R-Conn., chair; Larry Halloran, staff director. Internet, http://www.house.gov/reform.

Oversight jurisdiction of the Veterans Affairs Dept. (shares oversight jurisdiction with the House Veterans' Affairs Committee).

House Veterans' Affairs Committee, 335 CHOB 20515; (202) 225-3527. Bob Stump, R-Ariz., chair; Carl Commenator, staff director.

Jurisdiction over the Veterans Affairs Dept. (jurisdiction shared with House Government Reform and Oversight Committee).

House Veterans' Affairs Committee, *Subcommittee on Benefits,* 337 CHOB 20515; (202) 225-9164. Fax, (202) 225-6392. Jack Quinn, R-N.Y., chair; Michael Brink, staff director.

Jurisdiction over legislation on veterans' pensions and life insurance; service-connected disability payments to veterans, survivors, and dependents; and burial benefits for veterans. Jurisdiction over legislation on education, training, vocational rehabilitation, employment, housing loans, special housing for paraplegics, readjustment to civilian life for veterans and disabled veterans and educational assistance for survivors of deceased veterans.

Senate Appropriations Committee, *Subcommittee on VA, HUD, and Independent Agencies,* SD-127 20510; (202) 224-7211. Christopher S. Bond, R-Mo., chair; John K. Mark, staff director. Internet, http://www.senate.gov/~appropriations.

Jurisdiction over legislation to appropriate funds for the Veterans Affairs Dept., the Board of Veterans Appeals, the U.S. Court of Veterans Appeals, and other veterans' programs.

Senate Veterans' Affairs Committee, *SR-412 20510;* *(202) 224-9126. Fax, (202) 224-9575. Arlen Specter, R-Pa., chair; Charles C. Battaglia, staff director.*

Jurisdiction over veterans' legislation, including pensions; service-connected disability payments to veterans, survivors, and dependents; education and training; vocational rehabilitation for disabled veterans; veterans' life insurance, hospitals, medical programs, and outpatient programs; construction of medical facilities; readjustment to civilian life; housing loans and special housing loans for paraplegics; employment; cemetery and burial benefits; state veterans' homes; and educational assistance for survivors of deceased veterans. Oversight of and legislative jurisdiction over the Veterans Affairs Dept.

NONPROFIT

American Legion National Organization, *1608 K St. N.W. 20006; (202) 861-2711. Fax, (202) 861-2786. John F. Sommer Jr., executive director.*

Membership: honorably discharged wartime veterans of World War I, World War II, the Korean War, the Vietnam War, or conflicts in Lebanon, Grenada, Panama, and the Persian Gulf. Chartered by Congress to assist veterans with claims for benefits.

American Red Cross, *Armed Forces Emergency Services, 8111 Gatehouse Rd., Falls Church, VA 22042; (703) 206-7481. Fax, (703) 206-8533. Sue Richter, vice president. Internet, http://www.crossnet.org.*

Assists veterans and their dependents with claims for benefits on a limited basis; provides emergency services for active duty armed forces personnel and their families.

American Veterans Committee, *6309 Bannockburn Dr., Bethesda, MD 20817; (301) 320-6490. June A. Willenz, executive director.*

Membership: veterans of the World Wars and the Korean, Vietnam, and Persian Gulf wars. Promotes the philosophy, "citizens first, veterans second"; works for international cooperation and peace. (Affiliated with World Veterans Federation, headquartered in Paris.)

American Veterans of World War II, Korea, and Vietnam (Amvets), *4647 Forbes Blvd., Lanham, MD 20706-4380; (301) 459-9600. Fax, (301) 459-7924. Robert Carbonneau, executive director.*

Membership: those who served honorably in the military after September 15, 1940. Helps members obtain benefits; participates in community programs; operates a volunteer service that donates time to hospitalized veterans. Monitors legislation and regulations.

Blinded Veterans Assn., *477 H St. N.W. 20001; (202) 371-8880. Fax, (202) 371-8258. John Williams, director, Administration. Toll-free, (800) 669-7079. Internet, bva@bva.org or http://www.bva.org.*

Chartered by Congress to assist veterans with claims for benefits. Seeks out blinded veterans to make them aware of benefits and services available to them.

Catholic War Veterans U.S.A., *441 N. Lee St., Alexandria, VA 22314; (703) 549-3622. Fax, (703) 684-5196. Gilman Udell, executive director.*

Recognized by the Veterans Affairs Dept. to assist veterans with claims for benefits. Conducts community service programs; offers scholarships for children; supports benefits for Vietnam veterans commensurate with those received by World War II veterans.

Coast Guard Combat Veterans Assn., *17718 Striley Dr., Ashton, MD 20861-9763; (301) 570-5664. Joseph L. Kleinpeter, president.*

Membership: Coast Guard combat veterans. Maintains records of Coast Guard combat veterans; sponsors biennial conference; conducts fundraising campaigns.

Disabled American Veterans, *807 Maine Ave. S.W. 20024; (202) 554-3501. Fax, (202) 554-3581. Arthur H. Wilson, national adjutant. Internet, http://www.dav.org.*

Chartered by Congress to assist veterans with claims for benefits; represents veterans seeking to correct alleged errors in military records. Assists families of veterans with disabilities.

Jewish War Veterans of U.S.A., *1811 R St. N.W. 20009; (202) 265-6280. Fax, (202) 234-5662. Col. Herb Rosenbleeth (USA, ret.), national executive director. Internet, http://www.penfed.org/jwv/home.htm.*

Recognized by the Veterans Affairs Dept. to assist veterans with claims for benefits. Offers programs in community relations and services, foreign affairs, national defense, and veterans' affairs. Monitors legislation and regulations that affect veterans.

Marine Corps League, *8626 Lee Hwy., Fairfax, VA (mailing address: P.O. Box 3070, Merrifield, VA 22116); (703) 207-9588. Fax, (703) 207-0047. William "Brooks" Corley Jr., executive director. Internet, mcl@mcleague.org or http://www.mcleague.org.*

Membership: active duty, retired, and reserve Marine Corps groups. Chartered by Congress to assist veterans with claims for benefits. Operates a volunteer service program in VA hospitals.

Military Order of the Purple Heart of the U.S.A., *5413-B Backlick Rd., Springfield, VA 22151; (703) 642-*

5360. Fax, (703) 642-2054. John B. Kirby, adjutant general. Internet, http://www.purpleheart.org.

Membership: veterans awarded the Purple Heart for combat wounds. Chartered by Congress to assist veterans with claims for benefits. Conducts service and welfare work on behalf of disabled and needy veterans and their families.

National Coalition for Homeless Veterans, *333 1/2 Pennsylvania Ave. S.E. 20003-1148; (202) 546-1969. Fax, (202) 546-2063. Linda Boone, executive director. Internet, nchv@nchv.org or http://www.nchv.org.*

Provides technical assistance to service providers; advocates on behalf of homeless veterans.

National Veterans Legal Services Program, *2001 S St. N.W., #610 20009-1125; (202) 265-8305. Fax, (202) 328-0063. David F. Addlestone and Bart Stichman, co-directors. Internet, nvlsp@aol.com or http://www.nvlsp.org.*

Represents the interests of veterans through educational programs, advocacy, and litigation.

Non-Commissioned Officers Assn., *225 N. Washington St., Alexandria, VA 22314; (703) 549-0311. Fax, (703) 549-0245. Charles R. Jackson, president.*

Congressionally chartered and accredited by the Veterans Affairs Dept. to assist veterans and widows of veterans with claims for benefits. Provides legislative assistance. (Headquarters in San Antonio, Texas.)

Paralyzed Veterans of America, *801 18th St. N.W. 20006; (202) 872-1300. Fax, (202) 785-4452. Gordon H. Mansfield, executive director. Toll-free, (800) 424-8200. TDD, (202) 416-7622. Internet, http://www.pva.org.*

Congressionally chartered organization that assists veterans with claims for benefits. Distributes information on special education for paralyzed veterans; supports and raises funds for medical research.

Retired Enlisted Assn., *909 N. Washington St., #301, Alexandria, VA 22314; (703) 684-1981. Fax, (703) 548-4876. Mark H. Olanoff, national legislative director. Internet, treadc@erols.com or http://www.trea.org.*

Membership: enlisted personnel who have retired for length of service or medical reasons from the active, reserve, or guard components of the armed forces. Runs scholarship, legislative, and veterans service programs. (Headquarters in Aurora, Colo.)

Retired Officers Assn., *201 N. Washington St., Alexandria, VA 22314; (703) 549-2311. Fax, (703) 838-8173. Michael A. Nelson, president. Internet, troa@troa.org or http://www.troa.org.*

Membership: officers and former officers of the uniformed services. Assists members, their dependents, and survivors with service status and retirement problems; provides employment assistance. Monitors legislation affecting veterans affairs, health, and military compensation issues.

Veterans of Foreign Wars of the United States, *National Veterans Service, 200 Maryland Ave. N.E. 20002; (202) 543-2239. Fax, (202) 547-3196. Frederico Juarbe Jr., director. Internet, vfw@vfw.org or http://www.vfw.org.*

Chartered by Congress to assist veterans with claims for benefits.

Veterans of the Battle of the Bulge, *P.O. Box 11129, Arlington, VA 22210-2129; (703) 528-4058. Nancy Monson, administrative director.*

Membership: veterans who were awarded the Ardennes Campaign battle star and their families. Maintains historical data on the Battle of the Bulge; sponsors reunions, memorial services, and educational programs; fosters international peace.

Veterans of World War I of the U.S.A., *P.O. Box 8027, Alexandria, VA 22306; (703) 780-5660. Fax, (703) 780-8465. Muriel Sue Parkhurst, executive director.*

Fraternal organization of veterans of wartime service in World War I. Chartered by Congress to assist veterans with claims for benefits. Maintains representatives in VA hospitals.

Vietnam Veterans of America, *1224 M St. N.W. 20005-5183; (202) 628-2700. Fax, (202) 628-5880. George Duggins, president. Toll free, (800) 882-1316. Internet, 71154.702@compuserve.com or http://www.vva.org.*

Membership organization that provides information on legislation that affects Vietnam era veterans and their families. Engages in legislative and judicial advocacy in areas relevant to Vietnam era veterans.

Appeals of VA Decisions

AGENCIES

Defense Dept., *Legal Policy, The Pentagon, #4C763 20301-4000; (703) 697-3387. Fax, (703) 693-6708. Col. Paul Black (USAF), director.*

Coordinates policy for armed services boards charged with correcting military records and reviewing discharges.

Veterans Affairs Dept., *Board of Veterans Appeals, 810 Vermont Ave. N.W. 20420; (202) 565-5001. Fax, (202) 565-5587. Richard B. Standefer, acting chair. Information, (202) 565-3336. Press, (202) 565-4059.*

Final appellate body within the department; reviews claims for veterans' benefits on appeal from agencies of original jurisdiction. Decisions of the board are subject to review by the U.S. Court of Veterans' Appeals.

JUDICIARY

U.S. Court of Appeals for the Federal Circuit, *717 Madison Pl. N.W. 20439; (202) 633-6556. Fax, (202) 633-6353. Haldane Robert Mayer, chief judge; Jan Horbaly, clerk, (202) 633-9613. Electronic bulletin board, (202) 633-9608 or (202) 786-6584.*

Reviews decisions concerning the Veteran's Judicial Review Provisions.

U.S. Court of Veterans Appeals, *625 Indiana Ave. N.W., #900 20004-2950; (202) 501-5970. Fax, (202) 501-5849. Frank Q. Nebeker, chief judge. Information, (202) 501-5971. Toll-free, (800) 869-8650.*

Independent court that reviews decisions of the VA's Board of Veterans Appeals concerning benefits. Focuses primarily on disability benefits claims.

NONPROFIT

American Legion National Organization, *Claims Service, 1608 K St. N.W. 20006; (202) 861-2762. Fax, (202) 833-4452. Philip R. Wilkerson, deputy director, Operations.*

Membership: honorably discharged wartime veterans of World War I, World War II, the Korean War, the Vietnam War, or conflicts in Lebanon, Grenada, Panama, and the Persian Gulf. Assists veterans with appeals before the Veterans Affairs Dept. for benefits claims.

American Legion National Organization, *Review and Correction Boards Unit, 1608 K St. N.W. 20006; (202) 861-2766. Fax, (202) 833-4452. Thomas Holland, supervisor. Information, (202) 861-2700.*

Membership: honorably discharged wartime veterans of World War I, World War II, the Korean War, the Vietnam War, or conflicts in Lebanon, Grenada, Panama, and the Persian Gulf. Represents, before the Defense Dept., former military personnel seeking to upgrade less-than-honorable discharges and to correct alleged errors in military records.

National Veterans Legal Services Program, *2001 S St. N.W., #610 20009-1125; (202) 265-8305. Fax, (202) 328-0063. David F. Addlestone and Bart Stichman, co-directors. Internet, nvlsp@aol.com or http://www.nvlsp.org.*

Represents the interests of veterans through educational programs, advocacy, and litigation.

Veterans of Foreign Wars of the United States, *Appeals, 200 Maryland Ave. N.E. 20002; (202) 543-2239.*

Fax, (202) 547-3196. George Estry, chief of appeals. Internet, http://www.vfw.org.

Assists veterans and their dependents and survivors with appeals before the Veterans Affairs Dept. for benefits claims. Assists with cases in the U.S. Court of Veterans Appeals.

Veterans of Foreign Wars of the United States, *Military Claims, 200 Maryland Ave. N.E. 20002; (202) 543-2239. Fax, (202) 547-3196. Robert Gardner, chief.*

Represents, before the Defense Dept., veterans seeking to upgrade less-than-honorable discharges.

Education/Economic Opportunity

AGENCIES

Office of Personnel Management, *Diversity, 1900 E St. N.W., #2445 20415-0001; (202) 606-2817. Fax, (202) 606-0927. Armando E. Rodriguez, director.*

Responsible for government recruiting policies and guidelines. Advises and assists federal agency offices in the recruitment and employment of minorities, women, veterans, and people with disabilities. Collects and maintains statistics on the federal employment of these groups. Administers the Disabled Veterans Affirmative Action Program.

Small Business Administration, *Veterans Affairs, 409 3rd St. S.W., #6500 20416; (202) 205-6773. Fax, (202) 205-7292. Cliff Toulson, assistant administrator. TDD, (202) 205-5988.*

Coordinates programs to give special consideration to veterans in loan, counseling, procurement, and training programs and in transition training sessions.

Veterans Affairs Dept., *Education Service, 1800 G St. N.W. (mailing address: 810 Vermont Ave. N.W., Washington, DC 20420); (202) 273-7133. Fax, (202) 275-1653. Celia P. Dollarhide, director. Student inquiries, (800) 827-1000. Internet, wasco22@vba.va.gov or http://www.va.gov/education.*

Administers VA's education program, including financial support for veterans' education and for spouses and dependent children of disabled and deceased disabled veterans; provides eligible veterans and dependents with educational assistance under the G.I. Bill and Veterans Educational Assistance Program. Provides postsecondary institutions with funds, based on their eligible veterans' enrollment. Emphasis is on helping disabled and educationally disadvantaged veterans.

Veterans Affairs Dept., *Loan Guaranty Service, 810 Vermont Ave. N.W. 20420; (202) 273-7332. Fax, (202) 275-3523. R. Keith Pedigo, director.*

Guarantees private institutional financing of home loans (including manufactured home loans) for veterans; provides disabled veterans with direct loans and grants for specially adapted housing; administers a direct loan program for Native American veterans living on trust land.

Veterans Affairs Dept., *Vocational Rehabilitation and Counseling Service,* 1800 G St. N.W., #501 (mailing address: 810 Vermont Ave. N.W., Washington, DC 20420); (202) 273-7419. Fax, (202) 275-5122. Julius M. Williams Jr., director. TDD, (202) 275-5119.

Administers VA's vocational rehabilitation and counseling program, which provides service-disabled veterans with services and assistance; helps veterans to become employable and to obtain and maintain suitable employment.

Veterans' Employment and Training Service *(Labor Dept.),* 200 Constitution Ave. N.W., #S1315 20210; (202) 219-9116. Fax, (202) 219-4773. Al Borrego, assistant secretary.

Works with and monitors state employment offices to see that preference is given to veterans seeking jobs; advises the secretary on veterans' affairs.

Veterans' Employment and Training Service *(Labor Dept.),* **Operations and Programs,** 200 Constitution Ave. N.W., #S1316 20210; (202) 219-9110. Fax, (202) 219-7341. Vacant, director.

Investigates veterans' complaints of job or benefits loss because of active or reserve duty military service.

NONPROFIT

Blinded Veterans Assn., 477 H St. N.W. 20001; (202) 371-8880. Fax, (202) 371-8258. John Williams, director, Administration. Toll-free, (800) 669-7079. Internet, bva@bva.org or http://www.bva.org.

Provides blind and disabled veterans with vocational rehabilitation and employment services.

Disabled American Veterans, *Employment,* 807 Maine Ave. S.W. 20024; (202) 554-3501. Fax, (202) 554-3581. Ronald W. Drach, national employment director.

Recommends veterans' employment policy to federal agencies. Monitors legislation and regulations on veterans' employment.

Interstate Conference of Employment Security Agencies, 444 N. Capitol St. N.W., #142 20001; (202) 628-5588. Fax, (202) 783-5023. Emily DeRocco, executive director. Internet, http://www.icesa.org.

Membership: state employment security administrators. Provides veterans' employment and training professionals with opportunities for networking and information exchange. Monitors legislation and regulations that affect veterans' employment and training programs involving state employment security agencies.

Paralyzed Veterans of America, 801 18th St. N.W. 20006; (202) 872-1300. Fax, (202) 785-4452. Gordon H. Mansfield, executive director. Toll-free, (800) 424-8200. TDD, (202) 416-7622. Internet, http://www.pva.org.

Congressionally chartered organization that assists veterans with claims for benefits. Promotes access to educational and public facilities and to public transportation for people with disabilities; seeks modification of workplaces.

Health Care/VA Hospitals

AGENCIES

Defense Dept., *Special Assistant for Gulf War Illnesses,* 5113 Leesburg Pike, #901, Falls Church, VA 22041; (703) 578-8500. Fax, (703) 578-8501. Bernard D. Rostker, special assistant. Incident reporting line, (800) 472-6719. Internet, http://www.dtic.mil/gulflink.

Coordinates Defense Dept. investigation of illnesses suffered by Gulf War veterans. Researches links between these illnesses and possible exposure to Iraqi nerve agents. Responds to inquiries from veterans and their families.

Defense Special Weapons Agency *(Defense Dept.),* **Nuclear Test Personnel Review Program,** 6801 Telegraph Rd., Alexandria, VA 22310-3398; (703) 325-2407. Fax, (703) 325-2951. D. Michael Schaeffer, program manager. Information, (703) 325-7095. Veterans hotline, (800) 462-3683.

Manages a database of participants in U.S. atmospheric nuclear tests and in the post-war occupation of Hiroshima and Nagasaki, Japan; provides participation information to veterans, their families, and government organizations representing their interests.

Public Health and Science *(Health and Human Services Dept.),* **Veterans Affairs and Military Liaison,** 200 Independence Ave. S.W., #701H 20201; (202) 260-0576. Fax, (202) 690-7425. Capt. Peter Mazzella (U.S. Public Health Service), director.

Advises the assistant secretary on health issues that affect veterans and military personnel. Works to identify the health-related needs of veterans and their families and to facilitate the delivery of services.

Veterans Affairs Dept., *Committee on the Readjustment of Vietnam Veterans and Other War Veterans,* 801

Eye St. N.W. (mailing address: 810 Vermont Ave. N.W., Washington, DC 20420); (202) 861-2711. Fax, (202) 861-2786. John F. Sommer Jr., chair.

Studies veteran readjustment issues such as medical service, compensation, and pension for posttraumatic stress disorder; examines Vet Center operations and veteran employment issues.

Veterans Health Administration *(Veterans Affairs Dept.),* 810 Vermont Ave. N.W., #800 20420; (202) 273-5781. Fax, (202) 273-5787. Dr. Kenneth W. Kizer, under secretary for health.

Recommends policy and administers medical and hospital services for eligible veterans. Publishes guidelines on treatment of veterans exposed to Agent Orange.

Veterans Health Administration *(Veterans Affairs Dept.), Academic Affiliations,* 810 Vermont Ave. N.W. 20420; (202) 273-8946. Fax, (202) 273-9031. David P. Stevens, chief academic affiliations officer.

Administers education and training programs for health professionals, students, and residents through partnerships with affiliated academic institutions.

Veterans Health Administration *(Veterans Affairs Dept.), Dentistry,* 810 Vermont Ave. N.W. 20420; (202) 273-8503. Fax, (202) 273-9105. Dr. Robert T. Frame, assistant chief medical director.

Administers VA oral health care programs; coordinates oral research, education, and training of VA oral health personnel and outpatient dental care in private practice.

Veterans Health Administration *(Veterans Affairs Dept.), Facilities Management,* 810 Vermont Ave. N.W. 20420; (202) 565-5009. Fax, (202) 565-4155. C. V. Yarbrough, chief.

Reviews construction policies for VA hospitals.

Veterans Health Administration *(Veterans Affairs Dept.), Geriatrics and Extended Care,* 810 Vermont Ave. N.W. 20420; (202) 273-8540. Fax, (202) 273-9131. Dr. Judith Salerno, chief consultant.

Administers research, educational, and clinical health care programs in geriatrics, including VA and community nursing homes, personal care homes, VA domiciliaries, state veterans' homes, and hospital-based home care.

Veterans Health Administration *(Veterans Affairs Dept.), Mental Health Strategic Health Care,* 810 Vermont Ave. N.W. 20420; (202) 273-8440. Fax, (202) 273-9069. Dr. Thomas B. Horvath, chief.

Develops ambulatory and inpatient psychiatry and psychology programs for the mentally ill and for drug and alcohol abusers; programs are offered in VA facilities and networks. Incorporates special programs for veterans suffering from post-traumatic stress disorders, serious mental illness, addictive disorders, and homelessness.

Veterans Health Administration *(Veterans Affairs Dept.), Patient Care Services,* 810 Vermont Ave. N.W. 20420; (202) 273-8474. Fax, (202) 273-9274. Dr. Thomas Holohan, chief officer.

Manages clinical programs of the VA medical care system.

Veterans Health Administration *(Veterans Affairs Dept.), Policy, Planning, and Performance,* 810 Vermont Ave. N.W. 20420; (202) 273-8932. Fax, (202) 273-9030. Greg Pane, director.

Coordinates and develops departmental planning to distribute funds to VA field facilities.

Veterans Health Administration *(Veterans Affairs Dept.), Readjustment Counseling,* 810 Vermont Ave. N.W., Mail Code 15 20420; (202) 273-8967. Fax, (202) 273-9071. Alfonso R. Batres, director.

Responsible for community-based centers for veterans nationwide. Provides outreach and counseling services for war-related psychological problems.

Veterans Health Administration *(Veterans Affairs Dept.), Research and Development,* 810 Vermont Ave. N.W. 20420; (202) 273-8284. Fax, (202) 273-6526. Dr. John Feussner, chief medical director.

Formulates and implements policy for the research and development program of the Veterans Health Administration; advises the undersecretary for health on research-related matters and on management of the VA's health care system; represents the VA in interactions with external organizations in matters related to biomedical and health services research.

Veterans Health Administration *(Veterans Affairs Dept.), Voluntary Service,* 810 Vermont Ave. N.W., Mail Code 10C2 20420; (202) 273-8952. Fax, (202) 273-9040. Jim W. Delgado, director.

Supervises volunteer programs in VA medical centers.

CONGRESS

House Veterans' Affairs Committee, *Subcommittee on Health,* 338 CHOB 20515; (202) 225-9154. Fax, (202) 226-4536. Cliff Stearns, R-Fla., chair; Ralph Ibson, staff director.

Jurisdiction over legislation on hospitals, medical programs, outpatient programs, state veterans' homes, and construction of medical facilities.

Senate Veterans' Affairs Committee, *Special Investigations Unit on Gulf War Illnesses,* SD B40-2 20510; *(202) 224-4316. Michael J. Rotko, special counsel. Internet, http://www.senate.gov/~veterans.*

Coordinates committee efforts to determine the causes and incidence of Gulf War illnesses; provides liaison to the Veterans Affairs Dept. and the General Accounting Office.

NONPROFIT

American Gold Star Mothers, *2128 LeRoy Pl. N.W. 20008-1893; (202) 265-0991. Jeanne K. Penfold, national service officer.*

Membership: mothers who have lost sons or daughters in military service (World War I to the present). Members serve as volunteers in VA hospitals.

American War Mothers, *2615 Woodley Pl. N.W. 20008; (202) 462-2791. Maydell McLain, president.*

Membership: mothers and stepmothers of military personnel from all branches of service. Members serve as volunteers in VA hospitals.

National Assn. of Veterans Administration Physicians and Dentists, *1414 Prince St., #202, Alexandria, VA 22314; (703) 548-0280. Fax, (703) 548-8024. Samuel Spagnolo, president. Internet, navapd@dgs.dgsys.com.*

Seeks to improve the quality of care and conditions at VA hospitals. Monitors legislation and regulations on veterans' health care.

National Conference on Ministry in the Armed Forces, *Endorsers Conference for Veterans Affairs Chaplaincy,* 4141 N. Henderson Rd., #13, Arlington, VA 22203; (703) 276-7905. Fax, (703) 276-7906. Clifford T. Weathers, coordinator.

Encourages religious ministry to veterans in VA hospitals and centers.

National Gulf War Resource Center, Inc., *1224 M St. N.W. 20005 (mailing address: P.O. Box 622, Decatur, GA 30031); (202) 628-2700. Fax, (202) 628-6997. Chris Kornkven, president; Paul Sullivan, director. Internet, ngwrc@mindspring.com or http://www.gulfweb.org/ngwrc.*

Supports grassroots efforts of various Gulf War veterans associations. Provides information and referrals on health and benefits. Monitors legislation and regulations.

Paralyzed Veterans of America, *801 18th St. N.W. 20006; (202) 872-1300. Fax, (202) 785-4452. Gordon H. Mansfield, executive director. Toll-free, (800) 424-8200. TDD, (202) 416-7622. Internet, http://www.pva.org.*

Congressionally chartered veterans' service organization. Consults with the Veterans Affairs Dept. on the establishment and operation of spinal cord injury treatment centers.

Spouses, Dependents, and Survivors

AGENCIES

Air Force Dept. *(Defense Dept.), Personnel,* The Pentagon, #4E194 20330-1040; (703) 697-6088. Fax, (703) 614-5436. Lt. Gen. Michael D. McGinty, deputy chief of staff. Toll-free casualty assistance, (800) 433-0048.

Military office that responds to inquiries concerning deceased Air Force personnel and their beneficiaries; refers inquiries to the Military Personnel Center at Randolph Air Force Base in San Antonio, Texas.

Army Dept. *(Defense Dept.), Casualty Operations,* 2461 Eisenhower Ave., #920, Alexandria, VA 22331-0481; (703) 325-7990. Fax, (703) 325-0134. Lt. Col. Gene Samanka, chief.

Verifies beneficiaries of deceased Army personnel for benefits distribution.

Marine Corps *(Defense Dept.), Casualty Section,* 3033 Wilson Blvd., Arlington, VA (mailing address: Headquarters, U.S. Marine Corps, 2 Navy Annex, Code MHP-10, Washington, DC 20380-1775); (703) 696-2069. Fax, (703) 696-2072. Maj. M. L. Ward, head.

Confirms beneficiaries of deceased Marine Corps personnel for benefits distribution.

Navy Dept. *(Defense Dept.), Casualty Assistance and Retired Activities,* Navy Annex, #1720, Arlington, VA 20370; (703) 697-2171. Fax, (703) 614-3345. Cmdr. Jonie Parker, director.

Confirms beneficiaries of deceased Navy personnel for benefits distribution; oversees retired activities for the Navy.

NONPROFIT

American Gold Star Mothers, *2128 LeRoy Pl. N.W. 20008-1893; (202) 265-0991. Jeanne K. Penfold, national service officer.*

Membership: mothers who have lost sons or daughters in military service (World War I to the present). Members serve as volunteers in VA hospitals.

American War Mothers, *2615 Woodley Pl. N.W. 20008; (202) 462-2791. Betty A. Hughes, president.*

Membership: mothers and stepmothers of military personnel from all branches of service. Members serve as volunteers in VA hospitals.

Army and Air Force Mutual Aid Assn., *102 Sheridan Ave., Fort Myer, VA 22211-1110; (703) 522-3060. Fax, (703) 522-1336. Bradley J. Snyder, president. Toll-free, (800) 336-4538. Internet, info@aafmaa.com or http://www.aafmaa.com.*

Private service organization that offers member and family insurance services to Army and Air Force officers. Recognized by the Veterans Affairs Dept. to assist veterans and their survivors with claims for benefits.

Army Distaff Foundation, *6200 Oregon Ave. N.W. 20015; (202) 541-0105. Fax, (202) 364-2856. Maj. Gen. Calvert P. Benedict (USA, ret.), executive director. Toll-free, (800) 541-4255.*

Nonprofit continuing care retirement community for career military officers and their families. Provides retirement housing and health care services.

EXPOSE, Ex-partners of Servicemen (Women) for Equality, *P.O. Box 11191, Alexandria, VA 22312; (703) 941-5844. Fax, (703) 212-6951. Kathleen Rogers, director.*

Membership: former spouses of military personnel, both officers and enlisted, and other interested parties. Seeks federal laws to restore to ex-spouses benefits lost through divorce, including retirement pay; survivors' benefits; and medical, commissary, and exchange benefits. Provides information concerning related federal laws and regulations. Serves as an information clearinghouse.

National Assn. of Military Widows, *4023 N. 25th Rd., Arlington, VA 22207; (703) 527-4565. Jean Arthurs, president.*

Provides military widows with referral information on survivor benefit programs; helps locate widows eligible for benefits. Interests include health and education. Monitors legislation.

No Greater Love, *1750 New York Ave. N.W. 20006; (202) 783-4665. Fax, (202) 783-1168. Carmella LaSpada, chief executive officer. Internet, http://www.ngl.org.*

Provides programs of remembrance, friendship, and care for families of Americans killed in war or by acts of terrorism.

Society of Military Widows, *5535 Hempstead Way, Springfield, VA 22151; (703) 750-1342. Fax, (703) 354-4380. Caroline Hunter, president.*

Serves the interests of widows of servicemen who died while in active military service; provides support programs and information. Monitors legislation concerning military widows' benefits. (Affiliated with the National Assn. for Uniformed Services.)

16 National Security

GENERAL POLICY

See also Caucuses (chap. 20); International Law and Agreements (chap. 13)

AGENCIES

Air Force Dept. *(Defense Dept.), Chief of Staff,* The Pentagon, #4E924 20330-1670; (703) 697-9225. Fax, (703) 693-9297. Gen. Michael E. Ryan, chief of staff. Internet, http://www.hq.af.mil.

Military office that develops and directs Air Force national security policies in conjunction with the secretary of the Air Force and the secretary of defense.

Air Force Dept. *(Defense Dept.), Secretary,* The Pentagon, #4E871 20330-1670; (703) 697-7376. Fax, (703) 695-8809. Vacant, secretary; F. Whitten Peters, under secretary, (703) 697-1361. Information, (703) 695-0640.

Civilian office that develops and reviews Air Force national security policies in conjunction with the chief of staff of the Air Force and the secretary of defense.

Army Dept. *(Defense Dept.), Chief of Staff,* The Pentagon, #3E668 20310-0200; (703) 695-2077. Fax, (703) 614-5268. Gen. Dennis Reimer, chief of staff. Information, (703) 614-0741. Press, (703) 697-7589.

Military office that develops and administers Army national security policies in conjunction with the secretary of the Army and the secretary of defense.

Army Dept. *(Defense Dept.), Secretary,* The Pentagon 20310-1500; (703) 695-3211. Fax, (703) 697-2159. Vacant, secretary; Robert M. Walker, under secretary, (703) 695-4311. Press, (703) 697-2564. Internet, http://www.army.mil or http://www.dtic.mil/armylink.

Civilian office that develops and reviews Army national security policies in conjunction with the chief of staff of the Army and the secretary of defense.

Defense Dept., *The Pentagon 20301-1000; (703) 695-5261. Fax, (703) 695-1149. William S. Cohen, secretary; John J. Hamre, deputy secretary. Information, (703) 697-5737. Press, (703) 695-0192 (defense news); (703) 697-5131 (armed forces news). (703) 695-3324 (tours). Locator, (703) 697-5371. Internet, http://www.defenselink.mil.*

Civilian office that develops national security policies and has overall responsibility for administering national defense; responds to public and congressional inquiries about national defense matters.

Defense Dept., *Environmental Security,* 3400 Defense Pentagon, #3E792 20301-3400; (703) 695-6639. Fax, (703) 693-7011. Sherri W. Goodman, deputy under secretary. Internet, http://www.acq.osd.mil/ens.

Integrates environmental, safety, and occupational health considerations into U.S. defense and economic policies. Works to ensure responsible performance in defense operations, to maintain quality installations, to reduce the costs of complying with environmental laws, and to clean up past contamination.

Defense Dept., *Joint Chiefs of Staff,* The Pentagon, #2E872 20318-9999; (703) 697-9121. Fax, (703) 697-8758. Gen. Henry H. Shelton (USA), chair; V. Adm. Dennis C. Blair (USN), joint staff director, (703) 614-5221. Information, (703) 697-4272. Internet, http://www.dtic.mil/jcs.

Joint military staff office that assists the president, the National Security Council, and the secretary of defense in developing national security policy and in coordinating operations of the individual armed services.

Defense Dept., *Policy,* The Pentagon, #4E808 20301-2000; (703) 697-7200. Fax, (703) 697-9680. Walter Slocombe, under secretary.

Civilian office responsible for policy matters relating to international security issues and political military affairs. Oversees such areas as arms control, foreign military sales, intelligence collection and analysis, and NATO and regional security affairs.

Defense Dept., *Special Operations and Low Intensity Conflict,* The Pentagon, #2E258 20301-2500; (703) 693-2895. Fax, (703) 693-6335. H. Allen Holmes, assistant secretary.

Serves as special staff assistant and civilian adviser to the defense secretary on matters related to special operations and low intensity conflict. Responsible for the Army's Green Berets, the Navy Seals, and other special operations forces. Oversees counterdrug efforts and humanitarian and refugee affairs for the Defense Dept.

Defense Dept., *Strategy and Threat Reduction,* The Pentagon, #4E817 20301-2600; (703) 697-7728. Fax, (703) 693-9146. Edward L. Warner III, assistant secretary.

Develops and coordinates national security strategy and defense strategy and advises on the resources, forces, and contingency plans necessary to implement those strategies. Ensures the integration of defense strategy into the department's resource allocation, force structure development, weapons system acquisition, and budgetary processes. Evaluates the capability of forces to accomplish defense strategy.

Marine Corps *(Defense Dept.), Commandant,* Navy Annex, Arlington, VA (mailing address: Marine Corps Headquarters, Washington, DC 20380-1775); (703) 614-2500. Fax, (703) 697-7246. Gen. Charles Krulak,

DEFENSE DEPARTMENT

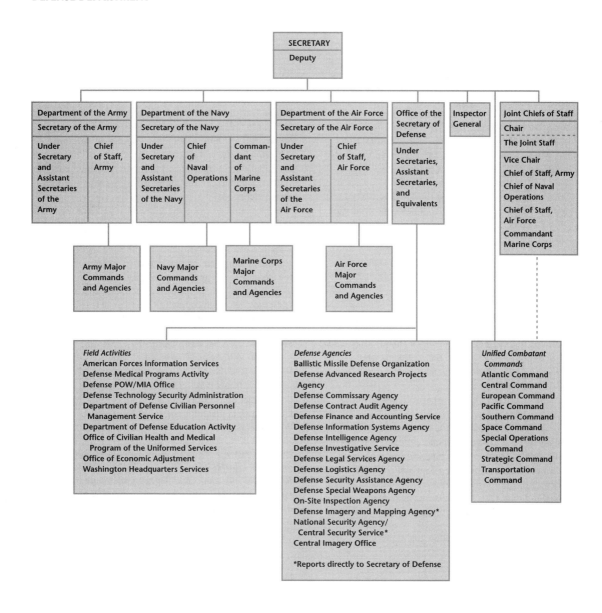

commandant. *Information, (703) 614-8010. Press, (703) 614-1492. Internet, http://www.hqmc.usmc.mil.*

Military office that develops and directs Marine Corps national security policies in conjunction with the secretary of defense and the secretary of the Navy.

National Security Council (*Executive Office of the President*), *The White House 20504; (202) 456-9471.*

Fax, (202) 456-9460. Samuel R. "Sandy" Berger, assistant to the president for national security affairs. Press, (202) 456-9271. Internet, http://www.whitehouse.gov.

Advises the president on foreign policy and defense issues, including participation and proposed participation of U.S. armed forces in international peacekeeping operations.

Navy Dept. *(Defense Dept.), Chief of Naval Operations,* The Pentagon, #4E660 20350-2000; (703) 695-6007. Fax, (703) 697-6290. Adm. Jay Johnson, chief of naval operations. Information, (703) 695-0965. Press, (703) 697-5342.

Military office that develops Navy national security policies in conjunction with the secretary of defense and the secretary of the Navy and in cooperation with the commandant of the Marine Corps.

Navy Dept. *(Defense Dept.), Secretary,* The Pentagon, #4E686 20350-1200; (703) 695-3131. Fax, (703) 614-3477. John Dalton, secretary; Jerry Hultin, under secretary, (703) 695-3141. Information, (703) 695-0965. Press, (703) 697-5342. Internet, http://www.navy.mil.

Civilian office that develops and reviews Navy and Marine Corps national security policies in conjunction with the chief of naval operations, the commandant of the Marine Corps, and the secretary of defense.

State Dept., *Political-Military Affairs,* Main State Bldg., #7325 20520; (202) 647-9022. Fax, (202) 736-4779. Eric D. Newsom, acting assistant secretary.

Responsible for security affairs policy; acts as a liaison between the Defense Dept. and the State Dept.

U.S. Coast Guard *(Transportation Dept.),* 2100 2nd St. S.W. 20593; (202) 267-2390. Fax, (202) 267-4158. Adm. Robert Kramek, commandant. Information, (202) 267-1587. Internet, http://www.uscg.mil.

Carries out search-and-rescue missions in and around navigable waters and on the high seas; enforces federal laws on the high seas and navigable waters of the United States and its possessions; conducts marine environmental protection programs; administers boating safety programs; inspects and regulates construction, safety, and equipment of merchant marine vessels; establishes and maintains a system of navigation aids; carries out domestic icebreaking activities; maintains a state of military readiness to assist the Navy in time of war or when directed by the president.

CONGRESS

House Appropriations Committee, *Subcommittee on National Security,* H149 CAP 20515; (202) 225-2847. Fax, (202) 225-2822. C. W. Bill Young, R-Fla., chair; Kevin M. Roper, staff director. Internet, http://www.house.gov/appropriations.

Jurisdiction over legislation to appropriate funds for the Defense Dept. (excluding military construction, civil defense, military assistance to foreign countries, and nuclear warhead program), the Central Intelligence Agency, and the intelligence community.

House Appropriations Committee, *Subcommittee on Treasury, Postal Service, and General Government,* B307 RHOB 20515; (202) 225-5834. Fax, (202) 225-5895. Jim Kolbe, R-Ariz., chair; Michelle Mrdeza, clerk. Internet, http://www.house.gov/appropriations.

Jurisdiction over legislation to appropriate funds for the Executive Office of the President, including the National Security Council.

House National Security Committee, 2120 RHOB 20515; (202) 225-4151. Fax, (202) 225-9077. Floyd D. Spence, R-S.C., chair; Andrew K. Ellis, staff director. Internet, http://www.house.gov/nsc.

Jurisdiction over defense legislation. Oversight of the Defense Dept., including the Army, Navy, and Air Force departments.

Senate Appropriations Committee, *Subcommittee on Defense,* SD-122 20510; (202) 224-7255. Ted Stevens, R-Alaska, chair; Steve Cortese, staff director.

Jurisdiction over legislation to appropriate funds for the Defense Dept. (excluding military construction, family housing, civil defense, nuclear materials, and military assistance to foreign countries), the Central Intelligence Agency, and the intelligence community.

Senate Armed Services Committee, SR-228 20510; (202) 224-3871. Strom Thurmond, R-S.C., chair; Les Brownlee, staff director. Internet, http://www.senate.gov/committee/armed_services.html.

Jurisdiction over defense legislation. Oversight of the Defense Dept., including the Army, Navy, and Air Force departments.

Senate Armed Services Committee, *Subcommittee on Airland Forces,* SR-228 20510; (202) 224-3871. Daniel R. Coats, R-Ind., chair; John Barnes, professional staff member. Internet, http://www.senate.gov/committee/armed_services.html.

Jurisdiction over legislation concerning NATO and East Asia defenses, cooperation with allies, defense modeling and simulation, equipment requirements and programs for reserve forces, and, to the extent not covered by the full committee, issues of peacekeeping and peace enforcement.

Senate Armed Services Committee, *Subcommittee on Seapower,* SR-228 20510; (202) 224-3871. John W. Warner, R-Va., chair; Gary M. Hall, professional staff member. Internet, http://www.senate.gov/committee/armed_services.html.

Jurisdiction over legislation concerning Southwest Asia defenses and defense-related programs of the U.S. Coast Guard. Oversees policy aspects of security assis-

AIR FORCE DEPARTMENT

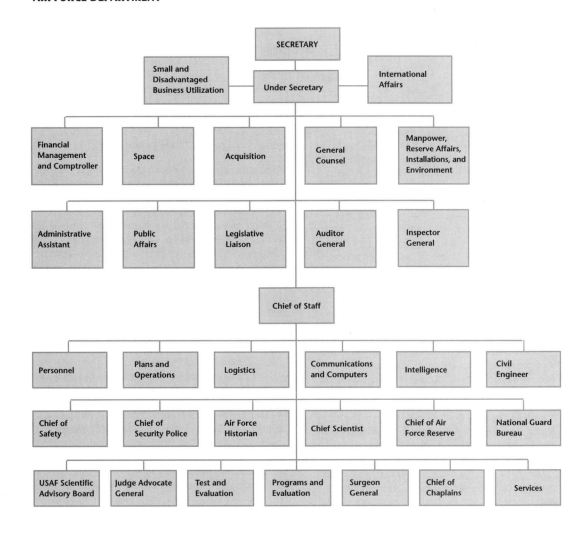

tance programs and the Defense Security Assistance Agency; oversees the Military Sealift Command, Military Transportation Command, and budget accounts for research, development, and procurement of airlift and sealift capability.

Senate Governmental Affairs Committee, *SD-340 20510; (202) 224-4751. Fax, (202) 224-9603. Fred Thompson, R-Tenn., chair; Hannah Sistare, staff director. Internet, http://www.senate.gov/committee/governmental_ affairs.html.*

Oversees operations of the National Security Council.

NONPROFIT

Air Force Assn., *1501 Lee Hwy., Arlington, VA 22209-1198; (703) 247-5800. Fax, (703) 247-5853. Gen. John A. Shaud (USAF, ret.), executive director. Press, (703) 247-5850. Library, (703) 247-5829. Internet, http://www. afa.org.*

Membership: civilians and active, reserve, retired, and cadet personnel of the Air Force. Informs members and the public of developments in the aerospace field. Monitors legislation and Defense Dept. policies. Library on aviation history open to the public by appointment.

American Conservative Union, *1007 Cameron St., Alexandria, VA 22314; (703) 836-8602. Fax, (703) 836-8606. Vacant, executive director. Toll-free, (800) 228-7345. Internet, acu@conservative.org or http://www.conservative.org.*

Legislative interest organization concerned with national defense policy, legislation related to nuclear weapons, U.S. strategic position vis-à-vis the former Soviet Union, missile defense programs, U.S. troops under U.N. command, and U.S. strategic alliance commitments.

American Defense Institute, *Pride in America, 1055 N. Fairfax St., #200, Alexandria, VA 22314; (703) 519-7000. Fax, (703) 519-8627. Capt. Eugene B. McDaniel (USN, ret.), president. Internet, rdt2@americandefinst.org.*

Nonpartisan organization that advocates a strong national defense. Acts as an information clearinghouse on issues related to national security. Seeks to educate young Americans on matters of defense and foreign policy.

American Enterprise Institute for Public Policy Research, *Foreign and Defense Policy Studies, 1150 17th St. N.W. 20036; (202) 862-5814. Fax, (202) 862-7177. Jeane Kirkpatrick, director. Information, (202) 862-6158. Press, (202) 862-5829.*

Research and educational organization that conducts conferences, seminars, and debates and sponsors research on national security, defense policy, and arms control.

American Security Council, *5545 Security Circle, Boston, VA 22713 (mailing address: P.O. Box 8, Boston, VA 22713); (540) 547-1776. Fax, (540) 547-9737. John M. Fisher, chair.*

Bipartisan, prodefense organization that advocates continuation of the strategic modernization program and stable funding for the space program, new technologies, and conventional forces. Monitors legislation and conducts educational activities.

Assn. of the United States Army, *2425 Wilson Blvd., Arlington, VA 22201; (703) 841-4300. Fax, (703) 525-9039. Gen. Gordon Sullivan (USA, ret.), president. Internet, http://www.ausa.org.*

Membership: civilians and active and retired members of the armed forces. Conducts symposia on defense issues and researches topics that affect the military.

Atlantic Council of the United States, *910 17th St. N.W., 10th Floor 20006; (202) 463-7226. Fax, (202) 463-7241. David C. Acheson, president. Internet, info@acgate.acus.org.*

Conducts studies and makes policy recommendations on American foreign security and international economic policies in the Atlantic and Pacific communities; sponsors conferences and educational exchanges.

Brookings Institution, *Foreign Policy Studies, 1775 Massachusetts Ave. N.W. 20036-2188; (202) 797-6400. Fax, (202) 797-6004. Richard Haass, director. Information, (202) 797-6000. Press, (202) 797-6105. Publications, (202) 797-6258. Internet, http://www.brook.edu.*

Research and educational organization that focuses on major national security topics, including U.S. armed forces, weapons decisions, employment policies, and the security aspects of U.S. foreign relations.

Center for Defense Information, *1779 Massachusetts Ave. N.W., #615 20036; (202) 332-0600. Fax, (202) 462-4559. Vacant, director. Toll-free, (800) 234-3334. Internet, info@cdi.org or http://www.cdi.org.*

Educational organization that advocates a strong defense while opposing excessive expenditures for weapons and policies that increase the risk of war. Interests include the defense budget, weapons systems, and troop levels. Provides Congress, the Pentagon, State Dept., media, and public with appraisals of military matters. Library open to the public.

Center for Naval Analyses, *4401 Ford Ave., Alexandria, VA 22302-0268; (703) 824-2000. Fax, (703) 824-2942. Robert J. Murray, president. Internet, http://www.cna.org.*

Conducts research on weapons acquisitions, tactical problems, and naval operations.

Center for Security Policy, *1250 24th St. N.W., #350 20037; (202) 466-0515. Fax, (202) 466-0518. Frank J. Gaffney Jr., director. Internet, http://www.security-policy.org.*

Educational institution concerned with U.S. defense and foreign policy. Interests include relations between the United States and the former Soviet Union, arms control compliance and verification policy, and technology transfer policy.

Conservative Caucus, *450 Maple Ave. East, Vienna, VA 22180; (703) 938-9626. Fax, (703) 281-4108. Howard Phillips, chair. Internet, http://www.conservativeusa.org.*

Legislative interest organization that promotes grassroots activity on national defense and foreign policy.

Defense Orientation Conference Assn., *9271 Old Keene Mill Rd., #200, Burke, VA 22015-4202; (703) 451-1200. Fax, (703) 451-1201. John W. Ohlsen, executive vice president. Internet, doca@erols.com.*

Membership: citizens interested in national defense. Promotes continuing education of members on national security issues through tours of defense installations in the United States and abroad.

ARMY DEPARTMENT

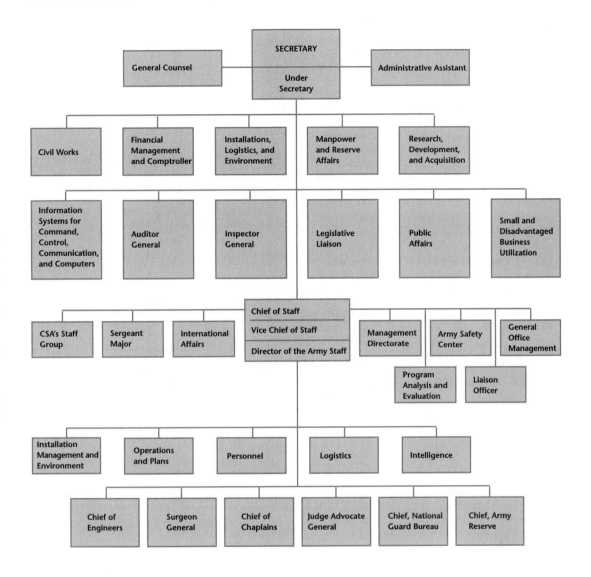

Ethics and Public Policy Center, *Foreign Policy Program,* 1015 15th St. N.W., #900 20005; (202) 682-1200. *Fax, (202) 408-0632. Elliott Abrams, president. Internet, ethics@eppc.org or http://www.eppc.org.*

Conducts research and holds conferences on foreign policy, including the role of the U.S. military abroad.

Henry L. Stimson Center, 11 Dupont Circle N.W., 9th Floor 20036; (202) 223-5956. *Fax, (202) 238-9604. Michael Krepon, president. Internet, info@stimson.org or http://www.stimson.org.*

Research and educational organization that studies arms control and international security, focusing on policy, technology, and politics.

Hudson Institute, *National Security Studies,* 1015 18th St. N.W., #300 20036; (202) 223-7770. *Fax, (202) 223-8537. Lt. Gen. William E. Odom (USA, ret.), director. Internet, http://www.hudson.org.*

Public policy research organization that conducts studies on U.S. overseas bases, U.S.-NATO relations, and missile defense programs. Focuses on long-range implications for U.S. national security. (Headquarters in Indianapolis.)

Marine Corps League, *8626 Lee Hwy., Fairfax, VA (mailing address: P.O. Box 3070, Merrifield, VA 22116); (703) 207-9588. Fax, (703) 207-0047. William "Brooks" Corley Jr., executive director. Internet, mcl@mcleague.org or http://www.mcleague.org.*

Membership: active duty, retired, and reserve Marine Corps groups. Promotes the interests of the Marine Corps and works to preserve its traditions; assists veterans and their survivors. Monitors legislation and regulations.

Navy League of the United States, *2300 Wilson Blvd., Arlington, VA 22201; (703) 528-1775. Fax, (703) 528-2333. Charles L. Robinson, executive director. Internet, mail@navyleague.org or http://www.navyleague.org.*

Membership: retired and reserve military personnel and civilians interested in the U.S. Navy, Marine Corps, Coast Guard, and Merchant Marine. Distributes literature, provides speakers, and conducts seminars to promote interests of the sea services. Monitors legislation.

Rand Corporation, *1333 H St. N.W., #800 20005; (202) 296-5000. Fax, (202) 296-7960. David Chu, director, Washington Office. Internet, http://www.rand.org.*

Conducts research on national security issues, including political/military affairs of the former Soviet Union and U.S. strategic policy. (Headquarters in Santa Monica, Calif.)

Defense Budget

See also Federal Budget (chap. 5)

AGENCIES

Defense Contract Audit Agency *(Defense Dept.),* *8725 John Jay Kingman Rd., #2135, Fort Belvoir, VA 22060-6219; (703) 767-3200. Fax, (703) 767-3267. William H. Reed, director; Michael J. Thibault, deputy director, (703) 274-7281. Internet, http://www.dtic.mil/dcaa.*

Performs all contract audits for the Defense Dept. Provides Defense Dept. personnel responsible for procurement and contract administration with accounting and financial advisory services regarding the negotiation, administration, and settlement of contracts and subcontracts.

Defense Dept., Comptroller, *The Pentagon, #3E822 20301-1100; (703) 695-3237. Fax, (703) 693-0582. William Lynn, comptroller.*

Supervises and reviews the preparation and implementation of the defense budget. Advises the secretary

of defense on fiscal matters. Collects and distributes information on the department's management of resources.

Office of Management and Budget *(Executive Office of the President),* **National Security,** *New Executive Office Bldg., #1001 20503; (202) 395-4572. Fax, (202) 395-3307. David H. Morrison, deputy associate director.*

Supervises preparation of the Defense Dept.'s portion of the federal budget.

CONGRESS

General Accounting Office, *National Security and International Affairs, 441 G St. N.W., #4035 20548; (202) 512-2800. Fax, (202) 512-7686. Henry L. Hinton, assistant comptroller general.*

Independent, nonpartisan agency in the legislative branch. Audits, analyzes, and evaluates defense spending programs; makes unclassified reports available to the public.

NONPROFIT

Campaign for New Priorities, *424 C St. N.E., Lower Level 20002; (202) 544-8222. Fax, (202) 544-8226. Robert L. Borosage, director. Internet, cnp@igc.apc.org or http://www.newpriorities.org.*

Coordinates efforts of citizens and organizations to increase federal domestic-program funding by reducing military spending. Works to increase spending on education, job retraining, the environment and infrastructure, and civilian research and development.

Center for Strategic and Budgetary Assessments, *1730 Rhode Island Ave., #912 20036; (202) 331-7990. Fax, (202) 331-8019. Andrew Krepinevich, director. Internet, http://www.csbahome.com.*

Conducts detailed analyses of defense spending; makes results available to members of Congress, the executive branch, the media, academics, other organizations, and the general public.

Institute for Policy Studies, *National Commission for Economic Conversion and Disarmament, 733 15th St. N.W., #1020 20005; (202) 234-9382. Fax, (202) 387-7915. Miriam Pemberton, executive director. Internet, ncecd@ igc.apc.org or http://www.webcom.com/ncecd.*

Supports cutbacks in the U.S. military budget and reallocation of funds for civilian economic development. Advocates investment in civilian research and development, transportation, housing, health, education, and the environment.

NAVY DEPARTMENT

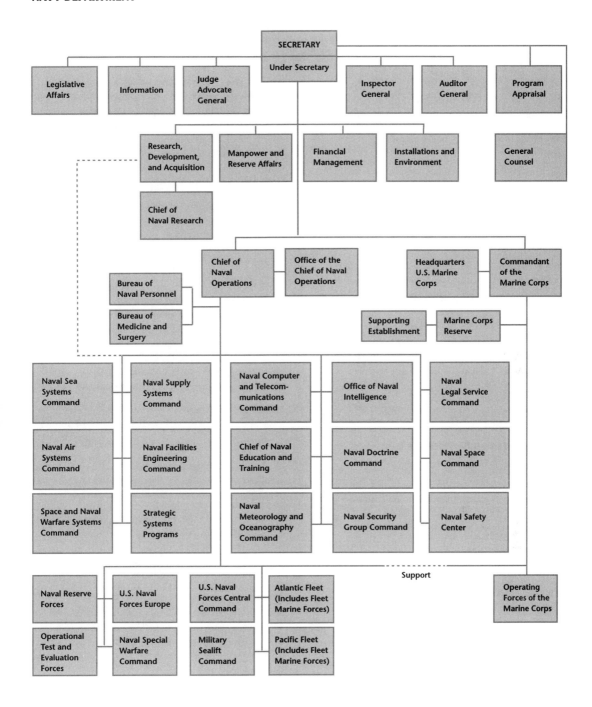

SECRETARY

Under Secretary

Legislative Affairs

Information

Judge Advocate General

Inspector General

Auditor General

Program Appraisal

Research, Development, and Acquisition

Manpower and Reserve Affairs

Financial Management

Installations and Environment

General Counsel

Chief of Naval Research

Chief of Naval Operations

Office of the Chief of Naval Operations

Headquarters U.S. Marine Corps

Commandant of the Marine Corps

Bureau of Naval Personnel

Bureau of Medicine and Surgery

Supporting Establishment

Marine Corps Reserve

Naval Sea Systems Command

Naval Supply Systems Command

Naval Computer and Telecommunications Command

Office of Naval Intelligence

Naval Legal Service Command

Naval Air Systems Command

Naval Facilities Engineering Command

Chief of Naval Education and Training

Naval Doctrine Command

Naval Space Command

Space and Naval Warfare Systems Command

Strategic Systems Programs

Naval Meteorology and Oceanography Command

Naval Security Group Command

Naval Safety Center

Support

Naval Reserve Forces

U.S. Naval Forces Europe

U.S. Naval Forces Central Command

Atlantic Fleet (Includes Fleet Marine Forces)

Operating Forces of the Marine Corps

Operational Test and Evaluation Forces

Naval Special Warfare Command

Military Sealift Command

Pacific Fleet (Includes Fleet Marine Forces)

National Campaign for a Peace Tax Fund,
2121 Decatur Pl. N.W. 20008; (202) 483-3751. Fax, (202) 986-0667. Marian Franz, executive director. Internet, peacetaxfund@igc.org or http://www.nonviolence.org/peacetax.

Membership: individuals opposed to military spending. Supports legislation permitting taxpayers who are conscientiously opposed to military expenditures to have the military portion of their income tax money placed in a separate, nonmilitary fund.

Women's Action for New Directions, *110 Maryland Ave. N.E., #205 20002; (202) 543-8505. Fax, (202) 675-6469. Kimberly Robson, director of policy and programs. Legislative hotline, (800) 444-9263. Internet, wandwill@wand.org or http://www.wand.org.*

Seeks to redirect federal spending priorities from military spending toward domestic needs; works to develop citizen expertise through education and political involvement; provides educational programs and material about nuclear and conventional weapons; monitors defense legislation, budget policy legislation, and legislation affecting women. (Headquarters in Arlington, Mass.)

Military Aid and Peacekeeping

See also Regional Affairs (chap. 13)

AGENCIES

Commission on Security and Cooperation in Europe *(Helsinki Commission), 234 Ford Bldg. 20515; (202) 225-1901. Fax, (202) 226-4199. Sen. Alfonse M. D'Amato, R-N.Y., and Rep. Christopher H. Smith, R-N.J., co-chairs; Michael Hathaway, staff director. Internet, http://www.house.gov/csce.*

Independent agency created by Congress. Membership includes individuals from the executive and legislative branches. Studies and evaluates international peacekeeping and peace enforcement operations, particularly as they relate to the Helsinki Accords.

Defense Dept., *Defense Security Assistance Agency, Crystal Gateway North, #303, 1111 Jefferson Davis Hwy., Arlington, VA 22202-4306; (703) 604-6604. Fax, (703) 602-5403. Lt. Gen. Michael S. Davison (USA), director. Information, (703) 604-6633. Press, (703) 604-5131.*

Develops budgetary proposals and Defense Dept. policies on arms transfers. Selects and manages U.S. personnel in security assistance assignments overseas; manages weapons systems sales; maintains special defense acquisition funds and priority defense items information systems. Administers foreign military sales programs.

Defense Dept., *European and NATO Affairs, The Pentagon, #4D800 20301-2400; (703) 697-7207. Fax, (703) 697-5992. Brig. Gen. Thomas K. Longstreth, deputy assistant secretary.*

Advises the assistant secretary for international security affairs on matters dealing with Europe and NATO.

Defense Dept., *International Security Affairs, The Pentagon, #4E838 20301-2400; (703) 695-4351. Fax, (703) 697-7230. Franklin D. Kramer, assistant secretary.*

Advises the secretary of defense and recommends policies on regional security issues (except those involving countries of the former Soviet Union).

State Dept., *Arms Control and International Security Affairs, Main State Bldg., #7208 20520-7512; (202) 647-1049. Fax, (202) 736-4397. John D. Holum, acting under secretary.*

Works with the secretary of state to develop policy on foreign security assistance programs and technology transfer.

State Dept., *European Security and Political Affairs, Main State Bldg., #6227 20520; (202) 647-1626. Fax, (202) 647-1369. Barbaro Owens-Kirkpatrick, director.*

Coordinates and advises, with the Defense Dept. and other agencies, the U.S. mission to the North Atlantic Treaty Organization and the U.S. delegation to the Organization on Security and Cooperation in Europe regarding political, military, and arms control matters.

State Dept., *International Organization Affairs, Main State Bldg., #6323 20520-6319; (202) 647-9600. Fax, (202) 736-4116. Princeton N. Lyman, assistant secretary. Press, (202) 647-2492.*

Coordinates and develops policy guidelines for U.S. participation in the United Nations and in other international organizations and conferences.

State Dept., *Policy Planning Staff, Main State Bldg., #7311 20520; (202) 647-2372. Fax, (202) 647-4147. Gregory Craig, director.*

Advises the secretary and other State Dept. officials on foreign policy matters, including international peacekeeping and peace enforcement operations.

State Dept., *Political-Military Affairs, Main State Bldg., #7325 20520; (202) 647-9022. Fax, (202) 736-4779. Eric D. Newsom, acting assistant secretary.*

Responsible for security affairs policy and operations for the non-European area.

State Dept., *United Nations Political Affairs, Main State Bldg., #6334 20520-6319; (202) 647-2392. Fax, (202) 647-0039. William Imbrie, director.*

Deals with United Nations political and institutional matters and international security affairs.

U.S. Institute of Peace, *1550 M St. N.W., #700 20005-1708; (202) 457-1700. Fax, (202) 429-6063. Richard H. Solomon, president. TDD, (202) 457-1719. Internet, http://www.usip.org.*

Independent organization created and funded by Congress to promote the peaceful resolution of international conflict through negotiation and mediation. Provides federal agencies and individuals with training, research programs, and information. Awards grants to institutions and individuals and provides fellowships to scholars from the United States and abroad. Library open to the public by appointment.

CONGRESS

General Accounting Office, *National Security and International Affairs, 441 G St. N.W., #4035 20548; (202) 512-2800. Fax, (202) 512-7686. Henry L. Hinton, assistant comptroller general.*

Independent, nonpartisan agency in the legislative branch. Audits, analyzes, and evaluates international programs, including U.S. participation in international peacekeeping and peace enforcement operations; makes unclassified reports available to the public.

INTERNATIONAL ORGANIZATIONS

Inter-American Defense Board, *2600 16th St. N.W. 20441; (202) 939-6600. Fax, (202) 939-6620. Maj. Gen. John C. Thompson (USA), chair. Internet, http://www.jid.org.*

Membership: military officers from twenty countries of the Western Hemisphere. Plans and prepares for the collective self-defense of the American continents. Develops procedures for standardizing military organization and operations; operates the Inter-American Defense College.

Joint Mexican-United States Defense Commission, U.S. Section, *1111 Jefferson Davis Hwy., #509, Arlington, VA 22202; (703) 604-0483. Fax, (703) 604-0266. Maj. Gen. David S. Weisman (USA), chair.*

Comprises military delegates of the two countries. Studies problems concerning the common defense of the United States and Mexico.

Permanent Joint Board on Defense/United States and Canada, *1111 Jefferson Davis Hwy., #511, Arlington, VA 22202-4306; (703) 604-0487. Fax, (703) 604-0486. Dwight N. Mason, chair; Lt. Col. Michael J. Muolo (USAF), military secretary.*

Comprises representatives from the State Dept. and Defense Dept.; chair appointed by the president. Con-

ducts studies relating to sea, land, and air defense problems. (Canadian counterpart located in Ottawa.)

NONPROFIT

National Peace Foundation, *1835 K St. N.W., #610 20006; (202) 223-1770. Fax, (202) 223-1718. Stephen P. Strickland, president. Toll-free, (800) 237-3223. Internet, http://www.nationalpeace.org.*

Supports conflict resolution education and the U.S. Institute of Peace. Holds conferences and provides information on peace education and managing and resolving conflict.

Peace Links, *729 8th St. S.E., #300 20003; (202) 544-0805. Fax, (202) 544-0809. Mary Neznek, director. Internet, peacelinks@igc.apc.org.*

Seeks to educate Americans about alternatives to war as a means of resolving conflicts; promotes improved relations between people from the former Soviet Union and Americans through an exchange program and a letter-writing program; provides educational information, primarily to women's groups, concerning the arms race and national security issues.

⚔ ARMS CONTROL AND DISARMAMENT

AGENCIES

Defense Dept., *Counterproliferation Policy, The Pentagon, #4B856 20301-2600; (703) 697-6963. Fax, (703) 693-5193. James N. Miller Jr., deputy assistant secretary.*

Formulates national policies to prevent and counter the proliferation of nuclear, chemical, and biological weapons; missiles; and conventional technologies. Devises arms control agreements, export controls, technology transfer policies, and military planning policies.

Defense Dept., *Nuclear, Chemical, and Biological Defense Programs, The Pentagon, #3E808 20301-3050; (703) 697-5161. Fax, (703) 695-0476. George Singley, acting assistant secretary.*

Civilian office responsible for the safety, security, and survivability of nuclear and chemical weapons and for the modernization and upgrading of the nuclear and chemical weapons stockpile. Coordinates nuclear weapons policy with the Energy Dept.

Defense Dept., *On-Site Inspection Agency, 45045 Aviation Dr. Dulles International Airport, Chantilly, VA (mailing address: P.O. Box 17498, Washington, DC 20041-0498); (703) 810-4449. Fax, (703) 810-4343. Brig. Gen. John C.*

Reppert (USA), director. Information, (703) 810-4326. Toll-free, (888) 240-1232.

Implements all activities associated with the inspection process of the Intermediate-range Nuclear Forces (INF) Treaty and other U.S. international arms control agreements. Recruits, trains, and manages U.S. teams inspecting treaty-related facilities in Europe and the former Soviet Union; escorts inspectors from the former Soviet Union visiting U.S. facilities; plans inspection activities for proposed agreements, including Conventional Forces in Europe, Chemical Weapons, Strategic Arms Reductions Talks (START), and Nuclear Testing Talks. Provides support to U.N. Special Commission on Iraq.

Defense Dept., *Strategy and Threat Reduction,* The Pentagon, #4E817 20301-2600; (703) 697-7728. Fax, (703) 693-9146. Edward L. Warner III, assistant secretary.

Advises the secretary on reducing and countering nuclear, biological, chemical, and missile threats to the United States and its forces and allies; arms control negotiations, implementation, and verification policy; nuclear weapons policy, denuclearization, threat reduction, and nuclear safety, and security; and technology transfer.

National Security Council *(Executive Office of the President), Defense Policy/Arms Control,* The White House 20506; (202) 456-9191. Fax, (202) 456-9190. Robert G. Bell, director.

Advises the assistant to the president for national security affairs on matters concerning weapons policy.

State Dept., *Strategic Policy and Negotiations,* Main State Bldg., #7418 20520; (202) 647-7775. Fax, (202) 647-8998. Richard A. Davis, acting director.

Develops policies related to nuclear and conventional arms control, strategic defenses, nuclear testing, and assistance to the former Soviet Union aimed toward eliminating weapons of mass destruction.

U.S. Arms Control and Disarmament Agency, Main State Bldg., 2201 C St. N.W. (mailing address: 320 21st St. N.W., Washington, DC 20451); (202) 647-9610. Fax, (202) 647-4920. John D. Holum, director; Ralph Earle II, deputy director, (202) 647-8463. Press, (202) 647-8677. Locator, (202) 647-2034. Internet, http://www.acda.gov.

Advises the president and the secretary of state on arms control policy. Conducts and coordinates research for arms control policy formulation. Prepares for and manages U.S. participation in arms control negotiations; develops verification procedures for arms control agreements; disseminates information to the public.

CONGRESS

House International Relations Committee, *Subcommittee on International Operations and Human Rights,* B-358 RHOB 20515; (202) 225-5748. Fax, (202) 225-7485. Christopher H. Smith, R-N.J., chair; Grover Joseph Rees, staff director. Internet, http://www.house.gov/international_relations.

Jurisdiction over arms control, disarmament, and nuclear nonproliferation legislation. Oversight of the U.S. Arms Control and Disarmament Agency and State and Defense department activities involving arms transfers and arms sales.

House National Security Committee, 2120 RHOB 20515; (202) 225-4151. Fax, (202) 225-9077. Floyd D. Spence, R-S.C., chair; Andrew K. Ellis, staff director. Internet, http://www.house.gov/nsc.

Oversight of international arms control and disarmament matters (jurisdiction shared with House International Relations Committee).

Senate Armed Services Committee, SR-228 20510; (202) 224-3871. Strom Thurmond, R-S.C., chair; Les Brownlee, staff director. Internet, http://www.senate.gov/committee/armed_services.html.

Oversight of arms control and disarmament matters. (Jurisdiction shared with Senate Foreign Relations Committee.)

Senate Foreign Relations Committee, SD-450 20510; (202) 224-4651. Fax, (202) 224-0836. Jesse Helms, R-N.C., chair; James W. "Bud" Nance, staff director. Internet, http://www.senate.gov/committee/foreign.html.

Jurisdiction over arms control, disarmament, and nuclear nonproliferation legislation. (Jurisdiction shared with Senate Armed Services Committee.)

NONPROFIT

Arms Control Assn., 1726 M St. N.W., #201 20036; (202) 463-8270. Fax, (202) 463-8273. Spurgeon M. Keeny Jr., executive director. Internet, aca@armscontrol.org or http://www.armscontrol.org.

Nonpartisan organization interested in arms control. Seeks to broaden public interest in arms control, disarmament, and national security policy.

Center for Defense Information, 1779 Massachusetts Ave. N.W., #615 20036; (202) 332-0600. Fax, (202) 462-4559. Vacant, director. Toll-free, (800) 234-3334. Internet, info@cdi.org or http://www.cdi.org.

Educational organization that advocates a strong defense while opposing excessive expenditure for weapons and policies that increase the risk of war. Interests include the defense budget, weapons systems, and troop levels. Library open to the public.

Chemical and Biological Arms Control Institute, *2111 Eisenhower Ave., #302, Alexandria, VA 22314; (703) 739-1538. Fax, (703) 739-1525. Michael Moodie, president. Internet, cbaci@pressroom.com or http://www.pressroom.com/~cbaci.*

Promotes arms control, nonproliferation, and the elimination of chemical, biological, and other weapons of mass destruction through research, analysis, technical support, and education.

Council for a Livable World, *110 Maryland Ave. N.E., #409 20002; (202) 543-4100. Fax, (202) 543-6297. John Isaacs, president. Arms control hotline, (202) 543-0006. Internet, clw@clw.org or http://www.clw.org/pub/clw/welcome.html.*

Citizens' interest group that supports arms control treaties, reduced military spending, peacekeeping, and tight restrictions on international arms sales.

Federation of American Scientists, *307 Massachusetts Ave. N.E. 20002; (202) 546-3300. Fax, (202) 675-1010. Jeremy J. Stone, president. Internet, fas@fas.org or http://www.fas.org.*

Conducts studies and monitors legislation on U.S. nuclear arms policy; provides the public with information on arms control and related issues. Interests include the Strategic Defense Initiative (SDI) and arms control compliance.

Friends Committee on National Legislation, *245 2nd St. N.E. 20002-5795; (202) 547-6000. Fax, (202) 547-6019. Joe Volk, executive secretary. Recorded information, (202) 547-4343. Internet, fcnl@igc.apc.org or http://www.fas.org/pub/gen/fcnl.*

Supports world disarmament; international cooperation; domestic, economic, peace, and social justice issues; and improvement in relations between the United States and the former Soviet Union. Opposes conscription. Affiliated with the Religious Society of Friends (Quakers).

Friends of the Earth, *1025 Vermont Ave. N.W., #300 20005-6303; (202) 783-7400. Fax, (202) 783-0444. Brent Blackwelder, president. Internet, foe@foe.org or http://www.foe.org.*

Citizens' interest group that advocates a freeze on the production and testing of nuclear weapons and the transfer of federal funds from production to cleanup efforts. Advises other organizations on political strategy and organizational techniques. Monitors military compliance with environmental law. Library open to the public by appointment.

High Frontier, *2800 Shirlington Rd., #405, Arlington, VA 22206-3601; (703) 671-4111. Fax, (703) 931-6432. Henry Cooper, director. Internet, hifront@erols.com or http://www.erols.com/hifront.*

Educational organization that provides information on missile defense programs and proliferation. Advocates development of a single-stage-to-orbit space vehicle and research of space solar power. Operates speakers bureau. Monitors defense legislation.

Lawyers Alliance for World Security, *1901 Pennsylvania Ave. N.W., #802 20006; (202) 745-2450. Fax, (202) 667-0444. Thomas Graham Jr., president. Internet, laws@lawscns.org or http://www.lawscns.org.*

Public education organization that seeks to broaden interest in and understanding of arms control and disarmament with regard to nuclear, conventional, chemical, and biological weapons. Sponsors educational programs for government officials, including legislators from the Commonwealth of Independent States. (Affiliated with the Committee for National Security.)

Peace Action, *1819 H St. N.W., #420 20006-3603; (202) 862-9740. Fax, (202) 862-9762. Gordon Clark, executive director. Internet, pamembers@igc.apc.org or http://www.webcom.com/peaceact.*

Grassroots organization that supports a negotiated comprehensive test ban treaty. Seeks a reduction in the military budget and a transfer of those funds to nonmilitary programs. Works for an end to international arms trade.

Physicians for Social Responsibility, *1101 14th St. N.W., #700 20005; (202) 898-0150. Fax, (202) 898-0172. Robert Musil, executive director. Internet, psrnatl@psr.org or http://www.psr.org.*

Membership: doctors, dentists, and other individuals. Works toward the elimination of nuclear and other weapons of mass destruction, the achievement of a sustainable environment, and the reduction of violence and its causes. Conducts public education programs, monitors policy decisions on arms control, and serves as a liaison with other concerned groups.

Union of Concerned Scientists, *1616 P St. N.W., #310 20036; (202) 332-0900. Fax, (202) 332-0905. Alden Meyer, director, Government Relations; Todd Perry, arms control program director. Internet, ucs@ucsusa.org or http://www.ucsusa.org.*

Works to advance the international security policies and agreements that restrict the spread of weapons of mass destruction and reduce the risk of war. Promotes international nonproliferation through reductions in fissile materials, arms control measures including a comprehensive nuclear testing ban, restrictions on ballistic missile defenses and dismantlement of nuclear warheads. Encourages the use of collective security forces such as the United Nations to alleviate conflicts. (Headquarters in Cambridge, Mass.)

Nuclear Weapons and Power

See also Nuclear Energy (chap. 8)

AGENCIES

Defense Special Weapons Agency *(Defense Dept.),* 6801 Telegraph Rd., Alexandria, VA 22310-3398; (703) 325-7004. Fax, (703) 325-2960. Maj. Gen. Gary L. Curtin (USAF), director; George W. Ullrich, deputy director, (703) 325-7300. Information, (703) 325-7095. Internet, http://www.dfwa.mil.

Military office responsible for researching, developing, and testing advanced weapons systems; coordinates Defense Dept. nuclear weapons activities with civilian nuclear research agencies; manages nuclear weapons stockpile; coordinates inspections of nuclear weapons storage sites; publishes technical documents on nuclear weaponry.

Defense Special Weapons Agency *(Defense Dept.),* *Nuclear Test Program Personnel Review Program,* 6801 Telegraph Rd., Alexandria, VA 22310-3398; (703) 325-2407. Fax, (703) 325-2951. D. Michael Schaeffer, program manager. Information, (703) 325-7095. Veterans hotline, (800) 462-3683.

Manages database of participants in U.S. atmospheric nuclear tests and in the post-war occupation of Hiroshima and Nagasaki, Japan; provides participation information to veterans, their families, and government organizations representing their interests.

Energy Dept., *Arms Control and Nonproliferation,* 1000 Independence Ave. S.W. (mailing address: NN40, Washington, DC 20585-0001); (202) 586-2102. Fax, (202) 586-4452. Leonard Spector, director.

Develops and implements policies concerning nuclear materials and equipment; participates in international negotiations involving nuclear policy; supports activities of the International Atomic Energy Agency; develops policies concerning nuclear reprocessing requests.

Energy Dept., *Defense Programs,* 1000 Independence Ave. S.W., #4A019 20585; (202) 586-2177. Fax, (202) 586-1567. Victor H. Reis, assistant secretary.

Responsible for nuclear weapons research, development, engineering, testing, and production; performs laser fusion research and development; provides the director of nonproliferation and national security with support in the area of nonproliferation controls.

Energy Dept., *Naval Reactors,* 2521 Jefferson Davis Hwy., Arlington, VA 22242-5106; (703) 603-7321. Fax, (703) 603-1906. Adm. F. L. Bowman, director.

Designs, develops, and maintains naval nuclear propulsion plants.

Navy Dept. *(Defense Dept.), Naval Sea Systems Command,* National Center 2, 2521 Jefferson Davis Hwy., Arlington, VA 22242-5160; (703) 602-3887. Fax, (703) 603-1906. Adm. F. L. Bowman, director, Naval Nuclear Propulsion.

Responsible for naval nuclear propulsion.

State Dept., *Nuclear Energy Affairs,* Main State Bldg., #7828 20520; (202) 647-3310. Fax, (202) 647-0775. Richard J. K. Stratford, director.

Coordinates U.S. government activities that support safeguards against proliferation of nuclear weapons.

CONGRESS

House Appropriations Committee, *Subcommittee on Energy and Water Development,* 2362 RHOB 20515; (202) 225-3421. Joseph M. McDade, R-Pa., chair; James Ogsbury, staff director. Internet, http://www.house.gov/appropriations.

Jurisdiction over legislation to appropriate funds for atomic energy defense activities within the Energy Dept., Defense Nuclear Facilities Safety Board, Nuclear Regulatory Commission, Nuclear Waste Technical Review Board, Nuclear Safety Oversight Commission, and Office of Nuclear Waste Negotiator.

House National Security Committee, *Subcommittee on Military Procurement,* 2340 RHOB 20515; (202) 225-4440. Fax, (202) 226-0105. Duncan Hunter, R-Calif., chair; Steve Thompson, professional staff member. Internet, http://www.house.gov/nsc.

Jurisdiction over military applications of nuclear energy.

Senate Appropriations Committee, *Subcommittee on Energy and Water Development,* SD-127 20510; (202) 224-7260. Pete V. Domenici, R-N.M., chair; Alex Flint, majority clerk. Internet, http://www.senate.gov/~appropriations/energy.

Jurisdiction over legislation to appropriate funds for the Nuclear Regulatory Commission, Nuclear Safety Oversight Commission, Nuclear Waste Technical Review Board, Office of Nuclear Waste Negotiator, Defense Nuclear Facilities Safety Board, and atomic energy defense activities within the Energy Dept.

Senate Armed Services Committee, SR-228 20510; (202) 224-3871. Strom Thurmond, R-S.C., chair; Les

Brownlee, staff director. Internet, http://www.senate.gov/committee/armed_services.html.

Jurisdiction over national security aspects of nuclear energy.

NONPROFIT

Institute for Science and International Security,
236 Massachusetts Ave. N.E., #500 20002; (202) 547-3633. Fax, (202) 547-3634. David Albright, director. Internet, 73744.3675@compuserve.com.

Conducts research and analysis on nuclear weapons production and nonproliferation issues.

Nuclear Control Institute, 1000 Connecticut Ave. N.W., #804 20036; (202) 822-8444. Fax, (202) 452-0892. Paul Leventhal, president. Internet, nci@access.digex.net or http://www.nci.org/nci.

Promotes nuclear nonproliferation; works to prevent the use of nuclear explosive materials (plutonium and highly enriched uranium) as reactor fuels; advocates terminating the export of nuclear technologies and facilities that could be used in the manufacture of nuclear weaponry; works to reduce the nuclear arsenals of nuclear weapons states; studies and recommends measures to prevent nuclear terrorism.

Women Strike for Peace, 110 Maryland Ave. N.E., #102 20002; (202) 543-2660. Fax, (202) 544-9613. Edith Villastrigo, national legislative coordinator.

Promotes opposition to nuclear weapons, nuclear power plants, and U.S. intervention in developing countries. Supports nuclear disarmament with international controls. Provides the public with information on foreign policy, and prevention of nuclear war.

🗝 DEFENSE TRADE AND TECHNOLOGY

See also Procurement, Acquisition, and Logistics (this chapter)

AGENCIES

Bureau of Export Administration (Commerce Dept.),
14th St. and Constitution Ave. N.W., #3898 20230; (202) 482-1427. Fax, (202) 482-2387. William Alan Reinsch, under secretary. Information, (202) 482-2721. Export licensing information, (202) 482-4811. Internet, http://www.bxa.doc.gov.

Administers Export Administration Act; maintains control lists and performs export licensing for the purposes of national security, foreign policy, and prevention of short supply.

Bureau of Export Administration (Commerce Dept.),
Export Enforcement, 14th St. and Constitution Ave. N.W., #3721 20230; (202) 482-1561. Fax, (202) 482-4173. F. Amanda Debusk, assistant secretary. Internet, http://www.bxa.doc.gov.

Enforces regulation of exports of U.S. goods and technology for purposes of national security, foreign policy, and prevention of short supply. Enforces foreign boycotts and compliance with antiboycott provisions of the Export Administration Act.

Defense Dept., Defense Technology Security Administration, 400 Army-Navy Dr., #300, Arlington, VA 22202-2884; (703) 604-5215. Fax, (703) 602-5838. Dave Tarbell, director.

Analyzes export control factors affecting national security; develops and implements Defense Dept. policies for trade security and for the transfer and control of advanced military technology.

Energy Dept., Arms Control and Nonproliferation,
1000 Independence Ave. S.W. 20585-0001; (202) 586-2102. Fax, (202) 586-1348. Patricia Dedik, director, Nuclear Transfer and Supplier Policy.

Develops policies concerning nuclear material and equipment exports, nuclear material transfers and retransfers, and regional nonproliferation.

Export Administration Review Board (Commerce Dept.), 14th St. and Constitution Ave. N.W., #2639 20230; (202) 482-5863. Fax, (202) 501-2815. Carol A. Kalinoski, acting executive secretary.

Committee of Cabinet-level secretaries and heads of other government offices. Considers export licensing policies and actions, especially those concerning national security and other major policy matters; advises the secretary of commerce on export licensing; reviews contentious export licensing applications.

National Security Council (Executive Office of the President), The White House 20506; (202) 456-9301. Fax, (202) 456-9290. Malcolm Lee, director, International Economic Affairs, (202) 456-9291; Robert G. Bell, director, Defense Policy/Arms Control, (202) 456-9191.

Advises the president, in conjunction with the National Economic Council, on national security issues, including export controls on dual-use commodities and technologies.

Nuclear Regulatory Commission, Nonproliferation, Exports, and Multilateral Relations, 11555 Rockville Pike, Rockville, MD 20852; (301) 415-2344. Fax, (301) 415-2395. Ronald D. Hauber, director.

Coordinates application review process for exports and imports of nuclear materials, facilities, and components; makes recommendations on licensing upon completion of review; conducts related policy reviews.

President's Export Council *(Commerce Dept.), Subcommittee on Export Administration,* 14th St. and Constitution Ave. N.W., #3886C 20230; (202) 482-2583. Fax, (202) 501-8024. Lee Ann Carpenter, committee control officer.

Advises the president and secretary of commerce on matters related to the Export Administration Act of 1979, which deals with controlling trade for reasons of national security, foreign policy, and short supply. Seeks ways to minimize the negative effect of export controls while protecting U.S. national security and foreign policy interests.

State Dept., *Defense Trade Controls,* 2201 C St. N.W. (mailing address: State Dept., Rm. 200, PM/DTC, SA-6, Washington, DC 20520-0602); (703) 875-6644. Fax, (703) 875-6647. William J. Lowell, director. Internet, http://www. pmdtc.org.

Administers government control over the commercial export of defense articles, services, and related technical data and other authorizations related to the permanent export and temporary import of such items.

State Dept., *Economic Sanctions Policy,* Main State Bldg., #3329 20520; (202) 647-5673. Fax, (202) 647-4064. David R. Moran, director.

Coordinates U.S. participation in multilateral strategic trade control and revisions related to the export of strategically critical high-technology goods. Cooperates with the Commerce, Defense, and Treasury departments regarding export controls and economic sanctions.

Treasury Dept., *Foreign Assets Control,* 1500 Pennsylvania Ave. N.W., Annex Bldg., 2nd Floor 20220; (202) 622-2510. Fax, (202) 622-1657. R. Richard Newcomb, director. Internet, http://www.ustreas.gov/treasury/services/fac.

Authorized under the revised Trading with the Enemy Act, the International Emergency Economic Powers Act, and the United Nations Participation Act to control financial and commercial dealings with certain countries and their foreign nationals in times of war or emergencies. Regulations involving foreign assets control and commercial transactions currently apply in varying degrees to Cuba, Iran, Iraq, Libya, North Korea, and Angola.

U.S. Arms Control and Disarmament Agency, *Nonproliferation and Regional Arms Control,* Main State Bldg., #4936 20451; (202) 647-3466. Fax, (202) 647-3259. Vacant, assistant director. Information, (202) 647-8677. Publications, (202) 647-4800.

Advises the president and the secretary of state on exports of conventional, nuclear, chemical, and biological weapons and missiles that deliver them.

CONGRESS

House International Relations Committee, *Subcommittee on International Economic Policy and Trade,* 702 O'Neill Bldg. 20515; (202) 225-3345. Fax, (202) 225-0432. Ileana Ros-Lehtinen, R-Fla., chair; Mauricio Tamargo, staff director. Internet, http://www. house.gov/international_relations.

Jurisdiction over foreign trade legislation and legislation related to export control, including the Export Administration Act and the revised Trading with the Enemy Act, which authorize trade restrictions, and the International Emergency Economic Powers Act. Oversight of State and Defense department operations regarding arms transfers, export licenses, and sales.

House National Security Committee, *Subcommittee on Military Procurement,* 2340 RHOB 20515; (202) 225-4440. Fax, (202) 226-0105. Duncan Hunter, R-Calif., chair; Steve Thompson, professional staff member. Internet, http://www.house.gov/nsc.

Jurisdiction over legislation on foreign military sales and the proliferation of weapons technology.

House Science Committee, *Subcommittee on Technology,* 2319 RHOB 20515; (202) 225-8844. Fax, (202) 225-4438. Constance A. Morella, R-Md., chair; Richard Russell, staff director. Internet, http://www.house.gov/science.

Jurisdiction over legislation on transfers of technology between the United States and foreign countries.

Senate Armed Services Committee, *Subcommittee on Acquisition and Technology,* SR-228 20510; (202) 224-3871. Rick Santorum, R-Pa., chair; Jonathan L. Etherton, professional staff member. Internet, http://www. senate.gov/committee/armed_services.html.

Jurisdiction over legislation on foreign military sales and the proliferation of weapons technology.

Senate Banking, Housing, and Urban Affairs Committee, *Subcommittee on International Finance,* SD-534 20510; (202) 224-7391. Fax, (202) 224-5137. Rod Grams, R-Minn., chair; Dave Berson, staff director. Internet, http://www.senate.gov/~banking.

Jurisdiction over foreign trade legislation and legislation related to export control, including the Export Administration Act and the revised Trading with the Enemy Act, which authorizes trade restrictions.

Senate Foreign Relations Committee, SD-450 20510; (202) 224-4651. Fax, (202) 224-0836. Jesse Helms, R-N.C., chair; James W. "Bud" Nance, staff director. Internet, http://www.senate.gov/committee/foreign.html.

Oversight of State and Defense department operations regarding arms transfers, export licenses, and sales.

Senate Governmental Affairs Committee, *Permanent Subcommittee on Investigations, SH-432 20510; (202) 224-3721. Fax, (202) 224-7042. Susan Collins, R-Maine, chair; Tim Shea, chief of staff. Internet, http://www.senate.gov/~gov_affairs/psi.htm.*

Investigates transfers of technology between the United States and foreign countries.

NONPROFIT

American League for Exports and Security Assistance, *122 C St. N.W., #310 20001; (202) 783-0051. Fax, (202) 737-4727. Toby Roth Jr., executive vice president. Internet, alesa@erols.com.*

Membership: defense-related and high-technology companies. Supports government policies that promote the export of defense-related goods consistent with U.S. security interests.

Business Executives for National Security, *1717 Pennsylvania Ave. N.W., #350 20006; (202) 296-2125. Fax, (202) 296-2490. Stanley Weiss, chair. Internet, http://www.bens.org.*

Monitors legislation on national security issues from a business perspective; holds conferences, congressional forums, and other meetings on national security issues; works with other organizations on defense policy issues.

Research and Development

AGENCIES

Air Force Dept. *(Defense Dept.), Acquisition, 1060 Air Force Pentagon 20330-1060; (703) 697-6361. Fax, (703) 693-6400. Arthur L. Money, assistant secretary.*

Civilian office that directs and reviews Air Force research, development, and acquisition of weapons systems.

Air Force Dept. *(Defense Dept.), Scientific Research, 110 Duncan Ave., #B115, Bolling Air Force Base 20332-8050; (202) 767-5017. Fax, (202) 767-6213. Joseph F. Janni, director. Internet, http://www.afosr.af.mil.*

Sponsors and sustains basic research; assists in the transfer of research results to the fleet; supports Air Force goals of control and maximum utilization of air and space.

Army Corps of Engineers *(Defense Dept.), Research and Development, 20 Massachusetts Ave. N.W., #6207*

20314; (202) 761-1839. Fax, (202) 761-0907. Lewis E. Link, director. Internet, http://www.usace.army.mil.

Coordinates the Corps of Engineers' research efforts; acts as advocate for its research laboratories in the Pentagon and with Congress; develops management procedures for laboratories.

Army Dept. *(Defense Dept.), Research and Technology, 2511 Jefferson Davis Hwy., Arlington, VA 22122; (703) 601-1500. Fax, (703) 607-5989. A. Fenner Milton, deputy assistant secretary.*

Sponsors and supports basic research at Army laboratories, universities, and other public and private organizations; assists in the transfer of research and technology to the field.

Army Dept. *(Defense Dept.), Research, Development, and Acquisition, The Pentagon 20310-0103; (703) 695-6153. Fax, (703) 697-4003. Kenneth Oscar, acting assistant secretary.*

Civilian office that directs and reviews Army research and development of weapons systems and missiles.

Defense Advanced Research Projects Agency *(Defense Dept.), 3701 N. Fairfax Dr., Arlington, VA 22203-1714; (703) 696-2400. Fax, (703) 696-2207. Larry Lynn, director; H. Lee Buchanan III, deputy director, (703) 696-2402. Information, (703) 696-2404. Internet, http://www.darpa.mil.*

Helps maintain U.S. technological superiority and guard against unforeseen technological advances by potential adversaries; determines which proposals for future projects related to national security deserve further research.

Defense Dept., *Ballistic Missile Defense Organization, The Pentagon 20301-7100; (703) 614-7059. Fax, (703) 693-1693. Lt. Gen. Lester L. Lyles (USAF), director; Rear Adm. Richard West (USN), deputy director. Information, (703) 695-8743. Internet, http://www.acq.osd.mil/bmdo/bmdolink/html.*

Manages and directs the ballistic missile defense acquisition and research and development programs. Seeks to deploy improved theater missile defense systems and to develop options for effective national missile defenses while increasing the contribution of defensive systems to U.S. and allied security.

Defense Dept., *Defense Research and Engineering, The Pentagon, #3E1045 20301-3080; (703) 695-0598. Fax, (703) 614-6829. Vacant, deputy director.*

Civilian office responsible for policy, guidance, and oversight of the Defense Dept.'s Science and Technology Program. Serves as focal point for in-house laboratories, university research, and other science and technology matters.

Defense Dept., *Research and Engineering,* *The Pentagon, #3E1014 20301-3030; (703) 697-5776. Fax, (703) 693-7167. Vacant, director.*

Formulates, plans, and reviews the Defense Dept. Science and Technology program. This includes all research, exploratory development, and advanced technology development programs; oversees federally funded research and development centers.

Defense Technical Information Center *(Defense Dept.), 8725 John Jay Kingman Rd., #0944, Fort Belvoir, VA 22060-6218; (703) 767-9100. Fax, (703) 767-9183. Kurt N. Molholm, administrator. Registration, (703) 767-8201. Internet, http://www.dtic.mil.*

Acts as a central repository for the Defense Dept.'s collection of current and completed research and development efforts in all fields of science and technology. Disseminates research and development information to contractors, grantees, and registered organizations working on government research and development projects, particularly for the Defense Dept. Users must register with the center.

Marine Corps *(Defense Dept.), Systems Command, 2033 Barnett Ave., #315, Quantico, VA 22134-5010; (703) 784-2411. Fax, (703) 784-3792. Maj. Gen. Michael J. Williams, commander.*

Military office that directs Marine Corps research, development, and acquisition.

Naval Research Laboratory *(Defense Dept.), Research, 4555 Overlook Ave. S.W. 20375-5320; (202) 767-3301. Fax, (202) 404-2676. Timothy Coffey, director. Information, (202) 767-2541. Internet, http://www.nrl.navy.mil.*

Conducts scientific research and develops advanced technology for the Navy. Areas of research include radar systems, radiation technology, tactical electronic warfare, and weapons guidance systems.

Navy Dept. *(Defense Dept.), Naval Research, 800 N. Quincy St., #907, Arlington, VA 22217-5660; (703) 696-4767. Fax, (703) 696-4065. Rear Adm. Paul G. Gaffney II, chief. Internet, http://www.onr.navy.mil.*

Oversees the offices of Naval Research, Naval Technology, and Advanced Technology; works to ensure transition of research and technology to the fleet; sponsors and supports basic research at Navy laboratories, universities, and other public and private organizations.

Navy Dept. *(Defense Dept.), Research, Development, and Acquisition,* *The Pentagon 20350-1000; (703) 695-*

6315. Fax, (703) 697-0172. John W. Douglass, assistant secretary.

Civilian office that directs and reviews Navy and Marine Corps research and development of weapons systems.

Navy Dept. *(Defense Dept.), Test Evaluation and Technology Requirements,* *The Pentagon 20350-2000; (703) 601-1870. Fax, (703) 601-2011. Rear Adm. Richard A. Ridell, director.*

Military office that directs Navy testing, evaluation, and science and technology.

Office of Science and Technology Policy *(Executive Office of the President), National Security and International Affairs, Old Executive Office Bldg., #494 20502; (202) 456-2894. Fax, (202) 456-6028. Kerri-Ann Jones, associate director.*

Supports and advises the president on national security policy, international science matters, and other science policy areas. Coordinates international science and technology issues at the interagency level.

President's National Security Telecommunications Advisory Committee, *c/o National Communications System, 701 S. Courthouse Rd., Arlington, VA 22204-2198; (703) 607-6221. Fax, (703) 607-4826. Janet Jefferson, manager. Internet, http://www.ncs.gov.*

Advises the president on specific measures to improve national security telecommunications.

State Dept., *Intelligence and Research,* *Main State Bldg., #6531 20520-6531; (202) 647-9177. Fax, (202) 736-4688. Phyllis E. Oakley, assistant secretary.*

Coordinates foreign-policy-related research, analysis, and intelligence programs for the State Dept. and other federal agencies.

U.S. Coast Guard *(Transportation Dept.), Systems, 2100 2nd St. S.W., #6120 20593-0001; (202) 267-1844. Fax, (202) 267-4245. Rear Adm. John T. Tozzi, assistant commandant.*

Develops and maintains engineering standards for the building of ships and other Coast Guard craft.

CONGRESS

House National Security Committee, *Subcommittee on Military Research and Development, 2340 RHOB 20515; (202) 225-0883. Fax, (202) 226-0105. Steve Ansley, R-Pa., chair; Doug Roach, professional staff member. Internet, http://www.house.gov/nsc.*

Jurisdiction over legislation on military research and development, reinvestment, and conversion.

Senate Armed Services Committee, *SR-228 20510; (202) 224-3871. Strom Thurmond, R-S.C., chair; Les Brownlee, staff director. Internet, http://www.senate.gov/ committee/armed_services.html.*

Jurisdiction over military research and development legislation.

NONPROFIT

American Society of Naval Engineers, *1452 Duke St., Alexandria, VA 22314-3458; (703) 836-6727. Fax, (703) 836-7491. Capt. Dennis K. Kruse (USN, ret.), executive director. Internet, asnehq.asne@mcimail.com or http:// www.jhuapl.edu/ASNE.*

Membership: civilian, active duty, and retired naval engineers. Provides forum for an exchange of information between industry and government involving all phases of naval engineering.

ANSER (Analytic Services), *1215 Jefferson Davis Hwy., #800, Arlington, VA 22202; (703) 416-2000. Fax, (703) 416-4451. John M. Fabian, president. Internet, http://www.anser.org.*

Systems analysis organization funded by government contracts. Conducts weapon systems analysis.

Armed Forces Communications and Electronics Assn., *4400 Fair Lakes Court, Fairfax, VA 22033-3899; (703) 631-6100. Fax, (703) 631-4693. C. Norman Wood, president. Internet, http://www.afcea.com.*

Membership: industrial organizations, scientists, and military and government personnel in the fields of communications, electronics, computers, and electrical engineering. Consults with the Defense Dept. and other federal agencies on design and maintenance of command, control, communications, computer, and intelligence systems; holds shows displaying latest communications products.

Institute for Defense Analyses, *1801 N. Beauregard St., Alexandria, VA 22311; (703) 845-2300. Fax, (703) 845-2569. Gen. Larry D. Welch (USAF, ret.), president.*

Federally funded research and development center that focuses on national security and defense. Conducts research, systems evaluation, and policy analysis for Defense Dept. and other agencies.

Johns Hopkins University Applied Physics Laboratory, *Johns Hopkins Rd., Laurel, MD 20723-6099; (240) 228-5000. Fax, (240) 228-1093. G. L. Smith, director. Information, (240) 228-5021. Internet, http://www.jhuapl.edu.*

Research and development organization that conducts research for the Defense Dept. (primarily the

Navy) and other state and federal agencies. Interests include weapons systems and satellites.

Logistics Management Institute, *2000 Corporate Ridge Rd., McLean, VA 22102-7805; (703) 917-7437. Fax, (703) 917-7591. William G. T. Tuttle Jr., president. Library, (703) 917-7249. Internet, http://www.lmi.org.*

Conducts research on military and nonmilitary logistics, including transportation, supply and maintenance, force management, weapons support, acquisition, health systems, international programs, energy and environment, mathematical modeling, installations, operations, and information systems. Library open to the public by appointment.

Military Operations Research Society, *101 S. Whiting St., #202, Alexandria, VA 22304; (703) 751-7290. Fax, (703) 751-8171. Robert I. Wiles, executive vice president. Internet, http://www.mors.org.*

Membership: professional analysts of military operations. Fosters information exchange; promotes professional development and high ethical standards; educates members on emerging issues, analytical techniques, and applications of research.

Society of American Military Engineers, *607 Prince St., Alexandria, VA 22314; (703) 549-3800. Fax, (703) 684-0231. A. B. Beran, executive director. Internet, http:// www.same.org.*

Membership: military and civilian engineers and architects. Conducts research on subjects related to military engineering.

SRI International, *1611 N. Kent St., #700, Arlington, VA 22209; (703) 524-2053. Fax, (703) 247-8569. Jack F. Scherrer, vice president, Washington Office. Internet, http:// www.sri.com.*

Research organization supported by government and private contracts. Conducts research on military technology, including lasers and computers. Other interests include strategic planning and armed forces interdisciplinary research. (Headquarters in Menlo Park, Calif.)

EMERGENCY PREPAREDNESS

AGENCIES

Army Corps of Engineers *(Defense Dept.), Readiness, 20 Massachusetts Ave. N.W., #6215 20314; (202) 761-0251. Fax, (202) 761-4150. Edward J. Hecker, chief.*

Assists in repairing and restoring damaged flood control structures and federally authorized hurricane and shore protection projects damaged by wind or water;

provides emergency assistance during floods or coastal storms. Supplies emergency power, removes debris, provides temporary housing, rebuilds public infrastructure, and performs other services at request of the Federal Emergency Management Agency.

Civil Air Patrol, *National Capital Wing, Bolling Air Force Base, 222 Luke Ave., #2 20332-5114; (202) 767-5689. Fax, (202) 767-5695. Col. Roland Butler, wing commander.*

Official auxiliary of the U.S. Air Force. Conducts search-and-rescue missions for the Air Force; participates in emergency airlift and disaster relief missions. (Headquarters at Maxwell Air Force Base, Ala.)

Energy Dept., *Emergency Management, 1000 Independence Ave. S.W., #GH060 20585; (202) 586-9892. Fax, (202) 586-3904. John J. Nettles Jr., director. Internet, http://www2.nn.doe.gov/nn/emerga/emerg.htm.*

Assists federal agencies, state and local governments, and industry in preparing for and responding to energy emergencies.

Federal Emergency Management Agency, *500 C St. S.W. 20472; (202) 646-3923. Fax, (202) 646-3930. James Lee Witt, director. Press, (202) 646-4600. Locator, (202) 646-2500; disaster assistance, (800) 462-9029; radio network, (800) 323-5248; fax-on-demand, (202) 646-FEMA. Internet, http://www.fema.gov.*

Assists state and local governments in preparing for and responding to natural, man-made, and national security-related emergencies. Develops plans and policies for hazard mitigation, preparedness planning, emergency response, and recovery. Coordinates emergency preparedness and planning for all federal agencies and departments.

Federal Emergency Management Agency, *Emergency Management Institute, 16825 S. Seton Ave., Emmitsburg, MD 21727; (301) 447-1286. Fax, (301) 447-1497. John W. McKay, superintendent. Internet, http://www.fema.gov/home/emi/index.htm.*

Provides federal, state, and local government personnel and private organizations engaged in emergency management with technical, professional, and vocational training. Educational programs include hazard mitigation, emergency preparedness, and disaster response.

Federal Emergency Management Agency, *National Emergency Coordination Center, 500 C St. S.W. (mailing address: P.O. Box 129, Berryville, VA 22611); (202) 898-6100. Fax, (202) 898-6175. Harold Aldrich, chief, Operations Center. Information, (202) 646-4600. Operations, (202) 646-2400.*

Serves as a central point of contact for federal agencies and members of Congress for coordinating national response to disasters and emergencies.

Federal Emergency Management Agency, *Response and Recovery, 500 C St. S.W. 20472; (202) 646-3692. Fax, (202) 646-4060. Lacy E. Suiter, executive director. Press, (202) 646-4600. Internet, http://www.fema.gov.*

Administers the president's disaster relief program, including disaster research, preparedness, temporary housing, funding for repair of damaged public facilities, debris removal, and hazard mitigation; provides financial and technical assistance in the event of natural or technological disasters including earthquakes; assists in developing civil emergency planning. Coordinates other federal agency disaster assistance activities.

Federal Insurance Administration *(Federal Emergency Management Agency), 500 C St. S.W., #430 20472; (202) 646-2781. Fax, (202) 646-3445. Joann Howard, administrator. Internet, http://www.fema.gov.*

Administers federal crime and flood insurance programs, including the National Flood Insurance Program. Makes available to eligible homeowners low-cost flood and crime insurance. Flood insurance information: (202) 731-5300; (800) 427-4661, toll-free, nationwide non-claims business; (800) 638-6831, Alaska and Hawaii; (800) 492-6605, Maryland. Crime insurance information: (202) 251-1660; (800) 638-8780, nationwide customer service.

President's Commission on Critical Infrastructure Protection, *Transition Office, P.O. Box 46258 20050-6258; (703) 696-9395. Fax, (703) 696-9411. David V. Keyes, acting director. Internet, comments@pccip.gov or http://www.pccip.gov.*

Advises the president on a national stategy for protecting critical infrastructures from physical and electronic threats. Focus includes information and communications systems, banking and finance, water supplies, transportation, and government services.

Public Health and Science *(Health and Human Services Dept.), Emergency Preparedness, 12300 Twinbrook Pkwy., #360, Rockville, MD 20852; (301) 443-1167. Fax, (301) 443-5146. Robert Knouss, director.*

Works with the Federal Emergency Management Agency and other federal agencies and departments to develop plans and maintain operational readiness for responding to requests for assistance during presidentially declared disasters; develops and coordinates medical equipment and training plans for catastrophic disasters; maintains logistical plans and communication networks with federal, state, and local emergency preparedness organizations.

Research and Special Programs Administration *(Transportation Dept.), Emergency Transportation, 400 7th St. S.W., #8404 20590; (202) 366-5270. Fax, (202) 366-3769. John Porco, acting director. Internet, http://www. rspa.dot.gov/oet.*

Develops, coordinates, and reviews transportation emergency preparedness programs for use in emergencies affecting national defense and in emergencies caused by natural disasters and crisis situations.

Small Business Administration, *Disaster Assistance, 409 3rd St. S.W., #6050 20416; (202) 205-6734. Fax, (202) 205-7728. Bernard Kulik, associate administrator. Internet, http://www.sba.gov.*

Provides victims of physical disasters with disaster and economic injury loans for homes, businesses, and personal property. Lends to individual homeowners, business concerns of all sizes, and nonprofit institutions funds to repair or replace damaged structures and furnishings, business machinery, equipment, and inventory.

U.S. Coast Guard *(Transportation Dept.), Defense Operations, 2100 2nd St. S.W. 20593; (202) 267-1502. Fax, (202) 267-4278. Capt. Keith Coddington, chief.*

Ensures that the Coast Guard can mobilize effectively during national emergencies, including those resulting from enemy military attack. (The Coast Guard is part of the Transportation Dept. during peacetime; in certain emergency circumstances, including war, some of its functions become components of the Navy and come under the jurisdiction of the Defense Dept.)

CONGRESS

House Appropriations Committee, *Subcommittee on VA, HUD, and Independent Agencies, H143 CAP 20515; (202) 225-3241. Jerry Lewis, R-Calif., chair; Frank Cushing, staff director. Internet, http://www.house.gov/ appropriations.*

Jurisdiction over legislation to appropriate funds for the Federal Emergency Management Agency.

House Banking and Financial Services Committee, *Subcommittee on Housing and Community Opportunity, B303 RHOB 20515; (202) 225-6634. Rick A. Lazio, R-N.Y., chair; Joseph M. Ventrone, staff director.*

Jurisdiction over federal insurance, including flood insurance.

House National Security Committee, *2120 RHOB 20515; (202) 225-4151. Fax, (202) 225-9077. Floyd D. Spence, R-S.C., chair; Andrew K. Ellis, staff director. Internet, http://www.hous.gov/nsc.*

Jurisdiction over legislation for emergency communications and industrial planning and mobilization.

House National Security Committee, *Subcommittee on Military Readiness, 2117 RHOB 20515; (202) 226-1036. Fax, (202) 225-7102. Herbert H. Bateman, R-Va., chair; Peter Steffes, professional staff member. Internet, http://www.house.gov/nsc.*

Jurisdiction over legislation concerning civil defense, emergency mobilization of merchant fleets, and national defense stockpiles, including military, civilian, and industrial requirements.

House Transportation and Infrastructure Committee, *Subcommittee on Water Resources and Environment, B376 RHOB 20515; (202) 225-4360. Fax, (202) 226-5435. Sherwood Boehlert, R-N.Y., chair; Ben Grumbles, counsel. Internet, http://www.house.gov/transportation.*

Jurisdiction over disaster relief and emergency response programs of the Federal Emergency Management Agency.

Senate Appropriations Committee, *Subcommittee on VA, HUD, and Independent Agencies, SD-127 20510; (202) 224-7211. Christopher S. Bond, R-Mo., chair; John K. Mark, staff director. Internet, http://www.senate.gov/ ~appropriations.*

Jurisdiction over legislation to appropriate funds for the Federal Emergency Management Agency.

Senate Armed Services Committee, *Subcommittee on Readiness, SR-228 20510; (202) 224-3871. Fax, (202) 228-3781. James M. Inhofe, R-Okla., chair; Cord Sterling, professional staff member.*

Jurisdiction over legislation concerning national defense stockpiles, including military, civilian, and industrial requirements. Jurisdiction over emergency preparedness legislation, including civil defense, emergency mobilization of merchant fleets, emergency communications, and industrial planning and mobilization.

Senate Banking, Housing, and Urban Affairs Committee, *Subcommittee on Housing Opportunity and Community Development, SD-534 20510; (202) 224-7391. Connie Mack, R-Fla., chair; Christopher Lord, staff director. Internet, http://www.senate.gov/~banking.*

Jurisdiction over federal insurance, including flood insurance.

Senate Environment and Public Works Committee, *Subcommittee on Clean Air, Wetlands, Private Property, and Nuclear Safety, SD-407 20510; (202) 224-6176. James M. Inhofe, R-Okla., chair; Chris Hessler, staff contact. Internet, http://www.senate.gov/committee/ environment.html.*

Jurisdiction over the Federal Emergency Management Agency.

NONPROFIT

American Red Cross, *Disaster Services,* 8111 Gatehouse Rd., Falls Church, VA 22042; (703) 206-7460. Fax, (703) 206-8835. Donald W. Jones, vice president.

Chartered by Congress to administer disaster relief. Provides disaster victims with food, clothing, shelter, first aid, and medical care; promotes disaster preparedness and prevention.

International Assn. of Chiefs of Police, *Advisory Committee for Patrol and Tactical Operations,* 515 N. Washington St., Alexandria, VA 22314-2357; (703) 836-6767. Fax, (703) 836-4543. Robert DelCore, staff liaison. Internet, http://www.amdahl.com/ext/iacp.

Membership: foreign and U.S. police executives and administrators. Maintains liaison with civil defense and emergency service agencies; prepares guidelines for police cooperation with emergency and disaster relief agencies during emergencies.

Salvation Army Disaster Service, 503 E St. N.W. 20001; (202) 783-9085. Fax, (202) 347-4070. Capt. Brack Dodd, emergency disaster services coordinator. Internet, http://www.salvationarmyusa.org.

Provides disaster victims and rescuers with emergency support, including food, clothing, and counseling services.

Emergency Communications

AGENCIES

Air Force Dept. *(Defense Dept.), Communications and Information,* The Pentagon, #5B477 20330-1250; (703) 695-6324. Fax, (703) 614-0156. Lt. Gen. William J. Donahue, director.

Responsible for policy, planning, programming, and evaluating performance of the Air Force's C-4 system.

Army Dept. *(Defense Dept.), Information Systems for Command, Control, Communications, and Computers,* The Pentagon, #3E458 20310-0107; (703) 695-4366. Fax, (703) 695-3091. Lt. Gen. William H. Campbell, director.

Oversees policy and budget for the Army's information systems and programs.

Defense Dept., *Command, Control, and Communications,* The Pentagon, #3E194 20301-6000; (703) 695-2396. Fax, (703) 693-7013. James Soos, deputy assistant secretary.

Civilian office with policy oversight for all C-3 matters.

Defense Dept., *Command, Control, Communications, and Computer Systems,* The Pentagon, #2D866 20318-6000; (703) 695-6478. Fax, (703) 614-2945. Lt. Gen. Douglas D. Buchholz, director.

Military office that sets policy throughout the Defense Dept. for C-4 matters.

Defense Dept., *White House Communications Agency,* U.S. Naval Station—Anacostia, 2701 S. Capitol St. S.W. 20373-5815; (202) 757-5530. Fax, (202) 757-5529. Col. Joseph J. Simmons IV (USA), commander.

Responsible for presidential communications.

Federal Communications Commission, *Emergency Alert System,* 1919 M St. N.W. 20554; (202) 418-1220. Fax, (202) 418-2817. John Winston, director. Information, (202) 418-1100. Internet, http://www.fcc.gov/cib/eas.

Develops rules and regulations for the Emergency Alert System, which issues radio reports during local, state, and national emergencies, including war, natural disasters, or major accidents involving hazardous materials. Assists officials of state and local Emergency Alert Systems.

National Communications System *(Defense Dept.),* 701 S. Courthouse Rd., Arlington, VA 22204-2199; (703) 607-6100. Fax, (703) 607-4802. Lt. Gen. David J. Kelley (USA), manager. Information, (703) 607-6214. Internet, http://www.disa.mil.

Ensures that the federal government has the necessary communications capabilities to permit its continued operation during a national emergency, including war; provides the Federal Emergency Management Agency with communications support as it directs the nation's recovery from a major disaster.

Navy Dept. *(Defense Dept.), Naval Computer and Telecommunications Command,* 4401 Massachusetts Ave. N.W. 20394-5460; (202) 764-0550. Fax, (202) 764-0357. Capt. George B. Allison, commander.

Provides, operates, and maintains all Navy onshore communications resources; nontactical information resources for command, control, and administration of the Navy; and the Defense Communication System.

President's National Security Telecommunications Advisory Committee, c/o National Communications System, 701 S. Courthouse Rd., Arlington, VA 22204-2198; (703) 607-6221. Fax, (703) 607-4826. Janet Jefferson, manager. Internet, http://www.ncs.gov.

Advises the president on specific measures to improve national security telecommunications.

Industrial Planning and Mobilization

AGENCIES

Bureau of Export Administration *(Commerce Dept.), Strategic Industries and Economic Security,* 14th St. and Constitution Ave. N.W., #3876 20230; (202) 482-4506. Fax, (202) 482-5650. William Denk, acting director. Information, (202) 482-2721.

Administers the Defense Production Act and provides industry with information on the allocation of resources falling under the jurisdiction of the act; conducts studies on industrial mobilization for the federal government.

Defense Dept., *International and Commercial Programs,* The Pentagon, #3E1082 20301-3070; (703) 697-4172. Fax, (703) 693-2026. Paul J. Hoeper, deputy assistant secretary.

Advises the under secretary of defense on cooperative research and development, production, procurement, and follow-on support programs with foreign nations; monitors the transfer of secure technologies to foreign nations.

Defense Logistics Agency *(Defense Dept.), Defense Logistics Support Command,* 8725 John Jay Kingman Rd., Fort Belvoir, VA 22060; (703) 767-1600. Fax, (703) 767-1588. Rear Adm. David P. Keller (USN), deputy director. Information, (703) 767-6200. Internet, http://www.supply.dla.mil.

Oversees operations of Emergency Supply Operations Centers that acquire, maintain, and distribute items used in first-line weapons systems.

Maritime Administration *(Transportation Dept.), National Security Plans,* 400 7th St. S.W., #PI-1303 20590; (202) 366-5900. Fax, (202) 366-5904. Thomas M. P. Christensen, director. Internet, http://marad.dot.gov/national_security.html.

Plans for the transition of merchant shipping from peacetime to wartime operations under the direction of the National Shipping Authority. (The National Shipping Authority is a stand-by organization that is activated upon the declaration of a war or other national emergency.)

Maritime Administration *(Transportation Dept.), Ship Operations,* 400 7th St. S.W. 20590; (202) 366-1875. Fax, (202) 366-3954. Michael Delpercio Jr., director. Internet, http://marad.dot.gov/ship_operations.html.

Maintains the National Defense Reserve Fleet, a fleet of older vessels traded in by U.S. flag operators that are called into operation during emergencies; manages and administers the Ready Reserve Force, a fleet of ships available for operation within four to twenty days, to meet the nation's sealift readiness requirements.

NONPROFIT

National Defense Industrial Assn., 2111 Wilson Blvd., #400, Arlington, VA 22201-3061; (703) 522-1820. Fax, (703) 522-1885. Lt. Gen. Lawrence F. Skibbie (USA, ret.), president. Internet, http://www.ndia.org.

Membership: U.S. citizens and businesses interested in national security. Also open to individuals and businesses in nations with defense agreements with the United States. Provides information and expertise on defense preparedness issues; works to increase public awareness of national defense preparedness through education programs; serves as a forum for dialogue between the defense industry and the government.

National Defense Transportation Assn., 50 S. Pickett St., #220, Alexandria, VA 22304; (703) 751-5011. Fax, (703) 823-8761. Lt. Gen. Edward Honor (USA, ret.), president. Internet, ndta@pop.erols.com or http://web2.volpe.dot.gov/ndta.

Membership: transportation service and manufacturing companies. Maintains liaison with the Defense Dept., Transportation Dept., and Federal Emergency Management Agency to prepare emergency transportation plans.

Shipbuilders Council of America, 901 N. Washington St., #204, Alexandria, VA 22314; (703) 548-7447. Fax, (703) 518-0276. Penny L. Eastman, president. Internet, http://www.shipbuilders.org.

Membership: commercially focused shipyards that repair and build ships, and allied industries and associations. Promotes the maintenance of a privately owned reserve fleet for times of national emergency. Serves as a liaison between the government and the shipbuilding and ship repairing industries.

Selective Service

AGENCIES

Selective Service System, 1515 Wilson Blvd., Arlington, VA 22209-2425; (703) 605-4010. Fax, (703) 605-4006. Gil Coronado, director; Willie L. Blanding Jr., executive director. Locator, (703) 605-4000. Internet, http://www.sss.gov.

Supplies the armed forces with manpower when authorized; registers male citizens of the United States ages 18 to 25. In an emergency, would institute a draft and would provide alternative service assignments to men classified as conscientious objectors.

CONGRESS

House Appropriations Committee, *Subcommittee on VA, HUD, and Independent Agencies, H143 CAP 20515; (202) 225-3241. Jerry Lewis, R-Calif., chair; Frank Cushing, staff director. Internet, http://www.house.gov/ appropriations.*

Jurisdiction over legislation to appropriate funds for the Selective Service System.

House Government Reform and Oversight Committee, *Subcommittee on National Security, International Affairs, and Criminal Justice, B373 RHOB 20515; (202) 225-2577. Fax, (202) 225-1154. Dennis Hastert, R-Ill., chair; Robert Charles, staff director. Internet, http:// www.house.gov/reform.*

Oversees operations of the Selective Service System.

House National Security Committee, *Subcommittee on Military Personnel, 2340 RHOB 20515; (202) 225-7560. Fax, (202) 226-0789. Steve Buyer, R-Ind., chair; John Chapla, professional staff member. Internet, http://www. house.gov/nsc.*

Jurisdiction over selective service legislation.

Senate Appropriations Committee, *Subcommittee on VA, HUD, and Independent Agencies, SD-127 20510; (202) 224-7211. Christopher S. Bond, R-Mo., chair; John K. Mark, staff director. Internet, http://www.senate.gov/ ~appropriations.*

Jurisdiction over legislation to appropriate funds for the Selective Service System.

Senate Armed Services Committee, *Subcommittee on Personnel, SR-228 20510; (202) 224-3871. Fax, (202) 228-3781. Dirk Kempthorne, R-Idaho, chair; Charles S. Abell, professional staff member.*

Oversees operations of the Selective Service System.

NONPROFIT

National Interreligious Service Board for Conscientious Objectors, *1830 Connecticut Ave. N.W. 20009; (202) 483-2220. Fax, (202) 483-1246. Raymond Toney, executive director. Internet, nisbco@igc.apc.org or http:// www.nonviolence.org/nisbco.*

Seeks to defend and extend the rights of conscientious objectors. Provides information and advocacy about the military draft and national service. Offers counseling and information to military personnel seeking discharge or transfer to noncombatant positions within the military.

Public Law Education Institute, *454 New Jersey Ave. S.E. 20003; (202) 544-8646. Thomas Alder, president.*

Conducts research and serves as an information clearinghouse on military law, the draft, selective service, veterans' affairs, and tort law related to military affairs.

Strategic Stockpiles

AGENCIES

Defense Dept., *Defense National Stockpile Center, 8725 John Jay Kingman Rd., Fort Belvoir, VA 22060-6223; (703) 767-5525. Fax, (703) 767-5538. Richard J. Connelly, administrator. Internet, http://www.dnsc.dla.mil.*

Stockpiles strategic and critical materials for use in wartime or national emergencies.

Defense Dept., *Industrial Affairs and Installations, The Pentagon, #2A318 20301-3000; (703) 695-0123. Fax, (703) 693-7038. Paul Halpern, director, Industrial Programs. Internet, http://www.acq.osd.mil.*

Develops and oversees strategic and critical materials policies including oversight of the National Defense Stockpile.

Defense Dept., *Materiel and Distribution Management, The Pentagon, #3B730 20301-3500; (703) 697-9238. Fax, (703) 697-3428. Walter Atchley, acting director. Internet, http://www.acq.osd.mil/log/mdm.*

Civilian office that develops energy policy for the Defense Dept. Works with the Energy Dept. to develop policy for strategic petroleum reserves, petroleum logistics, facilities energies, and naval petroleum and oil shale reserves. Promotes conservation and efficiency of energy resources.

Fossil Energy *(Energy Dept.), Naval Petroleum and Oil Shale Reserves, 1000 Independence Ave. S.W., #3H076 20585; (202) 586-4685. Fax, (202) 586-4446. R. Dobie Langenkamp, deputy assistant secretary.*

Develops, conserves, operates, and maintains naval petroleum and oil shale reserves for producing oil, natural gas, and other petroleum products as authorized by the Naval Petroleum Reserves Production Act of 1976.

National Institute of Standards and Technology *(Commerce Dept.), Materials Science and Engineering Laboratory, Route I-270 and Quince Orchard Rd., Gaithersburg, MD (mailing address: Bldg. 223, #B309, Gaithersburg, MD 20899); (301) 975-5658. Fax, (301) 975-5012. Dale Hall, acting director.*

Advises the secretary and Congress on strategic resources issues. Conducts studies; coordinates development of departmental positions on federal policies and programs; develops and maintains consultation program with business interests; prepares reports on critical and strategic materials for members of the Council for Mutual Economic Assistance.

🖾 INTELLIGENCE AND COUNTERTERRORISM

AGENCIES

Air Force Dept. *(Defense Dept.), Intelligence,* The Pentagon, #4A932 20330-1700; (703) 695-5613. Fax, (703) 697-4903. Maj. Gen. John P. Casciano, director, Intelligence, Surveillance, and Reconnaissance.

Military office that directs Air Force intelligence activities and coordinates activities with other intelligence agencies.

Army Dept. *(Defense Dept.), Intelligence,* The Pentagon, #2E464 20310-1000; (703) 695-3033. Fax, (703) 697-7605. Lt. Gen. Claudia J. Kennedy, deputy chief of staff.

Military office that directs Army intelligence activities and coordinates activities with other intelligence agencies.

Central Intelligence Agency, Langley, VA; (703) 482-1100. Fax, (703) 482-6790. George J. Tenet, director. Information, (703) 482-7677. Internet, http://www.odci.gov/cia.

Coordinates the intelligence functions of government agencies as they relate to national security and advises the National Security Council on those functions; gathers and evaluates intelligence relating to national security and distributes the information to government agencies in the national security field.

Criminal Division *(Justice Dept.), Terrorism and Violent Crime,* 601 D St. N.W., #6500 20530; (202) 514-0849. Fax, (202) 514-8714. James S. Reynolds, chief.

Investigates and prosecutes incidents of international terrorism involving U.S. interests, domestic violent crime, firearms, and explosives violations. Provides legal advice on federal statutes relating to murder, assault, kidnapping, threats, robbery, weapons and explosives control, malicious destruction of property, and aircraft and sea piracy.

Defense Dept., *Command, Control, Communications, and Intelligence,* The Pentagon, #3E172 20301-6000; (703) 695-0348. Fax, (703) 614-8060. Anthony M. Valletta, assistant secretary.

Civilian office that advises and makes recommendations to the secretary of defense on the management of all Defense Dept. intelligence and communications programs, resources, and activities.

Defense Dept., *Intelligence Oversight,* 4035 Ridgetop Rd., #210, Fairfax, VA 22030; (703) 275-6552. Fax, (703) 275-6590. Christopher Mellon, assistant to the secretary.

Responsible for the independent oversight of all Defense Dept. intelligence, counterintelligence, and related activities, and for the formulation of intelligence policy; reviews intelligence operations and investigates and reports on possible violations of federal law or regulations.

Defense Dept., *Special Operations and Low Intensity Conflict,* The Pentagon, #2E258 20301-2500; (703) 693-2895. Fax, (703) 693-6335. H. Allen Holmes, assistant secretary.

Serves as special staff assistant and civilian adviser to the defense secretary on matters related to special operations and international terrorism.

Defense Information Systems Agency *(Defense Dept.),* 701 S. Courthouse Rd., Arlington, VA 22204-2199; (703) 607-6100. Fax, (703) 607-4802. Lt. Gen. David J. Kelley (USA), director. Information, (703) 607-6214. Internet, http://www.disa.mil.

Division of Command, Control, Communications, and Intelligence; the Defense Dept. agency responsible for information technology and the central manager for major portions of the Defense Information Infrastructure. Units include the White House Communications Agency; the DISA director is also manager of the National Communications System.

Defense Intelligence Agency *(Defense Dept.),* The Pentagon, #3E258 20301-7400; (703) 695-7353. Fax, (703) 695-7336. Lt. Gen. Patrick M. Hughes (USA), director. Information, (703) 695-0071. Internet, http://www.dia.osis.com.

Collects and evaluates foreign military-related intelligence information to satisfy the requirements of the secretary of defense, Joint Chiefs of Staff, selected components of the Defense Dept., and other authorized agencies.

Energy Dept., *Intelligence,* 1000 Independence Ave. S.W., #GA-301 20585; (202) 586-2610. Fax, (202) 586-0751. Garnetta Pickett, director.

Gathers and maintains information as it relates to national security, including military applications of nuclear energy.

Federal Bureau of Investigation *(Justice Dept.), International Terrorism Operations,* 935 Pennsylvania Ave. N.W., #5222 20535; (202) 324-4664. Fax, (202) 324-1524. Dale Watson, chief. Press, (202) 324-3691.

Federal law enforcement agency with primary jurisdiction over the U.S. government's counterterrorism activities. Responsible for preventing, interdicting, and investigating the criminal activities of international terrorist groups and individuals.

Justice Dept., *Intelligence Policy and Review,* 950 *Pennsylvania Ave. N.W., #3305 20530; (202) 514-5600. Fax, (202) 514-7858. Frances Fragos Townsend, counsel.*

Provides the attorney general with legal advice and recommendations on national security matters. Reviews executive orders, directives, and procedures relating to the intelligence community; approves certain intelligence-gathering activities. Provides interpretations and applications of the Constitution, statutes, regulations, and directives relating to U.S. national security activities. Represents the United States before the Foreign Intelligence Surveillance Court.

Marine Corps *(Defense Dept.), Intelligence,* 2 *Navy Annex 20380-1775; (703) 614-2443. Fax, (703) 614-5888. Maj. Gen. Joseph T. Anderson, director.*

Military office that directs Marine Corps intelligence activities and coordinates activities with other intelligence agencies.

National Imagery and Mapping Agency *(Defense Dept.),* 1400 *Sangamore Rd., Bethesda, MD 20816; (301) 227-7300. Fax, (301) 227-3696. Rear Adm. Joseph J. Dantone Jr., acting director. Internet, http://www.nima.mil.*

Combat support agency that provides imagery and geospatial information to national policymakers and military forces in support of national defense objectives; incorporates the missions and functions of the former Defense Mapping Agency, Central Imaging Office, and Defense Dissemination Program Office.

National Reconnaissance Office *(Defense Dept.),* 14675 *Lee Rd., Chantilly, VA 20151-1715; (703) 808-1017. Fax, (703) 808-1171. Keith R. Hall, director. Press, (703) 808-1015. Internet, http://www.nro.odci.gov.*

Researches, develops, and operates intelligence satellites. Gathers intelligence for various purposes, including indications and warning, monitoring of arms control agreements, military operations and exercises, and monitoring of natural disasters and other environmental issues.

National Security Agency *(Defense Dept.),* 9800 *Savage Rd., Fort Meade, MD 20755-6000; (301) 688-6311. Fax, (301) 497-2844. Lt. Gen. Kenneth A. Minihan (USAF), director; Barbara A. McNamara, deputy director. Information, (301) 688-6524. Internet, http://www. nsa.gov.*

Provides technical advice and services to protect classified and unclassified national security systems against exploitation through interception, unauthorized access, or related technical intelligence threats. Collects data on foreign signals and transmissions in the United States.

National Security Council *(Executive Office of the President), The White House 20504; (202) 456-9471. Fax, (202) 456-9460. Samuel R. "Sandy" Berger, assistant to the president for national security affairs. Press, (202) 456-9271. Internet, http://www.whitehouse.gov.*

Advises the president on national security matters; collects information on foreign policy and defense issues; coordinates the national security, defense, and intelligence functions of departments such as State and Defense.

Navy Dept. *(Defense Dept.), Naval Intelligence, The Pentagon, #5C600 20350-2000; (703) 695-0124. Fax, (703) 614-0230. Rear Adm. Lowell E. Jacoby, director.*

Military office that directs Navy intelligence activities and coordinates activities with other intelligence agencies.

President's Foreign Intelligence Advisory Board *(Executive Office of the President), Old Executive Office Bldg., #340 20502; (202) 456-2352. Fax, (202) 395-3403. Warren Rudman, chair; Randy Deitering, acting executive director.*

Members appointed by the president. Advises the president and makes recommendations to government intelligence agencies on the improvement of U.S. intelligence-gathering efforts. Assesses the quality, quantity, and propriety of intelligence collection and analysis and of counterintelligence activities. Advises the president on matters concerning national security.

State Dept., *Counterterrorism, Main State Bldg., #2507 20520; (202) 647-9892. Fax, (202) 647-0221. Kenneth R. McKume, acting coordinator. Press, (202) 647-7633.*

Implements U.S. counterterrorism policy and coordinates activities with foreign governments; responds to terrorist acts; works to promote a stronger counterterrorism stance worldwide.

State Dept., *Diplomatic Security Bureau, Main State Bldg., #6316 20520; (202) 647-6290. Fax, (202) 647-0953. Eric J. Boswell, assistant secretary.*

Conducts Anti-Terrorism Assistance Program, which provides training to foreign governments fighting terrorism.

State Dept., *Intelligence and Research, Main State Bldg., #6531 20520-6531; (202) 647-9177. Fax, (202) 736-4688. Phyllis E. Oakley, assistant secretary.*

Coordinates foreign-policy-related research, analysis, and intelligence programs for the State Dept. and other federal agencies.

Transportation Dept., *Intelligence and Security, 400 7th St. S.W., #10401 20590; (202) 366-6535. Fax, (202) 366-7261. Rear Adm. Paul J. Pluta (USCG), director.*

Advises the secretary on transportation intelligence and security policy. Acts as liaison with the intelligence community, federal agencies, corporations, and interest groups; administers counterterrorism strategic planning processes.

U.S. Coast Guard *(Transportation Dept.),* **Intelligence,** *2100 2nd St. S.W. 20593-0001; (202) 267-2126. Fax, (202) 267-6954. Dennis L. Hager, chief.*

Manages all Coast Guard intelligence activities and programs.

CONGRESS

House Government Reform and Oversight Committee, *Subcommittee on National Security, International Affairs, and Criminal Justice, B373 RHOB 20515; (202) 225-2577. Fax, (202) 225-1154. Dennis Hastert, R-Ill., chair; Robert Charles, staff director. Internet, http://www.house.gov/reform.*

Oversight responsibilities for the operations of agencies related to intelligence and security, including the Defense Dept., Central Intelligence Agency, National Security Agency, and Defense Intelligence Agency.

House International Relations Committee, *2170 RHOB 20515; (202) 225-5021. Fax, (202) 225-2035. Benjamin A. Gilman, R-N.Y., chair; Richard J. Garon Jr., chief of staff. Internet, http://www.house.gov/international_relations.*

Jurisdiction over legislation on international terrorism, including counterterrorism policy, embassy security, and the Anti-Terrorism Assistance Program (jurisdiction shared with House Judiciary Committee).

House Judiciary Committee, *2138 RHOB 20515; (202) 225-3951. Fax, (202) 225-7682. Henry J. Hyde, R-Ill., chair; Thomas Mooney, chief counsel. Internet, http://www.house.gov/judiciary.*

Jurisdiction over legislation on control of international terrorism (shared with House International Relations Committee).

House National Security Committee, *Subcommittee on Military Procurement, 2340 RHOB 20515; (202) 225-4440. Fax, (202) 226-0105. Duncan Hunter, R-Calif., chair; Steve Thompson, professional staff member. Internet, http://www.house.gov/nsc.*

Jurisdiction over military intelligence activities affecting national security.

House Select Committee on Intelligence, *H405 CAP 20515; (202) 225-4121. Fax, (202) 225-1991. Porter J. Goss, R-Fla., chair; John I. Millis, staff director.*

Studies, makes recommendations, and proposes legislation on intelligence agencies' activities and policies, including the attorney general's implementation of guidelines for Federal Bureau of Investigation intelligence activities and the conduct of electronic surveillance for foreign intelligence purposes; oversees the Central Intelligence Agency, National Security Agency, Defense Intelligence Agency, and other intelligence activities of the U.S. government to ensure conformity with the U.S. Constitution and laws; authorizes budgets for the intelligence community.

Senate Armed Services Committee, *Subcommittee on Strategic Forces, SR-228 20510; (202) 224-3871. Fax, (202) 228-3781. Robert C. Smith, R-N.H., chair; Eric Thomas, professional staff member. Internet, http://www.senate.gov/armed_services.html.*

Jurisdiction over military intelligence activities affecting national security.

Senate Foreign Relations Committee, *SD-450 20510; (202) 224-4651. Fax, (202) 224-0836. Jesse Helms, R-N.C., chair; James W. "Bud" Nance, staff director. Internet, http://www.senate.gov/committee/foreign.html.*

Oversight of foreign intelligence activities. Jurisdiction over international counterterrorism policy, including the Anti-Terrorism Assistance Program (shared with Senate Judiciary Committee).

Senate Judiciary Committee, *SD-224 20510; (202) 224-5225. Fax, (202) 224-9102. Orrin G. Hatch, R-Utah, chair; Manus Cooney, chief counsel. Internet, http://www.senate.gov/committee/judiciary.html.*

Jurisdiction over legislation relating to the control of international terrorism (jurisdiction shared with the Senate Foreign Relations Committee).

Senate Select Committee on Intelligence, *SH-211 20510; (202) 224-1700. Richard C. Shelby, R-Ala., chair; Taylor Lawrence, staff director. Internet, http://www.senate.gov/committee/intelligence.html.*

Studies, makes recommendations, and proposes legislation on intelligence agencies' activities, policies, and funds; oversees the Central Intelligence Agency, National Security Agency, Defense Intelligence Agency, the intelligence activities of the Federal Bureau of Investigation, and other intelligence operations of the U.S. government to ensure conformity with the U.S. Constitution and laws; authorizes appropriations for the intelligence community. Oversight of directives and procedures governing intelligence activities affecting the rights of Americans abroad.

INTERNATIONAL ORGANIZATIONS

INTERPOL *(Justice Dept.)*, *600 E St. N.W. (mailing address: U.S. Justice Dept., Washington, DC 20530); (202) 616-9000. Fax, (202) 616-8400. John J. Imhoff, chief. Internet, http://www.usdoj.gov/usncb.*

U.S. national central bureau for INTERPOL; interacts in international investigations of terrorism on behalf of U.S. police. Serves as liaison between foreign and U.S. law enforcement agencies. Headquarters office sponsors forums enabling foreign governments to discuss counterterrorism policy. (Headquarters in Lyons, France.)

NONPROFIT

American Society for Industrial Security, *1655 N. Fort Myer Dr., #1200, Arlington, VA 22209-3198; (703) 522-5800. Fax, (703) 243-4954. Michael Stack, executive director. Internet, http://www.asisonline.org.*

Membership: security administrators from around the world who protect the assets and personnel of private and public organizations. Sponsors seminars and workshops on counterterrorism.

Assn. of Former Intelligence Officers, *6723 Whittier Ave., #303A, McLean, VA 22101; (703) 790-0320. Fax, (703) 790-0264. Roy K. Jonkers, executive director. Toll-free, (800) 234-6717. Internet, afio@his.com or http://www.his.com/afio.*

Membership: former military and civilian intelligence officers. Encourages public support for intelligence agencies; supports increased intelligence education in colleges and universities.

Center for National Security Studies, *Gelman Library, 2130 H St. N.W., #701 20037; (202) 994-7060. Fax, (202) 994-7005. Kate Martin, director. Internet, cnss@gwis2.circ.gwu.edu or cnss@nicom.com.*

A project of the Fund for Peace. Monitors and conducts research on civil liberties and intelligence and national security, including activities of the Central Intelligence Agency and the Federal Bureau of Investigation.

National Security Archive, *Gelman Library, 2130 H St. N.W., #701 20037; (202) 994-7000. Fax, (202) 994-7005. Thomas Blanton, executive director. Internet, nsarchiv@ gwis2.circ.gwu.edu or http://www.seas.gwu.edu/nsarchive.*

Research institute and library that provides information on U.S. foreign policy and national security affairs.

Maintains collection of declassified and unclassified national security documents. Archive open to the public by appointment.

Internal Security

See also Defense Trade and Technology (this chapter); Emergency Preparedness (this chapter)

AGENCIES

Air Force Dept. *(Defense Dept.), Special Investigations, The Pentagon, #4E1081 20330-1140; (703) 697-1955. Fax, (703) 695-4346. Col. Charles P. Azukas, director.*

Develops and implements policy with regard to investigations of foreign intelligence, terrorism, and other crimes as they relate to Air Force security.

Army Dept. *(Defense Dept.), Counterintelligence and Human Intelligence, 2511 Jefferson Davis Hwy., 9th Floor, Arlington, VA 22202; (703) 601-1962. Lt. Col. Brian McGill, director.*

Responsible for the security and effectiveness of the Army's electronic warfare systems. Develops new ways to interfere with enemy electronic warfare systems.

Defense Dept., *Counterintelligence and Investigations, The Pentagon, #3C260 20301-6000; (703) 697-9586. Fax, (703) 695-8217. David A. Burtt II, director.*

Responsible for security and effectiveness of the military's information warfare systems. Develops new ways to interfere with enemy information warfare systems.

Defense Security Service *(Defense Dept.), 1340 Braddock Pl., Alexandria, VA 22314-1651; (703) 325-5308. Fax, (703) 325-3916. Steven T. Schanzer, director. Information, (703) 325-5396. Internet, http://www.dis.mil.*

Administers programs to protect classified government information and resources, including the Personnel Security Investigations and Defense Industrial Security programs. Serves the Defense Dept. and other executive departments, as well as federal agencies.

Federal Bureau of Investigation *(Justice Dept.), National Security, 935 Pennsylvania Ave. N.W., #7110 20535; (202) 324-4880. Fax, (202) 324-0027. John F. Lewis Jr., assistant director. Information, (202) 324-3000. Press, (202) 324-2727.*

Investigates violations of federal law relating to sabotage, espionage, treason, sedition, international terrorism, and other matters affecting national security. Conducts counterespionage activities against hostile intelligence services and their agents in the United States.

Justice Dept., *Internal Security*, *1400 New York Ave. N.W., 20530; (202) 514-1187. Fax, (202) 514-2836. John J. Dion, acting chief.*

Enforces criminal statutes relating to national security, including treason, espionage, sedition, sabotage, and the export of military and strategic commodities and technology; supervises registration requirements of the Foreign Agents Registration Act.

National Archives and Records Administration, *Information Security Oversight, 700 Pennsylvania Ave. N.W., #5W 20408-0001; (202) 219-5250. Fax, (202) 219-5385. Steven Garfinkel, director.*

Administers governmentwide national security classification program under which information is classified, declassified, and safeguarded for national security purposes.

National Security Agency *(Defense Dept.), 9800 Savage Rd., Fort Meade, MD 20755-6000; (301) 688-6311. Fax, (301) 497-2844. Lt. Gen. Kenneth A. Minihan (USAF), director; Barbara A. McNamara, deputy director. Information, (301) 688-6524. Internet, http://www. nsa.gov.*

Maintains and operates the Defense Dept.'s Computer Security Center; ensures communications and computer security within the government.

Navy Dept. *(Defense Dept.), Naval Criminal Investigative Service, Washington Navy Yard, Bldg. 111, 901 M St. S.E. 20388-5000; (202) 433-8800. Fax, (202) 433-9619. David L. Brant, director. Information, (202) 433-9624. Internet, http://www.ncis.navy.mil.*

Handles investigative responsibilities for naval counterintelligence and security; processes security clearances for the Navy.

State Dept., *Countermeasures and Information Security, 2121 Virginia Ave. N.W. 20522-1003; (202) 663-0538. Fax, (202) 663-0653. Wayne S. Rychak, deputy assistant secretary.*

Safeguards all electronic information and systems in the State Dept., both domestically and abroad. Also responsible for Physical Security Program for State Dept. officials and for the Diplomatic Courier Service.

State Dept., *Diplomatic Security Service, 2121 Virginia Ave. N.W. 20520-1003; (202) 663-0473. Fax, (202) 663-0831. Peter E. Bergin, acting director.*

Oversees the safety and security of all U.S. government employees at U.S. embassies and consulates abroad. Responsible for the safety of the secretary of state and all foreign dignitaries. Conducts background investigations of potential government employees, investigates passport

and visa fraud, and warns government employees of any counterintelligence dangers they might encounter.

State Dept., *Foreign Missions, Main State Bldg., #2238 20520-7207; (202) 647-3416. Fax, (202) 647-1919. Vacant, director; Thomas E. Burns Jr., deputy director.*

Authorized to control the numbers, locations, and travel privileges of foreign diplomats and diplomatic staff in the United States.

🖼️ MILITARY INSTALLATIONS

AGENCIES

Defense Dept., *Environmental Security, 3400 Defense Pentagon, #3E792 20301-3400; (703) 695-6639. Fax, (703) 693-7011. Sherri W. Goodman, deputy under secretary. Internet, http://www.acq.osd.mil/ens.*

Integrates environmental, safety, and occupational health considerations into U.S. defense and economic policies. Works to ensure responsible performance in defense operations, to maintain quality installations, to reduce the costs of complying with environmental laws, and to clean up past contamination.

Defense Dept., *International Security Affairs, The Pentagon, #4E838 20301-2400; (703) 695-4351. Fax, (703) 697-7230. Franklin D. Kramer, assistant secretary.*

Negotiates and monitors defense cooperation agreements, including base rights, access and prepositioning, exchange programs, and status of forces agreements with foreign governments in assigned geographic areas of responsibility.

CONGRESS

House National Security Committee, *Subcommittee on Military Installations and Facilities, 2340 RHOB 20515; (202) 225-7120. Fax, (202) 226-0789. Joel Hefley, R-Colo., chair; Phil Grone, professional staff member. Internet, http://www.house.gov/nsc.*

Jurisdiction over legislation on military base operations and closings, military construction, military housing, and military real estate leasing and buying.

Senate Armed Services Committee, *Subcommittee on Readiness, SR-228 20510; (202) 224-3871. Fax, (202) 228-3781. James M. Inhofe, R-Okla., chair; Cord Sterling, professional staff member.*

Jurisdiction over legislation on military base operations and closings, military construction, military housing, and military real estate leasing and buying.

Base Closings/Economic Impact

AGENCIES

Air Force Dept. *(Defense Dept.)*, ***Base Realignment and Transition,*** *The Pentagon, #5D973 20330-1660; (703) 695-6766. Fax, (703) 693-9707. Lt. Col. Gray Donnalley, chief.*

Military office that plans for the closing of Air Force bases.

Air Force Dept. *(Defense Dept.)*, ***Bases and Units,*** *The Pentagon, #5C966 20330-1480; (703) 697-7706. Fax, (703) 697-5143. Col. Richard Comley, chief.*

Manages Air Force bases and units worldwide.

Air Force Dept. *(Defense Dept.)*, ***Installations,*** *The Pentagon, #4C940 20330-1660; (703) 695-3592. Fax, (703) 693-7568. Jimmy G. Dishner, deputy assistant secretary.*

Civilian office that plans and reviews the closing of Air Force bases.

Army Dept. *(Defense Dept.)*, ***Installations and Housing,*** *The Pentagon, #3E581 20310-0110; (703) 697-8161. Fax, (703) 614-7394. Paul W. Johnson, deputy assistant secretary.*

Civilian office that manages all Army installations and reviews the closing of Army facilities.

Army Dept. *(Defense Dept.)*, ***Policy and Program Development,*** *200 Stovall St., #4S43, Alexandria, VA 22322-0300; (703) 325-9650. Fax, (703) 325-2601. Elizabeth B. Throckmorton, chief.*

Military office responsible for employment policies to assist civilian personnel in cases of Defense Dept. program changes, including base closings.

Defense Dept., ***Base Closure and Community Reinvestment,*** *400 Army-Navy Dr., #200, Arlington, VA 22202-2884; (703) 604-6020. Fax, (703) 604-5843. Paul J. Dempsey, director; Helene O'Connor, acting director, Economic Adjustment, (703) 604-5948.*

Civilian office that helps community officials develop strategies and coordinate plans to alleviate the economic effect of major defense program changes, including base closings, reductions in forces, and contract cutbacks. Assists communities where defense activities are being expanded. Serves as the staff for the Economic Adjustment Committee, an interagency group that coordinates federal defense economic adjustment activities.

Defense Dept., ***Civilian Assistance and Re-Employment (CARE),*** *1400 Key Blvd., B-200, Arlington, VA 22209-5144; (703) 696-1798. Fax, (703) 696-5416. Charles Rogers, chief.*

Manages transition programs for Defense Dept. civilians, including placement, early retirement, and transition assistance programs.

Marine Corps *(Defense Dept.)*, ***Land Use and Military Construction,*** *2 Navy Annex 20380-1775; (703) 696-0865. Fax, (703) 696-0903. Col. Lawrence Larson, head.*

Military office that reviews studies on base closings.

Navy Dept. *(Defense Dept.)*, ***Facilities Engineering,*** *200 Stovall St., Alexandria, VA 22332-2300; (703) 325-0400. Fax, (703) 325-0024. Rear Adm. David J. Nash, commander.*

Military office that plans for program changes at Navy facilities and assists in planning for the economic and personnel adjustments that accompany such changes, including base closings.

Navy Dept. *(Defense Dept.)*, ***Installations and Facilities,*** *The Pentagon, #4A686 20350-1000; (703) 693-0661. Fax, (703) 695-2574. Duncan Holaday, deputy assistant secretary.*

Civilian office that assists in planning for the economic and personnel adjustments that accompany program changes at Navy facilities, including base closings.

Commissaries, PXs, and Service Clubs

AGENCIES

Air Force Dept. *(Defense Dept.)*, ***Defense Commissary Liaison Office,*** *The Pentagon, #5E487 20330-3000; (703) 695-3265. Fax, (703) 695-3650. Dan Sclater, legislative liaison; Harry Witt, operations liaison.*

Serves as a liaison for defense commissary services. Monitors legislation and regulations.

Army Dept. *(Defense Dept.)*, ***Troop Support,*** *The Pentagon, #1E583 20310-0500; (703) 695-2711. Fax, (703) 614-4031. Vacant, chief.*

Military office that monitors operations and policies regarding clothing, equipment, food, field, and Army commissary services.

Defense Dept., ***Army and Air Force Exchange,*** *2511 Jefferson Davis Hwy., #11600, Arlington, VA 22202-3922; (703) 604-7523. Fax, (703) 604-7510. Robert Ellis, director, Washington Office.*

Coordinates Army and Air Force PX matters with other Defense Dept. offices. (Headquarters in Dallas.)

Defense Dept., ***Morale, Welfare, and Recreation,*** *The Pentagon, OASD (FMP) PSTS 20301-4000; (703) 697-7197. Fax, (703) 614-3375. Steve Rossetti, director.*

Directs the operations and policies of armed forces commissaries, PXs, and service clubs.

Navy Dept. *(Defense Dept.),* **Manpower and Reserve Affairs,** *The Pentagon 20350-1000; (703) 697-2179. Fax, (703) 614-4103. Bernard D. Rostker, assistant secretary.*

Civilian office that develops policies for Navy and Marine Corps commissaries, exchanges, and service clubs and reviews their operations.

Navy Dept. *(Defense Dept.),* **Navy Exchange Program,** *Crystal Square 4, 1745 Jefferson Davis Hwy., #501, Arlington, VA 22902; (703) 607-0072. Fax, (703) 607-1167. Alexander Douvres, director.*

Military office that serves as a liaison between Navy Supply Command and Navy Exchange Service Command. (Headquarters located in Virginia Beach, Va.)

CONGRESS

House National Security Committee, *Subcommittee* **on Military Readiness,** *2117 RHOB 20515; (202) 225-1036. Fax, (202) 225-7102. Herbert H. Bateman, R-Va., chair; Peter Steffes, professional staff member. Internet, http://www.house.gov/nsc.*

Jurisdiction over legislation on military commissaries, PXs, and service clubs.

Senate Armed Services Committee, *SR-228 20510; (202) 224-3871. Strom Thurmond, R-S.C., chair; Les Brownlee, staff director. Internet, http://www.senate.gov/committee/armed_services.html.*

Jurisdiction over legislation on military commissaries, PXs, and service clubs.

NONPROFIT

American Logistics Assn., *1133 15th St. N.W., #640 20005; (202) 466-2520. Fax, (202) 296-4419. Robert F. Swarts, president.*

Membership: suppliers of military commissaries, PXs, and service clubs. Acts as liaison between the Defense Dept. and service contractors; monitors legislation and testifies on issues of interest to members.

International Military Community Executives Assn., *1800 Diagonal Rd., #285, Alexandria, VA 22314; (703) 548-0093. Fax, (703) 548-0095. Col. Donald Pavlik (USA, ret.), executive director.*

Provides members with education and training seminars on government affairs, public relations, hospitality and recreation management, and communication. Operates certification program.

United Service Organizations (USO), *901 M St. S.E., Bldg. #198 20374-5096; (202) 610-5700. Fax, (202) 610-5701. Carl E. Mundy Jr., president, World USO.*

Voluntary civilian organization chartered by Congress. Provides military personnel and their families in the United States and overseas with social, educational, and recreational programs.

Construction, Housing, and Real Estate

AGENCIES

Air Force Dept. *(Defense Dept.),* **Civil Engineering,** *Headquarters USAF/ILE, The Pentagon 20330-1260; (703) 607-0200. Fax, (703) 604-0610. Maj. Gen. Eugene Lupia, director.*

Military office that plans and directs construction of Air Force facilities (except housing) in the United States and overseas.

Air Force Dept. *(Defense Dept.),* **Housing,** *The Pentagon 20330-1260; (703) 601-0478. Fax, (703) 604-2484. Col. Donald E. Murphy, director.*

Military office that plans and manages construction of Air Force housing on military installations in the United States and overseas.

Air Force Dept. *(Defense Dept.),* **Installations,** *The Pentagon, #4C940 20330-1660; (703) 695-3592. Fax, (703) 693-7568. Jimmy G. Dishner, deputy assistant secretary.*

Civilian office that plans and reviews construction policies and programs of Air Force military facilities (including the Military Construction Program), housing programs, and real estate buying, selling, and leasing in the United States.

Air Force Dept. *(Defense Dept.),* **Real Estate Agency,** *112 Luke Ave., #104, AFREA/MI, Bolling Air Force Base 20332-8020; (202) 767-4275. Fax, (202) 767-4384. William E. Edwards, director.*

Acquires, manages, and disposes of land for the Air Force worldwide. Maintains a complete land and facilities inventory; establishes instructions and operating procedures.

Army Corps of Engineers *(Defense Dept.), 20 Massachusetts Ave. N.W. 20314-1000; (202) 761-0001. Fax, (202) 761-4463. Lt. Gen. Joe N. Ballard (USACE), chief of engineers. Internet, http://www.usace.army.mil.*

Military office that establishes policy and designs, directs, and manages civil works and military construction projects of the Army Corps of Engineers; directs the Army's real estate leasing and buying for military installations and civil works projects.

Army Dept. *(Defense Dept.),* **Army Housing,** *DAIM-FDH 7701 Telegraph Rd., Alexandria, VA 22315-3000; (703) 428-8378. Fax, (703) 428-8359. Dean Stefanides, chief.*

Military office that plans, directs, and administers the construction and maintenance of Army family housing. Also responsible for unaccompanied personnel, temporary duty, and guest housing.

Army Dept. *(Defense Dept.)*, **Installations and Housing**, *The Pentagon, #3E581 20310-0110; (703) 697-8161. Fax, (703) 614-7394. Paul W. Johnson, deputy assistant secretary.*

Civilian office that reviews construction of Army military facilities, housing programs, and the buying and leasing of real estate in the United States and overseas.

Defense Dept., *Installation Management,* *400 Army-Navy Dr., #206, Arlington, VA 22202-2884; (703) 604-5763. Fax, (703) 604-5934. Joe Terry, director.*

Develops Defense Dept. policy for acquisition, management, and disposal of military real property. Ensures responsiveness of military physical plant to the changing needs of the military; seeks to improve business and management processes on military installations; monitors Defense Dept. experiment with decentralized management of military commands.

Marine Corps *(Defense Dept.)*, **Facilities**, *3033 Wilson Blvd., Arlington, VA (mailing address: Headquarters, U.S. Marine Corps, Code LFF, 2 Navy Annex, Washington, DC 20380-1775); (703) 696-0864. Fax, (703) 696-0849. Col. Larry Johnson, head.*

Military office that develops and implements Marine Corps policy for family housing and maintenance of real property.

Marine Corps *(Defense Dept.)*, **Land Use and Military Construction**, *2 Navy Annex 20380-1775; (703) 696-0865. Fax, (703) 696-0903. Col. Lawrence Larson, head.*

Military office responsible for military construction and the acquisition, management, and disposal of Marine Corps real property.

Navy Dept. *(Defense Dept.)*, **Facilities Engineering**, *200 Stovall St., Alexandria, VA 22332-2300; (703) 325-0400. Fax, (703) 325-0024. Rear Adm. David J. Nash, commander.*

Military office that oversees the development of construction programs for Navy military facilities in the United States and abroad; directs construction of Navy housing at military installations.

Navy Dept. *(Defense Dept.)*, **Installations and Facilities**, *The Pentagon, #4A686 20350-1000; (703) 693-0661. Fax, (703) 695-2574. Duncan Holaday, deputy assistant secretary.*

Civilian office that monitors and reviews construction of Navy military facilities and housing and the buy-

ing and leasing of real estate in the United States and overseas.

Navy Dept. *(Defense Dept.)*, **Real Estate**, *200 Stovall St., Alexandria, VA 22332-2300; (703) 325-0474. Fax, (703) 325-2839. Howard D. Kelsey, director.*

Military office that directs the Navy's real estate leasing and buying for military installations.

U.S. Coast Guard *(Transportation Dept.)*, **Housing Programs**, *2100 2nd St. S.W., #6400, G-WPW-1 20593-0001; (202) 267-6263. Fax, (202) 267-4862. Herbert Levin, chief.*

Provides temporary housing for active personnel and their families.

CONGRESS

House Appropriations Committee, *Subcommittee on Military Construction*, *B300 RHOB 20515; (202) 225-3047. Fax, (202) 225-3099. Ron Packard, R-Calif., chair; Elizabeth G. Dawson, staff director. Internet, http://www.house.gov/appropriations.*

Jurisdiction over legislation to appropriate funds for military construction, including family housing and NATO infrastructure.

Senate Appropriations Committee, *Subcommittee on Military Construction*, *SD-187 20510; (202) 224-2644. Conrad Burns, R-Mont., chair; Jennifer Chartrand, staff director.*

Jurisdiction over legislation to appropriate funds for military construction, including family housing and NATO infrastructure.

PROCUREMENT, ACQUISITION, AND LOGISTICS

See also Defense Trade and Technology (this chapter); Federal Contracts and Procurement (chap. 10)

AGENCIES

Air Force Dept. *(Defense Dept.)*, **Acquisition**, *1060 Air Force Pentagon 20330-1060; (703) 697-6361. Fax, (703) 693-6400. Arthur L. Money, assistant secretary.*

Civilian office that directs and reviews Air Force procurement policies and programs.

Air Force Dept. *(Defense Dept.)*, **Contracting**, *The Pentagon 20330-1060; (703) 588-7004. Fax, (703) 588-1067. Brig. Gen. Frank Anderson, deputy assistant secretary.*

Develops, implements, and enforces contracting policies on Air Force acquisitions worldwide, including research and development services, weapons systems, logistics services, and operational contracts.

Air Force Dept. *(Defense Dept.), Global Power Programs,* The Pentagon 20330-1060; (703) 588-7170. Fax, (703) 588-6196. Brig. Gen. Bruce Carlson, director.

Military office that directs Air Force acquisition and development programs within the tactical arena.

Army Dept. *(Defense Dept.), Operations Research,* 102 Army Pentagon, #2E660 20310-0102; (703) 695-0083. Fax, (703) 693-3897. Walter W. Hollis, deputy under secretary. Internet, http://www.odusa-or.army.mil.

Establishes policy for operations research and systems analysis activities for the Army. Supports acquisition review committees within the Army and the Defense Dept.

Army Dept. *(Defense Dept.), Procurement,* The Pentagon 20310-0103; (703) 695-2488. Fax, (703) 614-9505. Edward G. Elgart, acting deputy assistant secretary.

Directs and reviews Army procurement policies and programs.

Defense Contract Audit Agency *(Defense Dept.),* 8725 John Jay Kingman Rd., #2135, Fort Belvoir, VA 22060-6219; (703) 767-3200. Fax, (703) 767-3267. William H. Reed, director; Michael J. Thibault, deputy director, (703) 274-7281. Internet, http://www.dtic.mil/dcaa.

Performs all contract audits for the Defense Dept. Provides Defense Dept. personnel responsible for procurement and contract administration with accounting and financial advisory services regarding the negotiation, administration, and settlement of contracts and subcontracts.

Defense Dept., *Acquisition and Technology,* The Pentagon, #3E933 20301-3010; (703) 695-2381. Fax, (703) 693-2576. Jacques S. Gansler, under secretary.

Formulates and directs policy relating to the department's purchasing system. Oversees all defense procurement and acquisition programs.

Defense Dept., *Acquisition Reform,* 3600 Defense Pentagon, #3E1034 20301-3600; (703) 695-6413. Fax, (703) 695-2760. Donna S. Richbourg, acting deputy under secretary. Internet, http://www.acq.osd.mil/ar.

Seeks to improve and streamline Defense Dept. policies and practices governing the development and procurement of defense materiel and weapons systems, including associated education and training.

Defense Dept., *Armed Services Board of Contract Appeals,* 5109 Leesburg Pike, Falls Church, VA 22041-3208; (703) 681-8500. Fax, (703) 681-8535. Paul Williams, chair.

Adjudicates disputes arising under Defense Dept. contracts.

Defense Dept., *Defense Acquisition Regulations Council,* The Pentagon 20301-3062; (703) 602-0131. Fax, (703) 602-0350. Vacant, director.

Develops procurement regulations for the Defense Dept.

Defense Dept., *Logistics,* The Pentagon 20301-3500; (703) 697-5530. Fax, (703) 693-0555. Vacant, deputy under secretary.

Formulates and implements department policies and programs regarding spare parts management. Helps determine Defense Dept. spare parts requirements and oversees acquisition of spare parts.

Defense Dept., *Operational Test and Evaluation,* The Pentagon 20301-1700; (703) 697-3654. Fax, (703) 693-5248. Philip E. Coyle III, director.

Ensures that major acquisitions, including weapons systems, are operationally effective and suitable prior to full-scale investment. Provides the secretary of defense and Congress with independent assessment of these programs.

Defense Logistics Agency *(Defense Dept.),* 8725 John Jay Kingman Rd., #2533, Fort Belvoir, VA 22060-6221; (703) 767-5200. Fax, (703) 767-5207. Rear Adm. E.R. Chamberlin (USN), director; Lt. Gen. Henry T. Glisson (USA), principal deputy director. Information, (703) 767-6200. Internet, http://www.dla.mil.

Administers defense contracts; acquires, stores, and distributes food, clothing, medical, and other supplies used by the military services and other federal agencies; administers programs related to logistical support for the military services; and assists military services with developing, acquiring, and using technical information and defense materiel and disposing of materiel no longer needed.

Defense Systems Management College *(Defense Dept.),* 9820 Belvoir Rd., #G38, Fort Belvoir, VA 22060-5565; (703) 805-3360. Fax, (703) 805-2639. Rear Adm. Leonard Vincent (USN), commandant. Registrar, (703) 805-2227. Internet, http://www.dsmc.dsm.mil.

Academic institution that offers courses to military and civilian personnel who specialize in acquisition and procurement. Conducts research to support and improve management of defense systems acquisitions programs.

Justice Dept., *Federal Procurement Fraud,* 1400 New York Ave. N.W., #3100 (mailing address: P.O. Box 28188, Washington, DC 20038); (202) 616-0440. Fax, (202) 514-0152. Barbara Corprew, chief.

Interdepartmental unit that investigates fraud in federal procurement contracting.

Marine Corps *(Defense Dept.),* **Installations and Logistics, Contracts Division,** 2 Navy Annex 20380-1775; (703) 696-1013. Fax, (703) 696-1016. Philip E. Zanfagna Jr., assistant deputy chief of staff.

Military office that directs Marine Corps procurement programs.

Navy Dept. *(Defense Dept.),* **Acquisition and Business Management,** Crystal Plaza 5, #578, 2211 S. Clark Pl., Arlington, VA 22244-5104; (703) 602-2338. Fax, (703) 602-4643. Rear Adm. Richard T. Ginman, deputy.

Directs and reviews Navy acquisition and procurement policy.

Navy Dept. *(Defense Dept.),* **Logistics,** 2000 Navy Pentagon 20350-2000; (703) 695-2154. Fax, (703) 695-1117. Vice Adm. William J. Hancock, deputy chief.

Military office that directs overall Navy logistics policy.

Navy Dept. *(Defense Dept.),* **Military Sealift Command,** Washington Navy Yard, Bldg. 210 20398-5100; (202) 685-5001. Fax, (202) 685-5020. Vice Adm. James B. Perkins, commander.

Transports Defense Dept. and other U.S. government cargo by sea; operates ships that maintain supplies for the armed forces and scientific agencies.

U.S. Coast Guard *(Transportation Dept.),* **Acquisition,** 2100 2nd St. S.W., #5120 20593-0001; (202) 267-2007. Fax, (202) 267-4279. Rear Adm. Roy Casto, chief.

Administers all procurement made through the Acquisition Contract Support division.

U.S. Coast Guard *(Transportation Dept.),* **Logistics Management,** 2100 2nd St. S.W. 20593-0001; (202) 267-1407. Fax, (202) 267-4516. Capt. Robert Kirk Jones, chief.

Sets policy and procedures for the procurement, distribution, maintenance, and replacement of materiel and personnel.

CONGRESS

General Accounting Office, *National Security and International Affairs,* 441 G St. N.W., #4035 20548; (202) 512-2800. Fax, (202) 512-7686. Henry L. Hinton, assistant comptroller general.

Independent, nonpartisan agency in the legislative branch. Audits, analyzes, and evaluates Defense Dept.

acquisition programs; makes unclassified reports available to the public.

House Government Reform and Oversight Committee, *Subcommittee on National Security, International Affairs, and Criminal Justice,* B373 RHOB 20515; (202) 225-2577. Fax, (202) 225-1154. Dennis Hastert, R-Ill., chair; Robert Charles, staff director. Internet, http://www.house.gov/reform.

Oversight of defense procurement.

House National Security Committee, *Subcommittee on Military Procurement,* 2340 RHOB 20515; (202) 225-4440. Fax, (202) 226-0105. Duncan Hunter, R-Calif., chair; Steve Thompson, professional staff member. Internet, http://www.house.gov/nsc.

Jurisdiction over legislation on military procurement (excluding construction) and military contract services.

House National Security Committee, *Subcommittee on Military Readiness,* 2117 RHOB 20515; (202) 226-1036. Fax, (202) 225-7102. Herbert H. Bateman, R-Va., chair; Peter Steffes, professional staff member. Internet, http://www.house.gov/nsc.

Jurisdiction over legislation on naval petroleum reserves and leasing of capital equipment.

Senate Armed Services Committee, SR-228 20510; (202) 224-3871. Strom Thurmond, R-S.C., chair; Les Brownlee, staff director. Internet, http://www.senate.gov/committee/armed_services.html.

Jurisdiction over legislation on military procurement (excluding construction), naval petroleum reserves, and military contract services.

NONPROFIT

Contract Services Assn., 1200 G St. N.W., #750 20005; (202) 347-0600. Fax, (202) 347-0608. Gary Engebretson, president. Internet, http://www.csa-dc.org.

Membership: companies that, under contract, provide federal, state, and local governments and other agencies with various technical and support services. Analyzes the process by which the government awards contracts to private firms. Monitors legislation and regulations.

Council of Defense and Space Industry Assns., 1250 Eye St. N.W., #1200 20005-3922; (202) 371-8414. Fax, (202) 371-8470. Ruth W. Franklin, administrative officer.

Makes recommendations on federal procurement policies. Interests include estimating and accounting systems, contract clauses, defective pricing data, industrial security, management systems control, patents and technical data, property acquisition and control, and contract cost principles.

Electronic Industries Assn., *Government Division,*
2500 Wilson Blvd., #400, Arlington, VA 22201-3834; (703)
907-7500. Fax, (703) 907-7501. Dan C. Heinemeier, vice
president. Internet, http://www.eia.org.

Membership: companies engaged in the research, development, integration, or manufacture of electronic equipment or services for government applications.

Monitors federal policy and practices in acquiring electronic products and services; represents the industry's views on acquisition regulations in federal agencies; serves as the focal point through which the government communicates with the electronics industry on procurement policy and other matters affecting the business-government relationship.

See also Center for Naval Analyses (p. 560)

17 Science and Technology

⬛ GENERAL POLICY

See also Science and Mathematics Education (chap. 6)

AGENCIES

Energy Research *(Energy Dept.), 1000 Independence Ave. S.W., #7B058 20585; (202) 586-5430. Fax, (202) 586-4120. Martha A. Krebs, director.*

Advises the secretary on the department's physical science and energy research and development programs; the management of the nonweapons multipurpose laboratories; and education and training activities required for basic and applied research activities. Manages the department's high energy physics, nuclear physics, fusion energy sciences, basic energy sciences, health and environmental research, and computational and technology research. Provides and operates the large-scale facilities required for research in the physical and life sciences.

National Museum of Natural History *(Smithsonian Institution), 10th St. and Constitution Ave. N.W. 20560; (202) 357-2664. Fax, (202) 357-4779. Robert W. Fry, director. Internet, http://www.sil.si.edu.*

Conducts research and maintains exhibitions and collections relating to the natural sciences. Collections are organized into seven research and curatorial departments: anthropology, botany, entomology, invertebrate zoology, mineral sciences, paleobiology, and vertebrate zoology.

National Science and Technology Council *(Executive Office of the President), Old Executive Office Bldg., #435 20500; (202) 456-6100. Fax, (202) 456-6026. John H. Gibbons, chair. Internet, http://www.whitehouse.gov/White_House/EOP/OSTP.*

Coordinates research and development activities and programs that involve more than one federal agency. Activities concern biotechnology; earth sciences; human subjects; international science; engineering and technology; life sciences; food, agriculture, and forestry; and research, computing, materials, and radiation policy coordination.

National Science Board *(National Science Foundation), 4201 Wilson Blvd., #1220, Arlington, VA 22230; (703) 306-2000. Fax, (703) 306-0181. Richard N. Zare, chair; Marta Cehelsky, executive officer. Information, (703) 306-1234. Internet, http://www.nsf.gov.*

Formulates policy for the National Science Foundation; advises the president on national science policy.

National Science Foundation, *4201 Wilson Blvd., #1205, Arlington, VA 22230; (703) 306-1234. Fax, (703) 306-0109. Neal Lane, director, (703) 306-1000. TDD, (703) 306-0090. Publications, (703) 306-1130. Government Affairs, (703) 306-1070. Internet, pubs@nsf.gov or http://www.nsf.gov.*

Sponsors scientific and engineering research; develops and helps implement science and engineering education programs; fosters dissemination of scientific information; promotes international cooperation within the scientific community; and assists with national science policy planning.

National Science Foundation, *Science Resources Studies, 4201 Wilson Blvd., #965, Arlington, VA 22230; (703) 306-1780. Fax, (703) 306-0510. Jeanne E. Griffith, director. Internet, http://www.nsf.gov/sbe/srs.*

Projects national scientific and technical resources and requirements.

Office of Management and Budget *(Executive Office of the President), Energy and Science, New Executive Office Bldg., #8002 20503; (202) 395-3404. Fax, (202) 395-3049. Kathleen Peroff, deputy associate director.*

Assists and advises the OMB director in budget preparation; analyzes and evaluates programs in space and science, including the activities of the National Science Foundation and the National Aeronautics and Space Administration; coordinates OMB science, energy, and space policies and programs.

Office of Science and Technology Policy *(Executive Office of the President), Old Executive Office Bldg., #424 20502; (202) 456-7116. Fax, (202) 456-6021. John H. Gibbons, director. Press, (202) 456-6018. Internet, http://www.whitehouse.gov/White_House/EOP/OSTP.*

Serves as the president's principal adviser on science and technology policy. Assists with review of research and development budgets of federal agencies, including the departments of Energy, Commerce, and Health and Human Services; the National Science Foundation; and the National Aeronautics and Space Administration. Works with the Office of Management and Budget, other executive offices, Congress, and federal agencies to develop research programs consistent with the president's science and technology goals. Administers the Federal Coordinating Council for Science, Engineering, and Technology.

Office of Science and Technology Policy *(Executive Office of the President), Science, Old Executive Office Bldg., #436 20502; (202) 456-6130. Fax, (202) 456-6027. Arthur Bienenstock, associate director.*

Analyzes policies and advises the president on biological, physical, social, and behavioral sciences and on engineering; coordinates executive office and federal agency actions related to these issues. Evaluates the effectiveness of government science programs.

Office of Science and Technology Policy *(Executive Office of the President), Technology,* Old Executive Office Bldg., #423 20502; (202) 456-6046. Fax, (202) 456-6023. Duncan Moore, associate director.

Analyzes policies and advises the president on technology and related issues of physical, computational, and space sciences; coordinates executive office and federal agency actions related to these issues.

Technology Administration *(Commerce Dept.),* 14th St. and Constitution Ave. N.W., #4824 20230; (202) 482-1575. Fax, (202) 501-2492. Gary R. Bachula, acting under secretary. Information, (202) 482-8321. Internet, http://www.ta.doc.gov.

Seeks to enhance U.S. competitiveness by encouraging the development of new technologies and the conversion of technological knowledge into products and services. Oversees the National Institute of Standards and Technology and the National Technical Information Service.

CONGRESS

General Accounting Office, *Resources, Community, and Economic Development,* 441 G St. N.W., #2T23 20548; (202) 512-3200. Fax, (202) 512-8774. Keith Fultz, assistant comptroller general. Internet, http://www.gao.gov.

Independent, nonpartisan agency in the legislative branch. Reviews and analyzes issues involving federal science, technology, and public policy; audits and oversees the National Science Foundation and the Office of Science and Technology Policy; serves as liaison with the National Academy of Sciences and the National Academy of Engineering; audits and evaluates the performance of the Commerce Dept. (including the National Oceanic and Atmospheric Administration and the National Institute of Standards and Technology); makes reports available to the public.

House Appropriations Committee, *Subcommittee on Commerce, Justice, State, and Judiciary,* H309 Capitol 20515; (202) 225-3351. Harold Rogers, R-Ky., chair; Jim Kulikowski, staff director. Internet, http://www.house.gov/appropriations.

Jurisdiction over legislation to appropriate funds for the Commerce Dept., including the National Oceanic and Atmospheric Administration, the National Institute of Standards and Technology, and the National Technical Information Service.

House Appropriations Committee, *Subcommittee on Interior,* B308 RHOB 20515; (202) 225-3081. Fax, (202) 225-9069. Ralph Regula, R-Ohio, chair; Deborah A. Weatherly, clerk. Internet, http://www.house.gov/appropriations.

Jurisdiction over legislation to appropriate funds for the Smithsonian Institution and the U.S. Geological Survey.

House Appropriations Committee, *Subcommittee on VA, HUD, and Independent Agencies,* H143 CAP 20515; (202) 225-3241. Jerry Lewis, R-Calif., chair; Frank Cushing, staff director. Internet, http://www.house.gov/appropriations.

Jurisdiction over legislation to appropriate funds for the National Science Foundation and the Office of Science and Technology Policy.

House Oversight Committee, *1309 LHOB 20515;* (202) 225-8281. Fax, (202) 225-9957. Bill Thomas, R-Calif., chair; Cathy Abernathy, acting staff director. Internet, http://www.house.gov/cho.

Oversight of and jurisdiction over legislation on the Smithsonian Institution.

House Science Committee, *2320 RHOB 20515;* (202) 225-6371. Fax, (202) 226-0113. F. James Sensenbrenner Jr., R-Wis., chair; Todd Schultz, chief of staff. Internet, http://www.house.gov/science.

Jurisdiction over legislation on scientific research and development; science scholarships, programs, policy, resources, employment, and exploration; and technology.

House Science Committee, *Subcommittee on Basic Research,* B374 RHOB 20515; (202) 225-7858. Fax, (202) 225-7815. Vacant, chair; Steve Eule, staff director. Press, (202) 225-0584. Internet, http://www.house.gov/science.

Jurisdiction over legislation on the National Science Foundation and the Office of Science and Technology Policy; science research and development programs; math, science, and engineering education; international scientific cooperation; and nuclear research and development projects.

House Science Committee, *Subcommittee on Technology,* 2319 RHOB 20515; (202) 225-8844. Fax, (202) 225-4438. Constance A. Morella, R-Md., chair; Richard Russell, staff director. Internet, http://www.house.gov/science.

Jurisdiction over technology policy (including technology transfer), cooperative research and development, patent and intellectual property policy, biotechnology, and recombinant DNA research. Legislative jurisdiction over the National Institute of Standards and Technology and the National Technical Information Service.

Senate Appropriations Committee, *Subcommittee on Commerce, Justice, State, and Judiciary, SR-393 20510; (202) 224-7277. Judd Gregg, R-N.H., chair, (202) 224-3324; Vas Alexopoulos, legislative assistant. Chair's fax, (202) 224-4952. Internet, http://www.senate.gov/~appropriations.*

Jurisdiction over legislation to appropriate funds for the Commerce Dept., including the National Oceanic and Atmospheric Administration, National Institute of Standards and Technology, and the National Technical Information Service.

Senate Appropriations Committee, *Subcommittee on Interior, SD-131 20510; (202) 224-7233. Slade Gorton, R-Wash., chair; Bruce Evans, staff director. Internet, http://www.senate.gov/~appropriations.*

Jurisdiction over legislation to appropriate funds for the Smithsonian Institution and the U.S. Geological Survey.

Senate Appropriations Committee, *Subcommittee on VA, HUD, and Independent Agencies, SD-127 20510; (202) 224-7211. Christopher S. Bond, R-Mo., chair; John K. Mark, staff director. Internet, http://www.senate.gov/~appropriations.*

Jurisdiction over legislation to appropriate funds for the National Science Foundation, the Office of Science and Technology Policy, and the National Institute of Building Science.

Senate Commerce, Science, and Transportation Committee, *SD-508 20510; (202) 224-5115. Fax, (202) 224-1259. John McCain, R-Ariz., chair; John Raidt, staff director. Internet, http://www.senate.gov/~commerce.*

Jurisdiction over legislation on the Commerce Dept. and its scientific activities and science aspects of the Office of Science and Technology Policy.

Senate Commerce, Science, and Transportation Committee, *Subcommittee on Science, Technology, and Space, SH-427 (mailing address: SD-508, Washington, DC 20510); (202) 224-4852. Fax, (202) 228-0326. Bill Frist, R-Tenn., chair; Rosalind Parker, professional staff member. Internet, http://www.senate.gov/~commerce.*

Oversight of the National Institute of Standards and Technology and other departments and agencies with an emphasis on science. Jurisdiction over scientific research and development; science fellowships, scholarships, grants, programs, policy, resources, employment, and exploration; and technology. Jurisdiction over international scientific cooperation, technology transfer, and cooperative research and development (including global change and the space station); resolutions of joint cooperation with foreign governments on science and technology.

Senate Labor and Human Resources Committee, *SD-428 20510; (202) 224-5375. Fax, (202) 224-6510. James M. Jeffords, R-Vt., chair; Mark Powden, staff director. Internet, http://www.senate.gov/~labor.*

Oversees and has jurisdiction over legislation on the National Science Foundation.

Senate Rules and Administration Committee, *SR-305 20510; (202) 224-6352. Fax, (202) 224-3036. John W. Warner, R-Va., chair; Grayson Winterling, staff director. Internet, http://www.senate.gov/~rules.*

Jurisdiction over legislation concerning the Smithsonian Institution and the U.S. Botanic Garden.

NONPROFIT

ACIL, *1629 K St. N.W., #400 20006; (202) 887-5872. Fax, (202) 887-0021. Joseph F. O'Neil, executive director. Laboratory Referral Service, (202) 887-5872. Internet, http://www.acil.org.*

Membership: independent commercial laboratories. Promotes professional and ethical business practices in providing analysis, testing, and research in engineering, microbiology, analytical chemistry, life sciences, and environmental geosciences.

American Assn. for Laboratory Accreditation, *656 Quince Orchard Rd., #620, Gaithersburg, MD 20878-1405; (301) 670-1377. Fax, (301) 869-1495. Peter Unger, president. Internet, http://www.a2la.org.*

Accredits and monitors laboratories that test construction materials and perform acoustics and vibration, biological, chemical, electrical, geotechnical, nondestructive, environmental, mechanical, metals and metal fasteners, calibration, asbestos, radon, and thermal testing. Certifies laboratory reference materials and registers laboratory quality systems.

American Assn. for the Advancement of Science, *1200 New York Ave. N.W. 20005; (202) 326-6640. Fax, (202) 371-9526. Richard S. Nicholson, executive officer. Information, (202) 326-6400. Internet, http://www.aaas.org.*

Membership: scientists, affiliated scientific organizations, and individuals interested in science. Fosters scientific education; monitors and seeks to influence public policy and public understanding of science and technology; encourages scientific literacy among minorities and women. Sponsors national and international symposia, workshops, and meetings; publishes *Science* magazine.

American Assn. for the Advancement of Science, Scientific Freedom, Responsibility, and Law Program, *1200 New York Ave. N.W. 20005; (202) 326-6793. Fax, (202) 289-4950. Mark S. Frankel, director. Internet, http://www.aaas.org/spp/dspp/SFRL/SFRL.htm.*

Focuses on professional ethics and law in science and engineering and on the social implications of science and technology. Collaborates with other professional groups on these activities; provides technical assistance to organizations developing codes of ethics or educational programs on research integrity.

Assn. for Women in Science, *1200 New York Ave. N.W., #650 20005; (202) 326-8940. Fax, (202) 326-8960. Catherine Didion, executive director. Internet, awis@awis. org or http://www.awis.org.*

Promotes equal opportunity for women in scientific professions; provides career and funding information. Interests include international developments.

Council of Scientific Society Presidents, *1155 16th St. N.W. 20036; (202) 872-6230. Fax, (202) 872-4079. Martin Apple, executive director. Internet, cssp@acs.org or http://www.science-presidents.org.*

Membership: presidents, presidents-elect, and immediate past presidents of professional scientific societies. Supports professional science education. Serves as a forum for discussion of emerging scientific issues, formulates national science policy, and develops the nation's scientific leadership.

Federation of American Scientists, *307 Massachusetts Ave. N.E. 20002; (202) 546-3300. Fax, (202) 675-1010. Jeremy J. Stone, president. Internet, fas@fas.org or http:// www.fas.org.*

Conducts studies and monitors legislation on issues and problems related to science and technology, especially U.S. nuclear arms policy, energy, arms transfer, and civil aerospace issues.

George C. Marshall Institute, *1730 K St. N.W., #905 20006; (202) 296-9655. Fax, (202) 296-9714. Jeffrey Salmon, executive director. Internet, info@marshall.org or http://www.marshall.org.*

Analyzes the technical and scientific aspects of public policy issues; produces publications on environmental science, space, national security, and technology policy.

Government-University-Industry Research Roundtable, *2101 Constitution Ave. N.W., #340 20418; (202) 334-3486. Fax, (202) 334-1505. Thomas Moss, executive director. Internet, http://www.nas.edu.*

Forum sponsored by the National Academy of Sciences, National Academy of Engineering, and Institute of

Medicine. Provides scientists, engineers, and members of government, academia, and industry with an opportunity to discuss ways of improving the infrastructure for science and technology research.

National Academy of Sciences, *2101 Constitution Ave. N.W. 20418; (202) 334-2000. Fax, (202) 334-2419. Bruce M. Alberts, president; Jack Halpern, vice president, (202) 334-2151. Press, (202) 334-2138. Library, (202) 334-2125. Publications, (800) 624-6242; in Washington, (202) 334-3313. Internet, news@nas.edu or http://www. nas.edu.*

Congressionally chartered independent organization that advises the federal government on questions of science, technology, and health. Library open to the public by appointment. (Affiliated with the National Academy of Engineering, the Institute of Medicine, and the National Research Council.)

National Geographic Society, *Committee for Research and Exploration, 1145 17th St. N.W. 20036-4688; (202) 857-7439. George Stewart, chair. Internet, http://www.nationalgeographic.com.*

Sponsors basic research grants in the sciences, including anthropology, archeology, astronomy, biology, botany, ecology, physical and human geography, geology, oceanography, paleontology, and zoology. To apply for grants, mail one- to two-page prospectus of project, estimated budget, and curriculum vitae.

National Research Council, *2101 Constitution Ave. N.W. 20418; (202) 334-2000. Fax, (202) 334-2419. Bruce M. Alberts, president; Jack Halpern, vice president, (202) 334-2151. Press, (202) 334-2138. Library, (202) 334-2125. Publications, (800) 624-6242; in Washington, (202) 334-3313. Internet, news@nas.edu or http://www. nas.edu/nrc.*

Serves as the principal operating agency of the National Academy of Sciences, National Academy of Engineering, and Institute of Medicine. Program units focus on physical, social, and life sciences; applications of science including medicine, transportation, and education; international affairs; and U.S. government policy. Library open to the public by appointment.

SAMA Group of Assns., *225 Reinekers Lane, #625, Alexandria, VA 22314-2875; (703) 836-1360. Fax, (703) 836-6644. Mike Duff, executive director.*

Membership: manufacturers and distributors of high technology scientific and industrial instruments and laboratory apparatus. Works to increase worldwide demand for products. (Affiliated with the Laboratory Products Assn.)

Data, Statistics, and Reference

AGENCIES

National Aeronautics and Space Administration, *National Space Science Data Center, Goddard Space Flight Center, Code 633, Greenbelt, MD 20771; (301) 286-7355. Fax, (301) 286-1771. Joseph H. King, head. Internet, http://www.nssdc.gsfc.nasa.gov.*

Acquires, catalogs, and distributes NASA mission data to the international space science community, including research organizations, universities, and other interested organizations worldwide. Provides software tools and network access to promote collaborative data analysis. (Mail data requests to above address, attention: Code 633.4/Request Coordination Office, or phone (301) 286-6695.)

National Aeronautics and Space Administration, *Space Science Data Operations, Goddard Space Flight Center, Code 630, Greenbelt, MD 20771; (301) 286-7354. Fax, (301) 286-1771. James L. Green, chief. Information, (301) 286-6695. Internet, http://www.nssds.gsfc.nasa.gov.*

Develops and operates systems for processing, archiving, and disseminating space physics and astrophysics data.

National Institute of Standards and Technology *(Commerce Dept.), Information Services, Route I-270 and Quince Orchard Rd., Administration Bldg., #E106, Gaithersburg, MD 20899-0001; (301) 975-2786. Fax, (301) 869-8071. Paul Vassallo, director. Reference desk, (301) 975-3052. Internet, http://nvl.nist.gov.*

Conducts publications program for the institute and maintains a research information center, which includes material on engineering, chemistry, physics, mathematics, and the materials and computer sciences.

National Institute of Standards and Technology *(Commerce Dept.), Measurement Services, 820 W. Diamond Ave., Gaithersburg, MD (mailing address: Bldg. 820, #306, Gaithersburg, MD 20899); (301) 975-4500. Fax, (301) 948-3825. Peter Heydenmann, director. Internet, http://www.nist.gov.*

Disseminates physical, chemical, and engineering measurement standards and provides services to ensure accurate and compatible measurements, specifications, and codes on a national and international scale.

National Institute of Standards and Technology *(Commerce Dept.), Standard Reference Data, 820 W. Diamond Ave., Bldg. 820, #113, Gaithersburg, MD 20899; (301) 975-2200. Fax, (301) 926-0416. John Rumble Jr., chief. Information and publications, (301) 975-2208. Internet, srdata@enh.nist.gov or http://www.nist.gov/srd.*

Collects and disseminates critically evaluated physical, chemical, and materials properties data in the physical sciences and engineering for use by industry, government, and academic laboratories. Develops databases in a variety of formats, including disk, CD-ROM, online, and magnetic tape.

National Institute of Standards and Technology *(Commerce Dept.), Statistical Engineering, 820 W. Diamond Ave., #353, Gaithersburg, MD 20899; (301) 975-2839. Fax, (301) 990-4127. Keith Eberhardt, chief. Internet, http://www.nist.gov/itl/div898.*

Promotes within industry and government the use of effective statistical techniques for planning analysis of experiments in the physical sciences; interprets experiments and data collection programs.

National Museum of American History *(Smithsonian Institution), Library, 14th St. and Constitution Ave. N.W., MRC 630 20560; (202) 357-2414. Fax, (202) 357-4256. Rhoda Ratner, chief librarian. Internet, http://www.sil.si.edu/nmahhp.htm.*

Collection includes materials on the history of science and technology, with concentrations in engineering, transportation, and applied science. Maintains collection of trade catalogs and materials about expositions and world fairs. Open to the public by appointment.

National Oceanic and Atmospheric Administration *(Commerce Dept.), Library and Information Services, 1315 East-West Hwy., SSMC3, 2nd Floor, Silver Spring, MD 20910; (301) 713-2607. Fax, (301) 713-4598. Carol Watts, director. Reference service, (301) 713-2600. Internet, reference@nodc.noaa.gov or http://www.lib.noaa.gov.*

Collection includes reports, journals, monographs, and microforms on atmospheric and oceanic science. Maintains bibliographic database of other NOAA libraries, an online service, and reference materials on CD-ROM. Makes interlibrary loans; open to the public.

National Oceanic and Atmospheric Administration *(Commerce Dept.), National Environmental Satellite, Data, and Information Service, 4401 Suitland Rd., #2069, Suitland, MD 20746 (mailing address: 4700 Silver Hill Rd., STOP 9909, Washington, DC 20233-9909); (301) 457-5115. Fax, (301) 457-5276. Robert S. Winokur, assistant administrator. Internet, orders@ncdc.noaa.gov (National Climatic Data Center).*

Acquires and disseminates global environmental (marine, atmospheric, solid earth, and solar-terrestrial) data. Operates the following data facilities: National Climatic Data Center, Asheville, N.C.; National Geophysical Data Center, Boulder, Colo.; and National Oceanographic Data Center, Washington, D.C. Maintains comprehensive data and information referral service.

National Oceanic and Atmospheric Administration *(Commerce Dept.), National Oceanographic Data Center, 1315 East-West Hwy., 4th Floor, Silver Spring, MD 20910-3282; (301) 713-3267. Fax, (301) 713-3300. Henry R. Frey, director. Information and requests, (301) 606-4549. Internet, services@nodc.noaa.gov or http://www. nodc.gov.*

Offers a wide range of oceanographic data on magnetic tape, disk, CD-ROM, and hard copy; provides research scientists with data processing services; prepares statistical summaries and graphical data products. (Fee charged for some services.)

National Technical Information Service *(Commerce Dept.), 5285 Port Royal Rd., #200F, Springfield, VA 22161; (703) 605-6400. Fax, (703) 321-8547. Donald R. Johnson, director. TDD, (703) 605-6043. Sales center, (703) 605-6000; rush orders, (800) 553-6847. Internet, http://www. ntis.gov.*

Distribution center that catalogs and sells U.S. and foreign government-sponsored research, development, and scientific engineering reports and other technical analyses prepared by federal and local government agencies. Offers microfiche and computerized bibliographic search services. Online database available through commercial vendors and in machine-readable form through lease agreement.

Smithsonian Institution, *Central Reference and Loan Services, 10th St. and Constitution Ave. N.W., MRC 154 20560; (202) 357-2139. Fax, (202) 786-2443. Martin A. Smith, chief librarian. TDD, (202) 357-2328.*

Maintains collection of general reference, biographical, and interdisciplinary materials; serves as an information resource on institution libraries, a number of which have collections in scientific subjects, including horticulture, botany, science and technology, and anthropology.

Smithsonian Institution, *Dibner Library of the History of Science and Technology, 14th St. and Constitution Ave. N.W., NMAH 5016/MRC 630 20560; (202) 357-1577. Fax, (202) 633-9102. William E. Baxter, head, Special Collections. Internet, http://www.sil.si.edu.*

Collection includes major holdings in the history of science and technology dating from the fifteenth to the twentieth centuries. Extensive collections in natural history, archeology, almanacs, physical and mathematical sciences, and scientific instrumentation. Open to the public by appointment.

U.S. Geological Survey *(Interior Dept.), Earth Science Information Center, 507 National Center, Reston, VA 20192-1507; (703) 648-6045. Fax, (703) 648-5548. Susan*

Russell-Robinson, chief. U.S. maps, (800) 872-6277. Internet, http://www.usgs.gov.

Collects, organizes, and distributes cartographic, geographic, hydrologic, and other earth science information; offers maps, reports, and other publications, digital cartographic data, aerial photographs, and space imagery and manned spacecraft photographs for sale. Acts as clearinghouse on cartographic and geographic data covering the United States.

U.S. Geological Survey *(Interior Dept.), Library, 12201 Sunrise Valley Dr., MS 950, Reston, VA 22092; (703) 648-4305. Fax, (703) 648-6373. Edward H. Liszewski, chief librarian.*

Maintains collection of books, periodicals, serials, maps, and technical reports on geology, mineral and water resources, mineralogy, paleontology, petrology, soil and environmental sciences, and physics and chemistry as they relate to earth sciences. Open to the public; makes interlibrary loans.

CONGRESS

General Accounting Office, *Document Distribution Center, 700 4th St. N.W. (mailing address: P.O. Box 37050, Washington, DC 20013); (202) 512-6000. Fax, (202) 512-6061. Paula DeRoy, staff contact. Press, (202) 512-4800. Locator, (202) 512-3000. Internet, info@www.gao.gov.*

Provides information to the public on many federal programs. GAO technical publications and information about GAO publications are available upon request.

Library of Congress, *Science and Technology, 10 1st St. S.E. 20540-4750; (202) 707-5664. Fax, (202) 707-1925. William J. Sittig, chief. Science reading room, (202) 707-6401. Technical reports, (202) 707-5655.*

Offers reference service by telephone, by correspondence, and in person. Maintains a collection of more than three million technical reports.

NONPROFIT

American Statistical Assn., *1429 Duke St., Alexandria, VA 22314; (703) 684-1221. Fax, (703) 684-2037. Ray Waller, executive director. Internet, asainfo@amstat.org or http://www.amstat.org.*

Membership: individuals interested in statistics and related quantitative fields. Advises government agencies on statistics and methodology in agency research; promotes development of statistical techniques for use in business, industry, finance, government, agriculture, and science.

Commission on Professionals in Science and Technology, *1200 New York Ave. N.W., #390 20005; (202)*

326-7080. Fax, (202) 842-1603. Catherine D. Gaddy, executive director. Internet, http://www.aaas.org/cpst.

Membership: scientific societies, corporations, academicians, and individuals. Analyzes and publishes data on scientific and engineering human resources in the United States.

International Programs

See also Information and Exchange Programs (chap. 13)

AGENCIES

International Trade Administration *(Commerce Dept.), Technology and Aerospace Industries, 14th St. and Constitution Ave. N.W., #2800A 20230; (202) 482-1872. Fax, (202) 482-0856. Ellis R. Mottur, deputy assistant secretary. Internet, http://www.ita.doc.gov.*

Conducts analyses and competitive assessments of high-tech industries, including aerospace, telecommunications, computer and business equipment, microelectronics, and medical equipment and instrumentation. Develops trade policies for these industries, negotiates market access for U.S. companies, assists in promoting exports through trade missions, shows, and fairs in major overseas markets.

National Institute of Standards and Technology *(Commerce Dept.), International and Academic Affairs, Route I-270 and Quince Orchard Rd., Administration Bldg., #A505, Gaithersburg, MD 20899; (301) 975-4119. Fax, (301) 975-3530. B. Stephen Carpenter, director. Internet, http://www.nist.gov/oiaa/oiaa1.htm.*

Represents the institute in international functions; coordinates programs with foreign institutions; assists scientists from foreign countries who visit the institute for consultation. Administers a postdoctoral research associates program.

National Oceanic and Atmospheric Administration *(Commerce Dept.), National Environmental Satellite, Data, and Information Service, 4401 Suitland Rd., #2069, Suitland, MD 20746 (mailing address: 4700 Silver Hill Rd., STOP 9909, Washington, DC 20233-9909); (301) 457-5115. Fax, (301) 457-5276. Robert S. Winokur, assistant administrator. Internet, orders@ncdc.noaa.gov (National Climatic Data Center).*

Participates, with the National Meteorological Center, in the World Weather Watch Programme developed by the United Nations' World Meteorological Organization. Manages U.S. civil earth-observing satellite systems and atmospheric, oceanographic, geophysical, and solar data centers. Provides the public, businesses, and govern-ment agencies with environmental data and information products and services.

National Science Foundation, *International Programs, 4201 Wilson Blvd., #935, Arlington, VA 22230; (703) 306-1710. Fax, (703) 306-0476. Pierre Perrolle, director. Internet, http://www.nsf.gov/sbe/int.*

Coordinates and manages the foundation's international scientific activities and cooperative research and exchange programs; promotes new partnerships between U.S. scientists and engineers and their foreign colleagues; provides support for U.S. participation in international scientific organizations.

National Weather Service *(National Oceanic and Atmospheric Administration), National Center for Environmental Prediction, 5200 Auth Rd., Camp Springs, MD 20746; (301) 763-8016. Fax, (301) 763-8434. Ronald D. McPherson, director. Internet, http://www.ncep.noaa.gov.*

The National Center for Environmental Prediction and the National Environmental Satellite, Data, and Information Service are part of the World Weather Watch Programme developed by the United Nations' World Meteorological Organization. Collects data and exchanges it with other nations; provides other national weather service offices, private meteorologists, and government agencies with products, including forecast guidance products.

Office of Science and Technology Policy *(Executive Office of the President), National Security and International Affairs, Old Executive Office Bldg., #494 20502; (202) 456-2894. Fax, (202) 456-6028. Kerri-Ann Jones, associate director.*

Advises the president on international science and technology matters as they affect national security; coordinates international science and technology initiatives at the interagency level.

Smithsonian Institution, *International Relations, 1100 Jefferson Dr. S.W., #3123, MRC 705 20560; (202) 357-4282. Fax, (202) 786-2557. Francine C. Berkowitz, director.*

Fosters the development and coordinates the international aspects of Smithsonian scientific activities; facilitates basic research in the natural sciences and encourages international collaboration among individuals and institutions.

State Dept., *Oceans and International Environmental and Scientific Affairs, Main State Bldg., #7831 20520-7818; (202) 647-1554. Fax, (202) 647-0217. Melinda L. Kimble, acting assistant secretary. Press, (202) 647-0978.*

Formulates and implements policies and proposals for U.S. international scientific, technological, environmental, oceanic and marine, arctic and antarctic, and space programs; coordinates international science and technology policy with other federal agencies.

State Dept., *Scientific Programs, Main State Bldg., #5336 20520; (202) 647-2752. Fax, (202) 647-8902. Raymond E. Wanner, deputy director.*

Oversees U.S. participation in international scientific and technical organizations, including the International Atomic Energy Agency, the United Nations Environment Programme, the World Meteorological Organization, and the United Nations Educational, Scientific, and Cultural Organization. Works to ensure that United Nations agencies follow United Nations Conference on Environment and Development recommendations on sustainable growth.

Technology Administration *(Commerce Dept.), International Technology Policy, 14th St. and Constitution Ave. N.W., #4411 20230; (202) 482-1287. Fax, (202) 219-3310. Phyllis Yoshida, acting director.*

Develops and implements policies to enhance the competitiveness of U.S. technology-based industry. Provides information on foreign research and development; coordinates, on behalf of the Commerce Dept., negotiation of international science and technology agreements. Manages the Japan Technology program, which seeks to ensure access for U.S. researchers and industry to Japanese science and technology.

INTERNATIONAL ORGANIZATIONS

InterAcademy Panel on International Issues, *2101 Constitution Ave. N.W., FO 2050 20418; (202) 334-2800. Fax, (202) 334-3094. John P. Campbell, NAS contact. Internet, http://www2.nas.edu/iap.*

Membership: academies of science in countries worldwide. Promotes communication among leading authorities in the natural and social sciences; advises governments and international organizations; interests include scientific aspects of population, sustainable development, energy and other resources, and environmental protection. (National Academy of Sciences is U.S. member.)

NONPROFIT

American Assn. for the Advancement of Science, *International Programs, 1200 New York Ave. N.W., 7th Floor 20005; (202) 326-6650. Fax, (202) 289-4958. Richard Getzinger, director. Internet, http://www.aaas.org.*

Administers programs concerned with international science and engineering; works to further understanding

of global problems with scientific and technological components; provides policymakers at national and international levels with information from the scientific community.

Japan Information Access Project, *2000 P St. N.W., #620 20036; (202) 822-6040. Fax, (202) 822-6044. Mindy Kotler, director. Internet, access@nmjc.org or http://www.nmjc.org/jiap.*

Membership organization that works to strengthen international understanding of Japanese science, technology, management, and business information. Teaches professionals how to access, use, and evaluate Japanese information for research and planning. Studies Japanese and Western science, technology, industry, management, and trade issues.

National Research Council, *International Affairs, 2101 Constitution Ave. N.W., FO 2050 20418; (202) 334-2800. Fax, (202) 334-3094. John Boright, executive director. Internet, http://www2.nas.edu/oia.*

Serves the international interests of the National Research Council, National Academy of Sciences, National Academy of Engineering, and Institute of Medicine. Promotes effective application of science and technology to the economic and social problems of industrialized and developing countries; advises U.S. government agencies; participates in international organizations, conferences, and cooperative activities.

Research Applications

AGENCIES

Defense Technical Information Center *(Defense Dept.), 8725 John Jay Kingman Rd., #0944, Fort Belvoir, VA 22060-6218; (703) 767-9100. Fax, (703) 767-9183. Kurt N. Molholm, administrator. Registration, (703) 767-8201. Internet, http://www.dtic.mil.*

Acts as a central repository for the Defense Dept.'s collection of current and completed research and development efforts in all fields of science and technology. Disseminates research and development information to contractors, grantees, and registered organizations working on government research and development projects, particularly for the Defense Dept. Users must register with the center.

National Aeronautics and Space Administration, *Space Science, 300 E St. S.W. (mailing address: NASA Headquarters, Mail Code S, Washington, DC 20546); (202) 358-1409. Fax, (202) 358-3092. Wesley T. Huntress Jr., associate administrator. Information, (202) 358-1547. Internet, http://www.hq.nasa.gov/office/oss.*

Provides information on technology developed during NASA's activities that have practical applications in other fields; maintains a data bank. (Accepts written requests for specific technical information.)

National Institute of Standards and Technology *(Commerce Dept.), Route I-270 and Quince Orchard Rd., Gaithersburg, MD (mailing address: Bldg. 101, #A1134, Gaithersburg, MD 20899); (301) 975-2300. Fax, (301) 869-8972. Raymond Kammer, director. Information, (301) 975-2762. Internet, http://www.nist.gov.*

Nonregulatory agency that serves as national reference and measurement laboratory for the physical and engineering sciences. Works with industry, government agencies, and academia; conducts research in electronics, manufacturing, physics, chemistry, radiation, materials science, applied mathematics, computer science and technology, and engineering sciences.

National Science Foundation, *Human Resource Development, 4201 Wilson Blvd., #815, Arlington, VA 22230; (703) 306-1640. Fax, (703) 306-0423. Roosevelt Calbert, director.*

Supports and encourages participation in scientific and engineering research by women, minorities, and people with disabilities. Awards grants and scholarships.

Technology Administration *(Commerce Dept.), Technology Policy, 14th St. and Constitution Ave. N.W., #4814C 20230; (202) 482-1581. Fax, (202) 482-4817. Vacant, assistant secretary. Internet, http://www.ta.doc. gov/OTPolicy/default.html.*

Promotes the removal of barriers to the commercialization of technology; analyzes federal research and development funding; acts as an information clearinghouse.

NONPROFIT

American National Standards Institute, *7315 Wisconsin Ave., #250-E, Bethesda, MD 20814; (301) 469-3360. Fax, (301) 469-3361. John Donaldson, vice president, Conformity Assessment. Customer service, (888) 267-4783. Internet, info@ansi.org or http://www.ansi.org.*

Administers and coordinates the voluntary standardization system for the U.S. private sector; maintains staff contacts for specific industries. Serves as U.S. member of the International Organization for Standardization (ISO) and hosts the U.S. National Committee of the International Electrotechnical Commission (IEC). (ANSI headquarters in New York.)

National Center for Advanced Technologies, *1250 Eye St. N.W., #1100 20005-3922; (202) 371-8451. Fax,* *(202) 371-8573. Stan Siegel, president. Internet, ncat@ncat.com or http://www.access.digex.net/~ncat.*

Encourages U.S. competition in the world market by uniting government, industry, and university efforts to develop advanced technologies. (Affiliated with the Aerospace Industries Assn. of America.)

Public Technology, *1301 Pennsylvania Ave. N.W., #800 20004; (202) 626-2400. Fax, (202) 626-2498. Costis Toregas, president. Press, (202) 626-2412. Library, (202) 626-2456. Toll-free, (800) 852-4934. Internet, press@pti.nw. dc.us or http://pti.nw.dc.us.*

Cooperative research, development, and technology-transfer organization of cities and counties in North America. Applies available technological innovations and develops other methods to improve public services. Participates in international conferences.

Rand Corporation, *1333 H St. N.W., #800 20005; (202) 296-5000. Fax, (202) 296-7960. David Chu, director, Washington Office. Internet, http://www.rand.org.*

Research organization. Interests include energy, emerging technologies and critical systems, space and transportation, technology policies, international cooperative research, water resources, ocean and atmospheric sciences, and other technologies in defense and nondefense areas. (Headquarters in Santa Monica, Calif.)

SRI International, *1611 N. Kent St., #700, Arlington, VA 22209; (703) 524-2053. Fax, (703) 247-8569. Jack F. Scherrer, vice president, Washington Office. Internet, http://www.sri.com.*

Research and consulting organization that conducts basic and applied research for government, industry, and business. Interests include engineering, physical and life sciences, and international research. (Headquarters in Menlo Park, Calif.)

See also Industrial Research Institute (p. 154)

 # BIOLOGY AND LIFE SCIENCES

AGENCIES

Animal and Plant Health Inspection Service *(Agriculture Dept.), National Biological Control Institute, 4700 River Rd., Unit 5, Riverdale, MD 20737-1229; (301) 734-4329. Fax, (301) 734-7823. Michael Oraze, acting director. Internet, http://www.aphis.gov/nbci/nbci.html.*

Division of APHIS Plant Protection and Quarantine. Oversees efforts to control animal and plant pests; works to develop a national and international biological control network, and to document and improve procedures for importation, interstate movement, and release of biological control agents.

Armed Forces Radiobiology Research Institute *(Defense Dept.), National Naval Medical Center, 8901 Wisconsin Ave., Bethesda, MD 20889-5603; (301) 295-1210. Fax, (301) 295-4967. Col. Robert Eng (MSUSA), director. Internet, http://www.afrri.usuhs.mil.*

Serves as the principal ionizing radiation radiobiology research laboratory under the jurisdiction of the Uniformed Services University of the Health Sciences. Participates in international conferences and projects. Library open to the public.

National Aeronautics and Space Administration, *Life Sciences, 300 E St. S.W. 20546; (202) 358-2530. Fax, (202) 358-4168. Joan Vernikos, director.*

Conducts NASA's life sciences research.

National Institute of General Medical Sciences *(National Institutes of Health), 45 Center Dr., MSC-6200, #2AN12B, Bethesda, MD 20892-6200; (301) 594-2172. Fax, (301) 402-0156. Marvin Cassman, director. Internet, http://www.nih.gov/nigms.*

Supports basic biomedical research and training that are not targeted to specific diseases; focus includes cell biology, genetics, pharmacology, and systemic response to trauma and anesthesia.

National Museum of Natural History *(Smithsonian Institution), Library, 10th St. and Constitution Ave. N.W., #51 20560; (202) 357-1496. Fax, (202) 357-1896. Ann Juneau, chief librarian.*

Maintains reference collections covering systematic biology and taxonomy, invertebrate biology and vertebrate zoology, paleobiology, botany, general geology and mineral sciences, oceanography, entomology, ecology, evolution, limnology, anthropology, and ethnology; permits on-site use of the collections. Open to the public by appointment; makes interlibrary loans.

National Museum of Natural History *(Smithsonian Institution), Naturalist Center, 741 Miller Dr. S.E., #G2, Leesburg, VA 20175; (703) 779-9712. Fax, (703) 779-9715. Richard H. Efthim, manager. Toll-free, (800) 729-7725. Internet, natcenter@aol.com or http://nmnhgoph.si.edu/museum/learn.html.*

Maintains natural history research and reference library with books and 30,000 objects, including minerals, rocks, plants, animals, shells and corals, insects, invertebrates, micro- and macrofossil materials, and microbiological and anthropological materials. Facilities include study equipment such as microscopes, dissecting instruments, and plant presses. Operates a teachers' ref-

erence center. Library open to the public; reservations required for groups of six or more.

National Oceanic and Atmospheric Administration *(Commerce Dept.), National Marine Fisheries Service, 1315 East-West Hwy., Silver Spring, MD 20910; (301) 713-2239. Fax, (301) 713-2258. Rolland A. Schmitten, assistant administrator. Press, (301) 713-2370. Internet, http://kingfish.ssp.nmfs.gov.*

Conducts research and collects data on marine ecology and biology; collects, analyzes, and provides information through the Marine Resources Monitoring, Assessment, and Prediction Program. Administers the Magnuson Fishery Conservation and Management Act and marine mammals and endangered species protection programs. Works with the Army Corps of Engineers on research into habitat restoration and conservation.

National Science Foundation, *Biological Sciences, 4201 Wilson Blvd., #605, Arlington, VA 22230; (703) 306-1400. Fax, (703) 306-0343. Mary E. Clutter, assistant director. Information, (703) 306-1234. Internet, http://www.nsf.gov/bio.*

Directorate that provides grants for research in the cellular and molecular biosciences, environmental biology, integrative biology and neuroscience, and biological infrastructure.

Naval Medical Research Institute *(Defense Dept.), 8901 Wisconsin Ave., Bethesda, MD 20889-5607; (301) 295-0021. Fax, (301) 295-2720. Capt. Thomas J. Contreares Jr., commanding officer. Internet, http://131.158.70.70.*

Performs basic and applied biomedical research in areas of military importance, including infectious diseases, hyperbaric medicine, wound repair enhancement, environmental stress, and immunobiology. Provides support to field laboratories and naval hospitals; monitors research internationally.

U.S. Geological Survey *(Interior Dept.), Biological Resources, 12201 Sunrise Valley Dr., Reston, VA 20192; (703) 648-4050. Fax, (703) 648-4042. Dennis B. Fenn, chief biologist. Internet, http://www.nbs.gov.*

Performs research in support of biological resource management. Monitors and reports on the status of the nation's biotic resources. Conducts research on wildlife, fish, insects, and plants, including the effects of disease and environmental contaminants on endangered and other species.

NONPROFIT

American Institute of Biological Sciences, *1444 Eye St. N.W., #200 20005; (202) 628-1500. Fax, (202) 628-*

1509. Richard O'Grady, executive director. Toll-free, (800) 992-2427. Internet, http://www.aibs.org.

Membership: biologists, biological associations, industrial research laboratories, and others interested in biology. Promotes interdisciplinary cooperation among members engaged in biological research and education; conducts educational programs for members; sponsors Congressional Science Fellowship; administers projects supported by government grants. Monitors legislation and regulations.

American Society for Biochemistry and Molecular Biology, 9650 Rockville Pike, Bethesda, MD 20814; (301) 530-7145. Fax, (301) 571-1824. Charles C. Hancock, executive officer. Internet, asbmb@asbmb.faseb.org or http://www.faseb.org/asbmb.

Professional society of biological chemists; membership by election. Participates in International Union of Biochemistry and Molecular Biology (headquartered in Berlin). Monitors legislation and regulations.

American Society for Cell Biology, 9650 Rockville Pike, Bethesda, MD 20814-3992; (301) 530-7153. Fax, (301) 530-7139. Elizabeth Marincola, executive director. Internet, ascbinfo@ascb.org or http://www.acsb.org.

Membership: scientists who have education or research experience in cell biology or an allied field. Promotes scientific exchange worldwide; organizes courses, workshops, and symposia. Monitors legislation and regulations.

American Society for Microbiology, 1325 Massachusetts Ave. N.W. 20005; (202) 737-3600. Fax, (202) 942-9333. Michael I. Goldberg, executive director. Press, (202) 942-9297. Internet, oed@asmusa.org or http://www.asmusa.org.

Membership: microbiologists. Encourages education, training, scientific investigation, and application of research results in microbiology and related subjects; participates in international research.

American Type Culture Collection, 12301 Parklawn Dr., Rockville, MD 20852; (301) 881-2600. Fax, (301) 816-4363. Raymond H. Cypess, president. Internet, help@atcc.org or http://www.atcc.org.

Independent organization devoted to preserving cultures of microorganisms, viruses, and plant and animal cell lines; distributes them for study among scientists. Conducts workshops and training courses on using these materials.

AOAC International, 481 N. Frederick Ave., #500, Gaithersburg, MD 20877; (301) 924-7077. Fax, (301) 924-7089. Ronald R. Christensen, executive director. Toll-free,

(800) 379-2622. Internet, info@aoac.org or http://www.aoac.org.

International association of analytical science professionals, companies, government agencies, nongovernmental organizations, and institutions. Promotes methods validation and quality measurements in the analytical sciences. Supports the development, testing, validation, and publication of reliable chemical and biological methods of analyzing foods, drugs, feed, fertilizers, pesticides, water, forensic materials, and other substances.

Biophysical Society, 9650 Rockville Pike, #L0512, Bethesda, MD 20814-3998; (301) 530-7114. Fax, (301) 530-7133. Rosalba Kampman, executive director. Internet, http://www.biophysics.org/biophys.

Membership: scientists, professors, and researchers engaged in biophysics or related fields. Encourages development and dissemination of knowledge in biophysics.

Carnegie Institution of Washington, 1530 P St. N.W. 20005-1910; (202) 387-6400. Fax, (202) 387-8092. Maxine F. Singer, president. Library, (202) 939-1120. Internet, http://www.ciw.edu.

Conducts research in the physical and biological sciences at the following centers: the observatories of the Carnegie Institution with headquarters in Pasadena, Calif.; Geophysical Laboratory and Department of Terrestrial Magnetism in Washington, D.C.; Department of Plant Biology in Stanford, Calif.; and Department of Embryology in Baltimore, Md. Refers specific inquiries to appropriate department. Library open to the public by appointment.

Ecological Society of America, 2010 Massachusetts Ave. N.W., #400 20036; (202) 833-8773. Fax, (202) 833-8775. Kathryn McCarter, executive director. Internet, esahq@esa.org or http://esa.sdsc.edu.

Promotes research in ecology, the scientific study of the relationship between organisms and their past, present, and future environments. Interests include biotechnology; management of natural resources, habitats, and ecosystems to protect biological diversity; and ecologically sound public policies.

Federation of American Societies for Experimental Biology, 9650 Rockville Pike, Bethesda, MD 20814-3998; (301) 530-7090. Fax, (301) 571-0686. Michael J. Jackson, executive director. Information, (301) 571-0657. Internet, http://www.faseb.org.

Federation of fourteen scientific and educational groups: American Physiological Society, American Society for Biochemistry and Molecular Biology, American Society for Pharmacology and Experimental Therapeutics, Society for Investigative Pathology, American Institute of Nutrition, American Assn. of Immunologists, American Society for Cell Biology, Biophysical Society, The Protein Society, American Assn. of Anatomists, American Society for Bone and Mineral Research, Society for Developmental Biology, American Peptide Society, and Assn. of Biomolecular Resource Facilities. Serves as support group for member societies; participates in international conferences.

See also American Assn. for the Advancement of Science (p. 593); Howard Hughes Medical Institute (p. 386); National Geographic Society (p. 594)

Biotechnology

See also Agricultural Research/Education (chap. 2); Genetic Disorders (chap. 11)

AGENCIES

Cooperative State Research, Education, and Extension Service *(Agriculture Dept.), Competitive Research Grants and Awards Management, 901 D St. S.W., #322 20250-2240; (202) 401-1761. Fax, (202) 401-3237. Sally Rockey, deputy administrator.*

Administers competitive research grants for biotechnology in the agricultural field. Oversees research in biotechnology.

Environmental Protection Agency, *Prevention, Pesticides, and Toxic Substances, 401 M St. S.W., #627 East Tower 20460; (202) 260-6900. Fax, (202) 260-0949. Elizabeth Milewski, special assistant, Biotechnology.*

Regulates certain agricultural and industrial products of biotechnology.

National Institute of Standards and Technology *(Commerce Dept.), Chemical Science and Technology Laboratory, Route I-270 and Quince Orchard Rd., Gaithersburg, MD 20899; (301) 975-3145. Fax, (301) 975-3845. Hratch G. Semerjian, director.*

Conducts basic and applied research in biotechnology.

National Institutes of Health *(Health and Human Services Dept.), Recombinant DNA Activities, 6000 Executive Blvd., #302, MSC 7010, Bethesda, MD 20892-7010; (301) 496-9838. Fax, (301) 496-9839. Deborah Knorr, acting director. Internet, http://www.nih.gov/od/orda.*

Reviews requests submitted to the National Institutes of Health involving recombinant DNA technology and implements research guidelines.

National Library of Medicine *(National Institutes of Health), National Center for Biotechnology Information, 8600 Rockville Pike, Bldg. 38A, 8th Floor, Bethesda, MD 20894; (301) 496-2475. Fax, (301) 480-9241. Dr. David J. Lipman, director. Internet, http://www.ncbi.nlm.nih.gov.*

Creates automated systems for storing and analyzing knowledge of molecular biology and genetics. Develops new information technologies to aid in understanding the molecular processes that control human health and disease. Conducts basic research in computational molecular biology.

Office of Science and Technology Policy *(Executive Office of the President), Biotechnology Subcommittee of the Committee on Fundamental Science, 4201 Wilson Blvd., #605, Arlington, VA 22250; (703) 306-1400. Fax, (703) 306-0343. Mary E. Clutter, chair.*

Serves as a forum for addressing biotechnology research issues, sharing information, identifying gaps in scientific knowledge, and developing consensus among concerned federal agencies. Facilitates continuing cooperation among federal agencies on topical issues.

NONPROFIT

Biotechnology Industry Organization, *1625 K St. N.W., #1100 20006-1604; (202) 857-0244. Fax, (202) 857-0237. Carl B. Feldbaum, president. Internet, bio@bio.org or http://www.bio.org.*

Membership: companies engaged in biotechnology. Monitors government activities at all levels; promotes educational activities; conducts workshops.

Friends of the Earth, *1025 Vermont Ave. N.W., #300 20005-6303; (202) 783-7400. Fax, (202) 783-0444. Brent Blackwelder, president. Internet, foe@foe.org or http://www.foe.org.*

Monitors legislation and regulations on issues related to seed industry consolidation and patenting laws and on business developments in agricultural biotechnology and their effect on farming, food production, genetic resources, and the environment.

Kennedy Institute of Ethics *(Georgetown University), 1437 37th St. N.W. 20057; (202) 687-8099. Fax, (202) 687-8089. Dr. Leroy Walters, director. Library, (800) 633-3849; in Washington, D.C., (202) 687-3885. Internet, http://guweb.georgetown.edu/kennedy.*

Sponsors research on medical ethics. Interests include legal and ethical definitions of death, allocation of scarce health resources, and recombinant DNA and human gene therapy. Supplies National Library of Medicine with online database on bioethics; publishes annual bibliography. Library open to the public by appointment.

Botany

See also Horticulture and Gardening (chap. 2)

AGENCIES

National Arboretum *(Agriculture Dept.), 3501 New York Ave. N.E. 20002; (202) 245-4539. Fax, (202) 245-4575. Thomas S. Elias, director. Library, (202) 245-4967.*

Maintains public display of plants on 444 acres; provides information and makes referrals concerning cultivated plants (exclusive of field crops and fruits); conducts plant breeding and research; maintains herbarium. Library open to the public by appointment.

National Museum of Natural History *(Smithsonian Institution), Botany, 10th St. and Constitution Ave. N.W., MRC 166 20560-0166; (202) 357-2534. Fax, (202) 786-2563. John Kress, chair. Internet, http://nmnhwww.si.edu/departments/botany.html.*

Conducts botanical research worldwide; furnishes information on the identification, distribution, and local names of flowering plants; studies threatened and endangered plant species.

Smithsonian Institution, *Botany Branch Library, 10th St. and Constitution Ave. N.W., MRC 166 (National Museum of Natural History) 20560; (202) 357-2715. Fax, (202) 357-1896. Ruth F. Schallert, librarian. Internet, http://www.sil.si.edu.*

Collections include taxonomic botany, plant morphology, general botany, history of botany, grasses, and algae. Permits on-site use of collections (appointment preferred); makes interlibrary loans.

CONGRESS

U.S. Botanic Garden, *245 1st St. S.W. 20024; (202) 225-8333. Fax, (202) 225-1561. Jeffrey P. Cooper-Smith, executive director. Flower show information, (202) 225-7099 (recording).*

Collects, cultivates, and grows various plants for public display and study; identifies botanic specimens and furnishes information on proper growing methods. Conducts horticultural classes and tours. Sponsors four seasonal flower shows annually.

NONPROFIT

American Society for Horticultural Science, *600 Cameron St., Alexandria, VA 22314-2562; (703) 836-4606. Fax, (703) 836-2024. Michael Neff, executive director. Internet, ashs@ashs.org or http://www.ashs.org.*

Membership: educators, government workers, firms, associations, and individuals interested in horticultural science. Promotes scientific research and education in horticulture, including international exchange of information.

American Society of Plant Physiologists, *15501 Monona Dr., Rockville, MD 20855-2768; (301) 251-0560. Fax, (301) 279-2996. Kenneth M. Beam, executive director. Internet, aspp@aspp.org or http://aspp.org.*

Membership: plant physiologists, plant biochemists, and molecular biologists. Seeks to educate and promote public interest in plant physiology. Publishes journals; provides placement service for members; sponsors annual meeting of plant scientists.

National Assn. of Plant Patent Owners, *1250 Eye St. N.W., #500 20005-3922; (202) 789-2900. Fax, (202) 789-1893. Craig Regelbrugge, administrator.*

Membership: owners of patents on newly propagated horticultural plants. Informs members of plant patents issued, provisions of patent laws, and changes in practice. Promotes the development, protection, production, and distribution of new varieties of horticultural plants. Works with international organizations of plant breeders on matters of common interest. (Affiliated with the American Nursery and Landscape Assn.)

Zoology

See also Animals and Plants (chap. 9)

AGENCIES

National Museum of Natural History *(Smithsonian Institution), Entomology, 10th St. and Constitution Ave. N.W., MRC 105 20560; (202) 357-2078. Fax, (202) 786-2894. Robert K. Robbins, chair. Library, (202) 357-2354. Internet, http://nmnhwww.si.edu/departments/entom.html.*

Conducts worldwide research in entomology. Maintains the national collection of insects; lends insect specimens to specialists for research and classification. Library open to the public by appointment.

National Museum of Natural History *(Smithsonian Institution), Invertebrate Zoology, 10th St. and Constitution Ave. N.W., MRC 163 20560; (202) 357-2030. Fax, (202) 357-3043. Kristian Fauchald, chair. Internet, http://nmnhwww.si.edu/departments/invert.html.*

Conducts research on the identity, morphology, histology, life history, distribution, classification, and ecology of marine, terrestrial, and fresh water invertebrate animals (except insects); maintains the national collection of invertebrate animals; aids exhibit and educational programs; conducts pre- and postdoctoral fellowship programs; provides facilities for visiting scientists in the profession.

National Museum of Natural History (*Smithsonian Institution*), *Vertebrate Zoology,* 10th St. and Constitution Ave. N.W., MRC 109 20560; (202) 357-2740. Fax, (202) 786-2979. G. David Johnson, chair. Internet, http://nmnhwww.si.edu/departments/vert.html.

Conducts research worldwide on the systematics, ecology, and behavior of mammals, birds, reptiles, amphibians, and fish; maintains the national collection of specimens.

NONPROFIT

American Zoo and Aquarium Assn., 7970-D Old Georgetown Rd., Bethesda, MD 20814-2493; (301) 907-7777. Fax, (301) 907-2980. Sydney J. Butler, executive director. Internet, http://www.aza.org.

Membership: interested individuals and professionally run zoos and aquariums in North America. Administers professional accreditation program; participates in worldwide conservation, education, and research activities. (Membership services office in Wheeling, W.Va.)

Entomological Society of America, 9301 Annapolis Rd., Lanham, MD 20706; (301) 731-4535. Fax, (301) 731-4538. Doug Kleine, executive director. Internet, esa@entsoc.org or http://www.entsoc.org.

Scientific association that promotes the science of entomology and the interests of professionals in the field. Advises on crop protection, food chain, and individual and urban health matters dealing with insect pests.

⬛ ENGINEERING

See also Construction (chap. 12)

AGENCIES

National Institute of Standards and Technology (*Commerce Dept.*), *Electronics and Electrical Engineering Laboratory,* Route I-270 and Quince Orchard Rd., Bldg. 220, #B358, Gaithersburg, MD 20899; (301) 975-2220. Fax, (301) 975-4091. Judson French, director. Internet, eeel@nist.gov or http://www.eeel.nist.gov.

Provides focus for research, development, and applications in the fields of electrical, electronic, quantum electric, and electromagnetic materials engineering. Interests include fundamental physical constants, practical data, measurement methods, theory, standards, technology, technical services, and international trade.

National Institute of Standards and Technology (*Commerce Dept.*), *Manufacturing Engineering Laboratory,* Route I-270 and Quince Orchard Rd., Bldg. 220,

#B322, Gaithersburg, MD 20899; (301) 975-3400. Fax, (301) 948-5668. Richard H. F. Jackson, director. Internet, http://www.mel.nist.gov.

Collects technical data, develops standards in production engineering, and publishes findings; produces the technical base for proposed standards and technology for industrial and mechanical engineering; provides instrument design, fabrication, and repair. Helps establish international standards.

National Science Foundation, *Engineering,* 4201 Wilson Blvd., #505, Arlington, VA 22230; (703) 306-1300. Fax, (703) 306-0289. Elbert L. Marsh, acting assistant director. Internet, http://www.eng.nsf.gov.

Directorate that supports fundamental research and education in engineering through grants and special equipment awards. Programs are designed to enhance international competitiveness and to improve the quality of engineering in the United States. Oversees the following divisions: Electrical and Communications Systems; Chemical and Transport Systems; Engineering Education and Centers; Civil and Mechanical Systems; Design, Manufacture, and Industrial Innovation; and Bioengineering and Environmental Systems.

See also National Institute of Standards and Technology, Information Services (p. 595)

NONPROFIT

American Assn. of Engineering Societies, 1111 19th St. N.W., #403 20036-3690; (202) 296-2237. Fax, (202) 296-1151. Tom Price, executive director. Internet, http://www.aaes.org.

Federation of engineering societies; members work in industry, construction, government, academia, and private practice. Advances the knowledge, understanding, and practice of engineering. Serves as delegate to the World Federation of Engineering Organizations.

American Consulting Engineers Council, 1015 15th St. N.W., #802 20005; (202) 347-7474. Fax, (202) 898-0068. Howard M. Messner, executive vice president. Internet, http://www.acec.org.

Membership: practicing consulting engineering firms and state, local, and regional consulting engineers councils. Serves as an information clearinghouse for member companies in such areas as legislation, legal cases, marketing, management, professional liability, business practices, and insurance. Monitors legislation and regulations.

American Consulting Engineers Council, *Research and Management Foundation,* 1015 15th St. N.W., #802

20005; (202) 347-7474. Fax, (202) 898-0068. Thomas Kern, executive director.

Conducts research and educational activities to improve engineering practices, professional cooperation, and ties to government. Provides information and training to member organizations on research and analysis, management training, access to international markets, and community involvement.

American Society for Engineering Education, *1818 N St. N.W., #600 20036; (202) 331-3500. Fax, (202) 265-8504. Frank L. Huband, executive director. Press, (202) 331-3537. Internet, http://www.asee.org.*

Membership: engineering faculty and administrators, professional engineers, government agencies, and engineering colleges, corporations, and professional societies. Conducts research, conferences, and workshops on engineering education. Monitors legislation and regulations.

American Society of Civil Engineers, *1801 Alexander Bell Dr., Reston, VA 20191-4400; (703) 295-6000. Fax, (703) 295-6333. James E. Davis, executive director. Internet, http://www.asce.org.*

Membership: professionals and students in civil engineering. Develops and produces consensus standards for construction documents and building codes. Maintains the Civil Engineering Research Foundation, which focuses national attention and resources on the research needs of the civil engineering profession. Participates in international conferences.

American Society of Mechanical Engineers, *1828 L St. N.W., #906 20036; (202) 785-3756. Fax, (202) 429-9417. Philip W. Hamilton, managing director, Public Affairs. Internet, grdept@asme.org or http://www.asme.org.*

Serves as a clearinghouse for sharing of information among federal, state, and local governments and the engineering profession. Monitors legislation and regulations. (Headquarters in New York.)

ASFE/Assn. of Professional Firms Practicing in the Geosciences, *8811 Colesville Rd., #G106, Silver Spring, MD 20910; (301) 565-2733. Fax, (301) 589-2017. John P. Bachner, executive vice president. Internet, info@asfe.org or http://www.asfe.org.*

Membership: consulting geotechnical and geoenvironmental engineering firms. Conducts seminars and a peer review program on quality control policies and procedures in geotechnical engineering.

Institute of Electrical and Electronics Engineers— United States Activities, *1828 L St. N.W., #1202 20036-5104; (202) 785-0017. Fax, (202) 785-0835. W. Thomas Suttle, managing director, Professional Activities. Internet, ieeeusa@ieee.org or http://www.ieee.org/usab.*

U.S. arm of an international technological and professional organization concerned with all areas of electrotechnology policy, including aerospace, computers, communications, biomedicine, electric power, and consumer electronics. (Headquarters in New York.)

International Federation of Professional and Technical Engineers, *8630 Fenton St., #400, Silver Spring, MD 20910; (301) 565-9016. Fax, (301) 565-0018. Paul E. Almeida, president. Internet, http://www.ifpte.org.*

Membership: approximately 50,000 technicians, engineers, scientists, professionals, and other workers, including government employees. Helps members negotiate pay, benefits, and better working conditions; conducts training programs and workshops. Monitors legislation and regulations. (Affiliated with the AFL-CIO and the Canadian Labour Congress.)

International Microelectronics and Packaging Society, *1850 Centennial Park Dr., #105, Reston, VA 20191-1517; (703) 758-1060. Fax, (703) 758-1066. Richard Breck, executive director. Toll-free, (800) 535-4746. Internet, imaps@imaps.org or http://www.imaps.org.*

Membership: persons involved in the microelectronics industry worldwide. Integrates disciplines of science and engineering; fosters exchange of information among complementary technologies, including ceramics, thin and thick films, surface mounts, semiconductor packaging, discrete semiconductor devices, monolithic circuits, and multichip modules; disseminates technical knowledge.

International Test and Evaluation Assn., *4400 Fair Lakes Court, Fairfax, VA 22033-3899; (703) 631-6220. Fax, (703) 631-6221. R. Alan Plishker, executive director. Internet, http://www.itea.org.*

Membership: engineers, scientists, managers, and other industry, government, and academic professionals interested in testing and evaluating products and complex systems. Provides a forum for information exchange; monitors international research.

National Academy of Engineering, *2101 Constitution Ave. N.W., #218 20418; (202) 334-3200. Fax, (202) 334-1680. William A. Wulf, president; William Salmon, executive officer, (202) 334-3677. Information, (202) 334-2138. Library, (202) 334-2125. Publications, (800) 624-6242; in Washington, (202) 334-3313. Internet, http://www.nae.edu.*

Independent society whose members are elected in recognition of important contributions to the field of engineering and technology. Shares responsibility with the National Academy of Sciences for examining questions of science and technology at the request of the federal government; promotes international cooperation

Library open to the public by appointment. (Affiliated with the National Academy of Sciences.)

National Society of Professional Engineers, *1420 King St., Alexandria, VA 22314; (703) 684-2800. Fax, (703) 836-4875. Russell Jones, executive director. Internet, http://www.nspe.org.*

Membership: U.S. licensed professional engineers from all disciplines. Holds engineering seminars; operates an information center; interests include international practice of engineering.

🗺️ ENVIRONMENTAL AND EARTH SCIENCES

See also Resources Management (chap. 9)

AGENCIES

Arctic Research Commission, *4350 N. Fairfax Dr., #630, Arlington, VA 22203; (703) 525-0111. Fax, (703) 525-0114. Garrett W. Brass, executive director.*

Presidential advisory commission that develops policy for arctic research; assists the interagency Arctic Research Policy Committee in implementing a national plan of arctic research; recommends improvements in logistics, data management, and dissemination of arctic information.

National Aeronautics and Space Administration, *Earth Science, 300 E St. S.W. (mailing address: NASA Headquarters, Mail Code Y, Washington, DC 20546); (202) 358-1700. Fax, (202) 358-3092. Ghassem R. Asrar, associate administrator.*

Conducts programs dealing with the earth as observed from space; conducts upper atmospheric and terrestrial studies and meteorological and ocean research.

National Oceanic and Atmospheric Administration *(Commerce Dept.), 14th St. and Constitution Ave. N.W. 20230; (202) 482-3436. Fax, (202) 408-9674. D. James Baker, under secretary. Information, (202) 482-2000. Press, (202) 482-6090. Internet, http://www.noaa.gov.*

Conducts research in marine and atmospheric sciences; issues weather forecasts and warnings vital to public safety and the national economy; surveys resources of the sea; analyzes economic aspects of fisheries operations; develops and implements policies on international fisheries; provides states with grants to conserve coastal zone areas; protects marine mammals; maintains a national environmental center with data from satellite observa-

tions and other sources including meteorological, oceanic, geodetic, and seismological data centers; provides colleges and universities with grants for research, education, and marine advisory services; prepares and provides nautical and aeronautical charts and maps.

National Oceanic and Atmospheric Administration *(Commerce Dept.), Library and Information Services, 1315 East-West Hwy., SSMC3, 2nd Floor, Silver Spring, MD 20910; (301) 713-2607. Fax, (301) 713-4598. Carol Watts, director. Reference service, (301) 713-2600. Internet, reference@nodc.noaa.gov or http://www.lib.noaa.gov.*

Collection includes books, periodicals, and microforms on earth, marine, and atmospheric sciences. Maintains bibliographic database of other NOAA libraries, an online service, and reference materials on CD-ROM. Makes interlibrary loans; open to the public.

National Science Foundation, *Geosciences, 4201 Wilson Blvd., #705N, Arlington, VA 22230; (703) 306-1500. Fax, (703) 306-0372. Robert W. Corell, assistant director. Internet, http://www.geo.nsf.gov.*

Directorate that supports research about Earth, including its atmosphere, continents, oceans, and interior. Works to improve the education and human resource base for the geosciences; participates in international and multidisciplinary activities, especially to study changes in the global climate.

National Science Foundation, *Polar Programs, 4201 Wilson Blvd., #755S, Arlington, VA 22230; (703) 306-1030. Fax, (703) 306-0645. John Hunt, acting director; Dennis Peacock, program manager, Antarctica Science, (703) 306-1031. Internet, http://www.nsf.gov/od/opp.*

Funds and manages U.S. activity in Antarctica; provides grants for arctic programs in polar biology and medicine, earth sciences, atmospheric sciences, meteorology, ocean sciences, and glaciology. The Polar Information Program serves as a clearinghouse for polar data and makes referrals on specific questions.

Smithsonian Environmental Research Center *(Smithsonian Institution), 647 Contees Wharf Rd., Edgewater, MD (mailing address: P.O. Box 28, Edgewater, MD 21037); (410) 798-4424. Fax, (301) 261-7954. Ross Simons, acting director. Internet, http://www.serc.si.edu.*

Performs laboratory and field research that measures physical, chemical, and biological interactions to determine the mechanisms of environmental responses to humans' use of air, land, and water. Evaluates properties of the environment that affect the functions of living organisms. Maintains research laboratories, public education program, facilities for controlled environments, and estuarine and terrestrial lands.

U.S. Geological Survey *(Interior Dept.),* *12201 Sunrise Valley Dr., Reston, VA 20192; (703) 648-7411. Fax, (703) 648-4454. Thomas J. Casadevall, director. Information, (703) 648-7469. Press, (703) 648-4460. Library, (703) 648-4305. Internet, http://www.usgs.gov.*

Provides reports, maps, and databases that describe and analyze water, energy, and mineral resources; the land surface; and the underlying geological structure and dynamic processes of the earth.

U.S. Geological Survey *(Interior Dept.), Library,* *12201 Sunrise Valley Dr., MS 950, Reston, VA 22092; (703) 648-4305. Fax, (703) 648-6373. Edward H. Liszewski, chief librarian.*

Maintains collection of books, periodicals, serials, maps, and technical reports on geology, mineral and water resources, mineralogy, paleontology, petrology, soil and environmental sciences, and physics and chemistry as they relate to earth sciences. Open to the public; makes interlibrary loans.

CONGRESS

House Government Reform and Oversight Committee, *Subcommittee on National Economic Growth, Natural Resources, and Regulatory Affairs, B377 RHOB 20515; (202) 225-4407. Fax, (202) 225-2441. David M. McIntosh, R-Ind., chair; Mildred Webber, staff director. Internet, http://www.house.gov/reform.*

Oversees operations of the National Oceanic and Atmospheric Administration.

House Resources Committee, *Subcommittee on Energy and Mineral Resources, 1626 LHOB 20515; (202) 225-9297. Fax, (202) 225-5255. Barbara Cubin, R-Wyo., chair; William Condit, staff director. Internet, http://www.house.gov/resources.*

Jurisdiction over U.S. Geological Survey legislation, except water-related programs.

House Resources Committee, *Subcommittee on Fisheries, Conservation, Wildlife, and Oceans, 805 O'Neill Bldg. 20515; (202) 226-0200. Fax, (202) 225-1542. Rep. H. James Saxton, R-N.J., chair; Harry Burroughs, staff director. Internet, http://www.house.gov/resources.*

Jurisdiction over legislation on most oceanographic matters, including ocean engineering, ocean charting, and certain programs of the National Oceanic and Atmospheric Administration.

House Resources Committee, *Subcommittee on Water and Power, 1522 LHOB 20515; (202) 225-8331. John T. Doolittle, R-Calif., chair; Robert Faber, staff director. Internet, http://www.house.gov/resources.*

Jurisdiction over water-related programs of the U.S. Geological Survey.

Senate Commerce, Science, and Transportation Committee, *SD-508 20510; (202) 224-5115. Fax, (202) 224-1259. John McCain, R-Ariz., chair; John Raidt, staff director. Internet, http://www.senate.gov/~commerce.*

Jurisdiction over legislation on most oceanographic matters, including ocean charting and the National Oceanic and Atmospheric Administration.

Senate Commerce, Science, and Transportation Committee, *Subcommittee on Oceans and Fisheries, SH-428 (mailing address: SD-508, Washington, DC 20510); (202) 224-8172. Fax, (202) 228-0326. Olympia J. Snowe, R-Maine, chair; Clark LeBlanc, professional staffer. Internet, http://www.senate.gov/~commerce.*

Studies national ocean policy and programs, including ocean-specific satellite and atmospheric systems of the National Oceanic and Atmospheric Administration. (Subcommittee does not report legislation.)

Senate Energy and Natural Resources Committee, *Subcommittee on Energy Research, Development, Production, and Regulation, SD-364 20510; (202) 224-6567. Fax, (202) 228-0302. Don Nickles, R-Okla., chair; David Garman, professional staff member. Internet, http://www.senate.gov/~energy.*

Jurisdiction over legislation on the U.S. Geological Survey.

NONPROFIT

American Geophysical Union, *2000 Florida Ave. N.W. 20009-1277; (202) 462-6910. Fax, (202) 328-0566. A. F. Spilhaus Jr., executive director. Information, (202) 939-3212. Internet, http://www.agu.org.*

Membership: scientists and technologists who study the environments and components of the Earth, Sun, and solar system. Promotes international cooperation; disseminates information.

Atmospheric Sciences

See also Air Pollution (chap. 9)

AGENCIES

National Science Foundation, *Atmospheric Sciences, 4201 Wilson Blvd., #775, Arlington, VA 22230; (703) 306-1520. Fax, (703) 306-0377. Richard S. Greenfield, director. Internet, http://www.geo.nsf.gov/atm.*

Supports research on the earth's atmosphere and the sun's effect on it, including studies of the physics, chemistry, and dynamics of the earth's upper and lower atmospheres and its space environment; climate processes and variations; and the natural global cycles of gases and particles in the earth's atmosphere.

National Weather Service *(National Oceanic and Atmospheric Administration)*, *1325 East-West Hwy., Silver Spring, MD 20910; (301) 713-0689. Fax, (301) 713-0662. Robert S. Winokur, acting director. Internet, http:// www.nws.noaa.gov.*

Issues warnings of hurricanes, severe storms, and floods; provides weather forecasts and services for the general public and for aviation and marine interests. National Weather Service forecast office, (703) 260-0107; weather forecast for Washington, D.C., and vicinity, (703) 260-0307; marine forecast, (703) 260-0505; recreational forecast, (703) 260-0705; climate data, (703) 271-4800; river stages, (703) 260-0305; pilot weather, (800) 992-7433.

National Weather Service *(National Oceanic and Atmospheric Administration)*, *National Center for Environmental Prediction, 5200 Auth Rd., Camp Springs, MD 20746; (301) 763-8016. Fax, (301) 763-8434. Ronald D. McPherson, director. Internet, http://www.ncep. noaa.gov.*

The National Center for Environmental Prediction and the National Environmental Satellite, Data, and Information Service are part of the World Weather Watch Programme developed by the United Nations' World Meteorological Organization. Collects data and exchanges it with other nations; provides other national weather service offices, private meteorologists, and government agencies with products, including forecast guidance products.

National Weather Service *(National Oceanic and Atmospheric Administration)*, *Science and History Center, 1325 East-West Hwy., Silver Spring, MD 20910; (301) 713-0692. Fax, (301) 713-0662. Gloria Walker, program manager.*

Maintains and exhibits historical collection of the National Weather Service. Displays include meteorological instruments, weather satellites, photographs, and a re-creation of a 19th century weather office. Forecasting office in Sterling, Va.

U.S. Geological Survey *(Interior Dept.)*, *Global Change and Climate History, 12201 Sunrise Valley Dr., MS 906, Reston, VA 20192; (703) 648-5270. Fax, (703) 648-6032. Richard Z. Poore, program coordinator. Internet, http://geochange.er.usgs.gov.*

Manages geological investigations and analyses to document variability of the climate system in the past and future; helps build and test predictive climate mod-

els, and document the contribution of volcano emissions to atmospheric greenhouse gases.

NONPROFIT

Alliance for Responsible Atmospheric Policy, *2111 Wilson Blvd., #850, Arlington, VA 22201; (703) 243-0344. Fax, (703) 243-2874. David Stirpe, executive director.*

Coalition of users and producers of chlorofluorocarbons (CFCs). Seeks further study of the ozone depletion theory.

Climate Institute, *120 Maryland Ave. N.E. 20002; (202) 547-0104. Fax, (202) 547-0111. John C. Topping Jr., president. Internet, climateinst@igc.apc.org or http://www. climate.org.*

Educates the public and policymakers on climate change (greenhouse effect, or global warming) and on the depletion of the ozone layer. Develops strategies on mitigating climate change in developing countries.

Global Climate Coalition, *1275 K St. N.W., #890 20005; (202) 682-9161. Fax, (202) 638-1043. Gail McDonald, president. Internet, gcc@globalclimate.org or http://www.globalclimate.org.*

Membership: business trade associations and private companies. Promotes scientific research on global climate change; analyzes economic and social impacts of policy options; produces educational materials and conducts programs.

Geology and Earth Sciences

AGENCIES

National Museum of Natural History *(Smithsonian Institution)*, *Mineral Sciences, 10th St. and Constitution Ave. N.W., MRC-119 20560; (202) 357-1412. Fax, (202) 357-2476. Glenn J. MacPherson, chair. Internet, http:// nmnhwww.si.edu/departments/minsci.html.*

Conducts research on meteorites. Interests include mineralogy, petrology, volcanology, and geochemistry. Maintains the Global Volcanism Network, which reports worldwide volcanic and seismic activity.

National Museum of Natural History *(Smithsonian Institution)*, *Naturalist Center, 741 Miller Dr. S.E., #G2, Leesburg, VA 20175; (703) 779-9712. Fax, (703) 779-9715. Richard H. Efthim, manager. Toll-free, (800) 729-7725. Internet, natcenter@aol.com or http://nmnhgoph.si.edu/ museum/learn.html.*

Maintains natural history research and reference library with books and 30,000 objects, including minerals, rocks, plants, animals, shells and corals, insects, invertebrates, micro- and macrofossil materials, and microbiological and anthropological materials. Facilities include study equipment such as microscopes, dissecting instruments, and plant presses. Operates a teachers' reference center. Library open to the public; reservations required for groups of six or more.

National Museum of Natural History *(Smithsonian Institution)*, *Paleobiology, 10th St. and Constitution Ave. N.W., MRC 121 20560; (202) 357-2162. Fax, (202) 786-2832. Richard H. Benson, chair. Internet, http:// nmnhwww.si.edu/departments/paleo.html.*

Conducts research worldwide on invertebrate pale-ontology, paleobotany, sedimentology, and vertebrate paleontology; provides information on paleontology. Maintains national collection of fossil organisms and sediment samples.

National Science Foundation, *Earth Sciences, 4201 Wilson Blvd., #785, Arlington, VA 22230; (703) 306-1550. Fax, (703) 306-0382. Ian MacGregor, director. Internet, http://www.geo.nsf.gov/ear.*

Provides grants for research in geology, geophysics, geochemistry, and related fields, including tectonics, hydrologic sciences, and continental dynamics.

U.S. Geological Survey *(Interior Dept.)*, *Earthquake Hazards, 12201 Sunrise Valley Dr., Reston, VA (mailing address: 905 National Center, Reston, VA 20192); (703) 648-6714. Fax, (703) 648-6717. John Filson, acting program coordinator.*

Manages geologic, geophysical, and engineering investigations, including assessments of hazards from earthquakes and landslides; conducts research on the mechanisms and occurrences of earthquakes worldwide and their relationship to the behavior of the crust and upper mantle; develops methods for predicting the time, place, and magnitude of earthquakes; conducts engineering and geologic studies on landslides and ground failures.

U.S. Geological Survey *(Interior Dept.)*, *Geologic Division, 12201 Sunrise Valley Dr., MS 911, Reston, VA 20192; (703) 648-6600. Fax, (703) 648-6683. P. Patrick Leahy, chief geologist. Internet, http://geology.usgs.gov.*

Conducts a onshore and offshore geologic research and investigation. Produces information on geologic hazards, such as earthquakes and volcanoes; geologic information for use in the management of public lands and national policy determinations; information on the chemistry and physics of the Earth; and geologic, geophysical, and geochemical maps and analyses to address environmental, resource, and geologic hazards concerns.

U.S. Geological Survey *(Interior Dept.)*, *National Cooperative Geologic Mapping, 12201 Sunrise Valley Dr., MS 908, Reston, VA 22092; (703) 648-6960. Fax, (703) 648-6937. John S. Pallister, program coordinator.*

Produces geologic maps; makes maps available to public and private organizations.

U.S. Geological Survey *(Interior Dept.)*, *Volcano Hazards, 12201 Sunrise Valley Dr., Reston, VA (mailing address: 905 National Center, Reston, VA 20192); (703) 648-6708. Fax, (703) 648-5483. Marianne C. Guffanti, program coordinator. Internet, http://volcanoes.usgs.gov.*

Manages geologic, geophysical, and engineering investigations, including assessments of hazards from volcanoes; conducts research worldwide on the mechanisms of volcanoes and on igneous and geothermal systems. Issues warnings of potential volcanic hazards.

NONPROFIT

American Geological Institute, *4220 King St., Alexandria, VA 22302; (703) 379-2480. Fax, (703) 379-7563. Marcus E. Milling, executive director. Internet, http://www. agiweb.org.*

Membership: earth science societies and associations. Maintains a computerized database with worldwide information on geology, engineering and environmental geology, oceanography, and other geological fields (available to the public for a fee).

Oceanography

See also Ocean Resources (chap. 9)

AGENCIES

National Museum of Natural History *(Smithsonian Institution)*, *Botany, 4210 Silver Hill Rd., Suitland, MD (mailing address: Smithsonian Institution, Washington, DC 20560); (301) 238-3548. Fax, (301) 238-3361. Ernani Menez, marine biologist.*

Investigates the biology, evolution, and classification of tropical and subtropical marine algae and seagrasses. Acts as curator of the national collection in this field. Develops and participates in scholarly programs.

National Museum of Natural History *(Smithsonian Institution)*, *Invertebrate Zoology, 10th St. and Constitution Ave. N.W., MRC 163 20560; (202) 357-4673. Fax, (202) 357-3043. Rafael Lemaitre, curator, Crustaceans.*

Conducts worldwide research and answers scientific inquiries on the Smithsonian's marine invertebrate collections; engages in taxonomic identification, community analysis, and specimen and sample data management.

National Museum of Natural History *(Smithsonian Institution), Library,* 10th St. and Constitution Ave. N.W., #51 20560; (202) 357-1496. Fax, (202) 357-1896. *Ann Juneau, chief librarian.*

Maintains collections covering oceanography; permits on-site use of the collections. Open to the public by appointment; makes interlibrary loans.

National Museum of Natural History *(Smithsonian Institution), Vertebrate Zoology,* 4210 Silver Hill Rd., Suitland, MD (mailing address: Smithsonian Institution, Washington, DC 20560); (301) 238-3798. Fax, (301) 238-3361. *Leslie Knapp, marine biologist.*

Processes, sorts, and distributes to scientists specimens of marine vertebrates; engages in taxonomic sorting, community analysis, and specimen and sample data management.

National Oceanic and Atmospheric Administration *(Commerce Dept.), Commissioned Corps,* 1315 East-West Hwy., 12th Floor, Silver Spring, MD 20910-3282; (301) 713-1045. Fax, (301) 713-1541. *Rear Adm. William L. Stubblefield, director.* Recruiting, (301) 713-3470. *Internet, http://www.noaa.gov/nchome.*

Uniformed service of the Commerce Dept. that operates and manages NOAA's fleet of hydrographic, oceanographic, and fisheries research ships and aircraft. Supports NOAA's scientific programs.

National Oceanic and Atmospheric Administration *(Commerce Dept.), National Ocean Service,* 1305 East-West Hwy., SSMC4, Silver Spring, MD 20910; (301) 713-3074. Fax, (301) 713-4269. *Nancy Foster, assistant administrator. Internet, http://www.nos.noaa.gov.*

Manages charting and geodetic services, oceanography and marine services, coastal resource coordination, and marine survey operations.

National Oceanic and Atmospheric Administration *(Commerce Dept.), National Oceanographic Data Center,* 1315 East-West Hwy., 4th Floor, Silver Spring, MD 20910-3282; (301) 713-3267. Fax, (301) 713-3300. *Henry R. Frey, director.* Information and requests, (301) 606-4549. *Internet, services@nodc.noaa.gov or http://www.nodc.gov.*

Offers a wide range of oceanographic data on magnetic tape, disk, CD-ROM, and hard copy; provides research scientists with data processing services; prepares statistical summaries and graphical data products. (Fee charged for some services.)

National Science Foundation, *Ocean Sciences Research,* 4201 Wilson Blvd., #725, Arlington, VA 22230; (703) 306-1582. Fax, (703) 306-0390. *Michael Reeve, head. Internet, http://www.geo.nsf.gov/oce.*

Awards grants to academic institutions and private corporations for research in all areas of the marine sciences, including biological, chemical, and physical oceanography, marine geology, and marine geophysics.

National Science Foundation, *Oceanographic Centers and Facilities,* 4201 Wilson Blvd., #725, Arlington, VA 22230; (703) 306-1576. Fax, (703) 306-0390. *Donald F. Heinrichs, head.*

Awards grants and contracts for acquiring, upgrading, and operating oceanographic research facilities that lend themselves to shared usage. Facilities supported include ships, submersibles, and shipboard and shore-based data logging and processing equipment. Supports development of new drilling techniques and systems.

U.S. Geological Survey *(Interior Dept.), Marine and Coastal Geologic Surveys,* 12201 Sunrise Valley Dr., Reston, VA (mailing address: 915B National Center, Reston, VA 20192); (703) 648-6511. Fax, (703) 648-5464. *S. Jeffress Williams, program coordinator.*

Surveys the continental margins and the ocean floor to provide information on the mineral resources potential of submerged lands.

NONPROFIT

Marine Technology Society, 1828 L St. N.W., #906 20036-5104; (202) 775-5966. Fax, (202) 429-9417. *Martin J. Finerty Jr., executive director. Internet, mtsadmin@erols. com or http://www.cms.udel.edu/mts.*

Membership: scientists, engineers, technologists, and others interested in marine science and technology. Provides information on marine science, technology, and education.

National Ocean Industries Assn., 1120 G St. N.W., #900 20005; (202) 347-6900. Fax, (202) 347-8650. *Robert B. Stewart, president. Internet, noia@noia.org.*

Membership: manufacturers, producers, suppliers, and support and service companies involved in marine, offshore, and ocean work. Interests include offshore oil and gas supply and production, deep-sea mining, ocean thermal energy, and new energy sources.

MATHEMATICAL, COMPUTER, AND PHYSICAL SCIENCES

See also Space Sciences (this chapter)

AGENCIES

National Institute of Standards and Technology *(Commerce Dept.),* Route I-270 and Quince Orchard Rd.,

Gaithersburg, MD (mailing address: Bldg. 101, #A1134, Gaithersburg, MD 20899); (301) 975-2300. Fax, (301) 869-8972. Raymond Kammer, director. Information, (301) 975-2762. Internet, http://www.nist.gov.

Nonregulatory agency that serves as national reference and measurement laboratory for the physical and engineering sciences. Works with industry, government agencies, and academia; conducts research in electronics, manufacturing, physics, chemistry, radiation, materials science, applied mathematics, computer science and technology, and engineering sciences.

National Institute of Standards and Technology *(Commerce Dept.), Information Technology Laboratory, Bldg. 225, #B263, Gaithersburg, MD 20899; (301) 975-2904. Fax, (301) 840-1357. Shukri Wakid, director. Internet, http://www.nist.gov/itl.*

Offers support in mathematical and computer sciences to all institute programs and federal agencies; provides consultations, methods, and research supporting the institute's scientific and engineering projects. Manages and operates NIST central computing facilities.

National Science Foundation, *Mathematical and Physical Sciences, 4201 Wilson Blvd., #1005N, Arlington, VA 22230; (703) 306-1800. Fax, (703) 306-0545. Robert A. Eisenstein, assistant director. Internet, http://www.nsf. gov/mps.*

Directorate that supports research in the mathematical and physical sciences; divisions focus on physics, chemistry, materials research, mathematical sciences, and astronomical sciences. Works to improve the education and human resource base for these fields.

NONPROFIT

Carnegie Institution of Washington, *1530 P St. N.W. 20005-1910; (202) 387-6400. Fax, (202) 387-8092. Maxine F. Singer, president. Library, (202) 939-1120. Internet, http://www.ciw.edu.*

Conducts research in the physical and biological sciences at the following centers: the observatories of the Carnegie Institution with headquarters in Pasadena, Calif.; Geophysical Laboratory and Department of Terrestrial Magnetism in Washington, D.C.; Department of Plant Biology in Stanford, Calif.; and Department of Embryology in Baltimore, Md. Refers specific inquiries to appropriate department. Library open to the public by appointment.

See also American Assn. for the Advancement of Science (p. 593)

Chemistry

AGENCIES

National Institute of Standards and Technology *(Commerce Dept.), Chemical Science and Technology Laboratory, Route I-270 and Quince Orchard Rd., Gaithersburg, MD 20899; (301) 975-3145. Fax, (301) 975-3845. Hratch G. Semerjian, director.*

Develops uniform chemical measurement methods; provides federal agencies and industry with advisory and research services in the areas of analytical chemistry, biotechnology, chemical engineering, and physical chemistry; conducts interdisciplinary research efforts with other NIST laboratories.

National Institute of Standards and Technology *(Commerce Dept.), Materials Science and Engineering Laboratory, Route I-270 and Quince Orchard Rd., Gaithersburg, MD (mailing address: Bldg. 223, #B309, Gaithersburg, MD 20899); (301) 975-5658. Fax, (301) 975-5012. Dale Hall, acting director.*

Provides measurements, data, standards, reference materials, concepts, and technical information fundamental to the processing, microstructure, properties, and performance of materials; addresses the scientific basis for new advanced materials; operates a research nuclear reactor for advanced materials characterization measurements; operates four materials data centers.

National Science Foundation, *Chemistry, 4201 Wilson Blvd., #1055, Arlington, VA 22230; (703) 306-1845. Fax, (703) 306-0534. Janet Osteryoung, director. Toll-free fax, (800) 338-3128. Internet, http://www.nsf.gov/chem.*

Awards grants to research programs in organic and macromolecular chemistry, materials chemistry, physical chemistry, analytical and surface chemistry, and inorganic, bioinorganic, and organometallic chemistry; provides funds for instruments needed in chemistry research; coordinates interdisciplinary programs. Monitors international research.

National Science Foundation, *Materials Research, 4201 Wilson Blvd., #1065, Arlington, VA 22230; (703) 306-1811. Fax, (703) 306-0515. Thomas A. Weber, director. Internet, http://www.nsf.gov/MPS/dmr.*

Provides grants for research in condensed matter physics; solid state chemistry and polymers; metals, ceramics, and electronic materials; and materials theory. Provides major instrumentation for these activities. Supports multidisciplinary research in these areas through materials research science and engineering centers.

See also National Institute of Standards and Technology, Information Services (p. 595)

NONPROFIT

American Assn. for Clinical Chemistry, Inc., *2101 L St. N.W., #202 20037-1526; (202) 857-0717. Fax, (202) 887-5093. Richard G. Flaherty, executive vice president. Internet, http://www.aacc.org.*

International society of chemists, physicians, and other scientists specializing in clinical chemistry. Provides educational and professional development services; presents awards for outstanding achievement. Monitors legislation and regulations.

American Chemical Society, *1155 16th St. N.W. 20036; (202) 872-4600. Fax, (202) 872-4615. John K. Crum, executive director. Library, (202) 872-6000. Internet, http://www.acs.org.*

Membership: professional chemists and chemical engineers. Maintains educational programs, including those that evaluate college chemistry departments and high school chemistry curricula. Administers grants and fellowships for basic research; sponsors international exchanges; presents achievement awards. Library open to the public.

American Chemical Society, Petroleum Research Fund, *1155 16th St. N.W. 20036; (202) 872-4481. Fax, (202) 872-6319. Joseph E. Rogers Jr., administrator.*

Makes grants to nonprofit institutions for advanced scientific education and fundamental research related to the petroleum industry (chemistry, geology, engineering).

American Institute of Chemical Engineers, *1300 Eye St. N.W., #1090 East 20005-3314; (202) 962-8690. Fax, (202) 962-8699. Sean Devlin Bersell, director, Government Relations. Internet, dc@aiche.org or http://www.aiche.org.*

Membership: professionals from industry, government, academia, and consulting, including students and retirees. Sponsors research in chemical engineering and promotes public understanding of the profession.

American Institute of Chemists, *501 Wythe St., Alexandria, VA 22314; (703) 836-2090. Fax, (703) 836-2091. Sharon Dobson, executive director. Internet, theaic@aol.com or http://www.theaic.org.*

Professional society of chemists and chemical engineers. Sponsors a national certification program. Publishes annual professional directory. AIC Foundation sponsors the Student Award Program. Monitors legislation and regulations.

AOAC International, *481 N. Frederick Ave., #500, Gaithersburg, MD 20877; (301) 924-7077. Fax, (301) 924-7089. Ronald R. Christensen, executive director. Toll-free, (800) 379-2622. Internet, info@aoac.org or http://www.aoac.org.*

International association of analytical science professionals, companies, government agencies, nongovernmental organizations, and institutions. Promotes methods validation and quality measurements in the analytical sciences. Supports the development, testing, validation, and publication of reliable chemical and biological methods of analyzing foods, drugs, feed, fertilizers, pesticides, water, forensic materials, and other substances.

Chemical Manufacturers Assn., *1300 Wilson Blvd., Arlington, VA 22209; (703) 741-5000. Fax, (703) 741-6097. Frederick L. Webber, president. Internet, http://www.cmahq.com.*

Membership: manufacturers of basic industrial chemicals. Provides members with technical research, communications services, and legal affairs counseling. Interests include environmental safety and health, transportation, energy, and international trade. Monitors legislation and regulations.

Society of the Plastics Industry, *1801 K St. N.W., #600K 20006; (202) 974-5200. Fax, (202) 296-7005. Larry Thomas, president. Internet, http://www.socplas.org.*

Promotes the plastics industry. Monitors legislation and regulations.

Synthetic Organic Chemical Manufacturers Assn., *1850 M St. N.W., #700 20036; (202) 296-8577. Fax, (202) 296-8120. Graydon R. Powers, president. Internet, http://www.socma.com.*

Membership: companies that manufacture, distribute, and market organic chemicals, and providers of custom chemical services. Interests include international trade, environmental and occupational safety, and health issues; conducts workshops and seminars. Promotes commercial opportunities for members. Monitors legislation and regulations.

See also American Industrial Health Council (p. 353)

Computer Sciences

See also Internet and Related Technologies (chap. 3)

AGENCIES

National Coordination Office for Computing, Information, and Communications, *4201 Wilson Blvd., #665, Arlington, VA 22230; (703) 306-4722. Fax, (703) 306-4727. Kay Howell, director. Internet, http://www.ccic.gov.*

Coordinates multi-agency research and development projects that involve computing, information, and communications, including the High Performance Computing and Communications (HPCC) Program. Reports to the National Science and Technology Council; provides information to Congress, U.S. and foreign organizations, and the public.

National Institute of Standards and Technology *(Commerce Dept.), Information Technology Laboratory, Bldg. 225, #B263, Gaithersburg, MD 20899; (301) 975-2904. Fax, (301) 840-1357. Shukri Wakid, director. Internet, http://www.nist.gov/itl.*

Advises federal agencies on automatic data processing management and use of information technology; helps federal agencies maintain up-to-date computer technology support systems, emphasizing computer security techniques; recommends federal information processing standards; conducts research in computer science and technology.

National Science Foundation, *Computer and Information Sciences and Engineering, 4201 Wilson Blvd., Arlington, VA 22230; (703) 306-1900. Fax, (703) 306-0577. Juris Hartmanis, assistant director. Internet, http://www.cise.nsf.gov.*

Directorate that promotes basic research and education in computer and information sciences and engineering; helps maintain U.S. preeminence in these fields. Coordinates NSF involvement in the High-Performance Computing and Communications (HPCC) program; develops computer resources for scholarly communication, including links with foreign research and education networks; helps set Internet policy.

National Science Foundation, *Computer Communications Research, 4201 Wilson Blvd., #1145, Arlington, VA 22230; (703) 306-1910. Fax, (703) 306-1947. John Lehmann, director. Internet, http://www.cise.nsf.gov/ccr.*

Awards grants for research in computer science and engineering, including programs in computer and computation theory; numeric, symbolic, and geometric computation; computer systems; and software engineering.

National Science Foundation, *Information and Intelligence Systems, 4201 Wilson Blvd., #1115, Arlington, VA 22230; (703) 306-1930. Fax, (703) 306-0599. Michael Lesk, director. Internet, http://www.cise.nsf.gov/iis.*

Supports research on designing, developing, managing, and using information systems, including database and expert systems, knowledge models and cognitive systems, machine intelligence and robotics, information technology and organizations, and interactive systems.

See also National Institute of Standards and Technology, Information Services (p. 595)

NONPROFIT

Computer and Communications Industry Assn., *666 11th St. N.W., #600 20001; (202) 783-0070. Fax, (202) 783-0534. Edward J. Black, president. Internet, ccia@aol.com or http://www.ccianet.org.*

Membership: manufacturers and suppliers of computer data processing and communications-related products and services. Interests include telecommunications policy, capital formation and tax policy, federal procurement policy, communications and computer industry standards, intellectual property policies, encryption, international trade, and antitrust reform.

Computer Law Assn., *3028 Javier Rd., #402, Fairfax, VA 22031-4622; (703) 560-7747. Fax, (703) 207-7028. Barbara Fieser, executive director. Internet, clanet@aol.com or http://cla.org.*

Membership: lawyers, law students, and nonattorneys concerned with the legal aspects of computers and computer communications. Sponsors programs and provides information on such issues as software protection, contracting, telecommunications, international distribution, financing, taxes, copyrights, patents, and electronic data interchange. Focus includes the Internet and year 2000 issues.

Industry Advisory Council, *3601E Chain Bridge Rd., Fairfax, VA 22030; (703) 218-1965. Fax, (703) 218-1960. Mary Ellen Geoffroy, executive director. Internet, http://www.iaconline.org.*

Membership: producers of computer hardware and software and systems integrators. Serves as liaison between government and industry; offers programs on development and acquisition of information technology. Monitors legislation and regulations. (Affiliated with the Federation of Government Information Processing Councils.)

Information Technology Assn. of America, *1616 N. Fort Myer Dr., #1300, Arlington, VA 22209; (703) 284-5300. Fax, (703) 525-2279. Harris N. Miller, president. Internet, http://www.itaa.org.*

Membership: organizations in the computer software and services industry. Conducts research; holds seminars and workshops; interests include small business, government procurement, competitive practices, communications, software, trade, and international copyright issues. Monitors legislation and regulations.

Information Technology Industry Council, *1250 Eye St. N.W., #200 20005; (202) 737-8888. Fax, (202) 638-4922. Rhett Dawson, president. Press, (202) 626-5725. Internet, http://www.itic.org.*

Membership: providers of information technology products and services. Promotes the global competitiveness of its members and advocates free trade. Seeks to protect intellectual property and encourages the use of voluntary standards.

Institute for Artificial Intelligence *(George Washington University), 707 22nd St. N.W., #206 20052; (202) 994-5079. Fax, (202) 994-0245. Barry G. Silverman, director. Internet, http://www.seas.gwu.edu/seas/institutes/iai.*

Researches, develops, tests, and evaluates artificial intelligence programs and organizational knowledge asset management. Interests include new information technologies, intelligent agents for the World Wide Web, and multimedia, knowledge-based tools.

Institute of Electrical and Electronics Engineers— United States Activities, *1828 L St. N.W., #1202 20036-5104; (202) 785-0017. Fax, (202) 785-0835. W. Thomas Suttle, managing director, Professional Activities. Internet, ieeeusa@ieee.org or http://www.ieee.org/usab.*

U.S. arm of an international technological and professional organization. Interests include promoting career and technology policy interests of members. (Headquarters in New York.)

International Council for Computer Communication, *P.O. Box 9745 20016; (703) 836-7787. John D. McKendree, treasurer. Internet, http://www.iccc.inter.net.*

Membership: industry, government, and academic leaders interested in computer communications issues. Promotes scientific research in and development of computer communication; encourages evaluation of applications of computer communication for educational, scientific, medical, economic, legal, cultural, and other peaceful purposes; sponsors international conferences, seminars, and workshops. (Affiliated with the International Federation for Information Processing in Vienna, Austria.)

ITRA: Information Technology Resellers Assn., *11921 Freedom Dr., #550, Reston, VA 20190; (703) 904-4337. Fax, (703) 904-4339. Steven Worth, president.*

Membership: companies that buy, sell, and lease new and used computers and other high-technology equipment. Acts as liaison with equipment manufacturers; enforces industry code of ethics; conducts industry surveys. Monitors legislation and regulations.

Software Publishers Assn., *1730 M St. N.W., #700 20036; (202) 452-1600. Fax, (202) 223-8756. Kenneth A. Wasch, president. Internet, http://www.spa.org.*

Membership: publishers of microcomputer software. Promotes the industry worldwide; conducts investiga-

tions and litigation to protect members' copyrights; collects data, including monthly sales information; offers contracts reference and credit information exchange services; sponsors conferences and seminars. Monitors legislation and regulations.

See also American Institutes for Research (p.617); American Medical Informatics Assn. (p. 360); Institute for Alternative Futures (p. 386)

Mathematics

AGENCIES

National Institute of Standards and Technology *(Commerce Dept.), Information Technology Laboratory, Bldg. 225, #B263, Gaithersburg, MD 20899; (301) 975-2904. Fax, (301) 840-1357. Shukri Wakid, director. Internet, http://www.nist.gov/itl.*

Develops improved mathematical and statistical models and computational methods; consults on their use. Manages and operates NIST central computing facilities.

National Science Foundation, *Mathematical Sciences, 4201 Wilson Blvd., #1025, Arlington, VA 22230; (703) 306-1870. Fax, (703) 306-0555. Donald J. Lewis, director. Internet, http://www.nsf.gov/MPS/dms.*

Provides grants for research in the mathematical sciences in the following areas: classical and modern analysis, geometric analysis, topology and foundations, algebra and number theory, applied and computational mathematics, and statistics and probability. Maintains special projects program, which supports scientific computing equipment for mathematics research and several research institutes. Sponsors conferences, workshops, and postdoctoral research fellowships. Monitors international research.

See also National Institute of Standards and Technology, Information Services (p. 595)

NONPROFIT

American Statistical Assn., *1429 Duke St., Alexandria, VA 22314; (703) 684-1221. Fax, (703) 684-2037. Ray Waller, executive director. Internet, asainfo@amstat.org or http://www.amstat.org.*

Membership: individuals interested in statistics and related quantitative fields. Advises government agencies on statistics and methodology in agency research; promotes development of statistical techniques for use in business, industry, finance, government, agriculture, and science.

Conference Board of the Mathematical Sciences, *1529 18th St. N.W. 20036; (202) 293-1170. Fax, (202) 265-2384. Ronald C. Rosier, administrative officer. Internet, http://www.maa.org/cbms/cbms.html.*

Membership: presidents of fifteen mathematical sciences professional societies. Serves as a forum for discussion of issues of concern to the mathematical sciences community.

Mathematical Assn. of America, *1529 18th St. N.W. 20036-1358; (202) 387-5200. Fax, (202) 265-2384. Marcia P. Sward, executive director. Internet, maahq@maa.org or http://www.maa.org.*

Membership: mathematics professors and individuals with a professional interest in mathematics. Seeks to improve the teaching of collegiate mathematics. Conducts professional development programs.

Physics

AGENCIES

Energy Research *(Energy Dept.), **High Energy and Nuclear Physics,** 19901 Germantown Rd., Germantown, MD 20874-1290; (301) 903-3713. Fax, (301) 903-5079. S. Peter Rosen, associate director. Internet, http://www.er.doe.gov.*

Provides grants and facilities for research in high energy and nuclear physics. Constructs, operates, and maintains particle accelerators used in high energy and nuclear physics research.

National Institute of Standards and Technology *(Commerce Dept.), **Materials Science and Engineering Laboratory,** Route I-270 and Quince Orchard Rd., Gaithersburg, MD (mailing address: Bldg. 223, #B309, Gaithersburg, MD 20899); (301) 975-5658. Fax, (301) 975-5012. Dale Hall, acting director.*

Provides measurements, data, standards, reference materials, concepts, and technical information fundamental to the processing, microstructure, properties, and performance of materials; addresses the scientific basis for new advanced materials; operates a research nuclear reactor for advanced materials characterization measurements; operates four materials data centers.

National Institute of Standards and Technology *(Commerce Dept.), **Physics Laboratory,** Route I-270 and Quince Orchard Rd., Bldg. 221, #B160, Gaithersburg, MD 20899; (301) 975-4200. Fax, (301) 975-3038. Katharine B. Gebbie, director. Internet, http://physics.nist.gov.*

Conducts research to improve measurement capability and quantitative understanding of basic physical processes that underlie measurement science; investi-

gates structure and dynamics of atoms and molecules; provides national standards for time and frequency and for measurement of radiation; develops radiometric and wavelength standards; analyzes national measurement needs.

National Science Foundation, *Materials Research, 4201 Wilson Blvd., #1065, Arlington, VA 22230; (703) 306-1811. Fax, (703) 306-0515. Thomas A. Weber, director. Internet, http://www.nsf.gov/MPS/dmr.*

Provides grants for research in condensed matter physics; solid state chemistry and polymers; metals, ceramics, and electronic materials; and materials theory. Provides major instrumentation for these activities. Supports multidisciplinary research in these areas through materials research science and engineering centers. Supports national facilities and instrumentation in the areas of synchrotron radiation, high magnetic fields.

National Science Foundation, *Physics, 4201 Wilson Blvd., #1015, Arlington, VA 22230; (703) 306-1890. Fax, (703) 306-0566. Marcel Bardon, director. Internet, http://www.nsf.gov/MPS/phy.*

Awards grants for research and special programs in atomic, molecular, and optical physics; elementary particle physics; and nuclear, theoretical, and gravitational physics. Monitors international research.

See also National Institute of Standards and Technology, Information Services (p. 595)

NONPROFIT

American Institute of Physics, *1 Physics Ellipse, College Park, MD 20740-3843; (301) 209-3000. Fax, (301) 209-0843. Marc H. Brodsky, executive director. Internet, http://www.api.org.*

Fosters cooperation among the physics community; improves public understanding of science; disseminates information on scientific research.

American Physical Society, *529 14th St. N.W., #1050 20045-2001; (202) 662-8700. Fax, (202) 662-8711. Robert L. Park, director, Public Information. Internet, opa@aps.org or http://www.aps.org.*

Scientific and educational society of educators, students, citizens, and scientists, including industrial scientists. Sponsors studies on issues of public concern related to physics, such as reactor safety and energy use. Informs members of national and international developments. (Headquarters in College Park, Md.)

Optical Society of America, *2010 Massachusetts Ave. N.W. 20036; (202) 223-8130. Fax, (202) 223-1096. Vacant, executive director. Internet, http://www.osa.org.*

Membership: researchers, educators, manufacturers, students, and others interested in optics and photonics worldwide. Promotes research and information exchange; conducts conferences. Interests include use of optics in medical imaging and surgery.

Weights and Measures/ Metric System

AGENCIES

National Institute of Standards and Technology *(Commerce Dept.), Measurement Services, 820 W. Diamond Ave., Gaithersburg, MD (mailing address: Bldg. 820, #306, Gaithersburg, MD 20899); (301) 975-4500. Fax, (301) 948-3825. Peter Heydenmann, director. Internet, http://www.nist.gov.*

Disseminates physical, chemical, and engineering measurement standards and provides services to ensure accurate and compatible measurements, specifications, and codes on a national and international scale.

National Institute of Standards and Technology *(Commerce Dept.), Metric Program, Route I-270 and Quince Orchard Rd., Bldg. 820, Gaithersburg, MD 20899; (301) 975-3690. Fax, (301) 948-1416. Gerard Iannelli, director. Internet, metric_prg@nist.gov or http://www.nist.gov/metric.*

Coordinates federal metric conversion transition to ensure consistency; provides the public with technical and general information about the metric system; assists state and local governments, businesses, and educators with metric conversion activities.

National Institute of Standards and Technology *(Commerce Dept.), National Conference on Weights and Measures, 820 W. Diamond St., #223, Gaithersburg, MD 20899; (301) 975-4005. Fax, (301) 926-0647. Gilbert M. Ugiansky, executive secretary.*

Membership: state and local officials who deal with weights and measures, industry and business representatives, individuals, and associations. Serves as a national forum on issues related to weights and measures administration; develops consensus on uniform laws and regulations, specifications, and tolerances for weighing and measuring devices.

National Institute of Standards and Technology *(Commerce Dept.), Weights and Measures, 820 W. Diamond St., #223, Gaithersburg, MD 20899; (301) 975-4004. Fax, (301) 926-0647. Gilbert M. Ugiansky, chief, (301) 975-4005.*

Promotes uniformity in weights and measures law and enforcement. Provides weights and measures agen-

cies with training and technical assistance; assists state and local agencies in adapting their weights and measures to meet national standards; conducts research; sets uniform standards and regulations; sponsors the National Conference on Weights and Measures.

CONGRESS

House Science Committee, *Subcommittee on Technology, 2319 RHOB 20515; (202) 225-8844. Fax, (202) 225-4438. Constance A. Morella, R-Md., chair; Richard Russell, staff director. Internet, http://www.house.gov/science.*

Jurisdiction over legislation on weights and measurement systems; monitors the National Institute of Standards and Technology.

Senate Commerce, Science, and Transportation Committee, *Subcommittee on Science, Technology, and Space, SH-427 (mailing address: SD-508, Washington, DC 20510); (202) 224-4852. Fax, (202) 228-0326. Bill Frist, R-Tenn., chair; Rosalind Parker, professional staff member. Internet, http://www.senate.gov/~commerce.*

Jurisdiction over legislation on weights and measurement systems; monitors the National Institute of Standards and Technology.

NONPROFIT

American National Metric Council, *4340 East-West Hwy., #401, Bethesda, MD 20814-4408; (301) 718-6508. Fax, (301) 656-0989. Gian Argenentati, president. Internet, anmc@paimgnt.com.*

Membership: companies, libraries, organizations, and individuals. Coordinates voluntary transition to the metric system in the United States and assists with industry transition; serves as information source on U.S. and international metric planning and use.

SOCIAL SCIENCES

See also History and Preservation (chap. 4)

AGENCIES

National Museum of Natural History *(Smithsonian Institution), Anthropology, 10th St. and Constitution Ave. N.W., MRC 112 20560; (202) 357-2363. Fax, (202) 357-2208. Dennis J. Stanford, chair. Information, (202) 357-1592. Internet, http://nmnhwww.si.edu/departments/anthro.html.*

Conducts research on paleo-Indian archeology and prehistory, New World origins, and paleoecology. Maintains anthropological and human studies film archives. Museum maintains public exhibitions of human cultures.

National Museum of Natural History *(Smithsonian Institution), Library,* 10th St. and Constitution Ave. N.W., #51 20560; (202) 357-1496. Fax, (202) 357-1896. Ann Juneau, chief librarian.

Maintains reference collections covering anthropology and ethnology; permits on-site use of the collections. Open to the public by appointment; makes interlibrary loans.

National Science Foundation, *Social, Behavioral, and Economic Sciences,* 4201 Wilson Blvd., #905, Arlington, VA 22230; (703) 306-1700. Fax, (703) 306-0495. Bennett I. Bertenthal, assistant director. Internet, http://www.nsf.gov/sbe.

Directorate that awards grants for research in behavioral and cognitive sciences, social and economic sciences, science resources studies, and international programs. Provides support for workshops, symposia, and conferences.

NONPROFIT

American Anthropological Assn., 4350 N. Fairfax Dr., #640, Arlington, VA 22203-1620; (703) 528-1902. Fax, (703) 528-3546. William Davis III, executive director. Internet, http://www.ameranthassn.org.

Membership: anthropologists, educators, students, and others interested in anthropological studies. Publishes research studies of member organizations, sponsors workshops, and disseminates to members information concerning developments in anthropology worldwide.

American Institutes for Research, 3333 K St. N.W., #300 20007; (202) 342-5000. Fax, (202) 342-5033. David A. Goslin, president. Internet, http://www.air-dc.org.

Conducts research and analysis in the behavioral and social sciences, including education and health research and data analysis to assess fairness and equity in the workplace; assists in designing and writing documents; assesses usability of software, systems, and other products; studies human-machine interface.

American Psychological Assn., 750 1st St. N.E. 20002-4242; (202) 336-5500. Fax, (202) 336-6069. Raymond D. Fowler, executive vice president. Library, (202) 336-5640. TDD, (202) 336-6123. Internet, http://www.apa.org.

Membership: professional psychologists, educators, and behavioral research scientists. Supports research, training, and professional services; works toward

improving the qualifications, competence, and training programs of psychologists. Monitors international research and U.S. legislation on mental health.

American Sociological Assn., 1722 N St. N.W. 20036; (202) 833-3410. Fax, (202) 785-0146. Felice Levine, executive officer. TDD, (202) 872-0486. Internet, executive.office@asanet.org or http://www.asanet.org.

Membership: sociologists, social scientists, and others interested in research, teaching, and application of sociology in the United States and internationally. Sponsors professional development program, teaching resources center, and education programs; offers fellowships for minorities.

Consortium of Social Science Assns., 1522 K St. N.W., #836 20005; (202) 842-3525. Fax, (202) 842-2788. Howard J. Silver, executive director. Internet, http://members.aol.com/socscience/COSSAindex.htm.

Consortium of associations in the fields of anthropology, criminology, economics, history, political science, psychology, sociology, statistics, geography, linguistics, law, and social science. Advocates support for research and monitors federal funding in the social and behavioral sciences; conducts seminars.

Human Resources Research Organization, 66 Canal Center Plaza, #400, Alexandria, VA 22314; (703) 549-3611. Fax, (703) 549-9025. Lauress L. Wise, president. Internet, http://www.humrro.org.

Research and development organization in the fields of industrial and behavioral psychology. Studies, designs, develops, and evaluates personnel systems, chiefly in the workplace. Interests include personnel selection and promotion, career progression, performance appraisal, training, and program evaluation.

Institute for the Study of Man, 1133 13th St. N.W., #C2 20005-4297; (202) 371-2700. Fax, (202) 371-1523. Roger Pearson, executive director.

Publishes academic journals, books, and monographs in areas related to anthropology, psychology, genetics, archeology, linguistics, and cultural history.

See also National Geographic Society (p. 594)

Geography and Mapping

AGENCIES

Census Bureau *(Commerce Dept.), Geography,* 8903 Presidential Pkwy., Upper Marlboro, MD; (301) 457-1132. Fax, (301) 457-4710. Joel Morrison, chief. Internet, http://www.census.gov.

Manages the TIGER system, a nationwide geographic database; prepares maps for use in conducting censuses and surveys and for showing their results geographically; determines names and current boundaries of legal geographic units; defines names and boundaries of selected statistical areas; develops geographic code schemes; maintains computer files of area measurements, geographic boundaries, and map features with address ranges.

National Archives and Records Administration, *Cartographic and Architectural Branch,* 8601 Adelphi Rd., #3320, College Park, MD 20740-6001; (301) 713-7030. Fax, (301) 713-7488. Robert Richardson, branch chief. TDD, (301) 713-7030. Internet, carto@arch2. nara.gov.

Makes information available on federal government cartographic records, architectural drawings, and aerial mapping films; prepares descriptive guides and inventories of records. Library open to the public. Records may be reproduced for a fee.

National Imagery and Mapping Agency *(Defense Dept.),* 1400 Sangamore Rd., Bethesda, MD 20816; (301) 227-7300. Fax, (301) 227-3696. Rear Adm. Joseph J. Dantone Jr., acting director. Internet, http://www.nima.mil.

Combat support agency that provides imagery and geospatial information to national policymakers and military forces in support of national defense objectives; incorporates the missions and functions of the former Defense Mapping Agency, Central Imaging Office, and Defense Dissemination Program Office.

National Oceanic and Atmospheric Administration *(Commerce Dept.), National Geodetic Survey,* 1315 East-West Hwy., SSMC3, Silver Spring, MD 20910-3282; (301) 713-3222. Fax, (301) 713-4175. Charles Challstrom, acting director. Internet, http://www.ngs.noaa.gov.

Develops and maintains the National Spatial Reference System, a national geodetic reference system which serves as a common reference for latitude, longitude, height, scale, orientation, and gravity measurements. Maps the nation's coastal zone and waterways; conducts research and development programs to improve the collection, distribution, and use of spatial data; coordinates the development and application of new surveying instrumentation and procedures; and assists state, county, and municipal agencies through a variety of cooperative programs.

State Dept., *Office of the Geographer and Global Issues,* Main State Bldg., #8742 20520; (202) 647-2021. Fax, (202) 647-0504. William B. Wood, director.

Advises the State Dept. and other federal agencies on geographic and cartographic matters. Furnishes technical and analytical research and advice in the field of geography.

U.S. Board on Geographic Names, *12201 Sunrise Valley Dr., Reston, VA 20192-0523; (703) 648-4544. Fax, (703) 648-4165. Roger L. Payne, executive secretary, Domestic Names Committee; Randall Flynn, executive secretary, Foreign Names Committee, (301) 227-3050. Internet, http://mapping.usgs.gov/www/gnis/bgn.html.*

Interagency organization established by Congress to standardize geographic names. Board members are representatives from the departments of Agriculture, Commerce, Defense, Interior, and State; the Central Intelligence Agency; the Government Printing Office; the Library of Congress; and the Postal Service. Sets policy governing the use of both domestic and foreign geographic names as well as underseas and Antarctic feature names.

U.S. Geological Survey *(Interior Dept.), Data and Information Delivery,* 12201 Sunrise Valley Dr., Reston, VA (mailing address: 508 National Center, Reston, VA 20192); (703) 648-5780. Fax, (703) 648-5939. Hedy J. Rossmeissl, senior program advisor.

Plans and coordinates information dissemination activities of the National Mapping Division; manages inventory and assures proper storage and preservation for all products.

U.S. Geological Survey *(Interior Dept.), Earth Science Information Center,* 507 National Center, Reston, VA 20192-1507; (703) 648-6045. Fax, (703) 648-5548. Susan Russell-Robinson, chief. U.S. maps, (800) 872-6277. Internet, http://www.usgs.gov.

Collects, organizes, and distributes cartographic, geographic, hydrologic, and other earth science information; offers maps, reports, and other publications, digital cartographic data, aerial photographs, and space imagery and manned spacecraft photographs for sale. Acts as clearinghouse on cartographic and geographic data covering the United States.

U.S. Geological Survey *(Interior Dept.), National Mapping,* 12201 Sunrise Valley Dr., MS 516, Reston, VA 20192; (703) 648-5748. Fax, (703) 648-5792. Richard E. Witmer, chief. Information and data services, (703) 648-5780. Internet, http://www.nmd.usgs.gov.

Provides government agencies and the public with geographic and cartographic information, maps, and technical assistance; conducts research; collects, compiles, and analyzes information about features of the earth's surface; develops and maintains a digital geographic/cartographic database and assists users in applying spatial data; coordinates federal mapping activities;

encourages the development of surveying and mapping techniques.

CONGRESS

Library of Congress, *Geography and Map Division,* 101 Independence Ave. S.E., #B02 20540; (202) 707-8530. Fax, (202) 707-8531. Ralph Ehrenberg, chief. Reference, (202) 707-6277.

Maintains cartographic collection of maps, atlases, globes, and reference books. Reference service provided; reading room open to the public. Interlibrary loans available through the library's loan division; photocopies, when not limited by copyright or other restriction, available through the library's photoduplication service.

NONPROFIT

American Congress on Surveying and Mapping, 5410 Grosvenor Lane, #100, Bethesda, MD 20814-2122; (301) 493-0200. Fax, (301) 493-8245. John Lisack Jr., executive director. Internet, http://www.servemap.org.

Membership: professionals working worldwide in surveying, cartography, geodesy, and geographic/land information systems (computerized mapping systems used in urban, regional, and environmental planning). Sponsors workshops and seminars for surveyors and mapping scientists; participates in accreditation of college and university surveying and related degree programs; grants fellowships; develops and administers certification programs for hydrographers and technician surveyors. Monitors legislation and regulations.

American Society for Photogrammetry and Remote Sensing, 5410 Grosvenor Lane, #210, Bethesda, MD 20814-2160; (301) 493-0290. Fax, (301) 493-0208. Vacant, executive director. Internet, asprs@asprs.org or http://www.asprs.org/asprs.

Promotes use of photogrammetry, remote sensing, and geographic information systems (computerized mapping systems used in urban, regional, and environmental planning) for earth resource evaluation and preparation of maps; interests include global applications of mapping. Sponsors continuing education programs.

Assn. of American Geographers, 1710 16th St. N.W. 20009; (202) 234-1450. Fax, (202) 234-2744. Ronald F. Abler, executive director. Internet, gaia@aag.org or http://www.aag.org.

Membership: educators, students, business executives, government employees, and scientists in the field of geography. Seeks to advance professional studies in geography and encourages the application of geographic research in education, government, and business.

National Geographic Maps, 1145 17th St. N.W. 20036-4688; (202) 857-7799. Fax, (202) 429-5704. Allen Carroll, director. Library, (202) 775-6173. Map orders, (800) 962-1643. Internet, http://www.nationalgeographic.com.

Educational and scientific organization. Supports and conducts research on cartography, mapping, and geography. Produces and sells to the public political, physical, and thematic maps, atlases, and globes. (Affiliated with National Geographic Society.)

SPACE SCIENCES

AGENCIES

Air Force Dept. *(Defense Dept.), Space,* 1640 Air Force Pentagon, #4E998 20330-1640; (703) 693-5799. Fax, (703) 693-6567. Richard M. McCormick, assistant secretary.

Formulates, reviews, and executes Air Force policies and programs relating to space.

Commerce Dept., *Air and Space Commercialization,* 14th St. and Constitution Ave. N.W., #4817 20230; (202) 482-6125. Fax, (202) 482-5173. Keith Calhoun-Senghor, director. Internet, oascinfo@doc.gov or http://www.ta.doc.gov/oasc.

Promotes private investment in space activities; seeks to remove legal, policy, and institutional impediments to space commerce; represents private sector interests at the federal level; coordinates commercial space policy for the Commerce Dept. Monitors international developments.

Federal Aviation Administration *(Transportation Dept.), Commercial Space Transportation,* 800 Independence Ave. S.W., #331 20591; (202) 267-7793. Fax, (202) 267-5450. Patricia Grace Smith, acting associate administrator. Internet, http://ast.faa.gov.

Promotes and facilitates the operation of commercial expendable space launch vehicles by the private sector; licenses and regulates these activities.

National Aeronautics and Space Administration, 300 E St. S.W. (mailing address: NASA Headquarters, Mail Code A, Washington, DC 20546); (202) 358-1801. Fax, (202) 358-2811. Daniel Goldin, administrator; Gen. John R. Dailey, acting deputy administrator, (202) 358-1820. Information, (202) 358-1000. TDD, (800) 735-2258. Locator, (202) 358-0000. Internet, http://www.nasa.gov.

Conducts research on problems of flight within and outside the earth's atmosphere; develops, constructs, tests, and operates experimental aeronautical and space vehicles; conducts activities for manned and unmanned exploration of space; maintains information center.

NATIONAL AERONAUTICS AND SPACE ADMINISTRATION

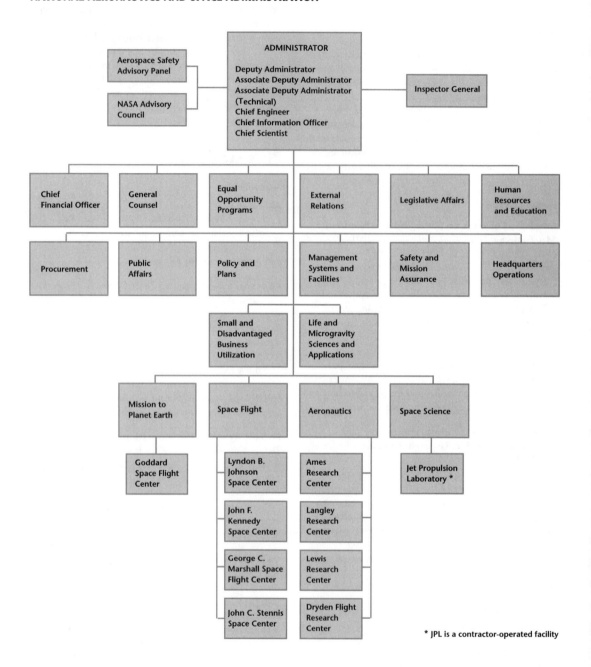

* JPL is a contractor-operated facility

National Aeronautics and Space Administration,
Aeronautics and Space Transportation Technology, 300
E St. S.W. (mailing address: NASA Headquarters, Mail
Code R, Washington, DC 20546); (202) 358-2693. Fax,
(202) 358-4066. Richard Christensen, acting associate
administrator. Internet, http://www.hq.nasa.gov/office/aero.

Conducts research in aerodynamics, materials, structures, avionics, propulsion, human factors, and safety;
helps apply new technologies to the U.S. aeronautics
industry and international projects. Manages the following NASA research centers: Marshal (Huntsville, Ala.);
Goddard (Greenbelt, Md.); Ames (Moffett, Calif.); Dryden (Edwards, Calif.); Langley (Hampton, Va.); and
Lewis (Cleveland, Ohio).

National Aeronautics and Space Administration,
Goddard Space Flight Center, Code 130, Greenbelt, MD
20771; (301) 286-5121. Fax, (301) 286-1714. Al Diaz,
director. Information, (301) 286-8955. Internet, http://pao.
gsfc.nasa.gov.

Conducts space and earth science research; performs
advanced planning for space missions; develops and
manages spacecraft and scientific instrumentation;
functions as the control center for earth orbital satellites;
operates the NASA tracking and data relay satellite
system.

National Aeronautics and Space Administration,
International Space Station, 300 E St. S.W. (mailing
address: NASA Headquarters, Mail Code M-4, Washington, DC 20546); (202) 358-4424. Fax, (202) 358-2848.
Gretchen W. McClain, director. Internet, http://station.
nasa.gov.

Responsible for developing a permanently manned
orbiting space station to serve as a research facility for
scientific, technological, and commercial activities.

National Aeronautics and Space Administration,
Life and Microgravity Sciences and Applications, 300 E
St. S.W. (mailing address: NASA Headquarters, Mail Code
U, Washington, DC 20546); (202) 358-0122. Fax, (202)
358-4174. Dr. Arnold E. Nicogossian, associate administra-
tor. Internet, http://www.hq.nasa.gov/office/olmsa.

Conducts all in-orbit exploration of space. Areas of
research include life sciences (people, animals, and
plants), materials (crystals and minerals), and microgravity effects observed in space. Participates in international projects and conferences.

National Aeronautics and Space Administration,
National Space Science Data Center, Goddard Space
Flight Center, Goddard Code 633, Greenbelt, MD 20771;
(301) 286-7355. Fax, (301) 286-1771. Joseph H. King,
head. Internet, http://www.nssdc.gsfc.nasa.gov.

Acquires, catalogs, and distributes NASA mission
data to the international space science community,
including research organizations, universities, and other
interested organizations worldwide. Provides software
tools and network access to promote collaborative data
analysis. (Mail data requests to above address, attention:
Code 633.4/Request Coordination Office, or phone (301)
286-6695.)

National Aeronautics and Space Administration,
NASA Advisory Council, 300 E St. S.W. (mailing address:
NASA Headquarters, Mail Code Z, Washington, DC
20546); (202) 358-2096. Fax, (202) 358-4336. Anne L.
Accola, executive secretary. Internet, http://www.hq.nasa.
gov/office/codez.nac.htm.

Advises the administrator on NASA's aeronautics and
space plans and programs. The council is comprised of
the following advisory committees: Aeronautics, Technology and Commercialization, Life and Microgravity
Sciences and Applications, Space Science, International
Space Station, Minority Business Resource, and Earth
Systems Science and Applications.

National Aeronautics and Space Administration,
Safety and Mission Assurance, 300 E St. S.W. (mailing
address: NASA Headquarters, Mail Code Q, Washington,
DC 20546); (202) 358-2406. Fax, (202) 358-2699. Frederick D. Gregory, associate administrator.

Evaluates the safety and reliability of NASA systems
and programs. Alerts officials to technical execution and
physical readiness of NASA projects.

National Aeronautics and Space Administration,
Space Communications, 300 E St. S.W. (mailing address:
NASA Headquarters, Mail Code M-3, Washington, DC
20546); (202) 358-2020. Fax, (202) 358-3530. Robert
Spearing, deputy associate administrator. Internet, http://
www.nasa.gov.

Plans, develops, and operates worldwide tracking,
data acquisition, data processing, and communications
systems, facilities, and services essential to the agency's
space flight missions, including the Space Tracking Data
Network at Goddard Space Flight Center in Greenbelt,
Md., and the Deep Space Network operated by the Jet
Propulsion Laboratory in Pasadena, Calif. Gives support
to planetary spacecraft, earth-orbiting satellites, shuttle
missions, sounding rockets, balloons, and aeronautical
test vehicles.

National Aeronautics and Space Administration,
Space Flight, 300 E St. S.W. (mailing address: NASA Headquarters, Mail Code M, Washington, DC 20546); (202)
358-2015. Fax, (202) 358-2838. Joseph Rothenberg, associate administrator. Internet, http://www.osf.hq.nasa.gov.

Responsible for space transportation systems operations, including U.S. participation in international missions. Manages the Johnson Space Center, Kennedy Space Center, Marshall Space Flight Center, and Stennis Space Center. Administers the development, testing, and production phases of the space shuttle. Manages the shuttle space lab program and the space station.

National Aeronautics and Space Administration, *Space Science, 300 E St. S.W. (mailing address: NASA Headquarters, Mail Code S, Washington, DC 20546); (202) 358-1409. Fax, (202) 358-3092. Wesley T. Huntress Jr., associate administrator. Information, (202) 358-1547. Internet, http://www.hq.nasa.gov/office/oss.*

Makes information available on technological developments that have resulted from NASA programs. (Accepts written requests for specific technical information.)

National Aeronautics and Space Administration, *Space Science and Aeronautics, 300 E St. S.W. (mailing address: NASA Headquarters, Mail Code IS, Washington, DC 20546); (202) 358-0900. Fax, (202) 358-3029. James B. Higgins, acting director. Information, (202) 358-1639. Internet, http://www.hq.nasa.gov.*

Acts as liaison with space agencies of foreign countries; negotiates and implements international agreements for cooperation in space; works with other U.S. government agencies on international issues regarding space and aeronautics.

National Aeronautics and Space Administration, *Space Shuttle, 300 E St. S.W., #7A70 20546; (202) 358-1200. Fax, (202) 358-2848. Steve Oswald, director.*

Directs policy related to operation of the space shuttle program, including U.S.-Russian cooperative programs and commercial uses of the shuttle.

National Air and Space Museum *(Smithsonian Institution), 6th St. and Independence Ave. S.W., MRC 310 20560; (202) 357-1745. Fax, (202) 357-2426. Donald D. Engan, director. Press, (202) 357-1552. Library, (202) 357-3133. TDD, (202) 357-1505. Education office, (202) 786-2106. Daily space and earth phenomena report, (202) 357-2000 (recording). Tours, (202) 357-1400. Internet, http://www.nasm.si.edu.*

Collects, preserves, and exhibits astronautical objects and equipment of historical interest, including manned spacecraft and communications and weather satellites. Library open to the public by appointment.

See also Civil Air Patrol (p. 574)

CONGRESS

General Accounting Office, *National Security and International Affairs, 441 G St. N.W., #4035 20548;*

(202) 512-2800. Fax, (202) 512-7686. Henry L. Hinton, assistant comptroller general.

Independent, nonpartisan agency in the legislative branch. Audits, analyzes, and evaluates the performance of the National Aeronautics and Space Administration. Makes unclassified reports available to the public.

House Appropriations Committee, *Subcommittee on VA, HUD, and Independent Agencies, H143 CAP 20515; (202) 225-3241. Jerry Lewis, R-Calif., chair; Frank Cushing, staff director. Internet, http://www.house.gov/appropriations.*

Jurisdiction over legislation to appropriate funds for the National Aeronautics and Space Administration.

House Government Reform and Oversight Committee, *Subcommittee on National Security, International Affairs, and Criminal Justice, B373 RHOB 20515; (202) 225-2577. Fax, (202) 225-1154. Dennis Hastert, R-Ill., chair; Robert Charles, staff director. Internet, http://www.house.gov/reform.*

Oversees operations of the National Aeronautics and Space Administration (jurisdiction shared with the House Science Committee).

House Science Committee, *Subcommittee on Space and Aeronautics, 2320 RHOB 20515; (202) 225-7858. F. James Sensenbrenner Jr., R-Wis., chair; Shana Dale, staff director. Internet, http://www.house.gov/science.*

Jurisdiction over legislation on space programs, national research and development in space exploration, space commercialization, earth-observing systems, the National Aeronautics and Space Administration (jurisdiction shared with House Government Reform and Oversight Committee), and space-related activities of the Transportation and Commerce departments.

Senate Appropriations Committee, *Subcommittee on VA, HUD, and Independent Agencies, SD-127 20510; (202) 224-7211. Christopher S. Bond, R-Mo., chair; John K. Mark, staff director. Internet, http://www.senate.gov/~appropriations.*

Jurisdiction over legislation to appropriate funds for the National Aeronautics and Space Administration.

Senate Commerce, Science, and Transportation Committee, *Subcommittee on Science, Technology, and Space, SH-427 (mailing address: SD-508, Washington, DC 20510); (202) 224-4852. Fax, (202) 228-0326. Bill Frist, R-Tenn., chair; Rosalind Parker, professional staff member. Internet, http://www.senate.gov/~commerce.*

Jurisdiction over legislation on nonmilitary space programs, national research and development in space exploration, space commercialization, and earth-observing systems. Oversight and legislative jurisdiction over NASA.

INTERNATIONAL ORGANIZATIONS

European Space Agency (ESA), *955 L'Enfant Plaza S.W., #7800 20024; (202) 488-4158. Fax, (202) 488-4930. I. W. Pryke, head, Washington office. Internet, http://www.esa.int.*

Intergovernmental agency that promotes international collaboration in space research and development and the use of space technology for peaceful purposes. Members include Australia and fourteen European countries: Austria, Belgium, Denmark, Finland, France, Germany, Ireland, Italy, the Netherlands, Norway, Spain, Sweden, Switzerland, and the United Kingdom; Canada participates in some programs. (Headquarters in Paris.)

NONPROFIT

Aerospace Education Foundation, *1501 Lee Hwy., Arlington, VA 22209; (703) 247-5839. Fax, (703) 247-5853. Darryl Hayes, managing director. Toll-free, (800) 727-3337. Internet, aefstaff@aef.org or http://www.aef.org.*

Promotes knowledge and appreciation of U.S. military and civilian aerospace development and history. Sponsors educational symposia and scholarships for enlisted personnel and officers on active duty or in the National Guard and Reserves. (Affiliated with the Air Force Assn.)

Aerospace Industries Assn. of America, *1250 Eye St. N.W., #1200 20005-3922; (202) 371-8400. Fax, (202) 371-8470. Don Fuqua, president. Press, (202) 371-8544. Internet, http://www.aia-aerospace.org.*

Represents U.S. manufacturers of commercial, military, and business aircraft; helicopters; aircraft engines; missiles; spacecraft; and related components and equipment. Interests include international standards and trade.

American Astronautical Society, *6352 Rolling Mill Pl., #102, Springfield, VA 22152; (703) 866-0020. Fax, (703) 866-3526. Carolyn Brown, executive director. Internet, aas@astronautical.org or http://www.astronautical.org.*

Scientific and technological society of researchers, scientists, astronauts, and other professionals in the field of astronautics and spaceflight engineering. Organizes national and local meetings and symposia.

American Institute of Aeronautics and Astronautics, *1801 Alexander Bell Dr., #500, Reston, VA 20191; (703) 264-7500. Fax, (703) 264-7551. Cort Durocher, executive director. Toll-free, (800) 639-2422. Internet, custserv@aiaa.org or http://www.aiaa.org.*

Membership: engineers, scientists, and students in the fields of aeronautics and astronautics. Holds workshops on aerospace technical issues for congressional subcommittees; sponsors international conferences. Offers computerized database through its Technical Information Service in New York.

National Research Council, *Aeronautics and Space Engineering Board, 2001 Wisconsin Ave. N.W. (mailing address: 2101 Constitution Ave. N.W., #HA292, Washington, DC 20418); (202) 334-2855. Fax, (202) 334-2482. George Levin, director. Press, (202) 334-2138. Library, (202) 334-2125. Publications, (202) 334-2855. Internet, http://www.nas.edu/cets/aseb.*

Membership: aeronautics and space experts. Advises government agencies on aeronautics and space engineering research, technology, experiments, international programs, and policy. Library open to the public by appointment.

National Research Council, *Space Studies Board, 2001 Wisconsin Ave. N.W. (mailing address: 2101 Constitution Ave. N.W., #HA584, Washington, DC 20418); (202) 334-3477. Fax, (202) 334-3701. Joseph K. Alexander, director. Press, (202) 334-2138. Library, (202) 334-2125. Internet, ssb@nas.edu or http://www.nas.edu/ssb/ssb.html.*

Provides assessments for NASA and other federal agencies on space science and applications, including international programs; provides research assessments and long-term research strategies. Interests include astronomy, lunar and planetary exploration, solar and space physics, earth science, space biology and medicine, and microgravity materials research. Library open to the public by appointment.

National Space Society, *600 Pennsylvania Ave. S.E., #201 20003-4316; (202) 543-1900. Fax, (202) 546-4189. Patricia Dasch, executive director. Internet, nsshq@nss.org or http://www.nss.org.*

Membership: individuals interested in space programs and applications of space technology. Provides information on NASA, commercial space activities, and international cooperation; promotes public education on space exploration and development; conducts conferences and workshops. Monitors legislation and regulations.

Resources for the Future, *1616 P St. N.W. 20036; (202) 328-5000. Fax, (202) 939-3460. Paul Portney, president. Library, (202) 328-5089. Internet, info@rff.org or http://www.rff.org.*

Examines the economic aspects of U.S. space policy, including policy on the space shuttle, unmanned rockets, communications satellites, and the space station. Focuses on the role of private business versus that of government.

Space Policy Institute *(George Washington University), 2013 G St. N.W., Stuart Hall, #201 20052; (202) 994-7292. Fax, (202) 994-1639. John M. Logsdon, director. Internet, cistp@gwis2.circ.gwu.edu or http://www.gwu.edu/~spi.*

Conducts research on space policy issues; organizes seminars, symposia, and conferences. Focuses on civilian space activities, including competitive and cooperative interactions on space between the United States and other countries.

Young Astronaut Council, *1308 19th St. N.W. 20036; (202) 682-1984. Fax, (202) 775-1773. T. Wendell Butler, president. Internet, yac1@aol.com or http://www.yac.org.*

Promotes improved math and science skills through aerospace activities for children ages 3 to 16. Encourages children to pursue careers in aerospace fields.

See also George C. Marshall Institute (p. 594); National Aviation Club (p. 663)

Astronomy

AGENCIES

National Aeronautics and Space Administration, *Space Science, 300 E St. S.W. (mailing address: NASA Headquarters, Mail Code S, Washington, DC 20546); (202) 358-1409. Fax, (202) 358-3092. Wesley T. Huntress Jr., associate administrator. Information, (202) 358-1547. Internet, http://www.hq.nasa.gov/office/oss.*

Administers programs that study the composition, energy, mass, position, size, and properties of celestial bodies within the universe, as observed from Earth; participates in international research efforts. Administers NASA's rocket programs.

National Science Foundation, *Astronomical Sciences, 4201 Wilson Blvd., #1045, Arlington, VA 22230; (703) 306-1820. Fax, (703) 306-0525. Hugh M. Van Horn, director. Internet, http://www.nsf.gov/MPS/ast.*

Provides grants for ground-based astronomy and astronomical research on planetary astronomy, stellar astronomy and astrophysics, galactic astronomy, extragalactic astronomy and cosmology, and advanced technologies and instrumentation. Maintains astronomical facilities.

U.S. Naval Observatory *(Defense Dept.), 3450 Massachusetts Ave. N.W. 20392-5420; (202) 762-1467. Fax, (202) 762-1461. Capt. Dennis G. Larsen, superintendent. Information, (202) 762-1438. Internet, http://www.usno.navy.mil.*

Determines the precise positions and motions of celestial bodies. Operates the U.S. master clock. Provides the U.S. Navy and Defense Dept. with astronomical and timing data for navigation, precise positioning, and command, control, and communications.

NONPROFIT

American Astronomical Society, *2000 Florida Ave. N.W., #400 20009-1231; (202) 328-2010. Fax, (202) 234-2560. Robert W. Milkey, executive officer. Press, (301) 286-5154. Internet, aas@aas.org or http://www.aas.org.*

Membership: astronomers and other professionals interested in the advancement of astronomy in the United States, Canada, and Mexico. Holds scientific meetings; awards research grants.

American Geophysical Union, *2000 Florida Ave. N.W. 20009-1277; (202) 462-6910. Fax, (202) 328-0566. A. F. Spilhaus Jr., executive director. Information, (202) 939-3212. Internet, http://www.agu.org.*

Membership: scientists and technologists who study the environments and components of the Earth, Sun, and solar system. Promotes international cooperation; disseminates information.

Assn. of Universities for Research in Astronomy, *1200 New York Ave. N.W., #350 20005; (202) 483-2101. Fax, (202) 483-2106. Goetz Oertel, president. Internet, http://www.aura-astronomy.org.*

Consortium of universities. Manages three ground-based observatories and the international Gemini Project for the National Science Foundation and manages the Space Telescope Science Institute for the National Aeronautics and Space Administration.

18

Social Services
and Disabilities

▦ GENERAL POLICY

AGENCIES

Administration for Children and Families *(Health and Human Services Dept.)*, 901 D St. S.W. (mailing address: 370 L'Enfant Promenade S.W., Washington, DC 20447); (202) 401-9200. Fax, (202) 401-5770. Olivia A. Golden, assistant secretary. Information, (202) 401-9215. Internet, http://www.acf.dhhs.gov.

Administers and funds programs for Native Americans, low-income families and individuals, and persons with disabilities. Responsible for Social Services Block Grants to the states; coordinates Health and Human Services Dept. policy and regulations on child protection, day care, foster care, adoption services, child abuse and neglect, and special services for those with disabilities. Administers Head Start program and funds the National Runaway Switchboard, (800) 621-4000, and the Domestic Violence Hotline, (800) 799-7233; TDD, (800) 787-3224.

Administration for Children and Families *(Health and Human Services Dept.)*, *Community Services*, 901 D St. S.W. (mailing address: 370 L'Enfant Promenade S.W., Washington, DC 20447); (202) 401-9333. Fax, (202) 401-4694. Donald Sykes, director.

Administers the Community Services Block Grant and Discretionary Grant programs and the Low Income Home Energy Assistance Block Grant Program for heating, cooling, and weatherizing low-income households.

Administration for Children and Families *(Health and Human Services Dept.)*, *State Systems*, 200 Independence Ave. S.W., 3rd Floor 20447; (202) 401-6959. Fax, (202) 401-6400. Mark Ragan, director. Internet, http://www.acf.dhhs.gov/programs/oss.

Oversees the development of state social services information systems; coordinates development of automated systems that states will use to implement the welfare reform law, including electronic transfer of benefits.

Administration for Native Americans *(Health and Human Services Dept.)*, 200 Independence Ave. S.W., #348F 20201; (202) 690-7776. Fax, (202) 690-7441. Gary N. Kimble, commissioner.

Awards grants for locally determined social and economic development strategies; promotes Native American economic and social self-sufficiency; funds tribes and Native American and native Hawaiian organizations. Commissioner chairs the Intradepartmental Council on Indian Affairs, which coordinates Native American-related programs.

AmeriCorps *(Corporation for National Service)*, *Volunteers in Service to America (VISTA)*, 1201 New York Ave. N.W., 9th Floor 20525; (202) 606-5000. Fax, (202) 565-2789. Diana London, deputy director. Volunteer recruiting information, (800) 942-2677; TDD, (800) 833-3722. Internet, http://www.cns.gov/americorps/ac_vista.html.

Assigns full-time volunteers to public and private nonprofit organizations to alleviate poverty in local communities. Volunteers receive stipends.

Bureau of Indian Affairs *(Interior Dept.)*, *Social Services*, 1849 C St. N.W., Mail Stop 4641 20240-4001; (202) 208-2721. Fax, (202) 208-2648. Larry R. Blair, chief.

Gives assistance, in accordance with state payment standards, to native Americans who do not qualify for other forms of direct aid. Provides family and individual counseling and child welfare services. Administers the Indian Child Welfare Act grants to native American tribes and organizations to establish and operate native American child protection services.

Corporation for National Service, 1201 New York Ave. N.W. 20525; (202) 606-5000. Fax, (202) 565-2784. Harris L. Wofford, chief executive officer; Shirley Sagawa, executive director. TDD, (202) 565-2799. Volunteer recruiting information, (800) 942-2677. Internet, http://www.cns.gov.

Independent corporation that administers federally sponsored domestic volunteer programs that provide disadvantaged citizens with services, including AmeriCorps, AmeriCorps-VISTA (Volunteers in Service to America), AmeriCorps-NCCC (National Civilian Community Corps), Learn and Serve America, and the National Senior Service Corps.

Food and Consumer Service *(Agriculture Dept.)*, 3101 Park Center Dr., #803, Alexandria, VA 22302; (703) 305-2062. Fax, (703) 305-2908. Yvette S. Jackson, administrator. Information, (703) 305-2276. Internet, http://www.usda.gov/fcs.

Administers all Agriculture Dept. domestic food assistance, including the distribution of funds and food for school breakfast and lunch programs (preschool through secondary) to public and nonprofit private schools; the food stamp program; and a supplemental nutrition program for women, infants, and children (WIC).

Food and Consumer Service *(Agriculture Dept.)*, *Food Distribution*, 3101 Park Center Dr., #503, Alexandria, VA 22302; (703) 305-2680. Fax, (703) 305-2420. Les Johnson, director.

Administers the purchasing and distribution of food to state agencies for child care centers, public and private schools, public and nonprofit charitable institutions, and summer camps. Coordinates the distribution of special commodities, including surplus cheese and butter. Administers the National Commodity Processing Program, which facilitates distribution, at reduced prices, of processed foods to state agencies.

Food and Consumer Service *(Agriculture Dept.),* *Food Stamp Program, 3101 Park Center Dr., #710, Alexandria, VA 22302; (703) 305-2026. Fax, (703) 305-2454. Susan Carr Gossman, deputy administrator.*

Administers, through state welfare agencies, the Food Stamp Program, which provides needy persons with food coupons to increase food purchasing power. Provides matching funds to cover half the cost of coupon issuance.

Health and Human Services Dept., *200 Independence Ave. S.W., #615F 20201; (202) 690-7000. Fax, (202) 690-7203. Donna E. Shalala, secretary; Walter D. Broadnax, deputy secretary, (202) 690-7431. Press, (202) 690-6343. TDD, (800) 877-8339. Locator, (202) 619-0257. Internet, http://www.os.dhhs.gov.*

Acts as principal adviser to the president on health and welfare plans, policies, and programs of the federal government. Encompasses the Health Care Financing Administration, the Administration for Children and Families, the Public Health Service, and the Centers for Disease Control and Prevention.

Health and Human Services Dept., *Disability, Aging, and Long-Term Care Policy, 200 Independence Ave. S.W., #424E 20201; (202) 690-6443. Fax, (202) 401-7733. Bob Williams, deputy assistant secretary.*

Coordinates policy and evaluation procedures for social services programs to ensure efficient use of resources. Conducts research and analyses of programs, including long-term care services for the elderly; social services programs for families; and programs for the disabled.

Health and Human Services Dept., *Human Services Policy, 200 Independence Ave. S.W., #404E 20201; (202) 690-7148. Fax, (202) 690-6562. Canta Pian, director, Economic Support for Families.*

Collects and disseminates information on human services programs that provide nonelderly populations, including families and their children, with cash, employment, training, and related assistance.

CONGRESS

General Accounting Office, *Health, Education, and Human Services, 441 G St. N.W. 20548; (202) 512-6806. Fax, (202) 512-5806. Richard L. Hembra, assistant comptroller general.*

Independent, nonpartisan agency in the legislative branch. Audits, analyzes, and evaluates Health and Human Services Dept. and Corporation for National Service programs; makes reports available to the public.

House Agriculture Committee, *Subcommittee on Department Operations, Nutrition, and Foreign Agriculture, 1430 LHOB 20515; (202) 225-0171. Fax, (202) 225-4464. Robert W. Goodlatte, R-Va., chair; Kevin Kramp, staff director. Internet, http://www.house.gov/agriculture.*

Jurisdiction over food stamp legislation.

House Appropriations Committee, *Subcommittee on Labor, Health and Human Services, and Education, 2358 RHOB 20515; (202) 225-3508. John Edward Porter, R-Ill., chair; Tony McCann, staff director. Internet, http://www.house.gov/appropriations.*

Jurisdiction over legislation to appropriate funds for the Health and Human Services Dept. (except the Food and Drug Administration and Native American health programs), Corporation for National Service programs, and the National Council on Disability.

House Education and the Workforce Committee, *Subcommittee on Early Childhood, Youth, and Families, 2181 RHOB 20515; (202) 225-4527. Fax, (202) 225-9571. Frank Riggs, R-Calif., chair; Kevin Talley, staff director. Internet, http://www.house.gov/eeo.*

Jurisdiction over legislation on Community Services Block Grant Program, Head Start, Native Americans programs, antipoverty programs, applications of the Older Americans Act (including volunteer older Americans programs under the Corporation for National Service) and related legislation, runaway youth, child and youth development, Child Care Development Block Grant, and child-family services.

House Education and the Workforce Committee, *Subcommittee on Oversight and Investigations, 2181 RHOB 20515; (202) 225-7101. Fax, (202) 225-9571. Peter Hoekstra, R-Mich., chair; Kevin Talley, staff director. Internet, http://www.house.gov/eeo.*

Oversees and investigates matters relating to child abuse and domestic violence, child adoption, education of children with disabilities, vocational rehabilitation for people with disabilities and developmental disabilities, day care, and domestic volunteer programs, including the Corporation for National Service. No legislative jurisdiction.

House Ways and Means Committee, *Subcommittee on Human Resources, B317 RHOB 20515; (202) 225-1025. Fax, (202) 225-9480. E. Clay Shaw Jr., R-Fla., chair;*

Ronald Haskins, staff director. Internet, http://www.house. gov/ways_means.

Jurisdiction over legislation on welfare programs, child support enforcement, child welfare, child care, foster care, adoption assistance, supplemental security income, unemployment compensation and insurance, low-income energy assistance, eligibility of welfare recipients for food stamps, and social services for the elderly and persons with disabilities.

Senate Agriculture, Nutrition, and Forestry Committee, SR-328A 20510; (202) 224-2035. Fax, (202) 224-1725. Richard G. Lugar, R-Ind., chair; Randy Green, staff director. Internet, http://www.senate.gov/~agriculture.

Jurisdiction over legislation on low-income energy assistance programs.

Senate Appropriations Committee, *Subcommittee on Labor, Health and Human Services, and Education,* SD-184 20510; (202) 224-7230. Arlen Specter, R-Pa., chair; Craig A. Higgins, staff director. Internet, http://www. senate.gov/~appropriations/labor.

Jurisdiction over legislation to appropriate funds for the Health and Human Services Dept. (except the Food and Drug Administration and Native American health programs), Corporation for National Service, and the National Council on Disability.

Senate Finance Committee, *Subcommittee on Social Security and Family Policy,* SD-219 20510; (202) 224-4515. Fax, (202) 228-0578. John H. Chafee, R-R.I., chair; Alec Bachon, staff contact. Internet, http://www.senate. gov/~finance.

Holds hearings on legislation concerning welfare programs, child support enforcement, child welfare, child care, foster care, adoption assistance, supplemental security income, unemployment compensation and insurance, and social services for the elderly and persons with disabilities.

NONPROFIT

American Enterprise Institute for Public Policy Research, *Social and Individual Responsibility Project,* 1150 17th St. N.W. 20036; (202) 862-5904. Fax, (202) 862-7178. Douglas J. Besharov, director.

Research and education organization that conducts studies on social welfare policies, including family and welfare policies. Interests include children, child abuse and neglect, divorce, drug abuse, family breakdown, poverty, out-of-wedlock births, and welfare programs.

American Public Welfare Assn., 810 1st St. N.E., #500 20002-4267; (202) 682-0100. Fax, (202) 289-6555. Linda Wolf, executive director. Internet, http://www.apwa.org.

Membership: state and local human services agencies and individuals working or interested in public welfare. Develops national social policy positions; promotes professional development for members.

Assn. of Community Organizations for Reform Now (ACORN), 739 8th St. S.E. 20003; (202) 547-2500. Fax, (202) 547-2483. Melanie Marcus, head, Washington Office. Internet, dcnatacorn@igc.apc.org.

Works to advance the interests of minority and low-income families through community organizing and action. Interests include jobs, living wages, housing, welfare reform, and community reinvestment. (Headquarters in New Orleans.)

Catholic Charities USA, 1731 King St., #200, Alexandria, VA 22314; (703) 549-1390. Fax, (703) 549-1656. Fred Kammer (SJ), president. Press, (703) 549-1390. Internet, http://catholiccharitiesusa.org.

Member agencies and institutions provide persons of all backgrounds with social services, including adoption, education, counseling, food, and housing services. National office promotes public policies that address human needs and social injustice. Provides members with advocacy and professional support, including technical assistance, training, and resource development; disseminates publications.

Center for Community Change, 1000 Wisconsin Ave. N.W. 20007; (202) 342-0519. Fax, (202) 342-1132. Pablo Eisenberg, executive director.

Provides community-based organizations serving minorities and the economically disadvantaged with technical assistance. Areas of assistance include community development block grants, housing, economic and resource development, rural development projects, and program planning.

Center for Law and Social Policy, 1616 P St. N.W., #150 20036; (202) 328-5141. Fax, (202) 328-5195. Alan W. Houseman, director. Information, (202) 328-5140. Internet, http://www.class.org.

Public interest organization with expertise in law and policy affecting low-income Americans. Seeks to improve the economic conditions of low-income families with children and to secure access for persons in poverty to the civil justice system.

Center for the Study of Social Policy, 1250 Eye St. N.W., #503 20005-3922; (202) 371-1565. Fax, (202) 371-1472. Tom Joe, director.

Conducts research on government financing and delivery of social services programs, especially those related to children and families. Research focuses on long-term care for the elderly, health care reform, social welfare, the working poor, and people with disabilities. Offers technical assistance to states implementing reform in child and family services.

Center on Budget and Policy Priorities, *820 1st St. N.E., #510 20002; (202) 408-1080. Fax, (202) 408-1056. Robert Greenstein, executive director. Internet, http:// www.cbpp.org.*

Research group that analyzes federal, state, and local government policies affecting low- and moderate-income Americans.

Christian Relief Services, *8815 Telegraph Rd., Lorton, VA 22079; (703) 550-2472. Fax, (703) 550-2473. Eugene L. Krizek, president. Internet, crserv@access.digex.net or http://www.christianrelief.org.*

Promotes economic development and the alleviation of poverty in urban areas of the United States, Native American reservations, and developing countries around the world. Donates medical supplies and food; administers housing, hospital, and school construction programs.

Coalition on Human Needs, *1000 Wisconsin Ave. N.W. 20007; (202) 342-0726. Fax, (202) 338-1856. Jennifer A. Vasiloff, executive director. Internet, chn@chn.org.*

Promotes public policies that address the needs of low-income Americans. Members include civil rights, religious, labor, and professional organizations and individuals concerned with the well-being of children, women, the elderly, and people with disabilities.

Council of Jewish Federations, *1640 Rhode Island Ave. N.W., #500 20036; (202) 785-5900. Fax, (202) 785-7043. Diana Aviv, director, Washington Office. Internet, http:// jewishfedna.org.*

Membership: Jewish Federations, which are community organizations serving localities in the United States and Canada. Serves federations in areas of fundraising, operations, planning, and government relations; assists Jewish communities overseas. Interests include health, welfare, immigration, and human rights. (Headquarters in New York.)

Council on Social Work Education, *1600 Duke St., #300, Alexandria, VA 22314-3421; (703) 683-8080. Fax, (703) 683-8099. Donald W. Beless, executive director. Internet, membership@cswe.org or http://www.cswe.org.*

Promotes quality education in social work. Accredits social work programs.

Food Research and Action Center, *1875 Connecticut Ave. N.W., #540 20009-5728; (202) 986-2200. Fax, (202) 986-2525. James Weil, president. Internet, http://www. frac.org.*

Public interest advocacy, research, and legal center that works to end hunger and poverty in the United States; offers legal assistance, organizational aid, training, and information to groups seeking to improve or expand federal food programs, including food stamp, child nutrition, and WIC (women, infants, and children) programs; conducts studies relating to hunger and poverty; coordinates network of antihunger organizations. Monitors legislation and regulations.

Goodwill Industries International, Inc., *9200 Rockville Pike, Bethesda, MD 20814-3896; (301) 530-6500. Fax, (301) 530-1516. Fred Grandy, president. Internet, goodwill@goodwill.org or http://www.goodwill.org.*

Membership: 185 autonomous organizations that provide disabled and disadvantaged individuals with Goodwill Industries services, which include vocational rehabilitation evaluation, job training, employment, and placement services.

Hudson Institute, *1015 18th St. N.W., #300 20036; (202) 223-7770. Fax, (202) 223-8537. Tom Duesterberg, director, Washington Office. Internet, http://www.hudson.org.*

Studies welfare policy; helps states create welfare reform programs. (Headquarters in Indianapolis.)

Institute for Women's Policy Research, *1400 20th St. N.W., #104 20036; (202) 785-5100. Fax, (202) 833-4362. Heidi I. Hartmann, director. Internet, http://www.iwpr.org.*

Public policy research organization that focuses on women's issues, including welfare reform, family and work policies, employment and wages, and discrimination based on gender, race, or ethnicity.

National Assn. for the Advancement of Colored People (NAACP), *1025 Vermont Ave. N.W., #1120 20005; (202) 638-2269. Fax, (202) 638-5936. Hilary Shelton, deputy director. Internet, http://www.naacp.org.*

Membership: persons interested in civil rights for all minorities. Interests include welfare reform and related social welfare matters. Administers programs that create employment and affordable housing opportunities and that improve health care. Monitors legislation and regulations. (Headquarters in Baltimore.)

National Assn. of Community Action Agencies, *1100 17th St. N.W., #500 20036; (202) 265-7546. Fax, (202) 265-8850. John Buckstead, executive director. Internet, http://www.nacaa.org.*

Provides community action agencies with information, training, and technical assistance; advocates, at all levels of government, for low-income people.

National Assn. of Social Workers, *750 1st St. N.E., #700 20002-4241; (202) 408-8600. Fax, (202) 336-8310.*

Josephine Nieves, executive director. Internet, nasw@capcon.net or http://www.naswdc.org.

Membership: graduates of accredited social work education programs and students in accredited programs. Promotes the interests of social workers and their clients; promotes professional standards; certifies members of the Academy of Certified Social Workers; conducts research.

National Community Action Foundation, 2100 M St. N.W., #604 20037; (202) 775-0223. Fax, (202) 775-0225. David Bradley, executive director. Internet, http://www.ncas.org.

Organization for community action agencies concerned with issues that affect the poor. Provides information on Community Services Block Grant, low-income energy assistance, employment and training, weatherization for low-income housing, nutrition, and the Head Start program.

National Urban Coalition, 2120 L St. N.W., #510 20037; (202) 986-1460. Fax, (202) 986-1468. Ramona H. Edelin, president.

Membership: urban community action groups. Operates Say Yes to a Youngster's Future, a community-based education program for low-income students in math, science, and technology, and the M. Carl Holman Leadership Development Institute, which gives students opportunities to learn from local and national leaders, including scholars, entrepreneurs, and other experts.

National Urban League, 1111 14th St. N.W., #1001 20005-5603; (202) 898-1604. Fax, (202) 408-1965. Robert McAlpine, director, Policy and Government Relations. Internet, http://www.nul.org.

Federation of affiliates concerned with the social welfare of African Americans and other minorities. Social Welfare Division disseminates welfare rights information to local leagues. (Headquarters in New York.)

Poverty and Race Research Action Council, 1711 Connecticut Ave. N.W., #207 20009; (202) 387-9887. Fax, (202) 387-0764. Chester W. Hartman, executive director. Internet, prrac@aol.com.

Facilitates cooperative links between researchers and activists who work on race and poverty issues. Provides nonprofit organizations with funding for research on race and poverty.

Salvation Army, 615 Slaters Lane, Alexandria, VA (mailing address: P.O. Box 269, Alexandria, VA 22313); (703) 684-5500. Fax, (703) 684-3478. Robert A. Watson, commissioner. Internet, http://www.salvationarmyusa.org.

International religious social welfare organization that provides social services, including counseling, youth and senior citizens' services, emergency help, foster care, settlement and day care, tutoring for the retarded, programs for people with disabilities, prison work, summer camps, community centers, employment services, rehabilitation programs for alcoholics, missing persons bureaus, and residences for the homeless. (International headquarters in London.)

Social Legislation Information Service, 440 1st St. N.W. 20001-2085; (202) 638-2952. Fax, (202) 638-4004. Marjorie Kopp, editor. Internet, hn3898@handsnet.org.

Membership: individuals; libraries; and national, state, and local agencies interested in social welfare. Reports on federal legislation and activities of federal agencies relating to children, the elderly, and people with disabilities; delinquents; health, education, and welfare; and housing, employment, and other social welfare issues. (Division of the Child Welfare League of America.)

Urban Institute, 2100 M St. N.W. 20037; (202) 833-7200. Fax, (202) 429-0687. William Gorham, president. Information, (202) 857-8702. Library, (202) 857-8688. Internet, paffairs@ui.urban.org or http://www.urban.org.

Nonpartisan, public policy research and education organization. Interests include states' use of federal funds; delivery of social services to specific groups, including children of mothers in welfare reform programs; retirement policy, income, and community-based services for the elderly; job placement and training programs for welfare recipients; health care cost containment and access; food stamps; child nutrition; the homeless; housing; immigration; and tax policy. Library open to the public by appointment.

U.S. Conference of City Human Services Officials, 1620 Eye St. N.W. 20006; (202) 861-6707. Fax, (202) 293-2352. Laura DeKoven Waxman, deputy executive director.

Promotes improved social services for specific urban populations through meetings, technical assistance, and training programs for members; fosters information exchange among federal, state, and local governments, human services experts, and other groups concerned with human services issues. (Affiliate of the U.S. Conference of Mayors.)

 CHILDREN AND FAMILIES

See also Caucuses (chap. 20)

AGENCIES

Administration for Children and Families *(Health and Human Services Dept.),* 901 D St. S.W. *(mailing* *address: 370 L'Enfant Promenade S.W., Washington, DC 20447); (202) 401-9200. Fax, (202) 401-5770. Olivia A. Golden, assistant secretary. Information, (202) 401-9215. Internet, http://www.acf.dhhs.gov.*

Plans, manages, and coordinates national assistance programs that promote stability, economic security, responsibility, and self-support for families; supervises programs and use of funds to provide the most needy with aid and to increase alternatives to public assistance. Programs include Temporary Assistance to Needy Families, Child Welfare, Head Start, Child Support Enforcement, Low-Income Home Energy Assistance, Community Services Block Grant, and Refugee Resettlement Assistance.

Administration for Children and Families *(Health and Human Services Dept.), Child Support Enforcement, 901 D St. S.W. (mailing address: 370 L'Enfant Promenade S.W., Washington, DC 20447); (202) 401-9370. Fax, (202) 401-5559. Olivia A. Golden, acting director. Information, (202) 401-9373. Internet, http://www. acf.dhhs.gov.*

Helps states develop, manage, and operate child support programs. Maintains the Federal Parent Locator Service, which provides state and local child support agencies with information for locating absent parents. State enforcement agencies locate absent parents, establish paternity, establish and enforce support orders, and collect child support payments.

Administration for Children and Families *(Health and Human Services Dept.), Family Assistance—Job Opportunities and Basic Skills Training, 901 D St. S.W. (mailing address: 370 L'Enfant Promenade S.W., Washington, DC 20447); (202) 401-9275. Fax, (202) 205-5887. Lavinia Limon, director.*

Provides recipients of Aid to Families with Dependent Children with job search assistance, vocational training, and educational aid (including remedial programs, literacy training, and instruction in English as a second language); focuses on women with young children; provides child care options and other support services to make participation possible. Coordinates programs, under the Family Support Act of 1988, with departments of Education and Labor.

Administration for Children, Youth, and Families *(Health and Human Services Dept.), Children's Bureau, 330 C St. S.W. (mailing address: P.O. Box 1182, Washington, DC 20013); (202) 205-8618. Fax, (202) 260-9345. Carol W. Williams, associate commissioner.*

Administers grants to agencies and institutes of higher learning for research projects and for training personnel in the child welfare field. Administers formula grants to strengthen child welfare services provided by state and local public welfare agencies. Provides states with technical assistance in group and foster care, adoption, and family services.

Administration for Children, Youth, and Families *(Health and Human Services Dept.), Family and Youth Services, 330 C St. S.W. (mailing address: P.O. Box 1182, Washington, DC 20013); (202) 205-8102. Fax, (202) 260-9333. Terry Lewis, associate commissioner.*

Administers federal discretionary grant programs for projects serving runaway and homeless youth and for projects that deter youth involvement in gangs. Provides youth service agencies with training and technical assistance. Monitors federal policies, programs, and legislation. Supports research on youth development issues, including gangs, runaways, and homeless youth. Operates national clearinghouse on families and youth.

Administration for Children, Youth, and Families *(Health and Human Services Dept.), National Center on Child Abuse and Neglect, 330 C St. S.W. (mailing address: P.O. Box 1182, Washington, DC 20013); (202) 205-8586. Fax, (202) 260-9351. Emily Cook, acting director. Information, (703) 385-7565.*

Maintains clearinghouse of programs for preventing and treating child abuse and neglect; makes grants to agencies and states for identification and treatment programs.

Cooperative State Research, Education, and Extension Service *(Agriculture Dept.), Family, 4-H, and Nutrition, 1400 Independence Ave. S.W., #3441S (mailing address: P.O. Box 2225, Washington, DC 20250-2225); (202) 720-2908. Fax, (202) 690-2469. Alma C. Hobbs, deputy administrator. Internet, http://www.reeusda.gov.*

Administers education programs with state land-grant universities and county governments for rural and urban youth ages 5 to 19. Projects provide youth with experience in the fields of science and technological literacy, environment, natural resources, health, leadership, citizenship, service, and personal development.

Food and Consumer Service *(Agriculture Dept.), Child Nutrition, 3101 Park Center Dr., #1006, Alexandria, VA 22302; (703) 305-2590. Fax, (703) 305-2879. Stanley Garnett, director. Press, (703) 305-2286.*

Administers the transfer of funds to state agencies for the National School Lunch Program; the School Breakfast Program; the Special Milk Program, which helps schools and institutions provide children who do not have access to full meals under other child nutrition programs with fluid milk; the Child and Adult Care Food

Program, which provides children in nonresidential child-care centers and family day care homes with year-round meal service; and the Summer Food Service Program, which provides children from low-income families with meals during the summer months.

Food and Consumer Service *(Agriculture Dept.), Nutrition and Technical Services, 3101 Park Center Dr., #607, Alexandria, VA 22302; (703) 305-2585. Fax, (703) 305-2549. Patricia Daniels, director.*

Administers the Nutrition Education and Training Program, which provides states with grants for disseminating nutrition information to children and for in-service training of food service and teaching personnel; administers the Child Nutrition Labeling Program, which certifies that foods served in school lunch and breakfast programs meet nutritional requirements; provides information and technical assistance in nutrition and food service management.

Food and Consumer Service *(Agriculture Dept.), Supplemental Food Program, 3101 Park Center Dr., #540, Alexandria, VA 22302; (703) 305-2746. Fax, (703) 305-2196. Ronald J. Vogel, acting director.*

Provides health departments and agencies with federal funding for food supplements and administrative expenses to make food, nutrition education, and health services available to infants, young children, and pregnant, nursing, and postpartum women.

Health and Human Services Dept., *Head Start, 330 C St. S.W., #2050 (mailing address: P.O. Box 1182, Washington, DC 20013); (202) 205-8572. Fax, (202) 260-9336. Helen Taylor, associate commissioner.*

Awards grants to nonprofit organizations and local governments for operating community Head Start programs (comprehensive development programs for children, ages 3 to 5, of low-income families); manages a limited number of parent and child centers for families with children up to age 3. Conducts research and manages demonstration programs, including those under the Comprehensive Child Care Development Act of 1988; administers the Child Development Associate scholarship program, which trains individuals for careers in child development, often as Head Start teachers.

Health and Human Services Dept., *Human Services Policy, 200 Independence Ave. S.W., #450G 20201; (202) 690-6461. Fax, (202) 690-5514. Barbara Broman, director, Children and Youth Policy.*

Develops policies and procedures for programs that benefit children, youth, and families. Interests include child protection, family support, gang violence, child

care and development, and care for drug-exposed, runaway, and homeless children and their families.

National Institute of Child Health and Human Development *(National Institutes of Health), National Center for Medical Rehabilitation Research, 6100 Executive Blvd., Bldg. 6100E, #2A-03, Bethesda, MD 20892-7510; (301) 402-2242. Fax, (301) 402-0832. Dr. Marcus Fuhrer, director. TDD, (301) 402-2554. Internet, http://silk.nih.gov/silk/NCMRR.*

Conducts and supports research to develop improved technologies, techniques, and prosthetic and orthotic devices for people with disabilities; promotes medical rehabilitation training.

Office of Justice Programs *(Justice Dept.), Juvenile Justice and Delinquency Prevention, 810 7th St. N.W., 8th Floor 20531; (202) 307-5911. Fax, (202) 307-2093. Shay Bilchik, administrator. Technical information, (202) 307-0751. Clearinghouse, (800) 638-8736. Internet, http://www.ncjrs.org/ojjhome.htm.*

Administers most federal programs related to prevention and treatment of juvenile delinquency, missing and exploited children, and research and evaluation of juvenile justice system; coordinates youth programs of the departments of Agriculture, Education, Housing and Urban Development, Interior, and Labor, and of the Substance Abuse and Mental Health Services Administration, including the Center for Studies of Crime and Delinquency. Operates the Juvenile Justice Clearinghouse.

Office of Justice Programs *(Justice Dept.), Violence Against Women, 10th and Constitution Ave. N.W., #5302 20530; (202) 616-8894. Fax, (202) 307-3911. Bonnie Campbell, director. Internet, http://www.usdoj.gov/vawo.*

Seeks more effective policies and services to combat domestic violence, sexual assault, stalking, and other crimes against women. Helps administer grants to states to fund shelters, crisis centers, and hotlines, and to hire law enforcement officers, prosecutors, and counselors specializing in cases of sexual violence and other violent crimes against women.

See also Bureau of Indian Affairs (p. 6)

CONGRESS

House Education and the Workforce Committee, *Subcommittee on Early Childhood, Youth, and Families, 2181 RHOB 20515; (202) 225-4527. Fax, (202) 225-9571. Frank Riggs, R-Calif., chair; Kevin Talley, staff director. Internet, http://www.house.gov/eeo.*

Jurisdiction over legislation on the National School Lunch Program, the School Breakfast Program, the Summer Food Program for Children, the Special Milk Program for Children, and the Special Supplemental Food Program for Women, Infants, and Children (WIC).

Senate Agriculture, Nutrition, and Forestry Committee, *Subcommittee on Research, Nutrition, and General Legislation, SR-361A 20510; (202) 224-2035. Fax, (202) 224-1725. Mitch McConnell, R-Ky., chair; David Hovermale, legislative assistant. Internet, http:// www.senate.gov/~agriculture.*

Jurisdiction over legislation on commodity donations, the Food Stamp Program, the National School Lunch Program, the School Breakfast Program, the Summer Food Program for Children, the Special Milk Program for Children, the Special Supplemental Food Program for Women, Infants, and Children (WIC), and nutritional programs for the elderly.

Senate Labor and Human Resources Committee, *Subcommittee on Children and Families, SH-625 20510; (202) 224-5800. Fax, (202) 228-4137. Daniel R. Coats, R-Ind., chair; Stephanie Monroe, staff director. Internet, http://www.senate.gov/~labor.*

Jurisdiction over legislation on day care, child abuse and domestic violence, family and medical leave, low-income energy assistance, adoption reform, Community Services Block Grant Program, Head Start, youth, child and youth development, Child Care Development Block Grant, and child-family services.

NONPROFIT

Adoptees in Search, *P.O. Box 41016, Bethesda, MD 20824; (301) 656-8555. Fax, (301) 652-2106. Joanne W. Small, executive director. Internet, ais20824@aol.com.*

Membership: adult adoptees, adoptive parents, and birth relatives. Provides members with professional consultation, guidance, and support services. Promotes awareness of adoption practice and laws that affect adopted people and their families. Advocates legislation that restores full civil rights to adult adoptees.

Adoption Service Information Agency, *7720 Alaska Ave. N.W. 20012; (202) 726-7193. Fax, (202) 722-4928. Theodore Kim, president. Internet, http://www.clocknet/ pub/asia/asia.html.*

Provides information on international adoption; sponsors seminars and workshops for adoptive and prospective adoptive parents.

American Assn. for Marriage and Family Therapy, *1133 15th St. N.W., #300 20005-2710; (202) 452-0109. Fax, (202) 223-2329. Michael Bowers, executive director. Internet, http://www.aamft.org.*

Membership: professional marriage and family therapists. Promotes professional standards in marriage and family therapy through training programs; provides the public with educational material and referral service for marriage and family therapy.

American Bar Assn., *Center on Children and the Law, 740 15th St. N.W., 9th Floor 20005; (202) 662-1720. Fax, (202) 662-1755. Howard Davidson, director. Internet, ctrchildlaw@abanet.org or http://www.abanet.org.*

Works to increase lawyer representation of children; sponsors speakers and conferences; monitors legislation and provides information. Interests include child sexual abuse and exploitation, missing and runaway children, parental kidnapping, child support, foster care, and adoption of children with special needs.

American Family Society, *5013 Russett Rd., Rockville, MD 20853; (301) 460-4455. Fax, (301) 460-6422. K. Wayne Scott, president. Internet, famtime@aol.com.*

Provides families and organizations with self-help resource materials.

American Humane Assn., *236 Massachusetts Ave. N.E., #203 20002; (202) 543-7780. Fax, (202) 546-3266. Adele Douglass, director, Washington Office. Internet, tuam@ aol.com or http://www.amerhumane.org.*

Membership: humane societies, individuals, and government agencies concerned with child protection laws. Prepares model state legislation on child abuse and its prevention; publishes surveys on child abuse and state abuse laws. (Headquarters in Denver.)

American Youth Work Center, *1200 17th St. N.W., 4th Floor 20036; (202) 785-0764. Fax, (202) 728-0657. William Treanor, executive director. Internet, hn2759@ handsnet.org.*

International citizens' interest group concerned with juvenile justice and community-based youth services, including runaway shelters, hotlines, crisis intervention centers, drug programs, alternative education, and job training and placement. Provides youth programs with technical assistance; works with agencies and individuals dealing with young people; serves as clearinghouse and resource center; sponsors a college internship program.

Boy Scouts of America, *9190 Wisconsin Ave., Bethesda, MD 20814; (301) 530-9360. Fax, (301) 564-3648. Ron L. Carroll, scout executive.*

Educational services organization for boys ages 7 to 17. Promotes citizen participation and physical fitness. The Explorers Program, which includes young men and women ages 14 to 20, provides vocational opportunities. (Headquarters in Irving, Texas.)

Boys and Girls Clubs of America, *600 Jefferson Plaza, #401, Rockville, MD 20852-1150; (301) 251-6676. Fax, (301) 294-3052. Robbie Callaway, senior vice president. Internet, http://www.bgca.org.*

Educational service organization for boys and girls, most from disadvantaged circumstances. Works to prevent juvenile delinquency; promotes youth employment, health and fitness, leadership, and citizenship. Interests include child care, child safety and protection, drug and alcohol abuse prevention, runaway and homeless youth, youth employment, child nutrition, tax reform and charitable contributions, and other issues that affect disadvantaged youth. (Headquarters in Atlanta.)

Center for the Support of Children, *5141 Linnean Ave. N.W. 20008; (202) 363-7271. Fax, (202) 363-7354. Laurene T. McKillop, executive director.*

Assists state and local decisionmakers and service providers in creating and implementing policy for children and families; seeks to strengthen relationships among policymakers, service providers and recipients, and funding sources; provides training, technical assistance, and strategic planning; focuses on child support, paternity, child welfare, child care, and other family responsibility issues that affect adolescents, young families, and child support service professionals.

Child Nutrition Forum, *1875 Connecticut Ave. N.W., #540 20009-5728; (202) 986-2200. Fax, (202) 986-2525. Ellen Teller, coordinator.*

Membership: agriculture, labor, education, and health and nutrition specialists; school food service officials; and consumer and religious groups. Supports federal nutrition programs for children; provides information on school nutrition programs. Monitors legislation and regulations concerning hunger issues.

Child Welfare League of America, *440 1st St. N.W., #310 20001-2085; (202) 638-2952. Fax, (202) 638-4004. David Liederman, executive director. Internet, http://www. cwla.org.*

Membership: public and private child welfare agencies and individuals. Develops standards for the field; provides information on adoption, day care, foster care, group home services, child protection, residential care for children and youth, services to pregnant adolescents and young parents, and other child welfare issues.

Children's Defense Fund, *25 E St. N.W. 20001; (202) 628-8787. Fax, (202) 662-3510. Marian Wright Edelman, president. Internet, http://www.childrensdefense.org.*

Advocacy group concerned with programs and policies for children and youth, particularly poor and minority children. Interests include health care, education,

child care, job training and employment, and family support; works to ensure educational and job opportunities for youth.

Children's Defense Fund, *Child Care Division, 25 E St. N.W. 20001; (202) 628-8787. Fax, (202) 662-3510. Helen Blank, director.*

Advocacy group concerned with federal and state programs for children and youth; provides parents and child-care advocates with information on child-care policy.

Children's Foundation, *725 15th St. N.W., #505 20005-2109; (202) 347-3300. Fax, (202) 347-3382. Kay Hollestelle, executive director. Internet, cfwashdc@aol.com.*

Advocacy group for children and those who care for them. Works to improve available child care; promotes enforcement of child support; offers information, technical assistance, and professional training to child care providers and parents.

Children's Rights Council, *300 Eye St. N.E., #401 20002-4362; (202) 547-6227. Fax, (202) 546-4272. David L. Levy, president. Internet, http://www.vix.com/crc.*

Membership: parents and professionals. Works to strengthen families through education and advocacy. Supports family formation and preservation. Conducts conferences and serves as an information clearinghouse. Interests include children whose parents are separated, unwed, or divorced.

Christian Children's Fund, *1400 16th St. N.W., #420 20036; (202) 462-2161. Fax, (202) 462-0601. Betty Meyer, director, Washington Liaison Office. Internet, http://www. christianchildrensfund.org.*

Works internationally to ensure the survival, protection, and development of children. Promotes the improvement in quality of life of children within the context of family, community, and culture. Helps children in unstable situations brought on by war, natural disasters, and other high-risk circumstances. (Headquarters in Richmond, Va.)

Council for Early Childhood Professional Recognition, *Child Development Associate National Credentialing Program, 2460 16th St. N.W. 20009-3575; (202) 265-9090. Fax, (202) 265-9161. Carol Brunson Phillips, executive director. Toll-free, (800) 424-4310.*

Promotes and establishes standards for quality child care through an accrediting program. Awards credentials to family day care, preschool, home visitor, and infant-toddler caregivers.

Family Service America, Inc., *1319 F St. N.W., #204 20004; (202) 347-1124. Fax, (202) 393-4517. Ronald H.*

Field, senior vice president, Public Policy. Toll-free information and referrals, (800) 221-3726. Internet, http://www.fsanet.org.

Membership: family service agencies in the United States and abroad. Provides families with support services and counseling. Promotes affordable and accessible family-centered health and mental health care, affordable housing and safe neighborhoods, education and job training, family and child welfare, and fiscal and workplace policies that strengthen family viability. Monitors legislation. (Headquarters in Milwaukee.)

Girl Scouts of the U.S.A., 1025 Connecticut Ave. N.W., #309 20036; (202) 659-3780. Fax, (202) 331-8065. LaVern Alexander, acing director, Government Relations. Internet, http://www.gsusa.org.

Educational service organization for girls ages 5 to 17. Promotes personal development through social action, leadership, and other projects. Interests include career education, youth camp safety, prevention of child sexual exploitation, child health care, runaways, and juvenile justice. (Headquarters in New York.)

Mothers at Home, 8310-A Old Courthouse Rd., Vienna, VA 22182; (703) 827-5903. Fax, (703) 790-8587. Betty Walter, executive director. Toll-free, (800) 783-4666. Press, (703) 534-7858. Internet, mah@mah.org or http://www.mah.org.

Provides information and support for mothers who stay home, or who would like to stay home, to raise their children. Monitors legislation and regulations relating to mothers and family issues.

National Assn. for the Education of Young Children, 1509 16th St. N.W. 20036-1426; (202) 232-8777. Fax, (202) 328-1846. Marilyn M. Smith, executive director. Toll-free, (800) 424-2460. Internet, http://www.naeyc.org.

Membership: early childhood professionals and parents. Works to improve the quality of early childhood care and education. Administers national accreditation system for early childhood programs. Maintains information service.

National Assn. of Child Advocates, 1522 K St. N.W., #600 20005; (202) 289-0777. Fax, (202) 289-0776. Tamara Lucas Copeland, president. Internet, http://www.childadvocacy.org.

Membership: private, nonprofit, state- and community-based child advocacy organizations. Works for safety, security, health, and education for all children by strengthening and building child advocacy organizations.

National Black Child Development Institute, 1023 15th St. N.W., #600 20005; (202) 387-1281. Fax, (202) 234-1738. Evelyn K. Moore, president. Internet, moreinfo@nbcdi.org or http://www.nbcdi.org.

Advocacy group for African American children, youth, and families. Interests include child care, foster care, adoption, health, and education. Provides information on government policies that affect African American children, youth, and families.

National Campaign to Prevent Teen Pregnancy, 2100 M St. N.W., #300 20037; (202) 857-8655. Fax, (202) 331-7735. Sarah S. Brown, director. Internet, campaign@teenpregnancy.org or http://www.teenpregnancy.org.

Nonpartisan initiative that seeks to reduce the U.S. teen pregnancy rate by one-third by the year 2005.

National Center for Missing and Exploited Children, 2101 Wilson Blvd., #550, Arlington, VA 22201-3052; (703) 235-3900. Fax, (703) 235-4067. Ernest Allen, president. TDD, (800) 826-7653. Toll-free hotline, (800) 843-5678. Internet, http://www.missingkids.org.

Private organization funded primarily by the Justice Dept. Assists parents and citizens' groups in locating and safely returning missing children; offers technical assistance to law enforcement agencies; coordinates public and private missing children programs; maintains database that coordinates information on missing children.

National Child Support Enforcement Assn., 444 N. Capitol St. N.W., #414 20001; (202) 624-8180. Fax, (202) 624-8828. Joel Bankes, executive director. Internet, ncsea@sso.org or http://www.ncsea.org.

Promotes enforcement of child support obligations and educates professionals on child support issues; fosters exchange of ideas among child support professionals. Monitors legislation and regulations.

National Collaboration for Youth, 1319 F St. N.W. 20004; (202) 347-2080. Fax, (202) 393-4517. Gordon A. Raley, executive director.

Membership: national youth-serving organizations. Works to improve members' youth development programs through information exchange and other support. Raises public awareness of youth issues. Monitors legislation and regulations. (Affiliate of the National Assembly of National Voluntary Health and Social Welfare Organizations.)

National Congress of Parents and Teachers, 1090 Vermont Ave. N.W., #1200 20005; (202) 289-6790. Fax, (202) 289-6791. Vacant, director, Governmental Relations. Internet, http://www.pta.org.

Membership: parent-teacher associations at the preschool, elementary, and secondary levels. Supports school lunch and breakfast programs; works as an active member of the Child Nutrition Forum, which supports federally funded nutrition programs for children. (Headquarters in Chicago.)

National Council for Adoption, *1930 17th St. N.W. 20009; (202) 328-1200. Fax, (202) 332-0935. William L. Pierce, president. Internet, ncfa@juno.com or http://www. ncfa-usa.org.*

Organization of individuals, agencies, and corporations interested in adoption. Supports adoption through legal agencies; advocates the right to confidentiality in adoption. Conducts research and holds conferences; supports pregnancy counseling, maternity services, and counseling for infertile couples.

National Family Caregivers Assn., *10605 Concord St., #501, Kensington, MD 20895-2504; (301) 942-6430. Fax, (301) 942-2302. Suzanne Mintz, president. Toll-free, (800) 896-3650. Internet, info@nfcacares.org or http://www. nfcacares.org.*

Seeks to increase the quality of life of family caregivers by providing support and information; works to raise public awareness of caregiving through educational activities and a speakers bureau.

National 4-H Council, *7100 Connecticut Ave., Chevy Chase, MD 20815-4999; (301) 961-2820. Fax, (301) 961-2894. Richard J. Sauer, president. Press, (301) 961-2915. Internet, http://www.fourhcouncil.edu.*

Educational organization incorporated to expand and strengthen the 4-H program (for young people ages 7 to 19) of the Cooperative Extension System and state land-grant universities. Programs include citizenship and leadership training.

National Head Start Assn., *1651 Prince St., Alexandria, VA 22314; (703) 739-0875. Fax, (703) 739-0878. Sarah M. Greene, chief executive officer. Internet, http://www. nhsa.org.*

Membership organization that represents Head Start children, families, and staff. Recommends strategies on issues affecting Head Start programs; provides training and professional development opportunities. Monitors legislation and regulations.

National Network for Youth, *1319 F St. N.W., #401 20004; (202) 783-7949. Fax, (202) 783-7955. Della M. Hughes, executive director. AIDS hotline for youth-serving agencies, (800) 878-2437. Internet, nn4youth@aol.com or http://www.nn4youth.org.*

Membership: providers of services related to runaway and homeless youth. Offers technical assistance to new and existing youth projects; operates Safe Choices Project, which provides youth with AIDS prevention education. Monitors legislation and regulations.

National Urban League, *1111 14th St. N.W., #1001 20005-5603; (202) 898-1604. Fax, (202) 408-1965. Robert McAlpine, director, Policy and Government Relations. Internet, http://www.nul.org.*

Federation of affiliates concerned with the social welfare of African Americans and other minorities. Youth Development division provides local leagues with technical assistance for youth programs and seeks training opportunities for youth within Urban League programs. (Headquarters in New York.)

Orphan Foundation of America, *380 Maple Ave. West, #LL5, Vienna, VA 22180-5616; (703) 281-4226. Fax, (703) 281-0116. Eileen McCaffrey, executive director. Toll-free, (800) 950-4673. Internet, orphans@erols.com or http://www.orphan.org.*

Advocates for orphaned, abandoned, and homeless teenagers. Provides research, scholarships, emergency cash grants, volunteer programs, guidance, and support. Interests include the rights of orphaned children, transition from foster care to adult independence, and breaking the welfare cycle. Learning center provides training and education materials.

Rape, Abuse, and Incest National Network (RAINN), *635-B Pennsylvania Ave. S.E. 20003; (202) 544-1034. Fax, (202) 544-1401. Debbie Andrews, executive director. Toll-free, (800) 656-HOPE. Internet, rainnmail@ aol.com or http://www.rainn.org.*

Publicizes the issue of sexual assault and the availability of local counseling services for rape and incest survivors. RAINN's 24-hour sexual assault hotline provides free counseling services through a national network of rape crisis centers.

See also National Center for Prosecution of Child Abuse (p. 511); National Organization on Adolescent Pregnancy, Parenting, and Prevention (p. 382)

Elderly

See also Health Services for Special Groups (chap. 11); Pensions and Benefits (chap. 7); Senior Citizens (chap. 1); Social Security (this chapter)

AGENCIES

Administration on Aging *(Health and Human Services Dept.), 200 Independence Ave. S.W., #309F 20201;*

(202) 401-4634. Fax, (202) 401-7741. Jeanette C. Taka-mura, assistant secretary. Press, (202) 401-4541. Internet, http://www.aoa.dhhs.gov.

Acts as advocate for older people; serves as the principal agency for implementing programs under the Older Americans Act. Coordinates with other federal agencies to improve services. Develops programs to promote the economic welfare and personal independence of older people; provides advice and assistance to promote the development of state-administered, community-based social services for older people; supports curriculum development and training in gerontology.

National Senior Service Corps (*Corporation for National Service), Retired and Senior Volunteer Program, Foster Grandparent Program, and Senior Companion Program, 1201 New York Ave. N.W. 20525; (202) 606-5000. Fax, (202) 565-2789. Tom Endres, director. Volunteer recruiting information, (800) 942-2677; TDD, (800) 833-3722; in Washington, (202) 606-5000. Internet, http://www.cns.gov.*

Network of programs that help older Americans find service opportunities in their communities, including the Retired and Senior Volunteer Program, which encourages older citizens to use their talents and experience in community service; the Foster Grandparent Program, which gives older citizens opportunities to work with exceptional children and children with special needs; and the Senior Companion Program, which recruits older citizens to help homebound adults, especially seniors with special needs.

See also Administration for Children and Families (p. 630)

CONGRESS

House Education and the Workforce Committee, *Subcommittee on Early Childhood, Youth, and Families,* 2181 RHOB 20515; (202) 225-4527. Fax, (202) 225-9571. Frank Riggs, R-Calif., chair; Kevin Talley, staff director. Internet, http://www.house.gov/eeo.

Jurisdiction over legislation on all matters dealing with programs and services for the elderly, including nutrition programs and the Older Americans Act.

Senate Labor and Human Resources Committee, *Subcommittee on Aging,* SH-615 20510; (202) 224-0136. Judd Gregg, R-N.H., chair; Kimberly Spalding, staff director. Internet, http://www.senate.gov/~labor.

Jurisdiction over applications of the Older Americans Act and related legislation.

Senate Special Committee on Aging, SD-G31 20510; (202) 224-5364. Fax, (202) 224-8660. Charles E. Grassley, R-Iowa, chair; Ted Totman, staff director.

Oversight of all matters affecting older Americans. Studies and reviews public and private policies and programs that affect the elderly, including retirement income and maintenance, housing, health, welfare, employment, education, recreation, and participation in family and community life; provides other Senate committees with information. Cannot report legislation.

NONPROFIT

American Assn. of Retired Persons, 601 E St. N.W. 20049; (202) 434-2277. Fax, (202) 434-2320. Horace B. Deets, executive director. Press, (202) 434-2560. Library, (202) 434-6240. TDD, (202) 434-6554. Internet, http://www.aarp.org.

Conducts educational and counseling programs in areas concerning the elderly such as widowed persons services, health promotion, housing, and consumer protection. Library open to the public.

Families USA, 1334 G St. N.W., #300 20005; (202) 737-6340. Fax, (202) 347-2417. Ron Pollack, executive director. Internet, info@familiesusa.org or http://www.familiesusa.org.

Organization of American families whose interests include health care and long-term care, Social Security, Medicare, and Medicaid. Monitors legislation and regulations affecting the elderly.

Jewish Council for the Aging, *National Center for Productive Aging,* 11820 Parklawn Dr., #200, Rockville, MD 20852; (301) 881-8782. Fax, (301) 231-9360. David N. Gamse, executive director. TDD, (301) 881-5263.

Nonsectarian organization that provides programs and services to help older people continue living independent lives. Offers employment related services, computer training, adult day care, in-home care, transportation, information and referrals, volunteer opportunties, and consultation.

National Alliance of Senior Citizens, 1744 Riggs Pl. N.W., 3rd Floor 20009-2508; (202) 986-0117. Fax, (202) 986-2974. Peter J. Luciano, chief executive officer.

Membership: persons of any age who want to improve the quality of life for senior Americans. Interests include Social Security, health care, Medicare, pensions, crime against older Americans, intergenerational support, and improvement of care for the dying.

National Assn. of Area Agencies on Aging, 1112 16th St. N.W., #100 20036; (202) 296-8130. Fax, (202)

296-8134. Janice Jackson, executive director. Internet, jjf@ n4a.org or http://www.n4a.org.

Works to establish an effective national policy on aging; provides local agencies with training and technical assistance; disseminates information to these agencies and the public. Monitors legislation and regulations.

National Assn. of State Units on Aging, *1225 Eye St. N.W., #725 20005; (202) 898-2578. Fax, (202) 898-2583. Daniel A. Quirk, executive director. Internet, staff@ NASUA.org.*

Membership: state and territorial governmental units that deal with the elderly. Provides members with information, technical assistance, and professional training. Monitors legislation and regulations.

National Caucus and Center on Black Aged, *1424 K St. N.W., #500 20005-2410; (202) 637-8400. Fax, (202) 347-0895. Samuel J. Simmons, president.*

Concerned with issues that affect elderly African Americans. Sponsors employment and housing programs for the elderly and education and training for professionals in gerontology. Monitors legislation and regulations.

National Council of Senior Citizens, *8403 Colesville Rd., #1200, Silver Spring, MD 20910-3314; (301) 578-8800. Fax, (301) 578-8999. Steve Protulis, executive director. Internet, http://www.ncscinc.org.*

Seeks to strengthen benefits to the elderly, including improved Social Security payments, increased employment, and education and health programs.

National Council on the Aging, *409 3rd St. S.W., 2nd Floor 20024; (202) 479-1200. Fax, (202) 479-0735. James Firman, president. Information, (202) 479-6653. Press, (202) 479-6610. Library, (202) 479-6669. TDD, (202) 479-6674. Internet, info@ncoa.org or http://www.ncoa.org.*

Serves as an information clearinghouse on training, technical assistance, advocacy, and research on every aspect of aging. Provides information on social services for older persons. Monitors legislation and regulations. Library open to the public.

National Hispanic Council on Aging, *2713 Ontario Rd. N.W. 20009; (202) 265-1288. Fax, (202) 745-2522. Marta Sotomayor, president. Internet, nhcoa@worldnet. att.net or http://www.incacorp.com/nhcoa.*

Membership: senior citizens, health care workers, professionals in the field of aging, and others in the United States and Puerto Rico who are interested in topics related to Hispanics and aging. Provides research training, consulting, and technical assistance; sponsors seminars, workshops, and management internships.

See also Catholic Charities U.S.A. (p. 628); National Senior Citizens Law Center (p. 8)

 DISABILITIES

See also Employment and Training Programs (chap. 7); Special Groups in Education (chap. 6)

AGENCIES

Administration for Children and Families *(Health and Human Services Dept.), Administration on Developmental Disabilities, 200 Independence Ave. S.W., #351D 20201; (202) 690-6590. Fax, (202) 690-6904. Reginald Wells, acting commissioner. TDD, (202) 690-6415.*

Establishes state protection and advocacy systems for people with developmental disabilities, including persons with mental retardation, cerebral palsy, epilepsy, and autism; awards discretionary grants to university-affiliated programs and to programs of national significance. Administers formula grants to states for persons who incurred developmental disabilities before the age of 22.

Architectural and Transportation Barriers Compliance Board (Access Board), *1331 F St. N.W., #1000 20004-1111; (202) 272-5434. Fax, (202) 272-5447. Lawrence W. Roffee, executive director. TDD, (202) 272-5449. Toll-free technical assistance, (800) 872-2253. Internet, http://www.access-board.gov.*

Enforces standards requiring that buildings and telecommunications and transportation systems be accessible to persons with disabilities; provides technical assistance and information on designing these facilities; sets accessibility guidelines for the Americans with Disabilities Act and the Telecommunications Act of 1996.

Committee for Purchase From People Who Are Blind or Severely Disabled, *1215 Jefferson Davis Hwy., #310, Arlington, VA 22202; (703) 603-7740. Fax, (703) 603-0655. Beverly L. Milkman, executive director.*

Presidentially appointed committee. Determines which products and services are suitable for federal procurement from qualified nonprofit agencies that employ people who are blind or have other severe disabilities; seeks to increase employment opportunities for these individuals.

Education Dept., *Special Education and Rehabilitative Services, 330 C St. S.W. 20202-2500; (202) 205-5465. Fax, (202) 205-9252. Judith Heumann, assistant secretary.*

Information, (202) 205-8241. Main phone is voice and TDD accessible.

Provides information on federal legislation and programs and national organizations concerning individuals with disabilities.

Employment Standards Administration *(Labor Dept.), Coal Mine Workers' Compensation, 200 Constitution Ave. N.W. 20210; (202) 219-6692. Fax, (202) 219-8568. James L. DeMarce, director.*

Provides direction for administration of the black lung benefits program. Adjudicates claims filed on or after July 1, 1973; certifies these benefit payments and maintains black lung beneficiary rolls. *(For claims filed before July 1, 1973, contact Social Security Administration, Disability.)*

Equal Employment Opportunity Commission, *Americans with Disabilities Act, 1801 L St. N.W., #6027 20507; (202) 663-4503. Fax, (202) 663-4639. Christopher J. Kuczynski, director. TDD, (800) 669-6820. Toll-free, (800) 669-4000.*

Division of the Office of Legal Counsel. Provides interpretations, opinions, and technical assistance on the ADA provisions relating to employment.

Justice Dept., *Disability Rights, 1425 New York Ave. N.W., #4039 20005 (mailing address: P.O. Box 66738, Washington, DC 20035-6738); (202) 307-2227. Fax, (202) 307-1198. John L. Wodatch, chief. TDD, (800) 514-0383. Toll-free, (800) 514-0301. Internet, http://www.usdoj.gov/crt/ada/adahom1.htm.*

Litigates cases under Title II and III of the Americans with Disabilities Act, which prohibits discrimination on the basis of disability in places of public accommodation and in all activities of state and local government. Provides technical assistance to business and individuals affected by the law.

National Council on Disability, *1331 F St. N.W., #1050 20004-1107; (202) 272-2004. Fax, (202) 272-2022. Marca Bristo, chair. Internet, http://www.ncd.gov.*

Reviews and reports to the president on all laws, programs, and policies of the federal government affecting individuals with disabilities. Focus includes health insurance; sponsors conferences for families caring for persons with disabilities.

National Institute on Disability and Rehabilitation Research *(Education Dept.), 330 C St. S.W. (mailing address: 600 Independence Ave. S.W., Washington, DC 20202-2572); (202) 205-8134. Fax, (202) 205-8997. Katherine D. Seelman, director. TDD, (202) 205-9136.*

Assists research programs in rehabilitating people with disabilities; provides information on developments in the field; awards grants and contracts for scientific, technical, and methodological research; coordinates federal research programs on rehabilitation; offers fellowships to individuals conducting research in the field.

President's Committee on Employment of People with Disabilities, *1331 F St. N.W., #300 20004-1107; (202) 376-6200. Fax, (202) 376-6219. John Lancaster, executive director. TDD, (202) 376-6205. Internet, http://www.pcepd.gov.*

Seeks to eliminate physical and psychological barriers to the disabled through education and information programs; promotes education, training, rehabilitation, and employment opportunities for people with disabilities.

Rehabilitation Services Administration *(Education Dept.), 330 C St. S.W. 20202-2531; (202) 205-5482. Fax, (202) 205-9874. Fredric K. Schroeder, commissioner. TDD, (202) 205-9295.*

Coordinates and directs major federal programs for eligible physically and mentally disabled persons. Administers distribution of grants for training and employment programs and for establishing supported-employment and independent-living programs. Provides vocational training and job placement.

Smithsonian Institution, *Accessibility Program, 900 Jefferson Dr. S.W., #1239 MRC 426 20560; (202) 786-2942. Fax, (202) 786-2210. Janice Majewski, coordinator. TDD, (202) 786-2414.*

Coordinates Smithsonian efforts to improve accessibility of its programs and facilities to visitors and staff with disabilities. Serves as a resource for museums and individuals nationwide.

Social Security Administration, *Disability, 6401 Security Blvd., #560, Baltimore, MD 21235; (410) 965-3424. Fax, (410) 965-6503. Susan M. Daniels, associate commissioner. Information, (410) 965-7700.*

Administers and regulates the disability insurance program and disability provisions of the Supplemental Security Income (SSI) program.

Very Special Arts, *1300 Connecticut Ave. N.W., #700 20036; (202) 628-2800. Fax, (202) 737-0725. John Kemp, chief executive officer. Toll-free, (800) 933-8721. TDD, (202) 737-0645. Internet, http://www.vsarts.org.*

Initiates and supports research and program development providing arts training and demonstration for persons with disabilities. Provides technical assistance and training to Very Special Arts state organizations; acts as an information clearinghouse for arts and persons with disabilities. (Affiliated with the Kennedy Center education office.)

CONGRESS

House Appropriations Committee, *Subcommittee on Transportation, 2358 RHOB 20515; (202) 225-2141. Frank R. Wolf, R-Va., chair; John T. Blazey, staff director. Internet, http://www.house.gov/appropriations.*

Jurisdiction over legislation to appropriate funds for the Architectural and Transportation Barriers Compliance Board.

House Commerce Committee, *Subcommittee on Health and the Environment, 2125 RHOB 20515; (202) 225-2927. Fax, (202) 225-1919. Michael Bilirakis, R-Fla., chair; James E. Derderian, staff director. Internet, http://www.house.gov/commerce/health.html.*

Jurisdiction over developmental disability legislation.

House Education and the Workforce Committee, *Subcommittee on Early Childhood, Youth, and Families, 2181 RHOB 20515; (202) 225-4527. Fax, (202) 225-9571. Frank Riggs, R-Calif., chair; Kevin Talley, staff director. Internet, http://www.house.gov/eeo.*

Jurisdiction over legislation on special education programs including, but not limited to, alcohol and drug abuse and education of the disabled.

Library of Congress, *National Library Service for the Blind and Physically Handicapped, 1291 Taylor St. N.W. 20542; (202) 707-5104. Fax, (202) 707-0712. Frank Kurt Cylke, director. TDD, (202) 707-0744. Reference, (202) 707-5100; outside D.C. area, (800) 424-8567. Internet, nls@loc.gov or http://lcweb.loc.gov/nls.*

Administers a national program of free library services for persons with physical disabilities in cooperation with regional and subregional libraries. Produces and distributes full-length books and magazines in recorded form (disc and cassette) and in Braille. Reference section answers questions relating to blindness and physical disabilities and on library services available to persons with disabilities.

Senate Appropriations Committee, *Subcommittee on Transportation, SD-133 20510; (202) 224-7281. Fax, (202) 224-4401. Richard C. Shelby, R-Ala., chair; Wally Burnett, majority clerk. Internet, http://www.senate.gov/ ~appropriations.*

Jurisdiction over legislation to appropriate funds for the Architectural and Transportation Barriers Compliance Board.

Senate Labor and Human Resources Committee, *SD-428 20510; (202) 224-5375. Fax, (202) 224-6510. James M. Jeffords, R-Vt., chair; Mark Powden, staff director. Internet, http://www.senate.gov/~labor.*

Jurisdiction over legislation on people with disabilities, including vocational rehabilitation for people with physical and developmental disabilities. Jurisdiction over the Americans with Disabilities Act.

NONPROFIT

American Assn. of University Affiliated Programs for Persons with Developmental Disabilities, *8630 Fenton St., #410, Silver Spring, MD 20910; (301) 588-8252. Fax, (301) 588-2842. William E. Jones, executive director. TDD, (301) 588-3319. Internet, http://www. waisman.wisc.edu/aauap.*

Network of facilities that diagnose and treat the developmentally disabled. Trains graduate students and professionals in the field; helps state and local agencies develop services. Interests include interdisciplinary training and services, early screening to prevent developmental disabilities, and development of equipment and programs to serve persons with disabilities.

American Bar Assn., *Commission on Mental and Physical Disability Law, 740 15th St. N.W. 20005; (202) 662-1570. Fax, (202) 662-1032. John Parry, director. Internet, http://www.abanet.org/disability/home.html.*

Serves as a clearinghouse for information on mental and physical disability law and offers legal research services.

American Medical Rehabilitation Providers Assn., *606 20th St. N.W., 3rd Floor 20009; (202) 265-3916. Fax, (202) 833-9168. Dale Eazell, president. Toll-free, (800) 368-3513.*

Promotes improved rehabilitation facilities; sponsors workshops, seminars, and on-the-job training contracts.

American Network of Community Options and Resources, *4200 Evergreen Lane, #315, Annandale, VA 22003; (703) 642-6614. Fax, (703) 642-0497. Joni Fritz, executive director. Internet, ancor@radix.net or http:// www.ancor.org.*

Membership: privately operated agencies and corporations that provide support and services to people with disabilities. Advises and works with regulatory and consumer agencies that serve people with disabilities; provides information and sponsors seminars and workshops; publishes directory that lists services offered by member agencies. Monitors legislation and regulations.

American Occupational Therapy Assn., *4720 Montgomery Lane, Bethesda, MD (mailing address: P.O. Box 31220, Bethesda, MD 20824-1220); (301) 652-2682. Fax, (301) 652-7711. Jeanette Bair, executive director. TDD, (800) 377-8555. Internet, http://www.aota.org.*

Membership: registered occupational therapists, certified occupational therapy assistants, and students. Associate members include businesses and organizations supportive of occupational therapy. Accredits colleges and universities and certifies therapists.

American Orthotic and Prosthetic Assn., *1650 King St., #500, Alexandria, VA 22314; (703) 836-7116. Fax, (703) 836-0838. Charles Unger, president. Internet, http:// www.theaopa.org.*

Membership: companies that manufacture or supply artificial limbs and braces. Provides information on the profession.

American Physical Therapy Assn., *1111 N. Fairfax St., Alexandria, VA 22314-1488; (703) 684-2782. Fax, (703) 684-7343. Francis Mallon, executive vice president. Toll-free, (800) 999-2782. TDD, (703) 683-6748. Internet, svcctr@apta.org or http://www.apta.org.*

Membership: physical therapists, assistants, and students. Establishes professional standards and accredits physical therapy programs; seeks to improve physical therapy education, practice, and research.

American Rehabilitation Counseling Assn., *5999 Stevenson Ave., Alexandria, VA 22304; (703) 823-9800. Fax, (703) 823-0252. Vilia Tarvydas, president. Toll-free, (800) 347-6647. TDD, (703) 370-1943.*

Membership: rehabilitation counselors, counselor educators and graduate students in the rehabilitation field, and other interested persons. Establishes counseling and research standards; encourages establishment of rehabilitation facilities; conducts leadership training and continuing education programs; serves as a liaison between counselors and clients. Monitors legislation and regulations. Library open to the public. (Affiliated with the American Counseling Assn.)

American Speech-Language-Hearing Assn., *10801 Rockville Pike, Rockville, MD 20852; (301) 897-5700. Fax, (301) 571-0457. Frederick T. Spahr, executive director. Press, (301) 897-0156. TDD, (301) 897-0157. Toll-free hotline (except Alaska, Hawaii, and Maryland), (800) 498-2071 (voice and TDD accessible). Internet, http://www.asha.org.*

Membership: specialists in speech-language pathology and audiology. Sponsors professional education programs; acts as accrediting agent for graduate college programs and for public clinical education programs in speech-language pathology and audiology. Advocates the rights of the communicatively disabled; provides information on speech, hearing, and language problems. Provides referrals to speech-language pathologists and audiologists. Interests include national and international standards for bioacoustics and noise.

Brain Injury Assn., *105 N. Alfred St., Alexandria, VA 22314; (703) 236-6000. Fax, (703) 236-6001. George Zitnay, president. Family helpline, (800) 444-6443.*

Works to improve the quality of life for persons with traumatic brain injuries and for their families. Promotes the prevention of head injuries through public awareness and education programs. Offers state-level support services for individuals and their families. Monitors legislation and regulations.

Center on Disability and Health, *1522 K St. N.W., #800 20005; (202) 842-4408. Fax, (202) 842-2402. Bob Griss, director. Internet, bgrisscdh@aol.com.*

Promotes changes in the financing and delivery of health care to meet the needs of persons with disabilities and other chronic health conditions. Conducts research; provides technical assistance to disability groups and agencies. Monitors legislation and regulations.

Consortium for Citizens with Disabilities, *1730 K St. N.W., #1212 20006; (202) 785-3388. Fax, (202) 467-4179. Paul Marchand, chair. Internet, CCD@radix.net or http:// www.radix.net/~ccd.*

Coalition of national disability organizations. Advocates national public policy that ensures the self-determination, independence, empowerment, and integration in all aspects of society for children and adults with disabilities.

Council of American Building Officials, *5203 Leesburg Pike, Falls Church, VA 22041; (703) 931-4533. Fax, (703) 379-1546. Richard P. Kuchnicki, chief executive officer. Internet, http://www.cabo.org.*

Provides review board for the American National Standards Institute accessibility standards, which ensure that buildings are accessible to persons with physical disabilities.

Council of State Administrators of Vocational Rehabilitation, *P.O. Box 3776 20007; (202) 638-4634. Joseph H. Owens, executive director.*

Membership: chief administrative officers of public rehabilitation agencies that prepare persons with mental and physical disabilities for competitive employment. Provides a forum to study and act on matters affecting the rehabilitation of persons with disabilities.

Disability Rights Center, *4031 University Dr., #301, Fairfax, VA 22030; (703) 934-2021. Fax, (703) 352-5762. Susan Ferris, executive director. TDD, (703) 218-5377. Internet, drc@patriot.net.*

Advocates for the rights of people with physical and mental disabilities; seeks to educate the public about these rights; conducts research. Monitors legislation and regulations.

Disabled American Veterans, *807 Maine Ave. S.W. 20024; (202) 554-3501. Fax, (202) 554-3581. Arthur H. Wilson, national adjutant. Internet, http://www.dav.org.*

Chartered by Congress to assist veterans with claims for benefits; represents veterans seeking to correct alleged errors in military records. Assists families of veterans with disabilities.

Disability Rights Education and Defense Fund, *1629 K St. N.W. 20006; (202) 986-0375. Fax, (202) 775-7465. Pat Wright, director, Governmental Affairs.*

Law and policy center working to protect and advance the civil rights of people with disabilities through legislation, litigation, advocacy, and technical assistance. Educates and trains attorneys, advocates, persons with disabilities, and parents of children with disabilities. (Headquarters in Berkeley, Calif.)

Disabled Sports USA, *451 Hungerford Dr., #100, Rockville, MD 20850; (301) 217-0960. Fax, (301) 217-0968. Kirk M. Bauer, executive director. TDD, (301) 217-0963. Internet, dsusa@dsusa.org or http://www.dsusa.org/~dsusa.*

Conducts sports and recreation activities and physical fitness programs for people with disabilities and their families and friends; produces videotaped exercise programs for people with physical disabilities; conducts workshops and competitions; participates in world championships.

Epilepsy Foundation of America, *4351 Garden City Dr., Landover, MD 20785; (301) 459-3700. Fax, (301) 577-2684. Paulette V. Maehara, chief executive officer. Toll-free, (800) 332-1000. Library, (800) 332-4050. Internet, postmaster@efa.org or http://www.efa.org.*

Promotes research and treatment of epilepsy; makes research grants; disseminates information and educational materials. Affiliates provide direct services for people with epilepsy and make referrals when necessary. Library open to the public by appointment.

Girl Scouts of the U.S.A., *1025 Connecticut Ave. N.W., #309 20036; (202) 659-3780. Fax, (202) 331-8065. LaVern Alexander, acting director, Government Relations. Internet, http://www.gsusa.org.*

Educational service organization for girls ages 5 to 17. Promotes personal development through social action, leadership, and programs such as Girl Scouting for Handicapped Girls. (Headquarters in New York.)

Goodwill Industries International, Inc., *9200 Rockville Pike, Bethesda, MD 20814-3896; (301) 530-6500. Fax, (301) 530-1516. Fred Grandy, president. Internet, goodwill@goodwill.org or http://www.goodwill.org.*

Membership: 185 autonomous organizations that provide disabled and disadvantaged individuals with Goodwill Industries services, which include vocational rehabilitation evaluation, job training, employment, and placement services.

National Assn. of Developmental Disabilities Councils, *1234 Massachusetts Ave. N.W., #103 20005; (202) 347-1234. Fax, (202) 347-4023. Susan A. Zierman, executive director. Internet, NADDC@igc.apc.org or http://www.igc.apc.org/NADDC.*

Membership: state and territorial councils authorized by the Development Disabilities Act, which promotes the interests of people with developmental and other disabilities and their families. Monitors legislation and regulations.

National Council on Independent Living, *1916 Wilson Blvd., #209, Arlington, VA 22201; (703) 525-3406. Fax, (703) 525-4153. Anne-Marie Hughey, executive director.*

Membership: independent living centers, their staff and volunteers, and individuals with disabilities. Seeks to strengthen independent living centers; facilitates the integration of people with disabilities into society; provides training and technical assistance; sponsors referral service and speakers' bureau.

National Easter Seal Society, *700 13th St. N.W. 20005; (202) 347-3066. Fax, (202) 737-7914. Joseph D. Romer, executive vice president. TDD, (202) 347-7385. Internet, http://www.seals.com.*

Federation of state and local groups with programs that help people with disabilities achieve independence. Washington office monitors legislation and regulations. Affiliates assist individuals with a broad range of disabilities, including muscular dystrophy, cerebral palsy, stroke, speech and hearing loss, blindness, amputation, and learning disabilities. Services include physical, occupational, vocational, and speech therapy; speech, hearing, physical, and vocational evaluation; psychological testing and counseling; personal and family counseling; supported employment; special education programs; social clubs and day and residential camps; and transportation, referral, and follow-up programs. (Headquarters in Chicago.)

National Information Center for Children and Youth with Disabilities, *P.O. Box 1492 20013; (202) 884-8200. Fax, (202) 884-8441. Suzanne Ripley, director. Toll-free, (800) 695-0285. Internet, http://www.nichey.org.*

Federally funded clearinghouse that provides free information to parents, educators, caregivers, advocates, and others who help children and youth with disabilities become active participants in school, work, and the community. Offers personal responses to specific questions, referrals to other organizations, prepared information packets, and technical assistance to families and professional groups.

National Multiple Sclerosis Society, *2021 K St. N.W., #715 20006; (202) 296-9891. Fax, (202) 296-3425. Jeanne Oates Angulo, president, Washington Office. Internet, http://www.dcw.nmss.org.*

Seeks to advance medical knowledge of multiple sclerosis, a disease of the central nervous system; disseminates information worldwide. Patient services include individual and family counseling, exercise programs, equipment loans, medical and social service referrals, transportation assistance, back-to-work training programs, and in-service training seminars for nurses, homemakers, and physical and occupational therapists. (Headquarters in New York.)

National Organization on Disability, *910 16th St. N.W., #600 20006-2988; (202) 293-5960. Fax, (202) 293-7999. Alan A. Reich, president. TDD, (202) 293-5968. Internet, http://www.nod.org.*

Administers the Community Partnership Program, a network of communities that works to remove barriers and address educational, employment, social, and transportation needs of people with disabilities. Provides members with information and technical assistance; sponsors annual community awards competition; makes referrals. Monitors legislation and regulations.

National Parent Network on Disabilities, *1200 G St. N.W., #800 20005; (202) 434-8686. Fax, (202) 638-0509. Patricia McGill Smith, executive director. Internet, npnd@ aol.com or http://www.npnd.org.*

Works to improve the lives of people with disabilities by providing parents and family member groups with information, education, and training. Monitors legislation and regulations.

National Rehabilitation Assn., *633 S. Washington St., Alexandria, VA 22314; (703) 836-0850. Fax, (703) 836-0848. Michelle Vaughn, executive director. TDD, (703) 836-0849. Internet, http://www.nationalrehab.org.*

Membership: administrators, counselors, therapists, disability examiners, vocational evaluators, instructors, job placement specialists, disability managers in the corporate sector, and others interested in rehabilitation of the physically and mentally disabled. Sponsors conferences and workshops. Monitors legislation and regulations.

National Rehabilitation Information Center, *8455 Colesville Rd., #935, Silver Spring, MD 20910-3319; (301) 588-9284. Fax, (301) 587-1967. Mark Odum, director. TDD, (301) 495-5626. Toll-free, (800) 346-2742. Internet, http://www.cais.com/naric.*

Library and information center funded by the National Institute on Disability and Rehabilitation Research. Provides information on adaptive equipment for people with all types of disabilities; assists in identifying technology solutions for specific functional limitations.

Paralyzed Veterans of America, *801 18th St. N.W. 20006; (202) 872-1300. Fax, (202) 785-4452. Gordon H. Mansfield, executive director. Toll-free, (800) 424-8200. TDD, (202) 416-7622. Internet, http://www.pva.org.*

Congressionally chartered organization that assists veterans with claims for benefits. Distributes information on special education for paralyzed veterans; supports and raises funds for medical research.

RESNA, *1700 N. Moore St., #1540, Arlington, VA 22209; (703) 524-6686. Fax, (703) 524-6630. James R. Geletka, executive director. TDD, (703) 524-6639. Internet, natloffice@resna.org or http://www.resna.org.*

Membership: engineers, health professionals, persons with disabilities, and others concerned with rehabilitation engineering technology. Promotes and supports developments in rehabilitation engineering; acts as an information clearinghouse.

Special Olympics International, *1325 G St. N.W., #500 20005; (202) 628-3630. Fax, (202) 824-0200. Robert Sargent Shriver Jr., chair. Internet, specialolympics@msn.com or http://www.specialolympics.org.*

Offers individuals with mental retardation opportunities for year-round sports training; sponsors athletic competition worldwide in twenty two individual and team sports.

Spina Bifida Assn. of America, *4590 MacArthur Blvd. N.W., #250 20007-4226; (202) 944-3285. Fax, (202) 944-3295. Lawrence Pencak, executive director. Toll-free, (800) 621-3141. Internet, sbaa@sbaa.org or http://www.sbaa.org.*

Membership: individuals with spina bifida, their supporters, and concerned professionals. Offers educational programs and support services; acts as a clearinghouse; provides referrals. Serves as U.S. member of the International Federation for Hydrocephalus and Spina Bifida, which is headquartered in Geneva. Monitors legislation and regulations.

United Cerebral Palsy Assns., *1660 L St. N.W., #700 20036; (202) 776-0406. Fax, (202) 776-0414. Vacant, exec-*

utive director. Toll-free, (800) 872-5827. Main phone is voice and TDD accessible. Internet, http://www.ucpa.org.

National network of state and local affiliates that assists individuals with cerebral palsy and other developmental disabilities and their families. Provides parent education, early intervention, employment services, family support and respite programs, therapy, assistive technology, and vocational training. Promotes research on cerebral palsy; supports the use of assistive technology and community-based living arrangements for persons with cerebral palsy and other developmental disabilities.

Blind and Visually Impaired

AGENCIES

Committee for Purchase From People Who Are Blind or Severely Disabled, *1215 Jefferson Davis Hwy., #310, Arlington, VA 22202; (703) 603-7740. Fax, (703) 603-0655. Beverly L. Milkman, executive director.*

Presidentially appointed committee. Determines which products and services are suitable for federal procurement from qualified nonprofit agencies that employ people who are blind or have other severe disabilities; seeks to increase employment opportunities for these individuals.

CONGRESS

Library of Congress, *National Library Service for the Blind and Physically Handicapped, 1291 Taylor St. N.W. 20542; (202) 707-5104. Fax, (202) 707-0712. Frank Kurt Cylke, director. TDD, (202) 707-0744. Reference, (202) 707-5100; outside D.C. area, (800) 424-8567. Internet, nls@loc.gov or http://lcweb.loc.gov/nls.*

Administers a national program of free library services for persons with physical disabilities in cooperation with regional and subregional libraries. Produces and distributes full-length books and magazines in recorded form (disc and cassette) and in Braille. Reference section answers questions relating to blindness and physical disabilities and on library services available to persons with disabilities.

NONPROFIT

Affiliated Leadership League of and for the Blind of America, *2915 34th St. N.W. 20008; (202) 298-8151. Robert R. Humphreys, administrator and counsel.*

Membership: service and educational organizations and public and private agencies serving the blind and visually impaired. Advocates rights of blind consumers. Promotes accreditation for organizations serving the blind; acts as an information clearinghouse. Monitors legislation and regulations.

American Blind Lawyers Assn., *1155 15th St. N.W., #720 20005; (202) 467-5081. Fax, (202) 467-5085. Gary Austin, president.*

Membership: blind lawyers and law students. Provides members with legal information; acts as an information clearinghouse on legal materials available in Braille, in large print, on computer disc, and on tape. (Affiliated with American Council of the Blind.)

American Council of the Blind, *1155 15th St. N.W., #720 20005; (202) 467-5081. Fax, (202) 467-5085. Oral O. Miller, executive director. Toll-free, 2:30-5:30 p.m. E.S.T., (800) 424-8666. Internet, http://www.acb.org.*

Membership organization serving blind and visually impaired individuals. Interests include Social Security, telecommunications, rehabilitation services, transportation, education, and architectural access. Provides blind individuals with information and referral services, including legal referrals; advises state organizations and agencies serving the blind; sponsors scholarships for the blind and visually impaired.

American Foundation for the Blind, *820 1st St. N.E., #400 20005; (202) 408-0200. Fax, (202) 289-7880. Scott Marshall, vice president, Governmental Relations. Toll-free, (800) 232-5463. Internet, afbgov@afb.org or http://www.afb.org.*

Advocates equality of access and opportunity for the blind and visually impaired. Provides services; conducts informational and educational programs; develops and implements public policy and legislation. Maintains the Helen Keller Archives and M.C. Migel Memorial Library. (Headquarters in New York.)

Assn. for Education and Rehabilitation of the Blind and Visually Impaired, *P.O. Box 22397, Alexandria, VA 22304; (703) 823-9690. Fax, (703) 823-9695. Denise Rozell, executive director. Internet, aernet@laser.net or http://www.aerbvi.org.*

Membership: professionals and paraprofessionals who work with the blind and visually impaired. Provides information on services for people who are blind and visually impaired and on employment opportunities for those who work with them. Works to improve quality of education and rehabilitation services. Monitors legislation and regulations.

Blinded Veterans Assn., *477 H St. N.W. 20001; (202) 371-8880. Fax, (202) 371-8258. John Williams, director, Administration. Toll-free, (800) 669-7079. Internet, bva@bva.org or http://www.bva.org.*

Chartered by Congress to assist veterans with claims for benefits. Seeks out blinded veterans to make them aware of benefits and services available to them.

National Industries for the Blind, *1901 N. Beauregard St., #200, Alexandria, VA 22311; (703) 998-0770. Fax, (703) 671-9053. Bill Cramer, director, Legislative Affairs. Internet, http://www.nib.org.*

Works to develop and improve opportunities for evaluating, training, employing, and advancing people who are blind and multidisabled blind. Assists associated agencies for the blind in acquiring quality products and services for procurement by state and federal government and the private sector.

Prevention of Blindness Society, *1775 Church St. N.W. 20036; (202) 234-1010. Fax, (202) 234-1020. Arnold Simonse, executive director.*

Conducts preschool and elementary school screening program and glaucoma testing; provides information and referral service on eye health care; assists low-income persons in obtaining eye care and provides eyeglasses for a nominal fee to persons experiencing financial stress; conducts macular degeneration support group.

Deaf and Hearing Impaired

AGENCIES

General Services Administration, *Federal Information Relay Service, 13221 Woodland Park Rd., 3rd Floor, Herndon, VA 20171-3022; (800) 877-8339. Carolyn Thomas, director. Information, (703) 904-2848. TDD, (800) 877-8845. Internet, http://www.gsa.gov/et/fic-firs/firs.htm.*

Assures that the federal telecommunications system is fully accessible to deaf, hearing-impaired, and speech-impaired individuals, including federal workers. Operates 8 a.m. to 8 p.m., weekdays, Eastern time. Produces a directory of TDD/TTY services within the federal government.

National Institute on Deafness and Other Communication Disorders *(National Institutes of Health), 31 Center Dr., MSC-2320, #3C02, Bethesda, MD 20892-2320; (301) 402-0900. Fax, (301) 402-1590. Dr. James F. Battey Jr., director. Information, (301) 496-7243. TDD, (301) 496-6596. Internet, http://www.nih.gov/nidcd.*

Conducts and supports research and research training and disseminates information on hearing disorders and other communication processes, including diseases that affect hearing, balance, smell, taste, voice, speech, and language. Monitors international research.

NONPROFIT

Alexander Graham Bell Assn. for the Deaf, *3417 Volta Pl. N.W. 20007-2778; (202) 337-5220. Donna M.*

Dickman, executive director. Main phone is voice and TDD accessible. Internet, agbell2@aol.com or http://www.agbell.org.

Provides hearing-impaired children in the United States and abroad with information and special education programs; works to improve employment opportunities for deaf persons; acts as a support group for parents of deaf persons.

American Academy of Audiology, *8201 Greensboro Dr., #300, McLean, VA 22102; (703) 610-9022. Fax, (703) 610-9005. Carol Fraser Fisk, executive director. Internet, http://www.audiology.org.*

Membership: audiologists. Provides comsumer information on testing and treatment for hearing loss; sponsors research, awards, and continuing education for audiologists.

American Speech-Language-Hearing Assn., *10801 Rockville Pike, Rockville, MD 20852; (301) 897-5700. Fax, (301) 571-0457. Frederick T. Spahr, executive director. Press, (301) 897-0156. TDD, (301) 897-0157. Toll-free hotline (except Alaska, Hawaii, and Maryland), (800) 498-2071 (voice and TDD accessible). Internet, http://www.asha.org.*

Membership: specialists in speech-language pathology and audiology. Sponsors professional education programs; acts as accrediting agent for graduate college programs and for public clinical education programs in speech-language pathology and audiology. Advocates the rights of the communicatively disabled; provides information on speech, hearing, and language problems. Provides referrals to speech-language pathologists and audiologists. Interests include national and international standards for bioacoustics and noise.

Better Hearing Institute, *5021-B Backlick Rd., Annandale, VA 22003; (703) 642-0580. Fax, (703) 750-9302. Joseph J. Rizzo, executive director. Hearing Helpline, (800) 327-9355. Main phone is voice and TDD accessible.*

Educational organization that conducts national public information programs on hearing loss and on available medical, surgical, hearing aid, and rehabilitation assistance for those with uncorrected hearing problems.

Center for Global Education, *Gallaudet University, 800 Florida Ave. N.E. 20002-3695; (202) 651-6050. Fax, (202) 651-6038. Donalda Ammons, director. Information, (202) 651-5217. Internet, http://www.gallaudet.edu/~cgeweb.*

Coordinates Gallaudet University's international outreach programs. Fosters cooperative research, education, and training to increase opportunities for deaf people worldwide. Conducts educational programs serving the international community. Sponsors international internship program.

Gallaudet University, *800 Florida Ave. N.E. 20002-3695; (202) 651-5005. Fax, (202) 651-5508. I. King Jordan, president. Phone numbers are voice and TDD accessible. Internet, http://www.gallaudet.edu.*

Offers undergraduate and graduate degree programs for the deaf and hard of hearing and graduate training for teachers and other professionals who work with the deaf; conducts research; maintains outreach and regional centers and demonstration doctoral, continuing education, secondary, elementary, and preschool programs (Model Secondary School for the Deaf, Kendall Demonstration Elementary School). Sponsors the Center for Global Education, the National Information Center on Deafness, and the National Center for the Law and the Deaf.

Hearing Industries Assn., *515 King St., #420, Alexandria, VA 22314; (703) 684-5744. Fax, (703) 684-6048. Carole M. Rogin, president. Internet, http://www.hiallears.org.*

Membership: hearing aid manufacturers and companies that supply hearing aid components. Provides information on hearing loss and hearing aids.

National Assn. of the Deaf, *814 Thayer Ave., Silver Spring, MD 20910-4500; (301) 587-1788. Fax, (301) 587-1791. Nancy J. Bloch, executive director. TDD, (301) 587-1789. Internet, nadhq@juno.com or http://www.nad.org.*

Membership: deaf and hard-of-hearing individuals; hearing, speech, and language professionals; associations; parents; and others concerned with the problems of the deaf. Works to ensure that deaf Americans have acccess to education, employment, health care, and telecommunications; administers the American Sign Language Teachers Assn. (ASTLA), which certifies sign language instructors.

National Information Center on Deafness, *800 Florida Ave. N.E. 20002-3695; (202) 651-5051. Fax, (202) 651-5054. Loraine DiPietro, director. TDD, (202) 651-5052. Internet, http://www.gallaudet.edu/~nicd.*

Provides information on topics dealing with hearing loss and deafness. (Affiliated with Gallaudet University.)

Registry of Interpreters for the Deaf, *8630 Fenton St., #324, Silver Spring, MD 20910; (301) 608-0050. Fax, (301) 608-0508. Daniel D. Burch, president. Internet, ridnts@aol.com or http://www.rid.org.*

Trains and certifies interpreters; maintains registry of certified interpreters; establishes certification standards. Sponsors training workshops and conferences.

Self Help for Hard of Hearing People, *7910 Woodmont Ave., #1200, Bethesda, MD 20814; (301) 657-2248. Fax, (301) 913-9413. Donna Sorkin, executive director. TDD, (301) 657-2249. Internet, national@shhh.org or http://www.shhh.org.*

Promotes understanding of the nature, causes, and remedies of hearing loss. Provides hearing-impaired people with support and information. Seeks to educate the public about hearing loss and the problems of the hard of hearing. Provides travelers with information on assistive listening devices in museums, theaters, and places of worship.

Telecommunications for the Deaf, Inc., *8630 Fenton St., #604, Silver Spring, MD 20910; (301) 589-3786. Fax, (301) 589-3797. Claude Stout, executive director. TDD, (301) 589-3006. Internet, tdiexdir@aol.com.*

Membership: individuals, organizations, and businesses using text telephone (TTY) equipment. Provides information on TTY equipment. Interests include closed captioning for television, emergency access (911), TTY relay services, visual alerting systems, and TTY/computer conversion. Publishes a national TTY telephone directory.

Mental Disabilities

AGENCIES

Administration for Children and Families *(Health and Human Services Dept.),* **Administration on Developmental Disabilities,** *200 Independence Ave. S.W., #351D 20201; (202) 690-6590. Fax, (202) 690-6904. Reginald Wells, acting commissioner. TDD, (202) 690-6415.*

Establishes state protection and advocacy systems for people with developmental disabilities, including persons with mental retardation, cerebral palsy, epilepsy, and autism; awards discretionary grants to university-affiliated programs and to programs of national significance. Administers formula grants to states for persons who incurred developmental disabilities before the age of 22.

President's Committee on Mental Retardation *(Health and Human Services Dept.), 200 Independence Ave. S.W., #352G 20201; (202) 619-0634. Fax, (202) 205-9519. Gary H. Blumenthal, executive director. Information, (202) 619-3636.*

Compiles information, conducts studies, and promotes research on mental retardation; advises the president and the secretary of health and human services; acts as a liaison among federal, state, local, and private organizations concerned with mental retardation.

NONPROFIT

American Assn. on Mental Retardation,
444 N. Capitol St. N.W., #846 20001; (202) 387-1968. Fax, (202) 387-2193. M. Doreen Croser, executive director. Toll-free, (800) 424-3688. Internet, aamr@access.digex.net or http://www.aamr.org.

Membership: physicians, educators, administrators, social workers, psychologists, psychiatrists, lawyers, students, and others interested in mental retardation and related developmental disabilities. Provides information on legal rights, services, and facilities for people with mental retardation.

American Foundation for Autistic Children,
4917 Dorset Ave., Chevy Chase, MD 20815; (301) 656-9213. Mooza V. P. Grant, president.

Works with children and parents of autistic and self-injurious children. Conducts research and provides information on autism; works with education and health institutions. Interests include developing residential facilities for older children.

The Arc,
1730 K St. N.W., #1212 20006; (202) 785-3388. Fax, (202) 467-4179. Paul Marchand, director, Governmental Affairs. Internet, arcga@radix.net or http://thearc.org.

Membership: individuals interested in assisting people with mental retardation. Provides information on government programs and legislation concerning mental retardation; oversees and encourages support for local groups that provide direct services for people with mental retardation. (Headquarters in Arlington, Texas.)

Autism Society of America,
7910 Woodmont Ave., #650, Bethesda, MD 20814-3015; (301) 657-0881. Fax, (301) 657-0869. Joan S. Zaro, executive director. Toll-free, (800) 328-8476. Internet, http://www.autism-society.org.

Monitors legislation and regulations affecting support, education, training, research, and other services for individuals with autism. Offers referral service and information to the public.

Best Buddies International,
1325 G St. N.W., #500 20005; (202) 347-7265. Fax, (202) 824-0200. Sarah Grabowski, program manager. Toll-free, (800) 892-8339. Internet, http://www.bestbuddies.org.

Volunteer organization that pairs high school students, college students, or working individuals in one-to-one friendships with mentally retarded persons worldwide. (Headquarters in Miami.)

International Assn. of Psychosocial Rehabilitation
Services, 10025 Gov. Warfield Pkwy., #301, Columbia, MD 21044-3357; (410) 730-7190. Fax, (410) 730-5965.

Ruth A. Hughes, chief executive officer. TDD, (410) 730-1723. Internet, iapsrs33@aol.com.

Membership: agencies, mental health practitioners, policymakers, family groups, and consumer organizations. Supports the community adjustment of persons with psychiatric disabilities; promotes the role of rehabilitation in mental health systems; opposes discrimination based on mental disability.

National Assn. of Protection and Advocacy
Systems, 900 2nd St. N.E., #211 20002; (202) 408-9514. Fax, (202) 408-9520. Curtis Decker, executive director. TDD, (202) 408-9521. Internet, http://www.protectionandadvocacy.org.

Membership: agencies working for the rights of the mentally ill or developmentally disabled and clients of the vocational rehabilitation system. Provides state agencies with training and technical assistance; maintains an electronic mail network. Monitors legislation and regulations.

National Assn. of State Directors of Developmental
Disability Services, 113 Oronoco St., Alexandria, VA 22314; (703) 683-4202. Fax, (703) 684-1395. Robert M. Gettings, executive director. Internet, http://www.nasddds.org.

Membership: chief administrators of state mental retardation programs. Coordinates exchange of information on mental retardation programs among the states; provides information on state programs.

National Children's Center,
6200 2nd St. N.W. 20011; (202) 722-2300. Fax, (202) 722-2383. Arthur Ginsburg, executive director.

Provides educational, social, and clinical services to infants, children, and adults with mental retardation and other developmental disabilities. Services provided through a 24-hour intensive treatment program, group homes and independent living programs, educational services, adult treatment programs, and early intervention programs for infants with disabilities or infants at high risk. Operates a child development center for children with and without disabilities.

HOMELESSNESS

AGENCIES

Education Dept., *Adult Education and Literacy, 330 C St. S.W., #4428 (mailing address: 600 Independence Ave. S.W., Washington, DC 20202-7240); (202) 205-8270. Fax, (202) 205-8973. Ronald S. Pugsley, director. Literacy clearinghouse, (202) 205-9996.*

Provides state and local agencies and community-based organizations with assistance in establishing education programs for homeless adults.

Education Dept., *Education for Homeless Children and Youth,* *600 Independence Ave. S.W., Portals Bldg., #4400 20202; (202) 260-0997. Fax, (202) 260-7764. Vacant, coordinator.*

Provides formula grants to education agencies in the states and Puerto Rico to educate homeless children and youth and to establish an office of coordinator of education for homeless children and youth in each jurisdiction.

Federal Emergency Management Agency, *Emergency Food and Shelter,* *500 C St. S.W. 20472; (202) 646-3107. Fax, (202) 646-4557. Carol Coleman, program officer.*

Administers the Emergency Food and Shelter Program under the McKinney Act. Gives supplemental assistance to programs that provide the homeless and persons in need with shelter, food, and support services.

Housing and Urban Development Dept., *Community Planning and Development,* *451 7th St. S.W., #7100 20410; (202) 708-2690. Fax, (202) 708-3336. Saul Ramirez Jr., assistant secretary.*

Gives supplemental assistance to facilities that aid the homeless; awards grants for innovative programs that address the needs of homeless families with children.

Housing and Urban Development Dept., *Special Needs Assistance Programs,* *451 7th St. S.W., #7262 20410; (202) 708-4300. Fax, (202) 708-3617. John D. Garrity, director.*

Advises and represents the secretary on homelessness matters; promotes cooperation among federal agencies on homelessness issues; coordinates assistance programs for the homeless under the McKinney Act. Trains HUD field staff in administering homelessness programs. Distributes funds to eligible nonprofit organizations, cities, counties, tribes, and territories for shelter, care, transitional housing, and permanent housing for the disabled homeless. Programs provide for acquisition and rehabilitation of buildings, prevention of homelessness, counseling, and medical care. Administers the Federal Surplus Property Program and spearheads the initiative to lease HUD-held homes to the homeless.

NONPROFIT

Housing Assistance Council, *1025 Vermont Ave. N.W., #606 20005-3516; (202) 842-8600. Fax, (202) 347-3441. Moises Loza, executive director. Toll-free, (800) 989-4422. Internet, hn0143@handsnet.org.*

Provides low-income housing development groups in rural areas with seed money loans and technical assistance; assesses programs designed to respond to rural housing needs; makes recommendations for federal and state involvement; publishes technical guides and reports on rural housing issues.

National Alliance to End Homelessness, *1518 K St. N.W., #206 20005; (202) 638-1526. Fax, (202) 638-4664. Paula Van Ness, president. Internet, naeh@naeh.org.*

Seeks to form a public-private partnership to alleviate problems of the homeless; promotes policies and programs that reduce the homeless population.

National Coalition for Homeless Veterans, *333 ½ Pennsylvania Ave. S.E. 20003-1148; (202) 546-1969. Fax, (202) 546-2063. Linda Boone, executive director. Internet, nchv@nchv.org or http://www.nchv.org.*

Provides technical assistance to service providers; advocates on behalf of homeless veterans.

National Coalition for the Homeless, *1012 14th St. N.W., #600 20005-3406; (202) 737-6444. Fax, (202) 737-6445. Mary Ann Gleason, executive director. Recorded hotline, (202) 737-6442. Internet, nch@ari.net or http://nch. ari.net.*

Works to ensure housing for all people; conducts research and provides information on homelessness, job creation, counseling, and family and child care; litigates on behalf of homeless people. Monitors legislation and regulations.

National Law Center on Homelessness and Poverty, *918 F St. N.W., #412 20004-1406; (202) 638-2535. Fax, (202) 628-2737. Maria Foscarinis, executive director. Internet, nlchp@nlchp.org or http://www. nlchp.org.*

Legal advocacy group that works to protect and expand the rights of the homeless through impact litigation, and conducts research on homelessness issues. Acts as a clearinghouse for legal information and technical assistance. Monitors legislation and regulations.

Salvation Army, *615 Slaters Lane, Alexandria, VA (mailing address: P.O. Box 269, Alexandria, VA 22313); (703) 684-5500. Fax, (703) 684-3478. Robert A. Watson, commissioner. Internet, http://www.salvationarmyusa.org.*

International religious social welfare organization that provides the homeless with residences and social services, including counseling, emergency help, and employment services. (International headquarters in London.)

Share Our Strength, *1511 K St. N.W., #940 20005; (202) 393-2925. Fax, (202) 347-5868. Bill Shore, executive*

director. Toll-free, (800) 969-4767. Internet, sos@
charitiesusa.com or http://www.strength.org.

Works to alleviate and prevent hunger and poverty in
the United States and around the world. Meets immediate demands for food by providing food assistance; treats
malnutrition and other consequences of hunger; promotes economic independence among people in need,
while seeking long-term solutions to hunger and poverty.
Helps mobilize industries, organizations, and individuals
to contribute their talents to anti-hunger efforts.

U.S. Conference of Mayors, *Task Force on Hunger
and Homelessness, 1620 Eye St. N.W. 20006; (202) 861-
6707. Fax, (202) 293-2352. Laura DeKoven Waxman,
assistant executive director.*

Tracks trends in hunger, homelessness, and community programs that address homelessness and hunger
in U.S. cities; issues reports. Monitors legislation and
regulations.

SOCIAL SECURITY

AGENCIES

Employment Standards Administration *(Labor
Dept.), Coal Mine Workers' Compensation, 200 Constitution Ave. N.W. 20210; (202) 219-6692. Fax, (202) 219-
8568. James L. DeMarce, director.*

Provides direction for administration of the black
lung benefits program. Adjudicates claims filed on or
after July 1, 1973; certifies these benefit payments and
maintains black lung beneficiary rolls. *(For claims filed
before July 1, 1973, contact Social Security Administration,
Disability.)*

Social Security Administration, *6401 Security Blvd.,
Baltimore, MD 21235; (410) 965-3120. Fax, (410) 966-
1463. Kenneth Apfel, commissioner; John R. Dyer, acting
principal deputy commissioner. Toll-free, (800) 772-1213.
Press, (410) 965-8904. TDD, (800) 325-0778. Internet,
http://www.ssa.gov.*

Administers national social security programs and
the supplemental security income program.

Social Security Administration, *Disability, 6401 Security Blvd., #560, Baltimore, MD 21235; (410) 965-3424.
Fax, (410) 965-6503. Susan M. Daniels, associate commissioner. Information, (410) 965-7700.*

Provides direction for administration of the disability
insurance program, which is paid out of the Social Security Trust Fund. Administers disability and blindness
provisions of the Supplemental Security Income (SSI)

program. Responsible for claims filed under black lung
benefits program before July 1, 1973.

Social Security Administration, *Disability and
International Operations, 1500 Woodlawn Dr., Baltimore, MD (mailing address: 7000 Security West Tower,
Baltimore, MD 21241); (410) 966-7000. Fax, (410) 966-
6005. W. Burnell Hurt, director. Toll-free, (800) 772-1213.*

Reviews and authorizes claims for benefits under the
disability insurance program and all claims for beneficiaries living abroad; certifies benefits payments; maintains
beneficiary rolls.

Social Security Administration, *Hearings and
Appeals, 5107 Leesburg Pike, #1600, Falls Church, VA
22041-3255; (703) 605-8200. Fax, (703) 605-8201. Rita S.
Geier, associate commissioner.*

Administers a nationwide system of administrative
law judges who conduct hearings and decide appealed
cases concerning benefits provisions. Reviews decisions
for appeals council action, if necessary, and renders the
secretary's final decision. Reviews benefits cases on
health insurance, disability, retirement and survivors'
benefits, and supplemental security income.

Social Security Administration, *Operations, 6401
Security Blvd., #1204, Baltimore, MD 21235; (410) 965-
3143. Fax, (410) 965-1344. Janice L. Warden, deputy commissioner. Toll-free, (800) 772-1213. TDD, (410)
965-4404.*

Issues Social Security numbers, maintains earnings
and beneficiary records, authorizes claims, certifies benefits, and makes postadjudicative changes in beneficiary
records for retirement, survivors', and disability insurance and black lung claims. Maintains toll-free number
for workers who want information on future Social
Security benefits.

Social Security Administration, *Program, Benefits,
Policy, 6401 Security Blvd., #760, Baltimore, MD 21235;
(410) 965-7100. Fax, (410) 965-8582. Marilyn O'Connell,
acting associate commissioner.*

Develops policies and procedures for administering
the retirement and survivors' insurance programs. Provides direction and technical guidance for administration of the Supplemental Security Income (SSI) program
for the elderly, blind, and disabled. Provides guidance on
administration of state supplementary benefits programs; monitors state compliance with mandatory minimum federal supplements.

Social Security Administration, *Research, Evaluation, and Statistics, 6401 Security Blvd., Operations
Building, #4C-15, Baltimore, MD 21235; (410) 965-2841.*

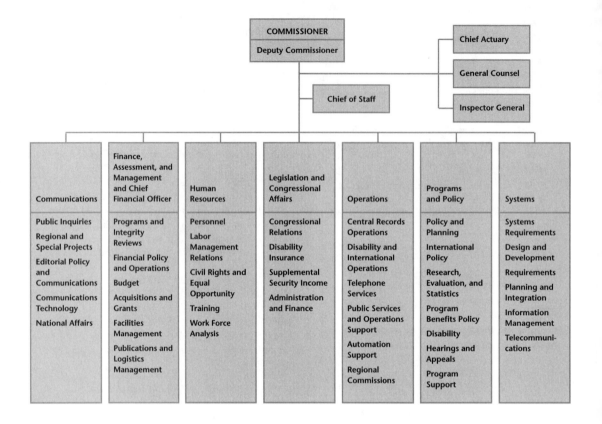

Fax, (410) 965-3308. Peter M. Wheeler, associate commissioner. Publications, (202) 358-6263.

Compiles statistics on beneficiaries; conducts research on the economic status of beneficiaries and the relationship between Social Security, the American people, and the economy; analyzes the effects of proposed Social Security legislation, especially on lower- and middle-income individuals and families; disseminates results of research and statistical programs through publications.

CONGRESS

General Accounting Office, *Health, Education, and Human Services, 441 G St. N.W. 20548; (202) 512-6806. Fax, (202) 512-5806. Richard L. Hembra, assistant comptroller general.*

Independent, nonpartisan agency in the legislative branch that audits, analyzes, and evaluates Health and Human Services Dept. programs, including Social Security, Medicare, and Medicaid; makes reports available to the public.

House Appropriations Committee, *Subcommittee on Labor, Health and Human Services, and Education, 2358 RHOB 20515; (202) 225-3508. John Edward Porter, R-Ill., chair; Tony McCann, staff director. Internet, http:// www.house.gov/appropriations.*

Jurisdiction over legislation to appropriate funds for the Social Security Administration.

House Ways and Means Committee, *Subcommittee on Human Resources, B317 RHOB 20515; (202) 225-1025. Fax, (202) 225-9480. E. Clay Shaw Jr., R-Fla., chair; Ronald Haskins, staff director. Internet, http://www. house.gov/ways_means.*

Jurisdiction over legislation on supplemental security income for the elderly, blind, and disabled.

House Ways and Means Committee, *Subcommittee on Social Security, B316 RHOB 20515; (202) 225-9263.*

Fax, (202) 225-9480. Jim Bunning, R-Ky., chair; Kim Hildred, staff director. Internet, http://www.house.gov/ways_means.

Jurisdiction over Social Security disability and retirement and survivors' legislation.

Senate Appropriations Committee, *Subcommittee on Labor, Health and Human Services, and Education, SD-184 20510; (202) 224-7230. Arlen Specter, R-Pa., chair; Craig A. Higgins, staff director. Internet, http://www.senate.gov/~appropriations/labor.*

Jurisdiction over legislation to appropriate funds for the Social Security Administration.

Senate Finance Committee, *Subcommittee on Social Security and Family Policy, SD-219 20510; (202) 224-4515. Fax, (202) 228-0578. John H. Chafee, R-R.I., chair; Alec Bachon, staff contact. Internet, http://www.senate.gov/~finance.*

Holds hearings on supplemental security income for the elderly, blind, and disabled; Social Security disability; and retirement and survivors' legislation.

Senate Special Committee on Aging, *SD-G31 20510; (202) 224-5364. Fax, (202) 224-8660. Charles E. Grassley, R-Iowa, chair; Ted Totman, staff director.*

Studies and makes recommendations on Social Security and other retirement benefits for the elderly.

NONPROFIT

National Academy of Social Insurance, *1776 Massachusetts Ave. N.W., #615 20036-1904; (202) 452-8097. Fax, (202) 452-8111. Pamela J. Larson, executive vice president. Internet, nasi@nasi.org or http://www.nasi.org.*

Promotes research and education on Social Security, health care financing, and related programs; assesses social insurance programs and their relationship to others; supports research and leadership development. Acts as a clearinghouse for social insurance information.

National Committee to Preserve Social Security and Medicare, *10 G St. N.E., #600 20002; (202) 216-0420. Fax, (202) 216-0451. Martha McSteen, president. Internet, http://www.ncpssm.org.*

Education and advocacy organization that focuses on Social Security, Medicare programs, and related health issues. Interests include retirement income protection, health care reform, and the quality of life of seniors. Monitors legislation and regulations.

2030 Center, *1511 K St. N.W., #709 20005; (202) 393-2485. Fax, (202) 393-2486. Hans Riemer, director. Internet, security@nicom.com.*

Public policy research and advocacy organization. Promotes policies that ensure the long-term viability of the social security system and expanded economic opportunities for younger Americans.

19

Transportation

GENERAL POLICY

AGENCIES

Architectural and Transportation Barriers Compliance Board (Access Board), *1331 F St. N.W., #1000 20004-1111; (202) 272-5434. Fax, (202) 272-5447. Lawrence W. Roffee, executive director. TDD, (202) 272-5449. Toll-free technical assistance, (800) 872-2253. Internet, http://www.access-board.gov.*

Enforces standards requiring that buildings and telecommunications and transportation systems be accessible to persons with disabilities; provides technical assistance and information on designing these facilities; sets accessibility guidelines for the Americans with Disabilities Act and the Telecommunications Act of 1996.

Bureau of Transportation Statistics *(Transportation Dept.), 400 7th St. S.W. 20590; (202) 366-1270. Fax, (202) 366-3640. Vacant, director. Information, (202) 366-3282. Internet, http://www.bts.gov.*

Works to improve public awareness of the nation's transportation systems. Compiles, analyzes, and makes accessible information on transportation.

Census Bureau *(Commerce Dept.), Services Division, Suitland and Silver Hill Rds., Suitland, MD; (301) 457-2797. Fax, (301) 457-2374. Kimberly P. Moore, survey statistician.*

Provides data and explains proper use of data for the bureau's Truck Inventory and Use Survey.

National Transportation Safety Board, *490 L'Enfant Plaza East S.W. 20594; (202) 314-6010. Fax, (202) 314-6018. James E. Hall, chair; Robert T. Francis, vice chair. Internet, http://www.ntsb.gov.*

Promotes transportation safety through independent investigations of accidents and other safety problems. Makes recommendations for safety improvement.

National Transportation Safety Board, *Research and Engineering, 490 L'Enfant Plaza East S.W. 20594; (202) 314-6500. Fax, (202) 314-6599. Vernon Ellingstad, director.*

Evaluates effectiveness of federal, state, and local safety programs. Identifies transportation safety issues not addressed by government or industry. Conducts studies on specific safety problems.

Office of Management and Budget *(Executive Office of the President), Transportation, New Executive Office Bldg., #9208 20503; (202) 395-5704. Fax, (202) 395-4797. David Tornquist, chief.*

Assists and advises the OMB director on budget preparation, proposed legislation, and evaluations of Transportation Dept. programs, policies, and activities.

Research and Special Programs Administration *(Transportation Dept.), 400 7th St. S.W., #8410 20590; (202) 366-4433. Fax, (202) 366-3666. Kelley Coyner, acting administrator. Internet, http://www.rspa.dot.gov.*

Coordinates research and development programs to improve safety of transportation systems; focus includes hazardous materials shipments, pipeline safety, and preparedness for transportation emergencies. Oversees Volpe National Transportation Systems Center in Cambridge, Mass., and Transportation Safety Institute in Oklahoma City.

Research and Special Programs Administration *(Transportation Dept.), Emergency Transportation, 400 7th St. S.W., #8404 20590; (202) 366-5270. Fax, (202) 366-3769. John Porco, acting director. Internet, http://www.rspa.dot.gov/oet.*

Develops, coordinates, and reviews transportation emergency preparedness programs for use in emergencies affecting national defense and in emergencies caused by natural disasters and crisis situations.

Research and Special Programs Administration *(Transportation Dept.), Research, Technology, and Analysis, 400 7th St. S.W., #8417 20590; (202) 366-4434. Fax, (202) 366-3671. Fenton Carey, associate administrator. Internet, http://www.rspa.dot.gov/dra.*

Supports transportation research, engineering, education, and safety training. Focus includes intermodal transportation; partnerships among government, universities, and industry; and economic growth and competitiveness through use of new technologies. Monitors international research.

Transportation Dept., *400 7th St. S.W. 20590; (202) 366-1111. Fax, (202) 366-7202. Rodney Slater, secretary; Mortimer L. Downey, deputy secretary. Information, (202) 366-4570. Locator, (202) 366-4000. Internet, http://www.dot.gov.*

Deals with most areas of transportation. Comprises the Coast Guard, Federal Aviation Administration, Federal Highway Administration, Federal Railroad Administration, Maritime Administration, National Highway Traffic Safety Administration, Research and Special Programs Administration, Federal Transit Administration, and Saint Lawrence Seaway Development Corp.

Transportation Dept., *Aviation and International Affairs, 400 7th St. S.W., #10232 20590; (202) 366-4551. Fax, (202) 493-2005. Charles Hunnicutt, assistant secretary. Internet, http://www.dot.gov/ost/aviation.*

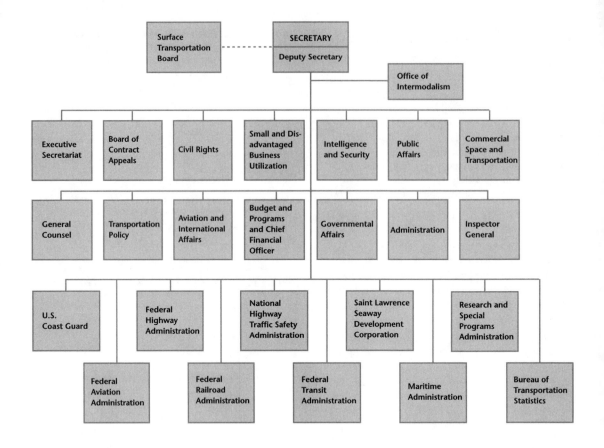

Formulates domestic aviation policy. Formulates international aviation, maritime, and across-the-border railroad and trucking policy.

Transportation Dept., *Consumer Affairs,* 400 7th St. S.W., #10405 (mailing address: Transportation Dept., C75, Washington, DC 20590); (202) 366-2220. Fax, (202) 366-7907. Hoyte Decker, assistant director.

Refers consumer complaints to appropriate departmental offices; advises the secretary on consumer issues; coordinates citizen participation activities and promotes joint projects with consumer interest groups; serves as ombudsman for consumer protection affairs; publishes educational materials.

Transportation Dept., *Environment, Energy, and Safety,* 400 7th St. S.W., P-10, #9222 20590; (202) 366-4220. Fax, (202) 366-7618. Donald R. Trilling, director.

Reviews environmental and safety regulatory issues, and accessibility issues affecting the private transportation industries and state and local transportation agencies. Prepares material for filings before various regulatory agencies and boards.

Transportation Dept., *Environmental Division,* 400 7th St. S.W., #9217 20590-0001; (202) 366-4366. Fax, (202) 366-7618. Camille Mittelholtz, chief.

Develops environmental policy and makes recommendations to the secretary; monitors Transportation Dept. implementation of environmental legislation; acts as liaison with other federal agencies and state and local governments on environmental matters related to transportation.

Transportation Dept., *Intelligence and Security,* 400 7th St. S.W., #10401 20590; (202) 366-6535. Fax, (202) 366-7261. Rear Adm. Paul J. Pluta (USCG), director.

NATIONAL TRANSPORTATION SAFETY BOARD

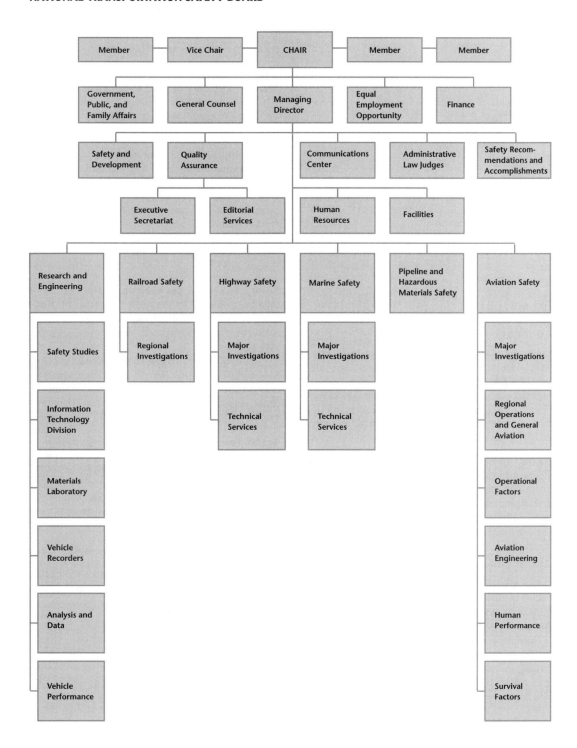

Advises the secretary on transportation intelligence and security policy. Acts as liaison with the intelligence community, federal agencies, corporations, and interest groups; administers counterterrorism strategic planning processes.

Transportation Dept., *Transportation Policy,* 400 7th St. S.W., #10228 20590; (202) 366-4544. Fax, (202) 366-7127. John Lieber, acting assistant secretary.

Oversees policy development for all domestic transportation except aviation. Assesses the performance of the domestic transportation network; analyzes the effect of government policies on domestic transportation industries.

U.S. Customs Service *(Treasury Dept.), Field Operations,* 1400 Pennsylvania Ave. N.W., #5.5C 20229; (202) 927-0100. Fax, (202) 927-0837. Robert S. Trotter, assistant commissioner.

Enforces statutes relating to the processing and regulation of people, baggage, cargo, and mail in and out of the United States; assesses and collects customs duties, excise taxes, fees, and penalties due on imported merchandise; administers certain navigation laws.

CONGRESS

General Accounting Office, *Transportation Issues,* 441 G St. N.W., #2T23 20548; (202) 512-3650. Fax, (202) 512-3766. John H. Anderson Jr., director.

Independent, nonpartisan agency in the legislative branch. Audits, analyzes, and evaluates performance of the Transportation Dept. and its component agencies; makes reports available to the public.

House Appropriations Committee, *Subcommittee on Commerce, Justice, State, and Judiciary,* H309 Capitol 20515; (202) 225-3351. Harold Rogers, R-Ky., chair; Jim Kulikowski, staff director. Internet, http://www.house.gov/appropriations.

Jurisdiction over legislation to appropriate funds for the Maritime Administration and Federal Maritime Commission.

House Appropriations Committee, *Subcommittee on Transportation,* 2358 RHOB 20515; (202) 225-2141. Frank R. Wolf, R-Va., chair; John T. Blazey, staff director. Internet, http://www.house.gov/appropriations.

Jurisdiction over legislation to appropriate funds for the Transportation Dept. (except the Maritime Administration) and related agencies, including the National Transportation Safety Board and the Surface Transportation Board.

House Government Reform and Oversight Committee, *Subcommittee on Government Management,*

Information, and Technology, B373 RHOB 20515; (202) 225-5147. Steve Horn, R-Calif., chair; J. Russell George, staff director. Internet, http://www.house.gov/cho.

Oversees operations of the Transportation Dept. and the National Transportation Safety Board.

House Transportation and Infrastructure Committee, 2165 RHOB 20515; (202) 225-9446. Fax, (202) 225-6782. Bud Shuster, R-Pa., chair; Jack Schenendorf, chief of staff. Internet, http://www.house.gov/transportation.

Jurisdiction over legislation on transportation.

Senate Appropriations Committee, *Subcommittee on Commerce, Justice, State, and Judiciary,* SR-393 20510; (202) 224-7277. Judd Gregg, R-N.H., chair, (202) 224-3324; Vas Alexopoulos, legislative assistant. Chair's fax, (202) 224-4952. Internet, http://www.senate.gov/~appropriations.

Jurisdiction over legislation to appropriate funds for the Maritime Administration and the Federal Maritime Commission.

Senate Appropriations Committee, *Subcommittee on Transportation,* SD-133 20510; (202) 224-7281. Fax, (202) 224-4401. Richard C. Shelby, R-Ala., chair; Wally Burnett, majority clerk. Internet, http://www.senate.gov/~appropriations.

Jurisdiction over legislation to appropriate funds for the Transportation Dept. (except the Maritime Administration) and related agencies, including the National Transportation Safety Board and the Surface Transportation Board.

Senate Commerce, Science, and Transportation Committee, SD-508 20510; (202) 224-5115. Fax, (202) 224-1259. John McCain, R-Ariz., chair; John Raidt, staff director. Internet, http://www.senate.gov/~commerce.

Jurisdiction over legislation on transportation; oversight of the Transportation Dept. and the National Transportation Safety Board.

Senate Special Committee on Aging, SD-G31 20510; (202) 224-5364. Fax, (202) 224-8660. Charles E. Grassley, R-Iowa, chair; Ted Totman, staff director.

Studies and makes recommendations on the availability of transportation for the elderly.

NONPROFIT

American Public Works Assn., 1301 Pennsylvania Ave. N.W., #501 20004; (202) 393-2792. Fax, (202) 737-9153. William J. Bertera, executive director. Internet, apwadc@us.net.

Membership: engineers, architects, and others who maintain and manage public works facilities and services. Conducts research and promotes exchange of information on transportation-related issues. (Headquarters in Kansas City.)

Assn. for Transportation Law, Logistics, and Policy, *19564 Club House Rd., Montgomery Village, MD 20886; (301) 670-6733. Fax, (301) 670-6735. E. Dale Jones, executive director. Internet, atllp@aol.com or http://www. transportlink.com/atllp.*

Provides members with continuing educational development in transportation law and practice. Interests include railroad, motor, energy, pipeline, antitrust, labor, logistics, safety, and environmental matters.

Institute of Navigation, *1800 Diagonal Rd., #480, Alexandria, VA 22314-2840; (703) 683-7101. Fax, (703) 683-7105. Lisa Beaty, director of operations. Internet, membership@ion.org or http://www.ion.org.*

Membership: individuals and organizations interested in navigation. Encourages research in navigation and establishment of uniform practices in navigation operations and education; conducts symposia on air, space, marine, and land navigation.

Institute of Transportation Engineers, *525 School St. S.W., #410 20024-2797; (202) 554-8050. Fax, (202) 863-5486. Thomas W. Brahms, executive director. Internet, http://www.ite.org.*

Membership: international professional transportation engineers. Conducts research, seminars, and training sessions; provides professional and scientific information on transportation standards and recommended practices.

International Brotherhood of Teamsters, *25 Louisiana Ave. N.W. 20001; (202) 624-6800. Fax, (202) 624-8102. Tom Sever, acting president. Internet, http://www.teamsters.org.*

Membership: more than 1.4 million workers in the transportation and construction industries, factories, offices, hospitals, warehouses, and other workplaces. Helps members negotiate pay, benefits, and better working conditions; conducts training programs and workshops. Monitors legislation and regulations. (Affiliated with the AFL-CIO.)

National Defense Transportation Assn., *50 S. Pickett St., Alexandria, VA 22304-7296; (703) 751-5011. Fax, (703) 823-8761. Edward Honor, president. Internet, http://web2.volpe.dot.gov/ndta.*

Membership: transportation users, manufacturers, and mode carriers; information technology firms; and related military, government, and civil interests worldwide. Promotes a strong U.S. transportation capability through coordination of private industry, government, and the military.

National Research Council, *Transportation Research Board, 2001 Wisconsin Ave. N.W. (mailing address: 2101 Constitution Ave. N.W., Washington, DC 20418); (202) 334-2936. Fax, (202) 334-2003. Robert E. Skinner, executive director. Information, (202) 334-2933. Library, (202) 334-2990. Publications, (202) 334-3213. Toll-free, (800) 424-9818. Internet, http://www.nas.edu/trb/index.html.*

Promotes research in transportation systems planning and administration and in the design, construction, maintenance, and operation of transportation facilities. Provides information to state and national highway and transportation departments; operates research information services; conducts special studies, conferences, and workshops; publishes technical reports. Library open to the public by appointment.

Rebuild America Coalition, *c/o American Public Works Assn., 1301 Pennsylvania Ave. N.W., #501 20004; (202) 347-7254. Fax, (202) 737-9153. William J. Bertera, executive director. Internet, http://www.rebuildamerica.org.*

Coalition of public and private organizations concerned with maintaining the infrastructure of the United States. Advocates government encouragement of innovative technology, financing, and public-private partnerships to build and rebuild public facilities, including highways, ports, airports, and transit systems.

Sheet Metal Workers' International Assn., *1750 New York Ave. N.W. 20006; (202) 783-5880. Fax, (202) 662-0895. Arthur Moore, president. Internet, http://smwia.org.*

Membership: more than 130,000 U.S. and Canadian workers in the building and construction trades, manufacturing, and the railroad and shipyard industries. Assists members with contract negotiation and grievances; conducts training programs and workshops. Monitors legislation and regulations. (Affiliated with the Sheet Metal and Air Conditioning Contractors' Assn., the AFL-CIO, and the Canadian Labour Congress.)

Surface Transportation Policy Project, *1100 17th St. N.W., 10th Floor 20036; (202) 466-2636. Fax, (202) 466-2247. Hank Dittmar, executive Director. Internet, stpp@transact.org or http://www.transact.org/stpp.htm.*

Advocates transportation policy and investments that conserve energy, protect environmental and aesthetic quality, strengthen the economy, promote social equity, and make communities more livable.

Union of Concerned Scientists, *1616 P St. N.W., #310 20036; (202) 332-0900. Fax, (202) 332-0905. Alden Meyer, director, Government Relations. Internet, ucs@ucsusa.org or http://www.ucsusa.org.*

Develops and promotes market-based strategies to reduce the adverse environmental, economic, and public health impacts of the U.S. transportation system. Advocates price incentives to promote transportation reform; development of cleaner, more fuel-efficient vehicles; and advancement of transportation technology and alternative fuels. (Headquarters in Cambridge, Mass.)

United Transportation Union, *400 N. Capitol St. N.W., #370 20001; (202) 347-0900. Fax, (202) 347-0958. James Brunkenhoefer, legislative director.*

Membership: approximately 150,000 workers in the transportation industry. Helps members negotiate pay, benefits, and better working conditions; conducts training programs and workshops. Monitors legislation and regulations. (Headquarters in Lakewood, Ohio; affiliated with the AFL-CIO.)

See also National Assn. of Regional Councils (p. 411)

Freight and Intermodalism

See also specific modes of transportation (this chapter)

AGENCIES

Federal Railroad Administration *(Transportation Dept.), Industry and Intermodal Policy, 1120 Vermont Ave. N.W., #7077 20005 (mailing address: 400 7th St. S.W, #15, Washington, DC 20590); (202) 632-3131. Fax, (202) 632-3705. Jane H. Bachner, deputy associate administrator.*

Promotes intermodal movement of freight involving rail transportation; studies economics and industry practices.

Maritime Administration *(Transportation Dept.), Intermodal Development, 400 7th St. S.W., #7209 20590; (202) 366-8888. Fax, (202) 366-6988. Richard L. Walker, director. Internet, http://marad.dot.gov/intermodal_development.html.*

Promotes development and improved use of marine-related intermodal transportation systems; provides technical information and advice to other agencies and organizations concerned with intermodal development.

Surface Transportation Board *(Transportation Dept.), 1925 K St. N.W. 20423-0001; (202) 565-1500. Fax, (202) 565-9004. Linda J. Morgan, chair; Gus A. Owen, vice chair. Internet, http://www.stb.dot.gov.*

Regulates rates for intermodal connections to or from water in noncontiguous domestic trade (between the mainland and Alaska, Hawaii, or U.S. territories).

Transportation Dept., *Intermodalism, 400 7th St. S.W., #10126 20590; (202) 366-5781. Fax, (202) 366-0263. Richard Biter, acting director.*

Coordinates departmental efforts to develop an intermodal transportation system to move people and goods; promotes energy efficiency and optimal use of national transportation resources.

NONPROFIT

American Moving and Storage Assn., *1611 Duke St., Alexandria, VA 22314; (703) 683-7410. Fax, (703) 683-7527. Gary F. Petty, president. Internet, http://www.amconf.org.*

Represents members' views before the Transportation Dept. and other government agencies. Conducts certification and training programs. Provides financial support for research on the moving and storage industry.

Distribution and LTL Carriers Assn., *211 N. Union St., #102, Alexandria, VA 22314; (703) 739-3101. Fax, (703) 739-3105. A. D. Garner Jr., president.*

Membership: movers of general freight. Provides networking opportunities; conducts workshops and seminars. Monitors legislation and regulations.

Intermodal Assn. of North America, *7501 Greenway Center Dr., #720, Greenbelt, MD 20770-3514; (301) 982-3400. Fax, (202) 982-3414. Joanne Casey, president. Internet, IANA@intermodal.org or http://www.intermodal.org.*

Membership: railroads, stacktrain operators, water carriers, motor carriers, marketing companies, and suppliers to the intermodal industry. Promotes intermodal transportation of freight. Monitors legislation and regulations.

National Assn. of Chemical Distributors, *1525 Wilson Blvd., #750, Arlington, VA 22209; (703) 527-6223. Fax, (703) 527-7747. D. Christopher Cathcart, executive vice president. Internet, http://www.nacd.com.*

Membership: firms involved in purchasing, processing, blending, storing, transporting, and marketing, chemical products. Provides members with information on such topics as training, safe handling and transport of chemicals, liability insurance, and environmental issues. Manages the NACD Educational Foundation. Monitors legislation and regulations.

National Customs Brokers and Forwarders Assn. of America, *1200 18th St. N.W., #901 20036; (202) 466-0222. Fax, (202) 466-0226. Eric Scharf, executive vice president. Internet, staff@ncbfaa.org or http://www.ncbfaa.org.*

Membership: customs brokers and freight forwarders in the United States. Fosters information exchange within the industry. Monitors legislation and regulations.

National Industrial Transportation League, *1700 N. Moore St., #1900, Arlington, VA 22209-1904; (703) 524-5011. Fax, (703) 524-5017. Edward M. Emmett, president. Internet, http://www.nitl.org.*

Membership: air, water, and surface shippers and receivers, including industries, corporations, chambers of commerce, and trade associations. Monitors legislation and regulations.

AIR TRANSPORTATION

AGENCIES

Civil Air Patrol, *National Capital Wing, Bolling Air Force Base, 222 Luke Ave., #2 20332-5114; (202) 767-5689. Fax, (202) 767-5695. Col. Roland Butler, wing commander.*

Official civilian auxiliary of the U.S. Air Force. Primary function is to conduct search-and-rescue missions for the Air Force. Maintains an aerospace education program for adults and a cadet program for junior and senior high school students. (Headquarters at Maxwell Air Force Base, Ala.)

Federal Aviation Administration *(Transportation Dept.), 800 Independence Ave. S.W. 20591; (202) 267-3111. Fax, (202) 267-5047. Jane Garvey, administrator. Press, (202) 267-3883. Internet, http://www.faa.gov.*

Regulates air commerce to improve aviation safety; promotes development of a national system of airports; develops and operates a common system of air traffic control and air navigation for both civilian and military aircraft; prepares the annual National Aviation System Plan.

Federal Aviation Administration *(Transportation Dept.), Aviation Education, 800 Independence Ave. S.W., #515 20591; (202) 267-3788. Phillip S. Woodruff, director.*

Provides schools and colleges with educational materials; sponsors aviation education activities for the public and the education community. Administers science curriculum that promotes aviation education by developing and certifying school curricula.

Federal Aviation Administration *(Transportation Dept.), Aviation Policy and Plans, 800 Independence Ave. S.W., #939, APO-1 20591; (202) 267-3274. Fax, (202) 267-3278. John M. Rodgers, director.*

Responsible for economic and regulatory policy and analysis, aviation activity forecasts, and strategic planning within the FAA.

Federal Aviation Administration *(Transportation Dept.), Environment and Energy, 800 Independence Ave. S.W., #900W 20591; (202) 267-3576. Fax, (202) 267-5594. James Erickson, director.*

Responsible for environmental affairs and energy conservation for aviation, including implementation and administration of various aviation-related environmental acts.

Federal Aviation Administration *(Transportation Dept.), International Aviation, 800 Independence Ave. S.W., #1028, AIA-1 20591; (202) 267-3213. Fax, (202) 267-5306. Joan W. Bauerlein, director.*

Coordinates all activities of the FAA that involve foreign relations; acts as liaison with the State Dept. and other agencies concerning international aviation; provides other countries with technical assistance on civil aviation problems; formulates international civil aviation policy for the United States.

Federal Aviation Administration *(Transportation Dept.), Research and Acquisitions, 800 Independence Ave. S.W., #1019 20591; (202) 267-7222. Fax, (202) 267-5085. George Donohue, associate administrator. Internet, http://www.faa.gov/ara/arahome.htm.*

Advises and assists in developing concepts for applying new technologies to meet long-range national airspace system requirements and for system acquisition, engineering, and management activities.

Federal Aviation Administration *(Transportation Dept.), Statistics and Forecast, 800 Independence Ave. S.W., #935, APO-110 20591; (202) 267-3355. Fax, (202) 267-5370. Robert L. Bowles, manager.*

Maintains statistics relating to civil aircraft, air personnel and airports, age and type of pilots and air personnel, passenger data, activity counts at FAA air traffic control facilities, and related information. Forecasts activity demand at FAA facilities and aviation demand for commercial and general aviation sectors; holds two annual forecast conferences.

Federal Aviation Administration *(Transportation Dept.), System Architecture and Investment Analysis, 1250 Maryland Ave. S.W. (mailing address: 800 Independence Ave. S.W., ASD-1, Washington, DC 20591); (202) 358-5238. Fax, (202) 358-5207. Steve Zaidman, director.*

Advises and assists in developing advanced technologies to meet National Airspace System Development requirements. Works with internal FAA customers, other government agencies, and the aviation industry to understand and respond to user requirements.

Justice Dept., *Civil Division, 1425 New York Ave. N.W., #10100 (mailing address: P.O. Box 14271, Washington, DC*

20044-4271); (202) 616-4000. Fax, (202) 616-4002. Gary W. Allen, director, Torts Branch, Aviation/Admiralty Litigation.

Represents the federal government in civil suits arising from aviation incidents and accidents. Handles tort litigation for the government's varied activities in the operation of the air traffic control system, the regulation of air commerce, weather services, aeronautical charting, and the government's operation of its own civil and military aircraft.

National Aeronautics and Space Administration, Aeronautics and Space Transportation Technology, 300 E St. S.W. (mailing address: NASA Headquarters, Mail Code R, Washington, DC 20546); (202) 358-2693. Fax, (202) 358-4066. Richard Christensen, acting associate administrator. Internet, http://www.hq.nasa.gov/office/aero.

Conducts research in aerodynamics, materials, structures, avionics, propulsion, human factors, and safety; helps apply new technologies to the U.S. aeronautics industry and international projects. Manages the following NASA research centers: Marshals (Huntsville, Ala.); Goddard (Greenbelt, Md.); Ames (Moffett, Calif.); Dryden (Edwards, Calif.); Langley (Hampton, Va.); and Lewis (Cleveland, Ohio).

National Air and Space Museum (Smithsonian Institution), 6th St. and Independence Ave. S.W., MRC 310 20560; (202) 357-1745. Fax, (202) 357-2426. Donald D. Engan, director. Press, (202) 357-1552. Library, (202) 357-3133. TDD, (202) 357-1505. Education office, (202) 786-2106. Daily space and earth phenomena report, (202) 357-2000 (recording). Tours, (202) 357-1400. Internet, http://www.nasm.si.edu.

Maintains exhibits and collections on aeronautics, pioneers of flight, and early aircraft through modern air technology. Library open to the public by appointment.

National Mediation Board, 1301 K St. N.W., #250E 20572; (202) 523-5920. Fax, (202) 523-2179. Kenneth B. Hipp, chair. Information, (202) 523-5335. TDD, (202) 523-8560.

Mediates labor disputes in the airline industry; determines and certifies labor representatives for the industry.

Transportation Dept., Airline Information, 400 7th St. S.W., #4125, MC K-25 20590; (202) 366-9059. Fax, (202) 366-3383. Timothy E. Carmody, director.

Develops, interprets, and enforces accounting and reporting regulations for the aviation industry; issues air carrier reporting instructions, waivers, and due-date extensions.

Transportation Dept., Aviation Analysis, 400 7th St. S.W., #6401, X-50 20590; (202) 366-5903. Fax, (202) 366-7638. John V. Coleman, director.

Analyzes essential air service needs of communities; directs subsidy policy and programs; guarantees air service to small communities; conducts research for the department on airline mergers, international route awards, and employee protection programs; administers the air carrier fitness provisions of the Federal Aviation Act; registers domestic and foreign air carriers; enforces charter regulations for tour operators.

Transportation Dept., Aviation and International Affairs, 400 7th St. S.W., #10232 20590; (202) 366-4551. Fax, (202) 493-2005. Charles Hunnicutt, assistant secretary. Internet, http://www.dot.gov/ost/aviation.

Formulates domestic and international aviation policy. Assesses the performance of the U.S. aviation network in meeting public needs. Studies the social and economic conditions of the aviation industry, including airline licensing, antitrust concerns, and the effect of government policies.

Transportation Dept., Consumer Affairs, 400 7th St. S.W., #10405 (mailing address: Transportation Dept., C75, Washington, DC 20590); (202) 366-2220. Fax, (202) 366-7907. Hoyte Decker, assistant director.

Addresses complaints about airline service and consumer-protection matters. Conducts investigations, provides assistance, and reviews regulations affecting air carriers.

Transportation Dept., Information Technology, Financial, and Secretarial Audits, 400 7th St. S.W., #7102, JA-20 20590-0001; (202) 366-1496. Fax, (202) 366-3530. John Meche, director.

Provides auditing services for airline economic programs.

CONGRESS

House Appropriations Committee, Subcommittee on Transportation, 2358 RHOB 20515; (202) 225-2141. Frank R. Wolf, R-Va., chair; John T. Blazey, staff director. Internet, http://www.house.gov/appropriations.

Jurisdiction over legislation to appropriate funds for the Federal Aviation Administration.

House Science Committee, Subcommittee on Space and Aeronautics, B374 RHOB 20515; (202) 225-9662. F. James Sensenbrenner Jr., R-Wis., chair; Shana Dale, staff director. Internet, http://www.house.gov/science.

Legislative jurisdiction over the Transportation Dept. (relating to space activities and aeronautics) and the National Aeronautics and Space Administration.

House Science Committee, *Subcommittee on Technology,* 2319 RHOB 20515; (202) 225-8844. Fax, (202) 225-4438. Constance A. Morella, R-Md., chair; Richard Russell, staff director. Internet, http://www.house.gov/science.

Jurisdiction over legislation on civil aviation research and development, including the Federal Aviation Administration.

House Transportation and Infrastructure Committee, *Subcommittee on Aviation,* 2251 RHOB 20515; (202) 226-3220. Fax, (202) 225-4629. John J. "Jimmy" Duncan Jr., R-Tenn., chair; David Schaffer, staff director. Internet, http://www.house.gov/transportation.

Jurisdiction over legislation on civil aviation, including airport funding, airline deregulation, safety issues, the National Transportation Safety Board, and the Federal Aviation Administration (except research and development). Jurisdiction over aviation noise pollution legislation.

Senate Appropriations Committee, *Subcommittee on Transportation,* SD-133 20510; (202) 224-7281. Fax, (202) 224-4401. Richard C. Shelby, R-Ala., chair; Wally Burnett, majority clerk. Internet, http://www.senate.gov/~appropriations.

Jurisdiction over legislation to appropriate funds for the Federal Aviation Administration.

Senate Commerce, Science, and Transportation Committee, SD-508 20510; (202) 224-5115. Fax, (202) 224-1259. John McCain, R-Ariz., chair; John Raidt, staff director. Internet, http://www.senate.gov/~commerce.

Jurisdiction over legislation on the National Aeronautics and Space Administration, including nonmilitary aeronautical research and development.

Senate Commerce, Science, and Transportation Committee, *Subcommittee on Aviation,* SH-427 (mailing address: SD-508, Washington, DC 20510); (202) 224-4852. Fax, (202) 228-0326. Slade Gorton, R-Wash., chair; Ann Hodges, professional staff member. Internet, http://www.senate.gov/~commerce.

Jurisdiction over legislation on civil aviation, including airport funding, airline deregulation, safety issues, research and development, the National Transportation Safety Board, and the Federal Aviation Administration. Jurisdiction over aviation noise pollution legislation.

NONPROFIT

Aeronautical Repair Station Assn., 121 N. Henry St., Alexandria, VA 22314-2903; (703) 739-9543. Fax, (703) 739-9488. Sarah MacLeod, executive director. Internet, arsa@arsa.org or http://www.arsa.org.

Membership: Federal Aviation Administration-certified repair stations; associate members are suppliers and distributors of components and parts. Works to improve relations between repair stations and manufacturers. Interests include reducing costs and problems associated with product liability and establishing uniformity in the application, interpretation, and enforcement of FAA regulations. Monitors legislation and regulations.

Aerospace Education Foundation, 1501 Lee Hwy., Arlington, VA 22209; (703) 247-5839. Fax, (703) 247-5853. Darryl Hayes, managing director. Toll-free, (800) 727-3337. Internet, aefstaff@aef.org or http://www.aef.org.

Promotes knowledge and appreciation of U.S. civilian and military aerospace development and history. (Affiliated with the Air Force Assn.)

Aerospace Industries Assn. of America, 1250 Eye St. N.W., #1200 20005-3922; (202) 371-8400. Fax, (202) 371-8470. Don Fuqua, president. Press, (202) 371-8544. Internet, http://www.aia-aerospace.org.

Represents U.S. manufacturers of commercial, military, and business aircraft; helicopters; aircraft engines; missiles; spacecraft; and related components and equipment. Interests include international standards and trade.

Air Care Alliance, P.O. Box 1940, Manassas, VA 20108-0804; (703) 361-1191. Fax, (703) 361-1792. Ed Boyer, executive vice president. Toll-free, (800) 296-1217. Internet, http://www.angelflightfla.org/aircareall.org/acahome.html.

Coordinates the efforts of national and regional volunteer pilot associations; seeks to save lives by providing safe air transportation to health care facilities. (Affiliated with Mercy Air Flights.)

AIR Conference (Airline Industrial Relations Conference), 1920 N St. N.W., #250 20036; (202) 861-7550. Fax, (202) 861-7557. Robert J. DeLucia, vice president. Internet, office@aircon.org or http://www.aircon.org.

Membership: domestic and international scheduled air carriers. Monitors developments and collects data on trends in airline labor relations.

Air Freight Assn., 1220 19th St. N.W., #400 20036; (202) 293-1030. Fax, (202) 293-4377. Stephen A. Alterman, president.

Membership: cargo airlines and other firms interested in the development and promotion of air freight.

Air Line Pilots Assn. International, 1625 Massachusetts Ave. N.W. 20036; (703) 689-2270. Fax, (703) 689-4370. J. Randolph Babbitt, president. Press, (703) 481-4440. Internet, http://www.airspacemag.com/ALPA.

Membership: airline pilots in the United States and Canada. Promotes air travel safety; assists investigations of aviation accidents. Monitors legislation and regulations. (Affiliated with the AFL-CIO.)

Air Transport Assn. of America, *1301 Pennsylvania Ave. N.W., #1100 20004; (202) 626-4000. Fax, (202) 626-4166. Carol Hallett, president. Internet, http://www.air-transport.org.*

Membership: U.S. scheduled air carriers. Promotes aviation safety and the facilitation of air transportation for passengers and cargo. Monitors legislation and regulations.

American Helicopter Society, *217 N. Washington St., Alexandria, VA 22314; (703) 684-6777. Fax, (703) 739-9279. Morris E. Flater, executive director. Internet, ahs703@aol.com or http://www.vtol.org.*

Membership: individuals and organizations interested in vertical flight. Acts as an information clearinghouse for technical data on helicopter design improvement, aerodynamics, and safety. Awards the Vertical Flight Foundation Scholarship to students interested in helicopter technology.

American Institute of Aeronautics and Astronautics, *1801 Alexander Bell Dr., #500, Reston, VA 20191; (703) 264-7500. Fax, (703) 264-7551. Cort Durocher, executive director. Toll-free, (800) 639-2422. Internet, custserv@aiaa.org or http://www.aiaa.org.*

Membership: engineers, scientists, and students in the fields of aeronautics and astronautics. Holds workshops on aerospace technical issues for congressional subcommittees; sponsors international conferences. Offers computerized database through its Technical Information Service in New York.

AOPA Legislative Action, *500 E St. S.W., #250 20024; (202) 479-4050. Fax, (202) 484-1312. Bill Deere, executive director.*

Membership: owners and pilots of general aviation aircraft. Washington office monitors legislation and regulations. Headquarters office provides members with maps, trip planning, speakers bureau, and other services; issues airport directory and handbook for pilots; sponsors the Air Safety Foundation. (Headquarters in Frederick, Md.)

Assn. of Flight Attendants, *1275 K St. N.W. 20005-4006; (202) 712-9799. Fax, (202) 712-9798. Patricia A. Friend, president. Internet, afatalk@flightattendant-afa.org or http://www.flightattendant-afa.inter.net.*

Membership: approximately 42,000 flight attendants. Helps members negotiate pay, benefits, and better working conditions; conducts training programs and work-

shops. Monitors legislation and regulations. (Affiliated with the AFL-CIO.)

Aviation Consumer Action Project, *2001 S St. N.W., #410 20009 (mailing address: P.O. Box 19029, Washington, DC 20036); (202) 638-4000. Fax, (202) 638-0746. Paul S. Hudson, director. Internet, acap71@erols.com or http://www.acap1971.org.*

Consumer advocacy organization that represents interests of airline passengers before the Federal Aviation Administration on safety issues and before the Transportation Dept. on economic and regulatory issues; testifies before Congress.

General Aviation Manufacturers Assn., *1400 K St. N.W., #801 20005; (202) 393-1500. Fax, (202) 842-4063. Edward M. Bolen, president. Internet, http://www.generalaviation.org.*

Membership: U.S. manufacturers of business, commuter, and personal aircraft and manufacturers of engines, avionics, and equipment. Sponsors safety and public information programs. Monitors legislation and regulations.

Helicopter Assn. International, *1635 Prince St., Alexandria, VA 22314; (703) 683-4646. Fax, (703) 683-4745. Frank Jensen, president. Internet, http://www.rotor.com.*

Membership: owners, manufacturers, and operators of helicopters, and affiliated companies in the civil helicopter industry. Provides information on use and operation of helicopters; offers business management and aviation safety courses; sponsors annual industry exposition. Monitors legislation and regulations.

International Assn. of Machinists and Aerospace Workers, *9000 Machinists Pl. 20772-2687; (301) 967-4500. Fax, (301) 967-4588. Thomas Buffenbarger, president. Internet, http://www.iamaw.org.*

Membership: machinists in more than 200 industries. Helps members negotiate pay, benefits, and better working conditions; conducts training programs and workshops. Monitors legislation and regulations. (Affiliated with the AFL-CIO, the Canadian Labour Congress, the Railway Labor Executives Assn., the International Metalworkers Federation, and the International Transport Workers' Federation.)

National Aeronautic Assn., *1815 N. Fort Myer Dr., #700, Arlington, VA 22209-1805; (703) 527-0226. Fax, (703) 527-0229. Steven J. Brown, president. Internet, naa@ids2.idsonline.com or http://www.naa.ycg.org.*

Membership: persons interested in development of general and sporting aviation. Supervises sporting aviation competitions; oversees and approves official U.S.

aircraft, aeronautics, and astronautics records. Interests include aeromodeling, aerobatics, helicopters, ultralights, home-built aircraft, parachuting, soaring, hang gliding, and ballooning. Serves as U.S. representative to the International Aeronautical Federation in Paris.

National Agricultural Aviation Assn., *1005 E St. S.E. 20003; (202) 546-5722. Fax, (202) 546-5726. James Boillot, executive director. Internet, naaa@aol.com.*

Membership: qualified agricultural pilots; operating companies that seed, fertilize, and spray land by air; and allied industries. Monitors legislation and regulations.

National Air Carrier Assn., *1730 M St. N.W., #806 20036; (202) 833-8200. Fax, (202) 659-9479. Edward J. Driscoll, president.*

Membership: air carriers certified for charter and scheduled operations. Monitors legislation and regulations.

National Air Transportation Assn., *4226 King St., Alexandria, VA 22302-1507; (703) 845-9000. Fax, (703) 845-8176. James K. Coyne, president. Toll-free, (800) 808-6282. Internet, http://www.nata-online.org.*

Membership: companies that provide on-demand air charter, aircraft sales, flight training, maintenance and repair, avionics, and other services. Manages education foundation; compiles statistics; provides business assistance programs. Monitors legislation and regulations.

National Assn. of State Aviation Officials, *8401 Colesville Rd., #505, Silver Spring, MD 20910; (301) 588-0587. Fax, (301) 585-1803. Henry Ogrodzinski, executive vice president. Internet, http://www.nasao.org.*

Membership: state aeronautics agencies that deal with aviation issues, including regulation. Seeks uniform aviation laws; manages an aviation research and education foundation.

National Aviation Club, *1500 N. Beauregard St., #104, Alexandria, VA 22311; (703) 379-1506. Fax, (703) 379-1507. Daniel McGrath, executive vice president. Internet, natavclub@aol.com.*

Membership: individuals and corporations interested in aviation and aerospace. Sponsors speakers and seminars on aviation and aerospace issues; presents awards for achievements in aviation.

National Business Aircraft Assn., *1200 18th St. N.W., #400 20036; (202) 783-9000. Fax, (202) 331-8364. John W. Olcott, president. Internet, http://www.nbaa.org.*

Membership: companies owning and operating aircraft for business use, suppliers, and maintenance and air fleet service companies. Conducts seminars and work-

shops in business aviation management. Sponsors annual civilian aviation exposition. Monitors legislation and regulations.

Regional Airline Assn., *1200 19th St. N.W., #300 20036-2401; (202) 857-1170. Fax, (202) 429-5113. Walter S. Coleman, president. Internet, http://www.raa.org.*

Membership: regional airlines that provide passenger, scheduled cargo, and mail service. Issues annual report on the industry.

RTCA Inc., *1140 Connecticut Ave. N.W., #1020 20036; (202) 833-9339. Fax, (202) 833-9434. David S. Watrous, president. Internet, http://www.rtca.org.*

Membership: federal agencies, aviation organizations, and commercial firms interested in aeronautical systems. Develops and publishes standards for aviation, including minimum operational performance standards for specific equipment; conducts research, makes recommendations, and issues reports on the field of aviation electronics and telecommunications.

See also Transportation Communications International Union (p. 682)

Airports

AGENCIES

Animal and Plant Health Inspection Service *(Agriculture Dept.),* **Wildlife Services,** *1400 Independence Ave. S.W., #1624S 20250-3402; (202) 720-2054. Fax, (202) 690-0053. Bobby R. Acord, deputy administrator. Internet, http://www.aphis.usda.gov/ws.*

Works to minimize damage caused by wildlife to human health and safety. Interests include aviation safety; works with airport managers to reduce the risk of bird strikes. Oversees the National Wildlife Research Center in Denver, Colo.

Bureau of Land Management *(Interior Dept.),* **Lands and Realty,** *1620 L St. N.W. (mailing address: 1849 C St. N.W., MC 1000LS, Washington, DC 20240); (202) 452-7780. Fax, (202) 452-7708. Ray Brady, manager. Internet, http://www.blm.gov.*

Operates the Airport Lease Program, which leases public lands for use as public airports.

Federal Aviation Administration *(Transportation Dept.),* **Airports,** *800 Independence Ave. S.W., #600E, ARP-1 20591; (202) 267-9471. Fax, (202) 267-5301. Susan Kurland, associate administrator. Internet, http://www.faa.gov/arp/arphome.htm.*

Makes grants for development and improvement of publicly operated and owned airports and some privately owned airports; certifies airports; oversees construction and accessibility standards for people with disabilities. Questions about local airports are usually referred to a local FAA field office. *(See Regional Information Sources in appendix.)*

Maryland Aviation Administration, *P.O. Box 8766 21240; (410) 859-7060. Fax, (410) 850-4729. Theodore E. Mathison, executive director; Jay D. Huber, director, BWI Operations, (410) 859-7022.*

Responsible for aviation operations, planning, instruction, and safety in Maryland; operates Baltimore/Washington International Airport (BWI).

Metropolitan Washington Airports Authority, *44 Canal Center Plaza, #219, Alexandria, VA 22314-1562; (703) 417-8600. Fax, (703) 417-8949. James A. Wilding, president. Internet, http://www.metwashairports.com.*

Independent interstate agency created by Virginia and the District of Columbia with the consent of Congress; operates Washington Dulles International Airport and Ronald Reagan Washington National Airport.

NONPROFIT

Airports Council International, *1775 K St. N.W., #500 20006; (202) 293-8500. Fax, (202) 331-1362. David Z. Plavin, president. Internet, http://www.aci-na.org.*

Membership: authorities, boards, commissions, and municipal departments operating public airports. Serves as liaison with government agencies and other aviation organizations; works to improve passenger and freight facilitation; acts as clearinghouse on engineering and operational aspects of airport development. Monitors legislation and regulations.

American Assn. of Airport Executives, *4212 King St., Alexandria, VA 22302; (703) 824-0500. Fax, (703) 820-1395. Charles M. Barclay, president. Internet, http://www.airportnet.org.*

Membership: airport managers, superintendents, consultants, authorities and commissions, government officials, and others interested in the construction, management, and operation of airports. Conducts examination for and awards the professional designation of Accredited Airport Executive.

Aviation Safety and Security

AGENCIES

Federal Aviation Administration *(Transportation Dept.), Accident Investigation, 800 Independence Ave. S.W., AAI-1 20591; (202) 267-9612. Fax, (202) 267-5043. David F. Thomas, director.*

Investigates aviation accidents and incidents to detect unsafe conditions and trends in the national airspace system and to coordinate corrective action.

Federal Aviation Administration *(Transportation Dept.), Air Traffic Services, 800 Independence Ave. S.W., ATS-1 20591; (202) 267-7111. Fax, (202) 267-5621. Ron Morgan, acting associate administrator. Internet, http://www.faa.gov/ats/atshome,htm.*

Operates the national air traffic control system; employs air traffic controllers at airport towers, en route air traffic control centers, and flight service stations; maintains the National Flight Data Center.

Federal Aviation Administration *(Transportation Dept.), Aircraft Certification Service, 800 Independence Ave. S.W., AIR-1 20591; (202) 267-8235. Fax, (202) 267-5364. Thomas E. McSweeny, director.*

Certifies all aircraft for airworthiness; approves designs and specifications for new aircraft, aircraft engines, propellers, and appliances; supervises aircraft manufacturing and testing.

Federal Aviation Administration *(Transportation Dept.), Airway Facilities, 800 Independence Ave. S.W., #700E, AAF-1 20591; (202) 267-8181. Fax, (202) 267-5015. Stanley Rivers, director.*

Conducts research and development programs aimed at providing procedures, facilities, and devices needed for a safe and efficient system of air navigation and air traffic control.

Federal Aviation Administration *(Transportation Dept.), Aviation Medicine, 800 Independence Ave. S.W., #800, AAM-1 20591; (202) 267-3535. Fax, (202) 267-5399. Dr. Jon L. Jordan, federal air surgeon.*

Responsible for the medical activities and policies of the FAA; designates, through regional offices, aviation medical examiners who conduct periodic medical examinations of all air personnel; maintains a Civil Aeromedical Institute in Oklahoma City.

Federal Aviation Administration *(Transportation Dept.), Civil Aviation Security, 800 Independence Ave. S.W., #300E, ACS-1 20591; (202) 267-9863. Fax, (202) 267-8496. Cathal L. Flynn, associate administrator. Internet, http://cas.faa.gov.*

Responsible for domestic and foreign air carrier and airport security, including FAA antihijacking, antitheft, and sabotage prevention programs; formulates regulations for airport security, antihijacking controls, air cargo security, and hazardous materials; enforces regulations; inspects airports for compliance.

Federal Aviation Administration *(Transportation Dept.), Flight Standards Service,* 800 Independence Ave. S.W., AFS-1 20591; (202) 267-8237. Fax, (202) 267-5230. *Thomas Stuckey, acting director.*

Sets certification standards for air carriers, commercial operators, air agencies, and airmen (except air-traffic control tower operators); directs and executes certification and inspection of flight procedures, operating methods, airmen qualification and proficiency, and maintenance aspects of airworthiness programs; manages the registry of civil aircraft and all official airmen records; supports law enforcement agencies responsible for drug interdiction.

Federal Aviation Administration *(Transportation Dept.), System Safety,* 800 Independence Ave. S.W., #1040A 20591; (202) 267-3611. Fax, (202) 267-5496. *Christopher A. Hart, assistant administrator. Internet, http://nasdac.faa.gov.*

Responsible for safety promotion and for the quality and integrity of safety-data studies and analyses.

Federal Bureau of Investigation *(Justice Dept.), Criminal Investigative Division,* 935 Pennsylvania Ave. N.W., #7116 20535; (202) 324-4260. Fax, (202) 324-0027. *John F. Lewis Jr., assistant director. Internet, http://www.fbi.gov.*

Investigates cases of aircraft hijacking, destruction of aircraft, and air piracy. Works with FAA to ensure security of national air carrier systems against terrorist and nonterrorist threats.

Federal Communications Commission, *Compliance and Information Bureau,* 1919 M St. N.W. 20554; (202) 418-1100. Richard Lee, chief. Toll-free, (888) 225-5322. TDD, (888) 835-5322. 24-hour watch officer, (202) 632-6975. Internet, http://www.fcc.gov/cib.

Provides technical services to aid the Federal Aviation Administration in locating aircraft in distress; provides interference resolution for air traffic control radio frequencies.

National Oceanic and Atmospheric Administration *(Commerce Dept.), National Ocean Service,* 1305 East-West Hwy., SSMC4, #5430, Silver Spring, MD 20910; (301) 713-2619. Fax, (301) 713-4587. Nancy Foster, assistant administrator. Internet, http://www.nos.noaa.gov.

Directs programs and conducts research to support fundamental scientific and engineering activities and resource development for safe navigation of national airspace. Maintains the National Spatial Reference System. Prints and distributes aeronautical charts.

National Transportation Safety Board, *Aviation Safety,* 490 L'Enfant Plaza East S.W., #5400 20594; (202) 314-6300. Fax, (202) 314-6309. Bernard Loeb, director.

Responsible for management, policies, and programs in aviation safety and for aviation accident investigations. Manages programs on special investigations, safety issues, and safety objectives. Acts as U.S. representative in international investigations.

NONPROFIT

Aerospace Medical Assn., *320 S. Henry St., Alexandria, VA 22314-3579; (703) 739-2240. Fax, (703) 739-9652. Dr. Russell B. Rayman, executive director.*

Membership: physicians, flight surgeons, aviation medical examiners, flight nurses, scientists, technicians, and specialists in clinical, operational, and research fields of aerospace medicine. Promotes programs to improve aerospace medicine and maintain safety in aviation by examining and monitoring the health of aviation personnel; participates in aircraft investigation and cockpit design.

Air Traffic Control Assn., *2300 Clarendon Blvd., #711, Arlington, VA 22201; (703) 522-5717. Fax, (703) 527-7251. Gabriel A. Hartl, president. Internet, http://www.atca.org.*

Membership: air traffic controllers, flight service station specialists, pilots, aviation engineers and manufacturers, and others interested in air traffic control systems. Compiles and publishes information and data concerning air traffic control; provides information to members, Congress, and federal agencies; acts as liaison between members and Congress.

Flight Safety Foundation, *601 Madison St., #300, Alexandria, VA 22314; (703) 739-6700. Fax, (703) 739-6708. Stuart Matthews, president. Internet, http://www.flightsafety.org.*

Membership: aerospace manufacturers, domestic and foreign airlines, energy and insurance companies, educational institutions, and organizations and corporations interested in flight safety. Sponsors seminars and conducts studies on air safety for governments and industries. Administers award programs that recognize achievements in air safety.

International Society of Air Safety Investigators, *Technology Trading Park, 5 Export Dr., Sterling, VA 20164-4421; (703) 430-9668. Fax, (703) 450-1745. Ann Schull, office manager. Internet, isasi@erols.com.*

Membership: specialists who investigate and seek to define the causes of aircraft accidents. Encourages improvement of air safety and investigative procedures.

National Air Traffic Controllers Assn., *1150 17th St. N.W., #701 20036; (202) 223-2900. Michael McNally, president. Internet, http://www.natca.org.*

Seeks to increase air traffic controller staffing levels, improve working conditions, and encourage procurement of more modern, reliable equipment.

National Assn. of Air Traffic Specialists, *11303 Amherst Ave., #4, Wheaton, MD 20902; (301) 933-6228. Fax, (301) 933-3902. Walter W. Pike, chief executive officer. Internet, naatshq@aol.com or http://www.naats.org.*

Membership: flight service station controllers from the FAA. Assists members with contract negotiation and grievances; conducts training programs and workshops. Monitors legislation and regulations.

See also National Safety Council (p. 680)

🚢 MARITIME TRANSPORTATION

AGENCIES

Army Corps of Engineers *(Defense Dept.), 20 Massachusetts Ave. N.W. 20314-1000; (202) 761-0001. Fax, (202) 761-4463. Lt. Gen. Joe N. Ballard (USACE), chief of engineers. Internet, http://www.usace.army.mil.*

Provides local governments with navigation, flood control, disaster relief, and hydroelectric power services.

Federal Maritime Commission, *800 N. Capitol St. N.W., #1046 20573; (202) 523-5725. Fax, (202) 523-0014. Harold J. Creel Jr., chair; Edward P. Walsh, managing director, (202) 523-5800. Library, (202) 523-5762. TDD, (202) 343-3679. Locator, (202) 523-5773. Internet, http://www.fmc.gov.*

Regulates foreign and domestic ocean shipping of the United States; enforces maritime shipping laws and regulations regarding rates and charges, freight forwarding, passengers, and port authorities. Library open to the public.

Federal Maritime Commission, *Tariffs, Certification, and Licensing, 800 N. Capitol St. N.W., 9th Floor 20573; (202) 523-5796. Fax, (202) 523-5830. Bryant L. VanBrakle, director. Internet, http://www.fmc.gov.*

Regulates the rates charged for shipping in domestic commerce and monitors the rates in foreign commerce; licenses and enforces regulations concerning ocean freight forwarders; issues certificates of financial responsibility to ensure that carriers refund fares and meet their liability in case of death, injury, or nonperformance.

Justice Dept., *Civil Division, 1425 New York Ave. N.W., #10100 (mailing address: P.O. Box 14271, Washington, DC 20044-4271); (202) 616-4000. Fax, (202) 616-4002. Gary*

W. Allen, director, Torts Branch, Aviation/Admiralty Litigation.

Represents the federal government in civil suits concerning the maritime industry, including ships, shipping, and merchant marine personnel. Handles civil cases arising from admiralty incidents and accidents, including oil spills.

Maritime Administration *(Transportation Dept.), 400 7th St. S.W., #7206, MAR-100 20590; (202) 366-5823. Fax, (202) 366-3890. John E. Graykowski, acting administrator. Information, (202) 366-5807. Internet, http://marad.dot.gov.*

Conducts research on shipbuilding and operations; administers subsidy programs; provides financing guarantees and a tax-deferred fund for shipbuilding; operates the U.S. Merchant Marine Academy in Kings Point, N.Y.

Maritime Administration *(Transportation Dept.), Costs and Rates, 400 7th St. S.W., #8117, MAR-560 20590; (202) 366-2324. Fax, (202) 366-7901. Michael P. Ferris, director.*

Calculates rates for commercial American steamship lines to enable them to compete with foreign shipping lines that operate at lower cost. Conducts financial analysis of commercial shipping and calculates guideline rates for carriage of preference cargos.

Maritime Administration *(Transportation Dept.), Maritime Labor, Training, and Safety, 400 7th St. S.W., #7302 20590; (202) 366-5755. Fax, (202) 493-2288. Taylor Jones II, director. Internet, http://marad.dot.gov/labor_training.html.*

Supports the training of merchant marine officers at the U.S. Merchant Marine Academy in Kings Point, N.Y., and at maritime academies in California, Maine, Massachusetts, Michigan, New York, and Texas. Monitors maritime industry labor practices and policies; promotes consonant labor relations and safety practices.

Maritime Administration *(Transportation Dept.), Maritime Subsidy Board, 400 7th St. S.W., #7210, MAR-120 20590; (202) 366-5746. Fax, (202) 366-9206. Joel C. Richard, secretary.*

Administers subsidy contracts for the construction and operation of U.S.-flag ships engaged in foreign trade.

Maritime Administration *(Transportation Dept.), Policy and International Trade, 400 7th St. S.W., #7218, MAR-400 20590; (202) 366-2762. Fax, (202) 366-3746. Bruce Carlton, associate administrator. Internet, http://marad.dot.gov/policy.html.*

Conducts studies and makes policy recommendations to the administrator. Compiles data gathered by foreign maritime representatives on the operating and construction costs of ships; implements bilateral maritime agreements; participates in international maritime policymaking.

Maritime Administration *(Transportation Dept.), Research and Development,* 400 7th St. S.W., #7328, MAR-130 20590; (202) 366-1925. Fax, (202) 366-1922. Paul Mentz, coordinator. Internet, http://marad.dot.gov/ coor_res_dev.html.

Conducts technology assessment activities related to the development and use of water transportation systems for commercial and national security purposes. Makes recommendations concerning future trends in such areas as trade, emerging technologies, fuels, and materials.

Maritime Administration *(Transportation Dept.), Ship Construction,* 400 7th St. S.W., MAR-720 20590; (202) 366-5737. Fax, (202) 366-3954. Edwin Schimler, director.

Works with private industry to develop standardized ship designs and improved shipbuilding techniques and materials.

Maritime Administration *(Transportation Dept.), Ship Financial Assistance and Cargo Preference,* 400 7th St. S.W., #8126, MAR-500 20590; (202) 366-0364. Fax, (202) 366-7901. James J. Zok, associate administrator. Internet, http://marad.dot.gov/aa_financial.html.

Administers ship finance and cargo preference programs, including Capital Construction Funds, Operating Differential Subsidy, Financing Guarantees, and Marine Insurance programs.

Maritime Administration *(Transportation Dept.), Ship Financing,* 400 7th St. S.W., #8122 20590; (202) 366-5744. Fax, (202) 366-7901. Mitchell D. Lax, director.

Provides ship financing guarantees and administers the Capital Construction Fund Program.

Maritime Administration *(Transportation Dept.), Subsidy and Insurance,* 400 7th St. S.W., #8117 20590; (202) 366-2400. Fax, (202) 366-7901. Edmond J. Fitzgerald, director.

Recommends subsidies for ship operation to the Maritime Subsidy Board. Administers war risk insurance.

Navy Dept. *(Defense Dept.), Military Sealift Command,* Washington Navy Yard, Bldg. 210 20398-5100; (202) 685-5001. Fax, (202) 685-5020. Vice Adm. James B. Perkins, commander.

Transports Defense Dept. and other U.S. government cargo by sea; operates ships that maintain supplies for the armed forces and scientific agencies; transports fuels for the Energy Dept.

Surface Transportation Board *(Transportation Dept.),* 1925 K St. N.W. 20423-0001; (202) 565-1500. Fax, (202) 565-9004. Linda J. Morgan, chair; Gus A. Owen, vice chair. Internet, http://www.stb.dot.gov.

Regulates rates for water transportation and intermodal connections in noncontiguous domestic trade (between the mainland and Alaska, Hawaii, or U.S. territories).

U.S. Coast Guard *(Transportation Dept.),* 2100 2nd St. S.W. 20593; (202) 267-2390. Fax, (202) 267-4158. Adm. Robert Kramek, commandant. Information, (202) 267-1587. Internet, http://www.uscg.mil.

Carries out search-and-rescue missions in and around navigable waters and on the high seas; enforces federal laws on the high seas and navigable waters of the United States and its possessions; conducts marine environmental protection programs; administers boating safety programs; inspects and regulates construction, safety, and equipment of merchant marine vessels; establishes and maintains a system of navigation aids; carries out domestic icebreaking activities; maintains a state of military readiness to assist the Navy in time of war or when directed by the president.

U.S. Coast Guard *(Transportation Dept.), Investigations and Analysis,* 2100 2nd St. S.W., #2404, G-MOA 20593; (202) 267-1430. Fax, (202) 267-1416. Capt. Scott P. Cooper, chief.

Handles disciplinary proceedings for merchant marine personnel. Compiles and analyzes records of marine casualties.

U.S. Coast Guard *(Transportation Dept.), Licensing and Manning,* 4200 Wilson Blvd., #510, NMC-4C, Arlington, VA 22203-1804; (703) 235-0018. Fax, (703) 235-5333. Stewart Walker, chief.

Provides guidance to marine inspection efforts and regional examination centers regarding evaluation of personnel qualifications, licensing, certification, shipment, and discharge of merchant mariners. Monitors operation of the Regional Examination Center; evaluates requests for medical waivers, vessel manning scales, and exemptions from citizenship requirements; advises the State Dept. concerning merchant marine personnel procedures abroad.

U.S. Coast Guard *(Transportation Dept.), Strategic Planning and Analysis,* 2100 2nd St. S.W. 20593-0001; (202) 267-2690. Fax, (202) 267-4234. Capt. Joel Whitehead, chief.

Makes five-to-fifteen-year projections on trends in politics, economics, sociology, technology, and society, and how those trends will affect the Coast Guard.

CONGRESS

House Appropriations Committee, *Subcommittee on Commerce, Justice, State, and Judiciary,* H309 Capitol 20515; (202) 225-3351. Harold Rogers, R-Ky., chair; Jim Kulikowski, staff director. Internet, http://www.house. gov/appropriations.

Jurisdiction over legislation to appropriate funds for the Maritime Administration and Federal Maritime Commission.

House Appropriations Committee, *Subcommittee on Energy and Water Development,* 2362 RHOB 20515; (202) 225-3421. Joseph M. McDade, R-Pa., chair; James Ogsbury, staff director. Internet, http://www.house.gov/ appropriations.

Jurisdiction over legislation to appropriate funds for the civil programs of the Army Corps of Engineers.

House Appropriations Committee, *Subcommittee on Transportation,* 2358 RHOB 20515; (202) 225-2141. Frank R. Wolf, R-Va., chair; John T. Blazey, staff director. Internet, http://www.house.gov/appropriations.

Jurisdiction over legislation to appropriate funds for the U.S. Coast Guard, Saint Lawrence Seaway Development Corp., and Panama Canal Commission.

House Government Reform and Oversight Committee, *Subcommittee on National Economic Growth, Natural Resources, and Regulatory Affairs,* B377 RHOB 20515; (202) 225-4407. Fax, (202) 225-2441. David M. McIntosh, R-Ind., chair; Mildred Webber, staff director. Internet, http://www.house.gov/reform.

Oversees operations of the Federal Maritime Commission.

House Science Committee, *Subcommittee on Technology,* 2319 RHOB 20515; (202) 225-8844. Fax, (202) 225-4438. Constance A. Morella, R-Md., chair; Richard Russell, staff director. Internet, http://www.house.gov/ science.

Oversight of research and development activities of the U.S. Coast Guard and the Maritime Administration.

House Transportation and Infrastructure Committee, *Subcommittee on Coast Guard and Maritime Transportation,* 507 Ford Bldg. 20515; (202) 226-3552. Fax, (202) 226-2524. Wayne T. Gilchrest, R-Md., chair; Rebecca Dye, counsel. Internet, http://www.house.gov/ transportation.

Jurisdiction over legislation on most merchant marine matters, including government subsidies and assistance; merchant marine personnel programs; port regulation, safety, and security; and ship and freight regulation and rates. Jurisdiction over legislation on the

maritime safety, marine pollution control and abatement, U.S. Coast Guard, and the Saint Lawrence Seaway (jursidiction shared with Subcommitee on Water Resources and Environment).

House Transportation and Infrastructure Committee, *Subcommittee on Water Resources and Environment,* B376 RHOB 20515; (202) 225-4360. Fax, (202) 226-5435. Sherwood Boehlert, R-N.Y., chair; Ben Grumbles, counsel. Internet, http://www.house.gov/ transportation.

Jurisdiction over legislation on deepwater ports and the Saint Lawrence Seaway, including the Saint Lawrence Seaway Development Corp. (Jurisdiction shared with the Subcommittee on Coast Guard and Maritime Transportation.)

Senate Appropriations Committee, *Subcommittee on Commerce, Justice, State, and Judiciary,* SR-393 20510; (202) 224-7277. Judd Gregg, R-N.H., chair, (202) 224-3324; Vas Alexopoulos, legislative assistant. Chair's fax, (202) 224-4952. Internet, http://www.senate.gov/ ~appropriations.

Jurisdiction over legislation to appropriate funds for the Maritime Administration and the Federal Maritime Commission.

Senate Appropriations Committee, *Subcommittee on Energy and Water Development,* SD-127 20510; (202) 224-7260. Pete V. Domenici, R-N.M., chair; Alex Flint, majority clerk. Internet, http://www.senate.gov/ ~appropriations/energy.

Jurisdiction over legislation to appropriate funds for the civil functions of the Army Corps of Engineers.

Senate Appropriations Committee, *Subcommittee on Transportation,* SD-133 20510; (202) 224-7281. Fax, (202) 224-4401. Richard C. Shelby, R-Ala., chair; Wally Burnett, majority clerk. Internet, http://www.senate. gov/~appropriations.

Jurisdiction over legislation to appropriate funds for the U.S. Coast Guard, Saint Lawrence Seaway Development Corp., and Panama Canal Commission.

Senate Commerce, Science, and Transportation Committee, SD-508 20510; (202) 224-5115. Fax, (202) 224-1259. John McCain, R-Ariz., chair; John Raidt, staff director. Internet, http://www.senate.gov/~commerce.

Oversight of and legislative jurisdiction over the U.S. Coast Guard, the Maritime Administration, maritime safety, and ports, including security and regulation; oversight of the Federal Maritime Commission.

Senate Commerce, Science, and Transportation Committee, *Subcommittee on Oceans and Fisheries,*

SH-428 (mailing address: SD-508, Washington, DC 20510); (202) 224-8172. Fax, (202) 228-0326. Olympia J. Snowe, R-Maine, chair; Clark LeBlanc, professional staffer. Internet, http://www.senate.gov/~commerce.

Studies issues involving deepwater ports (jurisdiction shared with Senate Energy and Natural Resources and Senate Environment and Public Works committees). Studies legislation on the U.S. Coast Guard. (Subcommittee does not report legislation.)

Senate Commerce, Science, and Transportation Committee, *Subcommittee on Surface Transportation and Merchant Marine,* SH-427 20510; (202) 224-4852. Kay Bailey Hutchison, R-Texas, chair; Charlotte Casey, professional staff member. Internet, http://www.senate.gov/~commerce.

Jurisdiction over legislation on Saint Lawrence Seaway and merchant marine matters, including ship and freight regulation and rates, merchant marine personnel programs, and government subsidies and assistance to foreign and U.S. vessels.

Senate Energy and Natural Resources Committee, *Subcommittee on Energy Research, Development, Production, and Regulation,* SD-364 20510; (202) 224-6567. Fax, (202) 228-0302. Don Nickles, R-Okla., chair; David Garman, professional staff member. Internet, http://www.senate.gov/~energy.

Jurisdiction over legislation on deepwater ports (jurisdiction shared with Senate Commerce, Science, and Transportation and Senate Environment and Public Works committees).

Senate Environment and Public Works Committee, *Subcommittee on Transportation and Infrastructure,* SD-410 20510; (202) 224-6176. John W. Warner, R-Va., chair; Dan Corbett, staff contact.

Jurisdiction over legislation authorizing construction, operation, and maintenance of inland waterways and harbors (jurisdiction on deepwater ports beyond three-mile limit shared with Senate Energy and Natural Resources and Senate Commerce, Science, and Transportation committees).

NONPROFIT

AFL-CIO Maritime Committee, 1150 17th St. N.W., #700 20036; (202) 835-0404. Fax, (202) 872-0912. Talmage E. Simpkins, executive director.

Membership: AFL-CIO maritime unions. Provides information on the maritime industry and unions. Interests include seamen's service contracts and pension plans, maritime safety, U.S. merchant marine, and the rights of Panama Canal residents. Monitors legislation and regulations.

American Maritime Congress, 1300 Eye St. N.W., #250W 20005-3314; (202) 842-4900. Fax, (202) 842-3492. Gloria Cataneo Tosi, executive director.

Organization of U.S.-flag carriers engaged in ocean-borne transportation. Conducts research and provides information on the U.S.-flag merchant marine.

Boat Owners Assn. of the United States, 880 S. Pickett St., Alexandria, VA 22304; (703) 461-2864. Fax, (703) 461-2845. Michael Sciulla, vice president, Government Affairs.

Membership: owners of recreational boats. Represents boat-owner interests before the federal government; offers consumer protection and other services to members.

Chamber of Shipping of America, 1730 M St. N.W., #407 20036; (202) 775-4399. Fax, (202) 659-3795. Joseph J. Cox, president.

Represents U.S.-based companies that own, operate or charter oceangoing tankers, container ships, and other merchant vessels engaged in domestic and international trade.

Maritime Institute for Research and Industrial Development, 1775 K St. N.W., #200 20006; (202) 463-6505. Fax, (202) 223-9093. C. James Patti, president. Internet, miraid@worldnet.att.net.

Membership: U.S.-flag ship operators. Promotes the development of the U.S. Merchant Marine. Interests include bilateral shipping agreements, the use of private commercial merchant vessels by the Defense Dept., and enforcement of cargo preference laws for U.S.-flag ships.

National Marine Manufacturers Assn., 1819 L St. N.W., #700 20036; (202) 861-1180. Fax, (202) 861-1181. Jacque Johnson, director, Federal Government Relations.

Membership: recreational marine equipment manufacturers. Promotes boating safety and the development of boating facilities. Serves as liaison with Congress and regulatory agencies. Monitors legislation and regulations. (Headquarters in Chicago.)

Shipbuilders Council of America, 901 N. Washington St., #204, Alexandria, VA 22314; (703) 548-7447. Fax, (703) 518-0276. Penny L. Eastman, president. Internet, http://www.shipbuilders.org.

Membership: commercially focused shipyards that repair and build ships and allied industries and associations. Works to ensure a stable shipbuilding and ship repairing industry in the United States. Promotes the maintenance of a privately owned reserve fleet for times of national emergency. Sponsors lectures; conducts discussions to promote industry consensus and cooperation. Monitors legislation and regulations.

Transportation Institute, *5201 Auth Way, Camp Springs, MD 20746; (301) 423-3335. Fax, (301) 423-0634. James L. Henry, president. Internet, http://www.trans-inst. org.*

Membership: U.S.-flag maritime shipping companies. Conducts research on freight regulation and rates, government subsidies and assistance, domestic and international maritime matters, maritime safety, ports, Saint Lawrence Seaway, shipbuilding, and regulation of shipping.

See also Intermodal Assn. of North America (p. 658)

Maritime Safety

AGENCIES

Federal Communications Commission, *Compliance and Information Bureau, 1919 M St. N.W. 20554; (202) 418-1100. Richard Lee, chief. Toll-free, (888) 225-5322. TDD, (888) 835-5322. 24-hour watch officer, (202) 632-6975. Internet, http://www.fcc.gov/cib.*

Provides technical services to the U.S. Coast Guard for locating ships in distress. Provides policy and program support for maritime radiotelegraph inspection.

National Oceanic and Atmospheric Administration *(Commerce Dept.), National Ocean Service, 1315 East-West Hwy., SSMC3, #6147, Silver Spring, MD 20910-3282; (301) 713-2770. Fax, (301) 713-4019. Frank Maloney, director, Coast Survey. Internet, http://www.nos.noaa.gov.*

Directs programs and conducts research to support fundamental scientific and engineering activities and resource development for safe navigation of the nation's waterways and territorial seas. Prints and distributes nautical charts.

National Response Center *(Transportation Dept.), 2100 2nd St. S.W., #2611 20593; (202) 267-2675. Fax, (202) 267-2165. Cmdr. Syed Qadir, chief. Toll-free hotline, (800) 424-8802. Internet, http://www.nrc.uscg.mil.*

Maintains 24-hour hotline for reporting oil spills or hazardous materials accidents. Notifies appropriate federal officials to reduce the effects of accidents.

National Transportation Safety Board, *Marine Safety, 490 L'Enfant Plaza East S.W., #6313 20594; (202) 314-6450. Fax, (202) 314-6454. Marjorie Murtagh, director.*

Investigates selected marine transportation accidents, including major marine accidents that involve U.S. Coast Guard operations or functions. Determines the facts upon which the board establishes probable cause; makes recommendations on matters pertaining to marine transportation safety and accident prevention.

Occupational Safety and Health Administration *(Labor Dept.), General Industry Compliance, 200 Constitution Ave. N.W., #N3107 20210; (202) 219-8041. Fax, (202) 219-5533. Herbert Washington, director.*

Interprets maritime compliance safety standards for agency field personnel and private employees and employers.

U.S. Coast Guard *(Transportation Dept.), Boating Safety, 2100 2nd St. S.W., G-OPB 20593-0001; (202) 267-1077. Fax, (202) 267-4285. Capt. J. A. Stimatz, chief. Internet, http://www.USCGBoating.org.*

Establishes and enforces safety standards for recreational boats and associated equipment; sets boater education standards; coordinates nationwide public awareness and information programs.

U.S. Coast Guard *(Transportation Dept.), Design and Engineering Standards, 2100 2nd St. S.W., #1218, G-MSE 20593; (202) 267-2967. Fax, (202) 267-4816. Capt. Mark Van Haverbeke, chief.*

Develops standards; responsible for general vessel arrangements, naval architecture, vessel design and construction, and transport of bulk dangerous cargoes. Supports national advisory committees and national professional organizations to achieve industry standards.

U.S. Coast Guard *(Transportation Dept.), Investigations and Analysis, 2100 2nd St. S.W., #2404, G-MOA 20593; (202) 267-1430. Fax, (202) 267-1416. Capt. Scott P. Cooper, chief.*

Investigates accidents involving commercial vessels that result in loss of life, serious injury, or substantial damage.

U.S. Coast Guard *(Transportation Dept.), Marine Safety Center, 400 7th St. S.W., #6302 20590; (202) 366-6480. Fax, (202) 366-3877. Capt. J. G. Lantz, commanding officer.*

Reviews and approves commercial vessel plans and specifications to ensure technical compliance with federal safety and pollution abatement standards.

U.S. Coast Guard *(Transportation Dept.), Marine Safety, Security, and Environmental Protection, 2100 2nd St. S.W., #2408 20593; (202) 267-2200. Fax, (202) 267-4839. Rear Adm. R. C. North, chief. Internet, http://www.uscg.mil/hq/g-m/gmhome.htm.*

Establishes and enforces regulations for port safety and security; environmental protection; vessel safety, inspection, design, documentation, and investigation; licensing of merchant vessel personnel; and shipment of hazardous materials.

U.S. Coast Guard *(Transportation Dept.), Operations Policy Directorate,* 2100 2nd St. S.W. (mailing address: Commandant G-OP, Washington, DC 20593); (202) 267-2267. Fax, (202) 267-4674. Rear Adm. James D. Hull, director.

Administers Long Range and Short Range Aids to Navigation programs; regulates the construction, maintenance, and operation of bridges across U.S. navigable waters. Conducts search-and-rescue and polar and domestic ice-breaking operations. Regulates waterways under U.S. jurisdiction. Operates the Coast Guard Command Center; participates in defense operations; assists with law enforcement/drug interdictions.

NONPROFIT

National Safe Boating Council, 2100 2nd St. S.W. (mailing address: c/o Commandant G-OPB-2, U.S. Coast Guard, Washington, DC 20593); (202) 267-1060. Fax, (202) 267-4285. Jo Calkin, grant manager, (202) 267-0994.

Membership: national organizations that promote recreational boating safety. Conducts annual seminar; works with the U.S. Coast Guard to sponsor activities during National Safe Boating Week.

U.S. Coast Guard Auxiliary, 2100 2nd St. S.W. 20593-0001; (202) 267-1001. Fax, (202) 267-4460. Alan Summy, chief director. Internet, http://www.cgaux.gov.

Volunteer, nonmilitary organization created by Congress to assist the Coast Guard in promoting water safety. Offers public education programs; administers the Courtesy Marine Examination Program, a safety equipment check provided free to the public; works with the Coast Guard and state boating officials to maintain marine safety.

Ports and Waterways

AGENCIES

Army Corps of Engineers *(Defense Dept.), Civil Works,* 20 Massachusetts Ave. N.W. 20314; (202) 761-0099. Fax, (202) 761-8992. Maj. Gen. Russell L. Fuhrman (USA), director. Internet, http://www.usace.army.mil.

Coordinates field offices that oversee harbors, dams, levees, waterways, locks, reservoirs, and other construction projects designed to facilitate transportation and flood control. Major projects include the Mississippi, Missouri, and Ohio Rivers.

Federal Maritime Commission, *Agreements and Information Management,* 800 N. Capitol St. N.W. 20573; (202) 523-5793. Fax, (202) 523-4372. Jeremiah Hospital, chief.

Analyzes agreements between terminal operators and shipping companies for docking facilities.

Maritime Administration *(Transportation Dept.), Inland Waterways and Great Lakes,* 400 7th St. S.W., MAR-115 20590; (202) 366-1718. Fax, (202) 366-3890. John E. Graykowski, deputy administrator.

Coordinates agency policies affecting U.S. inland waterways and the Great Lakes. Works with industry, unions, state and local governments, and other federal agencies; interests include streamlining of regulatory requirements and improved integration of maritime with other modes of transportation.

Maritime Administration *(Transportation Dept.), Port, Intermodal, and Environmental Activities,* 400 7th St. S.W., #7214, MAR-800 20590; (202) 366-4721. Fax, (202) 366-6988. Margaret Blum, associate administrator. Internet, http://marad.dot.gov/aa_port_inter_env.html.

Responsible for direction and administration of port and intermodal transportation development and port readiness for national defense.

Panama Canal Commission, 1825 Eye St. N.W., #1050 20006-5402; (202) 634-6441. Fax, (202) 634-6439. John A. Mills, secretary. Internet, http://www.pananet.com/pancanal.

Independent federal agency that manages, operates, and maintains the Panama Canal and its complementary works, installations, and equipment; provides for the orderly transit of vessels through the canal.

Saint Lawrence Seaway Development Corp. *(Transportation Dept.),* 400 7th St. S.W., #5424 20590; (202) 366-0118. Fax, (202) 366-7147. David G. Sanders, acting administrator. Information, (202) 366-0091. Internet, http://www.dot.gov/slsdc.

Operates and maintains the Saint Lawrence Seaway within U.S. territorial limits; conducts development programs and coordinates activities with its Canadian counterpart.

Tennessee Valley Authority, 1 Massachusetts Ave. N.W., #300 20001; (202) 898-2999. Fax, (202) 898-2998. Vacant, administrative officer, Washington Office. Internet, http://www.tva.gov.

Operates the river control system on the Tennessee River and its tributaries; projects include flood control, navigation development, and multiple-use reservoirs. (Headquarters in Knoxville, Tenn.)

U.S. Coast Guard *(Transportation Dept.),* 2100 2nd St. S.W. 20593; (202) 267-2390. Fax, (202) 267-4158. Adm. Robert Kramek, commandant. Internet, http://www.uscg.mil.

Enforces rules and regulations governing the safety and security of ports and anchorages and the movement of vessels in U.S. waters. Supervises cargo transfer operations, storage, and stowage; conducts harbor patrols and waterfront facility inspections; establishes security zones and monitors vessel movement.

NONPROFIT

American Assn. of Port Authorities, *1010 Duke St., Alexandria, VA 22314; (703) 684-5700. Fax, (703) 684-6321. Kurt J. Nagle, president. Internet, aapa@ix.netcom. com or http://www.aapa-ports.org.*

Membership: port authorities in the Western Hemisphere. Provides technical and economic information on port finance, construction, operation, and security.

American Waterways Operators, *1600 Wilson Blvd., #1000, Arlington, VA 22209; (703) 841-9300. Fax, (703) 841-0389. Thomas Allegretti, president.*

Membership: commercial shipyard owners and operators of barges, tugboats, and towboats on navigable coastal and inland waterways. Acts as liaison with Congress, the U.S. Coast Guard, the Army Corps of Engineers, and the Maritime Administration. Monitors legislation and regulations.

International Longshore and Warehouse Union, *1775 K St. N.W., #200 20006; (202) 463-6265. Fax, (202) 467-4875. Lindsay McLaughlin, legislative director.*

Membership: approximately 45,000 longshore and warehouse personnel. Helps members negotiate pay, benefits, and better working conditions; conduct training programs and workshops. Monitors legislation and regulations. (Headquarters in San Francisco; affiliated with the AFL-CIO.)

International Longshoremen's Assn., *1101 17th St. N.W., #400 20036; (202) 955-6305. Fax, (202) 955-6048. John Bowers Jr., legislative director.*

Membership: approximately 61,000 longshore personnel. Helps members negotiate pay, benefits, and better working conditions; conducts training programs and workshops. Monitors legislation and regulations. (Headquarters in New York; affiliated with the AFL-CIO.)

National Assn. of Waterfront Employers, *2011 Pennsylvania Ave. N.W., #301 20006; (202) 296-2810. Fax, (202) 331-7479. Charles T. Carroll Jr., executive director.*

Membership: private stevedore and marine terminal companies, their subsidiaries, and other waterfront-related employers. Legislative interests include trade, antitrust, insurance, and user-fee issues. Monitors legislation and regulations.

National Waterways Conference, Inc., *1130 17th St. N.W. 20036-4676; (202) 296-4415. Fax, (202) 835-3861. Harry N. Cook, president. Internet, http://www.waterways. org.*

Membership: petroleum, coal, chemical, electric power, building materials, iron and steel, and grain companies; port authorities; water carriers; and other waterways interests. Conducts research on the economics of water transportation; sponsors educational programs on waterways. Monitors legislation and regulations.

Passenger Vessel Assn., *1600 Wilson Blvd., #1000A, Arlington, VA 22209; (703) 807-0100. Fax, (703) 807-0103. John R. Groundwater, executive director. Internet, http://www.p-v-a.com.*

Membership: owners, operators, and suppliers for U.S. and Canadian passenger vessels; and international vessel companies. Interests include dinner and excursion boats, car and passenger ferries, overnight cruise ships, and riverboat casinos. Monitors legislation and regulations.

See also Transportation Institute (p. 670)

🚗 MOTOR VEHICLES

See also Air Pollution (chap. 9); Caucuses (chap. 20); Insurance (chap. 5)

AGENCIES

Federal Highway Administration *(Transportation Dept.), 400 7th St. S.W. 20590; (202) 366-0650. Fax, (202) 366-3244. Kenneth R. Wykle, administrator. Information, (202) 366-0660. Internet, http://www.fhwa.dot.gov.*

Administers federal-aid highway programs with money from the Highway Trust Fund; works to improve highway and motor vehicle safety; coordinates research and development programs on highway and traffic safety, construction, costs, and environmental impact of highway transportation; administers regional and territorial highway building programs and the highway beautification program.

Federal Highway Administration *(Transportation Dept.), Motor Carrier Research and Standards, 400 7th St. S.W., #3107 20590; (202) 366-1790. Fax, (202) 366-8842. Paul L. Brennan, director. Internet, http://www.fhwa. dot.gov/omc/omchome.html.*

Regulates motor vehicle size and weight on federally aided highways; conducts studies on issues relating to motor carrier transportation; promotes uniformity in state and federal motor carrier laws and regulations.

CONGRESS

House Appropriations Committee, *Subcommittee on Transportation,* 2358 RHOB 20515; (202) 225-2141. *Frank R. Wolf, R-Va., chair; John T. Blazey, staff director. Internet, http://www.house.gov/appropriations.*

Jurisdiction over legislation to appropriate funds for the Transportation Dept., including the Federal Highway Administration and the National Highway Traffic Safety Administration.

House Commerce Committee, *Subcommittee on Telecommunications, Trade, and Consumer Protection,* 2125 RHOB 20515; (202) 225-2927. Fax, (202) 225-1919. *W.J. "Billy" Tauzin, R-La., chair; James E. Derderian, staff director. Internet, http://www.house.gov/commerce.*

Jurisdiction over motor vehicle safety legislation and the National Highway Traffic Safety Administration. (Jurisdiction shared with House Transportation and Infrastructure Committee.)

House Science Committee, *Subcommittee on Technology,* 2319 RHOB 20515; (202) 225-8844. Fax, (202) 225-4438. *Constance A. Morella, R-Md., chair; Richard Russell, staff director. Internet, http://www.house.gov/science.*

Special oversight of surface transportation research and development programs of executive branch departments and agencies.

House Transportation and Infrastructure Committee, *Subcommittee on Surface Transportation,* B370A RHOB 20515; (202) 225-6715. Fax, (202) 225-4623. *Tom Petri, R-Wis., chair; Roger Nober, counsel. Internet, http://www.house.gov/transportation.*

Jurisdiction over legislation on regulation of commercial vehicles and interstate surface transportation, including the Federal Highway Administration, National Highway Traffic Safety Administration (jurisdiction shared with House Commerce Committee), Federal Aid to Highways, and highway trust fund programs and activities.

Senate Appropriations Committee, *Subcommittee on Transportation,* SD-133 20510; (202) 224-7281. Fax, (202) 224-4401. *Richard C. Shelby, R-Ala., chair; Wally Burnett, majority clerk. Internet, http://www.senate.gov/ ~appropriations.*

Jurisdiction over legislation to appropriate funds for the Transportation Dept., including the Federal Highway Administration and National Highway Traffic Safety Administration.

Senate Commerce, Science, and Transportation Committee, SD-508 20510; (202) 224-5115. Fax, (202) 224-1259. *John McCain, R-Ariz., chair; John Raidt, staff director. Internet, http://www.senate.gov/~commerce.*

Jurisdiction over motor vehicle safety legislation; oversight of the Surface Transportation Board.

Senate Commerce, Science, and Transportation Committee, *Subcommittee on Surface Transportation and Merchant Marine,* SH-427 20510; (202) 224-4852. *Kay Bailey Hutchison, R-Texas, chair; Charlotte Casey, professional staff member. Internet, http://www.senate.gov/ ~commerce.*

Jurisdiction over legislation on regulation of commercial motor carriers and interstate buses. Oversight of surface transportation research and development, including Federal Highway Administration activities (except federal highway construction).

Senate Environment and Public Works Committee, *Subcommittee on Transportation and Infrastructure,* SD-410 20510; (202) 224-6176. *John W. Warner, R-Va., chair; Dan Corbett, staff contact.*

Jurisdiction over legislation on the Federal Highway Administration, National Highway Traffic Safety Administration, highway trust fund programs, and federal aid to highways.

NONPROFIT

American Assn. of Motor Vehicle Administrators, 4301 Wilson Blvd., #400, Arlington, VA 22203; (703) 522-4200. Fax, (703) 522-1553. *John Strandquist, president. Internet, http://www.aamva.net.*

Membership: officials responsible for administering and enforcing motor vehicle and traffic laws in the United States and Canada. Promotes uniform laws and regulations for vehicle registration, drivers' licenses, and motor carrier services; provides administrative evaluation services for safety equipment.

American Automobile Assn. (AAA), 1440 New York Ave. N.W., #200 20005-2111; (202) 942-2050. Fax, (202) 783-4798. *Steve Hayes, managing director.*

Membership: state and local automobile associations. Provides members with travel services. Interests include all aspects of highway transportation, travel and tourism, safety, drunk driving, economics, federal aid, and legislation that affects motorists. (Headquarters in Heathrow, Fla.)

American Bus Assn., 1100 New York Ave. N.W., #1050 20005-3934; (202) 842-1645. Fax, (202) 842-0850. *Peter J. Pantuso, president. Internet, http://www.buses.org.*

Membership: intercity privately owned bus companies, state associations, travel/tourism businesses, bus manufacturers, and those interested in the bus industry. Monitors legislation and regulations.

American Trucking Assns., *2200 Mill Rd., Alexandria, VA 22314-4677; (703) 838-1700. Fax, (703) 684-4326. Walter B. McCormick, president. Toll-free, (800) 282-5463. Press, (703) 838-1873. Library, (703) 838-1880. Internet, membership@trucking.org or http://www.trucking.org.*

Membership: state trucking associations, individual trucking and motor carrier organizations, and related supply companies. Maintains departments on industrial relations, law, management systems, research, safety, traffic, state laws, taxation, communications, legislation, economics, and engineering. Library open to the public by appointment.

Highway Loss Data Institute, *1005 N. Glebe Rd., #800, Arlington, VA 22201; (703) 247-1600. Fax, (703) 247-1595. Brian O'Neill, president. Internet, http://www.carsafety.org.*

Research organization that gathers, processes, and publishes data on the ways in which insurance losses vary among different kinds of vehicles. (Affiliated with Insurance Institute for Highway Safety.)

International Parking Institute, *701 Kenmore Ave., Fredericksburg, VA 22404-7167 (mailing address: P.O. Box 7167, Fredericksburg, VA 22404-7167); (540) 371-7535. Fax, (540) 371-8022. David Ivey, president. Internet, http://www.parking.org.*

Membership: operators, designers, and builders of parking lots and structures. Provides leadership to the parking industry; supports professional development; works with transportation and related fields.

Interstate Truckload Carriers Conference, *2200 Mill Rd., Alexandria, VA 22314; (703) 838-1950. Fax, (703) 836-6610. Lana R. Batts, president.*

Represents intercity common and contract trucking companies before Congress, federal agencies, courts, and the media.

Motor Freight Carriers Assn., *499 S. Capitol St. S.W. 20003; (202) 554-3060. Fax, (202) 554-3160. Timothy P. Lynch, president. Internet, http://www.mfca.org.*

Represents trucking employers. Negotiates and administers labor contracts with the Teamsters Union.

Motorcycle Industry Council, *1235 Jefferson Davis Hwy., #600, Arlington, VA 22202; (703) 416-0444. Fax, (703) 416-2269. Kathy Van Kleeck, vice president.*

Membership: manufacturers and distributors of motorcycles, mopeds and related parts, accessories, and

equipment. Monitors legislation and regulations. (Headquarters in Irvine, Calif.)

National Assn. of Regulatory Utility Commissioners, *12th St. and Constitution Ave. N.W. (mailing address: P.O. Box 684, Washington, DC 20044-0684); (202) 898-2200. Fax, (202) 898-2213. Peggy Welsh, executive director. Press, (202) 898-2205. Internet, http://www.naruc.org.*

Membership: members of federal, state, municipal, and Canadian regulatory commissions that have jurisdiction over motor and common carriers. Interests include motor carriers.

National Institute for Automotive Service Excellence, *13505 Dulles Technology Dr., #2, Herndon, VA 20171-3421; (703) 713-3800. Fax, (703) 713-0727. Ronald H. Weiner, president. Internet, http://www.asecert.org.*

Administers program for testing and certifying automotive technicians; researches methods to improve technician training.

National Motor Freight Traffic Assn., *2200 Mill Rd., 4th Floor, Alexandria, VA 22314; (703) 838-1810. Fax, (703) 683-1094. Martin E. Foley, executive director. Internet, http://www.erols.com/nmfta.*

Membership: motor carriers of general goods in interstate and intrastate commerce. Publishes *National Motor Freight Classification.*

National Parking Assn., *1112 16th St. N.W., #300 20036; (202) 296-4336. Fax, (202) 331-8523. Barbara O'Dell, executive director. Internet, http://www.npapark.org.*

Membership: parking garage owners, operators, consultants, and university municipalities. Offers information and research services; sponsors seminars and educational programs on garage design and equipment. Monitors legislation and regulations.

National Private Truck Council, *66 Canal Center Plaza, #600, Alexandria, VA 22314; (703) 683-1300. Fax, (703) 683-1217. John A. McQuaid, president. Internet, http://www.nptc.org.*

Membership: manufacturers, producers, distributors, and retail establishments that operate fleets of vehicles incidental to their nontransportation businesses. Interests include truck safety, maintenance, and economics. Supports economic deregulation of the trucking industry and uniformity in state taxation of the industry. Private Management Fleet Institute conducts continuing education, truck research, and certification programs.

NATSO, Inc., *1199 N. Fairfax St., #801, Alexandria, VA (mailing address: P.O. Box 1285, Alexandria, VA 22313-*

1285); (703) 549-2100. Fax, (703) 684-4525. W. Dewey Clower, president. Internet, natsoinc@aol.com or http://www.natso.com.

Membership: travel plaza and truck stop operators and suppliers to the truck stop industry. Provides credit information and educational training programs. Monitors legislation and regulations. Operates the NATSO Foundation, which promotes highway safety.

Natural Gas Vehicle Coalition, *1515 Wilson Blvd., #1030, Arlington, VA 22209; (703) 527-3022. Fax, (703) 527-3025. Richard R. Kolodziej, president. Internet, http://www.ngvc.org.*

Membership: natural gas distributors; pipeline, automobile, and engine manufacturers; environmental groups; research and development organizations; and state and local government agencies. Advocates installation of compressed natural gas fuel stations and development of industry standards. Helps market new natural gas products and equipment.

See also Oil and Natural Gas (chap. 8)

Highways

AGENCIES

Federal Highway Administration *(Transportation Dept.), National Highway Institute, 901 N. Stuart St., #300, Arlington, VA 22203; (703) 235-0500. Fax, (703) 235-0593. Moges Ayele, director. Internet, http://www.nhi.fhwa.dot.gov.*

Develops and administers, in cooperation with state highway departments, training programs for agency, state, and local highway department employees.

Federal Highway Administration *(Transportation Dept.), Policy, 400 7th St. S.W., #3317 20590; (202) 366-0585. Fax, (202) 366-9626. Vacant, associate administrator.*

Develops policy and administers the Federal Highway Administration's international programs. Conducts policy studies and legislation analyses; makes recommendations; compiles and reviews highway-related data. Represents the administration at international conferences; administers foreign assistance programs.

Federal Highway Administration *(Transportation Dept.), Program Development, 400 7th St. S.W., #3212 20590; (202) 366-0371. Fax, (202) 366-3043. Tom Ptak, associate administrator.*

Provides guidance and oversight for planning, design, construction, and maintenance operations relating to federal aid, direct federal construction, environmental analysis and planning, right-of-way issues, and other

highway programs; establishes design guidelines and specifications for highways built with federal funds.

Federal Highway Administration *(Transportation Dept.), Real Estate Services, 400 7th St. S.W. 20590; (202) 366-0142. Fax, (202) 366-3780. Cynthia Burbank, director.*

Funds and oversees acquisition of land by states for federally assisted highways; provides financial assistance to relocate people and businesses forced to move by highway construction; cooperates in administering program for the use of air rights in connection with federally aided highways; administers Highway Beautification Act to control billboards and junkyards along interstate and federally aided primary highways.

Federal Highway Administration *(Transportation Dept.), Research and Development, 6300 Georgetown Pike, McLean, VA 22101; (703) 285-2051. Fax, (703) 285-2379. Robert Betsole, associate administrator.*

Conducts highway research and development programs; studies safety, location, design, construction, operation, and maintenance of highways; cooperates with state and local highway departments in utilizing results of research.

U.S. Coast Guard *(Transportation Dept.), 2100 2nd St. S.W. 20593; (202) 267-2390. Fax, (202) 267-4158. Adm. Robert Kramek, commandant. Information, (202) 267-1587. Internet, http://www.uscg.mil.*

Regulates the construction, maintenance, and operation of bridges across U.S. navigable waters.

NONPROFIT

American Assn. of State Highway and Transportation Officials, *444 N. Capitol St. N.W., #249 20001; (202) 624-5800. Fax, (202) 624-5806. Francis B. Francois, executive director. Internet, http://www.aashto.org.*

Membership: the Federal Highway Administration and transportation departments of the states, District of Columbia, Guam, and Puerto Rico. Maintains committees on transportation planning, finance, maintenance, safety, and construction.

American Road and Transportation Builders Assn., *1010 Massachusetts Ave. N.W., 6th Floor 20001; (202) 289-4434. Fax, (202) 289-4435. T. Peter Ruane, president. Internet, artba@artba.com or http://www.artba-hq.org.*

Membership: highway and transportation contractors; federal, state, and local engineers and officials; construction equipment manufacturers and distributors; and others interested in the transportation construction industry. Serves as liaison with government; provides information on highway engineering and construction developments.

Intelligent Transportation Society of America, *400 Virginia Ave. S.W., #800 20024-2730; (202) 484-4847. Fax, (202) 484-3483. James Constantino, president. Publications, (202) 484-4540. Internet, http://www.itsa.org.*

Advocates application of electronic, computer, and communications technology to make surface transportation more efficient. Coordinates development and implementation of intelligent transportation systems.

International Bridge, Tunnel, and Turnpike Assn., *2120 L St. N.W., #305 20037-1527; (202) 659-4620. Fax, (202) 659-0500. Neil D. Schuster, executive director. Internet, ibtta@ibtta.org or http://www.ibtta.org.*

Membership: public and private operators of toll facilities and associated industries. Conducts research; compiles statistics.

International Road Federation, *2600 Virginia Ave. N.W., #208 20037; (202) 338-4641. Fax, (202) 338-8104. Richard B. Robertson, director general. Internet, info@ irfnet.org or http://www.irfnet.org.*

Membership: road associations, automobile construction, and related industries. Administers fellowship program for foreign engineering students to study at U.S. schools. Maintains interest in roads and highways worldwide.

Road Information Program, *1200 18th St. N.W., #314 20036; (202) 466-6706. Fax, (202) 785-4722. William M. Wilkins, executive director. Internet, trip@novanetwork. com or http://www.tripnet.org.*

Organization of transportation specialists; conducts research on economic and technical transportation issues; promotes consumer awareness of the condition of the national road and bridge system.

Manufacturing and Sales

AGENCIES

International Trade Administration, *Automotive Affairs,* *14th St. and Constitution Ave. N.W., #4036 20230; (202) 482-0554. Fax, (202) 482-0784. Henry Misisco, director. Internet, http://www.ita.doc.gov/auto.*

Promotes the export of U.S. automotive products; analyzes auto industry data; seeks to secure a favorable position for the U.S. auto industry in global markets.

NONPROFIT

American Automobile Manufacturers Assn., *1401 H St. N.W., #900 20005; (202) 326-5500. Fax, (202) 326-*5567. Andrew H. Card Jr., president. Press, (202) 326-5538. Internet, http://www.aama.com.*

Membership: domestic manufacturers of passenger and commercial cars for highway use.

American Automotive Leasing Assn., *700 13th St. N.W., #350 20005; (202) 393-7292. Fax, (202) 393-7293. Mary T. Tavenner, executive director. Internet, aala@ bolandmadigan.com.*

Membership: automotive commercial fleet leasing and management companies. Monitors legislation and regulations.

American Car Rental Assn., *1225 Eye St. N.W., #500 20005; (202) 682-4778. Fax, (202) 789-4512. Jan M. Armstrong, executive vice president.*

Membership: companies involved in the renting of cars. Acts as liaison with legislative bodies and regulatory agencies. Maintains information clearinghouse.

American International Automobile Dealers Assn., *99 Canal Center Plaza, #500, Alexandria, VA 22314; (703) 519-7800. Fax, (703) 519-7810. Walter E. Huizenga, president. Internet, http://www.aiada.org.*

Promotes a free market for international nameplate automobiles in the United States. Monitors legislation and regulations.

American Retreaders Assn., *1707 Pepper Tree Court, Bowie, MD 20721; (301) 577-5040. Fax, (301) 731-0039. Roy Littlefield, director, Government Affairs.*

Membership: manufacturers, distributors, and retailers of retreaded tires. Interests include environmental and small-business issues and quality control in the industry. Promotes government procurement of retreaded tires. Monitors legislation and regulations. (Headquarters in Louisville, Ky.)

Assn. of International Automobile Manufacturers, *1001 N. 19th St., #1200, Arlington, VA 22209; (703) 525-7788. Fax, (703) 525-8817. Philip A. Hutchinson Jr., president. Internet, http://www.aiam.org.*

Membership: importers of cars and automotive equipment. Serves as an information clearinghouse on import regulations at the state and federal levels.

Automotive Parts and Accessories Assn., *4600 East-West Hwy., #300, Bethesda, MD 20814; (301) 654-6664. Fax, (301) 654-3299. Alfred L. Gaspar, president. Internet, http://www.apaa.org.*

Membership: manufacturers, retailers, and distributors in the automotive aftermarket industry, which involves service of a vehicle after it leaves the dealership. Offers educational programs, conducts research, and provides members with technical and international trade services; acts as liaison with government; sponsors annual marketing conference and trade shows.

Automotive Parts Rebuilders Assn., *4401 Fair Lakes Court, #210, Fairfax, VA 22033; (703) 968-2772. Fax, (703) 968-2878. William C. Gager, president. Internet, mail@apra.org or http://www.apra.org.*

Membership: rebuilders of automotive parts. Conducts educational programs on transmission, brake, clutch, water pump, air conditioning, electrical parts, heavy duty brake, and carburetor rebuilding.

Automotive Recyclers Assn., *3975 Fair Ridge Dr., #20N, Fairfax, VA 22033-2924; (703) 385-1001. Fax, (703) 385-1494. William P. Steinkuller, executive vice president. Internet, http://www.autorecyc.org.*

Membership: retail and wholesale firms selling recycled auto and truck parts. Works to increase the efficiency of businesses in the automotive recycling industry. Cooperates with public and private agencies to encourage further automotive recycling efforts.

Electronic Industries Assn., *2500 Wilson Blvd., #400, Arlington, VA 22201-3834; (703) 907-7500. Fax, (703) 907-7501. Peter F. McCloskey, president. Internet, http://www.eia.org.*

Membership: manufacturers, dealers, installers, and distributors of consumer electronics products. Provides consumer information and data on industry trends; advocates an open market. Monitors legislation and regulations.

Japan Automobile Manufacturers Assn., *1050 17th St. N.W., #410 20036; (202) 296-8537. Fax, (202) 872-1212. William C. Duncan, general director, Washington Office. Internet, http://www.japanauto.com.*

Membership: Japanese motor vehicle manufacturers. Interests include energy, market, trade, and environmental issues. (Headquarters in Tokyo.)

National Automobile Dealers Assn., *8400 Westpark Dr., McLean, VA 22102-3591; (703) 821-7000. Fax, (703) 821-7075. Frank E. McCarthy, president. Internet, nada@nadanet.com or http://www.nadanet.com.*

Membership: domestic and imported franchised new car and truck dealers. Publishes the *National Automobile Dealers Used Car Guide* (Blue Book).

Recreation Vehicle Dealers Assn. of North America, *3930 University Dr., Fairfax, VA 22030-2515; (703) 591-7130. Fax, (703) 591-0734. Michael A. Molino, president. Toll-free, (800) 336-0355. Internet, rvda@aol.com or http://www.rvda.org.*

Serves as liaison between the recreation vehicle industry and government; interests include government regulation of safety, trade, warranty, and franchising; provides members with educational services; works to improve service standards for consumers.

Recreation Vehicle Industry Assn., *1896 Preston White Dr., Reston, VA (mailing address: P.O. Box 2999, Reston, VA 20195-0999); (703) 620-6003. Fax, (703) 620-5071. David J. Humphreys, president. Internet, rvia@rvia.org or http://www.rvamerica.com.*

Membership: manufacturers of recreation vehicles and their suppliers. Compiles shipment statistics and other technical data; provides consumers and the media with information on the industry. Assists members' compliance with American National Standards Institute requirements for recreation vehicles. Monitors legislation and regulations.

Tire Assn. of North America, *11921 Freedom Dr., #550, Reston, VA 20190; (703) 736-8082. Fax, (703) 904-4339. Dave Poisson, executive vice president.*

Membership: independent tire dealers and retreaders. Conducts seminars and market research. Monitors federal and state legislation and regulations.

Truck Renting and Leasing Assn., *1725 Duke St., #600, Alexandria, VA 22314-3457; (703) 299-9120. Fax, (703) 299-9115. J. Michael Payne, president.*

Membership: truck renting and leasing companies and system suppliers to the industry. Acts as liaison with legislative bodies and regulatory agencies. Interests include federal motor carrier safety issues, highway funding, operating taxes and registration fees at the state level, and uniformity of state taxes.

Truck Trailer Manufacturers Assn., *1020 Princess St., Alexandria, VA 22314; (703) 549-3010. Fax, (703) 549-3014. Richard P. Bowling, president.*

Membership: truck trailer manufacturing and supply companies. Serves as liaison between its members and government agencies; works to improve safety standards and industry efficiency.

Union of Needletrades Industrial and Textile Employees (UNITE), *888 16th St. N.W., #303 20006; (202) 347-7417. Fax, (202) 347-0708. Jay Mazur, president. Internet, unite@bellatlantic.net or http://www.unite.org.*

Membership: approximately 285,000 workers in basic apparel and textiles, millinery, shoe, laundry, retail, and related industries; and in auto parts and auto supply. Assists members with contract negotiation and grievances; conducts training programs and workshops.

Monitors legislation and regulations. (Headquarters in New York; affiliated with the AFL-CIO.)

United Auto Workers, *1757 N St. N.W. 20036; (202) 828-8500. Fax, (202) 293-3457. Steven P. Yokich, president. Toll-free, (800) 243-8829; in Canada, (800) 387-0538. Internet, FAQs@www.uaw.org or http://www.uaw.org.*

Membership: approximately 775,000 active and 500,000 retired North America workers in aerospace, automotive, defense, manufacturing, steel, technical, and other industries. Assists members with contract negotiation and grievances; conducts training programs and workshops. Monitors legislation and regulations. (Headquarters in Detroit; affiliated with the AFL-CIO.)

Traffic Safety

See also Beverages (chap. 2)

AGENCIES

Federal Highway Administration *(Transportation Dept.), Highway Safety, 400 7th St. S.W., #3414 20590; (202) 366-2171. Fax, (202) 366-2249. Michael Trentacoste, director. Internet, http://www.ohs.fhwa.dot.gov.*

Develops roadway safety standards, including standards for traffic control systems and devices. Administers program to make safety improvements to highways.

Federal Highway Administration *(Transportation Dept.), Motor Carrier Field Operations, 400 7th St. S.W., #3103 20590; (202) 366-2952. Fax, (202) 366-7298. Clinton Magby, director.*

Assigns safety fitness ratings based on motor carrier safety data. Monitors the federal and state Motor Carrier Safety Assistance programs to improve commercial vehicle safety on U.S. highways.

Federal Highway Administration *(Transportation Dept.), Motor Carrier Research and Standards, 400 7th St. S.W., #3107 20590; (202) 366-1790. Fax, (202) 366-8842. Paul L. Brennan, director. Internet, http://www.fhwa. dot.gov/omc/omchome.html.*

Interprets and disseminates national safety regulations regarding commercial drivers' qualifications, maximum hours of service, accident reporting, and transportation of hazardous materials. Sets minimum levels of financial responsibility for trucks and buses. Responsible for Commercial Driver's License Information Program.

Federal Highway Administration *(Transportation Dept.), Traffic Management and Intelligent Transportation Systems Applications, 400 7th St. S.W., #3401, HTV-1 20590; (202) 366-0372. Fax, (202) 366-8518. Susan B. Lauffer, director.*

Fosters the efficient operation of streets and highways. Facilitates the deployment of transportation management and traveller information ITS technologies.

National Highway Traffic Safety Administration *(Transportation Dept.), 400 7th St. S.W., #5220 20590; (202) 366-1836. Fax, (202) 366-2106. Ricardo Martinez, administrator. Information, (202) 366-9550. Toll-free 24-hour hotline, (800) 424-9393; in Washington, (202) 366-0123. Internet, http://www.nhtsa.dot.gov.*

Implements motor vehicle safety programs; issues federal motor vehicle safety standards; conducts testing programs to determine compliance with these standards; funds local and state motor vehicle and driver safety programs; conducts research on motor vehicle development, equipment, and auto and traffic safety. The Auto Safety Hotline provides safety information and handles consumer problems and complaints involving safety-related defects.

National Highway Traffic Safety Administration *(Transportation Dept.), Motor Vehicle Safety Research Advisory Committee, 400 7th St. S.W. 20590; (202) 366-1537. Fax, (202) 366-5930. Raymond Owings, acting chair.*

Serves as an independent source of ideas for motor vehicle safety research; provides the National Highway Traffic Safety Administration with information and recommendations.

National Highway Traffic Safety Administration *(Transportation Dept.), National Driver Register, 400 7th St. S.W., #6124 20590; (202) 366-4800. Fax, (202) 366-2746. Bill Holden, chief; Cheryl Schuler, committee management coordinator.*

Maintains and operates the National Driver Register, a program in which states exchange information on motor vehicle driving records to ensure that drivers with suspended licenses in one state cannot obtain licenses in any other state.

National Transportation Safety Board, *Highway Safety, 490 L'Enfant Plaza East S.W., HS-1 20594; (202) 314-6440. Fax, (202) 314-6482. Joseph Osterman, director.*

In cooperation with states, investigates selected highway transportation accidents to compile the facts upon which the board determines probable cause; works to prevent similar recurrences; makes recommendations on matters pertaining to highway safety and accident prevention.

NONPROFIT

AAA Foundation for Traffic Safety, *1440 New York Ave. N.W., #201 20005; (202) 638-5944. Fax, (202) 638-*

5943. David K. Willis, president. Internet, http://www. aaafts.org/aaa.

Sponsors research on traffic safety issues; supplies traffic safety educational materials to elementary and secondary schools, commercial driving schools, and programs for older drivers.

Advocates for Highway and Auto Safety, *750 1st St. N.E., #901 20002; (202) 408-1711. Fax, (202) 408-1699. Judith Lee Stone, president. Internet, http://www. saferoads.org.*

Coalition of insurers, citizens' groups, and public health and safety organizations. Advocates public policy designed to reduce deaths, injuries, and economic costs associated with motor vehicle crashes and fraud and theft involving motor vehicles. Interests include safety belts and child safety seats, air bags, drunk driving abuse, motorcycle helmets, vehicle crashworthiness, and speed limits. Monitors legislation and regulations.

American Highway Users Alliance, *1776 Massachusetts Ave. N.W., #500 20036; (202) 857-1200. Fax, (202) 857-1220. William D. Fay, president. Internet, http:// www.highways.org.*

Membership: companies and associations representing major industry and highway user groups. Develops information, analyzes public policy, and advocates legislation to improve roadway safety and efficiency and to increase the mobility of the American public. (Affiliated with the Roadway Safety Foundation.)

American Trucking Assns., *Safety, 2200 Mill Rd., Alexandria, VA 22314; (703) 838-1847. Fax, (703) 683-1934. Joel Dandrea, vice president. Internet, http://www. truckline.com.*

Membership: state trucking associations, individual trucking and motor carrier organizations, and related supply companies. Provides information on safety for the trucking industry. Develops safety training programs for motor carriers and drivers.

Center for Auto Safety, *2001 S St. N.W., #410 20009; (202) 328-7700. Clarence M. Ditlow III, executive director. Internet, http://www.essential.org/orgs/cas.*

Public interest group. Receives consumer complaints against auto manufacturers; monitors government agencies that enforce auto safety and fuel economy rules.

Commercial Vehicle Safety Alliance, *5430 Grosvenor Lane, #130, Bethesda, MD 20814; (301) 564-1623. Fax, (301) 564-0588. William R. Fiste, executive director. Internet, cvsahq@aol.com or http://www.cvsa.org.*

Membership: U.S., Canadian, and Mexican officials responsible for administering and enforcing commercial motor carrier safety laws. Works to increase on-highway inspections, prevent duplication of inspections, improve the safety of equipment operated on highways, and improve compliance with hazardous materials transportation regulations.

Institute of Transportation Engineers, *525 School St. S.W., #410 20024-2797; (202) 554-8050. Fax, (202) 863-5486. Thomas W. Brahms, executive director. Internet, http://www.ite.org.*

Membership: international professional transportation engineers. Interests include safe and efficient surface transportation; provides professional and scientific information on transportation standards and recommended practices.

Insurance Institute for Highway Safety, *1005 N. Glebe Rd., Arlington, VA 22201; (703) 247-1500. Fax, (703) 247-1678. Brian O'Neill, president. Internet, http:// highwaysafety.org.*

Membership: property and casualty insurance associations and individual insurance companies. Conducts research and provides data on highway safety; seeks ways to reduce losses from vehicle crashes. (Affiliated with Highway Loss Data Institute.)

Mothers Against Drunk Driving (MADD), *1001 G St. N.W., #400 East 20001; (202) 638-3735. Fax, (202) 638-3516. Tom Howarth, Washington contact. Internet, peyser@ix.netcom.com.*

Works to increase public awareness of the problem of drunk driving; advocates strict enforcement of drunk driving laws; operates sobriety checkpoints; supports victims of drunk driving offenses. Monitors legislation and regulations. (Headquarters in Irving, Texas.)

National Assn. of Governors' Highway Safety Representatives, *750 1st St. N.E., #720 20002-4241; (202) 789-0942. Fax, (202) 789-0946. Barbara L. Harsha, executive director. Internet, naghsr@naghsr.org or http://www. naghsr.org.*

Membership: state officials who manage highway safety programs. Maintains information clearinghouse on state highway safety programs; interprets technical data concerning highway safety. Represents the states in policy debates on national highway safety issues.

National Commission Against Drunk Driving, *1900 L St. N.W., #705 20036; (202) 452-6004. Fax, (202) 223-7012. Terrance Schiavone, president. Internet, http:// www.ncadd.com.*

Works to increase public awareness of the problem of drunk and impaired drivers, especially repeat offenders. Administers work site traffic safety programs for corporate managers. Monitors the implementation of recommendations made by the Presidential Commission Against Drunk Driving.

National Crash Analysis Center *(George Washington University), 20101 Academic Way, Ashburn, VA 20147; (703) 729-8361. Fax, (703) 729-8359. Nabih E. Bedewi, director. Internet, http://gwuva.gwu.edu/ncac.*

Conducts advanced research on transportation safety. Serves as a resource for the transportation research community on all Federal Highway Administration and National Highway Traffic Safety Administration crash test films and documentation. Research interests include biomechanics, crash-related injury, vehicle dynamics, and vehicle-to-object analysis.

National Safety Council, *1019 19th St. N.W., #401 20036-5105; (202) 293-2270. Fax, (202) 293-0032. Jane S. Roemer, executive director, Public Policy. Internet, ehc@ cais.com or http://www.nsc.org.*

Chartered by Congress. Conducts research and provides educational and informational services on motor vehicle crash prevention; promotes policies to reduce accidental deaths and injuries. Monitors legislation and regulations. (Headquarters in Itasca, Ill.)

National School Transportation Assn., *6213 Old Keene Mill Court, Springfield, VA (mailing address: P.O. Box 2639, Springfield, VA 22152-2639); (703) 644-0700. Fax, (703) 644-9385. Karen Finkel, executive director. Internet, http://www.schooltrans.com.*

Membership: private owners who operate school buses on contract, bus manufacturers, and allied companies. Primary area of interest and research is school bus safety.

Roadway Safety Foundation, *1776 Massachusetts Ave. N.W., #500 20036; (202) 857-1200. Fax, (202) 857-1220. William D. Fay, president.*

Conducts highway safety programs to reduce automobile-related accidents and deaths. (Affiliated with American Highway Users Alliance.)

Tire Industry Safety Council, *1400 K St. N.W., #900 20005; (202) 783-1022. Fax, (202) 783-3512. Kristen Udowitz, director. Internet, kristen@tmn.com or http:// www.tisc.org.*

Membership: American tire manufacturers. Provides consumers with information on tire care and safety.

United Motorcoach Assn., *113 S. West St., 4th Floor, Alexandria, VA 22314; (703) 838-2929. Fax, (703) 838-2950. Stephen Sprague, interim executive director. Internet, http://www.uma.org.*

Provides information, offers technical assistance, conducts research, and monitors legislation. Interests include insurance, safety programs, and credit.

See also NATSO, Inc. (p. 674)

🚆 RAIL TRANSPORTATION

AGENCIES

Federal Railroad Administration *(Transportation Dept.), 400 7th St. S.W. 20590; (202) 632-3114. Fax, (202) 632-3700. Jolene M. Molitoris, administrator. Information, (202) 632-3123. Internet, http://www.fra.dot.gov.*

Develops national rail policies; enforces rail safety laws; administers financial assistance programs available to states and the rail industry; conducts research and development on improved rail safety.

Federal Railroad Administration *(Transportation Dept.), Policy and Program Development, 1120 Vermont Ave. N.W., 7th Floor (mailing address: 400 7th St. S.W, #15, Washington, DC 20590); (202) 632-3131. Fax, (202) 632-3705. Charles White, associate administrator.*

Plans, coordinates, and administers activities related to railroad economics, finance, traffic and network analysis, labor management, and transportation planning, as well as intermodal, environmental, emergency response, and international programs.

Federal Railroad Administration *(Transportation Dept.), Railroad Development, 1120 Vermont Ave. N.W., 6th Floor (mailing address: 400 7th St. S.W., MS-20, Washington, DC 20590); (202) 632-3281. Fax, (202) 632-3855. James T. McQueen, associate administrator.*

Administers federal assistance programs for national, regional, and local rail services, including freight service assistance, service continuation, and passenger service. Conducts research and development on new rail technologies.

Federal Railroad Administration *(Transportation Dept.), Safety, 1120 Vermont Ave. N.W., 6th Floor (mailing address: 400 7th St. S.W., #25, Washington, DC 20590); (202) 632-3333. Fax, (202) 632-3877. George Gavalla, acting associate administrator. Internet, http://www.fra.dot. gov/safindex.htm.*

Administers and enforces federal laws and regulations that promote railroad safety, including track maintenance, inspection and equipment standards, operating practices, and transportation of explosives and other hazardous materials. Conducts inspections and reports on railroad equipment facilities and accidents.

National Mediation Board, *1301 K St. N.W., #250E 20572; (202) 523-5920. Fax, (202) 523-2179. Kenneth B. Hipp, chair. Information, (202) 523-5335. TDD, (202) 523-8560.*

Mediates labor disputes in the railroad industry; determines and certifies labor representatives in the industry.

National Railroad Passenger Corp. (Amtrak), *60 Massachusetts Ave. N.E. 20002; (202) 906-3960. Fax, (202) 906-2850. George D. Warrington, acting president. Information, (202) 906-3000. Press, (202) 906-3860. Consumer relations/complaints, (202) 906-2121; travel and ticket information, (800) 872-7245. Internet, http://www. amtrak.com.*

Quasi-public corporation created by the Rail Passenger Service Act of 1970 to improve and develop intercity passenger rail service.

National Transportation Safety Board, *Railroad Safety, 490 L'Enfant Plaza East S.W. 20594; (202) 314-6430. Fax, (202) 314-6497. Robert Lauby, director.*

Investigates passenger train accidents, including rapid rail transit and rail commuter systems, and freight rail accidents with substantial damage to determine probable cause; investigates all employee and passenger fatalities; makes recommendations on rail transportation safety and accident prevention.

Railroad Retirement Board, *Legislative Affairs, 1310 G St. N.W., #500 20005; (202) 272-7742. Fax, (202) 272-7728. Marian Powers Gibson, director.*

Assists congressional offices with inquiries on retirement, spouse, survivor, and unemployment benefits for railroad employees and retirees. Assists with legislation. (Headquarters in Chicago.)

Surface Transportation Board *(Transportation Dept.), 1925 K St. N.W. 20423-0001; (202) 565-1500. Fax, (202) 565-9004. Linda J. Morgan, chair; Gus A. Owen, vice chair. Internet, http://www.stb.dot.gov.*

Regulates rail rate disputes, railroad consolidations, rail line construction proposals, line abandonments, rail car service, and motor carrier undercharge cases.

Surface Transportation Board *(Transportation Dept.), Congressional and Public Services, 1925 K St. N.W. 20423-0001; (202) 565-1592. Fax, (202) 565-9016. Dan King, director.*

Assists small-business owners and transportation firms in filing protests on rates and filing for new operating authority or extensions for rail carriers. Provides information on how to obtain service where there is none.

U.S. Coast Guard *(Transportation Dept.), 2100 2nd St. S.W. 20593; (202) 267-2390. Fax, (202) 267-4158. Adm. Robert Kramek, commandant. Information, (202) 267-1587. Internet, http://www.uscg.mil.*

Regulates the construction, maintenance, and operation of bridges across U.S. navigable waters, including railway bridges.

CONGRESS

House Appropriations Committee, *Subcommittee on Transportation, 2358 RHOB 20515; (202) 225-2141. Frank R. Wolf, R-Va., chair; John T. Blazey, staff director. Internet, http://www.house.gov/appropriations.*

Jurisdiction over legislation to appropriate funds for the Federal Railroad Administration, National Railroad Passenger Corp. (Amtrak), and Surface Transportation Board.

House Government Reform and Oversight Committee, *Subcommittee on Government Management, Information, and Technology, B373 RHOB 20515; (202) 225-5147. Steve Horn, R-Calif., chair; J. Russell George, staff director. Internet, http://www.house.gov/cho.*

Oversees operations of the Federal Railroad Administration, Surface Transportation Board, and National Railroad Passenger Corp. (Amtrak).

House Transportation and Infrastructure Committee, *Subcommittee on Railroads, B376 RHOB 20515; (202) 226-0727. Fax, (202) 226-3475. Vacant, chair; Glenn Scammel, counsel.*

Jurisdiction over railroad legislation, including railroad labor and retirement. Oversees operations of the Federal Railroad Administration, the Surface Transportation Board (jurisdiction shared with Subcommittee on Surface Transportation), and the National Railroad Passenger Corp. (Amtrak).

House Transportation and Infrastructure Committee, *Subcommittee on Surface Transportation, B370A RHOB 20515; (202) 225-6715. Fax, (202) 225-4623. Tom Petri, R-Wis., chair; Roger Nober, counsel. Internet, http://www.house.gov/transportation.*

Oversees operations of the Surface Transportation Board (jurisdiction shared with Subcommittee on Railroads.)

Senate Appropriations Committee, *Subcommittee on Transportation, SD-133 20510; (202) 224-7281. Fax, (202) 224-4401. Richard C. Shelby, R-Ala., chair; Wally Burnett, majority clerk. Internet, http://www.senate.gov/ ~appropriations.*

Jurisdiction over legislation to appropriate funds for the Federal Railroad Administration, the National Railroad Passenger Corp. (Amtrak), and the Surface Transportation Board.

Senate Commerce, Science, and Transportation Committee, *Subcommittee on Surface Transportation and Merchant Marine, SH-427 20510; (202) 224-4852. Kay Bailey Hutchison, R-Texas, chair; Charlotte Casey, professional staff member. Internet, http://www.senate.gov/~commerce.*

Jurisdiction over railroad legislation (except railroad labor and retirement); oversees the Federal Railroad Administration, Surface Transportation Board, and National Railroad Passenger Corp. (Amtrak).

Senate Labor and Human Resources Committee, *SD-428 20510; (202) 224-5375. Fax, (202) 224-6510. James M. Jeffords, R-Vt., chair; Mark Powden, staff director. Internet, http://www.senate.gov/~labor.*

Jurisdiction over legislation on railroad labor and retirement.

NONPROFIT

American Short Line Railroad Assn., *1120 G St. N.W., #520 20005-3889; (202) 628-4500. Fax, (202) 628-6430. William E. Loftus, president. Internet, http://www.aslrra.org.*

Membership: independently owned short line railroad systems. Assists members with technical and legal questions; compiles information on laws, regulations, and other matters affecting the industry.

Assn. of American Railroads, *50 F St. N.W., 4th Floor 20001; (202) 639-2100. Fax, (202) 639-2558. M.B. Oglesby Jr., president. Press, (202) 639-2555. Library, (202) 639-2333. Internet, http://www.aar.org.*

Provides information on freight railroad operations, safety and maintenance, economics and finance, management, and law and legislation; conducts research; issues statistical reports. Library open to the public by appointment.

Brotherhood of Maintenance of Way Employees, *10 G St. N.E., #460 20002; (202) 638-2135. Fax, (202) 737-3085. Mac A. Fleming, president. Internet, http://www.bmwe.org.*

Membership: rail industry workers and others. Assists members with contract negotiation and grievances; conducts training programs and workshops. Monitors legislation and regulations. (Headquarters in Southfield, Mich.; affiliated with the AFL-CIO.)

National Assn. of Railroad Passengers, *900 2nd St. N.E., #308 20002-3557; (202) 408-8362. Fax, (202) 408-8287. Ross Capon, executive director. Internet, narp@worldweb.net.*

Consumer organization. Works to expand and improve U.S. intercity and commuter rail passenger service, increase federal funds for mass transit, ensure fair treatment for rail freight transportation, and address environmental concerns pertaining to mass transit. Opposes subsidies for intercity trucking; works with Amtrak on scheduling, new services, fares, and advertising.

National Assn. of Regulatory Utility Commissioners, *12th St. and Constitution Ave. N.W. (mailing address: P.O. Box 684, Washington, DC 20044-0684); (202) 898-2200. Fax, (202) 898-2213. Peggy Welsh, executive director. Press, (202) 898-2205. Internet, http://www.naruc.org.*

Membership: members of federal, state, municipal, and Canadian regulatory commissions that have jurisdiction over motor and common carriers. Interests include railroads.

National Railway Labor Conference, *1901 L St. N.W., #500 20036; (202) 862-7200. Fax, (202) 862-7230. Robert F. Allen, chair.*

Assists member railroad lines with labor matters; negotiates with railroad labor representatives.

Railway Progress Institute, *700 N. Fairfax St., #601, Alexandria, VA 22314; (703) 836-2332. Fax, (703) 548-0058. Robert A. Matthews, president. Internet, http://www.rpi.org.*

Membership: railroad and rail rapid transit suppliers. Conducts research on safety and new technology; monitors legislation.

Transportation Communications International Union, *3 Research Pl., Rockville, MD 20850; (301) 948-4910. Fax, (301) 948-1369. Robert A. Scardelletti, president.*

Membership: approximately 120,000 railway workers. Assists members with contract negotiation and grievances; conducts training programs and workshops. Monitors legislation and regulations. (Affiliated with the AFL-CIO and Canadian Labour Congress.)

See also Intermodal Assn. of North America (p. 658)

🚈 TRANSIT SYSTEMS

AGENCIES

Federal Transit Administration *(Transportation Dept.), 400 7th St. S.W. 20590; (202) 366-4040. Fax, (202) 366-9854. Gordon J. Linton, administrator. Information, (202) 366-4319. Internet, http://www.fta.dot.gov.*

Responsible for developing improved mass transportation facilities, equipment, techniques, and methods; assists state and local governments in financing mass transportation systems.

Federal Transit Administration *(Transportation Dept.), Budget and Policy, 400 7th St. S.W., #9310 20590; (202) 366-4050. Fax, (202) 366-7116. Michael A. Winter, associate administrator. Internet, http://www.fta.dot.gov/office/budget.*

Develops budgets, programs, legislative proposals, and policies for the federal transit program; evaluates program proposals and their potential impact on local communities; coordinates private sector initiatives of the agency.

Federal Transit Administration *(Transportation Dept.), Program Management, 400 7th St. S.W., #9315 20590; (202) 366-4020. Fax, (202) 366-7951. Hiram J. Walker, associate administrator. Internet, http://www.fta.dot.gov/office/program.*

Administers capital planning and operating assistance grants and loan activities; monitors transit projects in such areas as environmental impact, special provisions for the elderly and people with disabilities, efficiency, and investment.

Federal Transit Administration *(Transportation Dept.), Research, Demonstration, and Innovation, 400 7th St. S.W., #6431 20590; (202) 366-4052. Fax, (202) 366-3765. Edward L. Thomas, associate administrator. Internet, http://www.fta.dot.gov/office/research.*

Provides industry, transit properties, and state and local governments with contracts, cooperative agreements, and grants for testing, developing, and demonstrating methods of improved mass transportation service and technology. Supports security, safety, and drug control efforts in transit systems.

Maryland Mass Transit Administration, *6 St. Paul St., Baltimore, MD 21202; (410) 767-3943. Fax, (410) 333-3279. Ronald L. Freeland, administrator; Charles S. Carnaggio, director, operations, (410) 767-8758. Toll-free, (800) 325-7245. TDD, (410) 539-3497. Wheelchair accessibility, (410) 859-7420. Internet, http://www.libertynet.org/dvarp/MARC.*

Responsible for mass transit programs in Maryland; provides MARC commuter rail service between Baltimore, Washington, and suburbs in Maryland and West Virginia. (Mailing address for MARC: 5 Amtrak Way, P.O. Box 8718, Baltimore, MD 21240-8718K.)

National Transportation Safety Board, *Railroad Safety, 490 L'Enfant Plaza East S.W. 20594; (202) 314-6430. Fax, (202) 314-6497. Robert Lauby, director.*

Investigates passenger train accidents, including rapid rail transit and rail commuter systems, and freight rail accidents with substantial damage to determine probable cause; investigates all employee and passenger fatalities; makes recommendations on rail transportation safety and accident prevention.

Surface Transportation Board *(Transportation Dept.), 1925 K St. N.W. 20423-0001; (202) 565-1500. Fax, (202) 565-9004. Linda J. Morgan, chair; Gus A. Owen, vice chair. Internet, http://www.stb.dot.gov.*

Regulates mergers and through-route requirements for the intercity bus industry.

Virginia Railway Express, *1500 King St., #202, Alexandria, VA 22314; (703) 684-1001. Fax, (703) 684-1313. Stephen T. Roberts, director of operations. Information, (703) 684-0400. TDD, (703) 684-0551. Toll-free, (800) 743-3873. Internet, gotrains@vre.org or http://www.vre.org.*

Regional transportation partnership that provides commuter rail service from the northern Virginia suburbs to Alexandria, Arlington, and Washington, D.C.

Washington Metropolitan Area Transit Authority, *600 5th St. N.W. 20001; (202) 962-1234. Richard A. White, general manager. Information, (202) 637-7000. Internet, http://www.wmata.com.*

Provides bus and rail transit service to Washington, D.C., and the neighboring Maryland and Virginia communities; assesses and plans for transportation needs. Provides fare, schedule, and route information; promotes accessibiliity for persons with disabilities and the elderly.

CONGRESS

House Appropriations Committee, *Subcommittee on Transportation, 2358 RHOB 20515; (202) 225-2141. Frank R. Wolf, R-Va., chair; John T. Blazey, staff director. Internet, http://www.house.gov/appropriations.*

Jurisdiction over legislation to appropriate funds for the Federal Transit Administration and intercity mass transit systems, including the Washington Metropolitan Area Transit Authority.

House Transportation and Infrastructure Committee, *Subcommittee on Surface Transportation, B370A RHOB 20515; (202) 225-6715. Fax, (202) 225-4623. Tom Petri, R-Wis., chair; Roger Nober, counsel. Internet, http://www.house.gov/transportation.*

Jurisdiction over legislation on urban mass transportation and intercity mass transit systems.

Senate Appropriations Committee, *Subcommittee on Transportation, SD-133 20510; (202) 224-7281. Fax,*

(202) 224-4401. Richard C. Shelby, R-Ala., chair; Wally Burnett, majority clerk. Internet, http://www.senate.gov/~appropriations.

Jurisdiction over legislation to appropriate funds for the Federal Transit Administration, urban mass transportation, and intercity mass transit systems, including the Washington Metro Area Transit Authority.

Senate Banking, Housing, and Urban Affairs Committee, *SD-534 20510; (202) 224-7391. Fax, (202) 224-5137. Alfonse M. D'Amato, R-N.Y., chair; Howard Menell, staff director. Internet, http://www.senate.gov/~banking.*

Jurisdiction over legislation on urban mass transportation and intercity mass transit systems.

NONPROFIT

Amalgamated Transit Union, *5025 Wisconsin Ave. N.W., 3rd Floor 20016; (202) 537-1645. Fax, (202) 244-7824. Jim La Sala, president. Internet, http://www.atu.org/atu.*

Membership: transit workers in the United States and Canada, including bus, van, subway, and light rail operators; clerks, baggage handlers, and maintenance employees in urban transit, over-the-road, and school bus industries; and municipal workers. Assists members with contract negotiations and grievances; conducts training programs and seminars. Monitors legislation and regulations. (Affiliated with the AFL-CIO.)

American Bus Assn., *1100 New York Ave. N.W., #1050 20005-3934; (202) 842-1645. Fax, (202) 842-0850. Peter J. Pantuso, president. Internet, http://www.buses.org.*

Membership: intercity privately owned bus companies, state associations, travel/tourism businesses, bus manufacturers, and those interested in the bus industry. Monitors legislation and regulations.

American Public Transit Assn., *1201 New York Ave. N.W., #400 20005; (202) 898-4000. Fax, (202) 898-4049. William W. Millar, president. Information, (202) 898-4089. Internet, http://www.apta.com.*

Membership: rapid rail and motor bus systems and manufacturers, suppliers, and consulting firms. Compiles data on the industry; promotes research. Monitors legislation and regulations.

Assn. for Commuter Transportation, *1518 K St. N.W., #503 20005; (202) 393-3497. Fax, (202) 638-4833. Kenneth Sufka, executive director. Internet, acthq@aol.com or http://finat.cob.fsu.edu/act.htm.*

Membership: corporations, public agencies, transit authorities, transport management associations, vanpool management companies, and individuals. Serves as a clearinghouse for ride-sharing information and materials; maintains speaker referral service. Interests include tax equity for commuters and employer transportation requirements of the Clean Air Act amendments. Monitors legislation and regulations.

Community Transportation Assn. of America, *1341 G St. N.W., #600 20005; (202) 628-1480. Fax, (202) 737-9197. Dale Marsico, executive director. Toll-free, (800) 527-8279. Internet, http://www.ctaa.org.*

Works to improve mobility for the elderly, the poor, and persons with disabilities; concerns include rural, small-city, and specialized transportation.

National Assn. of Railroad Passengers, *900 2nd St. N.E., #308 20002-3557; (202) 408-8362. Fax, (202) 408-8287. Ross Capon, executive director. Internet, narp@worldweb.net.*

Consumer organization. Works to expand and improve U.S. intercity and commuter rail passenger service, increase federal funds for mass transit, ensure fair treatment for rail freight transportation, and address environmental concerns pertaining to mass transit. Opposes subsidies for intercity trucking; works with Amtrak on scheduling, new services, fares, and advertising.

National Research Council, *Transportation Research Information Services, 2001 Wisconsin Ave. N.W. (mailing address: 2101 Constitution Ave. N.W., Washington, DC 20418); (202) 334-3250. Fax, (202) 334-3495. Jerome Maddock, manager. Internet, http://www.nas.edu/trb/about/trisfram.html.*

Provides information on research projects and publications covering such topics as public transportation technology and management, elderly and disabled passenger needs, and rural transport systems. Fee for services.

United Motorcoach Assn., *113 S. West St., 4th Floor, Alexandria, VA 22314; (703) 838-2929. Fax, (703) 838-2950. Stephen Sprague, interim executive director. Internet, http://www.uma.org.*

Provides information, offers technical assistance, conducts research, and monitors legislation. Interests include insurance, safety programs, and credit.

20

U.S. Congress and Politics

ACCESS TO CONGRESSIONAL INFORMATION

AGENCIES

National Archives and Records Administration,
Federal Register, 800 N. Capitol St., #700 20408; (202)
523-5230. Fax, (202) 523-6866. Frances D. McDonald,
editor-in-chief. TDD, (202) 523-5229. Public Laws Update
Service (PLUS), (202) 523-6641. Internet, http://www.
nara.gov/nara/fedreg/fedreg.html.

Assigns public law numbers to enacted legislation,
executive orders, and proclamations; responds to
inquiries on public law numbers; assists inquirers in
finding presidential signing or veto messages in the
Weekly Compilation of Presidential Documents and the
Public Papers of the Presidents series; compiles slip laws
and annual *United States Statutes at Large;* compiles
indexes for finding statutory provisions. Operates Public
Laws Update Service (PLUS), which provides information by telephone on new legislation. Publications available from the U.S. Government Printing Office,
Washington, DC 20402; (202) 783-3238.

CONGRESS

Government Printing Office, *Documents, 732 N.*
Capitol St. N.W. (mailing address: Superintendent of Doc-
uments, Government Printing Office, Washington, DC
20402); (202) 512-0571. Fax, (202) 512-1434. Francis J.
Buckley Jr., superintendent. Congressional order desk and
publications, (202) 512-1800; fax for orders, (202) 512-
2168. Internet, http://www.gpo.gov/su_docs.

Prints, distributes, and sells congressional documents, prints, public laws, reports, and House calendars.
Orders, P.O. Box 371954, Pittsburgh, PA 15250-7954
(See also GPO Regional Depository Libraries in the
appendix.)

House Oversight Committee, *1309 LHOB 20515;*
(202) 225-8281. Fax, (202) 225-9957. Bill Thomas, R-
Calif., chair; Cathy Abernathy, acting staff director. Inter-
net, http://www.house.gov/cho.

Jurisdiction over the printing, cost of printing, binding, and distribution of congressional publications; jurisdiction (in conjunction with the Joint Committee on
Printing) over the Government Printing Office, executive
papers, and depository libraries; jurisdiction over federal
election law.

Joint Committee on Printing, *SH-818 20510; (202)*
224-5241. Fax, (202) 224-1176. Sen. John W. Warner, R-
Va., chair; Eric Peterson, staff director.

Controls arrangement and style of the *Congressional*
Record; determines which congressional prints, documents, and reports are inserted; oversees public printing,
binding, and distribution of government publications;
oversees activities of the Government Printing Office (in
conjunction with the House Oversight and Senate Rules
and Administration committees).

Legislative Resource Center, *B-106 CHOB 20515;*
(202) 226-5200. Fax, (202) 226-5208. Catherine Keller,
director. Documents fax, (202) 226-4362. Internet, http://
clerkweb.house.gov/lrc/lrc.htm.

Maintains and distributes House bills, reports, public
laws, and documents to members' offices, committee
staffs, and the general public. (Telephone requests are
accepted.)

Legislative Resource Center, *Office of the Historian,*
B-106 CHOB 20515; (202) 226-5200. Fax, (202) 226-
5208. Cynthia Miller, historian. Internet, http://clerkweb.
house.gov/histrecs/history/history.htm.

Conducts historical research. Advises members on
the disposition of their records and papers; maintains
information on manuscript collections of former members; maintains biographical files on former members.
Makes data available online; print publications include
Biographical Directory of the United States Congress, 1774-
1989; Guide to Research Collections of Former Members of
the United States House of Representatives, 1789-1987;
Black Americans in Congress, 1870-1989; and *Women in*
Congress, 1917-1989.

Senate Document Room, *SH-B04 20510; (202) 224-*
7860. Fax, (202) 228-2815. Barry Wolk, superintendent.

Maintains and distributes Senate bills, reports, public
laws, and documents. (To obtain material send a self-
addressed mailing label or fax with request. Telephone
requests are not accepted.)

Senate Executive Clerk, *5138 CAP 20510; (202) 224-*
4341. David Marcos, executive clerk.

Maintains and distributes copies of treaties submitted
to the Senate for ratification; provides information on
submitted treaties and nominations. (Shares distribution
responsibility with Senate Document Room, (202) 224-
7860.)

Senate Historical Office, *SH-201 20510; (202) 224-*
6900. Fax, (202) 224-5329. Richard Baker, historian. Inter-
net, http://www.senate.gov/history.

Serves as an information clearinghouse on Senate
history, traditions, and members. Collects, organizes, and
distributes to the public previously unpublished Senate
documents; collects and preserves photographs and pic-

tures related to Senate history; conducts an oral history program; advises senators and Senate committees on the disposition of their noncurrent papers and records. Produces publications on the history of the Senate.

Senate Office of Conservation and Preservation,
S410 CAP 20510; (202) 224-4550. Carl Fritter, bookbinder.

Develops and coordinates programs related to the conservation and preservation of Senate records and materials for the secretary of the Senate.

Senate Rules and Administration Committee, *SR-305 20510; (202) 224-6352. Fax, (202) 224-3036. John W. Warner, R-Va., chair; Grayson Winterling, staff director. Internet, http://www.senate.gov/~rules.*

Jurisdiction (in conjunction with the Joint Committee on Printing) over the Government Printing Office and legislation on printing of and corrections to the *Congressional Record.*

NEWS SERVICES

Congressional Quarterly Inc., *1414 22nd St. N.W. 20037; (202) 887-8500. Fax, (202) 728-1863. Robert W. Merry, president. Information, (202) 887-6279. Internet, http://www.cq.com.*

Provides news, analysis, and information on government. Products include the *CQ Weekly;* online legislative tracking services; print and electronic news updates; abstracts and full text of the *Congressional Record; Campaigns and Elections* magazine; the *Congressional Staff Directory;* and books on Congress. (Affiliated with the St. Petersburg Times.)

Congressional Record

The Congressional Record, *published daily when Congress is in session, is a printed account of proceedings on the floor of the House and Senate. A Daily Digest section summarizes the day's action on the floor and in committees, and lists committee meetings scheduled for the following day. An index is published monthly and at the close of sessions of Congress. Since January 1995, House members have not been allowed to edit their remarks before they appear in the* Record, *but senators retain this privilege. Material not spoken on the floor may be inserted through unanimous consent to revise or extend a speech, and is published in a distinctive typeface. Grammatical, typographical, and technical corrections are also permitted.*

CONGRESS

Government Printing Office Main Bookstore, *Congressional Order Desk, 710 N. Capitol St. N.W. (mailing address: Superintendent of Documents, Government Print-*

ing Office, Washington, DC 20402); (202) 512-1808. Fax, (202) 512-2250. Congressional order desk and publications, (202) 512-1800. Internet, http://www.access.gpo.goc/su_docs.

Sells copies of and subscriptions to the *Congressional Record.* Orders, P.O. Box 371954, Pittsburgh, PA 15250-7954. *(See also GPO Regional Depository Libraries in the appendix.)*

Library of Congress, *Law Library Reading Room, 101 Independence Ave. S.E., #LM240 20540; (202) 707-5079. Fax, (202) 707-3585. Rubens Medina, head, Law Library.*

Copies of the *Congressional Record* are available for reading. Terminals in the reading room provide access to a computer system containing bill digests from the 93rd Congress to date.

NONPROFIT

Martin Luther King Memorial Library, *901 G St. N.W., #400 20001; (202) 727-1101. Fax, (202) 727-1129. Molly Raphael, director. Information, (202) 727-0321. Hours of operation, (202) 727-1111 (recording).*

Maintains collection of *Congressional Record* paperback volumes (1980 to date), bound volumes (1939-1976), microfilm (1827-1964), and microfiche (1977-1985).

U.S. Capitol Historical Society, *Information Center, East-Front Lobby, CAP 20515; (202) 543-8919. Toll-free, (800) 887-9318.*

Sells copies of the *Congressional Record.*

Schedules/Status of Legislation

Information can also be obtained from the Congressional Record (Daily Digest) and from individual congressional committees (see 105th Congress, p. 721)

CONGRESS

Calendars of the U.S. House of Representatives and History of Legislation, *Senate Document Room, SH-B04 20510; (202) 224-7860. Fax, (202) 228-2815. Barry Wolk, superintendent.*

Issued daily when the House is in session. Provides capsule legislative history of all measures reported by House and Senate committees; provides additional reference material. Subject index included in each Monday edition or in the edition published on the first day the House is in session. (Also available from the House Document Room, B-18 Ford Bldg., 2nd and D Sts. S.W. 20515; (202) 225-3456, and from the Superintendent of

Documents, Government Printing Office, Washington, DC 20402; (202) 512-1808.)

House Democratic Cloakroom, *H222 CAP 20515; (202) 225-7330. Barry K. Sullivan, manager. Recorded message: House floor action, (202) 225-7400; legislative program, (202) 225-1600.*

Provides information about House floor proceedings.

House Republican Cloakroom, *H223 CAP 20515; (202) 225-7350. Timothy J. Harroun, manager. Recorded message: House floor action, (202) 225-7430; legislative program, (202) 225-2020.*

Provides information about House floor proceedings.

Legislative Information Service, *696 Ford Bldg. 20515; (202) 225-1772. Fax, (202) 226-1399. Deborah Turner, chief.*

Records, stores, and provides legislative status information on all bills and resolutions pending in Congress. Provides information through LEGIS, a computer-based service, on all legislation introduced since the 96th Congress. Measures that became law (public or private) between the 93rd and 96th Congress are also available.

Legislative Resource Center, *Records and Registration,* B-106 CHOB 20515; (202) 226-5200. Fax, (202) 226-5208. Catherine Keller, director.

Provides videotapes of House floor proceedings.

Library of Congress, *Computer Catalog Center,* 101 Independence Ave. 20540; (202) 707-3370. Fax, (202) 707-1957. Barbara Moreland, Head, Main Reading Room.

Makes available a computer system containing information on all legislation introduced since the 93rd Congress (1973), arranged by member's name, subject, committee, and bill or resolution number.

Senate Democratic Cloakroom, *S225 CAP 20510; (202) 224-4691. Recorded message: Senate floor action, (202) 224-8541.*

Provides information about Senate floor proceedings.

Senate Republican Cloakroom, *S226 CAP 20510; (202) 224-6191. Recorded message: Senate floor action, (202) 224-8601.*

Provides information about Senate floor proceedings.

NEWS SERVICES

Associated Press, *2021 K St. N.W., #600 20006; (202) 776-9400. Fax, (202) 776-9570. Jonathan P. Wolman, bureau chief. Daybook editor, (202) 736-9699.*

Publishes daybook that lists congressional committee meetings and hearings and their location and subject matter. No fee for listing events in daybook. (Headquarters in New York.)

CQ Daily Monitor, *1414 22nd St. N.W. 20037; (202) 887-6515. Fax, (202) 835-1635. Subscriptions, (202) 887-6258.*

Provides daily news and analysis about Congress; lists daily committee meetings and hearings, complete witness list, floor proceedings, and future scheduled committee meetings and hearings. Fee for services. (A publication of Congressional Quarterly Inc.)

Legi-Slate, *10 G St. N.E., #500 20002; (202) 898-2300. Fax, (202) 898-3030. Toll-free, (800) 733-1131. Internet, http://www.legislate.com.*

Provides online congressional hearing and markup schedules, including time and location, meeting agendas, and full witness listings. Fee for services. (Affiliated with the Washington Post Company.)

United Press International, *1510 H St. N.W., #700 20005; (202) 898-8000. Fax, (202) 898-8057.*

Wire service that lists congressional committee meetings and hearings, location, and subject matter. Fee for services.

Washington Alert, *1414 22nd St. N.W. 20037; (202) 887-8511. Fax, (202) 728-1863. Subscriptions and demonstrations, (202) 887-6258.*

Provides online congressional news and analysis, including legislative summaries, votes, testimony, and archival and reference materials. Provides hearing and markup schedules, including time and location, meeting agendas, and full witness listings. Fee for services. (Affiliated with Congressional Quarterly Inc.)

Washington Post, *1150 15th St. N.W. 20071; (202) 334-7410. Information, (202) 334-6000. Internet, http://www.washingtonpost.com.*

Lists congressional committee meetings and hearings, locations, and subject matter. Fee for services.

CAMPAIGNS AND ELECTIONS

See also Political Activity and the Hatch Act (chap. 10); Standards of Conduct (this chapter)

AGENCIES

Federal Communications Commission, *Complaints and Political Programming,* 2025 M St. N.W., #8202 20554; (202) 418-1440. Fax, (202) 653-1124. Norman Goldstein, chief. Information, (202) 418-0200.

Handles complaints and inquiries concerning the equal time rule, which requires equal broadcast opportunities for all legally qualified candidates for the same office. Enforces related Communications Act provisions, including the requirement for sponsorship identification of all paid broadcast announcements.

Federal Election Commission, *999 E St. N.W. 20463; (202) 694-1000. Fax, (202) 219-8494. Joan D. Aikens, chair. Information, (202) 694-1100. Press, (202) 694-1220. Library, (202) 694-1600. Toll-free information, (800) 424-9530. Internet, http://www.fec.gov.*

Formulates, administers, and enforces policy with respect to the Federal Election Campaign Act of 1971 as amended, including campaign disclosure requirements, contribution and expenditure limitations, and public financing of presidential nominating conventions and campaigns. Receives campaign finance reports; makes rules and regulations; conducts audits and investigations. Serves as an election information clearinghouse. Copies of campaign finance reports available for inspection. Library open to the public.

Federal Election Commission, *Election Administration, 999 E St. N.W., #209 20463; (202) 694-1095. Fax, (202) 219-8500. Penelope Bonsall, director. Toll-free, (800) 424-9530.*

Conducts studies on voter registration, voting procedures, and election administration; serves as an information clearinghouse on election administration; provides information on National Voter Registration Act of 1993; produces research publications, which are available through the Government Printing Office.

Federal Election Commission, *Public Records, 999 E St. N.W. 20463; (202) 694-1120. Fax, (202) 501-0693. Patricia Young, assistant staff director. Toll-free, (800) 424-9530.*

Makes available for public inspection and copying the detailed campaign finance reports on contributions and expenditures filed by candidates for federal office, their supporting political committees, and individuals and committees making expenditures on behalf of a candidate. Maintains copies of all reports and statements filed since 1972.

Justice Dept., *Election Crimes, 1400 New York Ave. N.W. (mailing address: P.O. Box 27518, McPherson Station, Washington, DC 20038); (202) 514-1421. Fax, (202) 514-3003. Craig Donsanto, director.*

Supervises enforcement of federal criminal laws related to campaigns and elections. Oversees investigation of deprivation of voting rights; intimidation and coercion of voters; denial or promise of federal employ-

ment or other benefits; illegal political contributions, expenditures, and solicitations; and all other election violations referred to the division.

CONGRESS

House Appropriations Committee, *Subcommittee on Treasury, Postal Service, and General Government, B307 RHOB 20515; (202) 225-5834. Fax, (202) 225-5895. Jim Kolbe, R-Ariz., chair; Michelle Mrdeza, clerk. Internet, http://www.house.gov/appropriations.*

Jurisdiction over legislation to appropriate funds for the Federal Election Commission.

House Commission on Congressional Mailing Standards, *140 CHOB 20515; (202) 225-9337. Fax, (202) 226-0047. Bill Thomas, R-Calif., chair; Jack Dail, staff director.*

Receives complaints, conducts investigations, and issues decisions on disputes arising from the alleged abuse of franked mail by House members during congressional election campaigns.

House Government Reform and Oversight Committee, *Subcommittee on the District of Columbia, B-349A 20515; (202) 225-6751. Thomas M. Davis III, R-Va., chair; Ronald P. Hamm, staff director.*

Oversight of election laws in the District of Columbia.

House Judiciary Committee, *Subcommittee on the Constitution, 362 Ford Bldg. 20515; (202) 226-7680. Fax, (202) 225-3746. Charles T. Canady, R-Fla., chair; Keri Folmar, counsel. Internet, http://www.house.gov/judiciary.*

Jurisdiction over proposed constitutional amendments related to the electoral college, campaign reform, and presidential succession.

House Oversight Committee, *1309 LHOB 20515; (202) 225-8281. Fax, (202) 225-9957. Bill Thomas, R-Calif., chair; Cathy Abernathy, acting staff director. Internet, http://www.house.gov/cho.*

Jurisdiction over legislation and other matters related to all federal elections, including campaign finance; corrupt practices; contested House elections; voter registration; overseas voters; and broadcast of early election projections. Oversees operations of the Federal Election Commission.

House Ways and Means Committee, *1102 LHOB 20515; (202) 225-3625. Bill Archer, R-Texas, chair; Peter Singleton, chief of staff. Internet, http://www.house.gov/ways_means.*

Jurisdiction over legislation on taxes and credits for public financing of federal elections.

Legislative Resource Center, *Records and Registration,* *B-106 CHOB 20515; (202) 226-5200. Fax, (202) 226-5208. Catherine Keller, director.*

Receives reports of campaign receipts and expenditures of House candidates and committees. Open for public inspection.

Secretary of the Senate, *Public Records, S220 20510; (202) 224-0329. Fax, (202) 224-1851. Raymond Davis, chief, Campaign Financing and FEC Liaison.*

Receives reports of campaign receipts and expenditures of Senate candidates and committees. Open for public inspection.

Senate Appropriations Committee, *Subcommittee on Treasury and General Government, SD-190 20510; (202) 224-7337. Ben Nighthorse Campbell, R-Colo., chair; Patricia Raymond, staff director. Internet, http://www. senate.gov/~appropriations.*

Jurisdiction over legislation to appropriate funds for the Federal Election Commission.

Senate Finance Committee, *SD-219 20510; (202) 224-4515. Fax, (202) 224-5920. William V. Roth Jr., R-Del., chair; Lindy L. Paull, staff director. Internet, http://www. senate.gov/~finance.*

Jurisdiction over legislation on taxes and credits for public financing of federal elections.

Senate Governmental Affairs Committee, *Subcommittee on Oversight of Government Management, Restructuring, and the District of Columbia, SH-604 20510; (202) 224-3682. Fax, (202) 224-3328. Sam Brownback, R-Kan., chair; Michael Rubin, acting staff director. Internet, http://www.senate.gov/committee/ governmental_affairs.html.*

Oversight of election laws in the District of Columbia.

Senate Judiciary Committee, *Subcommittee on the Constitution, Federalism, and Property Rights, SD-164 20510; (202) 224-8081. John Ashcroft, R-Mo., chair; David Miller, chief counsel. Internet, http://www.senate.gov/ committee/judiciary.html.*

Jurisdiction over proposed constitutional amendments related to the electoral college, campaign reform, and presidential succession.

Senate Rules and Administration Committee, *SR-305 20510; (202) 224-6352. Fax, (202) 224-3036. John W. Warner, R-Va., chair; Grayson Winterling, staff member. Internet, http://www.senate.gov/~rules.*

Jurisdiction over legislation and other matters related to all federal elections, including presidential succession; campaign finance; corrupt practices; political action

committees; election law changes; and broadcast of early election projections. Oversees voter registration by mail and operations of the Federal Election Commission.

NONPROFIT

American Assn. of Political Consultants, *900 2nd St. N.E., #217 20002; (202) 371-9585. Fax, (202) 371-6751. Richard Woodward, president. Internet, aapcmail@aol. com.*

Membership: political consultants, media specialists, campaign managers, corporate public affairs officers, pollsters, public officials, academicians, fundraisers, lobbyists, and congressional staffers. Focuses on ethics of the profession; provides members with opportunities to meet industry leaders and learn new techniques and emerging technologies.

American Bar Assn., *Standing Committee on Election Law, 740 15th St. N.W. 20005; (202) 662-1692. Fax, (202) 638-3844. Elizabeth Yang, staff director. Internet, http:// www.abanet.org.*

Studies ways to improve the U.S. election and campaign process.

Center for Responsive Politics, *1320 19th St. N.W., #620 20036; (202) 857-0044. Fax, (202) 857-7809. Kent Cooper, executive director. Internet, http://www.crp.org.*

Conducts research on Congress and related issues, with particular interest in campaign finance and congressional operations.

Commission on Presidential Debates, *1200 New Hampshire Ave. N.W., #445 20036; (202) 872-1020. Fax, (202) 783-5923. Frank J. Fahrenkopf Jr. and Paul G. Kirk, co-chairs.*

Independent, nonpartisan organization established to sponsor general election presidential and vice presidential debates, and to undertake educational and research activities related to the debates.

Common Cause, *1250 Connecticut Ave. N.W., #600 20036; (202) 833-1200. Fax, (202) 659-3716. Ann McBride, president; John Anthony, press secretary. Press, (202) 736-5770. Internet, http://www.commoncause.org.*

Citizens' legislative interest group. Records and analyzes campaign contributions to congressional candidates and campaign committees, particularly those from political action committees, and soft money contributions to national political parties.

Congressional Accountability Project, *1611 Connecticut Ave. N.W., #3A 20009; (202) 296-2787. Fax, (202) 833-2406. Gary Ruskin, director. Internet, http://www. essential.org/orgs/CAP/CAP.html.*

Seeks to reform rules on campaign finance, gifts, pensions, and ethics for members of Congress; advocates free online access to congressional documents; files ethics complaints against individual members of Congress.

National Library on Money and Politics, *1320 19th St. N.W., #620 20036; (202) 857-0318. Fax, (202) 857-7809. Kent Cooper, executive director. Internet, http://www.crp.org.*

Conducts research and analysis of political money and provides the media and others with direct assistance on the subject. A project of the Center for Responsive Politics.

Public Campaign, *1320 19th St. N.W., #M1 20036; (202) 293-0222. Fax, (202) 293-0202. Ellen Miller, executive director. Internet, info@publicampaign.org or http://www.publicampaign.org.*

Grassroots organization interested in campaign finance reform. Supports the Clean Money Campaign, a voluntary program in which candidates receive a set amount of public financing for elections if they reject private money and limit spending.

Election Statistics and Apportionment

AGENCIES

Census Bureau *(Commerce Dept.),* **Administrative and Customer Services,** *4700 Silver Hill Rd., FB3, #1587, Suitland, MD (mailing address: Customer Service, Bureau of the Census, Washington, DC 20233); (301) 457-4100. Fax, (301) 457-4714. Don Wynegar, chief. Fax after hours (orders only), (301) 457-3842.*

Disseminates census data on counties, municipalities, and other small areas to state legislatures for use in redrawing congressional district boundaries.

Census Bureau *(Commerce Dept.),* **Population,** *Suitland and Silver Hill Rds., Suitland, MD; (301) 457-2071. Fax, (301) 457-2644. John F. Long, chief.*

Computes every ten years the population figures that determine the number of representatives each state may have in the House of Representatives.

CONGRESS

Clerk of the House of Representatives, *H154 CAP 20515; (202) 225-7000. Robin H. Carle, clerk. Internet, http://clerkweb.house.gov.*

Publishes biennial compilation of statistics on congressional and presidential elections. Receives population figures compiled by the Census Bureau that form the basis for reapportionment of the House; informs state governors of new apportionment figures.

House Judiciary Committee, *2138 RHOB 20515; (202) 225-3951. Fax, (202) 225-7682. Henry J. Hyde, R-Ill., chair; Thomas Mooney, chief counsel. Internet, http://www.house.gov/judiciary.*

Jurisdiction over reapportionment legislation.

Senate Judiciary Committee, *SD-224 20510; (202) 224-5225. Fax, (202) 224-9102. Orrin G. Hatch, R-Utah, chair; Manus Cooney, chief counsel. Internet, http://www.senate.gov/committee/judiciary.html.*

Jurisdiction over reapportionment legislation.

Senate Rules and Administration Committee, *SR-305 20510; (202) 224-6352. Fax, (202) 224-3036. John W. Warner, R-Va., chair; Grayson Winterling, staff director. Internet, http://www.senate.gov/~rules.*

Distributes *Senate Election Law Guidebook,* a compilation of Senate campaign information, including federal and state laws governing election to the U.S. Senate. Available from the Senate Document Room.

NONPROFIT

Common Cause, *State Issues Development,* *1250 Connecticut Ave. N.W., #600 20036; (202) 833-1200. Fax, (202) 659-3716. Ed Davis, director, State Issues. Internet, http://www.commoncause.org.*

Citizens' interest group. Seeks to alter procedures governing redistricting by the establishment of independent redistricting commissions. Serves as an information clearinghouse; provides research and support for regional field offices.

Voting/Political Participation

See also Civil Rights (chap. 1)

NONPROFIT

AARP/VOTE, *601 E St. N.W. 20049; (202) 434-3730. Fax, (202) 434-3745. Molly Daniels, director.*

Nonpartisan voter education program of the American Association of Retired Persons. Maintains nationwide volunteer network that raises issues of concern to older persons in political campaigns.

Arab American Institute, *918 16th St. N.W., #601 20006; (202) 429-9210. Fax, (202) 429-9214. James J. Zogby, president. Internet, aai@arab-aai.org.*

Advocacy group concerned with political issues affecting Arab Americans. Seeks to involve the Arab-American community in party politics and the electoral process.

Center for Voting and Democracy, *P.O. Box 60037 20039; (301) 270-4616. Fax, (301) 270-4133. Robert*

Richie, executive director. Information, (202) 828-3062. Internet, fairvote@compuserve.com or http://www.igc. org/cvd.

Researches and disseminates information on electoral systems that promote voter participation and fair representation. Supports a broad range of proportional representation systems and reforms in plurality elections. Holds conferences; provides technical assistance to localities.

Coalition of Black Trade Unionists, *1625 L St. N.W. (mailing address: P.O. Box 66268, Washington, DC 20035); (202) 429-1203. Fax, (202) 429-1102. Wil Duncan, executive director.*

Monitors legislation affecting African American and other minority trade unionists. Focuses efforts on equal employment opportunity, unemployment, and voter education and registration.

Committee for the Study of the American Electorate, *421 New Jersey Ave. S.E. 20003; (202) 546-3221. Fax, (202) 546-3571. Curtis Gans, director.*

Nonpartisan research group that studies issues involving low and declining American voter participation.

Democratic National Committee, *Campaign Division, 430 S. Capitol St. S.E. 20003; (202) 863-8000. Fax, (202) 488-5025. Steve Grossman, director. Internet, dnc@democrat.org or http://www.democrat.org.*

Responsible for electoral activities at the federal, state, and local levels; sponsors workshops to recruit Democratic candidates and to provide instruction in campaign techniques; conducts party constituency outreach programs; coordinates voter registration.

Joint Center for Political and Economic Studies, *1090 Vermont Ave. N.W., #1100 20005-4961; (202) 789-3500. Fax, (202) 789-6390. Eddie N. Williams, president. Internet, http://www.jointctr.org.*

Research and educational organization that analyzes issues of concern to African Americans, focusing on economic and social policy issues and African American political participation; publishes a biannual profile of African American elected officials in federal, state, and local government.

Labor Council for Latin American Advancement, *888 16th St. N.W., #5330 20006; (202) 347-4223. Fax, (202) 347-5095. Oscar Sanchez, executive director. Internet, http://www.lclaa.org.*

Membership: Hispanic trade unionists. Conducts nonpartisan voter registration and education programs; encourages increased participation by Hispanic workers in the political process. (Affiliated with the AFL-CIO.)

League of Women Voters of the United States, *1730 M St. N.W., #1000 20036; (202) 429-1965. Fax, (202) 429-0854. Judy Conover, executive director. Internet, http://www.lwv.org.*

Membership: women and men interested in nonpartisan political action and study. Works to increase participation in government; provides information on voter registration and balloting. Interests include social policy, natural resources, international relations, and representative government.

National Assn. of Latino Elected and Appointed Officials, *514 C St. N.E. 20002-5810; (202) 546-2536. Fax, (202) 546-4121. Ingrid Duran, assistant director, Policy Development.*

Research and advocacy group that provides civic affairs information and assistance on legislation affecting Hispanics. Encourages Hispanic participation in local, state, and national politics. Interests include the health and social, economic, and educational welfare of Hispanics. (Headquarters in Los Angeles.)

National Black Caucus of Local Elected Officials, *c/o National League of Cities, 1301 Pennsylvania Ave. N.W., #550 20004; (202) 626-3169. Fax, (202) 626-3103. Paul Richards, president. Press, (202) 626-3000.*

Membership: elected officials at the local level and other interested individuals. Concerned with issues affecting African Americans, including housing, economics, the family, and human rights.

National Black Caucus of State Legislators, *444 N. Capitol St. N.W., #622 20001; (202) 624-5457. Fax, (202) 508-3826. Ivan Lanier, executive director.*

Membership: African American state legislators. Promotes effective leadership among African American state legislators; serves as an information network and clearinghouse for members.

National Coalition on Black Voter Participation, Inc., *1629 K St. N.W., #801 20006; (202) 659-4929. Fax, (202) 659-5025. Melanie Campbell Hill, acting executive director. Internet, ncobvp@igc.apc.org.*

Seeks to increase black voter registration and turnout and to eliminate barriers to political participation for African Americans. Sponsors Operation Big Vote that conducts voter education, registration, and get-out-the-vote activities in African Americans communities. Operates an information resource center. Monitors legislation and regulations.

National Political Congress of Black Women, *8401 Colesville Rd., #400, Silver Spring, MD 20910; (301) 562-8000. Fax, (301) 562-8303. C. DeLores Tucker, chair.*

Nonpartisan political organization that encourages African American women to participate in the political process. Advocates nonpartisan voter registration and encourages African American women to engage in other political activities. Develops positions and participates in platform development and strategies that address the needs of communities at every level of government.

National Women's Political Caucus, *1211 Connecticut Ave. N.W., #425 20036; (202) 785-1100. Fax, (202) 785-3605. Anita Perez Ferguson, president. Toll-free, (800) 729-6972. Internet, mailnwpc@aol.com or http://www.feminist.com/nwpc.htm.*

Advocacy group that seeks greater involvement of women in politics. Seeks to identify, recruit, and train women for elective and appointive political office, regardless of party affiliation; serves as an information clearinghouse on women in politics, particularly during election campaigns; publishes directory of women holding federal and state offices.

Project Vote, *739 8th St. S.E., #202 20003; (202) 546-3492. Fax, (202) 546-2483. Zachary Pollett, executive director.*

Civic organization that registers low-income and minority individuals and educates them on the power of the vote.

Republican National Committee, *Political Operations, 310 1st St. S.E. 20003; (202) 863-8600. Fax, (202) 863-8657. Tony Hammond, director. Internet, http://www.rnc.org.*

Responsible for electoral activities at the federal, state, and local levels; operates party constituency outreach programs; coordinates voter registration.

 CAPITOL

Capitol switchboard, (202) 224-3121. See also 105th Congress (p. 720) for each member's office.

CONGRESS

Architect of the Capitol, *SB15 CAP 20515; (202) 228-1793. Fax, (202) 228-1893. Alan M. Hantman, architect. Internet, http://www.aoc.gov.*

Maintains the Capitol and its grounds, the House and Senate office buildings, Capitol power plant, Robert A. Taft Memorial, and buildings and grounds of the Supreme Court and the Library of Congress; operates the Botanic Garden and Senate restaurants. Acquires property and plans and constructs buildings for Congress, the Supreme Court, and the Library of Congress.

Assists in deciding which artwork, historical objects, and exhibits are to be accepted for display in the Capitol. Flag office flies American flags over the Capitol at legislators' request.

Architect of the Capitol, *Office of the Curator, HT3 CAP 20515; (202) 228-1222. Fax, (202) 228-1893. Barbara A. Wolanin, curator. Press, (202) 228-1205. Internet, http://www.aoc.gov.*

Preserves artwork; maintains collection of drawings, photographs, and manuscripts on and about the Capitol and the House and Senate office buildings. Maintains records of the architect of the Capitol. Library open to the public.

Capitol Police, *119 D St. N.E. 20510; (202) 224-9806. Fax, (202) 228-2592. Gary L. Abrecht, chief.*

Responsible for security for the Capitol, House and Senate office buildings, and Botanic Garden; approves demonstration permits.

House Appropriations Committee, *Subcommittee on Legislative Branch, H147 CAP 20515; (202) 225-5338. James T. Walsh, R-N.Y., chair; Edward E. Lombard, staff assistant. Internet, http://www.house.gov/appropriations.*

Jurisdiction over legislation to appropriate funds for the House of Representatives, the Architect of the Capitol (except Senate items), the Botanic Garden, the Library of Congress, and House offices.

House Office Building Commission, *H326 CAP 20515; (202) 225-0600. Fax, (202) 226-1047. Newt Gingrich, R-Ga., chair; Ann Beighey, staff contact.*

Studies and approves all matters related to construction and alterations of House office buildings. Assigns office space to House committees.

House Oversight Committee, *1309 LHOB 20515; (202) 225-8281. Fax, (202) 225-9957. Bill Thomas, R-Calif., chair; Cathy Abernathy, acting staff director. Internet, http://www.house.gov/cho.*

Responsible for all matters related to security of the House office buildings and the House wing of the Capitol; jurisdiction over operations of the Botanic Garden, Library of Congress, Smithsonian Institution, and Capitol art collection (in conjunction with the Joint Committee on the Library).

House Transportation and Infrastructure Committee, *Subcommittee on Public Buildings and Economic Development, 586 Ford Bldg. 20515; (202) 225-3014. Fax, (202) 226-1898. Jay C. Kim, R-Calif., chair; Richard C. Barnett, staff director. Internet, http://www.house.gov/transportation.*

Jurisdiction over legislation relating to the Capitol and House office buildings, including naming of buildings and facilities. Oversees planning, construction, renovation, maintenance, and care of the grounds and buildings of the Capitol, House, Library of Congress, and Botanic Garden (in conjunction with the Joint Committee on the Library). Participates with other House committees in the oversight of security.

Joint Committee on the Library, *1309 LHOB 20515; (202) 225-8281. Rep. Bill Thomas, R-Calif., chair; Deborah Weiss, contact.*

Oversees the placing of all works of art in the Capitol (in conjunction with the House Oversight and Senate Rules and Administration committees); oversees development and maintenance of the Botanic Garden and the Library of Congress (in conjunction with the House Transportation and Infrastructure and Senate Rules and Administration committees).

Senate Appropriations Committee, *Subcommittee on Legislative Branch, S125 CAP 20510; (202) 224-8921. Robert F. Bennett, R-Utah, chair; Christine Ciccone, staff director. Internet, http://www.senate.gov/~appropriations.*

Jurisdiction over legislation to appropriate funds for the Senate, the Architect of the Capitol (except House items), the Botanic Garden, the Library of Congress, and Senate offices.

Senate Commission on Art, *S411 CAP 20510-7102; (202) 224-2955. Fax, (202) 224-8799. Trent Lott, R-Miss., chair; Diane Skvarla, curator of the Senate. Internet, http://www.senate.gov/curator/collections.htm.*

Accepts artwork and historical objects for display in Senate office buildings and the Senate wing of the Capitol. Maintains and exhibits Senate collections (paintings, sculpture, furniture, and manuscripts); oversees and maintains old Senate and Supreme Court chambers.

Senate Rules and Administration Committee, *SR-305 20510; (202) 224-6352. Fax, (202) 224-3036. John W. Warner, R-Va., chair; Grayson Winterling, staff director. Internet, http://www.senate.gov/~rules.*

Responsible for all matters related to the Senate office buildings, including oversight of alterations, and the Senate wing of the Capitol; jurisdiction over authorization of funds for constructing and acquiring additional office space; oversees the maintenance and care of the grounds and buildings of the Botanic Garden and the Library of Congress and the placement of all works of art in the Capitol (in conjunction with the Joint Committee on the Library). Assigns office space to Senate members and committees.

Superintendent of the House Office Buildings, *B341 RHOB 20515; (202) 225-4141. Fax, (202) 225-3003. Robert R. Miley, superintendent.*

Oversees construction, maintenance, and operation of House office buildings; assigns office space to House members under rules of procedure established by the Speaker's office and the House Office Building Commission.

Superintendent of the Senate Office Buildings, *SD-G45 20510; (202) 224-3141. Fax, (202) 224-0652. Larry R. Stoffel, superintendent.*

Oversees construction, maintenance, and operation of Senate office buildings.

U.S. Botanic Garden, *245 1st St. S.W. 20024; (202) 225-8333. Fax, (202) 225-1561. Jeffrey P. Cooper-Smith, executive director. Flower show information, (202) 225-7099 (recording). Internet, http://www.aoc.gov/pages/usbgpage.htm.*

Collects, cultivates, and grows various plants for public display and study. Sponsors four seasonal flower shows annually. Operates conservatory on the Capitol grounds (conservatory closed for renovations from 1997 to 2000).

NONPROFIT

U.S. Capitol Historical Society, *200 Maryland Ave. N.E. 20002; (202) 543-8919. Fax, (202) 544-8244. Clarence J. Brown, president. Library, (202) 543-0629. Internet, uschs@uschs.org or http://www.uschs.org.*

Membership: members of Congress, individuals, and organizations interested in the preservation of the history and traditions of the U.S. Capitol. Conducts historical research; offers tours, lectures, and films; maintains information centers in the Capitol; produces a historical calendar annually.

Tours and Events

CONGRESS

The House and Senate public galleries are open daily from 9:00 a.m. to 4:30 p.m. (Hours are extended when chamber is in session.) Free gallery passes are available from any congressional office.

Capitol Police, *Special Events, 119 D St. N.E. 20510; (202) 224-8891. Fax, (202) 228-2429. Steven Bahrns, deputy chief, Protective Services.*

Handles administrative and protective aspects of all special events held on the Capitol grounds. Accepts applications for demonstration permits and for visiting musical performances and submits them to the police board for approval. Coordinates all VIP arrivals.

Office of the Speaker, *Special Projects, H326 CAP 20515; (202) 225-0600. Fax, (202) 226-1996. Kathleen Taylor, special projects coordinator. Internet, georgia6@hr. house.gov.*

Approves events permits and visiting band performances on the House side of the Capitol. To arrange for performances and events, contact your representative.

Sergeant at Arms of the Senate, *S321 CAP 20510-7200; (202) 224-2341. Fax, (202) 224-7690. Gregory S. Casey, sergeant at arms; Loretta Symms, deputy sergeant at arms.*

Enforces rules and regulations of the Senate public gallery. Approves visiting band performances on the Senate steps; to arrange for performances, contact your senator.

Sergeant at Arms of the Senate, *Capitol Guide Service, Rotunda CAP 20510; (202) 224-3235. Ted Daniel, director, Guide Service. Visitor information, (202) 225-6827.*

Offers the general public free guided tours of the interior of the U.S. Capitol, 9:00 a.m. to 3:45 p.m. daily.

NONPROFIT

U.S. Capitol Historical Society, *200 Maryland Ave. N.E. 20002; (202) 543-8919. Fax, (202) 544-8244. Clarence J. Brown, president. Library, (202) 543-0629. Internet, uschs@uschs.org or http://www.uschs.org.*

Offers tours, lectures, and films; maintains information centers in the Capitol.

CAUCUSES: ORGANIZATIONS OF MEMBERS

HOUSE AND SENATE

Ad Hoc Congressional Committee on Irish Affairs, *2235 RHOB 20515; (202) 225-3965. Fax, (202) 225-1909. Rep. Peter T. King, R-N.Y., Rep. Benjamin A. Gilman, R-N.Y., Rep. Thomas J. Manton, D-N.Y., and Rep. Richard E. Neal, D-Mass., co-chairs; John Feeney, legislative assistant.*

California Democratic Congressional Delegation, *2435 RHOB 20515; (202) 225-1766. Rep. Lucille Roybal-Allard, D-Calif., chair; Sherry Greenberg, staff contact.*

Commission on Security and Cooperation in Europe, *234 Ford Bldg. 20515; (202) 225-1901. Fax, (202) 226-4199. Sen. Alfonse M. D'Amato, R-N.Y., and Rep.*

Christopher H. Smith, R-N.J., co-chairs; Michael Hathaway, staff director. Internet, http://www.house.gov/csce.

Congressional Arts Caucus, *2347 RHOB 20515; (202) 225-3615. Fax, (202) 225-7822. Rep. Louise M. Slaughter, D-N.Y., chair; Julie Kashen, staff contact.*

Congressional Asian Pacific American Caucus, *2135 RHOB 20515; (202) 225-4906. Rep. Patsy T. Mink, D-Hawaii, chair; Laura Efurd, legislative director.*

Congressional Black Caucus, *2344 RHOB 20515; (202) 225-2201. Fax, (202) 225-7854. Rep. Maxine Waters, D-Calif., chair; Donna Crews, staff contact.*

Congressional Competitiveness Caucus, *SH-511 20510; (202) 224-2651. Fax, (202) 224-4379. Sen. Max Baucus, D-Mont., Sen. Charles E. Grassley, R-Iowa, Sen. Jeff Bingaman, D-N.M., Rep. Marcy Kaptur, D-Ohio, and Rep. Jim Kolbe, R-Ariz., co-chairs; Ed Gresser, staff contact.*

Congressional Fire Services Caucus, *2439 RHOB 20515; (202) 225-6501. Rep. Robert E. Andrews, D-N.J., chair; Maureen Doherty, staff contact.*

Congressional Fire Services Institute, *900 2nd St. N.E., #303 20002; (202) 371-1277. Fax, (202) 682-3473. Rep. Robert E. Andrews, D-N.J., chair; William Webb, executive director.*

Congressional Grace Caucus, *2402 RHOB 20515; (202) 225-5611. Fax, (202) 225-9177. Rep. Christopher Cox, R-Calif., chair; Brad Campbell, staff contact.*

Bipartisan coalition; focuses on recommendations made by the Grace commission (President's Private Sector Survey on Cost Control) and other commissions.

Congressional Hispanic Caucus, *1119 LHOB 20515; (202) 225-6235. Rep. Xavier Becerra, D-Calif., chair; Deirdre Martinez, legislative director.*

Congressional International AIDS Task Force, *2349 RHOB 20515; (202) 225-3106. Fax, (202) 225-6197. Rep. Jim McDermott, D-Wash., chair; Rita Patel, staff contact.*

Studies the spread of HIV/AIDS in the developing world; helps plan the U.S. government response.

Fine Arts Board, *SH-522 20510; (202) 224-3004. Ted Stevens, R-Alaska, vice chair; Liz Connell, staff contact.*

Flat Tax Caucus, *301 CHOB 20515; (202) 225-7772. Rep. Dick Armey, R-Texas and Sen. Richard C. Shelby, R-Ala., co-chairs; Andy LaPerriere, staff contact.*

Global Legislators Organization for a Balanced Environment U.S.A., *409 3rd St. N.W., #204 20024;*

(202) 863-0153. Rep. John Edward Porter, R-Ill. and Sen. John Kerry, D-Mass., co-chairs; John Bond, director.

Internet Caucus, *116 CHOB 20515-4701; (202) 225-6311. Rep. Rick White, R-Wash., Rep. Rick Boucher, D-Va., Sen. Patrick J. Leahy, D-Vt., and Sen. Conrad Burns, R-Mont., co-chairs; Dan Horowitz, staff contact. Internet, http://www.netcaucus.org.*

Promotes growth of the Internet, including government participation; educates members and congressional staff about the Internet.

Long Island Congressional Delegation, *2243 RHOB 20515; (202) 225-2601. Fax, (202) 225-1589. Rep. Gary L. Ackerman, D-N.Y., chair; Jedd Moskowitz, chief of staff.*

New York Bipartisan Congressional Delegation, *2354 RHOB 20515; (202) 225-4365. Fax, (202) 225-0816. Rep. Charles B. Rangel, D-N.Y., chair; Patricia Bradley, staff contact.*

Pennsylvania Congressional Delegation, *2423 RHOB 20515; (202) 225-2065. Fax, (202) 225-5709. Rep. John P. Murtha, D-Pa., chair; Debra Tekavec, staff contact.*

Porkbusters Coalition, *1415 LHOB 20515; (202) 225-2331. Fax, (202) 226-0836. Rep. David Minge, D-Minn., and Rep. Ed Royce, R-Calif., co-chairs; Tim Bromelkamp, staff contact.*

U.S. Assn. of Former Members of Congress, *330 A St. N.E. 20002; (202) 543-8676. Fax, (202) 543-7145. Louis Frey Jr., president.*

Nonpartisan organization of former members of Congress. Acts as a congressional alumni association; sponsors educational projects, including the Congressional Fellows program, which provides support for colleges and universities to host visits of former representatives and senators.

U.S. Holocaust Memorial Council, *100 Raoul Wallenberg Pl. S.W. 20024; (202) 488-2626. Fax, (202) 488-2613. Jane Rizer, staff contact.*

Vietnam Veterans in Congress, *2335 RHOB 20515; (202) 225-5905. Fax, (202) 225-5396. Sen. Tom Daschle, D-S.D., Sen. John Kerry, D-Mass., and Rep. Lane Evans, D-Ill., co-chairs; Tom O'Donnell, staff contact.*

Women's Policy, Inc., *409 12th St. S.W., #705 20024; (202) 554-2323. Fax, (202) 554-2346. Marjorie Sims, executive director. Internet, wpic@erols.com or http:// www.womenconnect.com/wpi/index.htm.*

Tracks legislative and executive branch actions affecting women and children.

HOUSE

Albanian Issues Caucus, *2303 RHOB 20515; (202) 225-2464. Fax, (202) 225-5513. Eliot L. Engel, D-N.Y., and Peter T. King, R-N.Y., co-chairs; Jason Steinbaum, staff contact.*

Army Caucus, *2441 RHOB 20515; (202) 225-4611. Fax, (202) 226-0621. Chet Edwards, D-Texas, and John M. McHugh, R-N.Y., co-chairs; Cary Brick, chief of staff.*

The Coalition, *1127 LHOB 20515; (202) 225-4714. Gary A. Condit, D-Calif., co-chair, Administration; John Tanner, D-Tenn., co-chair; Jeff Fleming, legislative director.*

Congressional Alcohol Fuels Caucus, *303 CHOB 20515; (202) 225-2911. Fax, (202) 225-9129. Jon Christensen, R-Neb., Lane Evans, D-Ill., David Minge, D-Minn., and Jim Nussle, R-Iowa, co-chairs; Scott Bruns, staff contact.*

Congressional Automotive Caucus, *2187 RHOB 20515; (202) 225-3611. Fax, (202) 225-6393. Dale E. Kildee, D-Mich., and Bud Shuster, R-Pa., co-chairs; Michelle Arnold, staff contact.*

Congressional Bearing Caucus, *343 CHOB 20515; (202) 225-4476. Fax, (202) 225-4488. Nancy L. Johnson, R-Conn., and John M. Spratt Jr., D-S.C., co-chairs; Scott Cahill, chief of staff.*

Congressional Children's Working Group, *2348 RHOB 20515; (202) 225-3915. Tim Roemer, D-Ind., chair; Gina Mahoney, staff contact.*

Congressional Friends of Animals, *2217 RHOB 20515; (202) 225-3531. Tom Lantos, D-Calif., and Christopher Shays, R-Conn., co-chairs; Winthrop Wulsin, staff contact.*

Congressional Hispanic Caucus Institute, *504 C St. N.E. 20002; (202) 543-1771. Fax, (202) 546-2143. Xavier Becerra, D-Calif., chair; Rita Elizondo, executive director.*

Congressional Human Rights Caucus, *2217 RHOB 20515; (202) 225-3531. John Edward Porter, R-Ill., and Tom Lantos, D-Calif., co-chairs; Hans Hogrefe and Kellie Currie, directors.*

Congressional Older Americans Caucus, *2309 RHOB 20515; (202) 225-3876. Fax, (202) 225-3059. Ralph Regula, R-Ohio, Constance A. Morella, R-Md., and Joseph P. Kennedy II, D-Mass., co-chairs; Lynne Davis, staff contact.*

Congressional Pro-Life Caucus, *2370 RHOB 20515; (202) 225-7669. Fax, (202) 225-7768. Christopher H. Smith, R-N.J., co-chair; Maggie Wynne, director.*

Congressional Social Security Caucus, *2407 RHOB 20515; (202) 225-5961. Fax, (202) 225-9764. C. W. Bill Young, R-Fla., chair; Harry Glenn, staff contact.*

Congressional Space Caucus, *2350 RHOB 20515; (202) 225-4261. Herbert H. Bateman, R-Va., co-chair; Chris Wenk, staff contact.*

Congressional Steel Caucus, *2309 RHOB 20515; (202) 225-3876. Fax, (202) 225-3059. Ralph Regula, R-Ohio, chair; Karen Buttaro, staff contact.*

Congressional Task Force on Haiti, *2305 RHOB 20515; (202) 225-6231. Fax, (202) 226-0112. Major R. Owens, D-N.Y., chair; Jacqueline Ellis, staff contact.*

Congressional Task Force on International HIV/AIDS, *2347 RHOB 20515; (202) 225-3106. Fax, (202) 225-6197. Jim McDermott, D-Wash., chair; Rita Patel, staff contact.*

Congressional Task Force on Tobacco and Health, *2434 RHOB 20515; (202) 225-3411. Fax, (202) 226-0771. Martin T. Meehan, D-Mass., and James V. Hansen, R-Utah, co-chairs; Bill McCann, legislative assistant.*

Congressional Task Force to End the Arab Boycott, *2211 RHOB 20515; (202) 225-6616. Fax, (202) 225-4183. Ileana Ros-Lehtinen, R-Fla., and Charles E. Schumer, D-N.Y., co-chairs; Kate Scheeler, staff contact.*

Congressional Urban Caucus, *131 CHOB 20515; (202) 225-4372. Fax, (202) 226-0333. Bobby L. Rush, D-Ill., chair; Carol Richardson, staff contact.*

Congressional Women's Caucus, *343 CHOB 20515; (202) 225-4476. Fax, (202) 225-4488. Nancy Johnson, R-Conn., and Eleanor Holmes Norton, D-D.C., co-chairs.*

Congressional Working Group on China, *2457 RHOB 20515; (202) 225-4965. Nancy Pelosi, D-Calif., chair; Carolyn Bartholomew, staff contact.*

Conservative Action Team, *2185 RHOB 20515; (202) 225-2276. Dan Burton, R-Ind., John T. Doolittle, R-Calif., Ernest Istook, R-Okla., and Sam Johnson, R-Texas, co-chairs; Jennifer Larkin, staff contact.*

Export Task Force, *343 CHOB 20515; (202) 225-4476. Fax, (202) 225-4488. Nancy L. Johnson, R-Conn., co-chair; Dave Karvelis, chief of staff.*

Firearms Legislation Task Force, *1130 LHOB 20515; (202) 225-2931. Bob Barr, R-Ga., chair; Glee Smith, staff contact.*

House Republican Task Force on Agriculture, *1527 LHOB 20515; (202) 225-2006. Fax, (202) 225-3392. George Nethercutt, R-Wash., chair; Jack Silzel, staff contact.*

Long Island Sound Congressional Caucus, *1502 LHOB 20515; (202) 225-5541. Fax, (202) 225-9629. Christopher Shays, R-Conn., and Nita M. Lowey, D-N.Y., co-chairs; Allison Rak, legislative assistant.*

Mainstream Conservative Alliance, *2183 RHOB 20515; (202) 225-4031. W. J. "Billy" Tauzin, R-La., and Dan Schaefer, R-Colo., co-chairs; Janet Friedman, staff contact.*

Medical Technology Caucus, *103 CHOB 20515; (202) 225-2871. Fax, (202) 225-6351. Anna G. Eshoo, D-Calif., and Jim Ramstad, R-Minn., co-chairs; Megan Ivory, staff contact.*

Narcotics Abuse and Control Caucus, *2354 RHOB 20515; (202) 225-4365. Fax, (202) 225-0816. Charles B. Rangel, D-N.Y., chair; Jim Griffin, staff contact.*

Northeast Agricultural Caucus, *2246 RHOB 20515; (202) 225-3665. Fax, (202) 225-1891. Sherwood Boehlert, R-N.Y., and Tim Holden, D-Pa., co-chairs; Eric Webster, staff contact.*

Peace Accord Monitoring Group, *2303 RHOB 20515; (202) 225-2464. Fax, (202) 225-5513. Eliot L. Engel, D-N.Y., and H. James Saxton, R-N.J., co-chairs; Jason Steinbaum, staff contact.*

Permanent U.S. Congressional Delegation to the European Parliament, *2170 RHOB 20515; (202) 225-5021. Benjamin A. Gilman, R-N.Y., chair; Laura Rush, staff contact.*

Rural Health Care Coalition, *303 CHOB 20515; (202) 225-2911. Fax, (202) 225-9129. Jim Nussle, R-Iowa, and Glenn Poshard, D-Ill., co-chairs; Steven Berry, staff contact.*

SENATE

Democratic Technology and Communications Committee, *SH-619 20510; (202) 224-1430. Fax, (202) 224-1431. John D. Rockefeller IV, D-W.Va., chair; Laura Quinn, staff contact.*

Northeast-Midwest Senate Coalition, *SH-513 20510; (202) 224-0606. Fax, (202) 224-8330. James M. Jeffords, R-Vt., and Daniel Patrick Moynihan, D-N.Y., co-chairs; Jeff Brown, staff contact.*

Senate Auto Caucus, *SR-459 20510; (202) 224-6221. Carl Levin, D-Mich., co-chair; Chris Miller, staff contact.*

Senate Cancer Coalition, *SH-517 20510; (202) 224-5274. Fax, (202) 224-8022. Dianne Feinstein, D-Calif., and Connie Mack, R-Fla., co-chairs; Mark Smith, staff contact.*

Senate Democratic Task Force on Hispanic Issues, *SH-703 20510; (202) 224-5521. Fax, (202) 224-2852. Jeff Bingaman, D-N.M., chair; Chris Harrington, staff contact.*

Senate Great Lakes Task Force, *SH-503 20510; (202) 224-3353. Fax, (202) 224-7983. John Glenn, D-Ohio, co-chair; Rochelle Sturtevant, staff contact.*

Senate Rural Health Caucus, *SH-731 20510; (202) 224-3254. Fax, (202) 228-2923. Tom Harkin, D-Iowa, and Craig Thomas, R-Wyo., co-chairs; Sabrina Corlette, staff contact.*

Senate Steel Caucus, *SH-711 20510; (202) 224-4254. Fax, (202) 224-1893. Arlen Specter, R-Pa., and John D. Rockefeller IV, D-W.Va., co-chairs; Bill Morley, staff contact.*

Senate Textile Caucus, *SR-125 20510; (202) 224-6121. Fax, (202) 228-0327. Ernest F. Hollings, D-S.C., chair; Greg Elias, staff contact.*

U.S. Interparliamentary Group—Mexico, *SH-808 20510; (202) 224-3047. Kay Bailey Hutchison, R-Texas, chair; Sally Walsh, director.*

U.S. Senate—Interparliamentary Services (Executive Committee), *SH-808 20510; (202) 224-3047. Fax, (202) 224-2373. Vacant, chair; Vacant, director.*

Membership: elected parliamentarians throughout the world. All members of Congress are members.

Western States Senate Coalition, *SH-522 20510; (202) 224-3004. Fax, (202) 224-2354. Ben Nighthorse Campbell, R-Colo., Byron L. Dorgan, D-N.D., Orrin G. Hatch, R-Utah, and Ted Stevens, R-Alaska, co-chairs; Dick Cocozza, staff contact.*

CONGRESS AT WORK

See 105th Congress (p. 720) for individual members' offices and committee assignments and for rosters of congressional committees and subcommittees.

CONGRESS

Clerk of the House of Representatives, *Communications Media, B310 RHOB 20515; (202) 225-3941. Fax, (202) 225-0707. Mike Allen, director. Internet, http://www.onlinecao.house.gov.*

Assists House members in making tape recordings. Provides daily gavel-to-gavel television coverage of House floor proceedings.

Office of Photography, *B302 RHOB 20515; (202) 225-2840. Dwight Comedy, director.*

Provides House members with photographic assistance.

House Rules Committee, *H312 CAP 20515; (202) 225-9191. Gerald B. H. Solomon, R-N.Y., chair; Dan Keniry, staff director.*

Sets rules for floor debate on legislation reported by regular standing committees; grants emergency waivers, under the House rules and the Congressional Budget Act of 1974, of required reporting dates for bills and resolutions authorizing new budget authority; has jurisdiction over resolutions creating committees; has legislative authority to recommend changes in the rules of the House; has jurisdiction over recesses and final adjournments of Congress.

Parliamentarian of the House of Representatives, *H209 CAP 20515; (202) 225-7373. Charles W. Johnson III, parliamentarian.*

Advises presiding officers on parliamentary procedures and committee jurisdiction over legislation; prepares and maintains a compilation of the precedents of the House.

Parliamentarian of the Senate, *S133 CAP 20510; (202) 224-6128. Robert B. Dove, parliamentarian; Alan S. Frumin, senior assistant parliamentarian.*

Advises presiding officers on parliamentary procedures and committee jurisdiction over legislation; prepares and maintains a compilation of the precedents of the Senate.

Senate Rules and Administration Committee, *SR-305 20510; (202) 224-6352. Fax, (202) 224-3036. John W. Warner, R-Va., chair; Grayson Winterling, staff director. Internet, http://www.senate.gov/~rules.*

Jurisdiction over all matters related to the rules governing the conduct of business in the Senate, including floor, committee, and gallery procedures. Also studies and makes recommendations on computer and other technical services in the Senate; oversees operation of the computer information system for the Senate.

Sergeant at Arms of the Senate, *Senate Photographic Studio, SDG-10 20510; (202) 224-3669. Fax, (202) 228-3584. Steve Benza, supervisor.*

Provides Senate members with photographic assistance.

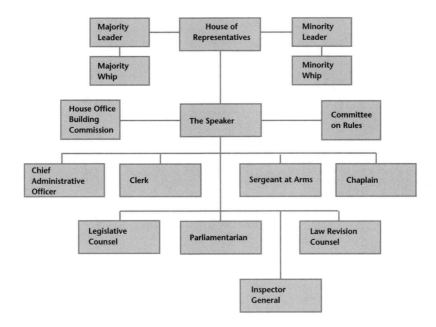

Sergeant at Arms of the Senate, *Senate Recording Studio,* ST71 CAP 20510; (202) 224-4977. Fax, (202) 224-8701. David Bass, director.

Assists Senate members in making radio and video tape recordings and live satellite broadcasts; televises Senate floor proceedings for broadcast by C-SPAN (Cable-Satellite Public Affairs Network).

Leadership

HOUSE

See House Leadership (p. 749); Partisan Committees (p. 747).

House Democratic Caucus, *1420 LHOB 20515; (202) 226-3210. Fax, (202) 225-0282. Vic Fazio, D-Calif., chair; Julie Tippens, chief of staff. Internet, http://www. dcaucus.gov.*

Membership: House Democrats. Selects Democratic leadership; formulates party rules and floor strategy; considers caucus members' recommendations on major issues; votes on the Democratic Steering and Policy Committee's recommendations for Democratic committee assignments.

House Democratic Policy Committee, *H204 CAP 20515; (202) 225-6760. Fax, (202) 226-0938. Richard A. Gephardt, D-Mo., chair; Craig Hannah, executive director. Internet, http://www.house.gov/democrats.*

Studies and makes recommendations to the Democratic leadership on party policy and priorities. Assisted in decisionmaking by the House Democratic Leadership Advisory Group.

House Democratic Steering Committee, *H204 CAP 20515; (202) 225-0100. Fax, (202) 226-0938. Richard A. Gephardt, D-Mo., ; Steny H. Hoyer, D-Md., co-chairs; Craig Hannah, executive director. Internet, http://www. house.gov/democrats.*

Makes Democratic committee assignments, subject to approval by the House Democratic Caucus.

House Republican Conference, *1010 LHOB 20515; (202) 225-5107. Fax, (202) 225-0809. John A. Boehner, R-Ohio, chair; Barry Jackson, executive director.*

Membership: House Republicans. Selects Republican leadership; formulates party rules and floor strategy, and considers party positions on major legislation; votes on Republican Committee on Committees' recommendations for House committee chairmen and Republican

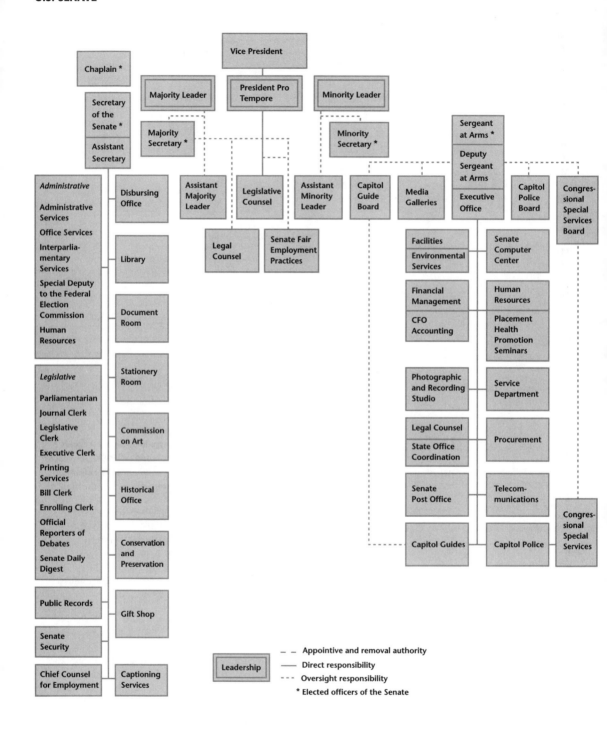

Vice President

Chaplain *

Majority Leader

President Pro Tempore

Minority Leader

Secretary of the Senate *

Majority Secretary *

Minority Secretary *

Sergeant at Arms *

Assistant Secretary

Deputy Sergeant at Arms

Administrative

Disbursing Office

Assistant Majority Leader

Legislative Counsel

Assistant Minority Leader

Capitol Guide Board

Media Galleries

Executive Office

Capitol Police Board

Congressional Special Services Board

Administrative Services

Office Services

Interparliamentary Services

Library

Legal Counsel

Senate Fair Employment Practices

Facilities

Environmental Services

Senate Computer Center

Special Deputy to the Federal Election Commission

Human Resources

Document Room

Financial Management

CFO Accounting

Human Resources

Placement Health Promotion Seminars

Legislative

Stationery Room

Parliamentarian

Journal Clerk

Legislative Clerk

Executive Clerk

Commission on Art

Photographic and Recording Studio

Service Department

Legal Counsel

State Office Coordination

Procurement

Printing Services

Bill Clerk

Enrolling Clerk

Historical Office

Official Reporters of Debates

Senate Daily Digest

Conservation and Preservation

Senate Post Office

Telecommunications

Public Records

Gift Shop

Congressional Special Services

Senate Security

Capitol Guides

Capitol Police

Chief Counsel for Employment

Captioning Services

Leadership

- - - Appointive and removal authority
——— Direct responsibility
- - - Oversight responsibility
* Elected officers of the Senate

committee assignments; publishes legislative digest analyzing pending legislation.

House Republican Policy Committee, *2471 RHOB 20515; (202) 225-6168. Fax, (202) 225-0931. Christopher Cox, R-Calif., chair; Benedict Cohen, executive director. Internet, http://www.house.gov/republican-policy.*

Studies legislation and makes recommendations on House Republican policies and positions on proposed legislation.

House Republican Steering Committee, *H230 CAP 20515; (202) 225-0600. Newt Gingrich, R-Ga., chair; Martha Morrison, staff contact.*

Makes Republican committee assignments and nominates committee chairmen subject to approval by the House Republican Conference and entire House of Representatives.

Majority Leader of the House of Representatives, *H329 CAP 20515; (202) 225-4000. Fax, (202) 226-8100. Dick Armey, R-Texas, majority leader; Peter Davidson, floor assistant.*

Serves as chief strategist and floor spokesman for the majority party in the House.

Majority Whip of the House of Representatives, *H107 CAP 20515; (202) 225-0197. Fax, (202) 225-5117. Tom DeLay, R-Texas, majority whip; Susan Hirschmann, chief of staff. Internet, http://majoritywhip.house.gov.*

Serves as assistant majority leader in the House; helps marshal majority forces in support of party strategy.

Minority Leader of the House of Representatives, *H204 CAP 20515-6502; (202) 225-0100. Fax, (202) 225-7414. Richard A. Gephardt, D-Mo., minority leader; Dan Turton, executive floor assistant. Internet, http://www. house.gov/democrats.*

Serves as chief strategist and floor spokesman for the minority party in the House.

Minority Whip of the House of Representatives, *H307 CAP 20515; (202) 225-3130. Fax, (202) 226-1169. David E. Bonior, D-Mich., minority whip; Sarah Dufendach, administrative assistant.*

Serves as assistant minority leader in the House; helps marshal minority forces in support of party strategy.

Speaker of the House of Representatives, *Speaker's Office, H326 CAP 20515; (202) 225-0600. Newt Gingrich, R-Ga., Speaker; Arne Christenson, chief of staff. Internet, georgia6@hr.house.gov.*

Presides over the House while in session; preserves decorum and order; announces vote results; recognizes members for debate and introduction of bills, amendments, and motions; refers bills and resolutions to committees; decides points of order; appoints House members to conference committees; votes at his own discretion.

SENATE

See Senate Leadership (p. 818); Partisan Committees, (p. 816).

Democratic Leader of the Senate, *S221 CAP 20510; (202) 224-5556. Tom Daschle, D-S.D., Democratic leader; Peter Rouse, chief of staff. Press, (202) 224-2939.*

Serves as chief strategist and floor spokesman for the Democratic party in the Senate.

Majority Leader of the Senate, *SR 487 20510; (202) 224-6253. Trent Lott, R-Miss., majority leader; Dave Hoppe, chief of staff.*

Serves as chief strategist and floor spokesman for the majority party in the Senate.

Majority Whip of the Senate, *S208 CAP 20510; (202) 224-2708. Fax, (202) 224-3913. Don Nickles, R-Okla., majority whip; Doug Badger, staff director.*

Serves as assistant majority leader in the Senate; helps marshal majority forces in support of party strategy.

Minority Whip of the Senate, *S148 CAP (mailing address: SR-173A, Washington, DC 20510); (202) 224-2158. Wendell H. Ford, D-Ky., minority whip; Missy Smith, executive assistant.*

Serves as assistant minority leader in the Senate; helps marshal minority forces in support of party strategy.

President Pro Tempore of the Senate, *S217 RSOB 20510; (202) 224-5972. Strom Thurmond, R-S.C., president pro tempore; R.J. "Duke" Short, administrative assistant.*

Presides over the Senate in the absence of the vice president.

Senate Democratic Conference, *S309 CAP 20510; (202) 224-3735. Tom Daschle, D-S.D., chair; Barbara A. Mikulski, D-Md., secretary; Martin P. Paone, secretary for the minority.*

Membership: Democratic senators. Selects Democratic leadership; formulates party rules and floor strategy and considers party positions on major legislation; votes on Democratic Steering Committee's recommendations for Democratic committee assignments.

Senate Democratic Policy Committee, *S118 CAP 20510; (202) 224-3232. Tom Daschle, D-S.D., chair; Joel Johnson, staff director. Internet, postmaster@dpc.senate.gov.*

Studies and makes recommendations to the Democratic leadership on legislation for consideration by the Senate.

Senate Democratic Steering and Coordination Committee, *SH-712 20510; (202) 224-9048. John Kerry, D-Mass., chair; Martin P. Paone, secretary for the minority.*

Makes Democratic committee assignments subject to approval by the Senate Democratic Conference.

Senate Republican Committee on Committees, *SH-320 20510; (202) 224-2752. Larry E. Craig, R-Idaho, chair; Gerry Fritz, staff contact.*

Makes Republican committee assignments and selects committee chairmen, subject to approval by the Senate Republican Conference. (The committee convenes once every two years at the beginning of each new Congress.)

Senate Republican Conference, *SH-405 20510; (202) 224-2764. Connie Mack, R-Fla., chair; Mark Mills, staff director.*

Membership: Republican senators. Serves as caucus and central coordinating body of the party. Organizes and elects Senate Republican leadership; votes on Republican Committee on Committees' recommendations for Senate committee chairs and Republican committee assignments. Staff provides various support and media services for Republican members.

Senate Republican Policy Committee, *SR-347 20510; (202) 224-2946. Larry E. Craig, R-Idaho, chair; Jade West, staff director.*

Studies and makes recommendations to the majority leader on the priorities and scheduling of legislation on the Senate floor; prepares policy papers and develops Republican policy initiatives.

Vice President of the United States, *President of the Senate, U.S. Capitol, S212 CAP 20510; (202) 224-8391. Albert Gore Jr., vice president; Kay Casstevens, director, legislative affairs. Senate office: SD-202 20510; (202) 224-8391. Executive office: White House 20500; (202) 456-2326. Internet, vice-president@whitehouse.gov.*

Presides over the Senate while in session; preserves decorum and order; announces vote results; recognizes members for debate and introduction of bills, amendments, and motions; decides points of order; votes only in the case of a tie. (President pro tempore of the Senate presides in the absence of the vice president.)

Officers

HOUSE

Chaplain of the House of Representatives, *HB25 CAP 20515; (202) 225-2509. James David Ford, chaplain.*

Opens each day's House session with a prayer; offers religious services to House members, their families, and staffs. (Prayer sometimes offered by visiting chaplain.)

Chief Administrative Officer of the House of Representatives, *H112 CAP 20515; (202) 225-6900. Fax, (202) 226-6300. James M. "Jay" Eagen III, chief administrative officer.*

Responsible for all administrative functions of the House, including services related to employee assistance, finance, payroll, benefits, food service, information resources, telecommunications, procurement, photography, postal operations, supplies and equipment, child care center, barber and beauty shop, and press galleries.

Clerk of the House of Representatives, *H154 CAP 20515; (202) 225-7000. Robin H. Carle, clerk. Internet, http://clerkweb.house.gov.*

Responsible for direction of duties of House employees; receives lobby registrations and reports of campaign expenditures and receipts of House candidates; disburses funds appropriated for House expenditures; responsible for other activities necessary for the continuing operation of the House.

Floor Assistant to the Speaker of the House of Representatives, *HB13 CAP 20515; (202) 225-4768. Fax, (202) 225-1488. Jay Pierson, floor assistant to the Speaker.*

Assists the majority leadership and members on legislative matters.

General Counsel of the House of Representatives, *219 CHOB 20515; (202) 225-9700. Fax, (202) 226-1360. Geraldine R. Gennet, general counsel.*

Advises House members and committees on legal matters.

Legislative Counsel of the House of Representatives, *136 CHOB 20515; (202) 225-6060. Fax, (202) 225-3437. Pope Barrow, legislative counsel.*

Assists House members and committees in drafting legislation.

Sergeant at Arms of the House of Representatives, *H124 CAP 20515; (202) 225-2456. Fax, (202) 225-3233. Wilson L. "Bill" Livingood, sergeant at arms.*

Maintains order on the House floor; executes orders from the Speaker of the House. Serves on the Capitol Police Board and Capitol Guide Board; oversees Capitol security (with Senate Sergeant at Arms) and protocol.

SENATE

Chaplain of the Senate, *SR-325B 20510; (202) 224-2510. Fax, (202) 224-9686. Lloyd Ogilvie, chaplain. Internet, chaplain@senate.gov.*

Opens each day's Senate session with a prayer and offers other religious services to Senate members, their families, and staffs. (Prayer sometimes offered by visiting chaplain.)

Legal Counsel of the Senate, *SH-642 20510; (202) 224-4435. Fax, (202) 224-3391. Thomas B. Griffith, legal counsel.*

Advises Senate members and committees on legal matters.

Legislative Counsel of the Senate, *SD-668 20510; (202) 224-6461. Fax, (202) 224-0567. Francis L. Burk Jr., legislative counsel.*

Assists Senate members and committees in drafting legislation.

Majority Secretary of the Senate, *S337 CAP 20510; (202) 224-3835. Elizabeth Letchworth, secretary; Dave Schiappa, assistant secretary.*

Assists the majority leader and majority party in the Senate.

Minority Secretary of the Senate, *S309 CAP 20510; (202) 224-3735. Martin P. Paone, secretary; Lula Davis, assistant secretary.*

Assists the minority leader and the minority party in the Senate.

Secretary of the Senate, *S220 CAP 20510; (202) 224-3622. Gary Sisco, secretary; Jon Lynn Kerchner, administrative assistant. Information, (202) 224-2115.*

Chief administrative officer of the Senate. Responsible for direction of duties of Senate employees and administration of oaths; receives lobby registrations and reports of campaign expenditures and receipts of Senate candidates; responsible for other Senate activities.

Sergeant at Arms of the Senate, *S321 CAP 20510-7200; (202) 224-2341. Fax, (202) 224-7690. Gregory S. Casey, sergeant at arms; Loretta Symms, deputy sergeant at arms.*

Oversees the Senate wing of the Capitol; doormen; Senate pages; and telecommunication, photographic, supply, and janitorial services. Maintains order on the Senate floor and galleries; oversees Capitol security (with House Sergeant at Arms); sits on the Capitol Police Board and Capitol Guide Board.

Pay and Perquisites

CONGRESS

Attending Physician, *H166 CAP 20515; (202) 225-5421. Dr. John F. Eisold, attending physician; Robert J. Burg, administrative assistant.*

Provides members with primary care, first-aid, emergency care, and environmental/occupational health services; provides House and Senate employees, visiting dignitaries, and tourists with first-aid and emergency care.

Chief Administrative Office, *Postal Operations of the House of Representatives,* *B225 LHOB 20515; (202) 225-3856. Fax, (202) 225-6530. Paul Lozito, assistant director.*

Supervises the postal facilities in the Capitol and the House office buildings.

Clerk of the House of Representatives, *H154 CAP 20515; (202) 225-7000. Robin H. Carle, clerk. Internet, http://clerkweb.house.gov.*

Prepares and submits quarterly reports covering the receipts and expenditures of the House for three months, including disbursements by each committee and each member's office and staff. Reports available from the House Document Room, (202) 225-3456.

House Commission on Congressional Mailing Standards, *140 CHOB 20515; (202) 225-9337. Fax, (202) 226-0047. Bill Thomas, R-Calif., chair; Jack Dail, staff director.*

Oversight of the use of franked mail by House members.

House Government Reform and Oversight Committee, *Subcommittee on Government Management, Information, and Technology,* *B373 RHOB 20515; (202) 225-5147. Steve Horn, R-Calif., chair; J. Russell George, staff director. Internet, http://www.house.gov/cho.*

Jurisdiction over proposed changes in the salary of members of Congress.

House Government Reform and Oversight Committee, *Subcommittee on the Postal Service,* *B349C RHOB 20515; (202) 225-3741. Fax, (202) 225-2544. John M. McHugh, R-N.Y., chair; Robert Taub, staff director. Internet, http://www.house.gov/reform.*

Jurisdiction over the use of the franking privilege.

House Oversight Committee, *1309 LHOB 20515; (202) 225-8281. Fax, (202) 225-9957. Bill Thomas, R-Calif., chair; Cathy Abernathy, acting staff director. Internet, http://www.house.gov/cho.*

Responsible for all matters related to the House's internal operational budget, including members' allowances and expenses, remuneration of House employees, and such unforeseen expenditures as special investigations. Oversight of the House Commission on Congressional Mailing Standards.

CONGRESSIONAL LIAISONS AT FEDERAL AGENCIES

DEPARTMENTS

Agriculture, J. David Carlin, (202) 720-7907

Commerce, Ellen Bloom, (202) 482-3663

Defense, Sandra Stuart, (703) 697-6210

  Air Force, Brig. Gen. Paul V. Hester, (703) 697-8153

  Army, Maj. Gen. Bruce Scott, (703) 697-6767

  Navy, Rear Adm. Norbert Ryan, (703) 697-7146

Education, Scott Fleming, acting, (202) 401-0020

Energy, John C. Angell, (202) 586-5450

Health and Human Services, Irene Bueno, (202) 690-6786

Housing and Urban Development, Hal Decell, (202) 708-0380

Interior, Melanie Beller, (202) 208-7693

Justice, Andrew Fois, (202) 514-3752

Labor, Geri D. Palast, (202) 219-4692

State, Barbara Larkin, (202) 647-4204

Transportation, Nadine Hamilton, acting, (202) 366-9714

Treasury, Linda L. Robertson, (202) 622-1900

Veterans Affairs, Phil Riggin, (202) 273-5615

AGENCIES

Agency for International Development, Ray Burn, (202) 712-4340

Commission on Civil Rights, James Cunningham, (202) 376-8317

Commodity Futures Trading Commission, Thomas Erickson, (202) 418-5075

Consumer Product Safety Commission, Robert J. Wager, (301) 504-0515

Corporation for National Service, Gene Sofer, (202) 606-5000

Environmental Protection Agency, Julie Anderson, (202) 260-5200

Equal Employment Opportunity Commission, Sylvia Anderson, (202) 663-4900

Export-Import Bank, David Carter, (202) 565-3235

Farm Credit Administration, Eileen McMahon, (703) 883-4056

Federal Communications Commission, Cheryl Wilderson, (202) 418-1900

Federal Deposit Insurance Corporation, Alice C. Goodman, (202) 898-8730

Federal Election Commission, Christina VanBrakle, (202) 219-4136

Federal Emergency Management Agency, Martha S. Braddock, (202) 646-4500

Federal Labor Relations Authority, Kim Weaver, (202) 482-6500

Federal Maritime Commission, David Miles, (202) 523-5740

Federal Mediation and Conciliation Service, Elizabeth G. Watson, (202) 606-8150

Federal Reserve System, Donald J. Winn, (202) 452-3456

Secretary of the Senate, *S220 CAP 20510; (202) 224-3622. Gary Sisco, secretary; Jon Lynn Kerchner, administrative assistant. Information, (202) 224-2115. Internet, http://www.senate.gov/senator/secretary.html*

Prepares and submits semiannual reports covering the receipts and expenditures of the Senate for six months, including data on each committee and each member's office and staff. Reports available from the Government Printing Office, (202) 275-3030.

Senate Governmental Affairs Committee, *SD-340 20510; (202) 224-4751. Fax, (202) 224-9603. Fred Thompson, R-Tenn., chair; Hannah Sistare, staff director. Internet, http://www.senate.gov/committee/government_affairs.html.*

Jurisdiction over proposed changes in the salary of members of Congress.

Senate Rules and Administration Committee, *SR-305 20510; (202) 224-6352. Fax, (202) 224-3036. John W. Warner, R-Va., chair; Grayson Winterling, staff director. Internet, http://www.senate.gov/~rules.*

Responsible for all matters related to the Senate's internal operational budget, including members' allowances and expenses, remuneration of Senate employees, and such unforeseen expenditures as special investigations. Oversees budgets of the Secretary of the Senate, the Sergeant at Arms, and the Architect of the Capitol. Jurisdiction over Senate use of the franking privilege.

Senate Select Committee on Ethics, *SH-220 20510; (202) 224-2981. Fax, (202) 224-7416. Robert C. Smith, R-N.H., chair; Victor M. Baird, staff director.*

Oversight of the use of franked mail by Senate members; takes action on misuse of the frank.

Federal Trade Commission, Lorraine Miller (202) 326-2195

General Services Administration, Bill Ratchford, (202) 501-0563

Legal Services Corporation, Vacant, (202) 336-8800

Merit Systems Protection Board, Susan Williams, (202) 653-7171

National Aeronautics and Space Administration, Mary D. Kerwin, (202) 358-1948

National Credit Union Administration, Robert Loftus, (703) 518-6300

National Endowment for the Arts, Richard Woodruff, (202) 682-5434

National Endowment for the Humanities, Ann S. Young-Orr, (202) 606-8328

National Labor Relations Board, John Toner, (202) 273-1944

National Mediation Board, Ronald M. Etters, (202) 523-5944

National Science Foundation, Julia Moore, (703) 306-1070

National Transportation Safety Board, Betty Scott, (202) 314-6120

Nuclear Regulatory Commission, Dennis K. Rathbun, (301) 415-1776

Occupational Safety and Health Review Commission, William A. Gainer, (202) 606-5398

Office of Personnel Management, Cynthia Brock-Smith, (202) 606-1300

Office of Special Counsel, Vacant, (202) 653-9001

Pension Benefit Guaranty Corporation, Judith Schub, (202) 326-4010

Postal Rate Commission, Margaret P. Crenshaw, (202) 789-6840

Securities and Exchange Commission, Kay Williams, (202) 942-0014

Selective Service System, Lewis C. Brodsky, (703) 605-4100

Small Business Administration, Kris Swedin, (202) 205-6700

Smithsonian Institution, Vacant, (202) 357-2962

Social Security Administration, Judy Chesser, (410) 965-3737

Surface Transportation Board, Dan King, (202) 565-1594

Tennessee Valley Authority, Joe Bailey, (202) 898-2999

U.S. Arms Control and Disarmament Agency, Ivo Spalatin, (202) 647-3612

U.S. Information Agency, Ronna Freibert, (202) 619-6828

U.S. International Trade Commission, Nancy Carmin, (202) 205-3151

U.S. Postal Service, Daborah Willhite, (202) 268-2506

NONPROFIT

National Taxpayers Union, *108 N. Alfred St., 3rd Floor, Alexandria, VA 22314; (703) 683-5700. Fax, (703) 683-5722. Peter Sepp, vice president, Communications. Internet, http://www.ntu.org.*

Citizens' interest group that publishes reports on congressional pay and perquisites, including pensions and the franking privilege.

Standards of Conduct

AGENCIES

Justice Dept., *Public Integrity, 10th St. and Constitution Ave. N.W. 20005; (202) 514-1412. Fax, (202) 514-3003. Lee J. Radek, chief.*

Conducts investigations of wrongdoing in selected cases that involve alleged corruption of public office or violations of election law by public officials, including members of Congress.

CONGRESS

House Standards of Official Conduct Committee, *HT-2 CAP 20515; (202) 225-7103. Fax, (202) 225-7392. James V. Hansen, R-Utah, chair; Theodore J. Van Der Meid, chief counsel.*

Enforces the House Code of Official Conduct (rules governing the behavior of House members and employees); has full legislative jurisdiction over all matters under that code; reviews members' financial disclosures.

Legislative Resource Center, *Records and Registration, B-106 CHOB 20515; (202) 226-5200. Fax, (202) 226-5208. Catherine Keller, director.*

Receives and maintains the financial disclosure records of House members, officers, employees, candidates, and certain legislative organizations. Receives reports from committee chairs on foreign travel by members and staff. Records open for public inspection.

Secretary of the Senate, *Public Records, SH-232 20510; (202) 224-0322. Fax, (202) 224-1851. Susan Morgan, staff contact, Ethics.*

Receives and maintains the financial disclosure records of Senate members, officers, employees, candidates, and legislative organizations. Receives reports from committee chairs on foreign travel by senators and staff. Records open for public inspection.

Senate Select Committee on Ethics, *SH-220 20510; (202) 224-2981. Fax, (202) 224-7416. Robert C. Smith, R-N.H., chair; Victor M. Baird, staff director.*

Receives complaints and investigates allegations of improper conduct; administers the code of official conduct; recommends disciplinary action; makes recommendations to the Senate on additional laws, rules, and regulations; investigates allegations of unauthorized disclosure of classified information and documents by members, officers, and employees of the Senate.

CONGRESSIONAL SUPPORT GROUPS

CONGRESS

Congressional Budget Office, *402 Ford Bldg. 20515; (202) 226-2700. Fax, (202) 225-7509. June O'Neill, director. Information, (202) 226-2600. Internet, http://www.cbo.gov.*

Nonpartisan office that provides the House and Senate with budget-related information and analyses of alternative fiscal policies.

General Accounting Office, *441 G St. N.W. 20548; (202) 512-5500. Fax, (202) 512-5507. James F. Hinchman, acting comptroller general. Information, (202) 512-4800. Library, (202) 512-5180. Documents, (202) 512-6000. Internet, http://www.gao.gov.*

Independent, nonpartisan agency in the legislative branch. Serves as the investigating agency for Congress; carries out legal, accounting, auditing, and claims settlement functions; makes recommendations for more effective government operations; publishes monthly lists of reports available to the public. Library open to the public by appointment.

Law Revision Counsel, *H2304 Ford Bldg. 20515; (202) 226-2411. Fax, (202) 225-0010. John R. Miller, law revision counsel. Internet, http://www.law.house.gov.*

Develops and updates an official classification of U.S. laws.

Legislative Counsel of the House of Representatives, *136 CHOB 20515; (202) 225-6060. Fax, (202) 225-3437. Pope Barrow, legislative counsel.*

Assists House members and committees in drafting legislation.

Legislative Counsel of the Senate, *SD-668 20510; (202) 224-6461. Fax, (202) 224-0567. Francis L. Burk Jr., legislative counsel.*

Assists Senate members and committees in drafting legislation.

Library of Congress, *Congressional Research Service, 101 Independence Ave. S.E. 20540; (202) 707-5775. Fax, (202) 707-6745. Daniel P. Mulhollan, director. Information, (202) 707-5700. (Services not available to public).*

Provides members of Congress and committees with general reference assistance; prepares upon request background reports, analytical studies, reading lists, bibliographies, and pros and cons of policy issues; conducts public issue seminars for committees, members, and staffs; makes available the services of subject specialists.

Liaison Offices

CONGRESS

Office of Personnel Management, *Congressional Liaison, B332 RHOB 20515; (202) 225-4955. Fax, (202) 632-0832. Charlene Luskey, chief.*

Provides House and Senate members with information on federal civil service matters, especially those pertaining to federal employment, retirement, and health benefits programs.

HOUSE

Air Force Liaison, *B322 RHOB 20515; (202) 225-6656. Fax, (202) 685-2592. Col. Steve Wood, chief.*

Provides House members with services and information on all matters related to the U.S. Air Force.

Army Liaison, *B325 RHOB 20515; (202) 225-3853. Fax, (202) 685-2674. Col. Dan Fleming, chief.*

Provides House members with services and information on all matters related to the U.S. Army.

Navy-Marine Corps Liaison, *B324 RHOB 20515; (202) 225-7124. Capt. Dale Snodgrass, director; Lt. Col. John F. Kelly, Marine Corps director.*

Provides House members with services and information on all matters related to the U.S. Navy and the U.S. Marine Corps.

U.S. Coast Guard Liaison, *B320 RHOB 20515; (202) 225-4775. Fax, (202) 426-6081. Cmdr. John Gentile, chief.*

Provides House members with services and information on all matters related to the U.S. Coast Guard.

Veterans Affairs Dept. Congressional Liaison Service, *B328 RHOB 20515; (202) 225-2280. Fax, (202) 453-5225. Philip R. Mayo, chief.*

Provides House members with services and information on all matters related to veterans' benefits and services.

White House Legislative Affairs, *White House 20502; (202) 456-2230. Fax, (202) 456-6220. Larry Stein, assistant to the president for legislative affairs; Janet Murguia, deputy assistant (House), (202) 456-6620.*

Serves as a liaison between the president and the House of Representatives.

SENATE

Air Force Liaison, *SR-182 20510; (202) 224-2481. Fax, (202) 685-2575. Col. Jeff McChesney, chief.*

Provides senators with services and information on all matters related to the U.S. Air Force.

Army Liaison, *SR-183 20510; (202) 224-2881. Fax, (202) 685-2570. Col. Randy Bookout, chief.*

Provides senators with services and information on all matters related to the U.S. Army.

Navy-Marine Corps Liaison, *SR-182 20510; (202) 224-4681. Fax, (202) 685-6005. Capt. Barry Costello, Navy director; Col. Terry Paul, Marine Corps director.*

Provides senators with services and information on all matters related to the U.S. Navy and the U.S. Marine Corps.

U.S. Coast Guard Liaison, *SR-183 20510; (202) 224-2913. Fax, (202) 755-1695. Cmdr. John Miko, chief.*

Provides senators with services and information on all matters related to the U.S. Coast Guard.

Veterans Affairs Dept. Congressional Liaison Service, *SH-321 20510; (202) 224-5351. Fax, (202) 453-5218. Philip R. Mayo, chief.*

Provides senators with services and information on all matters related to veterans' benefits and services.

White House Legislative Affairs, *White House 20502; (202) 456-2230. Fax, (202) 456-6220. Larry Stein, assistant to the president for legislative affairs; Tracy Thornton, deputy assistant (Senate), (202) 456-6493.*

Serves as a liaison between the president and the Senate.

Libraries

For Library of Congress divisions, see Libraries and Educational Media (chap. 6)

CONGRESS

House Oversight Committee, *1309 LHOB 20515; (202) 225-8281. Fax, (202) 225-9957. Bill Thomas, R-Calif., chair; Cathy Abernathy, acting staff director. Internet, http://www.house.gov/cho.*

Jurisdiction over legislation on the House library; manages, in conjunction with the Joint Library and the Senate Rules and Administration committees, policies and programs of the Library of Congress.

Joint Committee on the Library, *1309 LHOB 20515; (202) 225-8281. Rep. Bill Thomas, R-Calif., chair; Deborah Weiss, contact.*

Studies and makes recommendations on proposals concerning the management and expansion of the Library of Congress.

Legislative Resource Center, *Library of the House, B18 CHOB 20515; (202) 226-5200. Stephen R. Mayer, senior library assistant.*

Serves as the statutory and official depository of House reports, hearings, prints, and documents for the Clerk of the House.

Library of Congress, *Congressional Research Service, 101 Independence Ave. S.E. 20540; (202) 707-5775. Fax, (202) 707-6745. Daniel P. Mulhollan, director. Information, (202) 707-5700. (Services not available to public).*

Provides members of Congress and committees with general reference assistance.

Library of Congress, *Law Library, 101 Independence Ave. S.E., #LM201 20540; (202) 707-5065. Fax, (202) 707-1820. Rubens Medina, law librarian. Reading room, (202) 707-5080.*

Maintains collections of foreign, international, and comparative law organized jurisdictionally by country; covers all legal systems, including common law, civil law, Roman law, canon law, religious law, and ancient and medieval law. Reading room open to the public.

Library of the Senate, *S332 CAP 20510; (202) 224-7106. Gregory Harness, librarian.*

Maintains special collection for Senate private use of primary source legislative materials, including reports, hearings, prints, documents, and debate proceedings. (Not open to the public.)

Senate Rules and Administration Committee, *SR-305 20510; (202) 224-6352. Fax, (202) 224-3036. John*

W. Warner, R-Va., chair; Grayson Winterling, staff director. Internet, http://www.senate.gov/~rules.

Manages, in conjunction with the House Oversight and the Joint Library committees, policies and programs of the Library of Congress.

Pages

CONGRESS

House of Representatives Page Board, *109 CHOB 20515; (202) 225-2501. Fax, (202) 225-9318. Tillie Fowler, R-Fla., chair; David Gilliland, coordinator.*

Oversees and enforces rules and regulations concerning the House page program.

House of Representatives Page School, *LJ-A5, Library of Congress 20540-9996; (202) 225-9000. Fax, (202) 225-9001. Robert F. Knautz, principal.*

Provides pages of the House with junior year high school education.

Senate Page School, *U.S. Senate 20510-7248; (202) 224-3926. Fax, (202) 224-1838. Kathryn S. Weeden, principal.*

Provides education for pages of the Senate.

Sergeant at Arms of the Senate, *S321 CAP 20510-7200; (202) 224-2341. Fax, (202) 224-7690. Gregory S. Casey, sergeant at arms; Loretta Symms, deputy sergeant at arms.*

Oversees and enforces rules and regulations concerning Senate pages after they have been appointed.

Staff

CONGRESS

House Oversight Committee, *1309 LHOB 20515; (202) 225-8281. Fax, (202) 225-9957. Bill Thomas, R-Calif., chair; Cathy Abernathy, acting staff director. Internet, http://www.house.gov/cho.*

Jurisdiction over employment of persons by the House. Handles issues of compensation, retirement, and other benefits for members, officers, and employees. Oversight of the House contingent fund, office equipment, and police, parking, restaurant, and other related services.

Human Resources/Policy and Administration, *House Resume Referral Service, 263 CHOB 20515-6610; (202) 225-2926. Fax, (202) 226-0098. James M. "Jay" Eagen III, chief administrative officer. Information, (202) 226-6731.*

Provides members, committees, and administrative offices of the House of Representatives with placement and referral services.

Office of Compliance, *110 2nd St. S.E., #LA-200 20540-1999; (202) 724-9250. Fax, (202) 426-1913. Constance Miller, director, Education and Training. Information, (202) 724-9260. TDD, (202) 426-1912. Internet, http://www.compliance.gov.*

Provides general information to covered employees, applicants, and former employees of the legislative branch about their equal employment rights and protections under the Congressional Accountability Act of 1995.

Senate Placement Office, *SH-142 20510; (202) 224-9167. Yvonne Costello, manager.*

Provides members, committees, and administrative offices of the Senate with placement and referral services.

Senate Rules and Administration Committee, *SR-305 20510; (202) 224-6352. Fax, (202) 224-3036. John W. Warner, R-Va., chair; Grayson Winterling, staff director. Internet, http://www.senate.gov/~rules.*

Jurisdiction over Senate contingent fund, which provides salaries for professional committee staff members and general funds for personal Senate staffs.

NONPROFIT

Administrative Assistants Assn. of the U.S. House of Representatives, *1974 LHOB 20515; (202) 225-3915. Doug Ritter, president.*

Professional and social organization of House chiefs of staff. Meets to discuss mutual concerns and exchange information. Sponsors orientation program for new chiefs of staff. Meets with administrative, congressional, and international personnel for off-the-record briefings.

Capitol Hill Women's Political Caucus, *P.O. Box 599, LHOB 20515; (202) 986-0994. Victoria Sneed, chair.*

Membership: women and men from congressional offices, public interest groups, federal agencies, law firms, and lobbying organizations. Promotes legislation that supports equal employment policy, reproductive choice, child care, and other issues of concern to women; seeks to encourage participation, election, and appointment of women in the political and governing process; serves as an information clearinghouse for female members of Congress and the public. (Affiliated with the National Women's Political Caucus.)

Congressional Legislative Staff Assn., *c/o 1991 LHOB 20515; (202) 225-1986. Nelson Garcia, president.*

Nonpartisan professional organization of legislative assistants, legislative directors, legal counsels, and committee staff. Meets to discuss mutual concerns, exchange information, and hear guest speakers; holds seminars on issues pending on the House floor.

Congressional Management Foundation, *513 Capitol Court N.E., #300 20002; (202) 546-0100. Fax, (202) 547-0936. Richard Shapiro, executive director. Internet, cmf@ricochet.net.*

Nonpartisan organization that provides members of Congress and their staffs with management information and services through seminars, consultation, research, and publications.

Congressional Staff Club, *810 O'Neill Bldg. 20515; (202) 226-3250. Cary Brick, president.*

Organization of House and Senate staff members. Meets to discuss mutual concerns and promote better relationships among congressional offices.

Federal Bar Assn., *1815 H St. N.W., #408 20006; (202) 638-0252. Fax, (202) 775-0295. Michael E. Campiglia, executive director. Internet, fba@fedbar.org or http://www.fedbar.org.*

Organization of bar members who are present or former staff members of the House, Senate, Library of Congress, Supreme Court, General Accounting Office, or Government Printing Office, or attorneys in legislative practice before federal courts or agencies.

Senate Press Secretaries Assn., *SD-329 20510-2203; (202) 224-8833. Fax, (202) 224-8834. Joe McMonigle, president.*

Bipartisan organization of present and former senatorial press secretaries and assistant press secretaries. Meets to discuss mutual concerns and to hear guest speakers.

 POLITICAL ADVOCACY

See also Advocacy and Public Service (chap. 1)

AGENCIES

Justice Dept., *Foreign Agents Registration Unit, 1400 New York Ave. N.W. 20530; (202) 514-1216. Fax, (202) 514-2836. Marshall Williams, chief. Internet, http://www.usdoj.gov/criminal/fara.*

Receives and maintains the registration of agents representing foreign countries, companies, organizations, and individuals. Compiles semi-annual report on foreign agent registrations. Foreign agent registration files are open for public inspection.

CONGRESS

House Judiciary Committee, *Subcommittee on the Constitution, 362 Ford Bldg. 20515; (202) 226-7680. Fax, (202) 225-3746. Charles T. Canady, R-Fla., chair; Keri*

Folmar, counsel. Internet, http://www.house.gov/judiciary.

Jurisdiction over legislation on the federal regulation of lobbying and disclosure requirements for registered lobbyists.

Legislative Resource Center, *Records and Registration, B-106 CHOB 20515; (202) 226-5200. Fax, (202) 226-5208. Catherine Keller, director.*

Receives and maintains lobby registrations and quarterly financial reports of lobbyists. Administers the statutes of the Federal Regulation of Lobbying Act of 1995 and counsels lobbyists. Receives and maintains agency filings made under the requirements of Section 319 of the Department of the Interior and Related Agencies Appropriations Act for fiscal 1990 (known as the Byrd amendment). Open for public inspection.

Secretary of the Senate, *Public Records, SH-232 20510; (202) 224-0758. Fax, (202) 224-1851. Mark W. Ward, staff contact.*

Receives and maintains lobby registrations and quarterly financial reports of lobbyists. Open for public inspection.

Senate Governmental Affairs Committee, *Subcommittee on Oversight of Government Management, Restructuring, and the District of Columbia, SH-604 20510; (202) 224-3682. Fax, (202) 224-3328. Sam Brownback, R-Kan., chair; Michael Rubin, acting staff director. Internet, http://www.senate.gov/committee/governmental_affairs.html.*

Jurisdiction over legislation on regulation of lobbying and disclosure requirements for registered lobbyists.

NONPROFIT

American League of Lobbyists, *P.O. Box 30005, Alexandria, VA 22310; (703) 960-3011. Patti Jo Baber, executive director.*

Membership: lobbyists and government relations and public affairs professionals. Works to improve the skills, ethics, and public image of lobbyists. Monitors lobby legislation; conducts educational programs on public issues, lobbying techniques, and other topics of interest to membership.

Political Action Committees

The following are some key political action committees (PACs) based in Washington. Note that many other organizations listed in this book operate their own PACs.

LABOR

Active Ballot Club *(United Food and Commercial Workers International Union, AFL-CIO), 1775 K St.*

N.W. 20006; (202) 223-3111. Fax, (202) 728-1802. Joseph T. Hansen, treasurer.

Air Line Pilots Assn. PAC, 1625 Massachusetts Ave. N.W., 8th Floor 20036; (202) 797-4039. Fax, (202) 797-4052. Duane E. Woerth, treasurer.

Amalgamated Transit Union—Cope, 5025 Wisconsin Ave. N.W., 3rd Floor 20016; (202) 537-1645. Fax, (202) 244-7824. Oliver W. Green, treasurer.

American Federation of State, County, and Municipal Employees—PEOPLE, Qualified, 1625 L St. N.W. 20036; (202) 429-1000. Fax, (202) 429-1102. William Lucy, treasurer. Internet, http://www.afscme.org.

American Federation of Teachers Committee on Political Education, 555 New Jersey Ave. N.W. 20001; (202) 879-4436. Edward J. McElroy, treasurer. Internet, http://www.aft.com.

Carpenters' Legislative Improvement Committee *(United Brotherhood of Carpenters and Joiners of America, AFL-CIO),* 101 Constitution Ave. N.W. 20001; (202) 546-6206. Fax, (202) 546-3873. Douglas J. McCarron, treasurer.

Committee on Letter Carriers Political Education *(National Assn. of Letter Carriers),* 100 Indiana Ave. N.W. 20001; (202) 393-4695. Fax, (202) 737-1540. Florence Johnson, treasurer.

CWA-COPE Political Contributions Committee *(Communications Workers of America, AFL-CIO),* 501 3rd St. N.W., #1000 20001; (202) 434-1410. Fax, (202) 434-1481. Barbara J. Easterling, treasurer.

Democratic Republican Independent Voter Education Committee (DRIVE) *(International Brotherhood of Teamsters, Chauffeurs, Warehousemen, and Helpers of America),* 25 Louisiana Ave. N.W. 20001; (202) 624-8741. Fax, (202) 624-8973. Bob Nicklas, treasurer.

Engineers Political Education Committee/ International Union of Operating Engineers, 1125 17th St. N.W. 20036; (202) 429-9100. Fax, (202) 778-2691. Tim James, treasurer.

International Brotherhood of Electrical Workers Committee on Political Education, 1125 15th St. N.W., #1202 20005; (202) 728-6020. Fax, (202) 728-6099. Edwin Hill, treasurer.

Ironworkers Political Action League, 1750 New York Ave. N.W., #400 20006; (202) 383-4800. Fax, (202) 383-6483. James E. Cole, treasurer.

Laborers' Political League of Laborers' International Union of North America, 905 16th St. N.W. 20006; (202) 737-8320. Fax, (202) 737-2754. R. P. Vinall, treasurer.

Machinists Non-Partisan Political League *(International Assn. of Machinists and Aerospace Workers, AFL-CIO),* 9000 Machinists Pl., Upper Marlboro, MD 20772; (301) 967-4500. Fax, (301) 967-4588. Donald E. Wharton, treasurer.

National Education Assn. PAC, 1201 16th St. N.W. 20036; (202) 822-7300. Fax, (202) 822-7741. Mary Elizabeth Teasley, director.

Political Fund Committee of the American Postal Workers Union, AFL-CIO, 1300 L St. N.W. 20005; (202) 842-4210. Fax, (202) 842-8530. Douglas C. Holbrook, treasurer.

Seafarers Political Activity Donation *(Seafarers International Union of North America),* 5201 Auth Way, Camp Springs, MD 20746; (301) 899-0675. Fax, (301) 899-7355. Michael Neuman, treasurer.

Sheet Metal Workers International Assn. Political Action League, 1750 New York Ave. N.W. 20006; (202) 662-0887. Fax, (202) 662-0895. Michael J. Sullivan, treasurer.

United Mine Workers of America, *Coal Miners Political Action Committee,* 900 15th St. N.W. 20005; (202) 842-7200. Fax, (202) 842-7212. Carlo Tarley, treasurer.

NONCONNECTED

American AIDS PAC, 1808 Swann St. N.W. 20009; (202) 462-8061. Fax, (202) 483-1964. Thomas F. Sheridan, treasurer.

American Sugarbeet Growers Assn. Political Action Committee, 1156 15th St. N.W., #1101 20005; (202) 833-2398. Fax, (202) 833-2962. Luther Markwart, treasurer.

Americans for Free International Trade PAC Inc., 112 S. West St., #310, Alexandria, VA 22314; (703) 684-8880. Lee Maas, treasurer.

Arthur Andersen PAC (FKA) Arthur Andersen/ Andersen Consulting PAC, 1666 K St. N.W. 20006; (202) 862-3100. Jeffrey J. Peck, treasurer. Consulting PAC, (202) 327-8560.

Black America's PAC, 2029 P St. N.W., #302 20036; (202) 785-9619. Fax, (202) 785-9621. Alvin Williams, executive director. Internet, bampac@compuserve.com or http://www.bampac.org.

Committee for a Democratic Majority, *426 C St. N.E., Rear Bldg. 20002; (202) 544-4889. Fax, (202) 546-2285. William C. Oldaker, treasurer.*

Coopers and Lybrand PAC, *1900 K St. N.W. 20006; (202) 822-4274. Fax, (202) 822-5640. Allen J. Weltmann, treasurer.*

Council for a Livable World, *110 Maryland Ave. N.E., #409 20002; (202) 543-4100. Fax, (202) 543-6297. John Isaacs, president. Internet, clw@clw.org or http://www.clw.org/pub/clw/welcome.html.*

Supports congressional candidates who advocate arms control and cutting the military budget.

Deloitte and Touche LLP Federal Political Action Committee, *555 12th N.W., #500 20004; (202) 879-5600. Fax, (202) 879-5309. Wade S. Williams, treasurer.*

Effective Government Committee, *530 7th St. S.E. 20003; (202) 347-1767. Fax, (202) 544-8612. David Jones, treasurer.*

Promotes Democratic candidates in congressional elections.

EMILY's List, *805 15th St. N.W., #400 20005; (202) 326-1400. Fax, (202) 326-1415. Jennifer Boucher, treasurer. Internet, http://www.emilyslist.org.*

Raises money to support pro-choice Democratic women candidates for political office.

English Language PAC, *P.O. Box 9558 20016; (202) 775-1307. Jan C. Zall, treasurer. Internet, http://www.workings.com/elpac.htm.*

Supports candidates who favor declaring English the official language of the United States.

Ernst and Young PAC, *1225 Connecticut Ave. N.W., #200 20036; (202) 327-6410. Fax, (202) 327-8863. George H. McCallum, treasurer.*

GOPAC Inc., *122 C St. N.W., #505 20001; (202) 484-2282. Fax, (202) 783-3306. Tony Moonis, treasurer. Internet, http://www.gopac.com.*

Promotes conservative Republican candidates for local, state, and federal office.

National Committee for an Effective Congress, *122 C St. N.W., #650 20001; (202) 639-8300. Fax, (202) 639-5038. James E. Byron, treasurer. Internet, http://www.ncec.org.*

Supports liberal or progressive candidates in marginal races.

National PAC, *600 Pennsylvania Ave. S.E., #207 20003; (202) 879-7710. Fax, (202) 879-7728. Marvin Josephson, treasurer.*

Supports candidates who advocate close U.S.-Israeli relations.

New Republican Majority Fund, *1301 Pennsylvania Ave. N.W., #500 20004; (202) 347-1233. Fax, (202) 347-1238. J. Stanley Huckaby, treasurer; John Green, executive director. Internet, nrmf@msn.com.*

Peat Marwick Partners/Principals and Employees Political Action Committee, *P.O. Box 18254 20036; (202) 467-3974. Fax, (202) 296-6495. Stephen E. Allis, treasurer.*

Price Waterhouse Partners' Political Action Committee, *1301 K St. N.W., #800W 20005; (202) 414-1000. Fax, (202) 414-1301. Gilbert Simonetti Jr., treasurer.*

Voters for Choice/Friends of Family Planning, *P.O. Box 53301 20009-9301; (202) 588-5200. Fax, (202) 588-0600. Mary Jean Collins, treasurer.*

Wish List, *3205 N St. N.W. 20007; (202) 342-9111. Fax, (202) 342-9190. Kendall Wilson, treasurer. Internet, thwishlist@aol.com or http://www.thewishlist.org.*

Raises money for pro-choice Republican women candidates

Trade, Membership, and Health

Action Committee for Rural Electrification, *4301 Wilson Blvd., Arlington, VA 22203; (703) 907-5500. Patrick E. Gioffre, treasurer.*

American Bankers Assn. BankPAC, *1120 Connecticut Ave. N.W., #851 20036; (202) 663-5113. Fax, (202) 663-7544. Gary W. Fields, treasurer.*

American Dental PAC, *1111 14th St. N.W., 11th Floor 20005; (202) 898-2424. Fax, (202) 898-2437. Dr. Michael Donohoo, treasurer.*

American Health Care Assn. Political Action Committee (AHC-PAC), *1201 L St. N.W. 20005; (202) 842-4444. Fax, (202) 842-3860. Mary Ousley, treasurer. Internet, http://www.ahca.org.*

American Medical Assn. PAC, *1101 Vermont Ave. N.W. 20005; (202) 789-7400. Fax, (202) 789-7469. Kevin Walker, treasurer.*

Assn. of Trial Lawyers of America PAC, *1050 31st St. N.W. 20007; (202) 965-3500. Fax, (202) 338-8709. Heather Tureen, director.*

Build PAC of the National Assn. of Home Builders, *1201 15th St. N.W. 20005; (202) 822-0470. Fax, (202) 822-0572. Joe Barney, treasurer.*

Credit Union Legislative Action Council, *805 15th St. N.W., #300 20005; (202) 682-4200. Sonja Simmons, treasurer.*

Dealers Election Action Committee of the National Automobile Dealers Assn., *8400 Westpark Dr., McLean, VA 22102; (703) 821-7111. Fax, (703) 442-3168. Leonard Fichtner, treasurer. Internet, deac@nadanet.com or http://www.nadanet.com.*

Human Rights Campaign PAC, *1101 14th St. N.W., #200 20005; (202) 628-4160. Fax, (202) 347-5323. Elizabeth Birch, treasurer. Internet, hrc@hrc.org or http://www.hrc.org.*

Supports candidates for state and federal office who favor gay and lesbian rights.

Independent Insurance Agents of America Inc. Political Action Committee (INSURPAC), *412 1st St. S.E., #300 20003; (202) 863-7000. Fax, (202) 863-7015. Paul A. Equale, treasurer.*

National Assn. of Broadcasters Television and Radio Political Action Committee, *1771 N St. N.W. 20036; (202) 429-5300. Fax, (202) 775-2157. Rae Ann Bevington, manager. Internet, http://www.nab.org.*

National Assn. of Life Underwriters PAC, *1922 F St. N.W. 20006; (202) 331-6000. Paul M. Smith Sr., treasurer.*

National Assn. of Retired Federal Employees PAC, *606 N. Washington St., Alexandria, VA 22314; (703) 838-7760. Fax, (703) 838-7782. Frank G. Atwater, treasurer. Member relations, (800) 456-8410. Internet, narfehq@aol.com.*

National Assn. of Social Workers Political Action for Candidate Election, *750 1st St. N.E., #700 20002; (202) 408-8600. Fax, (202) 336-8311. Keith Umemoto, treasurer.*

National Beer Wholesalers' Assn. PAC, *1100 S. Washington St., Alexandria, VA 22314; (703) 683-4300. Fax, (703) 683-8965. Ronald A. Sarasin, treasurer.*

National Committee to Preserve Social Security and Medicare PAC, *10 G St. N.E., #600 20002; (202) 216-0420. Fax, (202) 216-0451. Shelly C. Shapiro, treasurer. Internet, http://www.ncpssm.org.*

NRA Political Victory Fund, *11250 Waples Mill Rd., Fairfax, VA 22030; (703) 267-1000. Fax, (703) 267-3918. Maryrose Jennison, treasurer.*

Physical Therapy Political Action Committee (PT-PAC), *1111 N. Fairfax St., Alexandria, VA 22314; (703) 684-2782. Fax, (202) 706-8519. Nancy Garland, treasurer.*

Women's Campaign Fund Inc., *734 15th St. N.W., #500 20005; (202) 393-8164. Fax, (202) 393-0649. Doreen Frasca, treasurer.*

Political Interest Groups

See also Advocacy and Public Service (chap. 1)

NONPROFIT

Alexis de Tocqueville Institution, *1611 N. Kent St., #901, Arlington, VA 22209; (703) 351-4969. Fax, (703) 351-0090. Merrick Carey, president. Internet, alexisde@aol.com or http://www.schoolreport.com/adti.*

Public policy research organization that conducts, sponsors and publishes research and analysis. Advocates individual political and economic freedom, limited government, and free markets. Provides research grants to journalists, scholars, and others.

American Conservative Union, *1007 Cameron St., Alexandria, VA 22314; (703) 836-8602. Fax, (703) 836-8606. Vacant, executive director. Toll-free, (800) 228-7345. Internet, acu@conservative.org or http://www.conservative.org.*

Legislative interest organization that focuses on defense, foreign policy, economics, the national budget, taxes, and legal and social issues. Monitors legislation and regulations.

Americans Back in Charge, *1225 Eye St. N.W., #500 20005; (202) 371-0450. Fax, (202) 682-4707. Paul Sullivan, director. Internet, abic@abic.org or http://www.abic.org.*

Works for congressional passage of a term limits constitutional amendment; provides information on term limits and congressional reform; advocates limited government. Term Limits Legal Institute project handles lawsuits regarding congressional term limits.

Americans for Democratic Action, *1625 K St. N.W., #210 20006; (202) 785-5980. Fax, (202) 785-5969. Jack Sheinkman, president; Amy F. Isaacs, director. Internet, adaction@ix.netcom.com or http://www.adaction.org.*

Legislative interest organization that seeks to strengthen civil, constitutional, women's, family, workers', and human rights.

Brookings Institution, *1775 Massachusetts Ave. N.W. 20036; (202) 797-6000. Fax, (202) 797-6004. Michael H. Armacost, president. Internet, brookinfo@brook.edu or http://www.brookings.org.*

Public policy research organization that seeks to improve the performance of American institutions, the effectiveness of government programs, and the quality of public policy through research and analysis. Sponsors lectures, debates, and policy forums.

Campaign for America's Future, *1101 14th St. N.W., #600 20005; (202) 371-6990. Fax, (202) 371-9669. Robert L. Borosage and Roger Hickey, co-directors. Internet, http://www.ourfuture.org.*

Advocates policies to help working people. Supports improved employee benefits, including health care, child care, and paid family leave; promotes life-long education and training of workers. Seeks full employment, higher wages, and increased productivity. Monitors legislation and regulations.

Cato Institute, *1000 Massachusetts Ave. N.W. 20001-5403; (202) 842-0200. Fax, (202) 842-3490. Edward H. Crane III, president. Library, (202) 789-5263. Internet, cato@cato.org or http://www.cato.org.*

Public policy research organization that advocates limited government and individual liberty. Interests include privatization and deregulation, low and simple taxes, and reduced government spending. Encourages voluntary solutions to social and economic problems. Library open to the public by appointment.

Center for National Policy, *1 Massachusetts Ave. N.W., #333 20001; (202) 682-1800. Fax, (202) 682-1818. Maureen Steinbruner, president. Internet, cnp@access.digex.net or http://www.access.digex.net/cnp.*

Public policy research and educational organization that serves as a forum for development of national policy alternatives. Studies issues of national and international concern including problems of governance; sponsors conferences and symposia.

Christian Coalition, *227 Massachusetts Ave. N.E., #101 20002; (202) 547-3600. Fax, (202) 543-2978. Heidi Stirrup, director, Government Affairs. Internet, http://www.cc.org.*

Membership: individuals who support traditional, conservative Christian values. Represents members' views to all levels of government and to the media. (Headquarters in Chesapeake, Va.)

Common Cause, *1250 Connecticut Ave. N.W., #600 20036; (202) 833-1200. Fax, (202) 659-3716. Ann*

McBride, president; John Anthony, press secretary. Press, (202) 736-5770. Internet, http://www.commoncause.org.

Citizens' legislative interest group that works for institutional reform in federal and state government. Advocates partial public financing of congressional election campaigns, ethics in government, nuclear arms control, oversight of defense spending, tax reform, and a reduction of political action committee influence in Congress.

Concerned Women for America, *901 D St. S.W., #800 20024; (202) 488-7000. Fax, (202) 488-0806. Jim Woodall, chief executive officer. Internet, http://www.cwfa.org.*

Educational organization that seeks to protect the rights of the family and preserve Judeo-Christian values. Monitors legislation affecting family and religious issues.

Concord Coalition, *1019 19th St. N.W., #810 20036; (202) 467-6222. Fax, (202) 467-6333. Martha Phillips, executive director. Internet, http://www.concordcoalition.org.*

Bipartisan citizens' interest group that promotes tax and spending policies intended to eliminate the federal budget deficit.

Congressional Economic Leadership Institute, *201 Massachusetts Ave. N.E., #C8 20002; (202) 546-5007. Fax, (202) 546-7037. John Weinfurter, president. Internet, http://www.celi.org.*

Nonpartisan research group that serves as a forum for the discussion of economic issues between Congress and the private sector.

Congressional Institute for the Future, *409 3rd St. S.W., #204 20024; (202) 863-1700. Fax, (202) 479-9447. Tom Hennessy, executive director. Internet, globe@igc.apc.org or http://policy.gmu.edu/cif/cif.html.*

Nonpartisan educational organization that offers information about emerging issues and trends to leaders in business and government. Conducts research; sponsors seminars and conferences; compiles and analyzes public opinion data.

Conservative Caucus, *450 Maple Ave. East, Vienna, VA 22180; (703) 938-9626. Fax, (703) 281-4108. Howard Phillips, chair. Internet, http://www.conservativeusa.org.*

Legislative interest organization that promotes grass-roots activity on issues such as national defense and economic and tax policy. The Conservative Caucus Research, Analysis, and Education Foundation studies public issues including Central American affairs, defense policy, and federal funding of political advocacy groups.

Council for Citizens Against Government Waste, *1301 Connecticut Ave. N.W., #400 20036; (202) 467-5300.*

RATINGS OF MEMBERS

The following organizations either publish voting records on selected issues or annually rate members of Congress; organizations marked with an asterisk (*) rate members biennially.

AFL—CIO, 815 16th St. N.W. 20006; (202) 637-5000.

American Conservative Union, 1007 Cameron St., Alexandria, VA 22314; (703) 836-8602.

*American Farm Bureau Federation, 600 Maryland Ave. S.W., #800 20024; (202) 484-3600.

*American Security Council, 5545 Security Circle, Boston, VA 22713; (540) 547-1776.

Americans for Democratic Action, 1625 K St. N.W., #210 20006; (202) 785-5980.

*Common Cause, 1250 Connecticut Ave. N.W., #600 20036; (202) 833-1200.

Competitive Enterprise Institute, 1001 Connecticut Ave. N.W., #1250 20036; (202) 331-1010.

Consumer Federation of America, 1424 16th St. N.W., #604 20036; (202) 387-6121.

Human Rights Campaign, 1101 14th St. N.W., #200 20005; (202) 628-4160

Leadership Conference on Civil Rights, 1629 K St. N.W., #1010 20006; (202) 466-3311.

League of Conservation Voters, 1707 L St. N.W., #750 20036; (202) 785-8683.

*Liberty Lobby, 300 Independence Ave. S.E. 20003; (202) 546-5611.

National Abortion and Reproductive Rights Action League-Political Action Committee (NARAL-PAC), 1156 15th St. N.W., 7th Floor 20005; (202) 973-3000.

*National Assn. for the Advancement of Colored People (NAACP), 1025 Vermont Ave. N.W., #1120 20005; (202) 638-2269.

National Assn. of Social Workers-PACE (Political Action for Candidate Election), 750 1st St. N.E., #700 20002; (202) 408-8600.

National Council of Senior Citizens, 8403 Colesville Rd., #1200, Silver Spring, MD 20910; (301) 578-8800.

National Federation of Independent Business, 600 Maryland Ave. S.W., #700 20024; (202) 554-9000.

National Gay and Lesbian Task Force Policy Institute, 2320 17th St. N.W. 20009; (202) 332-6483.

National Taxpayers Union, 108 N. Alfred St., Alexandria, VA 22314, (703) 683-5700.

National Women's Political Caucus, 1211 Connecticut Ave. N.W., #425 20036; (202) 785-1100.

Public Citizen, Congress Watch, 215 Pennsylvania Ave. S.E., 3rd Floor 20003; (202) 546-4996.

U.S. Chamber of Commerce Legislative and Public Affairs, 1615 H St. N.W. 20062; (202) 463-5604.

U.S. Student Assn., 1413 K St. N.W., 9th Floor 20005; (202) 347-8772.

The Woman Activist Fund, 2310 Barbour Rd., Falls Church, VA 22043; (703) 573-8716.

Fax, (202) 467-4253. Thomas A. Schatz, president. Toll-free, (800) 232-6479. Internet, http://www.cagw.org.

Nonpartisan organization that seeks to eliminate waste, mismanagement, and inefficiency in the federal government. Monitors legislation and regulations.

Eagle Forum, 316 Pennsylvania Ave. S.E., #203 20003; (202) 544-0353. Fax, (202) 547-6996. Vacant, legislative director. Internet, eagle@eagleforum.org or http://www.eagleforum.org.

Legislative interest group that supports conservative, pro-family policies at all levels of government. Concerns include abortion, affirmative action, taxes, and national defense. (Headquarters in St. Louis.)

Empower America, 1776 Eye St. N.W., #890 20006; (202) 452-8200. Fax, (202) 833-0388. Josette Shiner, president. Internet, fluet@erols.com or http://www.empower.org.

Public policy research organization that seeks to encourage economic growth through lower taxes, less government spending, and regulatory reform. Interests include social policy and the moral impact of popular culture.

Family Research Council, 801 G St. N.W. 20001; (202) 393-2100. Fax, (202) 393-2134. Gary L. Bauer, president. Internet, http://www.frc.org.

Legislative interest organization that analyzes issues affecting the family and seeks to ensure that the interests of the family are considered in the formulation of public policy.

Foundation for Public Affairs, 2033 K St. N.W., #700 20006; (202) 872-1750. Fax, (202) 835-8343. Leslie Swift-Rosenzweig, executive director.

Public policy research and educational foundation that serves as an information clearinghouse on interest groups and corporate public affairs programs. Monitors the activities of public policy groups and advises on methods of operation, staff, budget size, and other administrative topics. Provides third-party commentary on groups' effectiveness and political orientation. Library open to the public by appointment. (Affiliated with the Public Affairs Council.)

Free Congress Research and Education Foundation, *717 2nd St. N.E. 20002-4368; (202) 546-3004. Fax, (202) 543-8425. Paul M. Weyrich, president. Internet, net@fcref.org or http://www.fcref.org.*

Research and education foundation that promotes traditional values, conservative governance, and institutional reform. Studies judicial/political issues, electoral process, and public policy. Trains citizens to participate in a democracy. Operates a 24-hour satellite television network.

Frontiers of Freedom, *1100 Wilson Blvd., #1700, Arlington, VA 22209; (703) 527-8282. Fax, (703) 527-8388. Bob Schadler, executive director. Internet, http://www.ff.org.*

Grassroots organization that seeks to increase personal freedoms through a reduction in the size and scope of government. Interests include defense of property rights, regulatory reform, privatization of Social Security, and promotion of a flat tax system. Monitors legislation and regulations.

Fund for the Feminist Majority Foundation, *1600 Wilson Blvd., #801, Arlington, VA 22209; (703) 522-2214. Fax, (703) 522-2219. Eleanor Smeal, president. Internet, femmaj@feminist.org or http://www.feminist.org.*

Legislative interest group that seeks to increase the number of feminists running for public office; promotes a national feminist agenda.

Heritage Foundation, *214 Massachusetts Ave. N.E. 20002; (202) 546-4400. Fax, (202) 544-8328. Edwin J. Feulner Jr., president. Internet, http://www.heritage.org or http://www.townhall.com/heritage.*

Public policy research organization that conducts research and analysis and sponsors lectures, debates, and policy forums advocating individual freedom, limited government, the free market system, and a strong national defense.

Interfaith Alliance, *1012 14th St. N.W., #700 20005; (202) 639-6370. Fax, (202) 639-6375. Jay Philip Wogaman, president. Internet, TIAlliance@tialliance.org or http://www.tialliance.org.*

Membership: Protestant, Catholic, Jewish, and Muslim clergy; laity; and others who favor a positive, nonpartisan role for religious faith in public life. Advocates mainstream religious values; promotes tolerance and social opportunity; opposes the use of religion to promote political extremism at national, state, and local levels. Monitors legislation and regulations.

Liberty Lobby, *300 Independence Ave. S.E. 20003; (202) 546-5611. Fax, (202) 547-7492. Vince Ryan, chair, Board of Policy. Internet, http://www.spotlight.org.*

Legislative interest organization that opposes a balanced budget amendment, busing, gun control, hate crimes legislation, the Genocide Convention, foreign aid, and U.S. involvement in the United Nations. Supports states' rights, reduced government spending and lower taxes, protective immigration laws, and repeal of the Sixteenth, Seventeenth, and Twenty-Fifth amendments.

Log Cabin Republicans, *1633 Q St. N.W., #210 20009; (202) 347-5306. Fax, (202) 347-5224. Rich Tafel, executive director. Internet, logcabin@cais.com or http://www.lcr.org.*

Membership: lesbian and gay Republicans. Educates conservative politicians and voters on gay and lesbian issues; disseminates information; conducts seminars for members. Monitors legislation and regulations.

Millennium Institute, *1117 19th St. North, #900, Arlington, VA 22209-1708; (703) 841-0048. Fax, (703) 841-0050. Gerald O. Barney, president. Internet, millennium@igc.apc.org or http://www.igc.apc.org/millennium.*

Uses the significance of the year 2000 to focus attention on strategies for building a sustainable economic and ecological future. Conducts research; sponsors conferences; supports worldwide information sharing and coalition building.

National Jewish Coalition, *415 2nd St. N.E., #100 20002; (202) 547-7701. Fax, (202) 544-2434. Matt Brooks, executive director. Internet, http://www.njchq.org.*

Legislative interest group that works to build support among Republican party decisionmakers on issues of concern to the Jewish community; studies domestic and foreign policy issues affecting the Jewish community; supports a strong relationship between the United States and Israel.

National Jewish Democratic Council, *P.O. Box 75308 20013-0308; (202) 216-9060. Fax, (202) 216-9061. Ira Forman, executive director. Internet, NJDConline@aol.com or http://www.njdc.org.*

Encourages Jewish involvement in the Democratic party and its political campaigns. Monitors and analyzes domestic and foreign policy issues that concern the American Jewish community.

National Organization for Women (NOW), *1000 16th St. N.W., #700 20036; (202) 331-0066. Fax, (202) 785-8576. Patricia Ireland, president. TDD, (202) 331-9002. Internet, now@now.org or http://www.now.org.*

Advocacy organization that works for women's civil rights. Acts through demonstrations, court cases, and legislative efforts to improve the status of all women. Interests include increasing the number of women in elected and appointed office, improving women's economic status and health coverage, ending violence against women, preserving abortion rights, and abolishing discrimination based on gender, race, age, and sexual orientation.

National Rainbow Coalition, *1002 Wisconsin Ave. N.W. 20007; (202) 333-5270. Fax, (202) 728-1192. Jesse L. Jackson, president. Internet, http://www.rainbow.org.*

Independent political organization concerned with U.S. domestic and foreign policy. Interests include D.C. statehood, civil rights, defense policy, agriculture, poverty, the economy, energy, and the environment.

National Taxpayers Union, *108 N. Alfred St., 3rd Floor, Alexandria, VA 22314; (703) 683-5700. Fax, (703) 683-5722. Peter Sepp, vice president, Communications. Internet, http://www.ntu.org.*

Citizens' interest group that promotes tax and spending reduction at all levels of government. Supports constitutional amendments to balance the federal budget and limit taxes.

National Woman's Party, *144 Constitution Ave. N.E. 20002; (202) 546-1210. Fax, (202) 546-3997. Dorothy Ferrell, president.*

Membership: women seeking equality under the law. Supports the Equal Rights Amendment and other legislation to eliminate discrimination against women.

People for the American Way, *2000 M St. N.W., #400 20036; (202) 467-4999. Fax, (202) 293-2672. Carole Shields, president. Internet, pfaw@pfaw.org or http://www.pfaw.org.*

Nonpartisan organization that promotes protection of First Amendment rights through a national grassroots network of members and volunteers. Conducts public education programs on constitutional issues. Provides radio, television, and newspaper advertisements; maintains speakers bureau. Library open to the public by appointment.

Progress and Freedom Foundation, *1301 K St. N.W., #550E 20005; (202) 289-8928. Fax, (202) 289-6079. Jeffrey*

A. Eisenach, president. Internet, pff@aol.com or http://www.pff.org.

Studies the impact of the digital revolution and its implications for public policy; sponsors seminars, conferences, and broadcasts.

Progressive Policy Institute, *518 C St. N.E. 20002; (202) 547-0001. Fax, (202) 544-5014. Will Marshall, president. Internet, http://www.dlcppi.org.*

Public policy research and educational organization that supports individual opportunity, equal justice under law, and popular government.

Public Advocate of the U.S., *5613 Leesburg Pike, #17, Falls Church, VA 22041; (703) 845-1808. Eugene Delgaudio, executive director.*

Educational grassroots organization that promotes a limited role for the federal government.

Public Affairs Council, *2033 K St. N.W., #700 20006; (202) 872-1790. Fax, (202) 835-8343. Douglas G. Pinkham, president. Internet, http://www.pac.org.*

Membership: corporate public affairs executives. Informs and counsels members on public affairs programs. Sponsors conferences on election issues, government relations, and political trends. Sponsors the Foundation for Public Affairs.

Public Citizen, *Congress Watch, 215 Pennsylvania Ave. S.E., 3rd Floor 20003; (202) 546-4996. Fax, (202) 547-7392. Frank Clemente, director. Internet, http://www.citizen.org.*

Citizens' interest group. Interests include consumer protection, financial services, public health and safety, government reform, trade, and the environment.

Traditional Values Coalition, *139 C St. S.E. 20003; (202) 547-8570. Fax, (202) 546-6403. Andrea Sheldon, executive director. Internet, http://www.traditionalvalues.org.*

Legislative interest group that supports traditional, conservative Judeo-Christian values. Interests include anti-abortion issues, decreased federal funding for the arts, and the promotion of school prayer. Opposes gay rights legislation. (Headquarters in Anaheim, Calif.)

20/20 Vision, *1828 Jefferson Pl. N.W. 20036; (202) 833-2020. Fax, (202) 833-5307. Laura Kriv, legislative and field director. Internet, vision@2020vision.org or http://www.2020vision.org.*

Prodemocracy advocacy group that encourages members to spend twenty minutes each month in communicating their opinions to policymakers. Targets legislative issues in particular districts and provides information on current issues. Interests include reducing military spending and protecting the environment.

Urban Institute, *2100 M St. N.W. 20037; (202) 833-7200. Fax, (202) 429-0687. William Gorham, president. Information, (202) 857-8702. Library, (202) 857-8688. Internet, paffairs@ui.urban.org or http://www. urban.org.*

Public policy research and education organization. Investigates U.S. social and economic problems; encourages discussion on solving society's problems, improving and implementing government decisions, and increasing citizens' awareness of public choices. Library open to the public by appointment.

U.S. Chamber of Commerce, *Membership Grassroots Operations, 1615 H St. N.W. 20062-2000; (202) 463-5604. Fax, (202) 463-3190. R. Bruce Josten, senior vice president, Membership Policy. Press, (202) 463-5682. Internet, http://www.uschamber.org.*

Federation that works to enact probusiness legislation; tracks election law legislation; coordinates the chamber's candidate endorsement program and its grass-roots lobbying activities.

U.S. Term Limits, *1125 15th St. N.W., #501 20005; (202) 463-3200. Fax, (202) 463-3210. Paul Jacob, executive director. Internet, http://www.termlimits.org.*

Works with state and local activists to place initiatives before voters; supports term limits at all levels of government; seeks limits of three terms in the House and two in the Senate. Monitors legislation and regulations.

The Woman Activist, *2310 Barbour Rd., Falls Church, VA 22043; (703) 573-8716. Flora Crater, president.*

Advocacy group that conducts research on individuals and groups in elective and appointive office, especially those who make decisions affecting women and minorities. Publishes annual ratings of these officials.

Women Legislators' Lobby (WiLL), *110 Maryland Ave. N.E., #205 20002; (202) 543-8505. Fax, (202) 675-6469. Kimberly Robson, director, policy and programs. Internet, wandwill@clark.net or http://www. wand.org.*

Membership: women state legislators. Sponsors conferences, training workshops, issue briefings, and seminars. Interests include violence against women and children, employment, education, and the environment. Monitors legislation and regulations. (Affiliated with Women's Action for New Directions.)

See also Coalition of Black Trade Unionists (p. 228); Voters for Choice (p. 504)

POLITICAL PARTY ORGANIZATIONS

Democratic

Democratic Congressional Campaign Committee, *430 S. Capitol St. S.E. 20003; (202) 863-1500. Fax, (202) 485-3512. Rep. Martin Frost, D-Texas, chair; Matt Angle, executive director. Internet, http://www.dccc.org.*

Provides Democratic House candidates with financial and other campaign services.

Democratic Governors' Assn., *430 S. Capitol St. S.E. 20003; (202) 479-5153. Fax, (202) 479-5156. Gov. Pedro Rosello, D-Puerto Rico, chair; Katherine Whelan, executive director.*

Serves as a liaison between governors' offices and Democratic party organizations; assists Democratic gubernatorial candidates.

Democratic Leadership Council, *518 C St. N.E. 20002; (202) 546-0007. Fax, (202) 544-5002. Sen. Joseph I. Lieberman, D-Conn., chair; Alvin From, president. Internet, http://www.dlcppi.org.*

Organization of Democratic members of Congress, governors, state and local officials, and concerned citizens. Builds consensus within the Democratic party on public policy issues, including economic growth, national security, national service, and expansion of opportunity for all Americans.

Democratic National Committee, *430 S. Capitol St. S.E. 20003; (202) 863-8000. Fax, (202) 863-8174. Gov. Roy Romer, D-Colo., general chair; Steve Grossman, national chair. Press, (202) 479-5118. Internet, http:// www.democrats.org.*

Formulates Democratic party policies and positions; assists Democratic candidates for state and national office; organizes national political activities; works with state and local officials and organizations.

Democratic National Committee, *430 S. Capitol St. S.E. 20003; (202) 863-8000. Fax, (202) 863-8081. Joe Sandler, general counsel. Internet, http://www.democrats. org.*

Responsible for legal affairs of the DNC, including campaign finance and election laws, ethics, and related matters.

Democratic National Committee, *Assn. of State Democratic Chairs, 430 S. Capitol St. S.E. 20003; (202) 479-5120. Fax, (202) 479-5123. Ann Fishman, executive director. Internet, paradise@democrats.org.*

Acts as a liaison between state parties and the DNC; works to strengthen state parties for national, state, and local elections; conducts fundraising activities for state parties.

Democratic National Committee, *Communications,* *430 S. Capitol St. S.E. 20003; (202) 863-8148. Fax, (202) 863-7194. Melissa Bonney, acting director.*

Assists federal, state, and local Democratic candidates and officials in delivering a coordinated message on current issues; works to improve and expand relations with the press and to increase the visibility of Democratic officials and the Democratic party.

Democratic National Committee, *Finance, 430 S. Capitol St. S.E. 20003; (202) 863-7187. Fax, (202) 863-7109. Fran Katz, director.*

Responsible for developing the Democratic party's financial base. Coordinates fundraising efforts for and gives financial support to Democratic candidates in national, state, and local campaigns.

Democratic National Committee, *Research, 430 S. Capitol St. S.E. 20003; (202) 479-5130. Fax, (202) 479-5129. Doug Kelly, director.*

Provides Democratic elected officials, candidates, state party organizations, and the general public with information on Democratic party policy and programs.

Democratic Senatorial Campaign Committee, *430 S. Capitol St. S.E. 20003; (202) 224-2447. Fax, (202) 485-3120. Sen. Bob Kerrey, D-Neb., chair; Paul Johnson, executive director. Internet, http://www.dscc.org.*

Provides Democratic senatorial candidates with financial, research, and consulting services.

Women's National Democratic Club, *Committee on* **Public Policy,** *1526 New Hampshire Ave. N.W. 20036; (202) 232-7363. Fax, (202) 986-2791. Anne Goodrich, president.*

Studies issues and presents views to congressional committees, the Democratic Party Platform Committee, Democratic leadership groups, elected officials, and other interested groups.

Republican

College Republican National Committee, *600 Pennsylvania Ave. S.E., #301 20003; (202) 608-1411. Fax, (202) 608-1429. Evan Kozlow, executive director. Internet, http:// www.crnc.org.*

Membership: Republican college students. Promotes grassroots support for the Republican party and provides campaign assistance.

National Federation of Republican Women, *124 N. Alfred St., Alexandria, VA 22314; (703) 548-9688. Fax, (703) 548-9836. Mary Jo Arndt, president. Internet, http:// www.nfrw.org.*

Political education and volunteer arm of the Republican party. Organizes volunteers for support of Republican candidates for national, state, and local offices; encourages candidacy of Republican women; sponsors campaign management schools. Recruits Republican women candidates for office.

National Republican Congressional Committee, *320 1st St. S.E. 20003; (202) 479-7000. Fax, (202) 863-0693. Rep. John Linder, R-Ga., chair; Ted Maness, executive director. Internet, http://www.nrcc.org.*

Provides Republican House candidates with campaign assistance, including financial, public relations, media, and direct mail services.

National Republican Senatorial Committee, *425 2nd St. N.E. 20002; (202) 675-6000. Fax, (202) 675-6058. Sen. Mitch McConnell, R-Ky., chair; Steven Law, executive director. Internet, http://www.nrsc.org.*

Provides Republican senatorial candidates with financial and public relations services.

Republican Governors Assn., *310 1st St. S.E. 20003; (202) 863-8587. Fax, (202) 863-8659. Gov. David Beasley, R-S.C., chair; Clinton Key, executive director. Internet, http://www.rga.org.*

Serves as a liaison between governors' offices and Republican party organizations; assists Republican candidates for governor.

Republican National Committee, *310 1st St. S.E. 20003; (202) 863-8500. Fax, (202) 863-8820. Jim Nicholson, chair. Information, (202) 863-8790. Press, (202) 863-8550. Internet, http://www.rnc.org.*

Develops and promotes Republican party policies and positions; assists Republican candidates for state and national office; sponsors workshops to recruit Republican candidates and provide instruction in campaign techniques; organizes national political activities; works with state and local officials and organizations.

Republican National Committee, *310 1st St. S.E. 20003; (202) 863-8638. Fax, (202) 863-8654. Michael W. Grebe, general counsel.*

Responsible for legal affairs of the RNC, including equal time and fairness cases before the Federal Communications Commission. Advises the RNC and state parties on redistricting and campaign finance law compliance.

Republican National Committee, *Communications,* *310 1st St. S.E. 20003; (202) 863-8614. Fax, (202) 863-8773. Clifford May, director.*

Assists federal, state, and local Republican candidates and officials in delivering a coordinated message on current issues; works to improve and expand relations with the press and to increase the visibility of Republican officials and the Republican message.

Republican National Committee, *Finance, 310 1st St. S.E. 20003; (202) 863-8720. Fax, (202) 863-8634. Margaret Alexander Parker, director.*

Responsible for developing the Republican party's financial base. Coordinates fundraising efforts for and gives financial support to Republican candidates in national, state, and local campaigns.

Republican National Committee, *Republican National Hispanic Assembly, 600 Pennsylvania Ave. S.E., #300 20003; (202) 608-1400. Fax, (202) 602-1427. Jose Rivera, chair.*

Seeks to develop a strong, effective, and informed Hispanic Republican constituency. Encourages Hispanic Americans to seek office at all levels of government; provides information and offers advisory services to Republican candidates, officeholders, and party organizations.

Ripon Society, *501 Capitol Court N.E., #300 20002; (202) 546-1292. Fax, (202) 547-6560. Michael Gill, executive director. Internet, riponsoc@aol.com.*

Membership: moderate Republicans. Works for the adoption of moderate policies within the Republican party.

Other Political Parties

Democratic Socialists of America, *409 Butternut St. N.W. 20012; (202) 726-0745. Fax, (202) 726-6587. Christine R. Riddiough, political director. Internet, http://www. dsausa.org.*

Supports radical change in U.S. social policy. Major interests include unemployment, poverty, civil rights, economic insecurity, and tax reform issues. (U.S. affiliate of the Socialist International, which is headquartered in London.)

Libertarian Party, *P.O. Box 12075 20005; (202) 462-4390. Daniel Smith, chair, Libertarian Party of D.C.. Internet, http://www.lp.org.*

Nationally organized political party. Seeks to bring libertarian ideas into the national political debate. Believes in the primacy of the individual over government; supports property rights, free trade, and eventual elimination of taxes.

Natural Law Party, *P.O. Box 22254, Alexandria, VA 22304; (703) 823-6933. Fax, (703) 823-6934. Sarina Grosswald, treasurer. Internet, info@natural-law.org or http://www.natural-law.org.*

Nationally organized political party that seeks to infuse natural law philosophies into the U.S. political debate. Supports preventive medicine programs, use and development of renewable energy resources, sustainable agricultural practices, and alternative approaches to criminal justice. (Headquarters in Fairfield, Iowa.)

Reform Party, *P.O. Box 58112 20037-8112; (202) 728-3835. Fax, (202) 332-4270. Donna Waks, Washington contact. Internet, http://www.reformparty.org.*

Nationally organized political party. Promotes a balanced budget; campaign finance reform; congressional term limits; tax reform; Medicare, Medicaid, and Social Security reform; and lobbying restrictions. (Headquarters in Dallas, Texas.)

U.S. Taxpayers Party, *450 Maple Ave. East, Vienna, VA 22180; (703) 242-0613. Fax, (703) 242-0796. Alison Potter, administrative director. Toll-free, (800) 283-8647. Internet, ustaxpayer@aol.com or http://www.ustaxpayers.org.*

Nationally organized political party. Favors repeal of the Sixteenth Amendment, which established the federal income tax; elimination of the Education Dept.; termination of federal funding for the arts; appointment of pro-life federal judges; expansion of state powers; and comprehensive regulatory reform.

Workers World Party, *P.O. Box 57300 20037; (202) 588-1205. Malcolm Cummins, contact. Internet, dc@workers.org or http://www.workers.org.*

Nationally organized political party that promotes socialism. Seeks to achieve equal employment, housing, education, and health care for all people. (Headquarters in New York.)

105th Congress

PRONUNCIATION GUIDE FOR CONGRESS

The following is an informal guide for some of the most-often-mispronounced names of members of Congress:

SENATE

John B. Breaux, D-La. — BRO
Max Cleland, D-Ga. — CLEE-lend
Alfonse M. D'Amato, R-N.Y. — da-MAH-toe
Tom Daschle, D-S.D. — DASH-el
Pete V. Domenici, R-N.M. — da-MEN-ih-chee
Mike Enzi, R-Wyo. — EN-zee
Lauch Faircloth, R-N.C. — LOCK
Dianne Feinstein, D-Calif. — FINE-stine
James M. Inhofe, R-Okla. — IN-hoff
Daniel K. Inouye, D-Hawaii — in-NO-ay
Mary L. Landrieu, D-La. — LAN-drew
Rick Santorum, R-Pa. — san-TORE-um
Robert G. Torricelli, D-N.J. — tor-uh-SELL-ee

HOUSE

Robert Aderholt,, R-Ala. — ADD-er-holt
Spencer Bachus, R-Ala. — BACK-us
Scotty Baesler, D-Ky. — BAZ-ler
John Baldacci, D-Maine — ball-DATCH-ee
James A. Barcia, D-Mich. — BAR-sha
Xavier Becerra, D-Calif. — HAH-vee-air beh-SEH-ra
Doug Bereuter, R-Neb. — BEE-right-er
Michael Bilirakis, R-Fla. — bil-lee-RACK-us
Rod Blagojevich, D-Ill. — bla-GOY-a-vich
Earl Blumenauer, D-Ore. — BLUE-men-hour
Sherwood Boehlert, R-N.Y — BO-lert
John A. Boehner, R-Ohio — BAY-ner
Henry Bonilla, R-Texas — bo-NEE-uh
David E. Bonior, D-Mich. — BON-yer
Rick Boucher, D-Va. — BOUGH-cher
Steve Buyer, R-Ind. — BOO-yer
Charles T. Canady, R-Fla. — CAN-uh-dee
Steve Chabot, R-Ohio — SHAB-butt
Saxby Chambliss, R-Ga. — SAX-bee CHAM-bliss
Helen Chenoweth, R-Idaho — CHEN-o-weth
Michael D. Crapo, R-Idaho — CRAY-poe
Barbara Cubin, R-Wyo. — Q-ban
Peter A. DeFazio, D-Ore. — da-FAH-zee-o
Diana DeGette, D-Colo. — de-GET
William D. Delahunt, D-Mass. — DELL-a-hunt
Rosa DeLauro, D-Conn.. — da-LAUR-o
Peter Deutsch, D-Fla. — DOYCH
Lincoln Diaz-Balart, R-Fla. — dee-AZ baa-LART
Vernon J. Ehlers, R-Mich. — AY-lurz
Robert L. Ehrlich, R-Md. — ER-lick
Anna G. Eshoo, D-Calif. — EH-shoo
Eni F. H. Faleomavaega, D-Am. Samoa — EN-ee FOL-ee-oh-mav-ah-ENG-uh
Chaka Fattah, D-Pa. — SHOCK-ak fa-TAH
Harris W. Fawell, R-Ill. — FAY-well
Vic Fazio, D-Calif. — FAY-zee-o
Thomas M. Foglietta, D-Pa. — fo-lee-ET-uh
Rodney Frelinghuysen, R-N.J. — FREE-ling-highzen
Elton Gallegly, R-Calif. — GAL-uh-glee
Greg Ganske, R-Iowa — GAN-skee

Sam Gejdenson, D-Conn. — GAY-den-son
Robert W. Goodlatte, R-Va. — GOOD-lat
Luis V. Gutierrez, D-Ill. — loo-EES goo-tee-AIR-ez
Gil Gutknecht, R-Minn. — GOOT-neck
Van Hilleary, R-Tenn. — HILL-ary
Rubén Hinojosa, D-Texas — ru-BEN ee-na-HO-suh
Peter Hoekstra, R-Mich. — HOKE-struh
John Hostettler, R-Ind. — HO-stet-lur
Amo Houghton Jr., R-N.Y. — HO-tun
Kenny Hulshof, R-Mo. — HULLZ-hoff
Ernest Istook Jr., R-Okla. — IZ-took
John R. Kasich, R-Ohio — KAY-sick
Barbara B. Kennelly, D-Conn. — ka-NELL-ee
Gerald D. Kleczka, D-Wis. — KLETCH-kuh
Scott L. Klug, R-Wis. — KLOOG
Jim Kolbe, R-Ariz. — COLE-bee
Dennis Kucinich, D-Ohio — ku-SIN-itch
Steven LaTourette, R-Ohio — la-TUR-et
Rick A. Lazio, R-N.Y. — LAZZ-ee-o
Frank LoBiondo, R-N.J. — lo-BEE-on-dough
Zoe Lofgren, D-Calif. — ZO
Nita M. Lowey, D-N.Y. — LOW-ee
Donald Manzullo, R-Ill. — man-ZOO-low
David Minge, D-Minn. — MING-gee (hard G)
Jerrold Nadler, D-N.Y. — NAD-ler
David R. Obey, D-Wis. — O-bee
Frank Pallone Jr., D-N.J. — pa-LOAN
William J. Pascrell Jr., D-N.J. — pas-KRELL
Ed Pastor, D-Ariz. — pas-TORE
Nancy Pelosi, D-Calif. — pa-LOH-see
Thomas E. Petri, R-Wis. — PEE-try
Glenn Poshard, D-Ill. — pa-SHARD
George P. Radanovich, R-Calif. — ruh-DON-o-vitch
Ralph Regula, R-Ohio — REG-you-luh
Silvestre Reyes, D-Texas. — sil-VES-treh RAY-ess (rolled 'R's)
Dana Rohrabacher, R-Calif. — ROAR-ah-BAH-ker
Carlos Romero-Barceló, D/NPP-PR. — ro-MARE-oh bar-sell-O
Ileana Ros-Lehtinen, R-Fla. — il-ee-AH-na ross-LAY-tin-nen
Marge Roukema, R-N.J. — ROCK-ah-muh
Matt Salmon, R-Ariz. — SAM-men
Robert W. Schaffer, R-Colo. — SHAY-fer
José E. Serrano, D-N.Y. — ho-ZAY sa-RAH-no (rolled 'R')
John Shadegg, R-Ariz. — SHAD-egg
John M. Shimkus, R-Ill. — SHIM-kus
Mark Edward Souder, R-Ind. — SOW -dur
Deborah Ann Stabenow, D-Mich. — STAB-uh-now
Bart Stupak, D-Mich. — STEW-pack
W. J. "Billy" Tauzin, D-La. — TOE-zan
John Thune, R-S.D. — THOON
Todd Tiahrt, R-Kan. — TEE-hart
Nydia M. Velázquez, D-N.Y. — NID-ee-uh veh-LASS-kez
Peter J. Visclosky, D-Ind. — vis-KLOSS-key
Peter A. Weygand, D-R.I. — WAY-gend (hard G)

Delegations to the 105th Congress

The list below gives the names of senators and representatives of each state delegation for the 105th Congress, as of April 24, 1998. The senators are listed by seniority and the representatives by district. Italicized names indicate members serving their freshman terms.

Alabama

Richard C. Shelby (R)
Jeff Sessions (R)
1. Sonny Callahan (R)
2. Terry Everett (R)
3. *Bob Riley* (R)
4. *Robert B. Aderholt* (R)
5. Robert E. "Bud" Cramer (D)
6. Spencer Bachus (R)
7. Earl F. Hilliard (D)

Alaska

Ted Stevens (R)
Frank H. Murkowski (R)
AL Don Young (R)

American Samoa

AL Eni F. H. Faleomavaega (D)

Arizona

John McCain (R)
Jon Kyl (R)
1. Matt Salmon (R)
2. Ed Pastor (D)
3. Bob Stump (R)
4. John Shadegg (R)
5. Jim Kolbe (R)
6. J.D. Hayworth (R)

Arkansas

Dale Bumpers (D)
Tim Hutchinson (R)
1. *Marion Berry* (D)

2. *Vic Snyder* (D)
3. *Asa Hutchinson* (R)
4. Jay Dickey (R)

California

Dianne Feinstein (D)
Barbara Boxer (D)
1. Frank Riggs (R)
2. Wally Herger (R)
3. Vic Fazio (D)
4. John T. Doolittle (R)
5. Robert T. Matsui (D)
6. Lynn Woolsey (D)
7. George Miller (D)
8. Nancy Pelosi (D)
9. *Barbara Lee* (D)
10. *Ellen O. Tauscher* (D)
11. Richard W. Pombo (R)
12. Tom Lantos (D)
13. Pete Stark (D)
14. Anna G. Eshoo (D)
15. Tom Campbell (R)
16. Zoe Lofgren (D)
17. Sam Farr (D)
18. Gary A. Condit (D)
19. George P. Radanovich (R)
20. Cal Dooley (D)
21. Bill Thomas (R)
22. *Lois Capps* (D)
23. Elton Gallegly (R)
24. *Brad Sherman* (D)
25. Howard P. "Buck" McKeon (R)
26. Howard L. Berman (D)
27. *James E. Rogan* (R)

28. David Dreier (R)
29. Henry A. Waxman (D)
30. Xavier Becerra (D)
31. Matthew G. Martinez (D)
32. Julian C. Dixon (D)
33. Lucille Roybal-Allard (D)
34. Esteban E. Torres (D)
35. Maxine Waters (D)
36. Jane Harman (D)
37. Juanita Millender-McDonald (D)
38. Steve Horn (R)
39. Ed Royce (R)
40. Jerry Lewis (R)
41. Jay C. Kim (R)
42. George E. Brown Jr. (D)
43. Ken Calvert (R)
44. *Mary Bono* (R)
45. Dana Rohrabacher (R)
46. Loretta Sanchez (D)
47. Christopher Cox (R)
48. Ron Packard (R)
49. Brian P. Bilbray (R)
50. Bob Filner (D)
51. Randy "Duke" Cunningham (R)
52. Duncan Hunter (R)

Colorado

Ben Nighthorse Campbell (R)
Wayne Allard (R)
1. *Diana DeGette* (D)
2. David E. Skaggs (D)
3. Scott McInnis (R)
4. *Bob Schaffer* (R)

5. Joel Hefley (R)
6. Dan Schaefer (R)

Connecticut

Christopher J. Dodd (D)
Joseph I. Lieberman (D)
1. Barbara B. Kennelly (D)
2. Sam Gejdenson (D)
3. Rosa DeLauro (D)
4. Christopher Shays (R)
5. *Jim Maloney* (D)
6. Nancy L. Johnson (R)

Delaware

William V. Roth Jr. (R)
Joseph R. Biden Jr. (D)
AL Michael N. Castle (R)

District of Columbia

AL Eleanor Holmes Norton (D)

Florida

Bob Graham (D)
Connie Mack (R)
1. Joe Scarborough (R)
2. *Allen Boyd* (D)
3. Corrine Brown (D)
4. Tillie Fowler (R)
5. Karen L. Thurman (D)
6. Cliff Stearns (R)
7. John L. Mica (R)
8. Bill McCollum (R)
9. Michael Bilirakis (R)
10. C. W. Bill Young (R)
11. *Jim Davis* (D)
12. Charles T. Canady (R)
13. Dan Miller (R)
14. Porter J. Goss (R)
15. Dave Weldon (R)
16. Mark Foley (R)
17. Carrie P. Meek (D)
18. Ileana Ros-Lehtinen (R)
19. *Robert Wexler* (D)
20. Peter Deutsch (D)
21. Lincoln Diaz-Balart (R)
22. E. Clay Shaw Jr. (R)
23. Alcee L. Hastings (D)

Georgia

Paul Coverdell (R)
Max Cleland (D)
1. Jack Kingston (R)

2. Sanford D. Bishop Jr. (D)
3. Mac Collins (R)
4. Cynthia A. McKinney (D)
5. John Lewis (D)
6. Newt Gingrich (R)
7. Bob Barr (R)
8. Saxby Chambliss (R)
9. Nathan Deal (R)
10. Charlie Norwood (R)
11. John Linder (R)

Guam

AL Robert A. Underwood (D)

Hawaii

Daniel K. Inouye (D)
Daniel K. Akaka (D)
1. Neil Abercrombie (D)
2. Patsy T. Mink (D)

Idaho

Larry E. Craig (R)
Dirk Kempthorne (R)
1. Helen Chenoweth (R)
2. Michael D. Crapo (R)

Illinois

Carol Moseley-Braun (D)
Richard J. Durbin (D)
1. Bobby L. Rush (D)
2. Jesse L. Jackson Jr. (D)
3. William O. Lipinski (D)
4. Luis V. Gutierrez (D)
5. *Rod R. Blagojevich* (D)
6. Henry J. Hyde (R)
7. *Danny K. Davis* (D)
8. Philip M. Crane (R)
9. Sidney R. Yates (D)
10. John Edward Porter (R)
11. Jerry Weller (R)
12. Jerry F. Costello (D)
13. Harris W. Fawell (R)
14. Dennis Hastert (R)
15. Thomas W. Ewing (R)
16. Donald Manzullo (R)
17. Lane Evans (D)
18. Ray LaHood (R)
19. Glenn Poshard (D)
20. *John M. Shimkus* (R)

Indiana

Richard G. Lugar (R)
Daniel R. Coats (R)
1. Peter J. Visclosky (D)
2. David M. McIntosh (R)
3. Tim Roemer (D)
4. Mark Souder (R)
5. Steve Buyer (R)
6. Dan Burton (R)
7. *Ed Pease* (R)
8. John Hostettler (R)
9. Lee H. Hamilton (D)
10. *Julia Carson* (D)

Iowa

Charles E. Grassley (R)
Tom Harkin (D)
1. Jim Leach (R)
2. Jim Nussle (R)
3. Leonard L. Boswell (D)
4. Greg Ganske (R)
5. Tom Latham (R)

Kansas

Sam Brownback (R)
Pat Roberts (R)
1. *Jerry Moran* (R)
2. Jim Ryun (R)
3. *Vince Snowbarger* (R)
4. Todd Tiahrt (R)

Kentucky

Wendell H. Ford (D)
Mitch McConnell (R)
1. Edward Whitfield (R)
2. Ron Lewis (R)
3. *Anne M. Northup* (R)
4. Jim Bunning (R)
5. Harold Rogers (R)
6. Scotty Baesler (D)

Louisiana

John B. Breaux (D)
Mary L. Landrieu (D)
1. Robert L. Livingston (R)
2. *William J. Jefferson* (D)
3. W. J. "Billy" Tauzin (R)
4. Jim McCrery (R)
5. *John Cooksey* (R)
6. Richard H. Baker (R)
7. *Chris John* (D)

Maine

Olympia J. Snowe (R)
Susan Collins (R)
1. *Tom Allen* (D)
2. John Baldacci (D)

Maryland

Paul S. Sarbanes (D)
Barbara A. Mikulski (D)
1. Wayne T. Gilchrest (R)
2. Robert L. Ehrlich Jr. (R)
3. Benjamin L. Cardin (D)
4. Albert R. Wynn (D)
5. Steny H. Hoyer (D)
6. Roscoe G. Bartlett (R)
7. Elijah E. Cummings (D)
8. Constance A. Morella (R)

Massachusetts

Edward M. Kennedy (D)
John Kerry (D)
1. John W. Olver (D)
2. Richard E. Neal (D)
3. *Jim McGovern* (D)
4. Barney Frank (D)
5. Martin T. Meehan (D)
6. *John F. Tierney* (D)
7. Edward J. Markey (D)
8. Joseph P. Kennedy II (D)
9. Joe Moakley (D)
10. *Bill Delahunt* (D)

Michigan

Carl Levin (D)
Spencer Abraham (R)
1. Bart Stupak (D)
2. Peter Hoekstra (R)
3. Vernon J. Ehlers (R)
4. Dave Camp (R)
5. James A. Barcia (D)
6. Fred Upton (R)
7. Nick Smith (R)
8. *Debbie Stabenow* (D)
9. Dale E. Kildee (D)
10. David E. Bonior (D)
11. Joe Knollenberg (R)
12. Sander M. Levin (D)
13. Lynn Rivers (D)
14. John Conyers Jr. (D)
15. *Carolyn Cheeks Kilpatrick* (D)
16. John D. Dingell (D)

Minnesota

Paul Wellstone (D)
Rod Grams (R)
1. Gil Gutknecht (R)
2. David Minge (D)
3. Jim Ramstad (R)
4. Bruce F. Vento (D)
5. Martin Olav Sabo (D)
6. William P. "Bill" Luther (D)
7. Collin C. Peterson (D)
8. James L. Oberstar (D)

Mississippi

Thad Cochran (R)
Trent Lott (R)
1. Roger Wicker (R)
2. Bennie Thompson (D)
3. *Charles W. "Chip" Pickering Jr.* (R)
4. Mike Parker (R)
5. Gene Taylor (D)

Missouri

Christopher S. Bond (R)
John Ashcroft (R)
1. William L. Clay (D)
2. James M. Talent (R)
3. Richard A. Gephardt (D)
4. Ike Skelton (D)
5. Karen McCarthy (D)
6. Pat Danner (D)
7. *Roy Blunt* (R)
8. *Jo Ann Emerson* (R)
9. *Kenny Hulshof* (R)

Montana

Max Baucus (D)
Conrad Burns (R)
AL *Rick Hill* (R)

Nebraska

Bob Kerrey (D)
Chuck Hagel (R)
1. Doug Bereuter (R)
2. Jon Christensen (R)
3. Bill Barrett (R)

Nevada

Harry Reid (D)
Richard H. Bryan (D)
1. John Ensign (R)
2. Jim Gibbons (R)

New Hampshire

Robert C. Smith (R)
Judd Gregg (R)
1. *John E. Sununu* (R)
2. Charles Bass (R)

New Jersey

Frank R. Lautenberg (D)
Robert G. Torricelli (D)
1. Robert E. Andrews (D)
2. Frank A. LoBiondo (R)
3. Jim Saxton (R)
4. Christopher H. Smith (R)
5. Marge Roukema (R)
6. Frank Pallone Jr. (D)
7. Bob Franks (R)
8. *Bill Pascrell Jr.* (D)
9. *Steven R. Rothman* (D)
10. Donald M. Payne (D)
11. Rodney Frelinghuysen (R)
12. *Michael Pappas* (R)
13. Robert Menendez (D)

New Mexico

Pete V. Domenici (R)
Jeff Bingaman (D)
1. Vacant[1]
2. Joe Skeen (R)
3. *Bill Redmond* (R)

New York

Daniel Patrick Moynihan (D)
Alfonse M. D'Amato (R)
1. Michael P. Forbes (R)
2. Rick A. Lazio (R)
3. Peter T. King (R)
4. *Carolyn McCarthy* (D)
5. Gary L. Ackerman (D)
6. *Gregory W. Meeks* (D)
7. Thomas J. Manton (D)
8. Jerrold Nadler (D)
9. Charles E. Schumer (D)
10. Edolphus Towns (D)
11. Major R. Owens (D)
12. Nydia M. Velazquez (D)
13. Vito J. Fossella (R)
14. Carolyn B. Maloney (D)
15. Charles B. Rangel (D)
16. Jose E. Serrano (D)
17. Eliot L. Engel (D)
18. Nita M. Lowey (D)
19. Sue W. Kelly (R)

20. Benjamin A. Gilman (R)
21. Michael R. McNulty (D)
22. Gerald B.H. Solomon (R)
23. Sherwood Boehlert (R)
24. John M. McHugh (R)
25. James T. Walsh (R)
26. Maurice D. Hinchey (D)
27. Bill Paxon (R)
28. Louise M. Slaughter (D)
29. John J. LaFalce (D)
30. Jack Quinn (R)
31. Amo Houghton (R)

North Carolina

Jesse Helms (R)
Lauch Faircloth (R)
1. Eva Clayton (D)
2. *Bob Etheridge (D)*
3. Walter B. Jones Jr. (R)
4. *David E. Price (D)*
5. Richard M. Burr (R)
6. Howard Coble (R)
7. *Mike McIntyre (D)*
8. W. G. "Bill" Hefner (D)
9. Sue Myrick (R)
10. Cass Ballenger (R)
11. Charles H. Taylor (R)
12. Melvin Watt (D)

North Dakota

Kent Conrad (D)
Byron L. Dorgan (D)
AL Earl Pomeroy (D)

Ohio

John Glenn (D)
Mike DeWine (R)
1. Steve Chabot (R)
2. Rob Portman (R)
3. Tony P. Hall (D)
4. Michael G. Oxley (R)
5. Paul E. Gillmor (R)
6. *Ted Strickland (D)*
7. David L. Hobson (R)
8. John A. Boehner (R)
9. Marcy Kaptur (D)
10. *Dennis J. Kucinich (D)*
11. Louis Stokes (D)
12. John R. Kasich (R)
13. Sherrod Brown (D)
14. Tom Sawyer (D)
15. Deborah Pryce (R)

16. Ralph Regula (R)
17. James A. Traficant Jr. (D)
18. Bob Ney (R)
19. Steven C. LaTourette (R)

Oklahoma

Don Nickles (R)
James M. Inhofe (R)
1. Steve Largent (R)
2. Tom Coburn (R)
3. *Wes Watkins (R)*
4. J. C. Watts Jr. (R)
5. Ernest Istook (R)
6. Frank D. Lucas (R)

Oregon

Ron Wyden (D)
Gordon H. Smith (R)
1. Elizabeth Furse (D)
2. *Bob Smith (R)*
3. Earl Blumenauer (D)
4. Peter A. DeFazio (D)
5. *Darlene Hooley (D)*

Pennsylvania

Arlen Specter (R)
Rick Santorum (R)
1. Vacant[2]
2. Chaka Fattah (D)
3. Robert A. Borski (D)
4. Ron Klink (D)
5. *John E. Peterson (R)*
6. Tim Holden (D)
7. Curt Weldon (R)
8. James C. Greenwood (R)
9. Bud Shuster (R)
10. Joseph M. McDade (R)
11. Paul E. Kanjorski (D)
12. John P. Murtha (D)
13. Jon D. Fox (R)
14. William J. Coyne (D)
15. Paul McHale (D)
16. *Joseph R. Pitts (R)*
17. George W. Gekas (R)
18. Mike Doyle (D)
19. Bill Goodling (R)
20. Frank R. Mascara (D)
21. Phil English (R)

Puerto Rico

AL Carlos Romero-Barcelo (D)

Rhode Island

John H. Chafee (R)
Jack Reed (D)
1. Patrick J. Kennedy (D)
2. *Bob Weygand (D)*

South Carolina

Strom Thurmond (R)
Ernest F. Hollings (D)
1. Mark Sanford (R)
2. Floyd D. Spence (R)
3. Lindsey Graham (R)
4. Bob Inglis (R)
5. John M. Spratt Jr. (D)
6. James E. Clyburn (D)

South Dakota

Tom Daschle (D)
Tim Johnson (D)
AL *John Thune (R)*

Tennessee

Fred Thompson (R)
Bill Frist (R)
1. *Bill Jenkins (R)*
2. John J. "Jimmy" Duncan Jr. (R)
3. Zach Wamp (R)
4. Van Hilleary (R)
5. Bob Clement (D)
6. Bart Gordon (D)
7. Ed Bryant (R)
8. John Tanner (D)
9. *Harold E. Ford Jr. (D)*

Texas

Phil Gramm (R)
Kay Bailey Hutchison (R)
1. *Max Sandlin (D)*
2. *Jim Turner (D)*
3. Sam Johnson (R)
4. Ralph M. Hall (D)
5. *Pete Sessions (R)*
6. Joe L. Barton (R)
7. Bill Archer (R)
8. *Kevin Brady (R)*
9. *Nick Lampson (D)*
10. Lloyd Doggett (D)
11. Chet Edwards (D)
12. *Kay Granger (R)*
13. William M. "Mac" Thornberry (R)
14. *Ron Paul (R)*

15. *Rubén Hinojosa* (D)
16. *Silvestre Reyes* (D)
17. Charles W. Stenholm (D)
18. Sheila Jackson-Lee (D)
19. Larry Combest (R)
20. Henry B. Gonzalez (D)
21. Lamar Smith (R)
22. Tom DeLay (R)
23. Henry Bonilla (R)
24. Martin Frost (D)
25. Ken Bentsen (D)
26. Dick Armey (R)
27. Solomon P. Ortiz (D)
28. *Ciro Rodriguez* (D)
29. Gene Green (D)
30. Eddie Bernice Johnson (D)

Utah

Orrin G. Hatch (R)
Robert F. Bennett (R)
1. James V. Hansen (R)
2. *Merrill Cook* (R)
3. *Christopher B. Cannon* (R)

Vermont

Patrick J. Leahy (D)
James M. Jeffords (R)
AL   Bernard Sanders (I)

Virgin Islands

AL   *Donna M. Christian-Green* (D)

Virginia

John W. Warner (R)
Charles S. Robb (D)
1. Herbert H. Bateman (R)
2. Owen B. Pickett (D)
3. Robert C. Scott (D)
4. Norman Sisisky (D)
5. *Virgil H. Goode Jr.* (D)
6. Robert W. Goodlatte (R)
7. Tom Bliley (R)
8. James P. Moran (D)
9. Rick Boucher (D)
10. Frank R. Wolf (R)
11. Thomas M. Davis III (R)

Washington

Slade Gorton (R)
Patty Murray (D)
1. Rick White (R)
2. Jack Metcalf (R)
3. Linda Smith (R)
4. Richard "Doc" Hastings (R)
5. George R. Nethercutt Jr. (R)
6. Norm Dicks (D)
7. Jim McDermott (D)

8. Jennifer Dunn (R)
9. *Adam Smith* (D)

West Virginia

Robert C. Byrd (D)
John D. Rockefeller IV (D)
1. Alan B. Mollohan (D)
2. Bob Wise (D)
3. Nick J. Rahall II (D)

Wisconsin

Herb Kohl (D)
Russell D. Feingold (D)
1. Mark W. Neumann (R)
2. Scott L. Klug (R)
3. *Ron Kind* (D)
4. Jerry Kleczka (D)
5. Thomas M. Barrett (D)
6. Tom Petri (R)
7. David R. Obey (D)
8. *Jay W. Johnson* (D)
9. F. James Sensenbrenner Jr. (R)

Wyoming

Craig Thomas (R)
Michael B. Enzi (R)
AL   Barbara Cubin

1   Steven H. Schiff, R, died March 25, 1998.
2   Thomas M. Foglietta, D, resigned November 11, 1997. A special election will be held May 19, 1998, to fill the vacancy.

House Committees

The standing and select committees of the U.S. House of Representatives are listed below. The listing includes the room number, telephone number, party ratio, and jurisdiction for each full committee. Subcommittees are listed alphabetically under each committee. Membership is listed in order of seniority on the committee or subcommittee.

Members of the majority party, Republicans, are shown in roman type; the minority party, Democrats, are shown in italic type; Independents, in bold italic type. The word *vacancy* indicates that a committee or subcommittee seat had not been filled as of March 3, 1998. Subcommittee vacancies do not necessarily indicate vacancies on full committees, or vice versa. The partisan committees of the House are listed on p. 747. Members of these committees are listed in alphabetical order, not by seniority.

AGRICULTURE

Phone: (202) 225-0029 **Room:** 1301 LHOB
Staff Director: Paul Unger; (202) 225-2171; 1301 LHOB
Minority Staff Director: Stephen Haterius; (202) 225-0317; 1305 LHOB

Agriculture generally; forestry in general, and forest reserves other than those created from the public domain; adulteration of seeds, insect pests, and protection of birds and animals in forest reserves; agricultural and industrial chemistry; agricultural colleges and experiment stations; agricultural economics and research; agricultural education extension services; agricultural production and marketing and stabilization of prices of agricultural products, and commodities (not including distribution outside of the United States); animal industry and diseases of animals; commodities exchanges; crop insurance and soil conservation; dairy industry; entomology and plant quarantine; extension of farm credit and farm security; inspection of livestock, poultry, meat products, seafood and seafood products; human nutrition and home economics; plant industry, soils, and agricultural engineering; rural electrification; rural development; water conservation related to activities of the Agriculture Dept. The chair and ranking minority member are voting members ex officio of all subcommittees of which they are not regular members.
Party Ratio: R 27 - D 23

Bob Smith, Ore., chair	*Charles W. Stenholm, Texas, ranking member*
Larry Combest, Texas	*George E. Brown Jr., Calif.*
Bill Barrett, Neb.	*Gary A. Condit, Calif.*
John A. Boehner, Ohio	*Collin C. Peterson, Minn.*
Thomas W. Ewing, Ill.	*Cal Dooley, Calif.*
John T. Doolittle, Calif.	*Eva Clayton, N.C.*
Robert W. Goodlatte, Va.	*David Minge, Minn.*
Richard W. Pombo, Calif.	*Earl F. Hilliard, Ala.*
Charles T. Canady, Fla.	*Earl Pomeroy, N.D.*
Nick Smith, Mich.	*Tim Holden, Pa.*
Terry Everett, Ala.	*Scotty Baesler, Ky.*
Frank D. Lucas, Okla.	*Sanford D. Bishop Jr., Ga.*
Ron Lewis, Ky.	*Bennie Thompson, Miss.*
Helen Chenoweth, Idaho	*Sam Farr, Calif.*
John Hostettler, Ind.	*John Baldacci, Maine*
Ed Bryant, Tenn.	*Marion Berry, Ark.*
Mark Foley, Fla.	*Virgil H. Goode Jr., Va.*
Saxby Chambliss, Ga.	*Mike McIntyre, N.C.*
Ray LaHood, Ill.	*Debbie Stabenow, Mich.*
Jo Ann Emerson, Mo.	*Bob Etheridge, N.C.*
Jerry Moran, Kan.	*Chris John, La.*
Roy Blunt, Mo.	*Jay W. Johnson, Wis.*
Charles W. "Chip" Pickering Jr., Miss.	
Leonard L. Boswell, Iowa	
Bob Schaffer, Colo.	
John Thune, S.D.	
Bill Jenkins, Tenn.	
John Cooksey, La.	

AGRICULTURE (continued)

Subcommittees

Department Operations, Nutrition and Foreign Agriculture
Phone: (202) 225-0171 **Room:** 1430 LHOB

Goodlatte, chair	*Clayton*
Ewing	*Thompson*
Canady	*Berry*
Smith (Mich.)	*Brown (Calif.)*
Foley	*Bishop*
LaHood	
Thune	

Forestry, Resource Conservation and Research
Phone: (202) 225-0171 **Room:** 1430 LHOB

Combest, chair	*Dooley*
Barrett (Neb.)	*Brown (Calif.)*
Doolittle	*Farr*
Pombo	*Stabenow*
Smith (Mich.)	*John*
Everett	*Peterson (Minn.)*
Lucas	*Clayton*
Lewis (Ky.)	*Minge*
Chenoweth	*Hilliard*
Hostettler	*Pomeroy*
Chambliss	*Holden*
LaHood	*Baesler*
Emerson	*Baldacci*
Moran (Kan.)	*Berry*
Pickering	*Goode*
Schaffer	
Jenkins	
Cooksey	

General Farm Commodities
Phone: (202) 225-0171 **Room:** 1430 LHOB

Barrett (Neb.), chair	*Minge*
Combest	*Thompson*
Boehner	*McIntyre*
Lucas	*Stabenow*
Chambliss	*Etheridge*
Emerson	*John*
Moran (Kan.)	*Johnson (Wis.)*
Thune	
Cooksey	

Livestock, Dairy and Poultry
Phone: (202) 225-2171 **Room:** 1432P LHOB

Pombo, chair	*Peterson (Minn.)*
Boehner	*Hilliard*
Goodlatte	*Holden*
Smith (Mich.)	*Johnson (Wis.)*
Lucas	*Condit*

Lewis (Ky.)	*Dooley*
Hostettler	*Farr*
Blunt	*Boswell*
Pickering	
Jenkins	

Risk Management and Specialty Crops
Phone: (202) 225-4652 **Room:** 1741P LHOB

Ewing, chair	*Condit*
Combest	*Baesler*
Doolittle	*Bishop*
Pombo	*Pomeroy*
Smith (Mich.)	*Baldacci*
Everett	*Goode*
Lewis (Ky.)	*McIntyre*
Bryant	*Etheridge*
Foley	*Boswell*
Chambliss	
Moran (Kan.)	

APPROPRIATIONS

Phone: (202) 225-2771 **Room:** H-218 CAP
Clerk and Staff Director: James W. Dyer; (202) 225-2771; H-218 CAP
Minority Staff Director: R. Scott Lilly; (202) 225-3481; 1016 LHOB

Appropriation of the revenue for the support of the government; rescissions of appropriations contained in appropriation acts; transfers of unexpended balances; new spending authority under the Congressional Budget Act. The chair and ranking minority member are voting members ex officio of all subcommittees of which they are not regular members.

Party Ratio: R 34 - D 26

Robert L. Livingston, La., chair	*David R. Obey, Wis., ranking member*
Joseph M. McDade, Pa.	*Sidney R. Yates, Ill.*
C.W. Bill Young, Fla.	*Louis Stokes, Ohio*
Ralph Regula, Ohio	*John P. Murtha, Pa.*
Jerry Lewis, Calif.	*Norm Dicks, Wash.*
John Edward Porter, Ill.	*Martin Olav Sabo, Minn.*
Harold Rogers, Ky.	*Julian C. Dixon, Calif.*
Joe Skeen, N.M.	*Vic Fazio, Calif.*
Frank R. Wolf, Va.	*W.G. "Bill" Hefner, N.C.*
Tom DeLay, Texas	*Steny H. Hoyer, Md.*
Jim Kolbe, Ariz.	*Alan B. Mollohan, W.Va.*
Ron Packard, Calif.	*Marcy Kaptur, Ohio*
Sonny Callahan, Ala.	*David E. Skaggs, Colo.*
James T. Walsh, N.Y.	*Nancy Pelosi, Calif.*
Charles H. Taylor, N.C.	*Peter J. Visclosky, Ind.*
David L. Hobson, Ohio	*Esteban E. Torres, Calif.*
Ernest Istook, Okla.	*Nita M. Lowey, N.Y.*

Henry Bonilla, Texas
Joe Knollenberg, Mich.
Dan Miller, Fla.
Jay Dickey, Ark.
Jack Kingston, Ga.
Mike Parker, Miss.
Rodney Frelinghuysen, N.J.
Roger Wicker, Miss.
Michael P. Forbes, N.Y.
George R. Nethercutt Jr., Wash.
Mark W. Neumann, Wis.
Randy "Duke" Cunningham, Calif.
Todd Tiahrt, Kan.
Zach Wamp, Tenn.
Tom Latham, Iowa
Anne M. Northup, Ky.
Robert B. Aderholt, Ala.

Jose E. Serrano, N.Y.
Rosa DeLauro, Conn.
James P. Moran, Va.
John W. Olver, Mass.
Ed Pastor, Ariz.
Carrie P. Meek, Fla.
David E. Price, N.C.
Chet Edwards, Texas
Robert E. "Bud" Cramer, Ala.

Subcommittees

Agriculture, Rural Development, FDA and Related Agencies
Phone: (202) 225-2638 **Room:** 2362 RHOB

Skeen, chair	*Kaptur*
Walsh	*Fazio*
Dickey	*Serrano*
Kingston	*DeLauro*
Nethercutt	
Bonilla	
Latham	

Commerce, Justice, State and Judiciary
Phone: (202) 225-3351 **Room:** H-309 CAP

Rogers, chair	*Mollohan*
Kolbe	*Skaggs*
Taylor (N.C.)	*Dixon*
Regula	
Forbes	
Latham	

District of Columbia
Phone: (202) 225-5338 **Room:** H-147 CAP

Taylor (N.C.), chair	*Moran (Va.)*
Neumann	*Sabo*
Cunningham	*Dixon*
Tiahrt	
Northup	
Aderholt	

Energy and Water Development
Phone: (202) 225-3421 **Room:** 2362 RHOB

McDade, chair	*Fazio*
Rogers	*Visclosky*

Knollenberg	*Edwards*
Frelinghuysen	*Pastor*
Parker	
Callahan	
Dickey	

Foreign Operations, Export Financing and Related Programs
Phone: (202) 225-2041 **Room:** H-150 CAP

Callahan, chair	*Pelosi*
Porter	*Yates*
Wolf	*Lowey*
Packard	*Vacancy*
Knollenberg	*Torres*
Forbes	
Kingston	
Frelinghuysen	

Interior
Phone: (202) 225-3081 **Room:** B-308 RHOB

Regula, chair	*Yates*
McDade	*Murtha*
Kolbe	*Dicks*
Skeen	*Skaggs*
Taylor (N.C.)	*Moran (Va.)*
Nethercutt	
Miller (Fla.)	
Wamp	

Labor, Health and Human Services, and Education
Phone: (202) 225-3508 **Room:** 2358 RHOB

Porter, chair	*Obey*
Young (Fla.)	*Stokes*
Bonilla	*Hoyer*
Istook	*Pelosi*
Miller (Fla.)	*Lowey*
Dickey	*DeLauro*
Wicker	
Northup	

Legislative
Phone: (202) 225-5338 **Room:** H-147 CAP

Walsh, chair	*Serrano*
Young (Fla.)	*Fazio*
Cunningham	*Kaptur*
Wamp	
Latham	

Military Construction
Phone: (202) 225-3047 **Room:** B-300 RHOB

Packard, chair	*Hefner*
Porter	*Olver*
Hobson	*Edwards*
Wicker	*Dicks*
Kingston	*Hoyer*

APPROPRIATIONS (continued)

Parker
Tiahrt
Wamp

National Security
Phone: (202) 225-2847 **Room:** H-149 CAP

Young (Fla.), chair	*Murtha*
McDade	*Dicks*
Lewis (Calif.)	*Hefner*
Skeen	*Sabo*
Hobson	*Dixon*
Bonilla	*Visclosky*
Nethercutt	
Istook	
Cunningham	

Transportation
Phone: (202) 225-2141 **Room:** 2358 RHOB

Wolf, chair	*Sabo*
DeLay	*Vacancy*
Regula	*Torres*
Rogers	*Olver*
Packard	*Pastor*
Callahan	
Tiahrt	
Aderholt	

Treasury, Postal Service and General Government
Phone: (202) 225-5834 **Room:** B-307 RHOB

Kolbe, chair	*Hoyer*
Wolf	*Meek*
Istook	*Price*
Forbes	
Northup	
Aderholt	

Veterans Affairs, Housing and Urban Development and Independent Agencies
Phone: (202) 225-3241 **Room:** H-143 CAP

Lewis (Calif.), chair	*Stokes*
DeLay	*Mollohan*
Walsh	*Kaptur*
Hobson	*Meek*
Knollenberg	*Price*
Frelinghuysen	
Neumann	
Wicker	

BANKING AND FINANCIAL SERVICES

Phone: (202) 225-7502 **Room:** 2129 RHOB
Staff Director: Anthony F. Cole; (202) 225-7502; 2129 RHOB
Minority Staff Director: Kelsey R. Meek; (202) 225-4247; B-301C RHOB

Banks and banking, including deposit insurance and federal monetary policy; bank capital markets activities generally; depository institution securities activities generally, including the activities of any affiliates, except for functional regulation under applicable securities laws not involving safety and soundness; economic stabilization, defense production, renegotiation, and control of the price of commodities, rents, and services; financial aid to commerce and industry (other than transportation); international finance; international financial and monetary organizations; money and credit, including currency and the issuance of notes and redemption thereof; gold and silver, including the coinage thereof; valuation and revaluation of the dollar; public and private housing; urban development. The chair and ranking minority member are non-voting members ex officio of all subcommittees of which they are not regular members.

Party Ratio: R 30 - D 25 - I 1

Jim Leach, Iowa, chair	*Henry B. Gonzalez, Texas, ranking member*
Bill McCollum, Fla.	*John J. LaFalce, N.Y.*
Marge Roukema, N.J.	*Bruce F. Vento, Minn.*
Doug Bereuter, Neb.	*Charles E. Schumer, N.Y.*
Richard H. Baker, La.	*Barney Frank, Mass.*
Rick A. Lazio, N.Y.	*Paul E. Kanjorski, Pa.*
Spencer Bachus, Ala.	*Joseph P. Kennedy II, Mass.*
Michael N. Castle, Del.	*Maxine Waters, Calif.*
Peter T. King, N.Y.	*Carolyn B. Maloney, N.Y.*
Tom Campbell, Calif.	*Luis V. Gutierrez, Ill.*
Ed Royce, Calif.	*Lucille Roybal-Allard, Calif.*
Frank D. Lucas, Okla.	*Thomas M. Barrett, Wis.*
Jack Metcalf, Wash.	*Nydia M. Velazquez, N.Y.*
Bob Ney, Ohio	*Melvin Watt, N.C.*
Robert L. Ehrlich Jr., Md.	*Maurice D. Hinchey, N.Y.*
Bob Barr, Ga.	*Gary L. Ackerman, N.Y.*
Jon D. Fox, Pa.	*Ken Bentsen, Texas*
Sue W. Kelly, N.Y.	*Jesse L. Jackson Jr., Ill.*
Ron Paul, Texas	*Carolyn Cheeks Kilpatrick, Mich.*
Dave Weldon, Fla.	
Merrill Cook, Utah	*Jim Maloney, Conn.*
Vince Snowbarger, Kan.	*Darlene Hooley, Ore.*
Jim Ryun, Kan.	*Julia Carson, Ind.*
Bob Riley, Ala.	*Bob Weygand, R.I.*
Rick Hill, Mont.	*Esteban E. Torres, Calif.*
Pete Sessions, Texas	*Max Sandlin, Texas*
Steven C. LaTourette, Ohio	*Gregory W. Meeks, N.Y.*
Donald Manzullo, Ill.	*David E. Price, N.C.*
Mark Foley, Fla.	
Walter B. Jones Jr., N.C.	
Bill Redmond, N.M.	
Vito J. Fossella, N.Y.	***Bernard Sanders, Vt.***

Subcommittees

Capital Markets, Securities and Government Sponsored Enterprises
Phone: (202) 226-0469   **Room:** 2129 RHOB

Baker, chair	*Kanjorski*
Lucas	*Schumer*
Cook	*Vacancy*
Snowbarger	*Waters*
Riley	*Gutierrez*
Hill	*Vento*
Sessions	*Roybal-Allard*
Lazio	*Barrett (Wis.)*
Bachus	*Watt*
King	*Ackerman*
Campbell	
Jones	

Domestic and International Monetary Policy
Phone: (202) 226-0473   **Room:** B-303 RHOB

Castle, chair	*Vacancy*
Fox	*Frank*
LaTourette	*Kennedy (Mass.)*
Royce	*Sanders*
Lucas	*Kanjorski*
Metcalf	*Velazquez*
Ney	*Maloney (N.Y.)*
Barr	*Hinchey*
Paul	*Bentsen*
Weldon (Fla.)	*Jackson*
Manzullo	
Foley	

Financial Institutions and Consumer Credit
Phone: (202) 225-2258   **Room:** 2129 RHOB

Roukema, chair	*Vento*
McCollum	*LaFalce*
Bereuter	*Schumer*
King	*Maloney (N.Y.)*
Campbell	*Barrett (Wis.)*
Royce	*Watt*
Metcalf	*Roybal-Allard*
Ehrlich	*Ackerman*
Barr	*Bentsen*
Kelly	*Kilpatrick*
Paul	
Weldon (Fla.)	
Ryun	
Redmond	

General Oversight and Investigations
Phone: (202) 226-3280   **Room:** 212 OHOB

Bachus, chair	*Waters*
Riley	*Kilpatrick*
LaTourette	*Hooley*

King	
Ney	
Foley	

Housing and Community Opportunity
Phone: (202) 225-6634   **Room:** B-303 RHOB

Lazio, chair	*Kennedy (Mass.)*
Ney	*Sanders*
Roukema	*Gutierrez*
Bereuter	*Velazquez*
Baker	*Frank*
Castle	*Hinchey*
Ehrlich	*Jackson*
Fox	*LaFalce*
Kelly	*Maloney (Conn.)*
Cook	*Hooley*
Hill	*Carson*
Sessions	
Metcalf	
Jones	
Redmond	

BUDGET

Phone: (202) 226-7270   **Room:** 309 CHOB
Staff Director: Richard May; (202) 226-7270; 309 CHOB
Minority Staff Director: Thomas S. Kahn; (202) 226-7200; 214 CHOB

Congressional budget process generally; concurrent budget resolutions; measures relating to special controls over the federal budget; Congressional Budget Office.
Party Ratio: R 24 - D 19

John R. Kasich, Ohio, chair	*John M. Spratt Jr., S.C., ranking member*
David L. Hobson, Ohio	*Jim McDermott, Wash.*
Christopher Shays, Conn.	*Alan B. Mollohan, W.Va.*
Wally Herger, Calif.	*Jerry F. Costello, Ill.*
Jim Bunning, Ky.	*Patsy T. Mink, Hawaii*
Lamar Smith, Texas	*Earl Pomeroy, N.D.*
Dan Miller, Fla.	*Lynn Woolsey, Calif.*
Bob Franks, N.J.	*Lucille Roybal-Allard, Calif.*
Nick Smith, Mich.	*Lynn Rivers, Mich.*
Bob Inglis, S.C.	*Lloyd Doggett, Texas*
Jim Nussle, Iowa	*Bennie Thompson, Miss.*
Peter Hoekstra, Mich.	*Benjamin L. Cardin, Md.*
John Shadegg, Ariz.	*David Minge, Minn.*
George P. Radanovich, Calif.	*Scotty Baesler, Ky.*
	Ken Bentsen, Texas
Charles Bass, N.H.	*Jim Davis, Fla.*
Mark W. Neumann, Wis.	*Bob Weygand, R.I.*
Mike Parker, Miss.	*Eva Clayton, N.C.*
Robert L. Ehrlich Jr., Md.	
Gil Gutknecht, Minn.	
Van Hilleary, Tenn.	

BUDGET (continued)

Kay Granger, Texas
John E. Sununu, N.H.
Joseph R. Pitts, Pa.

COMMERCE

Phone: (202) 225-2927 **Room:** 2125 RHOB
Staff Director: James E. Derderian; (202) 225-2927;
  2125 RHOB
Minority Staff Director and Chief Counsel: Reid P. S.
  Stuntz; (202) 225-3641; 2322 RHOB

Interstate and foreign commerce generally; biomedical research and development; consumer affairs and consumer protection; health and health facilities, except health care supported by payroll deductions; interstate energy compacts; measures relating to the exploration, production, storage, supply, marketing, pricing, and regulation of energy resources, including all fossil fuels, solar energy, and other unconventional or renewable energy resources; measures relating to the conservation of energy resources; measures relating to energy information generally; measures relating to (A) the generation and marketing of power (except by federally chartered or federal regional power marketing authorities), (B) the reliability and interstate transmission of, and ratemaking for, all power, and (C) the siting of generation facilities, except the installation of interconnections between government water power projects; measures relating to general management of the Energy Dept. and the management and all functions of the Federal Energy Regulatory Commission; national energy policy generally; public health and quarantine; regulation of the domestic nuclear energy industry, including regulation of research and development reactors and nuclear regulatory research; regulation of interstate and foreign communications; securities and exchanges; travel and tourism; nuclear and other energy, and nonmilitary nuclear energy and research and development including the disposal of nuclear waste. The chair and ranking minority member are voting members ex officio of all subcommittees of which they are not regular members.

Party Ratio: R 28 - D 23

Tom Bliley, Va.,	John D. Dingell, Mich.,
chair	ranking member
W. J. "Billy" Tauzin, La.	Henry A. Waxman, Calif.
Michael G. Oxley, Ohio	Edward J. Markey, Mass.
Michael Bilirakis, Fla.	Ralph M. Hall, Texas
Dan Schaefer, Colo.	Rick Boucher, Va.
Joe L. Barton, Texas	Thomas J. Manton, N.Y.
Dennis Hastert, Ill.	Edolphus Towns, N.Y.
Fred Upton, Mich.	Frank Pallone Jr., N.J.

Cliff Stearns, Fla.	Sherrod Brown, Ohio
Bill Paxon, N.Y.	Bart Gordon, Tenn.
Paul E. Gillmor, Ohio	Elizabeth Furse, Ore.
Scott L. Klug, Wis.	Peter Deutsch, Fla.
James C. Greenwood, Pa.	Bobby L. Rush, Ill.
Michael D. Crapo, Idaho	Anna G. Eshoo, Calif.
Christopher Cox, Calif.	Ron Klink, Pa.
Nathan Deal, Ga.	Bart Stupak, Mich.
Steve Largent, Okla.	Eliot L. Engel, N.Y.
Richard M. Burr, N.C.	Tom Sawyer, Ohio
Brian P. Bilbray, Calif.	Albert R. Wynn, Md.
Edward Whitfield, Ky.	Gene Green, Texas
Greg Ganske, Iowa	Karen McCarthy, Mo.
Charlie Norwood, Ga.	Ted Strickland, Ohio
Rick White, Wash.	Diana DeGette, Colo.
Tom Coburn, Okla.	
Rick A. Lazio, N.Y.	
Barbara Cubin, Wyo.	
James E. Rogan, Calif.	
John M. Shimkus, Ill.	

Subcommittees

Energy and Power
Phone: (202) 225-2927 **Room:** 2125 RHOB

Schaefer, chair	Hall (Texas)
Crapo	Furse
Bilirakis	Rush
Hastert	McCarthy (Mo.)
Upton	Wynn
Stearns	Markey
Paxon	Boucher
Largent	Towns
Burr	Pallone
Whitfield	Brown (Ohio)
Norwood	Gordon
White	Deutsch
Coburn	
Rogan	
Shimkus	

Finance and Hazardous Materials
Phone: (202) 225-2927 **Room:** 2125 RHOB

Oxley, chair	Manton
Tauzin	Stupak
Paxon	Engel
Gillmor	Sawyer
Klug	Strickland
Greenwood	DeGette
Crapo	Markey
Deal	Hall (Texas)
Largent	Towns
Bilbray	Pallone

Ganske	Furse
White	
Lazio	
Cubin	

Health and Environment
Phone: (202) 225-2927 **Room:** 2125 RHOB

Bilirakis, chair	Brown (Ohio)
Hastert	Waxman
Barton	Towns
Upton	Pallone
Klug	Deutsch
Greenwood	Eshoo
Deal	Stupak
Burr	Green
Bilbray	Strickland
Whitfield	DeGette
Ganske	Hall (Texas)
Norwood	Furse
Coburn	
Lazio	
Cubin	

Oversight and Investigations
Phone: (202) 225-2927 **Room:** 2125 RHOB

Barton, chair	Klink
Cox	Waxman
Greenwood	Deutsch
Crapo	Stupak
Burr	Engel
Bilbray	Sawyer
Ganske	
Coburn	

Telecommunications, Trade and Consumer Protection
Phone: (202) 225-2927 **Room:** 2125 RHOB

Tauzin, chair	Markey
Oxley	Boucher
Schaefer	Gordon
Barton	Engel
Hastert	Sawyer
Upton	Manton
Stearns	Rush
Gillmor	Eshoo
Klug	Klink
Cox	Wynn
Deal	Green
Largent	McCarthy (Mo.)
White	
Rogan	
Shimkus	

EDUCATION AND THE WORKFORCE
Phone: (202) 225-4527 **Room:** 2181 RHOB
Staff Director: James M. "Jay" Eagen III; (202) 225-4527; 2181 RHOB
Minority Staff Director: Gail Weiss; (202) 225-3725; 2101 RHOB

Measures relating to education or labor generally; child labor; Columbia Institution for the Deaf, Dumb and Blind; Howard University; Freedmen's Hospital; convict labor and the entry of goods made by convicts into interstate commerce; food programs for children in schools; labor standards and statistics; mediation and arbitration of labor disputes; regulation or prevention of importation of foreign laborers under contract; U.S. Employees' Compensation Commission; vocational rehabilitation; wages and hours of labor; welfare of miners; work incentive programs. The chair and ranking minority member are non-voting members ex officio of all subcommittees of which they are not regular members.

Party Ratio: R 25 - D 20

Bill Goodling, Pa., chair	William L. Clay, Mo., ranking member
Tom Petri, Wis.	George Miller, Calif.
Marge Roukema, N.J.	Dale E. Kildee, Mich.
Harris W. Fawell, Ill.	Matthew G. Martinez, Calif.
Cass Ballenger, N.C.	Major R. Owens, N.Y.
Bill Barrett, Neb.	Donald M. Payne, N.J.
Peter Hoekstra, Mich.	Patsy T. Mink, Hawaii
Howard P. "Buck" McKeon, Calif.	Robert E. Andrews, N.J.
Michael N. Castle, Del.	Tim Roemer, Ind.
Sam Johnson, Texas	Robert C. Scott, Va.
James M. Talent, Mo.	Lynn Woolsey, Calif.
James C. Greenwood, Pa.	Carlos Romero-Barcelo, P.R.
Joe Knollenberg, Mich.	Chaka Fattah, Pa.
Frank Riggs, Calif.	Ruben Hinojosa, Texas
Lindsey Graham, S.C.	Carolyn McCarthy, N.Y.
Mark Souder, Ind.	John F. Tierney, Mass.
David M. McIntosh, Ind.	Ron Kind, Wis.
Charlie Norwood, Ga.	Loretta Sanchez, Calif.
Ron Paul, Texas	Harold E. Ford Jr., Tenn.
Bob Schaffer, Colo.	Dennis J. Kucinich, Ohio
John E. Peterson, Pa.	
Fred Upton, Mich.	
Nathan Deal, Ga.	
Van Hilleary, Tenn.	
Joe Scarborough, Fla.	

EDUCATION AND THE WORKFORCE (continued)

Subcommittees

Early Childhood, Youth and Families
Phone: (202) 225-4527 **Room:** 2181 RHOB

Riggs, chair	Martinez
Castle	Miller (Calif.)
Johnson	Kildee
Souder	Owens
Paul	Payne
Goodling	Mink
Greenwood	Roemer
McIntosh	Scott
Peterson (Pa.)	Kucinich
Upton	
Hilleary	

Employer-Employee Relations
Phone: (202) 225-4527 **Room:** 2181 RHOB

Fawell, chair	Payne
Talent	Fattah
Knollenberg	Hinojosa
Petri	McCarthy (N.Y.)
Roukema	Tierney
Ballenger	
Goodling	

Oversight and Investigations
Phone: (202) 225-4527 **Room:** 2181 RHOB

Hoekstra, chair	Mink
Norwood	Kind
Hilleary	Sanchez
Scarborough	Ford
Fawell	
Ballenger	

Postsecondary Education, Training and Life-Long Learning
Phone: (202) 225-4527 **Room:** 2181 RHOB

McKeon, chair	Kildee
Goodling	Andrews
Petri	Roemer
Roukema	Woolsey
Barrett (Neb.)	Romero-Barcelo
Greenwood	Fattah
Graham	Hinojosa
McIntosh	McCarthy (N.Y.)
Schaffer	Tierney
Peterson (Pa.)	Kind
Castle	Sanchez
Riggs	Ford
Souder	
Upton	
Deal	

Workforce Protections
Phone: (202) 225-4527 **Room:** 2181 RHOB

Ballenger, chair	Owens
Fawell	Miller (Calif.)
Barrett (Neb.)	Martinez
Hoekstra	Andrews
Graham	Woolsey
Paul	
Johnson	

GOVERNMENT REFORM AND OVERSIGHT

Phone: (202) 225-5074 **Room:** 2157 RHOB

Majority Staff Director: Kevin Binger; (202) 225-5074; 2157 RHOB

Minority Staff Director: Phil Schiliro; (202) 225-5051; B350-A RHOB

Civil service, including intergovernmental personnel; the status of officers and employees of the United States, including their compensation, classification, and retirement; measures relating to the municipal affairs of the District of Columbia in general, other than appropriations; federal paperwork reduction; budget and accounting measures, generally; holidays and celebrations; overall economy, efficiency and management of government operations and activities, including federal procurement; National Archives; population and demography generally, including the census; Postal Service generally, including the transportation of mail; public information and records; relationship of the federal government to the states and municipalities generally; reorganizations in the executive branch of the government. The chair and ranking minority member are voting members ex officio of all subcommittees of which they are not regular members.

Party Ratio: R 24 - D 19 - I 1

Dan Burton, Ind., chair	Henry A. Waxman, Calif., ranking member
Benjamin A. Gilman, N.Y.	Tom Lantos, Calif.
Dennis Hastert, Ill.	Bob Wise, W.Va.
Constance A. Morella, Md.	Major R. Owens, N.Y.
	Edolphus Towns, N.Y.
Christopher Shays, Conn.	Paul E. Kanjorski, Pa.
Steven H. Schiff, N.M.	Gary A. Condit, Calif.
Christopher Cox, Calif.	Carolyn B. Maloney, N.Y.
Ileana Ros-Lehtinen, Fla.	Thomas M. Barrett, Wis.
John M. McHugh, N.Y.	Eleanor Holmes Norton, D.C.
Steve Horn, Calif.	Chaka Fattah, Pa.
John L. Mica, Fla.	Elijah E. Cummings, Md.
Thomas M. Davis III, Va.	Dennis J. Kucinich, Ohio
David M. McIntosh, Ind.	Rod R. Blagojevich, Ill.
Mark Souder, Ind.	Danny K. Davis, Ill.
Joe Scarborough, Fla.	John F. Tierney, Mass.

John Shadegg, Ariz.

Steven C. LaTourette, Ohio

Mark Sanford, S.C.

John E. Sununu, N.H.

Pete Sessions, Texas

Michael Pappas, N.J.

Vince Snowbarger, Kan.

Bob Barr, Ga.

Dan Miller, Fla.

Jim Turner, Texas

Tom Allen, Maine

Harold E. Ford Jr., Tenn.

Bernard Sanders, Vt.

Subcommittees

Census

Phone (202) 226-1973 **Room:** 114 OHOB

Miller (Fla.), chair	*Maloney (N.Y.)*
Davis (Va.)	*Blagojevich*
Hastert	*Davis (Ill.)*
Shadegg	
Snowbarger	

Civil Service

Phone: (202) 225-6427 **Room:** B-371C RHOB

Mica, chair	*Cummings*
Pappas	*Norton*
Morella	*Ford*
Cox	
Sessions	

District of Columbia

Phone: (202) 225-6751 **Room:** B-349A RHOB

Davis (Va.), chair	*Norton*
Morella	*Allen*
Ros-Lehtinen	
Horn	

Government Management, Information and Technology

Phone: (202) 225-5147 **Room:** B-373 RHOB

Horn, chair	*Kucinich*
Sessions	*Kanjorski*
Davis (Va.)	*Owens*
Scarborough	*Blagojevich*
Sanford	*Davis (Ill.)*
Sununu	

Human Resources

Phone: (202) 225-2548 **Room:** B-372 RHOB

Shays, chair	*Towns*
Snowbarger	*Kucinich*
Gilman	*Allen*
McIntosh	*Lantos*
Souder	*Sanders*
Pappas	*Barrett (Wis.)*
Schiff	

National Economic Growth, Natural Resources and Regulatory Affairs

Phone: (202) 225-4407 **Room:** B-377 RHOB

McIntosh,	*Sanders*
Sununu	*Tierney*
Hastert	*Turner*
Scarborough	*Kanjorski*
Shadegg	*Condit*
LaTourette	*Kucinich*
Snowbarger	*Fattah*
Barr	
Vacancy	

National Security, International Affairs and Criminal Justice

Phone: (202) 225-2577 **Room:** B-373 RHOB

Hastert, chair	*Barrett (Wis.)*
Souder	*Lantos*
Shays	*Wise*
Schiff	*Condit*
Ros-Lehtinen	*Blagojevich*
McHugh	*Maloney (N.Y.)*
Mica	*Cummings*
Shadegg	*Turner*
LaTourette	
Barr	

Postal Service

Phone: (202) 225-3741 **Room:** B-349B RHOB

McHugh, chair	*Fattah*
Sanford	*Owens*
Gilman	*Davis (Ill.)*
LaTourette	
Sessions	

OVERSIGHT

Phone: (202) 225-8281 **Room:** 1309 LHOB

Majority Staff Director: Stacy Carlson; (202) 225-8281; 1309 LHOB

Minority Staff Director: Bob Baskin; (202) 225-2061; 1339 LHOB

Accounts of the house generally; assignment of office space for members and committees; disposition of useless executive papers; matters relating to the election of the president, vice president, or members of congress; corrupt practices; contested elections; credentials and qualifications; federal elections generally; appropriations from accounts for committee salaries and expenses (except for the Committee on Appropriations), House Information Systems, and allowances and expenses of members, House officers and administrative offices of the House; auditing and settling of all such accounts;

OVERSIGHT (continued)

expenditure of such accounts; employment of persons by the House, including clerks for members and committees, and reporters of debates; Library of Congress and the House Library; statuary and pictures; acceptance or purchase of works of art for the Capitol; the Botanic Garden; management of the Library of Congress; purchase of books and manuscripts; Smithsonian Institution and the incorporation of similar institutions; Franking Commission; printing and correction of the Congressional Record; services to the House, including the House restaurant, parking facilities and administration of the House office buildings and of the House wing of the Capitol; travel of members of the House; raising, reporting and use of campaign contributions for candidates for office of representative in the House of Representatives, of delegate, and of resident commissioner to the United States from Puerto Rico; compensation, retirement and other benefits of the members, officers and employees of the Congress.

Party Ratio: R 6 - D 3

Bill Thomas, Calif., chair	*Sam Gejdenson, Conn., ranking member*
Bob Ney, Ohio,	*Steny H. Hoyer, Md.*
John A. Boehner, Ohio	*Carolyn Cheeks*
Vernon J. Ehlers, Mich.	*Kilpatrick, Mich.*
Kay Granger, Texas	
John L. Mica, Fla.	

Task Forces

Contested Elections (Calif. 46th)
Phone: (202) 225-8281 **Room:** 1309 LHOB

Ehlers	*Hoyer*
Ney	

INTERNATIONAL RELATIONS

Phone: (202) 225-5021 **Room:** 2170 RHOB
Chief of Staff: Richard J. Garon Jr.; (202) 225-5021; 2170 RHOB
Minority Chief of Staff: Michael H. Van Dusen; (202) 225-6735; B-360 RHOB

Relations of the United States with foreign nations generally; acquisition of land and buildings for embassies and legations in foreign countries; establishment of boundary lines between the United States and foreign nations; export controls, including nonproliferation of nuclear technology and nuclear hardware; foreign loans; international commodity agreements (other than those involving sugar), including all agreements for cooperation in the export of nuclear technology and nuclear hardware; international conferences and congresses; international education; intervention abroad and declarations of war; measures relating to the diplomatic service; measures to foster commercial intercourse with foreign nations and to safeguard American business interests abroad; measures relating to international economic policy; neutrality; protection of American citizens abroad and expatriation; American National Red Cross; trading with the enemy; U.N. organizations. The chair and ranking minority member are non-voting members ex officio of all subcommittees of which they are not regular members.

Party Ratio: R 26 - D 22

Benjamin A. Gilman, N.Y., chair	*Lee H. Hamilton, Ind., ranking member*
Bill Goodling, Pa.	*Sam Gejdenson, Conn.*
Jim Leach, Iowa	*Tom Lantos, Calif.*
Henry J. Hyde, Ill.	*Howard L. Berman, Calif.*
Doug Bereuter, Neb.	*Gary L. Ackerman, N.Y.*
Christopher H. Smith, N.J.	*Eni F. H. Faleomavaega,*
Dan Burton, Ind.	*Am. Samoa*
Elton Gallegly, Calif.	*Matthew G. Martinez, Calif.*
Ileana Ros-Lehtinen, Fla.	*Donald M. Payne, N.J.*
Cass Ballenger, N.C.	*Robert E. Andrews, N.J.*
Dana Rohrabacher, Calif.	*Robert Menendez, N.J.*
Donald Manzullo, Ill.	*Sherrod Brown, Ohio*
Ed Royce, Calif.	*Cynthia A. McKinney, Ga.*
Peter T. King, N.Y.	*Alcee L. Hastings, Fla.*
Jay C. Kim, Calif.	*Pat Danner, Mo.*
Steve Chabot, Ohio	*Earl F. Hilliard, Ala.*
Mark Sanford, S.C.	*Brad Sherman, Calif.*
Matt Salmon, Ariz.	*Robert Wexler, Fla.*
Amo Houghton, N.Y.	*Steven R. Rothman, N.J.*
Tom Campbell, Calif.	*Bob Clement, Tenn.*
Jon D. Fox, Pa.	*William P. "Bill" Luther,*
John M. McHugh, N.Y.	*Minn.*
Lindsey Graham, S.C.	*Jim Davis, Fla.*
Roy Blunt, Mo.	
Kevin Brady, Texas	
Vacancy	

Subcommittees

Africa
Phone: 226-7812 **Room:** 705 OHOB

Royce, chair	*Menendez*
Houghton	*Payne*
Chabot	*Hastings (Fla.)*
Sanford	*Davis (Fla.)*
Campbell	
McHugh	

Asia and the Pacific
Phone: (202) 226-7825 **Room:** B-359 RHOB

Bereuter, chair	Berman
Leach	Faleomavaega
Rohrabacher	Andrews
King	Brown (Ohio)
Kim	Martinez
Salmon	Hastings (Fla.)
Fox	Wexler
McHugh	
Manzullo	
Royce	

International Economic Policy and Trade
Phone: (202) 225-3345 **Room:** 702 OHOB

Ros-Lehtinen, chair	Gejdenson
Manzullo	Danner
Chabot	Hilliard
Campbell	Sherman
Graham	Rothman
Blunt	Clement
Vacancy	Lantos
Brady	Luther
Bereuter	
Rohrabacher	

International Operations and Human Rights
Phone: (202) 225-5748 **Room:** B-358 RHOB

Smith (N.J.), chair	Lantos
Goodling	McKinney
Hyde	Ackerman
Burton	Faleomavaega
Ballenger	Payne
King	Hilliard
Salmon	Wexler
Graham	
Ros-Lehtinen	

Western Hemisphere
Phone: (202) 226-7820 **Room:** 2401-A RHOB

Gallegly, chair	Ackerman
Ballenger	Martinez
Sanford	Andrews
Smith (N.J.)	Menendez
Burton	McKinney
Ros-Lehtinen	Sherman
Kim	
Blunt	
Brady	

JUDICIARY

Phone: (202) 225-3951 **Room:** 2138 RHOB
Chief Counsel: Thomas E. Mooney; (202) 225-3951; 2138 RHOB

Minority Chief Counsel: Perry H. Apelbaum; (202) 225-6906; B-351C RHOB

The judiciary and judicial proceedings, civil and criminal; administrative practice and procedure; apportionment of representatives; bankruptcy, mutiny, espionage, and counterfeiting; civil liberties; constitutional amendments; federal courts and judges, and local courts in the territories and possessions; immigration and naturalization; interstate compacts, generally; measures relating to claims against the United States; meetings of Congress, attendance of members and their acceptance of incompatible offices; national penitentiaries; patents, the Patent Office, copyrights, and trademarks; presidential succession; protection of trade and commerce against unlawful restraints and monopolies; revision and codification of the Statutes of the United States; state and territorial boundaries; subversive activities affecting the internal security of the United States. The chair and ranking minority member are non-voting members ex officio of all subcommittees of which they are not regular members.
Party Ratio: R 20 - D 15

Henry J. Hyde, Ill., chair	John Conyers Jr., Mich., ranking member
F. James Sensenbrenner Jr., Wis.	Barney Frank, Mass.
Bill McCollum, Fla.	Charles E. Schumer, N.Y.
George W. Gekas, Pa.	Howard L. Berman, Calif.
Howard Coble, N.C.	Rick Boucher, Va.
Lamar Smith, Texas	Jerrold Nadler, N.Y.
Steven H. Schiff, N.M.	Robert C. Scott, Va.
Elton Gallegly, Calif.	Melvin Watt, N.C.
Charles T. Canady, Fla.	Zoe Lofgren, Calif.
Bob Inglis, S.C.	Sheila Jackson-Lee, Texas
Robert W. Goodlatte, Va.	Maxine Waters, Calif.
Steve Buyer, Ind.	Martin T. Meehan, Mass.
Ed Bryant, Tenn.	Bill Delahunt, Mass.
Steve Chabot, Ohio	Robert Wexler, Fla.
Bob Barr, Ga.	Steven R. Rothman, N.J.
Bill Jenkins, Tenn.	
Asa Hutchinson, Ark.	
Ed Pease, Ind.	
Christopher B. Cannon, Utah	
James E. Rogan, Calif.	

Subcommittees

Commercial and Administrative Law
Phone: (202) 225-2825 **Room:** B-353 RHOB

Gekas, chair	Nadler
Schiff	Jackson-Lee
Smith (Texas)	Meehan
Inglis	Delahunt

JUDICIARY (continued)

Bryant
Chabot

Constitution

Phone: (202) 226-7680 **Room:** H2-362 FHOB

Canady, chair	Scott
Hyde	Waters
Inglis	Conyers
Bryant	Nadler
Jenkins	Watt
Goodlatte	
Barr	
Hutchinson	

Courts and Intellectual Property

Phone: (202) 225-5741 **Room:** B-351A RHOB

Coble, chair	Frank
Sensenbrenner	Conyers
Gallegly	Berman
Goodlatte	Boucher
Pease	Lofgren
Cannon	Delahunt
McCollum	
Canady	
Vacancy	

Crime

Phone: (202) 225-3926 **Room:** 207 CHOB

McCollum, chair	Schumer
Schiff	Jackson-Lee
Buyer	Meehan
Chabot	Wexler
Barr	Rothman
Hutchinson	
Gekas	
Coble	

Immigration and Claims

Phone: (202) 225-5727 **Room:** B-370B RHOB

Smith (Texas), chair	Watt
Gallegly	Schumer
Jenkins	Berman
Pease	Lofgren
Cannon	Wexler
Bryant	
Vacancy	

NATIONAL SECURITY

Phone: (202) 225-4151 **Room:** 2120 RHOB
Majority Staff Director: Andrew K. Ellis; (202) 225-9648; 2120 RHOB
Minority Staff Director: Marilyn A. Elrod; (202) 225-4158; 2340 RHOB

Ammunition depots; forts; arsenals; Army, Navy, and Air Force reservations and establishments; common defense generally; conservation, development, and use of naval petroleum and oil shale reserves; the Defense Dept. generally, including the departments of the Army, Navy, and Air Force generally; interoceanic canals generally, including measures relating to the maintenance, operation, and administration of interoceanic canals; Merchant Marine Academy, and State Maritime Academies; military applications of nuclear energy; tactical intelligence and intelligence related activities of the Defense Dept.; national security aspects of merchant marine, including financial assistance for the construction and operation of vessels, the maintenance of the U.S. shipbuilding and ship repair industrial base, cabotage, cargo preference and merchant marine officers and seamen as these matters relate to the national security; pay, promotion, retirement, and other benefits and privileges of members of the armed forces; scientific research and development in support of the armed services; selective service; size and composition of the Army, Navy, Marine Corps, and Air Force; soldiers' and sailors' homes; strategic and critical materials necessary for the common defense. The chair and ranking minority member are non-voting members ex officio of all subcommittees of which they are not regular members.

Party Ratio: R 31 - D 26

Floyd D. Spence, S.C., chair	Ike Skelton, Mo., ranking member
Bob Stump, Ariz.	Norman Sisisky, Va.
Duncan Hunter, Calif.	John M. Spratt Jr., S.C.
John R. Kasich, Ohio	Solomon P. Ortiz, Texas
Herbert H. Bateman, Va.	Owen B. Pickett, Va.
James V. Hansen, Utah	Lane Evans, Ill.
Curt Weldon, Pa.	Gene Taylor, Miss.
Joel Hefley, Colo.	Neil Abercrombie, Hawaii
Jim Saxton, N.J.	Martin T. Meehan, Mass.
Steve Buyer, Ind.	Robert A. Underwood, Guam
Tillie Fowler, Fla.	Jane Harman, Calif.
John M. McHugh, N.Y.	Paul McHale, Pa.
James M. Talent, Mo.	Patrick J. Kennedy, R.I.
Terry Everett, Ala.	Rod R. Blagojevich, Ill.
Roscoe G. Bartlett, Md.	Silvestre Reyes, Texas
Howard P. "Buck" McKeon, Calif.	Tom Allen, Maine
Ron Lewis, Ky.	Vic Snyder, Ark.
J. C. Watts Jr., Okla.	Jim Turner, Texas
William M. "Mac" Thornberry, Texas	Allen Boyd, Fla.
	Adam Smith, Wash.
John Hostettler, Ind.	Loretta Sanchez, Calif.
Saxby Chambliss, Ga.	Jim Maloney, Conn.
Van Hilleary, Tenn.	Mike McIntyre, N.C.
Joe Scarborough, Fla.	Ciro D. Rodriguez, Texas
	Cynthia A. McKinney, Ga.

Walter B. Jones Jr., N.C. *Vacancy*
Lindsey Graham, S.C.
Jim Ryun, Kan.
Michael Pappas, N.J.
Bob Riley, Ala.
Jim Gibbons, Nev.
Bill Redmond, N.M.
Vacancy

Subcommittees

Merchant Marine
Phone: (202) 226-2578 **Room:** 2340 RHOB

Bateman, chair	*Abercrombie*
Hunter	*Taylor (Miss.)*
Weldon (Pa.)	*Harman*
Saxton	*Kennedy (R.I.)*
Fowler	*Allen*
Scarborough	*Smith*
Vacancy	
Vacancy	

Military Installations and Facilities
Phone: (202) 225-7120 **Room:** 2340 RHOB

Hefley, chair	*Ortiz*
McHugh	*Sisisky*
Hostettler	*Abercrombie*
Hilleary	*Underwood*
Scarborough	*Reyes*
Stump	*Snyder*
Saxton	*Boyd*
Buyer	*Smith*
Fowler	
Everett	

Military Personnel
Phone: (202) 225-7560 **Room:** 2340 RHOB

Buyer, chair	*Taylor (Miss.)*
Talent	*Skelton*
Bartlett	*Pickett*
Lewis (Ky.)	*Underwood*
Watts	*Harman*
Thornberry	*Kennedy (R.I.)*
Graham	*Maloney (Conn.)*
Vacancy	
Ryun	

Military Procurement
Phone: (202) 225-4440 **Room:** 2340 RHOB

Hunter, chair	*Skelton*
Spence	*Spratt*
Stump	*Evans*
Hansen	*Blagojevich*
Saxton	*Allen*

Talent	*Snyder*
Everett	*Turner*
McKeon	*Boyd*
Lewis (Ky.)	*Smith*
Watts	*Maloney (Conn.)*
Thornberry	*McIntyre*
Graham	*Vacancy*
Ryun	
Pappas	
Vacancy	

Military Readiness
Phone: (202) 225-6288 **Room:** 2117 RHOB

Bateman, chair	*Sisisky*
Kasich	*Ortiz*
Fowler	*Pickett*
Chambliss	*Evans*
Jones	*Taylor (Miss.)*
Riley	*Meehan*
Gibbons	*Underwood*
Hunter	*McHale*
Hansen	*Rodriguez*
Weldon (Pa.)	*McKinney*
McKeon	
Redmond	

Military Research and Development
Phone: (202) 225-1967 **Room:** 2340 RHOB

Weldon (Pa.), chair	*Pickett*
Bartlett	*Abercrombie*
Kasich	*Meehan*
Bateman	*Harman*
Hefley	*McHale*
McHugh	*Kennedy (R.I.)*
Hostettler	*Blagojevich*
Chambliss	*Reyes*
Hilleary	*Allen*
Scarborough	*Turner*
Jones	*Sanchez*
Pappas	*Rodriguez*
Riley	
Gibbons	
Redmond	

Morale, Welfare and Recreation
Phone: (202) 225-8281 **Room:** 2117 RHOB

McHugh, chair	*Meehan*
Stump	*Sisisky*
Bateman	*Ortiz*
Bartlett	*Pickett*
Watts	*Underwood*
Chambliss	*Sanchez*
Scarborough	
Jones	

RESOURCES

Phone: (202) 225-2761 **Room:** 1324 LHOB
Majority Staff Director: Daniel Val Kish; (202) 225-2761; 1324 LHOB
Minority Staff Director: John A. Lawrence; (202) 225-6065; 1329 LHOB

Public lands generally, including entry, easements, and grazing; mining interests generally; fisheries and wildlife, including research, restoration, refuges, and conservation; forest reserves and national parks created from the public domain; forfeiture of land grants and alie ownership, including alien ownership of mineral lands; U.S. Geological Survey; international fishing agreements; interstate compacts relating to apportionment of waters for irrigation purposes; irrigation and reclamation, including water supply for reclamation projects, and easements of public lands for irrigation projects, and acquisition of private lands when necessary to complete irrigation projects; measures relating to the care and management of Indians, including the care and allotment of Indian lands and general and special measures relating to claims which are paid out of Indian funds; measures relating generally to the insular possessions of the United States, except those affecting the revenue and appropriations; military parks and battlefields, national cemeteries administered by the secretary of the Interior, parks within the District of Columbia, and the erection of monuments to the memory of individuals; mineral land laws and claims and entries thereunder; mineral resources of the public lands; mining schools and experimental stations; marine affairs (including coastal zone management), except for measures relating to oil and other pollution of navigable waters; oceanography; petroleum conservation on the public lands and conservation of the radium supply in the United States; preservation of prehistoric ruins and objects of interest on the public domain; relations of the United States with the Indians and the Indian tribes; Trans-Alaska Oil Pipeline (except ratemaking). The chair and ranking minority member are non-voting members ex officio of all subcommittees of which they are not regular members.

Party Ratio: R 27 - D 23

Don Young, Alaska, chair	George Miller, Calif., ranking member
W.J. "Billy" Tauzin, La.	Edward J. Markey, Mass.
James V. Hansen, Utah	Nick J. Rahall II, W.Va.
Jim Saxton, N.J.	Bruce F. Vento, Minn.
Elton Gallegly, Calif.	Dale E. Kildee, Mich.
John J. "Jimmy" Duncan Jr., Tenn.	Peter A. DeFazio, Ore.
Joel Hefley, Colo.	Eni F. H. Faleomavaega, Am. Samoa

John T. Doolittle, Calif.	Neil Abercrombie, Hawaii
Wayne T. Gilchrest, Md.	Solomon P. Ortiz, Texas
Ken Calvert, Calif.	Owen B. Pickett, Va.
Richard W. Pombo, Calif.	Frank Pallone Jr., N.J.
Barbara Cubin, Wyo.	Cal Dooley, Calif.
Helen Chenoweth, Idaho	Carlos Romero-Barcelo, P.R.
Linda Smith, Wash.	Maurice D. Hinchey, N.Y.
George P. Radanovich, Calif.	Robert A. Underwood, Guam
Walter B. Jones Jr., N.C.	Sam Farr, Calif.
William M. "Mac" Thornberry, Texas	Patrick J. Kennedy, R.I.
	Adam Smith, Wash.
John Shadegg, Ariz.	Bill Delahunt, Mass.
John Ensign, Nev.	Chris John, La.
Bob Smith, Ore.	Donna M. Christian-Green, Virgin Is.
Christopher B. Cannon, Utah	Ron Kind, Wis.
Kevin Brady, Texas	Lloyd Doggett, Texas
John E. Peterson, Pa.	
Rick Hill, Mont.	
Bob Schaffer, Colo.	
Jim Gibbons, Nev.	
Michael D. Crapo, Idaho	

Subcommittees

Energy and Mineral Resources
Phone: (202) 225-9297 **Room:** 1626 LHOB

Cubin, chair	Romero-Barcelo
Tauzin	Rahall
Duncan	Ortiz
Calvert	Dooley
Thornberry	John
Cannon	Christian-Green (Virgin Is.)
Brady	Vacancy
Gibbons	

Fisheries Conservation, Wildlife and Oceans
Phone: (202) 226-0200 **Room:** 805 OHOB

Saxton, chair	Abercrombie
Tauzin	Ortiz
Gilchrest	Pallone
Jones	Farr
Peterson (Pa.)	Kennedy (R.I.)
Crapo	

Forests and Forest Health
Phone: (202) 225-8331 **Room:** 1337 LHOB

Chenoweth, chair	Hinchey
Hansen	Vento
Doolittle	Kildee
Radanovich	Faleomavaega
Peterson (Pa.)	Vacancy
Hill	Vacancy
Schaffer	

National Parks and Public Lands
Phone: (202) 226-7736 **Room:** 814 OHOB

Hansen, chair	*Faleomavaega*
Gallegly	*Markey*
Duncan	*Vento*
Hefley	*Kildee*
Gilchrest	*Romero-Barcelo*
Pombo	*Hinchey*
Chenoweth	*Underwood*
Smith	*Kennedy (R.I.)*
Radanovich	*Delahunt*
Jones	*Christian-Green (Virgin Is.)*
Shadegg	*Kind*
Ensign	*Doggett*
Smith (Ore.)	*Vacancy*
Hill	
Gibbons	

Water and Power
Phone: (202) 225-8331 **Room:** 1337 LHOB

Doolittle, chair	*DeFazio*
Calvert	*Miller (Calif.)*
Pombo	*Pickett*
Chenoweth	*Dooley*
Smith	*Farr*
Radanovich	*Smith*
Thornberry	*Kind*
Shadegg	*Doggett*
Ensign	*Vacancy*
Smith (Ore.)	*Vacancy*
Cannon	
Crapo	

RULES

Phone: (202) 225-9191 **Room:** H-312 CAP
Majority Staff Director: Dan Keniry; (202) 225-9191; H-312 CAP
Minority Staff Director: George C. Crawford; (202) 225-9091; H-152 CAP

Rules and joint rules (other than rules or joint rules relating to the Code of Official Conduct), and order of business of the House; recesses and final adjournments of Congress.

Party Ratio: R 9 - D 4

Gerald B. H. Solomon, N.Y., chair	*Joe Moakley, Mass., ranking member*
David Dreier, Calif.	*Martin Frost, Texas*
Porter J. Goss, Fla.	*Tony P. Hall, Ohio*
John Linder, Ga.	*Louise M. Slaughter, N.Y.*
Deborah Pryce, Ohio	
Lincoln Diaz-Balart, Fla.	
Scott McInnis, Colo.	

Richard "Doc" Hastings, Wash.
Sue Myrick, N.C.

Subcommittees
Legislative and Budget Process
Phone: (202) 225-1547 **Room:** 421 CHOB

Goss, chair	*Frost*
Linder	*Moakley*
Pryce	
Hastings (Wash.)	
Solomon	

Rules and Organization of the House
Phone: (202) 225-8925 **Room:** 421 CHOB

Dreier, chair	*Hall (Ohio)*
Diaz-Balart	*Slaughter*
McInnis	
Myrick	
Solomon	

SCIENCE

Phone: (202) 225-6371 **Room:** 2320 RHOB
Majority Staff Director: Todd Schultz; (202) 225-6371; 2320 RHOB
Minority Staff Director: Robert E. Palmer; (202) 225-6375; 822 OHOB

All energy research, development, and demonstration, and projects therefor, and all federally owned or operated nonmilitary energy laboratories; astronautical research and development, including resources, personnel, equipment, and facilities; civil aviation research and development; environmental research and development; marine research; measures relating to the commercial application of energy technology; National Institute of Standards and Technology, standardization of weights and measures and the metric system; National Aeronautics and Space Administration; National Space Council; National Science Foundation; National Weather Service; outer space, including exploration and control thereof; science scholarships; scientific research, development, and demonstration, and projects therefor. The chair and ranking minority member are members ex officio of all subcommittees of which they are not regular members.

Party Ratio: R 25 - D 21

F. James Sensenbrenner Jr., Wis., chair	*George E. Brown Jr., Calif., ranking member*
Sherwood Boehlert, N.Y.	*Ralph M. Hall, Texas*
Harris W. Fawell, Ill.	*Bart Gordon, Tenn.*
Constance A. Morella, Md.	*James A. Traficant Jr., Ohio*
Curt Weldon, Pa.	*Tim Roemer, Ind.*
Dana Rohrabacher, Calif.	*James A. Barcia, Mich.*
Steven H. Schiff, N.M.	*Paul McHale, Pa.*

SCIENCE (continued)

Joe L. Barton, Texas	*Eddie Bernice Johnson, Texas*
Ken Calvert, Calif.	*Alcee L. Hastings, Fla.*
Roscoe G. Bartlett, Md.	*Lynn Rivers, Mich.*
Vernon J. Ehlers, Mich.	*Zoe Lofgren, Calif.*
Dave Weldon, Fla.	*Mike Doyle, Pa.*
Matt Salmon, Ariz.	*Sheila Jackson-Lee, Texas*
Thomas M. Davis III, Va.	*William P. "Bill" Luther,*
Gil Gutknecht, Minn.	*Minn.*
Mark Foley, Fla.	*Debbie Stabenow, Mich.*
Thomas W. Ewing, Ill.	*Bob Etheridge, N.C.*
Charles W. "Chip"	*Nick Lampson, Texas*
Pickering Jr., Miss.	*Darlene Hooley, Ore.*
Christopher B. Cannon,	*Ellen O. Tauscher, Calif.*
Utah	*Vacancy*
Kevin Brady, Texas	
Merrill Cook, Utah	
Phil English, Pa.	
George R. Nethercutt	
Jr., Wash.	
Tom Coburn, Okla.	
Pete Sessions, Texas	

Subcommittees

Basic Research
Phone: (202) 225-9662 **Room:** B-374 RHOB

Schiff, chair	*Barcia*
Boehlert	*Etheridge*
Morella	*Rivers*
Barton	*Jackson-Lee*
Gutknecht	*Luther*
Ewing	
Pickering	
Sessions	

Energy and Environment
Phone: (202) 225-9662 **Room:** B-374 RHOB

Calvert, chair	*Roemer*
Fawell	*McHale*
Weldon (Pa.)	*Doyle*
Rohrabacher	*Hooley*
Schiff	*Hall (Texas)*
Ehlers	*Johnson*
Salmon	*Lofgren*
Foley	*Vacancy*
English	
Coburn	

Space and Aeronautics
Phone: (202) 225-7858 **Room:** 2320 RHOB

Rohrabacher, chair	*Hall (Texas)*
Barton	*Traficant*
Calvert	*Hastings (Fla.)*

Bartlett	*Jackson-Lee*
Weldon (Fla.)	*Luther*
Salmon	*Lofgren*
Davis (Va.)	*Lampson*
Foley	*Gordon*
Pickering	*Vacancy*
Cannon	
Brady	
Cook	
Nethercutt	

Technology
Phone: (202) 225-8844 **Room:** 2319 RHOB

Morella, chair	*Gordon*
Weldon (Pa.)	*Johnson*
Bartlett	*Rivers*
Ehlers	*Stabenow*
Davis (Va.)	*Barcia*
Gutknecht	*McHale*
Ewing	*Doyle*
Cannon	*Vacancy*
Brady	
Cook	

SELECT INTELLIGENCE

Phone: (202) 225-4121 **Room:** H-405 CAP
Staff Director: John I. Millis; (202) 225-4121; H-405 CAP
Minority Staff Director: Michael W. Sheehy; (202) 225-7690; H-405 CAP

Legislative and budget authority over the National Security Agency and the director of central intelligence, the Defense Intelligence Agency, the National Security Agency, intelligence activities of the Federal Bureau of Investigation and other components of the federal intelligence community. The Speaker of the House and minority leader are non-voting members ex officio of the full committee.

Party Ratio: R 9 - D 7

Porter J. Goss, Fla.,	*Norm Dicks, Wash.,*
chair	*ranking member*
C.W. Bill Young, Fla.	*Julian C. Dixon, Calif.*
Jerry Lewis, Calif.	*David E. Skaggs, Colo.*
Bud Shuster, Pa.	*Nancy Pelosi, Calif.*
Bill McCollum, Fla.	*Jane Harman, Calif.*
Michael N. Castle, Del.	*Ike Skelton, Mo.*
Sherwood Boehlert, N.Y.	*Sanford D. Bishop Jr., Ga.*
Charles Bass, N.H.	
Jim Gibbons, Nev.	

Subcommittees

Human Intelligence, Analysis and Counterintelligence
Phone: (202) 225-4121 **Room:** H-405 CAP

McCollum, chair	*Dixon*
Shuster	*Skaggs*
Castle	*Pelosi*
Bass	*Bishop*

Technical and Tactical Intelligence
Phone: (202) 225-4121 **Room:** H-405 CAP

Lewis (Calif.), chair	*Skaggs*
Young (Fla.)	*Dicks*
Boehlert	*Harman*
Gibbons	*Skelton*

SMALL BUSINESS

Phone: (202) 225-5821 **Room:** 2361 RHOB
Chief of Staff: Mary McKenzie; (202) 225-5821; 2361 RHOB
Minority Staff Director: Jeanne Roslanowick; (202) 225-4038; B-343C RHOB

Assistance to and protection of small business, including financial aid, regulatory flexibility, and paperwork reduction; participation of small business enterprises in federal procurement and government contracts.

Party Ratio: R 19 - D 16

James M. Talent, Mo., chair	*John J. LaFalce, N.Y., ranking member*
Larry Combest, Texas	*Norman Sisisky, Va.*
Joel Hefley, Colo.	*Glenn Poshard, Ill.*
Donald Manzullo, Ill.	*Nydia M. Velazquez, N.Y.*
Roscoe G. Bartlett, Md.	*John Baldacci, Maine*
Linda Smith, Wash.	*Jesse L. Jackson Jr., Ill.*
Frank A. LoBiondo, N.J.	*Juanita Millender-McDonald, Calif.*
Sue W. Kelly, N.Y.	*Bob Weygand, R.I.*
Walter B. Jones Jr., N.C.	*Danny K. Davis, Ill.*
Mark Souder, Ind.	*Allen Boyd, Fla.*
Steve Chabot, Ohio	*Carolyn McCarthy, N.Y.*
Jim Ryun, Kan.	*Bill Pascrell Jr., N.J.*
Vince Snowbarger, Kan.	*Virgil H. Goode Jr., Va.*
Michael Pappas, N.J.	*Ruben Hinojosa, Texas*
Phil English, Pa.	*Marion Berry, Ark.*
David M. McIntosh, Ind.	*Vacancy*
Jo Ann Emerson, Mo.	*Vacancy*
Rick Hill, Mont.	
John E. Sununu, N.H.	
Joseph R. Pitts, Pa.	

Subcommittees

Empowerment
Phone: (202) 226-2630 **Room:** B-363 RHOB

Souder, chair	*Velazquez*
LoBiondo	*Millender-McDonald*
Chabot	*Davis (Ill.)*
English	*Pascrell*
Emerson	*Vacancy*
Pitts	

Government Programs and Oversight
Phone: (202) 226-2630 **Room:** B-363 RHOB

Bartlett, chair	*Poshard*
Manzullo	*Boyd*
Smith	*McCarthy (N.Y.)*
Hill	*Davis (Ill.)*
Sununu	*Vacancy*
Vacancy	

Regulatory Reform and Paperwork Reduction
Phone: (202) 226-2630 **Room:** B-363 RHOB

Kelly, chair	*Jackson*
Combest	*Sisisky*
LoBiondo	*Goode*
Ryun	*Boyd*
McIntosh	*Vacancy*
Emerson	

Tax, Finance and Exports
Phone: (202) 226-2630 **Room:** B-363 RHOB

Manzullo, chair	*Baldacci*
Smith	*Hinojosa*
Snowbarger	*Berry*
Pappas	*Millender-McDonald*
English	

STANDARDS OF OFFICIAL CONDUCT

Phone: (202) 225-7103 **Room:** HT-2 CAP
Staff Director and Chief Counsel: Theodore J. Van Der Meid; (202) 225-7103; HT-2 CAP
Minority Counsel: Bernard Raimo Jr.; (202) 225-7103; HT-2 CAP

Measures relating to the Code of Official Conduct.

Party Ratio: R 5 - D 5

James V. Hansen, Utah, chair	*Howard L. Berman, Calif., ranking member*
Joel Hefley, Colo.	*Martin Olav Sabo, Minn.*
Robert W. Goodlatte, Va.	*Chaka Fattah, Pa.*
Joe Knollenberg, Mich.	*Zoe Lofgren, Calif.*
Lamar Smith, Texas	*Ed Pastor, Ariz.*

Subcommittee

Bud Shuster Inquiry
Phone: (202) 225-7103 **Room:** HT-2 CAP

Hefley, chair	*Lofgren*
McCrery	*Edwards*

TRANSPORTATION AND INFRASTRUCTURE

Phone: (202) 225-9446 **Room:** 2165 RHOB
Majority Chief of Staff: Jack Schenendorf; (202) 225-9446; 2165 RHOB
Minority Staff Director: David Heymsfeld; (202) 225-4472; 2163 RHOB

Transportation, including civil aviation, railroads, water transportation, transportation safety (except automobile safety), transportation infrastructure, transportation labor, and railroad retirement and unemployment (except revenue measures); water power; the Coast Guard; federal management of emergencies and natural disasters; flood control and improvement of waterways; inspection of merchant marine vessels; navigation and related laws; rules and international arrangements to prevent collisions at sea; measures, other than appropriations, that relate to construction, maintenance and safety of roads; buildings and grounds of the Botanic Gardens, the Library of Congress and the Smithsonian Institution and other governmental buildings within the District of Columbia; post offices, customhouses, federal courthouses, and the merchant marine, except for national security aspects; pollution of navigable waters; and bridges and dams and related transportation regulatory agencies. The chair and ranking minority member are voting members ex officio of all subcommittees of which they are not regular members.

Party Ratio: R 40 - D 33

Bud Shuster, Pa., chair	*James L. Oberstar, Minn., ranking member*
Don Young, Alaska	*Nick J. Rahall II, W.Va.*
Tom Petri, Wis.	*Robert A. Borski, Pa.*
Sherwood Boehlert, N.Y.	*William O. Lipinski, Ill.*
Herbert H. Bateman, Va.	*Bob Wise, W.Va.*
Howard Coble, N.C.	*James A. Traficant Jr., Ohio*
John J. "Jimmy" Duncan Jr., Tenn.	*Peter A. DeFazio, Ore.*
Thomas W. Ewing, Ill.	*Bob Clement, Tenn.*
Wayne T. Gilchrest, Md.	*Jerry F. Costello, Ill.*
Jay C. Kim, Calif.	*Glenn Poshard, Ill.*
Steve Horn, Calif.	*Eleanor Holmes Norton, D.C.*
Bob Franks, N.J.	*Jerrold Nadler, N.Y.*
John L. Mica, Fla.	*Pat Danner, Mo.*
Jack Quinn, N.Y.	*Robert Menendez, N.J.*
Tillie Fowler, Fla.	*James E. Clyburn, S.C.*
Vernon J. Ehlers, Mich.	*Corrine Brown, Fla.*
Spencer Bachus, Ala.	*James A. Barcia, Mich.*
Steven C. LaTourette, Ohio	*Bob Filner, Calif.*
	Eddie Bernice Johnson, Texas
	Frank R. Mascara, Pa.

Sue W. Kelly, N.Y.	*Gene Taylor, Miss.*
Ray LaHood, Ill.	*Juanita Millender-McDonald, Calif.*
Richard H. Baker, La.	
Frank Riggs, Calif.	*Elijah E. Cummings, Md.*
Charles Bass, N.H.	*Earl Blumenauer, Ore.*
Bob Ney, Ohio	*Max Sandlin, Texas*
Jack Metcalf, Wash.	*Ellen O. Tauscher, Calif.*
Jo Ann Emerson, Mo.	*Bill Pascrell Jr., N.J.*
Ed Pease, Ind.	*Jay W. Johnson, Wis.*
Roy Blunt, Mo.	*Leonard L. Boswell, Iowa*
Joseph R. Pitts, Pa.	*Jim McGovern, Mass.*
Asa Hutchinson, Ark.	*Tim Holden, Pa.*
Merrill Cook, Utah	*Nick Lampson, Texas*
John Cooksey, La.	
John Thune, S.D.	
Charles W. "Chip" Pickering Jr., Miss.	
Kay Granger, Texas	
Jon D. Fox, Pa.	
Thomas M. Davis III, Va.	
Frank A. LoBiondo, N.J.	
J.C. Watts Jr., Okla.	
Jerry Moran, Kan.	
Vito J. Fossella, N.Y.	

Subcommittees

Aviation
Phone: (202) 226-3220 **Room:** 2251 RHOB

Duncan, chair	*Lipinski*
Blunt	*Boswell*
Ewing	*Poshard*
Ehlers	*Rahall*
LaHood	*Traficant*
Bass	*DeFazio*
Metcalf	*Costello*
Pease	*Danner*
Pitts	*Clyburn*
Hutchinson	*Brown (Fla.)*
Cook	*Johnson*
Cooksey	*Millender-McDonald*
Pickering	*Cummings*
Granger	*Vacancy*
Fox	
Davis (Va.)	
Watts	

Coast Guard and Maritime Transportation
Phone: (202) 226-3552 **Room:** 507 FHOB

Gilchrest, chair	*Clement*
LoBiondo	*Johnson (Wis.)*
Young (Alaska)	*Borski*
Coble	

Public Buildings and Economic Development
Phone: (202) 225-3014 **Room:** 586 FHOB

Kim, chair	*Traficant*
Cooksey	*Norton*
Duncan	*Holden*
LaTourette	*Lampson*
Davis (Va.)	

Railroads
Phone: (202) 226-0727 **Room:** B-376 RHOB

Vacancy, chair	*Wise*
Granger	*Blumenauer*
Boehlert	*Borski*
Franks	*Lipinski*
Mica	*Clement*
Quinn	*Nadler*
Fowler	*Filner*
Bachus	*Sandlin*
Pitts	
Fox	

Surface Transportation
Phone: (202) 225-6715 **Room:** B-370A RHOB

Petri, chair	*Rahall*
Pickering	*DeFazio*
Bateman	*Danner*
Coble	*Clyburn*
Ewing	*Brown (Fla.)*
Horn	*Barcia*
Franks	*Filner*
Mica	*Johnson*
Quinn	*Mascara*
Fowler	*Millender-McDonald*
Bachus	*Costello*
LaTourette	*Norton*
Kelly	*Nadler*
LaHood	*Menendez*
Baker	*Taylor (Miss.)*
Riggs	*Cummings*
Bass	*Sandlin*
Ney	*Tauscher*
Metcalf	*Pascrell*
Emerson	*McGovern*
Pease	*Vacancy*
Pitts	
Hutchinson	
Cook	
Thune	
Granger	
Watts	

Water Resources and Environment
Phone: (202) 225-4360 **Room:** B-375 RHOB

Boehlert, chair	*Borski*
Thune	*Johnson (Wis.)*
Young (Alaska)	*Wise*
Petri	*Poshard*
Bateman	*Menendez*
Gilchrest	*Barcia*
Kim	*Mascara*
Horn	*Taylor (Miss.)*
Franks	*Blumenauer*
Quinn	*Tauscher*
Ehlers	*Pascrell*
LaTourette	*Boswell*
Kelly	*McGovern*
Baker	*Rahall*
Riggs	*Lampson*
Ney	
Emerson	
LoBiondo	
Vacancy	

VETERANS' AFFAIRS

Phone: (202) 225-3527 **Room:** 335 CHOB
Staff Director: Carl Commenator; (202) 225-3527; 335 CHOB
Minority Staff Director: Mike Durishin; (202) 225-9756; 333 CHOB

Veterans' measures generally; cemeteries of the United States in which veterans of any war or conflict are or may be buried, whether in the United States or abroad, except cemeteries administered by the secretary of the Interior; compensation, vocational rehabilitation, and education of veterans; life insurance issued by the government on account of service in the armed forces; pensions of all the wars of the United States; readjustment of servicemen to civil life; soldiers' and sailors' civil relief; veterans' hospitals, medical care and treatment of veterans.

Party Ratio: R 16 - D 13

Bob Stump, Ariz., chair	*Lane Evans, Ill., ranking member*
Christopher H. Smith, N.J.	*Joseph P. Kennedy II, Mass.*
Michael Bilirakis, Fla.	*Bob Filner, Calif.*
Floyd D. Spence, S.C.	*Luis V. Gutierrez, Ill.*
Terry Everett, Ala.	*James E. Clyburn, S.C.*
Steve Buyer, Ind.	*Corrine Brown, Fla.*
Jack Quinn, N.Y.	*Mike Doyle, Pa.*
Spencer Bachus, Ala.	*Frank R. Mascara, Pa.*
Cliff Stearns, Fla.	*Collin C. Peterson, Minn.*
Dan Schaefer, Colo.	*Julia Carson, Ind.*
Jerry Moran, Kan.	*Silvestre Reyes, Texas*
John Cooksey, La.	*Vic Snyder, Ark.*

VETERANS' AFFAIRS (continued)

Asa Hutchinson, Ark. *Ciro D. Rodriguez, Texas*
J.D. Hayworth, Ariz.
Helen Chenoweth, Idaho
Ray LaHood, Ill.
Bill Redmond, N.M.

Subcommittees

Benefits

Phone: (202) 225-9164 **Room:** 335 CHOB
Quinn, chair   *Filner*
Schaefer   *Mascara*
Hayworth   *Reyes*
LaHood   *Vacancy*
Vacancy
Redmond

Health

Phone: (202) 225-9154 **Room:** 335 CHOB
Stearns, chair   *Gutierrez*
Smith (N.J.)   *Kennedy (Mass.)*
Bilirakis   *Brown (Fla.)*
Bachus   *Doyle*
Moran (Kan.)   *Peterson (Minn.)*
Cooksey   *Carson*
Hutchinson
Chenoweth

Oversight and Investigations

Phone: (202) 225-3527 **Room:** 335 CHOB
Everett, chair   *Clyburn*
Stump   *Snyder*
Spence   *Vacancy*
Buyer

WAYS AND MEANS

Phone: (202) 225-3625 **Room:** 1102 LHOB
Chief of Staff: A. L. Singleton; (202) 225-3625; 1102 LHOB
Minority Chief Counsel: Janice A. Mays; (202) 225-4021; 1106 LHOB

Revenue measures generally; reciprocal trade agreements; customs, collection districts, and ports of entry and delivery; revenue measures relating to the insular possessions; bonded debt of the United States; deposit of public moneys; transportation of dutiable goods; tax-exempt foundations and charitable trusts; national Social Security, except (A) health care and facilities programs that are supported from general revenues as opposed to payroll deductions and (B) work incentive programs. The chair and ranking minority member are non-voting members ex officio of all subcommittees of which they are not regular members.

Party Ratio: R 23 - D 16

Bill Archer, Texas,   *Charles B. Rangel, N.Y.,*
  chair   *ranking member*
Philip M. Crane, Ill.   *Pete Stark, Calif.*
Bill Thomas, Calif.   *Robert T. Matsui, Calif.*
E. Clay Shaw Jr., Fla.   *Barbara B. Kennelly, Conn.*
Nancy L. Johnson, Conn.   *William J. Coyne, Pa.*
Jim Bunning, Ky.   *Sander M. Levin, Mich.*
Amo Houghton, N.Y.   *Benjamin L. Cardin, Md.*
Wally Herger, Calif.   *Jim McDermott, Wash.*
Jim McCrery, La.   *Jerry Kleczka, Wis.*
Dave Camp, Mich.   *John Lewis, Ga.*
Jim Ramstad, Minn.   *Richard E. Neal, Mass.*
Jim Nussle, Iowa   *Michael R. McNulty, N.Y.*
Sam Johnson, Texas   *William J. Jefferson, La.*
Jennifer Dunn, Wash.   *John Tanner, Tenn.*
Mac Collins, Ga.   *Xavier Becerra, Calif.*
Rob Portman, Ohio   *Karen L. Thurman, Fla.*
Phil English, Pa.
John Ensign, Nev.
Jon Christensen, Neb.
Wes Watkins, Okla.
J.D. Hayworth, Ariz.
Jerry Weller, Ill.
Kenny Hulshof, Mo.

Subcommittees

Health

Phone: (202) 225-3943 **Room:** 1136 LHOB
Thomas, chair   *Stark*
Johnson (Conn.)   *Cardin*
McCrery   *Kleczka*
Ensign   *Lewis (Ga.)*
Christensen   *Becerra*
Crane
Houghton
Johnson

Human Resources

Phone: (202) 225-1025 **Room:** B-317 RHOB
Shaw, chair   *Levin*
Camp   *Stark*
McCrery   *Matsui*
Collins   *Coyne*
English   *Jefferson*
Ensign
Hayworth
Watkins

Oversight

Phone: (202) 225-7601 **Room:** 1136 LHOB
Johnson (Conn.), chair *Coyne*
Portman   *Kleczka*

Ramstad
Dunn
English
Watkins
Weller
Hulshof

McNulty
Tanner
Thurman

Social Security
Phone: (202) 225-9263 **Room:** B-316 RHOB

Bunning, chair
Johnson
Collins
Portman
Christensen
Hayworth
Weller
Hulshof

Kennelly
Neal
Levin
Jefferson
Tanner

Trade
Phone: (202) 225-6649 **Room:** 1104 LHOB

Crane, chair
Thomas
Shaw
Houghton
Camp
Ramstad
Dunn
Herger
Nussle

Matsui
Rangel
Neal
McDermott
McNulty
Jefferson

PARTISAN COMMITTEES

DEMOCRATIC CONGRESSIONAL CAMPAIGN COMMITTEE

Phone: (202) 863-1500 **Room:** 430 S. Capitol St., S.E. 20003

Martin Frost, Texas, chair

DEMOCRATIC POLICY COMMITTEE

Phone: (202) 225-6760 **Room:** H-204 Capitol

Richard A. Gephardt, Mo., chair
George Miller, Calif., policy co-chair
Charles W. Stenholm, Texas, policy co-chair
Martin Olav Sabo, Minn., policy co-chair
Nita M. Lowey, N.Y., policy co-chair
Rosa DeLauro, Conn., communications co-chair
Frank Pallone Jr., N.J., communications co-chair
Jesse L. Jackson Jr., Ill., communications co-chair
Nydia M. Velazquez, N.Y., communications co-chair
David R. Obey, Wis., research co-chair
Eva Clayton, N.C., research co-chair
Louise M. Slaughter, N.Y., research co-chair

DEMOCRATIC STEERING COMMITTEE

Phone: (202) 225-0100 **Room:** H-204 Capitol

Richard A. Gephardt, Mo., co-chair
Steny H. Hoyer, Md., co-chair
Jose E. Serrano, N.Y., vice chair
Maxine Waters, Calif., vice chair

Gary L. Ackerman, N.Y.	*Edward J. Markey, Mass.*
Tom Allen, Maine	*Robert T. Matsui, Calif.*
Xavier Becerra, Calif.	*Jim McDermott, Wash.*
David E. Bonior, Mich.	*Joe Moakley, Mass.*
Robert A. Borski, Pa.	*John P. Murtha, Pa.*
Leonard L. Boswell, Iowa	*Richard E. Neal, Mass.*
Sherrod Brown, Ohio	*David R. Obey, Wis.*
Benjamin L. Cardin, Md.	*Frank Pallone Jr., N.J.*
Rosa DeLauro, Conn.	*Ed Pastor, Ariz.*
Norm Dicks, Wash.	*Nancy Pelosi, Calif.*
John D. Dingell, Mich.	*Charles B. Rangel, N.Y.*
Chet Edwards, Texas	*John M. Spratt Jr., S.C.*
Vic Fazio, Calif.	*Debbie Stabenow, Mich.*
Martin Frost, Texas	*Charles W. Stenholm, Texas*
Jane Harman, Calif.	*John Tanner, Tenn.*
William J. Jefferson, La.	*Gene Taylor, Miss.*
Barbara B. Kennelly, Conn.	*Peter J. Visclosky, Ind.*
Dale E. Kildee, Mich.	*Melvin Watt, N.C.*
John Lewis, Ga.	*Henry A. Waxman, Calif.*
William O. Lipinski, Ill.	*Vacancy*

NATIONAL REPUBLICAN CONGRESSIONAL COMMITTEE

Phone: (202) 479-7020 **Room:** 320 First St., S.E. 20003

John Linder, Ga., chair
Deborah Pryce, Ohio, vice chair
Jim McCrery, La., vice chair
Michael D. Crapo, Idaho, vice chair
Ed Royce, Calif., executive committee chair
Newt Gingrich, Ga., ex officio
Dick Armey, Texas, ex officio
Tom DeLay, Texas, ex officio
John A. Boehner, Ohio, ex officio
Jennifer Dunn, Wash., ex officio
Christopher Cox, Calif., ex officio
John Linder, Ga., ex officio

Bob Barr, Ga.	Thomas M. Davis III, Va.
Charles Bass, N.H.	John T. Doolittle, Calif.
Sherwood Boehlert, N.Y.	Jo Ann Emerson, Mo.
Dave Camp, Mich.	John Ensign, Nev.
Christopher B. Cannon, Utah	Thomas W. Ewing, Ill.
	Mark Foley, Fla.
Jon Christensen, Neb.	Bob Franks, N.J.
Tom Coburn, Okla.	Gil Gutknecht, Minn.

NATIONAL REPUBLICAN CONGRESSIONAL COMMITTEE (continued)

Richard "Doc" Hastings, Wash.
David L. Hobson, Ohio
Ray LaHood, Ill.
Rick A. Lazio, N.Y.
Jerry Moran, Kan.
Sue Myrick, N.C.

Anne M. Northup, Ky.
Charles W. "Chip" Pickering Jr., Miss.
John Thune, S.D.
Jerry Weller, Ill.
Roger Wicker, Miss.

REPULICAN POLICY COMMITTEE

Phone: (202) 225-6168   **Room:** 1616 LHOB

Christopher Cox, Calif., chair

Bill Archer, Texas
Dick Armey, Texas
Bob Barr, Ga.
Doug Bereuter, Neb.
Tom Bliley, Va.
John A. Boehner, Ohio
Tom Coburn, Okla.
Tom DeLay, Texas
Jennifer Dunn, Wash.
Jim Gibbons, Nev.
Benjamin A. Gilman, N.Y.

Newt Gingrich, Ga.
Robert W. Goodlatte, Va.
Rick Hill, Mont.
John R. Kasich, Ohio
Joe Knollenberg, Mich.
Ron Lewis, Ky.
John Linder, Ga.
Robert L. Livingston, La.
David M. McIntosh, Ind.
Jack Metcalf, Wash.
Sue Myrick, N.C.
Bill Paxon, N.Y.

Charles W. "Chip" Pickering Jr., Miss.
Richard W. Pombo, Calif.
Rob Portman, Ohio
Frank Riggs, Calif.
Bob Schaffer, Colo.
Nick Smith, Mich.
Gerald B. H.. Solomon, N.Y

Floyd D. Spence, S.C.
Cliff Stearns, Fla.
John E. Sununu, N.H.
John Thune, S.D.
Todd Tiahrt, Kan.
Curt Weldon, Pa.
Vacancy
Vacancy

REPUBLICAN STEERING COMMITTEE

Phone: (202) 225-0600   **Room:** H-230 Capitol

Newt Gingrich, Ga.
Bill Archer, Texas
Dick Armey, Texas
Cass Ballenger, N.C.
Joe L. Barton, Texas
Roy Blunt, Mo.
John A. Boehner, Ohio
Saxby Chambliss, Ga.
Christopher Cox, Calif.
Tom DeLay, Texas
David Dreier, Calif.
Jennifer Dunn, Wash.
Lindsey Graham, S.C.

Dennis Hastert, Ill.
John R. Kasich, Ohio
Tom Latham, Iowa
John Linder, Ga.
Robert L. Livingston, La.
John M. McHugh, N.Y.
Bill Paxon, N.Y.
Bud Shuster, Pa.
Gerald B. H. Solomon, N.Y.
Bob Stump, Ariz.
C.W. Bill Young, Fla.
Don Young, Alaska

House Leadership

DEMOCRATIC LEADERS

Minority Leader   *Richard A. Gephardt, Mo.*
Minority Whip   *David E. Bonior, Mich.*
Caucus Chair   *Vic Fazio, Calif.*
Caucus Vice Chair   *Barbara B. Kennelly, Conn.*
Chief Deputy Whip

Rosa DeLauro, Conn.

Chet Edwards, Texas

John Lewis, Ga.

Robert Menendez, N.J.

Parliamentarian

Barney Frank, Mass.

Bob Wise, W.Va.

Ex-Officio   *Joe Moakley, Mass.*

Deputy Whip

Gene Green, Texas	*Charles W. Stenholm, Texas*
W.G. "Bill" Hefner, N.C.	*Esteban E. Torres, Calif.*
Eddie Bernice Johnson, Texas	*Nydia M. Velazquez, N.Y.*
Charles B. Rangel, N.Y.	*Lynn Woolsey, Calif.*
Bobby L. Rush, Ill.	*Albert R. Wynn, Md.*
Martin Olav Sabo, Minn.	

At-Large Whip

Neil Abercrombie, Hawaii	*Sam Gejdenson, Conn.*
Howard L. Berman, Calif.	*Bart Gordon, Tenn.*
Sanford D. Bishop Jr., Ga.	*Maurice D. Hinchey, N.Y.*
Rick Boucher, Va.	*Sheila Jackson-Lee, Texas*
Sherrod Brown, Ohio	*William J. Jefferson, La.*
Benjamin L. Cardin, Md.	*Paul E. Kanjorski, Pa.*
Norm Dicks, Wash.	*Patrick J. Kennedy, R.I.*
Lloyd Doggett, Texas	*Dale E. Kildee, Mich.*
Mike Doyle, Pa.	*Carolyn Cheeks*
Anna G. Eshoo, Calif.	* Kilpatrick, Mich.*
Bob Etheridge, N.C.	*Ron Klink, Pa.*
Lane Evans, Ill.	*Nita M. Lowey, N.Y.*
Elizabeth Furse, Ore.	*Frank R. Mascara, Pa.*

Robert T. Matsui, Calif.	*Charles E. Schumer, N.Y.*
Michael R. McNulty, N.Y.	*Jose E. Serrano, N.Y.*
George Miller, Calif.	*David E. Skaggs, Colo.*
Alan B. Mollohan, W.Va.	*Louise M. Slaughter, N.Y.*
Richard E. Neal, Mass.	*John M. Spratt Jr., S.C.*
James L. Oberstar, Minn.	*Robert A. Underwood,*
David R. Obey, Wis.	* Guam*
John W. Olver, Mass.	*Bruce F. Vento, Minn.*
Donald M. Payne, N.J.	*Peter J. Visclosky, Ind.*
Nancy Pelosi, Calif.	*Maxine Waters, Calif.*
Silvestre Reyes, Texas	*Bob Wise, W.Va.*
Max Sandlin, Texas	*Sidney R. Yates, Ill.*

Regional Whip

John Baldacci, Maine	*Cynthia A. McKinney, Ga.*
Robert A. Borski, Pa.	*Juanita Millender-*
Bob Clement, Tenn.	* McDonald, Calif.*
James E. Clyburn, S.C.	*Patsy T. Mink, Hawaii*
Danny K. Davis, Ill.	*Jerrold Nadler, N.Y.*
Diana DeGette, Colo.	*Earl Pomeroy, N.D.*
Sam Farr, Calif.	*Bobby L. Rush, Ill.*
Maurice D. Hinchey, N.Y.	*Adam Smith, Wash.*
Ruben Hinojosa, Texas	*Bart Stupak, Mich.*
Marcy Kaptur, Ohio	*Bennie Thompson, Miss.*
William P. "Bill" Luther,	*Jim Turner, Texas*
* Minn.*	*Bob Wise, W.Va.*
Jim McGovern, Mass.	*Albert R. Wynn, Md.*

Steering Committee

   Co-Chair   *Richard A. Gephardt, Mo.*

   Co-Chair   *Steny H. Hoyer, Md.*

Democratic Congressional Campaign Committee Chair   *Martin Frost, Texas*

REPUBLICAN LEADERS

Speaker of the House   Newt Gingrich, Ga.
Majority Leader   Dick Armey, Texas
Majority Whip   Tom DeLay, Texas

Conference Chair   John A. Boehner, Ohio

Conference Vice Chair   Jennifer Dunn, Wash.

Conference Secretary   Deborah Pryce, Ohio

Chief Deputy Whip   Dennis Hastert, Ill.

Deputy Whip

Cass Ballenger, N.C.
Jim Bunning, Ky.
Mac Collins, Ga.
Michael D. Crapo, Idaho
Barbara Cubin, Wyo.
John T. Doolittle, Calif.
Thomas W. Ewing, Ill.
Mark Foley, Fla.

Tillie Fowler, Fla.
Porter J. Goss, Fla.
Van Hilleary, Tenn.
Rick A. Lazio, N.Y.
Bob Ney, Ohio
Deborah Pryce, Ohio
W. J. "Billy" Tauzin, La.
Roger Wicker, Miss.

Assistant Whip

Charles Bass, N.H.
Roy Blunt, Mo.
Henry Bonilla, Texas
Richard M. Burr, N.C.
Steve Buyer, Ind.
Sonny Callahan, Ala.
Dave Camp, Mich.
Randy "Duke"
  Cunningham, Calif.

Thomas M. Davis III, Va.
Nathan Deal, Ga.
Robert L. Ehrlich Jr., Md.
Jon D. Fox, Pa.
Bob Franks, N.J.
Paul E. Gillmor, Ohio
Robert W. Goodlatte, Va.
Lindsey Graham, S.C.
Kay Granger, Texas

J.D. Hayworth, Ariz.
David L. Hobson, Ohio
Bob Inglis, S.C.
Ernest Istook, Okla.
Sam Johnson, Texas
Sue W. Kelly, N.Y.
Jack Kingston, Ga.
Scott L. Klug, Wis.
Frank A. LoBiondo, N.J.
Frank D. Lucas, Okla.
Scott McInnis, Colo.
David M. McIntosh, Ind.
Howard P. "Buck"
  McKeon, Calif.
Dan Miller, Fla.
Michael Pappas, N.J.
Ed Pease, Ind.

Charles W. "Chip"
  Pickering Jr., Miss.
Joseph R. Pitts, Pa.
Richard W. Pombo, Calif.
Rob Portman, Ohio
George P. Radanovich,
  Calif.
Bob Riley, Ala.
James E. Rogan, Calif.
Ed Royce, Calif.
John Shadegg, Ariz.
Vince Snowbarger, Kan.
Mark Souder, Ind.
John Thune, S.D.
Todd Tiahrt, Kan.
James T. Walsh, N.Y.
Jerry Weller, Ill.

Policy Committee Chair   Christopher Cox, Calif.

Steering Committee Chair   Newt Gingrich, Ga.

**National Republican Congressional
  Committee Chair**   John Linder, Ga.

House Members' Offices

The list below gives the names of House members and their party, state, and district affiliation, followed by addresses and telephone numbers for their Washington offices. The list also gives the name of a top administrative aide for each member.

The address, telephone number, and director for the members' district offices are listed. Each representative's committee assignments are given as the final entry. For partisan committee assignments, see p. 747.

As of March 14, 1998, there were 203 Republicans, 205 Democrats, 1 independent, and 4 vacancies in the House of Representatives. This information was gathered by Congressional Quarterly from House offices in Washington, D.C.

ABERCROMBIE, NEIL, D-HAWAII (1)

Capitol Hill office: 1233 LHOB 20515; (202) 225-2726; Fax: (202) 225-4580; Internet: neil.abercrombie@ mail.house.gov or www.house.gov/abercrombie; *Chief of Staff:* Alan Yamamoto
District office(s): 300 Ala Moana Blvd., #4104, Honolulu 96850; (808) 541-2570; Fax: (808) 533-0133.
Committee assignment(s): National Security; Resources

ACKERMAN, GARY L., D-N.Y. (5)

Capitol Hill office: 2243 RHOB 20515; (202) 225-2601; Fax: (202) 225-1589; Internet: www.house.gov/ ackerman; *Administrative Assistant:* Jedd Moskowitz
District office(s): 218-14 Northern Blvd., Bayside 11361; (718) 423-2154; *District Administrator:* Arthur Flug.
229 Main St., Huntington 11743; (516) 423-2154; *Nassau, Suffolk Administrator:* Anne McShane.
Committee assignment(s): Banking and Financial Services; International Relations

ADERHOLT, ROBERT B., R-ALA. (4)

Capitol Hill office: 1007 LHOB 20515; (202) 225-4876; Fax: (202) 225-5587; *Chief of Staff:* Brian Rell
District office(s): 102 Federal Bldg., Cullman 35055; (205) 734-6043; Fax: (205) 737-0885; *District Coordinator:* Evelyn Stevens.
247 Federal Bldg., Jasper 35501; (205) 221-2310; Fax: (205) 221-9035; *District Coordinator:* Hood Harris.
Committee assignment(s): Appropriations

ALLEN, TOM, D-MAINE (1)

Capitol Hill office: 1630 LHOB 20515; (202) 225-6116; Fax: (202) 225-5590; Internet: rep.tomallen@mail. house.gov or www.house.gov/allen; *Chief of Staff:* Jackie Potter
District office(s): 234 Oxford St., Portland 04101; (207) 774-5019; Fax: (207) 871-0720; *District Director:* Bill Johnson.
Committee assignment(s): Government Reform and Oversight; National Security

ANDREWS, ROBERT E., D-N.J. (1)

Capitol Hill office: 2439 RHOB 20515; (202) 225-6501; Fax: (202) 225-6583; Internet: rob.andrews@mail. house.gov; *Administrative Assistant:* David Socolow
District office(s): 506 A White Horse Pike, Haddon Heights 08035; (609) 546-5100; Fax: (609) 546-9529; *Chief of Staff:* David B. Applebaum.
63 N. Broad St., Woodbury 08096; (609) 848-3900; *District Representative:* Leanne Hasbrouck.
Committee assignment(s): Education and Workforce; International Relations

ARCHER, BILL, R-TEXAS (7)

Capitol Hill office: 1236 LHOB 20515; (202) 225-2571; Fax: (202) 225-4381; Internet: www.house.gov/ archer; *Chief of Staff:* Don Carlson
District office(s): 1000 Memorial Dr., #620, Houston 77024; (713) 682-8828; Fax: (713) 680-8070; *District Representative:* Camille Cromwell.

Committee assignment(s): Ways and Means (chair); Joint Taxation (chair)

ARMEY, DICK, R-TEXAS (26)

Capitol Hill office: 301 CHOB 20515; (202) 225-7772; Internet: armey.house.gov; *Administrative Assistant:* Paul Morrell

District office(s): 9901 Valley Ranch Parkway East, #3050, Irving 75063; (972) 556-2500; *District Director:* Jean Campbell.

BACHUS, SPENCER, R-ALA. (6)

Capitol Hill office: 442 CHOB 20515; (202) 225-4921; Fax: (202) 225-2082; Internet: sbachus@hr.house.gov or www.house.gov/bachus; *Administrative Assistant:* Jennifer Hatcher

District office(s): 1900 International Park Dr., #107, Birmingham 35243; (205) 969-2296; Fax: (205) 969-3958; *District Director:* Judy White.

3500 McFarland Blvd., P.O. Drawer 569, Northport 35476; (205) 333-9894; *Congressional Aide:* Margaret Pyle.

Committee assignment(s): Banking and Financial Services; Transportation and Infrastructure; Veterans' Affairs

BAESLER, SCOTTY, D-KY. (6)

Capitol Hill office: 2463 RHOB 20515; (202) 225-4706; Fax: (202) 225-2122; Internet: scotty.baesler@mail. house.gov or www.house.gov/baesler; *Chief of Staff:* Chuck Atkins

District office(s): 401 W. Main St., #318, Lexington 40507; (606) 253-1124; Fax: (606) 253-1740; *District Director:* Robert D. Wiseman.

Committee assignment(s): Agriculture; Budget

BAKER, RICHARD H., R-LA. (6)

Capitol Hill office: 434 CHOB 20515; 225-3901; Fax: 225-7313; *Administrative Assistant:* Christy Casteel

District office(s): 5555 Hilton Ave., #100, Baton Rouge 70808; (504) 929-7711.

Committee assignment(s): Banking and Financial Services; Transportation and Infrastructure

BALDACCI, JOHN, D-MAINE (2)

Capitol Hill office: 1740 LHOB 20515; (202) 225-6306; Fax: (202) 225-2943; Internet: baldacci@hr.house.gov or www.house.gov/baldacci; *Administrative Assistant:* Larry Benoit

District office(s): 157 Main St., Lewiston 04240; (207) 782-3704; Fax: (207) 782-5330; *Field Representative:* Judy Cadorette.

P.O. Box 858, Bangor 04402; (207) 942-6935; Fax: (207) 942-5907; *Field Representative:* Janet Dennis.

445 Main St., Presque Isle 04769; (207) 764-1036; Fax: (207) 764-1060; *Field Representative:* Marcia Gartley.

500 Main St., Madawaska 04756; (207) 728-6160; *Field Representative:* Bob Parent.

Committee assignment(s): Agriculture; Small Business

BALLENGER, CASS, R-N.C. (1)

Capitol Hill office: 2182 RHOB 20515; (202) 225-2576; Fax: (202) 225-0316; Internet: cass.ballenger@mail. house.gov; *Chief of Staff:* Patrick Murphy

District office(s): P.O. Box 1881, Clemmons 27012; (910) 766-9455; Fax: (910) 766-1602; *District Representative:* Marsha Sucharski.

P.O. Box 1830, Hickory 28603; (704) 327-6100; *District Director:* Thomas D. Luckadoo.

Committee assignment(s): Education and Workforce; International Relations

BARCIA, JAMES A., D-MICH. (5)

Capitol Hill office: 2419 RHOB 20515; (202) 225-8171; Internet: jim.barcia-pub@mail.house.gov or www.house.gov/barcia; *Administrative Assistant:* Roger Szemraj

District office(s): 5409 W. Pierson Rd., Flushing 48433; (810) 732-7501; Fax: (810) 732-7504; *District Representative:* Mark Salogar.

301 E. Genesee St., #502, Saginaw 48607; (517) 754-6075; Fax: (517) 754-6571; *District Director:* James C. Lewis.

503 N. Euclid St., #11, Bay City 48706; (517) 667-0003; Fax: (517) 667-0921; *District Representative:* Marla N. Schutt.

Committee assignment(s): Science; Transportation and Infrastructure

BARR, BOB, R-GA. (7)

Capitol Hill office: 1130 LHOB 20515; (202) 225-2931; Fax: (202) 225-2944; Internet: barr.ga@mail.house. gov or www.house.gov/barr; *Chief of Staff:* Dan R. Levinson

District office(s): 423 College St., Suite B, #503, Carrollton 30117; (770) 836-1776; Fax: (770) 838-0436; *Constituent Services Representative:* Catherine Brock.

200 Ridley Ave., LaGrange 30240; (706) 812-1776; Fax: (706) 885-9019; *Constituent Services Representative:* Jan Haralson.

999 Whitlock Ave., #13, Marietta 30064; (770) 429-1776; Fax: (770) 795-9551; *District Director:* Fred Aiken.

600 E. 1st St., Rome 30161; (706) 290-1776; Fax: (706) 232-7864; *Constituent Services Representative:* Linda Shiver.

Committee assignment(s): Banking and Financial Services; Government Reform and Oversight; Judiciary

BARRETT, BILL, R-NEB. (3)

Capitol Hill office: 2458 RHOB 20515; 225-6435; Internet: barrett.ntouch@mail.house.gov or www.house.gov/billbarrett; *Administrative Assistant:* Jeri Finke

District office(s): 312 W. 3rd St., Grand Island 68801; (308) 381-5555; *Deputy Chief of Staff:* Bruce R. Rieker.

1811 Ave. A, Scottsbluff 69361; (308) 632-3333; *District Office Manager:* Greg Beam.

Committee assignment(s): Agriculture; Education and Workforce

BARRETT, THOMAS M., D-WIS. (5)

Capitol Hill office: 1224 LHOB 20515; (202) 225-3571; Fax: (202) 225-2185; Internet: telltom@mail.house.gov or www.house.gov/barrett; *Chief of Staff:* Sharon Robinson

District office(s): 135 W. Wells St., #618, Milwaukee 53203; (414) 297-1331; *District Office Director:* Terry Perry.

Committee assignment(s): Banking and Financial Services; Government Reform and Oversight

BARTLETT, ROSCOE G., R-MD. (6)

Capitol Hill office: 322 CHOB 20515; (202) 225-2721; Fax: (202) 225-2193; Internet: www.house.gov/bartlett; *Chief of Staff:* Jim Backlin

District office(s): 15 E. Main St., #110, Westminster 21157; (410) 857-1115; Fax: (410) 857-1329; *District Assistant:* Phil Straw.

48-50 Broadway, Frostburg 21532; (301) 689-0034; *District Assistant:* Myra Kidd.

5831 Buckeystown Pike, Suite E, Frederick 21701; (301) 694-3030; Fax: (301) 694-6674; *District Coordinator:* Gregg Cox.

100 W. Franklin St., Hagerstown 21740; (301) 797-6043; *District Assistant:* Rita Downs.

Committee assignment(s): National Security; Science; Small Business

BARTON, JOE L., R-TEXAS (6)

Capitol Hill office: 2264 RHOB 20515; (202) 225-2002; Fax: (202) 225-3052; Internet: rep.barton@mail.house.gov or www.house.gov/barton; *Administrative Assistant:* Cathy Gillespie

District office(s): 303 W. Knox St., #201, Ennis 75119; (817) 543-1000; Fax: (817) 875-1907; *District Representative:* Linda Gillespie.

805 Washington Dr., Suite F, Arlington 76011; (817) 543-1000; Fax: (817) 548-7029; *District Director:* Harold Samuels.

4521 S. Hulen St., #210, Fort Worth 76109; (817) 543-1000; Fax: (817) 926-2618; *District Representative:* Christi Townsend.

Committee assignment(s): Commerce; Science

BASS, CHARLES, R-N.H. (2)

Capitol Hill office: 218 CHOB 20515; (202) 225-5206; Fax: (202) 225-2946; Internet: cbass@hr.house.gov or www.house.gov/bass; *Staff Director:* David B. Leland

District office(s): 142 N. Main St., Concord 03301; (603) 226-0249; Fax: (603) 226-0476; *Chief of Staff:* Darwin Cusack.

170 Main St., Nashua ; (603) 889-8772; Fax: (603) 889-6890; *Constituent Services Representative:* Madeline Saulnier.

1 W. St., #208, Keene 03431; (603) 358-4094; Fax: (603) 358-5092; *Constituent Services Representative:* Jane Lane.

69 Main St., Littleton 03561; (603) 444-1271; Fax: (603) 444-5343; *Constituent Services Representative:* Christopher Hodgdon.

Committee assignment(s): Budget; Select Intelligence; Transportation and Infrastructure

BATEMAN, HERBERT H., R-VA. (1)

Capitol Hill office: 2350 RHOB 20515; (202) 225-4261; Fax: (202) 225-4382; Internet: www.house.gov/bateman; *Administrative Assistant:* Dan Scandling

District office(s): 4712 Southpoint Parkway, Fredericksburg 22407; (540) 898-2975; Fax: (540) 898-3280; *District Representative:* John Goolrick.

P.O. Box 447, Accomac 23301; (757) 787-7836; Fax: (757) 787-9540; *District Representative:* Suzanne Beasley.

739 Thimble Shoals Blvd., #803, Newport News 23606; (757) 873-1132; Fax: (757) 599-0424; *District Director:* Dee Benton.

Committee assignment(s): National Security; Transportation and Infrastructure

BECERRA, XAVIER, D-CALIF. (3)

Capitol Hill office: 1119 LHOB 20515; (202) 225-6235; Fax: (202) 225-2202; *Administrative Assistant:* Krista Atteberry

District office(s): 1910 Sunset Blvd., #560, Los Angeles 90026; (213) 483-1425; Fax: (213) 483-1429; *District Administrative Assistant:* Henry Lozano.

Committee assignment(s): Ways and Means

BENTSEN, KEN, D-TEXAS (25)

Capitol Hill office: 128 CHOB 20515; (202) 225-7508; Fax: (202) 225-2947; Internet: bentsen@hr.house.gov or www.house.gov/bentsen; *Administrative Assistant:* Vince Willmore

District office(s): 515 Rusk St., #12102, Houston 77002; (713) 229-2244; *District Director:* Pat Strong.

Committee assignment(s): Banking and Financial Services; Budget

BEREUTER, DOUG, R-NEB. (1)

Capitol Hill office: 2184 RHOB 20515; (202) 225-4806; *Chief of Staff:* Susan Olson

District office(s): 502 N. Broad St., P.O. Box 377, Fremont 68025; (402) 727-0888; *District Assistant:* Judy Larson.

1045 K St., P.O. Box 82887, Lincoln 68501; (402) 438-1598; *District Office Manager:* Roger Massey.

Committee assignment(s): Banking and Financial Services; International Relations

BERMAN, HOWARD L., D-CALIF. (26)

Capitol Hill office: 2330 RHOB 20515; (202) 225-4695; Internet: www.house.gov/berman; *Chief of Staff:* Gene Smith

District office(s): 10200 Sepulveda Blvd., #300, Mission Hills 91345; (818) 891-0543; *Executive Secretary:* Pearl Ricci.

Committee assignment(s): International Relations; Judiciary; Standards of Official Conduct (ranking member)

BERRY, MARION, D-ARK. (1)

Capitol Hill office: 1407 LHOB 20515; (202) 225-4076; Internet: www.house.gov/berry; *Administrative Assistant:* Bruce Harris

District office(s): 615 S. Main, #211, Jonesboro 72401; (870) 972-4600.

Committee assignment(s): Agriculture; Small Business

BILBRAY, BRIAN P., R-CALIF. (49)

Capitol Hill office: 1530 LHOB 20515; (202) 225-2040; Fax: 225-2948; Internet: brian.bilbray@mail.house.gov or www.house.gov/bilbray; *Chief of Staff:* John Woodard

District office(s): 1101 Camino del Rio South, #330, San Diego 92108; (619) 291-1430; Fax: (619) 291-8956; *District Director:* Greg Stein.

Committee assignment(s): Commerce

BILIRAKIS, MICHAEL, R-FLA. (9)

Capitol Hill office: 2369 RHOB 20515; 225-5755; Fax: 225-4085; Internet: www.house.gov/bilirakis; *Administrative Assistant:* Patricia DeLoatche

District office(s): 1100 Cleveland St., #1600, Clearwater 34615; (813) 441-3721; *Scheduler:* Patti Caccamo.

4111 Land O'Lakes Blvd., #306, Land O'Lakes 34639; (813) 996-7441; *Caseworker:* Shirley Miaoulis.

Committee assignment(s): Commerce; Veterans' Affairs

BISHOP, SANFORD D., JR., D-GA. (2)

Capitol Hill office: 1433 LHOB 20515; (202) 225-3631; Fax: (202) 225-2203; *Administrative Assistant:* Katreice Lindley-Banks

District office(s): 401 N. Patterson St., #255, Valdosta 31601; (912) 247-9705; Fax: (912) 241-1035; *Staff Assistant:* Nancy Webb.

225 Pine St., Albany 31701; (912) 439-8067; Fax: (912) 436-2099; *District Director:* Hobby Stripling.

105 Main St., Dawson 31742; (912) 995-3991; Fax: (912) 995-4894; *Staff Assistant:* Tonya Griggs.

Committee assignment(s): Agriculture; Select Intelligence

BLAGOJEVICH, ROD R., D-ILL. (5)

Capitol Hill office: 501 CHOB 20515; (202) 225-4061; Fax: (202) 225-5603; Internet: www.house.gov/blagojevich; *Chief of Staff:* John Wyma

District office(s): 4064 N. Lincoln Ave., Chicago 60618; (773) 868-3240; Fax: (773) 868-0036; *District Director:* Lucy Moog.

Committee assignment(s): Government Reform and Oversight; National Security

BLILEY, TOM, R-VA. (7)

Capitol Hill office: 2409 RHOB 20515; (202) 225-2815; Internet: www.house.gov/bliley; *Chief of Staff:* Linda Pedigo

District office(s): 763 Madison Rd., #207, Culpeper 22701; (703) 825-8960; *District Office Representative:* Anita Essalih.

4914 Fitzhugh Ave., #101, Richmond 23230; (804) 771-2809; *District Director:* Kathy Costigan.

Committee assignment(s): Commerce (chair)

BLUMENAUER, EARL, D-ORE. (3)

Capitol Hill office: 1113 LHOB 20515; (202) 225-4811; Internet: write.earl@mail.house.gov or www.house.gov/blumenauer; *Administrative Assistant:* Bob Crane

District office(s): 516 S.E. Morrison St., #250, Portland 97214; (503) 321-3200; *District Director:* Julia Pomeroy.

Committee assignment(s): Transportation and Infrastructure

BLUNT, ROY, R-MO. (7)

Capitol Hill office: 508 CHOB 20515; (202) 225-6536; Internet: www.house.gov/blunt; *Chief of Staff:* Gregg Hartley

District office(s): 2247-B E. Sunshine St., Springfield 65804; (417) 889-1800.

Committee assignment(s): Agriculture; International Relations; Transportation and Infrastructure

BOEHLERT, SHERWOOD, R-N.Y. (23)

Capitol Hill office: 2246 RHOB 20515; (202) 225-3665; Fax: (202) 225-1891; Internet: rep.boehlert@mail.house.gov or www.house.gov/boehlert; *Chief of Staff:* Dean D'Amore

District office(s): 10 Broad St., #200, Utica 13501; (315) 793-8146; *District Director:* Jeanne Donalty.

66 S. Broad St., Norwich 13815; (607) 336-7160.

41 S. Main St., Oneonta 13820; (607) 432-5524.

Committee assignment(s): Select Intelligence; Science; Transportation and Infrastructure

BOEHNER, JOHN A., R-OHIO (8)

Capitol Hill office: 1011 LHOB 20515; (202) 225-6205; Internet: www.house.gov/boehner; *Chief of Staff:* Barry Jackson

District office(s): 5617 Liberty-Fairfield Rd., Hamilton 45011; (513) 894-6003; Fax: (513) 894-6127; *District Deputy Chief of Staff:* William C. Krieger.

12 S. Plum St., Troy 45373; (513) 339-1524; Fax: (513) 339-1878; *Field Representative:* Bill Wolke.

Committee assignment(s): Agriculture; House Oversight

BONILLA, HENRY, R-TEXAS (23)

Capitol Hill office: 1427 LHOB 20515; (202) 225-4511; Fax: (202) 225-2237; *Administrative Assistant:* Steve Ruhlen

District office(s): 1300 Matamoros St., #113B, Laredo 78040; (210) 726-4682; Fax: (210) 726-4684; *Constituent Liaison:* Viola Martinez.

11120 Wurzbach Rd., #300, San Antonio 78230; (210) 697-9055; *District Director:* Phil Ricks.

111 E. Broadway, #101, Del Rio 78840; (210) 774-6547; Fax: (210) 774-5693; *Constituent Liaison:* Ida Nino.

4400 N. Big Spring, #211, Midland 79705; (915) 686-8833; Fax: (915) 686-8819; *Constituent Liaison:* Tony Carillo.

Committee assignment(s): Appropriations

BONIOR, DAVID E., D-MICH. (1)

Capitol Hill office: 2207 RHOB 20515; (202) 225-2106; Fax: (202) 226-1169; *Administrative Assistant:* Sarah Dufendach

District office(s): 59 N. Walnut St., #305, Mt. Clemens 48043; (810) 469-3232; *Administrative Assistant:* Edward Bruley.

526 Water St., #101, Port Huron 48060; (810) 987-8889; *Congressional Aide:* Timothy Morse.

BORSKI, ROBERT A., D-PA. (3)

Capitol Hill office: 2267 RHOB 20515; (202) 225-8251; Fax: (202) 225-4628; *Administrative Assistant:* Mark Vieth

District office(s): 2630 Memphis St., Philadelphia 19125; (215) 426-4616; Fax: (215) 426-7741; *Congressional Aide:* Peg Rzepski.

7141 Frankford Ave., Philadelphia 19135; (215) 335-3355; Fax: (215) 333-4508; *District Director:* John F. Dempsey.

Committee assignment(s): Transportation and Infrastructure

BOSWELL, LEONARD L., D-IOWA (3)

Capitol Hill office: 1029 LHOB 20515; (202) 225-3806; Fax: (202) 225-5608; *Chief of Staff:* John Norris

District office(s): 709 Furnas Dr., Osceola 50213; (515) 342-4801; Fax: (515) 342-4354.

Committee assignment(s): Agriculture; Transportation and Infrastructure

BOUCHER, RICK, D-VA. (9)

Capitol Hill office: 2329 RHOB 20515; (202) 225-3861; Fax: (202) 225-0442; Internet: ninthnet@mail.house. gov or www.house.gov/boucher; *Chief of Staff:* Andy Wright

District office(s): 188 E. Main St., Abingdon 24210; (703) 628-1145; Fax: (703) 628-2203; *District Administrator:* Linda DeYorio.

311 Shawnee Ave. East, Big Stone Gap 24219; (703) 523-5450; Fax: (703) 523-1412; *Senior Staff Assistant:* Janet Cantrell.

106 N. Washington Ave., P.O. Box 1268, Pulaski 24301; (703) 980-4310; Fax: (703) 980-0629; *Casework Supervisor:* Becki Gunn.

Committee assignment(s): Commerce; Judiciary

BOYD, ALLEN, D-FLA. (2)

Capitol Hill office: 1237 LHOB 20515; (202) 225-5235; Internet: www.house.gov/boyd; *Administrative Assistant:* Jennifer Cannon

District office(s): 930 Thomasville Rd., #101, Tallahassee 32303; (850) 561-3979; Fax: (850) 681-2902.

3030 W. Government St., #703, Panama City 32401; (850) 785-0812; Fax: (850) 763-3764; *District Representative:* Jerry Smithwick.

Committee assignment(s): National Security; Small Business

BRADY, KEVIN, R-TEXAS (8)

Capitol Hill office: 1531 LHOB 20515; (202) 225-4901; Fax: (202) 225-5524; *Chief of Staff:* Doug Centilli

District office(s): 200 River Point Dr., #304, Conroe 77304; (409) 441-5700; Fax: (409) 441-5757; *District Director:* Jamey Webster.

616 FM 1960 W #325, Houston 77090; (281) 895-8892; Fax: (281) 895-8912.

111 E. University Dr., #216, College Station 77840; (409) 846-6068; Fax: (409) 260-2916.

Committee assignment(s): International Relations; Resources; Science

BROWN, CORRINE, D-FLA. (3)

Capitol Hill office: 1610 LHOB 20515; (202) 225-0123; Fax: (202) 225-2256; *Administrative Assistant:* Elias Ronnie Simmons

District office(s): 314 Palmetto St., Jacksonville 32202; (904) 354-1652; Fax: (904) 354-2721; *District Director:* Glenel Bowden.

75 Ivanhoe Blvd., Orlando 32801; (407) 872-0656; Fax: (407) 872-5763; *Area Director:* Reginald McGill.

Committee assignment(s): Transportation and Infrastructure; Veterans' Affairs

BROWN, GEORGE E., JR., D-CALIF. (42)

Capitol Hill office: 2300 RHOB 20515; (202) 225-6161; Fax: (202) 225-8671; Internet: talk2geb@mail.house. gov or www.house.gov/georgebrown; *Administrative Assistant:* Bill Grady

District office(s): 657 La Cadena Dr., Colton 92324; (909) 825-2472; Fax: (909) 824-3825; *District Administrator:* Wilmer D. Carter.

Committee assignment(s): Agriculture; Science (ranking member)

BROWN, SHERROD, D-OHIO (13)

Capitol Hill office: 328 CHOB 20515; (202) 225-3401; Fax: (202) 225-2266; Internet: sherrod@hr.house.gov or www.house.gov/sherrodbrown; *Chief of Staff:* Donna Pignatelli

District office(s): 5201 Abbe Rd., Elyria 44035; (440) 934-5100; *District Director:* Elizabeth Thames.

15561 W. High St., Middlefield 44062; (440) 632-5913; *Caseworker:* Joyce Edelinsky.

144 N. Broadway, Medina 44256; (216) 722-9262; *Caseworker:* Colin Cranston.

Committee assignment(s): Commerce; International Relations

BRYANT, ED, R-TENN. (7)

Capitol Hill office: 408 CHOB 20515; (202) 225-2811; Fax: (202) 225-2989; Internet: www.house.gov/ bryant; *Chief of Staff:* P. K. Rehbein

District office(s): 330 N. 2nd St., Clarksville 37040; (615) 503-0391; Fax: (615) 503-0393; *Staff Assistant:* Woody Parker.

5909 Shelby Oaks Dr., #213, Memphis 38134; (901) 382-5811; Fax: (901) 373-8215; *Staff Assistant:* Susan McCord.

810 1/2 S. Garden St., Columbia 38401; (615) 381-8100; Fax: (615) 381-1956; *Staff Assistant:* Becky Moon.

Committee assignment(s): Agriculture; Judiciary

BUNNING, JIM, R-KY. (4)

Capitol Hill office: 2437 RHOB 20515; (202) 225-3465; Fax: (202) 225-0003; Internet: rep.jim.bunning@ mail.house.gov or www.house.gov/bunning; *Chief of Staff:* David A. York

District office(s): 1405 Greenup Ave., Ashland 41011; (606) 325-9898; Fax: (606) 325-9892; *Office Manager:* Darlynn Barber.

1717 Dixie Hwy., #160, Fort Wright 41011; (606) 341-2602; Fax: (606) 292-3188; *District Administrator:* Debbie McKinney.

Committee assignment(s): Budget; Ways and Means

BURR, RICHARD M., R-N.C. (5)

Capitol Hill office: 1513 LHOB 20515; (202) 225-2071; Fax: (202) 225-2995; Internet: richard.burrnc05@ mail.house.gov or www.house.gov/burr; *Chief of Staff:* Alicia Peterson

District office(s): 2000 W. 1st St., #508, Winston Salem 27104; (910) 631-5125; Fax: (910) 725-4495; *District Director:* L. Dean Myers.

Committee assignment(s): Commerce

BURTON, DAN, R-IND. (6)

Capitol Hill office: 2185 RHOB 20515; (202) 225-2276; Fax: (202) 225-0016; Internet: www.house.gov/ burton; *Chief of Staff:* Mark Walker

District office(s): 435 E. Main St., #J3, Greenwood 46142; (317) 882-3640; *Special Assistant:* Mary Frederick.

8900 Keystone at the Crossing, #1050, Indianapolis 46240; (317) 848-0201; Fax: (317) 846-7306; *District Director:* James D. Atterholt.

Committee assignment(s): Government Reform and Oversight (chair); International Relations

BUYER, STEVE, R-IND. (5)

Capitol Hill office: 326 CHOB 20515; (202) 225-5037; Internet: www.house.gov/buyer; *Chief of Staff:* Kelly Craven

District office(s): 120 E. Mulberry St., #106, Kokomo 46901; (765) 454-7551; *District Manager:* Linda Worsham.

204A N. Main St., Monticello 47960; (219) 583-9819; *Staff Assistant:* Janet Faker.

Committee assignment(s): Judiciary; National Security; Veterans' Affairs

CALLAHAN, SONNY, R-ALA. (1)

Capitol Hill office: 2418 RHOB 20515; (202) 225-4931; Fax: (202) 225-0562; Internet: sonny.callahan@mail. house.gov or www.house.gov/callahan; *Chief of Staff:* Jo Bonner

District office(s): 2970 Cottage Hill Rd., #126, Mobile 36606; (334) 690-2811; *District Office Manager:* Eliska Roe.

Committee assignment(s): Appropriations

CALVERT, KEN, R-CALIF. (43)

Capitol Hill office: 1034 LHOB 20515; (202) 225-1986; Internet: www.house.gov/calvert; *Administrative Assistant:* Dave Ramey

District office(s): 3400 Central Ave., #200, Riverside 92506; (909) 784-4300; Fax: (909) 784-5255; *District Director:* Sue Miller.

Committee assignment(s): Resources; Science

CAMP, DAVE, R-MICH. (4)

Capitol Hill office: 137 CHOB 20515; (202) 225-3561; Fax: (202) 225-9679; Internet: davecamp@mail. house.gov or www.house.gov/camp; *Chief of Staff:* John Guzik

District office(s): 3508 Houghton Lake Dr., Houghton Lake 48629; (517) 366-4922; *Office Manager:* Tarin Boven.

135 Ashman St., Midland 48640; (517) 631-2552; *District Director:* Dan Keelean.

308 W. Main St., Owosso 48867; (517) 723-6759; *Constituent Representative:* Donna Conklin.

Committee assignment(s): Ways and Means

CAMPBELL, TOM, R-CALIF. (15)

Capitol Hill office: 2442 RHOB 20515; (202) 225-2631; Fax: (202) 225-6788; Internet: campbell@mail.house. gov or www.house.gov/campbell; *Chief of Staff:* Casey Beyer

District office(s): #1C, 910 Campisi Way, Campbell 95008; (408) 371-7337; Fax: (408) 371-7925; *District Manager:* Casey Beyer.

Committee assignment(s): Banking and Financial Services; International Relations

CANADY, CHARLES T., R-FLA. (12)

Capitol Hill office: 2432 RHOB 20515;(202) 225-1252; Fax: (202) 225-2279; Internet: rep.charles.canady@ mail.house.gov or www.house.gov/canady; *Chief of Staff:* Stacey Windham

District office(s): 129 S. Kentucky Ave., #910, Lakeland 33801; (941) 688-2651; *District Director:* Sue Loftin.

Committee assignment(s): Agriculture; Judiciary

CANNON, CHRISTOPHER B., R-UTAH (3)

Capitol Hill office: 118 CHOB 20515; (202) 225-7751; Fax: (202) 225-5629; Internet: cannon.ut03@mail. house.gov or www.house.gov/cannon; *Administrative Assistant:* Steven Taggart

District office(s): 51 S. University Ave., #317, Provo 84606; (801) 379-2500; Fax: (801) 379-2509; *District Director:* Mike Mower.

Committee assignment(s): Judiciary; Resources; Science

CARDIN, BENJAMIN L., D-MD. (3)

Capitol Hill office: 104 CHOB 20515; (202) 225-4016; Internet: rep.cardin@mail.house.gov or www.house. gov/cardin; *Administrative Assistant:* David Koshgarian

District office(s): 540 E. Belvedere Ave., #201, Baltimore 21212; (410) 433-8886; *District Office Director:* Bailey E. Fine.

Committee assignment(s): Budget; Ways and Means

CARSON, JULIA, D-IND. (1)

Capitol Hill office: 1541 LHOB 20515; (202) 225-4011; Fax: (202) 225-5633; Internet: rep.carson@mail. house.gov or www.house.gov/carson; *Chief of Staff:* Marie McGlone

District office(s): 300 E. Fall Creek Parkway, #201, Indianapolis 46205; (317) 283-6516; Fax: (317) 283-6567; *District Director:* Lena Hackett.

Committee assignment(s): Banking and Financial Services; Veterans' Affairs

CASTLE, MICHAEL N., R-DEL. (AL)

Capitol Hill office: 1227 LHOB 20515; (202) 225-4165; Fax: (202) 225-2291; Internet: delaware@mail.house. gov or www.house.gov/castle; *Chief of Staff:* Paul Leonard

District office(s): 3 Christina Centre, 201 N. Walnut St., #107, Wilmington 19801; (302) 428-1902; Fax: (302) 428-1950; *District Director:* Jeffrey A. Dayton.

2005 Frear Federal Bldg., #2005, Dover 19901; (302) 736-1666; Fax: (302) 736-6580; *Kent and Sussex County Coordinator:* Kate Johnson.

Committee assignment(s): Banking and Financial Services; Education and Workforce; Select Intelligence

CHABOT, STEVE, R-OHIO (1)

Capitol Hill office: 129 CHOB 20515; (202) 225-2216; Fax: (202) 225-3012; *Administrative Assistant:* Gary Lindgren

District office(s): 105 W. 4th St., #1115, Cincinnati 45202; (513) 684-2723; Fax: (513) 421-8722; *Chief of Staff:* Shannon W. Jones.

Committee assignment(s): International Relations; Judiciary; Small Business

CHAMBLISS, SAXBY, R-GA. (8)

Capitol Hill office: 1019 LHOB 20515; (202) 225-6531; Fax: (202) 225-3013; Internet: saxby@mail.house.gov or www.house.gov/chambliss; *Chief of Staff:* Rob Leebern

District office(s): 3312 Northside Dr., Bldg. D, Macon 31210; (912) 475-0665; Fax: (912) 475-0673; *District Director:* Bill Stembridge.

208 Tebean St., Waycross 31501; (912) 287-1180; Fax: (912) 287-1182; *District Administrator:* Debbie Cannon.

Committee assignment(s): Agriculture; National Security

CHENOWETH, HELEN, R-IDAHO (1)

Capitol Hill office: 1727 LHOB 20515; (202) 225-6611; Fax: (202) 225-3029; Internet: askhelen@mail.house. gov or www.house.gov/chenoweth; *Chief of Staff:* Keith Lee Rupp

District office(s): 304 N. 8th St., #454, Boise 83702; (208) 336-9831; Fax: (208) 336-9891; *District Director:* Jim Gambrell.

Committee assignment(s): Agriculture; Resources; Veterans' Affairs

CHRISTENSEN, JON, R-NEB. (2)

Capitol Hill office: 413 CHOB 20515; (202) 225-4155; Fax: (202) 225-3032; Internet: talk2jon@hr.house.gov or www.house.gov/christensen; *Administrative Assistant:* Lori Wall

District office(s): 8712 W. Dodge St., #350, Omaha 68114; (402) 397-9944; Fax: (402) 397-8787; *Chief of Staff:* Bill Protexter.

Committee assignment(s): Ways and Means

CHRISTIAN-GREEN, DONNA M., D-VIRGIN IS. (AL)

Capitol Hill office: 1711 LHOB 20515; (202) 225-1790; Internet: donna.green@mail.house.gov or www. house.gov/christian-green; *Administrative Assistant:* Lorraine Hill

District office(s): Vitraco Mall, Bldg. 2, Bay 3, St. Thomas 00801; (340) 774-4408; Fax: (340) 774-8033; *District Director:* James A. O'Bryan.

Sunny Isle Shopping Center, P.O. Box 5980, St. Croix 00823; (340) 773-5900; Fax: (340) 773-5111: Claire Roker.

Committee assignment(s): Resources

CLAY, WILLIAM L., D-MO. (1)

Capitol Hill office: 2306 RHOB 20515; (202) 225-2406; Internet: www.house.gov/clay; *Chief of Staff:* Harriet Pritchett Grigsby

District office(s): 5261 Delmar Blvd., Suite B, St. Louis 63108; (314) 367-1970; Fax: (314) 367-1341; *District Assistant:* Pearlie I. Evans.

Central City Shopping Center North, #49, St. Louis 63136; (314) 388-0321; *District Coordinator:* Virginia Cook.

Committee assignment(s): Education and Workforce (ranking member)

CLAYTON, EVA, D-N.C. (1)

Capitol Hill office: 2440 RHOB 20515; (202) 225-3101; Fax: (202) 225-3354; Internet: eclayton@hr.house. gov or www.house.gov/clayton; *Administrative Assistant:* Johnny Barnes

District office(s): 134 N. Main St., Warrenton 27589; (919) 257-4800; Fax: (919) 257-2088; *District Manager:* Charles Worth.

400 W. 5th St., Greenville 27838; (919) 758-8800; Fax: (919) 758-1021; *District Manager:* Charles Worth.

313 S. Union St., #111, Fayetteville 28301; (910) 323-9003; Fax: (910) 323-8810; *Caseworker:* Judy Lowe.

Committee assignment(s): Agriculture; Budget

CLEMENT, BOB, D-TENN. (5)

Capitol Hill office: 2229 RHOB 20515; (202) 225-4311; Fax: (202) 226-1035; Internet: bob.clement@mail. house.gov or www.house.gov/clement; *Chief of Staff:* Alex Haught

District office(s): 552 U.S. Courthouse, Nashville 37203; (615) 736-5295; *Chief of Staff:* Dottie Moore.

2701 Jefferson St., #103, Nashville 37208; (615) 320-1363; Fax: (615) 736-7479; *Nashville Coordinator:* Gail Stafford.

101 5th Ave. West, #201, Springfield 37172; (615) 384-6600; Fax: (615) 384-6600; *Field Coordinator:* Christi Ray.

Committee assignment(s): International Relations; Transportation and Infrastructure

CLYBURN, JAMES E., D-S.C. (6)

Capitol Hill office: 319 CHOB 20515; (202) 225-3315; Fax: (202) 225-2313; Internet: jclyburn@mail.house. gov or www.house.gov/clyburn; *Chief of Staff:* Yelberton Watkins

District office(s): 1703 Gervais St., Columbia 29201; (803) 799-1100; Fax: (803) 799-9060; *District Director:* Robert M. Nance.

2106 Mount Pleasant St., P.O. Box 6099, Charleston 29405; (803) 965-5570; Fax: (803) 965-5581; *Area Director:* Davis Marshall.

181 E. Evans St., #314, Florence 29502; (803) 662-1212; *Area Director:* Charlene Lowery.

Committee assignment(s): Transportation and Infrastructure; Veterans' Affairs

COBLE, HOWARD, R-N.C. (6)

Capitol Hill office: 2239 RHOB 20515;(202) 225-3065; Fax: (202) 225-8611; Internet: repcoble@mail.house. gov; *Administrative Assistant:* Edward McDonald

District office(s): 241 Sunset Ave., #101, Asheboro 27203; (910) 626-3060; Fax: (910) 626-4533; *District Representative:* Rebecca Williams.

124 W. Elm St., P.O. Box 814, Graham 27253; (910) 229-0159; Fax: (910) 228-7974; *District Representative:* Janine Osborne.

1912 Eastchester Dr., #430, High Point 27265; (910) 886-5106; Fax: (910) 886-8740; *District Representative:* Carolyn McGahey.

1404 Piedmont Ave., Suite A, P.O. Box 1813, Lexington 27293; (910) 248-8230; Fax: (910) 248-4275; *District Representative:* Connie Leonard.

324 W. Market St., #247, Greensboro 27401; (910) 333-5005; Fax: (910) 333-5048; *Community Liaison:* Jan Scott.

Committee assignment(s): Judiciary; Transportation and Infrastructure

COBURN, TOM, R-OKLA. (2)

Capitol Hill office: 429 CHOB 20515; (202) 225-2701; Fax: (202) 225-3038; Internet: rep.coburn@mail.house.gov or www.house.gov/coburn; *Chief of Staff:* Karl E. Ahlgren

District office(s): 215 State St., #815, Muskogee 74401; (918) 687-2533; Fax: (918) 682-8503.

Committee assignment(s): Commerce; Science

COLLINS, MAC, R-GA. (3)

Capitol Hill office: 1131 LHOB 20515; (202) 225-5901; Fax: (202) 225-2515; Internet: mac.collins@mail.house.gov or www.house.gov/maccollins; *Administrative Assistant:* Betty Monro

District office(s): 173 N. Main St., Jonesboro 30236; (770) 603-3395; *Press Secretary:* Clark Reid.

2121 Wynnton Rd., Columbus 31906; (706) 327-7229; Fax: (706) 324-7969; *Constituent Services Manager:* Shirley Gillespie.

Committee assignment(s): Ways and Means

COMBEST, LARRY, R-TEXAS (19)

Capitol Hill office: 1026 LHOB 20515; (202) 225-4005; Internet: www.house.gov/combest; *Administrative Assistant:* Rob Lehman

District office(s): 5809 S. Western Ave., #205, Amarillo 79110; (806) 353-3945; *Office Manager:* Danelle Barber.

1205 Texas Ave., #810, Lubbock 79401; (806) 763-1611; *District Representative:* Jimmy Clark.

3800 E. 42nd St., Odessa 79762; (915) 550-0743; *Office Manager:* Jenny Welch.

Committee assignment(s): Agriculture; Small Business

CONDIT, GARY A., D-CALIF. (18)

Capitol Hill office: 2245 RHOB 20515; (202) 225-6131; Fax: (202) 225-0819; Internet: gary.condit@mail.house.gov or www.house.gov/gcondit; *Administrative Assistant:* Mike Dayton

District office(s): 415 W. 18th St., Merced 95340; (209) 383-4455; Fax: (209) 726-1065; *Staff Assistant:* Ruth Daleth.

920 16th St., Suite C, Modesto 95354; (209) 527-1914; Fax: (209) 527-5748; *Chief of Staff:* Mike Lynch.

Committee assignment(s): Agriculture; Government Reform and Oversight

CONYERS, JOHN, JR., D-MICH. (14)

Capitol Hill office: 2426 RHOB 20515; (202) 225-5126; Fax: (202) 225-0072; Internet: jconyers@hr.house.gov or www.house.gov/conyers

District office(s): 231 W. Lafayette Blvd., #669, Detroit 48226; (313) 961-5670; Fax: (313) 226-2085; *District Director:* Ray Plowden.

Committee assignment(s): Judiciary (ranking member)

COOK, MERRILL, R-UTAH (2)

Capitol Hill office: 1431 LHOB 20515; (202) 225-3011; Fax: (202) 225-5638; Internet: cong.merrill.cook@mail.house.gov or www.house.gov/cook; *Chief of Staff:* Janet Jenson

District office(s): 125 S. State, #2311, Salt Lake City 84138; (801) 524-4395; Fax: (801) 524-5994; *District Director:* Rob Jeppson.

Committee assignment(s): Banking and Financial Services; Science; Transportation and Infrastructure

COOKSEY, JOHN, R-LA. (5)

Capitol Hill office: 317 CHOB 20515; (202) 225-8490; Fax: (202) 225-5639; Internet: congressman.cooksey@mail.house.gov or www.house.gov/cooksey; *Administrative Assistant:* Lee Fletcher

District office(s): 1101 Hudson Lane, Suite B, Monroe 71201; (318) 330-9998; Fax: (318) 330-9950; *District Director:* Del Vines.

2019 MacArthur Dr., Suite B, Alexandria 71301; (318) 448-1777; Fax: (318) 473-8163; *District Director:* Susan DeKeyzer.

Committee assignment(s): Agriculture; Transportation and Infrastructure; Veterans' Affairs

COSTELLO, JERRY F., D-ILL. (12)

Capitol Hill office: 2454 RHOB 20515;(202) 225-5661; Fax: (202) 225-0285; Internet: jfc.il12@mail.house.gov or www.house.gov/costello; *Administrative Assistant:* Brian Lott

District office(s): 1363 Neidringhaus Ave., Granite City 62040; (618) 451-7065; Fax: (618) 451-2126; *Staff Assistant:* David Cueto.

8787 State St., E. St. Louis 62203; (618) 397-8833; *Staff Assistant:* Mel Frierson.

327 W. Main St., Belleville 62220; (618) 233-8026; Fax: (618) 233-8765; *Office Manager:* Anne-Marie Risavy.

1330 Swanwick St., Chester 62233; (618) 826-3043; *Staff Assistant:* Patsie Lindsey.

250 W. Cherry St., Carbondale 62901; (618) 529-3791; *Staff Assistant:* Alice Tucker.

Committee assignment(s): Budget; Transportation and Infrastructure

COX, CHRISTOPHER, R-CALIF. (47)

Capitol Hill office: 2402 RHOB 20515; (202) 225-5611; Fax: (202) 225-9177; Internet: christopher.cox@mail. house.gov or www.house.gov/chriscox; *Chief of Staff:* C. Dean McGrath

District office(s): 4000 MacArthur Blvd., #430 E. Tower, Newport Beach 92660; (714) 756-2244; Fax: (714) 251-9309; *District Representative:* Greg Haskin.

Committee assignment(s): Commerce; Government Reform and Oversight

COYNE, WILLIAM J., D-PA. (14)

Capitol Hill office: 2455 RHOB 20515; (202) 225-2301; *Administrative Assistant:* Coleman J. Conroy

District office(s): 1000 Liberty Ave., #2009, Pittsburgh 15222; (412) 644-2870; *Executive Assistant:* James Rooney.

Committee assignment(s): Ways and Means

CRAMER, ROBERT E. "BUD," D-ALA. (5)

Capitol Hill office: 2416 RHOB 20515; (202) 225-4801; Internet: budmail@mail.house.gov or www.house. gov/cramer; *Administrative Assistant:* John Hay

District office(s): Morgan County Courthouse, Box 668, Decatur 35602; (205) 355-9400; *Caseworker:* Peggy Allen.

737 E. Avalon Ave., Muscle Shoals 35661; (205) 381-3450; *Caseworker:* Ethel McDonald.

403 Franklin St., Huntsville 35801; (205) 551-0190; *District Coordinator:* Joe Vallely.

Committee assignment(s): Appropriations

CRANE, PHILIP M., R-ILL. (8)

Capitol Hill office: 233 CHOB 20515; (202) 225-3711; Fax: (202) 225-7830; Internet: www.house.gov/crane; *Chief of Staff:* Kirt C. Johnson

District office(s): 300 N. Milwaukee Ave., Suite C, Lake Villa 60046; (847) 265-9000; *Caseworker:* Carol Toft.

1100 W. Northwest Hwy., Palatine 60067; (847) 358-9160; Fax: (847) 358-9185; *District Representative:* Jack McKenney.

Committee assignment(s): Ways and Means; Joint Taxation

CRAPO, MICHAEL D., R-IDAHO (2)

Capitol Hill office: 437 CHOB 20515; (202) 225-5531; Fax: (202) 225-8216; Internet: askmike@mail.house. gov or www.house.gov/crapo; *Administrative Assistant:* Susan Wheeler

District office(s): 250 S. 4th Ave., #220, Pocatello 83201; (208) 236-6734; Fax: (208) 236-6735; *Field Representative:* Katy Fischer.

628 Blue Lakes Blvd. North, Twin Falls 83301; (208) 734-7219; Fax: (208) 734-7244; *Field Representative:* Linda Norris.

2539 Channing Way, #260, Idaho Falls 83404; (208) 523-6701; Fax: (208) 523-2384; *Field Representative:* Laurel Hall.

304 N. 8th St., #325, Boise 83702; (208) 334-1953.

Committee assignment(s): Commerce; Resources

CUBIN, BARBARA, R-WYO. (AL)

Capitol Hill office: 1114 LHOB 20515; (202) 225-2311; Fax: (202) 225-3057; *Administrative Assistant:* Patty McDonald

District office(s): 2015 Federal Center, Cheyenne 82001; (307) 772-2595; Fax: (307) 772-2597; *Caseworker:* Elaine McCauley.

4003 Federal Bldg., Casper 82601; (307) 261-6595; Fax: (307) 261-5597; *Caseworker:* Mantha Phillips.

2515 Foothills Blvd., #202, Rock Springs 82901; (307) 362-4095; Fax: (307) 362-4097; *State Chair:* Katie Legerski.

Committee assignment(s): Commerce; Resources

CUMMINGS, ELIJAH E., D-MD. (7)

Capitol Hill office: 1632 LHOB 20515; (202) 225-4741; Fax: (202) 225-3178; Internet: www.house.gov/ cummings; *Chief of Staff:* Darleen Taylor

District office(s): 3000 Druid Park Dr., Baltimore 21215; (410) 367-1900; Fax: (410) 367-5331; *District Manager:* Deborah Perry.

754 Frederick Rd., Catonsville 21228; (410) 719-8777; Fax: (410) 455-0110; *Special Assistant:* William Cole.

7900 Liberty Rd., Baltimore 21244; (410) 496-2010; Fax: (410) 496-2015; *District Administrator:* Vernon Simms.

Committee assignment(s): Government Reform and Oversight; Transportation and Infrastructure

CUNNINGHAM, RANDY "DUKE," R-CALIF. (51)

Capitol Hill office: 2238 RHOB 20515; (202) 225-5452; Fax: (202) 225-2558; Internet: www.house.gov/ cunningham; *Chief of Staff:* Patrick McSwain

District office(s): 613 W. Valley Parkway, #320, Escondido 92025; (619) 737-8438; Fax: (619) 737-9132; *District Director:* Kathy Stafford.

Committee assignment(s): Appropriations

DANNER, PAT, D-MO. (6)

Capitol Hill office: 1207 LHOB 20515; (202) 225-7041; Fax: (202) 225-8221; *Chief of Staff:* Cathie McCarley

District office(s): 5754 N. Broadway, Kansas City 64118; (816) 455-2256; Fax: (816) 455-2153; *District Coordinator:* Donna Padgett.

201 S. 8th St., #330, St. Joseph 64501; (816) 233-9818; Fax: (816) 233-9848; *District Administrator:* Rose M. Grinstead.

Committee assignment(s): International Relations; Transportation and Infrastructure

DAVIS, DANNY K., D-ILL. (7)

Capitol Hill office: 1218 LHOB 20515; (202) 225-5006; Fax: (202) 225-5641; *Chief of Staff:* Roxanne Smith

District office(s): 3333 W. Arthington, Chicago 60624; (773) 533-7520; Fax: (773) 533-7530; *District Administrator:* F. Daniel Cantrell.

Committee assignment(s): Government Reform and Oversight; Small Business

DAVIS, JIM, D-FLA. (11)

Capitol Hill office: 327 CHOB 20515; (202) 225-3376; Internet: www.house.gov/writerep or www.house.gov/jimdavis; *Chief of Staff:* Suzanne Farmer

District office(s): 3315 Henderson Blvd., Tampa 33609; (813) 354-9217; Fax: (813) 354-9514; *District Director:* Clay Phillips.

Committee assignment(s): Budget; International Relations

DAVIS, THOMAS M., III, R-VA. (11)

Capitol Hill office: 224 CHOB 20515; (202) 225-1492; Fax: (202) 225-3071; Internet: www.house.gov/writerep or www.house.gov/tomdavis; *Administrative Assistant:* John Hishta

District office(s): 7018 Evergreen Ct., #6-A, Annandale 22003; (703) 916-9617; Fax: (703) 916-9617; *District Director:* Linda O'Meara.

Committee assignment(s): Government Reform and Oversight; Science; Transportation and Infrastructure

DEAL, NATHAN, R-GA. (9)

Capitol Hill office: 1406 LHOB 20515; (202) 225-5211; Fax: (202) 225-8272; Internet: www.house.gov/deal; *Chief of Staff:* Mark Maddox

District office(s): 311 Green St., #302, Gainesville 30501; (770) 535-2592; Fax: (770) 535-2765; *Staff Assistant:* Jim Adams.

415 E. Walnut Ave., #108, Dalton 30721; (706) 226-5320; *Staff Assistant:* Vivian Campbell.

109 N. Main St., Lafayette 30728; (706) 638-7042; Fax: (706) 638-7049; *Staff Assistant:* Lonna Hightower.

Committee assignment(s): Commerce; Education and Workforce

DEFAZIO, PETER A., D-ORE. (4)

Capitol Hill office: 2134 RHOB 20515; (202) 225-6416; Internet: peter.defazio@mail.house.gov or www.house.gov/defazio; *Administrative Assistant:* Penny Dodge

District office(s): 211 E. 7th Ave., #287, Eugene 97401; (541) 465-6732; *District Director:* Betsy Boyd.

P.O. Box 1557, Coos Bay 97420; (541) 269-2609; *Coastal Field Representative:* Jana R. Doerr.

612 S.E. Jackson St., P.O. Box 2460, Roseburg 97470; (541) 440-3523; *Field Representative:* Chris Conroy.

Committee assignment(s): Resources; Transportation and Infrastructure

DEGETTE, DIANA, D-COLO. (1)

Capitol Hill office: 1404 LHOB 20515; (202) 225-4431; Fax: (202) 225-5657; Internet: degette@mail.house.gov or www.house.gov/degette; *Administrative Assistant:* Lisa Cohen

District office(s): 1400 Glenarm Place, #202, Denver 80202; (303) 844-4988; Fax: (303) 844-4996; *Acting District Director:* Selina Dunham.

Committee assignment(s): Commerce

DELAHUNT, BILL, D-MASS. (1)

Capitol Hill office: 1517 LHOB 20515; (202) 225-3111; Fax: (202) 225-5658; *Administrative Assistant:* Steve Schwadron

District office(s): 15 Cottage Ave., 4th Floor, Quincy 02169; (617) 770-3700; Fax: (617) 770-2984; *District Director:* P.J. O'Sullivan.

146 Main St., Hyannis 02601; (508) 771-0666; Fax: (508) 790-1959; *Regional Representative:* Mark Forest.

Committee assignment(s): Judiciary; Resources

DELAURO, ROSA, D-CONN. (3)

Capitol Hill office: 436 CHOB 20515; (202) 225-3661; Fax: (202) 225-4890; Internet: delauro.ct03@mail.house.gov or www.house.gov/delauro; *Administrative Assistant:* Maura Keefe

District office(s): 59 Elm St., 2nd Floor, New Haven 06510; (203) 562-3718; *District Director:* Jennifer Emra.

Committee assignment(s): Appropriations

DELAY, TOM, R-TEXAS (22)

Capitol Hill office: 341 CHOB 20515; (202) 225-5951; Fax: (202) 225-5241; Internet: thewhip@mail.house.gov or tomdelay.house.gov; *Administrative Assistant:* Susan Hirschmann

District office(s): 12603 Southwest Freeway, #285, Stafford 77477; (713) 240-3700; *District Director:* Ann Swischer.

Committee assignment(s): Appropriations

DEUTSCH, PETER, D-FLA. (2)

Capitol Hill office: 204 CHOB 20515; (202) 225-7931; Fax: (202) 225-8456; Internet: pdeutsch@hr.house. gov; *Chief of Staff:* Robin Rorapaugh

District office(s): 10100 Pines Blvd., Pembroke Pines 33025; (954) 437-3936; *Administrative Assistant:* Robin Rorapaugh.

1010 Kennedy Dr., Key W. 33040; (305) 294-5815; Fax: (305) 294-4193; *Key W. Representative:* Debbie Robertson.

Committee assignment(s): Commerce

DIAZ-BALART, LINCOLN, R-FLA. (21)

Capitol Hill office: 404 CHOB 20515; (202) 225-4211; Fax: (202) 225-8576; Internet: www.house.gov/ diaz-balart; *Administrative Assistant:* Stephen Vermillion

District office(s): 8525 N.W. 53rd Terrace, #102, Miami 33166; (305) 470-8555; *District Director:* Ana M. Carbonell.

Committee assignment(s): Rules

DICKEY, JAY, R-ARK. (4)

Capitol Hill office: 2453 RHOB 20515; (202) 225-3772; Fax: (202) 225-1314; Internet: talk2jay@mail.house. gov or www.house.gov/dickey; *Chief of Staff:* Allen W. Maxwell

District office(s): 100 E. 8th Ave., #2521, Pine Bluff 76701; (870) 536-3376; Fax: (870) 536-4058; *District Director:* Allen Maxwell.

100 Reserve St., #201, Hot Springs National Park 71901; (501) 623-5800; Fax: (501) 623-5363; *District Field Representative:* Glenda Peacock.

Committee assignment(s): Appropriations

DICKS, NORM, D-WASH. (6)

Capitol Hill office: 2467 RHOB 20515; (202) 225-5916; Fax: 226-1176; *Office Manager:* Donna Taylor

District office(s): 500 Pacific Ave., #301, Bremerton 98310; (206) 479-4011; Fax: (206) 553-7445; *Congressional Aide:* Cheri Williams.

1717 Pacific Ave., #2244, Tacoma 98402; (206) 593-6536; Fax: (206) 593-6551; *District Representative:* Kurt Beckett.

Committee assignment(s): Appropriations; Select Intelligence (ranking member)

DINGELL, JOHN D., D-MICH. (16)

Capitol Hill office: 2328 RHOB 20515; (202) 225-4071; Internet: www.house.gov/dingell; *Administrative Assistant:* Marda Robillard

District office(s): 5465 Schaefer Rd., Dearborn 48126; (313) 846-1276; *District Administrator:* Connie Shorter.

214 E. Elm St., #105, Monroe 48161; (313) 243-1849; *Office Manager:* Donna Hoffer.

Committee assignment(s): Commerce (ranking member)

DIXON, JULIAN C., D-CALIF. (32)

Capitol Hill office: 2252 RHOB 20515; (202) 225-7084; Fax: (202) 225-3073; *Administrative Assistant:* Andrea Tracy Holmes

District office(s): Wateridge, 5100 W. Goldleaf Circle, #208, Los Angeles 90056; (213) 678-5424; Fax: (213) 678-6026; *Administrative Assistant:* Patricia Miller.

Committee assignment(s): Appropriations; Select Intelligence

DOGGETT, LLOYD, D-TEXAS (1)

Capitol Hill office: 126 CHOB 20515; (202) 225-4865; Internet: lloyd.doggett@mail.house.gov or www.house. gov/doggett; *Administrative Assistant:* Leo Coco

District office(s): 300 E. 8th St., #763, Austin 78701; (512) 916-5921; Fax: (512) 916-5108; *District Director:* Patti Everitt.

Committee assignment(s): Budget; Resources

DOOLEY, CAL, D-CALIF. (2)

Capitol Hill office: 1201 LHOB 20515; (202) 225-3341; Fax: (202) 225-9308; Internet: www.house.gov/ dooley; *Chief of Staff:* Lisa Quigley

District office(s): 224 W. Lacey Blvd., Hanford 93230; (209) 585-8171; Fax: (209) 585-8199; *District Director:* Victoria Hight.

Committee assignment(s): Agriculture; Resources

DOOLITTLE, JOHN T., R-CALIF. (4)

Capitol Hill office: 1526 LHOB 20515; (202) 225-2511; Fax: (202) 225-5444; Internet: doolittle@mail.house. gov or www.house.gov/doolittle; *Chief of Staff:* David Lopez

District office(s): 2130 Professional Dr., #190, Roseville 95661; (916) 786-5560; *Chief of Staff:* David G. Lopez.

Committee assignment(s): Agriculture; Resources; Joint Economic

DOYLE, MIKE, D-PA. (18)

Capitol Hill office: 133 CHOB 20515; (202) 225-2135; Fax: (202) 225-3084; Internet: rep.doyle@mail.house. gov or www.house.gov/doyle; *Chief of Staff:* David Lucas

District office(s): 541 5th Ave., McKeesport 15132; (412) 664-4049; Fax: (412) 664-4053; *District Director:* Paul D'Alesandro.

11 Duff Rd., Penn Hills 15235; (412) 241-6055; Fax: (412) 241-6820; *District Director:* Paul D'Alesandro.

Committee assignment(s): Science; Veterans' Affairs

DREIER, DAVID, R-CALIF. (28)

Capitol Hill office: 237 CHOB 20515; (202) 225-2305; Internet: www.house.gov/dreier; *Staff Director:* Brad Smith

District office(s): 112 N. 2nd Ave., Covina 91723; (909) 592-2857; *Field Representative:* Mark S. Harmsen.

Committee assignment(s): Rules

DUNCAN, JOHN J. "JIMMY," JR., R-TENN. (2)

Capitol Hill office: 2400 RHOB 20515; (202) 225-5435; Fax: (202) 225-6440; Internet: jjduncan@mail.house. gov or www.house.gov/duncan; *Chief of Staff:* Judy Whitbred

District office(s): 6 W. Madison Ave., Athens 37303; (615) 745-4671; *Caseworker:* Linda Higdon.

262 E. Broadway, Maryville 37804; (615) 984-5464; *Caseworker:* Denise Lambert.

800 Market St., #110, Knoxville 37902; (423) 523-3772; *District Director:* Bob Griffitts.

Committee assignment(s): Resources; Transportation and Infrastructure

DUNN, JENNIFER, R-WASH. (8)

Capitol Hill office: 432 CHOB 20515; (202) 225-7761; Fax: (202) 225-8673; Internet: dunnwa08@mail. house.gov or www.house.gov/dunn; *Chief of Staff:* Phil Bond

District office(s): 9 Lake Bellevue Dr., #204, Bellevue 98005; (206) 450-0161; *District Director:* Julie Collins.

Committee assignment(s): Ways and Means

EDWARDS, CHET, D-TEXAS (11)

Capitol Hill office: 2459 RHOB 20515; (202) 225-6105; Fax: (202) 225-0350; *Chief of Staff:* Jay Neel

District office(s): 700 S. University Parks Dr., #710, Waco 76706; (817) 752-9600; Fax: (817) 752-7769; *Deputy District Director:* Myril Thompson.

116 S. E. St., Belton 76513; (817) 933-2904; Fax: (817) 933-2913; *District Director:* Sam Murphy.

Committee assignment(s): Appropriations

EHLERS, VERNON J., R-MICH. (3)

Capitol Hill office: 1717 LHOB 20515; (202) 225-3831; Fax: (202) 225-5144; Internet: rep.ehlers@mail. house.gov or www.house.gov/ehlers; *Chief of Staff:* Bill McBride

District office(s): 110 Michigan Ave., #166, Grand Rapids 49503; (616) 451-8383; Fax: (616) 454-5630; *Constituent Services Director:* Nancy Ostapowicz.

Committee assignment(s): House Oversight; Science; Transportation and Infrastructure; Joint Library

EHRLICH, ROBERT L., JR., R-MD. (2)

Capitol Hill office: 315 CHOB 20515; (202) 225-3061; Fax: (202) 225-3094; Internet: ehrlich@mail.house. gov or www.house.gov/ehrlich; *Chief of Staff:* Steven Kreseski

District office(s): 1407 York Rd., #304, Lutherville 21093; (410) 337-7222; Fax: (410) 337-0021; *District Director:* Karl Aumann.

45 N. Main St., Bel Air 21014; (410) 838-2517; Fax: (410) 838-7823; *District Representative:* Shirley Stoyer.

Committee assignment(s): Banking and Financial Services; Budget

EMERSON, JO ANN, R-MO. (8)

Capitol Hill office: 132 CHOB 20515; (202) 225-4404; Internet: joann.emerson@mail.house.gov or www. house.gov/emerson; *Legislative Director:* David La Valle

District office(s): 339 Broadway, Cape Girardeau 63701; (573) 335-0101; Fax: (573) 335-1931; *Chief of Staff (dist.):* Lloyd Smith.

Committee assignment(s): Agriculture; Small Business; Transportation and Infrastructure

ENGEL, ELIOT L., D-N.Y. (17)

Capitol Hill office: 2303 RHOB 20515; (202) 225-2464; Fax: (202) 225-5513; Internet: engeline@hr.house. gov or www.house.gov/engel; *Administrative Assistant:* John Calvelli

District office(s): 3655 Johnson Ave., Bronx 10463; (718) 796-9700; *Chief of Staff:* Arnold I. Linhardt.

655 E. 233rd St., Bronx 10466; (718) 652-0400; *Caseworker:* Brian Anderson.

177 Dreiser Loop, #3, Bronx 10475; (718) 320-2314; *Caseworker:* Shirley Saunders.

87 Nepperhan Ave., Yonkers 10701; (914) 423-0700; *Caseworker:* Cynthia Miller.

250 S. 6th Ave., Mount Vernon 10550; (914) 699-4100; *Caseworker:* Cynthia Miller.

Committee assignment(s): Commerce

ENGLISH, PHIL, R-PA. (21)

Capitol Hill office: 1721 LHOB 20515; (202) 225-5406; Fax: (202) 225-3103; Internet: www.house.gov/ english; *Chief of Staff:* Robert Holste

District office(s): 310 French St., #107, Erie 16507; (814) 456-2038; Fax: (814) 454-0163; *District Representative:* Jerry Knight.

312 Chestnut St., #114, Meadville 16335; (814) 724-8414; Fax: (814) 333-8824; *District Representative:* Kim Green.

Butler Mall, 310 Newcastle, Butler 16001; (412) 285-7005; Fax: (412) 285-5616; *District Representative:* Marci Mustella.

900 N. Hermitage Rd., #6, Hermitage 16348; (412) 342-6132; Fax: (412) 342-3219; *District Representative:* Anne Coleman.

Committee assignment(s): Science; Small Business; Ways and Means

ENSIGN, JOHN, R-NEV. (1)

Capitol Hill office: 414 CHOB 20515; (202) 225-5965; Fax: (202) 225-3119; Internet: ensign@mail.house.gov or www.house.gov/ensign; *Administrative Assistant:* Mark Emerson

District office(s): 1000 E. Sahara, Las Vegas 89104; (702) 873-1994; Fax: (702) 731-1863; *District Office Manager:* Sonia Joya.

Committee assignment(s): Resources; Ways and Means

ESHOO, ANNA G., D-CALIF. (14)

Capitol Hill office: 308 CHOB 20515; (202) 225-8104; Fax: (202) 225-8890; Internet: annagram@mail.house.gov or www-eshoo.house.gov; *Chief of Staff:* Jill Ehrlich

District office(s): 698 Emerson St., Palo Alto 94301; (650) 323-2984; Fax: (650) 323-7283; *District Director:* Karen Chapman.

Committee assignment(s): Commerce

ETHERIDGE, BOB, D-N.C. (2)

Capitol Hill office: 1641 LHOB 20515; (202) 225-4531; Internet: bob.etheridge@mail.house.gov; *Administrative Assistant:* Julie Dwyer

District office(s): 3310 Croasdaile Dr., #301, Durham 27705; (919) 383-7548; Fax: (919) 309-2740; *District Director:* Glenn Keever.

607 N. 1st St., Lillington 27546; (910) 814-0335; Fax: (910) 814-2264; *Office Manager:* Leonore Tuck.

Committee assignment(s): Agriculture; Science

EVANS, LANE, D-ILL. (17)

Capitol Hill office: 2335 RHOB 20515; (202) 225-5905; Fax: (202) 225-5396; Internet: lane.evans@mail.house.gov or www.house.gov/evans; *Administrative Assistant:* Dennis J. King

District office(s): 1535 47th Ave., #5, Moline 61265; (309) 793-5760; Fax: (309) 793-5764; *District Representative:* Philip G. Hare.

1640 N. Henderson St., Galesburg 61401; (309) 342-4411; *Office Manager:* Joyce Bean.

Committee assignment(s): National Security; Veterans' Affairs (ranking member)

EVERETT, TERRY, R-ALA. (2)

Capitol Hill office: 208 CHOB 20515; (202) 225-2901; Internet: everett@hr.house.gov; *Administrative Assistant:* H. Clay Swanzy

District office(s): 3001 Zelda Rd., #100, Montgomery 36106; (334) 277-9113; *Field Representative:* Steve Pelhem.

100 W. Troy St., #101, Dothan 36303; (334) 794-9680; *District Aide:* Joe Williams.

108 N. Main St., Opp 36467; (334) 493-9253; *Staff Assistant:* Frances Spurlin.

Committee assignment(s): Agriculture; National Security; Veterans' Affairs

EWING, THOMAS W., R-ILL. (15)

Capitol Hill office: 2417 RHOB 20515; (202) 225-2371; Fax: (202) 225-8071; Internet: www.house.gov/ewing; *Administrative Assistant:* Brad Close

District office(s): 2401 E. Washington St., #101, Bloomington 61704; (309) 662-9371; Fax: (309) 663-9806; *Caseworker:* Karen McCall.

P.O. Box 20, Pontiac 61764; (815) 844-7660; Fax: (815) 844-3473; *District Scheduler:* Joe Alexander.

102 E. Main St., #30, Urbana 61801; (217) 328-0165; Fax: (217) 328-0169; *Chief of Staff:* Terry Greene.

4 N. Vermillion St., #503-504, Danville 61832; (217) 431-8230; Fax: (217) 436-5338; *Caseworker:* Ginny Mulholland.

Committee assignment(s): Agriculture; Science; Transportation and Infrastructure

FALEOMAVAEGA, ENI F.H., D-AM. SAMOA (AL)

Capitol Hill office: 2422 RHOB 20515; (202) 225-8577; Fax: (202) 225-8757; Internet: as00@pop3.house.gov or www.house.gov/faleomavaega; *Administrative Assistant:* Aliimau Scanlan

District office(s): P.O. Drawer X, Pago Pago 96799; (684) 633-1372; Fax: (684) 633-2680; *District Manager:* Oreta M. Togafau.

Committee assignment(s): International Relations; Resources

FARR, SAM, D-CALIF. (17)

Capitol Hill office: 1117 LHOB 20515; (202) 225-2861; Fax: (202) 225-6791; Internet: samfarr@mail.house.gov or www.house.gov/farr; *Administrative Assistant:* Rochelle Dornatt

District office(s): 100 W. Alisal St., Salinas 93901; (408) 424-2229; *Congressional Aide:* Tisha Hutchins.

380 Alvarado St., Monterey 93940; (408) 649-3555; *District Director:* Donna Blitzer.

701 Ocean Ave., #318, Santa Cruz 95060; (408) 429-1976; *Congressional Aide:* Naomi Brauner.

Committee assignment(s): Agriculture; Resources

FATTAH, CHAKA, D-PA. (2)

Capitol Hill office: 1205 LHOB 20515; (202) 225-4001; Fax: (202) 225-5392; Internet: www.house.gov/fattah; *Administrative Assistant:* Claudia Pharis

District office(s): 4104 Walnut St., Philadelphia 19104; (215) 387-6404; Fax: (215) 387-6407; *District Director:* Gregory Naylor.

Committee assignment(s): Education and Workforce; Government Reform and Oversight; Standards of Official Conduct

FAWELL, HARRIS W., R-ILL. (13)

Capitol Hill office: 2368 RHOB 20515; (202) 225-3515; Fax: (202) 225-9420; Internet: hfawell@hr.house.gov or www.house.gov/fawell; *Chief of Staff:* Alan Mertz

District office(s): 115 W. 55th St., #100, Clarendon Hills 60514; (630) 655-2052; *District Director:* Jane Motl.

Committee assignment(s): Education and Workforce; Science

FAZIO, VIC, D-CALIF. (3)

Capitol Hill office: 2113 RHOB 20515; (202) 225-5716; Fax: (202) 225-5141; Internet: dcaucus@mail.house. gov or www.house.gov/fazio; *Chief of Staff:* Monica Maples-Dixon

District office(s): 722B Main St., Woodland 95695; (916) 666-5521; *District Director:* Val Dolcini.

332 Pine St., Suite F, Red Bluff 96080; (916) 529-5629.

Committee assignment(s): Appropriations

FILNER, BOB, D-CALIF. (5)

Capitol Hill office: 330 CHOB 20515; (202) 225-8045; Fax: (202) 225-9073; *Chief of Staff:* Francisco Estrada

District office(s): 333 F St., Suite A, Chula Vista 91910; (619) 422-5963; Fax: (619) 422-7290; *District Director:* Francisco Estrada.

Committee assignment(s): Transportation and Infrastructure; Veterans' Affairs

FOLEY, MARK, R-FLA. (16)

Capitol Hill office: 113 CHOB 20515; (202) 225-5792; Fax: (202) 225-3132; Internet: mark.foley@mail. house.gov or www.house.gov/foley; *Administrative Assistant:* Kirk Fordham

District office(s): 4440 PGA Blvd., #406, Palm Beach Gardens 33410; (561) 627-6192; Fax: (561) 626-4749; *District Director:* Ed Chase.

250 N.W. Country Club Dr., Port St. Lucie 34986; (561) 878-3181; *District Manager:* Ann Decker.

Committee assignment(s): Agriculture; Banking and Financial Services; Science

FORBES, MICHAEL P., R-N.Y. (1)

Capitol Hill office: 416 CHOB 20515; (202) 225-3826; Fax: (202) 225-3143; Internet: mpforbes@hr.house. gov or www.house.gov/forbes; *Chief of Staff:* Diana Weir

District office(s): 1500 William Floyd Parkway, Shirley 11967; (516) 345-9000; Fax: (516) 345-3891; *District Director:* Mark Wooley.

Committee assignment(s): Appropriations

FORD, HAROLD E., JR., D-TENN. (9)

Capitol Hill office: 1523 LHOB 20515; (202) 225-3265; Internet: rep.harold.ford.jr@mail.house.gov or www.house.gov/ford; *Chief of Staff:* David Sutphen

District office(s): 107 N. Main St., #369, Memphis 38103; (901) 544-4131; Fax: (901) 544-4329; *District Chief of Staff:* Mark Yates.

Committee assignment(s): Education and Workforce; Government Reform and Oversight

FOSSELLA, VITO J., R-N.Y. (13)

Capitol Hill office: 2411 RHOB 20515; (202) 225-3371; Fax: 226-1272; Internet: vitofossella@mail.house.gov; *Chief of Staff:* Tom Quaadman

District office(s): 14 New Dorp Lane, Staten Island 10306; (718) 987-8400; Fax: (718) 987-8938; *District Director:* Sherry Diamond.

Committee assignment(s): Banking and Financial Services; Transportation and Infrastructure

FOWLER, TILLIE, R-FLA. (4)

Capitol Hill office: 109 CHOB 20515; (202) 225-2501; Fax: (202) 225-9318; Internet: www.house.gov/ fowler; *Administrative Assistant:* David Gilliland

District office(s): 140 S. Atlantic Ave., Ormond Beach 32174; (904) 672-0754; Fax: (904) 673-8964; *Caseworker:* Chris Calabucci.

4452 Hendricks Ave., Jacksonville 32207; (904) 739-6600; Fax: (904) 367-0066; *District Director:* Susan Siegmund.

Committee assignment(s): National Security; Transportation and Infrastructure

FOX, JON D., R-PA. (13)

Capitol Hill office: 435 CHOB 20515; (202) 225-6111; Fax: (202) 225-3155; Internet: jonfox@hr.house.gov; *Administrative Assistant:* Jan Friis

District office(s): 1768 Markey St., Norristown 19401; (610) 272-8400; Fax: (610) 272-8532; *District Administrator:* Eric Wilkox.

Eason Rd. at Edge Hill Rd., Abington 19001; (215) 885-3500; Fax: (215) 885-6828; *Office Manager:* Janice Harvey.

Narberth Borough Hall, 100 Conway Ave., Narberth 19072; (610) 667-6020; *District Administrator:* Eric Wilkox.

Committee assignment(s): Banking and Financial Services; International Relations; Transportation and Infrastructure

FRANK, BARNEY, D-MASS. (4)

Capitol Hill office: 2210 RHOB 20515; (202) 225-5931; Fax: (202) 225-0182; Internet: www.house.gov/frank; *Administrative Assistant:* Peter Kovar

District office(s): 29 Crafts St., Newton 02158; (617) 332-3920; Fax: (617) 332-2822; *District Director:* Dorothy M. Reichard.

89 Main St., Bridgewater 02324; (508) 697-9403; Fax: (508) 674-3030; *Staff Assistant:* Garth Patterson.

222 Milliken Place, 3rd floor, Fall River 02721; (508) 674-3551; *Office Manager:* Amelia Wright.

558 Pleasant St., #309, New Bedford 02740; (508) 999-6462; Fax: (508) 697-0263; *Office Manager:* Elsie Souza.

Committee assignment(s): Banking and Financial Services; Judiciary

FRANKS, BOB, R-N.J. (7)

Capitol Hill office: 225 CHOB 20515; (202) 225-5361; Fax: (202) 225-9460; Internet: franksnj@mail.house.gov or www.house.gov/bobfranks; *Chief of Staff:* Bill Ulrey

District office(s): 2333 Morris Ave., #B17, Union 07083; (908) 686-5576.

73 Main St., #4, Woodbridge 70095; (732) 602-0075; *Community Service Director:* Barbara Ballard.

Committee assignment(s): Budget; Transportation and Infrastructure

FRELINGHUYSEN, RODNEY, R-N.J. (11)

Capitol Hill office: 228 CHOB 20515; (202) 225-5034; Fax: (202) 225-3186; Internet: rodney.frelinghuysen@mail.house.gov or www.house.gov/frelinghuysen; *Administrative Assistant:* Donna F. Mullins

District office(s): 1 Morris St., Morristown 07960; (201) 984-0711; *District Representative:* Betty Denecke.

Committee assignment(s): Appropriations

FROST, MARTIN, D-TEXAS (24)

Capitol Hill office: 2256 RHOB 20515; (202) 225-3605; Fax: (202) 225-4951; Internet: frost@hr.house.gov or www.house.gov/frost; *Administrative Assistant:* Ronnie P. Carleton

District office(s): 100 N. Main St., #534, Corsicana 75110; (903) 874-0760; Fax: (903) 874-0468; *Staff Assistant:* Penny Jones.

400 S. Zang Blvd., #506, Dallas 75208; (214) 948-3401; *Staff Assistant:* Marsha Price.

3020 S.E. Loop 820, Fort Worth 76140; (817) 293-9231; *District Director:* Cinda M. Crawford.

Committee assignment(s): Rules

FURSE, ELIZABETH, D-ORE. (1)

Capitol Hill office: 316 CHOB 20515; (202) 225-0855; Fax: (202) 225-9497; Internet: rep.elizabeth.furse@mail.house.gov or www.house.gov/furse; *Administrative Assistant:* Jennie Kugel

District office(s): 2701 N.W. Vaughn, #860, Portland 97210; (503) 326-2901; Fax: (503) 326-5066; *District Director:* Mary K. Elliott-Parham.

Committee assignment(s): Commerce

GALLEGLY, ELTON, R-CALIF. (23)

Capitol Hill office: 2427 RHOB 20515; (202) 225-5811; Fax: (202) 225-1100; Internet: www.house.gov/gallegly; *Administrative Assistant:* Joel Cassidy

District office(s): 300 Esplanade Dr., #1800, Oxnard 93030; (805) 485-2300; *District Director:* Paula Sheil.

Committee assignment(s): International Relations; Judiciary; Resources

GANSKE, GREG, R-IOWA (4)

Capitol Hill office: 1108 LHOB 20515; (202) 225-4426; Fax: (202) 225-3193; Internet: rep.ganske@mail.house.gov or www.house.gov/ganske; *Administrative Assistant:* John Barnes

District office(s): 210 Walnut St., #717, Des Moines 50309; (515) 284-4634; Fax: (515) 280-1412; *District Director:* Luke Roth.

40 Pearl St., Council Bluffs 51503; (712) 323-5976; Fax: (712) 323-7903; *Field Representative:* Ben Post.

Committee assignment(s): Commerce

GEJDENSON, SAM, D-CONN. (2)

Capitol Hill office: 1401 LHOB 20515; (202) 225-2076; Fax: (202) 225-4977; Internet: bozrah@mail.house.gov or www.house.gov/gejdenson; *Chief of Staff:* Vacant

District office(s): 2 Courthouse Square, 5th Floor, Norwich 06360; (860) 886-0139; Fax: (860) 886-2974; *District Director:* Naomi Otterness.

94 Court St., Middletown 06457; (860) 346-1123; *Congressional Aide:* Patricia Shea.

Committee assignment(s): International Relations; House Oversight (ranking member); Joint Library; Joint Printing

GEKAS, GEORGE W., R-PA. (17)

Capitol Hill office: 2410 RHOB 20515; (202) 225-4315; Fax: (202) 225-8440; Internet: www.house.gov/gekas; *Administrative Assistant:* Allan Cagnoli

District office(s): 222 S. Market St., #102-A, Elizabethtown 17022; (717) 367-6731; Fax: (717) 367-6602; *Office Director:* Shelley Whitcomb.

400 S. 8th St., #108B, Lebanon 17042; (717) 273-1451; Fax: (717) 273-1673; *Office Director:* Reg Nyman.

3605 Vartan Way, 2nd Floor, Harrisburg 17110; (717) 541-5507; Fax: (717) 541-5518; *District Secretary:* Arlene Eckels.

Committee assignment(s): Judiciary

GEPHARDT, RICHARD A., D-MO. (3)

Capitol Hill office: 1226 LHOB 20515; (202) 225-2671; Fax: (202) 225-7452; Internet: gephardt@mail.house. gov or www.house.gov/gephardt; *Chief of Staff:* Steve A. Elmendorf

District office(s): 11140 S. Towne Square, #201, St. Louis 63123; (314) 894-3400; Fax: (314) 845-7088; *Administrative Assistant:* Mary Renick.

998 E. Gannon Dr., Festus 63208; (314) 937-6399; Fax: (314) 845-8675; *Administrative Assistant:* Mary Renick.

GIBBONS, JIM, R-NEV. (2)

Capitol Hill office: 100 CHOB 20515; (202) 225-6155; Fax: (202) 225-5629; Internet: mail.gibbons@ mail.house.gov or www.house.gov/gibbons; *Chief of Staff:* Mike Dayton

District office(s): 400 S. Virginia St., #502, Reno 89501; (702) 686-5760; Fax: (702) 686-5711; *District Office Manager:* Deanna Lazovich.

850 S. Durango Dr., #107, Las Vegas 89128; (702) 255-1651; Fax: (702) 255-1927; *District Office Manager:* Judy Ray.

501 Railroad St., #202, Elko 89801; (702) 777-7920; Fax: (702) 777-7922; *Regional Representative:* Claude Ackerman.

Committee assignment(s): Select Intelligence; National Security; Resources

GILCHREST, WAYNE T., R-MD. (1)

Capitol Hill office: 332 CHOB 20515; (202) 225-5311; Fax: (202) 225-0254; Internet: www.house.gov/ writerep or www.house.gov/gilchrest; *Administrative Assistant:* Tony Caligiuri

District office(s): 44 Calvert St., #320, Annapolis 21401; (410) 263-6321; Fax: (410) 263-7619; *Office Manager:* Kathy Hicks.

315 High St., #105, Chestertown 21620; (410) 778-9407; Fax: (410) 778-4560; *District Director:* Emmett Duke.

1 Plaza East, Salisbury 21801; (410) 749-3184; Fax: (410) 749-8458; *District Office Manager:* Sue Sullivan.

Committee assignment(s): Resources; Transportation and Infrastructure

GILLMOR, PAUL E., R-OHIO (5)

Capitol Hill office: 1203 LHOB 20515; (202) 225-6405; Internet: www.house.gov/gillmor; *Administrative Assistant:* Mark Wellman

District office(s): 120 Jefferson St., 2nd Floor, Port Clinton 43452; (419) 734-1999; *Office Manager:* Cathy Bivens.

1655 N. Clinton St., #C2, Defiance 43512; (419) 782-1996; *District Aide:* Barb Barker.

148 E. S. Boundary St., Perrysburg 43551; (419) 872-2500; *District Representative:* Brian Dicken.

County Administration Bldg., Norwalk 44857; (419) 668-0206.

Committee assignment(s): Commerce

GILMAN, BENJAMIN A., R-N.Y. (2)

Capitol Hill office: 2449 RHOB 20515; (202) 225-3776; Fax: (202) 225-2541; Internet: ben@mail.house.gov or www.house.gov/gilman; *Administrative Assistant:* Robert Becker

District office(s): 32 Main St., Hastings-on-Hudson 10706; (914) 478-5550.

407 E. Main St., P.O. Box 358, Middletown 10940; (914) 343-6666; *Office Manager:* Molly Aumick.

377 Route 59, Monsey 10952; (914) 357-9000; *District Assistant:* Peggy Dandridge.

Committee assignment(s): Government Reform and Oversight; International Relations (chair)

GINGRICH, NEWT, R-GA. (6)

Capitol Hill office: 2428 RHOB 20515; (202) 225-4501; Fax: (202) 225-4656; Internet: georgia6@mail.house. gov or www.house.gov/gingrich; *Chief of Staff:* Arne L. Christenson

District office(s): 3823 Roswell Rd. N.E., #200, Marietta 30062; (404) 565-6398; *Chief of Staff:* Nancy J. Desmond.

Committee assignment(s):

GONZALEZ, HENRY B., D-TEXAS (2)

Capitol Hill office: 2413 RHOB 20515; (202) 225-3236; Fax: (202) 225-1915; :

District office(s): 727 E. Durango Blvd., #B-124, San Antonio 78206; (210) 472-6195; Fax: (210) 472-4009; *Senior District Representative:* Mary Jesse Roque.

Committee assignment(s): Banking and Financial Services (ranking member)

GOODE, VIRGIL H., JR., D-VA. (5)

Capitol Hill office: 1520 LHOB 20515; (202) 225-4711; Fax: (202) 225-5681; Internet: rep.goode@mail. house.gov; *Administrative Assistant:* Jim Severt

District office(s): 104 S. 1st St., Charlottesville 22902; (804) 295-6372; Fax: (804) 295-6059; *Caseworker:* Greg Kelly.

103 S. Main St., Farmville 23901; (804) 392-8331; *Caseworker:* Margie Watkins.

437 Main St., Danville 24541; (804) 792-1208; *Press Secretary:* Linwood Duncan.

70 E. Court St., #215, Rocky Mount 24151; (540) 484-1254; *Caseworker:* Lacy Ward.

Committee assignment(s): Agriculture; Small Business

GOODLATTE, ROBERT W., R-VA. (6)

Capitol Hill office: 123 CHOB 20515; (202) 225-5431; Internet: talk2bob@mail.house.gov or www.house.gov/goodlatte; *Chief of Staff:* Chip Nottingham

District office(s): 2 S. Main St., 1st Floor, Suite A, Harrisonburg 22801; (540) 432-2391; *District Representative:* Charles Evans-Haywood.

10 Franklin Rd., #540, Roanoke 24011; (540) 857-2672; *District Director:* Pete Larkin.

114 N. Central Ave., Staunton 24401; (540) 885-3861; *District Representative:* Blair Lovern.

916 Main St., #300, Lynchburg 24504; (804) 845-8306; Fax: (804) 845-8245; *District Representative:* Clarkie Jester.

Committee assignment(s): Agriculture; Judiciary; Standards of Official Conduct

GOODLING, BILL, R-PA. (19)

Capitol Hill office: 2263 RHOB 20515; (202) 225-5836; Internet: www.house.gov/goodling; *Executive Assistant:* Kimberly Strycharz

District office(s): 2020 Yale Ave., Camp Hill 17011; (717) 763-1988; *District Coordinator:* Tom Davidson.

212 N. Hanover St., Carlisle 17013; (717) 243-5432; *District Staffer:* Ped Young.

140 Baltimore St., #210, Gettysburg 17325; (717) 334-3430; *District Secretary:* Georgiana Spangler.

Federal Bldg, 200 S. George St., York 17405; (717) 843-8887; *District Secretary:* Betty Lou Tarasovic.

44 Frederick St., Hanover 17331; (717) 632-7855.

Committee assignment(s): Education and Workforce (chair); International Relations

GORDON, BART, D-TENN. (6)

Capitol Hill office: 2201 RHOB 20515; (202) 225-4231; Fax: (202) 225-6887; Internet: bart.gordon@mail.house.gov or www.house.gov/gordon; *Administrative Assistant:* Brent Ayer

District office(s): 106 S. Maple St., P.O. Box 1986, Murfreesboro 37133; (615) 896-1986; Fax: (615) 896-8218; *District Administrative Assistant:* Kent Syler.

17 S. Jefferson St., P.O. Box 1140, Cookville 38503; (615) 528-5907; Fax: (615) 528-1165; *Field Representative:* Billy Smith.

Committee assignment(s): Commerce; Science

GOSS, PORTER J., R-FLA. (14)

Capitol Hill office: 108 CHOB 20515; (202) 225-2536; Fax: (202) 225-6820; Internet: www.house.gov/goss; *Chief of Staff:* Sheryl V. Wooley

District office(s): 2000 Main St., #303, Fort Myers 33901; (813) 332-4677; Fax: (813) 332-1743; *Chief of Staff:* Sheryl V. Wooley.

3301 Tamiami Trail East, Bldg. F, #212, Naples 33962; (813) 774-8060; Fax: (813) 774-7262; *Special Projects Coordinator:* Scott Odenbach.

Charlotte Memorial Auditorium, 75 Taylor St., Punta Gorda 33950; (813) 639-0051; Fax: (813) 639-0714.

Committee assignment(s): Select Intelligence (chair); Rules

GRAHAM, LINDSEY, R-S.C. (3)

Capitol Hill office: 1429 LHOB 20515; (202) 225-5301; Fax: (202) 225-3216; Internet: www.house.gov/graham; *Chief of Staff:* Richard Perry

District office(s): 315 S. McDuffie St., P.O. Box 4126, Anderson 29622; (864) 885-9600; Fax: (864) (202) 225-7049; *District Coordinator:* Jane Goolsby.

120 Main St., #129, Greenwood 29646; (864) 223-8251.

211 York St. N.E., #5, Aiken 29801; (803) 649-5571.

Committee assignment(s): Education and Workforce; International Relations; National Security

GRANGER, KAY, R-TEXAS (12)

Capitol Hill office: 515 CHOB 20515; (202) 225-5071; Fax: (202) 225-5683; Internet: texas.granger@mail.house.gov or www.house.gov/granger; *Chief of Staff:* Ken Mehlman

District office(s): 1600 W. 7th St., #740, Ft. Worth 76102; (817) 338-0909; Fax: (817) 335-5852; *District Director:* Lacie Chambers.

Committee assignment(s): Budget; House Oversight; Transportation and Infrastructure; Joint Printing

GREEN, GENE, D-TEXAS (29)

Capitol Hill office: 2429 RHOB 20515; (202) 225-1688; Fax: (202) 225-9903; Internet: ask.gene@mail.house.gov or www.house.gov/green; *Administrative Assistant:* Marc Gonzales

District office(s): 256 N. Sam Houston Parkway East, #29, Houston 77060; (281) 999-5879; *District Director:* Rhonda Jackson.

11811 1-10 East, #430, Houston 77029; (713) 330-0761; Fax: (713) 330-0807.

Committee assignment(s): Commerce

GREENWOOD, JAMES C., R-PA. (8)

Capitol Hill office: 2436 RHOB 20515; (202) 225-4276; Fax: (202) 225-9511; Internet: www.house.gov/writerep or www.house.gov/greenwood; *Chief of Staff:* Jordan "Pete" Krauss

District office(s): 69 E. Oakland Ave., Doylestown 18901; (215) 348-7511.

1 Oxford Valley, #800, Langhorne 19047; (215) 752-7711; *District Director:* Peter Johnson.

Committee assignment(s): Commerce; Education and Workforce

GUTIERREZ, LUIS V., D-ILL. (4)

Capitol Hill office: 2438 RHOB 20515; (202) 225-8203; Fax: (202) 225-7810; Internet: luisg@gutierrez. house.gov; *Chief of Staff:* Doug Scofield
District office(s): 3181 N. Elston Ave., Chicago 60618; (773) 509-0999; Fax: (773) 509-0152; *Director:* Lori Baas.
2132 W. 21st St., Chicago 60608; (773) 579-0902.
Committee assignment(s): Banking and Financial Services; Veterans' Affairs

GUTKNECHT, GIL, R-MINN. (1)

Capitol Hill office: 425 CHOB 20515; (202) 225-2472; Fax: (202) 225-3246; Internet: gil.gutknecht@mail. house.gov or www.house.gov/gutknecht
District office(s): 1530 Greenview Dr., #108, Rochester 55902; (507) 252-9841; *Chief of Staff:* John Wade.
Committee assignment(s): Budget; Science

HALL, RALPH M., D-TEXAS (4)

Capitol Hill office: 2221 RHOB 20515; (202) 225-6673; Fax: (202) 225-3332; Internet: rmhall@hr.house.gov; *Chief of Staff:* Janet Perry
District office(s): 104 N. San Jacinto St., Rockwall 75087; (972) 771-9118; *District Director:* Diane Milliken.
119 Federal Bldg., Sherman 75090; (903) 892-1112; Fax: (903) 868-0264; *District Assistant:* Judy Rowton.
211 Federal Bldg., Tyler 75702; (903) 597-3729; Fax: (903) 597-0726; *District Assistant:* Martha Glover.
Cooke County Courthouse, Gainesville 76240; (817) 668-6370; Fax: (817) 668-6478; *District Assistant:* Tom Hughes.
Committee assignment(s): Commerce; Science

HALL, TONY P., D-OHIO (3)

Capitol Hill office: 1432 LHOB 20515; (202) 225-6465; Fax: (202) 225-9272; Internet: www.house.gov/ tonyhall; *Chief of Staff:* Rick Carne
District office(s): 200 W. 2nd St., #501, Dayton 45402; (937) (202) 225-2843; Fax: (937) (202) 225-2706; *District Director:* Jim Vangrov.
Committee assignment(s): Rules

HAMILTON, LEE H., D-IND. (9)

Capitol Hill office: 2314 RHOB 20515; (202) 225-5315; Fax: (202) 225-1101; Internet: hamilton@hamilton. house.gov or www.house.gov/hamilton; *Chief of Staff:* Jonathan Friedman
District office(s): 1201 E. 10th St., Bldg. 66, #107, Jeffersonville 47130; (812) 288-3999; Fax: (812) 288-3877; *Administrative Assistant:* Wayne Vance.
Committee assignment(s): International Relations (ranking member); Joint Economic

HANSEN, JAMES V., R-UTAH (1)

Capitol Hill office: 2466 RHOB 20515; (202) 225-0453; Internet: www.house.gov/hansen; *Chief of Staff:* Nancee W. Blockinger
District office(s): 324 25th St., #1017, Ogden 84401; (801) 393-8362; *State Director:* Steve Petersen.
435 E. Tabernacle St., #301, St. George 84770; (801) 628-1071; *Field Office Manager:* Rick Arial.
Committee assignment(s): National Security; Resources; Standards of Official Conduct (chair)

HARMAN, JANE, D-CALIF. (36)

Capitol Hill office: 325 CHOB 20515; (202) 225-8220; Fax: 226-0684; Internet: rep.harman@mail.house.gov or www.house.gov/harman; *Chief of Staff:* Mike Monasmith
District office(s): 1217 El Prado Ave., Torrance 90501; (310) 783-8220; *District Director:* Doane Liu.
Committee assignment(s): Select Intelligence; National Security

HASTERT, DENNIS, R-ILL. (14)

Capitol Hill office: 2241 RHOB 20515; (202) 225-2976; Fax: (202) 225-0697; Internet: dhastert@mail.house. gov; *Chief of Staff:* Scott B. Palmer
District office(s): 27 N. River St., Batavia 60510; (630) 406-1114; Fax: (630) 406-1808; *Chief of Staff:* Scott B. Palmer.
Committee assignment(s): Commerce; Government Reform and Oversight

HASTINGS, ALCEE L., D-FLA. (23)

Capitol Hill office: 1039 LHOB 20515; (202) 225-1313; Fax: 226-0690; Internet: hastings@hr.house.gov or www.house.gov/alceehastings; *Administrative Assistant:* Ann Jacobs
District office(s): 2701 Oakland Park Blvd., #200, Ft. Lauderdale 33311; (305) 733-2800; Fax: (305) 735-9444; *District Director:* Art W. Kennedy.
5725 Corporate Way, W. Palm Beach 33407; (407) 684-0565; Fax: (407) 684-3613; *Congressional Aide:* Mikel Jones.
Committee assignment(s): International Relations; Science

HASTINGS, RICHARD "DOC," R-WASH. (4)

Capitol Hill office: 1323 LHOB 20515; (202) 225-5816; Fax: (202) 225-3251; *Chief of Staff:* Ed Cassidy
District office(s): 2715 St. Andrews Loop, Suite D, Pasco 99302; (509) 543-9396; Fax: (509) 543-1972; *District Director:* Joyce DeFelice.
302 E. Chestnut St., Yakima 98901; (509) 452-3243; Fax: (509) 452-3438.
Committee assignment(s): Rules

HAYWORTH, J.D., R-ARIZ. (6)

Capitol Hill office: 1023 LHOB 20515; (202) 225-2190; Fax: (202) 225-3263; Internet: www.house.gov/writerep or www.house.gov/hayworth; *Chief of Staff:* Joseph Eule

District office(s): 1017 S. Gilbert Rd., #203, Mesa 85204; (602) 926-4151; Fax: (602) 926-3998; *District Director:* Doug Nick.

1300 S. Milton St., #207, Flagstaff 06001; (520) 556-8760; Fax: (520) 556-8764: Eileen Moffitt.

Committee assignment(s): Veterans' Affairs; Ways and Means

HEFLEY, JOEL, R-COLO. (5)

Capitol Hill office: 2230 RHOB 20515; (202) 225-4422; Fax: (202) 225-1942; *Administrative Director:* Jeff G. Crank

District office(s): 6059 S. Quebec #103, Englewood 80111; (303) 843-0401; *Staff Assistant:* Angie D'Aurio.

104 S. Cascade Ave., #105, Colorado Springs 80903; (719) 520-0055; *District Director:* Connie Solomon.

Committee assignment(s): National Security; Resources; Small Business; Standards of Official Conduct

HEFNER, W.G. "BILL," D-N.C. (8)

Capitol Hill office: 2470 RHOB 20515; (202) 225-3715; Fax: (202) 225-4036; *Administrative Assistant:* Bill McEwen

District office(s): 101 Union St. South, P.O. Box 385, Concord 28026; (704) 786-1612; Fax: (704) 782-1004; *Office Manager:* Virginia M. Jochems.

507 W. Innes St., #225, Salisbury 28145; (704) 636-0635; Fax: (704) 636-6271; *Office Manager:* Sharon Banner-Sheelor.

P.O. Box 372, Carthage 28327; (910) 949-2912; *District Administrator:* J. Elvin Jackson.

230 E. Franklin St., P.O. Box 1503, Rockingham 28379; (910) 997-2070; Fax: (910) 997-7987; *Office Manager:* Linda Samuels.

Committee assignment(s): Appropriations

HERGER, WALLY, R-CALIF. (2)

Capitol Hill office: 2433 RHOB 20515; (202) 225-3076; Internet: www.house.gov/writerep or www.house.gov/herger; *Administrative Assistant:* John P. Magill

District office(s): 55 Independence Circle, #104, Chico 95926; (916) 893-8363; *District Office Manager:* Fran Peace.

410 Hemsted Dr., #115, Redding 96002; (916) 223-5898; *Field Representative:* David Meurer.

Committee assignment(s): Budget; Ways and Means

HILL, RICK, R-MONT. (AL)

Capitol Hill office: 1037 LHOB 20515; (202) 225-3211; Fax: (202) 225-5687; Internet: rick.hill@mail.house.gov or www.house.gov/hill; *Chief of Staff:* Mike Pieper

District office(s): 33 S. Last Chance Gulch, #2C, Helena 59601; (406) 443-7878; Fax: (406) 449-3736; *State Director:* Peggy Olson Trenk.

27 N. 27th, Billings 59101; (406) 256-1019; Fax: (406) 256-3185; *Eastern Field Representative:* Larry Herzog.

200 E. Broadway, Missoula 59802; (406) 543-9550; Fax: (406) 543-9560; *Field Representative:* Amy Hallmark.

Committee assignment(s): Banking and Financial Services; Resources; Small Business

HILLEARY, VAN, R-TENN. (4)

Capitol Hill office: 114 CHOB 20515; (202) 225-6831; Fax: (202) 225-3272; Internet: van.hilleary@mail.house.gov or www.house.gov/hilleary; *Chief of Staff:* Elaine Roberson

District office(s): 300 S. Jackson St., Tullahoma 37388; (615) 393-4764; Fax: (615) 393-4767; *Field Representative:* Janice Bowling.

1502 N. Main St., Crossville 38555; (615) 484-1114; Fax: (615) 484-5097; *Caseworker:* Pam Kenner.

400 W. Main St., #304, Morristown 37814; (423) 587-0396; Fax: (423) 587-0065; *District Representative:* Paul Chapman.

Committee assignment(s): Budget; Education and Workforce; National Security

HILLIARD, EARL F., D-ALA. (7)

Capitol Hill office: 1314 LHOB 20515; (202) 225-2665; Fax: 226-0772; Internet: callearl@mail.house.gov or www.house.gov/hilliard; *Chief of Staff:* Phyllis Hallmon

District office(s): 319 17th St. North, #204, Birmingham 35203; (205) 328-2841; Fax: (205) 251-6817; *District Manager:* Elvira Williams.

204 Federal Bldg., Tuscaloosa 35401; (205) 752-3578; Fax: (205) 349-2450; *District Manager:* Kay Presley.

3800 Norman Bridge Rd., Montgomery 36105; (334) 281-0513; *Montgomery District Manager:* Robert A. Lane.

Federal Bldg., Selma 36701; (334) 872-2684; Fax: (334) 875-8270; *Selma District Manager:* Betty A. Callaway.

Committee assignment(s): Agriculture; International Relations

HINCHEY, MAURICE D., D-N.Y. (26)

Capitol Hill office: 2431 RHOB 20515; (202) 225-6335; Internet: maurice.hinchey@mail.house.gov or www.house.gov/hinchey; *Chief of Staff:* Eleanor Nash-Brown

District office(s): 291 Wall St., Kingston 12401; (914) 331-4466; *District Representative:* Christine Avlon-Nelson.

100A Federal Bldg., Binghamton 13901; (607) 773-2768; Fax: (607) 772-1789; *District Representative:* Jim Testani.

123 S. Cayuga St., #201, Ithaca 14850; (607) 273-1388; *Federal Liaison:* Dan Lamb.

Committee assignment(s): Banking and Financial Services; Resources; Joint Economic

HINOJOSA, RUBEN, D-TEXAS (15)

Capitol Hill office: 1032 LHOB 20515; (202) 225-2531; Fax: (202) 225-5688; Internet: rep.hinojosa@mail.house.gov or www.house.gov/hinojosa; *Chief of Staff:* Rita Jaramillo

District office(s): 311 N. 15th St., McAllen 78501; (210) 682-5545; Fax: (210) 682-0141; *District Director:* Nick Gonzalez.

Committee assignment(s): Education and Workforce; Small Business

HOBSON, DAVID L., R-OHIO (7)

Capitol Hill office: 1514 LHOB 20515; (202) 225-4324; Internet: www.house.gov/hobson; *Chief of Staff:* Mary Beth Carozza

District office(s): 212 S. Broad St., Lancaster 43130; (614) 654-5149; *Senior Constituent Aide:* Bob Clark.

150 N. Limestone St., #220, Springfield 45501; (513) 325-0474; *District Director:* Eileen Austria.

Committee assignment(s): Appropriations; Budget

HOEKSTRA, PETER, R-MICH. (2)

Capitol Hill office: 1122 LHOB 20515; (202) 225-4401; Fax: 226-0779; Internet: tellhoek@mail.house.gov or www.house.gov/hoekstra; *Administrative Assistant:* Jon Vanden Heuvel

District office(s): 31 E. 8th St., #320, Holland 49423; (616) 395-0030; Fax: (616) 395-0271; *Director of Public Policy:* Bill Huizenga.

900 3rd St., #203, Muskegon 49440; (616) 722-8386; Fax: (616) 722-0176; *Director of Constituent Services:* Jerry Kooiman.

120 W. Harris St., Cadillac 49601; (616) 775-0050; Fax: (616) 775-0298; *Cadillac Area Representative:* Jill Brown.

Committee assignment(s): Budget; Education and Workforce

HOLDEN, TIM, D-PA. (6)

Capitol Hill office: 1421 LHOB 20515; (202) 225-5546; Fax: 226-0996; *Chief of Staff:* Tom Gajewski

District office(s): Northumberland County Courthouse, Market Square, Sunbury 17801; (717) 988-1902; *Staff Assistant:* Annabelle Litchard.

303 Meridian Bank Bldg., Pottsville 17901; (717) 622-4212; Fax: (717) 628-2561; *Office Manager:* Connie Caldonetti.

633 Court St., 1st Floor, Reading 19601; (215) 371-9931; Fax: (215) 371-9939; *Staff Assistant:* Tim Smith.

310 High St., 2nd Floor, Pottstown 19464; (610) 970-9492; *Staff Assistant:* Beryle Glassmoyer.

Committee assignment(s): Agriculture; Transportation and Infrastructure

HOOLEY, DARLENE, D-ORE. (5)

Capitol Hill office: 1419 LHOB 20515; (202) 225-5711; Fax: (202) 225-5699; Internet: darlene@mail.house.gov; *Chief of Staff:* Joan Mooney

District office(s): #101, 315 Mission St., Salem 97301; (503) 588-9100; Fax: (503) 588-5711; *District Director:* Dave Hunt.

914 Mollalla Ave., #103, Oregon City 97045; (503) 557-1324; Fax: (503) 557-1981; *Field Representative:* Connie Sealy.

Committee assignment(s): Banking and Financial Services; Science

HORN, STEVE, R-CALIF. (38)

Capitol Hill office: 438 CHOB 20515; (202) 225-6676; Fax: 226-1012; Internet: steve.horn@mail.house.gov or www.house.gov/horn; *Chief of Staff:* David Bartel

District office(s): 4010 Watson Plaza Dr., #160, Lakewood 90712; (310) 425-1336; Fax: (310) 425-4591; *District Director:* Connie Sziebl.

Committee assignment(s): Government Reform and Oversight; Transportation and Infrastructure

HOSTETTLER, JOHN, R-IND. (8)

Capitol Hill office: 431 CHOB 20515; (202) 225-4636; Fax: (202) 225-3284; Internet: john.hostettler@mail.house.gov or www.house.gov/hostettler; *Administrative Assistant:* Curt Smith

District office(s): 120 N. 7th St., #208, Bloomington 47404; (812) 334-1111; Fax: (812) 333-6928; *Deputy District Director:* Chris Crabtree.

101 Martin Luther King Blvd., Evansville 47708; (812) 465-6484; Fax: (812) 422-4761; *District Director:* Rob Krieg.

Committee assignment(s): Agriculture; National Security

HOUGHTON, AMO, R-N.Y. (31)

Capitol Hill office: 1110 LHOB 20515; (202) 225-3161; Fax: (202) 225-5574; Internet: houghton@mail.house.gov or www.house.gov/houghton; *Staff Director:* Brian Fitzpatrick

District office(s): 122 Federal Bldg., Prendergast and 3rd Sts., Jamestown 14701; (716) 484-0252; Fax: (716) 484-8178; *Director of Economic Development:* Mickey Brown.

700 Westgate Plaza, Olean 14760; (716) 372-2127; Fax: (716) 373-4750; *Office Manager:* Nancy Clark.

32 Denison Parkway West, Corning 14830; (607) 937-3333; Fax: (607) 937-6047; *District Director:* John Meier.

268 Genesee St., Auburn 13021; (315) 255-3045.

Committee assignment(s): International Relations; Ways and Means

HOYER, STENY H., D-MD. (5)

Capitol Hill office: 1705 LHOB 20515; (202) 225-4131; Fax: (202) 225-4300; Internet: www.house.gov/hoyer; *Administrative Assistant:* Betsy Bossart

District office(s): 6500 Cherrywood Lane, #310, Greenbelt 20770; (301) 474-0119; Fax: (301) 474-4697; *Caseworker:* Betty Richardson.

21A Industrial Park Dr., #101, Waldorf 20602; (301) 843-1577; Fax: (301) 843-1331; *District Director:* John Bohanan.

Committee assignment(s): Appropriations; House Oversight; Joint Printing (ranking member)

HULSHOF, KENNY, R-MO. (9)

Capitol Hill office: 1728 LHOB 20515; (202) 225-2956; Fax: (202) 225-5712; Internet: www.house.gov/ writerep or www.house.gov/hulshof; *Administrative Assistant:* Matt Miller

District office(s): 33 E. Broadway St., #280, Columbia 65203; (573) 449-5111; Fax: (573) 449-5312; *District Representative:* Eric Feltner.

109 Virginia St., #157, Hannibal 63401; (573) 221-1200; Fax: (573) 221-5349; *District Representative:* Scott Callicott.

317 Lafayette St., Washington 63090; (314) 239-4001; Fax: (314) 239-1987; *District Representative:* David O'Brien.

Committee assignment(s): Ways and Means

HUNTER, DUNCAN, R-CALIF. (52)

Capitol Hill office: 2265 RHOB 20515; (202) 225-5672; Fax: (202) 225-0235; *Chief of Staff:* Victoria J. Middleton

District office(s): 366 S. Pierce St., El Cajon 92020; (619) 579-3001; Fax: (619) 579-2251; *District Chief of Staff:* Wendell Cutting.

1410 Main St., Suite C, Ramona 92065; (619) 788-3630; *Field Representative:* Val Snesko.

1101 Airport Rd., Suite G, Imperial 92251; (619) 353-5420; Fax: (619) 353-0653; *Field Representative:* Carole Starr.

Committee assignment(s): National Security

HUTCHINSON, ASA, R-ARK. (3)

Capitol Hill office: 1535 LHOB 20515; (202) 225-4301; Fax: (202) 225-5713; Internet: asa.hutchinson@mail. house.gov or www.house.gov/hutchinson; *Chief of Staff:* Westbrook Doss

District office(s): 402 N. Walnut, P.O. Box 579, Harrison 72601; (501) 741-6900; Fax: (501) 741-7741; *District Representative:* Karen Hopper.

30 S. 6th St., #248, Fort Smith 72901; (501) 782-7787; Fax: (501) 783-7662; *District Representative:* Kathy Watson.

35 E. Mountain St., #423, Fayetteville 72701; (501) 442-5258; Fax: (501) 442-0937; *District Representative:* Ralph Hudson.

Committee assignment(s): Judiciary; Transportation and Infrastructure; Veterans' Affairs

HYDE, HENRY J., R-ILL. (6)

Capitol Hill office: 2110 RHOB 20515; (202) 225-4561; Fax: (202) 225-1166; Internet: www.house.gov/hyde; *Chief of Staff:* Judy Wolverton

District office(s): 50 E. Oak St., #200, Addison 60101; (708) 832-5950; Fax: (708) 832-5969; *Administrative Assistant:* Judy Wolverton.

Committee assignment(s): International Relations; Judiciary (chair)

INGLIS, BOB, R-S.C. (4)

Capitol Hill office: 320 CHOB 20515; (202) 225-6030; Fax: 226-1177; Internet: www.citizendirect.net; *Administrative Assistant:* Bruce Haynes

District office(s): 201 Magnolia St., #108, Spartanburg 29301; (864) 582-6422; Fax: (864) 573-9478; *Legislative Assistant:* Jerry Setzer.

405 W. Main St., Union 29379; (864) 427-2205; Fax: (864) 429-8879; *Constituent Services Manager:* Ray Wynn.

300 E. Washington St., #101, Greenville 29601; (864) 232-1141; Fax: (864) 233-2160; *District Director:* Wayne Roper.

Committee assignment(s): Budget; Judiciary

ISTOOK, ERNEST, R-OKLA. (5)

Capitol Hill office: 119 CHOB 20515; (202) 225-2132; Fax: 226-1463; Internet: istook@mail.house.gov or www.house.gov/istook; *Administrative Assistant:* Steve Jones

District office(s): 5400 N. Grand Blvd., #505, Oklahoma City 73112; (405) 942-3636; *District Director:* Dwight A. Dissler.

1st Court Place, #205, Bartlesville 74003; (918) 336-5546; Fax: (918) 336-5740; *Northern Region Field Representative:* Mary Lynn Mihm.

5th and Grand, Ponca City 74601; (405) 762-6778; Fax: (405) 762-7049; *Northern Region Field Representative:* Mary Lynn Mihm.
Committee assignment(s): Appropriations

JACKSON, JESSE L., JR., D-ILL. (2)
Capitol Hill office: 313 CHOB 20515; (202) 225-0773; Fax: (202) 225-0899; *Chief of Staff:* Licia Green
District office(s): 10327 S. Halsted St., Homewood 60628; (773) 238-2100; Fax: (773) 238-7984; *District Administrator:* Edward J. Hamb.
17927 S. Halsted St., Homewood 60430; (708) 798-6000; Fax: (708) 798-6160; *Deputy District Administrator:* Richard Bryant.
Committee assignment(s): Banking and Financial Services; Small Business

JACKSON-LEE, SHEILA, D-TEXAS (18)
Capitol Hill office: 410 CHOB 20515; (202) 225-3816; Fax: (202) 225-3317; Internet: tx.18@mail.house.gov or www.house.gov/jacksonlee; *Deputy Chief of Staff:* Leon Buck
District office(s): 1919 Smith St., #1180, Houston 77002; (713) 655-6060; Fax: (713) 655-1612; *District Director:* Vacant.
6719 W. Montgomery Rd., Houston 77091; (713) 691-4882; Fax: (713) 699-8292; *District Field Representative:* Dorothy Hubbard.
420 W. 19th St., Houston 77008; (713) 861-4070; Fax: (713) 861-4323; *Staff Assistant:* Suzanne James.
Committee assignment(s): Judiciary; Science

JEFFERSON, WILLIAM J., D-LA. (2)
Capitol Hill office: 240 CHOB 20515; (202) 225-6636; Fax: (202) 225-1988; *Chief of Staff:* Lionel Collins
District office(s): 501 Magazine St., New Orleans 70130; (504) 589-2274; Fax: (504) 589-4513; *Executive Assistant:* Stephanie Butler.
Committee assignment(s): Ways and Means

JENKINS, BILL, R-TENN. (1)
Capitol Hill office: 1708 LHOB 20515; (202) 225-6356; Fax: (202) 225-5714; Internet: rep.jenkins@mail.house.gov or www.house.gov/jenkins; *Chief of Staff:* Jeff Anderson
District office(s): 320 W. Center St., P.O. Box 769, Kingsport 37662; (423) 247-8161; Fax: (423) 247-1834; *District Director:* Bill Snodgrass.
Committee assignment(s): Agriculture; Judiciary

JOHN, CHRIS, D-LA. (7)
Capitol Hill office: 1504 LHOB 20515; (202) 225-2031; Fax: (202) 225-5724; Internet: chrisjohn@mail.house.gov or www.house.gov/john; *Chief of Staff:* Lynn Hershey

District office(s): #100, 556 Jefferson St., Lafayette 70501; (318) 235-6322; Fax: (318) 235-6072; *District Director:* Louis Perret.
1011 Lakeshore Dr., #306, Lake Charles 70601; (318) 433-1747; Fax: (318) 433-0974; *Executive Assistant:* Lynn Jones.
Committee assignment(s): Agriculture; Resources

JOHNSON, EDDIE BERNICE, D-TEXAS (3)
Capitol Hill office: 1123 LHOB 20515; (202) 225-8885; Fax: 226-1477; Internet: ejohnson@mail.house.gov or www.house.gov/ebjohnson; *Chief of Staff:* Horace Jennings
District office(s): 2515 McKinney Ave., #1565, Dallas 75201; (214) 922-8885; *District Director:* Mollie Johnson-Williams.
1634B W. Irving Blvd., Irving 75061; (972) 253-8885; Fax: (972) 253-3034; *Staff Assistant:* Bernard Williams.
Committee assignment(s): Science; Transportation and Infrastructure

JOHNSON, JAY W., D-WIS. (8)
Capitol Hill office: 1313 LHOB 20515; (202) 225-5665; Internet: jay.johnson@mail.house.gov or www.house.gov/jayjohnson; *Chief of Staff:* Karisa Johnson
District office(s): 211 N. Broadway St., #103, Green Bay 54303; (920) 430-1776; *District Director:* Paul Williams.
300 N. Woods Edge Dr., #101, Appleton 54914; (920) 731-7586.
Committee assignment(s): Agriculture; Transportation and Infrastructure

JOHNSON, NANCY L., R-CONN. (6)
Capitol Hill office: 343 CHOB 20515; (202) 225-4476; Fax: (202) 225-4488; Internet: njohnson@mail.house.gov or www.house.gov/nancyjohnson; *Chief of Staff:* Dave Karvelas
District office(s): 480 Myrtle St., #200, New Britain 06053; (860) 223-8412; Fax: (860) 827-9009; *District Director:* Marianne Calnen.
Committee assignment(s): Ways and Means

JOHNSON, SAM, R-TEXAS (3)
Capitol Hill office: 1030 LHOB 20515; (202) 225-4201; Fax: (202) 225-1485; Internet: sam.tx03@mail.house.gov or www.house.gov/samjohnson; *Chief of Staff:* Mark Franz
District office(s): 801 E. Campbell Rd., #425, Richardson 75081; (972) 470-0892; Fax: (972) 470-9937; *District Director:* Mary Lynn Murrell.

Committee assignment(s): Education and Workforce; Ways and Means

JONES, WALTER B., JR., R-N.C. (3)

Capitol Hill office: 422 CHOB 20515; (202) 225-3415; Fax: (202) 225-3286; Internet: www.house.gov/writerep or www.house.gov/jones; *Administrative Assistant:* Glen Downs

District office(s): 102-C Eastbrook Dr., Greenville 27858; (919) 931-1003; Fax: (919) 931-1002; *Office Manager:* Millie Lillie.

Committee assignment(s): Banking and Financial Services; National Security; Resources; Small Business

KANJORSKI, PAUL E., D-PA. (11)

Capitol Hill office: 2353 RHOB 20515; (202) 225-6511; Internet: paul.kanjorski@mail.house.gov; *Chief of Staff:* Karen Feather

District office(s): 7 N. Wilkes-Barre Blvd., #400 M, Wilkes-Barre 18702; (717) 825-2200; *District Director:* Joseph J. Terrana.

Committee assignment(s): Banking and Financial Services; Government Reform and Oversight

KAPTUR, MARCY, D-OHIO (9)

Capitol Hill office: 2311 RHOB 20515; (202) 225-4146; Fax: (202) 225-7711; Internet: rep.kaptur@mail. house.gov or www.house.gov/kaptur; *Chief of Staff:* Fariborz S. Fatemi

District office(s): 234 Summit St., #719, Toledo 43604; (419) 259-7500; Fax: (419) 255-9623; *District Manager:* Steve Katich.

Committee assignment(s): Appropriations

KASICH, JOHN R., R-OHIO (12)

Capitol Hill office: 1111 LHOB 20515; (202) 225-5355; Internet: www.house.gov/kasich; *Chief of Staff:* Don Thibaut

District office(s): 2700 E. Dublin Granville Rd., Columbus 43231; (614) 469-7318; *Office Manager,Caseworker:* Sally Testa.

Committee assignment(s): Budget (chair); National Security

KELLY, SUE W., R-N.Y. (19)

Capitol Hill office: 1222 LHOB 20515; (202) 225-5441; Fax: (202) 225-3289; Internet: dearsue@hr.house.gov or www.house.gov/suekelly; *Chief of Staff:* Steve Hall

District office(s): 21 Old Main St., #205, Fishkill 12524; (914) 897-5200; Fax: (914) 897-5800; *District Director:* Chris Fish.

105 S. Bedford Rd., #312A, Mount Kisco 10549; (914) 241-6340; Fax: (914) 241-3502; *District Director:* Chris Fish.

Committee assignment(s): Banking and Financial Services; Small Business; Transportation and Infrastructure

KENNEDY, JOSEPH P., II, D-MASS. (8)

Capitol Hill office: 2242 RHOB 20515; (202) 225-5111; Fax: (202) 225-9322; Internet: www.house.gov/josephkennedy; *Chief of Staff:* Amy Simmons

District office(s): 529 Main St., #605, Charlestown 02129; (617) 242-0200; Fax: (617) 241-7593; *District Director:* Ray Dooley.

Committee assignment(s): Banking and Financial Services; Veterans' Affairs

KENNEDY, PATRICK J., D-R.I. (1)

Capitol Hill office: 312 CHOB 20515; (202) 225-4911; Fax: (202) 225-3290; Internet: www.house.gov/patrickkennedy; *Chief of Staff:* Anthony C. Marcella

District office(s): 286 Main St., #600, Pawtucket 02860; (401) 729-5600; Fax: (401) 729-5608; *District Director:* Michael Mello.

Committee assignment(s): National Security; Resources

KENNELLY, BARBARA B., D-CONN. (1)

Capitol Hill office: 201 CHOB 20515; (202) 225-2265; Fax: (202) 225-1031; Internet: kennelly@mail.house. gov or www.house.gov/kennelly; *Administrative Assistant:* Ross Brown

District office(s): 1 Corporate Center, 11th Floor, Hartford 06103; (860) 278-8888; Fax: (860) 278-2111; *District Director:* Robert J. Croce.

Committee assignment(s): Ways and Means

KILDEE, DALE E., D-MICH. (9)

Capitol Hill office: 2187 RHOB 20515; (202) 225-3611; Fax: (202) 225-6393; Internet: dale.kildee@mail. house.gov; *Administrative Assistant:* Christopher Mansour

District office(s): 1829 N. Perry St., Pontiac 48340; (248) 373-9337; Fax: (248) 373-6955; *District Director:* Tiffany Flynn.

432 N. Saginaw St., #410, Flint 48502; (810) 239-1437; Fax: (810) 239-1439.

Committee assignment(s): Education and Workforce; Resources

KILPATRICK, CAROLYN CHEEKS, D-MICH. (15)

Capitol Hill office: 503 CHOB 20515; (202) 225-2261; Fax: (202) 225-5730; Internet: www.house.gov/kilpatrick; *Administrative Assistant:* Beverlyn C. Hilton

District office(s): 1274 Library St., #1B, Detroit 48226; (313) 965-9004; Fax: (313) 965-9006; *District Director:* Derrick Miller.

Committee assignment(s): Banking and Financial Services; House Oversight; Joint Library

KIM, JAY C., R-CALIF. (41)
Capitol Hill office: 227 CHOB 20515; (202) 225-3201; Internet: www.house.gov/writerep or www.house.gov/kim; *Chief of Staff:* Matt Reynolds
District office(s): 1131 W. 6th St., Ontario 91762; (909) 988-1055; Fax: (909) 988-5723; *District Manager:* Peter Stevens.
18200 Yorba Linda Blvd., #203A, Yorba Linda 92686; (714) 572-8574; Fax: (714) 572-8577; *Field Director:* Steve Schuyler.
Committee assignment(s): International Relations; Transportation and Infrastructure

KIND, RON, D-WIS. (3)
Capitol Hill office: 1713 LHOB 20515; (202) 225-5506; Fax: (202) 225-5739; Internet: ron.kind@mail.house.gov or www.house.gov/kind; *Administrative Assistant:* Alan MacCleod
District office(s): 202 5th Ave. South, #227, LaCrosse 54601; (608) 782-2558; *District Director:* Loren Kannenberg.
131 S. Barstow St., #301, Eau Claire 54701; (715) 831-9214; *District Director:* Loren Kannenberg.
Committee assignment(s): Education and Workforce; Resources

KING, PETER T., R-N.Y. (3)
Capitol Hill office: 403 CHOB 20515; (202) 225-7896; Fax: 226-2279; Internet: pete.king@mail.house.gov or www.house.gov/king; *Chief of Staff:* Robert O'Connor
District office(s): 1003 Park Blvd., Massapequa Park 11762; (516) 541-4225; Fax: (516) 541-6602; *District Administrator:* Gene Turner.
Committee assignment(s): Banking and Financial Services; International Relations

KINGSTON, JACK, R-GA. (1)
Capitol Hill office: 1507 LHOB 20515; (202) 225-5831; Fax: 226-2269; Internet: www.house.gov/kingston; *Chief of Staff:* Karleen Mahn
District office(s): 52 N. Main St., #220, Statesboro 30458; (912) 489-8797; Fax: (912) 233-0712; *Office Manager:* Floy Thackston.
6605 Abercorn St., #102, Savannah 31405; (912) 352-0101; Fax: (912) 352-0105; *Casework Manager:* Trish DePriest.
805 Gloucester St., #304, Brunswick 31520; (912) 265-9010; Fax: (912) 265-9013; *Office Manager:* Russ Graham.
Committee assignment(s): Appropriations

KLECZKA, JERRY, D-WIS. (4)
Capitol Hill office: 2301 RHOB 20515; (202) 225-4572; Fax: (202) 225-8135; Internet: jerry.4wi@mail.house.gov; *Administrative Assistant:* Janet Brown
District office(s): 414 W. Moreland Blvd., #105, Waukesha 53188; (414) 549-6360; Fax: (414) 549-6723.
5032 W. Forest Home Ave., Milwaukee 53219; (414) 297-1140; Fax: (414) 327-6151; *Chief of Staff:* Kathryn Hein.
Committee assignment(s): Ways and Means

KLINK, RON, D-PA. (4)
Capitol Hill office: 125 CHOB 20515; (202) 225-2565; Fax: 226-2274; Internet: www.house.gov/klink; *Administrative Assistant:* Mary Kiernan
District office(s): 250 Insurance St., #305, Beaver 15009; (412) 728-3005; Fax: (412) 728-3095; *Caseworker:* Brian Hayden.
2692 Leechburg Rd., Lower Burrell 15068; (412) 335-4518; *Caseworker:* Melanie Polydence.
11279 Center Hwy., N. Huntingdon 15642; (412) 864-8681; Fax: (412) 864-8691; *Press Secretary:* Nancy Smith.
2700 D Rochester Rd., Mars 16046; (412) 772-6080; Fax: (412) 772-6099; *District Director:* Joe Brimmeier.
134 N. Mercer St., New Castle 16101; (412) 654-9036; Fax: (412) 654-9076; *Caseworker:* Rita Foley.
Committee assignment(s): Commerce

KLUG, SCOTT L., R-WIS. (2)
Capitol Hill office: 2331 RHOB 20515; (202) 225-2906; Fax: (202) 225-6942; Internet: badger02@hr.house.gov or www.house.gov/klug; *Chief of Staff:* Kris Andrews
District office(s): 16 N. Carroll St., #600, Madison 53703; (608) 257-9200; Fax: (608) 257-3116; *District Director:* Sam Gold.
Committee assignment(s): Commerce

KNOLLENBERG, JOE, R-MICH. (11)
Capitol Hill office: 1511 LHOB 20515; (202) 225-5802; Fax: 226-2356; Internet: www.house.gov/knollenberg; *Chief of Staff:* Paul Welday
District office(s): 15439 Middlebelt, Livonia 48154; (313) 425-7557; *Field Representative:* Denise Radtke.
30833 N. Western Hwy., #214, Farmington Hills 48334; (810) 851-1366; *District Representative:* Trent Wisecop.
Committee assignment(s): Appropriations; Education and Workforce; Standards of Official Conduct

KOLBE, JIM, R-ARIZ. (5)
Capitol Hill office: 205 CHOB 20515; (202) 225-2542; Fax: (202) 225-0378; Internet: www.house.gov/

writerep or www.house.gov/kolbe; *Chief of Staff:* Frances McNaught

District office(s): 77 Calle Portal, #B-160, Sierra Vista 85635; (520) 459-3115; *District Aide:* Melissa Rodriguez.

1661 N. Swan Rd., #112, Tucson 85712; (520) 881-3588; *District Director:* Patricia Klein.

Committee assignment(s): Appropriations

KUCINICH, DENNIS J., D-OHIO (1)

Capitol Hill office: 1730 LHOB 20515; (202) 225-5871; Fax: (202) 225-5745; *Administrative Assistant:* John Edgell

District office(s): 14400 Detroit Ave., Lakewood 44107; (216) 228-6465; *District Director:* Pat Vecchio.

Committee assignment(s): Education and Workforce; Government Reform and Oversight

LAFALCE, JOHN J., D-N.Y. (29)

Capitol Hill office: 2310 RHOB 20515; (202) 225-3231; Fax: (202) 225-8693; *Administrative Assistant:* Roy Dye

District office(s): 111 W. Huron St., Buffalo 14202; (716) 846-4056; Fax: (716) 856-3821; *Staff Assistant:* Mary Fitzgerald.

614 Main St., Niagara Falls 14302; (716) 284-9976; Fax: (716) 284-8870; *Staff Assistant:* Becky Muscoreis.

409 S. Union St., Spencerport 14559; (716) 352-4777; Fax: (716) 352-4747; *Staff Assistant:* Hannelore Heyen.

Committee assignment(s): Banking and Financial Services; Small Business (ranking member)

LAHOOD, RAY, R-ILL. (18)

Capitol Hill office: 329 CHOB 20515; (202) 225-6201; Fax: (202) 225-9249; Internet: www.house.gov/ writerep or www.house.gov/lahood; *Administrative Assistant:* Diane R. Liesman

District office(s): 100 N.E. Monroe St., Peoria 61602; (309) 671-7027; Fax: (309) 671-7309; *Administrative Assistant:* Mary Alice Erickson.

236 W. State St., Jacksonville 62650; (217) 245-1431; Fax: (217) 243-6852; *Office Manager:* Sally Dahman.

3050 Montvale Dr., Suite D, Springfield 62704; (217) 793-0808; Fax: (217) 793-9724; *Office Manager:* Donna Rapps Miller.

Committee assignment(s): Agriculture; Transportation and Infrastructure; Veterans' Affairs

LAMPSON, NICK, D-TEXAS (9)

Capitol Hill office: 417 CHOB 20515; (202) 225-6565; Fax: (202) 225-5547; Internet: www.house.gov/ writerep or www.house.gov/lampson; *Administrative Assistant:* Jacquelyn B. Davis

District office(s): 300 Willow St., #B104, Beaumont 77701; (409) 838-0061; Fax: (409) 832-0738; *District Director:* Joe Arnold.

601 Rosenberg, #216, Galveston 77550; (409) 762-5877; Fax: (409) 763-4133; *Galveston Director:* Dorethea Lewis.

Committee assignment(s): Science; Transportation and Infrastructure

LANTOS, TOM, D-CALIF. (12)

Capitol Hill office: 2217 RHOB 20515; (202) 225-3531; Internet: talk2tom@mail.house.gov or www.house. gov/lantos; *Administrative Assistant:* Robert R. King

District office(s): 400 El Camino Real, #820, San Mateo 94402; (415) 342-0300; Fax: (415) 375-8270; *District Representative:* Evelyn Szelenyi.

Committee assignment(s): Government Reform and Oversight; International Relations

LARGENT, STEVE, R-OKLA. (1)

Capitol Hill office: 426 CHOB 20515; (202) 225-2211; Fax: (202) 225-9187; Internet: ok01.largent@mail. house.gov or www.house.gov/largent; *Chief of Staff:* Terry Allen

District office(s): 2424 E. 21st St., #510, Tulsa 74114; (918) 749-0014; Fax: (918) 749-0781; *District Director:* Mike Willis.

Committee assignment(s): Commerce

LATHAM, TOM, R-IOWA (5)

Capitol Hill office: 516 CHOB 20515; (202) 225-5476; Fax: (202) 225-3301; Internet: www.house.gov/ writerep or www.house.gov/latham; *Washington Operations Director:* James D. Carstensen

District office(s): 1411 1st Ave. South, Suite A, Fort Dodge 50501; (515) 573-2738; Fax: (515) 576-7141; *Staff Assistant:* Andrew Warren.

123 Albany Ave. S.E., #1, Orange City 51041; (712) 737-8708; Fax: (712) 737-3456; *Chief of Staff:* Vicky Vermaat.

526 Pierce St., Sioux City 51101; (712) 277-2114; Fax: (712) 277-0932; *Special Assistant:* Michele Wing.

20 W. 6th St., Spencer 51301; (712) 262-6480; Fax: (712) 262-6673; *Staff Assistant:* Lois Clark.

Committee assignment(s): Appropriations

LATOURETTE, STEVEN C., R-OHIO (19)

Capitol Hill office: 1239 LHOB 20515; (202) 225-5731; Fax: (202) 225-3307; Internet: www.house.gov/ writerep or www.house.gov/latourette; *Administrative Assistant:* Brian Durdle

District office(s): 1 Victoria Place, #320, Painesville 44077; (216) 352-3939; Fax: (216) 352-3662; *Administrative Assistant:* Brian Durdle.

Committee assignment(s): Banking and Financial Services; Government Reform and Oversight; Transportation and Infrastructure

LAZIO, RICK A., R-N.Y. (2)

Capitol Hill office: 2444 RHOB 20515; (202) 225-3335; Fax: (202) 225-4669; Internet: lazio@mail.house.gov or www.house.gov/lazio; *Chief of Staff:* David Horne

District office(s): 126 W. Main St., Babylon 11702; (516) 893-9010; Fax: (516) 893-9017; *District Director:* Barbara Vogl.

Committee assignment(s): Banking and Financial Services; Commerce

LEACH, JIM, R-IOWA (1)

Capitol Hill office: 2186 RHOB 20515; (202) 225-6576; Fax: 226-1278; Internet: talk2jim@mail.house.gov or www.house.gov/leach; *Administrative Assistant:* Bill Tate

District office(s): 308 10th St. S.E., Cedar Rapids 52403; (319) 363-4773; Fax: (319) 363-5008; *Staff Assistant:* Gary Grant.

209 W. 4th St., Davenport 52801; (319) 326-1841; Fax: (319) 326-5464; *Staff Assistant:* Rita Lowry.

102 S. Clinton St., Iowa City 52240; (319) 351-0789; Fax: (319) 351-5789; *Staff Assistant:* Ginny Burrus.

Committee assignment(s): Banking and Financial Services (chair); International Relations

LEVIN, SANDER M., D-MICH. (12)

Capitol Hill office: 2209 RHOB 20515; (202) 225-4961; Fax: 226-1033; Internet: slevin@mail.house.gov or www.house.gov/levin; *Administrative Assistant:* Hilarie Chambers

District office(s): 2107 E. Fourteen Mile Rd., Sterling Heights 48310; (810) 268-4444; Fax: (810) 268-0918; *District Administrator:* Hilarie Chambers.

Committee assignment(s): Ways and Means

LEWIS, JERRY, R-CALIF. (4)

Capitol Hill office: 2112 RHOB 20515; (202) 225-5861; Fax: (202) 225-6498; Internet: www.house.gov/jerrylewis; *Administrative Assistant:* Arlene Willis

District office(s): 1150 Brookside Ave., #J5, Redlands 92373; (909) 862-6030; Fax: (909) 792-9510; *District Representative:* Janet Scott.

Committee assignment(s): Appropriations; Select Intelligence

LEWIS, JOHN, D-GA. (5)

Capitol Hill office: 229 CHOB 20515; (202) 225-3801; Fax: (202) 225-0351; Internet: www.house.gov/johnlewis; *Chief of Staff:* Robert H. Bassin

District office(s): 100 Peachtree St. N.W., #1920, Atlanta 30303; (404) 659-0116; Fax: (404) 331-0947; *Constituent Services Director:* Love Williams.

Committee assignment(s): Ways and Means

LEWIS, RON, R-KY. (2)

Capitol Hill office: 223 CHOB 20515; (202) 225-3501; *Administrative Assistant:* Greg Van Tatenhove

District office(s): 241 E. Main St., #B20, Bowling Green 42101; (502) 842-9896; Fax: (502) 842-9061; *District Representative:* Phyllis Causey.

312 N. Mulberry St., Elizabethtown 42701; (502) 765-4360; Fax: (502) 686-8372; *District Director:* Keith Rogers.

423 Frederica St., #B17, Owensboro 42302; (502) 688-8858; *Field Representative:* Darla Tomes.

Committee assignment(s): Agriculture; National Security

LINDER, JOHN, R-GA. (11)

Capitol Hill office: 1005 LHOB 20515; (202) 225-4272; Fax: (202) 225-4696; Internet: john.linder@mail.house.gov or www.house.gov/linder; *Administrative Assistant:* Henry Plaster

District office(s): 220 College Ave., #520, Athens 30601; (706) 355-9909; Fax: (706) 355-9968; *District Director:* Jeff Finger.

3675 Crestwood Blvd., #530, Duluth 30136; (770) 931-9550; Fax: (770) 931-2775; *District Field Manager:* Allan Hayes.

Committee assignment(s): Rules

LIPINSKI, WILLIAM O., D-ILL. (3)

Capitol Hill office: 1501 LHOB 20515; (202) 225-5701; Fax: (202) 225-1012; *Administrative Assistant:* Colleen Corr

District office(s): 5239 W. 95th St., Oak Lawn 60453; (708) 371-7460; *Staff Assistant:* Rita Pula.

5832 S. Archer Ave., Chicago 60638; (312) 886-0481; *Administrative Assistant:* Jerry Hurckes.

Committee assignment(s): Transportation and Infrastructure

LIVINGSTON, ROBERT L., R-LA. (1)

Capitol Hill office: 2406 RHOB 20515; (202) 225-3015; Fax: (202) 225-0739; *Administrative Assistant:* J. Allen Martin

District office(s): 111 Veterans Blvd., #700, Metairie 70005; (504) 589-2753; Fax: (504) 589-2607; *District Representative:* Rick Legendre.

300 E. Thomas St., Hammond 70401; (504) 542-9616; *Staff Assistant:* Mona Crapanzano.

2055 2nd St., Slidell 70458; (504) 643-7733; *Staff Assistant:* Carol Thurston.

428 E. Boston St., Covington 70433; (504) 542-9617;
Staff Assistant: Carol Thurston.
Committee assignment(s): Appropriations (chair)

LOBIONDO, FRANK A., R-N.J. (2)

Capitol Hill office: 222 CHOB 20515; (202) 225-6572; Fax: (202) 225-3318; Internet: lobiondo@mail.house. gov or www.house.gov/lobiondo; *Chief of Staff:* Mary Annie Harper

District office(s): 5914 Main St., Mays Landing 08330; (609) 625-5008; Fax: (609) 625-5071; *District Director:* Todd Noon.

Committee assignment(s): Small Business; Transportation and Infrastructure

LOFGREN, ZOE, D-CALIF. (16)

Capitol Hill office: 318 CHOB 20515; (202) 225-3072; Fax: (202) 225-3336; Internet: zoegram@logfren. house.gov or www.house.gov/lofgren

District office(s): 635 N. 1st St., San Jose 95110; (408) 271-8700; Fax: (408) 271-8713; *District Director:* Mavis Toscano.

Committee assignment(s): Judiciary; Science; Standards of Official Conduct

LOWEY, NITA M., D-N.Y. (18)

Capitol Hill office: 2421 RHOB 20515; (202) 225-6506; Fax: (202) 225-0546; Internet: nita.lowey@mail. house.gov or www.house.gov/lowey; *Chief of Staff:* Howard Wolfson

District office(s): 222 Mamaroneck Ave., #310, White Plains 10605; (914) 428-1707; Fax: (914) 328-1505; *District Director:* Patricia Keegan.

97-45 Queens Blvd., #505, Rego Park 11374; (718) 897-3602; Fax: (718) 897-3804; *District Representative:* Charlie Kasalaro.

Committee assignment(s): Appropriations

LUCAS, FRANK D., R-OKLA. (6)

Capitol Hill office: 107 CHOB 20515; (202) 225-5565; Fax: (202) 225-8698; Internet: www.house.gov/ writerep or www.house.gov/lucas; *Chief of Staff:* Shelly White

District office(s): 500 N. Broadway, #300, Oklahoma City 73102; (405) 231-5511; Fax: (405) 231-5811.

Federal Bldg., P.O. Box 3612, Enid 73701; (405) 233-9224; *Field Representative:* Tim Millacek.

1007 Main St., P.O. Box 1927, Woodward 73802; (405) 256-5752; Fax: (405) 254-3047; *Field Representative:* Tammie Smith.

703-A Frusco, Clinton 73601; (405) 323-6232; Fax: (405) 323-3431; *Field Representative:* David Thompson.

Committee assignment(s): Agriculture; Banking and Financial Services

LUTHER, WILLIAM P. "BILL," D-MINN. (6)

Capitol Hill office: 117 CHOB 20515; (202) 225-2271; Fax: (202) 225-3368; Internet: tell.bill@mail.house. gov or www.house.gov/luther; *Chief of Staff:* Ted Thompson

District office(s): 1811 Weir Dr., #150, Woodbury 55125; (612) 730-4949; Fax: (612) 730-0507; *District Director:* Corinne Hoeft.

Committee assignment(s): International Relations; Science

MALONEY, CAROLYN B., D-N.Y. (14)

Capitol Hill office: 1330 LHOB 20515; (202) 225-7944; Fax: (202) 225-4709; Internet: rep.carolyn. maloney@mail.house.gov or www.house.gov/ maloney; *Administrative Assistant:* Ben Chevat

District office(s): 110 E. 59th St., New York 10022; (212) 832-6531; Fax: (212) 832-7576; *Chief of Staff:* Minna Elias.

28-11 Astoria Blvd., Astoria 11102; (718) 932-1804; *District Representative:* Dominick Fucile.

619 Lorimer St., Brooklyn 11211; (718) 349-1260; *District Representative:* Mary Odomirok.

Committee assignment(s): Banking and Financial Services; Government Reform and Oversight; Joint Economic

MALONEY, JIM, D-CONN. (5)

Capitol Hill office: 1213 LHOB 20515; (202) 225-3822; Fax: (202) 225-5746; Internet: www.house.gov/ jimmaloney; *Chief of Staff:* Jim Hart

District office(s): 20 E. Main St., #240, Waterbury 06702; (203) 573-1418; Fax: (203) 573-9329; *District Director:* Philip D. Lewis.

Committee assignment(s): Banking and Financial Services; National Security

MANTON, THOMAS J., D-N.Y. (7)

Capitol Hill office: 2235 RHOB 20515; (202) 225-3965; Internet: tmanton@mail.house.gov or www.house. gov/manton; *Administrative Assistant:* James H. Mathews

District office(s): 2114 Williamsbridge Rd., Bronx 10461; (718) 931-1400; Fax: (718) 931-1340; *Community Liaison:* Fran Mahoney.

46-12 Queens Blvd., Sunnyside 11104; (718) 706-1400; Fax: (718) 472-0489; *District Director:* Brian Browne.

Committee assignment(s): Commerce

MANZULLO, DONALD, R-ILL. (16)

Capitol Hill office: 409 CHOB 20515; (202) 225-5676; Fax: (202) 225-5284; Internet: www.house.gov/ manzullo; *Chief of Staff:* Doug Thomas

District office(s): 181 Virginia Ave., Crystal Lake 61014; (815) 356-9800; *Caseworker:* Nada Johnson.

415 S. Mulford, Rockford 61107; (815) 394-1231;
District Director: Pamela Sexton.

Committee assignment(s): Banking and Financial Services; International Relations; Small Business; Joint Economic

MARKEY, EDWARD J., D-MASS. (7)

Capitol Hill office: 2133 RHOB 20515; (202) 225-2836; Internet: www.house.gov/writerep or www.house.gov/markey; *Administrative Assistant:* David Moulton

District office(s): 5 High St., #101, Medford 02155; (617) 396-2900; *Office Manager:* Carol Lederman.

188 Concord St., #102, Framingham 01701; (508) 875-2900.

Committee assignment(s): Commerce; Resources

MARTINEZ, MATTHEW G., D-CALIF. (31)

Capitol Hill office: 2234 RHOB 20515; (202) 225-5464; Fax: (202) 225-5467; Internet: www.house.gov/writerep or www.house.gov/martinez; *Administrative Assistant:* Maxine Grant

District office(s): 320 S. Garfield Ave., #214, Alhambra 91801; (818) 458-4524; Fax: (818) 458-7457; *Office Manager:* Sally Martinez.

Committee assignment(s): Education and Workforce; International Relations

MASCARA, FRANK R., D-PA. (2)

Capitol Hill office: 314 CHOB 20515; (202) 225-4665; Fax: (202) 225-3377; *Administrative Assistant:* Bill Sember

District office(s): 96 N. Main St., Washington 15301; (412) 228-4326; Fax: (412) 228-5839; *Field Representative:* Tina Dallatore.

625 Lincoln Ave., #210, N. Charleroi 15022; (412) 483-9016; Fax: (412) 483-9044; *District Director:* Lou Lignelli.

47 E. Penn St., Uniontown 15401; (412) 437-5078; Fax: (412) 437-5189; *Field Representative:* Chris Buckelew.

93 E. High St., #303, Waynesburg 15370; (412) 852-2182; *Field Representative:* Pam Snyder.

416 S. Main St., Greensburg 15601; (412) 834-6441; Fax: (412) 834-6514; *Field Representative:* David McCormick.

Committee assignment(s): Transportation and Infrastructure; Veterans' Affairs

MATSUI, ROBERT T., D-CALIF. (5)

Capitol Hill office: 2308 RHOB 20515; (202) 225-7163; Fax: (202) 225-0566; Internet: www.house.gov/matsui; *Administrative Assistant:* Tom Keaney

District office(s): 650 Capitol Mall, #8058, Sacramento 95814; (916) 498-5600; Fax: (916) 444-6117; *District Director:* Anne Valenti.

Committee assignment(s): Ways and Means

MCCARTHY, CAROLYN, D-N.Y. (4)

Capitol Hill office: 1725 LHOB 20515; (202) 225-5516; Fax: (202) 225-5758; Internet: www.house.gov/writerep or www.house.gov/carolynmccarthy; *Administrative Assistant:* Beneva Schulte

District office(s): 1 Fulton Ave., #12, Hempstead 11550; (516) 489-7066; Fax: (516) 489-7283; *District Director:* Mary Ellen Mendelsohn.

Committee assignment(s): Education and Workforce; Small Business

MCCARTHY, KAREN, D-MO. (5)

Capitol Hill office: 1232 LHOB 20515; (202) 225-4535; Fax: (202) 225-4403

District office(s): 811 Grand Ave., #935, Kansas City 64106; (816) 842-4545; Fax: (816) 471-5213; *Chief of Staff:* Phil Scaglia.

Committee assignment(s): Commerce

MCCOLLUM, BILL, R-FLA. (8)

Capitol Hill office: 2266 RHOB 20515; (202) 225-2176; Fax: (202) 225-0999; Internet: www.house.gov/mccollum; *Administrative Assistant:* Doyle Bartlett

District office(s): 605 E. Robinson St., #650, Orlando 32801; (407) 872-1962; *District Office Manager:* Sue Lancaster.

Committee assignment(s): Banking and Financial Services; Select Intelligence; Judiciary

MCCRERY, JIM, R-LA. (4)

Capitol Hill office: 2104 RHOB 20515; (202) 225-2777; Fax: (202) 225-8039; Internet: jim.mccrery@mail.house.gov or www.house.gov/mccrery; *Chief of Staff:* Richard Hunt

District office(s): 6425 Youree Dr., Shreveport 71115; (318) 798-2254; Fax: (318) 798-2063; *District Manager:* Linda Sentell Wright.

1606 S. 5th St., Leesville 71446; (318) 238-0778; Fax: (318) 238-0566; *District Manager:* Lee Turner.

Committee assignment(s): Ways and Means; Joint Economic

MCDADE, JOSEPH M., R-PA. (1)

Capitol Hill office: 2107 RHOB 20515; (202) 225-3731; Fax: (202) 225-9594; Internet: www.house.gov/mcdade; *Chief of Staff:* John Enright

District office(s): 240 W. 3rd St., #230, Williamsport 17701; (717) 327-8161; Fax: (717) 327-9359; *Staff Assistant:* Ruth Calistri.

Scranton Life Bldg., #514, Scranton 18503; (717) 346-3834; Fax: (717) 346-8577; *Field Representative:* Michael Russen.

Committee assignment(s): Appropriations

MCDERMOTT, JIM, D-WASH. (7)

Capitol Hill office: 2349 RHOB 20515; (202) 225-3106; Internet: www.house.gov/writerep or www.house.gov/mcdermott; *Administrative Assistant:* Charles M. Williams

District office(s): 1809 7th Ave., #1212, Seattle 98101; (206) 553-7170; *District Administrator:* Nancy F. James.

Committee assignment(s): Budget; Ways and Means

MCGOVERN, JIM, D-MASS. (3)

Capitol Hill office: 512 CHOB 20515; (202) 225-6101; Fax: (202) 225-5759; Internet: www.house.gov/mcgovern; *Chief of Staff:* Bernie Robinson

District office(s): 34 Mechanic St., 1st Floor, Worcester 01608; (508) 831-7356; Fax: (508) 754-0982; *District Director:* Gladys Rodriguez-Parker.

1 Park St., Attleboro 02703; (508) 431-8025; Fax: (508) 431-8017; *District Representative:* Shirley Coelho.

218 S. Main St., #204, Fall River 02721; (508) 677-0140; Fax: (508) 677-0992; *District Representative:* Patrick Norton.

Committee assignment(s): Transportation and Infra-structure

MCHALE, PAUL, D-PA. (15)

Capitol Hill office: 217 CHOB 20515; (202) 225-6411; Fax: (202) 225-5320; Internet: mchale@mail.house.gov or www.house.gov/mchale; *Chief of Staff:* Christine Messina-Boyer

District office(s): 26 E. 3rd St., Bethlehem 18015; (610) 866-0916; Fax: (610) 867-8210; *District Administrator:* Thomas Mohr.

1603 Lehigh St., Easton 18042; (610) 258-8383; Fax: (610) 258-3465; *Senior Staff Assistant:* Cindy Duelley.

168 Main St., Pennsburg 18073; (215) 541-0614; Fax: (215) 541-0617; *Senior Staff Assistant:* Judy Edwards.

1 Center Square, #203, Allentown 18101; (610) 439-8861; Fax: (610) 439-0598; *Senior Staff Assistant:* John Gormley.

Committee assignment(s): National Security; Science

MCHUGH, JOHN M., R-N.Y. (24)

Capitol Hill office: 2441 RHOB 20515; (202) 225-4611; Internet: www.house.gov/mchugh; *Chief of Staff:* Cary Brick

District office(s): 223 W. Main St., Johnstown 12095; (518) 762-0379; *District Office Manager:* Diane Henderson.

104 Federal Bldg., Plattsburgh 12901; (518) 563-1406; *District Office Manager:* Ruth Ortloff.

200 Washington St., Watertown 13601; (315) 782-3150; *District Office Manager:* Elaine Grabiec.

Committee assignment(s): Government Reform and Oversight; International Relations; National Security

MCINNIS, SCOTT, R-COLO. (3)

Capitol Hill office: 215 CHOB 20515; (202) 225-4761; Fax: 226-0622; Internet: www.house.gov/mcinnis; *Chief of Staff:* Stephannie Finley

District office(s): 132 W. B St., Pueblo 81003; (719) 543-8200; *District Director:* Roger Gomez.

1060 Main Ave., #107, Durango 81301; (970) 259-2754; Fax: (970) 259-2762; *Area Representative:* Debbie Egger.

225 N. 5th St., #702, Grand Junction 81501; (970) 245-7107; Fax: (970) 245-2194; *Area Representative:* Jake Cambrano.

526 Pine St., #112, Glenwood Springs 81601; (970) 928-0637; *Area Representative:* Lynne Kerst.

Committee assignment(s): Rules

MCINTOSH, DAVID M., R-IND. (2)

Capitol Hill office: 1208 LHOB 20515; (202) 225-3021; Fax: (202) 225-3382; Internet: mcintosh@hr.house.gov or www.house.gov/mcintosh; *Administrative Assistant:* Jeff Taylor

District office(s): 2900 W. Jackson St., #101, Muncie 47303; (765) 747-5546; Fax: (765) 747-5586; *District Director:* Jim Huston.

Paramount Centre, 1134 Meridian, Anderson 46016; (800) 382-8655; Fax: (800) 640-2922; *Field Representative:* Kathleen Aherholt.

Committee assignment(s): Education and Workforce; Government Reform and Oversight; Small Business

MCINTYRE, MIKE, D-N.C. (7)

Capitol Hill office: 1605 LHOB 20515; (202) 225-2731; Fax: (202) 225-5773; Internet: congmcintyre@mail.house.gov or www.house.gov/mcintyre; *Chief of Staff:* Dean Mitchell

District office(s): 218 Federal Bldg., Fayetteville 28301; (910) 323-0260; Fax: (910) 323-0069; *District Director:* Judith Kirchman.

208 Post Office Bldg., Wilmington 28401; (910) 815-4959; Fax: (910) 815-4543; *Constituent Service Assistant:* Pamela Campbell-Dereef.

701 N. Elm St., Lumberton 28358; (910) 671-6223; Fax: (910) 739-5085; *District Executive Assistant:* Marie Thompson.

Committee assignment(s): Agriculture; National Security

MCKEON, HOWARD P. "BUCK," R-CALIF. (25)

Capitol Hill office: 307 CHOB 20515; (202) 225-1956; Fax: 226-0683; Internet: tellbuck@mail.house.gov or www.house.gov/mckeon; *Chief of Staff:* Bob Cochran

District office(s): 23929 W. Valencia Blvd., #410, Santa Clarita 91355; (805) 254-2111; Fax: (805) 254-2380.

1008 W. Ave. M-4, Suite D, Palmdale 93551; (805) 948-7833; Fax: (805) 948-0398; *Field Representative:* Kristen Stark.

Committee assignment(s): Education and Workforce; National Security

MCKINNEY, CYNTHIA A., D-GA. (4)

Capitol Hill office: 124 CHOB 20515; (202) 225-1605; Fax: 226-0691; Internet: myck@hr.house.gov or www.house.gov/mckinney; *Chief of Staff:* Gary Cox

District office(s): 246 Sycamore Dr., #110, Decatur 30030; (404) 377-6900; Fax: (404) 377-6909.

Committee assignment(s): International Relations; National Security

MCNULTY, MICHAEL R., D-N.Y. (21)

Capitol Hill office: 2161 RHOB 20515; (202) 225-5076; Fax: (202) 225-5077; Internet: mike.mmcnulty@mail.house.gov or www.house.gov/mcnulty; *Chief of Staff:* Lana Helfrich

District office(s): 9 Market St., Amsterdam 12010; (518) 843-3400; *Secretary:* Elaine DeVito.

33 2nd St., Troy 12180; (518) 271-0822; *Office Manager:* Tom Matthews.

827 Leo W. O'Brien Federal Bldg., Albany 12207; (518) 465-0700; Fax: (518) 427-5107; *Administrative Assistant:* Charles J. Diamond.

29 Jay St., Schenectady 12305; (518) 374-4547; *District Representative:* Bob Carr.

Committee assignment(s): Ways and Means

MEEHAN, MARTIN T., D-MASS. (5)

Capitol Hill office: 2434 RHOB 20515; (202) 225-3411; Fax: 226-0771; Internet: mtmeehan@hr.house.gov or www.house.gov/meehan; *Administrative Assistant:* Will Keyser

District office(s): 255 Main St., #102, Marlborough 01752; (508) 460-9292; Fax: (508) 460-6869; *Congressional Aide:* Chris Doherty.

11 Lawrence St., #806, Lawrence 01840; (508) 681-6200; Fax: (508) 682-6070; *Special Assistant:* Junert Black.

11 Kearney Square, Lowell 01852; (508) 459-0101; Fax: (508) 459-1907; *Special Assistant:* Patti McCafferty.

Committee assignment(s): Judiciary; National Security

MEEK, CARRIE P., D-FLA. (17)

Capitol Hill office: 401 CHOB 20515; (202) 225-4506; Fax: 226-0777; Internet: www.house.gov/meek; *Chief of Staff:* Peggy Demon

District office(s): 25 W. Flagler St., #1015, Miami 33130; (305) 381-9541; Fax: (305) 381-8376.

Committee assignment(s): Appropriations

MEEKS, GREGORY W., D-N.Y. (6)

Capitol Hill office: 1035 LHOB 20515; (202) 225-3461; Fax: 226-4169; *Administrative Assistant:* Shawn Peterson

District office(s): Unavailable.

Committee assignment(s): Banking and Financial Services

MENENDEZ, ROBERT, D-N.J. (13)

Capitol Hill office: 405 CHOB 20515; (202) 225-7919; Fax: 226-0792; Internet: www.house.gov/menendez; *Administrative Assistant:* Michael Hutton

District office(s): 654 Ave. C, Bayonne 07002; (201) 823-2900; *Staff Assistant:* Dennis Collins.

911 Bergen Ave., Jersey City 07302; (201) 222-2828; Fax: (201) 222-0188; *District Director:* Jose Alvarez.

275 Hobart St., Perth Amboy 08861; (908) 324-6212; Fax: (908) 324-7470; *District Director:* Jose Alvarez.

Committee assignment(s): International Relations; Transportation and Infrastructure

METCALF, JACK, R-WASH. (2)

Capitol Hill office: 1510 LHOB 20515; (202) 225-2605; Fax: (202) 225-4420; Internet: www.house.gov/writerep or www.house.gov/metcalf; *Chief of Staff:* Lew Moore

District office(s): 2930 Wetmore Ave., #901, Everett 98201; (206) 252-3188; Fax: (206) 252-6606.

Committee assignment(s): Banking and Financial Services; Transportation and Infrastructure

MICA, JOHN L., R-FLA. (7)

Capitol Hill office: 106 CHOB 20515; (202) 225-4035; Fax: 226-0821; Internet: john.mica@mail.house.gov or www.house.gov/mica/mica.htm; *Chief of Staff:* Russell Roberts

District office(s): 1396 Dunlawton Ave., #2B, Port Orange 32127; (904) 756-9798; Fax: (904) 756-9903; *District Representative:* Greg Davis.

840 Deltona Blvd., Suite G, Deltona 32725; (407) 860-1499; Fax: (407) 860-5730; *District Representative:* C. J. Drake.

1211 Semoran Blvd., #117, Casselberry 32707; (407) 657-8080; Fax: (407) 657-5353; *District Representative:* Dick Harkey.

Committee assignment(s): Government Reform and Oversight; House Oversight; Transportation and Infrastructure

MILLENDER-MCDONALD, JUANITA, D-CALIF. (37)

Capitol Hill office: 419 CHOB 20515; (202) 225-7924; Fax: (202) 225-7926; Internet: millender-mcdonald@mail.house.gov or www.house.gov/millender-mcdonald; *Chief of Staff:* Andrea Martin

District office(s): 970 W. 190th St., #900 E. Tower, Torrence 90502; (310) 538-1190; Fax: (310) 538-9672; *District Director:* Steve Bradford.

Committee assignment(s): Small Business; Transportation and Infrastructure

MILLER, DAN, R-FLA. (13)

Capitol Hill office: 102 CHOB 20515; (202) 225-5015; Fax: 226-0828; Internet: www.house.gov/danmiller; *Chief of Staff:* Marty Reiser

District office(s): 2424 Manatee Ave., #104, Bradenton 34205; (941) 747-9081; Fax: (941) 749-5310; *District Director:* Glenda Wright.

1751 Mound St., #A2, Sarasota 34236; (941) 951-6643; Fax: (941) 951-2972; *District Representative:* Geedee Kerr.

Committee assignment(s): Appropriations; Budget; Government Reform and Oversight

MILLER, GEORGE, D-CALIF. (7)

Capitol Hill office: 2205 RHOB 20515; (202) 225-2095; Internet: george.miller-pub@mail.house.gov or www.house.gov/georgemiller; *Administrative Assistant:* Daniel Weiss

District office(s): 1333 Willow Pass Rd, #203, Concord 94520; (510) 602-1880; *District Director:* David Tucker.

1924 Springs Rd., Vallejo 94591; (707) 645-1888; *Staff Assistant:* Katherine Hoffman.

3220 Blume Dr., #281, Richmond 94806; (510) 262-6500; *Staff Assistant:* Hank Royal.

Committee assignment(s): Education and Workforce; Resources (ranking member)

MINGE, DAVID, D-MINN. (2)

Capitol Hill office: 1415 LHOB 20515; (202) 225-2331; Fax: 226-0836; Internet: www.house.gov/writerep or www.house.gov/minge; *Chief of Staff:* Ross Peterson

District office(s): 108 E. 3rd St., Chaska 55318; (612) 448-6567; *Constituent Services Director:* Jocelyn Batko.

938 4th Ave., Windom 56101; (507) 831-0115; *District Director:* Herb Halvorson.

542 1st St. South, Montevideo 56265; (320) 269-9311; Fax: (320) 269-8651; *Constituent Services Director:* Ruthann Lee.

Committee assignment(s): Agriculture; Budget

MINK, PATSY T., D-HAWAII (2)

Capitol Hill office: 2135 RHOB 20515; (202) 225-4906; Fax: (202) 225-4987; *Office Manager:* Helen E. Lewis

District office(s): 4104 Prince Kuhio Federal Bldg., P.O. Box 50124, Honolulu 96850; (808) 541-1986; Fax: (808) 538-0233; *District Director:* Joan Manke.

Committee assignment(s): Budget; Education and Workforce

MOAKLEY, JOE, D-MASS. (9)

Capitol Hill office: 235 CHOB 20515; (202) 225-8273; Fax: (202) 225-3984; Internet: jmoakley@mail.house.gov or www.house.gov/moakely; *Chief of Staff:* Kevin Ryan

District office(s): World Trade Center, #220, Boston 02210; (617) 565-2920; Fax: (617) 439-5157; *District Director:* Frederick W. Clark.

166 Main St., Brockton 02401; (508) 586-5555; Fax: (508) 580-4692; *Staff Assistant:* John Montagano.

4 Court St., Taunton 02780; (617) 824-6676; Fax: (617) 880-3520; *Congressional Assistant:* Karen Harraghy.

Committee assignment(s): Rules (ranking member)

MOLLOHAN, ALAN B., D-W.VA. (1)

Capitol Hill office: 2346 RHOB 20515; (202) 225-4172; Fax: (202) 225-7564; *Chief of Staff:* Liz Whyte

District office(s): 1125 Chapline St., #315, Wheeling 26003; (304) 232-5390; Fax: (304) 232-5722; *Area Representative:* Cathy Abraham.

425 Juliana St., #4311, P.O. Box 145, Parkersburg 26102; (304) 428-0493; Fax: (304) 428-5980; *Area Representative:* Betsy Moore.

500 W. Pike St., #209, P.O. Box 1400, Clarksburg 26302; (304) 623-4422; Fax: (304) 623-0571; *Area Representative:* Ann Marie Merandi.

Federal Bldg., Morgantown 26505; (304) 292-3019; Fax: (304) 292-3027; *Area Representative:* Lotta Neer.

Committee assignment(s): Appropriations; Budget

MORAN, JAMES P., D-VA. (8)

Capitol Hill office: 1214 LHOB 20515; (202) 225-4376; Fax: (202) 225-0017; Internet: jim.moran@mail.house.gov or www.house.gov/moran; *Chief of Staff:* Paul Reagan

District office(s): 5115B Franconia Rd., Alexandria 22310; (703) 971-4700; Fax: (703) 922-9436; *District Director:* Susie Warner.

Committee assignment(s): Appropriations

MORAN, JERRY, R-KAN. (1)

Capitol Hill office: 1217 LHOB 20515; (202) 225-2715; Fax: (202) 225-5124; Internet: jerry.moran@mail.house.gov or www.house.gov/moranks01; *Administrative Assistant:* Tom Hemmer

District office(s): #203, Davis Hall, Fort Hays State University, Hays 67601; (913) 628-6401; Fax: (913) 628-3791; *Constituent Services Representative:* Karla Werth.

P.O. Box 1128, Hutchinson 67504; (316) 665-6138; Fax: (316) 665-6360.

Committee assignment(s): Agriculture; Transportation and Infrastructure; Veterans' Affairs

MORELLA, CONSTANCE A., R-MD. (8)

Capitol Hill office: 2228 RHOB 20515; (202) 225-5341; Fax: (202) 225-1389; Internet: rep.morella@mail. house.gov or www.house.gov/morella; *Chief of Staff:* Bill Miller

District office(s): 51 Monroe St., #507, Rockville 20850; (301) 424-3501; Fax: (301) 424-5992; *District Director:* Minnie Anderson.

Committee assignment(s): Government Reform and Oversight; Science

MURTHA, JOHN P., D-PA. (12)

Capitol Hill office: 2423 RHOB 20515; (202) 225-2065; Internet: murtha@mail.house.gov or www.house. gov/murtha; *Executive Assistant:* Bill Allen

District office(s): P.O. Box 780, Johnstown 15907; (814) 535-2642; Fax: (814) 539-6229; *District Administrative Assistant:* John A. Hugya.

Committee assignment(s): Appropriations

MYRICK, SUE, R-N.C. (9)

Capitol Hill office: 230 CHOB 20515; (202) 225-1976; Fax: (202) 225-3389; Internet: myrick@mail.house. gov or www.house.gov/myrick; *Administrative Assistant:* Dave Redmond

District office(s): 224 S. New Hope Rd., Suite H, Gastonia 28054; (704) 861-1976; Fax: (704) 864-2445; *Assistant District Director:* Jason Bradley.

1901 Roxborough Rd., Charlotte 28211; (704) 362-1060; Fax: (704) 367-0852; *District Director:* Hal Weatherman.

Committee assignment(s): Rules

NADLER, JERROLD, D-N.Y. (8)

Capitol Hill office: 2448 RHOB 20515; (202) 225-5635; Fax: (202) 225-6923; Internet: jerrold.nadler@mail. house.gov or www.house.gov/nadler; *Chief of Staff:* Amy Green

District office(s): 11 Beach St., #910, New York 10013; (212) 334-3207; Fax: (212) 334-5259; *District Administrator:* Linda Rosenthal.

532 Neptune Ave., Brooklyn 11224; (718) 373-3198; *Brooklyn Director:* Bradley Korn.

Committee assignment(s): Judiciary; Transportation and Infrastructure

NEAL, RICHARD E., D-MASS. (2)

Capitol Hill office: 2236 RHOB 20515; (202) 225-5601; Fax: (202) 225-8112; Internet: www.house.gov/neal; *Administrative Assistant:* Ann Brozek-Jablon

District office(s): 1550 Main St., Springfield 01103; (413) 785-0325; Fax: (413) 747-0604; *Administrative Assistant:* James B. Leydon.

4 Congress St., P.O. Box 216, Milford 01757; (508) 634-8198; Fax: (508) 634-8398; *Staff Assistant:* Virginia Purcell.

Committee assignment(s): Ways and Means

NETHERCUTT, GEORGE R., JR., R-WASH. (5)

Capitol Hill office: 1527 LHOB 20515; (202) 225-2006; Fax: (202) 225-3392; Internet: george. nethercutt-pub@mail.house.gov or www.house. gov/nethercutt; *Chief of Staff:* Edward Feddeman

District office(s): W. 920 Riverside, #594, Spokane 99201; (509) 353-2374; Fax: (509) 353-2412; *District Director:* Mike Gruber.

Committee assignment(s): Appropriations; Science

NEUMANN, MARK W., R-WIS. (1)

Capitol Hill office: 415 CHOB 20515; (202) 225-3031; Fax: (202) 225-3393; Internet: mneumann@mail. house.gov or www.house.gov/neumann; *Chief of Staff:* Chuck Pike

District office(s): 1 Parker Place, #495, Janesville 53545; (608) 752-4050; Fax: (608) 752-4711; *District Director:* Scot Hudson.

Committee assignment(s): Appropriations; Budget

NEY, BOB, R-OHIO (18)

Capitol Hill office: 1024 LHOB 20515; (202) 225-6265; Fax: (202) 225-3394; Internet: www.house.gov/ney; *Chief of Staff:* Dave DiStefano

District office(s): 3201 Belmont St., #604, Bellaire 43906; (614) 676-1960; Fax: (614) 676-1983; *District Director:* Joseph Rose.

401 Market St., #719, Steubenville 43952; (614) 283-3716; Fax: (614) 283-1915; *Office Manager:* Dennis Watson.

38 N. 4th St., #502, Zanesville 43701; (614) 452-7023; Fax: (614) 452-7191; *Casework Manager:* Joe Miller.

Committee assignment(s): Banking and Financial Services; House Oversight; Transportation and Infrastructure; Joint Library; Joint Printing

NORTHUP, ANNE M., R-KY. (3)

Capitol Hill office: 1004 LHOB 20515; (202) 225-5401; Fax: (202) 225-5776; *Chief of Staff:* Terry Carmack

District office(s): 600 Martin Luther King Jr. Pl., #216, Louisville 40202; (502) 582-5129; Fax: (502) 582-5897; *District Director:* Sherry Craig.

Committee assignment(s): Appropriations

NORTON, ELEANOR HOLMES, D-D.C. (AL)

Capitol Hill office: 1424 LHOB 20515; (202) 225-8050; Fax: (202) 225-3002; Internet: www.house.gov/ norton; *Chief of Staff:* Donna Brazile

District office(s): 815 15th St. N.W., #100, Washington 20005; (202) 783-5065; Fax: (202) 783-5211; *Constituent Services Coordinator:* Cherry Gillis.

2101 Martin Luther King, Jr. Ave. S.E., Washington 20020; (202) 678-8900; Fax: (202) 678-8844; *Caseworker:* Edward Cartwright Moore.

Committee assignment(s): Government Reform and Oversight; Transportation and Infrastructure

NORWOOD, CHARLIE, R-GA. (1)

Capitol Hill office: 1707 LHOB 20515; (202) 225-4101; Fax: (202) 225-0279; Internet: www.house.gov/ writerep or www.house.gov/norwood; *Chief of Staff:* John S. Walker

District office(s): 1056 Claussen Rd., #226, Augusta 30907; (706) 733-7066; Fax: (706) 733-7725; *District Director:* Michael Shaffer.

1776 N. Jefferson St., Suite B, Milledgeville 31061; (912) 453-0373; Fax: (912) 453-7302: Tanya Reding.

101 N. Jefferson St., #109, Dublin 31021; (912) 275-2814; Fax: (912) 275-2063: Tanya Reding.

Committee assignment(s): Commerce; Education and Workforce

NUSSLE, JIM, R-IOWA (2)

Capitol Hill office: 303 CHOB 20515; (202) 225-2911; Fax: (202) 225-9129; Internet: nussleia@mail. house.gov or www.house.gov/nussle; *Chief of Staff:* Rich Meade

District office(s): 23 3rd St. N.W., Mason City 50401; (515) 423-0303; *District Representative:* Dan McGuire.

3641 Kimball Ave., Waterloo 50702; (319) 235-1109; *District Representative:* Chad Dennie.

2255 John F. Kennedy Rd., Dubuque 52002; (319) 557-7740; *District Representative:* Kathy Reed.

712 W. Main St., Manchester 52057; (319) 927-5141; *District Administrator:* Cheryl Madlom.

Committee assignment(s): Budget; Ways and Means

OBERSTAR, JAMES L., D-MINN. (8)

Capitol Hill office: 2366 RHOB 20515; (202) 225-6211; Fax: (202) 225-0699; Internet: oberstar@mail.house. gov or www.house.gov/oberstar; *Administrative Assistant:* William G. Richard

District office(s): 13065 Orono Parkway, Elk River 55330; (612) 241-0188; Fax: (612) 241-0233; *Staff Assistant:* Ken Hasskamp.

316 Lake St., Chisholm 55719; (218) 254-5761; Fax: (218) 254-5132; *Staff Assistant:* Jacquelyn Hirvela.

501 Laurel St., Brainerd 56401; (218) 828-4400; Fax: (218) 828-1412; *Staff Assistant:* Ken Hasskamp.

515 W. 1st St., #231, Duluth 55802; (218) 727-7474; Fax: (218) 727-8270; *District Office Director:* Jackie Morris.

Committee assignment(s): Transportation and Infrastructure (ranking member)

OBEY, DAVID R., D-WIS. (7)

Capitol Hill office: 2462 RHOB 20515; (202) 225-3365; *Staff Director:* William Stone

District office(s): 317 1st St., Wausau 54401; (715) 842-5606; *District Representative:* Jerry M. Madison.

Committee assignment(s): Appropriations (ranking member)

OLVER, JOHN W., D-MASS. (1)

Capitol Hill office: 1027 LHOB 20515; (202) 225-5335; Fax: 226-1224; Internet: john.olver@mail.house.gov or www.house.gov/olver; *Chief of Staff:* R. Hunter Ridgway

District office(s): 490 Westfield Rd., Holyoke 01040; (413) 532-7010; Fax: (413) 532-6543.

78 Center St., Pittsfield 01201; (413) 442-0946; Fax: (413) 443-2792; *District Director:* Deborah Guachione.

463 Main St., Fitchburg 01420; (508) 342-8722; Fax: (508) 343-8156.

Committee assignment(s): Appropriations

ORTIZ, SOLOMON P., D-TEXAS (27)

Capitol Hill office: 2136 RHOB 20515; (202) 225-7742; Fax: 226-1134; *Chief of Staff:* Florencio Rendon

District office(s): 3649 Leopard St., #510, Corpus Christi 78408; (512) 883-5868; Fax: (512) 884-9201; *Office Manager:* Gerald Sawyer.

3505 Boca Chica Blvd., #200, Brownsville 78521; (210) 541-1242; Fax: (210) 544-6915; *District Director:* Denise Blanchard.

Committee assignment(s): National Security; Resources

OWENS, MAJOR R., D-N.Y. (11)

Capitol Hill office: 2305 RHOB 20515; (202) 225-6231; Fax: 226-0112; *Administrative Assistant:* Jacqueline Ellis

District office(s): 289 Utica Ave., Brooklyn 11213; (718) 773-3100; Fax: (718) 735-7143; *District Director:* Fred Price.

Committee assignment(s): Education and Workforce; Government Reform and Oversight

OXLEY, MICHAEL G., R-OHIO (4)

Capitol Hill office: 2233 RHOB 20515; (202) 225-2676; Internet: mike.oxley@mail.house.gov or www.house. gov/oxley; *Chief of Staff:* Jim Conzelman

District office(s): 24 W. 3rd St., #314, Mansfield 44902; (419) 522-5757; *District Representative:* R. Philip Holloway.

3121 W. Elm Plaza, Lima 45805; (419) 999-6455; *District Representative:* Kelly Kirk.

100 E. Main Cross St., Findlay 45840; (419) 423-3210; *District Representative:* Bonnie Dunbar.

Committee assignment(s): Commerce

PACKARD, RON, R-CALIF. (48)

Capitol Hill office: 2372 RHOB 20515; (202) 225-3906; Fax: (202) 225-0134; Internet: rep.packard@mail. house.gov or www.house.gov/packard; *Chief of Staff:* Ray Mock

District office(s): 221 E. Vista Way, #205, Vista 92084; (760) 631-1364; Fax: (760) 631-1367; *District Director:* Don Polese.

629 Camino de los Mares, #204, San Clemente 92673; (714) 496-2343; Fax: (714) 496-2988; *District Representative:* Wyatt Hart.

Committee assignment(s): Appropriations

PALLONE, FRANK, JR., D-N.J. (6)

Capitol Hill office: 420 CHOB 20515; (202) 225-4671; Fax: (202) 225-9665; *Administrative Assistant:* Timothy J. Yehl

District office(s): I.E.I. Airport Plaza, #104, Hwy. 36, Hazlet 07730; (732) 264-9104; Fax: (732) 739-4668; *Staff Assistant:* Paul Dement.

504 Broadway, #118, Long Branch 07740; (732) 571-1140; Fax: (732) 870-3890; *District Director:* Michael Beson.

67/69 Church St., New Brunswick 08901; (732) 249-8892; Fax: (732) 249-1335; *District Representative:* Jim McCann.

Committee assignment(s): Commerce; Resources

PAPPAS, MICHAEL, R-N.J. (12)

Capitol Hill office: 1710 LHOB 20515; (202) 225-5801; Fax: (202) 225-6025; Internet: pappas@mail.house. gov or www.house.gov/pappas; *Administrative Assistant:* Jeff Krilla

District office(s): 8 Main St., Flemington 08822; (908) 284-1138; Fax: (908) 284-2577; *District Director:* Diane Naar.

3 Broad St., Freehold 07728; (908) 462-8499; Fax: (908) 462-8467; *Senior Staff Assistant:* Phyllis Deroian.

Committee assignment(s): Government Reform and Oversight; National Security; Small Business

PARKER, MIKE, R-MISS. (4)

Capitol Hill office: 2445 RHOB 20515; (202) 225-5865; Fax: (202) 225-5886; Internet: www.house.gov/ parker; *Chief of Staff:* Arthur D. Rhodes

District office(s): 176 W. Court Ave., Mendenhall 39114; (601) 847-0873; *Economic Development Liaison:* Malone Bryant.

118 N. Pearl St., #111, Natchez 39120; (601) 446-7250; *Staff Assistant:* Connie Merrick.

245 E. Capitol St., #222, Jackson 39201; (601) 352-1355; Fax: (601) 352-9044; *Executive Administrative Assistant:* Ed Cole.

250 Broad St., Columbia 39429; (601) 731-1622; *Community Develop. Liaison:* Rick Hux.

728 1/2 Sawmill Rd., Laurel 39440; (601) 425-4999; *Staff Assistant:* Donna Gibbes.

230 S. Whitworth St., Brookhaven 39601; (601) 835-0706; *Staff Assistant:* Carol Games.

Committee assignment(s): Appropriations; Budget

PASCRELL, BILL, JR., D-N.J. (8)

Capitol Hill office: 1722 LHOB 20515; (202) 225-5751; Internet: www.house.gov/pascrell; *Chief of Staff:* Thomas J. Edwards

District office(s): 200 Federal Plaza, Paterson 07505; (973) 523-5152; Fax: (973) 523-0637: Bill Maer.

Committee assignment(s): Small Business; Transportation and Infrastructure

PASTOR, ED, D-ARIZ. (2)

Capitol Hill office: 2465 RHOB 20515; (202) 225-4065; Fax: (202) 225-1655; Internet: ed.pastor@mail.house. gov or www.house.gov/pastor; *Administrative Assistant:* Laura Campos

District office(s): 802 N. 3rd Ave., Phoenix 85003; (602) 256-0551; Fax: (602) 257-9103; *District Director:* Ron Piceno.

281 W. 24th St., #118, Yuma 85364; (520) 726-2234; Fax: (520) 726-2235; *Caseworker:* Charlene Fernandez.

2432 E. Broadway Blvd., Tucson 85716; (520) 624-9986; Fax: (520) 624-3872; *S. Arizona Director:* Linda Leatherman.

Committee assignment(s): Appropriations; Standards of Official Conduct

PAUL, RON, R-TEXAS (14)

Capitol Hill office: 203 CHOB 20515; (202) 225-2831; Fax: 226-4871; Internet: rep.paul@mail.house.gov or www.house.gov/paul; *Chief of Staff:* Tom Lizardo

District office(s): 200 W. 2nd, #210, Freeport 77547; (409) 230-0000; Fax: (409) 230-0030; *District Representative:* Eric Rittberg.

312 W. Main, Victoria 77901; (512) 576-1231; Fax: (512) 576-0381; *District Representative:* Jackie Glour.

301 Guadalupe, #105, San Marcos 78666; (512) 396-1400; Fax: (512) 396-1434.

Committee assignment(s): Banking and Financial Services; Education and Workforce

PAXON, BILL, R-N.Y. (27)

Capitol Hill office: 2412 RHOB 20515; (202) 225-5265; Fax: (202) 225-5910; Internet: rep.paxon@mail.house. gov or www.house.gov/paxon; *Chief of Staff:* David Marventano

District office(s): 5500 Main St., Williamsville 14221; (716) 634-2324; Fax: (716) 631-7610; *Chief of Staff:* Michael J. Hook.

10 E. Main St., Victor 14564; (716) 742-1600; Fax: (716) 742-1976; *Staff Assistant:* John Haldow.

Committee assignment(s): Commerce

PAYNE, DONALD M., D-N.J. (1)

Capitol Hill office: 2244 RHOB 20515; (202) 225-3436; Fax: (202) 225-4160; Internet: donald.payne@mail. house.gov or www.house.gov/payne; *Administrative Assistant:* Maxine James

District office(s): 50 Walnut St., Newark 07102; (973) 645-3213; Fax: (973) 645-5902; *District Representative:* Robert Cottingham.

333 N. Broad St., Elizabeth 07208; (908) 629-0222; Fax: (908) 629-0221; *Caseworker:* Louis Copeland.

Committee assignment(s): Education and Workforce; International Relations

PEASE, ED, R-IND. (7)

Capitol Hill office: 226 CHOB 20515; (202) 225-5805; Internet: www.house.gov/pease; *Chief of Staff:* Bill Maxam

District office(s): 1071 Federal Bldg., Terre Haute 47808; (812) 238-1619; Fax: (812) 238-5638; *Constituent Representative:* Brandie Davis.

107 Charles A. Halleck Federal Bldg., Lafayette 47901; (765) 423-1661; Fax: (765) 423-2808; *Constituent Representative:* Steve Luts.

355 S. Washington St., Danville 46122; (317) 718-0307; Fax: (317) 718-0310; *Constituent Representative:* Dennis Campbell.

Committee assignment(s): Judiciary; Transportation and Infrastructure

PELOSI, NANCY, D-CALIF. (8)

Capitol Hill office: 2457 RHOB 20515; (202) 225-4965; Fax: (202) 225-8259; Internet: sf.nancy@mail.house. gov or www.house.gov/pelosi; *Administrative Assistant:* Judith Lemons

District office(s): 450 Golden Gate Ave., #145378, San Francisco 94102; (415) 556-4862; Fax: (415) 861-1670; *District Representative:* Fred Ross.

Committee assignment(s): Appropriations; Select Intelligence

PETERSON, COLLIN C., D-MINN. (7)

Capitol Hill office: 2159 RHOB 20515; (202) 225-2165; Internet: tocollin.peterson@mail.house.gov or www. house.gov/collinpeterson; *Administrative Assistant:* Mark Brownell

District office(s): 110 2nd St. South, #112, Waite Park 56387; (320) 259-0559; Fax: (320) 259-0413; *Staff Assistant:* Mary Bertram.

714 Lake Ave., #107, Detroit Lakes 56501; (218) 847-5056; *Staff Assistant:* Sharon Josephson.

2603 Wheat Dr., Red Lake Falls 56750; (218) 253-4356; Fax: (218) 253-4373; *Staff Assistant:* Deb Hams.

Committee assignment(s): Agriculture; Veterans' Affairs

PETERSON, JOHN E., R-PA. (5)

Capitol Hill office: 1020 LHOB 20515; (202) 225-5121; *Administrative Assistant:* Bob Ferguson

District office(s): 115 W. Spring St., Titusville 16354; (814) 827-3985; Fax: (814) 827-7307; *District Director:* Peter Winkler.

1524 W. College Ave., State College 16801; (814) 238-1776; Fax: (814) 238-1918; *Office Manager:* Lugene Keys.

224 Liberty St., #3, Warren 16365; (814) 726-3910; *Field Representative:* Leota Mack.

Committee assignment(s): Education and Workforce; Resources

PETRI, TOM, R-WIS. (6)

Capitol Hill office: 2262 RHOB 20515; (202) 225-2476; Fax: (202) 225-2356; Internet: tompetri@mail.house. gov or www.house.gov/petri; *Administrative Assistant:* Joseph Flader

District office(s): 115 Washington Ave., Oshkosh 54901; (920) 231-6333; Fax: (920) 231-0464; *Staff Assistant:* Frank Frassetto.

490 W. Rolling Meadows Dr., Fond du Lac 54937; (920) 922-1180; Fax: (920) 922-4498; *District Director:* Sue Kerkman-Jung.

Committee assignment(s): Education and Workforce; Transportation and Infrastructure

PICKERING, CHARLES W. "CHIP," JR., R-MISS. (3)

Capitol Hill office: 427 CHOB 20515; (202) 225-5031; Fax: (202) 225-5797; Internet: c.pickering@mail. house.gov or www.house.gov/pickering; *Chief of Staff:* Susan Connell

District office(s): 110-D Airport Rd., Pearl 39208; (601) 932-2410; Fax: (601) 965-4598; *Deputy District Director:* Kathy Henry.

2100 9th St., #302, Meridian 39301; (601) 693-6681; Fax: (601) 693-1801; *Special Assistant:* Carol Mabry.

Golden Triangle Airport, 2080 Airport Rd., Suite D, Columbus 39701; (601) 327-2766; Fax: (601) 328-4570; *Special Assistant:* Hank Moseley.

Committee assignment(s): Agriculture; Science; Transportation and Infrastructure

PICKETT, OWEN B., D-VA. (2)

Capitol Hill office: 2430 RHOB 20515; (202) 225-4215; Fax: (202) 225-4218; Internet: owen.pickett@mail. house.gov or www.house.gov/pickett; *Administrative Assistant:* Jeanne Evans

District office(s): 2710 Virginia Beach Blvd., Virginia Beach 23452; (757) 486-3710; Fax: (757) 498-8253; *Constituent Service Manager:* Kathy Vaughan.

112 E. Little Creek Rd., Norfolk 23505; (757) 583-5892; Fax: (757) 622-4038; *Constituent Service Manager:* Julia Jacobs-Hopkins.

Committee assignment(s): National Security; Resources

PITTS, JOSEPH R., R-PA. (16)

Capitol Hill office: 504 CHOB 20515; (202) 225-2411; Internet: pitts.pa16@mail.house.gov or www.house. gov/pitts; *Chief of Staff:* Bill Wichterman

District office(s): 50 N. Duke St., Lancaster 17602; (717) 393-0667; *District Director:* Tom Tillett.

36 W. Lancaster Ave., Downingtown 19335; (610) 518-5823; *District Representative:* Gabe Neville.

P.O. Box 837, Unionville 19375; (610) 429-1540; *District Representative:* Dot Willsie.

Committee assignment(s): Budget; Small Business; Transportation and Infrastructure

POMBO, RICHARD W., R-CALIF. (11)

Capitol Hill office: 1519 LHOB 20515; (202) 225-1947; Fax: 226-0861; Internet: rpombo@mail.house.gov or www.house.gov/pombo/pombo.htm; *Chief of Staff:* Steve Ding

District office(s): 2495 W. March Lane, #104, Stockton 95207; (209) 951-3091; Fax: (209) 951-1910; *District Director:* Stephen Reid.

3348 Mather Field Rd., Suite A, Sacramento 95670; (916) 361-1681; *District Representative:* Dave Calhoun.

Committee assignment(s): Agriculture; Resources

POMEROY, EARL, D-N.D. (AL)

Capitol Hill office: 1533 LHOB 20515; (202) 225-2611; Fax: 226-0893; Internet: rep.earl.pomeroy@mail. house.gov; *Chief of Staff:* Karen Frederickson

District office(s): 657 2nd Ave. North, #266, Fargo 58102; (701) 235-9760; Fax: (701) 235-9767; *Eastern Field Director:* Joan Carlson.

220 E. Rosser Ave., #376, Bismarck 58501; (701) 224-0355; Fax: (701) 224-0431; *State Director:* Gail Skaley.

Committee assignment(s): Agriculture; Budget

PORTER, JOHN EDWARD, R-ILL. (1)

Capitol Hill office: 2373 RHOB 20515; (202) 225-4835; Internet: www.house.gov/writerep or www.house. gov/porter; *Administrative Assistant:* Rob Bradner

District office(s): 115 N. Arlington Heights Rd., Arlington Heights 60004; (847) 392-0303; Fax: (847) 392-5774; *Caseworker:* Mary Beth Hartman.

102 Wilmot Rd., #200, Deerfield 60015; (847) 940-0202; Fax: (847) 940-7143; *Chief of Staff:* Ginny Hotaling.

18 N. County St., #601-A, Waukegan 60085; (847) 662-0101; Fax: (847) 662-7519; *Caseworker:* Dee Jay Davis.

Committee assignment(s): Appropriations

PORTMAN, ROB, R-OHIO (2)

Capitol Hill office: 238 CHOB 20515; (202) 225-3164; Fax: (202) 225-1992; Internet: portmail@mail.house. gov or www.house.gov/portman; *Chief of Staff:* John Bridgeland

District office(s): 175 E. Main St., Batavia 45103; (513) 732-2948; Fax: (513) 732-3196; *District Representative:* Helen Hiestano.

8044 Montgomery Rd., #540, Cincinnati 45236; (513) 791-0381; Fax: (513) 791-1696; *District Office Manager:* Gloria Griffiths.

Committee assignment(s): Ways and Means

POSHARD, GLENN, D-ILL. (19)

Capitol Hill office: 2334 RHOB 20515; (202) 225-5201; Fax: (202) 225-1541; *Administrative Assistant:* David Gilles

District office(s): 600 Airport Rd., Mattoon 61938; (217) 234-7032; *Staff Assistant:* Shane Rogers.

444 S. Willow St., Effingham 62401; (217) 342-7220; Fax: (217) 347-5014; *Staff Assistant:* Sam Medernach.

606 N. 13th St., #1, Lawrenceville 62439; (618) 943-6036; *Staff Assistant:* Shirley Stevenson.

363 S. Main St., Decatur 62521; (217) 362-9011; *Staff Assistant:* Robin Bolin.

201 E. Nolen St., W. Frankfort 62896; (618) 937-6402; *Staff Assistant:* James Kirkpatrick.

New Route 13 West, Marion 62959; (618) 993-8532; *District Office Manager:* Judy Hampton.

Committee assignment(s): Small Business; Transportation and Infrastructure

PRICE, DAVID E., D-N.C. (4)

Capitol Hill office: 2162 RHOB 20515; (202) 225-1784; Fax: (202) 225-2014; Internet: david.price@mail. house.gov; *Administrative Assistant:* Billy Moore

District office(s): 225 Hillsborough St., #490, Raleigh 27603; (919) 832-2456; Fax: (919) 832-2559; *District Director:* Rose Auman.

1777 Fordham Blvd., Chapel Hill 27514; (919) 967-7924; Fax: (919) 967-8324; *Constituent Services:* Gay Eddy.

Committee assignment(s): Appropriations; Banking and Financial Services

PRYCE, DEBORAH, R-OHIO (15)

Capitol Hill office: 221 CHOB 20515; (202) 225-2015; Internet: pryce@mail.house.gov or www.house.gov/pryce; *Chief of Staff:* Tim Day

District office(s): 500 S. Front St., #1130, Columbus 43215; (614) 469-5614; Fax: (614) 469-6937; *District Director:* Marcee C. McCreary.

Committee assignment(s): Rules

QUINN, JACK, R-N.Y. (3)

Capitol Hill office: 331 CHOB 20515; (202) 225-3306; Fax: 226-0347

District office(s): 403 Main St., #510, Buffalo 14203; (716) 845-5257; Fax: (716) 847-0323.

Committee assignment(s): Transportation and Infrastructure; Veterans' Affairs

RADANOVICH, GEORGE P., R-CALIF. (19)

Capitol Hill office: 213 CHOB 20515; (202) 225-4540; Fax: (202) 225-3402; Internet: george.radanovich@mail.house.gov or www.house.gov/radanovich; *Administrative Assistant:* John McCamman

District office(s): 2377 W. Shaw St., #105, Fresno 93711; (209) 248-0800; Fax: (209) 248-0169; *Field Director:* Steve Samuelian.

Committee assignment(s): Budget; Resources

RAHALL, NICK J., II, D-W.VA. (3)

Capitol Hill office: 2307 RHOB 20515; (202) 225-3452; Fax: (202) 225-9061; Internet: nrahall@mail.house.gov; *Administrative Assistant:* Kent Keyser

District office(s): 601 Federal St., #1005, Bluefield 24701; (304) 325-6222; Fax: (304) 325-0552; *Community Relations:* Deborah Stevens.

101 N. Court St., Lewisburg 24901; (304) 647-3228; Fax: (304) 647-3304; *Community Relations:* Kelly Dyke.

R. K. Bldg., Logan 25601; (304) 752-4934; Fax: (304) 752-8797; *Community Relations:* Debrina Workman.

815 5th Ave., Huntington 25701; (304) 522-6425; *District Representative:* Randy Cheetham.

110 1/2 Main St., Beckley 25801; (304) 252-5000; Fax: (304) 252-9083; *District Representative:* Dick Nevi.

Committee assignment(s): Resources; Transportation and Infrastructure

RAMSTAD, JIM, R-MINN. (3)

Capitol Hill office: 103 CHOB 20515; (202) 225-2871; Fax: (202) 225-6351; Internet: mn03@hr.house.gov or www.house.gov/ramstad; *Chief of Staff:* Dean Peterson

District office(s): 8120 Penn Ave. South, #152, Bloomington 55431; (612) 881-4600; Fax: (612) 881-1943; *Office Director:* Shari Nichols.

Committee assignment(s): Ways and Means

RANGEL, CHARLES B., D-N.Y. (15)

Capitol Hill office: 2354 RHOB 20515; (202) 225-4365; Fax: (202) 225-0816; Internet: www.house.gov/writerep; *Executive Assistant:* Patricia Bradley

District office(s): 163 W. 125th St., New York City 10027; (212) 663-3900; Fax: (212) 663-4277; *District Administrator:* Vivian Jones.

2110 1st Ave., New York City 10029; (212) 348-9630; Fax: (212) 423-0489; *Caseworker:* Juanita A. Laugier.

Committee assignment(s): Ways and Means (ranking member); Joint Taxation

REDMOND, BILL, R-N.M. (3)

Capitol Hill office: 2268 RHOB 20515; (202) 225-6190; Fax: 226-1331; *Chief of Staff:* Cathy Jewell

District office(s): 1494 S. Saint Francis Dr., Santa Fe 87505; (505) 988-7230; Fax: (505) 988-7296; *District Director:* Mike Burita.

3900 Southern Blvd. #101C, Rio Rancho 87124; (505) 892-0901; Fax: (505) 892-5387; *Constituent Liaison:* Kelly Holbrook.

800 Municipal Dr., Farmington 87401; (505) 599-1460; Fax: (505) 599-2463; *Field Representative:* Erik Ness.

321 Connelly, P.O. Box 1108, Clovis 88102; (505) 769-1223; Fax: (505) 769-1225; *District Representative:* Dennis Roch.

Committee assignment(s): Banking and Financial Services; National Security; Veterans' Affairs

REGULA, RALPH, R-OHIO (16)

Capitol Hill office: 2309 RHOB 20515; (202) 225-3876; Fax: (202) 225-3059; Internet: www.house.gov/regula; *Chief of Staff:* Connie Veillette

District office(s): 4150 Belden Village St. N.W., #408, Canton 44718; (330) 489-4414; Fax: (330) 489-4448; *District Staff Director:* Daryl Revoldt.

Committee assignment(s): Appropriations

REYES, SILVESTRE, D-TEXAS (16)

Capitol Hill office: 514 CHOB 20515; (202) 225-4831; Fax: (202) 225-6015; Internet: silvestrereyes@mail.house.gov or www.house.gov/reyes; *Chief of Staff:* Enrique Gallegos

District office(s): 310 N. Mesa, #400, El Paso 79901; (915) 534-4400; Fax: (915) 534-7426; *District Director:* Irma Sanchez.

Committee assignment(s): National Security; Veterans' Affairs

RIGGS, FRANK, R-CALIF. (1)

Capitol Hill office: 1714 LHOB 20515; (202) 225-3311; Internet: repriggs@hr.house.gov or www.house.gov/riggs; *Chief of Staff:* Beau Phillips

District office(s): 1700 2nd St., #378, Napa 94559; (707) 254-7308; *Southern District Director:* Darrell Shull.

710 E St., #100, Eureka 95501; (707) 441-8701; *Northern District Office Manager:* Vee Sorenson.

Committee assignment(s): Education and Workforce; Transportation and Infrastructure

RILEY, BOB, R-ALA. (3)

Capitol Hill office: 510 CHOB 20515; (202) 225-3261; Fax: (202) 225-5827; Internet: bob.riley@mail.house.gov or www.house.gov/riley; *Chief of Staff:* Earl Whipple

District office(s): 1129 Noble St., #104, Anniston 36201; (205) 236-5655; Fax: (205) 237-9203; *District Director:* Duane Higgins.

107 Federal Bldg., 7th and Ave. A, Opelika 36801; (334) 745-6222; Fax: (334) 742-0109; *Field Representative:* Thomas Casson.

Committee assignment(s): Banking and Financial Services; National Security

RIVERS, LYNN, D-MICH. (13)

Capitol Hill office: 1724 LHOB 20515; (202) 225-6261; Fax: (202) 225-3404; Internet: www.house.gov/writerep or www.house.gov/rivers; *Administrative Assistant:* Gayle Boesky

District office(s): 106 E. Washington St., Ann Arbor 48104; (313) 741-4210; Fax: (313) 742-4214; *District Director:* Marsha Lewis.

Federal Bldg., Wayne 48184; (313) 722-1418; Fax: (313) 722-1418; *District Director:* Marsha Lewis.

Committee assignment(s): Budget; Science

RODRIGUEZ, CIRO D., D-TEXAS (28)

Capitol Hill office: 323 CHOB 20515; (202) 225-1640; Fax: (202) 225-1641; *Chief of Staff:* Jeff Mendelsohn

District office(s): 1313 Southeast Military Dr., #119, San Antonio 78214; (210) 924-7383; Fax: (210) 927-6222; *District Director:* Norma Reyes.

202 E. St. Joseph, #5, San Diego 78384; (512) 279-3907; Fax: (512) 279-8117; *District Representative:* J. M. Rodriguez.

301 Lincoln St., Roma 78584; (956) 847-1111; Fax: (956) 849-1415; *District Representative:* Norma Pena.

Committee assignment(s): National Security; Veterans' Affairs

ROEMER, TIM, D-IND. (3)

Capitol Hill office: 2348 RHOB 20515; (202) 225-3915; Fax: (202) 225-6798; Internet: tim.roemer@mail.house.gov or www.house.gov/roemer; *Administrative Assistant:* Mark Brown

District office(s): 217 N. Main St., S. Bend 46601; (219) 288-3301; Fax: (219) 288-0527; *District Director:* Julie Vuckovich.

Committee assignment(s): Education and Workforce; Science

ROGAN, JAMES E., R-CALIF. (27)

Capitol Hill office: 502 CHOB 20515; (202) 225-4176; Fax: (202) 225-5828; Internet: www.house.gov/rogan; *Administrative Assistant:* Greg Mitchell

District office(s): 199 S. Los Robles Ave., #560, Pasadena 91101; (626) 577-3969; Fax: (626) 577-5588; *District Director:* Denise Milinkovich.

Committee assignment(s): Commerce; Judiciary

ROGERS, HAROLD, R-KY. (5)

Capitol Hill office: 2468 RHOB 20515; (202) 225-4601; Fax: (202) 225-0940; Internet: www.house.gov/rogers; *Administrative Assistant:* Kevin Fromer

District office(s): 806 Hambley Blvd., Pikeville 41501; (606) 432-4388; Fax: (606) 432-4262; *Field Representative:* Karen Engle.

601 Main St., Hazard 41701; (606) 439-0794; Fax: (606) 439-4647; *Caseworker:* Sandy Runyon.

203 E. Mt. Vernon St., Somerset 42501; (606) 679-8346; Fax: (606) 678-4856; *District Administrator:* Robert L. Mitchell.

Committee assignment(s): Appropriations

ROHRABACHER, DANA, R-CALIF. (45)

Capitol Hill office: 2338 RHOB 20515; (202) 225-2415; Fax: (202) 225-0145; Internet: www.house.gov/rohrabacher; *Administrative Assistant:* Rick Dykema

District office(s): 16162 Beach Blvd., #304, Huntington Beach 92647; (714) 847-2433; Fax: (714) 847-5153; *District Director:* Kathleen Hollingsworth.

Committee assignment(s): International Relations; Science

ROMERO-BARCELO, CARLOS, D-P.R. (AL)

Capitol Hill office: 2443 RHOB 20515; (202) 225-2615; Fax: (202) 225-2154; Internet: www.house.gov/romero-barcelo; *Administrative Assistant:* Pedro Rivera-Casiano

District office(s): Marvesa Bldg., #404, Rd. 14, Ponce 00731; (787) 841-3300; Fax: (787) 841-1008; *Caseworker:* Ada L. Hernandez.

P.O. Box 9023958, Old San Juan 00902; (787) 723-6333; Fax: (787) 729-6824; *District Director:* Domingo L. Garcia.

Committee assignment(s): Education and Workforce; Resources

ROS-LEHTINEN, ILEANA, R-FLA. (18)

Capitol Hill office: 2240 RHOB 20515; (202) 225-3931; Fax: (202) 225-5620; *Administrative Assistant:* Arturo Estopinan

District office(s): 9210 Sunset Dr., #100, Miami 33173; (305) 275-1800; Fax: (305) 275-1801; *Administrative Assistant:* Debbie Zimmerman.

Committee assignment(s): Government Reform and Oversight; International Relations

ROTHMAN, STEVEN R., D-N.J. (9)

Capitol Hill office: 1607 LHOB 20515; (202) 225-5061; Fax: (202) 225-5851; Internet: steven.rothman@mail.house.gov or www.house.gov/rothman; *Administrative Assistant:* Charles Young

District office(s): 25 Main St., Hackensack 07601; (201) 646-0808; Fax: (201) 646-1944; *District Director:* Adam Zellner.

130 Central Ave., Jersey City 07302; (201) 798-1366; Fax: (201) 798-1725.

Committee assignment(s): International Relations; Judiciary

ROUKEMA, MARGE, R-N.J. (5)

Capitol Hill office: 2469 RHOB 20515; (202) 225-4465; Fax: (202) 225-9048; Internet: www.house.gov/roukema; *Chief of Staff:* Steve Wilson

District office(s): 1200 E. Ridgewood Ave., Ridgewood 07450; (201) 447-3900; Fax: (201) 447-3749; *District Administrator:* David Zuidema.

1500 Route 517, #105, Hackettstown 07840; (908) 850-4747; Fax: (908) 850-3406; *Staff Assistant:* Carol Dougherty.

Committee assignment(s): Banking and Financial Services; Education and Workforce

ROYBAL-ALLARD, LUCILLE, D-CALIF. (33)

Capitol Hill office: 2435 RHOB 20515; (202) 225-1766; Fax: 226-0350; Internet: www.house.gov/roybal-allard; *Administrative Assistant:* Yolanda Chavez

District office(s): 255 E. Temple, #1860, Los Angeles 90012; (213) 628-9230; Fax: (213) 628-8578.

Committee assignment(s): Banking and Financial Services; Budget

ROYCE, ED, R-CALIF. (39)

Capitol Hill office: 1133 LHOB 20515; (202) 225-4111; Fax: 226-0335; Internet: www.house.gov/royce; *Chief of Staff:* Joan Bates Korich

District office(s): 305 N. Harbor Blvd., #300, Fullerton 92632; (714) 992-8081; Fax: (714) 992-1668; *Administrative Assistant:* Marcia Gilchrist.

Committee assignment(s): Banking and Financial Services; International Relations

RUSH, BOBBY L., D-ILL. (1)

Capitol Hill office: 131 CHOB 20515; (202) 225-4372; Fax: 226-0333; Internet: bobby.rush@mail.house.gov or www.house.gov/rush; *Chief of Staff:* Tim Wright

District office(s): 655 E. 79th St., Chicago 60619; (773) 224-6500; Fax: (773) 224-9624; *District Director:* Stan Watkins.

9730 S. Western Ave., #237, Evergreen Park 60642; (708) 422-4055; Fax: (708) 422-5199; *District Director:* Stan Watkins.

Committee assignment(s): Commerce

RYUN, JIM, R-KAN. (2)

Capitol Hill office: 511 CHOB 20515; (202) 225-6601; Fax: (202) 225-7986; Internet: www.house.gov/ryun; *Chief of Staff:* Daniel Schneider

District office(s): 820 Quincy St., Topeka 66612; (785) 232-4500; Fax: (785) 232-4512; *District Director:* Michelle Butler-Latham.

Committee assignment(s): Banking and Financial Services; National Security; Small Business

SABO, MARTIN OLAV, D-MINN. (5)

Capitol Hill office: 2336 RHOB 20515; (202) 225-4755; Fax: (202) 225-4886; Internet: martin.sabo@mail.house.gov or www.house.gov/sabo; *Administrative Assistant:* Michael Erlandson

District office(s): 250 2nd Ave. South, #286, Minneapolis 55401; (612) 664-8000; Fax: (612) 664-8004; *Office Director:* Kathleen C. Anderson.

Committee assignment(s): Appropriations; Standards of Official Conduct

SALMON, MATT, R-ARIZ. (1)

Capitol Hill office: 115 CHOB 20515; (202) 225-2635; Fax: (202) 225-3405; Internet: msalmon@mail.house.gov or www.house.gov/salmon; *Chief of Staff:* Michael Paranzino

District office(s): 401 W. Baseline Rd., #209, Tempe 85283; (602) 831-2900; Fax: (602) 831-2700; *District Director:* Terree P. Wasley.

Committee assignment(s): International Relations; Science

SANCHEZ, LORETTA, D-CALIF. (46)

Capitol Hill office: 1529 LHOB 20515; (202) 225-2965; Internet: loretta@mail.house.gov or www.house.gov/sanchez; *Chief of Staff:* Steve Jost

District office(s): 12397 Lewis St., #101, Garden Grove 92840; (714) 621-0102; Fax: (714) 621-0401; *District Director:* Nancy Ramirez.

Committee assignment(s): Education and Workforce; National Security

SANDERS, BERNARD, I-VT. (AL)

Capitol Hill office: 2202 RHOB 20515; (202) 225-4115; Fax: (202) 225-6790; Internet: bernie@mail.house.gov or www.house.gov/bernie; *Administrative Assistant:* William J. Goold

District office(s): 1 Church St., 2nd Floor, Burlington 05401; (802) 862-0697; Fax: (802) 860-6370; *Outreach Coordinator:* Phil Fiermonte.

Committee assignment(s): Banking and Financial Services; Government Reform and Oversight

SANDLIN, MAX, D-TEXAS (1)

Capitol Hill office: 214 CHOB 20515; (202) 225-3035; Fax: (202) 225-5866; Internet: www.house.gov/sandlin; *Administrative Assistant:* Paul Rogers

District office(s): 1300 E. Pinecrest Dr., #30, Marshall 75670; (903) 938-8386; Fax: (903) 935-5772; *District Assistant:* Cindy McGeorge.

P.O. Box 248, New Boston 75570; (903) 628-5594; Fax: (903) 628-3155; *District Assistant:* Molly Beth Malcolm.

P.O. Box 538, Sulphur Springs 75482; (903) 885-8682; Fax: (903) 885-2976; *District Assistant:* Delores Brown.

Committee assignment(s): Banking and Financial Services; Transportation and Infrastructure

SANFORD, MARK, R-S.C. (1)

Capitol Hill office: 1223 LHOB 20515; (202) 225-3176; Fax: (202) 225-3407; Internet: sanford@mail.house.gov or www.house.gov/sanford; *Chief of Staff:* Greg Engeman

District office(s): 334 Meeting St., #640, Charleston 29403; (803) 727-4175; Fax: (803) 577-6522; *District Administrator:* Ed Vaughan.

829-E Front St., Georgetown 29440; (803) 527-6868; *Caseworker:* Elma Harrelson.

206 Laurel St., Conway 29526; (803) 248-2660; Fax: (803) 248-2824; *Caseworker:* Elma Harrelson.

Committee assignment(s): Government Reform and Oversight; International Relations; Joint Economic

SAWYER, TOM, D-OHIO (14)

Capitol Hill office: 1414 LHOB 20515; (202) 225-5231; Fax: (202) 225-5278; *Chief of Staff:* Mary Anne Walsh

District office(s): 411 Wolf Ledges Parkway, #105, Akron 44311; (330) 375-5710; *District Director:* Judi Shapiro.

250 S. Chestnut St., Ravenna 44266; (330) 296-9810; *District Director:* Judi Shapiro.

Committee assignment(s): Commerce

SAXTON, JIM, R-N.J. (3)

Capitol Hill office: 339 CHOB 20515; (202) 225-4765; Fax: (202) 225-0778; *Administrative Assistant:* Gary Gallant

District office(s): 1 Maine Ave., Cherry Hill 08002; (609) 428-0520; Fax: (609) 428-2384; *Staff Assistant:* Dee Denton.

100 High St., #301, Mt. Holly 08060; (609) 261-5800; Fax: (609) 261-1275; *District Director:* Sandra R. Condit.

7 Hadley Ave., Toms River 08753; (908) 914-2020; Fax: (908) 914-8351; *Staff Assistant:* Patricia Brogan.

Committee assignment(s): National Security; Resources; Joint Economic (chair)

SCARBOROUGH, JOE, R-FLA. (1)

Capitol Hill office: 127 CHOB 20515; (202) 225-4136; Fax: (202) 225-3414; Internet: fl01@hr.house.gov or www.house.gov/scarborough; *Chief of Staff:* Bart Roper

District office(s): 4300 Bayou Blvd., #17C, #20, Pensacola 32503; (850) 479-1183; Fax: (850) 479-9394; *District Representative:* Nan Weaver.

438 Southwest Miracle Strip Parkway, Unit 21, Fort Walton Beach 32548; (850) 664-1266; Fax: (850) 664-0851; *Constituent Services Coordinator:* Louis Hoyt.

Committee assignment(s): Education and Workforce; Government Reform and Oversight; National Security

SCHAEFER, DAN, R-COLO. (6)

Capitol Hill office: 2160 RHOB 20515; (202) 225-7882; Fax: (202) 225-7885; Internet: rep.dan.schaefer@mail.house.gov or www.house.gov/schaefer; *Chief of Staff:* Holly Propst

District office(s): 3615 S. Huron St., #101, Englewood 80110; (303) 762-8890; Fax: (303) 762-7282; *District Director:* Andree R. Krause.

Committee assignment(s): Commerce; Veterans' Affairs

SCHAFFER, BOB, R-COLO. (4)

Capitol Hill office: 212 CHOB 20515; (202) 225-4676; Fax: (202) 225-5870; Internet: rep.schaffer@mail.house.gov or www.house.gov/schaffer; *Chief of Staff:* Susan M. Wadhams

District office(s): #307, 315 W. Oak St., Fort Collins 80521; (970) 493-9132; Fax: (970) 493-9144.

Committee assignment(s): Agriculture; Education and Workforce; Resources

SCHUMER, CHARLES E., D-N.Y. (9)

Capitol Hill office: 2211 RHOB 20515; (202) 225-6616; Fax: (202) 225-4183; *Chief of Staff:* Josh Isay

District office(s): 1628 Kings Hwy., Brooklyn 11229; (718) 627-9700; Fax: (718) 627-3411; *District Director:* Veronica Sullivan.

118-21 Queens Blvd., Forest Hills 11375; (718) 268-8200; *District Director:* Veronica Sullivan.

90-16 Rockaway Beach Blvd., Rockaway 11693; (718) 945-9200; *District Director:* Veronica Sullivan.

Committee assignment(s): Banking and Financial Services; Judiciary

SCOTT, ROBERT C., D-VA. (3)

Capitol Hill office: 2464 RHOB 20515; (202) 225-8351; Fax: (202) 225-8354; *Chief of Staff:* Joni Ivey

District office(s): 501 N. 2nd St., #401, Richmond 23219; (804) 644-4845; Fax: (804) 648-6026; *Legislative Assistant:* Nkechi George.

2600 Washington Ave., #1010, Newport News 23607; (757) 380-1000; Fax: (757) 928-6694; *District Manager:* Gisele P. Russell.

Committee assignment(s): Education and Workforce; Judiciary

SENSENBRENNER, F. JAMES, JR., R-WIS. (9)

Capitol Hill office: 2332 RHOB 20515; (202) 225-5101; Fax: (202) 225-3190; Internet: sensen09@mail.house.gov or www.house.gov/sensenbrenner; *Administrative Assistant:* Brian Dean

District office(s): 120 Bishops Way, #154, Brookfield 53005; (414) 784-1111; Fax: (414) 784-9437; *Home Secretary:* Thomas Schreibel.

Committee assignment(s): Judiciary; Science (chair)

SERRANO, JOSE E., D-N.Y. (16)

Capitol Hill office: 2342 RHOB 20515; (202) 225-4361; Fax: (202) 225-6001; Internet: serrano@mail.house.gov or www.house.gov/serrano; *Chief of Staff:* Ellyn M. Toscano

District office(s): 890 Grand Concourse, Bronx 10451; (718) 538-5400; Fax: (718) 588-3652; *District Director:* Cheryl Simmons-Oliver.

Committee assignment(s): Appropriations

SESSIONS, PETE, R-TEXAS (5)

Capitol Hill office: 1318 LHOB 20515; (202) 225-2231; Internet: petes@mail.house.gov or www.house.gov/sessions; *Administrative Assistant:* Scott Styles

District office(s): #410, 10677 E. Northwest Hwy., Dallas 75238; (214) 349-9996; Fax: (214) 349-0738; *District Director:* Chris Homan.

104 E. Corsicana, Athens 75751; (903) 675-8288; *Regional Director:* Charlie Hawn.

Committee assignment(s): Banking and Financial Services; Government Reform and Oversight; Science

SHADEGG, JOHN, R-ARIZ. (4)

Capitol Hill office: 430 CHOB 20515; (202) 225-3361; Fax: (202) 225-3462; Internet: j.shadegg@mail.house.gov or www.house.gov/shadegg; *Chief of Staff:* Elise Finley

District office(s): 301 E. Bethany Home Rd., #C178, Phoenix 85012; (602) 248-7779; *District Director:* Jennifer MacDonald.

Committee assignment(s): Budget; Government Reform and Oversight; Resources

SHAW, E. CLAY, JR., R-FLA. (22)

Capitol Hill office: 2408 RHOB 20515; (202) 225-3026; Fax: (202) 225-8398; Internet: www.house.gov/shaw; *Chief of Staff:* Scott A. Spear

District office(s): 1512 E. Broward Blvd., #101, Fort Lauderdale 33301; (954) 522-1800; Fax: (954) 768-0511; *District Office Director:* George Caldwell.

222 Lakeview Ave., #162, W. Palm Beach 33401; (561) 832-3007; Fax: (561) 832-0227; *District Representative:* Victoria Duxbury.

Committee assignment(s): Ways and Means

SHAYS, CHRISTOPHER, R-CONN. (4)

Capitol Hill office: 1502 LHOB 20515; (202) 225-5541; Fax: (202) 225-9629; Internet: rep.shays@mail.house.gov or www.house.gov/shays; *Chief of Staff:* Peter Carson

District office(s): 10 Middle St., Bridgeport 06604; (203) 579-5870; *District Director:* Ralph Loomis.

888 Washington Blvd., Stamford 06901; (203) 357-8277; *Caseworker:* Karen Charest.

Committee assignment(s): Budget; Government Reform and Oversight

SHERMAN, BRAD, D-CALIF. (24)

Capitol Hill office: 1524 LHOB 20515; (202) 225-5911; Fax: (202) 225-5879; Internet: www.house.gov/sherman; *Chief of Staff:* Peter Loge

District office(s): 21031 Ventura Blvd., #1010, Woodland Hills 91364; (818) 999-1990; Fax: (818) 999-2287; *District Director:* David Tierney.

2100 E. Thousand Oaks Blvd., Suite C, Thousand Oaks 91362; (805) 449-2372; Fax: (805) 449-2375; *Office Manager:* Glenda Lee.

Committee assignment(s): International Relations

SHIMKUS, JOHN M., R-ILL. (2)

Capitol Hill office: 513 CHOB 20515; (202) 225-5271; Internet: www.house.gov/shimkus; *Chief of Staff:* Craig Roberts

District office(s): 301 N. 6th St., #100, Springfield 62701; (217) 492-5090; Fax: (217) 492-5096; *Deputy Chief of Staff:* Deb Detmers.

1605 Vandalia St., Collinsville 62234; (618) 344-3065; Fax: (618) 344-4215; *Executive Assistant:* Dora Rohan.
Committee assignment(s): Commerce

SHUSTER, BUD, R-PA. (9)
Capitol Hill office: 2188 RHOB 20515; (202) 225-2431; Internet: www.house.gov/shuster; *Chief of Staff:* Tim Hugo
District office(s): RD 2, Box 711, Altoona 16601; (814) 946-1653; *District Aide:* Judy Giansante.
1214 Oldtown Rd., #4, Clearfield 16830; (814) 765-9106; *District Aide:* Robert Young.
179 E. Queen St., Chambersburg 17201; (717) 264-8308; *District Aide:* Geoffrey Mosebey.
Committee assignment(s): Select Intelligence; Transportation and Infrastructure (chair)

SISISKY, NORMAN, D-VA. (4)
Capitol Hill office: 2371 RHOB 20515; (202) 225-6365; Fax: 226-1170; Internet: www.house.gov/sisisky; *Chief of Staff:* Jan Faircloth
District office(s): 309 County St., #204, Portsmouth 23704; (757) 393-2068; Fax: (757) 399-1997; *District Representative:* Jeff Cunningham.
43 Rives Rd., Petersburg 23805; (804) 732-2544; Fax: (804) 733-4652; *District Representative:* Rick Franklin.
425H S. Main St., Emporia 23847; (804) 634-5575; *District Representative:* Rick Franklin.
Committee assignment(s): National Security; Small Business

SKAGGS, DAVID E., D-COLO. (2)
Capitol Hill office: 1124 LHOB 20515; (202) 225-2161; Internet: david.skaggs@mail.house.gov or www.house.gov/skaggs; *Chief of Staff:* Stephen Saunders
District office(s): 9101 Harlan St., #130, Westminster 80030; (303) 650-7886; Fax: (303) 650-7893; *District Director:* Susan B. Damour.
Committee assignment(s): Appropriations; Select Intelligence

SKEEN, JOE, R-N.M. (2)
Capitol Hill office: 2302 RHOB 20515; (202) 225-2365; Fax: (202) 225-9599; Internet: www.house.gov/skeen; *Chief of Staff:* Suzanne Eisold
District office(s): 1065B S. Main St., Suite A, Las Cruces 88005; (505) 527-1771; Fax: (505) 527-1774; *District Representative:* Dorothy C. Thomas.
500 N. Richardson Ave., #257, Roswell 88201; (505) 622-0055; Fax: (505) 625-9608; *District Representative:* Alice Eppers.
Committee assignment(s): Appropriations

SKELTON, IKE, D-MO. (4)
Capitol Hill office: 2227 RHOB 20515; (202) 225-2876; Internet: www.house.gov/skelton; *Administrative Assistant:* Jack Pollard
District office(s): 514-B Northwest Seven Hwy., Blue Springs 64014; (816) 228-4242; *District Representative:* Robert D. Hagedorn.
1401 Southwest Blvd., Jefferson City 65109; (573) 635-3499; *Staff Assistant:* Carol Scott.
319 S. Lamine St., Sedalia 65301; (660) 826-2675; *Staff Assistant:* Arletta Garrett.
219 N. Adams St., Lebanon 65536; (417) 532-7964; *Staff Assistant:* Shirley Clark.
Committee assignment(s): Select Intelligence; National Security (ranking member)

SLAUGHTER, LOUISE M., D-N.Y. (28)
Capitol Hill office: 2347 RHOB 20515; (202) 225-3615; Fax: (202) 225-7822; Internet: louiseny@mail.house.gov or www.house.gov/slaughter; *Chief of Staff:* Kim Simpson
District office(s): 100 State St., #3120, Rochester 14614; (716) 232-4850; Fax: (716) 232-1954.
Committee assignment(s): Rules

SMITH, ADAM, D-WASH. (9)
Capitol Hill office: 1505 LHOB 20515; (202) 225-8901; Fax: (202) 225-5893; Internet: adam.smith@mail.house.gov or www.house.gov/adamsmith; *Administrative Assistant:* Jeff Bjornstad
District office(s): 3600 Port of Tacoma Rd. East, #308, Tacoma 98424; (253) 926-6683; Fax: (253) 926-1321; *District Director:* Amy Ruble.
Committee assignment(s): National Security; Resources

SMITH, BOB, R-ORE. (2)
Capitol Hill office: 1126 LHOB 20515; (202) 225-6730; Fax: (202) 225-5774; Internet: bobsmith@mail.house.gov or www.house.gov/bobsmith; *Administrative Assistant:* Brian MacDonald
District office(s): 843 E. Main, #400, Medford 97504; (541) 776-4646; Fax: (541) 779-0204; *District Director:* John Snider.
707 Ponderosa Village, Burns 97720; (541) 573-3607; *District Director:* John Snider.
Committee assignment(s): Agriculture (chair); Resources

SMITH, CHRISTOPHER H., R-N.J. (4)
Capitol Hill office: 2370 RHOB 20515; (202) 225-3765; Fax: (202) 225-7768; Internet: www.house.gov/chrissmith; *Chief of Staff:* Mary Noonan
District office(s): 1540 Kuser Rd., #A9, Hamilton 08619; (609) 585-7878; Fax: (609) 585-9155; *Special Assistant:* Jean "Pidge" Carroll.

38A Whiting Shopping Center, Lacy Rd. and Cherry St., Whiting 08759; (908) 350-2300; Fax: (908) 350-6260; *Regional Director:* Lorretta Charbonneau.

Committee assignment(s): International Relations; Veterans' Affairs

SMITH, LAMAR, R-TEXAS (21)

Capitol Hill office: 2231 RHOB 20515; (202) 225-4236; Fax: (202) 225-8628; Internet: lamars@hr.house.gov or www.house.gov/lamarsmith; *Chief of Staff:* John Lampmann

District office(s): 33 E. Twohig St., #302, San Angelo 76903; (915) 653-3971; Fax: (915) 655-4687; *Office Manager:* Jo Anne Powell.

1006 Junction Hwy., Kerrville 78028; (210) 895-1414; Fax: (210) 895-2091; *Office Manager:* Kathy Temple.

1100 N.E. Loop 410, #640, San Antonio 78209; (210) 821-5024; Fax: (210) 821-5947; *District Director:* O'Lene Stone.

211 E. Main, #310, Round Rock 78664; (512) 218-4221; Fax: (512) 218-4208; *Staff Assistant:* Jodell Brooks.

4305 N. Garfield, #228B, Midland 79705; (915) 687-5232; Fax: (915) 687-5234; *Office Manager:* Ann Bradford.

Committee assignment(s): Budget; Judiciary; Standards of Official Conduct

SMITH, LINDA, R-WASH. (3)

Capitol Hill office: 1317 LHOB 20515; (202) 225-3536; Fax: (202) 225-3478; Internet: asklinda@mail.house.gov or www.house.gov/lindasmith; *Chief of Staff:* Patrick Fiske

District office(s): 2407 Pacific Ave. S.E., P.O. Box 1219, Olympia 98507; (360) 753-3073; Fax: (360) 753-3141; *District Assistant:* Glenna Gideon.

1220 Main St., #360, Vancouver 98660; (360) 695-6292; Fax: (360) 695-6197; *District Director:* Barb Holbrook.

Committee assignment(s): Resources; Small Business

SMITH, NICK, R-MICH. (7)

Capitol Hill office: 306 CHOB 20515; (202) 225-6276; Internet: www.house.gov/writerep or www.house.gov/nicksmith; *Administrative Assistant:* Kurt Schmautz

District office(s): 121 S. Cochran Ave., Charlotte 48813; (517) 543-0055; Fax: (517) 543-7116; *Admin Assistant:* Keith Brown.

209 E. Washington St., #217E, Jackson 49201; (517) 783-4486; Fax: (517) 783-3012; *Field Representative:* Pat Nelson.

4192 W. Maple St., Adrian 49221; (517) 265-5012; Fax: (517) 265-5012; *Field Representative:* Gayle Mitchell.

81 S. 20th St., Battle Creek 48813; (616) 965-9066; Fax: (616) 965-9036; *Field Representative:* Chris Gillette.

Committee assignment(s): Agriculture; Budget

SNOWBARGER, VINCE, R-KAN. (3)

Capitol Hill office: 509 CHOB 20515; (202) 225-2865; Fax: (202) 225-5897; Internet: rep.snowbarger@mail.house.gov or www.house.gov/snowbarger; *Chief of Staff:* Kevin Yowell

District office(s): 500 State Ave., #196, Kansas City 66101; (913) 621-0832; Fax: (913) 621-1533; *District Director:* Gary Haulmark.

8826 Santa Fe Dr., #350, Overland Park 66212; (913) 383-2013; Fax: (913) 383-1314; *District Representative:* Lori Rickert.

647 Massachusetts, #207, Lawrence 66044; (785) 842-9313; Fax: (785) 842-9276; *Staff Assistant:* Sandra London.

Committee assignment(s): Banking and Financial Services; Government Reform and Oversight; Small Business

SNYDER, VIC, D-ARK. (2)

Capitol Hill office: 1319 LHOB 20515; (202) 225-2506; Fax: (202) 225-5903; Internet: snyder.congress@mail.house.gov or www.house.gov/snyder; *Staff Director:* Ed Fry

District office(s): 700 W. Capitol Ave., #1527, Little Rock 72201; (501) 324-5941; Fax: (501) 324-6029; *District Director:* John Yates.

Committee assignment(s): National Security; Veterans' Affairs

SOLOMON, GERALD B. H., R-N.Y. (22)

Capitol Hill office: 2206 RHOB 20515; (202) 225-5614; Fax: (202) 225-6234; Internet: www.house.gov/solomon; *Chief of Staff:* Geoffrey Gleason

District office(s): 21 N. 7th St., Hudson 12534; (518) 828-0181; Fax: (518) 828-1657; *Staff Assistant:* Pat Hart.

21 Bay St., Glens Falls 12801; (518) 792-3031; Fax: (518) 792-3181; *Staff Assistant:* Dan Orsini.

285 Broadway, Saratoga Springs 12866; (518) 587-9800; Fax: (518) 587-1228; *District Representative:* Jeff Purner.

P.O. Box 71, Rhinebeck 12572; (914) 876-2200; *Staff Assistant:* Dan Orsini.

Committee assignment(s): Rules (chair)

SOUDER, MARK, R-IND. (4)

Capitol Hill office: 418 CHOB 20515; (202) 225-4436; Fax: (202) 225-3479; Internet: souder@hr.house.gov or www.house.gov/souder; *Chief of Staff:* Vacant

District office(s): 1300 S. Harrison St., #3105, Fort Wayne 46802; (219) 424-3041; *District Director:* Mark Wickersham.

Committee assignment(s): Education and Workforce; Government Reform and Oversight; Small Business

SPENCE, FLOYD D., R-S.C. (2)

Capitol Hill office: 2405 RHOB 20515; (202) 225-2452; *Chief of Staff:* Craig Metz

District office(s): 220 Stoneridge Dr., #202, Columbia 29210; (803) 254-5120; Fax: (803) 779-3406; *District Administrator:* Mary T. Howard.

1681 Chestnut St. N.E., P.O. Box 1609, Orangeburg 29116; (803) 536-4641; Fax: (803) 536-5754; *District Administrator:* Chessye B. Powell.

807 Port Republic, #2, P.O. Box 1538, Beaufort 29901; (803) 521-2530; Fax: (803) 521-2535; *Field Representative:* Katherine Ceips.

66 E. Railroad Ave., P.O. Box 550, Estill 29918; (803) 625-3177; Fax: (803) 625-4844; *Field Representative:* Mary Eleanor Bowers.

Committee assignment(s): National Security (chair); Veterans' Affairs

SPRATT, JOHN M., JR., D-S.C. (5)

Capitol Hill office: 1536 LHOB 20515; (202) 225-5501; Fax: (202) 225-0464; Internet: john.spratt@mail. house.gov or www.house.gov/spratt; *Chief of Staff:* Ellen Wallace Buchanan

District office(s): 39 E. Calhoun St., Sumter 29150; (803) 773-3362; Fax: (803) 773-7662; *District Aide:* Linda Mixon.

P.O. Box 25, Darlington 29532; (803) 393-3998; *District Aide:* Joanne Langley.

Courthouse Square, P.O. Box 350, Rock Hill 29731; (803) 327-1114; Fax: (803) 327-4330; *District Administrator:* Robert H. Hopkins.

Committee assignment(s): Budget (ranking member); National Security

STABENOW, DEBBIE, D-MICH. (8)

Capitol Hill office: 1516 LHOB 20515; (202) 225-4872; Fax: (202) 225-5820; Internet: debbie.stabenow@ mail.house.com; *Administrative Assistant:* Maggie Springer

District office(s): 3401 E. Saginaw, #214, Lansing 48912; (517) 336-7777; Fax: (517) 337-7236; *District Director:* Teresa Plachetka.

2900 E. Grand River, Howell 48843; (517) 545-2195; Fax: (517) 545-2430.

2503 S. Linden, Flint 48503; (810) 230-8275; Fax: (810) 230-8521.

Committee assignment(s): Agriculture; Science

STARK, PETE, D-CALIF. (13)

Capitol Hill office: 239 CHOB 20515; (202) 225-5065; Fax: (202) 225-3805; Internet: petemail@hr.house. gov or www.house.gov/stark; *Administrative Assistant:* Anne Raffaelli

District office(s): 39300 Civic Center Dr., #220, Fremont 94538; (510) 494-1388; Fax: (510) 494-5852; *District Representative:* Grace Davis.

Committee assignment(s): Ways and Means; Joint Economic (ranking member); Joint Taxation

STEARNS, CLIFF, R-FLA. (6)

Capitol Hill office: 2352 RHOB 20515; (202) 225-5744; Fax: (202) 225-3973; Internet: cstearns@hr.house.gov or www.house.gov/stearns; *Chief of Staff:* Jack Seum

District office(s): 115 S.E. 25th Ave., Ocala 34471; (352) 351-8777; Fax: (352) 351-8011; *District Manager:* Sharon Brooks.

734 N. 3rd St., #517 CD, Leesburg 34748; (352) 326-8285; Fax: (352) 326-9430; *Staff Assistant:* Catherine Potter.

1726 Kingsley Ave., #8, Orange Park 32073; (904) 269-3203; Fax: (904) 269-3343; *District Office Manager:* Sandi Schoonover.

Committee assignment(s): Commerce; Veterans' Affairs

STENHOLM, CHARLES W., D-TEXAS (17)

Capitol Hill office: 1211 LHOB 20515; (202) 225-6605; Fax: (202) 225-2234; Internet: texas17@mail.house. gov or www.house.gov/stenholm; *Administrative Assistant:* Lois Auer

District office(s): 33 E. Twohig Ave., #318, San Angelo 76903; (915) 655-7994; Fax: (915) 658-2798; *District Aide:* Jayne Schoonmaker.

903 E. Hamilton St., Stamford 79553; (915) 773-3623; Fax: (915) 773-3624; *District Manager:* Don Starr.

300 Pine St., #2101, P.O. Box 1101, Abilene 79604; (915) 673-7221; Fax: (915) 676-9547; *District Aide:* Elaine R. Talley.

Committee assignment(s): Agriculture (ranking member)

STOKES, LOUIS, D-OHIO (11)

Capitol Hill office: 2365 RHOB 20515; (202) 225-7032; Fax: (202) 225-1339; Internet: www.house.gov/ stokes; *Administrative Assistant:* Fredette West

District office(s): 3645 Warrensville Center Rd., #204, Shaker Heights 44122; (216) 522-4900; Fax: (216) 522-4908; *District Manager:* Jewell Gilbert.

Committee assignment(s): Appropriations

STRICKLAND, TED, D-OHIO (6)

Capitol Hill office: 336 CHOB 20515; (202) 225-5705; Internet: www.house.gov/strickland; *Chief of Staff:* Mark Lotwis

District office(s): 254 Front St., Marietta 45750; (614) 376-0868; Fax: (614) 376-0886; *Field Representative:* Denise Pittenger.

1236 Gallia St., Portsmouth 45662; (614) 353-5171; Fax: (614) 353-8014; *District Director:* John Haseley.

36 E. Locust St., Wilmington 45177; (937) 382-4585; Fax: (937) 383-0038; *Field Representative:* Greg Hargett.

Committee assignment(s): Commerce

STUMP, BOB, R-ARIZ. (3)

Capitol Hill office: 211 CHOB 20515; (202) 225-4576; Fax: (202) 225-6328; Internet: www.house.gov/va; *Chief of Staff:* Lisa Jackson

District office(s): 230 N. 1st Ave., #2001, Phoenix 85025; (602) 379-6923; Fax: (602) 271-0611; *District Assistant:* Bruce C. Bartholomew.

Committee assignment(s): National Security; Veterans' Affairs (chair)

STUPAK, BART, D-MICH. (1)

Capitol Hill office: 1410 LHOB 20515; (202) 225-4735; Fax: (202) 225-4744; Internet: stupak@mail.house. gov or www.house.gov/stupak; *Chief of Staff:* Scott Schloegel

District office(s): 346 E. Front St., Traverse City 49684; (616) 929-4711; Fax: (616) 929-7725; *District Aide:* Joanne Papenfuss.

111 W. Chisolm St., Alpena 49707; (517) 356-0690; Fax: (517) 356-0923; *Congressional Aide:* Sue Norkauski.

902 Ludington St., Escanaba 49829; (906) 786-4504; Fax: (906) 786-4534; *Congressional Aide:* Cindy Frazer Langdon.

1229 W. Washington St., Marquette 49855; (906) 228-3700; Fax: (906) 228-2305; *Congressional Aide:* Matt Johnson.

616 Sheldon Ave., #213, Houghton 49931; (906) 482-1371; *Congressional Aide:* Amy Wisti.

Committee assignment(s): Commerce

SUNUNU, JOHN E., R-N.H. (1)

Capitol Hill office: 1229 LHOB 20515; (202) 225-5456; Fax: (202) 225-5822; Internet: rep.sununu@mail. house.gov or www.house.gov/sununu; *Chief of Staff:* Paul Collins

District office(s): 1750 Elm St., #101, Manchester 03104; (603) 641-9536; Fax: (603) 641-9561; *Head Caseworker:* Kathy Schneiderat.

104 Washington St., Dover 03820; (603) 643-4813; Fax: (603) 743-5956; *District Director:* Pam Kocher.

35 Center St., Wolfeboro Falls 03896; (603) 569-8927; Fax: (603) 569-8926; *Caseworker:* Lynn Brownell.

Committee assignment(s): Budget; Government Reform and Oversight; Small Business

TALENT, JAMES M., R-MO. (2)

Capitol Hill office: 1022 LHOB 20515; (202) 225-2561; Fax: (202) 225-2563; Internet: rep.talent@mail.house. gov or www.house.gov/talent; *Administrative Assistant:* Mark Strand

District office(s): 555 N. New Ballas Rd., #315, St. Louis 63141; (314) 872-9561; Fax: (314) 872-3728; *District Director:* Barbara Cooper.

820 S. Main St., #206, St. Charles 63301; (314) 949-6826; Fax: (314) 949-3832; *District Office Manager:* Kerry Degregorio.

Committee assignment(s): Education and Workforce; National Security; Small Business (chair)

TANNER, JOHN, D-TENN. (8)

Capitol Hill office: 1127 LHOB 20515; (202) 225-4714; Fax: (202) 225-1765; Internet: john.tanner@mail. house.gov or www.house.gov/tanner/index.htm; *Administrative Assistant:* Vickie Walling

District office(s): 8120 Hwy. 51 North, #3, Millington 38053; (901) 873-5690; Fax: (901) 373-2996; *Office Manager:* Margaret Black.

203 W. Church St., Union City 38261; (901) 885-7070; Fax: (901) 885-7094; *District Director:* Joe H. Hill.

Federal Bldg., #B-7, Jackson 38301; (901) 423-4848; Fax: (901) 427-1539; *Constituent Services Director:* Shirlene Mercer.

Committee assignment(s): Ways and Means

TAUSCHER, ELLEN O., D-CALIF. (1)

Capitol Hill office: 1440 LHOB 20515; (202) 225-1880; Fax: (202) 225-5914; Internet: ellen.tauscher@mail. house.gov or www.house.gov/tauscher; *Administrative Assistant:* Katie Merrill

District office(s): 100 Civic Plaza, #242, Dublin 94549; (510) 829-0813; Fax: (510) 829-7318; *Caseworker:* Marco Milanese.

1801 N. California Blvd., #103, Walnut Creek 94596; (510) 932-8899; Fax: (510) 932-8159; *District Director:* Michelle Henry.

420 W. 3rd St., Antioch 94509; (510) 757-7187; *Caseworker:* Philip Arndt.

Committee assignment(s): Science; Transportation and Infrastructure

TAUZIN, W. J. "BILLY," R-LA. (3)

Capitol Hill office: 2183 RHOB 20515; (202) 225-4031; Fax: (202) 225-0563; Internet: www.house.gov/ tauzin; *Chief of Staff:* Wallace Henderson

District office(s): 423 Lafayette St., #107, Houma 70360; (504) 876-3033; Fax: (504) 872-4449; *Staff Assistant:* Jeri Theriot.

210 E. Main St., New Iberia 70560; (318) 367-8231; Fax: (318) 369-7084; *Staff Assistant:* Jan Viator.

828 S. Irma Blvd., #212A, Gonzales 70737; (504) 621-8490; Fax: (504) 621-8493; *Admin Assistant:* Martin Cancienne.

8201 W. Judge Perez Dr., Chalmette 70043; (504) 271-1707; Fax: (504) 271-1756; *District Representative:* Peggy T. Bourgeois.

Committee assignment(s): Commerce; Resources

TAYLOR, CHARLES H., R-N.C. (11)

Capitol Hill office: 231 CHOB 20515; (202) 225-6401; Internet: repcharles.taylor@mail.house.gov; *Chief of Staff:* Roger France

District office(s): 22 S. Pack Square, #330, Asheville 28801; (704) 251-1988; Fax: (704) 251-0794; *Executive Assistant:* Nancy Day.

200 S. Lafayette St., Shelby 28150; (704) 484-6971.

201 Peachtree St., Murphy 28906; (704) 837-3249; Fax: (704) 837-3249; *District Representative:* Judy Edwards.

Committee assignment(s): Appropriations

TAYLOR, GENE, D-MISS. (5)

Capitol Hill office: 2447 RHOB 20515; (202) 225-5772; Fax: (202) 225-7074; *Chief of Staff:* Wayne Weidie

District office(s): 701 Main St., #215, Hattiesburg 39401; (601) 582-3246; Fax: (601) 582-3246; *Office Manager:* L. J. Martin.

2424 14th St., Gulfport 39501; (228) 864-7670; Fax: (228) 864-3099; *District Manager:* Beau Gex.

1215-B Government St., Ocean Springs 39564; (228) 872-7950; Fax: (228) 872-7949; *Office Manager:* Brian Martin.

Committee assignment(s): National Security; Transportation and Infrastructure

THOMAS, BILL, R-CALIF. (21)

Capitol Hill office: 2208 RHOB 20515; (202) 225-2915; Fax: (202) 225-8798; Internet: www.house.gov/billthomas; *Administrative Assistant:* Cathy Abernathy

District office(s): 319 W. Murray St., Visalia 93291; (209) 627-6549; *Caseworker:* Marjorie Lancaster.

4100 Truxtun Ave., #220, Bakersfield 93309; (805) 327-3611; *Field Representative:* Kevin McCarthy.

Committee assignment(s): House Oversight (chair); Ways and Means; Joint Library (vice chair); Joint Printing (vice chair); Joint Taxation

THOMPSON, BENNIE, D-MISS. (2)

Capitol Hill office: 1408 LHOB 20515; (202) 225-5876; Fax: (202) 225-5898; Internet: chorhn@hr.house.gov or www.house.gov/thompson; *Administrative Assistant:* Marsha G. McCraven

District office(s): 220 Pecan St., Marks 38646; (601) 326-3090; *Field Representative:* Samuel McCray.

910 Courthouse Lane, Greenville 38701; (601) 335-9003; Fax: (601) 334-1304; *Field Director:* Marilyn Hansell.

106 W. Green St., #134, Mound Bayou 38762; (601) 741-9003; *Field Representative:* Geri Havard.

509 Hwy. 82 West, Greenwood 38930; (601) 455-9300; Fax: (601) 453-0118; *Office Manager:* Trina Nichols.

107 W. Madison St., Bolton 39041; (601) 866-9003; Fax: (601) 866-9036; *District Director:* Charles Horhn.

Committee assignment(s): Agriculture; Budget

THORNBERRY, WILLIAM M. "MAC," R-TEXAS (13)

Capitol Hill office: 412 CHOB 20515; (202) 225-3706; Fax: (202) 225-3486; Internet: www.house.gov/thornberry; *Chief of Staff:* Sylvia Nugent

District office(s): 724 S. Polk St., #400, Amarillo 79101; (806) 371-8844; Fax: (806) 371-7044; *District Representative:* Brent Oden.

811 6th St., #130, Wichita Falls 76301; (940) 767-0541; Fax: (940) 766-0570; *District Representative:* Durcie Scaling.

Committee assignment(s): National Security; Resources; Joint Economic

THUNE, JOHN, R-S.D. (AL)

Capitol Hill office: 506 CHOB 20515; (202) 225-2801; Fax: (202) 225-5823; Internet: jthune@mail.house.gov or www.house.gov/thune; *Chief of Staff:* Herb Jones

District office(s): 2310 W. 41st St., #101, Sioux Falls 57105; (605) 331-1010; Fax: (605) 331-0651; *District Representative:* Jill Schieffer.

621 6th St., #100A, Rapid City 57701; (605) 342-5135; Fax: (605) 342-5291; *District Representative:* Larry Russell.

Committee assignment(s): Agriculture; Transportation and Infrastructure

THURMAN, KAREN L., D-FLA. (5)

Capitol Hill office: 440 CHOB 20515; (202) 225-1002; Fax: 226-0329; Internet: kthurman@mail.house.gov or www.house.gov/thurman; *Chief of Staff:* Nora Matus

District office(s): 5700 S.W. 34th St., #425, Gainesville 32608; (352) 336-6614; Fax: (352) 336-6376; *Caseworker:* Marlene Corbett.

2224 Hwy. 44 West, Inverness 34453; (352) 344-3044; Fax: (352) 637-1769; *District Administrator:* Anne Morgan.

5609 U.S. 19 South, Suite H, New Port Richey 34652; (813) 849-4496; Fax: (813) 845-0462; *Caseworker:* Margaret Heal.

Committee assignment(s): Ways and Means

TIAHRT, TODD, R-KAN. (4)

Capitol Hill office: 428 CHOB 20515; (202) 225-6216; Fax: (202) 225-3489; Internet: tiahrt@hr.house.gov or www.house.gov/tiahrt; *Administrative Assistant:* Matt Schlapp

District office(s): 155 N. Market St., #400, Wichita 67202; (316) 262-8992; Fax: (316) 262-5309; *District Director:* Pam Porvaznik.

325 N. Penn St., Independence 67301; (316) 331-8056; Fax: (316) 331-8074.

Committee assignment(s): Appropriations

TIERNEY, JOHN F., D-MASS. (6)

Capitol Hill office: 120 CHOB 20515; (202) 225-8020; Fax: (202) 225-5915; Internet: www.house.gov/tierney; *Chief of Staff:* David Williams

District office(s): 17 Peabody Square, Peabody 01960; (978) 531-1669; Fax: (978) 531-1996; *District Director:* Gary Barrett.

Lynn City Hall, #410, Lynn 01902; (781) 595-7375; Fax: (781) 595-7492; *District Director:* Gary Barrett.

160 Main St., Haverhill 01830; (978) 469-1942; Fax: (978) 469-9021; *District Director:* Gary Barrett.

Committee assignment(s): Education and Workforce; Government Reform and Oversight

TORRES, ESTEBAN E., D-CALIF. (34)

Capitol Hill office: 2269 RHOB 20515; (202) 225-5256; Fax: (202) 225-9711; Internet: arcoiris@hr.house.gov or www.house.gov/torres; *Chief of Staff:* Albert Jacquez

District office(s): 8819 Whittier Blvd., #101, Pico Rivera 90660; (562) 695-0702; Fax: (562) 692-2216; *Chief of Staff:* James Casso.

Committee assignment(s): Appropriations; Banking and Financial Services

TOWNS, EDOLPHUS, D-N.Y. (1)

Capitol Hill office: 2232 RHOB 20515; (202) 225-5936; Fax: (202) 225-1018; Internet: www.house.gov/towns; *Chief of Staff:* Brenda Pillors

District office(s): 1110 Pennsylvania Ave. Store 5, Brooklyn 11207; (718) 272-1175; *District Manager:* Arelis Echavarria.

11670 Fulton St., Brooklyn 11213; (718) 387-8698; Fax: (718) 387-8045; *District Manager:* Arelis Echavarria.

16 Court St., #1505, Brooklyn 11241; (718) 855-8018; Fax: (718) 858-4542; *Staff Assistant:* Karen Johnson.

Committee assignment(s): Commerce; Government Reform and Oversight

TRAFICANT, JAMES A., JR., D-OHIO (17)

Capitol Hill office: 2446 RHOB 20515; (202) 225-5261; Fax: (202) 225-3719; Internet: telljim@hr.house.

gov or www.house.gov/traficant; *Chief of Staff:* Paul Marcone

District office(s): 109 W. 3rd St., E. Liverpool 43920; (330) 385-5921; Fax: (330) 385-7582; *Staff Representative:* Carrie Davis.

5555 Youngstown-Warren Rd., #503, Niles 44446; (330) 652-5649; *Staff Representative:* George Buccella.

125 Market St., Youngstown 44503; (330) 743-1914; Fax: (330) 743-4920; *Administrative Assistant:* Henry DiBlasio.

Committee assignment(s): Science; Transportation and Infrastructure

TURNER, JIM, D-TEXAS (2)

Capitol Hill office: 1508 LHOB 20515; (202) 225-2401; Fax: (202) 225-5955; Internet: tx02@mail.house.gov or www.house.gov/turner; *Chief of Staff:* Elizabeth Hurley

District office(s): 701 N. 1st St., #201, Lufkin 75901; (409) 637-1770; Fax: (409) 632-8588; *District Caseworker:* Lorri Donnahoe.

420 W. Green Ave., Orange 77630; (409) 883-4990; Fax: (409) 883-5149; *Field Representative:* Ann Grey.

605 E. Goliad, #102, Crockett 75835; (409) 544-8414; Fax: (409) 544-2181; *Field Representative:* Patricia Lucas.

Committee assignment(s): Government Reform and Oversight; National Security

UNDERWOOD, ROBERT A., D-GUAM (AL)

Capitol Hill office: 424 CHOB 20515; (202) 225-1188; Fax: 226-0341; Internet: guamtodc@hr.house.gov or www.house.gov/underwood; *Chief of Staff:* Terri Schroeder

District office(s): 120 Father Duenas Ave., #107, Agana 96910; (671) 477-4272; *District Director:* Vincent A. Leon Guerrero.

Committee assignment(s): National Security; Resources

UPTON, FRED, R-MICH. (6)

Capitol Hill office: 2333 RHOB 20515; (202) 225-3761; Fax: (202) 225-4986; Internet: talk2.fsu@mail.house. gov or www.house.gov/upton; *Administrative Assistant:* Joan Hillebrands

District office(s): 157 S. Kalamazoo Mall, #180, Kalamazoo 49007; (616) 385-0039; Fax: (616) 385-2888; *District Administrator:* Jeff Breneman.

800 Centre #106, 800 Ship St., St. Joseph 49085; (616) 982-1986; Fax: (616) 982-0237; *District Representative:* Art Fenrick.

Committee assignment(s): Commerce; Education and Workforce

VELAZQUEZ, NYDIA M., D-N.Y. (12)

Capitol Hill office: 1221 LHOB 20515; (202) 225-2361; Fax: 226-0327; Internet: www.house.gov/velazquez; *Chief of Staff:* Michael Bay

District office(s): 173 Ave. B, New York 10009; (212) 673-3997; Fax: (212) 473-5242; *Community Liaison:* Mickey Hernandez.

815 Broadway, Brooklyn 11206; (718) 599-3658; Fax: (718) 599-4537; *Staff Assistant:* Nelson Cruz.

50-07 108th St., 2nd Floor, Queens 11368; (718) 699-2602; Fax: (718) 760-0104; *N.Y. Scheduler:* Graciela Howard.

Committee assignment(s): Banking and Financial Services; Small Business

VENTO, BRUCE F., D-MINN. (4)

Capitol Hill office: 2304 RHOB 20515; (202) 225-6631; Fax: (202) 225-1968; Internet: vento@mail.house.gov or www.house.gov/vento; *Administrative Assistant:* Larry Romans

District office(s): Galtier Plaza, #727, Box 100, St. Paul 55101; (612) 224-4503; Fax: (612) 224-0575; *District Director:* John Van Hecke.

Committee assignment(s): Banking and Financial Services; Resources

VISCLOSKY, PETER J., D-IND. (1)

Capitol Hill office: 2313 RHOB 20515; (202) 225-2461; Fax: (202) 225-2493; Internet: www.house.gov/writerep or www.house.gov/visclosky; *Chief of Staff:* Chuck Brimmer

District office(s): 215 W. 35th Ave., Gary 46408; (219) 884-1177; *District Director:* Dave Rozmanich.

Committee assignment(s): Appropriations

WALSH, JAMES T., R-N.Y. (25)

Capitol Hill office: 2351 RHOB 20515; (202) 225-3701; Fax: (202) 225-4042; Internet: rep.james.walsh@mail.house.gov or www.house.gov/walsh; *Administrative Assistant:* Art Jutton

District office(s): 1 Lincoln St., Auburn 13021; (315) 255-0649; Fax: (315) 255-1369; *Staff Assistant:* Susan Dwyer.

45 Church St., Cortland 13045; (607) 758-3918; Fax: (607) 758-9007; *Staff Assistant:* Terre Dennis.

100 S. Clinton St., #1340, P.O. Box 7306, Syracuse 13261; (315) 423-5657; Fax: (315) 423-5669.

Committee assignment(s): Appropriations

WAMP, ZACH, R-TENN. (3)

Capitol Hill office: 423 CHOB 20515; (202) 225-3271; Fax: (202) 225-3494; Internet: www.house.gov/wamp/citdirect.html or www.house.gov/wamp; *Chief of Staff:* Helen Hardin

District office(s): 5741 Marlin Rd., #3400, Chattanooga 37411; (423) 894-7400; Fax: (423) 894-8621; *District Director:* Robin Derryberry.

200 Administration Rd., #100, Oak Ridge 37830; (423) 576-1976; Fax: (423) 576-3221; *District Director:* Ann Cook.

Committee assignment(s): Appropriations

WATERS, MAXINE, D-CALIF. (35)

Capitol Hill office: 2344 RHOB 20515; (202) 225-2201; Fax: (202) 225-7854; Internet: www.house.gov/waters; *Administrative Assistant:* Leah Allen

District office(s): 10124 S. Broadway, #1, Los Angeles 90037; (213) 757-8900; Fax: (213) 757-9506; *District Administrator:* I. Mike Murase.

Committee assignment(s): Banking and Financial Services; Judiciary

WATKINS, WES, R-OKLA. (3)

Capitol Hill office: 2312 RHOB 20515; (202) 225-4565; Fax: (202) 225-5966; Internet: www.house.gov/watkins; *Chief of Staff:* Leslie Belcher

District office(s): 118 Carl Albert Federal Bldg., McAlester 74501; (918) 423-5951; Fax: (918) 423-1457; *Caseworker:* Sue Bollinger.

1511 Cimarron Plaza, Stillwater 74075; (405) 743-1400; Fax: (405) 743-0680; *Caseworker:* Nancy Rogers.

P.O. Box 1600, Ada 74820; (580) 436-1980; Fax: (580) 332-7421; *Caseworker:* Dustin Rowe.

Committee assignment(s): Ways and Means

WATT, MELVIN, D-N.C. (12)

Capitol Hill office: 1230 LHOB 20515; (202) 225-1510; Fax: (202) 225-1512; Internet: melmail@hr.house.gov or www.house.gov/watt; *Administrative Assistant:* Joyce Brayboy Dalton

District office(s): 301 S. Greene St., #210, Greensboro 27401; (910) 379-9403; Fax: (910) 379-9429; *District Aide:* Pamlyn Stubbs.

315 E. Chapel Hill St., #202, Durham 27701; (919) 688-3004; Fax: (919) 688-0940; *District Aide:* Tracy Lovett.

324 N. College St., #201, Charlotte 28202; (704) 344-9950; Fax: (704) 344-9971; *District Director:* Don N. Baker.

Committee assignment(s): Banking and Financial Services; Judiciary

WATTS, J. C., JR., R-OKLA. (4)

Capitol Hill office: 1210 LHOB 20515; (202) 225-6165; Fax: (202) 225-3512; Internet: rep.jcwatts@mail.house.gov or www.house.gov/watts; *Chief of Staff:* Mike Hunter

District office(s): 2420 Springer Dr., #120, Norman 73069; (405) 329-6500; Fax: (405) 321-7369; *Executive Secretary:* Trish Gardener.

601 Southwest D Ave., #205, Lawton 73501; (580) 357-2131; Fax: (580) 357-7477; *Field Representative:* Suzanne Hogan.

Committee assignment(s): National Security; Transportation and Infrastructure

WAXMAN, HENRY A., D-CALIF. (29)

Capitol Hill office: 2204 RHOB 20515; (202) 225-3976; Fax: (202) 225-4099; Internet: www.house.gov/waxman; *Chief of Staff:* Philip Schiliro

District office(s): 8436 W. 3rd St., #600, Los Angeles 90048; (213) 651-1040; Fax: (213) 655-8037; *District Office Director:* Lisa Ellman.

Committee assignment(s): Commerce; Government Reform and Oversight (ranking member)

WELDON, CURT, R-PA. (7)

Capitol Hill office: 2452 RHOB 20515; (202) 225-2011; Fax: (202) 225-8137; Internet: curtpa7@mail.house. gov or www.house.gov/cweldon; *Administrative Assistant:* Doug Ritter

District office(s): 1554 Garrett Rd., Upper Darby 19082; (610) 259-0700; Fax: (610) 596-4665; *District Director:* John Fleitz.

30 S. Valley Rd., #212, Paoli 19301; (610) 640-9064; Fax: (610) 640-9071; *District Director:* John Fleitz.

Committee assignment(s): National Security; Science

WELDON, DAVE, R-FLA. (15)

Capitol Hill office: 216 CHOB 20515; (202) 225-3671; Fax: (202) 225-3516; Internet: fla15@mail.house.gov or www.house.gov/weldon; *Chief of Staff:* Dana Gartzke

District office(s): 2725 Judge Fran Jamison Way, Bldg. C., Melbourne 32940; (407) 632-1176; Fax: (407) 639-8595; *District Director:* J. B. Kump.

2000 16th Ave., #157, Vero Beach 32960; (561) 778-3534; Fax: (561) 562-5543; *District Representative:* Tammy Bogart.

Committee assignment(s): Banking and Financial Services; Science

WELLER, JERRY, R-ILL. (11)

Capitol Hill office: 130 CHOB 20515; (202) 225-3635; Fax: (202) 225-3521; Internet: www.house.gov/weller; *Administrative Assistant:* Jim Hayes

District office(s): 51 W. Jackson St., #100, Joliet 60432; (815) 740-2028; Fax: (815) 740-2037; *District Director:* Reed Wilson.

628-30 Columbus St., #205, Ottawa 61350; (815) 433-0085; Fax: (815) 433-0217; *District Scheduler:* Michelle Grundon.

Committee assignment(s): Ways and Means

WEXLER, ROBERT, D-FLA. (19)

Capitol Hill office: 1609 LHOB 20515; (202) 225-3001; Fax: (202) 225-5974; *Chief of Staff:* Suzanne Stoll

District office(s): #100, 2500 N. Military Trail, Boca Raton 33431; (561) 988-6302; Fax: (561) 988-6423; *District Administrator:* Wendi Lipsich.

5790 Margate Blvd., Margate 33063; (954) 972-6454; Fax: (954) 972-2982; *Broward Coordinator:* Lynn Brenes.

Committee assignment(s): International Relations; Judiciary

WEYGAND, BOB, D-R.I. (2)

Capitol Hill office: 507 CHOB 20515; (202) 225-2735; Internet: robert.weygand@mail.house.gov or www.house.gov/weygand; *Chief of Staff:* James M. Russo

District office(s): 300 Centreville Rd., #205, Warwick 02886; (401) 732-9400; *District Director:* Leigh Ann Woisard.

Committee assignment(s): Banking and Financial Services; Budget; Small Business

WHITE, RICK, R-WASH. (1)

Capitol Hill office: 116 CHOB 20515; (202) 225-6311; Fax: (202) 225-3524; Internet: repwhite@mail.house. gov or www.house.gov/white; *Administrative Assistant:* Connie J. Correll

District office(s): 21905 64th Ave. West, Mountlake Terrace 98043; (425) 640-0233; Fax: (425) 776-7168; *Chief of Staff:* Randy Pepple.

1050 N.E. Hostmark St., #204, Poulsbo 98370; (360) 697-3112; Fax: (360) 697-3477; *Constituent Liaison:* Shannon Childs.

Committee assignment(s): Commerce

WHITFIELD, EDWARD, R-KY. (1)

Capitol Hill office: 236 CHOB 20515; (202) 225-3115; Fax: (202) 225-3547; Internet: www.house.gov/writerep or www.house.gov/whitfield; *Policy Director:* Larry VanHoose

District office(s): Monroe County Courthouse, Tompkinsville 42167; (502) 487-9509; *Field Representative:* Sandy Simpson.

317 W. 9th St., Hopkinsville 42240; (502) 885-8079; Fax: (502) 885-8598; *Field Representative:* Michael Pape.

100 Fountain Ave., #104, Paducah 42001; (502) 442-6901; Fax: (502) 442-6805; *Field Representative:* Amy Bowland.

222 1st St., #307, Henderson 42420; (502) 826-4180; Fax: (502) 826-6783; *Field Representative:* Joe Bradford.

Committee assignment(s): Commerce

WICKER, ROGER, R-MISS. (1)

Capitol Hill office: 206 CHOB 20515; (202) 225-4306; Fax: (202) 225-3549; Internet: roger.wicker@mail. house.gov or www.house.gov/wicker; *Chief of Staff:* John Keast

District office(s): P.O. Box 1482, Tupelo 38802; (601) 844-5437; Fax: (601) 844-9096; *District Manager:* Bubba Lollar.

P.O. Box 70, Southaven 38671; (601) 342-3942; Fax: (601) 342-3883; *District Manager:* Merle Flowers.

Committee assignment(s): Appropriations

WISE, BOB, D-W.VA. (2)

Capitol Hill office: 2367 RHOB 20515; (202) 225-2711; Fax: (202) 225-7856; Internet: bobwise@mail.house. gov or www.house.gov/wise; *Administrative Assistant:* Lowell Johnson

District office(s): 4710 Chimney Dr., Charleston 25302; (304) 965-0865; *District Director:* Susan Small-Plante.

222 W. John St., Martinsburg 25401; (304) 264-8810; *District Director:* Chip Slaven.

Committee assignment(s): Government Reform and Oversight; Transportation and Infrastructure

WOLF, FRANK R., R-VA. (1)

Capitol Hill office: 241 CHOB 20515; (202) 225-5136; Fax: (202) 225-0437; Internet: www.house.gov/ writerep or www.house.gov/wolf; *Administrative Assistant:* Charles E. White

District office(s): 13873 Park Center Rd., #130, Herndon 20171; (703) 708-5800; Fax: (703) 709-5802; *Director of Constituent Services:* Judy McCary.

110 N. Cameron St., Winchester 22601; (540) 667-0990; Fax: (540) 678-0402; *Constituent Service Assistant:* Donna Crowley.

Committee assignment(s): Appropriations

WOOLSEY, LYNN, D-CALIF. (6)

Capitol Hill office: 439 CHOB 20515; (202) 225-5161; Fax: (202) 225-8714; Internet: lynn.woolsey@mail. house.gov or www.house.gov/woolsey; *Chief of Staff:* Mark Isaac

District office(s): 1050 Northgate Dr., #140, San Rafael 94903; (415) 507-9554; Fax: (415) 507-9601; *Field Representative:* Lucy Giovando.

1101 College Ave., #200, Santa Rosa 95404; (707) 542-7182; Fax: (707) 542-2745; *District Director:* Leslie Horak.

Committee assignment(s): Budget; Education and Work-force

WYNN, ALBERT R., D-MD. (4)

Capitol Hill office: 407 CHOB 20515; (202) 225-8699; Internet: albert.wynn@mail.house.gov or www. house.gov/wynn; *Chief of Staff:* James C. Ballentine

District office(s): 6009 Oxon Hill Rd., #208, Oxon Hill 20745; (301) 839-5570; Fax: (301) 839-9173; *Chief of Staff:* Bill Boston.

9200 Basil Court, #316, Landover 20785; (301) 773-4094; Fax: (301) 925-9674; *Senior Case Manager:* Annie Peters.

8601 Georgia Ave., #201, Silver Spring 20910; (301) 588-7328; Fax: (301) 588-1225; *Field Representative:* Melody Khalatbari.

Committee assignment(s): Commerce

YATES, SIDNEY R., D-ILL. (9)

Capitol Hill office: 2109 RHOB 20515; (202) 225-2111; Fax: (202) 225-3493; *Administrative Assistant:* Mary Bain

District office(s): 2100 Ridge Ave., Evanston 60204; (847) 328-2610; Fax: (847) 328-2618; *Staff Assistant:* Barbara Stein.

230 S. Dearborn St., Chicago 60604; (312) 353-4596; Fax: (312) 886-8046; *Staff Assistant:* Pat Fuller.

Committee assignment(s): Appropriations

YOUNG, C. W. BILL, R-FLA. (1)

Capitol Hill office: 2407 RHOB 20515; (202) 225-5961; *Administrative Assistant:* Harry Glenn

District office(s): 801 W. Bay Dr., #606, Largo 33540; (813) 581-0980; *District Assistant:* George N. Cretekos.

144 1st Ave. South, #627, St. Petersburg 33701; (813) 893-3191; *District Assistant:* George N. Cretekos.

Committee assignment(s): Appropriations; Select Intelligence

YOUNG, DON, R-ALASKA (AL)

Capitol Hill office: 2111 RHOB 20515; (202) 225-5765; Fax: (202) 225-0425; Internet: www.house.gov/ donyoung; *Administrative Assistant:* Colin Chapman

District office(s): 222 W. 7th Ave., Box 3, Anchorage 99513; (907) 271-5978; Fax: (907) 271-5950; *Special Assistant:* Chad Padgett.

130 Trading Bay Rd., #350, Kenai 99611; (907) 283-5808; Fax: (907) 283-4363; *Staff Assistant:* Peggy Arness.

101 12th Ave., Box 10, Fairbanks 99701; (907) 456-0210; Fax: (907) 456-0279; *Special Assistant:* Royce Chapman.

401 Federal Bldg., P.O. Box 21247, Juneau 99801; (907) 586-7400; Fax: (907) 586-8922; *Staff Assistant:* Lucy Hudson.

109 Main St., Ketchikan 99901; (907) (202) 225-6880; *Staff Assistant:* Sherrie Slick.

851 E. W. Point Dr. #307, Wasillah 99654; (907) 376-7665; Fax: (907) 376-8526; *Staff Assistant:* Carol Gustafson.

Committee assignment(s): Resources (chair); Transportation and Infrastructure

Joint Committees
of Congress

The joint committees of Congress are listed below. The listing includes the room number, telephone number, and jurisdiction for each committee. Membership is drawn from both the Senate and House and from both parties. Membership is given in order of seniority on the committees.

Republicans are shown on the left in roman type; Democrats are on the right in italic type. When a senator serves as chair, the vice chair usually is a representative, and vice versa. The office of chair usually rotates from one chamber to the other at the beginning of each Congress.

JOINT ECONOMIC

Phone: (202) 224-5171; **Room:** SD-G01
Executive Director: Christopher Frenze; (202) 224-5171; 1537 LHOB
Minority Staff Director: Vacant

Studies and investigates all recommendations in the president's annual Economic Report to Congress. Reports findings and recommendations to the House and Senate.

Senate Members

Connie Mack, Fla., vice chair	*Jeff Bingaman, N.M.*
William V. Roth Jr., Del.	*Paul S. Sarbanes, Md.*
Robert F. Bennett, Utah	*Edward M. Kennedy, Mass.*
Rod Grams, Minn.	*Charles S. Robb, Va.*
Sam Brownback, Kan.	
Jeff Sessions, Ala.	

House Members

Jim Saxton, N.J., chair	*Pete Stark, Calif., ranking member*
Donald Manzullo, Ill.	*Lee H. Hamilton, Ind.*
Mark Sanford, S.C.	*Maurice D. Hinchey, N.Y.*
William M. "Mac" Thornberry, Texas	*Carolyn B. Maloney, N.Y.*
John T. Doolittle, Calif.	
Jim McCrery, La.	

JOINT LIBRARY

Phone: (202) 225-8281; **Room:** 1309 LHOB
House Staff Contact: Catherine Fanucchi; (202) 225-8281; 1309 LHOB
Senate Staff Contact: Ed Edens; (202) 224-6352; SR-305

Management and expansion of the Library of Congress; receipt of gifts for the benefit of the library; development and maintenance of the Botanic Garden; placement of statues and other works of art in the Capitol.

Senate Members

John W. Warner, Va., chair	*Dianne Feinstein, Calif.*
Ted Stevens, Alaska	
Thad Cochran, Miss.	

House Members

Bill Thomas, Calif., vice chair	*Sam Gejdenson, Conn.*
Bob Ney, Ohio	
Vernon J. Ehlers, Mich.	

JOINT PRINTING

Phone: (202) 224-5241; **Room:** SH-818
Staff Director: Eric C. Peterson; (202) 224-5241; SH-818
Minority Staff Director: Bob Mansker; (202) 224-5241; SH-818

Probes inefficiency and waste in the printing, binding and distribution of federal government publications.

JOINT PRINTING (continued)

Oversees arrangement and style of the *Congressional Record*.

Senate Members

John W. Warner, Va., chair
Thad Cochran, Miss.
Mitch McConnell, Ky.

Wendell H. Ford, Ky., ranking member
Daniel K. Inouye, Hawaii

House Members

Bill Thomas, Calif., vice chair
Bob Ney, Ohio
Kay Granger, Texas

Steny H. Hoyer, Md., ranking member
Sam Gejdenson, Conn.

JOINT TAXATION

Phone: (202) 225-3621; **Room:** 1015 LHOB
Chief of Staff: Kenneth Kies; (202) 225-3621; 1015 LHOB

Operation, effects, and administration of the federal system of internal revenue taxes; measures and methods for simplification of taxes.

Senate Members

William V. Roth Jr., Del., vice chair
John H. Chafee, R.I.
Charles E. Grassley, Iowa

Daniel Patrick Moynihan, N.Y., ranking member
Max Baucus, Mont.

House Members

Bill Archer, Texas, chair
Philip M. Crane, Ill.
Bill Thomas, Calif.

Charles B. Rangel, N.Y.
Pete Stark, Calif.

Senate Committees

The standing and select committees of the U.S. Senate are listed below. The listing includes the room number, telephone number, party ratio, and jurisdiction for each full committee. Subcommittees are listed alphabetically under each committee. Membership is listed in order of seniority on the committee or subcommittee.

Members of the majority party, Republicans, are shown in roman type; the minority party, Democrats, are shown in italic type. The partisan committees of the Senate are listed on p. 816. Members of these committees are listed in alphabetical order, not by seniority.

AGRICULTURE, NUTRITION, AND FORESTRY

Phone: (202) 224-2035; **Room:** SR-328A
Staff Director: Charles F. Conner; (202) 224-2035; SR-328A
Minority Staff Director: Dan Smith; (202) 224-2035; SR-328

Agriculture in general; animal industry and diseases; crop insurance and soil conservation; farm credit and farm security; food from fresh waters; food stamp programs; forestry in general; home economics; human nutrition; inspection of livestock, meat and agricultural products; pests and pesticides; plant industry, soils and agricultural engineering; rural development, rural electrification and watersheds; school nutrition programs. The chair and ranking minority member are members ex officio of all subcommittees of which they are not regular members.
Party Ratio: R 10-D 8

Richard G. Lugar, Ind., chair	*Tom Harkin, Iowa, ranking member*
Jesse Helms, N.C.	*Patrick J. Leahy, Vt.*
Thad Cochran, Miss.	*Kent Conrad, N.D.*
Mitch McConnell, Ky.	*Tom Daschle, S.D.*
Paul Coverdell, Ga.	*Max Baucus, Mont.*
Rick Santorum, Pa.	*Bob Kerrey, Neb.*
Pat Roberts, Kan.	*Tim Johnson, S.D.*
Charles E. Grassley, Iowa	*Mary L. Landrieu, La.*
Phil Gramm, Texas	
Larry E. Craig, Idaho	

Subcommittees

Forestry, Conservation, and Rural Revitalization
Phone: (202) 224-2035; **Room:** SR-328A

Santorum, chair	*Conrad*
Grassley	*Leahy*
Coverdell	*Daschle*
Roberts	*Baucus*
Craig	

Marketing, Inspection, and Product Promotion
Phone: (202) 224-2035; **Room:** SR-328A

Coverdell, chair	*Baucus*
Helms	*Kerrey*
Cochran	*Landrieu*
McConnell	

Production and Price Competitiveness
Phone: (202) 224-2035; **Room:** SR-328A

Cochran, chair	*Kerrey*
Roberts	*Daschle*
Helms	*Johnson*
Grassley	*Landrieu*
Gramm	

Research, Nutrition, and General Legislation
Phone: (202) 224-2035; **Room:** SR-328A

McConnell, chair	*Leahy*
Gramm	*Conrad*
Craig	*Johnson*
Santorum	

APPROPRIATIONS

Phone: (202) 224-3471; **Room:** S-128 CAP
Staff Director: Steve Cortese; (202) 224-3471; S-128 CAP
Minority Staff Director: James H. English; (202) 224-7200; S-206 CAP

Appropriation of revenue; rescission of appropriations; new spending authority under the Congressional Budget Act. The chair and ranking minority member are non-voting members ex officio of all subcommittees.
Party Ratio: R 15-D 13

Ted Stevens, Alaska, chair	*Robert C. Byrd, W.Va., ranking member*
Thad Cochran, Miss.	*Daniel K. Inouye, Hawaii*
Arlen Specter, Pa.	*Ernest F. Hollings, S.C.*
Pete V. Domenici, N.M.	*Patrick J. Leahy, Vt.*
Christopher S. Bond, Mo.	*Dale Bumpers, Ark.*
Slade Gorton, Wash.	*Frank R. Lautenberg, N.J.*
Mitch McConnell, Ky.	*Tom Harkin, Iowa*
Conrad Burns, Mont.	*Barbara A. Mikulski, Md.*
Richard C. Shelby, Ala.	*Harry Reid, Nev.*
Judd Gregg, N.H.	*Herb Kohl, Wis.*
Robert F. Bennett, Utah	*Patty Murray, Wash.*
Ben Nighthorse Campbell, Colo.	*Byron L. Dorgan, N.D.*
Larry E. Craig, Idaho	*Barbara Boxer, Calif.*
Lauch Faircloth, N.C.	
Kay Bailey Hutchison, Texas	

Subcommittees

Agriculture, Rural Development, and Related Agencies
Phone: (202) 224-5270; **Room:** 136 SD

Cochran, chair	*Bumpers*
Specter	*Harkin*
Bond	*Kohl*
Gorton	*Byrd*
McConnell	*Leahy*
Burns	

Commerce, Justice, State, and Judiciary
Phone: (202) 224-7277; **Room:** S-146A CAP

Gregg, chair	*Hollings*
Stevens	*Inouye*
Domenici	*Bumpers*
McConnell	*Lautenberg*
Hutchison	*Mikulski*
Campbell	

Defense
Phone: (202) 224-7255; **Room:** 122 SD

Stevens, chair	*Inouye*
Cochran	*Hollings*
Specter	*Byrd*

Domenici	*Leahy*
Bond	*Bumpers*
McConnell	*Lautenberg*
Shelby	*Harkin*
Gregg	*Dorgan*
Hutchison	

District of Columbia
Phone: (202) 224-2731; **Room:** S-128 CAP

Faircloth, chair	*Boxer*
Hutchison	

Energy and Water Development
Phone: (202) 224-7260; **Room:** 127 SD

Domenici, chair	*Reid*
Cochran	*Byrd*
Gorton	*Hollings*
McConnell	*Murray*
Bennett	*Kohl*
Burns	*Dorgan*
Craig	

Foreign Operations
Phone: (202) 224-2104; **Room:** 142 SD

McConnell, chair	*Leahy*
Specter	*Inouye*
Gregg	*Lautenberg*
Shelby	*Harkin*
Bennett	*Mikulski*
Campbell	*Murray*
Stevens	

Interior
Phone: (202) 224-7233; **Room:** 131 SD

Gorton, chair	*Byrd*
Stevens	*Leahy*
Cochran	*Bumpers*
Domenici	*Hollings*
Burns	*Reid*
Bennett	*Dorgan*
Gregg	*Boxer*
Campbell	

Labor, Health, and Human Services and Education
Phone: (202) 224-7230; **Room:** 184 SD

Specter, chair	*Harkin*
Cochran	*Hollings*
Gorton	*Inouye*
Bond	*Bumpers*
Gregg	*Reid*
Faircloth	*Kohl*
Craig	*Murray*
Hutchison	

Legislative Branch
Phone: (202) 224-8921; **Room:** S-125 CAP

Bennett, chair	*Dorgan*
Stevens	*Boxer*
Craig	

Military Construction
Phone: (202) 224-7204; **Room:** 140 SD

Burns, chair	*Murray*
Hutchison	*Reid*
Faircloth	*Inouye*
Craig	

Transportation
Phone: (202) 224-7281; **Room:** 190 SD

Shelby, chair	*Lautenberg*
Domenici	*Byrd*
Specter	*Mikulski*
Bond	*Reid*
Gorton	*Kohl*
Bennett	*Murray*
Faircloth	

Treasury and General Government
Phone: (202) 224-7337; **Room:** 190 SD

Campbell, chair	*Kohl*
Shelby	*Mikulski*
Faircloth	

VA, HUD, and Independent Agencies
Phone: (202) 224-7211; **Room:** 130 SD

Bond, chair	*Mikulski*
Burns	*Leahy*
Stevens	*Lautenberg*
Shelby	*Harkin*
Campbell	*Boxer*
Craig	

ARMED SERVICES

Phone: (202) 224-3871; **Room:** SR-228
Staff Director: Romie L. Brownlee; (202) 224-3871; SR-228
Minority Staff Director: David Lyles; (202) 224-3871; SR-228

Defense and defense policy generally; aeronautical and space activities peculiar to or primarily associated with the development of weapons systems or military operations; maintenance and operation of the Panama Canal, including the Canal Zone; military research and development; national security aspects of nuclear energy; naval petroleum reserves (except Alaska); armed forces generally; Selective Service System; strategic and critical materials. The chair and ranking minority member are non-voting members ex officio of all subcommittees of which they are not regular members.
Party Ratio: R 10-D 08

Strom Thurmond, S.C., chair	*Carl Levin, Mich., ranking member*
John W. Warner, Va.	*Edward M. Kennedy, Mass.*
John McCain, Ariz.	*Jeff Bingaman, N.M.*
Daniel R. Coats, Ind.	*John Glenn, Ohio*
Robert C. Smith, N.H.	*Robert C. Byrd, W.Va.*
Dirk Kempthorne, Idaho	*Charles S. Robb, Va.*
James M. Inhofe, Okla.	*Joseph I. Lieberman, Conn.*
Rick Santorum, Pa.	*Max Cleland, Ga.*
Olympia J. Snowe, Maine	
Pat Roberts, Kan.	

Subcommittees

Acquisition and Technology
Phone: (202) 224-3871; **Room:** SR-228

Santorum, chair	*Lieberman*
Smith (N.H.)	*Kennedy*
Snowe	*Bingaman*
Roberts	

Airland Forces
Phone: (202) 224-3871; **Room:** SR-228

Coats, chair	*Glenn*
Warner	*Bingaman*
Kempthorne	*Byrd*
Inhofe	*Lieberman*
Santorum	*Cleland*
Roberts	

Personnel
Phone: (202) 224-3871; **Room:** SR-228

Kempthorne, chair	*Cleland*
McCain	*Kennedy*
Coats	*Robb*
Snowe	

Readiness
Phone: (202) 224-3871; **Room:** SR-228

Inhofe, chair	*Robb*
McCain	*Glenn*
Coats	*Cleland*
Roberts	

Seapower
Phone: (202) 224-3871; **Room:** SR-228

Warner, chair	*Kennedy*
McCain	*Byrd*
Smith (N.H.)	*Robb*
Santorum	*Lieberman*
Snowe	

ARMED SERVICES (continued)

Strategic Forces
Phone: (202) 224-3871; **Room:** SR-228

Smith (N.H.), chair	*Bingaman*
Warner	*Glenn*
Kempthorne	*Byrd*
Inhofe	

BANKING, HOUSING, AND URBAN AFFAIRS

Phone: (202) 224-7391; **Room:** SD-534
Staff Director: Howard Menell; (202) 224-0894; SD-534
Minority Staff Director: Steven Harris; (202) 224-1573; SD-542

Banks, banking and financial institutions; price controls; deposit insurance; economic stabilization and growth; defense production; export and foreign trade promotion; export controls; federal monetary policy, including Federal Reserve System; financial aid to commerce and industry; issuance and redemption of notes; money and credit, including currency and coinage; nursing home construction; public and private housing, including veterans' housing; renegotiation of government contracts; urban development and mass transit; international economic policy. The chair and ranking minority member are non-voting members ex officio of all subcommittees of which they are not regular members.

Party Ratio: R 10-D 8

Alfonse M. D'Amato, N.Y., chair	*Paul S. Sarbanes, Md., ranking rember*
Phil Gramm, Texas	*Christopher J. Dodd, Conn.*
Richard C. Shelby, Ala.	*John Kerry, Mass.*
Connie Mack, Fla.	*Richard H. Bryan, Nev.*
Lauch Faircloth, N.C.	*Barbara Boxer, Calif.*
Robert F. Bennett, Utah	*Carol Moseley-Braun, Ill.*
Rod Grams, Minn.	*Tim Johnson, S.D.*
Wayne Allard, Colo.	*Jack Reed, R.I.*
Michael B. Enzi, Wyo.	
Chuck Hagel, Neb.	

Subcommittees

Financial Institutions and Regulatory Relief
Phone: (202) 224-7391; **Room:** SD-534

Faircloth, chair	*Bryan*
Allard	*Johnson*
Enzi	*Boxer*
Shelby	*Moseley-Braun*
Mack	*Reed*
Grams	
Gramm	

Financial Services and Technology
Phone: (202) 224-7391; **Room:** SD-534

Bennett, chair	*Boxer*
Hagel	*Kerry*
Mack	*Dodd*
Grams	*Johnson*
Enzi	

Housing Opportunity and Community Development
Phone: (202) 224-7391; **Room:** SD-534

Mack, chair	*Kerry*
Faircloth	*Reed*
Enzi	*Dodd*
Shelby	*Bryan*
Allard	*Moseley-Braun*
Hagel	

International Finance
Phone: (202) 224-7391; **Room:** SD-534

Grams, chair	*Moseley-Braun*
Hagel	*Boxer*
Gramm	*Reed*
Bennett	

Securities
Phone: (202) 224-7391; **Room:** SD-534

Gramm, chair	*Dodd*
Shelby	*Johnson*
Allard	*Kerry*
Bennett	*Bryan*
Faircloth	

BUDGET

Phone: (202) 224-0642; **Room:** SD-621
Staff Director: G. William Hoagland; (202) 224-0642; SD-621
Minority Staff Director: William Dauster; (202) 224-3961; SD-634

Federal budget generally; concurrent budget resolutions; Congressional Budget Office.

Party Ratio: R 12-D 10

Pete V. Domenici, N.M., chair	*Frank R. Lautenberg, N.J., ranking member*
Charles E. Grassley, Iowa	*Ernest F. Hollings, S.C.*
Don Nickles, Okla.	*Kent Conrad, N.D.*
Phil Gramm, Texas	*Paul S. Sarbanes, Md.*
Christopher S. Bond, Mo.	*Barbara Boxer, Calif.*
Slade Gorton, Wash.	*Patty Murray, Wash.*
Judd Gregg, N.H.	*Ron Wyden, Ore.*
Olympia J. Snowe, Maine	*Russell D. Feingold, Wis.*
Spencer Abraham, Mich.	*Tim Johnson, S.D.*
Bill Frist, Tenn.	*Richard J. Durbin, Ill.*
Rod Grams, Minn.	
Gordon H. Smith, Ore.	

COMMERCE, SCIENCE, AND TRANSPORTATION

Phone: (202) 224-5115; **Room:** SD-508
Staff Director: John Raidt; (202) 224-1251; SR-254
Minority Staff Dir.: Ivan A. Schlager; (202) 224-0427; SD-558

Interstate commerce and transportation generally; Coast Guard; coastal zone management; communications; highway safety; inland waterways, except construction; marine fisheries; Merchant Marine and navigation; non-military aeronautical and space sciences; oceans, weather and atmospheric activities; interoceanic canals generally; regulation of consumer products and services; science, engineering and technology research, development and policy; sports; standards and measurement; transportation and commerce aspects of outer continental shelf lands. The chair and ranking minority member are non-voting members ex officio of all subcommittees of which they are not regular members.

Party Ratio: R 11-D 9

John McCain, Ariz., chair	*Ernest F. Hollings, S.C., ranking member*
Ted Stevens, Alaska	*Daniel K. Inouye, Hawaii*
Conrad Burns, Mont.	*Wendell H. Ford, Ky.*
Slade Gorton, Wash.	*John D. Rockefeller IV, W.Va.*
Trent Lott, Miss.	*John Kerry, Mass.*
Kay Bailey Hutchison, Texas	*John B. Breaux, La.*
Olympia J. Snowe, Maine	*Richard H. Bryan, Nev.*
John Ashcroft, Mo.	*Byron L. Dorgan, N.D.*
Bill Frist, Tenn.	*Ron Wyden, Ore.*
Spencer Abraham, Mich.	
Sam Brownback, Kan.	

Subcommittees

Aviation
Phone: (202) 224-4852; **Room:** SH-427

Gorton, chair	*Ford*
Stevens	*Hollings*
Burns	*Inouye*
Lott	*Bryan*
Hutchison	*Rockefeller*
Ashcroft	*Breaux*
Frist	*Dorgan*
Snowe	*Wyden*
Brownback	

Communications
Phone: (202) 224-5184; **Room:** SH-227

Burns, chair	*Hollings*
Stevens	*Inouye*
Gorton	*Ford*
Lott	*Kerry*
Ashcroft	*Breaux*
Hutchison	*Rockefeller*
Abraham	*Dorgan*
Frist	*Wyden*
Brownback	

Consumer Affairs, Foreign Commerce, and Tourism
Phone: (202) 224-5183; **Room:** SH-425

Ashcroft, chair	*Breaux*
Gorton	*Ford*
Abraham	*Bryan*
Burns	
Brownback	

Manufacturing and Competitiveness
Phone: (202) 224-1745; **Room:** SD-245

Abraham, chair	*Bryan*
Snowe	*Hollings*
Ashcroft	*Dorgan*
Frist	*Rockefeller*
Brownback	

Oceans and Fisheries
Phone: (202) 224-8172; **Room:** SH-428

Snowe, chair	*Kerry*
Stevens	*Inouye*
Gorton	*Breaux*
Hutchison	

Science, Technology, and Space
Phone: (202) 224-8172; **Room:** SH-428

Frist, chair	*Rockefeller*
Burns	*Kerry*
Hutchison	*Bryan*
Stevens	*Dorgan*
Abraham	

Surface Transportation and Merchant Marine
Phone: (202) 224-4852; **Room:** SH-427

Hutchison, chair	*Inouye*
Stevens	*Breaux*
Burns	*Dorgan*
Snowe	*Bryan*
Frist	*Wyden*
Abraham	
Ashcroft	

ENERGY AND NATURAL RESOURCES

Phone: (202) 224-4971; **Room:** SD-304
Staff Director: Gregg D. Renkes; (202) 224-4971; SD-304
Minority Staff Director: Tom Williams; (202) 224-4103; SD-312

Energy policy, regulation, conservation, research and development; coal; energy-related aspects of deep-water

ENERGY AND NATURAL RESOURCES (continued)

ports; hydroelectric power, irrigation and reclamation; mines, mining and minerals generally; national parks, recreation areas, wilderness areas, wild and scenic rivers, historic sites, military parks and battlefields; naval petroleum reserves in Alaska; non-military development of nuclear energy; oil and gas production and distribution; public lands and forests; solar energy systems; territorial possessions of the United States. The chair and ranking minority member are non-voting members ex officio of all subcommittees of which they are not regular members.

Party Ratio: R 11-D 9

Frank H. Murkowski, Alaska, chair	*Dale Bumpers, Ark., ranking member*
Pete V. Domenici, N.M.	*Wendell H. Ford, Ky.*
Don Nickles, Okla.	*Jeff Bingaman, N.M.*
Larry E. Craig, Idaho	*Daniel K. Akaka, Hawaii*
Ben Nighthorse Campbell, Colo.	*Byron L. Dorgan, N.D.*
Craig Thomas, Wyo.	*Bob Graham, Fla.*
Jon Kyl, Ariz.	*Ron Wyden, Ore.*
Rod Grams, Minn.	*Tim Johnson, S.D.*
Gordon H. Smith, Ore.	*Mary L. Landrieu, La.*
Slade Gorton, Wash.	
Conrad Burns, Mont.	

Subcommittees

Energy Research, Development, Production, and Regulation
Phone: (202) 224-6567; **Room:** SD-308

Nickles, chair	*Ford*
Domenici	*Bingaman*
Craig	*Graham*
Grams	*Wyden*
Gorton	*Johnson*
Campbell	*Landrieu*
Smith (Ore.)	

Forests and Public Land Management
Phone: (202) 224-6170; **Room:** SD-306

Craig, chair	*Dorgan*
Burns	*Graham*
Domenici	*Wyden*
Thomas	*Johnson*
Kyl	*Landrieu*
Smith (Ore.)	

National Parks, Historic Preservation, and Recreation
Phone: (202) 224-6969; **Room:** SD-354

Thomas, chair	*Bingaman*
Campbell	*Akaka*

Grams	*Graham*
Nickles	*Landrieu*
Burns	

Water and Power
Phone: (202) 224-2564; **Room:** SD-304

Kyl, chair	*Akaka*
Smith (Ore.)	*Ford*
Gorton	*Dorgan*
Campbell	*Wyden*
Craig	

ENVIRONMENT AND PUBLIC WORKS

Phone: (202) 224-6176; **Room:** SD-410
Majority Staff Director: Steven J. Shimberg; (202) 224-7854; SD-410
Minority Staff Director: J. Thomas Sliter; (202) 224-8832; SD-456

Environmental policy, research and development; air, water and noise pollution; construction and maintenance of highways; environmental aspects of outer continental shelf lands; environmental effects of toxic substances other than pesticides; fisheries and wildlife; flood control and improvements of rivers and harbors; non-military environmental regulation and control of nuclear energy; ocean dumping; public buildings and grounds; public works, bridges and dams; regional economic development; solid waste disposal and recycling; water resources. The chair is a non-voting member ex officio of all subcommittees.

Party Ratio: R 10-D 8

John H. Chafee, R.I., chair	*Max Baucus, Mont., ranking member*
John W. Warner, Va.	*Daniel Patrick Moynihan, N.Y.*
Robert C. Smith, N.H.	
Dirk Kempthorne, Idaho	*Frank R. Lautenberg, N.J.*
James M. Inhofe, Okla.	*Harry Reid, Nev.*
Craig Thomas, Wyo.	*Bob Graham, Fla.*
Christopher S. Bond, Mo.	*Joseph I. Lieberman, Conn.*
Tim Hutchinson, Ark.	*Barbara Boxer, Calif.*
Wayne Allard, Colo.	*Ron Wyden, Ore.*
Jeff Sessions, Ala.	

Subcommittees

Clean Air, Wetlands, Private Property, and Nuclear Safety
Phone: (202) 224-6176; **Room:** SD-410

Inhofe, chair	*Graham*
Hutchinson	*Lieberman*
Allard	*Boxer*
Sessions	

Drinking Water, Fisheries, and Wildlife
Phone: (202) 224-6176; **Room:** SD-410

Kempthorne, chair	*Reid*
Thomas	*Lautenberg*
Bond	*Lieberman*
Warner	*Wyden*
Hutchinson	

Superfund, Waste Control, and Risk Assessment
Phone: (202) 224-6176; **Room:** SD-410

Smith (N.H.), chair	*Lautenberg*
Warner	*Moynihan*
Inhofe	*Boxer*
Allard	*Graham*
Sessions	

Transportation and Infrastructure
Phone: (202) 224-6176; **Room:** SD-410

Warner, chair	*Baucus*
Smith (N.H.)	*Moynihan*
Kempthorne	*Reid*
Bond	*Graham*
Inhofe	*Boxer*
Thomas	

FINANCE

Phone: (202) 224-4515; **Room:** SD-219
Majority Staff Dir. and Chief Counsel: Lindy L. Paull; (202) 224-4515; SD-219
Minority Staff Director: Mark Patterson; (202) 224-5315; SH-203

Revenue measures generally; taxes; tariffs and import quotas; reciprocal trade agreements; customs; revenue sharing; federal debt limit; Social Security; health programs financed by taxes or trust funds. The chair and ranking minority member are non-voting members ex officio of all subcommittees of which they are not regular members.

Party Ratio: R 11–D 9

William V. Roth Jr., Del., chair	*Daniel Patrick Moynihan, N.Y., ranking member*
John H. Chafee, R.I.	*Max Baucus, Mont.*
Charles E. Grassley, Iowa	*John D. Rockefeller IV, W.Va.*
Orrin G. Hatch, Utah	*John B. Breaux, La.*
Alfonse M. D'Amato, N.Y.	*Kent Conrad, N.D.*
Frank H. Murkowski, Alaska	*Bob Graham, Fla.*
Don Nickles, Okla.	*Carol Moseley-Braun, Ill.*
Phil Gramm, Texas	*Richard H. Bryan, Nev.*
Trent Lott, Miss.	*Bob Kerrey, Neb.*
James M. Jeffords, Vt.	
Connie Mack, Fla.	

Subcommittees

Health Care
Phone: (202) 224-4515; **Room:** SD-219

Gramm, chair	*Rockefeller*
Roth	*Baucus*
Chafee	*Conrad*
Grassley	*Graham*
Hatch	*Moseley-Braun*
D'Amato	*Bryan*
Nickles	*Kerrey*
Jeffords	

International Trade
Phone: (202) 224-4515; **Room:** SD-219

Grassley, chair	*Moynihan*
Roth	*Baucus*
Chafee	*Rockefeller*
Hatch	*Breaux*
D'Amato	*Conrad*
Murkowski	*Graham*
Gramm	*Moseley-Braun*
Lott	*Kerrey*
Mack	

Long-Term Growth, Debt, and Deficit Reduction
Phone: (202) 224-4515; **Room:** SD-219

Mack, chair	*Graham*
Murkowski	*Bryan*
Lott	

Social Security and Family Policy
Phone: (202) 224-4515; **Room:** SD-219

Chafee, chair	*Breaux*
Nickles	*Moynihan*
Gramm	*Rockefeller*
Jeffords	*Moseley-Braun*

Taxation and IRS Oversight
Phone: (202) 224-4515; **Room:** SD-219

Nickles, chair	*Baucus*
Roth	*Moynihan*
Grassley	*Breaux*
Hatch	*Conrad*
D'Amato	*Bryan*
Murkowski	*Kerrey*
Lott	
Mack	
Jeffords	

FOREIGN RELATIONS

Phone: (202) 224-4651; **Room:** SD-450
Staff Director: James W. Nance; (202) 224-4651; SD-450
Minority Staff Director: Edwin K. Hall; (202) 224-3953; SD-439

FOREIGN RELATIONS (continued)

Relations of the United States with foreign nations generally; treaties; foreign economic, military, technical and humanitarian assistance; foreign loans; diplomatic service; International Red Cross; international aspects of nuclear energy; International Monetary Fund; intervention abroad and declarations of war; foreign trade; national security; oceans and international environmental and scientific affairs; protection of U.S. citizens abroad; United Nations; World Bank and other development assistance organizations. The chair and ranking minority member are non-voting members ex officio of all subcommittees of which they are not regular members.

Party Ratio: R 10-D 8

Jesse Helms, N.C., chair	*Joseph R. Biden Jr., Del., ranking member*
Richard G. Lugar, Ind.	*Paul S. Sarbanes, Md.*
Paul Coverdell, Ga.	*Christopher J. Dodd, Conn.*
Chuck Hagel, Neb.	*John Kerry, Mass.*
Gordon H. Smith, Ore.	*Charles S. Robb, Va.*
Craig Thomas, Wyo.	*Russell D. Feingold, Wis.*
John Ashcroft, Mo.	*Dianne Feinstein, Calif.*
Rod Grams, Minn.	*Paul Wellstone, Minn.*
Bill Frist, Tenn.	
Sam Brownback, Kan.	

Subcommittees

African Affairs
Phone: (202) 224-4651; **Room:** SD-450

Ashcroft, chair	*Feingold*
Grams	*Sarbanes*
Frist	

East Asian and Pacific Affairs
Phone: (202) 224-4651; **Room:** SD-450

Thomas, chair	*Kerry*
Frist	*Robb*
Lugar	*Feingold*
Coverdell	*Feinstein*
Hagel	

European Affairs
Phone: (202) 224-4651; **Room:** SD-450

Smith (Ore.), chair	*Biden*
Lugar	*Wellstone*
Ashcroft	*Sarbanes*
Hagel	*Dodd*
Thomas	

International Economic Policy, Export, and Trade Promotion
Phone: (202) 224-4651; **Room:** SD-450

Hagel, chair	*Sarbanes*
Thomas	*Biden*
Frist	*Wellstone*
Coverdell	

International Operations
Phone: (202) 224-4651; **Room:** SD-450

Grams, chair	*Feinstein*
Helms	*Dodd*
Brownback	*Kerry*
Smith (Ore.)	

Near Eastern and South Asian Affairs
Phone: (202) 224-4651; **Room:** SD-450

Brownback, chair	*Robb*
Smith (Ore.)	*Feinstein*
Grams	*Wellstone*
Helms	*Sarbanes*
Ashcroft	

Western Hemisphere, Peace Corps, Narcotics, and Terrorism
Phone: (202) 224-4651; **Room:** SD-450

Coverdell, chair	*Dodd*
Helms	*Kerry*
Lugar	*Robb*
Brownback	

GOVERNMENTAL AFFAIRS

Phone: (202) 224-4751; **Room:** SD-340
Staff Director: Hannah Sistare; (202) 224-4751; SD-340
Minority Staff Director: Leonard Weiss; (202) 224-2627; SD-326

Archives of the United States; budget and accounting measures; census and statistics; federal civil service; congressional organization; intergovernmental relations; government information; District of Columbia; organization and management of nuclear export policy; executive branch organization and reorganization; Postal Service; efficiency, economy and effectiveness of government. The chair and ranking minority member are non-voting members ex officio of all subcommittees of which they are not regular members.

Party Ratio: R 9-D 7

Fred Thompson, Tenn., chair	*John Glenn, Ohio, ranking member*
Robert C. Smith, N.H.	*Carl Levin, Mich.*
Robert F. Bennett, Utah	*Joseph I. Lieberman, Conn.*
Susan Collins, Maine	*Daniel K. Akaka, Hawaii*
Sam Brownback, Kan.	*Richard J. Durbin, Ill.*

Pete V. Domenici, N.M. *Robert G. Torricelli, N.J.*
Thad Cochran, Miss. *Max Cleland, Ga.*
Don Nickles, Okla.
Arlen Specter, Pa.

Subcommittees

International Security, Proliferation, and Federal Services
Phone: (202) 224-2254; **Room:** SH-442

Cochran, chair	*Levin*
Collins	*Akaka*
Domenici	*Durbin*
Nickles	*Torricelli*
Specter	*Cleland*
Smith (N.H.)	

Investigations
Phone: (202) 224-2254; **Room:** SH-601

Collins, chair	*Glenn*
Brownback	*Levin*
Domenici	*Lieberman*
Cochran	*Akaka*
Nickles	*Durbin*
Specter	*Torricelli*
Smith (N.H.)	*Cleland*
Bennett	

Oversight of Government Management, Restructuring, and the District of Columbia
Phone: (202) 224-3682; **Room:** SH-601

Brownback, chair	*Lieberman*
Specter	*Cleland*
Bennett	

INDIAN AFFAIRS

Phone: (202) 224-2251; **Room:** SH-838
Staff Director: Gary Bohnee; (202) 224-2251; SH-838
Minority Staff Director: Patricia Zell; (202) 224-2251; SH-838

Problems and opportunities of Indians, including Indian land management and trust responsibilities, education, health, special services, loan programs and claims against the United States.
Party Ratio: R 8-D 6

Ben Nighthorse Campbell, Colo., chair	*Daniel K. Inouye, Hawaii, ranking member*
Frank H. Murkowski, Alaska	*Kent Conrad, N.D.*
John McCain, Ariz.	*Harry Reid, Nev.*
Slade Gorton, Wash.	*Daniel K. Akaka, Hawaii*
Pete V. Domenici, N.M.	*Paul Wellstone, Minn.*
Craig Thomas, Wyo.	*Byron L. Dorgan, N.D.*

Orrin G. Hatch, Utah
James M. Inhofe, Okla.

JUDICIARY

Phone: (202) 224-5225; **Room:** SD-224
Chief Counsel and Staff Director: Manus Cooney; (202) 224-5225; SD-224
Minority Chief Counsel: Bruce Cohen; (202) 224-7703; SD-148

Civil and criminal judicial proceedings in general; penitentiaries; bankruptcy, mutiny, espionage and counterfeiting; civil liberties; constitutional amendments; apportionment of representatives; government information; immigration and naturalization; interstate compacts in general; claims against the United States; patents, copyrights and trademarks; monopolies and unlawful restraints of trade; holidays and celebrations. The chair and ranking minority member are non-voting members ex officio of all subcommittees of which they are not regular members.
Party Ratio: R 10-D 8

Orrin G. Hatch, Utah, chair	*Patrick J. Leahy, Vt., ranking member*
Strom Thurmond, S.C.	*Edward M. Kennedy, Mass.*
Charles E. Grassley, Iowa	*Joseph R. Biden Jr., Del.*
Arlen Specter, Pa.	*Herb Kohl, Wis.*
Fred Thompson, Tenn.	*Dianne Feinstein, Calif.*
Jon Kyl, Ariz.	*Russell D. Feingold, Wis.*
Mike DeWine, Ohio	*Richard J. Durbin, Ill.*
John Ashcroft, Mo.	*Robert G. Torricelli, N.J.*
Spencer Abraham, Mich.	
Jeff Sessions, Ala.	

Subcommittees

Administrative Oversight and the Courts
Phone: (202) 224-6736; **Room:** SH-308

Grassley, chair	*Durbin*
Thurmond	*Feingold*
Sessions	*Kohl*
Kyl	

Antitrust, Business Rights, and Competition
Phone: (202) 224-9494; **Room:** SD-161

DeWine, chair	*Kohl*
Hatch	*Torricelli*
Thurmond	*Leahy*
Specter	

Constitution, Federalism, and Property Rights
Phone: (202) 224-5710; **Room:** SD-164

Ashcroft, chair	*Feingold*
Hatch	*Kennedy*

JUDICIARY (continued)

Abraham	Torricelli
Thurmond	
Thompson	

Immigration
Phone: (202) 224-6098; **Room:** SD-323

Abraham, chair	Kennedy
Grassley	Feinstein
Kyl	Durbin
Specter	

Technology, Terrorism, and Government Information
Phone: (202) 224-4521; **Room:** SH-702

Kyl, chair	Feinstein
Hatch	Biden
Specter	Durbin
Thompson	

Youth Violence
Phone: (202) 224-2808; **Room:** SD-163

Sessions, chair	Biden
Thompson	Torricelli
DeWine	Kohl
Ashcroft	Feinstein
Grassley	

LABOR AND HUMAN RESOURCES

Phone: (202) 224-5375; **Room:** SD-428
Staff Director: Mark Powden; (202) 224-6770; SH-835
Minority Staff Director: Nick Littlefield; (202) 224-7675; SD-644

Education, labor, health and public welfare in general; aging; arts and humanities; biomedical research and development; child labor; convict labor; domestic activities of the Red Cross; equal employment opportunity; handicapped people; labor standards and statistics; mediation and arbitration of labor disputes; occupational safety and health; private pensions; public health; railway labor and retirement; regulation of foreign laborers; student loans; wages and hours; agricultural colleges; Gallaudet University; Howard University; St. Elizabeths Hospital in Washington, D.C. The chair and ranking minority member are non-voting members ex officio of all subcommittees of which they are not regular members.
Party Ratio: R 10-D 8

James M. Jeffords, Vt., chair	Edward M. Kennedy, Mass., ranking member
Daniel R. Coats, Ind.	Christopher J. Dodd, Conn.
Judd Gregg, N.H.	Tom Harkin, Iowa
Bill Frist, Tenn.	Barbara A. Mikulski, Md.
Mike DeWine, Ohio	Jeff Bingaman, N.M.

Michael B. Enzi, Wyo.	Paul Wellstone, Minn.
Tim Hutchinson, Ark.	Patty Murray, Wash.
Susan Collins, Maine	Jack Reed, R.I.
John W. Warner, Va.	
Mitch McConnell, Ky.	

Subcommittees

Aging
Phone: (202) 224-0136; **Room:** SH-615

Gregg, chair	Mikulski
Hutchinson	Murray
Warner	

Children and Families
Phone: (202) 224-5800; **Room:** SH-625

Coats, chair	Dodd
Gregg	Bingaman
Frist	Wellstone
Hutchinson	Murray
Collins	Reed
McConnell	

Employment and Training
Phone: (202) 224-2962; **Room:** SH-608

DeWine, chair	Wellstone
Jeffords	Kennedy
Enzi	Dodd
Warner	Harkin
McConnell	

Public Health and Safety
Phone: (202) 224-7139; **Room:** SD-422

Frist, chair	Kennedy
Jeffords	Harkin
Coats	Mikulski
DeWine	Bingaman
Enzi	Reed
Collins	

RULES AND ADMINISTRATION

Phone: (202) 224-6352; **Room:** SR-305
Staff Director: Grayson Winterling; (202) 224-6352; SR-305
Minority Staff Director: Kennie L. Gill; (202) 224-6351; SR-479

Senate administration in general; corrupt practices; qualifications of senators; contested elections; federal elections in general; Government Printing Office; Congressional Record; meetings of Congress and attendance of members; presidential succession; the Capitol, congressional office buildings, the Library of Congress, the Smithsonian Institution and the Botanic Garden.
Party Ratio: R 9-D 7

John W. Warner, Va., chair
Jesse Helms, N.C.
Ted Stevens, Alaska
Mitch McConnell, Ky.
Thad Cochran, Miss.
Rick Santorum, Pa.
Don Nickles, Okla.
Trent Lott, Miss.
Kay Bailey Hutchison, Texas

Wendell H. Ford, Ky., ranking member
Robert C. Byrd, W.Va.
Daniel K. Inouye, Hawaii
Daniel Patrick Moynihan, N.Y.
Christopher J. Dodd, Conn.
Dianne Feinstein, Calif.
Robert G. Torricelli, N.J.

SELECT ETHICS

Phone: (202) 224-2981; **Room:** SH-220
Staff Director and Chief Counsel: Victor M. Baird; (202) 224-2981; SH-220

Studies and investigates standards and conduct of Senate members and employees and may recommend remedial action.
Party Ratio: R 3-D 3

Robert C. Smith, N.H., chair
Pat Roberts, Kan.
Jeff Sessions, Ala.

Harry Reid, Nev., vice-chair
Patty Murray, Wash.
Kent Conrad, N.D.

SELECT INTELLIGENCE

Phone: (202) 224-1700; **Room:** SH-211
Majority Staff Director: Taylor Lawrence; (202) 224-1700; SH-211
Minority Staff Director: Christopher Straub; (202) 224-1700; SH-211

Legislative and budgetary authority over the Central Intelligence Agency, the Defense Intelligence Agency, the National Security Agency and intelligence activities of the Federal Bureau of Investigation and other components of the federal intelligence community. The majority leader and minority leader are members ex officio of the committee.
Party Ratio: R 10-D 9

Richard C. Shelby, Ala., chair
John H. Chafee, R.I.
Richard G. Lugar, Ind.
Mike DeWine, Ohio
Jon Kyl, Ariz.
James M. Inhofe, Okla.
Orrin G. Hatch, Utah
Pat Roberts, Kan.
Wayne Allard, Colo.
Daniel R. Coats, Ind.

Bob Kerrey, Neb., ranking member
John Glenn, Ohio
Richard H. Bryan, Nev.
Bob Graham, Fla.
John Kerry, Mass.
Max Baucus, Mont.
Charles S. Robb, Va.
Frank R. Lautenberg, N.J.
Carl Levin, Mich.

SMALL BUSINESS

Phone: (202) 224-5175; **Room:** SR-428A
Staff Director and Chief Counsel: Louis Taylor; (202) 224-5175; SR-428A
Minority Staff Director: Patricia Forbes; (202) 224-8496; SR-275

Problems of small business; Small Business Administration.
Party Ratio: R 10-D 8

Christopher S. Bond, Mo., chair
Conrad Burns, Mont.
Paul Coverdell, Ga.
Dirk Kempthorne, Idaho
Robert F. Bennett, Utah
John W. Warner, Va.
Bill Frist, Tenn.
Olympia J. Snowe, Maine
Lauch Faircloth, N.C.
Michael B. Enzi, Wyo.

John Kerry, Mass., ranking member
Dale Bumpers, Ark.
Carl Levin, Mich.
Tom Harkin, Iowa
Joseph I. Lieberman, Conn.
Paul Wellstone, Minn.
Max Cleland, Ga.
Mary L. Landrieu, La.

SPECIAL AGING

Phone: (202) 224-5364; **Room:** SD-G31
Staff Director: Ted Totman; (202) 224-5364; SD-G31
Minority Staff Director: Bruce Lesley; (202) 224-1467; SH-628

Problems and opportunities of older people including health, income, employment, housing, and care and assistance. Reports findings and makes recommendations to the Senate, but cannot report legislation.
Party Ratio: R 10-D 8

Charles E. Grassley, Iowa, chair
James M. Jeffords, Vt.
Larry E. Craig, Idaho
Conrad Burns, Mont.
Richard C. Shelby, Ala.
Rick Santorum, Pa.
John W. Warner, Va.
Chuck Hagel, Neb.
Susan Collins, Maine
Michael B. Enzi, Wyo.

John B. Breaux, La., ranking member
John Glenn, Ohio
Harry Reid, Nev.
Herb Kohl, Wis.
Russell D. Feingold, Wis.
Carol Moseley-Braun, Ill.
Ron Wyden, Ore.
Jack Reed, R.I.

VETERANS' AFFAIRS

Phone: (202) 224-9126; **Room:** SR-412
Staff Director: Charles C. Battaglia; (202) 224-9126; SR-412
Minority Staff Director: James R. Gottlieb; (202) 224-2074; SH-202

Veterans' measures in general; compensation; life insurance issued by the government on account of ser-

VETERANS' AFFAIRS (continued)

vice in the armed forces; national cemeteries; pensions; readjustment benefits; veterans' hospitals, medical care and treatment; vocational rehabilitation and education.
Party Ratio: R 7-D 5

Arlen Specter, Pa., chair
Strom Thurmond, S.C.,
Frank H. Murkowski, Alaska
James M. Jeffords, Vt.
Ben Nighthorse Campbell, Colo.
Larry E. Craig, Idaho
Tim Hutchinson, Ark.

John D. Rockefeller IV, W.Va., ranking member
Bob Graham, Fla.
Daniel K. Akaka, Hawaii
Paul Wellstone, Minn.
Patty Murray, Wash.

PARTISAN COMMITTEES

DEMOCRATIC POLICY COMMITTEE

Phone: (202) 224-5551   **Room:** S-118 CAP

Tom Daschle, S.D., chair
Harry Reid, Nev., co-chair
Paul S. Sarbanes, Md., vice chair
Charles S. Robb, Va., vice chair
Patty Murray, Wash., vice chair
John Glenn, Ohio, vice chair

Jack Reed, R.I.
Max Cleland, Ga.
Bob Kerrey, Neb.
Ernest F. Hollings, S.C.
Dale Bumpers, Ark.
Daniel Patrick Moynihan, N.Y.
John D. Rockefeller IV, W.Va.
Daniel K. Akaka, Hawaii
Byron L. Dorgan, N.D.

Carol Moseley-Braun, Ill.
Russell D. Feingold, Wis.
Joseph I. Lieberman, Conn.
Paul Wellstone, Minn.
Dianne Feinstein, Calif.
Ron Wyden, Ore.
Robert G. Torricelli, N.J.
Wendell H. Ford, Ky.
Barbara A. Mikulski, Md.

DEMOCRATIC SENATORIAL CAMPAIGN COMMITTEE

Phone: (202) 224-2447   **Room:** 430 S. Capitol St., S.E. 20003

Bob Kerrey, Neb., chair
Max Baucus, Mont., Majority Trust Co-Chair
Richard H. Bryan, Nev., Roundtable Co-Chair
Kent Conrad, N.D., Leadership Circle Co-Chair
Richard J. Durbin, Ill., Political Whips Co-Chair
Dianne Feinstein, Calif., Women's Council Co-Chair
Tom Harkin, Iowa, Majority Trust Co-Chair
Edward M. Kennedy, Mass., Labor Council Co-Chair
Mary L. Landrieu, La., Women's Council Co-Chair

Joseph I. Lieberman, Conn., Political Whips Co-Chair
Jack Reed, R.I., Roundtable Co-Chair
Charles S. Robb, Va., Leadership Circle Co-Chair
John D. Rockefeller IV, W.Va., Majority Trust Co-Chair
Robert G. Torricelli, N.J., vice-chair
Paul Wellstone, Minn., Labor Council Co-Chair

DEMOCRATIC STEERING AND COORDINATION COMMITTEE

Phone: (202) 224-9048   **Room:** SH-712
John Kerry, Mass., chair

Daniel K. Inouye, Hawaii
Robert C. Byrd, W.Va.
Edward M. Kennedy, Mass.
Joseph R. Biden Jr., Del.
Wendell H. Ford, Ky.
Patrick J. Leahy, Vt.
Christopher J. Dodd, Conn.
Tom Harkin, Iowa
Max Baucus, Mont.
Bob Graham, Fla.

Kent Conrad, N.D.
Carl Levin, Mich.
Richard H. Bryan, Nev.
Herb Kohl, Wis.
Barbara Boxer, Calif.
John B. Breaux, La.
Tom Daschle, S.D.
Frank R. Lautenberg, N.J.
Jeff Bingaman, N.M.

DEMOCRATIC TECHNOLOGY AND COMMUNICATIONS COMMITTEE

Phone: (202) 224-1430   **Room:** SH-619

John D. Rockefeller IV, W.Va., chair
Jeff Bingaman, N.M.
John B. Breaux, La.
Kent Conrad, N.D.
Tom Daschle, S.D.
Christopher J. Dodd, Conn.
Wendell H. Ford, Ky.

John Glenn, Ohio
Ernest F. Hollings, S.C.
Frank R. Lautenberg, N.J.
Barbara A. Mikulski, Md.
Patty Murray, Wash.
Charles S. Robb, Va.

NATIONAL REPUBLICAN SENATORIAL COMMITTEE

Phone: (202) 675-6000   **Room:** 425 Second St., N.E. 20002

Mitch McConnell, Ky., chair
Spencer Abraham, Mich.
Mike DeWine, Ohio
Bill Frist, Tenn.
Chuck Hagel, Neb.
Tim Hutchinson, Ark.

James M. Inhofe, Okla.
Jon Kyl, Ariz.
Pat Roberts, Kan.
Rick Santorum, Pa.
Robert C. Smith, N.H.

REPUBLICAN COMMITTEE ON COMMITTEES

Phone: (202) 224-2752   **Room:** SH-313

Slade Gorton, Wash., chair
John Ashcroft, Mo.
Bill Frist, Tenn.
Rod Grams, Minn.

Orrin G. Hatch, Utah
Ted Stevens, Alaska
John W. Warner, Va.

REPUBLICAN POLICY COMMITTEE

Phone: (202) 224-2946 **Room:** SR-347

Larry E. Craig, Idaho, chair
John H. Chafee, R.I.
Paul Coverdell, Ga.
Alfonse M. D'Amato, N.Y.
Pete V. Domenici, N.M.
Orrin G. Hatch, Utah
Jesse Helms, N.C.

James M. Jeffords, Vt.
Trent Lott, Miss.
Richard G. Lugar, Ind.
Connie Mack, Fla.
John McCain, Ariz.
Frank Murkowski, Alaska
Don Nickles, Okla.
William V. Roth Jr., Del.
Richard C. Shelby, Ala.
Arlen Specter, Pa.
Ted Stevens, Alaska
Fred Thompson, Tenn.
Strom Thurmond, S.C.
John W. Warner, Va.

Senate Leadership

DEMOCRATIC LEADERS

President   *Al Gore, Tenn.*

Minority Leader   *Tom Daschle, S.D.*

Minority Whip   *Wendell H. Ford, Ky.*

Conference Chair   *Tom Daschle, S.D.*

Conference Secretary   *Barbara A. Mikulski, Md.*

Chief Deputy Whip   *John B. Breaux, La.*

Assistant Floor Leader   *Byron L. Dorgan, N.D.*

Deputy Whip   *Jeff Bingaman, N.M.*

Deputy Whip   *Joseph I. Lieberman, Conn.*

Deputy Whip

Patty Murray, Wash.

Charles S. Robb, Va.

Policy Committee

  Co-Chair   *Tom Daschle, S.D.*

  Co-Chair   *Harry Reid, Nev.*

Steering and Coordination

  Committee Chair   *John Kerry, Mass.*

Technology and Communications

  Committee Chair   *John D. Rockefeller IV, W.Va.*

Democratic Senatorial Campaign

  Committee Chair   *Vacancy*

REPUBLICAN LEADERS

President Pro Tempore   Strom Thurmond, S.C.

Majority Leader   Trent Lott, Miss.

Assistant Majority Leader   Don Nickles, Okla.

Conference Chair   Connie Mack, Fla.

Conference Secretary   Paul Coverdell, Ga.

Chief Deputy Whip   Judd Gregg, N.H.

Deputy Whip

Spencer Abraham, Mich.	Kay Bailey Hutchison,
John Ashcroft, Mo.	Texas
Conrad Burns, Mont.	Dirk Kempthorne, Idaho
Daniel R. Coats, Ind.	Jon Kyl, Ariz.
Susan Collins, Maine	Gordon H. Smith, Ore.
Chuck Hagel, Neb.	Olympia J. Snowe, Maine

Policy Committee

  Chair   Larry E. Craig, Idaho

Committee on Committees

  Chair   Slade Gorton, Wash.

National Republican Senatorial

  Committee Chair   Mitch McConnell, Ky.

Senate Members' Offices

The list below gives the names of Senate members and their party, state, and district affiliation, followed by addresses and telephone numbers for their Washington offices. The list also gives the name of a top administrative aide for each member.

The address, telephone number, and director for the members' district offices are listed. Each senator's committee assignments are given as the final entry. For partisan committee assignments, see p. 816.

As of March 14, 1998, there were 55 Republicans and 45 Democrats. This information was gathered by Congressional Quarterly from Senate offices in Washington, D.C.

ABRAHAM, SPENCER, R-MICH.

Capitol Hill office: SD-329 20510; (202) 224-4822; Fax: (202) 224-8834; Internet: michigan@abraham.senate. gov or www.senate.gov/~abraham/; *Chief of Staff:* Jim Pitts

State office(s): 26222 Telegraph Rd., Southfield 48034; (810) 350-0510; Fax: (810) 350-0420; *State Director:* Laurie Bink.

3738 28th St. S.E., Grand Rapids 49512; (616) 975-1112; Fax: (616) 975-1119.

200 N. Capitol Ave., Lansing 48933; (517) 484-1984; Fax: (517) 484-3099.

202 W. Washington St., Marquette 49855; (906) 226-9466; Fax: (906) 226-9464.

301 E. Genesee St., Saginaw 48607; (517) 752-4400; Fax: (517) 752-4492.

Committee assignment(s): Budget; Commerce, Science and Transportation; Judiciary

AKAKA, DANIEL K., D-HAWAII

Capitol Hill office: SH-720 20510; (202) 224-6361; Fax: (202) 224-2126; Internet: www.senate.gov/senator/ akaka.html; *Administrative Assistant:* James Sakai

State office(s): 300 Ala Moana Blvd., #3104, Honolulu 96850; (808) 522-8970; Fax: (808) 545-4683; *Chief of Staff:* Mike Kitamura.

Committee assignment(s): Energy and Natural Resources; Governmental Affairs; Indian Affairs; Veterans' Affairs

ALLARD, WAYNE, R-COLO.

Capitol Hill office: SH-513 20510; (202) 224-5941; Fax: 225-8630; Internet: www.senate.gov/~allard/ webform.html or www.senate.gov/~allard/; *Administrative Assistant:* Mike Bennett

State office(s): 7340 E. Caley, #215, Englewood 80111; (303) 220-7414; Fax: (303) 220-8126; *Area Director:* Barb McTurks.

3400 16th St., #30, Greeley 80631; (970) 351-7582; Fax: (970) 351-7585; *District Press, Congressional Aide:* Sean P. Conway.

228 N. Cascade Ave., #106, Colorado Springs 80903; (719) 634-6071; Fax: (719) 636-2590; *Area Director:* Jim Bensberg.

411 Thatcher Bldg., Main St., Pueblo 81003; (719) 545-9751; Fax: (719) 545-3832; *Area Director:* Doris Morgan.

400 Rood Ave., #215, Grand Junction 81501; (970) 245-9553; Fax: (970) 245-9523; *Area Director:* Andy Colosimo.

Committee assignment(s): Banking, Housing and Urban Affairs; Environment and Public Works; Select Intelligence

ASHCROFT, JOHN, R-MO.

Capitol Hill office: SH-316 20510; (202) 224-6154; Fax: 228-0998; Internet: john_ashcroft@ashcroft.senate. gov or www.senate.gov/~ashcroft/; *Chief of Staff:* David T. Ayres

State office(s): 1233 Jefferson St., Jefferson City 65101; (573) 635-7292; *Constituent Services Director:* Liz Behrooz.

339 Broadway, #214, Cape Girardeau 63701; (573) 334-7044; Fax: (573) 334-7352; *District Office Director:* Tom Schulte.

600 Broadway, #100, Kansas City 64105; (816) 471-7141; Fax: (816) 471-7338; *District Office Director:* William Leathem.

1736 E. Sunshine St., #705, Springfield 65804; (417) 881-7068; Fax: (417) 881-8532; *District Office Director:* Steve Hilton.

8000 Maryland Av., #440, St. Louis 63105; (314) 725-4748; Fax: (314) 725-4268; *District Office Director:* Joe Messner.

Committee assignment(s): Commerce, Science and Transportation; Foreign Relations; Judiciary

BAUCUS, MAX, D-MONT.

Capitol Hill office: SH-511 20510; (202) 224-2651; Internet: max@baucus.senate.gov or www.senate.gov/~baucus/; *Chief of Staff:* David Castagnetti

State office(s): 207 N. Broadway, Billings 59101; (406) 657-6790; Fax: (406) 657-6793; *Assistant State Director:* Sharon Peterson.

18 5th St. South, Great Falls 59401; (406) 761-1574; Fax: (406) 761-3726; *Field Director:* Greg Eklund.

23 S. Last Chance Gulch, Helena 59601; (406) 449-5480; Fax: (406) 449-5484; *Mont. State Director:* Doug Mitchell.

125 W. Granite St., Butte 59701; (406) 782-8700; Fax: (406) 782-6553; *Field Director:* Kim Krueger.

32 E. Babcock St., Bozeman 59715; (406) 586-6104; Fax: (406) 586-9177; *Field Director:* Alicha Bradshaw.

211 N. Higgins Ave., #102, Missoula 59802; (406) 329-3123; *Field Representative:* Cheryl Sue Tillett.

220 1st Ave. East, Kalispell 59901; (406) 756-1150; Fax: (406) 756-1152; *Field Director:* Hazel Spencer.

Committee assignment(s): Joint Taxation; Agriculture, Nutrition and Forestry; Environment and Public Works (ranking member); Finance; Select Intelligence

BENNETT, ROBERT F., R-UTAH

Capitol Hill office: SD-431 20510; (202) 224-5444; Internet: senator@bennett.senate.gov or www.senate.gov/~bennett/; *Chief of Staff:* James C. Barker

State office(s): Federal Bldg, 125 S. State St., #4225, Salt Lake City 84138; (801) 524-5933; Fax: (801) 524-5730; *State Director:* Dixie L. Minson.

324 25th St., #1410, Ogden 84401; (801) 625-5676; Fax: (801) 625-5692; *Area Director:* Beth Maughn.

51 S. University Ave., #310, Provo 84601; (801) 379-2525; Fax: (801) 374-2938; *Area Director:* Brad Schaeffer.

196 E. Tabernacle St., #22, St. George 84770; (801) 628-5514; Fax: (801) 628-4160; *Area Director:* Bruce Richesson.

Committee assignment(s): Joint Economic; Appropriations; Banking, Housing and Urban Affairs; Governmental Affairs; Small Business

BIDEN, JOSEPH R., JR., D-DEL.

Capitol Hill office: SR-221 20510; (202) 224-5042; Fax: (202) 224-0139; Internet: senator@biden.senate.gov or www.senate.gov/~biden/; *Acting Chief of Staff:* Dennis Toner

State office(s): 844 King St., #6021, Wilmington 19801; (302) 573-6345; Fax: (302) 573-0351; *State Director:* Claire DeMatteis.

300 S. New St., Dover 19901; (302) 678-9483; Fax: (302) 678-2106; *Staff Assistant:* Lisa Williams.

Georgetown Professional Park, 600 N. DuPont Hwy., #108, Georgetown 19947; (302) 856-9275; Fax: (302) 856-9685; *Staff Assistant:* Kevin Smith.

Committee assignment(s): Foreign Relations (ranking member); Judiciary

BINGAMAN, JEFF, D-N.M.

Capitol Hill office: SH-703 20510; (202) 224-5521; Fax: (202) 224-2852; Internet: senator_bingaman@ bingaman.senate.gov or www.senate.gov/~bingaman/; *Administrative Assistant:* Patrick Von Bargen

State office(s): 625 Silver Ave. S.W., #130, Albuquerque 87102; (505) 766-3636; *State Director:* Sheila Hyde.

119 E. Marcy St., #101, Santa Fe 87501; (505) 988-6647; *Constituent Services Representative:* Dolores Garcia.

505 S. Main, #148, Las Cruces 88001; (505) 523-6561; *District Coordinator:* Alice Salcido.

105 W. 3rd, #101, Roswell 88201; (505) 622-7113; *Issues Director:* Lyn Ditto.

118 Bridge St., #3, Las Vegas 87701; (505) 454-8824; Fax: (505) 454-8959; : Rebecca Montoya.

Committee assignment(s): Joint Economic; Armed Services; Energy and Natural Resources; Labor and Human Resources

BOND, CHRISTOPHER S., R-MO.

Capitol Hill office: SR-274 20510; (202) 224-5721; Fax: (202) 224-8149; Internet: kit_bond@bond.senate.gov or www.senate.gov/~bond; *Chief of Staff:* Julie Dammann

State office(s): 8000 Maryland Ave., #1050, St. Louis 63105; (314) 727-7773; Fax: (314) 727-3548; *District Office Director:* Catharine Hanaway.

339 Broadway, #214, Cape Girardeau 63701; (573) 334-7044; Fax: (573) 334-7352; *Special Assistant:* Tom Schulte.

308 E. High St., #202, Jefferson City 65101; (573) 634-2488; Fax: (573) 634-6005; *Director of In-State Services:* Mary Beth Dobbs.

1736 E. Sunshine St., #705, Springfield 65804; (417) 881-7068; Fax: (417) 881-8532; *District Office Director:* Darren Ethridge.

600 Broadway, #400, Kansas City 64105; (816) 471-7141; Fax: (816) 471-7338; *District Office Director:* Brad Scott.

Committee assignment(s): Appropriations; Budget; Environment and Public Works; Small Business (chair)

BOXER, BARBARA, D-CALIF.

Capitol Hill office: SH-112 20510; (202) 224-3553; Internet: senator@boxer.senate.gov or www.senate.gov/~boxer/; *Administrative Assistant:* Karen Olick

State office(s): 2250 E. Imperial Hwy., #545, El Segundo 90245; (310) 414-5700; *Regional Director:* Larry Kaplan.

525 B St., #990, San Diego 92101; (619) 239-3884; *Community Representative:* Dan Hammer.

2300 Tulare St., #130, Fresno 93721; (209) 497-5109; *Community Representative:* Thomas Bohigian.

1700 Montgomery St., #240, San Francisco 94111; (415) 403-0100; *Chief of Staff:* Sam T. Chapman.

650 Capitol Mall, #6544, Sacramento 95814; (916) 448-2787; *Community Representative:* Charlotte Lopez-Rojas.

210 N. E St., #210, San Bernardino 92401; (909) 888-8525; *Community Representative:* Leannah Bradley.

Committee assignment(s): Appropriations; Banking, Housing and Urban Affairs; Budget; Environment and Public Works

BREAUX, JOHN B., D-LA.

Capitol Hill office: SH-516 20510; (202) 224-4623; Fax: 228-2577; Internet: senator@breaux.senate.gov or www.senate.gov/~breaux/; *Administrative Assistant:* Tommy Hudson

State office(s): 501 Magazine St., #1005, New Orleans 70130; (504) 589-2531; Fax: (504) 589-2531; *State Director:* Jim Nickel.

705 Jefferson St., #103, Lafayette 70501; (318) 262-6871; Fax: (318) 262-6874; *Executive Assistant:* Raymond Cordova.

1 American Place, #2030, Baton Rouge 70825; (504) 382-2050; Fax: (504) 382-2059; *Constituent Service Representative:* Suzy Warfield.

211 N. 3rd St., #102A, Monroe 71202; (318) 325-3320; Fax: (318) 325-3320; *Constituent Services Representative:* Jean Bates.

Committee assignment(s): Special Aging (ranking member); Commerce, Science and Transportation; Finance

BROWNBACK, SAM, R-KAN.

Capitol Hill office: SH-303 20510; (202) 224-6521; Fax: 228-1265; Internet: sam_brownback@brownback.senate.gov or www.senate.gov/~brownback/; *Administrative Assistant:* Tim McGivern

State office(s): 612 S. Kansas, Topeka 66603; (913) 233-2503; Fax: (913) 233-2616; *District Director:* Anne Emerson.

Committee assignment(s): Joint Economic; Commerce, Science and Transportation; Foreign Relations; Governmental Affairs

BRYAN, RICHARD H., D-NEV.

Capitol Hill office: SR-269 20510; (202) 224-6244; Fax: (202) 224-1867; Internet: senator@bryan.senate.gov or www.senate.gov/~bryan/; *Administrative Assistant:* Jean Marie Neal

State office(s): 300 Las Vegas Blvd., #1110, Las Vegas 89101; (702) 388-6605; *Southern Director:* Sara Besser.

400 S. Virginia St., #702, Reno 89501; (702) 686-5770; *Reno Area Director:* Kay Zunino.

600 E. William St., #304, Carson City 89701; (702) 885-9111; *Rural Field Representative:* Tom Baker.

Committee assignment(s): Banking, Housing and Urban Affairs; Commerce, Science and Transportation; Finance; Select Intelligence

BUMPERS, DALE, D-ARK.

Capitol Hill office: SD-229 20510; (202) 224-4843; Fax: (202) 224-6435; Internet: senator@bumpers.senate.gov or www.senate.gov/~bumpers; *Administrative Assistant:* Mary Hope Davis

State office(s): 700 W. Capitol Ave., #2527, Little Rock 72201; (501) 324-6286; *State Office Director:* Martha Perry.

Committee assignment(s): Appropriations; Energy and Natural Resources (ranking member); Small Business

BURNS, CONRAD, R-MONT.

Capitol Hill office: SD-187 20510; (202) 224-2644; Fax: (202) 224-8594; Internet: conrad_burns@burns.senate.gov or www.senate.gov/~burns; *Chief of Staff:* Leo Giacometto

State office(s): 2708 1st Ave. North, Billings 59101; (406) 252-0550; Fax: (406) 252-7768; *State Director:* Dwight MacKay.

324 W. Towne St., Glendive 59330; (406) 365-2391; Fax: (406) 365-8836; *Field Representative:* Pamela Tierney Crisafulli.

321 1st Ave. North, Great Falls 59401; (406) 452-9585; Fax: (406) 452-9586; *Field Representative:* Mike Brown.

208 N. Montana Ave., #202A, Helena 59601; (406) 449-5401; Fax: (406) 449-5462; *State Press Aide:* Betsy Allen.

125 W. Granite St., #211, Butte 59701; (406) 723-3277; Fax: (406) 782-4717; *Field Representative:* Cindy Perdue Dollan.

211 Haggerty Lane, Bozeman 59771; (406) 586-4450; Fax: (406) 586-7647; *Field Representative:* Mike Harris.

415 N. Higgins Ave., P. O. Box 8237, Missoula 59807; (406) 728-3606; Fax: (406) 728-2193; *Field Representative:* Amy Fischer.

575 Sunset Blvd., #101, Kalispell 59901; (406) 257-3360; Fax: (406) 257-3974; *Field Representative:* Stephanie Ryan.

Committee assignment(s): Special Aging; Appropriations; Commerce, Science and Transportation; Energy and Natural Resources; Small Business

BYRD, ROBERT C., D-W.VA.

Capitol Hill office: SH-311 20510; (202) 224-3954; Internet: senator_byrd@byrd.senate.gov or www.senate.gov/~byrd; *Administrative Assistant:* Lisa Tuite

State office(s): 500 Quarrier St., #1019, Charleston 25301; (304) 342-5855; *State Director:* Anne S. Barth.

Committee assignment(s): Appropriations (ranking member); Armed Services; Rules and Administration

CAMPBELL, BEN NIGHTHORSE, R-COLO.

Capitol Hill office: SR-380 20510; (202) 224-5852; Fax: (202) 224-1933; Internet: www.senate.gov/senator/campbell.html; *Chief of Staff:* Ginnie Kontnik

State office(s): 1129 Pennsylvania St., Denver 80203; (303) 866-1900; *Chief of Staff:* James Doyle.

19 Old Town Square, #238, Fort Collins 80524; (970) 224-1909; *District Director:* Keith Johnson.

105 E. Vermijo, #600, Colorado Springs 80903; (719) 636-9092; *District Director:* Dave Devendorf.

720 N. Main St., #402, Pueblo 81003; (719) 542-6987; *District Director:* Alberta Vega.

300 Main St., #306, Grand Junction 81501; (970) 241-6631; *District Director:* Dave Blair.

Committee assignment(s): Appropriations; Energy and Natural Resources; Indian Affairs (chair); Veterans' Affairs

CHAFEE, JOHN H., R-R.I.

Capitol Hill office: SD-505 20510; (202) 224-2921; Internet: senator_chafee@chafee.senate.gov or www.senate.gov/~chafee; *Chief of Staff:* David A. Griswold

State office(s): 10 Dorrance St., #221, Providence 02903; (401) 528-5294; Fax: (401) 528-5043; *Director:* Keith Lang.

Committee assignment(s): Joint Taxation; Environment and Public Works (chair); Finance; Select Intelligence

CLELAND, MAX, D-GA.

Capitol Hill office: SD-461 20510; (202) 224-3521; Fax: (202) 224-0072; Internet: senator_max_cleland@cleland.senate.gov or www.senate.gov/~cleland; *Administrative Assistant:* Wayne Howell

State office(s): 75 Spring St. S.W., #1700, Atlanta 30303; (404) 331-4811; Fax: (404) 331-5439; *State Director:* Bill Chapman.

120 12th St., #101, Columbus 31902; (706) 649-7705; *District Representative:* Bobbie Alexander.

Committee assignment(s): Armed Services; Governmental Affairs; Small Business

COATS, DANIEL R., R-IND.

Capitol Hill office: SR-404 20510; (202) 224-5623; Internet: www.senate.gov/~coats; *Chief of Staff:* Sharon Soderstrom

State office(s): 10 W. Market St., #1180, Indianapolis 46204; (317) 226-5555; *State Director:* Bill Dull.

8585 Browadway, Merrillville 46410; (219) 736-9084; *Northwest Regional Director:* Timothy J. Sanders.

1300 S. Harrison St., #3158, Fort Wayne 46802; (219) 422-1505; *Northeast Regional Director:* Phil Shaull.

1201 E. 10th St., #103, Jeffersonville 47132; (812) 288-3377; *Southeast Regional Director:* David Graham.

101 N.W. Martin Luther King Jr. Blvd., #122, Evansville 47708; (812) 465-6313; *Southwest Regional Director:* Mike Duckworth.

Committee assignment(s): Armed Services; Select Intelligence; Labor and Human Resources

COCHRAN, THAD, R-MISS.

Capitol Hill office: SR-326 20510; (202) 224-5054; Internet: senator@cochran.senate.gov or www.senate.gov/~cochran/; *Chief of Staff:* Mark Keenum

State office(s): 911 Jackson Ave., 2nd Floor, Oxford 38655; (601) 236-1018; Fax: (601) 236-7618; *Staff Assistant:* Ruthie Ervin.

188 E. Capitol St., #614, Jackson 39201; (601) 965-4459.

Committee assignment(s): Joint Library; Joint Printing; Agriculture, Nutrition and Forestry; Appropriations; Governmental Affairs; Rules and Administration

COLLINS, SUSAN, R-MAINE

Capitol Hill office: SR-172 20510; (202) 224-2523; Fax: (202) 224-2693; Internet: senator@collins.senate.gov or www.senate.gov/senator/collins.html; *Chief of Staff:* Steve Abbott

State office(s): 202 Harlow St., #204, P.O. Box 655, Bangor 04401; (207) 945-0417; Fax: (207) 990-4604; *State Office Representative:* Judy Cuddy.

150 Capitol St., 1st Floor, Augusta 04332; (207) 622-8414; Fax: (207) 622-5884.

109 Alfred St., Biddeford 04005; (207) 283-1101; Fax: (207) 283-4054; *State Office Representative:* Cliff Garvey.

11 Lisbon St., Lewiston 04240; (207) 784-6969; Fax: (207) 784-6475; *State Office Representative:* Dan Demeritt.

169 Academy St., Presque Isle 04769; (207) 764-3266; Fax: (207) 764-8412; *State Office Representative:* Phil Bosse.

10 Moulton St., Portland 04101; (207) 780-3575; Fax: (207) 828-0380; *State Office Representative:* Gary Reed.

Committee assignment(s): Special Aging; Governmental Affairs; Labor and Human Resources

CONRAD, KENT, D-N.D.

Capitol Hill office: SH-530 20510; (202) 224-2043; Fax: (202) 224-7776; Internet: senator@conrad.senate.gov or www.senate.gov/~conrad; *Chief of Staff:* Kent Hall

State office(s): 657 2nd Ave. North, #306, Fargo 58102; (701) 232-8030; *State Representative:* Lois E. Schneider.

102 N. 4th St., #104, Grand Forks 58203; (701) 775-9601; *State Representative:* James S. Hand.

228 Federal Bldg., 3rd St. and Rosser Ave., Bismarck 58501; (701) 258-4648; *State Director:* Lynn J. Clancy.

100 1st St. S.W., #105, Minot 58701; (701) 852-0703; *State Representative:* Gail Bergstad.

Committee assignment(s): Agriculture, Nutrition and Forestry; Budget; Select Ethics; Finance; Indian Affairs

COVERDELL, PAUL, R-GA.

Capitol Hill office: SR-200 20510; (202) 224-3643; Fax: 228-3783; Internet: senator_coverdell@coverdell. senate.gov or www.senate.gov/~coverdell; *Administrative Assistant:* Molly Dye

State office(s): 1175 Peachtree St., #300, Atlanta 30361; (404) 347-2202; Fax: (404) 347-2243; *State Director for Constituent Services:* Shirley A. Puchalski.

503 S. Thornton Ave., Dalton 30720; (706) 226-1925; Fax: (706) 226-2014; *Regional Representative:* Marc Peoples.

699 Broad St., #1208, Augusta 30901; (706) 722-0032; *Regional Representative:* Donald Stewart.

582 Walnut St., Macon 31297; (912) 742-0205; Fax: (912) 742-0900; *Regional Representative:* Patroski Lawson.

2 E. Bryan St., #1502, Savannah 31401; (912) 238-3244; Fax: (912) 238-1240; *Regional Representative:* Donald Stewart.

22 N. Main St., Moultrie 31768; (912) 985-8113; Fax: (912) 985-8018; *Regional Representative:* Kent Sole.

10 Eleventh St., Columbus 31901; (706) 322-7920; Fax: (706) 322-7967; *Regional Representative:* Dutsch Roberts.

Committee assignment(s): Agriculture, Nutrition and Forestry; Foreign Relations; Small Business

CRAIG, LARRY E., R-IDAHO

Capitol Hill office: SH-313 20510; (202) 224-2752; Internet: larry_craig@craig.senate.gov or www.senate. gov/~craig; *Chief of Staff:* Michael O. Ware

State office(s): 250 S. 4th Ave., Pocatello 83201; (208) 236-6817; Fax: (208) 236-6820; *Regional Director:* Greg Rice.

1292 Addison Ave. East, Twin Falls 83301; (208) 734-6780; Fax: (208) 734-3905; *Regional Director:* Michael Mathews.

2539 Channing Way, Idaho Falls 83404; (208) 523-5541; Fax: (208) 522-0135; *Regional Assistant:* Georgia Dixon.

633 Main St., Lewiston 83501; (208) 743-0792; Fax: (208) 746-7275; *Regional Assistant:* Susan Fagan.

304 N. 8th St., #149, Boise 83702; (208) 342-7985; Fax: (208) 342-8234; *Regional Director:* Ken Burgess.

103 N. 4th St., Coeur d'Alene 83814; (208) 667-6130; Fax: (208) 765-1743; *State Director:* Sandra Patano.

Committee assignment(s): Special Aging; Agriculture, Nutrition and Forestry; Appropriations; Energy and Natural Resources; Veterans' Affairs

D'AMATO, ALFONSE M., R-N.Y.

Capitol Hill office: SH-520 20510; (202) 224-6542; Fax: (202) 224-5871; Internet: senator_al@damato.senate. gov or www.senate.gov/~damato; *Administrative Assistant:* Michael T. Kinsella

State office(s): 250 W. 34th St., #600, New York 10001; (212) 947-7390; Fax: (212) 564-5066; *Executive Assistant:* Margaret Dillon.

1 Clinton Ave., #420, Albany 12207; (518) 472-4343; Fax: (518) 472-4414; *Upstate Coordinator:* David Poleto.

100 S. Clinton St., #1259, Syracuse 13260; (315) 423-5471; Fax: (315) 423-5185; *Executive Assistant:* Gretchen Ralph.

111 W. Huron St., #620, Buffalo 14202; (716) 846-4111; Fax: (716) 846-4113; *Executive Assistant:* Jane M. O'Bannon.

100 State St., #304, Rochester 14614; (716) 263-5866; Fax: (716) 263-3173; *Special Assistant:* Joan Mueller.

Committee assignment(s): Banking, Housing and Urban Affairs (chair); Finance

DASCHLE, TOM, D-S.D.

Capitol Hill office: SH-509 20510; (202) 224-2321; Internet: tom_daschle@daschle.senate.gov or www.senate.gov/~daschle/; *Chief of Staff:* Peter Rouse

State office(s): 810 S. Minnesota Ave., P.O. Box 1274, Sioux Falls 57101; (605) 334-9596; Fax: (605) 334-2591; *State Director:* Steve Erpenbach.

20 6th Ave. S.W., Suite B, Aberdeen 57401; (605) 225-8823; *Aberdeen Office Director:* Beth Smith.

816 6th St., P.O. Box 8168, Rapid City 57701; (605) 348-7551; Fax: (605) 348-7208; *W. River Area Director:* Ace Gallagher.

Committee assignment(s): Agriculture, Nutrition and Forestry

DEWINE, MIKE, R-OHIO

Capitol Hill office: SR-140 20510; (202) 224-2315; Fax: (202) 224-6519; Internet: senator_dewine@dewine.senate.gov or www.senate.gov/~dewine/; *Chief of Staff:* Laurel Pressler

State office(s): 37 W. Broad St., #970, Columbus 43215; (614) 469-6774; Fax: (614) 469-7419; *Chief of Staff:* Laurel A. Pressler.

550 Main St., #10411, Cincinnati 45202; (513) 684-3894; Fax: (513) 352-0625; *District Representative:* Jana Moreford.

1240 E. 9th St., #2915, Cleveland 44199; (216) 522-7272; Fax: (216) 522-2239; *District Representative:* Joshua Rubin.

200 Putnam St., #522, Marietta 45750; (614) 373-2317; Fax: (614) 373-8689; *District Representative:* Lynne M. Crow.

234 N. Summit St., #716, Toledo 43604; (419) 259-7535; Fax: (419) 259-7575; *District Representative:* Kathleen A. Teigland.

265 S. Allison Ave., #105, Xenia 45385; (937) 376-3080; Fax: (937) 376-3387; *State Director:* Barbara Briggs Schenck.

Committee assignment(s): Select Intelligence; Judiciary; Labor and Human Resources

DODD, CHRISTOPHER J., D-CONN.

Capitol Hill office: SR-444 20510; (202) 224-2823; Internet: sen_dodd@dodd.senate.gov or www.senate.gov/~dodd; *Chief of Staff:* Stephenie Foster

State office(s): Putnam Park, 100 Great Meadow Rd., Wethersfield 06109; (860) 240-3470; *State Director:* Ed Mann.

Committee assignment(s): Banking, Housing and Urban Affairs; Foreign Relations; Labor and Human Resources; Rules and Administration

DOMENICI, PETE V., R-N.M.

Capitol Hill office: SH-328 20510; (202) 224-6621; Internet: senator_domenici@domenici.senate.gov or www.senate.gov/~domenici; *Administrative Assistant:* Steve Bell

State office(s): 625 Silver Ave. S.W., #120, Albuquerque 87102; (505) 766-3481; *Northern Regional Director:* Lisa Breeden.

120 S. Federal Place, #302, Santa Fe 87501; (505) 988-6511; *Office Manager:* Maggie Murray.

1065 S. Main St., Bldg. D-13, Suite I, Las Cruces 88005; (505) 526-5475; *Southwest Regional Director:* Darlene Garcia.

140 Federal Bldg., Roswell 88201; (505) 623-6170; *Southern Regional Director:* Poe R. Corn.

Committee assignment(s): Appropriations; Budget (chair); Energy and Natural Resources; Governmental Affairs; Indian Affairs

DORGAN, BYRON L., D-N.D.

Capitol Hill office: SH-713 20510; (202) 224-2551; Fax: (202) 224-1193; Internet: senator@dorgan.senate.gov or www.senate.gov/~dorgan; *Chief of Staff:* Lucy Calautti

State office(s): 112 Roberts St., #110, P.O. Box 2250, Fargo 58107; (701) 239-5389; Fax: (701) 239-5512; *Fargo Coordinator:* Kevin Carvell.

312 Federal Bldg., 3rd and Rosser Ave., P.O. Box 2579, Bismarck 58502; (701) 250-4618; Fax: (701) 250-4484; *State Coordinator:* Bob Valeu.

102 N. 4th St., #10, Grand Forks 58201; (701) 746-9126; Fax: (701) 746-9122.

100 1st St. S.W., #105, Minot 58701; (701) 852-0703; Fax: (701) 838-8196; *State Representative:* Gail Bergstad.

Committee assignment(s): Appropriations; Commerce, Science and Transportation; Energy and Natural Resources; Indian Affairs

DURBIN, RICHARD J., D-ILL.

Capitol Hill office: SR-364 20510; (202) 224-2152; Fax: 228-0400; Internet: dick@durbin.senate.gov or www.senate.gov/~durbin; *Administrative Assistant:* Ed Greelegs

State office(s): 525 S. 8th St., P.O. Box 790, Springfield 62705; (217) 492-4062; *State Director:* Michael E. Daly.

230 S. Dearborn, Chicago 60604; (312) 353-4952; *Office Director:* Margaret Houlihan.

Committee assignment(s): Budget; Governmental Affairs; Judiciary

ENZI, MICHAEL B., R-WYO.

Capitol Hill office: SR-290 20510; (202) 224-3424; Internet: senator@enzi.senate.gov or www.senate.gov/~enzi/; *Chief of Staff:* Flip McConnaughey

State office(s): 2120 Capitol Ave., #2007, Cheyenne 82001; (307) 772-2477; Fax: (307) 772-2480; *State Director:* Dee Rodekohr.

510 S. Gillette Ave., Gillette 82716; (307) 682-6268; Fax: (307) 682-6501; *State Representative:* Robin Bailey.

100 E. B St., #3201, Casper 82801; (307) 261-6572; Fax: (307) 261-6574; *State Representative:* Cheri Burd.

1285 Sheridan Ave., #210, Cody 82414; (307) 527-9444; Fax: (307) 527-9478; *State Representative:* Karen McCreery.

545 W. Broadway, Jackson 83001; (307) 738-9507; Fax: (307) 739-9520; *State Representative:* Lyn Schanaghy.

Committee assignment(s): Special Aging; Banking, Housing and Urban Affairs; Labor and Human Resources; Small Business

FAIRCLOTH, LAUCH, R-N.C.

Capitol Hill office: SH-317 20510; (202) 224-3154; Internet: senator@faircloth.senate.gov or www.senate.gov/~faircloth; *Administrative Assistant:* Jonathan Hill

State office(s): 251 Main St., #422, Winston Salem 27101; (910) 631-5313; Fax: (910) 631-5315; *Director:* Mary Comer.

301 New Bern Ave., #120, Raleigh 27601; (919) 856-4791; Fax: (919) 856-4161; *Director:* Mary Bear.

401 W. Trade St., #219, Charlotte 28202; (704) 375-1993; Fax: (704) 334-0993; *Director:* Chuck Fuller.

109A W. Main St., Clinton 28328; (910) 590-3200; Fax: (910) 590-2806; *Regional Director:* Betty Jo Faircloth.

151 Patton Ave., #251, Asheville 28801; (704) 254-3099; Fax: (704) 251-0767; *Director:* Scotty Morgan.

Committee assignment(s): Appropriations; Banking, Housing and Urban Affairs; Small Business

FEINGOLD, RUSSELL D., D-WIS.

Capitol Hill office: SH-716 20510; (202) 224-5323; Fax: (202) 224-2725; Internet: senator@feingold.senate.gov or www.senate.gov/~feingold; *Administrative Assistant:* Mary Murphy

State office(s): 517 E. Wisconsin Ave., #408, Milwaukee 53202; (414) 276-7282; *Southeastern Regional Coordinator:* Cecilia B. Smith-Robertson.

8383 Greenway Blvd., Middleton 53562; (608) 828-1200; *Executive Assistant:* Nancy J. Mitchell.

425 State St., #232, La Crosse 54601; (608) 782-5585; *Northern and Western Regional Coordinator:* Matt Nikolay.

317 1st St., #107, Wausau 54403; (715) 848-5660; *Regional Coordinator:* Karen Graff.

1640 Main St., Green Bay 54302; (920) 465-7508; *Regional Coordinator:* Suzanne Pagel.

Committee assignment(s): Special Aging; Budget; Foreign Relations; Judiciary

FEINSTEIN, DIANNE, D-CALIF.

Capitol Hill office: SH-331 20510; (202) 224-3841; Fax: 228-3954; Internet: senator@feinstein.senate.gov or www.senate.gov/~feinstein/; *Chief of Staff:* Mike McGill

State office(s): 11111 Santa Monica Blvd., #915, Los Angeles 90025; (310) 914-7300; Fax: (310) 914-7318; *Director:* Ken Price.

705 B St., #1030, San Diego 92101; (619) 231-9712; Fax: (619) 231-1108; *Director:* Mike Richmond.

1130 O St., #2446, Fresno 93721; (209) 485-7430; Fax: (209) 485-7318; *Field Representative:* Stacy Krum.

525 Market St., #3670, San Francisco 94111; (415) 536-6868; Fax: (415) 536-6841; *State Director:* Bill Chandler.

Committee assignment(s): Joint Library; Foreign Relations; Judiciary; Rules and Administration

FORD, WENDELL H., D-KY.

Capitol Hill office: SR-173A 20510; (202) 224-4343; Fax: (202) 224-0046; Internet: wendell_ford@ford.senate.gov or www.senate.gov/~ford/; *Administrative Assistant:* Rob Mangas

State office(s): 600 Martin Luther King Blvd., #1072, Louisville 40202; (502) 582-6251; Fax: (502) 582-5117; *Field Representative:* Jesse C. McKnight.

343 Waller Ave., Suie 204, Lexington 40504; (606) 233-2484; *Field Representative:* Rusty Cheuvront.

U.S. Post Office and Courthouse, #19, Covington 41011; (606) 491-7929; *District Representative:* Janet Gerding Celella.

305 Federal Bldg., Frederica St., Owensboro 42301; (502) 685-5158; *District Representative:* Jo Anne Hawkins.

Committee assignment(s): Joint Printing (ranking member); Commerce, Science and Transportation; Energy and Natural Resources; Rules and Administration (ranking member)

FRIST, BILL, R-TENN.

Capitol Hill office: SD-565 20510; (202) 224-3344; Fax: 228-1264; Internet: senator_frist@frist.senate.gov or www.senate.gov/~frist/; *Administrative Assistant:* Lee Rawls

State office(s): 28 White Bridge Rd., #211, Nashville 37205; (615) 352-9411; Fax: (615) 352-9985; *State Director:* Emily Reynolds.

5704 Marlin Rd., Bldg. 6000, #2303, Chattanooga 37411; (423) 894-2203; Fax: (423) 894-5278; *Field Representative:* Cathy Kemp.

584 S. Royal St., Jackson 38301; (901) 424-9655; Fax: (901) 424-8322; *Field Representative:* John Garrard.

10368 Wallace Alley St., #7, Kingsport 37663; (423) 323-1252; Fax: (423) 323-0358; *Field Representative:* Jamey Campbell.

5401 Kingston Pike, Bldg. 1, #170, Knoxville 37919; (423) 602-7977; Fax: (423) 602-7979; *Field Representative:* Carolyn Jensen.

5100 Poplar Ave., #605, Memphis 38137; (901) 683-1910; Fax: (901) 683-3610; *Field Representative:* John Shannon.

Committee assignment(s): Budget; Commerce, Science and Transportation; Foreign Relations; Labor and Human Resources; Small Business

GLENN, JOHN, D-OHIO

Capitol Hill office: SH-503 20510; (202) 224-3353; Fax: (202) 224-7983; Internet: senator_glenn@glenn.senate.gov or little.nhlink.net/john-glenn; *Administrative Assistant:* Mary Jane Veno

State office(s): 200 N. High St., #600, Columbus 43215; (614) 469-6697; Fax: (614) 469-7733; *Communications Director:* Dale P. Butland.

234 N. Summit St., #726, Toledo 43604; (419) 259-7592; *Staff Assistant:* Mike Entinghe.

1240 E. 9th St., #2957, Cleveland 44199; (216) 522-7095; Fax: (216) 522-7097; *Special Projects Assistant:* Barbara Perry.

550 Main St., #10407, Cincinnati 45202; (513) 684-3265; Fax: (513) 684-3269; *Staff Assistant:* Rosemary Matthews.

Committee assignment(s): Special Aging; Armed Services; Governmental Affairs (ranking member); Select Intelligence

GORTON, SLADE, R-WASH.

Capitol Hill office: SH-730 20510; (202) 224-3441; Fax: (202) 224-9393; Internet: senator_gorton@gorton.senate.gov or www.senate.gov/~gorton; *Chief of Staff:* Tony Williams

State office(s): 10900 N.E. 4th St., #2110, Bellevue 98004; (206) 451-0103; Fax: (206) 451-0234; *State Director:* Veda Jellen.

500 W. 12th St., Vancouver 98660; (360) 696-7838; Fax: (360) 696-7844; *Southwest Washington Director:* Cathy Treadwell.

23 S. Wenatchee Ave., #119, E. Wenatchee 98801; (509) 884-1266; Fax: (509) 884-3447; *State Senior Policy Advisor:* Donald Moos.

402 E. Yakima Ave., P.O. Box 4083, Yakima 98901; (509) 248-8084; Fax: (509) 248-6167; *District Representative:* Sandra Linde.

W. 970 Riverside Ave., #697, Spokane 99201; (509) 353-2507; Fax: (509) 353-2547; *Eastern Washington Director:* Katherine O'Connell.

1350 Grandridge Blvd., #212, Kennewick 99336; (509) 783-0640; Fax: (509) 735-7559; *District Representative:* Suzanne Heaston.

11120 Gravelly Lake Dr., #8, Tacoma 98499; (253) 581-1614; Fax: (253) 581-0861; *Staff Assistant:* Doug Korba.

Committee assignment(s): Appropriations; Budget; Commerce, Science and Transportation; Energy and Natural Resources; Indian Affairs

GRAHAM, BOB, D-FLA.

Capitol Hill office: SH-524 20510; (202) 224-3041; Fax: (202) 224-2237; Internet: bob_graham@graham.senate.gov or www.senate.gov/~graham/; *Administrative Assistant:* Ken Klein

State office(s): 325 John Knox Rd., Bldg. 600, Tallahassee 32303; (850) 422-6100; *State Director:* Mary Chiles.

44 W. Flagler St., #1715, Miami 33130; (305) 536-7293; *District Representative:* Ellen Roth.

101 E. Kennedy Blvd., #3270, Tampa 33602; (813) 228-2476; *District Representative:* Adam Smith.

Committee assignment(s): Energy and Natural Resources; Environment and Public Works; Finance; Select Intelligence; Veterans' Affairs

GRAMM, PHIL, R-TEXAS

Capitol Hill office: SR-370 20510; (202) 224-2934; Fax: 228-2856; Internet: www.senate.gov/~gramm; *Chief of Staff:* Ruth Cymber

State office(s): 2323 Bryan St., Dallas 75201; (214) 767-3000; *Regional Director:* Kevin Brannon.

100 E. Ferguson St., #1004, Tyler 75702; (903) 593-0902; *Regional Director:* Gail Green.

712 Main St., #1704, Houston 77002; (713) 718-4000; *Regional Director:* Court Coenning.

404 E. Ramsey, #200, San Antonio 78216; (210) 366-9494; *Regional Director:* James Wilson.

222 E. Van Buren St., #404, Harlingen 78550; (956) 423-6118; *Office Manager:* Vacant.

1205 Texas Ave., #812, Lubbock 79401; (806) 743-7533; *Regional Director:* Hans Klinger.

310 N. Mesa St., #318, El Paso 79901; (915) 534-6896; *Office Manager:* Margie B. Velez.

Committee assignment(s): Agriculture, Nutrition and Forestry; Banking, Housing and Urban Affairs; Budget; Finance

GRAMS, ROD, R-MINN.

Capitol Hill office: SD-261 20510; (202) 224-3244; Fax: 228-0956; Internet: mail_grams@grams.senate.gov or www.senate.gov/~grams; *Chief of Staff:* Christine Rae Erikstrup

State office(s): 2013 2nd Ave. North, Anoka 55303; (612) 427-8872; Fax: (612) 427-8872; *Minnesota Director:* Merna Pease.

Committee assignment(s): Joint Economic; Banking, Housing and Urban Affairs; Budget; Energy and Natural Resources; Foreign Relations

GRASSLEY, CHARLES E., R-IOWA

Capitol Hill office: SH-135 20510; (202) 224-3744; Fax: (202) 224-6020; Internet: chuck_grassley@grassley. senate.gov or www.senate.gov/~grassley; *Administrative Assistant:* Kenneth C. Cunningham

State office(s): 210 Walnut St., #721, Des Moines 50309; (515) 284-4890; Fax: (515) 284-4069; *Iowa Administrator:* Henry Wulff.

531 Commercial St., #210, Waterloo 50701; (319) 232-6657; Fax: (319) 232-9965; *Regional Director:* Fred W. Schuster.

320 6th St., #103, Sioux City 51101; (712) 233-1860; Fax: (712) 233-1634; *Regional Director:* Marlise De Jong.

8 S. 6th St., #307, Council Bluffs 51501; (712) 322-7103; Fax: (712) 322-7196; *Regional Director:* Mary Ann Hansua.

101 1st St. S.E., #206, Cedar Rapids 52401; (319) 363-6832; Fax: (319) 363-7179; *Regional Director:* Mary Day.

131 E. 4th St., #116, Davenport 52801; (319) 322-4331; Fax: (319) 322-8552; *Regional Director:* Vada Reed.

Committee assignment(s): Joint Taxation; Special Aging (chair); Agriculture, Nutrition and Forestry; Budget; Finance; Judiciary

GREGG, JUDD, R-N.H.

Capitol Hill office: SR-393 20510; (202) 224-3324; Fax: (202) 224-4952; Internet: mailbox@gregg.senate.gov or www.senate.gov/~gregg; *Administrative Assistant:* Stan Sokul

State office(s): 28 Webster St., Manchester 03104; (603) 622-7979; Fax: (603) 622-0422; *Caseworker:* Peg Ouellette.

125 N. Main St., Concord 03301; (603) 225-7115; Fax: (603) 224-0198; *Chief of Staff:* Joel W. Maiola.

3 Glen Ave., Berlin 03570; (603) 752-2604; Fax: (603) 752-7351; *Caseworker:* Janet Woodward.

99 Pease Blvd., Portsmouth 03801; (603) 431-2171; Fax: (603) 431-1916; *Projects Assistant:* John Cavanaugh.

Committee assignment(s): Appropriations; Budget; Labor and Human Resources

HAGEL, CHUCK, R-NEB.

Capitol Hill office: SR-346 20510; (202) 224-4224; Fax: (202) 224-5213; Internet: chuck_hagel@hagel.senate. gov or www.senate.gov/~hagel; *Depty. Chief of Staff:* Kent Bonham

State office(s): 11301 Davenport St., #2, Omaha 68154; (402) 758-8981; Fax: (402) 758-9165; *Chief of Staff:* LouAnn Linehan.

100 Centennial Mall North, #294, Lincoln 68508; (402) 476-1400; Fax: (402) 476-0605; *Director of Constituent Services:* Dorothy Anderson.

4009 6th St., #9, Kearney 68847; (308) 236-7602; Fax: (308) 236-7473; *Constituent Services Representative:* Julie Booker.

300 E. 3rd St., N. Platte 69101; (308) 534-2006; Fax: (308) 534-1150; *Constituent Services Representative:* Carol Gale.

1010 Ave. I, Scottsbluff 69361; (308) 632-6032; Fax: (308) 632-6295; *Constituent Services Representative:* Diana Siewert.

Committee assignment(s): Special Aging; Banking, Housing and Urban Affairs; Foreign Relations

HARKIN, TOM, D-IOWA

Capitol Hill office: SH-731 20510; (202) 224-3254; Fax: (202) 224-9369; Internet: tom_harkin@harkin. senate.gov or www.senate.gov/~harkin/; *Administrative Assistant:* Jeff Link

State office(s): 210 Walnut St., #733, Des Moines 50309; (515) 284-4574; Fax: (515) 284-4937; *State Administrator:* Dianne Liepa.

320 6th St., #110, Sioux City 51101; (712) 252-1550; Fax: (712) 252-1638; *Regional Administrator:* Maureen Wilson.

350 W. St., #315, Dubuque 52001; (319) 582-2130; Fax: (319) 582-2342; *Regional Representative:* Linda Lucy.

150 1st Ave. North, #370, Cedar Rapids 52401; (319) 365-4504; Fax: (319) 393-6869; *Regional Administrator:* Beth Freeman.

131 E. 4th St., #314B, Davenport 52801; (319) 322-1338; Fax: (319) 322-0417; *Regional Representative:* Rita Vargas.

Committee assignment(s): Agriculture, Nutrition and Forestry (ranking member); Appropriations; Labor and Human Resources; Small Business

HATCH, ORRIN G., R-UTAH

Capitol Hill office: SR-131 20510; (202) 224-5251; Fax: (202) 224-6331; Internet: senator_hatch@hatch. senate.gov or www.senate.gov/~hatch; *Administrative Assistant:* Robert Dibblee

State office(s): 125 S. State St., #8402, Salt Lake City 84138; (801) 524-4380; *Utah State Director:* Melanie Bowen.

325 25th St., #1410, Ogden 84401; (801) 625-5672; *Northern Utah Director:* Norma S. Holmgren.

51 S. University Ave., #320, Provo 84606; (801) 375-7881; *Director:* Karen Thorn.

10 N. Main St., Cedar City 84720; (801) 586-8435; *Director:* Jeannine Holt.

197 E. Tabernacle, #2, St. George 84770; (801) 634-1795; *Director:* Jeannine Holt.

Committee assignment(s): Finance; Indian Affairs; Select Intelligence; Judiciary (chair)

HELMS, JESSE, R-N.C.

Capitol Hill office: SD-403 20510; (202) 224-6342; Fax: 228-1339; Internet: jesse_helms@helms.senate.gov or www.senate.gov/~helms; *Administrative Assistant:* Jimmy Broughton

State office(s): Century Post Office Bldg., #314, P.O. Box 2888, Raleigh 27602; (919) 856-4630; *State Director:* Marilyn Darnell.

Federal Bldg., P.O. Box 2944, Hickory 28603; (704) 322-5170; Fax: (704) 322-1255; *Staff Director:* Jo Murray.

Committee assignment(s): Agriculture, Nutrition and Forestry; Foreign Relations (chair); Rules and Administration

HOLLINGS, ERNEST F., D-S.C.

Capitol Hill office: SR-125 20510; (202) 224-6121; Fax: (202) 224-4293; Internet: senator@hollings.senate.gov or www.senate.gov/~hollings/; *Administrative Assistant:* David Rudd

State office(s): 1835 Assembly St., #1551, Columbia 29201; (803) 765-5731; Fax: (803) 765-5742; *State Director:* Sam B. King.

201 Magnolia St., #103, Spartanburg 29301; (864) 585-3702; Fax: (864) 585-2559; *Home Assistant:* Lynn Cazallis.

200 E. Bay St., Charleston 29401; (803) 727-4525; Fax: (803) 722-4923; *Low Country Representative:* Joe S. Maupin.

300 E. Washington St., #126, Greenville 29603; (864) 233-5366; Fax: (864) 233-2923; *Upstate Representative:* John Lummus.

Committee assignment(s): Appropriations; Budget; Commerce, Science and Transportation (ranking member)

HUTCHINSON, TIM, R-ARK.

Capitol Hill office: SD-245 20510; (202) 224-2353; Internet: senator.hutchinson@hutchinson.senate.gov or www.senate.gov/~hutchinson; *Chief of Staff:* Todd Deatherage

State office(s): 700 W. Capitol, #2527, Little Rock 72201; (501) 324-6336; *State Director:* Randi Fredholm.

Committee assignment(s): Environment and Public Works; Labor and Human Resources; Veterans' Affairs

HUTCHISON, KAY BAILEY, R-TEXAS

Capitol Hill office: SR-283 20510; (202) 224-5922; Fax: (202) 224-0776; Internet: senator@hutchison.senate.

gov or www.senate.gov/~hutchison; *Chief of Staff:* Tom Houston

State office(s): 10440 N. Central Expressway, Lock Box 606, #1160, Dallas 75231; (214) 361-3500; Fax: (214) 361-3502; *Regional Director:* Cynthia Hall.

1919 Smith St., #800, Houston 77002; (713) 653-3456; Fax: (713) 653-3459; *State Director:* Freida De La Morena.

8023 Vintage Dr., #460, San Antonio 78230; (210) 340-2885; Fax: (210) 349-6753; *Regional Director:* Marlene Pedrozza.

300 E. 8th St., #961, Austin 78701; (512) 916-5834; Fax: (512) 916-5839; *Regional Director:* Margaret Lauderback.

500 Chestnut St., #1570, Abilene 79602; (915) 676-2839; Fax: (915) 676-2937; *Regional Director:* Shea Woodard.

Committee assignment(s): Appropriations; Commerce, Science and Transportation; Rules and Administration

INHOFE, JAMES M., R-OKLA.

Capitol Hill office: SR-453 20510; (202) 224-4721; Fax: 228-0380; Internet: www.senate.gov/~inhofe; *Administrative Assistant:* Herbert H. Johnson

State office(s): 1924 S. Utica St., #530, Tulsa 74104; (918) 581-7111; Fax: (918) 581-7770; *Executive Assistant:* Kathie Lopp.

204 N. Robinson, #2701, Oklahoma City 73102; (405) 231-4381; Fax: (405) 231-4120; *Director of Constituent Services:* Linda Blaylock.

302 N. Independence, Enid 73701; (405) 234-5105; Fax: (405) 234-0929; *Northwest Field Representative:* Brent Kissling.

100 S. Main St., McAlester 74502; (918) 426-0933; Fax: (918) 426-0935; *Public Liason:* Lyndal Whitworth.

Committee assignment(s): Armed Services; Environment and Public Works; Indian Affairs; Select Intelligence

INOUYE, DANIEL K., D-HAWAII

Capitol Hill office: SH-722 20510; (202) 224-3934; Fax: (202) 224-6747; Internet: senator@inouye.senate.gov or www.senate.gov/~inouye; *Administrative Assistant:* Patrick DeLeon

State office(s): 300 Ala Moana Blvd., #7325, Honolulu 96850; (808) 541-2542; *Chief of Staff:* Jennifer Goto Sabas.

Committee assignment(s): Joint Printing; Appropriations; Commerce, Science and Transportation; Indian Affairs (ranking member); Rules and Administration

JEFFORDS, JAMES M., R-VT.

Capitol Hill office: SH-728 20510; (202) 224-5141; Internet: vermont@jeffords.senate.gov or www.senate.gov/~jeffords/; *Chief of Staff:* Susan Boardman Russ

State office(s): 95 St. Paul St., #100, Burlington 05401; (802) 658-6001; *Staff Assistant:* Jess Huber.

58 State St., Montpelier 05601; (802) 223-5273; *State Director:* Jolinda LaClair.

2 S. Main St., Rutland 05701; (802) 773-3875; *Office Coordinator:* Marie Pomaville.

Committee assignment(s): Special Aging; Finance; Labor and Human Resources (chair); Veterans' Affairs

JOHNSON, TIM, D-S.D.

Capitol Hill office: SH-502 20510; (202) 224-5842; Fax: 228-5765; Internet: tim@johnson.senate.gov or www.senate.gov/~johnson; *Administrative Assistant:* Greg Billings

State office(s): 715 S. Minnesota Ave., P.O. Box 1424, Sioux Falls 57101; (605) 332-8896; Fax: (605) 332-2824; *State Director:* Sharon Bertram.

320 S. 1st St., #103, Aberdeen 57402; (605) 226-3440; Fax: (605) 226-2439; *Northeast Area Director:* Sharon Stroschein.

405 E. Omaha, P.O. Box 1098, Rapid City 57701; (605) 341-3990; Fax: (605) 341-2207; *W. River Director:* Darrell W. Shoemaker.

Committee assignment(s): Agriculture, Nutrition and Forestry; Banking, Housing and Urban Affairs; Budget; Energy and Natural Resources

KEMPTHORNE, DIRK, R-IDAHO

Capitol Hill office: SR-304 20510; (202) 224-6142; Fax: (202) 224-5893; Internet: dirk_kempthorne@ kempthorne.senate.gov or www.senate.gov/ ~kempthorne/; *Chief of Staff:* Phil Reberger

State office(s): 250 S. 4th Ave., #207, Pocatello 83201; (208) 236-6775; Fax: (208) 236-6935; *State Assistant:* Sally Taniguchi.

401 2nd St. North, #106, Twin Falls 83301; (208) 734-2515; Fax: (208) 733-0414; *State Assistant:* Orrie Sinclair.

2539 Channing Way, #240, Idaho Falls 83404; (208) 522-9779; Fax: (208) 529-8367; *State Assistant:* Dixie Richardson.

618 D St., #E, Lewiston 83501; (208) 743-1492; Fax: (208) 743-6484; *State Assistant:* Carolyn Durant.

704 Blaine St., #1, Caldwell 83605; (208) 455-0360; Fax: (208) 455-0358; *Field Representative:* Ernie Guerra.

304 N. 8th St., #338, Boise 83702; (208) 334-1776; Fax: (208) 334-9044; *Chief of Staff:* J. Philip Reberger.

118 N. 2nd St., #1, Coeur d'Alene 83814; (208) 664-5490; Fax: (208) 664-0889; *State Assistant:* Rachel Riggs.

220 E. 5th St., #105, Moscow 83843; (208) 883-9783; Fax: (208) 883-8743; *State Assistant:* Cindy Agidius.

Committee assignment(s): Armed Services; Environment and Public Works; Small Business

KENNEDY, EDWARD M., D-MASS.

Capitol Hill office: SR-315 20510; (202) 224-4543; Fax: (202) 224-2417; Internet: senator@kennedy.senate. gov or www.senate.gov/~kennedy; *Administrative Assistant:* Gerry Kavanaugh

State office(s): John F. Kennedy Federal Bldg., #2400, Boston 02203; (617) 565-3170; *Staff Director:* Barbara Souliotis.

Committee assignment(s): Joint Economic; Armed Services; Judiciary; Labor and Human Resources (ranking member)

KERREY, BOB, D-NEB.

Capitol Hill office: SH-141 20510; (202) 224-6551; Fax: (202) 224-7645; Internet: bob@kerrey.senate.gov or www.senate.gov/~kerrey/; *Chief of Staff:* Shelia Nix

State office(s): 7602 Pacific St., #205, Omaha 68114; (402) 391-3411; *State Director:* Robert Holmstedt.

100 Centennial Mall North, #287, Lincoln 68508; (402) 437-5246; *Agricultural Representative:* Eugene T. Glock.

Western Nebraska Regional Office, 2106 1st Ave., Scottsbluff 69361; (308) 632-3595; *Western Nebraska Representative:* Mary Asmus.

Committee assignment(s): Agriculture, Nutrition and Forestry; Finance; Select Intelligence (ranking member)

KERRY, JOHN, D-MASS.

Capitol Hill office: SR-421 20510; (202) 224-2742; Fax: (202) 224-8525; Internet: john_kerry@kerry.senate. gov or www.senate.gov/~kerry/; *Acting Chief of Staff:* Richard Byers

State office(s): 145 State St., #504, Springfield 01103; (413) 785-4610; Fax: (413) 736-1049.

1 Bowdoin Square, 10th Floor, Boston 02114; (617) 565-8519; Fax: (617) 248-3870; *State Director:* Christopher J. Greeley.

222 Milliken Place, Fall River 02722; (508) 677-0522; Fax: (508) 677-0275.

90 Madison St., #205, Worcester 01680; (508) 831-7380; Fax: (508) 831-7381.

53 N. 6th St., #264, New Bedford 02740; (508) 994-7651.

Committee assignment(s): Banking, Housing and Urban Affairs; Commerce, Science and Transportation; Foreign Relations; Select Intelligence; Small Business (ranking member)

KOHL, HERB, D-WIS.

Capitol Hill office: SH-330 20510; (202) 224-5653; Internet: senator_kohl@kohl.senate.gov or www.senate.gov/~kohl; *Chief of Staff:* Paul Bock

State office(s): 205 E. Wisconsin Ave., Milwaukee 53202; (414) 297-4451; Fax: (414) 297-4455; *State Director:* JoAnn Anton.

14 W. Mifflin St., #312, Madison 53703; (608) 264-5338; Fax: (608) 264-5473; *Assistant State Director:* Eve Galanter.

3409 Golf Rd., Eau Claire 54701; (715) 832-8424; Fax: (715) 832-8492; *Regional Representative:* Marjorie Bunce.

4321 W. College Ave., #235, Appleton 54914; (920) 738-1640; Fax: (920) 738-1643; *Regional Representative:* Marlene Mielke.

Committee assignment(s): Special Aging; Appropriations; Judiciary

KYL, JON, R-ARIZ.

Capitol Hill office: SH-724 20510; (202) 224-4521; Fax: (202) 224-2207; Internet: info@kyl.senate.gov or www.senate.gov/~kyl/; *Chief of Staff:* Laurie Fenton

State office(s): 2200 E. Camelback Rd., #120, Phoenix 85016; (602) 840-1891; Fax: (602) 840-4848; *Regional Director:* Scott Celley.

7315 N. Oracle St., #220, Tucson 85704; (520) 575-8633; *Regional Director:* Hank Kenski.

Committee assignment(s): Energy and Natural Resources; Select Intelligence; Judiciary

LANDRIEU, MARY L., D-LA.

Capitol Hill office: SH-702 20510; (202) 224-5824; Internet: senator@landrieu.senate.gov or www.senate.gov/senator/landrieu.html; *Chief of Staff:* Norma Jane Sabiston

State office(s): 501 Magazine St., #1010, New Orleans 70130; (504) 589-2427; *Acting Office Manager:* Vionne Williams.

707 Florida St., #326, Baton Rouge 70801; (504) 389-0395; *Office Manager:* Shannon Langlois.

300 Fannin St., #2240, Shreveport 71101; (318) 676-3085; *Office Manager:* Tari Bradford.

Committee assignment(s): Agriculture, Nutrition and Forestry; Energy and Natural Resources; Small Business

LAUTENBERG, FRANK R., D-N.J.

Capitol Hill office: SH-506 20510; (202) 224-4744; Fax: (202) 224-9707; Internet: frank_lautenberg@lautenberg.senate.gov or www.senate.gov/~lautenberg; *Chief of Staff:* Eve Lubalin

State office(s): 1 Gateway Center, #1011, Newark 07102; (973) 645-3030; *State Director:* Christy Davis.

208 White Horse Pike, #18-19, Barrington 08007; (609) 757-5353; *Deputy State Director:* Karin Elkis.

Committee assignment(s): Appropriations; Budget (ranking member); Environment and Public Works; Select Intelligence

LEAHY, PATRICK J., D-VT.

Capitol Hill office: SR-433 20510; (202) 224-4242; Internet: senator_leahy@leahy.senate.gov or www.senate.gov/~leahy/; *Chief of Staff:* Luke Albee

State office(s): 199 Main St., Burlington 05401; (802) 863-2525; *Office Director:* Charles Ross.

338 Federal Bldg., P.O. Box 933, Montpelier 05602; (802) 229-0569; *Legislative Assistant:* Robert Paquin.

Committee assignment(s): Agriculture, Nutrition and Forestry; Appropriations; Judiciary (ranking member)

LEVIN, CARL, D-MICH.

Capitol Hill office: SR-459 20510; (202) 224-6221; Fax: (202) 224-1388; Internet: senator@levin.senate.gov or www.senate.gov/~levin/; *Administrative Assistant:* Gordon Kerr

State office(s): 30500 Van Dyke, #206, Warren 48093; (810) 759-0477; *Regional Representative:* Jan Jaffray.

477 Michigan Ave., #1860, Detroit 48226; (313) 226-6020; *Director:* Charles Wilbur.

301 E. Genesee St., Saginaw 48607; (517) 754-2494; *Committee Affairs Director:* Mary Washington.

124 W. Allegan St., #1810, Lansing 48933; (517) 377-1508; *Regional Representative:* James J. Turner.

110 Michigan St. N.W., #134, Grand Rapids 49503; (616) 456-2531; *Regional Representative:* Richard Tormala.

145 Water St., #102, Alpena 49707; (517) 354-5520; *Regional Representative:* Harold Chase.

623 Ludington St., #303, Escanaba 49829; (906) 789-0052; *Regional Representative:* Kevin Morter.

207 Grandview Parkway, #104, P.O. Box 4449, Traverse City 49864; (616) 947-9569; *Regional Representative:* Harold Chase.

15100 Northline Rd., #107, Southgate 48195; (313) 285-8596.

Committee assignment(s): Armed Services (ranking member); Governmental Affairs; Select Intelligence; Small Business

LIEBERMAN, JOSEPH I., D-CONN.

Capitol Hill office: SH-706 20510; (202) 224-4041; Fax: (202) 224-9750; Internet: senator_lieberman@lieberman.senate.gov or www.senate.gov/~lieberman; *Administrative Assistant:* William G. Andresen

State office(s): 1 State St., #1420, Hartford 06103; (860) 549-8463; Fax: (860) 549-8478; *State Director:* Sherry Brown.

Committee assignment(s): Armed Services; Environment and Public Works; Governmental Affairs; Small Business

LOTT, TRENT, R-MISS.

Capitol Hill office: SR-487 20510; (202) 224-6253; Fax: (202) 224-2262; Internet: senatorlott@lott.senate.gov or www.senate.gov/~lott; *Chief of Staff:* William Gottshall

State office(s): P.O. Box 1474, Oxford 38655; (601) 234-3774; Fax: (601) 234-1744; *Staff Assistant:* Geneise Hitt.

200 E. Washington St., #145, Greenwood 38930; (601) 453-5681; Fax: (601) 453-8974; *Staff Assistant:* Carolyn Overstreet.

245 E. Capitol St., #226, Jackson 39201; (601) 965-4644; Fax: (601) 965-4007; *State Director:* Guy Hovis.

1 Government Plaza, #428, Gulfport 39501; (601) 863-1988; Fax: (601) 863-9960; *Field Representative:* Robbie Maxwell.

3100 Pascagoula St., Pascagoula 39567; (601) 762-5400; Fax: (601) 762-0137; *Field Representative:* Bill Pope.

Committee assignment(s): Commerce, Science and Transportation; Finance; Rules and Administration

LUGAR, RICHARD G., R-IND.

Capitol Hill office: SH-306 20510; (202) 224-4814; Internet: senator_lugar@lugar.senate.gov or www.senate.gov/senator/lugar.html; *Chief of Staff:* Marty Morris

State office(s): 10 W. Market St., #1180, Indianapolis 46204; (317) 226-5555; *State Director:* Kevin S. Kellems.

5530 Sohl Ave., #103, Hammond 46320; (219) 937-5380; *Director:* Timothy J. Sanders.

1300 S. Harrison St., #3158, Fort Wayne 46802; (219) 422-1505; *Director:* Matthew G. Kelty.

1201 E. 10th St., #103, Jeffersonville 47132; (812) 288-3377; *Director:* David Graham.

101 N.W. Martin Luther King Jr. Blvd., #122, Evansville 47708; (812) 465-6313; *Director:* Mike Duckworth.

Committee assignment(s): Agriculture, Nutrition and Forestry (chair); Foreign Relations; Select Intelligence

MACK, CONNIE, R-FLA.

Capitol Hill office: SH-517 20510; (202) 224-5274; Fax: (202) 224-8022; Internet: connie@mack.senate.gov or www.senate.gov/~mack/; *Chief of Staff:* John Reich

State office(s): 1 San Jose Place, Jacksonville 32257; (904) 268-7915; *Regional Director:* Greg Williams.

150 S. Monroe, #305, Tallahassee 32301; (850) 425-1995; *Assistant Regional Director:* Andrea Heyman.

777 Brickell Ave., #704, Miami 33131; (305) 530-7100; Fax: (305) 530-7104; *District Manager:* Gladys Ferrer.

600 N. Westshore Blvd., #602, Tampa 33609; (813) 225-7683; Fax: (813) 289-8793; *District Manager:* Jamie Wilson.

1342 Colonial Blvd., #27, Fort Myers 33907; (941) 275-6252; Fax: (941) 275-0120; *Regional Director:* Sharon Thierer.

1 Palafox St., #158, Pensacola 32501; (850) 438-8875; *District Manager:* Aaron Wesc.

Committee assignment(s): Joint Economic (vice chair); Banking, Housing and Urban Affairs; Finance

MCCAIN, JOHN, R-ARIZ.

Capitol Hill office: SR-241 20510; (202) 224-2235; Fax: 228-2862; Internet: senator_mccain@mccain.senate.gov or www.senate.gov/~mccain; *Administrative Assistant:* Mark Salter

State office(s): 2400 E. Arizona Biltmore Circle, #1150, Bldg. 1, Phoenix 85016; (602) 952-2410; Fax: (602) 952-2410; *State Administrative Assistant:* Deb Gullet.

1839 S. Alma School Rd., #375, Mesa 85210; (602) 491-4300; *Office Manager:* Kaye Temple.

450 W. Paseo Redondo, #200, Tucson 85701; (520) 670-6334; *Office Manager:* Rosemary Alexander.

Committee assignment(s): Armed Services; Commerce, Science and Transportation (chair); Indian Affairs

MCCONNELL, MITCH, R-KY.

Capitol Hill office: SR-361A 20510; (202) 224-2541; Fax: (202) 224-2499; Internet: senator@mcconnell.senate.gov or www.senate.gov/~mcconnell; *Administrative Assistant:* Kyle Sinnows

State office(s): 601 W. Broadway, #630, Louisville 40202; (502) 582-6304; Fax: (502) 582-5326; *State Director:* Larry E. Cox.

771 Corporate Dr., #53D, Lexington 40503; (606) 224-8284; Fax: (606) 252-1783; *Field Representative:* Kevin Atkins.

301 S. Main St., London 40741; (606) 864-2026; Fax: (606) 864-2035; *Field Representative:* Scott Douglas.

1885 Dixie Hwy., #345, Forth Wright 41011; (606) 578-0188; Fax: (606) 261-9228; *Field Representative:* Kelly White.

602 Broadway, Paducah 42001; (502) 442-4554; Fax: (502) 443-3102; *Field Representative:* Tim Thomas.

241 E. Main St., #102, Bowling Green 42101; (502) 781-1673; Fax: (502) 782-1884; *Field Representative:* Robbin Morrison.

Committee assignment(s): Joint Printing; Agriculture, Nutrition and Forestry; Appropriations; Labor and Human Resources; Rules and Administration

MIKULSKI, BARBARA A., D-MD.

Capitol Hill office: SH-709 20510; (202) 224-4654; Fax: (202) 224-8858; Internet: senator@mikulski.senate.gov or www.senate.gov/~mikulski/; *Chief of Staff:* Shaila Aery

State office(s): 9658 Baltimore Ave., #208, College Park 20740; (301) 345-5517; *Caseworker:* Asumptha Chiang.

401 E. Pratt St., #253, Baltimore 21202; (410) 962-4510; Fax: (410) 962-4760; *State Administrator:* Mike Morrill.

60 W. St., #202, Annapolis 21401; (410) 263-1805; *Caseworker:* Denise Nooe.

94 W. Washington St., #301, Hagerstown 21740; (301) 797-2826; Fax: (301) 797-2241; *Western Maryland Representative:* Jennifer Maust.

1201 Pemberton Dr., #1E, Bldg. B, Salisbury 21801; (410) 546-7711; Fax: (410) 546-9324; *Eastern Shore Representative:* Cindy Betts.

Committee assignment(s): Appropriations; Labor and Human Resources

MOSELEY-BRAUN, CAROL, D-ILL.

Capitol Hill office: SH-324 20510; (202) 224-2854; Internet: senator@moseley-braun.senate.gov or www.senate.gov/~moseley-braun; *Chief of Staff:* Bill Mattea

State office(s): 230 S. Dearborn St., #3900, Chicago 60604; (312) 353-5420; Fax: (312) 353-2560; *Director:* Jill Zwick.

6 Executive Dr., #6, Fairview Heights 62208; (618) 632-7242.

Henson Robinson House, 520 S. 8th St., Springfield 62703; (217) 492-4126; *Director:* Bill Houlihan.

Committee assignment(s): Special Aging; Banking, Housing and Urban Affairs; Finance

MOYNIHAN, DANIEL PATRICK, D-N.Y.

Capitol Hill office: SR-464 20510; (202) 224-4451; Fax: 228-0406; Internet: senator@dpm.senate.gov or www.senate.gov/~moynihan/; *Administrative Assistant:* Tony Bullock

State office(s): 405 Lexington Ave., 41st Floor, New York 10174; (212) 661-5150; *Regional Director:* Adam Levine.

214 Main St., Oneonta 13820; (607) 433-2310; *Regional Director:* Ross Frommer.

28 Church St., Buffalo 14202; (716) 846-4097; *Regional Director:* James Kane.

Committee assignment(s): Joint Library; Joint Taxation (ranking member); Environment and Public Works; Finance (ranking member); Rules and Administration

MURKOWSKI, FRANK H., R-ALASKA

Capitol Hill office: SH-322 20510; (202) 224-6665; Fax: (202) 224-5301; Internet: email@murkowski.senate.gov or www.senate.gov/~murkowski/; *Chief of Staff:* David Garman

State office(s): 222 W. 7th Ave., Box 1, Anchorage 99513; (907) 271-3735; *State Director:* Patricia B. Heller.

130 Trading Bay Rd., #350, Kenai 99611; (907) 283-5808; *Special Assistant:* Susan Hett.

101 12th Ave., Box 7, Fairbanks 99701; (907) 456-0233; *Special Assistant:* Marcia Kozie.

Federal Bldg., P.O. Box 21647, Juneau 99802; (907) 586-7400; *Special Assistant:* Lucy Hudson.

109 Main St., Ketchikan 99901; (907) 225-6880; *Special Assistant:* Sherrie Slick.

851 E. Westpoint Dr., #307, Wasilla 99654; (907) 376-7665; Fax: (907) 376-8526; *Special Assistant:* Carol Gustafson.

Committee assignment(s): Energy and Natural Resources (chair); Finance; Indian Affairs; Veterans' Affairs

MURRAY, PATTY, D-WASH.

Capitol Hill office: SR-111 20510; (202) 224-2621; Fax: (202) 224-0238; Internet: senator_murray@murray.senate.gov or www.senate.gov/~murray; *Chief of Staff:* Patricia Akiyama

State office(s): 915 2nd Ave., #2988, Seattle 98174; (206) 553-5545; Fax: (206) 553-0891; *State Director:* John Engber.

500 W. 12th St., #140, Vancouver 98660; (360) 696-7797; Fax: (360) 696-7798; *Regional Representative:* Kaye Masco.

W. 601 1st Ave., Spokane 99201; (509) 624-9515; Fax: (509) 624-9561; *Eastern Regional Coordinator:* Judy Olson.

2930 Wetmore Ave., #903, Everett 98201; (206) 259-6515; Fax: (206) 259-7152; *Northwest Regional Coordinator:* Jill McKinnie.

402 E. Yakima Ave., #390, Yakima 98901; (509) 453-7462; Fax: (509) 453-7731; *Central Regional Coordinator:* Corky Mattingly.

Committee assignment(s): Appropriations; Budget; Select Ethics; Labor and Human Resources; Veterans' Affairs

NICKLES, DON, R-OKLA.

Capitol Hill office: SH-133 20510; (202) 224-5754; Fax: (202) 224-6008; Internet: senator@nickles.senate.gov or www.senate.gov/~nickles/; *Administrative Assistant:* Bret Bernhardt

State office(s): 100 N. Broadway, #1820, Oklahoma City 73102; (405) 231-4941; *Field Representative:* Brett Hamm.

601 D Ave., #201, Lawton 73501; (405) 357-9878; *Field Representative:* Billie Jo Penn.

409 S. Boston Ave., #3310, Tulsa 74103; (918) 581-7651; *Manager:* Sharon K. Keasler.

1916 Lake Rd., Ponca City 74601; (405) 767-1270; *State Director:* Cheryl Fletcher.

Committee assignment(s): Budget; Energy and Natural Resources; Finance; Governmental Affairs; Rules and Administration

REED, JACK, D-R.I.

Capitol Hill office: SH-320 20510; (202) 224-4642; Fax: (202) 224-4680; Internet: jack@reed.senate.gov or www.senate.gov/~reed; *Administrative Assistant:* J. B. Poersch

State office(s): 1 Exchange Terrace, #418, Providence 02903; *District Director:* Raymond Simone.

Committee assignment(s): Special Aging; Banking, Housing and Urban Affairs; Labor and Human Resources

REID, HARRY, D-NEV.

Capitol Hill office: SH-528 20510; (202) 224-3542; Fax: (202) 224-7327; Internet: senator_reid@reid.senate.gov or www.senate.gov/~reid/; *Chief of Staff:* Reynaldo Martinez

State office(s): 300 Las Vegas Blvd. South, #1610, Las Vegas 89104; (702) 474-0041; Fax: (702) 474-0137; *Regional Manager:* M. Connie Barker.

400 S. Virginia St., #902, Reno 89501; (702) 686-5750; Fax: (702) 686-5757; *Regional Manager:* Mary Conelly.

600 E. William St., Carson City 89701; (702) 882-7343; *Regional Representative:* Karen Denio.

Committee assignment(s): Special Aging; Appropriations; Environment and Public Works; Select Ethics (vice-chair); Indian Affairs

ROBB, CHARLES S., D-VA.

Capitol Hill office: SR-154 20510; (202) 224-4024; Fax: (202) 224-8689; Internet: senator@robb.senate.gov or www.senate.gov/~robb/; *Chief of Staff:* Thomas Lehner

State office(s): 1001 E. Broad St., #150, Richmond 23219; (804) 771-2221; *State Director:* Rob Jones.

999 Waterside Dr., #107, Norfolk 23510; (757) 441-3124; Fax: (757) 441-3133; *Director:* Rich Williams.

310 Church St. S.W., #102, Roanoke 24011; (540) 985-0103; *Regional Representative:* Debbie Lawson.

Dominion Bank Bldg., Main St., P.O. Box 1009, Clintwood 24288; (540) 926-4104; Fax: (540) 926-4823; *Regional Representative:* Jim F. O'Quinn.

530 Main St., Danville 24541; (804) 791-0330; *Regional Representative:* Anne Geyer.

Committee assignment(s): Joint Economic; Armed Services; Foreign Relations; Select Intelligence

ROBERTS, PAT, R-KAN.

Capitol Hill office: SH-302 20510; (202) 224-4774; Fax: (202) 224-3514; Internet: pat_roberts@roberts.senate.gov or www.senate.gov/~roberts/; *Chief of Staff:* Leroy Towns

State office(s): 100 Military Plaza, #203, P.O. Box 550, Dodge City 67801; (316) 227-2244; Fax: (316) 227-2264; *District Director:* Phyllis Ross.

155 N. Market St., #120, Wichita 67202; (316) 263-0416; Fax: (316) 263-0273; *District Director:* Karin Wisdom.

4200 Somerset, #152, Prairie Village 66208; (913) 648-3103; Fax: (913) 648-3106; *State Director:* Mike Harper.

444 S.E. Quincy, #392, Topeka 66683; (913) 295-2745; Fax: (913) 235-3665; *State Casework Director:* Betty Duwe.

Committee assignment(s): Agriculture, Nutrition and Forestry; Armed Services; Select Ethics; Select Intelligence

ROCKEFELLER, JOHN D., IV, D-W.VA.

Capitol Hill office: SH-531 20510; (202) 224-6472; Fax: (202) 224-7665; Internet: senator@rockefeller.senate.gov or www.senate.gov/~rockefeller/; *Administrative Assistant:* R. Lane Bailey

State office(s): 207 Prince St., Beckley 25801; (304) 253-9704; Fax: (304) 253-2578; *Area Coordinator:* Greg Ball.

118 Adams St., #301, Fairmont 26554; (304) 367-0122; Fax: (304) 367-0822; *Caseworker:* Meg Cianfrocca.

405 Capitol St., #608, Charleston 25301; (304) 347-5372; Fax: (304) 347-5371; *State Director:* Terri Giles.

225 W. King St., #1212, Martinsburg 25401; (304) 262-9285; Fax: (304) 262-9288; *Caseworker:* Penny Householder.

Committee assignment(s): Commerce, Science and Transportation; Finance; Veterans' Affairs

ROTH, WILLIAM V., JR., R-DEL.

Capitol Hill office: SH-104 20510; (202) 224-2441; Internet: comments@roth.senate.gov or www.senate.gov/~roth; *Administrative Assistant:* John M. Duncan

State office(s): 844 King St., #3021, Wilmington 19801; (302) 573-6291; *Communications Director:* Verna Hensley.

300 S. New St., #2215, Dover 19901; (302) 674-3308; *Assistant to the Senator:* Marlene Elliott.

12 The Circle, Georgetown 19947; (302) 856-7690; *Assistant to the Senator:* Marlene Elliott.

Committee assignment(s): Joint Economic; Joint Taxation (vice chair); Finance (chair)

SANTORUM, RICK, R-PA.

Capitol Hill office: SR-120 20510; (202) 224-6324; Fax: 228-0604; Internet: senator@santorum.senate.gov or www.senate.gov/~santorum; *Chief of Staff:* Mark D. Rodgers

State office(s): Regency Square, #202, Route 220 N, Altoona 16001; (814) 946-7023; Fax: (814) 946-7025.

1705 W. 26th St., Erie 16508; (814) 454-7114; Fax: (814) 459-2096.

221 Strawberry Square, Harrisburg 17101; (717) 231-7540; Fax: (717) 231-7542; *District Representative:* Jake Corman.

504 W. Hamilton St., #3804, Allentown 18015; (610) 770-0142; Fax: (610) 770-0911.

1 Station Square, #250, Pittsburgh 15219; (412) 562-0533; *District Representative:* Keith Schmidt.

527 Linden St., Scranton 18503; (717) 344-8805; *District Representative:* Susan Cox.

1 S. Penn Square, #960, Philadelphia 19107; (215) 864-6900; Fax: (215) 864-6910; *District Representative:* Skip Irvine.

Committee assignment(s): Special Aging; Agriculture, Nutrition and Forestry; Armed Services; Rules and Administration

SARBANES, PAUL S., D-MD.

Capitol Hill office: SH-309 20510; (202) 224-4524; Fax: (202) 224-1651; Internet: senator@sarbanes.senate. gov or www.senate.gov/~sarbanes; *Chief of Staff:* Peter Marudas

State office(s): 15499 Potomac River Dr., Box 331, Cobb Island 20625; (301) 724-0695; *Southern Maryland Representative:* Ursula Culver.

1110 Bonifant St., #450, Silver Spring 20910; (301) 589-0797; Fax: (301) 589-0598; *Field Representative:* Jeannie Lazerov.

100 S. Charles St., #1010, Baltimore 21201; (410) 962-4436; Fax: (410) 962-4156; *State Office Director:* Sharon Faraone.

141 Baltimore St., #206, Cumberland 21502; (301) 724-0695; Fax: (301) 724-4660; *Western Maryland Representative:* Tim Magrath.

110 W. Church St., Suite D, Salisbury 21801; (410) 860-2131; Fax: (410) 860-2134; *Eastern Shore Representative:* Lee Whaley.

Committee assignment(s): Joint Economic; Banking, Housing and Urban Affairs (ranking member); Budget; Foreign Relations

SESSIONS, JEFF, R-ALA.

Capitol Hill office: SR-495 20510; (202) 224-4124; Fax: (202) 224-3149; Internet: senator@sessions.senate. gov or www.senate.gov/~sessions; *Chief of Staff:* Armand DeKeyser

State office(s): 1 Court Square, #248, Montgomery 36104; (334) 265-9507; Fax: (334) 834-2823; *State Director:* Chuck Spurlock.

1800 5th Ave. North, #341, Birmingham 35203; (205) 731-1500; Fax: (205) 731-0221; *District Representative:* Keith Ensey.

200 Clinton Ave. N.W., #706, Huntsville 35801; (205) 533-0979; Fax: (205) 533-0745; *District Representative:* Angela Colvert.

113 St. Joseph St., #312, Mobile 36604; (334) 690-3167; Fax: (334) 690-3174; *District Representative:* Stormie Janzen.

Committee assignment(s): Joint Economic; Environment and Public Works; Select Ethics; Judiciary

SHELBY, RICHARD C., R-ALA.

Capitol Hill office: SH-110 20510; (202) 224-5744; Fax: (202) 224-3416; Internet: senator@shelby.senate.gov or www.senate.gov/senator/shelby.html; *Chief of Staff:* Tom Young

State office(s): 1800 5th Ave. North, #321, Birmingham 35203; (205) 731-1384; Fax: (205) 731-1386; *District Representative:* Blair Agricola.

1118 Greensboro Ave., #240, Tuscaloosa 35401; (205) 759-5047; Fax: (205) 759-5067; *District Representative:* Melissa Davis.

Huntsville International Airport, 1000 Glenn Hearn Blvd., P.O. Box 20127, Huntsville 35824; (205) 772-0460; Fax: (205) 772-8387; *District Representative:* LeAnn Hill.

15 Lee St., #B-28A, Montgomery 36104; (334) 223-7303; Fax: (334) 223-7317; *District Representative:* Carol Estes.

113 St. Joseph St., #438, Mobile 36602; (334) 694-4164; Fax: (334) 694-4166; *District Representative:* Laura Breland.

Committee assignment(s): Special Aging; Appropriations; Banking, Housing and Urban Affairs; Select Intelligence (chair)

SMITH, GORDON H., R-ORE.

Capitol Hill office: SD-359 20510; (202) 224-3753; Fax: 228-3997; Internet: oregon@gsmith.senate.gov or www.senate.gov/~gsmith/; *Chief of Staff:* Kurt Pfotenhauer

State office(s): 1220 S.W. 3rd Ave., #618, Portland 97204; (503) 326-3386; Fax: (503) 326-2900; *State Director:* Kerry Tymchuk.

1706 S.W. Frazer, Pendleton 97801; (541) 278-1129; Fax: (541) 278-4109; *District Representative:* Liz Lorenzen.

1175 E. Main, #2D, Medford 97504; (541) 608-9102; Fax: (541) 608-9104; *District Representative:* Esther Kennedy.

211 E. 7th Ave., #202, Eugene 97401; (541) 998-6439; Fax: (541) 465-6808; *District Representative:* Terri Moffett.

131 N.W. Hawthorne Av., #208, Bend 97701; (541) 318-1298; Fax: (541) 318-1396; *District Representative:* Susan Fitch.

Committee assignment(s): Budget; Energy and Natural Resources; Foreign Relations

SMITH, ROBERT C., R-N.H.

Capitol Hill office: SD-307 20510; (202) 224-2841; Internet: opinion@smith.senate.gov or www.senate.gov/~smith; *Chief of Staff:* Patrick Pettey

State office(s): 1750 Elm St., #100, Manchester 03104; (603) 634-5000; *State Director:* Mark F. Aldrich.

136 Pleasant St., Berlin 03570; (603) 752-2604; *Staff Assistant:* Sandra Patrick.

1 Harbour Place, #435, Portsmouth 03801; (603) 433-1667; *Staff Assistant:* Bonnie Spinnazola.

Committee assignment(s): Armed Services; Environment and Public Works; Select Ethics (chair); Governmental Affairs

SNOWE, OLYMPIA J., R-MAINE

Capitol Hill office: SR-250 20510; (202) 224-5344; Fax: (202) 224-1946; Internet: olympia@snowe.senate.gov or www.senate.gov/~snowe; *Chief of Staff:* Kevin Raye

State office(s): 231 Main St., #2, Biddeford 04005; (207) 282-4144; Fax: (207) 284-2358; *Regional Representative:* Peter Morin.

3 Canal Plaza, P.O. Box 188, Portland 04112; (207) 874-0883; Fax: (207) 874-7631; *State Director:* Charles Summers.

2 Great Falls Plaza, #7B, Auburn 04210; (207) 786-2451; Fax: (207) 782-1438; *Regional Representative:* Jane Desaulniers.

68 Sewall St., #101C, Augusta 04330; (207) 622-8292; Fax: (207) 622-7295; *Regional Representative:* John Cummings.

1 Cumberland Place, #306, Bangor 04401; (207) 945-0432; Fax: (207) 941-9525; *Regional Representative:* Gail Kelly.

169 Academy St., #3, Presque Isle 04769; (207) 764-5124; Fax: (207) 764-6420; *Regional Representative:* Marion A. Higgins.

Committee assignment(s): Armed Services; Budget; Commerce, Science and Transportation; Small Business

SPECTER, ARLEN, R-PA.

Capitol Hill office: SH-711 20510; (202) 224-4254; Fax: 228-1229; Internet: senator_specter@specter.senate.gov or www.senate.gov/~specter; *Chief of Staff:* David Urban

State office(s): 2031 Federal Bldg., Liberty Ave. and Grant St., Pittsburgh 15222; (412) 644-3400; *Executive Director:* Doug Saltzman.

617 State St., #118, Erie 16501; (814) 453-3010; *Executive Director:* Patricia Root.

228 Walnut St., #1159, Harrisburg 17101; (717) 782-3951; *Executive Director:* Steve Dunkle.

5th and Hamilton Sts., #102, Allentown 18101; (610) 434-1444; *Executive Director:* Mary Jo Bierman.

310 Spruce St., #201, Scranton 18503; (717) 346-2006; *Executive Director:* Andrew Wallace.

116 S. Main St., #306, Wilkes-Barre 18701; (717) 826-6265; *Executive Director:* Andrew Wallace.

600 Arch St., #9400, Philadelphia 19106; (215) 597-7200; *Executive Director:* Ken Braithewait.

Committee assignment(s): Appropriations; Governmental Affairs; Judiciary; Veterans' Affairs (chair)

STEVENS, TED, R-ALASKA

Capitol Hill office: SH-522 20510; (202) 224-3004; Fax: (202) 224-2354; Internet: senator_stevens@stevens.senate.gov or www.senate.gov/~stevens/; *Chief of Staff:* Mitch Rose

State office(s): 222 W. 7th Ave., #2, Anchorage 99513; (907) 271-5915; Fax: (907) 258-9305; *State Office Director:* Marie Nash.

120 Trading Bay Rd., #350, Kenai 99611; (907) 283-5808; Fax: (907) 283-4363; *Staff Assistant:* Susan Hett.

101 12th Ave., #206, P.O. Box 4, Fairbanks 99701; (907) 456-0261; Fax: (907) 456-7290; *Staff Assistant:* Ruth Burnet.

965 Federal Bldg., P.O. Box 020149, Juneau 99802; (907) 586-7400; Fax: (907) 586-7402; *Staff Assistant:* Lucy Hudson.

109 Main St., Ketchikan 99901; (907) 225-6880; Fax: (907) 225-0390; *Staff Assistant:* Sherrie Slick.

Committee assignment(s): Joint Library; Appropriations (chair); Commerce, Science and Transportation; Rules and Administration

THOMAS, CRAIG, R-WYO.

Capitol Hill office: SH-109 20510; (202) 224-6441; Fax: (202) 224-1724; Internet: craig@thomas.senate.gov or www.senate.gov/~thomas/; *Chief of Staff:* Elizabeth A. Brimmer

State office(s): 2100 Capitol Ave., #2009, Cheyenne 82009; (307) 772-2451; Fax: (307) 638-3512; *Field Representative:* Ruthann Norris.

325 W. Main, Suite F, Riverton 82501; (307) 856-6642; Fax: (307) 856-5901; *Field Representative:* Pam Buline.

2201 Federal Bldg., Casper 82601; (307) 261-6413; Fax: (307) 265-6413; *State Director:* Bobbi Brown.

2632 Foothill Blvd., #101, Rock Springs 82901; (307) 362-5012; Fax: (307) 362-5129; *Field Representative:* Pati L. Smith.

40 S. Main St., #206, Sheridan 82801; (307) 672-6456; Fax: (307) 672-8227; *Field Representative:* Jackie Van Mark.

Committee assignment(s): Energy and Natural Resources; Environment and Public Works; Foreign Relations; Indian Affairs

THOMPSON, FRED, R-TENN.

Capitol Hill office: SD-523 20510; (202) 224-4944; Fax: 228-3679; Internet: bob_davis@thompson.senate.gov or www.senate.gov/~thompson; *Chief of Staff:* Thomas A. Daffron

State office(s): 501 Main St., #305, Knoxville 37902; (615) 545-4253; Fax: (615) 545-4252; *Field Representative:* Dean Rice.

167 N. Main St., #403, Memphis 38103; (901) 544-4224; Fax: (901) 544-4227; *Field Representative:* Kelley Hankins.

3322 W. End Ave., #120, Nashville 37203; (615) 736-5129; Fax: (615) 269-4803; *State Director:* Bob Davis.

109 S. Highland St., #B-9, Jackson 38301; (901) 423-9344; Fax: (901) 423-8918; *Field Representative:* John Newman.

900 Georgia Ave., #260, Chattanooga 37402; (423) 752-5337; Fax: (423) 752-5341; *Field Representative:* Chris Devaney.

Terminal Bldg., #103, Tri-City Regional Airport, Blountville 37617; (423) 325-6217; Fax: (423) 325-6192; *Field Representative:* Tony DeVault.

Committee assignment(s): Governmental Affairs (chair); Judiciary

THURMOND, STROM, R-S.C.

Capitol Hill office: SR-217 20510; (202) 224-5972; Fax: (202) 224-1300; Internet: senator@thurmond.senate. gov or www.senate.gov/~thurmond/; *Chief of Staff:* R.J. Duke Short

State office(s): 1835 Assembly St., Columbia 29201; (803) 765-5494; *State Representative:* Warren Abernathy.

334 Meeting St., #600, Charleston 29401; (803) 727-4596; *District Representative:* Patricia Rones.

401 W. Evans St., Florence 29501; (803) 662-8873; *District Representative:* Raleigh Ward.

211 York St. N.E., #29, Aiken 29801; (803) 649-2591; *District Representative:* Elizabeth McFarland.

Committee assignment(s): Armed Services (chair); Judiciary; Veterans' Affairs

TORRICELLI, ROBERT G., D-N.J.

Capitol Hill office: SD-113 20510; (202) 224-3224; Fax: (202) 224-8567; Internet: senator_torricelli@torricelli. senate.com or www.senate.gov/~torricelli/; *Administrative Assistant:* James P. Fox

State office(s): 1 Riverfront Plaza, 3rd Floor, Newark 07102; (973) 624-5555; Fax: (973) 639-2878; *District Director:* Deborah Lux.

420 Benigno Blvd., Bellmawr 08031; (609) 933-2245; Fax: (609) 933-2711; Denise Velasquez.

Committee assignment(s): Governmental Affairs; Judiciary; Rules and Administration

WARNER, JOHN W., R-VA.

Capitol Hill office: SR-225 20510; (202) 224-2023; Fax: (202) 224-6295; Internet: senator@warner.senate.gov or www.senate.gov/~warner/; *Chief of Staff:* Susan Magill

State office(s): 600 E. Main St., 18th Floor, Richmond 23219; (804) 771-2579; Fax: (804) 782-2131; *State Representative:* Dan Hanley.

World Trade Center, #4900, Norfolk 23510; (757) 441-3079; Fax: (757) 441-6250; *Office Manager:* Loretta Tate.

213 S. Jefferson St., #1003, Roanoke 24011; (540) 857-2676; Fax: (540) 857-2800; *Caseworker:* Camellia Crowder.

180 W. Main St., #235, Abingdon 24210; (540) 628-8158; Fax: (540) 628-1036; *Office Manager:* Cathie Gollehon.

Committee assignment(s): Joint Library (chair); Joint Printing (chair); Special Aging; Armed Services; Environment and Public Works; Labor and Human Resources; Rules and Administration (chair); Small Business

WELLSTONE, PAUL, D-MINN.

Capitol Hill office: SH-136 20510; (202) 224-5641; Fax: (202) 224-8438; Internet: senator@wellstone.senate. gov or www.senate.gov/~wellstone/; *Chief of Staff:* Colin McGinnis

State office(s): 2550 University Ave. West, St. Paul 55104; (612) 645-0323; *State Office Director:* Connie Lewis.

105 2nd Ave. South, Virginia 55792; (218) 741-1075; Fax: (218) 741-8544; *Constituent Advocate:* Jim Shaw.

417 Litchfield Ave. S.W., Willmar 56201; (320) 231-0001; *Willmar Office Director:* Tom Meium.

Committee assignment(s): Foreign Relations; Indian Affairs; Labor and Human Resources; Small Business; Veterans' Affairs

WYDEN, RON, D-ORE.

Capitol Hill office: SH-717 20510; (202) 224-5244; Internet: senator@wyden.senate.gov or www.senate.gov/ ~wyden/; *Chief of Staff:* Josh R. Kardon

State office(s): 500 N.E. Multnomah St., #320, Portland 97232; (503) 326-7525; *State Director:* Terry Surguine.

151 W. 7th Ave., #435, Eugene 97401; (541) 431-0229; *State Director:* Terry Surguine.

310 W. 6th St., #118, Medford 97501; (541) 858-5122; *Regional Representative:* Traci Spillman.

131 N.W. Hawthorne Ave., #107, Bend 97701; (541) 330-9142; *Regional Representative:* Scott Bolton.

105 Fir St., #210, La Grande 97850; (541) 962-7691; *Regional Representative:* Wayne Kinney.

777 13th St. S.E., #110, Salem 97301; (503) 589-4555; *Regional Representative:* Brian Clem.

Committee assignment(s): Special Aging; Budget; Commerce, Science and Transportation; Energy and Natural Resources; Environment and Public Works

Ready Reference Lists

Regional Information Sources

DEPARTMENTS

Agriculture Dept.—Animal and Plant Health Inspection Service: Plant Protection and Quarantine Programs

AK, AZ, CA, CO, GU, HI, ID, MT, NM, NV, OR, UT, WA, WY, 9580 Micron Ave., Suite I, Sacramento, CA 95827; (916) 857-6065

AL, FL, GA, KY, MS, NC, PR, SC, TN, VI, 3505 25th Ave., Bldg. 1 North, Gulfport, MS 39501; (228) 863-1813

AR, IA, KS, LA, MO, NE, ND, OK, SD, TX, 3505 Boca Chica Blvd., #360, Brownsville, TX 78521-4065; (956) 504-4150

CT, DC, DE, IL, IN, MA, MD, ME, MI, MN, NH, NJ, NY, OH, PA, RI, VA, VT, WI, WV, 505 S. Lenola Rd., #201, Moorestown, NJ 08057-1549; (609) 968-4960

Agriculture Dept.—Animal and Plant Health Inspection Service: Regulatory Enforcement and Animal Care

AK, AZ, CA, CO, HI, ID, MT, NM, NV, OR, UT, WA, WY, 9580 Micron Ave., Suite J, Sacramento, CA 95827-2623; (916) 857-6205

AL, CT, DC, DE, FL, GA, IL, IN, KY, MA, MD, ME, MI, MN, MS, NC, NH, NJ, NY, OH, PA, PR, RI, SC, TN, VA, VI, VT, WI, WV, 2568-A Riva Rd., #302, Annapolis, MD 21401-7400; (410) 571-8692

AR, IA, KS, LA, MO, ND, NE, OK, SD, TX, 501 Felix St., Bldg. #11 (mailing address: P.O. Box 6258), Fort Worth, TX 76115-6258; (817) 885-6923

Agriculture Dept.—Animal and Plant Health Inspection Service: Veterinary Services

AK, AZ, CA, CO, HI, ID, MT, NM, NV, OR, UT, WA, WY, 384 Inverness Dr. South, #150, Englewood, CO 80112; (303) 784-6201

AL, FL, GA, KY, LA, MS, NC, PR, SC, TN, 501 E. Polk St., #880, Tampa, FL 33602-3945; (813) 228-2952

AR, IA, KS, MO, NE, ND, OK, SD, TX, 100 W. Pioneer Pkwy., #100, Arlington, TX 76010; (817) 885-7850

CT, DC, DE, IL, IN, MA, MD, ME, MI, MN, NH, NJ, NY, OH, PA, RI, VA, VT, WV, WI, 1 Winners Circle, #100, Albany, NY 12205; (518) 453-0103

Agriculture Dept.—Animal and Plant Health Inspection Service: Wildlife Services

AK, AS, AZ, CA, CO, GU, HI, ID, KS, MT, ND, NE, NM, NV, OK, OR, SD, TX, UT, WA, WY, 12345 W. Alameda Pkwy., #204, Lakewood, CO 80228; (303) 969-6560

AL, AR, CT, DC, DE, FL, GA, IA, IL, IN, KY, LA, MA, MD, ME, MI, MN, MO, MS, NC, NH, NJ, NY, OH, PA, RI, SC, TN, VA, VT, WI, WV, 3322 W. End Ave., #301, Nashville, TN 37203; (615) 736-2007

Agriculture Dept.—Cooperative State Research, Education, and Extension Service: Extension Offices

AK, University of Alaska, P.O. Box 756180, Fairbanks, AK 99775-6180; (907) 474-6567

AL, Auburn University, 109D Duncan Hall, Auburn, AL 36849-5612; (334) 844-4444

AR, University of Arkansas, P.O. Box 391, Little Rock, AR 72203; (501) 671-2117

AS, American Samoa Community College, c/o Grant Program, Pago Pago, AS 96799-2609; (684) 699-1575

AZ, College of Agriculture, University of Arizona, 301 Forbes Bldg., Tucson, AZ 85721; (520) 621-7209

CA, University of California, Agriculture and Natural Resources, 300 Lakeside Dr., 6th Floor, Oakland, CA 94612-3560; (510) 987-0060

STATE AND TERRITORY ABBREVIATIONS

Please refer to the following U.S. Postal Service abbreviations for the states and territories when using the list of Regional Information Sources.

AK	Alaska	**HI**	Hawaii	**MP**	Northern Marianas	**PR**	Puerto Rico
AL	Alabama	**IA**	Iowa	**MS**	Mississippi	**RI**	Rhode Island
AR	Arkansas	**ID**	Idaho	**MT**	Montana	**SC**	South Carolina
AS	American Samoa	**IL**	Illinois	**NC**	North Carolina	**SD**	South Dakota
AZ	Arizona	**IN**	Indiana	**ND**	North Dakota	**TN**	Tennessee
CA	California	**KS**	Kansas	**NE**	Nebraska	**TX**	Texas
CO	Colorado	**KY**	Kentucky	**NH**	New Hampshire	**UT**	Utah
CT	Connecticut	**LA**	Louisiana	**NJ**	New Jersey	**VA**	Virginia
CZ	Canal Zone	**MA**	Massachusetts	**NM**	New Mexico	**VI**	Virgin Islands
DC	District of Columbia	**MD**	Maryland	**NV**	Nevada	**VT**	Vermont
DE	Delaware	**ME**	Maine	**NY**	New York	**WA**	Washington
FL	Florida	**MI**	Michigan	**OH**	Ohio	**WI**	Wisconsin
GA	Georgia	**MN**	Minnesota	**OK**	Oklahoma	**WV**	West Virginia
GU	Guam	**MO**	Missouri	**OR**	Oregon	**WY**	Wyoming
				PA	Pennsylvania		

Agriculture Dept.—Cooperative State Research, Education, and Extension Service (Extension Offices) (continued)

CO, Colorado State University, 1 Administration Bldg., Fort Collins, CO 80523-4040; (970) 491-6281

CT, College of Agriculture & Natural Resources, University of Connecticut, 1376 Storrs Rd. (mailing address: Box U-66), Storrs, CT 06269-4036; (860) 486-6271

DC, University of the District of Columbia, 901 Newton St. N.E., Washington, DC 20017; (202) 274-6900

DE, University of Delaware, 131 Townsend Hall, S. College Ave., Newark, DE 19717-1303; (302) 831-2504

FL, University of Florida, 1038 McCarty Hall, Gainesville, FL 32611-0210; (352) 392-1761

GA, University of Georgia, 101 Conner Hall, Athens, GA 30602-7504; (706) 542-3824

GU, University of Guam, UOG Station, Mangilao, GU 96913; (671) 734-2562

HI, University of Hawaii, 3050 Maile Way, Gilmore 203, Honolulu, HI 96822; (808) 956-8397

IA, Iowa State University, 315 Beardshear, Ames, IA 50011; (515) 294-6192

ID, University of Idaho, Agricultural Science Bldg., #51, Moscow, ID 83843-2337; (208) 885-6639

IL, University of Illinois, 123 Mumford Hall, 1301 W. Gregory Dr., Urbana, IL 61801; (217) 333-5900

IN, Purdue University, 104 Agricultural Administration Bldg., West Lafayette, IN 47907; (888) 398-4636

KS, Kansas State University, 114 Waters Hall, Manhattan, KS 66506-3401; (785) 532-6147

KY, University of Kentucky, Agricultural Science Bldg. N, Lexington, KY 40546-0091; (606) 257-4772

LA, Louisiana State University, Knapp Hall, P.O. Box 25203, Baton Rouge, LA 70894-5203; (504) 388-4143

MA, University of Massachusetts, 1 Draper Hall, Amherst, MA 01003-2010; (413) 545-2716

MD, University of Maryland, Symons Hall, College Park, MD 20742; (410) 405-2027

ME, University of Maine, 102 Libby Hall, Orono, ME 04469-5741; (207) 581-3186

MI, Michigan State University, 108 Ag Hall, East Lansing, MI 48824; (517) 355-2308

MN, University of Minnesota, 240 Coffey Hall, 1420 Eckles Ave., St. Paul, MN 55108-6070; (612) 625-1915

**Agriculture Dept.—Cooperative State
Research, Education, and Extension Service
(Extension Offices)** (continued)

MO, University of Missouri, 309 University Hall, Columbia, MO 65211; (573) 882-7754

MS, Mississippi State University, Box 5446, Mississippi State, MS 39762; (601) 325-8594

MT, Montana State University, 204A Culberston Hall, Bozeman, MT 59717; (406) 994-4371

NC, North Carolina State University, Box 7602, Raleigh, NC 27695-7602; (919) 515-2811

ND, North Dakota State University, 315 Morrill Hall, Fargo, ND 58105-5437; (701) 231-8944

NE, University of Nebraska, 211 Ag Hall, Lincoln, NE 68583-0703; (402) 472-2966

NH, University of New Hampshire, 103 Taylor Hall, Durham, NH 03824-3587; (603) 862-1520

NJ, State University of Rutgers, Box 231, Cook College, New Brunswick, NJ 08903-0231; (732) 932-9306

NM, New Mexico State University, Box 30003, Dept. 3AE, Las Cruces, NM 88003; (505) 646-3015

NV, University of Nevada, 2317-A Renaissaru Dr., Reno, NV 89557-0106; (702) 784-1614

NY, Cornell University, 245 Roberts Hall, Ithaca, NY 14853-4203; (607) 255-2552

OH, Ohio State University, 2120 Fyffe Rd., Columbus, OH 43210; (614) 292-3897

OK, Oklahoma State University, 139 Agricultural Hall, Stillwater, OK 74078-0500; (405) 744-5398

OR, Oregon State University, 106 Ballard Hall, Corvallis, OR 97331; (541) 737-2713

PA, Penn State University, 201 Agriculture Administration Bldg., University Park, PA 16802; (814) 865-2541

PR, University of Puerto Rico, Mayaguez Campus, Mayaguez, PR 00681-5000; (787) 265-3850

RI, University of Rhode Island, 9 Alumni Ave., #7, Kingston, RI 02881; (401) 792-2474

SC, Clemson University, 104 Barre Hall, Clemson, SC 29634-0351; (803) 656-3382

SD, South Dakota State University, Ag Hall 154 (mailing address: P.O. Box 2207D), Brookings, SD 57007-9988; (605) 688-4792

TN, University of Tennessee, Box 1071, Knoxville, TN 37901-1071; (423) 974-7114

TX, Texas A&M University, 106 System Administration Bldg., College Station, TX 77843-7101; (409) 845-7967

UT, Utah State University, Ag. Science Bldg., Logan, UT 84322-4800; (801) 797-2200

VA, Virginia Polytechnic Institute and State University, 101 Hutcheson Hall, Blacksburg, VA 24061-0402; (540) 231-5299

VI, University of the Virgin Islands, RR #2-10,000, Kingshill, St. Croix, VI 00850; (340) 692-4022

VT, University of Vermont, 601 Main St., Burlington, VT 05401-3439; (802) 656-2980

WA, Washington State University, 421 Hulbert Hall, Pullman, WA 99164-6230; (509) 335-4563

WI, University of Wisconsin, 432 N. Lake St., 539 Ext. Bldg., Madison, WI 53706-1498; (608) 262-9781

WV, West Virginia University, 817 Knapp Hall (mailing address: P.O. Box 6031), Morgantown, WV 26506; (304) 293-5691

WY, University of Wyoming, P.O. Box 3354, College of Agriculture, Laramie, WY 82071-3354; (307) 766-5125

Agriculture Dept.—Farm Service Agency

AK, ID, OR, WA, 112 University Rd., #205, Spokane, WA 99206; (509) 353-2147

AL, FL, GA, SC, 401 N. Patterson St., #M-113, Valdosta, GA 31601; (912) 242-3044

AR, KY, LA, MS, TN, 100 W, Capitol St., Jackson, MS 39269; (601) 965-4771

AZ, CA, HI, NV, UT, 1303 J St., #450, Sacramento, CA 95814; (916) 498-5315

CO, KS, MO, NE, 3401 S.W. Van Buren, Topeka, KS 66611-2227; (785) 266-0248

CT, DE, MA, MD, ME, NC, NH, NJ, NY, PA, RI, VA, VT, WV, 4407 Bland Rd., #160, Raleigh, NC 27609; (919) 790-2749

IA, MN, WI, 30 E. 7th St., #910, St. Paul, MN 55101-4901; (612) 290-3304

IL, IN, MI, OH, 2305 W. Monroe St., Springfield, IL 62704; (217) 492-4186

MT, ND, SD, WY, 2110 Overland Ave., #106, Billings, MT 59102-6440; (406) 657-6447

NM, OK, TX, 205 N.W. 63rd St., #170, Oklahoma City, OK 73116-8209; (405) 879-2700

Agriculture Dept.—Food and Nutrition Service

AK, AZ, CA, GU, HI, ID, NV, OR, WA, 550 Kearny St., #400, San Francisco, CA 94108-2518; (415) 705-1311

AL, FL, GA, KY, MS, NC, SC, TN, 77 Forsyth St. S.W., #112, Atlanta, GA 30303-3427; (404) 730-2588

AR, LA, NM, OK, TX, 1100 Commerce St., #5C30, Dallas, TX 75242-9980; (214) 290-9802

CO, IA, KS, MO, MT, ND, NE, SD, UT, WY, 1244 Speer Blvd., #903, Denver, CO 80204-3581; (303) 844-0312

CT, MA, ME, NH, NY, RI, VT, 10 Causeway St., Boston, MA 02222-1069; (617) 565-6418

DC, DE, MD, NJ, PA, PR, VA, VI, WV, 300 Corporate Blvd., Robbinsville, NJ 08691-1518; (609) 259-5091

IL, IN, MI, MN, OH, WI, 77 W. Jackson Blvd., 20th Floor, Chicago, IL 60604-3507; (312) 353-1044

Agriculture Dept.—Food Safety and Inspection Service

AK, AS, GM, HI, ID, OR, WA, 530 Center St. N.E., #405, Salem OR 27609; (503) 399-5831

AL, MS, TN, 715 S. Pear Orchard Rd., #101, Ridgeland, MS 39157; (601) 965-4312

AR, LA, OK, (temporary location) 216 E. Emma Ave., 2nd Floor, Springdale AR 72764; (501) 751-8412

AZ, CO, NM, NV, UT, 665 S. Broadway, Suite B, Boulder, CO 80303; (303) 497-5411

CA, 620 Central Ave., Bldg. 2C, Alameda, CA 94501; (510) 337-5074

CT, MA, ME, NH, PR, RI, VI, VT, (temporary location) 10 Causeway St., #522, Boston, MA 02222; (617) 565-6570

DC, DE, MD, VA, 6303 Ivy Lane, #310, Greenbelt, MD 20770; (301) 344-2261

FL, GA, 100 Alabama St. S.W., #3R90, Atlanta, GA 30303; (404) 562-5900

IA, NE, 11338 Aurora Ave., Des Moines, IA 50322; (515) 284-6300

IL, IN, (temporary location) 1920 S. Highland Ave., #106, Lombard, IL 60148; (630) 620-7474

KS, MO, 4920 W. 15th St., Lawrence, KS 66049; (785) 841-5600

KY, OH, WV, 155 E. Columbus St., Pickerington, OH 43147; (614) 833-1405

MI, WI, (temporary location) 559 D'Onofrio Dr., #201, Madison, WI 53719; (608) 264-5600

MN, MT, ND, SD, WY, 100 N. 6th St., Minneapolis, MN 55403; (612) 370-2400

NC, SC, 6020 6 Forks Rd., Raleigh, NC 27609; (919) 844-8400

NJ, NY, 230 Washington Ave., Albany, NY 12203; (518) 452-6870

PA, 701 Market St., #2B South, Philadelphia, PA 19106; (215) 597-8735

TX, 1100 Commerce St., #5F41, Dallas, TX 75242; (214) 767-9116

Agriculture Dept.—Forest Service

AK, 709 W. 9th St. (mailing address: P.O. Box 21628), Juneau, AK 99802-1628; (907) 586-8863

AL, AR, FL, GA, KY, LA, MS, NC, OK, PR, SC, TN, TX, VA, VI, 1720 Peachtree Rd. N.W., Atlanta, GA 30367; (404) 347-4177

AZ, NM, 517 Gold Ave. S.W., Albuquerque, NM 87102; (505) 842-3300

CA, HI, 630 Sansome St., San Francisco, CA 94111; (415) 705-2870

CO, KS, NE, SD (southeastern), WY (eastern), 11177 W. 8th Ave. (mailing address: P.O. Box 25127), Lakewood, CO 80225; (303) 275-5450

CT, DE, IA, IL, IN, MA, MD, ME, MI, MN, MO, NH, NJ, NY, OH, PA, RI, VT, WI, WV, 310 W. Wisconsin Ave., #500, Milwaukee, WI 53203; (414) 297-3600

ID (northern), MT, ND, SD (northwestern), WY (northwestern), 200 E. Broadway St. (mailing address: P.O. Box 7669), Missoula, MT 59807-7669; (406) 329-3316

ID (southern), NV, UT, WY (western), 324 25th St., Ogden, UT 84401-2310; (801) 625-5605

OR, WA, 333 S.W. 1st Ave. (mailing address: P.O. Box 3623), Portland, OR 97208; (503) 326-3625

Agriculture Dept.—Rural Development

AK, 800 W. Evergreen, #201, Palmer, AK 99645-6539; (907) 745-2176

AL, 4121 Carmichael Rd. Sterling Center, #601, Montgomery, AL 36106-3683; (334) 279-3400

Agriculture Dept.—Rural Development
(continued)

AR, 700 W. Capitol Ave., #3416, Little Rock, AR 72201; (501) 324-6281

AZ, 3003 N. Central Ave., #900, Phoenix, AZ 85012; (602) 280-8700

CA, 194 W. Main St., Suite F, Woodland, CA 95695-2915; (916) 668-2000

CO, 655 Parfet St., #E-100, Lakewood, CO 80215; (303) 236-2801

CT, MA, RI, 451 West St., Amherst, MA 01002-2953; (413) 253-4302

DC, DE, MD, 4611 S. Dupont Hwy. (mailing address: P.O. Box 400), Camden, DE 19934-9998; (302) 697-4300

FL, 4440 N.W. 25th Pl. (mailing address: P.O. Box 147010), Gainesville, FL 32614-7010; (352) 338-3402

GA, 355 E. Hancock Ave., Athens, GA 30601-2768; (706) 546-2173

HI, 154 Waianuenue Ave., #311, Hilo, HI 96720; (808) 933-3000

IA, 210 Walnut St., #873, Des Moines, IA 50309; (515) 284-4663

ID, 3232 Elder St., Boise, ID 83705; (208) 378-5600

IL, 1817 S. Neil St., #103, Champaign, IL 61820; (217) 398-5235

IN, 5975 Lakeside Blvd., Indianapolis, IN 46278; (317) 290-3100

KS, 1200 S.W. Executive Dr. (mailing address: P.O. Box 4653), Topeka, KS 66604; (913) 271-2700

KY, 771 Corporate Plaza, #200, Lexington, KY 40503-5477; (606) 224-7300

LA, 3727 Government St., Alexandria, LA 71302; (318) 473-7920

ME, 444 Stillwater Ave., #2 (mailing address: P.O. Box 405), Bangor, ME 04402-0405; (207) 990-9106

MI, 3001 Coolidge Rd., #200, East Lansing, MI 48823; (517) 337-6635

MN, 375 Jackson St., #410, St. Paul, MN 55101-1853; (612) 602-7800

MO, 601 Business Loop 70 West, #235, Columbia, MO 65203; (573) 876-0976

MS, 100 W. Capitol St., #831, Jackson, MS 39269; (601) 965-4318

MT, 900 Technology Blvd., Suite B, (mailing address: P.O. Box 850) Bozeman, MT 59771; (406) 585-2580

NC, 4405 Bland Rd., #260, Raleigh, NC 27609; (919) 873-2000

ND, 220 E. Rosser, #208 (mailing address: P.O. Box 1737), Bismarck, ND 58502; (701) 250-4781

NE, 100 Centennial Mall North, #308, Lincoln, NE 68508; (402) 437-5551

NH, VI, VT, 89 Main St., 3rd Floor, Montpelier, VT 05602; (802) 828-6002

NJ, 790 Woodland Rd., #22, Mt. Holly, NJ 08060; (609) 265-3600

NM, 6200 Jefferson St. N.E., Albuquerque, NM 87109; (505) 761-4950

NV, 1390 S. Curry St., Carson City, NV 89703-5405; (702) 887-1222

NY, 441 S. Salina St., #357, Syracuse, NY 13202; (315) 477-6433

OH, 200 N. High St., #507, Columbus, OH 43215-2477; (614) 469-5608

OK, USDA Agricultural Center Bldg., #108, Stillwater, OK 74074-2654; (405) 742-1000

OR, 101 S.W. Main St., #1410, Portland, OR 97204-2333; (503) 414-3300

PA, 1 Credit Union Pl., #330, Harrisburg, PA 17110-2996; (717) 782-4476

PR, 159 Carlos E. Chardon St., #501, Hato Rey, PR 00918-5481; (787) 766-5095

SC, 1835 Assembly St., #1007, Columbia, SC 29201; (803) 253-3725

SD, 200 4th St. S.W., #308, Huron, SD 57350; (605) 352-1100

TN, 3322 West End Ave., #300, Nashville, TN 37203-1071; (615) 783-1300

TX, 101 S. Main, #102, Temple, TX 76501; (817) 774-1301

UT, 125 S. State St., #5438, Salt Lake City, UT 84138; (801) 524-4063

VA, 1606 Santa Rosa Rd., #238, Richmond, VA 23229-5014; (804) 287-1550

WA, 1835 Black Lake Blvd., Suite B, Olympia, WA 98512-5715; (360) 704-7742

WI, 4949 Kirschling Court, Stevens Point, WI 54481; (715) 345-7600

Agriculture Dept.—Rural Development
(continued)

WV, 75 High St., #320, Morgantown, WV 26505-7500; (304) 291-4793

WY, Federal Bldg., #1005, 100 East B (mailing address: P.O. Box 820), Casper, WY 82602; (307) 261-5271

Commerce Dept.—Census Bureau

AK, CA (northern), ID, OR, WA, 101 Stewart St., #500, Seattle, WA 98101-1098; (206) 728-5300

AL, FL, GA, 101 Marietta St. N.W., #3200, Atlanta, GA 30303-2700; (404) 730-3832

AR, IA, KS, MN, MO, OK, 400 State Ave., #600, Kansas City, KS 66101-2410; (913) 551-6728

AZ, CO, MT, ND, NE, SD, UT WY, 6900 W. Jefferson Ave., Denver, CO 80235-2032; (303) 969-6750

CA (southern), HI, 15350 Sherman Way, #300, Van Nuys, CA 91406-4224; (818) 904-6339

CT, MA, ME, NH, NY (upstate), PR, RI, VI, VT, 2 Copley Place, #301 (mailing address: P.O. Box 9108), Boston, MA 02117-9180; (617) 424-0500

DE, DC, MD, NJ (except New York area counties), PA, 105 S. 7th St., Philadelphia, PA 19106-3395; (215) 597-4920

IL, IN, WI, 2255 Enterprise Dr., #5501, Westchester, IL 60154-5800; (708) 562-1350

KY NC, SC, VA, 901 Center Park Dr., #106, Charlotte, NC 28217-2935; (704) 344-6142

LA, MS, TX, 6303 Harry Hines Blvd., #210, Dallas, TX 75235-5269; (214) 640-4400

MI, OH, WV, 1395 Brewery Park Blvd. (mailing address: P.O. Box 33405), Detroit, MI 48232-5405; (313) 259-1158

NJ (New York area counties), NY (downstate), 26 Federal Plaza, #37-100, New York, NY 10278-0044; (212) 264-3860

Commerce Dept.—Economic Development Administration

AK, AS, AZ, CA, GU, HI, ID, MP, NV, OR, WA, Marshall Islands, Micronesia, Palau, 915 2nd Ave., 1856, Seattle, WA 98174; (206) 220-7660

AL, FL, GA, KY, MS, NC, SC, TN, 401 W. Peachtree St. N.W., #1820, Atlanta, GA 30308-3510; (404) 730-3002

AR, LA, NM, OK, TX, 903 San Jacinto Blvd., #121, Austin, TX 78701-2450; (512) 916-5461

CO, IA, KS, MO, MT, ND, NE, SD, UT, WY, 1244 Speer Blvd., #670, Denver, CO 80204; (303) 844-4714

CT, DC, DE, MA, MD, ME, NH, NJ, NY, PA, PR, RI, VA, VI, VT, WV, Independence Square West, #140S, Philadelphia, PA 19106; (215) 597-4603

IL, IN, MI, MN, OH, WI, 111 N. Canal St., #855, Chicago, IL 60606-7204; (312) 353-7706

Commerce Dept.—International Trade Administration

AK, 3601 C St., #700, Anchorage, AK 99503; (907) 271-6237

AL, 950 22nd St. North, #707, Birmingham, AL 35203; (205) 731-1331

AR, 425 W. Capitol Ave., #700, Little Rock, AR 72201; (501) 324-5794

AZ, 2901 N. Central Ave., #970, Phoenix, AZ 85012; (602) 640-2513

CA, 390-B Fir Ave., Clovis, CA 93611; (209) 325-1619

1 World Trade Center, #1670, Long Beach, CA 90831; (310) 980-4550

350 S. Figueroa St., #172, Los Angeles, CA 90071; (213) 894-8784

11000 Wilshire Blvd., #9200, Los Angeles, CA 90024; (408) 641-9850

411 Pacific St., #200, Monterey, CA 93940; (408) 641-9850

3300 Irvine Ave., #305, Newport Beach, CA 92660; (714) 660-1688

330 Ignacio Blvd., #102, Novato, CA 94949; (415) 883-1966

530 Water St., #740, Oakland, CA 94607; (510) 273-7350

2940 Inland Empire Blvd., #121, Ontario, CA 91764; (909) 466-4134

300 Esplanade Dr., #2090, Oxnard, CA 93030; (805) 981-8150

917 7th St., 2nd Floor, Sacramento, CA 95814; (916) 498-5155

6363 Greenwich Dr., #230, San Diego, CA 92122; (619) 557-5395

345 California St., 7th Floor, San Francisco, CA 94104; (415) 705-1053

250 Montgomery St., 14th Floor, San Francisco, CA 94104; (415) 705-2300

5201 Great American Pkwy., #456, Santa Clara, CA 95054; (408) 970-4610

101 Park Center Plz., #1001, San Jose, CA 95113; (408) 271-7300

CO, WY, 1625 Broadway, #680, Denver, CO 80202; (303) 844-6622

CT, 213 Court St., #903, Middletown, CT 06457-3348; (860) 638-6950

DC, c/o National Institute of Standards and Technology, Bldg. 411, #A102, Gaithersburg, MD 20899; (301) 975-3904

DE, 615 Chestnut St., #1501, Philadelphia, PA 19106; (215) 597-6101

FL, 5600 N.W. 36th St., #617, Miami, FL 33166; (305) 526-7425

1130 Cleveland St., Clearwater, FL 34615; (813) 461-0011

200 E. Robinson St., #1270, Orlando, FL 32801; (407) 648-6235

The Capitol, #2001, Tallahassee, FL 32399-0001; (850) 488-6469

GA, 285 Peachtree Center Ave. N.E., #200, Atlanta, GA 30303-1229; (404) 657-1900

6001 Chatham Center Dr., #100, Savannah, GA 31405; (912) 652-4204

HI, 300 Ala Moana Blvd., #4106 (mailing address: P.O. Box 50026), Honolulu, HI 96850; (808) 541-1782

IA, 210 Walnut St., #817, Des Moines, IA 50309; (515) 284-4222

ID, MT, 700 W. State St., 2nd Floor, Boise, ID 83720; (208) 334-3857

IL, 55 W. Monroe St., #2440, Chicago, IL 60603; (312) 353-8045

610 Central Ave., #150, Highland Park, IL 60035; (847) 681-8010

515 N. Court St., Rockford, IL 61110; (815) 987-8123

c/o Illinois Institute of Technology, 201 E. Loop Rd., Wheaton, IL 60187; (630) 353-4332

IN, 11405 N. Pennsylvania St., #106, Carmel, IN 46032; (317) 582-2300

KS, 151 N. Volutsia, Wichita, KS 67214; (316) 269-6160

KY, 601 W. Broadway, #634B, Louisville, KY 40202; (502) 582-5066

2292 S. Hwy. 27, #320, Somerset, KY 42501; (606) 677-6160

LA, 365 Canal St., #2150, New Orleans, LA 70130; (504) 589-6546

5210 Hollywood Ave. Annex, Shreveport, LA 71109; (318) 676-3064

MA, 164 Northern Ave., #307, Boston, MA 02210; (617) 424-5990

100 Granger Blvd., #102, Marlborough, MA 01752; (508) 624-6000

MD, 401 E. Pratt St., #2432, Baltimore, MD 21202; (410) 962-4539

ME, 511 Congress St., Portland, ME 04101; (207) 541-7430

MI, 425 S. Main St., #103, Ann Arbor, MI 48104; (313) 741-2430

211 W. Fort St., #2220, Detroit, MI 48226; (313) 226-3650

301 W. Fulton St., #718S, Grand Rapids, MI 49504; (616) 458-3564

250 Elizabeth Lake Rd., Pontiac, MI 48314; (248) 975-9600

MN, ND, 110 S. 4th St., #108, Minneapolis, MN 55401; (612) 348-1638

MO, 8182 Maryland Ave., #303, St. Louis, MO 63105; (314) 425-3302

601 E. 12th St., #635, Kansas City, MO 64106; (816) 426-3141

MS, 201 W. Capital St., #310, Jackson, MS 39201-2005; (601) 965-4388

NC, 521 E. Morehead St., #435, Charlotte, NC 28202; (704) 333-4886

400 W. Market St., #400, Greensboro, NC 27401; (910) 333-5345

NE, 11135 O St., Omaha, NE 68137; (402) 221-3664

Commerce Dept.—International Trade Administration (continued)

NH, 17 New Hampshire Ave., Portsmouth, NH 03801-2838; (603) 334-6074

NJ, Gateway I, 9th Floor, Newark, NJ 07102; (973) 645-4682

    3131 Princeton Pike, #100, Trenton, NJ 08648; (609) 989-2100

NM, c/o New Mexico Dept. of Economic Development, 1100 St. Francis Dr. (mailing address: P.O. Box 20003), Santa Fe, NM 87504-5003; (505) 827-0350

NV, 1755 E. Plumb Lane, #152, Reno, NV 89502; (702) 784-5203

NY, 111 W. Huron St., #1304, Buffalo, NY 14202; (716) 555-4191

    111 E. Ave., #220, Rochester, NY 14604; (716) 263-6480

    6 World Trade Center, #635, New York, NY 10048; (212) 466-5222

    163 W. 125th St., #1301, New York, NY 10026; (212) 860-6200

    1550 Franklin Ave., #207, Mineola, NY 11501; (516) 739-1765

    707 West Chester Ave., White Plains, NY 10604; (914) 682-6218

OH, 36 E. Seventh St., #2860, Cincinnati, OH 45202; (513) 684-2944

    600 Superior Ave. E., #700, Cleveland, OH 44114; (216) 522-4750

    37 N. High St., 4th Floor, Columbus, OH 43215; (614) 365-9510

    300 Madison Ave., Toledo, OH 43604; (419) 241-0683

OK, 301 N.W. 63rd St., #330, Oklahoma City, OK 73116; (405) 231-5302

    700 N. Greenwood Ave., #1400, Tulsa, OK 74106; (918) 581-7650

OR, 1445 Willamette St., #13, Eugene, OR 97401-4003; (541) 465-6575

    121 S.W. Salmon St., #242, Portland, OR 97204; (503) 326-3001

PA, 1 Commerce St., 3rd Floor, Harrisburg, PA 17101; (717) 232-0051

615 Chestnut St., #1501, Philadelphia, PA 19106; (215) 597-6101

1000 Liberty Ave., Pittsburgh, PA 15222; (412) 395-5050

1 Montage Mountain Rd., Suite B, Moosic, PA 18507; (717) 969-2530

PR, 525 F. D. Roosevelt Ave., #905, San Juan, PR 00918; (787) 766-5555

RI, 1 W. Exchange St., Providence, RI 02903; (401) 528-5104

SC, 1835 Assembly St., #172, Columbia, SC 29201; (803) 765-5345

    81 Mary St., Charleston, SC 29402; (803) 727-4051

    555 N. Pleasantburg Dr., Bldg. #109, Greenville, SC 29607; (864) 271-1976

SD, 2001 S. Summit Ave., #SS29A, Sioux Falls, SD 57197; (605) 330-4264

TN, 22 N. Front St., #200, Memphis, TN 38103; (901) 544-4137

    301 E. Church Ave., Knoxville, TN 37915; (423) 545-4637

    404 James Robertson Pkwy., #114, Nashville, TN 37219; (615) 545-4637

TX, 2050 N. Stemmons Fwy., #170 (mailing address: P.O. Box 58130), Dallas, TX 75258; (214) 767-0542

    1700 Congress St., 2nd Floor, (mailing address: P.O. Box 12728), Austin, TX 78711; (512) 916-5939

    500 Dallas St., #1160, Houston, TX 77002; (713) 718-3062

    711 Houston St., Fort Worth, TX 76102; (214) 767-0542

    1222 N. Main St., #450, San Antonio, TX 78212; (210) 228-9878

UT, 324 S. State St., #211, Salt Lake City, UT 84111; (801) 524-5116

VA, 704 E. Franklin St., #550, Richmond, VA 23219; (804) 771-2246

VT, 109 State St., 4th Floor, Montpelier, VT 05609; (802) 828-4508

WA, 2001 6th Ave., #650, Seattle, WA 98121; (206) 553-5615

    c/o Greater Spokane Chamber of Commerce, 1020 W. Riverside, Spokane, WA 99201; (509) 353-2625

Commerce Dept.—International Trade Administration (continued)

WI, 517 E. Wisconsin Ave., #596, Milwaukee, WI 53202; (414) 297-3473

WV, 405 Capitol St., #807, Charleston, WV 25301; (304) 347-5123

   1310 Market St., 2nd Floor, Wheeling, WV 26003; (304) 233-7427

Commerce Dept.—Minority Business Development Agency

AK, AS, AZ, CA, HI, ID, NV, OR, WA, 221 Main St., #1280, San Francisco, CA 94105; (415) 744-3001

AL, FL, GA, KY, MS, NC, PR, SC, TN, VI, 401 W. Peachtree St. N.W., #1715, Atlanta, GA 30308-3516; (404) 730-3300

AR, CO, LA, MT, ND, NM, OK, SD, TX, UT, WY, 1100 Commerce St., #7B23, Dallas, TX 75242; (214) 767-8001

CT, DC, DE, MA, MD, ME, NH, NJ, NY, PA, RI, VA, VT, WV, 26 Federal Plaza, #3720, New York, NY 10278; (212) 264-3262

IA, IL, IN, KS, MI, MN, MO, NE, OH, WI, 55 E. Monroe St., #1406, Chicago, IL 60603-5792; (312) 353-0182

Commerce Dept.—National Oceanic and Atmospheric Administration: National Marine Fisheries Service

AK, P.O. Box 21668, Juneau, AK 99802; (907) 586-7221

AL, AR, FL, GA, IA, KS, LA, MO, MS, NC, NE, NM, OK, PR, SC, TN, TX, 9721 Executive Center Dr. North, St. Petersburg, FL 33702; (813) 570-5301

AS, AZ, CA, GU, HI, MP, NV, Pacific Island Territories, 501 W. Ocean Blvd., #4200, Long Beach, CA 90802; (562) 980-4001

CO, ID, MT, ND, OR, SD, UT, WA, WY, 7600 Sand Point Way N.E., Bldg. #1, Seattle, WA 98115; (206) 526-6150

CT, DC, DE, IL, IN, MA, MD, ME, MI, MN, NH, NJ, NY, OH, PA, RI, VA, WV, 1 Blackburn Dr., Gloucester, MA 01930; (978) 281-9250

Commerce Dept.—National Oceanic and Atmospheric Administration: National Weather Service

AK, 222 West 7th Avenue #23, Anchorage, AK 99513-7575; (907) 266-5102

AS, GU, HI, Pacific Island Territories, Grosvenor Center, Mauka Tower, 737 Bishop St., #2200, Honolulu, HI 96813; (808) 532-6416

AZ, CA, ID, MT, NV, OR, UT, WA, 125 S. State St., #1215, Salt Lake City, UT 84138-1102; (801) 524-5133

AL, AR, FL, GA, LA, MS, NM, OK, PR, TN, TX, VI, 819 Taylor St., #10A26, Fort Worth, TX 76102-6171; (817) 334-2651

CO, KS, KY, IA, IL, IN, MI, MN, MO, ND, NE, SD, WI, WY, 601 E. 12th St., #1836, Kansas City, MO 64106-2897; (816) 426-5400

CT, DC, DE, MA, MD, ME, NC, NH, NJ, NY, OH, PA, RI, SC, VA, VT, WV, 630 Johnson Ave., Bohemia, NY 11716-2626; (516) 244-0100

Education Dept.

AK, ID, OR, WA, 915 2nd Ave., #3362, Seattle, WA 98174-1099; (206) 220-7800

AL, FL, GA, KY, MS, NC, SC, TN, 101 Marietta Tower Bldg., #2221, Atlanta, GA 30323; (404) 331-2502

AR, LA, NM, OK, TX, 1200 Main Tower Bldg., #2125, Dallas, TX 75202-4309; (214) 767-3626

AS, AZ, CA, GU, HI, NV, Pacific Islands Territories, 50 United Nations Plaza, #205, San Francisco, CA 94102-4987; (415) 437-7250

CO, MT, ND, SD, UT, WY, 1244 Speer Blvd., #310, Denver, CO 80204-3582; (303) 844-3544

CT, MA, ME, NH, RI, VT, 540 McCormack Courthouse, Boston, MA 02109-4557; (617) 223-9317

DC, DE, MD, PA, VA, WV, 3535 Market St., #16350, Philadelphia, PA 19104-3398; (215) 596-1001

IA, KS, MO, NE, 10220 N. Executive Hills Blvd., #720, Kansas City, MO 64153-1367; (816) 880-4000

IL, IN, MI, MN, OH, WI, 111 N. Canal St., #1094, Chicago, IL 60606-7204; (312) 886-8215

NJ, NY, PR, VI, 75 Park Pl., 12th Floor, New York, NY 10007; (212) 264-7005

Energy Dept.—Federal Energy Regulatory Commission: Hydropower Licensing

AK, ID, MT, OR, WA, WY, 101 S.W. Main St., #905, Portland, OR 97204; (503) 326-5840

AL, AR, FL, GA, LA, MS, NC, OK, PR, SC, TN, TX, VA, 3125 Presidential Pkwy., #300, Atlanta, GA 30340; (770) 452-2360

Energy Dept.—Federal Energy Regulatory Commission: Hydropower Licensing

(continued)

AZ, CA, CO, HI, NM, NV, UT, 901 Market St., #350, San Francisco, CA 94103-1778; (415) 356-5300

CT, DC, DE, MA, MD, ME, NH, NJ, NY, PA, RI, VT, WV, 19 W. 34th St., #400, New York, NY 10001; (212) 273-5900

IA, IL, IN, KS, KY, MI, MN, MO, ND, NE, OH, SD, WI, 230 S. Dearborn St., #3130, Chicago, IL 60604; (312) 353-6173

Energy Dept.—Field Offices

These offices do not serve specific regions.

1301 Clay St., Oakland, CA 94612-5208; (510) 637-1800

1617 Cole Blvd., Golden, CO 80401-3393; (303) 275-4778

P.O. Box 928, Rocky Flats, CO 80402-0928; (303) 966-7657

850 Energy Dr., Idaho Falls, ID 83401-1563; (208) 526-1322

9800 S. Cass Ave., Argonne, IL 60439; (630) 252-2110

H and Pennsylvania Sts. S.E., (mailing address: P.O. Box 5400), Albuquerque, NM 87185-5400; (505) 845-6050

2753 S. Highland Ave. (mailing address: P.O. Box 98518) Las Vegas, NV 89193-8518; (702) 295-3211

P.O. Box 3020, Miamisburg, OH 45343-3020; (937) 865-3977

Road 1A, Aiken, SC 29802; (803) 725-2277

200 Administration Rd. (mailing address: P.O. Box 2001) Oak Ridge, TN 37831; (423) 576-4444

825 Jadwin Ave., Richland, WA 99352; (509) 376-7395

Health and Human Services Dept.

AK, ID, OR, WA, 2201 6th Ave., #RX-01, Seattle, WA 98121; (206) 615-2010

AL, FL, GA, KY, MS, NC, SC, TN, 101 Marietta Tower, #1515, Atlanta, GA 30323-0001; (404) 331-2442

AR, LA, NM, OK, TX, 1200 Main Tower Bldg., #1100, Dallas, TX 75202; (214) 767-3301

AS, AZ, CA, GU, HI, NV, Pacific Island Territories, 50 United Nations Plaza, #431, San Francisco, CA 94102-4988; (415) 437-8500

CO, MT, ND, SD, UT, WY, 1961 Stout St., #1076, Denver, CO 80294-1185; (303) 844-3372

CT, MA, ME, NH, RI, VT, John F. Kennedy Federal Bldg., #2100, Boston, MA 02203; (617) 565-1500

DC, DE, MD, PA, VA, WV, 3535 Market St. (mailing address: P.O. Box 13716), Philadelphia, PA 19101; (215) 596-6492

IA, KS, MO, NE, 601 E. 12th St., #210, Kansas City, MO 64106-2898; (816) 426-2821

IL, IN, MI, MN, OH, WI, 105 W. Adams, 23rd Floor, Chicago, IL 60603-6201; (312) 353-5160

NJ, NY, PR, VI, 26 Federal Plaza, New York, NY 10278-0022; (212) 264-4600

Health and Human Services Dept.—Administration for Children and Families

AK, ID, OR, WA, 2201 6th Ave., #610-MS-RX-70, Seattle, WA 98121; (206) 615-2547

AL, FL, GA, KY, MS, NC, SC, TN, 101 Marietta Tower, #821, Atlanta, GA 30323; (404) 331-5700

AR, LA, NM, OK, TX, 1200 Main Tower Bldg., #1700, Dallas, TX 75202; (214) 767-9648

AS, AZ, CA, GU, HI, MP, NV, Pacific Island Territories, 50 United Nations Plaza, #450, San Francisco, CA 94102; (415) 556-7800

CO, MT, ND, SD, UT, WY, 1961 Stout St., #1185, Denver, CO 80294-3538; (303) 844-3100

CT, MA, ME, NH, RI, VT, John F. Kennedy Federal Bldg., #2000, Boston, MA 02203; (617) 565-1020

DC, DE, MD, PA, VA, WV, 3535 Market St., #5450, Philadelphia, PA 19104; (215) 596-1351

IA, KS, MO, NE, 601 E. 12th St., #384, Kansas City, MO 64106; (816) 426-3981

IL, IN, MI, MN, OH, WI, 105 W. Adams St., 20th Floor, Chicago, IL 60603; (312) 353-4237

NJ, NY, PR, VI, 26 Federal Plaza, #4049, New York, NY 10278; (212) 264-2890

Health and Human Services Dept.—Food and Drug Administration

AS, AK, AZ, CA, GU, HI, ID, MT, NV, OR, WA, Pacific Island Territories, 1301 Clay St., #1180N, Oakland, CA 94102; (510) 637-3960

Health and Human Services Dept.—Food and Drug Administration (continued)

AL, FL, GA, LA, MS, NC, PR, SC, TN, 60 8th St. N.E., Atlanta, GA 30309; (404) 347-4344

AR, CO, IA, KS, MO, NE, NM, OK, TX, UT, WY, 7920 Elmbrook Dr., #102, Dallas, TX 75247-4982; (214) 655-8100

CT, MA, ME, NH, NY, RI, VT, 830 3rd Ave., Brooklyn, NY 11232; (718) 340-7000

DC, DE, IL, IN, KY, MD, MI, MN, NJ, ND, OH, PA, SD, VA, WI, WV, 2nd and Chestnut Sts., #900, Philadelphia, PA 19106; (215) 597-4390

Health and Human Services Dept.—Public Health and Science

AK, ID, OR, WA, 2201 6th Ave., MS-RX-20, Seattle, WA 98121; (206) 615-2469

AL, FL, GA, KY, MS, NC, SC, TN, 101 Marietta Tower Bldg., #1106 Atlanta, GA 30323; (404) 331-2316

AR, LA, NM, OK, TX, 1200 Main Tower Bldg., #1100, Dallas, TX 75202; (214) 767-3879

AS, AZ, CA, GU, HI, NV, 50 United Nations Plaza, #327, San Francisco, CA 94102; (415) 437-8096

CO, MT, ND, SD, UT, WY, 1961 Stout St., #498, Denver, CO 80294; (303) 844-6163

CT, MA, ME, NH, RI, VT, John F. Kennedy Federal Bldg., #1400, Boston, MA 02203; (617) 565-4999

DC, DE, MD, PA, VA, WV, 3535 Market St., #10200 (mailing address: P.O. Box 13716), Philadelphia, PA 19104; (215) 596-6637

IA, KS, MO, NE, 601 E. 12th St., #411, Kansas City, MO 64106; (816) 426-6513

IL, IN, MI, MN, OH, WI, 105 W. Adams St., 17th Floor, Chicago, IL 60603; (312) 353-6835

NJ, NY, PR, VI, 26 Federal Plaza, #3835, New York, NY 10278; (212) 264-2560

Housing and Urban Development Dept.

AK, ID, OR, WA, 909 1st Ave., #255, Seattle, WA 98104-1000; (206) 220-5101

AL, FL, GA, KY, MS, NC, PR, SC, TN, VI, 75 Spring St. S.W., Atlanta, GA 30303-3388; (404) 331-5136

AR, LA, NM, OK, TX, 1600 Throckmorton (mailing address: P.O. Box 2905), Fort Worth, TX 76113-2905; (817) 978-9000

AS, AZ, CA, GU, HI, NV, 450 Golden Gate Ave. (mailing address: P.O. Box 36003), San Francisco, CA 94102-3448; (415) 436-6532

CO, MT, ND, SD, UT, WY, 633 17th St., Denver, CO 80202-3607; (303) 633-5440

CT, MA, ME, NH, RI, VT, 10 Causeway St., #375, Boston, MA 02222-1092; (617) 565-5236

DC, DE, MD, PA, VA, WV, 100 Penn Square East, Philadelphia, PA 19107-3390; (215) 656-0600

IA, KS, MO, NE, 400 State Ave., #200, Kansas City, KS 66101-2406; (913) 551-5462

IL, IN, MI, MN, OH, WI, 77 W. Jackson Blvd., Chicago, IL 60604-3507; (312) 353-6236

NJ, NY, 26 Federal Plaza, New York, NY 10278-0068; (212) 264-8000

Interior Dept.—Bureau of Indian Affairs

AK, P.O. Box 25520, Juneau, AK 99802-5520; (907) 586-7177

AZ, CA, NV, UT (except Navajo Reservations), 1 N. 1st St. (mailing address: P.O. Box 10), Phoenix, AZ 85001-0010; (602) 379-6600

AZ, NM, UT (Navajo Reservations only) P.O. Box 1060, Gallup, NM 87305; (505) 863-8314

CA, 2800 Cottage Way, Sacramento, CA 95825-1884; (916) 978-4691

CO, NM, 615 1st St. N.W. (mailing address: Box 26567), Albuquerque, NM 87125-6567; (505) 766-3754

FL, LA, ME, MS, NC, NY, 3701 N. Fairfax Dr., MS-VASQ-260, Arlington, VA 22203; (703) 235-2571

IA, MI, MN, WI, 331 S. 2nd Ave., Minneapolis, MN 55401-2241; (612) 373-1000

ID, OR, WA, 911 11th Ave. N.E., Portland, OR 97232-4169; (503) 231-6702

KS, OK (western), WCD Office Complex (mailing address: P.O. Box 368) Anadarko, OK 73005-0368; (405) 247-6673

OK (eastern), 101 N. 5th St., Muskogee, OK 74401-6206; (918) 687-2296

MT, WY, 316 N. 26th St., Billings, MT 59101-1362; (406) 247-7943

ND, NE, SD, 115 4th Ave. S.E., Aberdeen, SD 57401-4382; (605) 226-7343

Interior Dept.—Bureau of Land Management

AK, 222 W. 7th Ave., #13, Anchorage, AK 99513-7599; (907) 271-5555

AZ, 3707 N. 7th St. (mailing address: P.O. Box 16563), Phoenix, AZ 85011; (602) 650-0504

CA, 2135 Butano Dr., Sacramento, CA 95825-0451; (916) 979-2835

CO, 2850 Youngfield St., Lakewood, CO 80215-7076; (303) 239-3670

Eastern States (headquarters), 7450 Boston Blvd., Springfield, VA 22153; (703) 440-1713

ID, 3383 S. Development Ave., Boise, ID 83706; (208) 384-3014

KS, NM, OK, TX, 1474 Rodeo Dr. (mailing address: P.O. Box 27115), Santa Fe, NM 87502-0115; (505) 438-7514

MT, ND, SD, 222 N. 32nd St. (mailing address: P.O. Box 36800), Billings, MT 59107-6800; (406) 255-2913

NE, WY, 5333 Yellowstone Rd. (mailing address: P.O. Box 1828) Cheyenne, WY 82003; (307) 775-6011

NV, 850 Harvard Way, Reno, NV 89520-6586; (702) 785-6586

OR, WA, 1515 S.W. 5th Ave. (mailing address: P.O. Box 2965), Portland, OR 97208-2965; (503) 957-6027

UT, 324 S. State St. (mailing address: P.O. Box 45155), Salt Lake City, UT 84145-0155; (801) 539-4021

Interior Dept.—National Park Service

AK, 2525 Gambell St., #107 Anchorage, AK 99503-2892; (907) 257-2574

AL, FL, GA, KY, MS, NC, PR, SC, TN, VI, 100 Alabama St. S.W., Bldg. 1924, Atlanta, GA 30303; (404) 567-3103

AR, AZ (northeast), CO, LA, MT, ND, NM, OK, SD, TX, UT, WY, 12795 Alameda Pkwy., Denver, CO 80225-0287; (303) 969-2500

AZ (except northeast), CA, HI, ID, NV, OR, WA, 600 Harrison St., #600, San Francisco, CA 94101; (415) 427-1320

CT, DE, MA, ME, NH, NJ, NY, PA, RI, and VT most of MD, VA, and WV, 200 Chestnut St., #322, Philadelphia, PA 19106; (215) 597-0865

DC and metro area parks in MD, VA, and WV, 1100 Ohio Dr. S.W., Washington, DC 20242; (202) 619-7256

IA, IL, IN, KS, MI, MN, MO, NE, OH, WI, 1709 Jackson St., Omaha, NE 68102; (402) 221-3431

Interior Dept.—U.S. Fish and Wildlife Service

AK, 1011 E. Tudor Rd., Anchorage, AK 99503; (907) 786-3652

AL, AR, FL, GA, KY, LA, MS, NC, PR, SC, TN, VI, 1875 Century Center Blvd., Atlanta, GA 30345; (404) 679-7289

AZ, NM, OK, TX, 500 Gold Ave. S.W. (mailing address: P.O. Box 1306), Albuquerque, NM 87103; (505) 248-6911

CA, HI, ID, NV, OR, WA, Pacific Islands, 911 N.E. 11th Ave., Portland, OR 97232-4181; (503) 231-6121

CO, KS, MT, ND, NE, SD, UT, WY, 134 Union Blvd., Lakewood, CO 80228; (303) 236-7917

CT, DC, DE, MA, MD, ME, NH, NJ, NY, PA, RI, VA, VT, WV, 300 Westgate Center Dr., Hadley, MA 01035-9589; (413) 253-8540

IA, IL, IN, MI, MN, MO, OH, WI, Whipple Federal Bldg., Fort Snelling, MN 55111-4056; (612) 725-3519

Interior Dept.—U.S. Geological Survey

AK, AZ, CA, HI, ID, NV, OR, WA, 345 Middlefield Rd., Menlo Park, CA 94025; (650) 329-4309

AL, AR, CT, DC, DE, FL, GA, IL, IN, KY, LA, MA, MD, ME, MI, MS, NC, NH, NJ, NY, OH, PA, PR, RI, SC, TN, VA, VI, VT, WI, WV, 12201 Sunrise Valley Dr., Reston, VA 22091; (703) 648-4000

CO, IA, KS, MN, MO, MT, ND, NE, NM, OK, SD, TX, UT, WY, P.O. Box 25406, Denver, CO 80225; (303) 236-5900

Justice Dept.—Drug Enforcement Administration

AK, ID, MT, OR, WA, 220 W. Mercer St., #104, Seattle, WA 98119; (206) 553-5443

AL, AR, LA, MS, 3838 N. Causeway Blvd., #1800, New Orleans, LA 70002; (504) 840-1100

AZ, 3010 N. 2nd St., #301, Phoenix, AZ 85012; (602) 664-5600

CA (Mexican border), 4560 Viewridge Ave., San Diego CA 92123; (619) 616-4100

Justice Dept.—Drug Enforcement Administration (continued)

CA (northern), 450 Golden Gate Ave., #12215 (mailing address: P.O. Box 36035) San Francisco, CA 94102; (415) 436-7900

CA (southern), GU, HI, NV, 225 E. Temple St., 20th Floor, Los Angeles, CA 90012; (213) 894-2650

CO, NM, UT, WY, 115 Inverness Dr. East, Englewood, CO 80112-5116; (303) 705-7300

CT, MA, ME, NH, RI, VT, 15 New Sudsbury St., #E400, Boston, MA 02203; (617) 557-2100

DC, MD, VA, WV, 400 6th St. S.W., #2558, Washington, DC 20024; (202) 401-7834

DE, PA, 600 Arch St., #10224 Philadelphia, PA 19106; (215) 597-9530

FL, Bahamas, 8400 N.W. 53rd St., Miami, FL 33166; (305) 590-4870

GA, NC, SC, TN, 75 Spring St. S.W., #740, Atlanta, GA 30303; (404) 331-4401

IA, IL (southern), KS, MO, NE, SD, 7911 Forsyth Blvd., #500, St. Louis, MO 63105; (314) 425-3241

IL (northern), IN, MN, ND, WI, 230 S. Dearborn St., #1200, Chicago, IL 60604; (312) 353-7875

KY, MI, OH, 431 Howard St., Detroit, MI 48226; (313) 234-4000

NJ, 970 Broad St., #806, Newark, NJ 07102; (201) 645-6060

NY, 99 10th Ave., New York, NY 10011; (212) 337-3900

OK, TX (northern), 1880 Regal Row, Dallas, TX 75235; (214) 640-0801

PR, VI, 2432 Loiza St., San Juan, PR 00913; (787) 253-4200

TX (southern), 1433 W. Loop South, Houston, TX 77027-9506; (713) 693-3000

Justice Dept.—Federal Bureau of Investigation

AK 101 E. 6th Ave., Anchorage, AK 99501; (907) 258-5322

AL, 2121 8th Ave., North., #1400, Birmingham, AL 35203; (205) 252-7705

1 St. Louis St., 3rd Floor, Mobile, AL 36602; (334) 438-3674

AR, 10825 Financial Centre Pkwy., #200, Little Rock, AR 72211-3552; (501) 221-9100

AZ, 201 E. Indianola Ave., #400, Phoenix, AZ 85012; (602) 279-5511

CA, 11000 Wilshire Blvd., #7700, Los Angeles, CA 90024; (310) 477-6565

4500 Orange Grove Ave., Sacramento, CA 95841-4205; (916) 481-9110

9797 Aero Dr., San Diego, CA 92123-1800; (619) 565-1255

450 Golden Gate Ave., 13th Floor, San Francisco, CA 94102-9523; (415) 553-7400

CO, WY, 1961 Stout St., #1823, Denver, CO 80294; (303) 629-7171

CT, 150 Court St., #535, New Haven, CT 06510; (203) 777-6311

DC (metro area), 601 4th St. N.W., Washington, DC 20535-0001; (202) 252-7801

DE, MD, 7142 Ambassador Rd., Baltimore, MD 21244-2754; (410) 265-8080

FL, 7820 Arlington Expwy., #200, Jacksonville, FL 32211; (904) 721-1211

16320 N.W. 2nd Ave., North Miami Beach, FL 33169; (305) 944-9101

500 Zack St., #610, Tampa, FL 33602-3917; (813) 273-4566

GA, 2635 Century Pkwy. N.E., #400, Atlanta, GA 30345; (404) 679-9000

HI, 300 Ala Moana Blvd., #4307, Honolulu, HI 96850; (808) 521-1411

IA, NE, 10755 Burt St., Omaha, NE 68114-2000; (402) 493-8688

ID, MT, UT, 257 E. 200 South St., #1200, Salt Lake City, UT 84111; (801) 579-1400

IL, 219 S. Dearborn St., #905, Chicago, IL 60604; (312) 431-1333

400 W. Monroe St., #400, Springfield, IL 62704; (217) 522-9675

IN, 575 N. Pennsylvania St., #679, Indianapolis, IN 46204; (317) 639-3301

KS, MO, 811 Grand Ave., #300, Kansas City, MO 64106; (816) 221-6100

Justice Dept.—Federal Bureau of Investigation (continued)

KY, 600 Martin Luther King Pl., #500, Louisville, KY 40202; (502) 583-3941

LA, 1250 Poydras St., #2200, New Orleans, LA 70113-1829; (504) 522-4671

MA, ME, NH, RI, 1 Center Plaza, #600, Boston, MA 02108; (617) 742-5533

MI, 477 Michigan Ave., 26th Floor, Detroit, MI 48226; (313) 965-2323

MN, ND, SD, 111 Washington Ave. South, #1100, Minneapolis, MN 55401-2176; (612) 376-3200

MO, 1520 Market St., #2704, St. Louis, MO 63103; (314) 241-5357

MS, 100 W. Capitol St., #1553, Jackson, MS 39269; (601) 948-5000

NC, 400 S. Tryon St., #900, Charlotte, NC 28285; (704) 377-9200

NJ (except Gloucester, Salem, and Camden counties), 1 Gateway One, Market St., 22nd Floor, Newark, NJ 07102; (973) 622-5613

NJ (Gloucester, Salem, and Camden counties), PA (eastern), 600 Arch St., 8th Floor, Philadelphia, PA 19106; (215) 829-2700

NM, 415 Silver Ave. S.W., #300, Albuquerque, NM 87102; (505) 224-2000

NV, 700 E. Charleston Blvd., Las Vegas, NV 89104-1545; (702) 385-1281

NY, VT, 445 Broadway, #502, Albany, NY 12207; (518) 465-7551

1 FBI Plaza, Buffalo, NY 14202-2698; (716) 856-7800

26 Federal Plaza, New York, NY 10278; (212) 384-1000

OH, 550 Main St., #9023, Cincinnati, OH 45273-8501; (513) 421-4310

1240 E. 9th St., #3005, Cleveland, OH 44199-9912; (216) 522-1400

OK, 50 Penn Pl., #1600, Oklahoma City, OK 73118-1886; (405) 842-7471

OR, 1500 S.W. 1st Ave., Portland, OR 97201-5828; (503) 224-4181

PA (western), WV, 700 Grant St., #300, Pittsburgh, PA 15219; (412) 471-2000

PR, 150 Carlos Chardon Ave., #526, Hato Rey, San Juan, PR 00918-1716; (787) 754-6000

SC, 1835 Assembly St., #1357, Columbia, SC 29201-2430; (803) 254-3011

TN, 710 Locust St., #600, Knoxville, TN 37901-9824; (423) 544-0751

225 N. Humphreys Blvd., #3000, Memphis, TN 38120-2107; (901) 747-4300

TX, 1801 N. Lamar, #300, Dallas, TX 75202; (214) 720-2200

700 E. San Antonio Ave., #C-600, El Paso, TX 79901-7020; (915) 533-7451

2500 East T. C. Jester, #200, Houston, TX 77008-1300; (713) 868-2266

615 E. Houston St., #200, San Antonio, TX 78205-9998; (512) 225-6741

VA, 150 Corporate Blvd., Norfolk, VA 23502; (757) 455-0100

FBI Academy, Marine Base, Quantico, VA 22315; (703) 640-6131

111 Greencourt Rd., Richmond, VA 23228; (804) 261-1044

WA, 915 2nd Ave., #710, Seattle, WA 98174-1096; (206) 622-0460

WI, 330 E. Kilbourn Ave., #600, Milwaukee, WI 53202-6627; (414) 276-4684

Justice Dept.— Federal Bureau of Prisons

AK, AZ, CA, HI, ID, MT, NV, OR, UT, WA, WY, 7950 Dublin Blvd., 3rd Floor, Dublin, CA 94568; (510) 803-4700

AL, FL, GA, MS, PR, SC, VI, 523 McDonough Blvd. S.E., Atlanta, GA 30315; (404) 624-5202

AR, LA, NM, OK, TX, 4211 Cedar Springs Rd., #300, Dallas, TX 75219; (214) 767-9700

CO, IA, IL, KS, MN, MO, ND, NE, SD, WI, 400 State Ave., Gateway Complex Tower II, 8th Floor, Kansas City, KS 66101-2492; (913) 621-3939

CT, MA, ME, NH, NJ, NY, PA, RI, VT, 2nd and Chestnut Sts., 7th Floor, Philadelphia, PA 19106; (215) 597-6317

DC, DE, IN, KY, MD, MI, NC, OH, TN, VA, WV, 10010 Junction Dr., #100N, Annapolis Junction, MD 20701; (410) 317-3100

Justice Dept.—Immigration and Naturalization Service

AK, AZ, CA, GU, HI, NV, OR, WA, 24000 Avila Rd. (mailing address: P.O. Box 30080), Laguna Niguel, CA 92607-8080; (714) 360-2995

AL, AR, CT, DC, DE, FL, GA, KY, LA, MA, MD, ME, MI, MS, NC, NH, NJ, NY, OH, PA, PR, RI, SC, TN, VA, VI, VT, WV, 70 Kimball Ave., South Burlington, VT 05403; (802) 660-5000

CO, IA, ID, IL, IN, KS, MN, MO, MT, ND, NE, NM, OK, SD, TX, UT, WI, WY, 7701 N. Stemmons Fwy., Dallas, TX 75247; (214) 767-7020

Labor Dept.—Bureau of Labor Statistics

AK, AS, AZ, CA, GU, HI, ID, NV, OR, WA, 71 Stevenson St., 6th Floor (mailing address: P.O. Box 193766), San Francisco, CA 94119-3766; (415) 975-4350

AL, FL, GA, KY, MS, NC, SC, TN, 61 Forsyth St. S.W., #7T50, Atlanta, GA 30303; (404) 562-2463

AR, LA, NM, OK, TX, 525 Griffin St., #221, Dallas, TX 75202-5028; (214) 767-6970

CO, IA, KS, MO, MT, ND, NE, SD, UT, WY, 1100 Main St., #600, Kansas City, MO 64105-2112; (816) 426-2378

CT, MA, ME, NH, RI, VT, John F. Kennedy Federal Bldg., #E310, Boston, MA 02203; (617) 565-2327

DC, DE, MD, PA, VA, WV, 3535 Market St., #8000 (mailing address: P.O. Box 13309) Philadelphia, PA 19104-3309; (215) 596-1154

IL, IN, MI, MN, OH, WI, 230 S. Dearborn St., 9th Floor, Chicago, IL 60604-1595; (312) 353-1880

NJ, NY, PR, VI, 201 Varick St., #808, New York, NY 10014-4811; (212) 337-2400

Labor Dept.—Employment and Training Administration

AK, ID, OR, WA, 1111 3rd Ave., #900, Seattle, WA 98101-3212; (206) 553-7700

AL, FL, GA, KY, MS, NC, SC, TN, 61 Forsyth St. S.W., Atlanta, GA 30303; (404) 562-2092

AR, LA, NM, OK, TX, 525 Griffin St., #317 Dallas, TX 75202; (214) 767-8263

AZ, CA, GU, HI, NV, 71 Stevenson St. (mailing address: P.O. Box 193767), San Francisco, CA 94105; (415) 975-4610

CO, MT, ND, SD, UT, WY, 1999 Broadway St., #1780, Denver, CO 80202-5716; (303) 391-5740

CT, MA, ME, NH, RI, VT, John F. Kennedy Bldg., Boston, MA 02203; (617) 565-3630

DC, DE, MD, PA, VA, WV, 3535 Market St. (mailing address: P.O. Box 8796), Philadelphia, PA 19104; (215) 596-6336

IA, KS, MO, NE, 1100 Main St., #1050, Kansas City, MO 64105; (816) 426-3796

IL, IN, MI, MN, OH, WI, 230 S. Dearborn St., #628, Chicago, IL 60604; (312) 353-0313

NJ, NY, PR, VI, 201 Varick St., #755, New York, NY 10014; (212) 337-2139

Labor Dept.—Occupational Safety and Health Administration

AK, ID, OR, WA, 1111 3rd Ave., #715, Seattle, WA 98101-3212; (206) 553-5930

AL, FL, GA, KY, MS, NC, SC, TN, 61 Forsyth St. S.W., Atlanta, GA 30303; (404) 562-2300

AR, LA, NM, OK, TX, 525 Griffin St., #602, Dallas, TX 75202; (214) 767-4731

AZ, CA, GU, HI, NV, 71 Stevenson St., #420, San Francisco, CA 94105; (415) 975-4310

CO, MT, ND, SD, UT, WY, 1999 Broadway St., #1960, Denver, CO 80202-5716; (303) 844-1600

CT, MA, ME, NH, RI, VT, John F. Kennedy, #E340, Boston, MA 02203; (617) 565-9860

DC, DE, MD, PA, VA, WV, 3535 Market St., #2100, Philadelphia, PA 19104; (215) 596-1201

IA, KS, MO, NE, 1100 Main St., #800, Kansas City, MO 64105; (816) 426-5861

IL, IN, MI, MN, OH, WI, 230 S. Dearborn St., #3244, Chicago, IL 60604; (312) 353-2220

NJ, NY, PR, VI, 201 Varick St., #670, New York, NY 10014; (212) 337-2378

Labor Dept.—Public Affairs

AK, ID, OR, WA, 1111 3rd Ave., #805, Seattle, WA 98101; (206) 553-7620

AL, FL, GA, KY, MS, NC, SC, TN, 61 Forsyth St., #6B75, Atlanta, GA 30303; (404) 562-2080

AR, LA, NM, OK, TX, 525 Griffin St., #734, Dallas, TX 75202; (214) 767-4776

Labor Dept.—Public Affairs (continued)

AZ, CA, GU, HI, NV, 71 Stevenson St., #1035, San Francisco, CA 94105; (415) 975-4742

CO, MT, ND, SD, UT, WY, 1999 Broadway, #1640, Denver, CO 80202-5716; (303) 844-1300

CT, MA, ME, NH, RI, VT, JFK Federal Bldg., #E120, Boston, MA 02203; (617) 565-2075

DC, DE, MD, PA, VA, WV, 3535 Market St., #14120, Philadelphia, PA 19104; (215) 596-1139

IA, KS, MO, NE, 1100 Maine St., #1220, Kansas City, MO 64105; (816) 426-5481

IL, IN, MI, MN, OH, WI, 230 S. Dearborn St., #3192, Chicago, IL 60604; (312) 353-6976

NJ, NY, PR, VI, 201 Varick St., #605A, New York, NY 10014; (212) 337-2319

State Dept.—Passport Offices

AK, CO, ID, MN, MT, ND, NE, OR, SD, WA, WY, 915 2nd Ave., #992, Seattle, WA 98174-1091; (206) 220-7788

AL, AR, IA, KY, LA, MO, MS, NC, OH, TN, VA (except D.C. suburbs), 701 Loyola Ave., #T-12005, New Orleans, LA 70113-1931; (504) 589-6728

AS, GU, HI, MP; Micronesia, 1132 Bishop St., #500, Honolulu, HI 96813-2809; (808) 522-8283

AZ, CA (northern), NV (except Clark County), UT, 95 Hawthorne St., 5th Floor, San Francisco, CA 94105-3901

CA (southern), NV (Clark County), 11000 Wilshire Blvd., #1000, Los Angeles, CA 90024-3615; (310) 235-7070

CT, NY (Westchester County), Broad and Atlantic Sts., 1 Landmark Square, Stamford, CT 06901-2667; (203) 325-4401

DC, MD, VA (DC suburbs), Diplomatic, 1111 19th St. N.W., #300, Washington, DC 20522-1705; (202) 647-0518

DE, NJ, PA, WV, 200 Chestnut St., #103, Philadelphia, PA 19106-2970; (215) 597-7480

FL, GA, PR, SC, VI, 51 S.W. 1st Ave., 3rd Floor, Miami, FL 33130-1680; (305) 536-4681

IL, IN, MI, WI, 230 S. Dearborn St., #380, Chicago, IL 60604-1564; (312) 353-7155

KS, OK, NM, TX, 1919 Smith St., #1100, Houston, TX 77002-8049; (713) 209-3153

MA, ME, NH, NY (upstate), RI, VT, 10 Causeway St., #247, Boston, MA 02222-1094; (617) 565-6990

NY (City and Long Island), emergency applications, 367 Hudson St., New York, NY 10014; (212) 206-3500

Transportation Dept.—Federal Aviation Administration

AK, 222 W. 7th Ave., #14, Anchorage, AK 99513-7587; (907) 271-5296

AL, CZ, FL, GA, KY, MS, NC, PR, SC, TN, VI, P.O. Box 20636, Atlanta, GA 30320; (404) 305-5000

AR, LA, NM, OK, TX, 2601 Meacham Blvd., Fort Worth, TX 76193-0005; (817) 222-5804

AZ, CA, HI, NV, P.O. Box 92007, Los Angeles, CA 90044; (562) 725-3550

CO, ID, MT, OR, UT, WA, WY, 1601 Lind Ave. S.W., #500, Renton, WA 98055-4056; (206) 227-2002

CT, MA, ME, NH, RI, VT, 12 New England Executive Park, #301, Burlington, MA 01803; (617) 238-7020

DC, DE, MD, NJ, NY, PA, VA, WV, JFK International Airport (Fitzgerald Federal Bldg., #207), Jamaica, NY 11430; (718) 553-2680

IA, KS, MO, NE, 601 E. 12th St., #1501, Kansas City, MO 64106; (816) 426-5626

IL, IN, MI, MN, ND, OH, SD, WI, 2300 E. Devon Ave., #366, Des Plaines, IL 60018-4686; (847) 294-7427

Transportation Dept.—Federal Highway Administration

AK, ID, OR, WA, 222 S.W. Columbia St., #600, Portland, OR 97201; (503) 326-2053

AL, FL, GA, KY, MS, NC, SC, TN, 61 Forsyth St. S.W., #17T26, Atlanta, GA 30367; (404) 562-3570

AR, LA, NM, OK, TX, 819 Taylor St., #8A00 (mailing address: P.O. Box 902003), Fort Worth, TX 76102; (817) 334-4393

AS, AZ, CA, GU, HI, NV, 201 Mission St., #2100, San Francisco, CA 94105; (415) 744-3102

CO, MT, ND, SD, UT, WY, 555 Zang St., #400, Lakewood, CO 80228; (303) 969-6722

CT, MA, ME, NH, NJ, NY, PR, RI, VI, VT, Clinton Ave. and N. Pearl St., #719, Albany, NY 12207; (518) 431-4224

Transportation Dept.—Federal Highway Administration (continued)

DC, DE, MD, PA, VA, WV, 10 S. Howard St., #4000, Baltimore, MD 21201; (410) 962-0077

IA, KS, MO, NE, 6301 Rockhill Rd. (mailing address: P.O. Box 419715), Kansas City, MO 64131-6715; (816) 276-2700

IL, IN, MI, MN, OH, WI, 19900 Governors Hwy., #301, Olympia Fields, IL 60461-1021; (708) 283-3510

Transportation Dept.—Federal Railroad Administration

AK, ID, MT, ND, OR, SD, WA, WY, 703 Broadway, #650, Vancouver, WA 98660; (360) 696-7536

AL, FL, GA, KY, MS, NC, SC, TN, 61 Forsyth St., S.W., #16T20, Atlanta, GA 30303; (404) 562-3800

AR, LA, NM, OK, TX, 8701 Bedford-Euless Rd., #425, Hurst, TX 76053; (817) 284-8142

AZ, CA, HI, NV, UT, 650 Capitol Mall, #7007, Sacramento, CA 95814; (916) 498-6540

CO, IA, KS, MO, NE, 1100 Maine St., #1130, Kansas City, MO 64105; (816) 426-2497

CT, MA, ME, NH, NJ, NY, RI, VT, 55 Broadway, #1077, Cambridge, MA 02142; (617) 494-2302

DE, MD, OH, PA, VA, WV, Scott Plaza II, #550, Philadelphia, PA 19113; (610) 521-8200

IL, IN, MI, MN, WI, 111 N. Canal St., #655, Chicago, IL 60606; (312) 353-6203

Transportation Dept.—Federal Transit Administration

AK, ID, OR, WA, 915 2nd Ave., #3142, Seattle, WA 98174-1002; (206) 220-7954

AL, FL, GA, KY, MS, NC, PR, SC, TN, 61 Forsyth St. S.W., #17T50, Atlanta, GA 30303; (404) 562-3500

AR, LA, NM, OK, TX, 524 E. Lamar Blvd, #175, Arlington, TX 76001-3900; (817) 860-9663

AZ, AS, CA, GU, HI, MP, NV, 201 Mission St., #2210, San Francisco, CA 94105; (415) 744-3133

CO, MT, ND, SD, UT, WY, 216 16th St., #650, Denver, CO 80202-5120; (303) 844-3242

CT, MA, ME, NH, RI, VT, 55 Broadway, #920, Cambridge, MA 02142-1093; (617) 494-2055

DC, DE, MD, PA, VA, WV, 1760 Market St., #500, Philadelphia, PA 19103-4124; (215) 656-7100

IA, KS, MO, NE, 6301 Rockhill Rd., #303, Kansas City, MO 64131-1117; (816) 523-0204

IL, IN, MI, MN, OH, WI, 55 E. Monroe St., #1415, Chicago, IL 60603-5704; (312) 353-2789

NJ, NY, VI, 26 Federal Plaza, #2940, New York, NY 10278-0194; (212) 264-8162

Transportation Dept.—Maritime Administration

AK, AZ, CA, CO, HI, ID, MT, NM, NV, OR, UT, WA, WY, 201 Mission St., #2200, San Francisco, CA 94105-1905; (415) 744-3125

AL, AR, FL (western), IA, KS, KY, LA, MO, MS, NE, OK, TN, TX, 365 Canal St., #2590, New Orleans, LA 70130-1137; (504) 589-6556

CT, DE, MA, MD, ME, NH, NJ, NY (downstate), PA (eastern), PR, RI, VT, 26 Federal Plaza, #3737, New York, NY 10278; (212) 264-1300

FL (eastern), GA, NC, SC, VA, WV, 7737 Hampton Blvd., #4D-211, Norfolk, VA 23505; (757) 441-6393

IL, IN, MI, MN, ND, NY (upstate), OH, PA (western), SD, WI, 2860 S. River Rd., #185, Des Plaines, IL 60018-2413; (847) 298-4535

Transportation Dept.—National Highway Traffic Safety Administration

AK, ID, OR, WA, 915 2nd Ave., #3140, Seattle, WA 98174; (206) 220-7640

AL, FL, GA, KY, MS, NC, SC, TN, 61 Forsyth St. S.W., #17T30, Atlanta, GA 30303; (404) 562-3739

AR, LA, NM, OK, TX, 819 Taylor St., #8A38, Fort Worth, TX 76102-6177; (817) 334-3653

AS, AZ, CA, GU, HI, MP, NV, 201 Mission St., #2230, San Francisco, CA 94105; (415) 744-3089

CO, MT, ND, SD, UT, WY, 555 Zang St., #430, Denver, CO 80228; (303) 969-6917

CT, MA, ME, NH, RI, VT, Volpe National Transportation System Center, Kendall Square, Code 903, Cambridge, MA 02142; (617) 494-3427

DC, DE, MD, PA, VA, WV, 10 S. Howard St., #4000, Baltimore MD 21201; (410) 962-0077

Transportation Dept.—National Highway Traffic Safety Administration (continued)

IA, KS, MO, NE, P.O. Box 412515, Kansas City, MO 64141; (816) 822-7233

IL, IN, MI, MN, OH, WI, 19900 Governors Dr., #201, Olympia Fields, IL 60461; (708) 503-8822

NJ, NY, PR, VI, 222 Mamaroneck Ave., #204, White Plains, NY 10605; (914) 682-6162

Treasury Dept.—Bureau of Alcohol, Tobacco, and Firearms: Criminal Enforcement

AK, HI, ID, MT, OR, WA, WY, 915 2nd Ave., #806, Seattle, WA 98174; (206) 220-6440

AL, MS, 1910 3rd Ave. North, Birmingham, AL 35203-3502; (205) 731-1205

AR, LA, 111 Veterans Memorial Blvd. #1050, Metairie, LA 70005; (504) 589-2048

AZ (except southwestern), NM, 3003 N. Central Ave., #1010, Phoenix, AZ 85012; (602) 640-2840

AZ (southwestern), CA (southern), 350 S. Figueroa St., #800, Los Angeles, CA 90071; (213) 894-4812

CA (northern), CO, NV, UT, 221 Main St., #1250, San Francisco, CA 94105; (415) 744-7001

CT, MA, ME, NH, RI, VT, 10 Causeway St., #253, Boston, MA 02222-1047; (617) 565-7042

DC, VA, 607 14th St. N.W., #620, Washington, DC 20005; (202) 219-7751

DE, MD, 22 S. Howard St., Baltimore, MD 21201; (410) 962-0897

FL, 8420 N.W. 52nd St., #120, Miami, FL 33166; (305) 597-4800

GA, 101 Marietta St. N.W., #406, Atlanta, GA 30303; (404) 331-6526

IA, KS, NE, 2600 Grand Ave., #200, Kansas City, MO 64108; (816) 421-3440

IL (northern), IN (northern), 300 S. Riverside Plaza, #350 South, Chicago, IL 60606; (312) 353-6935

IL (southern), MO, 100 S. 4th St., #550, St. Louis, MO 63102; (314) 425-5560

IN (southern), KY, WV (western), 600 Martin Luther King Pl., #322, Louisville, KY 40202; (502) 582-5211

MI, 1155 Brewery Park Blvd., #300, Detroit, MI 48207-2602; (313) 393-6000

MN, ND, SD, WI, 30 E. 7th St., #1870, St. Paul, MN 55101; (612) 290-3092

NC, SC, 4530 Park Rd., #400, Charlotte, NC 28209; (704) 344-6125

NJ (northern), NY, PR, 6 World Trade Center, #238, New York, NY 10048; (212) 264-4658

NJ (southern), PA, WV (eastern), 2nd and Chestnut Sts., #504, Philadelphia, PA 19106; (215) 597-7266

OH, 6745 Engle Rd., #200, Middleburg Heights, OH 44130; (440) 522-7210

OK, TX (northern), 1200 Main Tower Bldg., #2550, Dallas, TX 75250; (214) 767-2250

TN, 215 Centerview Dr., #215, Brentwood, TN 37027; (615) 781-5364

TX (southern), 15355 Vantage Pkwy. West, #210, Houston, TX 77032; (713) 449-2073

Treasury Dept.—Bureau of Alcohol, Tobacco, and Firearms: Regulatory Enforcement

AK, CA, HI, ID, MT, NV, OR, WA 221 Main St., 11th Floor, San Francisco, CA 94105; (415) 744-7013

AL, FL, GA, MS, NC, PR, SC, TN, VA, 2600 Century Pkwy. N.E., #300, Atlanta, GA 30345; (404) 679-5001

AR, AZ, CO, IA, KS, LA, MO, NE, NM, OK, TX, UT, WY, 1114 Commerce St., 7th Floor, Dallas, TX 75242; (214) 767-2280

CT, DC, DE, MA, MD, ME, NH, NJ, NY, PA, RI, VT, 6 World Trade Center, 6th Floor, New York, NY 10048; (212) 264-2328

IL, IN, KY, MI, MN, ND, OH, SD, WV, WI, 300 S. Riverside Plaza, #310, Chicago, IL 60606-6616; (312) 353-1967

Treasury Dept.—Comptroller of the Currency

AK, AZ, CA, CO, GU, HI, ID, MT, NV, OR, UT, WA, WY, 50 Fremont St., #3900, San Francisco, CA 94105-2292; (415) 545-5981

AL, FL, GA, MS, NC, SC, TN, VA, WV, 245 Peachtree Center Ave. N.E., #600, Atlanta, GA 30303-1223; (404) 659-8855

AR, LA, NM, OK, TX, 500 N. Ackard St., Dallas, TX 75201-3394; (214) 720-0656

Treasury Dept.—Comptroller of the Currency (continued)

CT, DC, DE, MA, MD, ME, NH, NJ, NY, PA, PR, RI, VI, VT, 1114 Ave. of the Americas, #3900, New York, NY 10036-7780; (212) 819-9860

IA, KS, MN, MO, ND, NE, SD, 2345 Grand Blvd., #700, Kansas City, MO 64108-2683; (816) 556-1800

IL, IN, KY, MI, OH, WI, 440 S. LaSalle St., #2700, Chicago, IL 60605-1073; (312) 360-8800

Treasury Dept.—Financial Management Services

AK, AZ, CA, CO, HI, ID, MT, ND, NV, OR, SD, UT, WA, WY, P.O. Box 193858, San Francisco, CA 94119-3858; (415) 744-7967

AL, FL, GA, KY, MS, NC, SC, TN, P.O. Box 2451, Birmingham, AL 35201-2451; (205) 912-6400

AR, LA, NM, OK, TX, P.O. Box 149058, Austin TX 78714-9058; (512) 342-7300

DC, DE, MA, MD, ME, NH, NJ, NY, PA, PR, RI, VA, VI, VT, WV, P.O. Box 8676; Philadelphia, PA 19101-8676; (215) 516-8015

IA, KS, MO, NE, P.O. Box 12599-0599, Kansas City, MO 64116-0599; (816) 414-2100

IL, IN, MI, MN, OH, WI, P.O. Box 8670, Chicago, IL 60680-8670; (312) 353-5622

Treasury Dept.—Internal Revenue Service

AK, AZ, CA, CO, HI, ID, MT, NM, NV, OR, UT, WA, WY, 1650 Mission St., #511, San Francisco, CA 94103; (415) 575-7000

AL, DC, DE, FL, GA, IN, KY, LA, MD, MS, NC, SC, TN, VA, WV, 401 W. Peachtree St. N.W., #201, Atlanta, GA 30365; (404) 331-6048

AR, IA, IL, KS, MN, MO, NE, ND, OK, SD, TX, WI, 4050 Alpha Rd., 12th Floor., Dallas, TX 75244-4203; (214) 308-7000

CT, MA, ME, MI, NH, NJ, NY, OH, PA, RI, VT, 290 Broadway, New York, NY 10008; (212) 298-2000

Treasury Dept.—Office of Thrift Supervision

AK, AZ, CA, GU, HI, ID, MP, MT, NV, OR, UT, WA, WY, 1 Montgomery St., #400 (mailing address: P.O. Box 7165), San Francisco, CA 94120; (415) 616-1500

AL, DC, FL, GA, MD, NC, PR, SC, VA, VI, 1475 Peachtree St. N.E. (mailing address: P.O. Box 105217), Atlanta, GA 30348-5217; (404) 888-0771

AR, CO, IA, KS, LA, MN, MO, MS, ND, NE, NM, OK, SD, TX, 122 W. John Carpenter Fwy., #600, Irving, TX (mailing address: P.O. Box 619027, Dallas/Fort Worth, TX 75261-9027); (972) 281-2000

CT, DE, MA, ME, NH, NJ, NY, PA, RI, VT, WV, 10 Exchange Place Centre, 18th Floor, Jersey City, NJ 07302; (201) 413-1000

IL, IN, KY, MI, OH, TN, WI, 200 W. Madison St., #1300, Chicago, IL 60606; (312) 917-5000

Treasury Dept.—U.S. Customs Service

AK, CO, ID (except northern), OR, WY, 511 N.W. Broadway, #592, Portland, OR 97209; (503) 326-7625

AL, AR, LA, MS, TN, 423 Canal St., #337, New Orleans, LA 70130; (504) 589-6324

AZ, 4740 N. Oracle Rd., #310, Tucson, AZ 85705; (520) 670-5900

CA (northern and central), HI, NV (except Las Vegas region), UT, 33 New Montgomery St., #1601, San Francisco, CA 94105; (415) 744-1530

CA (San Diego region), 610 W. Ash St., #1200, San Diego, CA 92101; (619) 557-5455

CA (southern except San Diego region), NV (Las Vegas region), 1 World Trade Center (mailing address: P.O. Box 32639) Long Beach, CA 90832; (310) 980-3100

CT, MA, ME, NH, RI, VT, 10 Causeway St., #801, Boston, MA 02222; (617) 565-6200

DC, DE, MD, NJ, PA, 103 S. Gay St., #208, Baltimore, MD 21202; (410) 962-6200

FL (northern and central), 1624 E. 7th Ave., #301, Tampa, FL 33605; (813) 228-2381

FL (southern), 909 S.E. 1st Ave., #968, Miami, FL 33131; (305) 536-6600

GA, NC, SC, VA, WV, 1691 Phoenix Blvd., #270, College Park, GA 30349; (770) 994-2306

IA, IL, IN, KS, KY, MN (southern), MO, NE, OH, SD (southern and central), WI (southern and central) 610 S. Canal St., #900, Chicago, IL 60607; (312) 353-4733

ID (northern), MN (northern), MT, ND, SD (northern), WA, WI (northwestern), 1000 2nd Ave., #2200, Seattle, WA 98104-1049; (206) 533-6944

Treasury Department—U.S. Customs Service
(continued)

MI, 613 Abbott St., #310, Detroit, MI 48226; (313) 226-2955

NM, TX (western), 9400 Viscount Blvd., #104, El Paso, TX 79925; (915) 540-5800

NY (upstate), 4455 Genesee St., Buffalo, NY 14225; (716) 626-0400

NJ (northern) NY (downstate), 6 World Trade Center, #716, New York, NY 10048; (212) 466-4444

OK, TX (eastern), 2323 S. Shephard St., #1200, Houston, TX 77019; (713) 313-2841

PR, 1 La Puntilla St., #203, San Juan, PR 00901; (787) 729-6950

TX (southern), P.O. Box 3130, Bldg. #2 Lincoln-Juarez Bridge, Laredo, TX 78044-3130; (210) 718-4161

Veterans Affairs Dept.—Veterans Benefits Administration

AK, AZ, CA, CO, HI, ID, MT, NM, NV, OR, UT, WA, WY 12600 W. Colfax Ave., Lakewood, CO 80215-3736; (303) 914-2900

AL, AR, FL, GA, LA, MS, NC, PR, SC, TN, TX, 6508 Dogwood View Pkwy., Suite E, Jackson, MS 39213-7859; (601) 965-5990

CT, DE, MA, MD, ME, NH, NJ, NY, PA, RI, VA, VT, WV, 200 St. Paul Pl., #2604, Baltimore, MD 21202-2004; (410) 962-0041

IA, IL, IN, KS, KY, MI, MN, MO, ND, NE, OH, SD, WI, 38701 7 Mile Rd., #345, Livonia, MI 48152-1058; (248) 953-8830

Veterans Affairs Dept.—Public Affairs

AK, CA, HI, ID (except Pocatello), NV, OR, WA, Philippines, 11301 Wilshire Blvd., Bldg. 218, #214, Los Angeles, CA 90073; (310) 268-4207

AL, FL (except Pensacola), GA, KY, PR, SC, TN, WV (Huntington), 730 Peachtree St. N.E., #710, Atlanta, GA 30365; (404) 347-3236

AR, AZ, FL (Pensacola), LA, MS, NM, OK, TX, 4500 S. Lancaster Rd., Bldg. 43, #124, Dallas, TX 75216; (214) 767-9270

CO, IA, ID (Pocatello), IL (E. Moline, Mariou, and Mount City), IN (Evansville), KS, MN, MO, MT, ND, NE, SD, UT, WI (Superior), WY, 155 Van Gordon St.

(mailing address: P.O. Box 25126), Denver, CO 80225; (303) 914-5855

CT, MA, ME, NH, NJ, NY, RI, VT, 245 W. Houston St., #315B, New York, NY 10014; (212) 807-3429

DC, DE, MD, NC, PA, VA, WV (except Huntington, WV), 810 Vermont Ave. N.W., #918, Washington, DC 20420; (202) 273-5740

IL (except East Moline, Marion, and Mound City), IN (except Evansville), MI, OH, WI (except Superior), 536 S. Clark St., #668, Chicago, IL 60605; (312) 353-4076

AGENCIES

Commission on Civil Rights

AK, AZ, CA, HI, ID, NM, NV, OR, TX, WA 3660 Wilshire Blvd., #810, Los Angeles, CA 90010; (213) 894-3437

AL, AR, IA, KS, LA, MO, MS, NE, OK, 400 State Ave., 9th Floor, Kansas City, MO 66106; (913) 551-1400

CO, MT, ND, SD, UT, WY, 1700 Broadway, #710, Denver, CO 80290; (303) 866-1040

CT, DC, DE, MA, MD, ME, NH, NJ, NY, PA, RI, VA, VT, WV, 624 9th St. N.W., #500, Washington, DC 20425; (202) 376-7533

FL, GA, KY, NC, SC, TN, 61 Forsyth St., Atlanta, GA 30303; (404) 562-7000

IL, IN, MI, MN, OH, WI, 55 W. Monroe St., #410, Chicago, IL 60603; (312) 353-8311

Commodity Futures Trading Commission

AK, AZ, CA, CO, GU, HI, ID, MT, NM, NV, OR, UT, WA, WY, 10900 Wilshire Blvd., #400, Los Angeles, CA 90024; (310) 235-6783

AL, CT, DE, FL, GA, KY, MA, MD, ME, MS, NC, NH, NJ, NY, PA, RI, SC, TN, VA, VI, VT, WV, 1 World Trade Center, #3747, New York, NY 10048; (212) 466-2061

AR, IA, KS, LA, MO, ND, NE, OK, SD, TX, 4900 Main St., #721, Kansas City, MO 64112; (816) 931-7600

IL, IN, MI, MN, OH, WI, 300 S. Riverside Plaza, #1600 North, Chicago, IL 60606; (312) 353-5990

Consumer Product Safety Commission

AK, AR, AS, AZ, CA, CO, GU, HI, ID, LA, MT, NM, NV, OK, OR, TX, UT, WA, WY, 600 Harrison St., #245, San Francisco, CA 94107-1370; (415) 744-2966

Consumer Product Safety Commission

(continued)

AL, GA, IA, IL, IN, KS, KY, MI, MN, MO, MS, ND, NE, OH, SD, TN, WI, 230 S. Dearborn St., #2944, Chicago, IL 60604-1601; (312) 353-8260

CT, DC, DE, FL, MA, MD, ME, NC, NH, NJ, NY, PA, PR, RI, SC, VA, VI, VT, WV, 6 World Trade Center, #350, New York, NY 10048-0206; (212) 466-1612

Corporation for National Service

AK, CA, HI, ID, MT, NV, OR, UT, VI, WA, WY, P.O. Box 29996, San Francisco, CA 94129; (415) 561-5960

AL, FL, GA, KY, MS, NC, SC, TN, VA, WV, 60 Forsyth St., #3M40, Atlanta, GA 30323-2301; (404) 562-4050

AR, AZ, CO, KS, LA, MO, NM, OK, TX, 1999 Bryan St. #2050, Dallas, TX 75242-0696; (214) 860-7050

CT, DC, DE, MA, MD, ME, NH, NJ, NY, PA, PR, RI, VT, 801 Arch St., #103, Philadelphia, PA 19107; (215) 597-9972

IA, IL, IN, MI, MN, ND, NE, OH, SD, WI, 77 W. Jackson Blvd., #442, Chicago, IL 60604-3511; (312) 353-7705

Environmental Protection Agency

AK, ID, OR, WA, 1200 6th Ave., Seattle, WA 98101; (206) 553-1200; (800) 424-4372

AL, FL, GA, KY, MS, NC, SC, TN, 61 Forsyth St. S.W., Atlanta, GA 30303-3104; (404) 562-9900

AR, LA, NM, OK, TX, 1445 Ross Ave., #1200, Dallas, TX 75202; (214) 655-2200

AS, AZ, CA, GU, HI, NV, 75 Hawthorne St., San Francisco, CA 94105; (415) 744-1305

CO, MT, ND, SD, UT, WY, 999 18th St., #500, Denver, CO 80202-2466; (303) 312-6312; (800) 227-8917

CT, MA, ME, NH, RI, VT, John F. Kennedy Federal Bldg., Boston, MA 02203; (617) 565-3420

DC, DE, MD, PA, VA, WV, 841 Chestnut St., Philadelphia, PA 19107-4431; (215) 566-5000

IA, KS, MO, NE, 726 Minnesota Ave., Kansas City, KS 66101; (913) 551-7282; (800) 551-7003

IL, IN, MI, MN, OH, WI, 77 W. Jackson Blvd., Chicago, IL 60604; (312) 353-2000; (800) 621-8431

NJ, NY, PR, VI, 290 Broadway, New York, NY 10007; (212) 637-3000

Equal Employment Opportunity Commission

AK, ID, OR, WA, 909 1st Ave., #400, Seattle, WA 98104-1061; (206) 220-6870

AL, MS, 1900 3rd Ave. North, #101, Birmingham, AL 35203-2397; (205) 731-1182

AR, TN, 1407 Union Ave., #621, Memphis, TN 38104; (901) 544-0116

AS, CA (northern), GU, HI, MP, 901 Market St., #500, San Francisco, CA 94103; (415) 356-5041

AZ, UT, 3300 N. Central Ave., #690, Phoenix, AZ 85012-9688; (602) 640-5011

CA (southern), NV, 255 E. Temple, 4th Floor, Los Angeles, CA 90012; (213) 894-1112

CO, MT, ND, NE, SD, WY, 303 E. 17th Ave., #510, Denver, CO 80203; (303) 866-1369

CT, MA, ME, NH, NY, PR, RI, VI, VT, 7 World Trade Center, 18th Floor, New York, NY 10048-0948; (212) 748-8400

DC, MD, VA, 10 S. Howard St., 3rd Floor, Baltimore, MD 21201; (410) 962-5634

DE, NJ, PA, WV, 21 S. 5th St., #400, Philadelphia, PA 19106-2515; (215) 451-5800

FL, CZ, 1 Biscayne Tower, #2700, Miami, FL 33131; (305) 530-6060

GA, 100 Alabama St., 4th Floor, Atlanta, GA 30303; (404) 562-6930

IA, MN, WI, 310 W. Wisconsin Ave., #800, Milwaukee, WI 53203-2292; (414) 297-1265

IL, 500 W. Madison St., #2800, Chicago, IL 60661; (312) 353-8550

IN, KY, 101 W. Ohio St., #1900, Indianapolis, IN 46204-4203; (317) 226-7215

KS, MO, 1222 Spurce St., #8.100, St. Louis, MO 63108; (314) 539-7830

LA, 701 Loyola Ave., #600, New Orleans, LA 70113-9936; (504) 589-3842

MI, 477 Michigan Ave., #865, Detroit, MI 48226-9704; (313) 226-7639

NC, SC, 129 W. Trade St., #400, Charlotte, NC 28202; (704) 344-6744

NM, 505 Marquette N.W., #900, Albuquerque, NM 87102; (505) 248-5201

Equal Employment Opportunity Commission (continued)

OH, 1660 W. 2nd St., #850, Cleveland, OH 44113-1454; (216) 522-4784

OK, TX (northern), 207 S. Houston St., 3rd Floor, Dallas, TX 75202-4726; (214) 655-3300

TX (central), 1919 Smith St., 7th Floor, Houston, TX 77002; (713) 209-3373

TX (southern), 5410 Fredericksburg Rd., #200, San Antonio, TX 78229-3555; (210) 229-4842

Federal Communications Commission

AK, AZ, CA, HI, ID, MT, NV, OR, UT, WA 3777 Depot Rd., #420, Hayward, CA 94545-2756; (510) 732-9046

AL, AR, CO, FL, GA, IA, KS, LA, MO, MS, NC, ND, NE, NM, OK, PR, SC, SD, TN, TX, VA, VI, WY, 8800 E. 63rd St., #320, Kansas City, MO 64133-4895; (816) 353-9035

CT, DC, DE, IL, IN, KY, MA, MD, ME, MI, MN, NH, NJ, NY, PA, OH, RI, VT, WI, WV, 1550 Northwest Hwy., Park Ridge, IL 60068-1460; (847) 298-5405

Federal Deposit Insurance Corp.

AK, AZ, CA, GU, HI, ID, MT, NV, OR, UT, WA, WY, 25 Ecker St., #2300, San Francisco, CA 94105; (415) 546-1810

AL, FL, GA, NC, SC, VA, WV, 1201 W. Peachtree St. N.E., #1800, Atlanta, GA 30309; (404) 817-2500

AR, KY, LA, MS, TN, 5100 Poplar Ave., #1900, Memphis, TN 38137; (901) 821-5201

CO, NM, OK, TX, 1910 Pacific Ave., #1900, Dallas, TX 75201; (214) 220-3393

CT, MA, ME, NH, RI, VT, 200 Lowder Brook Dr., Westwood, MA 02090; (781) 320-1700

DC, DE, MD, NJ, NY, PA, PR, VI, 452 5th Ave., 19th Floor, New York, NY 10018; (212) 704-1215

IA, KS, MN, MO, ND, NE, SD, 2345 Grand Ave., #1500, Kansas City, MO 64108; (816) 234-8037

IL, IN, MI, OH, WI, 500 W. Monroe St., #3200, Chicago, IL 60661; (312) 382-6456

Federal Emergency Management Agency

AK, ID, OR, WA, 130 228th St. S.W., Bothell, WA 98021-9796; (425) 487-4604

AL, FL, GA, KY, MS, NC, SC, TN, 3003 Chamblee-Tucker Rd., Atlanta, GA 30341; (770) 220-5200

AR, LA, NM, OK, TX, 800 N. Loop 288, #206, Denton, TX 76201-3698; (940) 898-5104

AZ, CA, HI, NV, Bldg. 105, Presidio of San Francisco, San Francisco, CA 94129-1250; (415) 923-7100

CO, MT, ND, SD, UT, WY, Denver Federal Center, Bldg. 710, Box 25267, Denver, CO 80225-0267; (303) 235-4812

CT, MA, ME, NH, RI, VT, John W. McCormack Post Office and Courthouse, #442, Boston, MA 02109-4595; (617) 223-9540

DC, DE, MD, PA, VA, WV, 105 S. 7th St., 2nd Floor, Philadelphia, PA 19106-3316; (215) 931-5608

IA, KS, MO, NE, 2323 Grand Blvd., #900, Kansas City, MO 64108-2670; (816) 283-7061

IL, IN, MI, MN, OH, WI, 175 W. Jackson Blvd., 4th Floor, Chicago, IL 60604-2698; (312) 408-5501

NJ, NY, PR, VI, 26 Federal Plaza, #1337, New York, NY 10278-0002; (212) 225-7209

Federal Labor Relations Authority

AK, CA, HI, OR, WA, 901 Market St., #220, San Francisco, CA 94103-1791; (415) 356-5000

AL, FL, GA, MS, NC, PR, SC, VI, 285 Peachtree Center Ave., #701, Atlanta, GA 30303-1270; (404) 331-5300

AR, CZ, LA, NM, OK, TX, 525 Griffin St., #926, LB 107, Dallas, TX 75202-1906; (214) 767-4996

AZ, CO, ID, KS, MO, MT, NE, NV, SD, UT, WY, 1244 Speer Blvd., #100, Denver, CO 80204-3581; (303) 844-5224

CT, MA, ME, NH, NJ, NY, PA, RI, VT, 99 Summer St., #1500, Boston, MA 02110-1200; (617) 424-5731

DC, MD, VA, WV, 1255 22nd St. N.W., #400, Washington, DC 20037-1206; (202) 653-8500

IA, IL, IN, KY, MI, MN, ND, OH, TN, WI, 55 W. Monroe, #1150, Chicago, IL 60603-9729; (312) 353-6306

Federal Maritime Commission

AK, OR, WA, 3236 16th St. S.W., Seattle, WA 98134; (206) 553-0221

AL, FL (northwest), LA, MS, TX, 423 Canal St., #303, New Orleans, LA 70130; (504) 589-6662

Federal Maritime Commission (continued)

AS, CA, GU, HI, 300 S. Ferry St., #1018 (mailing address: P.O. Box 3164), San Pedro, CA 90731; (562) 514-4905

CT, DC, DE, MA, MD, ME, NH, NJ, NY, PA, RI, VA, VT, WV, 800 N. Capitol St. N.W., #928, Washington, DC 20573; (202) 523-5900

FL (except northwest), GA, NC, PR, SC, VI, 909 S.E. 1st Ave., #736, Miami, FL 33131; (305) 536-4316

Federal Mediation and Conciliation Service

AK, CA (northern), ID (northern), OR, WA, 310 Westin Bldg., Seattle, WA 98121; (206) 553-5800

AL, AR, DC, FL, GA, IN (southwestern), KS, KY, LA, MO, MS, NC, OK, SC, TN, VA, WV, 401 W. Peachtree St. N.W., #472, Atlanta, GA 30308; (404) 331-3995

AZ, CA (southern), CO, HI, ID (southern), NM, NV, OR, TX, UT, WA, 225 W. Broadway, #610, Glendale, CA 91204; (213) 965-3814

CT, DE, MA, MD, ME, NH, NJ, NY (downstate), PA (eastern), RI, VT, 1633 Broadway, 2nd Floor, New York, NY 10019; (212) 399-5038

IA, IL, IN (except southwestern), MI (Upper Penninsula), MN, ND, NE, SD, WI, 1300 Godward St., #3950, Minneapolis, MN 55413; (612) 370-3300

MI, NY (upstate), OH, PA (western), WV, 6161 Oak Tree Blvd., #100, Independence, OH 44131; (216) 522-4800

Federal Reserve Districts

AK, AZ, CA, HI, ID, NV, OR, UT, WA, 101 Market St. (P.O. Box 7702), San Francisco, CA 94120; (415) 974-2000

AL, FL, GA, LA (southern), MS (southern), TN (central and eastern), 104 Marietta St. N.W. (P.O. Box 1731), Atlanta, GA 30303-2713; (404) 521-8500

AR, IL (southern), IN (southern), KY (western), MO (central and eastern), MS (northern), TN (western), 411 Locust St. (P.O. Box 442), St. Louis, MO 63166; (314) 444-8444

CO, KS, MO (western), NE, NM (northern), OK, WY, 925 Grand Blvd. (P.O. Box 2076), Kansas City, MO 64198-0001; (816) 881-2000

CT (northern), MA, ME, NH, RI, VT, 600 Atlantic Ave., Boston, MA 02106-2076; (617) 973-3000

CT (southern), NJ (northern), NY, PR, VI, 33 Liberty St., New York, NY 10045; (212) 720-5000

DC, MD, NC, SC, VA, WV (eastern and southern), 701 E. Byrd St. (P.O. Box 27622), Richmond, VA 23261; (804) 697-8000

DE, NJ (southern), PA (central and eastern), 10 Independence Mall (P.O. Box 66), Philadelphia, PA 19106; (215) 574-6000

IA, IL (northern), IN (central and northern), MI (except Upper Peninsula), WI (except northwestern), 230 S. LaSalle St. (P.O. Box 834), Chicago, IL 60604; (312) 322-5322

KY (eastern), OH, PA (western), WV (northern), 1455 E. 6th St. (P.O. Box 6387), Cleveland, OH 44101; (216) 579-2000

LA (northern), NM (southern), TX, 2200 N. Pearl St., Dallas, TX 75222; (214) 922-6000

MI (Upper Peninsula), MN, MT, ND, SD, WI (northwestern), 250 Marquette Ave. (P.O. Box 291), Minneapolis, MN 55401; (612) 340-2345

Federal Trade Commission

AK, ID, OR, WA 915 2nd Ave., #2806, Seattle, WA 98174; (206) 220-6350

AL, FL, GA, MS, NC, SC, TN, VA, 60 Forsyth St. S.W., #5M35, Atlanta, GA 30367; (404) 656-1399

AR, LA, NM, OK, TX, 1999 Bryan St., #2150, Dallas, TX 75201; (214) 979-0213

AZ, CA (southern), 10877 Wilshire Blvd., #700, Los Angeles, CA 90024; (310) 824-4300

CA (northern), HI, NV, 901 Market St., #570, San Francisco, CA 94103; (415) 356-5270

CO, KS, MT, ND, NE, SD, UT, WY, 1961 Stout St., #1523, Denver, CO 80294-0101; (303) 844-2271

CT, MA, ME, NH, RI, VT, 101 Merrimac St., #810, Boston, MA 02114-4719; (617) 424-5960

DC, DE, MD, MI, OH, PA, WV, 1101 Superior Ave., #200, Cleveland, OH 44114-2507; (216) 263-3410

IA, IL, IN, KY, MN, MO, WI, 55 E. Monroe St., #1860, Chicago, IL 60603-5701; (312) 353-4423

NJ, NY, 150 William St., #1300, New York, NY 10038; (212) 264-1207

General Accounting Office

The following national field offices do not serve specific regions.

Atlanta, GA, 2635 Century Pkwy., #700 30345; (404) 679-1900

Boston, MA, 10 Causeway St., #575 02222; (617) 565-7500

Chicago, IL, 200 W. Adams St., #700 60606; (312) 220-7600

Dallas, TX, 1999 Bryan St. 75201; (214) 777-5700

Denver, CO, 1224 Speer Blvd., #800 80204; (303) 572-7317

Los Angeles, CA, 350 S. Figueroa St., #1010 90071; (213) 830-1111

Mission, KS, 5799 Broadmoor, #600 66202; (913) 384-7419

San Francisco, CA, 301 Howard St., #1200 94105; (415) 904-2000

Seattle, WA, 701 5th Ave., #2700 98104; (206) 287-4810

Virginia Beach, VA, 5029 Corporate Woods Dr. #300, 23426; (757) 552-8100

General Services Administration

AK, ID, OR, WA, 400 15th St. S.W., Auburn, WA 98001; (253) 931-7000

AL, FL, GA, KY, MS, NC, SC, TN, 401 W. Peachtree St., #2900, Atlanta, GA 38365-2550; (404) 331-3200

AR, LA, NM, OK, TX, 819 Taylor St., Fort Worth, TX 76102; (817) 978-2856

AZ, CA, GU, HI, NV, 525 Market St., San Francisco, CA 94105; (415) 744-3001

CO, MT, ND, SD, UT, WY, Denver Federal Center, Bldg. 41, #200, Denver, CO 80225-0006; (303) 236-7329

CT, MA, ME, NH, RI, VT, 10 Causeway St., Boston, MA 02222; (617) 565-5860

DC, MD (Montgomery and Prince George's counties), VA (northern), 7th and D Sts. S.W., Washington, DC 20407; (202) 708-9100

DE, MD (except Montgomery and Prince George's counties), NJ (southern), PA, VA (southern), WV, 100 Penn Square East, #836, Philadelphia, PA 19107; (215) 656-5501

IA, KS, MO, NE, 1500 E. Bannister Rd., Kansas City, MO 64131; (816) 926-7201

IL, IN, MI, MN, OH, WI, 230 S. Dearborn St., Chicago, IL 60604; (312) 353-5395

NJ (northern), NY, PR, VI, 26 Federal Plaza, New York, NY 10278; (212) 264-2600

General Services Administration—Business Service Centers

These offices furnish advice and assistance to business persons interested in contracting with GSA and other federal agencies and departments; emphasis is placed on helping small and disadvantaged business.

AK, ID, OR, WA, 400 15th St. S.W., #2413, Auburn, WA 98001; (253) 931-7956

AL, FL, GA, KY, MS, NC, SC, TN, 401 W. Peachtree St., #2832, Atlanta, GA 38365-2550; (404) 331-5103

AR, LA, NM, OK, TX, 100 E. 15th St., #400, Fort Worth, TX 76102; (817) 871-6007

AZ, CA (southern), NV (Clark County), 300 N. Los Angeles St., #3459, Los Angeles, CA 90012-2000; (213) 894-3210

CA (northern), HI, NV (except Clark County), 450 Golden Gate Ave., 5th Floor., San Francisco, CA 94105; (415) 522-2700

CO, MT, ND, SD, UT, WY, Denver Federal Center, Bldg. 41, Denver, CO 80225-0006; (303) 236-7408

CT, MA, ME, NH, RI, VT, 10 Causeway St., #290, Boston, MA 02222; (617) 565-8100

DC and metro MD and VA, 7th and D Sts. S.W., #1050, Washington, DC 20407; (202) 708-5804

DE, MD, NJ (southern), PA, VA, WV, 100 Penn Square East, Philadelphia, PA 19107; (215) 656-5525

IA, KS, MO, NE, 1500 E. Bannister Rd., #1160 Kansas City, MO 64131; (816) 926-7203

IL, IN, MI, MN, OH, WI, 230 S. Dearborn St., #3714, Chicago, IL 60604; (312) 353-5383

NJ (northern), NY, PR, VI, 26 Federal Plaza, #18-130 New York, NY 10278; (212) 264-1234

Government Printing Office—Bookstores

These bookstores carry a limited stock of government publications. Titles not found in a bookstore may be ordered from the GPO in Washington, D.C., by call-

Government Printing Office—Bookstores
(continued)

ing (202) 783-3238. Many titles also can be ordered directly from departments and agencies: see list of Publications Offices in chap. 3. See also World Wide Web addresses in chap. 3.

Atlanta, GA, 999 Peachtree St. N.E., #120, 30309-3964; (404) 347-1900

Birmingham, AL, 2021 3rd Ave. North 35203-3301; (205) 731-1056

Boston, MA, 10 Causeway St., #169 02222-1001; (617) 720-4180

Chicago, IL, 401 S. State St., #124 60605-1225; (312) 353-5133

Cleveland, OH, 1240 E. 9th St., #1653 44199-2001; (216) 522-4922

Columbus, OH, 200 N. High St. 43215-2408; (614) 469-6956

Dallas, TX, 1100 Commerce St., #1C50 75242-0196; (214) 767-0076

Denver, CO, 1660 Wynkoop St., #130 80202; (303) 844-3964

Detroit, MI, 477 Michigan Ave., #160 48226-2500; (313) 226-7816

Houston, TX, 801 Travis St., #120 77002-5727; (713) 228-1187

Jacksonville, FL, 100 W. Bay St., #100 32202-3876; (904) 353-0569

Kansas City, MO, 5600 E. Bannister Rd., #120 64137-1000; (816) 765-2256

Laurel, MD, 8660 Cherry Lane, Laurel, MD 20707-4980; (301) 953-7974

Los Angeles, CA, 505 S. Flower St. 90071-2101; (213) 239-9844

Milwaukee, WI, 310 W. Wisconsin Ave., #150 53202-2211; (414) 297-1304

New York, NY, 26 Federal Plaza, #2-120 10278-0081; (212) 264-3825

Philadelphia, PA, 100 N. 17th St. 19103-2736; (215) 636-1900

Pittsburgh, PA, 1000 Liberty Ave., #118 15222-4003; (412) 395-5021

Portland, OR, 1305 S.W. 1st Ave. 97201-5887; (503) 221-6217

Pueblo, CO, 201 W. 8th St., #102 81003-3091; (719) 544-3142

San Francisco, CA, 303 2nd St., #141S 94107-1366; (415) 252-2770

Seattle, WA, 915 2nd Ave., #194 98174-1030; (206) 553-4270

Washington, DC, 710 N. Capitol St. N.W. 20401-0001; (202) 512-0132

1510 H St., N.W. 20005-1008; (202) 653-5075

Government Printing Office—Regional Depository Libraries

These libraries receive and retain one copy of all federal government documents which must be made available for public inspection. Selective depository libraries, not listed here, offer only certain types of documents chosen by the library. For a list of all depository libraries, write the GPO, 732 N. Capitol St. N.W., Washington, DC 20401.

AK, WA, Washington State Library, Government Publications, Olympia, WA 98504-2460; (360) 704-5225

AL, Auburn University at Montgomery, Library, Government Information, 7300 University Dr., Montgomery, AL 36124-4023; (334) 244-3211

University of Alabama, Gorgas Library, Tuscaloosa, AL 35487-0266; (205) 348-6047

AR, Arkansas State Library, Documents Service, 1 Capitol Mall, Little Rock, AR 72201-1081; (501) 682-2869

AS, GU, HI, MP, University of Hawaii, Hamilton Library, Government Documents and Maps, 2550 The Mall, Honolulu, HI 96822; (808) 956-8230

AZ, Arizona Dept. of Library, Archives and Public Records, 1700 W. Washington, Phoenix, AZ 85007; (602) 542-3701

CA, California State Library, Government Publications Section, 914 Capitol Mall, Sacramento, CA 95814-0001; (916) 654-0069

CO, University of Colorado at Boulder, Government Publications Library, Campus Box 184, Boulder, CO 80309-0184; (303) 492-8834

Denver Public Library, Government Documents, 10 W. 14th Ave., Denver, CO 80204; (303) 640-6220

CT, RI, Connecticut State Library, 231 Capitol Ave., Hartford, CT 06106; (860) 566-2507

DC, DE, MD, University of Maryland, McKeldin Library, College Park, MD 20742; (301) 405-9165

FL, PR, VI, University of Florida Libraries, Documents Dept. , #240, Library West, Gainesville, FL 32611; (352) 392-0366

GA, University of Georgia Libraries, Government Documents Dept., Jackson St., Athens, GA 30602-1645; (706) 542-8949

IA, University of Iowa Libraries, Government Publications Dept., Iowa City, IA 52242-1420; (319) 335-5925

ID, University of Idaho Libraries, Documents Section, Moscow, ID 83844-2353; (208) 885-6344

IL, Illinois State Library, Federal Documents, 300 S. 2nd St., Springfield, IL 62701-1796; (217) 782-7596

IN, Indiana State Library, Serials and Documents, 140 N. Senate Ave., Indianapolis, IN 46204-2296; (317) 232-3679

KS, University of Kansas, Government Documents and Maps, 6001 Malott Hall, Lawrence, KS 66045-2800; (785) 864-4660

KY, University of Kentucky, King Library, Lexington, KY 40506-0039; (606) 257-1631

LA, Louisiana State University, Middletown Library, Government Documents, Baton Rouge, LA 70803-3312; (504) 388-4019

Louisiana Tech University, Prescott Memorial Library, Documents Dept., Ruston, LA 71272-0046; (318) 257-4962

MA, Boston Public Library, Government Documents, 666 Boylston St., Boston, MA 02117-0286; (617) 536-5400, ext. 226

ME, NH, VT, University of Maine, Raymond Folger Library, Government Documents, Orono, ME 04469-5729; (207) 581-1673

MI, Detroit Public Library, 5201 Woodward Ave., Detroit, MI 48202-4093; (313) 833-1440

Library of Michigan, Government Documents Service, 717 W. Allegan St., Lansing, MI 48909-0007; (517) 373-1300

MN, SD, University of Minnesota, 10 Wilson Library, 309 19th Ave. South, Minneapolis, MN 55455-0414; (612) 625-4309

MO, University of Missouri at Columbia, 106B Ellis Library, Columbia, MO 65201-5149; (573) 882-6733

MS, University of Mississippi, Williams Library, Government Publications, University, MS 38677; (601) 232-5857

MT, University of Montana, Mansfield Library, Documents Dept., Missoula, MT 59812-1195; (406) 243-6700

NC, University of North Carolina at Chapel Hill, Davis Library, CB #3912, BA/SS Dept. - Documents, Chapel Hill, NC 27514-8890; (919) 962-1151

ND, North Dakota State University Library, Documents Office, P.O. Box 5599, Fargo, ND 58105-5599; (701) 231-8886

University of North Dakota, Chester Fritz Library, Documents Dept., Grand Forks, ND 58202-9000; (701) 777-3316

NE, University of Nebraska at Lincoln, Love Library, Federal Documents Dept., Lincoln, NE 68588-0410; (402) 472-4472

NJ, Newark Public Library, U.S. Documents Division, 5 Washington St., Newark, NJ 07101-0630; (973) 733-7815

NM, University of New Mexico, General Library, Government Information Dept., Albuquerque, NM 87131-1466; (505) 277-5441

New Mexico State Library, Documents Dept., 325 Don Gaspar Ave., Santa Fe, NM 87503; (505) 827-3824

NV, University of Nevada Library, Business and Government Information Center, 1664 N. Virginia St., Reno, NV 89557-0044; (702) 784-6500, ext. 257

NY, New York State Library, Legislative and Governmental Service, Cultural Education Center, Empire State Plaza, Albany, NY 12230-0001; (518) 474-5355

OH, State Library of Ohio, Research Services, 65 S. Front St., Columbus, OH 43215-4163; (614) 644-7051

OK, Oklahoma State University Library, Documents Dept., Stillwater, OK 74078-1071; (405) 744-6546

Oklahoma Dept. of Libaries, Government Information, 200 N.E. 18th St., Oklahoma City, OK 73105-3298; (405) 521-2502, ext. 253

OR, Portland State University, Millar Library, Documents Dept., P.O. Box 1151, Portland, OR 97207-1151; (503) 725-4126

PA, State Library of Pennsylvania, Government Publications, Box 1601, Harrisburg, PA 17105; (717) 787-2327

Government Printing Office—Regional Depository Libraries (continued)

SC, Clemson University, Cooper Library, Documents Dept., Box 343001, Clemson, SC 29634-3001; (803) 656-5174

University of South Carolina, Thomas Cooper Library, Documents/Microform Dept., Sumter and Green St., Columbia, SC 29208; (803) 777-4841

TN, University of Memphis Library, Government Documents Dept., Memphis, TN 38152-1000; (901) 678-2206

TX, Texas State Library, Documents Dept., 1201 Brazos, Austin, TX 78711-2927; (512) 463-5455

Texas Tech University Library, 17th and Boston Sts., Lubbock, TX 79409-0002; (806) 742-2268

UT, WY, Utah State University, Merrill Library, UMC-3000, Government Documents Dept., Logan, UT 84322-3000; (801) 797-2683

VA, University of Virginia, Alderman Library, Government Documents Dept., Charlottesville, VA 22903-2498; (804) 924-3133

WI, State Historical Society of Wisconsin Library, Government Publications, 816 State St., Madison, WI 53706-1488; (608) 264-6527

Milwaukee Public Library, Documents Dept., 814 W. Wisconsin Ave., Milwaukee, WI 53233-2385; (414) 286-3073

WV, West Virginia University Library, Government Documents Section, 1549 University Ave., Morgantown, WV 26506-6069; (304) 293-3051

Merit Systems Protection Board

AK, HI, ID, OR, WA; all Pacific overseas areas, including AS, GU, and MP, 915 2nd Ave., #1840, Seattle, WA 98174-1056; (206) 220-7975

AL, FL, GA, MS, SC, TN, 401 W. Peachtree St. N.W., #1050, Atlanta, GA 30308-3519; (404) 730-2751

AR, LA, OK, TX, 1100 Commerce St., #6F20, Dallas, TX 75242-9979; (214) 767-0555

AZ, CO, KS (except Kansas City), MT, ND, NE, NM, SD, UT, WY, 12567 W. Cedar Dr., #100, Lakewood, CO 80228-2009; (303) 969-5101

CA, NV, 250 Montgomery St., #400, San Francisco, CA 94104-3401; (415) 705-2935

CT, MA, ME, NH, RI, VT, 99 Summer St., #1810, Boston, MA 02110-1200; (617) 424-5700

DC, MD (Washington metro area), VA, overseas areas not otherwise covered, 5203 Leesburg Pike, #1109, Falls Church, VA 22041-3473; (703) 756-6250

DE, MD (except Washington metro area), NJ (southern), PA, WV, 2nd and Chestnut Sts., #501, Philadelphia, PA 19106-2987; (215) 597-9960

IA, IL, IN, KS (Kansas City), KY, MI, MN, MO, OH, WI, 230 S. Dearborn St., #3100, Chicago, IL 60604-1669; (312) 353-2923

NJ (northern), NY, PR, VI, 26 Federal Plaza, #3137A, New York, NY 10278-0022; (212) 264-9372

National Archives and Records Administration—Regional Records Facilities

The offices store documents for various geographic areas and federal agencies. For further information, please contact the closest facility.

Anchorage, AK, 654 W. 3rd Ave. 99501-2145; (907) 271-2443

Bayonne, NJ, 22 Military Ocean Terminal 07002-5388; (201) 823-7241

Chicago, IL, 7358 S. Pulaski Rd. 60629-5898; (773) 581-5898

Dayton, OH, 3150 Springboro Rd. 45439-1883; (937) 225-2852

Denver, CO, 48 Denver Federal Center (mailing address: P.O. Box 25307) 80225; (303) 236-0804

East Point, GA, 1557 St. Joseph Ave. 30344-2593; (404) 763-7477

Fort Worth, TX, 501 W. Felix St. (mailing address: P.O. Box 6216) 76115; (817) 334-5525

Kansas City, MO, 2312 E. Bannister Rd., 64131-3011; (816) 926-6272

Laguna Niguel, CA, 24000 Avila Rd. (mailing address: P.O. Box 6719) 92607; (714) 360-2641

New York, NY, 201 Varick St., New York, NY 10014-4811; (212) 337-1300

Philadelphia, PA, 14700 Towsend Rd. 19154-1025; (215) 671-9027

Philadelphia (Center City), PA, 900 Market St. 19107; (215) 957-3000

National Archives and Records Administration—Regional Records Facilities (continued)

Pittsfield, MA ,100 Dan Fox Dr. 01201-8230; (413) 445-6885

San Bruno, CA, 1000 Commodore Dr. 94066; (650) 876-9009

Seattle, WA, 6125 Sand Point Way N.E. 98115-7999; (206) 526-6507

St. Louis, MO (Civilian Personnel), 111 Winnebago St. 63118-4199; (314) 425-5719

St. Louis, MO (Military Personnel), 9700 Page Ave. 63132-5100; (314) 538-4201

Waltham, MA, 380 Trapelo Rd. 02154-6399; (617) 647-8100

National Credit Union Administration

AK, AS, CA, GU, HI, ID, MT, NV, OR, WA, 2300 Clayton Rd., #1350, Concord, CA 94520; (510) 825-6125

AL, AR, FL, GA, KY, LA, MS, NC, PR, SC, TN, VI, 7000 Central Pkwy., #1600, Atlanta, GA 30328; (770) 396-4042

AZ, CO, IA, KS, MN, ND, NE, NM, OK, SD, TX, UT, WY, 4807 Spicewood Springs Rd., #5200, Austin, TX 78759-8490; (512) 482-4500

CT, MA, ME, NH, NY, RI, VT, 9 Washington Square, Albany, NY 12205; (518) 464-4180

DC, DE, MD, NJ, PA, VA, WV, 1775 Duke St., #4206, Alexandria, VA 22314-3437; (703) 838-0401

IL, IN, MI, MO, OH, WI, 4225 Naperville Rd., #125, Lisle, IL 60532; (630) 245-1000

National Endowment for the Humanities

AK, 421 W. 1st Ave., #210, Anchorage, AK 99501; (907) 272-5341

AL, 2217 10th Court South, Birmingham, AL 35205; (205) 930-0540

AR, 10816 Executive Center Dr., #310, Little Rock, AR 72211-4383; (501) 221-0091

AS, P.O. Box 4074, Pago Pago, AS 96799; (684) 633-4870

AZ, 1242 N. Central Ave., Phoenix, AZ 85004; (602) 257-0335

CA, 312 Sutter St., #601, San Francisco, CA 94108; (415) 391-1474

CO, 1623 Blake St., #200, Denver, CO 80202; (303) 573-7733

CT, 41 Lawn Ave., Wesleyan Station, Middletown, CT 06459-0185; (860) 685-2260

DC, 1331 H St. N.W., #902, Washington, DC 20005; (202) 347-1732

DE, 1812 Newport Gap Pike, Wilmington, DE 19808-6179; (302) 633-2400

FL, 1725½ E. 7th Ave., Tampa, FL 33605-3708; (813) 272-3473

GA, 50 Hurt Plaza S.E., #1565, Atlanta, GA 30303-2915; (404) 523-6220

GU, 272 W. Route 8, #2A, Barrigada, GU 96913; (671) 734-1713

HI, 3599 Waialae Ave., #23, Honolulu, HI 96816; (808) 732-5402

IA, University of Iowa, Oakdale Campus N210 OH, Iowa City, IA 52242; (319) 335-4153

ID, 217 W. State St., Boise, ID 83702; (208) 345-5346

IL, 203 N. Wabash Ave., #2020, Chicago, IL 60601-2417; (312) 939-5212

IN, 1500 N. Delaware St., Indianapolis, IN 46202-2419; (317) 638-1500

KS, 112 S.W. 6th Ave., #210, Topeka, KS 66603-3895; (913) 357-0359

KY, 206 E. Maxwell St., Lexington, KY 40508; (606) 257-5932

LA, 225 Baronne St., New Orleans, LA 70112; (504) 523-4352

MA, 1 Woodbridge St., South Hadley, MA 01075; (413) 536-1385

MD, 601 N. Howard St., Baltimore, MD 21201; (410) 625-4830

ME, 371 Cumberland Ave. (mailing address: P.O. Box 7202), Portland, ME 04112; (207) 773-5051

MI, 119 Pere Marquette Dr., #3B, Lansing, MI 48912-1270; (517) 372-7770

MN, 987 East Ivy Ave., St. Paul, MN 55106; (612) 774-0105

MO, 911 Washington Ave., #215, St. Louis, MO 63101-1208; (314) 621-7705

MP, AAA 3394, Box 10001, Saipan, MP 96950; (670) 235-4785

National Endowment for the Humanities
(continued)

MS, 3825 Ridgewood Rd., #311, Jackson, MS 39211; (601) 982-6752

MT, 311 Brandly Hall, University of Montana, Missoula, MT 59812-8214; (406) 243-6022

NC, 425 Spring Garden St., Greensboro, NC 27401; (919) 334-5325

ND, 2900 Broadway East, #3 (mailing address: P.O. Box 2191), Bismarck, ND 58502-2191; (701) 255-3360

NE, 215 Centennial Mall South, #225, Lincoln, NE 68508; (402) 474-2131

NH, 19 Pillsbury St. (mailing address: P.O. Box 2228), Concord, NH 03302-2228; (603) 224-4071

NJ, 28 W. State St., 6th Floor, Trenton, NJ 08608; (609) 695-4838

NM, 209 Onate Hall, University of New Mexico, Albuquerque, NM 87131-1213; (505) 277-3705

NV, P.O. Box 8029, Reno, NV 89507-8029; (702) 784-6587

NY, 198 Broadway, 10th Floor, New York, NY 10038; (212) 233-1131

OH, 695 Bryden Rd. (mailing address: P.O. Box 06354), Columbus, OH 43206-0354; (614) 461-7802

OK, 428 W. California, #270, Oklahoma City, OK 73102; (405) 235-0280

OR, 812 S.W. Washington St., #225, Portland, OR 97205; (503) 241-0543

PA, 320 Walnut St., #305, Philadelphia, PA 19106-3892; (215) 925-1005

PR, 109 San Jose St., 3rd Floor, Box 9023920, San Juan, PR 00902-3920; (787) 721-2087

RI, 60 Ship St., Providence, RI 02903; (401) 273-2250

SC, P.O. Box 5287, Columbia, SC 29250; (803) 691-4100

SD, Box 7050, University Station, Brookings, SD 57007; (605) 688-6113

TN, 1003 18th Ave. South (mailing address: P.O. Box 24767), Nashville, TN 37202; (615) 320-7001

TX, 3809 S. 2nd St., Austin, TX 78704-7058; (512) 440-1991

UT, 350 S. 400 East, #110, Salt Lake City, UT 84111-2946; (801) 531-7868

VA, 145 Ednam Dr., Charlottesville, VA 22903-4629; (804) 924-3296

VI, 5-6 Kongens Gade, #200B, St. Thomas, VI 00803; (340) 776-4044

VT, 17 Park St. (mailing address: R.R. 1, Box 7285), Morrisville, VT 05661; (802) 888-3183

WA, 615 2nd Ave., #300, Seattle, WA 98104; (206) 682-1770

WI, 802 Regent St., 1st Floor, Madison, WI 53715-2610; (608) 262-0706

WV, 723 Kanawha Blvd. East, #800, Charleston, WV 25301; (304) 346-8500

WY, Box 3643, University Station, Laramie, WY 82071-3643; (307) 766-6496

National Labor Relations Board

Many area offices are responsible for serving parts of states; therefore, some states appear on this list more than once. For assistance, contact the nearest office.

AK, ID, MT, OR, WA, 915 2nd Ave., #2948, Seattle, WA 98174-1078; (206) 220-6300

AL, FL, LA, MS, 1515 Poydras St., #610, New Orleans, LA 70112-3723; (504) 589-6361

AL, GA, TN, 101 Marietta St. N.W., #2400, Atlanta, GA 30323-3301; (404) 331-2896

AR, KY, MS, TN, 1407 Union Ave., #800, Memphis, TN 38104-3627; (901) 544-0018

AR, TX, 819 Taylor St., #8A24, Fort Worth, TX 76102-6178; (817) 978-2921

AZ, NM, NV, TX, 234 N. Central Ave., #440, Phoenix, AZ 85004-2212; (602) 379-3361

CA, 888 S. Figueroa St., 9th Floor, Los Angeles, CA 90017-2803; (213) 894-5200

CA, HI, 901 Market St., #400, San Francisco, CA 94103-1735; (415) 356-5206

CA, NV, 1301 Clay St., #300N, Oakland, CA 94612-5211; (510) 637-3300

CO, MT, NE, UT, WY, 600 17th St., 3rd Floor, Denver, CO 80202-5433; (303) 844-3551

CT, NH, 1 Commercial Plaza, 21st Floor, Hartford, CT 06103-3599; (860) 240-3522

DC, DE, MD, PA, VA, WV, 103 S. Gay St., Baltimore, MD 21202-4026; (410) 962-2822

National Transportation Safety Board
(continued)

DE, NJ, PA, 615 Chestnut St., 7th Floor, Philadelphia, PA 19106-4404; (215) 597-7601

FL, 201 E. Kennedy Blvd., #530, Tampa, FL 33602-5824; (813) 228-2641

IA, IL, 300 Hamilton Blvd., #200, Peoria, IL 61602-1246; (309) 671-7080

IA, KS, MO, NE, OK, 8600 Farley St., #100 Overland Park, KS 66212-4677; (913) 236-3000

IA, MN, ND, SD, WI, 110 S. 4th St., #316, Minneapolis, MN 55401-2291; (612) 348-1757

IL, IN, 200 W. Adams St., #800, Chicago, IL 60606-5208; (312) 353-7570

IL, MO, 1222 Spuce St., #8.302, St. Louis, MO 63103-2829; (314) 539-7770

IN, KY, 575 N. Pennsylvania St., #238, Indianapolis, IN 46204-1577; (317) 226-7430

IN, KY, OH, WV, 550 Main St., #3003, Cincinnati, OH 45202-3271; (513) 684-3686

MA, ME, NH, RI, VT, 10 Causeway St., 6th Floor, Boston, MA 02222-1072; (617) 565-6700

MI, 477 Michigan Ave., #300, Detroit, MI 48226-2569; (313) 226-3200

MI, WI, 310 W. Wisconsin Ave., #700, Milwaukee, WI 53203; (414) 297-3861

NC, SC, TN, WV, 4035 University Pkwy., Winston-Salem, NC 27106-3325; (910) 631-5201

NJ, 970 Broad St., #1600, Newark, NJ 07102-2570; (973) 645-2100

NY, 26 Federal Plaza, #3614, New York, NY 10278-0104; (212) 264-0300

> 1 MetroTech Center, Jay St. and Myrtle Ave., 10th Floor, Brooklyn, NY 11201-4201; (718) 330-7713

> 111 W. Huron St., #901, Buffalo, NY 14202-2387; (716) 551-4931

OH, 1240 E. 9th St., #1695, Cleveland, OH 44191-2086; (216) 522-3715

PA, WV, 1000 Liberty Ave., #1501, Pittsburgh, PA 15222;-4173 (412) 395-6844

PR, VI, La Torre de Plaza, #1002, 525 F.D. Roosevelt Ave., San Juan, PR 00918-1002; (787) 766-5347

National Transportation Safety Board—Aviation Oversight

AK, ID, MT, OR, UT, WA, WY, 19518 Pacific Hwy. South, #201, Seattle, WA 98188; (206) 870-2200

AL, FL, GA, MS, NC, PR, SC, TN, VI, 8405 N.W. 53rd St., #B-103, Miami, FL 33166; (305) 597-4610

AR, CO, LA, NM, OK, TX, 624 Six Flags Dr., #150, Arlington, TX 76011; (817) 652-7800

AZ, CA, HI, NV, 1515 W. 190th St., #555, Gardena, CA 90248; (310) 380-5660

CT, DC, DE, KY, MA, MD, ME, NH, NJ, NY, OH, PA, RI, VA, VT, WV, 2001 Route 46, #203, Parsippany, NJ 07054; (973) 334-6420

IA, IL, IN, KS, MI, MN, MO, ND, NE, SD, WI, 31 W. 775 North Ave., West Chicago, IL 60185; (630) 377-8177

National Transportation Safety Board—Highway Oversight

AK, AZ, CA, CO, HI, ID, MT, NV, OR, UT, WA, WY, 1515 W. 190th St., #555, Gardena, CA 90248; (310) 380-5461

AL, FL, GA, KY, MS, NC, SC, TN, VA, WV, 60 Forsyth St. S.W., #3M25, Atlanta, GA 30303-3104; (404) 562-1655

AR, IA, IL, IN, KS, LA, MN, MO, ND, NE, NM, OK, SD, TX, WI, 624 Six Flags Dr., #150, Arlington, TX 76011; (817) 652-7840

CT, DC, DE, MA, MD, ME, MI, NH, NJ, NY, OH, PA, RI, VT, 2001 Rt. 46, #203, Parsippany, NJ 07054; (973) 334-6615

National Transportation Safety Board—Railroad Oversight

AK, AZ, CA, CO, HI, ID, MT, NM, NV, OR, UT, WA, WY, 1515 W. 190th St., #555, Gardena, CA 90248; (310) 380-5453

AL, AR, IA, IL, IN, KS, KY, LA, MI, MN, MO, MS, ND, NE, OK, SD, TN, TX, WI, 31 W. 775 North Ave., West Chicago, IL 60185; (630) 377-8177

CT, DC, DE, FL, GA, MA, MD, ME, NC, NH, NJ, NY, OH, PA, RI, SC, VA, VT, WV, 60 Forsyth St. S.W., #3M25, Atlanta, GA 30309; (404) 347-7385

Nuclear Regulatory Commission

AK, AR, AS, AZ, CA, CO, GU, HI, ID, KS, LA, MT, ND, NE, NM, NV, OK, OR, SD, TX, UT, WA, WY, 611 Ryan

Nuclear Regulatory Commission (continued)

Plaza Dr., #400, Arlington, TX 76011-8064; (817) 860-8225

AL, FL, GA, KY, MS, NC, PR, SC, TN, VA, VI, WV, 61 Forsyth St., #23T85, Atlanta, GA 30303; (404) 562-4410

CT, DC, DE, MA, MD, ME, NH, NJ, NY, PA, RI, VT, 475 Allendale Rd., King of Prussia, PA 19406-1415; (610) 337-5299

IA, IL, IN, MI, MN, MO, OH, WI, 801 Warrenville Rd., Lisle, IL 60532-4351; (630) 829-9657

Office of Personnel Management—Service Centers

OPM provides information about federal job opportunities and technical assistance to state and local governments. For assistance, contact the nearest service center.

Atlanta, GA, 75 Spring St. S.W., #940 30303; (404) 331-4588

Chicago, IL, 230 S. Dearborn St., DPN 30-3 60604; (312) 353-6234

Dayton, OH, 200 W. 2nd St., #507 45402; (513) 225-2576

Denver, CO, 12345 Alameda Pkwy. (mailing address: P.O. Box 25167) 80225; (303) 969-6931

Detroit, MI, 477 Michigan Ave., #594 48226; (313) 226-7522

Hato Rey, PR, Carlos E. Chardon St., #340 00918-1710; (787) 766-5259

Honolulu, HI, 300 Ala Moana Blvd., Box 50028 96850; (808) 541-2795

Huntsville, AL, 520 Wynn Dr. N.W. 35816-3426; (205) 837-1271

Norfolk, VA, 200 Granby St., #500 23510-1886; (757) 441-3373

Philadelphia, PA, 600 Arch St., #3400 19106; (215) 597-7670

Raleigh, NC, 4407 Bland Rd., #200 27609-6296; (919) 790-2817

San Antonio, TX, 8610 Broadway, #305 78217; (210) 805-2423

San Francisco, CA, 120 Howard St., #735 94105; (415) 281-7094

Seattle, WA, 700 5th Ave., #5950 98104-5012; (206) 553-0870

Peace Corps

AK, ID, MT, OR, WA, 2001 6th Ave., #1776, Seattle, WA 98121; (206) 553-5490

AL, FL, GA, TN, MS, SC, PR, 100 Alabama St., #2R70, Bldg. 1924, Atlanta, GA 30303; (404) 562-3456

AR, LA, NM, OK, TX, 207 S. Houston St., #527, Dallas, TX 75202; (214) 767-5435

AZ, CA (southern), 11000 Wilshire Blvd., #8104, Los Angeles, CA 90024; (310) 235-7444

CA (northern), HI, NV, 333 Market St., #600, San Francisco, CA 34105; (415) 977-8800

CO, KS, NE, UT, WY, 140 E. 19th Ave., #550, Denver, CO 80203; (303) 866-1057

CT, NJ, NY, PA, 6 World Trade Center, #611, New York, NY 10048; (212) 466-2477

DC, DE, MD, NC, VA, WV, 1400 Wilson Blvd., #400, Arlington, VA 22209; (703) 235-9191

IA, MN, ND, SD, WI, 330 2nd Ave. South, #420, Minneapolis, MN 55401; (612) 348-1480

IL, IN, KY, MI, MO, OH, 55 W. Monroe St., #450, Chicago, IL 60603; (312) 353-4990

MA, ME, NH, RI, VT, 10 Causeway St., #450, Boston, MA 02222; (617) 565-5555

Railroad Retirement Board

Main Office: 844 N. Rush St., Chicago, IL 60611-2092; (312) 751-4500

Legislative Liaison Office, 1310 G St. N.W., #520, Washington, DC 20005-3004; (202) 272-7742

AK, AZ, CA, CO, HI, IA, ID, KS, MN, MT, ND, NE, NM, NV, OR, SD, UT, WA, WI (western), WY, 1999 Broadway, #300, Denver, CO 80202-5737; (303) 884-0800

AL, AR, FL, GA, IL (southern), KY, LA, MO, MS, NC, OK, SC, TN, TX, VA, WV, 401 W. Peachtree St., #1703, Atlanta, GA 30065; (404) 331-2691

CT, DC, DE, IL (northern and central), IN, MA, MD, ME, NH, NJ, NY, OH, PA, RI, VT, WI (eastern), 1421 Cherry St., #660, Philadelphia, PA 19102-1493; (215) 656-6947

Securities and Exchange Commission

AK, AZ, CA, GU, HI, ID, MT, NV, OR, WA 5670 Wilshire Blvd., 11th Floor, Los Angeles, CA 90036-3648; (213) 965-3998

Securities and Exchange Commission
(continued)

AL, AR, FL, GA, LA, MS, NC, PR, SC, TN, VI, 1401 Brickell Ave., #200, Miami, FL 33131; (305) 536-4700

CO, KS, ND, NE, NM, OK, SD, TX, UT, WY, 1801 California St., #4800, Denver, CO 80202-2648; (303) 844-1000

CT, DC, DE, MA, MD, ME, NH, NJ, NY, PA, RI, VA, VT, WV, 7 World Trade Center, #1300, New York, NY 10048; (212) 748-8000

IA, IL, IN, KY, MI, MN, MO, OH, WI, 500 W. Madison St., #1400, Chicago, IL 60661-2511; (312) 353-7390

Small Business Administration

AK, ID, OR, WA, 1200 6th Ave., #1805, Seattle, WA 98101-1128; (206) 553-0291

AL, FL, GA, KY, MS, NC, SC, TN, 1720 Peachtree St. N.W., #496, Atlanta, GA 30309-2482; (404) 347-4999

AR, LA, NM, OK, TX, 4300 Amon Carter Blvd., #108, Fort Worth, TX 76155; (817) 885-6581

AZ, CA, GU, HI, NV, 455 Market St., #2200, San Francisco, CA 94105-2939; (415) 744-2108

CO, MT, ND, SD, UT, WY, 721 19th St., #400, Denver, CO 80202-2599; (303) 844-0500

CT, MA, ME, NH, RI, VT, 10 Causeway St., #812, Boston, MA 02222-1093; (617) 565-8415

DC, DE, MD, PA, VA, WV, 475 Allendale Rd., #201, King of Prussia, PA 19406; (610) 962-3710

IA, KS, MO, NE, 323 W. 8th St., #307, Kansas City, MO 64105-1500; (816) 374-6380

IL, IN, MI, MN, OH, WI, 500 W. Madison St., #1240, Chicago, IL 60606-6617; (312) 353-0357

NJ, NY, PR, VI, 26 Federal Plaza, #3108, New York, NY 10278; (212) 264-1450

Social Security Administration

AK, ID, OR, WA, 2201 6th Ave., Mail Stop RX-50, Seattle, WA 98121; (206) 615-2103

AL, FL, GA, KY, MS, NC, SC, TN, 101 Marietta Tower Bldg., #1902, Atlanta, GA 30323; (404) 331-2475

AR, LA, NM, OK, TX, 1200 Main Tower Bldg., #1440, Dallas, TX 75202; (214) 767-4210

AS, AZ, CA, GU, HI, NV, 75 Hawthorne St., 7th Floor, San Francisco, CA 94105; (415) 744-4676

CO, MT, ND, SD, UT, WY, 1961 Stout St., #325, Denver, CO 80294; (303) 844-2388

CT, MA, ME, NH, RI, VT, 10 Causeway St., Boston, MA 02222; (617) 565-2870

DC, DE, MD, PA, VA, WV, 3535 Market St. (mailing address: P.O. Box 8788), Philadelphia, PA 19101; (215) 597-5157

IA, KS, MO, NE, 601 E. 12th St., #436, Kansas City, MO 64106; (816) 426-6548

IL, IN, MI, MN, OH, WI, 600 W. Madison St., 10th Floor, Chicago, IL 60661; (312) 575-3000

NJ, NY, PR, VI, 26 Federal Plaza, #40-102, New York, NY 10278; (212) 264-3915

U.S. Postal Service

AK, AZ, CO, ID, MT, NM, NV, OR, UT, WA, WY, 1745 Stout St., #1000, Denver, CO 80299-5000; (303) 391-5100

AL, FL, GA, MS, TN, 225 N. Humphrey Blvd., Memphis, TN 38166; (901) 747-7333

AR, LA, OK, TX, P.O. Box 224748, Dallas, TX 75222-4748; (214) 819-8650

CA, HI, 400 Oyster Point Blvd., San Francisco, CA 94099-0100; (415) 635-3001

CT, MA, ME, NH, NY (except New York City), RI, VT, 6 Griffin Rd. North, Windsor, CT 06006-7010; (860) 285-7000

DC, KY, MD, NC, SC, VA, WV, 2800 Shirlington Rd., Arlington, VA 22206-7000; (703) 824-7050

DE, OH, PA, NJ (southern), 5315 Campbells Run Rd., Pittsburgh, PA 15277-7010; (412) 494-2510

IA, IL (southern), KS, MI (Upper Peninsula), MN, MO, NE, ND, SD, WI, P.O. Box 66601, St. Louis, MO 63166-6601; (314) 692-5611

IL (northern), IN, MI (except Upper Peninsula), 244 Knollwood Dr., Bloomingdale, IL 60117-1000; (630) 539-5858

NJ (northern), NY (New York City), PR, 142-02 20th Ave., #318, Flushing, NY 11351-0001; (718) 321-5823

Governors and Other State Officials

Political affiliations, when available, are indicated as follows: Democrat (D), Independent (I), Republican (R), and New Progressive Party (NPP). For key officials of the District of Columbia and other Washington area localities, see page 343.

Alabama

Gov. Fob James Jr. (R), 600 Dexter Ave., Montgomery 36130; Press: Alfred A. Sawyer, (334) 242-7150

Lt. Gov. Don Siegelman (D), 11 S. Union St., #725, Montgomery 36104, (334) 242-7900; fax, (334) 242-4661

Secy. of State Jim Bennett (D), P.O. Box 5616, Montgomery 36103, (334) 242-7205; fax, (334) 242-4993

Atty. Gen. William H. Pryor (R), 11 S. Union St., Montgomery 36130, (334) 242-7300

Treasurer Lucy Baxley (D), State Capitol, #S106, P.O. Box 302510, Montgomery 36130, (334) 242-7500; fax, (334) 242-7592

Alaska

Gov. Tony Knowles (D), State Capitol, P.O. Box 110001, Juneau, 99811-0001; Press: Bob King, (907) 465-3500

Lt. Gov. Fran Ulmer (D), State Capitol, P.O. Box 110015, Juneau, 99811-0015, (907) 465-3520; fax, (907) 463-5400

(No office of Secretary of State)

Atty. Gen. Bruce M. Botelho (D), State Capitol, P.O. Box 110300, Juneau, 99811-0300, (907) 465-3600

Treasurer Ross Kinney, State Capitol, P.O. Box 110405, Juneau, 99811, (907) 465-4800; fax, (907) 465-2389

In Washington, D.C.: John W. Katz, director, Washington Office of the Governor, State of Alaska, 444 N. Capitol St. N.W., #336 20001, (202) 624-5858; fax, (202) 624-5857

American Samoa

Gov. Tauese P. Sunia (D), Office of the Governor, Pago Pago 96799; Press: Vacant, (011) (684) 633-4116

Lt. Gov. Togiola T. Tulafono (D), Office of the Lieutenant Governor, Pago Pago 96799, (011) (684) 633-4116; fax, (011) (684) 633-2269

(No office of Secretary of State)

Atty. Gen. Toetagata Albert Mailo (D), P.O. Box 7, Pago Pago 96799, (011) (684) 633-4163

Treasurer Tifi Ale, Treasury Dept., Pago Pago 96799, (011) (684) 633-4155; fax, (011) (684) 633-4100

In Washington, D.C.: Janice Lipsan, representative, Washington Office of the Governor, 1000 16th St. N.W., #400 20036; (202) 785-0550

Arizona

Gov. Jane Dee Hull (R), 1700 W. Washington St., Phoenix 85007; Press: Francie Noyes, (602) 542-1342

(No office of Lieutenant Governor)

Secy. of State Betsey Bayless (R), 1700 W. Washington St., Phoenix 85007-2808, (602) 542-4285; fax, (602) 542-6172

Atty. Gen. Grant Woods (R), 1275 W. Washington St., Phoenix 85007, (602) 542-4266

Treasurer Tony West (R), 1700 W. Washington St., 1st Floor, Phoenix 85007, (602) 542-1463; fax, (602) 258-6627

Arkansas

Gov. Mike Huckabee (R), 250 State Capitol, Little Rock 72201; Press: Jim Harris, (501) 682-2345

Lt. Gov. Winthrop Rockefeller (R), 270 State Capitol, Little Rock 72201, (501) 682-2144; fax, (501) 682-2894

Secy. of State Sharon Priest (D), 256 State Capitol, Little Rock 72201, (501) 682-1010; fax, (501) 682-3510

Atty. Gen. Winston Bryant (D), 323 Center St., #200, Little Rock 72201-2610, (501) 682-2007

Treasurer Jimmie Lou Fisher (D), 220 State Capitol, Little Rock 72201, (501) 682-3835; fax, (501) 682-3842

California

Gov. Pete Wilson (R), State Capitol, 1st Floor, Sacramento 95814; Press: Sean Walsh, (916) 445-4571

Lt. Gov. Gray Davis (D), State Capitol, #1114, Sacramento 95814; (916) 445-8994

Secy. of State Bill Jones (R), 1500 11th St., Sacramento 95814, (916) 653-7244; fax, (916) 653-4620

Atty. Gen. Daniel E. Lungren (R), 1200 I St., Sacramento 95814, (916) 445-9555; fax, (916) 324-5205

Treasurer Matthew Fong (R), 915 Capitol Mall, #110 Sacramento 95814, (916) 653-2995; fax, (916) 653-3125

In Washington,D.C.: David Wetmore, director, Washington Office of the Governor, State of California, 444 N. Capitol St. N.W., #134 20001, (202) 624-5270; fax, (202) 624-5280

Colorado

Gov. Roy Romer (D), 136 State Capitol, Denver 80203-1792; Press: Jim Carpenter, (303) 866-4572

Lt. Gov. Gail Schoettler (D), 130 State Capitol, Denver 80203-1792, (303) 866-2087; fax, (303) 866-5469

Secy. of State Vikki Buckley (R), 1560 Broadway, #200, Denver 80202, (303) 894-2200; fax, (303) 894-7732

Atty. Gen. Gale A. Norton (R), 1525 Sherman St., Denver 80203, (303) 866-4500

Treasurer Bill Owens (R), 140 State Capitol, Denver 80203, (303) 866-2441; fax, (303) 866-2123

Connecticut

Gov. John G. Rowland (R), 211 Capitol Ave., Hartford 06106; Press: Dean Pagani, (860) 566-4840

Lt. Gov. Jodie Rell (R), State Capitol, #304, Hartford 06106, (860) 524-7384; fax, (860) 524-7304

Secy. of State Miles Rapoport (D), 30 Trinity St., Hartford 06115, (860) 509-6000; fax, (860) 509-6175

Atty. Gen. Richard Blumenthal (D), 55 Elm St., Hartford 06141-0120, (860) 566-2026

Treasurer Paul J. Silvester, 55 Elm St., Hartford 06106-1773, (860) 702-3001

In Washington, D.C.: Ruth B. Ravitz, director, Washington Office of the Governor, State of Connecticut, 444 N. Capitol St. N.W., #317 20001, (202) 347-4535; fax, (202) 347-7151

Delaware

Gov. Tom Carper (D), 820 N. French St., Wilmington 19801; Press: Sheri L. Woodruff, (302) 577-3210

Lt. Gov. Ruth Ann Minner (D), 820 N. French St., Wilmington 19801, (302) 577-8787; fax, (302) 577-3019

Secy. of State Edward J. Freel (D), Townsend Bldg., P.O. Box 898, Dover 19903, (302) 739-4111; fax, (302) 739-3811

Atty. Gen. M. Jane Brady (R), 820 N. French St., Wilmington 19801, (302) 577-3800

Treasurer Janet C. Rzewnicki (R), Thomas Collins Bldg., P.O. Box 1401, Dover 19904, (302) 739-3382; fax, (302) 739-5635

In Washington, D.C.: Jonathan Jones, director, Washington Office, State of Delaware, 444 N. Capitol St. N.W., #230 20001, (202) 624-7724; fax, (202) 624-5495

Florida

Gov. Lawton Chiles (D), State Capitol, Tallahassee 32399; Press: Ryan Banfill, (850) 488-5394

Lt. Gov. Buddy MacKay (D), State Capitol, Tallahassee 32399, (850) 488-4441

Secy. of State Sandy B. Mortham (R), State Capitol, Tallahassee 32399, (850) 922-0234; fax, (850) 487-2214

Atty. Gen. Robert A. Butterworth (D), PL01 State Capitol, Tallahassee 32399-1050, (850) 487-1963; fax, (850) 487-2561

Treasurer Bill Nelson (D), PL11 State Capitol, Tallahassee 32399-0300, (850) 922-3100; fax, (850) 488-6581

In Washington, D.C.: Charlie Salem, director, Washington Office, State of Florida, 444 N. Capitol St. N.W., #349 20001, (202) 624-5885; fax, (202) 624-5886

Georgia

Gov. Zell Miller (D), 203 State Capitol, Atlanta 30334; Press: Rick Dent, (404) 651-7774

Lt. Gov. Pierre Howard (D), 240 State Capitol, Atlanta 30334, (404) 656-5030; fax, (404) 656-6739

Secy. of State Lewis Massey (D), 214 State Capitol, Atlanta 30334, (404) 656-2881; fax, (404) 657-5804

Atty. Gen. Thurbert E. Baker (R), 40 Capitol Square S.W., Atlanta 30334-1300, (404) 656-3300

Treasurer Dan Ebersole, 200 Piedmont Ave. S.E., #1201 W. Tower, Atlanta 30334, (404) 656-2168; fax, (404) 656-9048

Guam

Gov. Carl T. C. Gutierrez (D), Executive Chambers, P.O. Box 2950, Agana 96932; Press: Ginger Cruz, (671) 472-8931

Lt. Gov. Madeleine Bordallo (D), Executive Chambers, P.O. Box 2950, Agana 96932, (671) 472-8931; fax, (671) 477-4826

(No office of Secretary of State)

Atty. Gen. Charles H. Troutman III (D), 120 W. O'Brien Dr., Judicial Court Bldg., #2-200E, Agana 96910, (671) 475-3324

Treasurer Y'Asela A. Pereira, Dept. of Administration, P.O. Box 884, Agana 96932, (671) 475-1122

In Washington, D.C.: John Hasselmann, director, Guam Liaison Office, 444 N. Capitol St. N.W., #532 20001, (202) 624-3670; fax, (202) 624-3679

Hawaii

Gov. Benjamin J. Cayetano (D), State Capitol, Honolulu 96813; Press: Kathleen Raenya-Markrich, (808) 586-0034

Lt. Gov. Mazie Hirono (D), State Capitol, 5th Floor, Honolulu 96813, (808) 586-0255; fax, (808) 586-0231

(No office of Secretary of State)

Atty. Gen. Margery S. Bronster (D), 425 Queen St., Honolulu 96813, (808) 586-1282

Treasurer Earl I. Anzai, P.O. Box 150, Honolulu 96810, (808) 586-1518; fax, (808) 586-1644

In Washington, D.C.: Kerrie Doerr, director, Washington Office, State of Hawaii, 700 13th St. N.W., #400 20005-5917, (202) 347-6253; fax, (202) 347-6255

Idaho

Gov. Philip E. Batt (R), State Capitol, P.O. Box 83720, Boise 83720-0034; Press: Julie Robinson, (208) 334-2100

Lt. Gov. C. L. Butch Otter (R), 225 State House, P.O. Box 83720, Boise 83720, (208) 334-2200; fax, (208) 334-3259

Secy. of State Pete T. Cenarrusa (R), 203 State Capitol, Boise 83720, (208) 334-2300; fax, (208) 334-2282

Atty. Gen. Alan G. Lance (R), P.O. Box 83720, Boise 83720-0010, (208) 334-2400; fax, (208) 334-2530

Treasurer Lydia Justice Edwards (R), 102 State Capitol, Boise 83720, (208) 334-3200; fax, (208) 334-2543

Illinois

Gov. Jim Edgar (R), 207 State Capitol, Springfield 62706; Press: Thomas Hardy, (217) 782-7355

Lt. Gov. Bob Kustra (R), 214 State Capitol, Springfield 62706, (217) 782-7884; fax, (217) 524-6262

Secy. of State George H. Ryan Sr. (R), 213 State Capitol, Springfield 62706, (217) 782-2201; fax, (217) 785-0358

Atty. Gen. Jim Ryan (R), 100 W. Randolph St., Chicago 60601, (312) 814-2503; toll-free, (800) 243-5377

Treasurer Judy Baar Topinka (R), 219 State House, Springfield 62706, (217) 782-2211; fax, (217) 785-2777

In Washington, D.C.: Terri Moreland, director, Washington Office, State of Illinois, 444 N. Capitol St. N.W., #240 20001, (202) 624-7760; fax, (202) 724-0689

Indiana

Gov. Frank L. O'Bannon (D), 206 State House, Indianapolis 46204; Press: Phil Bremen, (317) 232-4578

Lt. Gov. Joseph Kerman (D), 333 State House, Indianapolis 46204, (317) 232-4545; fax, (317) 232-4788

Secy. of State Sue Ann Gilroy (R), 201 State House, Indianapolis 46204, (317) 232-6531; fax, (317) 233-3283

Atty. Gen. Jeff Modisett (D), 219 State House, Indianapolis 46204, (317) 232-6201

Treasurer Joyce Brinkman (R), 242 State House, Indianapolis 46204, (317) 232-6386; fax, (317) 232-5656

In Washington, D.C.: Jeff Viohl, federal liaison, Washington Office, State of Indiana, 1001 G St. N.W., #E-400 20001, (202) 628-3343; fax, (202) 638-3516

Iowa

Gov. Terry E. Branstad (R), State Capitol, Des Moines 50319-0001; Press: Eric Woolson, (515) 281-3150

Lt. Gov. Joy Corning (R), State Capitol, Des Moines 50319, (515) 281-3421; fax, (515) 281-6611

Secy. of State Paul Danny Pate (R), State Capitol, Des Moines 50319, (515) 281-5204; fax, (515) 242-5952

Atty. Gen. Tom Miller (D), 1305 E. Walnut St., Des Moines 50319, (515) 281-8993

Treasurer Michael L. Fitzgerald (D), State Capitol, Des Moines 50319, (515) 281-5366; fax, (515) 281-6962

In Washington, D.C.: Phil Smith, director, Washington Office, State of Iowa, 444 N. Capitol St. N.W., #359 20001, (202) 624-5442; fax, (202) 624-8189

Kansas

Gov. Bill Graves (R), State Capitol, 2nd Floor, Topeka 66612; Press: Mike Matson, (785) 296-3232

Lt. Gov. Gary Sherrer (R), State Capitol, #222S, Topeka 66612, (785) 296-2213

Secy. of State Ron Thornburgh (R), State Capitol, 2nd Floor, Topeka 66612, (785) 296-4575; fax, (785) 296-4570

Atty. Gen. Carla J. Stovall (R), Judicial Bldg., 301 S.W. 10th St., Topeka 66612-1597, (785) 296-2215

Treasurer Sally Thompson (D), 900 S.W. Jackson St., #201N, Topeka 66612-1235, (785) 296-3171; fax, (785) 296-7950

Kentucky

Gov. Paul E. Patton (D), State Capitol, Frankfort 40601; Press: Melissa Forsythe, (502) 564-2611

Lt. Gov. Steve Henry (D), 100A State Capitol, Frankfort 40601, (502) 564-2611; fax, (502) 564-2517

Secy. of State John Y. Brown III (D), 152 State Capitol, Frankfort 40601, (502) 564-3490; fax, (502) 564-5687

Atty. Gen. Albert B. Chandler III (D), 118 State Capitol, Frankfort 40601, (502) 696-5300

Treasurer John Kennedy Hamilton (D), Capitol Annex, #183, Frankfort 40601, (502) 564-4722; fax, (502) 564-6545

Louisiana

Gov. Mike Foster (R), P.O. Box 94004, Baton Rouge 70804-9004; Press: Marsanne Golsby, (504) 342-9037

Lt. Gov. Kathleen Blanco (D), Pentagon Court Barracks, P.O. Box 44243, Baton Rouge 70804, (504) 342-7009; fax, (504) 342-1949

Secy. of State W. Fox McKeithen (R), P.O. Box 94125, Baton Rouge 70804, (504) 342-4479; fax, (504) 342-5577

Atty. Gen. Richard P. Ieyoub (D), Dept. of Justice, P.O. Box 94095, Baton Rouge 70804-9095, (504) 342-7013

Treasurer Ken Duncan (D), P.O. Box 44154, Baton Rouge 70804-0154, (504) 342-0010; fax, (504) 342-0046

Maine

Gov. Angus S. King (I), 1 State House Station, Augusta 04333-0001; Press: Dennis Bailey (207) 287-3531

(No office of Lieutenant Governor)

President of the Senate Mark Lawrence (D), 3 State House Station, Augusta 04333, (207) 287-1500

Secy. of State Dan A. Gwadowsky (D), 148 State House Station, Augusta 04333, (207) 626-8400; fax, (207) 287-8598

Atty. Gen. Andrew Ketterer (D), 6 State House Station, Augusta 04333, (207) 626-8800

Treasurer Dale McCormick (D), 39 State House Station, Augusta 04333, (207) 287-2771; fax, (207) 787-2367

Maryland

Gov. Parris N. Glendening (D), State House, Annapolis 21401; Press: JoAnne Trumbile, (410) 974-5267

Lt. Gov. Kathleen Kennedy Townsend (D), State House, Annapolis 21401, (410) 974-2804; fax, (410) 974-5252

Secy. of State John T. Willis (D), State House, Annapolis 21401, (410) 974-5521; fax, (410) 974-5190

Atty. Gen. J. Joseph Curran Jr. (D), 200 St. Paul Place, Baltimore 21202-2202, (410) 576-6300

Treasurer Richard N. Dixon (D), 80 Calvert St., #109, Annapolis 21401, (410) 974-3542; fax, (410) 974-3530

In Washington, D.C.: Steve Heyman, director, Washington Office of the Governor, State of Maryland, 444 N. Capitol St. N.W., #311 20001, (202) 624-1430; fax, (202) 783-3061

Massachusetts

Gov. Argeo Paul Cellucci (R), 360 State House, Boston 02133; Press: Ilene Hoffer, (617) 727-2759

Lt. Gov. (Vacant), 360 State House, Executive Office, Boston 02133, (617) 727-3600; fax, (617) 727-9731

Secy. of the Commonwealth William F. Galvin (D), 337 State House, Boston 02133, (617) 727-9180; fax, (617) 742-4722

Atty. Gen. Scott Harshbarger (D), 1 Ashburton Pl., Boston 02108-1698, (617) 727-2200

Treasurer Joseph Malone (R), 227 State House, Boston 02133, (617) 367-6900; (617) 248-0372

In Washington, D.C.: Charles Steele, director, Office of Federal-State Relations, Commonwealth of Massachusetts, 444 N. Capitol St. N.W., #400 20001, (202) 624-7713; fax, (202) 624-7714

Michigan

Gov. John Engler (R), P.O. Box 30013, Lansing 48909; Press: John Truscott, (517) 335-6397

Lt. Gov. Connie Binsfeld (R), 5215 Capitol Bldg., P.O. Box 30026, Lansing 48909, (517) 373-6800; fax, (517) 335-6763

Secy. of State Candice Miller (R), 430 W. Allegan St., 1st Floor, Lansing 48918, (517) 373-2510; fax, (517) 373-0727

Atty. Gen. Frank J. Kelley (D), P.O. Box 30212, Lansing 48909-0212, (517) 373-1110

Treasurer Douglas B. Roberts, P.O. Box 11097, Lansing 48901, (517) 373-3223; fax, (517) 335-1785

In Washington, D.C.: LeAnne Redick, director, Washington Office, State of Michigan, 444 N. Capitol St. N.W., #411 20001, (202) 624-5840; fax, (202) 624-5841

Minnesota

Gov. Arne H. Carlson (R), 130 State Capitol, St. Paul 55155; Press: Jackie Renner, (612) 296-0001

Lt. Gov. Joanne Benson (R), 130 State Capitol, St. Paul 55155, (612) 296-0078; fax, (612) 296-2089

Secy. of State Joan Growe (D), 180 State Office Bldg., 100 Constitution Ave., St. Paul 55155-1299, (612) 296-2079; fax, (612) 297-5844

Atty. Gen. Hubert H. Humphrey III (D), 102 State Capitol, St. Paul 55155, (612) 296-6196

Treasurer Michael A. McGrath (D), 50 Sherburne Ave., #303, St. Paul 55155, (612) 296-7091; fax, (612) 296-8615

In Washington, D.C.: Alison Englund Burns, director, Washington Office, State of Minnesota, 400 N. Capitol St. N.W., #365 20001, (202) 624-5308; fax, (202) 624-5425

Mississippi

Gov. Kirk Fordice (R), P.O. Box 139, Jackson 39205; Press: Kim Gallaspy, (601) 359-3150

Lt. Gov. Ronnie Musgrave (D), P.O. Box 1018, Jackson, 39215-1018, (601) 359-3200; fax, (601) 359-3935

Secy. of State Eric Clark (D), P.O. Box 136, Jackson 39205-0136, (601) 359-1350; fax, (601) 359-1499

Atty. Gen. Mike Moore (D), Dept. of Justice, P.O. Box 220, Jackson 39201-0220, (601) 359-3680

Treasurer Marshall G. Bennett (D), 404 Walter Sillers Bldg., P.O. Box 138, Jackson 39205, (601) 359-3600; fax, (601) 359-2001

Missouri

Gov. Mel Carnahan (D), 216 State Capitol, Jefferson City 65102; Press: Chris Sifford, (573) 751-3222

Lt. Gov. Roger B. Wilson (D), 121 State Capitol, Jefferson City 65101, (573) 751-4727

Secy. of State Rebecca McDonell Cook (D), 208 State Capitol, P.O. Box 778, Jefferson City 65102, (573) 751-4926

Atty. Gen. Jeremiah W. Jay Nixon (D), P.O. Box 899, Jefferson City 65102, (573) 751-3321

Treasurer Bob Holden (D), 229 State Capitol, Jefferson City 65102, (573) 751-2411; fax, (573) 751-7882

In Washington, D.C.: Susan Harris, director, Washington Office, State of Missouri, 400 N. Capitol St. N.W., #376 20001, (202) 624-7720; fax, (202) 624-5855

Montana

Gov. Marc Racicot (R), State Capitol, Helena 59620-0801; Press: Rone Hanrahan, (406) 444-3111

Lt. Gov. Judy Martz (R), 207 State Capitol, Helena 59620, (406) 444-5551

Secy. of State Mike Cooney (D), P.O. Box 202801, Helena 59620-2801, (406) 444-2034; fax, (406) 444-3976

Atty. Gen. Joseph P. Mazurek (D), 215 N. Sanders, P.O. Box 201401, Helena 59620-1401, (406) 444-2026

Treasurer Lois A. Menzies, Dept. of Administration, 155 Mitchell Bldg., Helena 59620, (406) 444-2032; fax, (406) 444-2812

Nebraska

Gov. E. Benjamin Nelson (D), P.O. Box 94848, Lincoln 68509-4848; Press: Karl Bieber, (402) 471-2244

Lt. Gov. Kim Robak (D), 2315 State Capitol, P.O. Box 94863, Lincoln, 68509-4863, (402) 471-2256; fax, (402) 471-6031

Secy. of State Scott Moore (R), 2300 State Capitol, P.O. Box 94608, Lincoln, 68509-4608, (402) 471-2554; fax, (402) 471-3237

Atty. Gen. Don Stenberg (R), State Capitol, P.O. Box 98920, Lincoln 68509-8920, (402) 471-2682

Treasurer David E. Heineman (R), 2003 State Capitol, P.O. Box 94788, Lincoln 68509-4788, (402) 471-2455; fax, (402) 471-4390

In Washington, D.C.: Thomas R. Litjen, Washington representative, State of Nebraska, 444 N. Capitol St. N.W., #406 20001, (202) 508-3838; fax, (202) 624-7714

Nevada

Gov. Bob Miller (D), State Capitol Complex, Carson City 89710; Press: Richard Urey, (702) 687-5670

Lt. Gov. Lonnie Hammargren (R), State Capitol Complex, Carson City 89710, (702) 687-3037; fax, (702) 687-3420

Secy. of State Dean Heller (R), State Capitol Complex, Carson City 89710, (702) 687-5203; fax, (702) 687-3471

Atty. Gen. Frankie Sue Del Papa (D), 100 N. Carson St., Carson City 89701, (702) 687-4170

Treasurer Robert L. Seale (R), State Capitol Complex, Carson City 89701, (702) 687-5200; fax, (702) 687-5532

In Washington, D.C.: R. Leo Penne, director, Washington Office, State of Nevada, 444 N. Capitol St. N.W., #209 20001, (202) 624-5405; fax, (202) 624-8181

New Hampshire

Gov. Jeanne Shaheen (D), State House, Concord 03301-4990; Press: Doug Hattaway, (603) 271-2121

(No office of Lieutenant Governor)

President of the Senate Joseph Delahunty (R), 302 State House, 107 N. Main St., Concord 03301-4951, (603) 271-2111; fax, (603) 271-2105

Secy. of State William Gardner (D), 204 State House, Concord 03301, (603) 271-3242; fax, (603) 271-6316

Atty. Gen. Philip McLaughlin (D), 25 Capitol St., Concord 03301-6397, (603) 271-3658

Treasurer Georgie A. Thomas (R), 25 Capitol St., #121, Concord 03301, (603) 271-2621; fax, (603) 271-3922

New Jersey

Gov. Christine Todd Whitman (R), 125 W. State St. (mailing address: P.O. Box 001), Trenton 08625; Press: Carl Golden, (609) 292-6000

(No office of Lieutenant Governor)

President of the Senate Donald T. DiFrancesco (R), P.O Box 099, Trenton 08625, (609) 292-5199; fax, (609) 599-3458

Secy. of State Lonna R. Hooks (R), P.O. Box 300, Trenton 08625, (609) 777-0884; fax, (609) 292-9897

Atty. Gen. Peter Verniero (R), 25 Market St., CN-080, Trenton 08625, (609) 292-4925; fax, (609) 292-3508

Treasurer James A. DiEleuterio, 121 W. State St., P.O. Box 002, Trenton 08625, (609) 984-3888

In Washington, D.C.: Marguerite Sullivan, director, Washington Office of the Governor, State of New Jersey, 444 N. Capitol St. N.W., #201 20001, (202) 638-0631; fax, (202) 638-2296

New Mexico

Gov. Gary E. Johnson (R), State Capitol, Santa Fe 87503; Press: Diane Kinderwater, (505) 827-3000

Lt. Gov. Walter Bradley (R), State Capitol, Santa Fe 87503, (505) 827-3050; fax, (505) 827-3057

Secy. of State Stephanie Gonzales (D), 420 State Capitol, Santa Fe 87503, (505) 827-3600; fax, (505) 827-3634

Atty. Gen. Tom Udall (D), P.O. Drawer 1508, Santa Fe 87504-1508, (505) 827-6000

Treasurer Michael A. Montoya (D), P.O. Box 608, Santa Fe 87504-0608, (505) 827-7835; fax, (505) 827-6395

New York

Gov. George E. Pataki (R), State Capitol, Albany 12224; Press: Zenia Mucha, (518) 474-8418

Lt. Gov. Betsy McCaughey Ross (R), 326 State Capitol, Albany 12224, (518) 474-4623

Secy. of State Alexander F. Treadwell (R), 41 State St., Albany 12231, (518) 474-0050; fax, (518) 474-4765

Atty. Gen. Dennis C. Vacco (R), Dept. of Law, State Capitol, Albany 12224, (518) 474-7330

Treasurer George H. Gasser, Dept. of Taxation and Finance, P.O. Box 7002, Albany 12225, (518) 474-4250; fax, (518) 428-5165

In Washington, D.C.: James Mazzarella, director, New York State Office of Federal Affairs, 444 N. Capitol St. N.W., #301 20001, (202) 434-7100; fax, (202) 434-7110

North Carolina

Gov. James B. Hunt Jr. (D), State Capitol, Raleigh 27603-2905; Press: Sean Walsh, (919) 733-5612

Lt. Gov. Dennis A. Wicker (D), 116 W. Jones St., Raleigh, 27603-8006, (919) 733-6248; fax, (919) 715-4239

Secy. of State Elaine Marshall (D), 300 N. Salisbury St., Raleigh 27603-5909, (919) 733-5140

Atty. Gen. Michael F. Easley (D), Dept. of Justice, P.O. Box 629, Raleigh 27602-0629, (919) 716-6400; fax, (919) 716-6750

Treasurer Harlan E. Boyles (D), 325 N. Salisbury St., #100, Raleigh 27603-1385, (919) 733-3951; fax, (919) 733-9586

In Washington, D.C.: Debra Bryant, director, Washington Office of the Governor, State of North Carolina, 444 N. Capitol St. N.W., #332 20001, (202) 624-5830; fax, (202) 624-5836

North Dakota

Gov. Edward T. Schafer (R), State Capitol, Bismarck 58505; Press: Julie Laffrig, (701) 328-2200

Lt. Gov. Rosemarie Myrdal (R), State Capitol, Bismarck 58505, (701) 328-4222; fax, (701) 328-2205

Secy. of State Alvin Jaeger (R), State Capitol, 1st Floor, Bismarck 58505-0500, (701) 328-2900; fax, (701) 328-2992

Atty. Gen. Heidi Heitkamp (D), State Capitol, Bismarck 58505-0040, (701) 328-2210; fax, (701) 328-2226

Treasurer Kathi Gilmore (D), State Capitol, Bismarck 58505-0600, (701) 328-2643; fax, (701) 328-3002

Northern Mariana Islands

Gov. Pedro. Tenorio (R), Capitol Hill, Saipan 96950; Press: Vacant, (011) (670) 664-2200

Lt. Gov. Jesus Sapalan (R), Capitol Hill, Saipan 96950, (011) (670) 322-5091; fax, (011) (670) 322-5096

Acting Atty. Gen. Robert B. Dunlap (D), Administration Bldg., Saipan 96950, (011) (670) 322-4311

Treasurer Dolores S. Guerrero, Dept. of Finance, P.O. Box 5243, Saipan 96950, (011) (670) 664-1300

In Washington, D.C.: Juan N. Babauta, Office of Representative to the United States, Commonwealth of the Northern Mariana Islands, 2121 R St., N.W., 20008; fax, (202) 637-5873

Ohio

Gov. George V. Voinovich (R), 77 S. High St., 30th Floor, Columbus 43266-0601; Press, John Meyer (614) 644-0957

Lt. Gov. Nancy Hollister (R), 77 S. High St., 30th Floor, Columbus 43266, (614) 466-3396; fax, (614) 644-0575

Secy. of State Bob Taft (R), 30 E. Broad St., 14th Floor, Columbus 43266-0418, (614) 466-2655

Atty. Gen. Betty D. Montgomery (R), 30 E. Broad St.,17th Floor, Columbus 43215-3428, (614) 466-4320

Treasurer J. Kenneth Blackwell (R), 30 E. Broad St., 9th Floor, Columbus 43215, (614) 466-2160; fax, (614) 644-7313

In Washington, D.C.: Ted Hollingsworth, director, Washington Office, State of Ohio, 444 N. Capitol St. N.W., #546 20001, (202) 624-5844; fax, (202) 624-5847

Oklahoma

Gov. Frank Keating (R), 212 State Capitol, Oklahoma City 73105; Press: Dan Mahoney, (405) 523-4278

Lt. Gov. Mary Fallin (R), 211 State Capitol, Oklahoma City 73105, (405) 521-2161

Secy. of State Tom Cole (R), 101 State Capitol, Oklahoma City 73105, (405) 521-3911

Atty. Gen. Drew Edmondson (D), 112 State Capitol, Oklahoma City 73105, (405) 521-3921

Treasurer Robert Butkin (D), 217 State Capitol, Oklahoma City 73105, (405) 521-3191; fax, (405) 521-4994

Oregon

Gov. John A. Kitzhaber (D), State Capitol, Salem 97310; Press: Bob Applegate, (503) 378-6496

(No office of Lieutenant Governor)

Secy. of State Phil Keisling (D), 136 State Capitol, Salem 97310, (503) 986-1523; fax, (503) 986-1616

Atty. Gen. Hardy Myers (D), 1162 Court St. N.E., Salem 97310, (503) 378-6002

Treasurer Jim Hill (D), 159 State Capitol, Salem 97310, (503) 378-4329; fax, (503) 373-7051

Pennsylvania

Gov. Tom Ridge (R), 225 Main Capitol, Harrisburg 17120; Press: Tim Reeves, (717) 787-2500

Lt. Gov. Mark Schwieker (R), 200 Main Capitol, Harrisburg 17120-0002, (717) 787-3300

Secy. of the Commonwealth, Yvette Kane (R), 302 N. Capitol Bldg., Harrisburg 17120, (717) 787-6458; fax, (717) 787-1734

Atty. Gen. Mike Fisher (R), Strawberry Square, 16th Floor, Harrisburg 17120, (717) 787-3391

Treasurer Barbara Hafer (R), 129 Finance Bldg., Harrisburg 17120, (717) 787-2465; fax, (717) 783-9760

In Washington, D.C.: Rebecca Halkias, Deputy Chief of Staff for Federal Affairs, Washington Office of the Governor, Commonwealth of Pennsylvania, 444 N. Capitol St. N.W., #700 20001, (202) 624-7828; fax, (202) 624-7831

Puerto Rico

Gov. Pedro J. Rosselló (NPP), La Fortaleza, P.O. Box 82, San Juan 00901; Press: Pedro Rosario, (787) 721-0646

(No office of Lieutenant Governor)

Secy. of State Norma Burgos Andujar (NPP), State Capitol, P.O. Box 3271, San Juan 00910-1398, (787) 723-4343

Atty. Gen. José Fuentes-Agostini (NPP), Dept. of Justice, P.O. Box 192, San Juan, 00902-0192, (787) 721-7700

Treasurer Xexia Velez Silva, P.O. Box 4515, San Juan, 00905, (787) 729-0916; fax, (787) 723-2838

In Washington, D.C.: Xavier Romeu, executive director, Puerto Rico Federal Affairs Administration, 1100 17th St. N.W., #800 20036, (202) 778-0710; fax, (202) 778-0721

Rhode Island

Gov. Lincoln Almond (R), 143 State House, Providence 02903; Press: Eric Cote, (401) 222-2080

Lt. Gov. Bernard A. Jackvony (R), 115 State House, Providence 02903, (401) 222-2371; fax, (401) 222-2012

Secy. of State James Langevin (D), 218 State House, Providence 02903, (401) 222-2357; fax, (401) 222-1356

Atty. Gen. Jeffrey B. Pine (R), 72 Pine St., Providence 02903, (401) 274-4400; fax, (401) 222-1331

Treasurer Nancy J. Mayer (R), 102 State House, Providence 02903, (401) 277-2397; fax, (401) 277-6140

In Washington, D.C.: Beth Meyer, acting director, Washington Office of the Governor, State of Rhode Island, 444 N. Capitol St. N.W., #619 20001, (202) 624-3605; fax, (202) 624-3607

South Carolina

Gov. David M. Beasley (R), P.O. Box 11369, Columbia 29211; Press: Gary Karr, (803) 734-9818

Lt. Gov. Bob Peeler (R), State House, Columbia 29202, (803) 734-2080

Secy. of State Jim Miles (R), Wade Hampton Bldg., P.O. Box 11350, Columbia 29211, (803) 734-2170; fax, (803) 734-2164

Atty. Gen. Charles M. Condon (R), Rembert C. Dennis Office Bldg., P.O. Box 11549, Columbia 29211-1549, (803) 734-3970

Treasurer Richard Eckstrom (R), P.O. Box 11778, Columbia 29211, (803) 734-2688; fax, (803) 734-2039

In Washington, D.C.: Lisa Chapman, director, Washington Office of the Governor, State of South Carolina, 444 N. Capitol St. N.W., #203 20001, (202) 624-7784; fax, (202) 624-7800

South Dakota

Gov. William J. Janklow (R), State Capitol, 2nd Floor, Pierre 57501; Press: Jim Soyer, (605) 773-3212

Lt. Gov. Carole Hillard (R), State Capitol, Pierre 57501, (605) 773-3661

Secy. of State Joyce Hazeltine (R), State Capitol, #204, Pierre 57501, (605) 773-3537; fax, (605) 773-6580

Atty. Gen. Mark Barnett (R), State Capitol, Pierre 57501-5070, (605) 773-3215

Treasurer Richard Butler (D), State Capitol, #212, Pierre 57501-5070, (605) 773-3378; fax, (605) 773-3115

Tennessee

Gov. Don Sundquist (R), State Capitol, Nashville 37243-0001; Press: Beth Fortune, (615) 741-3763

Lt. Gov. John S. Wilder (D), 1 Legislative Plaza, Nashville 37243, (615) 741-2368; fax, (615) 741-9349

Secy. of State Riley Darnell (D), State Capitol, 1st Floor, Nashville 37243-0305, (615) 741-2819; fax, (615) 741-5962

Atty. Gen. John Knox Walkup (R), 425 5th Ave. North, Nashville 37243, (615) 741-6474

Treasurer Stephen D. Adams (D), State Capitol, 1st Floor, Nashville 37243, (615) 741-2956; fax, (615) 741-7328

Texas

Gov. George W. Bush (R), P.O. Box 12428, Austin 78711; Press: Karen Hughes, (512) 463-1826

Lt. Gov. Bob Bullock (D), P.O. Box 12068, Austin 78711, (512) 463-0001; fax, (512) 463-0039

Secy. of State Al Gonzales (R), P.O. Box 12697, Austin 78711, (512) 463-5701; fax, (512) 475-2761

Atty. Gen. Dan Morales (D), P.O. Box 12548, Austin, 78711-2548, (512) 463-2100

Comptroller of Public Accounts John Sharp (D), P.O. Box 13528, Austin, 78711, (512) 463-4600; fax, (512) 463-4288

In Washington, D.C.: Laurie M. Rich, director, Office of State-Federal Relations, State of Texas, 122 C St. N.W., #200 20001, (202) 638-3927; fax, (202) 628-1943

Utah

Gov. Mike Leavitt (R), 210 State Capitol, Salt Lake City 84114; Press: Vicki Varela, (801) 538-1000

Lt. Gov. Olene S. Walker (R), 210 State Capitol, Salt Lake City 84114, (801) 538-1520; fax, (801) 538-1557

(No office of Secretary of State)

Atty. Gen. Jan Graham (D), 236 State Capitol, Salt Lake City 84114-0810, (801) 538-9600; fax, (801) 538-1121

Treasurer Edward T. Alter (R), 215 State Capitol, Salt Lake City 84114, (801) 538-1042; fax, (801) 538-1465

In Washington, D.C.: Joanne Snow Neumann, director, Washington Office, State of Utah, 444 N. Capitol St. N.W., #388 20001, (202) 624-7704; fax, (202) 624-7707

Vermont

Gov. Howard Dean (D), 109 State St., Montpelier 05609; Press: Sue Alan, (802) 828-3333

Lt. Gov. Douglas Racine (D), State House, Montpelier 05633, (802) 828-2226; fax, (802) 828-3198

Secy. of State James Milne (R), 109 State St., Montpelier 05609-1101, (802) 828-2148; fax, (802) 828-2496

Atty. Gen. William H. Sorrell (D), 109 State St., Montpelier 05633-6200, (802) 828-2301; fax, (802) 828-2772

Treasurer James H. Douglas (R), 133 State St., 2nd Floor, Montpelier 05609-1001, (802) 828-3171

Virgin Islands

Gov. Roy L. Schneider (I), 20-21 Government House, Charlotte Amalie, St. Thomas 00802; Press: Janette Millin, (340) 774-0294

Lt. Gov. Kenneth Mapp (I), 18 Kongens Gade, St. Thomas 00802, (340) 774-2991; fax, (340) 774-6953

(No office of Secretary of State)

Atty. Gen. Julio A. Brady (R), Dept. of Justice, G.E.R.S. Complex, #48B-50C Kronprinsdens Gade, St. Thomas 00802, (340) 774-5666

Acting Treasurer Bernice A. Turnbull, Dept. of Finance, 76 Kronprinsdens Gade, St. Thomas 00801-2515, (340) 774-4114; fax, (340) 776-4028

In Washington, D.C.: Terry Helenese, director, Washington Office of the Governor, Territory of the Virgin Islands, 444 N. Capitol St. N.W., #298 20001, (202) 624-3565; fax, (202) 785-2542

Virginia

Gov. Jim Gilmore (R), State Capitol, Richmond 23219; Press: Ken Stroupe, (804) 786-2211

Lt. Gov. John H. Hager (R), 900 E. Main St., #1400, Richmond 23219, (804) 786-2078; fax, (804) 786-7514

Secy. of the Commonwealth Anne Petera (R), Capitol Square, P.O. Box 2454, Richmond 23201, (804) 786-2441; fax, (804) 371-0017

Atty. Gen. Mark L. Earley (R), 900 E. Main St., Richmond 23219, (804) 786-2071

Treasurer Susan Dewey, P.O. Box 1879, Richmond 23218, (804) 371-6011

In Washington, D.C.: Mike McSherry, director, Virginia Liaison Office, 444 N. Capitol St. N.W., #214 20001, (202) 783-1769; fax, (202) 783-7687

Washington

Gov. Gary Locke (D), P.O Box 40002, Olympia 98504-0002; Press: Mary Lou Flynn, (360) 753-6780

Lt. Gov. Brad Owen (D), 304 Legislative Bldg., P.O. Box 40482, Olympia 98504-0482, (360) 786-7700

Secy. of State Ralph Munro (R), P.O. Box 40220, Olympia 98504-0220, (360) 902-4151

Atty. Gen. Christine O. Gregoire (D), 1125 Washington St. S.E., P.O. Box 40100, Olympia 98504-0100, (360) 753-6200; fax, (360) 664-0988

Treasurer Michael J. Murphy (D), Legislative Bldg., P.O. Box 40200, Olympia 98504-0200, (360) 902-9001; fax, (360) 586-6147

In Washington, D.C.: Jan Shinpoch, director, Washington Office of the Governor, State of Washington, 444 N. Capitol St. N.W., #617 20001, (202) 624-3680; fax, (202) 624-3682

West Virginia

Gov. Cecil H. Underwood (R), State Capitol, Charleston 25305-0370; Press: Dan Page, (304) 558-6345

(No office of Lieutenant Governor)

President of the Senate Earl Ray Tomblin (D), 229 Main Unit, Capitol Complex, Charleston 25305, 304-357-7801

Secy. of State Ken Hechler (D), 1900 Kanawha Blvd. East, Bldg. 1, #157K, Charleston 25305, (304) 558-6000; fax, (304) 558-0900

Atty. Gen. Darrell V. McGraw Jr. (D), State Capitol, 26 East Wing., Charleston 25305-0220, (304) 558-2021

Treasurer John Perdue (D), 1900 Kanawha Blvd. East, Bldg. 1, #E145, Charleston 25305, (304) 343-4000; fax, (304) 346-6602

Wisconsin

Gov. Tommy G. Thompson (R), State Capitol, P.O. Box 7863, Madison 53707; Press: Kevin Keane, (608) 266-1212

Lt. Gov. Scott McCallum (R), 22 E. State Capitol, Madison 53702, (608) 266-3516; fax, (608) 267-3571

Secy. of State Douglas La Follette (D), 30 W. Mifflin St., 10th Floors, Madison 53707, (608) 266-8888; fax, (608) 266-3159

Atty. Gen. James E. Doyle (D), 114 East State Capitol, P.O. Box 7857, Madison 53707-7857, (608) 266-1221; fax, (608) 267-2223

Treasurer Jack C. Voight (R), 101 E. Wilson St., 5th Floor, P.O. Box 7871, Madison 53707-7871, (608) 266-3712; fax, (608) 266-2647

In Washington, D.C.: Schuyler Baab, director, Washington Office, State of Wisconsin, 444 N. Capitol St. N.W., #613 20001, (202) 624-5870; fax, (202) 624-5871

Wyoming

Gov. Jim Geringer (R), State Capitol, Cheyenne 82002; Press: Jimmy Orr, (307) 777-7434

(No office of Lieutenant Governor)

Secy. of State Diana Ohman (R), State Capitol, Cheyenne 82002-0020, (307) 777-7378; fax, (307) 777-6217

Atty. Gen. William U. Hill (R), 200 W. 24th St., Cheyenne 82002, (307) 777-7841

Treasurer Stan Smith (R), State Capitol, Cheyenne 82002, (307) 777-7408; fax, (307) 777-5411

Foreign Embassies, U.S. Ambassadors, and Country Desk Officers

The list that follows includes key foreign diplomats in the United States, U.S. ambassadors or ranking diplomatic officials abroad, and offices or regional desks of the U.S. State Dept. and U.S. Commerce Dept. that follow political, cultural, and economic developments in each country. The Commerce Dept. also provides fax-on-demand services for selected regional desks, including the Asia Business Center (ABC), the Business Information Service for the Newly Independent States (BISNIS), and the Central and Eastern Europe Business Information Center (CEEBIC), all at (800) 872-8723; and the NAFTA Office at (202) 482-4464 or (202) 482-3101.

Afghanistan

Washington embassy suspended operations August 28, 1997.
Consul: Abdul Habib Seraj.
Chancery (consulate): 360 Lexington Ave., 11th Floor, New York, NY 10017; (212) 972-2276; fax, (212) 972-9046.
Embassy in Kabul temporarily closed.
State Dept.: Shelden Rapoport, (202) 647-9552.
Commerce Dept.: ABC, (202) 482-2522.

Albania

Ambassador: Petrit Bushati.
Chancery: 2100 S St. N.W. 20008; (202) 223-4942; fax, (202) 628-7342.
U.S. Ambassador in Tirane: Marisa R. Lino.
State Dept.: Eric Lundberg, (202) 647-3747.
Commerce Dept.: CEEBIC, (202) 482-2645.

Algeria

Ambassador: Ramtane Lamamra.
Chancery: 2118 Kalorama Rd. N.W. 20008; (202) 265-2800; fax, (202) 667-2174.
U.S. Ambassador in Algiers: Cameron R. Hume.
State Dept.: Cynthia Kierscht, (202) 647-4680.
Commerce Dept.: David Guglielmi, (202) 482-1860.

Andorra

Relations with Andorra are maintained by the U.S. Consulate in Barcelona, Spain. Maurice Parker, U.S. consul general.

Ambassador: Juli Minoves Triquell.
Chancery (U.N. Mission): 2 United Nations Plaza, 25th Floor, New York, NY 10017; (212) 750-8064; fax, (212) 750-6630.
State Dept.: Debra Glassman, (202) 647-1419.

Angola

Ambassador: Antonio Dos Santos Franca.
Chancery: 1050 Connecticut Ave. N.W., #760 20036; (202) 785-1156; fax, (202) 785-1258.
U.S. Ambassador in Luanda: Donald K. Steinberg.
State Dept.: Damian Leader, (202) 647-8434.
Commerce Dept.: Debra Rogers, (202) 482-4228.

Antigua and Barbuda

Ambassador: Lionel A. Hurst.
Chancery: 3216 New Mexico Ave. N.W. 20016; (202) 362-5211; fax, (202) 362-5225.
U.S. Ambassador: Jeanette Hyde (resident in Bridgetown, Barbados).
State Dept.: Annie Pforzheimer, (202) 647-2620.
Commerce Dept.: Michelle Brooks, (202) 482-1658.

Argentina

Ambassador: Diego Ramiro Guelar.
Chancery: 1600 New Hampshire Ave. N.W. 20009; (202) 939-6400; fax, (202) 332-3171.
U.S. Ambassador in Buenos Aires: James R. Cheek.
State Dept.: Richard Sanders, (202) 647-2401.
Commerce Dept.: Carrie Clark, (202) 482-0477.

CORRESPONDING WITH A FOREIGN SERVICE POST

Business correspondence to a foreign service post should be addressed to a section or position rather than to an officer by name in case that officer has transferred to another post. Do not combine any of the following address forms, since this can cause delays in delivery; in some cases the letter may be returned to you.

Posts with APO/FPO addresses:
use domestic postage
name of section
name of post
PSC or unit number, box number
APO + two-letter code (AA, AE, or AP) + ZIP Code

Posts without APO/FPO addresses (via diplomatic pouch):
use domestic postage
name of section
name of post
Department of State
Washington, DC 20521 + 4-digit postal code

When sending mail via diplomatic pouch (see address form above), add the 4-digit code of the destination post to the 20521 ZIP Code. Following are 4-digit codes for U.S. embassies abroad.

Abidjan 2010	**Brussels** 7600	**Jakarta** 8200	**Monrovia** 8800	**Riyadh** 6300
Abu Dhabi 6010	**Bucharest** 5260	**Kampala** 2190	**Montevideo** 3360	**Rome** 9500
Accra 2020	**Budapest** 5270	**Kathmandu** 6190	**Moscow** 5430	**St. George's** 3180
Addis Ababa 2030	**Buenos Aires** 3130	**Khartoum** 2200	**Muscat** 6220	**San José** 3440
Algiers 6030		**Kiev** 5850	**Nairobi** 8900	**San Salvador** 3450
Almaty 7030	**Bujumbura** 2100	**Kigali** 2210	**Nassau** 3370	**Sanaa** 6330
Amman 6050	**Cairo** 7700	**Kingston** 3210	**N'Djamena** 2410	**Santiago** 3460
Ankara 7000	**Canberra** 7800	**Kinshasa** 2220	**New Delhi** 9000	**Santo Domingo** 3470
Antananarivo 2040	**Caracas** 3140	**Kolonia** 4120	**Niamey** 2420	
Ashgabat 7070	**Chisinau** 7080	**Kuala Lumpur** 4210	**Nicosia** 5450	**Sarajevo** 7130
Asmara 7170	**Colombo** 6100		**Nouakchott** 2430	**Seoul** 9600
Asunción 3020	**Conakry** 2110	**Kuwait City** 6200	**Oslo** 5460	**Singapore** 4280
Athens 7100	**Copenhagen** 5280	**Lagos** 8300	**Ottawa** 5480	**Sofia** 5740
Baku 7050	**Cotonou** 2120	**La Paz** 3220	**Ouagadougou** 2440	**Stockholm** 5750
Bamako 2050	**Dakar** 2130	**Libreville** 2270		**Suva** 4290
Bandar Seri Begawan 4020	**Damascus** 6110	**Lilongwe** 2280	**Panama City** 9100	**Tallinn** 4530
	Dar Es Salaam 2140	**Lima** 3230	**Paramaribo** 3390	**Tashkent** 7110
Bangkok 7200	**Dhaka** 6120	**Lisbon** 5320	**Paris** 9200	**Tbilisi** 7060
Bangui 2060	**Djibouti** 2150	**Ljubljana** 7140	**Phnom Penh** 4540	**Tegucigalpa** 3480
Banjul 2070	**Doha** 6130	**Lome** 2300		**Tel Aviv** 9700
Barcelona 5400	**Dublin** 5290	**London** 8400	**Port-au-Prince** 3400	**Tirane** 9510
Beijing 7300	**Dushanbe** 7090	**Lusaka** 2310	**Port Louis** 2450	**Tokyo** 9800
Beirut 6070	**Florence** 5670	**Luxembourg** 5380	**Port Moresby** 4240	**Tunis** 6360
Belgrade 5070	**Freetown** 2160	**Madrid** 8500		**Ulaanbaatar** 4410
Belize City 3050	**Gaborone** 2170	**Majuro** 4380	**Port-of-Spain** 3410	**Valletta** 5800
Bern 5110	**Georgetown** 3170	**Malabo** 2320		**Vatican City** 5660
Bishkek 7040	**Guatemala City** 3190	**Managua** 3240	**Prague** 5630	**Victoria** 2510
Bissau 2080		**Manama** 6210	**Praia** 2460	**Vienna** 9900
Bogota 3030	**The Hague** 5770	**Manila** 8600	**Pretoria** 9300	**Vientiane** 4350
Bonn 7400	**Hanoi** 4550	**Maputo** 2330	**Quito** 3420	**Vilnius** 4510
Brasilia 7500	**Harare** 2180	**Maseru** 2340	**Rabat** 9400	**Warsaw** 5010
Bratislava 5840	**Havana** 3200	**Mbabane** 2350	**Rangoon** 4250	**Wellington** 4360
Brazzaville 2090	**Helsinki** 5310	**Mexico City** 8700	**Reykjavik** 5640	**Windhoek** 2540
Bridgetown 3120	**Islamabad** 8100	**Minsk** 7010	**Riga** 4520	**Yaounde** 2520
		Mogadishu 2360		**Yerevan** 7020
				Zagreb 5080
				Zurich 5130

Armenia

Ambassador: Rouben Robert Shugarian.
Chancery: 2225 R St. N.W. 20008; (202) 319-1976; fax, (202) 319-2982.
U.S. Ambassador in Yerevan: Peter Tomsen.
State Dept.: David Rodearmel, (202) 647-6795.
Commerce Dept.: BISNIS, (202) 482-4655.

Australia

Ambassador: Andrew Sharp Peacock.
Chancery: 1601 Massachusetts Ave. N.W. 20036; (202) 797-3000; fax, (202) 797-3168.
U.S. Ambassador in Canberra: Genta Hawkins Holmes.
State Dept.: David Henifin, (202) 647-9691.
Commerce Dept.: ABC, (202) 482-2522.

Austria

Ambassador: Helmut Tuerk.
Chancery: 3524 International Court N.W. 20008; (202) 895-6700; fax, (202) 895-6750.
U.S. Ambassador in Vienna: Kathryn Walt Hall.
State Dept.: John Feeney, (202) 647-2672.
Commerce Dept.: John Larsen, (202) 482-2434.

Azerbaijan

Ambassador: Hafiz Mir Jalal Pashayev.
Chancery (temp.): 927 15th St. N.W., #700 20005; (202) 842-0001; fax, (202) 842-0004.
U.S. Ambassador in Baku: Stanley T. Escudero.
State Dept.: Maria Germano, (202) 647-6048.
Commerce Dept. (BISNIS): BISNIS, (202) 482-4655.

Bahamas

Ambassador: Arlington Griffith Butler.
Chancery: 2220 Massachusetts Ave. N.W. 20008; (202) 319-2660; fax, (202) 319-2668.
U.S. Ambassador in Nassau: Sidney Williams.
State Dept.: Kathleen Lange, (202) 647-2621.
Commerce Dept.: Mark Siegelman, (202) 482-0704.

Bahrain

Ambassador: Muhammed Abdul Ghaffar.
Chancery: 3502 International Dr. N.W. 20008; (202) 342-0741; fax, (202) 362-2192.
U.S. Ambassador in Manama: Johnny Young.
State Dept.: Eric Gaudiosi, (202) 647-6571.
Commerce Dept.: David Guglielmi, (202) 482-1860.

Bangladesh

Ambassador: K. M. Shehabuddin.
Chancery: 2201 Wisconsin Ave. N.W. 20007; (202) 342-8372.
U.S. Ambassador in Dhaka: David N. Merrill.
State Dept.: Patricia Mahoney, (202) 647-9552.
Commerce Dept.: ABC, (202) 482-2522.

Barbados

Ambassador: Courtney N. Blackman.
Chancery: 2144 Wyoming Ave. N.W. 20008; (202) 939-9200.
U.S. Ambassador in Bridgetown: Jeanette Hyde.
State Dept.: Annie Pforzheimer, (202) 647-2620.
Commerce Dept.: Michelle Brooks, (202) 482-4464.

Belarus

Ambassador: Valery V. Tsepkalo.
Chancery: 1619 New Hampshire Ave. N.W. 20009; (202) 986-1604; fax, (202) 986-1805.
U.S. Ambassador in Minsk: Daniel V. Speckhard.
State Dept.: Maria Rudensky, (202) 647-6764.
Commerce Dept.: BISNIS, (202) 482-4655.

Belgium

Ambassador: Andre Adam.
Chancery: 3330 Garfield St. N.W. 20008; (202) 333-6900; fax, (202) 333-3079.
U.S. Ambassador in Brussels: Alan J. Blinken.
State Dept.: Marilyn Ereshefsky, (202) 647-6585.
Commerce Dept.: Maria Dorsett, (202) 482-6008.

Belize

Ambassador: James S. Murphy.
Chancery: 2535 Massachusetts Ave. N.W. 20008; (202) 332-9636; fax, (202) 332-6888.
U.S. Ambassador in Belize City: Carolyn Curiel.
State Dept.: Mary Sue Conaway, (202) 647-4986.
Commerce Dept.: Michelle Brooks, (202) 482-1658.

Benin

Ambassador: Lucien Edgar Tonoukouin.
Chancery: 2737 Cathedral Ave. N.W. 20008; (202) 232-6656; fax, (202) 265-1996.
U.S. Ambassador in Cotonou: John M. Yates.
State Dept.: Anne Sides, (202) 647-1540.
Commerce Dept.: Alicia Robinson, (202) 482-5149.

Bhutan

State Dept.: Gregory Fukutomi, (202) 647-1450.
Commerce Dept.: ABC, (202) 482-2522.

Bolivia

Ambassador: Marcelo Perez Monasterios.
Chancery: 3014 Massachusetts Ave. N.W. 20008; (202) 483-4410; fax, (202) 328-3712.
U.S. Ambassador in La Paz: Donna Jean Hrinak.
State Dept.: John Markey, (202) 647-4193.
Commerce Dept.: Tom Welch, (202) 482-0475.

Bosnia-Herzegovina

Ambassador: Sven Alkalaj.
Chancery: 1707 L St. N.W., #760 20036; (202) 833-3612; fax, (202) 833-2061.
U.S. Ambassador in Sarajevo: Richard Dale Kauzlarich.
State Dept.: Bert Braun, (202) 736-7024.
Commerce Dept.: CEEBIC, (202) 482-2645.

Botswana

Ambassador: Archibald Mooketsa Mogwe.
Chancery: 3400 International Dr. N.W., #7M 20008; (202) 244-4990; fax, (202) 244-4164.
U.S. Ambassador in Gaborone: Robert C. Krueger.
State Dept.: Patricia Kim-Scott, (202) 647-8432.
Commerce Dept.: Debra Rogers, (202) 482-4228.

Brazil

Ambassador: Paulo-Tarso Flecha de Lima.
Chancery: 3006 Massachusetts Ave. N.W. 20008; (202) 238-2700; fax, (202) 238-2827.
U.S. Ambassador in Brasilia: Melvyn Levitsky.
State Dept.: Keith Mines, (202) 647-2401.
Commerce Dept.: Paolo Mendes, (202) 482-3872.

Brunei

Ambassador: Pengiran Anak Dato Puteh.
Chancery: 2600 Virginia Ave. N.W., #300 20037; (202) 342-0159; fax, (202) 342-0158.
U.S. Ambassador in Bandar Seri Begawan: Glen Robert Rase.
State Dept.: Ike Reed, (202) 647-3276.
Commerce Dept.: ABC, (202) 482-2522.

Bulgaria

Ambassador: Snejana Damianova Botoucharova.
Chancery: 1621 22nd St. N.W. 20008; (202) 387-7969; fax, (202) 234-7973.
U.S. Ambassador in Sofia: Avist T. Bohlen.

State Dept.: Isabella Detweiler, (202) 647-0310.
Commerce Dept.: CEEBIC, (202) 482-2645.

Burkina Faso

Ambassador: Bruno Zidouemba.
Chancery: 2340 Massachusetts Ave. N.W. 20008; (202) 332-5577.
U.S. Ambassador in Ouagadougou: Sharon P. Wilkinson.
State Dept.: Natalie Brown, (202) 647-2791.
Commerce Dept.: Philip Michelini, (202) 482-4388.

Burma (See Myanmar)

Burundi

Chargé d'Affaires: Henri Simbakwira.
Chancery: 2233 Wisconsin Ave. N.W., #212 20007; (202) 342-2574; fax, (202) 342-2578.
U.S. Ambassador in Bujumbura: Morris N. Hughes.
State Dept.: Philip Nelson, (202) 647-1707.
Commerce Dept.: Philip Michelini, (202) 482-4388.

Cambodia

Ambassador: Huoth Var.
Chancery: 4500 16th St. N.W. 20011; (202) 726-7742; fax, (202) 726-8381.
U.S. Ambassador in Phnom Penh: Kenneth M. Quinn.
State Dept.: Brian Aggelar, (202) 647-0064.
Commerce Dept.: ABC, (202) 482-2522.

Cameroon

Ambassador: Jerome Mendouga.
Chancery: 2349 Massachusetts Ave. N.W. 20008; (202) 265-8790.
U.S. Ambassador in Yaounde: Charles H. Twining.
State Dept.: Donald Koran, (202) 647-1707.
Commerce Dept.: Alicia Robinson, (202) 482-5149.

Canada

Ambassador: Raymond A. J. Chretien.
Chancery: 501 Pennsylvania Ave. N.W. 20001; (202) 682-1740; fax, (202) 682-7726.
U.S. Ambassador in Ottawa: Gordon G. Giffin.
State Dept.: Stewart Smith, (202) 647-2170.
Commerce Dept.: NAFTA, (202) 482-0305.

Cape Verde

Chargé d'Affaires: Manuel de Matos.
Chancery: 3415 Massachusetts Ave. N.W. 20007; (202) 965-6820; fax, (202) 965-1207.

U.S. Ambassador in Praia: Lawrence M. Benedict.
State Dept.: Peter O'Donohue, (202) 647-1596.
Commerce Dept.: Philip Michelini, (202) 482-4388.

Central African Republic

Ambassador: Henry Koba.
Chancery: 1618 22nd St. N.W. 20008; (202) 483-7800; fax, (202) 332-9893.
Embassy in Bangui temporarily closed.
State Dept.: Deborah Odell, (202) 647-1707.
Commerce Dept.: Philip Michelini, (202) 482-4388.

Chad

Ambassador: Ahmat Mahamat-Saleh.
Chancery: 2002 R St. N.W. 20009; (202) 462-4009; fax, (202) 265-1937.
U.S. Ambassador in N'Djamena: David Halsted.
State Dept.: Deborah Odell, (202) 647-1707.
Commerce Dept.: Philip Michelini, (202) 482-4388.

Chile

Ambassador: John Biehl.
Chancery: 1732 Massachusetts Ave. N.W. 20036; (202) 785-1746; fax, (202) 887-5579.
U.S. Ambassador in Santiago: Gabriel Guerra-Mondragon.
State Dept.: James Roberts, (202) 647-2401.
Commerce Dept.: Roger Turner, (202) 482-0703.

China

Ambassador: Li Daoyu.
Chancery: 2300 Connecticut Ave. N.W. 20008; (202) 328-2500.
U.S. Ambassador in Beijing: James R. Sasser.
State Dept.: Pamela Slutz, (202) 647-6772.
Commerce Dept.: ABC, (202) 482-2522.

Colombia

Ambassador: Juan Carlos Esguerra.
Chancery: 2118 Leroy Pl. N.W. 20008; (202) 387-8338; fax, (202) 232-8643.
U.S. Ambassador in Bogota: Curtis Warren Kamman.
State Dept.: Harry O'Hara, (202) 647-3360.
Commerce Dept.: Matt Gaisford, (202) 482-0057.

Comoros

Ambassador: Ahmed Djabir.
Chancery (U.N. Mission): 336 E. 45th St., 2nd Floor, New York, NY 10017; (212) 972-8010; fax, (212) 983-4712.

U.S. Ambassador: Harold Geisel (resident in Port Louis, Mauritius).
State Dept.: Charles Gurney, (202) 647-6473.
Commerce Dept.: Debra Rogers, (202) 482-4228.

Congo, Democratic Republic of (Zaire)

Chargé d'Affaires: Mukendi Tambo A. Kabila.
Chancery: 1800 New Hampshire Ave. N.W. 20009; (202) 234-7690; fax, (202) 237-0748.
U.S. Ambassador in Kinshasa: Daniel H. Simpson.
State Dept.: Michael Goldschmidt, (202) 647-1707.
Commerce Dept.: Philip Michelini, (202) 482-4388.

Congo, Republic of

Chargé d'Affaires: Serge Mombouli.
Chancery: 4891 Colorado Ave. N.W. 20011; (202) 726-0825; fax, (202) 726-1860.
U.S. Ambassador in Brazzaville: Aubrey Hooks.
State Dept.: Michael Goldschmidt, (202) 647-1707.
Commerce Dept.: Alicia Robinson, (202) 482-5149.

Costa Rica

Chargé d'Affaires: Jose Thompson.
Chancery: 2114 S St. N.W. 20008; (202) 234-2945; fax, (202) 265-4795.
U.S. Ambassador in San Jose: Thomas J. Dodd.
State Dept.: Brad Johnson, (202) 647-4926.
Commerce Dept.: Mark Siegelman, (202) 482-0704.

Côte d'Ivoire

Ambassador: Koffi Moise Koumoue.
Chancery: 2424 Massachusetts Ave. N.W. 20008; (202) 797-0300.
U.S. Ambassador in Abidjan: Lannon Walker.
State Dept.: Anne Sides, (202) 647-1540.
Commerce Dept.: Philip Michelini, (202) 482-4388.

Croatia

Ambassador: Miomir Zuzul.
Chancery: 2343 Massachusetts Ave. N.W. 20008; (202) 588-5899; fax (202) 588-8936.
U.S. Ambassador in Zagreb: William D. Montgomery.
State Dept.: Lisa Tepper, (202) 647-2452.
Commerce Dept.: CEEBIC, (202) 482-2645.

Cuba

Chancery: Cuba's interests in the United States are represented by Switzerland.

The Cuban Interests Section is located at 2630 and 2639 16th St. N.W. 20009; (202) 797-8518. Fernando Ramirez, chief of section.

U.S. interests in Cuba are represented through the Swiss Embassy. Michael Kozak, U.S. principal officer in Havana.

State Dept.: Velia DePirro, (202) 647-9272.

Commerce Dept.: Mark Siegelman, (202) 482-0704.

Cyprus

Ambassador: Andros A. Nicolaides.

Chancery: 2211 R St. N.W. 20008; (202) 462-5772; fax, (202) 483-6710.

U.S. Ambassador in Nicosia: Kenneth Brill.

State Dept.: Conrad Tribble, (202) 647-6113.

Commerce Dept.: Ann Corro, (202) 482-3945.

Czech Republic

Ambassador: Alexandr Vondra.

Chancery: 3900 Spring of Freedom St. N.W. 20008; (202) 274-9100; fax, (202) 966-8540.

U.S. Ambassador in Prague: Jenonne R. Walker.

State Dept.: Tom Yazdgerdi, (202) 647-1457.

Commerce Dept.: CEEBIC, (202) 482-2645.

Denmark

Ambassador: K. Erik Tygesen.

Chancery: 3200 Whitehaven St. N.W. 20008; (202) 234-4300; fax, (202) 328-1470.

U.S. Ambassador in Copenhagen: Edward E. Elson.

State Dept.: Ingrid Kollist, (202) 647-6582.

Commerce Dept.: James Devlin, (202) 482-4414.

Djibouti

Ambassador: Roble Olhaye.

Chancery: 1156 15th St. N.W., #515 20005; (202) 331-0270; fax, (202) 331-0302.

State Dept.: George Fredrick, (202) 647-6453.

Commerce Dept.: Debra Rogers, (202) 482-4228.

Dominica

Ambassador: Edward I. Watty.

Chancery: 3216 New Mexico Ave. N.W. 20016; (202) 364-6781; fax, (202) 364-6791.

U.S. Ambassador: Jeanette Hyde (resident in Bridgetown, Barbados).

State Dept.: Annie Pforzheimer, (202) 647-2620.

Commerce Dept.: Michelle Brooks, (202) 482-1658.

Dominican Republic

Ambassador: Bernardo Vega.

Chancery: 1715 22nd St. N.W. 20008; (202) 332-6280; fax, (202) 265-8057.

Chargé d'Affaires in Santo Domingo: Linda Watts.

State Dept.: Ray Walser, (202) 647-2620.

Commerce Dept.: Mark Siegelman, (202) 482-0704.

Ecuador

Ambassador: Alberto F. Maspons.

Chancery: 2535 15th St. N.W. 20009; (202) 234-7200.

U.S. Ambassador in Quito: Leslie Alexander.

State Dept.: Andrew Simkim, (202) 647-3338.

Commerce Dept.: Matt Gaisford, (202) 482-0057.

Egypt

Ambassador: Ahmed Maher El Sayed.

Chancery: 3521 International Court N.W. 20008; (202) 895-5400; fax, (202) 244-4319.

U.S. Ambassador in Cairo: Daniel C. Kurtzer.

State Dept.: Thomas Duffy, (202) 647-4261.

Commerce Dept.: Thomas Sams, (202) 482-1860.

El Salvador

Ambassador: Rene A. Leon.

Chancery: 2308 California St. N.W. 20008; (202) 265-9671.

Chargé d'Affaires in San Salvador: Anne Patterson.

State Dept.: John Feeley, (202) 647-4986.

Commerce Dept.: Michelle Brooks, (202) 482-1658.

Equatorial Guinea

Ambassador: Micha Ondo Bile.

Chancery: 1511 K St. N.W., #405 20005; (202) 393-0525; fax, (202) 393-0348.

U.S. Ambassador in Malabo: Joseph O'Neill.

State Dept.: Donald Koran, (202) 647-1707.

Commerce Dept.: Philip Michelini, (202) 482-4388.

Eritrea

Ambassador: Semere Russom.

Chancery: 1708 New Hampshire Ave. N.W. 20009; (202) 319-1991; fax, (202) 319-1304.

U.S. Ambassador in Asmara: John F. Hicks Sr.

State Dept.: Joseph Cassidy, (202) 647-6485.

Commerce Dept.: Debra Rogers, (202) 482-4228.

Estonia

Ambassador: Grigore Kalev Stoicescu.
Chancery: 2131 Massachusetts Ave. N.W. 20008; (202) 588-0101; fax, (202) 588-0108.
U.S. Ambassador in Tallinn: Lawrence Palmer Taylor.
State Dept.: Trevor Evans, (202) 647-8908.
Commerce Dept.: CEEBIC, (202) 482-2645.

Ethiopia

Ambassador: Berhane Gebre-Christos.
Chancery: 2134 Kalorama Rd. N.W. 20008; (202) 234-2281; fax, (202) 328-7950.
U.S. Ambassador in Addis Ababa: David H. Shinn.
State Dept.: Joseph Cassidy, (202) 647-6485.
Commerce Dept.: Debra Rogers, (202) 482-4228.

Fiji

Ambassador: Napolioni Masirewa.
Chancery: 2233 Wisconsin Ave. N.W., #240 20007; (202) 337-8320; fax, (202) 337-1996.
U.S. Ambassador in Suva: Don Gevirtz.
State Dept.: Patricia Stigliani, (202) 736-4741.

Finland

Ambassador: Jaakko Tapani Laajava.
Chancery: 3301 Massachusetts Ave. N.W. 20008; (202) 298-5800; fax, (202) 298-6030.
U.S. Ambassador in Helsinki: Derek N. Shearer.
State Dept.: Josef Ruth, (202) 647-8431.
Commerce Dept.: James Devlin, (202) 482-4414.

France

Ambassador: Francois V. Bujon.
Chancery: 4101 Reservoir Rd. N.W. 20007; (202) 944-6000; fax, (202) 944-6166.
U.S. Ambassador in Paris: Felix George Rohatyn.
State Dept.: James Wojtasiewicz, (202) 647-3072.
Commerce Dept.: Maria Dorsett, (202) 482-6008.

Gabon

Ambassador: Paul Boundoukou-Latha.
Chancery: 2034 20th St. N.W., #200 20009; (202) 797-1000; fax, (202) 332-0668.
U.S. Ambassador in Libreville: Elizabeth Raspolic.
State Dept.: Michael Goldschmidt, (202) 647-1707.
Commerce Dept.: Alicia Robinson, (202) 482-5149.

Gambia

Ambassador: Crispin Grey-Johnson.
Chancery: 1155 15th St. N.W., #1000 20005; (202) 785-1399; fax, (202) 785-1430.

U.S. Ambassador in Banjul: Gerald W. Scott.
State Dept.: Michael Thomas, (202) 647-3469.
Commerce Dept.: Philip Michelini, (202) 482-4388.

Georgia

Ambassador: Tedo Japaridze.
Chancery: 1511 K St. N.W., #424 20005; (202) 393-5959; fax, (202) 393-6060.
Chargé d'Affaires in Tbilisi: Larry Kerr.
State Dept.: Sara Rosenberry, (202) 647-6795.
Commerce Dept.: BISNIS, (202) 482-4655.

Germany

Ambassador: Juergen Chrobog.
Chancery: 4645 Reservoir Rd. N.W. 20007; (202) 298-4000; fax, (202) 298-4249.
U.S. Ambassador in Bonn: John Kornblum.
State Dept.: Janice Weiner, (202) 647-2441.
Commerce Dept.: Brenda Fisher, (202) 482-2435.

Ghana

Ambassador: Kobina Arthur Koomson.
Chancery: 3512 International Dr. N.W. 20008; (202) 686-4520; fax, (202) 686-4527.
U.S. Ambassador in Accra: Edward P. Brynn.
State Dept.: Peter O'Donohue, (202) 647-1596.
Commerce Dept.: Alicia Robinson, (202) 482-5149.

Greece

Ambassador: Loucas Tsilas.
Chancery: 2221 Massachusetts Ave. N.W. 20008; (202) 939-5800; fax, (202) 939-5824.
U.S. Ambassador in Athens: R. Nicholas Burns.
State Dept.: Philip Kosnett, (202) 647-6113.
Commerce Dept.: Ann Corro, (202) 482-3945.

Grenada

Ambassador: Denis G. Antoine.
Chancery: 1701 New Hampshire Ave. N.W. 20009; (202) 265-2561.
U.S. Ambassador: Jeanette Hyde (resident in Bridgetown, Barbados).
State Dept.: Annie Pforzheimer, (202) 647-2620.
Commerce Dept.: Michelle Brooks, (202) 482-1658.

Guatemala

Ambassador: Pedro Miguel Lamport.
Chancery: 2220 R St. N.W. 20008; (202) 745-4952; fax, (202) 745-1908.
U.S. Ambassador in Guatemala City: Donald Planty.

State Dept.: Elise Kleinwaks, (202) 647-4986.
Commerce Dept.: Matt Gaisford, (202) 482-0057.

Guinea

Ambassador: Mohamed Aly Thiam.
Chancery: 2112 Leroy Pl. N.W. 20008; (202) 483-9420; fax, (202) 483-8688.
U.S. Ambassador in Conakry: Tibor Nagy.
State Dept.: Barbara Sand, (202) 647-3407.
Commerce Dept.: Philip Michelini, (202) 482-4388.

Guinea-Bissau

Ambassador: Rufino Jose Mendes.
Chancery: 1511 K St. N.W., #519 20005; (202) 347-3950; fax, (202) 347-3954.
U.S. Ambassador in Bissau: Peggy Blackford.
State Dept.: Peter O'Donohue, (202) 647-1596.
Commerce Dept.: Philip Michelini, (202) 482-4388.

Guyana

Ambassador: Mohammed Ali Odeen Ishmael.
Chancery: 2490 Tracy Pl. N.W. 20008; (202) 265-6900.
U.S. Ambassador in Georgetown: James F. Mack.
State Dept.: Joseph Pomper, (202) 647-2620.
Commerce Dept.: Michelle Brooks, (202) 482-1658.

Haiti

Chargé d'Affaires: Louis Harold Joseph.
Chancery: 2311 Massachusetts Ave. N.W. 20008; (202) 332-4090; fax, (202) 745-7215.
U.S. Ambassador in Port-au-Prince: Timothy M. Carney.
State Dept.: John Rath, (202) 647-5088.
Commerce Dept.: Mark Siegelman, (202) 482-0704.

The Holy See

Ambassador: The Most Reverend Agostino Cacciavillan, apostolic pro-nuncio.
Office: 3339 Massachusetts Ave. N.W. 20008; (202) 333-7121.
U.S. Ambassador in Vatican City: Lindy Boggs.
State Dept.: Jeanne Maloney, (202) 647-3746.

Honduras

Ambassador: Roberto Flores Bermudez.
Chancery: 3007 Tilden St. N.W. 20008; (202) 966-7702; fax, (202) 966-9751.
U.S. Ambassador in Tegucigalpa: James F. Creagan.
State Dept.: William Meara, (202) 647-4986.
Commerce Dept.: Matt Gaisford, (202) 482-0057.

Hungary

Ambassador: Gyorgy Banlaki.
Chancery: 3910 Shoemaker St. N.W. 20008; (202) 362-6730; fax, (202) 966-8135.
U.S. Ambassador in Budapest: Peter F. Tufo.
State Dept.: Liam Wasley, (202) 736-4136.
Commerce Dept.: CEEBIC, (202) 482-2645.

Iceland

Chargé d'Affaires: Sveinn Bjornsson.
Chancery: 1156 15th St. N.W., #1200 20005; (202) 265-6653; fax, (202) 265-6656.
U.S. Ambassador in Reykjavik: Day Olin Mount.
State Dept.: Andrew Silski, (202) 647-8378.
Commerce Dept.: James Devlin, (202) 482-4414.

India

Ambassador: Naresh Chandra.
Chancery: 2107 Massachusetts Ave. N.W. 20008; (202) 939-7000; fax, (202) 483-3972.
U.S. Ambassador in New Delhi: Richard F. Celeste.
State Dept.: Gregory Fukutomi, (202) 647-1450.
Commerce Dept.: ABC, (202) 482-2522.

Indonesia

Chargé d'Affaires: Nazaruddin Nasution.
Chancery: 2020 Massachusetts Ave. N.W. 20036; (202) 775-5200; fax, (202) 775-5365.
U.S. Ambassador in Jakarta: J. Stapleton Roy.
State Dept.: Frank Buckholz, (202) 647-3276.
Commerce Dept.: ABC, (202) 482-2522.

Iran

Chancery: Iran's interests in the United States are represented by Pakistan.
An Iranian Interests Section is located at 2209 Wisconsin Ave. N.W. 20007; (202) 965-4990. Framarz Fathnezhd, chief of section.
U.S. interests in Iran are represented through the Swiss Embassy in Tehran.
State Dept.: Chris Stevens, (202) 647-6111.
Commerce Dept.: Paul Thanos, (202) 482-1860.

Iraq

Chancery: Iraq's interests in the United States are represented by Algeria.
An Iraqi Interests Section is located at 1801 P St. N.W. 20036; (202) 483-7500; fax, (202) 462-5066. Khairi Al-Zubaidi, chief of section.
Embassy in Baghdad temporarily closed.

State Dept.: Andrew Schofer, (202) 647-9448.
Commerce Dept.: Thomas Sams, (202) 482-1860.

Ireland

Ambassador: Sean O'Huiginn.
Chancery: 2234 Massachusetts Ave. N.W. 20008; (202) 462-3939; fax, (202) 232-5993.
U.S. Ambassador in Dublin: Jean Kennedy Smith.
State Dept.: Steven Kashkett, (202) 647-6585.
Commerce Dept.: Robert McLaughlin, (202) 482-3748.

Israel

Ambassador: Eliahu Ben-Elissar.
Chancery: 3514 International Dr. N.W. 20008; (202) 364-5500; fax, (202) 364-5610.
U.S. Ambassador in Tel Aviv: Edward S. Walker Jr.
State Dept.: David Satterfield, (202) 647-3672.
Commerce Dept.: Paul Thanos, (202) 482-1860.

Italy

Ambassador: Ferdinando Salleo.
Chancery: 1601 Fuller St. N.W. 20009; (202) 328-5500; fax, (202) 483-2187.
U.S. Ambassador in Rome: Thomas M. Foglietta.
State Dept.: Clare Pierangelo, (202) 647-4395.
Commerce Dept.: Ann Corro, (202) 482-3945.

Jamaica

Ambassador: Richard Leighton Bernal.
Chancery: 1520 New Hampshire Ave. N.W. 20036; (202) 452-0660; fax, (202) 452-0081.
U.S. Ambassador in Kingston: Stanley L. McLelland.
State Dept.: Kathleen Lange, (202) 647-2621.
Commerce Dept.: Mark Siegelman, (202) 482-0704.

Japan

Ambassador: Kunihiko Saito.
Chancery: 2520 Massachusetts Ave. N.W. 20008; (202) 238-6700; fax, (202) 328-2187.
Chargé d'Affaires in Tokyo: Rust M. Deming.
State Dept.: Cecile Shea, (202) 647-2912.
Commerce Dept.: Eric Kennedy, (202) 482-2427.

Jordan

Ambassador: Marwan Jamil Muasher.
Chancery: 3504 International Dr. N.W. 20008; (202) 966-2664; fax, (202) 966-3110.
U.S. Ambassador in Amman: Wesley W. Egan Jr.
State Dept.: Julia Stanley, (202) 647-1022.
Commerce Dept.: Paul Thanos, (202) 482-1860.

Kazakhstan

Ambassador: Bolat K. Nurgaliyev.
Chancery (temp.): 3421 Massachusetts Ave. N.W. 20007; (202) 333-4504; fax, (202) 333-4509.
U.S. Ambassador in Almaty: A. Elizabeth Jones.
State Dept.: Juan Alsace, (202) 647-6859.
Commerce Dept.: BISNIS, (202) 482-4655.

Kenya

Chargé d'Affaires: Matthew K. M'Ithiri.
Chancery: 2249 R St. N.W. 20008; (202) 387-6101; fax, (202) 462-3829.
U.S. Ambassador in Nairobi: Prudence Bushnell.
State Dept.: Theodore Craig, (202) 647-6485.
Commerce Dept.: Debra Rogers, (202) 482-4228.

Kiribati

U.S. Ambassador: Don Gevirtz (resident in Suva, Fiji).
State Dept.: Theodore Craig, (202) 647-6479.

Korea, Democratic People's Republic of (North)

Ambassador: Li Hyong Chol.
U.N. Mission: 820 E. 2nd Ave., 13th Floor, New York, NY 10017; (212) 972-3105; fax, (212) 972-3154.
State Dept.: John Meakum, (202) 647-9330.

Korea, Republic of (South)

Ambassador: Kun Woo Park.
Chancery: 2450 Massachusetts Ave. N.W. 20008; (202) 939-5600.
U.S. Ambassador in Seoul: Stephen W. Bosworth.
State Dept.: John Meakum, (202) 647-9330.
Commerce Dept.: ABC, (202) 482-2522.

Kuwait

Ambassador: Mohammed Sabah Al-Salim Al-Sabah.
Chancery: 2940 Tilden St. N.W. 20008; (202) 966-0702; fax, (202) 966-0517.
U.S. Ambassador in Kuwait City: James A. Larocco.
State Dept.: Eric Gaudiosi, (202) 647-6571.
Commerce Dept.: Cherie Loustaunau, (202) 482-1860.

Kyrgyzstan

Ambassador: Baktybek Abdrissaev.
Chancery: 1732 Wisconsin Ave. N.W. 20007; (202) 338-5141; fax, (202) 338-5139.
U.S. Ambassador in Bishkek: Anne Marie Sigmund.
State Dept.: Steve Zate, (202) 647-6740.
Commerce Dept.: BISNIS, (202) 482-4655.

Laos

Ambassador: Hiem Phommachanh.

Chancery: 2222 S St. N.W. 20008; (202) 332-6416; fax, (202) 332-4923.

U.S. Ambassador in Vientiane: Wendy Jean Chamberlin.

State Dept.: Sandra Oudkirk, (202) 647-3132.

Commerce Dept.: ABC, (202) 482-2522.

Latvia

Ambassador: Ojars Eriks Kalnins.

Chancery: 4325 17th St. N.W. 20011; (202) 726-8213; fax, (202) 726-6785.

U.S. Ambassador in Riga: Larry C. Napper.

State Dept.: Trevor Evans, (202) 647-8908.

Commerce Dept.: CEEBIC, (202) 482-2645.

Lebanon

Ambassador: Mohammed B. Chatah.

Chancery: 2560 28th St. N.W. 20008; (202) 939-6300; fax, (202) 939-6324.

U.S. Ambassador in Beirut: Richard H. Jones.

State Dept.: Steve Bondy, (202) 647-1030.

Commerce Dept.: Thomas Sams, (202) 482-1860.

Lesotho

Ambassador: Eunice M. Bulane.

Chancery: 2511 Massachusetts Ave. N.W. 20008; (202) 797-5533; fax, (202) 234-6815.

U.S. Ambassador in Maseru: Bismark Myrick.

State Dept.: John Lowell, (202) 647-8434.

Commerce Dept.: Finn Holm-Olsen, (202) 482-4228.

Liberia

Ambassador: Rachel Diggs.

Chancery: 5201 16th St. N.W. 20011; (202) 723-0437.

Chief of Mission in Monrovia: William Milam.

State Dept.: Brian Browne, (202) 647-4512.

Commerce Dept.: Philip Michelini, (202) 482-4388.

Libya

State Dept.: Evan Reede, (202) 647-4674.

Commerce Dept.: David Guglielmi, (202) 482-1860.

Liechtenstein

Chancery: Represented by Switzerland, 2900 Cathedral Ave. N.W. 20008; (202) 745-7900; fax, (202) 387-2564.

U.S. interests represented by the consulate in Zurich, Switzerland. Sheldon I. Krebs, U.S. consul general.

State Dept.: Henry Kelly, (202) 647-2005.

Lithuania

Ambassador: Stasys Sakalauskas.

Chancery: 2622 16th St. N.W. 20009; (202) 234-5860; fax, (202) 328-0466.

U.S. Ambassador in Vilnius: Keith C. Smith.

State Dept.: Trevor Evans, (202) 647-8908.

Commerce Dept.: CEEBIC, (202) 482-2645.

Luxembourg

Ambassador: Alphonse Berns.

Chancery: 2200 Massachusetts Ave. N.W. 20008; (202) 265-4171; fax, (202) 328-8270.

U.S. Ambassador in Luxembourg: James Hormel (nominee).

State Dept.: Oscar DeSoto, (202) 647-6557.

Commerce Dept.: Maria Dorsett, (202) 482-6008.

Macedonia

Amassador: Lubica Z. Acevska.

Chancery: 3050 K St. N.W., #210 20007; (202) 337-3063; fax, (202) 337-3093.

U.S. Ambassador in Skopje: Christopher Robert Hill.

State Dept.: George Frowick, (202) 647-0757.

Commerce Dept.: CEEBIC, (202) 482-2645.

Madagascar

Chargé d'Affaires: Biclair Henri Andrianantoandro.

Chancery: 2374 Massachusetts Ave. N.W. 20008; (202) 265-5525.

U.S. Ambassador in Antananarivo: Vicki J. Huddleston.

State Dept.: Charles Gurney, (202) 647-6473.

Commerce Dept.: Philip Michelini, (202) 482-4388.

Malawi

Ambassador: Willie Chokani.

Chancery: 2408 Massachusetts Ave. N.W. 20008; (202) 797-1007.

U.S. Ambassador in Lilongwe: Peter R. Chaveas.

State Dept.: Philip Drouin, (202) 647-8432.

Commerce Dept.: Debra Rogers, (202) 482-4228.

Malaysia

Ambassador: Dato Dali Mahmud Hashim.

Chancery: 2401 Massachusetts Ave. N.W. 20008; (202) 328-2700; fax, (202) 483-7661.

U.S. Ambassador in Kuala Lumpur: John R. Malott.

State Dept.: Mary Hayes, (202) 647-3276.

Commerce Dept.: ABC, (202) 482-2522.

Maldives

Chief of Mission: Ahmad Rasheed.
Chancery (U.N. Mission): 820 2nd Ave., #800C, New York, NY 10017; (212) 599-6195; fax (212) 661-6405.
U.S. Ambassador: Shaun E. Donnelly (resident in Colombo, Sri Lanka).
State Dept.: Laura Lochman, (202) 647-2351.
Commerce Dept.: John Simmons, (202) 482-2954.

Mali

Ambassador: Cheick Oumar Diarrah.
Chancery: 2130 R St. N.W. 20008; (202) 332-2249; fax, (202) 332-6603.
U.S. Ambassador in Bamako: David P. Rawson.
State Dept.: Natalie Brown, (202) 647-2791.
Commerce Dept.: Philip Michelini, (202) 482-4388.

Malta

Ambassador: Mark Anthony Micallef.
Chancery: 2017 Connecticut Ave. N.W. 20008; (202) 462-3611; fax, (202) 387-5470.
U.S. Ambassador in Valletta: Kathryn L. H. Proffitt.
State Dept.: Debra Glassman, (202) 647-1419.
Commerce Dept.: Ann Corro, (202) 482-3945.

Marshall Islands

Ambassador: Banny De Brum.
Chancery: 2433 Massachusetts Ave. N.W. 20008; (202) 234-5414; fax, (202) 232-3236.
U.S. Ambassador in Majuro: Joan M. Plaisted.
State Dept.: Lynn Sicade, (202) 736-4741.

Mauritania

Ambassador: Ahmed Ould Sid Ahmed.
Chancery: 2129 Leroy Pl. N.W. 20008; (202) 232-5700; fax, (202) 319-2623.
U.S. Ambassador in Nouakchott: Dorothy Myers Sampas.
State Dept.: Barbara Sand, (202) 647-3407.
Commerce Dept.: Philip Michelini, (202) 482-4388.

Mauritius

Ambassador: Chitmansing Jesseramsing.
Chancery: 4301 Connecticut Ave. N.W., #441 20008; (202) 244-1491; fax, (202) 966-0983.
U.S. Ambassador in Port Louis: Harold W. Geisel.
State Dept.: Charles Gurney, (202) 647-6473.
Commerce Dept.: Debra Rogers, (202) 482-4228.

Mexico

Ambassador: Jesus Reyes Heroles.
Chancery: 1911 Pennsylvania Ave. N.W. 20006; (202) 728-1600; fax, (202) 728-1698.
Chargé d'Affaires in Mexico City: Charles Brayshaw.
State Dept.: James Davis, (202) 647-9292.
Commerce Dept.: NAFTA, (202) 482-0305.

Micronesia

Ambassador: Jesse B. Marehalau.
Chancery: 1725 N St. N.W. 20036; (202) 223-4383; fax, (202) 223-4391.
Chargé d'Affaires in Kolonia: Cheryl Martin.
State Dept.: Lynn Sicade, (202) 736-4741.

Moldova

Ambassador: Nicolae Tau.
Chancery: 2101 S St. N.W. 20008; (202) 667-1130; fax, (202) 667-1204.
U.S. Ambassador in Chisinau: John Todd Stewart.
State Dept.: David Hanzlik, (202) 647-6733.
Commerce Dept.: BISNIS, (202) 482-4655.

Monaco

Consul: Maguy Maccario-Doyle.
Chancery (consulate): 565 5th Ave., 23rd Floor, New York, NY 10017; (212) 286-0500; fax, (212) 286-1574.
Relations with Monaco are maintained by the U.S. Embassy in Paris, France. Felix George Rohatyn, U.S. ambassador in Paris.
State Dept.: Geoffrey Dafler, (202) 647-4361.

Mongolia

Ambassador: Jalbuu Choinhor.
Chancery: 2833 M St. N.W. 20007; (202) 333-7117; fax, (202) 298-9227.
U.S. Ambassador in Ulaanbaatar: Alfonse La Porta.
State Dept.: Pamela Slutz, (202) 647-6772.
Commerce Dept.: ABC, (202) 482-2522.

Morocco

Ambassador: Mohamed Benaissa.
Chancery: 1601 21st St. N.W. 20009; (202) 462-7979; fax, (202) 265-0161.
U.S. Ambassador in Rabat: Edward M. Gabriel.
State Dept.: Laura Byergo, (202) 647-4675.
Commerce Dept.: David Guglielmi, (202) 482-1860.

Mozambique

Ambassador: Marcus Geraldo Namashulua.
Chancery: 1990 M St. N.W., #570 20036; (202) 293-7146; fax, (202) 835-0245.
U.S. Ambassador in Maputo: Dean Curran.
State Dept.: Stephen Vann, (202) 647-8434.
Commerce Dept.: Debra Rogers, (202) 482-4228.

Myanmar (Burma)

Ambassador: Tin Winn.
Chancery: 2300 S St. N.W. 20008; (202) 332-9044; fax, (202) 332-9046.
U.S. Ambassador in Rangoon: Kent M. Weideman.
State Dept.: Chris Kraft, (202) 647-0064.
Commerce Dept.: ABC, (202) 482-2522.

Namibia

Ambassador: Veiccoh K. Nghiwete.
Chancery: 1605 New Hampshire Ave. N.W. 20009; (202) 986-0540; fax, (202) 986-0443.
U.S. Ambassador in Windhoek: George F. Ward Jr.
State Dept.: Philip Drouin, (202) 647-8432.
Commerce Dept.: Debra Rogers, (202) 482-4228.

Nauru

U.S. Ambassador: Edward Perkins (resident in Australia).
State Dept.: Patricia Stigliani, (202) 736-4741.

Nepal

Chargé d'Affaires: Lava Kumar Devacota.
Chancery: 2131 Leroy Pl. N.W. 20008; (202) 667-4550; fax, (202) 667-5534.
U.S. Ambassador in Kathmandu: Sandra L. Vogelgesang.
State Dept.: Erik Hall, (202) 647-2351.
Commerce Dept.: ABC, (202) 482-2522.

Netherlands

Ambassador: Joris M. Vos.
Chancery: 4200 Linnean Ave. N.W. 20008; (202) 244-5300; fax, (202) 362-3430.
U.S. Ambassador in The Hague: K. Terry Dornbush.
State Dept.: Oscar DeSoto, (202) 647-6557.
Commerce Dept.: Maria Dorsett, (202) 482-6008.

New Zealand

Ambassador: L. John Wood.
Chancery: 37 Observatory Circle N.W. 20008; (202) 328-4800.
U.S. Ambassador in Wellington: Josiah H. Beeman.

State Dept.: Dan Larsen, (202) 647-9691.
Commerce Dept.: ABC, (202) 482-2522.

Nicaragua

Ambassador: Francisco Javier Aguirre Sacasa.
Chancery: 1627 New Hampshire Ave. N.W. 20009; (202) 939-6570.
U.S. Ambassador in Managua: Lino Gutierrez.
State Dept.: David Alrid, (202) 647-4975.
Commerce Dept.: Mark Siegelman, (202) 482-0704.

Niger

Ambassador: Joseph Diatta.
Chancery: 2204 R St. N.W. 20008; (202) 483-4224.
U.S. Ambassador in Niamey: Charles Cecil.
State Dept.: Natalie Brown, (202) 647-2791.
Commerce Dept.: Philip Michelini, (202) 482-4388.

Nigeria

Ambassador: Wakili Hassan Adamu.
Chancery: 1333 16th St. N.W. 20036; (202) 986-8400.
U.S. Ambassador in Lagos: William H. Twaddell.
State Dept.: Dundas McCullough, (202) 647-1597.
Commerce Dept.: Alicia Robinson, (202) 482-5149.

Norway

Ambassador: Tom Eric Vraalsen.
Chancery: 2720 34th St. N.W. 20008; (202) 333-6000; fax, (202) 337-0870.
U.S. Ambassador in Oslo: David Hermelin.
State Dept.: Ingrid Kollist, (202) 647-6582.
Commerce Dept.: James Devlin, (202) 482-4414.

Oman

Ambassador: Abdulla Moh'd Aqueel Al-Dhahab.
Chancery: 2535 Belmont Rd. N.W. 20008; (202) 387-1980; fax, (202) 745-4933.
U.S. Ambassador in Muscat: Frances D. Cook.
State Dept.: Greg Hicks, (202) 647-6558.
Commerce Dept.: Cherie Loustaunau, (202) 482-1860.

Pakistan

Ambassador: Riez H. Khokhar.
Chancery: 2315 Massachusetts Ave. N.W. 20008; (202) 939-6205; fax, (202) 387-0484.
U.S. Ambassador in Islamabad: Thomas W. Simons Jr.
State Dept.: Edward J. Fendley, (202) 647-9823.
Commerce Dept.: ABC, (202) 482-2522.

Palau

Ambassador: Hersey Kyota.
Chancery: 1150 18th St. N.W., #750 20036; (202) 452-6814; fax, (202) 452-6281.
U.S. Ambassador in Korror: Thomas C. Hubbard.
State Dept.: Constance Arvis, (202) 647-0108.

Panama

Ambassador: Eduardo Morgan Gonzalez.
Chancery: 2862 McGill Terrace N.W. 20008; (202) 483-1407.
U.S. Ambassador in Panama City: William J. Hughes.
State Dept.: David Noble, (202) 647-4986.
Commerce Dept.: Matt Gaisford, (202) 482-0057.

Papua New Guinea

Ambassador: Nagora Y. Bogan.
Chancery: 1615 New Hampshire Ave. N.W., 3rd Floor 20009; (202) 745-3680; fax, (202) 745-3679.
U.S. Ambassador in Port Moresby: Arma Jean Karaer.
State Dept.: Patricia Stigliani, (202) 736-4741.

Paraguay

Ambassador: Jorge G. Prieto.
Chancery: 2400 Massachusetts Ave. N.W. 20008; (202) 483-6960; fax, (202) 234-4508.
U.S. Ambassador in Asunción: Maura Hardy.
State Dept.: Steven Liston, (202) 647-2401.
Commerce Dept.: Carrie Clark, (202) 482-0477.

Peru

Ambassador: Ricardo V. Luna.
Chancery: 1700 Massachusetts Ave. N.W. 20036; (202) 833-9860; fax, (202) 659-8124.
U.S. Ambassador in Lima: Dennis C. Jett.
State Dept.: Andrew Simkim, (202) 647-3360.
Commerce Dept.: Tom Welch, (202) 482-0475.

Philippines

Ambassador: Raul Chaves Rabe.
Chancery: 1600 Massachusetts Ave. N.W. 20036; (202) 467-9300; fax, (202) 328-7614.
U.S. Ambassador in Manila: Thomas C. Hubbard.
State Dept.: Philip Antweiler, (202) 647-3276.
Commerce Dept.: ABC, (202) 482-2522.

Poland

Ambassador: Jerzy Kozminski.
Chancery: 2640 16th St. N.W. 20009; (202) 234-3800; fax, (202) 328-6271.

U.S. Ambassador in Warsaw: Daniel Fried.
State Dept.: John Spilsbury, (202) 647-4139.
Commerce Dept.: CEEBIC, (202) 482-2645.

Portugal

Ambassador: Fernando Andresen Guimaraes.
Chancery: 2125 Kalorama Rd. N.W. 20008; (202) 328-8610; fax, (202) 462-3726.
U.S. Ambassador in Lisbon: Gerald S. McGowan.
State Dept.: Jean Maloney, (202) 647-3746.
Commerce Dept.: Ann Corro, (202) 482-3945.

Qatar

Ambassador: Saad Mohamed Al-Kobarsi.
Chancery: 4200 Wisconsin Ave. N.W. 20016; (202) 274-1600.
U.S. Ambassador in Doha: Patrick N. Theros.
State Dept.: Richard Bell, (202) 647-6572.
Commerce Dept.: Cherie Loustaunau, (202) 482-1860.

Romania

Ambassador: Mircea Dan Geoana.
Chancery: 1607 23rd St. N.W. 20008; (202) 332-4846; fax, (202) 232-4748.
U.S. Ambassador in Bucharest: James C. Rosapepe.
State Dept.: Katherine Kay, (202) 647-4272.
Commerce Dept.: CEEBIC, (202) 482-2645.

Russia

Ambassador: Yuli M. Vorontsov.
Chancery: 2650 Wisconsin Ave. N.W. 20007; (202) 298-5700; fax, (202) 298-5735.
U.S. Ambassador in Moscow: James F. Collins.
State Dept.: Julia Fuller, (202) 647-6763.
Commerce Dept.: BISNIS, (202) 482-4655.

Rwanda

Ambassador: Theogene N. Rudasingwa.
Chancery: 1714 New Hampshire Ave. N.W. 20009; (202) 232-2882; fax, (202) 232-4544.
U.S. Ambassador in Kigali: Robert Gribbin III.
State Dept.: Ava Rogers, (202) 647-1707.
Commerce Dept.: Philip Michelini, (202) 482-4388.

Saint Kitts and Nevis

Ambassador: Osbert W. Liburd.
Chancery: 3216 New Mexico Ave. N.W. 20016; (202) 686-2636; fax, (202) 686-5740.
U.S. Ambassador: Jeanette Hyde (resident in Bridgetown, Barbados).

State Dept.: Annie Pforzheimer, (202) 647-2620.
Commerce Dept.: Michelle Brooks, (202) 482-1658.

Saint Lucia

Chargé d'Affaires: Juliet Elaine Mallet Phillip.
Chancery: 3216 New Mexico Ave. N.W. 20016; (202) 364-6792; fax, (202) 364-6728.
U.S. Ambassador: Jeanette Hyde (resident in Bridgetown, Barbados).
State Dept.: Annie Pforzheimer, (202) 647-2620.
Commerce Dept.: Michelle Brooks, (202) 482-1658.

Saint Vincent and the Grenadines

Ambassador: Kingsley C. A. Layne.
Chancery: 3216 New Mexico Ave. N.W. 20016; (202) 364-6730; fax, (202) 364-6736.
U.S. Ambassador: Jeanette Hyde (resident in Bridgetown, Barbados).
State Dept.: Annie Pforzheimer, (202) 647-2620.
Commerce Dept.: Michelle Brooks, (202) 482-1658.

Samoa

Ambassador: Tuiloma Neroni Slade.
Chancery (U.N. Mission): 820 2nd Ave., #800D New York, NY 10017; (212) 599-6196; fax, (212) 599-0797.
U.S. Ambassador: Josiah H. Beeman (resident in Wellington, New Zealand).
State Dept.: Patricia Stigliani, (202) 736-4741.

San Marino

Consul: Baron Enrico di Porti-Nova, 1899 L St. N.W. 20036; (202) 223-3517.
Relations with San Marino are maintained by the U.S. Consulate in Florence, Italy. Louis McCall, U.S. consul general.
State Dept.: Clare Pierangelo, (202) 647-4395.

Sao Tome and Principe

Chargé d'Affaires: Domingos Ferreira.
Chancery (U.N. Mission): 122 E. 42nd St., #1604, New York, NY 10168; (212) 697-4211; fax, (212) 687-8389.
U.S. Ambassador: Elizabeth Raspolic (resident in Libreville, Gabon).
State Dept.: Michael Goldschmidt, (202) 647-1707.
Commerce Dept.: Philip Michelini, (202) 482-4388.

Saudi Arabia

Ambassador: Prince Bandar Bin Sultan.
Chancery: 601 New Hampshire Ave. N.W. 20037; (202) 342-3800.
U.S. Ambassador in Riyadh: Wyche Fowler Jr.
State Dept.: Mark Desjardins, (202) 647-7550.
Commerce Dept.: David Guglielmi, (202) 482-1860.

Senegal

Ambassador: Mamadou Mansour Seck.
Chancery: 2112 Wyoming Ave. N.W. 20008; (202) 234-0540.
U.S. Ambassador in Dakar: Dane F. Smith Jr.
State Dept.: Barbara Sand, (202) 647-3407.
Commerce Dept.: Philip Michelini, (202) 482-4388.

Serbia-Montenegro (See Yugoslavia)

Seychelles

Chargé d'Affaires: Claude Morel.
Chancery (U.N. Mission): 820 2nd Ave., #900F, New York, NY 10017; (212) 972-1785; fax, (212) 972-1786.
U.S. Ambassador: Harry Geisel (resident in Port Louis, Mauritius).
State Dept.: Charles Gurney, (202) 647-6473.
Commerce Dept.: Chandra Watkins, (202) 482-4564.

Sierra Leone

Ambassador: John Ernest Leigh.
Chancery: 1701 19th St. N.W. 20009; (202) 939-9261; fax, (202) 483-1793.
U.S. Ambassador in Freetown: John L. Hirsch.
State Dept.: Michael Thomas, (202) 647-3469.
Commerce Dept.: Philip Michelini, (202) 482-4388.

Singapore

Ambassador: Heng-Chee Chan.
Chancery: 3501 International Pl. N.W. 20008; (202) 537-3100; fax, (202) 537-0876.
U.S. Ambassador in Singapore: Steven J. Green.
State Dept.: Ike Reed, (202) 647-3276.
Commerce Dept.: ABC, (202) 482-2522.

Slovakia

Ambassador: Branislav Lichardus.
Chancery (temp.): 2201 Wisconsin Ave. N.W., #250 20007; (202) 965-5161; fax, (202) 965-5166.
U.S. Ambassador in Bratislava: Ralph Johnson.

State Dept.: Edward Johns, (202) 647-3191.
Commerce Dept.: CEEBIC, (202) 482-2645.

Slovenia

Ambassador: Dimitrij Rupel.
Chancery: 1525 New Hampshire Ave. N.W. 20036; (202) 667-5363; fax, (202) 667-4563.
U.S. Ambassador in Ljubljana: Victor Jackovich.
State Dept.: Paul Pfeuffer, (202) 736-7152.
Commerce Dept.: CEEBIC, (202) 482-2645.

Solomon Islands

Ambassador: Rex Stephen Horoi.
Chancery (U.N. Mission): 820 2nd Ave., #800, New York, NY 10017; (212) 599-6193; fax, (212) 661-8925.
U.S. Ambassador: Arma Jean Karaer (resident in Port Moresby, Papua New Guinea).
State Dept.: Patricia Stigliani, (202) 736-4741.

Somalia

Washington embassy ceased operations May 8, 1991.
Ambassador: Vacant.
U.S. embassy in Mogadishu is unstaffed.
State Dept.: George Fredrick, (202) 647-6453.
Commerce Dept.: Philip Michelini, (202) 482-4388.

South Africa

Ambassador: Franklin Abraham Sonn.
Chancery: 3051 Massachusetts Ave. N.W. 20008; (202) 232-4400; fax, (202) 265-1607.
U.S. Ambassador in Pretoria: James A. Joseph.
State Dept.: John Scott, (202) 647-9429.
Commerce Dept.: Finn Holm-Olsen, (202) 482-5148.

Spain

Ambassador: Antonio Oyarzabal.
Chancery: 2375 Pennsylvania Ave. N.W. 20037; (202) 452-0100; fax, (202) 833-5670.
U.S. Ambassador in Madrid: Richard N. Gardner.
State Dept.: Debra Glassman, (202) 647-1419.
Commerce Dept.: Ann Corro, (202) 482-3945.

Sri Lanka

Ambassador: Warnasena Rasaputram.
Chancery: 2148 Wyoming Ave. N.W. 20008; (202) 483-4025; fax, (202) 232-7181.
U.S. Ambassador in Colombo: Shaun E. Donnelly.
State Dept.: Laura Lochman, (202) 647-2351.
Commerce Dept.: ABC, (202) 482-2522.

Sudan

Ambassador: Mahdi Ibrahim Mohamed.
Chancery: 2210 Massachusetts Ave. N.W. 20008; (202) 338-8565; fax, (202) 667-2406.
Chargé d'Affaires in Khartoum: Don Teitelbaum.
State Dept.: Stephen Schwartz, (202) 647-9742.
Commerce Dept.: Philip Michelini, (202) 482-4388.

Suriname

Ambassador: Arnold T. Halfhide.
Chancery: 4301 Connecticut Ave. N.W., #460 20008; (202) 244-7488; fax, (202) 244-5878.
U.S. Ambassador in Paramaribo: Dennis K. Hays.
State Dept.: Linda Brown, (202) 647-2621.
Commerce Dept.: Michelle Brooks, (202) 482-1658.

Swaziland

Ambassador: Mary M. Kanya.
Chancery: 3400 International Dr. N.W. 20008; (202) 362-6683; fax, (202) 244-8059.
U.S. Ambassador in Mbabane: Alan R. McKee.
State Dept.: John Lowell, (202) 647-8434.
Commerce Dept.: Debra Rogers, (202) 482-4228.

Sweden

Ambassador: Rolf Ekeus.
Chancery: 1501 M St. N.W. 20005; (202) 467-2600; fax, (202) 467-2699.
U.S. Ambassador in Stockholm: Lyndon L. Olson Jr.
State Dept.: Josef Ruth, (202) 647-8431.
Commerce Dept.: James Devlin, (202) 482-4414.

Switzerland

Ambassador: Alfred Defago.
Chancery: 2900 Cathedral Ave. N.W. 20008; (202) 745-7900; fax, (202) 387-2564.
U.S. Ambassador in Bern: Madeleine M. Kunin.
State Dept.: John Feeney, (202) 647-2682.
Commerce Dept.: John Larsen, (202) 482-2434.

Syria

Ambassador: Walid Al-Moualem.
Chancery: 2215 Wyoming Ave. N.W. 20008; (202) 232-6313; fax, (202) 234-9548.
U.S. Ambassador in Damascus: Christopher W. S. Ross.
State Dept.: E. Candace Putnam, (202) 647-1131.
Commerce Dept.: Thomas Sams, (202) 482-1860.

Taiwan

Representation maintained by the Coordination Council for North American Affairs, 4201 Wisconsin Ave. N.W. 20016; (202) 895-1800.

The United States maintains unofficial relations with Taiwan through the American Institute in Taiwan.

Washington office: 1700 N. Moore St., Arlington, VA 22209-1996; (703) 525-8474; Richard Bush III, managing director.

State Dept.: Michael Finegan, (202) 647-7711.

Commerce Dept.: ABC, (202) 482-2522.

Tajikistan

U.S. Ambassador in Dushanbe: R. Grant Smith.

State Dept.: Daria Fane, (202) 647-6757.

Commerce Dept.: BISNIS, (202) 482-4655.

Tanzania

Ambassador: Mustafa Salim Nyang'Anyi.

Chancery: 2139 R St. N.W. 20008; (202) 939-6125; fax, (202) 797-7408.

U.S. Ambassador in Dar Es Salaam: J. Brady Anderson.

State Dept.: Charles Gurney, (202) 647-6473.

Commerce Dept.: Debra Rogers, (202) 482-4228.

Thailand

Ambassador: Nitya Pibulsonggram.

Chancery: 1024 Wisconsin Ave. N.W. 20007; (202) 944-3600; fax, (202) 944-3611.

U.S. Ambassador in Bangkok: William H. Itoh.

State Dept.: Chris Rich, (202) 647-0064.

Commerce Dept.: ABC, (202) 482-2522.

Togo

Ambassador: Kossivi Osseyi.

Chancery: 2208 Massachusetts Ave. N.W. 20008; (202) 234-4212; fax, (202) 232-3190.

U.S. Ambassador in Lomé: Brenda Schoonover.

State Dept.: Ann Sides, (202) 647-1540.

Commerce Dept.: Alicia Robinson, (202) 482-5149.

Tonga

Ambassador: Akosita Fineanganofo (resident in London).

U.S. Ambassador: Don Gevirtz (resident in Suva, Fiji).

State Dept.: Patricia Stigliani, (202) 736-4741.

Trinidad and Tobago

Ambassador: Michael Arneaud.

Chancery: 1708 Massachusetts Ave. N.W. 20036; (202) 467-6490; fax, (202) 785-3130.

U.S. Ambassador in Port-of-Spain: Edward E. Schumaker III.

State Dept.: Joseph Pomper, (202) 647-2620.

Commerce Dept.: Michelle Brooks, (202) 482-1658.

Tunisia

Ambassador: Noureddine Mejdoub.

Chancery: 1515 Massachusetts Ave. N.W. 20005; (202) 862-1850.

U.S. Ambassador in Tunis: Robin Lynn Raphael.

State Dept.: Evan Reede, (202) 647-4674.

Commerce Dept.: David Guglielmi, (202) 482-1860.

Turkey

Ambassador: Nuzhet Kandemir.

Chancery: 1714 Massachusetts Ave. N.W. 20036; (202) 659-8200.

U.S. Ambassador in Ankara: Mark Robert Parris.

State Dept.: Stephen Klemp, (202) 647-6114.

Commerce Dept.: Ann Corro, (202) 482-3945.

Turkmenistan

Ambassador: Halil Ugur.

Chancery: 2207 Massachusetts Ave. N.W. 20008; (202) 588-1500; fax, (202) 588-0697.

U.S. Ambassador in Ashgabat: Michael W. Cotter.

State Dept.: Adam Sterling, (202) 647-6831.

Commerce Dept.: BISNIS, (202) 482-4655.

Tuvalu

U.S. Ambassador: Don Gevirtz (resident in Suva, Fiji).

State Dept.: Patricia Stigliani, (202) 736-4741.

Uganda

Ambassador: Edith G. Ssempala.

Chancery: 5911 16th St. N.W. 20011; (202) 726-7100; fax, (202) 726-1727.

U.S. Ambassador in Kampala: E. Michael Southwick.

State Dept.: Theodore Craig, (202) 647-6479.

Commerce Dept.: Debra Rogers, (202) 482-4228.

Ukraine

Ambassador: Yuriy M. Shcherbak.

Chancery: 3350 M St. N.W. 20007; (202) 333-0606; fax, (202) 333-0817.

U.S. Ambassador in Kiev: Steven K. Piper.

State Dept.: Edward Salazar, (202) 647-8671.

Commerce Dept.: BISNIS, (202) 482-4655.

United Arab Emirates

Ambassador: Mohammad Bin Hussein Al-Shaali.
Chancery: 1255 22nd St. N.W., #700 20037; (202) 955-7999.
U.S. Ambassador in Abu Dhabi: David Litt.
State Dept.: Richard Bell, (202) 647-6572.
Commerce Dept.: David Guglielmi, (202) 482-1860.

United Kingdom

Ambassador: Christopher Meyer.
Chancery: 3100 Massachusetts Ave. N.W. 20008; (202) 588-6500; fax, (202) 588-7870.
U.S. Ambassador in London: Philip Lader.
State Dept.: Val Martinez, (202) 647-6587.
Commerce Dept.: Robert McLaughlin, (202) 482-3748.

Uruguay

Ambassador: Alvaro Diez de Medina.
Chancery: 2715 M St. N.W. 20007; (202) 331-1313; fax, (202) 331-8142.
U.S. Ambassador in Montevideo: Christopher C. Ashby.
State Dept.: Robert Benson, (202) 647-2296.
Commerce Dept.: Roger Turner, (202) 482-0703.

Uzbekistan

Ambassador: Sodiq Safaev.
Chancery: 1746 Massachusetts Ave. N.W. 20036; (202) 887-5300; fax, (202) 293-6804.
U.S. Ambassador in Tashkent: Joseph A. Presel.
State Dept.: Ladd Connell, (202) 647-6765.
Commerce Dept.: BISNIS, (202) 482-4655.

Vanuatu

U.S. Ambassador: Arma Jean Karaer (resident in Port Moresby, Papua New Guinea).
State Dept.: Patricia Stigliani, (202) 736-4741.

Venezuela

Ambassador: Pedro Luis Echeverria.
Chancery: 1099 30th St. N.W. 20007; (202) 342-2214; fax, (202) 342-6820.
U.S. Ambassador in Caracas: John F. Maisto.
State Dept.: Cynthia Akuetteh, (202) 647-3023.
Commerce Dept.: Tom Welch, (202) 482-0475.

Vietnam

Ambassador:: Bang Le.
Chancery: 1233 20th St. N.W., #400 20036; (202) 861-0737; fax, (202) 861-0917.
U.S. Ambassador in Hanoi: Pete Peterson.
State Dept.: Don Coleman, (202) 647-3133.
Commerce Dept.: ABC, (202) 482-2522.

Western Samoa (See Samoa)

Yemen

Ambassador: Abdulwahab A. Al-Hajjri.
Chancery: 2600 Virginia Ave. N.W., #705 20037; (202) 965-4760; fax, (202) 337-2017.
U.S. Ambassador in Sanaa: Barbara K. Bodine.
State Dept.: Greg Hicks, (202) 647-6558.
Commerce Dept.: Cherie Loustaunau, (202) 482-1860.

Yugoslavia

Chargé d'Affaires: Nebojsa Vujovic.
Chancery: 2410 California St. N.W. 20008; (202) 462-6566.
U.S. Ambassador in Belgrade: Richard M. Miles.
State Dept.: Matthew Palmer, (202) 736-7478.
Commerce Dept.: CEEBIC, (202) 482-2645.

Zaire (See Congo)

Zambia

Ambassador: Dunstan Weston Kamana.
Chancery: 2419 Massachusetts Ave. N.W. 20008; (202) 265-9717; fax, (202) 332-0826.
U.S. Ambassador in Lusaka: Arlene Render.
State Dept.: Philip Drouin, (202) 647-8432.
Commerce Dept.: Debra Rogers, (202) 482-4228.

Zimbabwe

Ambassador: Amos Bernard Muvengwa Midzi.
Chancery: 1608 New Hampshire Ave. N.W. 20009; (202) 332-7100; fax, (202) 483-9326.
U.S. Ambassador in Harare: Tom McDonald.
State Dept.: Patricia Kim-Scott, (202) 647-8432.
Commerce Dept.: Debra Rogers, (202) 482-4228.

Freedom of Information Act

Public access to government information remains a key issue in Washington. In 1966 Congress passed legislation to broaden access: the Freedom of Information Act (PL 89–487; codified in 1967 by PL 90–23). Amendments to expand access even further were passed into law over President Ford's veto in 1974 (PL 93–502).

Several organizations in Washington specialize in access to government information. See "Freedom of Information" section in the Communications and the Media chapter for details.

1966 Act

The 1966 act requires executive branch agencies and independent commissions of the federal government to make records, reports, policy statements, and staff manuals available to citizens who request them, unless the materials fall into one of nine exempted categories:

- secret national security or foreign policy information
- internal personnel practices
- information exempted by law (e.g., income tax returns)
- trade secrets, other confidential commercial or financial information
- inter-agency or intra-agency memos
- personal information, personnel, or medical files
- law enforcement investigatory information
- information related to reports on financial institutions
- geological and geophysical information

1974 Amendments

Further clarification of the rights of citizens to gain access to government information came in late 1974, when Congress enacted legislation to remove some of the obstacles that the bureaucracy had erected since 1966. Included in the amendments are provisions that:

- Require federal agencies to publish their indexes of final opinions on settlements of internal cases, policy statements, and administrative staff manuals. If, under special circumstances, the indexes are not published, they are to be furnished to any person requesting them for the cost of duplication. The 1966 law simply required agencies to make such indexes available for public inspection and copying.
- Require agencies to release unlisted documents to someone requesting them with a reasonable description (a change designed to ensure that an agency could not refuse to provide material simply because the applicant could not give its precise title).
- Direct each agency to publish a uniform set of fees for providing documents at the cost of finding and copying them. The amendment allows waiver or reduction of those fees when in the public interest.
- Set time limits for agency responses to requests: 10 working days for an initial request; 20 working days for an appeal from an initial refusal to produce documents; a possible 10–working-day extension which can be granted only once in a single case.
- Set a 30–day time limit for an agency response to a complaint filed in court under the act; provides that such cases should be given priority attention by the courts at the appeal, as well as the trial, level.
- Empower federal district courts to order agencies to produce withheld documents and to examine the contested materials privately *(in camera)* to determine if they are properly exempted.
- Require annual agency reports to Congress, including a list of all agency decisions to withhold information requested under the act; the reasons; the appeals; the results; all relevant rules; the fee schedule; and the names of officials responsible for each denial of information.
- Allow courts to order the government to pay attorneys' fees and court costs for persons winning suits against them under the act.
- Authorize a court to find that an agency employee has acted capriciously or arbitrarily in withholding information; disciplinary action is determined by Civil Service Commission proceedings.
- Amend and clarify the wording of the national defense and national security exemption to make

clear that it applies only to *properly* classified information.

• Amend the wording of the law enforcement exemption to allow withholding of information which, if disclosed, would interfere with enforcement proceedings, deprive someone of a fair trial or hearing, invade personal privacy in an unwarranted way, disclose the identity of a confidential source, disclose investigative techniques, or endanger law enforcement personnel; protect from disclosure all information from a confidential source obtained by a criminal law enforcement agency or a lawful national security investigation.

• Provide that separable non-exempt portions of requested material be released after deletion of the exempt portions.

• Require an annual report from the attorney general to Congress.

1984 Amendments

In 1984 Congress enacted legislation that clarified the requirements of the Central Intelligence Agency to respond to citizen requests for information. Included in the amendments are provisions that:

• Authorize the CIA to close from FOIA review certain operational files that contain information on the identities of sources and methods. The measure removed the requirement that officials search the files for material that might be subject to disclosure.

• Reverse a ruling by the Justice Dept. and the Office of Management and Budget that invoked the Privacy Act to deny individuals FOIA access to information about themselves in CIA records. HR 5164 required the CIA to search files in response to FOIA requests by individuals for information about themselves.

• Require the CIA to respond to FOIA requests for information regarding covert actions or suspected CIA improprieties.

All agencies of the executive branch have issued regulations to implement the Freedom of Information Act. To locate a specific agency's regulations, consult the general index of the *Code of Federal Regulations* under "Information availability."

Electronic Freedom of Information Act of 1996

In 1996 Congress enacted legislation which clarified that electronic documents are subject to the same Freedom of Information Act (FOIA) disclosure rules as printed documents. The 1996 law also requires federal agencies to make records available to the public in various electronic formats, such as e-mail, compact disc, and files accessible via the Internet. An additional measure seeks to improve the government's response time on FOIA requests by requiring agencies to report annually on the number of pending requests and how long it will take to respond.

Privacy Act

To protect citizens from invasions of privacy by the federal government, Congress passed the Privacy Act of 1974 (PL 93–579). The act permitted individuals for the first time to inspect information about themselves contained in federal agency files and to challenge, correct, or amend the material. The major provisions of the act:

• Permit an individual to have access to personal information in federal agency files and to correct or amend that information.

• Prevent an agency maintaining a file on an individual from making it available to another agency without the individual's consent.

• Require federal agencies to keep records that are necessary, lawful, accurate, and current, and to disclose the existence of all data banks and files containing information on individuals.

• Bar the transfer of personal information to other federal agencies for non-routine use without the individual's prior consent or written request.

• Require agencies to keep accurate accountings of transfers of records and make them available to the individual.

• Prohibit agencies from keeping records on an individual's exercise of First Amendment rights unless the records are authorized by statute, approved by the individual, or within the scope of an official law enforcement activity.

• Permit an individual to seek injunctive relief to correct or amend a record maintained by an agency and permit the individual to recover actual damages when an agency acts in a negligent manner that is "willful or intentional."

• Exempt from disclosure: records maintained by the Central Intelligence Agency; records maintained by law enforcement agencies; Secret Service records; statistical information; names of persons providing material used for determining the qualification of an individual for federal government service; federal testing material; and National Archives historical records.

• Provide that an officer or employee of an agency who violates provisions of the act be fined no more than $5,000.

• Prohibit an agency from selling or renting an individual's name or address for mailing list use.

• Require agencies to submit to Congress and to the Office of Management and Budget any plan to establish or alter records.

• Virtually all agencies of the executive branch have issued regulations to implement the Privacy Act. To locate a specific agency's regulations, consult the general index of the *Code of Federal Regulations* under "Privacy Act."

Name Index

In the name index, page numbers in **boldface** indicate the main entries of senators and representatives.

Collie, H. Cris, 220
Collins, Allyson, 457
Collins, Dennis, 781
Collins, Francis S., 394
Collins, James F., 892
Collins, Julie, 763
Collins, Keith J., 36
Collins, Kelly, 391
Collins, Kenneth L., 197, 199
Collins, Lionel, 773
Collins, Mac, R-Ga., 723, 746–747, 750, **759**
Collins, Mary Jean, 711
Collins, Paul, 796
Collins, Samuel J., 265, 267
Collins, Susan, R-Maine, 150, 235, 338, 454, 508, 571, 724, 812–813, 814, 815, 818, **822**
Collom, Jonathan, 294
Colorado, Antonio, 482
Colosimo, Andy, 819
Colton, Kent W., 417, 431, 435
Colvert, Angela, 834
Colvin, Joe, 265
Combest, Larry, R-Texas, 36, 44, 302, 313, 412, 726, 727–728, 743, **759**
Comedy, Dwight, 698
Comer, Mary, 825
Comley, Richard, 584
Commenator, Carl, 547
Conaboy, Richard C., 516
Conaty, Joseph, 181
Conaway, Mary Sue, 882
Conccklin, Bert M., 328
Condeelis, Mary, 148, 473
Condit, Gary A., D-Calif., 696, 722, 727–728, 734–735, **759**
Condit, Sandra R., 791
Condit, William, 245, 257, 269, 304, 306, 309, 607
Condon, Charles M., 877
Conell, Marion F., 420
Conelly, Mary, 833
Conklin, Donna, 757
Conley, Sydney M., 324
Connell, Ladd, 896
Connell, Liz, 695
Connell, Susan, 786
Connelly, Barry, 148
Connelly, Richard J., 152, 578
Conner, Charles S., 50
Conner, Roger, 495
Connor, Tim, 134
Conover, Judy, 203, 692
Conrad, Joseph, Jr., 33
Conrad, Kent, D-N.D., 725, 805, 808, 811, 813, 815, 816, **823**
Conrad, Rodrick, 4
Conroy, Chris, 761
Conroy, Coleman J., 760
Constantine, Thomas A., 458, 511
Constantino, James, 676
Contee, Martha, 13
Contreares, Thomas J., Jr., 385, 532, 600
Conway, John T., 266

Conway, Sean P., 819
Conyers, John, Jr., D-Mich., 724, 737–738, **759**
Conzelman, Jim, 784
Cooch, Anthony, 325
Cook, Ann, 799
Cook, Emily, 631
Cook, Frances D., 891
Cook, Harry N., 672
Cook, John, 259
Cook, Kenneth A., 54, 278
Cook, Merrill, R-Utah, 726, 730–731, 741–742, 744–745, **759**
Cook, Michael B., 298
Cook, Peter L., 315
Cook, Rebecca McDonell, 875
Cook, Thomas M., 66
Cook, Virginia, 758
Cooksey, John, R-La., 723, 727–728, 744–746, **759**
Cooksie, Caroline B., 53, 412
Cooney, Manus, 99, 139, 162, 352, 493, 498, 505, 509, 518, 581
Cooney, Mike, 875
Cooney, Nelson J., 422
Coonrod, Robert T., 73
Coonts, John J., 425, 432
Cooper, Barbara, 796
Cooper, Ben, 262
Cooper, Henry, 567
Cooper, Jo, 302
Cooper, Kent, 690, 691
Cooper, Scott P., 667, 670
Cooper, Yvonne, 96
Cooper-Levy, Herbert J., 435
Cooper-Smith, Jeffrey P., 43, 603, 694
Cope, James D., 364
Copeland, Louis, 786
Copeland, Tamara Lucas, 635
Copper, Kevin K., 332
Copts, Michael J., 153, 408, 416
Corbett, Dan, 331, 669, 673
Corbett, Marlene, 797
Corcoran, Carla, 334
Corcoran, Kevin, 357
Cordaro, John, 58
Cordova, Raymond, 821
Corell, Robert W., 606
Corey, Beverly, 167
Corlette, Sabrina, 698
Corley, William "Brooks," Jr., 525, 548, 562
Corman, Jake, 834
Corn, Poe R., 824
Cornell, Peter, 534
Corning, Joy, 873
Cornish, Edward, 208
Coronado, Gil, 524, 577
Corprew, Barbara, 588
Corr, Colleen, 777
Correll, Connie J., 800
Corrigan, Susan, 26
Corro, Ann, 885, 886, 888, 890, 892, 894, 895
Cortese, Steve, 132, 558

Costello, Barry, 707
Costello, Jerry F., D-Ill., 723, 731–732, 744–745, **759**
Costello, John H., 441
Costello, Yvonne, 708
Costigan, Kathy, 754
Cote, Eric, 877
Cotter, Michael W., 895
Cottingham, Robert, 786
Coughlan, William D., 360
Coulter, K. Jane, 40
Covall, Mark, 403
Coverdell, Paul, R-Ga., 46, 63, 440, 478, 481, 723, 805, 811–812, 815, 817, 818, **823**
Cowdrill, Olivia, 380
Cowings, John S., 536
Cox, Christopher, R-Calif., 695, 701, 722, 732–733, 734–735, 747, 748, 750, **760**
Cox, Courtland, 167, 327
Cox, Gary, 781
Cox, J. E., 421
Cox, Jim, 506
Cox, Joseph J., 669
Cox, Larry E., 831
Cox, Queen E., 333
Coy, Robert E., 494
Cox, Susan, 834
Coya, Steve, 88
Coyle, Philip E., III, 587
Coyne, James K., 663
Coyne, William J., D-Pa., 725, 746–747, **760**
Coyner, Kelley, 293, 653
Crabb, Juanita, 450
Crable, Stephen E., 230
Crabtree, Chris, 771
Craig, Gregory, 437, 564, 753
Craig, John, 483
Craig, Larry E., R-Idaho, 302, 305, 307, 702, 723, 805, 806–807, 809–810, 815–816, 817, 818, **823**
Craig, Sherry, 783
Craig, Theodore, 888, 895
Cramer, Bill, 645
Cramer, Judy A., 351
Cramer, Linda, 380
Cramer, Robert E. "Bud," D-Ala., 722, 728–730, **760**
Crandall, Derrick A., 122, 311
Crane, Bob, 754
Crane, Edward H., III, 713
Crane, Maureen, 284
Crane, Philip M., R-Ill., 215, 464, 723, 746–747, **760**, 804
Crane, Stacey, 345
Crane, Stephen C., 370
Craner, Lorne, 442
Crank, Jeff G., 770
Cranston, Colin, 756
Crapanzano, Mona, 777
Crapo, Michael D., R-Idaho, 723, 732–733, 740–741, 747, 750, **760**
Crater, Flora, 9, 717
Craven, Kelly, 756

Golodner, Linda F., 16, 21
Golsby, Marsanne, 874
Gomez, Roger, 780
Gondles, James A., Jr., 516
Gonzales, Al, 878
Gonzales, Ciriaco, 365
Gonzales, Marc, 768
Gonzales, Stephanie, 876
Gonzalez, Eduardo, 518
Gonzalez, Henry B., D-Texas, 726, 730–731, **767**
Gonzalez, Lillian, 528
Gonzalez, Nick, 771
Good, David P., 484
Goode, Virgil H., Jr., D-Va., 727–728, 743, **767**
Goodfellow, William, 482
Goodlatte, Robert W., R-Va., 40, 41, 46, 56, 63, 283, 627, 726, 727–728, 737–738, 743, 748, 750, **768**
Goodling, Bill, R-Pa., 200, 212, 219, 725, 733–734, 736–737, **768**
Goodman, Alice C., 704
Goodman, Mark, 94
Goodman, Sherri W., 292, 556, 583
Goodrich, Anne, 718
Goodwin, Michael, 233
Goodwin, Robert, 27
Goold, William J., 791
Goolrick, John, 753
Goosby, Eric, 387
Gorden, Phillip, 384
Gordis, Enoch, 398
Gordley, John, 50
Gordon, Bart, D-Tenn., 725, 732–733, 741–742, 749, **768**
Gordon, Derek, 101
Gore, Albert, Jr., 702, 818
Gorham, William, 630, 717
Gorin, Susan, 180
Gorman, Carolyn, 160
Gormley, John, 780
Gortenberg, Gary, 221
Gorton, Slade, R-Wash., 99, 201, 246, 277, 489, 593, 661, 726, 806–807, 808, 809–810, 813, 816, 818, **826**
Goslin, David A., 617
Goss, Kay, 265
Goss, Porter J., R-Fla., 508, 581, 723, 741, 742–743, 750, **768**
Gossman, Susan Carr, 55, 627
Goto Sabas, Jennifer, 828
Gottemoeller, Rose, 242
Gottshall, William, 831
Gould, Martha, 182
Gould, W. Scott, 78, 332
Gould, William B., IV, 230
Grabiec, Elaine, 780
Grabowski, Sarah, 647
Gradison, Willis D., Jr., 356
Grady, Bill, 756
Grady, Patricia A., 370
Grafeld, Margaret, 82
Graff, Brian, 159, 236
Graff, John, 125

Graff, Karen, 825
Graham, Bob, D-Fla., 723, 809–811, 815–816, **826**
Graham, David, 822, 831
Graham, Jan, 878
Graham, John H., IV, 391
Graham, Lawrence T., 52
Graham, Leslie H., 78
Graham, Lindsey, R-S.C., 725, 733–734, 736–737, 738–739, 748, 750, **768**
Graham, Lowell E., 543
Graham, Russ, 775
Graham, Thomas, Jr., 567
Gramm, Phil, R-Texas, 150, 356, 376, 725, 805, 808, 811, **826**
Grams, Rod, R-Minn., 69, 152, 454, 464, 472, 508, 570, 724, 803, 808, 809–810, 811–812, 816, **826**
Granahan, Thomas F., 539
Grandmaison, J. Joseph, 463
Grandy, Fred, 629, 642
Granger, Kay, R-Texas, 725, 731–732, 735–736, 744–745, 750, **768**, 803–804
Grant, Gary, 777
Grant, Maxine, 779
Grant, Mooza V. P., 647
Grassley, Charles E., R-Iowa, 7, 215, 220, 235, 246, 341, 377, 464, 493, 500, 637, 651, 656, 695, 723, 804, 805, 808, 811, 813–814, **827**
Grau, John, 157, 255, 418
Graves, David, 41, 47, 413
Graves, Jorja L., 535
Graves, Bill, R-Kan., 873
Gravitz, Alisa, 278
Gray, Beverly, 474, 484
Gray, John, 168
Gray, Nellie J., 504
Gray, William H., III, 202
Graykowski, John E., 666, 671
Graz, John, 33, 506
Greaney, John F., 143, 498
Greaux, Cheryl Prejean, 53, 427
Grebe, Michael W., 718
Greelegs, Ed, 824
Greeley, Christopher J., 829
Greeley, Paul J., Jr., 133
Green, Amy, 783
Green, Gail, 826
Green, Gene, D-Texas, 726, 726, 732–733, 749, **768**
Green, Gordon W., Jr., 139, 342, 408
Green, James L., 595
Green, Jeralene B., 82
Green, John, 711
Green, Jonathan Clark, 520
Green, Kim, 763
Green, Kimberly, 210
Green, Licia, 773
Green, Micah S., 150
Green, Oliver W., 710
Green, Randy, 37, 46, 628
Green, Steven J., 893
Greenbaum, Leon J., Jr., 387
Greenberg, Judith H., 394

Greenberg, Marjorie S., 349
Greenberg, Robert, 391
Greenberg, Sherry, 695
Greenberger, Marcia, 9, 202, 229
Greenberger, Phyllis, 401
Greene, Joe L., 179
Greene, Marilyn J., 94
Greene, Richard L., 332
Greene, Sarah M., 195, 636
Greene, Terry, 764
Greenfield, Richard S., 607
Greenspan, Alan, 127, 137, 144, 149
Greenstein, Robert, 629
Greenwald, Peter, 390
Greenwood, James C., R-Pa., 725, 732–734, **768**
Gregg, Judd, R-N.H., 15, 69, 132, 220, 317, 439, 464, 493, 593, 637, 656, 668, 724, 806–807, 808, 814, 818, **827**
Gregg, Richard, 130, 137
Gregoire, Christine O., 878
Gregory, Bruce, 448
Gregory, Frederick D., 622
Gregory, Hayden, 162
Grese, Sandra, 527
Gresser, Ed, 695
Gretch, JoAnn, 82
Gretch, Paul L., 453
Gretzinger, Carolyn M., 444
Greve, Michael S., 503
Grewe, Joan, 531
Grey, Ann, 798
Grey-Johnson, Crispin, 886
Gribbin, Robert, III, 892
Griffee, Ellen, 207
Griffin, Jim, 697
Griffin, Michelle, 221
Griffin, Richard, 334
Griffith, Jeanne E., 207, 591
Griffith, Patricia Browning, 105
Griffith, Reginald W., 114, 414
Griffith, Thomas B., 703
Griffiths, Ann Mills, 533
Griffiths, Barbara J., 471
Griffiths, Gloria, 787
Griffitts, Bob, 763
Griggs, Tonya, 754
Grigsby, Harriet Pritchett, 758
Grinstead, Rose M., 761
Grishaw, Letitia J., 289
Griss, Bob, 377, 641
Griswold, David A., 822
Grogan, Jack H., Jr., 543
Grone, Phil, 583
Groppel, Thomas L., 543
Gross, George, 96
Gross, Joel M., 289, 292
Gross, Richard J., 345
Gross, Roberta L., 334
Gross, Thomas J., 248
Gross, William, 217
Grossi, Ralph, 44
Grossman, Marc, 477
Grossman, Steve, 692, 717
Grosswald, Sarina, 719

Groundwater, John R., 125, 672
Grover, Kevin, 6
Growe, Joan, 874
Gruber, Mike, 783
Gruenburg, Drew, 43
Grumbles, Ben, 254, 293, 296, 299, 313, 575, 668
Grundon, Michelle, 800
Guachione, Deborah, 784
Gubser, Peter, 485
Guelar, Diego Ramiro, 880
Guenther, Kenneth A., 148
Guerra, Ernie, 829
Guerra-Mondragon, Gabriel, 884
Guerrero, Dolores S., 876
Guerrero, Peter F., 275
Guertin, Donald L., 253
Guffanti, Marianne C., 270, 609
Guglielmi, David, 880, 882, 889, 890, 893, 895, 896
Guitteau, Robert, 457
Gulledge, Maurice, 432
Gullet, Deb, 831
Gundersen, Jerry, 205
Gundersheimer, Werner, 104
Gunn, Becki, 755
Gunter, Rene, 206
Gupta, Sarita, 191
Gupton, Richard, 46, 63
Gurney, Charles, 884, 889, 890, 893, 895
Gustafson, Carol, 832, 802
Gustafson, John S., 60, 400, 513
Gutierrez, Carl T. C., 872
Gutierrez, Lino, 891
Gutierrez, Luis V., D-Ill., 723, 723, 730–731, 745–746, **769**
Gutierrez Nestor, Loretta, 520
Gutknecht, Gil, R-Minn., 724, 731–732, 741–742, 747, **769**
Guttentag, Joseph, 453
Gutting, Dick, 286
Guttman, Barbara, 83
Guzik, John, 757
Gwadowsky, Dan A., 874
Gwin, Rose, 323

Haas, Larry, 329
Haass, Richard, 441, 560
Habib Seraj, Abdul, 880
Hackett, David L., 178
Hackett, Lena, 757
Hadge, Nadine, 87
Hafer, Barbara, 877
Hagan, Timothy F., 326
Hagedorn, Robert D., 793
Hagel, Chuck, R-Neb., 281, 464, 472, 724, 808, 811–812, 815, 816, 818, **827**
Hager, Dennis L., 581
Hager, John H., 878
Hagood, Reginald, 312
Hagy, William F., III, 270
Hahn, Bruce, 430,
Hahn, Lorna, 441
Haig, Barbara, 442
Hailes, Edward A., Jr., 226

Al-Hajjri, Abdulwahab A., 896
Hajost, Scott, 281
Hakes, Jay, 243
Hakim, Peter, 482
Halamandaris, Val J., 25, 361, 379
Haldow, John, 786
Hale, Ralph, 372, 381
Hale, Robert F., 332, 530
Hales, David, 250, 339
Haley, George, 339
Halfhide, Arnold T., 894
Halicki, Thomas, 346
Halkias, Rebecca, 877
Hall, Betty Jean, 240
Hall, Cynthia, 828
Hall, Dale, 578, 611, 615
Hall, Erik, 891
Hall, Fletcher, 454, 520
Hall, Gary M., 558
Hall, Hannah R., 82
Hall, James E., 653
Hall, Kathryn Walt, 882
Hall, Keith R., 580
Hall, Kent, 823
Hall, Laurel, 760
Hall, Ralph M., D-Texas, 725, 732–733, 741–742, **769**
Hall, Steve, 774
Hall, Terre McFillan, 354, 386
Hall, Thomas F., 545
Hall, Tony P., D-Ohio, 58, 725, 741, **769**
Hall, Woody, 78
Hallett, Carol, 662
Hallion, Richard P., 540
Hallman, Linda, 43
Hallmark, Amy, 770
Hallmon, Phyllis, 770
Halloran, Larry, 2, 25, 57, 172, 227, 231, 319, 344, 352, 407, 507, 547
Halperin, Jerome A., 365
Halpern, Jack, 594
Halpern, Paul, 578
Halsted, David, 884
Halvorsen, Jerald V., 262
Halvorson, Herb, 782
Hamb, Edward J., 773
Hamburg, Margaret A., 349
Hamilton, Earl G., 152
Hamilton, John Kennedy, 873
Hamilton, Lee H., D-Ind., 723, 736–737, **769,** 803
Hamilton, Mary, 341
Hamilton, Nadine, 704
Hamilton, Philip W., 605
Hamm, Brett, 832
Hamm, Ronald P., 344, 689
Hammargren, Lonnie, 875
Hammer, Dan, 821
Hammer, John H., 100
Hammond, Peirce A., 181
Hammond, Tony, 693
Hammonds, Timothy, 61
Hampton, Judy, 787
Hampton, Ronald, 519
Hamre, John J., 556

Hams, Deb, 786
Hanaway, Catharine, 820
Hancock, Charles C., 601
Hancock, Mike, 222
Hancock, William J., 588
Hand, James S., 823
Hankerson, Terry, 527
Hankins, Kelley, 836
Hanley, Dan, 836
Hanley, Edward T., 61, 125
Hanley, Frank, 423
Hanna, Jack, 497
Hannah, Craig, 699
Hanneman, Richard L., 307
Hanrahan, Patricia, 454
Hanrahan, Rone, 875
Hansell, Marilyn, 797
Hansell, William H., Jr., 342
Hansen, C. Russell, 135
Hansen, Fred, 273
Hansen, James V., R-Utah, 115, 302, 304, 311, 341, 697, 705, 726, 738–739, 740–741, 743, **769**
Hansen, Joseph T., 710
Hansen, Kenneth, 494
Hansen, Paul W., 279, 314
Hansen, William D., 192
Hanson, Walter, 529
Hansua, Mary Ann, 827
Hantman, Alan M., 693
Hanzlik, David, 890
Harada, Daisaku, 476
Haralson, Jan, 752
Harbison, George, 332
Harden, Atif, 10, 31
Hardesty, Lesley J., 16
Hardin, Helen, 799
Hardin, Kristina, 116
Hardwick, Ray, 266
Hardy, Maura, 892
Hardy, Stew, 39, 247, 300
Hardy, Thomas, 873
Hare, Philip G., 764
Hargett, Greg, 796
Harkey, Dick, 781
Harkin, Tom, D-Iowa, 698, 723, 805, 806–807, 814, 815, 816, **827**
Harles, Charles, 224
Harley, William G., 315, 418
Harman, Jane, D-Calif., 722, 738–739, 742–743, 747, **769**
Harmon, James A., 459
Harmon, Linda, 381
Harmon, Rita, 9
Harmsen, Mark S., 763
Harnage, Bobby L., 321
Harness, Gregory, 707
Harper, Mary Annie, 777
Harper, Mike, 833
Harraghy, Karen, 782
Harrelson, Elma, 791
Harrington, Chris, 698
Harrington, Kathleen, 448
Harris, Bruce, 754
Harris, Cheryl, 537, 539

Metcalf, Jack, R-Wash., 726, 730–731, 744–745, 748, **781**
Metcalfe, Daniel J., 81
Metelits, Michael, 280, 293
Metz, Craig, 795
Metz, Douglas W., 60
Metzger, Philip, 463
Metzger, Richard, 72, 75, 499
Meurer, David, 770
Meyer, Alden, 39, 250, 265, 280, 567, 657
Meyer, Beth, 877
Meyer, Betty, 446, 634
Meyer, Christopher, 896
Meyer, John, 876
Meyer, Maureen, 521
Meyer, Tony, 153, 459
Meyers, Bob, 91
Meyers, Harry, 331
Meyers, Lynn, 205, 220
Meyers, Sherry, 368
Mezainis, Valdis, 300
Miailovich, Robert F., 5
Miaoulis, Shirley, 754
Mica, Daniel A., 148
Mica, John L., R-Fla., 99, 231, 317, 318, 335, 336, 723, 734–736, 744–745, **781**
Micallef, Mark Anthony, 890
Michael, Terry, 178
Michelini, Philip, 883, 884, 885, 886, 887, 889, 890, 891, 892, 893, 894
Michelman, Kate, 504
Miconi, Americo S., 344
Middleton, Victoria J., 772
Midzi, Amos Bernard Muvengwa, 896
Mielke, Marlene, 830
Migliaccio, Gene, 375
Mihm, Mary Lynn, 772, 773
Miko, John, 707
Mikowicz, Jerome, 324
Mikulski, Barbara A., D-Md., 701, 724, 806–807, 814, 816, 818, **831**
Milam, William, 889
Milanese, Marco, 796
Miles, David, 704
Miles, Jim, 877
Miles, John B., 237
Miles, Richard M., 896
Milewski, Elizabeth, 602
Miley, Robert R., 694
Milinkovich, Denise, 789
Milion, Al, 333
Milkey, Robert W., 624
Milkman, Beverly L., 223, 325, 638, 644
Millacek, Tim, 778
Millane, David M., 333
Millar, James R., 488
Millar, William W., 684
Millender-McDonald, Juanita, D-Calif., 722, 743, 744–745, 749, **781**
Miller, Amy, 362
Miller, Bill, 783
Miller, Bob, D-Nev., 875
Miller, C. Lowell, 258
Miller, Candice, 874
Miller, Chris, 697

Miller, Constance, 227, 708
Miller, Cynthia, 686, 763
Miller, Dan, R-Fla., 723, 728–730, 731–732, 734–735, 750, **782**
Miller, David, 3, 21, 426, 502, 503, 506, 507, 690
Miller, Derrick, 774
Miller, Donna Rapps, 776
Miller, Ellen, 691
Miller, Ethel P., 216
Miller, George, D-Calif., 722, 733–734, 740–741, 747, 749, **782**
Miller, Harris N., 87, 613
Miller, James N., Jr., 565
Miller, Jerome G., 517
Miller, Jill, 230
Miller, Joe, 783
Miller, John R., 706
Miller, Judith A., 494
Miller, Lorraine, 705
Miller, Marcia E., 463
Miller, Margaret, 188
Miller, Mary H., 32
Miller, Matt, 772
Miller, Michael F., 337
Miller, Michael L., 78
Miller, Miriam, 82
Miller, Oral O., 644
Miller, Patricia, 762
Miller, Richard T., 62
Miller, Stephen L., 254
Miller, Sue, 757
Miller, Tom, 873
Miller, Zell, D-Ga., 872
Milliken, Christine, 510
Milliken, Diane, 769
Millin, Janette, 878
Milling, Marcus E., 305, 609
Millis, John I., 508, 581
Millman, Amy, 129, 167
Mills, Jim, 93
Mills, John A., 480, 671
Mills, Mark, 702
Milne, James, 878
Milne, Thomas L., 354, 368
Milner, Neil, 148
Milovanic, Gillian, 478
Milton, A. Fenner, 571
Minchew, Daniel, 188
Mines, Keith, 883
Mines, Kenneth A., 200
Minge, David, D-Minn., 696, 724, 727–728, 731–732, **782**
Minihan, Kenneth A., 580, 583
Mink, Patsy T., D-Hawaii, 695, 723, 731–732, 733–734, 749, **782**
Minner, Ruth Ann, 872
Minoves Triquell, Juli, 880
Minson, Dixie L., 820
Minton, Mark, 475
Mintz, Suzanne, 636
Mirabal, Manuel, 5
Mirin, Steven, 373, 402
Mishoe, Helena, 393
Misisco, Henry, 676

Mitchell, Dean, 780
Mitchell, Denise, 231
Mitchell, Doug, 820
Mitchell, Gayle, 794
Mitchell, Greg, 789
Mitchell, Nancy J., 825
Mitchell, Robert L., 789
Mitchell, Susan, 82, 255
Mitchem, Arnold L., 202
M'Ithiri, Matthew K., 888
Mittelholtz, Camille, 275, 654
Mittermeier, Russell, 281
Mixon, Linda, 795
Mize, David M., 544
Moakley, Joe, D-Mass., 724, 741, 747, 749, **782**
Mock, Ray, 785
Modecki, Carl A., 160
Modisett, Jeff, 873
Modzeleski, William, 193, 398
Moe, Richard, 116, 411
Moeller, G. Martin, Jr., 419
Moffett, Charles S., 109
Moffett, Terri, 834
Moffitt, Eileen, 770
Moffitt, Kristine A., 547
Mogwe, Archibald Mooketsa, 883
Mohamed, Mahdi Ibrahim, 894
Mohr, Jan, 179, 530
Mohr, Thomas, 780
Moler, Elizabeth, 242
Molholm, Kurt N., 572, 598
Molino, Michael A., 677
Molique, Jerry, 435
Molitoris, Jolene M., 680
Mollohan, Alan B., D-W.Va., 726, 728–730, 731–732, 749, **782**
Molpus, C. Manly, 61
Mombouli, Serge, 884
Monasmith, Mike, 769
Money, Arthur L., 78, 571, 586
Monigan, Michael F., 541
Moniz, Ernest, 242
Monk, Carl C., 189, 520
Monk, C. Harvey, Jr., 250, 459
Monreig, Emma, 82
Monro, Betty, 759
Monroe, A. L. "Mike," 423
Monroe, Stephanie, 633
Monson, Nancy, 549
Montagano, John, 782
Montalbano, Ann, 22
Montes, J. Henry, 369
Montgomery, Betty D., 876
Montgomery, F. Kendall, 443
Montgomery, Kathryn C., 70
Montgomery, William D., 884
Montoya, Michael A., 876
Montoya, Rebecca, 820
Moodie, Michael, 567
Moody, Corlis S., 167, 242
Moody, Jim, 470
Moog, Lucy, 754
Moon, Becky, 756
Mooney, Joan, 771

Olson, Judy, 832
Olson, Lyndon L., Jr., 894
Olson, Susan, 754
Olver, John W., D-Mass., 724, 728–730, 749, **784**
O'Meara, Linda, 761
Ondo Bile, Micha, 885
O'Neil, Joseph F., 593
O'Neill, Anthony R., 19, 421
O'Neill, Brian, 674, 679
O'Neill, Joseph, 387, 885
O'Neill, June, 138, 706
O'Neill, Robert J., Jr., 343
Onieal, Denis, 18
Ooms, Van Doorn, 134
Opfer, George, 334
Oppy, James A., 328
O'Quinn, Jim F., 833
Oraze, Michael, 599
Orr, James C., 473
Orr, Jimmy, 879
Orr, Lois, 217
Orsini, Dan, 794
Ortiz, Solomon P., D-Texas, 726, 733–735, **784**
Ortloff, Ruth, 780
Osborne, Janine, 758
Osburn, C. Dixon, 6, 528, 539
Oscar, Kenneth, 571
Osseyi, Kossivi, 895
Ostapowicz, Nancy, 763
O'Steen, David N., 504
Osterman, Joseph, 678
Osteryoung, Janet, 611
O'Sullivan, P.J., 761
Oswald, Steve, 621
Otis, Lee Lieberman, 220, 445, 451
O'Toole, Jim, 115, 311
Ottaway, Lucretia, 118
Otter, C. L. Butch, 873
Otterness, Naomi, 766
Ottinger, Dick, 278
Otton, Charles, 111
Oudkirk, Sandra, 889
Ouellette, Peg, 827
Ould Sid Ahmed, Ahmed, 890
Ouseley, Jill K., 138
Ousley, Mary, 711
Overby, Charles L., 89
Overman, Joanne, 129
Overstreet, Carolyn, 831
Owen, Brad, 878
Owen, Gus A., 499, 658, 667, 683
Owendoff, James M., 267
Owens, Bill, 872
Owens, Joseph H., 641
Owens, Major R., D-N.Y., 697, 724, 733–735, **784**
Owens-Kirkpatrick, Barbaro, 477, 564
Owings, Raymond, 678
Oxley, Michael G., R-Ohio, 124, 159, 276, 293, 296, 725, 732–733, **789**
Oyarzabal, Antonio, 894

Packard, Ron, R-Calif., 586, 722, 728–730, **785**
Padgett, Chad, 801
Padgett, Donna, 761
Paemen, Hugo, 252, 440, 465, 479
Pagani, Dean, 872
Page, Dan, 879
Pagel, Suzanne, 825
Palast, Geri D., 704
Pale Moon, Princess, 119
Palguta, John M., 322
Palladino, Vincent, 339
Pallister, John S., 609
Pallone, Frank, Jr., D-N.J., 724, 732–733, 740–741, 747, **785**
Palmer, Matthew, 896
Palmer, Scott B., 769
Pamerleau, Susan, 535
Panagopoulos, Jennifer, 509, 512
Pane, Greg, 552
Pantuso, Peter J., 673, 684
Paone, Martin P., 701, 702, 703
Pape, Michael, 800
Papenfuss, Joanne, 796
Paperiello, Carl J., 265, 267
Pappas, Michael, R-N.J., 724, 734–735, 738–739, 743, 750, **785**
Paquin, Robert, 830
Paranzino, Michael, 790
Parde, Duane, 344
Parent, Bob, 752
Paris, Susan E., 283
Parish, Lael, 483
Park, Kun Woo, 888
Park, Robert L., 265, 615
Parker, Bruce, 290, 296
Parker, David, 260
Parker, Douglas L., 29, 70
Parker, J. A., 3, 474
Parker, James V., 45
Parker, Jonie, 529, 553
Parker, Karen, 535
Parker, Margaret Alexander, 719
Parker, Maurice, 880
Parker, Mike, R-Miss., 724, 728–730, 731–732, **785**
Parker, Rosalind, 593, 616, 622
Parker, Woody, 756
Parkhurst, Muriel Sue, 549
Parmelee, Carol, 329
Parmentier, Michael, 536
Parris, Mark Robert, 895
Parron, Delores, 401
Parry, John, 28, 402, 640
Pascrell, Bill, Jr., D-N.J., 724, 743, 744–745, **785**
Pashayev, Hafiz Mir Jalal, 882
Pasqual, Patricia, 26, 177
Passage, David, 480
Passiment, Elissa, 370
Pastin, John R., 544
Pastor, Ed, D-Ariz., 722, 728–730, 743, 747, **785**
Pataki, George E., R-N.Y., 876
Patano, Sandra, 823

Patchan, Joseph, 500
Pate, Paul Danny, 873
Patel, Rita, 695, 697
Patelunas, Gail, 143
Patrick, Erline M., 226
Patrick, Sandra, 835
Patterson, Garth, 766
Patti, C. James, 669
Pattie, Kenton, 142
Patterson, Anne, 885
Patton, Paul E., D-Ky., 873
Paugh, Jon, 153
Paul, Heather, 16
Paul, Ron, R-Texas, 725, 730–731, 733–734, **785**
Paul, Terry, 707
Paull, Lindy L., 25, 47, 133, 235, 246, 252, 352, 410, 472, 690
Pavlik, Donald, 585
Paxon, Bill, R-N.Y., 725, 732–733, 748, **785**
Payne, Donald M., D-N.J., 724, 733–734, 736–737, 749, **786**
Payne, J. Michael, 677
Payne, Joyce, 202
Payne, Roger L., 618
Payton, Tom, 120
Peace, Fran, 770
Peacock, Andrew Sharp, 882
Peacock, Dennis, 606
Peacock, Glenda, 762
Pearson, Cynthia, 400, 504
Pearson, Orin, 267, 295
Pearson, Roger, 135, 617
Pease, Ed, R-Ind., 723, 737–738, 744–745, 750, **786**
Pease, Merna, 826
Peasley, Carol A., 473
Peck, Jeffrey J., 710
Peck, Robert A., 329, 337, 416, 429
Peck, William, 540
Pedigo, Linda, 754
Pedigo, R. Keith, 550
Pedrozza, Marlene, 828
Peel, Ken, 281, 464, 472
Peeler, Bob, 877
Peeler, C. Lee, 23, 165
Pelhem, Steve, 764
Pelosi, Nancy, D-Calif., 697, 722, 728–730, 742–743, 747, 749, **786**
Pemberton, Miriam, 139, 562
Peña, Federico F., 242
Pena, Norma, 789
Pencak, Lawrence, 378, 643
Penfold, Jeanne K., 553
Penn, Audrey S., 395, 397
Penn, Billie Jo, 832
Penna, Richard, 188, 362, 366
Penne, R. Leo, 875
Pennington, James C., 525
Pennybacker, Albert M., 34, 197, 506
Peoples, Marc, 823
Pepple, Randy, 800
Perdue, John, 879
Perdue Dollan, Cindy, 822

Reid, Robert J., 407, 426
Reid, Stephen, 787
Reimer, Dennis, 556
Reinsch, William Alan, 459, 569
Reis, Robert, 475
Reis, Victor H., 568
Reiser, Marty, 782
Rell, Brian, 751
Rell, Jodie, 872
Remez, Shereen, 78
Render, Arlene, 896
Rendon, Florencio, 784
Rendon, Martin S., 446
Renick, Mary, 767
Renkes, Gregg D., 246, 252, 263, 277, 310, 489
Renner, Jackie, 874
Renninger, Karen, 81, 439
Reno, Janet, 451
Rényi, Judith, 180
Reppert, John C., 565
Retsinas, Nicolas P., 145, 425, 433
Reum, Josef, 372
Reuter, James, 354
Revoldt, Daryl, 788
Rey, Mark, 302, 305, 307
Reyes, Norma, 789
Reyes, Silvestre, D-Texas, 726, 738–739, 745–746, 749, **788**
Reynolds, Dennis, 86, 360
Reynolds, Emily, 825
Reynolds, James S., 515, 579
Reynolds, Margaret W., 105
Reynolds, Matt, 775
Reynoso, Cruz, 2
Rezendes, Victor S., 244, 275
Rhodes, Arthur D., 785
Rhodes, Robert, 537
Ricci, Pearl, 754
Rice, Dean, 836
Rice, Edmund B., 466
Rice, Greg, 823
Rice, Susan E., 473
Rich, Chris, 895
Rich, Dorothy, 194
Rich, Laurie M., 878
Richard, Joel C., 666
Richard, John, 29, 95, 495
Richard, William G., 784
Richards, Cory L., 380, 392
Richards, Jeff B., 88
Richards, Paul, 4, 692
Richardson, Alan H., 255
Richardson, Betty, 772
Richardson, Carol, 697
Richardson, Dixie, 829
Richardson, Kermit W., 38
Richardson, Robert, 114, 618
Richbourg, Donna S., 587
Richesson, Bruce, 820
Richie, Robert, 692
Richland, Jordan, 355
Richmond, Mike, 825
Richter, Sue, 530, 548
Rickard, Stephen, 457, 517

Rickert, Jonathan B., 478
Rickert, Lori, 794
Ricks, Phil, 755
Riddiough, Christine R., 719
Ridell, Richard A., 572
Ridge, Tom, R-Pa., 877
Ridgway, Delissa A., 455
Ridgway, R. Hunter, 784
Ridings, Dorothy, 26, 177
Riegg, Nick, 46
Rieker, Bruce R., 753
Riemenschneider, Charles H., 63, 465
Riemer, Hans, 651
Riep-Dice, Patricia M., 82
Riggin, Phil, 704
Riggs, Frank, R-Calif., 7, 57, 99, 172, 194, 200, 376, 508, 529, 627, 632, 637, 640, 722, 733–734, 744–745, 748, **789**
Riggs, Jean, 226
Riggs, Rachel, 829
Riley, Bob, R-Ala., 722, 730–731, 738–739, 750, **789**
Riley, Meg A., 34
Riley, Michael J., 148, 333
Riley, Richard W., 172
Rimas, Algis, 480
Ripley, Suzanne, 642
Risavy, Anne-Marie, 759
Risher, Carol A., 162
Ritchie, De, 530
Rittberg, Eric, 785
Ritter, Doug, 708, 800
Rivera, Charles, 12
Rivera, Jose, 719
Rivera-Casiano, Pedro, 789
Rivers, Lynn, D-Mich., 724, 731–732, 741–742, **789**
Rivers, Stanley, 664
Rivlin, Alice M., 127
Rizer, Jane, 696
Rizzo, Joseph J., 645
Roach, Doug, 572
Roadman, Charles H., Jr., 531
Robak, Kim, 875
Robb, Charles S., D-Va., 726, 803, 807–808, 811–812, 815, 816, 818, **833**
Robbins, Robert K., 603
Roberson, Elaine, 770
Roberts, Alan I., 262, 268, 293
Roberts, Cecil E., 259
Roberts, Craig, 792
Roberts, Douglas B., 874
Roberts, Dutsch, 823
Roberts, James, 884
Roberts, Pat, R-Kan., 723, 805, 807–808, 815, 816, **833**
Roberts, Russell, 781
Roberts, Stephen T., 683
Robertson, A. Haeworth, 236
Robertson, Debbie, 762
Robertson, Linda L., 704
Robertson, Richard B., 676
Robillard, Marda, 762
Robinson, Alicia, 882, 883, 886, 891, 895
Robinson, Anthony W., 169

Robinson, B. H., 39, 45, 55, 204
Robinson, Bernie, 780
Robinson, British, 33
Robinson, Charles L., 526, 537, 562
Robinson, Julie, 873
Robinson, Kenneth L., 148
Robinson, Laurie, 491
Robinson, Michael H., 282
Robinson, Randall, 474
Robinson, Reginald, 508
Robinson, Robert A., 36
Robinson, Sharon, 753
Robson, Kimberly, 9, 564, 717
Roch, Dennis, 788
Rockefeller, John D., IV, D-W.Va., 697, 698, 726, 809, 811, 815–816, 818, **833**
Rockefeller, Winthrop, 871
Rockey, Sally, 39, 602
Rodearmel, David, 882
Rodekohr, Dee, 825
Rodgers, David, 268
Rodgers, John M., 659
Rodgers, Kirk P., 281
Rodgers, Mark D., 833
Rodgers, Michael F., 378, 428
Rodriguez, Armando E., 200, 224, 227, 229, 322, 550
Rodriguez, Ciro D., D-Texas, 726, 738–739, 745–746, **789**
Rodriguez, J.M., 789
Rodriguez, Melissa, 776
Rodriguez-Parker, Gladys, 780
Roe, Eliska, 756
Roemer, Jane S., 239, 680
Roemer, Tim, D-Ind., 696, 726, 733–734, 741–742, **789**
Roffee, Lawrence W., 419, 638, 653
Rogan, James E., R-Calif., 722, 732–733, 737–738, 750, **789**
Rogers, Ava, 892
Rogers, Charles, 527, 584
Rogers, Debra, 880, 883, 884, 885, 886, 888, 889, 890, 891, 894, 895, 896
Rogers, Diane, 192
Rogers, Georgia A., 455
Rogers, Harold, R-Ky., 14, 68, 132, 275, 317, 439, 463, 491, 592, 656, 668, 723, 728–730, **789**
Rogers, Joseph E., Jr., 612
Rogers, Kathleen, 530, 554
Rogers, Keith, 777
Rogers, Ken, 459
Rogers, Kenneth W., 127
Rogers, Leonard, 445
Rogers, Nancy, 799
Rogers, Paul, 791
Rogers, Richard M., 491
Rogers, Shane, 787
Rogers, Thomas, 137
Rogerson, Lynn K., 108
Rogin, Carole M., 646
Rogstad, Barry K., 133
Rogus, David F., 481
Rohan, Dora, 793
Rohatyn, Felix George, 886, 890

Rohrabacher, Dana, R-Calif., 722, 736–737, 741–742, **789**
Rohrbaugh, Karl, 333
Roker, Claire, 758
Roldan, Richard R., 261
Romanowski, Alina, 483
Romans, Larry, 799
Romer, Joseph D., 377, 642
Romer, Roy, D-Colo., 717, 872
Romero, Bernice, 64
Romero, Henry, 318
Romero-Barceló, Carlos, D-Puerto Rico, 489, 725, 733–734, 740–741, **789**
Romeu, Xavier, 489, 877
Rominger, Richard, 36
Ronan, Mary, 82
Rones, Patricia, 836
Rooney, Frank, 61
Rooney, James, 760
Root, Patricia, 835
Roozenbeck, Yvette, 520
Roper, Bart, 791
Roper, Kevin M., 558
Roper, Ray, 96
Roper, Wayne, 772
Roque, Mary Jesse, 767
Rorapaugh, Robin, 762
Rosan, Richard, 416
Rosapepe, James C., 892
Rosario, Pedro, 877
Rose, John N., 75
Rose, Joseph, 783
Rose, Mitch, 835
Rosello, Pedro, D-Puerto Rico, 717
Rosen, S. Peter, 615
Rosenbaum, Eli M., 451
Rosenberg, Norman, 486
Rosenberg, Robert M., 42
Rosenberry, Sara, 886
Rosenblatt, Daniel N., 518
Rosenbleeth, Herb, 548
Rosendall, Rick, 5
Rosenstein, Peter D., 197
Rosenstock, Linda, 237, 351
Rosenthal, Linda, 783
Rosenthal, Neal H., 217
Rosenthal, Roger C., 29, 42, 223
Rosenthal, Steve, 231
Rosier, Ronald C., 615
Ros-Lehtinen, Ileana, R-Fla., 46, 281, 464, 570, 697, 723, 734–735, 736–737, **790**
Ross, Ann, 82
Ross, Betsy McCaughey, 876
Ross, Carl, 303
Ross, Charles, 830
Ross, Christopher W. S., 894
Ross, Fred, 786
Ross, Phyllis, 833
Rossello, Pedro J., 877
Rossetti, Steve, 12, 584
Rossides, Eugene, 479
Rossmeissl, Hedy J., 618
Rossotti, Charles, 141
Rostker, Bernard D., 538, 551, 585

Rotenberg, Marc, 21, 87
Roth, Ellen, 826
Roth, Luke, 766
Roth, Stanley, 475
Roth, Toby, Jr., 466, 571
Roth, William V., Jr., R-Del., 25, 47, 133, 235, 246, 252, 344, 352, 410, 472, 690, 723, 803, 804, 811, 817, **833**
Rothenberg, Joseph, 622
Rothman, Steven R., D-N.J., 724, 736–738, **790**
Rothrosen, Daniel, 394, 396
Rotko, Michael J., 553
Rotondaro, Alfred M., 119
Roukema, Marge, R-N.J., 14, 146, 430, 499, 530, 724, 730–731, 733–734, **790**
Rouse, Peter, 701, 824
Rowe, Dustin, 799
Rowe, Sylvia, 59
Rowland, John G., R-Conn., 872
Rowland, Pat, 22, 161
Rowton, Judy, 769
Roy, J. Stapleton, 887
Roy, Paula M., 326
Royal, Hank, 782
Roybal, Richard, 5, 201
Roybal-Allard, Lucille, D-Calif., 695, 722, 730–732, **790**
Royce, Ed, R-Calif., 474, 696, 722, 730–731, 736–737, 747, 750, **790**
Rozell, Denise, 198, 644
Rozmanich, Dave, 799
Ruane, T. Peter, 675
Rubillo, Jim, 180, 208
Rubin, James, 92
Rubin, Joshua, 824
Rubin, Michael, 327, 332, 341, 344, 709
Rubin, Robert E., 129, 137, 690
Rubinoff, Roberta, 176
Rubinson, Gail, 9
Ruble, Amy, 793
Ruble, Blair A., 487
Rudasingwa, Theogene N., 892
Rudd, David, 828
Rudder, Catherine E., 179
Rudensky, Maria, 882
Rudman, Warren, 329, 437, 580
Rudolph, Lawrence, 495
Ruff, Charles F. C., 329
Ruffin, John, 384
Rugh, William, 485
Ruhlen, Steve, 755
Ruiz-Casares, Monica, 469
Rumble, John, Jr., 595
Runyon, Sandy, 789
Rupel, Dimitrij, 894
Rupp, Keith Lee, 758
Rush, Bobby L., D-Ill., 697, 723, 732–733, 749, **790**
Rush, Jeffrey, Jr., 334
Rush, Laura, 697
Ruskin, Gary, 690
Russ, Maryann, 429
Russ, Susan Boardman, 828

Russell, Donald J., 72
Russell, Gisele P., 792
Russell, Larry, 797
Russell, Richard, 162, 570, 592, 616, 661, 668, 673
Russell, William J., 182
Russell-Robinson, Susan, 596, 618
Russen, Michael, 779
Russo, James M., 800
Russom, Semere, 885
Ruth, Josef, 886, 894
Ryan, Don, 380
Ryan, George H., Sr., 873
Ryan, Jim, 872
Ryan, Kevin, 782
Ryan, Mary A., 437
Ryan, Michael E., 556
Ryan, Michael W. S., 332
Ryan, Norbert, 704
Ryan, Stephanie, 822
Ryan, Tony, 323
Ryan, Vince, 715
Rychac, Wayne S., 583
Ryscavage, Richard, 447
Ryun, Jim, R-Kan., 723, 730–731, 738–739, 743, **790**
Rzepski, Peg, 755
Rzewnicki, Janet C., 872

Al-Sabah, Mohammed Sabah Al-Salim, 888
Sabiston, Norma Jane, 830
Sabo, Kevin, 15, 57, 124
Sabo, Martin Olav, D-Minn., 724, 728–730, 743, 747, 749, **790**
Sacco, Michael, 231
Sachtleben, Paul, 332
Safaev, Sodiq, 896
Safer, Nancy, 197, 198
Sagawa, Shirley, 24, 626
Saito, Kunihiko, 888
Sakai, James, 819
Sakalauskas, Stasys, 889
Sakanawa, Bob, 10
Salak, Rosemary, 532
Salazar, Edward, 895
Salcido, Alice, 820
Salem, Charlie, 872
Salerno, Judith, 552
Salett, Elizabeth, 203
Salisbury, Dallas L., 236, 356
Salleo, Ferdinando, 888
Salmon, Jeffrey, 594
Salmon, Matt, R-Ariz., 722, 736–737, 741–742, **790**
Salmon, William, 605
Salogar, Mark, 752
Salter, Mark, 831
Saltzman, Doug, 835
Samanka, Gene, 528, 553
Sambaiew, Nancy, 451
Samet, Andrew James, 215
Sampas, Dorothy Myers, 890
Sampson, Carol L., 255
Sampson, Neil H., 365

Sampson, Walter D., 68
Sams, Thomas, 885, 888, 889, 894
Samuelian, Steve, 788
Samuels, Harold, 753
Samuels, Linda, 770
Sanchez, Irma, 788
Sanchez, Loretta, D-Calif., 722, 733–734, 738–739, **790**
Sanchez, Oscar, 228, 232, 692
Sanchez, Viola J., 167
Sand, Barbara, 887, 890, 893
Sander, Nancy, 395
Sanders, Bernard, I-Vt., 726, 730–731, 734–735, **790**
Sanders, David G., 455, 671
Sanders, Richard, 880
Sanders, Timothy J., 822, 831
Sanders, Timothy K., 37, 56, 352
Sanders, William, 193, 292
Sandherr, Stephen, 417
Sandler, Joe, 717
Sandler, Roger W., 545
Sandlin, Max, D-Texas, 725, 730–731, 744–745, 749, **791**
Sandoval, Catherine, 89
Sanford, Mark, R-S.C., 725, 734–735, 736–737, **791,** 803
Santiful, Luther L., 226, 527
Santorum, Rick, R-Pa., 38, 44, 54, 276, 302, 313, 570, 725, 805, 807–808, 814–815, 816, **833**
Sapalan, Jesus, 876
Saperstein, David, 34
Saporta, Vicki, 393, 504
Sarasin, Ronald A., 60, 712
Sarbanes, Paul S., D-Md., 724, 803, 808, 811–812, 816, **834**
Sarbib, Jean-Louis, 474
Sasser, James R., 884
Sasso, John A., 411
Satagaj, John, 170
Satcher, David, 351
Satloff, Robert, 486
Satterfield, David, 484, 888
Sattler, Duane, 212, 217, 218, 220, 227, 231, 235
Sauer, Richard J., 41, 203, 636
Saulnier, Madeline, 753
Saunders, Lacy E., 524
Saunders, Margot, 29, 521
Saunders, Shirley, 763
Saunders, Stephen, 793
Sava, Samuel G., 195
Savage, Michael T., 414
Savage, Roberta Haley, 299
Sawhill, John C., 279, 288
Sawkiw, Michael, 488
Sawyer, Alfred A., 871
Sawyer, Gerald, 784
Sawyer, Tom, D-Ohio, 725, 732–733, **791**
Saxton, H. James, R-N.J., 132, 141, 248, 276, 285, 287, 298, 309, 456, 464, 607, 697, 724, 738–739, 740–741, **791,** 803
El Sayed, Ahmed Maher, 885
Scaglia, Phil, 779

Scalia, Antonin, 498
Scaling, Durcie, 797
Scammel, Glenn, 681
Scandling, Dan, 753
Scanlan, Aliimau, 764
Scanlon, Terrence, 25
Scarborough, Joe, R-Fla., 723, 733–735, 738–739, **791**
Scardelletti, Robert A., 682
Schadler, Bob, 715
Schaefer, Dan, R-Colo., 245, 248, 254, 257, 263, 269, 313, 697, 723, 732–733, 745–746, **791**
Schaeffer, Brad, 820
Schaeffer, D. Michael, 546, 551, 568
Schafer, Edward T., R-N.D., 876
Schaffer, Bob, R-Colo., 722, 727–728, 733–734, 740–741, 748, **791**
Schaffer, David, 661
Schaffer, Laurie, 14, 146, 430, 499, 530
Schagh, Catherine, 193
Schallert, Ruth F., 603
Schambra, Philip E., 382
Schanaghy, Lyn, 825
Schanzer, Steven T., 582
Schapiro, Leslie, 149
Schardt, Arlie, 278
Scharf, Eric, 467, 658
Scharpf, Norm, 87, 95
Schatz, Thomas A., 335
Schauble, Jeanne, 81
Schear, James A., 445
Schecter, Jason, 329
Scheeler, Kate, 697
Schenendorf, Jack, 656
Scheppach, Raymond C., 346
Scherrer, Jack F., 247, 386, 573, 599
Schiappa, Dave, 703
Schiavone, Terrance, 679
Schieffer, Jill, 797
Schiffer, Lois J., 274, 505
Schiliro, Philip, 800
Schimansky, H. Joseph, 323
Schimler, Edwin, 667
Schimpff, Barbara S., 537
Schiraldi, Vincent, 509
Schlagenhauf, Jeffery L., 52
Schlapp, Matt, 798
Schleicher, Carl, 271
Schlesinger, Steven R., 522
Schlicher, Ronald, 483
Schlickeisen, Rodger, 288
Schlitt, Lyn M., 495
Schloegel, Scott, 796
Schloss, Howard, 14
Schlosser, Lawrence A., 167
Schmautz, Kurt, 794
Schmidt, Keith, 834
Schmidt, Richard M., Jr., 94
Schmidt, William T., 392
Schmitten, Rolland A., 285, 456, 600
Schneider, Carol, 188
Schneider, Daniel, 790
Schneider, Elizabeth G., 346
Schneider, Karl F., 539

Schneider, Lois E., 823
Schneider, Mark L., 480
Schneider, Roy L., 878
Schneiderat, Kathy, 796
Schnurr, Dennis M., 33
Schoem, Alan H., 22
Schoenberg, Mark G., 331
Schoenbrun, Lois, 374
Schoettler, Gail, 872
Schofer, Andrew, 888
Scholz, Wesley, 462
Schonwalder, Chris, 274
Schoonmaker, Jayne, 795
Schoonover, Brenda, 895
Schoonover, Sandi, 795
Schopfer, Richard, 469
Schosberg, Paul A., 147, 433
Schott, Tina M., 374
Schrage, Barbara, 476
Schreibel, Thomas, 792
Schreibman, Mike, 111
Schroeder, Fredric K., 224, 376, 639
Schroeder, Terri, 798
Schub, Judith, 705
Schuhart, Robin, 57
Schuler, Cheryl, 678
Schull, Ann, 665
Schulte, Beneva, 779
Schulte, Tom, 820, 821
Schultz, Todd, 245, 592
Schumacher, August, Jr., 45, 53
Schumaker, Edward E., III, 895
Schumer, Charles E., D-N.Y., 697, 724, 730–731, 737–738, 749, **791**
Schuster, Fred W., 827
Schuster, Neil D., 676
Schutt, Marla N., 752
Schuyler, Steve, 775
Schwab, Ellen, 391
Schwadron, Steve, 761
Schwalb, Steve, 515
Schwartz, Eli, 369
Schwartz, Gary, 100
Schwartz, Robert, 154, 419
Schwartz, Stephen, 894
Schwartzman, Andrew Jay, 70
Schwarze, Robert C., 163
Schwieker, Mark, 877
Sciulla, Michael, 122, 669
Sclater, Dan, 584
Sclater, Jeanne, 14
Scofield, Doug, 769
Scorca, Marc A., 111
Scott, Betty, 705
Scott, Brad, 821
Scott, Bruce, 704
Scott, Carol, 793
Scott, Deven L., 66
Scott, Gerald W., 886
Scott, Jan, 759
Scott, Janet, 777
Scott, John, 371, 894
Scott, K. Wayne, 633
Scott, Robert C., D-Va., 726, 733–734, 737–738, **792**

Thomas, Bill, R-Calif., 80, 99, 183, 352, 355, 366, 592, 686, 689, 693, 694, 703, 707, 708, 722, 735–736, 746–747, **797**, 803–804
Thomas, Carolyn, 77, 645
Thomas, Clarence, 498
Thomas, Craig, R-Wyo., 115, 311, 475, 698, 726, 809–812, 813, **835**
Thomas, David F., 664
Thomas, Dorothy C., 793
Thomas, Doug, 778
Thomas, Edward L., 683
Thomas, Eric, 581
Thomas, Georgie A., 875
Thomas, Larry, 612
Thomas, Michael, 886, 893
Thomas, Ralph C., III, 167
Thomas, Solly J., Jr., 323
Thomas, Tim, 831
Thompson, Bennie, D-Miss., 724, 727–728, 731–732, 749, **797**
Thompson, David, 778
Thompson, Fred, R-Tenn., 133, 227, 317, 319, 335, 336, 344, 410, 508, 559, 704, 725, 812–813, 817, **836**
Thompson, Jill Long, 412
Thompson, John, 317
Thompson, John C., 565
Thompson, Jose, 884
Thompson, Joseph, 547
Thompson, Louis M., Jr., 151
Thompson, Marie, 780
Thompson, Myril, 763
Thompson, Sally, 873
Thompson, Steve, 568, 570, 581, 588
Thompson, Ted, 778
Thompson, Tommy G., R-Wis., 879
Thorn, Karen, 827
Thornberry, William M. "Mac," R-Texas, 725, 738–739, 740–741, **797**, 803
Thornburgh, Ron, 873
Thornton, Elizabeth M., 225
Thornton, Kathy, 34
Thornton, Stephanie, 308
Thornton, Tracy, 707
Throckmorton, Elizabeth B., 584
Thum, Jeanne, 449
Thune, John, R-S.D., 725, 727–728, 744–745, 748, 750, **797**
Thurm, Gil, 261
Thurman, Karen L., D-Fla., 723, 746–747, **797**
Thurman, Sandy, 387
Thurmond, J. C., 82
Thurmond, Strom, R-S.C., 558, 566, 568, 573, 585, 588, 701, 725, 807–808, 813–814, 815–816, 817, 818, **836**
Thurston, Carol, 777, 778
Tiahrt, Todd, R-Kan., 723, 728–729, 748, 750, **798**
Tice, Dean, 123, 311
Tierney, David, 792
Tierney, John F., D-Mass., 724, 733–734, 734–735, **798**
Tierney, Michael, 411

Tigner, Robert S., 21
Till, Alice E., 364
Tillett, Tom, 787
Timko, David M., 391
Timmer, Gloria, 135, 345
Tindell, Steve, 533
Tinsley, Nikki, 334
Tippens, Julie, 699
Tipton, E. Linwood, 49
Tirozzi, Gerald, 193
Tischler, Bonni G., 512, 515
Titus, C. Richard, 423
Titus, Frank D., 324
Tobe, Amy Weiss, 329
Tobias, Robert M., 323
Toft, Carol, 760
Togafau, Oreta M., 764
Tolbert, James C., Jr., 340
Toll, Deborah, 89
Tollison, Robert D., 134
Tomblin, Earl Ray, 879
Tomes, Darla, 777
Tomlinson, Tom, 100
Tomsen, Peter, 882
Tondro, LaRene, 73
Toner, Dennis, 820
Toner, Gerald A., 230, 234
Toner, John, 705
Toner, John J., 230
Toney, Raymond, 526, 538, 578
Tonoukouin, Lucien Edgar, 882
Topinka, Judy Baar, 873
Topping, John C., Jr., 291, 608
Toregas, Costis, 346, 599
Torgerson, Randall E., 40, 45
Tormala, Richard, 830
Tornquist, David, 653
Torrado, Miguel, 226
Torres, Esteban E., D-Calif., 722, 728–731, 749, **798**
Torres, Lisa, 5
Torricelli, Robert G., D-N.J., 724, 812–815, 816, **836**
Toscano, Ellyn M., 792
Toscano, Mavis, 778
Tosi, Gloria Cataneo, 669
Totman, Ted, 7, 220, 235, 246, 377, 426, 637, 651, 656
Toulson, Cliff, 550
Towns, Edolphus, D-N.Y., 724, 732–733, 734–735, **798**
Towns, Leroy, 833
Townsend, Ann Van Devanter, 110
Townsend, Christi, 753
Townsend, Frances Fragos, 456, 580
Townsend, Kathleen Kennedy, 874
Toy, Charles D., 495
Tozzi, John T., 572
Tracey, Patricia, 536
Trachtenberg, Stephen Joel, 187
Tracy, Alan, 51
Traficant, James A., Jr., D-Ohio, 725, 741–742, 744–745, **798**
Trahan, Paul, 535
Trapp, Kenneth, 108

Travis, Jeremy, 507, 511, 516, 521
Travis, L. E., III, 424
Traynham, Vella M., 230
Treadwell, Alexander F., 876
Treadwell, Cathy, 826
Treanor, William, 633
Treiber, Kathleen, 9
Treichel, Janet M., 180
Trenk, Peggy Olson, 770
Trentacoste, Michael, 678
Tribble, Conrad, 885
Trilling, Donald R., 654
Triplitt, Jim, 44
Trotter, Robert S., 656
Troutman, Charles H., III, 872
Troy, Pat, 92
Troyer, Michael, 386
Truby, Roy, 195
Trueheart, William, 196, 206
Trujillo, Michael H., 376
Trull, Frankie L., 284
Truman, Edwin M., 471
Trumbile, JoAnne, 874
Truscott, John, 874
Tsepkalo, Valery V., 882
Tsilas, Loucas, 886
Tsui, Pauline W., 10
Tubbesing, Carl, 346
Tuck, Leonore, 764
Tucker, Alice, 759
Tucker, C. DeLores, 692
Tucker, David, 782
Tucker, Karen, 361, 366
Tuerk, Helmut, 882
Tufo, Peter F., 887
Tuite, Lisa, 822
Tulafono, Togiola T., 871
Tull, John, 28
Tunheim, John R., 116
Tureen, Heather, 711
Turnbull, Bernice A., 878
Turner, Archie, 333
Turner, Deborah, 688
Turner, Gene, 775
Turner, James C., 496, 497
Turner, James J., 830
Turner, Jim, D-Texas, 725, 734–735, 738–739, 749, **798**
Turner, John F., 278
Turner, Lee, 779
Turner, Roger, 884, 896
Turton, Dan, 701
Tuttle, William G. T., Jr., 573
Tvardek, Steven F., 472
Twaddell, William H., 891
Tweedie, St. Clair, 135
Twining, Charles H., 883
Twiss, John R., Jr., 286
Tydings, John, 135, 414
Tygesen, K. Erik, 885
Tymchuk, Kerry, 834
Tyson, Samuel, 258

Udall, Tom, 876
Udell, Gilman, 548

Walsh, Sally, 698
Walsh, Sean, 871, 876
Walter, Betty, 635
Walters, Leroy, 394, 602
Walton, Kimberly, 226
Wamp, Zach, R-Tenn., 725, 728–730, **799**
Wamsley, Herbert C., 162
Wanner, Raymond E., 598
Ward, Emmett, 384
Ward, George F., Jr., 891
Ward, Lacy, 767
Ward, Mark W., 709
Ward, M. L., 529, 533, 553
Ward, Raleigh, 836
Warden, Janice L., 649
Ware, Michael O., 823
Warfield, Suzy, 821
Wargo, Andrea A., 292
Wargo, John R., 338
Warner, Edward L., III, 556, 566
Warner, John W., R-Va., 80, 81, 100, 185, 331, 558, 593, 669, 673, 686, 687, 690, 691, 694, 698, 704, 708, 726, 803–804, 807–808, 810–811, 814–815, 816, 817, **836**
Warner, Susie, 782
Warren, Andrew, 776
Warren, David L., 191
Warren, H. Michael, 72
Warrington, George D., 681
Warthin, T. Whittier, 463
Wasch, Kenneth A., 89, 614
Washington, Herbert, 670
Washington, Mary, 830
Wasley, Liam, 887
Wasley, Terree P., 790
Waszck, Steve, 540
Waters, Jackie, 226
Waters, Maxine, D-Calif., 695, 722, 730–731, 737–738, 747, 749, **799**
Wathen, Phyllis P., 115
Watkins, Chandra, 893
Watkins, Dayton J., 412
Watkins, Margie, 767
Watkins, Shirley R., 36, 55
Watkins, Stan, 790
Watkins, Wes, R-Okla., 725, 746–747, **799**
Watkins, Yelberton, 758
Watkins-Foote, Kimberly, 193
Watrous, David S., 663
Watson, Bruce, 307
Watson, Dale, 579
Watson, Dennis, 783
Watson, Elizabeth, 495, 704
Watson, Harlan, 248, 254, 257, 263, 269, 276, 293, 296, 313
Watson, Kathy, 772
Watson, Robert A., 630, 648
Watt, Melvin, D-N.C., 725, 730–731, 747, **799**
Wattenmaker, Richard J., 117
Watts, Carol, 595, 606
Watts, George B., 65

Watts, J. C., Jr., R-Okla., 725, 738–739, 744–745, **799**
Watts, Linda, 885
Watts, Ralph S., Jr., 469
Watty, Edward I., 885
Waugh, David A., 220
Waxman, Henry A., D-Calif., 722, 732–733, 734–735, 747, **800**
Waxman, Laura DeKoven, 630, 649
Waxman, Seth P., 491
Wayands, Dennis, 333
Wayne, Karen, 361
Wayne, Kirk, 53
Weatherly, Deborah A., 99, 200, 245, 276, 489, 592
Weatherman, Hal, 783
Weathers, Clifford T., 527, 553
Weaver, David A., 340
Weaver, Donald L., 365
Weaver, James, 110, 114
Weaver, Kim, 704
Weaver, Nan, 791
Weaver, Paul, 544
Webb, David O., 261
Webb, Frances, 321, 336
Webb, Nancy, 754
Webb, William, 695
Webber, Frederick L., 612
Webber, Mildred, 15, 37, 132, 147, 150, 168, 231, 245, 276, 287, 341, 464, 607
Weber, Thomas A., 43, 304, 611, 615
Weber, William L., 240
Weber, William R., 54, 412
Webster, Duane, 86, 185
Webster, Eric, 697
Webster, Jamey, 755
Webster, R. Tim, 367
Wechsler, Steve, 151, 431
Weckstein, Paul, 28, 173
Weeden, Kathryn S., 708
Wehrwein, Charles W., 425
Weideman, Kent M., 891
Weidie, Wayne, 797
Weiff, Betty, 415
Weil, James, 59, 629
Weill-Hallé, Vera P., 63
Weinberg, Daniel H., 317, 408
Weinberg, Myrl, 354
Weinberg, Wendy, 16
Weiner, Bennett M., 26
Weiner, Janice, 886
Weiner, Ronald H., 674
Weinfurter, John, 713
Weingarten, William, 251
Weinman, Janice, 201
Weinstein, Allen, 441
Weinstock, Lawrence, 267, 290, 295, 420
Weir, Diana, 765
Weir, Jeff, 544
Weisberg, Stuart E., 238
Weisman, David S., 565
Weisman, Steve, 5
Weiss, Daniel, 782
Weiss, Deborah, 183, 694, 707
Weiss, Joan C., 522

Weiss, Marina, 381, 394
Weiss, Nancy, 82
Weiss, Stanley, 571
Welburn, Brenda L., 174
Welch, Betty S., 226, 527
Welch, Jenny, 759
Welch, Larry D., 573
Welch, Richard, 504
Welch, Tom, 883, 892, 896
Welday, Paul, 775
Weldon, Curt, R-Pa., 725, 738–739, 741–742, 748, **800**
Weldon, Dave, R-Fla., 723
Weller, Jerry, R-Ill., 723, 746–747, 748, 750, **800**
Wellman, Mark, 767
Wells, John Calhoun, 230
Wells, Reginald, 638, 646
Wellstone, Paul, D-Minn., 724, 811–812, 813, 814, 815–816, 816, **836**
Welsch, Federico, 390
Welsh, Fred, 157
Welsh, Peggy, 71, 247, 256, 315, 674, 682
Welt, Leo G. B., 479
Weltmann, Allen J., 711
Wenk, Chris, 697
Werner-Ramirez, Constance, 116
Werth, Karla, 782
Wesc, Aaron, 831
West, Cheryl, 396
West, Fredette, 795
West, Jade, 702
West, Jake, 158, 423
West, Mary Beth, 456
West, Richard, 571
West, Togo D., Jr., 546
West, Tony, 871
West, W. Richard, 107
Westwood, John, 527
Wetherill, Rick, 409
Wetmore, David, 872
Wexler, Chuck, 519
Wexler, Robert, D-Fla., 723, 736–738, **800**
Weygand, Bob, D-R.I., 725, 730–732, 743, **800**
Weyrich, Paul M., 488, 715
Whaley, Lee, 834
Wharton, Donald E., 710
Wheat, Richard, 527
Wheeler, Gerry, 181, 208
Wheeler, Peter M., 650
Wheeler, Susan, 760
Wheeler, Thomas E., 76
Whelan, Katherine, 717
Whelihan, Alice M., 106
Whiley, Flora, 231
Whipple, Earl, 789
Whiston, Julia D., 91
Whitbred, Judy, 763
Whitcomb, Shelley, 766
White, Charles, 680
White, Charles E., 801
White, Daryl Y., 78
White, David E., 527

Subject Index

Entries in **BOLD CAPITALS** are the names of chapters and appendices; those in **bold** indicate major subsections. Page numbers in bold indicate the main entries for congressional committees and subcommittees (**pp. 727-748, 803-817**).

AAA Foundation for Traffic Safety, 678
AARP. *See American Assn. of Retired Persons*
Abbreviations, state and territory (list), 840
ABC News, 90
Abortion, 503-505
Academic Collective Bargaining Information Service, 178, 231
Academy for Educational Development, 41, 181, 469
Academy for State and Local Government, 344
Access to Congressional Information, 686-688
Accreditation
    colleges and universities, 191-192, 209
    media representatives, 92-93
Accrediting Commission of Career Schools and Colleges of Technology, 209
Accuracy in Academia, 188
Accuracy in Media, 70
ACIL, 593
ACLU. *See American Civil Liberties Union.*
Acquired Immune Deficiency Syndrome (AIDS), 387-389
    toll-free numbers, 12
ACT*American College Testing, 188
Action Committee for Rural Electrification, 711
Action on Smoking and Health, 23
Active Ballot Club, 709
Ad Hoc Congressional Committee on Irish Affairs, 695
Adjutants General Assn. of the United States, 545
Administration for Children and Families, 375, 626, 630
    Administration on Developmental Disabilities, 638, 646
    Child Support Enforcement, 631
    Community Services, 408, 626
    Family Assistance-Job Opportunities and Basic Skills Training, 631
    Information, 375, 626, 630
    Refugee Resettlement, 222, 444, 450
    regional offices, 848
    Repatriate Program, 454
    State Systems, 626
Administration for Children, Youth, and Families
    Children's Bureau, 631
    Family and Youth Services, 510, 631
    National Center on Child Abuse and Neglect, 631
Administration for Native Americans, 6, 408, 626
Administration on Aging, 7, 637
Administrative Assistants Assn. of the U.S. House of Representatives, 708

Administrative Office of the U.S. Courts, 493, 498, 516, 522
    Bankruptcy Judges Division, 500
    Federal Corrections and Supervision, 516
    Information, 493, 498, 516, 522
    personnel office, 320
    Statistics, 522
Adolescents. *See Children and Families.*
Adoptees in Search, 633
Adoption information, 12
Adoption Service Information Agency, 633
Adult education, 209-210
    GED hotline, 13
Adventist Development and Relief Agency International, 469
Advertising, 165
Advertising Mail Marketing Assn., 340
Advisory Committee for Trade Policy and Negotiations, 458
Advisory Council on Employee Welfare and Pension Benefit Plans, 233
Advisory Council on Historic Preservation, 114
    financial officer, 332
    general counsel, 494
Advocacy
    health policy, 382-401
    political, 709-717
ADVOCACY AND PUBLIC SERVICE (chap. 1), 1-34
Advocacy Institute, 25
Advocates for Highway and Auto Safety, 679
Advocates for Youth, 380, 392
Aeronautical Repair Station Assn., 661
Aerospace Education Foundation, 541, 623, 661
Aerospace Industries Assn. of America, 623, 661
Aerospace Medical Assn., 665
Affiliated Leadership League of and for the Blind of America, 644
AFL-CIO (American Federation of Labor-Congress of Industrial Organizations), 212, 232
    congressional ratings, 714
    departments (box), 231
    Human Resources Development Institute, 205, 220
    trade and industrial departments (box), 231
AFL-CIO Maritime Committee, 669
Africa, 473-475
African-American Institute, 474

African Americans
civil rights advocacy, 3-4
African Development Foundation, 473
Africare, 474
Aged persons. *See Elderly persons.*
Agence France-Presse, 90
Agency for Health Care Policy and Research, 349
Agency for International Development (AID), 62, 468
Africa Bureau, 473
Asia and Near East Bureau, 475, 483
Center for Environment, 250
Center for Human Capacity Development, 468
Center for Population, Health, and Nutrition, 445
Center for Trade and Investment Services, 459
congressional liaison, 704
Europe and the New Independent States Bureau, 477, 486
financial officer, 332
fraud and abuse hotline, 334
freedom of information contact, 82
general counsel, 494
Global Programs, Field Support and Research Bureau, 468
Humanitarian Response Bureau, 445
Information, 62, 468
inspector general, 334
Latin America and the Caribbean Bureau, 480
library, 184
Population, 392
small and disadvantaged business contact, 167
Small and Disadvantaged Business Utilization/Minority Resource Center, 165
U.S. Foreign Disaster Assistance, 445
Agency for Toxic Substances and Disease Registry, 291
Agribusiness Council, 47
Agricultural Cooperative Development International, 63
Agricultural Marketing Service, 36
Cotton, 47
Dairy, 48
Fruit and Vegetable, 49
Information, 36
Livestock and Seed, 50, 64, 65
Poultry, 65
Science and Technology, 54
Seed Regulatory and Testing, 44
Tobacco, 52
Transportation and Marketing, 44
Agricultural Research Institute, 41
Agricultural Research Service, 39, 55
National Agricultural Pesticide Impact Assessment Program, 41
National Plant Germplasm System, 45
AGRICULTURE AND NUTRITION (chap. 2), 35-66
commodities, 44-53
cotton, 47-48
dairy products, 48-49
eggs, 48-49
farm loans, insurance, and subsidies, 53-54
fertilizer and pesticides, 41-42
fruits and vegetables, 49-50
general policy, 36-39
grains and oilseeds, 50-51
horticulture and gardening, 42-43
livestock and poultry, 64-66
migrant and seasonal farm workers, 222-223
nutrition issues. *See Food and Nutrition.*
research and education, 39-41

soil and watershed conservation, 43-44
sugar, 51-52
tobacco and peanuts, 52-53
world food assistance, 62-64
Agriculture Department (USDA), 36
Agricultural Marketing Service. *See that heading.*
Agricultural Research Service. *See that heading.*
Animal and Plant Health Inspection Service. *See that heading.*
Board of Contract Appeals, 36
Chief Economist, 36
Commodity Credit Corp., 45, 53
congressional liaison, 704
Consumer Affairs, 12
Cooperative State Research, Education, and Extension Service. *See that heading.*
Economic Research Service, 40, 49, 51, 52, 140, 242
equal employment opportunity contact, 226
Farm Service Agency. *See that heading.*
financial officer, 332
Food and Consumer Service. *See that heading.*
Food and Nutrition Service, 842
Food, Nutrition, and Consumer Services, 36, 55
Food Safety and Inspection Service. *See that heading.*
Foreign Agricultural Service. *See that heading.*
Forest Service. *See that heading.*
fraud and abuse hotline, 334
freedom of information contact, 82
general counsel, 494
Graduate School, 187, 209
International Institute for Training and Education, 448
Grain Inspection, Packers, and Stockyards Administration, 50, 65
Information, 36
information officer, 78
inspector general, 334
Internet world wide web site, 84
library, 36, 184
Marketing and Regulatory Programs, 45
meat and poultry safety inquiries, 12
National Agricultural Library, 40, 56, 193
National Agricultural Statistics Service, 40, 140
National Arboretum, 42, 106, 603
Natural Resources and Environment, 273
Natural Resources Conservation Service, 43, 304
organization (chart), 37
personnel office, 320
procurement officer, 326
publications office, 79
Research, Education, and Economics, 39, 204
Risk Management Agency, 53
Rural Business-Cooperative Service, 40, 45, 270, 412
Rural Development, 53, 412, 427, 842-844
Rural Housing Service, 412, 425
Rural Utilities Service, 255, 312, 412
secretary, 36
small and disadvantaged business contact, 167
Special Emphasis Outreach Program, 39
Women's Executive Leadership Program, 229
World Agricultural Outlook Board, 63
Agri-Energy Roundtable, 47
AID. *See Agency for International Development.*
AIDS Action Council, 388

American Academy of Pediatrics, 22, 381
American Academy of Physician Assistants, 370
American Advertising Federation, 165
American African Affairs Assn., 474
American AIDS PAC, 710
American Alliance for Health, Physical Education, Recreation, and Dance, 121
American Anthropological Assn., 617
American Apparel Manufacturers Assn., 156
American-Arab Anti-Discrimination Committee, 10
American Arbitration Assn., 232, 454, 497
American Architectural Foundation, 177
American Arts Alliance, 100
American Assn. for Adult and Continuing Education, 209
American Assn. for Clinical Chemistry, Inc., 369, 612
American Assn. for Health Education, 366
American Assn. for Higher Education, 188
American Assn. for Laboratory Accreditation, 593
American Assn. for Marriage and Family Therapy, 633
American Assn. for Respiratory Care, 396
American Assn. for the Advancement of Science, 593
    Education and Human Resources Programs, 207
    International Programs, 598
    Scientific Freedom, Responsibility and Law Program, 594
American Assn. for World Health, 353
American Assn. of Advertising Agencies, 165
American Assn. of Airport Executives, 664
American Assn. of Blacks in Energy, 246
American Assn. of Blood Banks, 389
American Assn. of Children's Residential Centers, 381
American Assn. of Colleges for Teacher Education, 178
American Assn. of Colleges of Nursing, 370
American Assn. of Colleges of Osteopathic Medicine, 371
American Assn. of Colleges of Pharmacy, 188, 362, 366
American Assn. of Colleges of Podiatric Medicine, 371
American Assn. of Collegiate Registrars and Admissions Officers, 188
American Assn. of Community Colleges, 188
American Assn. of Dental Schools, 369
American Assn. of Engineering Societies, 604
American Assn. of Family and Consumer Sciences, 204
American Assn. of Health Plans, 356
American Assn. of Healthcare Consultants, 366
American Assn. of Homes and Services for the Aging, 378, 428
American Assn. of Immunologists, 369
American Assn. of Motor Vehicle Administrators, 673
American Assn. of Museums, 108
    Museum Assessment Program, 106
American Assn. of Pastoral Counselors, 30, 402
American Assn. of Pharmaceutical Scientists, 362
American Assn. of Physics Teachers, 207
American Assn. of Political Consultants, 690
American Assn. of Port Authorities, 671
American Assn. of Retired Persons, 7, 236, 637
    AARP Andrus Foundation, 378
    AARP/Vote, 691
    Consumer Issues, 428
    Health and Long Term Care, 378
    National Retired Teachers Assn., 178
    Senior Community Service Employment Program, 223
American Assn. of School Administrators, 178
American Assn. of State Colleges and Universities, 188
American Assn. of State Highway and Transportation Officials, 675
American Assn. of Suicidology, 402

American Assn. of University Affiliated Programs for Persons with Developmental Disabilities, 198, 640
American Assn. of University Professors, 188
American Assn. of University Women, 201
American Assn. of University Women Educational Foundation, 177
American Assn. on Mental Retardation, 647
American Astronautical Society, 623
American Astronomical Society, 624
American Automobile Assn. (AAA), 673
American Automobile Manufacturers Assn., 676
American Automotive Leasing Assn., 676
American Bakers Assn., 60
American Bankers Assn., 147
    BankPAC, 711
    Communications, 18
American Bankruptcy Institute, 501
American Baptist Churches U.S.A., 30
American Bar Assn.
    Center on Children and the Law, 511, 633
    Central and East European Law Initiative, 479, 487
    Commission on Mental and Physical Disability Law, 28, 402, 640
    Criminal Justice, 509, 516
    Dispute Resolution, 497
    Intellectual Property Law, 162
    International Law and Practice, 454, 520
    International Legal Exchange Program, 448
    Standing Committee on Election Law, 690
    Standing Committee on Environmental Law, 277
    Standing Committee on Law and Literacy, 205
    Standing Committee on World Order Under Law, 454
    Taxation Section, 501
    Washington Office, 494
American Battle Monuments Commission, 542
American Blind Lawyers Assn., 520, 644
American Board of Opticianry, 374
American Boiler Manufacturers Assn., 157, 246
American Bus Assn., 673, 684
American Business Conference, 133
American Butter Institute, 48
American Cancer Society, 390
American Canoe Assn., 121
American Car Rental Assn., 676
American Center for International Labor Solidarity, 215
American Chamber of Commerce Executives, 133
American Chemical Society, 612
    Petroleum Research Fund, 612
American Chiropractic Assn., 368
American Civil Liberties Union (ACLU), 81, 502
    internship programs, 176
    National Capital Area, 325
    Privacy and Technology, 21
American Civil Liberties Union Foundation
    National Prison Project, 516
American Clinical Laboratory Assn., 353
American Coal Ash Assn., 258
American Cocoa Research Institute, 52
American Coke and Coal Chemicals Institute, 259
American College of Cardiology, 371
American College of Dentists, 369
American College of Emergency Physicians, 371
American College of Health Care Administrators, 361, 366
American College of Nuclear Physicians, 371
American College of Nurse-Midwives, 370, 381

American College of Obstetricians and Gynecologists, 372, 381
American College of Osteopathic Surgeons, 372
American College of Physicians, 372
American College of Preventive Medicine, 372
American College of Radiology, 372
American College of Surgeons, 372
American Conference of Academic Deans, 188
American Congress on Surveying and Mapping, 619
American Conservative Union, 560, 712, 714
American Consulting Engineers Council, 604
   Research and Management Foundation, 604
American Corn Millers Federation, 50
American Corporate Counsel Assn., 500
American Correctional Assn., 516
American Cotton Shippers Assn., 48
American Council for an Energy-Efficient Economy, 249
American Council for Capital Formation, 133
American Council of Life Insurance, 159
American Council of State Savings Supervisors, 147
American Council of Teachers of Russian, 488
American Council of the Blind, 644
American Council of the Blind Government Employees, 321
American Council of Trustees and Alumni, 188
American Council of Young Political Leaders, 449
American Council on Education, 189
American Counseling Assn., 402
American Crop Protection Assn., 42
American Defense Institute, 533, 560
American Dental Assn., 369
   Political Action Committee, 711
American Dental Trade Assn., 369
American Design Drafting Assn., 418
American Diabetes Assn., 391
American Dietetic Assn., 57
American Educational Research Assn., 182
American Enterprise Institute for Public Policy Research
   Economic Policy Studies, 133, 212
   Fiscal Policy Studies, 142
   Foreign and Defense Policy Studies, 440, 560
   internship programs, 176
   Social and Individual Responsibility Project, 628
American Electronics Assn., 86
American Ethical Union
   Washington Ethical Action, 30
American Family Society, 633
American Farm Bureau Federation, 38, 714
American Farmland Trust, 44
American Federation of Government Employees, 321
American Federation of Police, 518
American Federation of School Administrators, 179
American Federation of State, County, and Municipal
  Employees
   PEOPLE, Qualified, 710
American Federation of Teachers, 179
   Committee on Political Education, 710
American Federation of Television and Radio Artists, 93
American Feed Industry Assn., 50
American Fiber Manufacturers Assn., 156
American Film Institute Theater, 102
American Financial Services Assn., 18
American Fisheries Society, 285
American Folklife Center, 119, 183
American Foreign Service Assn., 232, 444
American Forest and Paper Assn., 302, 421
American Forests, 302

American Foundation for AIDS Research (AmFAR), 388
American Foundation for Autistic Children, 647
American Foundation for the Blind, 644
American Friends Service Committee, 30
American Frozen Food Institute, 61
American Gaming Assn., 122
American Gas Assn., 260
   Statistics, 253
American Gastroenterological Assn., 391
American Gear Manufacturers Assn., 157
American Geological Institute, 305, 609
American Geophysical Union, 607, 624
American Gold Star Mothers, 553
American Hardwood Export Council, 302
American Health Care Assn., 361
   Political Action Committee, 711
American Health Quality Assn., 372
American Heart Assn., 395
American Helicopter Society, 662
American Hellenic Institute, 479
American Herbal Products Assn., 58, 283
American Highway Users Alliance, 679
American Hiking Society, 122, 311
American Historical Assn., 115
American history
   genealogy, 118
   military history, 540-544
   postal history, 340-341
   Washington area, 119-121
American Homeowners Assn., 430
American Horse Protection Assn., 283
American Horticultural Society, 43
American Hospital Assn., 358
American Hotel and Motel Assn., 124
American Humane Assn., 283, 633
American Immigration Lawyers Assn., 451
American Indian Heritage Foundation, 119
American Indians. *See* Native Americans.
American Industrial Health Council, 239, 353
American Industrial Hygiene Assn., 239
American Inns of Court Foundation, 520
American Institute for Cancer Research, 390
American Institute for Conservation of Historic and Artistic
  Works, 115
American Institute in Taiwan, 476
American Institute of Aeronautics and Astronautics, 623, 662
American Institute of Architects, 113, 419
   American Architectural Foundation, 177
American Institute of Biological Sciences, 600
American Institute of Certified Public Accountants, 147
American Institute of Chemical Engineers, 612
American Institute of Chemists, 612
American Institute of Physics, 615
American Institute of Ultrasound in Medicine, 360
American Institutes for Research, 617
American Insurance Assn., 159, 240
American Intellectual Property Law Assn., 162
American International Automobile Dealers Assn., 676
American Iron and Steel Institute, 307
American Israel Public Affairs Committee, 485
American Jewish Committee, 30
American Jewish Congress, 30, 485, 506
American Kidney Fund, 396
American Kurdish Information Network, 485
American Labor Education Center, 220

American Land Title Assn., 430
American League for Exports and Security Assistance, 466, 571
American League of Financial Institutions, 147, 433
American League of Lobbyists, 709
American Legion National Organization, 548
    Claims Service, 550
    Review and Correction Boards Unit, 550
American Legislative Exchange Council, 344
American Library Assn., 185
    Information Technology Policy, 86
American Logistics Assn., 585
American Lung Assn., 396
American Machine Tool Distributors Assn., 157
American Management Assn., 133
American Maritime Congress, 669
American Meat Institute, 61, 65
American Medical Assn., 356, 372
    Political Action Committee, 711
American Medical Athletic Assn., 122
American Medical Group Assn., 366
American Medical Informatics Assn., 360
American Medical Rehabilitation Providers Assn., 640
American Medical Women's Assn., 372400
American Mental Health Counselors Assn., 402
American Methanol Institute, 270
American Mobile Telecommunications Assn., 76
American Moving and Storage Assn., 658
American Music Therapy Assn., 111
American Muslim Council, 10, 31
American National Metric Council, 616
American National Standards Institute, 154, 599
American Near East Refugee Aid, 485
American Network of Community Options and Resources, 640
American News Women's Club, 89
American Nursery and Landscape Assn., 43, 419
American Nurses Assn., 370
American Occupational Therapy Assn., 371, 640
American Optometric Assn., 374
American Orthotic and Prosthetic Assn., 360, 641
American Osteopathic Assn., 372
American Osteopathic Healthcare Assn., 366
American Peace Society, 441
American Petroleum Institute, 260
    Finance, Accounting, and Statistics, 253
    Taxation Dept., 260
American Pharmaceutical Assn., 362
American Physical Society, 265, 615
American Physical Therapy Assn., 371, 641
American Physiological Society, 385
American Planning Assn., 410
American Plastics Council, 296
American Podiatric Medical Assn., 372
American Poetry and Literacy Project, 104, 205
American Political Science Assn., 179
    Congressional Fellowship Program, 177
American Portland Cement Alliance, 422
American Postal Workers Union, 339
    Political Fund Committee, 710
American Press Institute, 95
American Production and Inventory Control Society, 154
American Prosecutors Research Institute, 509
    National Drug Prosecution Center, 512
American Psychiatric Assn., 373, 402
American Psychological Assn., 402, 617
American Public Gas Assn., 260

American Public Health Assn., 353
American Public Power Assn., 255
American Public Transit Assn., 684
American Public Welfare Assn., 628
American Public Works Assn., 416, 656
American Pulpwood Assn., 303
American Recreation Coalition, 122, 311
American Red Cross
    Armed Forces Emergency Services, 529, 548
    Disaster Services, 576
    Emergency Communications, 530
    National Headquarters, 63, 388, 389, 446
American Rehabilitation Counseling Assn., 641
American Resort Development Assn., 122, 305, 410, 430
American Retreaders Assn., 676
American Rivers, 314
American Road and Transportation Builders Assn., 675
American Roentgen Ray Society, 360
American Running and Fitness Assn., 122
American Samoa's Delegate to Congress, 488
American School Food Service Assn., 194
American Security Council, 560, 714
American Seed Trade Assn., 47
American Sheep Industry Assn., 65
American Short Line Railroad Assn., 682
American Society for Biochemistry and Molecular Biology, 601
American Society for Cell Biology, 601
American Society for Clinical Laboratory Science, 370
American Society for Clinical Nutrition, 58
American Society for Engineering Education, 207, 605
American Society for Horticultural Science, 43, 603
American Society for Industrial Security, 21, 582
American Society for Information Science, 86, 185
American Society for Microbiology, 601
American Society for Nutritional Sciences, 58
American Society for Parenteral and Enteral Nutrition, 58
American Society for Pharmacology and Experimental Thera-
    peutics, 362
American Society for Photogrammetry and Remote Sensing,
    619
American Society for Public Administration, 341
American Society for the Protection of Cruelty to Animals
    (ASPCA), 283
American Society for Therapeutic Radiology and Oncology,
    390
American Society for Training and Development, 205, 220
American Society of Access Professionals, 81
American Society of Addiction Medicine, 373, 399
American Society of Appraisers, 431
American Society of Association Executives, 134
American Society of Civil Engineers, 421, 605
American Society of Clinical Oncology, 390
American Society of Clinical Pathologists, 370
American Society of Consultant Pharmacists, 367
American Society of Health-System Pharmacists, 362
American Society of Heating, Refrigerating, and Air
    Conditioning Engineers, 421
American Society of Interior Designers, 419
American Society of Internal Medicine, 373
American Society of International Law, 454
American Society of Landscape Architects, 419
American Society of Mechanical Engineers, 605
American Society of Naval Engineers, 573
American Society of Newspaper Editors, 95

Assn. of Community Cancer Centers, 390
Assn. of Community College Trustees, 189
Assn. of Community Organizations for Reform Now (ACORN), 428, 628
Assn. of Direct Response Fundraising Counsel, 21
Assn. of Farmworker Opportunity Programs, 223
Assn. of Financial Services Holding Companies, 147
Assn. of Flight Attendants, 662
Assn. of Foam Packaging Recyclers, 296
Assn. of Foreign Investors in U.S. Real Estate, 431, 466
Assn. of Former Intelligence Officers, 582
Assn. of Governing Boards of Universities and Colleges, 189
Assn. of Government Accountants, 341
Assn. of Higher Education Facilities Officers, 189
Assn. of Hispanic Serving Health Professions Schools, 367
Assn. of Independent Television Stations, 74
Assn. of International Automobile Manufacturers, 676
Assn. of Jesuit Colleges and Universities, 190
Assn. of Junior Leagues International, 25
Assn. of Local Air Pollution Control Officials, 291
Assn. of Local Housing Finance Agencies, 433
Assn. of Military Colleges and Schools of the U.S., 537
Assn. of Military Surgeons of the United States, 532
Assn. of National Advertisers, 165
Assn. of Oil Pipe Lines, 262
Assn. of Part-Time Professionals, 213
Assn. of Performing Arts Presenters, 100
Assn. of Private Pension and Welfare Plans, 236
Assn. of Professional Firms Practicing in the Geosciences, 605
Assn. of Professors of Medicine, 373
Assn. of Publicly Traded Companies, 150
Assn. of Reproductive Health Professionals, 367, 503
Assn. of Research Libraries, 86, 185
Assn. of Sales and Marketing Companies, 163
Assn. of School Business Officials International, 179
Assn. of Schools and Colleges of Optometry, 374
Assn. of Schools of Allied Health Professions, 367
Assn. of Schools of Public Health, 367
Assn. of Science-Technology Centers, 106, 207
Assn. of State and Interstate Water Pollution Control Administrators, 299
Assn. of State and Territorial Health Officials, 353, 367
Assn. of State and Territorial Public Health Laboratory Directors, 370
Assn. of State and Territorial Solid Waste Management Officials, 296
Assn. of State Drinking Water Administrators, 314
Assn. of Teacher Educators, 179
Assn. of Teachers of Preventive Medicine, 367
Assn. of the United States Army, 525, 560
Assn. of the Wall and Ceiling Industries, 422
Assn. of Trial Lawyers of America, 160, 495
    Political Action Committee, 711
Assn. of Universities for Research in Astronomy, 624
Assn. of University Programs in Health Administration, 367
Assn. of Women in International Trade, 466
Assn. on Third World Affairs, 441
Assn. to Unite the Democracies, 441
Associated Accounting Firms International, 147
Associated Builders and Contractors, 417
Associated Credit Bureaus, Inc., 148
Associated General Contractors of America, 417
Associated Landscape Contractors of America, 417
Associated Press, 90, 688
Asthma and Allergy Foundation of America, 395

Astronomy, 624
Atlantic Council of the United States, 441, 450
    Energy and Environment Program, 253
Atlantic States Marine Fisheries Commission, 284
Atmospheric sciences, 607-608
Autism Society of America, 647
Automobile transportation. *See Motor Vehicles.*
Automotive Consumer Action Program, 16
Automotive Parts and Accessories Assn., 676
Automotive Parts Rebuilders Assn., 677
Automotive Recyclers Assn., 677
Aviation. *See Air Transportation.*
Aviation Consumer Action Project, 662

Bakery, Confectionery, and Tobacco Workers' International Union, 23, 61
Balance of Payments Statistics Yearbook, 466
Balkan Institute, 479
Baltimore Sun, 90
Bands, military, 543-544
Bank Insurance Fund (FDIC), 143
Bank Marketing Assn., 148
Bankers Assn. for Foreign Trade, 148, 473
Bankers' Roundtable, 148, 500
Bankruptcy, 500-501
Banks and banking, 143-149
    complaints and inquiries, 13
    credit practices, 17-18
    departmental and agency financial officers (box), 332-333
    military personnel, 530-531
    mortgage banking, 432-434
Baptist Joint Committee on Public Affairs, 31
Baptist World Alliance, 31
Barbara Bush Foundation for Family Literacy, 206
Bazelon Center for Mental Health Law, 28, 402
Beer Institute, 59
Benefits, employee. *See Employee benefits.*
Best Buddies International, 647
Better Hearing Institute, 645
Beverages, 59-60
Bicycle Federation of America, 122
Bilingual education, 202-203
Biographical Directory of the United States Congress, 80, 686
Biology and Life Sciences, 599-604
Biophysical Society, 601
Biotechnology, 602
Biotechnology Industry Organization, 602
Biscuit and Cracker Manufacturers' Assn., 61
Bituminous Coal Operators Assn., 259
Black Americans
    civil rights advocacy, 3-4
Black Americans in Congress, 80, 686
Black America's PAC, 710
Black Revolutionary War Patriots Foundation, 543
Blacks in Government, 3, 321
Blind and visually impaired persons, 644-645
Blinded Veterans Assn., 548, 551, 644
Blood and bone marrow, 389-390
Blue Book (*National Automobile Dealers Used Car Guide*), 677
Blue Cross and Blue Shield Assn., 356, 359
B'nai B'rith International, 31
    Senior Citizens Housing Committee, 428
B'nai B'rith Klutznick Museum, 106
Boat Owners Assn. of the United States, 122, 669
Boating hotline, 12

Caring Institute, 25
Carnegie Endowment for International Peace, 441
Carnegie Institution of Washington, 601, 611
Carpenters' Legislative Improvement Committee, 710
Catalog of Federal Domestic Assistance, 343, 405
Catholic Charities USA, 31, 628
Catholic Foreign Mission Society of America (Maryknoll Fathers and Brothers), 33
Catholic Health Assn. of the United States, 377
Catholic Information Center, 31
Catholic University, 187
Catholic War Veterans U.S.A., 548
Catholics for a Free Choice, 504
Cato Institute, 176, 713
Catoctin Mountain Park, 120
Caucuses, 695-698
CBS News, 90
Cellular Telecommunications Industry Assn., 76
Cemeteries and memorials, 542-543
Census Bureau, 317
    Administrative and Customer Services, 691
    Agriculture and Financial Statistics, 39
    Decennial Census, 317
    Demographic Surveys, 218, 317
    Economic Programs, 127, 139
    Fertility and Family Statistics, 392
    Foreign Trade, 250, 459
    Geography, 617
    Governments Division, 139, 342, 408
    Housing and Household Economic Statistics, 317, 408
    Information, 317
    library, 317
    Manufacturing and Construction, 140, 153, 408, 416
    construction and minerals, 152
    Population, 317, 691
    publications office, 79
    regional offices, 844
    Services Division, 140, 163, 653
Census/Population Data, 317-318
Center for Applied Linguistics, 104, 206
Center for Auto Safety, 16, 291, 421, 679
Center for Clean Air Policy, 291
Center for Community Change, 410, 428, 628
Center for Contemporary Arab Studies, 485
Center for Corporate Public Involvement, 25
Center for Defense Information, 176, 560, 566
Center for Democracy, 441
Center for Democracy and Technology, 21, 86
Center for Dispute Settlement, 497
Center for Drug Evaluation and Research, 362, 387
Center for Economic Organizing, 236
Center for Education Reform, 173
Center for Energy and Economic Development, 254
Center for Equal Opportunity, 227
Center for Global Education, 645
Center for Health, Environment and Justice, 293
Center for Housing Policy, 407, 426
Center for Human Rights and Humanitarian Law, 457
Center for Immigration Studies, 452
Center for Individual Rights, 503
Center for Intercultural Education and Development, 449, 470
Center for International Policy, 482
Center for International Private Enterprise, 466
Center for Judeo-Christian Values, 31
Center for Law and Education, 28, 173

Center for Law and Social Policy, 29, 628
Center for Marine Conservation, 285, 288, 299
Center for Media and Public Affairs, 70
Center for Media Education, 70
Center for National Policy, 713
Center for National Security Studies
    Gelman Library, 83, 456, 582
Center for Naval Analyses, 560
Center for Patient Advocacy, 354, 386
Center for Policy Alternatives, 176, 344
Center for Public Integrity, 335
Center for Responsive Politics, 690
Center for Science in the Public Interest, 58, 60, 176
Center for Security Policy, 560
Center for Sickle Cell Disease, 394
Center for Strategic and Budgetary Assessments, 562
Center for Strategic and International Studies, 176, 441
Center for Study of Responsive Law, 29, 176, 495
Center for the Advancement of Language Learning, 103
Center for the Community Interest, 495
Center for the Study of Public Choice, 134
Center for the Study of Social Policy, 628
Center for the Support of Children, 634
Center for Voting and Democracy, 691
Center for Women Policy Studies, 9
Center for Women Veterans, 545
Center of Concern, 441
Center on Budget and Policy Priorities, 629
Center on Disability and Health, 377, 641
Center to Prevent Handgun Violence, 513
Centers for Disease Control and Prevention, 349, 379
    AIDS research, 387
    National Center for Health Statistics, 351
    National Institute for Occupational Safety and Health, 237, 351
    Smoking and Health/Liaison, 23
Central American Refugee Center, 446
Central Intelligence Agency (CIA), 579
    financial officer, 332
    freedom of information contact, 82
    general counsel, 494
    Information, 579
    information officer, 78
    inspector general, 334
    internship programs, 176
Central Liquidity Facility, 145
Challenger Center for Space Science Education, 207
Chamber of Shipping of America, 669
Charles F. Kettering Foundation, 173, 441
Chemical and Biological Arms Control Institute, 567
Chemical Manufacturers Assn., 612
Chemical Specialties Manufacturers Assn., 294
Chemistry, 611-612
Child Nutrition Forum, 58, 634
Child Welfare League of America, 634
Children and Families, 630-638
    abortion and reproductive issues, 503-505
    child abuse, 510-511
    congressional pages, 708
    domestic violence, 510-511
    education. *See Education; Postsecondary Education.*
    employment and training, 224-225
    family planning, 392-393
    health care, 379-382
    juvenile justice, 514

military support programs, 528-530
national runaway switchboard, 12
social services, 630-638
Children of the American Revolution, 115
Children's Defense Fund, 176, 381, 634
    Child Care Division, 634
Children's Foundation, 634
Children's Rights Council, 634
Chiropractors, 368
Chlorine Institute, 294
Chocolate Manufacturers Assn., 52
Christian Children's Fund, 446, 634
Christian Coalition, 713
Christian College Coalition, 190
Christian Legal Society, 506
Christian Life Commission of the Southern Baptist Convention, 31
Christian Relief Services, 629
Christian Science Committee on Publication, 31
Christian Science Monitor, 90
Church groups, 30-34
Church of Jesus Christ of Latter-Day Saints
    Family History Center, 118
Church of the Brethren, 32
Church Women United, 9
Church World Service, 446
CIA. *See Central Intelligence Agency.*
Cigar Assn. of America, 52
Cigars, cigarettes, and smoking, 23
Citizen Action, 16
Citizens' Commission on Civil Rights, 3
Citizens' Committee for the Right to Keep and Bear Arms, 513
Citizens Democracy Corps, 470
Citizens for a Sound Economy, 134, 142, 277
Citizens for Public Action on Blood Pressure and Cholesterol, 395
Citizens for State Power, 255
Citizens for Tax Justice, 142
Citizens Network for Foreign Affairs, 441
Citizenship education, 203-204
City governments. *See also State and Local Government.*
    in Washington area, 343
Civil Air Patrol
    National Capital Wing, 535, 574, 659
Civil liberties. *See Constitutional Law and Civil Liberties.*
Civil Rights, 2-10
    African Americans, 3-4
    employment. *See Equal Employment Opportunity.*
    gays and lesbians, 5-6
    Hispanics, 4-5
    housing discrimination hotline, 12
    native Americans, 6-7
    other minority groups, 10
    senior citizens, 7-8
    toll-free numbers, 12
    women, 8-10
Civil Service, 318-325
Civil War Trust, 115
Clara Barton National Historic Park, 120
Clean Sites, 294
Clean Water Action, 299
Clerkship Directors in Internal Medicine, 373
Climate Institute, 291, 608
Close Up Foundation, 203

Clothing and textiles, 156-157
Coal, 258-259
Coal and Slurry Technology Assn., 262
Coal Exporters Assn. of the United States, 259
Coal Miners Political Action Committee, 710
The Coalition, 696
Coalition for Employment Through Exports, 466
Coalition for Government Procurement, 327
Coalition for Juvenile Justice, 514
Coalition of Black Trade Unionists, 228, 232, 692
Coalition of Labor Union Women, 232
Coalition of Northeastern Governors (CONEG)
    Policy Research Center, Inc., 344
Coalition on Human Needs, 629
Coalition to Stop Gun Violence, 513
Coast Guard Combat Veterans Assn., 548
Coastal States Organization, 309
Codex Alimentarius Commission
    U.S. Codex Office, 57
Coins and currency, 137-138
College and University Personnel Assn., 190
College Board, 190, 192
College of American Pathologists, 373
College Republican National Committee, 718
College Work-Study Program, 192
Colleges and universities. *See also Postsecondary Education; specific college name.*
    Washington area (list), 187
Colonial Dames XVII Century, 116
Columbia Union College, 187
Commerce Business Daily, 325
Commerce Department, 127
    Air and Space Commercialization, 619
    Balance of Payments, 250, 471
    Bureau of Economic Analysis, 139
    Bureau of Export Administration. *See that heading.*
    Business Liaison, 166
    Census Bureau. *See that heading.*
    congressional liaison, 704
    Consumer Affairs, 12
    Economic Development Administration, 153, 405, 459, 844
    Economics and Statistics Administration, 127, 153
    equal employment opportunity contact, 226
    Export Administration Review Board, 569
    export enforcement toll-free number, 12
    financial officer, 332
    Foreign Trade Zones Board, 459
    fraud and abuse hotline, 334
    freedom of information contact, 82
    general counsel, 494
    Information, 127
    information officer, 78
    inspector general, 334
    International Investment, 459
    International Trade Administration. *See that heading.*
    Internet world wide web site, 84
    library, 127, 184
    Minority Business Development Agency, 167, 327, 847
    National Institute of Standards and Technology. *See that heading.*
    National Technical Information Service, 80, 103, 596
    National Telecommunications and Information Administration, 68, 85
    NOAA. *See National Oceanic and Atmospheric Administration.*

National Museum of Health and Medicine, 107, 541
National Reconnaissance Office, 580
National Security Agency, 580, 583
National War College, 536
Naval Medical Research Institute, 385, 532, 600
Naval Research Laboratory, 572
Navy Department. *See that heading.*
Near East and South Asia Affairs, 483
Nuclear, Chemical, and Biological Defense Programs, 565
On-Site Inspection Agency, 565
Operational Test and Evaluation, 587
organization (chart), 557
Peacekeeping and Humanitarian Assistance, 445
Personnel and Readiness, 524
personnel office (civilian), 320
Policy, 556
Prisoners of War and Missing Personnel, 533
procurement officer, 326
Public Affairs, 92
Public Communication, 524, 533
publications office, 79
Quality of Life, 529
Readiness and Training, 536
Research and Engineering, 572
Reserve Affairs, 544
secretary, 556
small and disadvantaged business contact, 167
Special Assistant for Gulf War Illnesses, 551
Special Operations and Low Intensity Conflict, 556, 579
Strategy and Threat Reduction, 556, 566
toll-free numbers, 12
Uniformed Services University of the Health Sciences, 536
U.S. Court of Appeals for the Armed Forces, 539
U.S. Naval Academy, 537, 544
U.S. Naval Observatory, 624
Walter Reed Army Institute of Research, 385, 388, 532
White House Communications Agency, 576
Defense Intelligence Agency, 579
Defense Information Systems Agency, 579
Defense Intelligence Agency, 579
Defense Logistics Agency, 587
Defense Logistics Support Command, 577
Information, 587
National Stockpile Center, 152, 578
personnel office, 320
Defense National Stockpile Center, 152, 578
Defense Nuclear Facilities Safety Board, 266
Defense Orientation Conference Assn., 560
Defense Personnel, 526-535
Defense policy. *See National Security.*
Defense Security Service, 582
Defense Special Weapons Agency, 568
Information, 568
Nuclear Test Program Personnel Review Program, 545, 551, 568
Defense Systems Management College, 536, 587
Defense Technical Information Center, 572, 598
Defense Trade and Technology, 569-573
Delaware River Basin Commission, 312, 414
Deloitte and Touche LLP Federal Political Action Committee, 711
Delphi International, 449
Democratic Congressional Campaign Committee, 717
Democratic Governors' Assn., 717
Democratic Leadership Council, 717

Democratic National Committee, 717
Assn. of State Democratic Chairs, 717
Campaign Division, 692
Communications, 718
Finance, 718
general counsel, 717
internships, 176
Research, 718
Democratic party
political organizations, 717-718
Democratic Republican Independent Voter Education Committee (DRIVE), 710
Democratic Senatorial Campaign Committee, 718, 816
Democratic Socialists of America, 719
Dental care, 368-369
Departments, executive. *See specific department names.*
Design arts, 418-419
Development assistance, 468-471
Development Group for Alternative Policies, 470
Diabetes, 391-392
Digestive diseases, 391-392
Dignity USA, 5
Diplomats and foreign agents, 443-444
Direct Marketing Assn., 21, 165, 340
Direction of Trade Statistics, 466
Directory of Health Philanthropy, 26
Disabilities, 638-647
Disability Rights Center, 641
Disability Rights Education and Defense Fund, 29, 642
Disabled American Veterans, 548, 642
Employment, 551
Disabled persons
education, 197-199
employment and training, 223-224
social services, 638-647
toll-free numbers, 12
Disabled Sports USA, 122, 642
Discovery Theater, 112
Discrimination. *See Civil Rights; Equal Employment Opportunity.*
Dislocated workers, 222
Dismissals and disputes, 321-322
Dispute resolution, 497
Distance Education and Training Council, 209
Distilled Spirits Council of the United States, 60
Distribution and LTL Carriers Assn., 658
Distributive Education Clubs of America, 174
District of Columbia
control board, 343
history and culture, 119-121
mayor, 343
Metropolitan Police Dept., 92
District of Columbia Tax Revision Commission, 342
Document Management Industries Assn., 95
Documents. *See Libraries and Educational Media.*
DOD. *See Defense Department.*
DOE. *See Energy Department.*
DOJ. *See Justice Department.*
DOL. *See Labor Department.*
Dole Foundation for Employment of People with Disabilities, 224
Domestic Policy Council, 328, 329
Domestic violence, 510-511
toll-free hotline, 12
Door and Hardware Institute, 422

Federation of Nurses and Health Professionals, 368, 370
Federation of Organizations for Professional Women, 229
Federation of State Humanities Councils, 100
Federation of Tax Administrators, 142
Fellowships and grants, 175-178
Feminists for Life of America, 504
Fertilizer and pesticides, 41-42
Fertilizer Institute, 42
Festival of American Folklife, 119
Films and filmmaking, 102-103
Finance and Investments, 143-153
    banking, 143-149
    credit practices, 17-18
    housing mortgages, 432-434
    international affairs, 471-473
    stocks, bonds, and securities, 149-152
    tangible assets, 152-153
Financial aid
    foreign. *See Foreign aid.*
    to students, 192
Financial Executives Institute, 135
Financial officers, departmental and agency (box), 332-333
Fine Arts Board, 695
Fire prevention and control, 18-19
First Lady, Office of, 329
Fish and fishing
    international agreements, 456-457
    resources, 284-286
Flat Tax Caucus, 695
Fleet Reserve Assn., 525
Flexible Packaging Assn., 20, 154, 296
Flight Safety Foundation, 665
Flood insurance, 13
Fogarty International Center, 382
Folger Shakespeare Library, 104, 106
Folk and native arts, 118-119
Food and Agriculture Organization of the United Nations, 63
    Liaison Office for North America, 465
Food and Consumer Service, 55, 626
    Child Nutrition, 55, 631
    Food Distribution, 55, 626
    Food Stamp Program, 55, 627
    Information, 55, 626
    Nutrition and Technical Services, 55, 632
    Supplemental Food Program, 56, 632
Food and Drug Administration (FDA), 23, 349
    Center for Biologics Evaluation and Research, 387
    Center for Devices and Radiological Health, 295, 360
    Center for Drug Evaluation and Research, 362, 387, 512
    Center for Food Safety and Applied Nutrition, 20, 56
    Center for Veterinary Medicine, 282
    Consumer Affairs, 14, 204
    Drug Marketing, Advertising, and Communication, 20, 165
    Generic Drugs, 362
    Health Affairs, 362, 398
    Information, 23, 349
    International Affairs, 349
    Internet world wide web site, 84
    organization (chart), 363
    personnel office, 320
    regional offices, 848-849
    Regulatory Affairs, 349
    Small Business, Scientific, and Trade Affairs, 167
    Small Manufacturers Assistance, 360
    Special Nutritionals, 56

Food and Drug Law Institute, 58, 364
Food and Nutrition, 54-64
    beverages, 59-60
    food industries, 60-62
    international organizations, 57
    meat and poultry safety inquiries, 12
    world food assistance, 62-64
Food and Nutrition Information Center, 56, 193
Food Marketing Institute, 61
Food Processing Machinery and Suppliers Assn., 61
Food Research and Action Center, 59, 629
Food Safety and Inspection Service, 20, 56, 65, 204
    consumer inquiries, 20, 56, 65, 204
    regional offices, 842
Food stamps, 627
Foodservice and Packaging Institute, 296
Footwear Distributors and Retailers of America, 156
Footwear Industries of America, 156
Ford's Theatre National Historic Site, 111, 120
Foreign agents, 443-444
Foreign Agricultural Service, 45, 468
    Export Credits, 62
    Information, 45, 468
    International Cooperation and Development, 62
Foreign aid
    development assistance, 468-471
    humanitarian aid, 444-448
    world food assistance, 62-64
Foreign Claims Settlement Commission of the United States, 455
Foreign Direct Investment in the United States: Transactions, 461
Foreign embassies (list), 880-896
Foreign policy. *See International Affairs.*
Foreign Press Center (USIA), 92
Foreign Service, 444
    postal service box numbers (box), 881
Foreign Service Institute, 443
Foreign Services Research Institute, 449
Foreign trade. *See International Trade and Development.*
Foreign Trade Zones Board, 459
Forest Service, 300
    Fire and Aviation Management, 18
    International Programs, 300
    National Forest System, 301
    Recreation Management, 310
    regional offices, 842
    Research, 301
    State and Private Forestry, 301
    Wildlife, Fisheries, and Rare Plants, 286
    Youth Conservation Corps, 224, 302
Forests and rangelands, 300-303
Fort Washington Park, 120
Fossil Energy (DOE), 257
    Coal and Power Import and Export, 251
    Coal Fuels and Industrial Systems, 258
    Natural Gas and Petroleum Technology, 260
    Naval Petroleum and Oil Shale Reserves, 260, 578
Fossil Fuels, 257-262
    coal, 258-259
    oil and natural gas, 259-262
    pipelines, 262
Foster Grandparent Program, 24, 637
Foundation Center, 26, 177
Foundation for Exceptional Children, 197, 198

Foundation for Middle East Peace, 485
Foundation for Public Affairs, 714
Foundation for the Advancement of Chiropractic Tenets and
    Science, 397
Fox News, 90
Fraud and abuse hotlines (box), 334
Freddie Mac (Federal Home Loan Mortgage Corp.), 432
    financial officer, 332
Frederick Douglass National Historic Site, 106, 120
Free Congress Research and Education Foundation, 488, 715
Freedom Forum, 89
Freedom Forum Museum, 109
Freedom of information, 81-83
    departmental and agency contacts (box), 82
Freedom of Information Act (provisions), 897-898
Freedom of Information Clearinghouse, 83
Freer Gallery of Art, 106
French-American Chamber of Commerce, 479
Friends Committee on National Legislation, 32, 442, 567
Friends of Art and Preservation in Embassies, 113
Friends of Family Planning, 711
Friends of the Earth, 249, 278, 567, 602
Friends of the Jessup, 520
Friends of the National Zoo, 106
Frontiers of Freedom, 715
Fruits and vegetables, 49-50
FTC. *See Federal Trade Commission.*
Fuels. *See Energy.*
Fund for American Studies, 178
The Fund for Animals, 284
Fund for Constitutional Government, 335
Fund for Investigative Journalism, 89
Fund for New American Plays, 112
Fund for the Feminist Majority, 176
Fund for the Feminist Majority Foundation, 715
Future Farmers of America, 41
Future Fisherman Foundation, 123
Future Homemakers of America, 204
Futures Industry Assn., 150

G7 Council, 467
Gadsby's Tavern Museum, 106
Gallaudet University, 187, 199, 646
    Center for Global Education, 645
    Library, 186
Gannett News Service, 90
GAO. *See General Accounting Office.*
Gardening, 42-43
Gas and oil, 259-262
Gas Appliance Manufacturers Assn., 157, 260
Gas Research Institute, 261
Gay and Lesbian Activists Alliance, 5
Gay and Lesbian Alliance Against Defamation (GLAAD), 5
Gay and lesbian rights, 5-6
Gay and Lesbian Victory Fund, 6
Gays and lesbians, 5-6
Genealogy, 118
General Accounting Office (GAO), 131, 331, 706
    comptroller general, 131, 331, 706
    Document Distribution Center, 80, 596
    Energy, Resources, and Science, 244
    Energy, Science, and Natural Resources Management
        Issues, 275
    Environmental Protection Issues, 275
    Federal Management and Workforce Issues, 85, 336

financial officer, 333
Food and Agriculture Issues, 36
fraud and abuse hotline, 334
General Government, 491
Health, Education, and Human Services, 24, 172, 212, 235,
    343, 351, 547, 627, 650
Information, 131, 331, 706
information officer, 78
Information Resources Management Policies and Issues, 85
Internet world wide web site, 84
internship programs, 176
libraries, 131, 184, 331
National Security and International Affairs, 439, 562, 565,
    588, 622
organization (chart), 330
personnel office, 320
Procurement Law Division, 327
publications office, 79
regional offices, 862
Resources, Community, and Economic Development, 592
Transportation Issues, 656
General Agents and Managers Assn., 160
General Aviation Manufacturers Assn., 662
General Board of Church and Society of the United Methodist
    Church, 32
General Conference of Seventh-day Adventists, 32
General Counsels for Federal Agencies (box), 494-495
General Federation of Women's Clubs, 26, 206
General Services Administration (GSA), 328
    Acquisition Policy, 326, 328
    Board of Contract Appeals, 328
    Business Performance, 337
    Business Service Centers, 862
    Center for Electronic Messaging Technology, 83
    congressional liaison, 705
    Consumer Information Center, 11, 14
    Cultural and Environmental Affairs, 98, 418
    Enterprise Development, 167, 326
    equal employment opportunity contact, 226
    Federal Acquisition Institute, 337
    Federal Domestic Assistance Catalog Staff, 343, 405
    Federal Information Center, 13, 77, 328
    Federal Information Relay Service, 77, 645
    Federal Protective Service, 337
    Federal Supply Service, 337
    Federal Telecommunications Service, 75
    financial officer, 333
    fraud and abuse hotline, 334
    freedom of information contact, 82
    general counsel, 495
    Governmentwide Information Systems, 326
    Governmentwide Information Technology Manage-
        ment, 83
    Governmentwide Policy, 327, 328
    Information, 328
    information officer, 78
    inspector general, 334
    Internet world wide web site, 84
    library, 184, 328
    Living Buildings Program, 98
    National Capital Region, 328
    personnel office, 320
    procurement officer, 326
    Public Buildings Service, 329, 337, 416, 429
    publications office, 79

dispute resolution, 497
general counsels, department and agency (box), 494-495
general policy, 491-497
immigration and naturalization, 450-452
international. *See International Law and Agreements.*
judicial appointments, 497-498
judicial jurisdiction, 493
law enforcement, 517-519
legal professions and resources, 520-522
military grievances and discipline, 537-540
tax violations, 501
Law Enforcement, 517-519
Law Enforcement Alliance of America, 519
Law of the Sea, 456-457
Law Revision Counsel, 706
Lawyers Alliance for World Security, 567
Lawyers' Committee for Civil Rights Under Law, 29
Lawyers Committee for Human Rights, 458
Lawyers for Civil Justice, 496
Leadership America, Inc., 9
Leadership Conference of Women Religious, 33
Leadership Conference on Civil Rights, 3, 714
League of Arab States, 484
League of Conservation Voters, 279, 714
League of United Latin American Citizens (LULAC), 5
League of Women Voters Education Fund, 203
    Natural Resources, 279, 299
League of Women Voters of the United States, 692
Learn and Serve America, 24
Learning disabled, 197-199
Legal Affairs Council, 503
Legal Professions and Resources, 520-522
Legal Services Corporation, 28
    congressional liaison, 705
    freedom of information contact, 82
Legi-Slate, 688
Legislative Information Service, 688
Legislative Resource Center, 80, 117, 686
    Library of the House, 707
    Office of the Historian, 686
    Records and Registration, 688, 690, 705, 709
Lesbians and gays, 5-6
Leukemia Society of America, 391
Libertarian Party, 719
Liberty Lobby, 714, 715
Libraries and Educational Media, 182-186
    agency and departmental libraries (box), 184
    archives and manuscripts, 116-118
    congressional, 707-708
    congressional documents, 686-687
    governmental regional depository libraries, 863-865
    presidential libraries, 78, 117
    Shakespeare and Renaissance, 104
    Washington area history, 119-121
Libraries at Federal Agencies (box), 184
Library of Congress, 183
    African and Middle Eastern Division, 183, 474, 484
    American Folklife Center, 119, 183
    American Memory Project, 183
    Archive of Folk Culture, 183
    Asian Division, 183, 475, 484
    Cataloging Distribution Service, 183
    Center for the Book, 104, 183, 205
    Children's Literature Center, 104, 183
    Computer Catalog Center, 183, 688

Concert Office, 183
Congressional Research Service, 706, 707
Copyright Office, 68, 162, 183
divisions (list), 183
European Division, 183, 478, 487
Federal Library and Information Center Committee, 80, 183, 185
Folklife Reading Room, 183
Geography and Map Division, 183, 619
Hispanic Division, 183, 481
Humanities and Social Sciences Division, 183
Information, 183
Interlibrary Loans, 183
Internet world wide web site, 84
internship programs, 176
Interpretive Programs, 108, 183
Law Library, 183, 521, 707
Law Library Reading Room, 183, 687
librarian, 183
Local History and Genealogy Reading Room, 118, 183
Manuscript Division, 117, 183
Mary Pickford Theater, 183
Microform Reading Room, 183
Motion Picture, Broadcasting, and Recorded Sound, 183
    Film and television reading room, 103
    Recorded sound reference center, 110
Music Division, 110, 183
National Film Preservation Board, 103
National Library Service for the Blind and Physically Handicapped, 183, 198, 640, 644
Photoduplication Service, 183
Poetry and Literature Center, 104, 183
Preservation Office, 183, 185
Prints and Photographs Division, 103, 113, 183
Rare Book and Special Collections Division, 117, 183
Science and Technology Division, 183, 596
Serial and Government Publications Division, 80, 183, 439
Life sciences and biology, 599-604
Lincoln Institute for Research and Education, 3
Linguistic Society of America, 105
The Links, 201
Literacy/basic skills education, 205-206
    toll-free number, 13
Literature, 103-105
Litigation Group, 17, 30, 507
Livestock and Poultry, 64-66
Living Buildings Program (GSA), 98
Local Government in the Washington Area (box), 343. *See also State and Local Government.*
Local Initiatives Support Corp., 411
Log Cabin Republicans, 6, 715
Logistics Management Institute, 573
Long Island Congressional Delegation, 696
Long Island Sound Congressional Caucus, 697
Los Angeles Times, 90
LULAC National Educational Service Centers, 201
Lung diseases, 396-397
Lutheran Educational Conference of North America, 196
Lutheran Immigration and Refugee Service, 452
Lutheran Volunteer Corps, 27
Lutheran World Relief, 447
Lyceum, 106

Machinery Dealers National Assn., 158
Machinists Non-Partisan Political League, 710

National Railroad Passenger Corp. (Amtrak), 681
    Consumer relations/complaints, 681
    financial officer, 333
    general counsel, 495
    Information, 681
    Internet world wide web site, 84
    travel and ticket information, 681
National Railway Labor Conference, 682
National Rainbow Coalition, 716
National Realty Committee, 432
National Reconnaissance Office, 580
National Recreation and Park Assn., 123, 311
National Recycling Coalition, 297
National Rehabilitation Assn., 643
National Rehabilitation Information Center, 643
National Renderers Assn., 66
National Republican Congressional Committee, 718, 747-748
National Republican Senatorial Committee, 718, 816
National Research Council, 594
    Aeronautics and Space Engineering Board, 623
    Board on International Comparative Studies in Education,
        182
    Institute of Laboratory Animal Resources, 284
    International Affairs, 598
    Space Studies Board, 623
    Transportation Research Board, 657
    Transportation Research Information Services, 684
National Response Center, 293, 670
National Restaurant Assn., 62
National Retail Federation, 18, 136, 164
National Retired Teachers Assn., 178
National Rifle Assn. of America, 513
National Right to Life Committee, 504
National Right to Work Committee, 233
National Right to Work Legal Defense Foundation, 233
National Runaway Switchboard, 12
National Rural Community Assistance Program, 315, 413
National Rural Electric Cooperative Assn., 256, 413
National Rural Housing Coalition, 427
National Rural Letter Carriers' Assn., 339
National Safe Boating Council, 671
National SAFE KIDS Campaign, 16
National Safety Council, 239, 680
National School Boards Assn., 163, 195
National School Public Relations Assn., 175
National School Transportation Assn., 680
National Science and Technology Council, 40, 275, 591
National Science Board, 591
National Science Foundation (NSF), 591
    Astronomical Sciences, 624
    Atmospheric Sciences, 607
    Biological Sciences, 600
    Chemistry, 611
    Computer and Information Sciences and Engineering, 85,
        613
    Computer Communications Research, 613
    congressional liaison, 705
    Earth Sciences, 609
    Education and Human Resources, 207
    Engineering, 604
    equal employment opportunity contact, 226
    financial officer, 333
    freedom of information contact, 82
    general counsel, 495
    Geosciences, 606

    Graduate Education, 176
    Human Resource Development, 599
    Information and Intelligence Systems, 613
    inspector general, 334
    International Programs, 597
    Internet world wide web site, 84
    library, 184
    Materials Research, 611, 615
    Mathematical and Physical Sciences, 611
    Mathematical Sciences, 614
    National Science Board, 591
    Ocean Sciences Research, 610
    Oceanographic Centers and Facilities, 610
    personnel office, 320
    Physics, 615
    Polar Programs, 606
    procurement officer, 326
    publications office, 79
    Science Resources Studies, 207, 591
    Small Business Innovation Research Program, 167
    Social, Behavioral, and Economic Sciences, 617
National Science Resources Center, 181, 208
National Science Teachers Assn., 181, 208
NATIONAL SECURITY (chap. 16), 555-589
    armed services. *See Military Personnel and Veterans.*
    arms control and disarmament, 565-569
    defense budget, 562, 564
    defense trade and technology, 569-573
    emergency preparedness, 573-579
    general policy, 556-562
    intelligence and counterterrorism, 579-583
    internal security, 582-583
    military aid and peacekeepings, 564-565
    military installations, 583-586
    nuclear weapons and power, 568-569
    procurement, acquisition, and logistics, 586-589
    research and development, 571-573
National Security Agency, 580, 583
National Security Archive, 442, 582
National Security Council, 437, 557, 569, 580
    Defense Policy/Arms Control, 566
National Senior Citizens Educational and Research Center
    Senior AIDES Program, 223
National Senior Citizens Law Center, 8
National Senior Service Corps, 24, 637
National Sheriffs' Assn., 519
National Sleep Foundation, 386
National Small Business United, 169
National Smokers Alliance, 23
National Society, Colonial Dames XVII Century, 116
National Society, Daughters of the American Colonists, 118
National Society, Daughters of the American Revolution, 116,
    118
    Museum, 106
National Society of Accountants, 149
National Society of Colonial Dames of America, 116
National Society of Fund Raising Executives, 27
National Society of Professional Engineers, 606
National Soft Drink Assn., 60
National Spa and Pool Institute, 421
National Space Society, 623
National Star Route Mail Contractors Assn., 339
National State Long Term Care Ombudsman Resource, 379
National Sudden Infant Death Syndrome Resource Center, 380
National Symphony Orchestra Education Program, 110

Talented and gifted children, 197
Tangible assets
    coins and currency, 137-138
    metals and minerals, 152-153
Task forces. *See specific task force name.*
Tax Council, 143
Tax Executives Institute, 143
Tax Foundation, 143
Taxes and tax reform, 141-143
    enforcement and violations, 501
    tax form requests, 12
    tax refund information, 12
    taxpayer assistance, 12
Teach for America, 196
Teachers. *See Education; Postsecondary Education.*
Teachers of English to Speakers of Other Languages, 181, 203
Technology. *See Science and Technology.*
Technology Administration, 592
    International Technology Policy, 453, 598
    Technology Competitiveness, 153
    Technology Policy, 599
Telecommunications. *See Communications and the Media.*
Telecommunications for the Deaf, Inc., 71, 646
Telecommunications Industry Assn., 71
Telephone and telegraph, 75-76
Telephone Contacts for Data Users, 317
Television, 73-75
    cable services, 71-72
    networks, 90
Tennessee Valley Authority, 254, 263, 300, 304, 311, 313, 414, 671
    congressional liaison, 705
Terminal Elevator Grain Merchants' Assn., 51
Territories and associated states, U.S., 488-489
Territory and state abbreviations (list), 840
Textile Museum, 106, 109
Theater, 111-112
Therapeutic Communities of America, 400
Thomas Stone National Historic Site, 120
Time magazine, 90
Tire Assn. of North America, 677
Tire Industry Safety Council, 680
Tobacco
    commodity, 52-53
    smoking, 23
Tobacco Associates, 53
Tobacco Institute, 53
Tourism, 124-125
Town Affiliation Assn. of the U.S., Inc.
    Sister Cities International, 450
Trade policy. *See International Trade and Development.*
Trade Promotion Coordinating Committee, 462
Trademarks and patents, 161-163
Tradeshow Exhibitors Assn., 164
Traditional Values Coalition, 716
Training. *See Employment and training.*
TransAfrica, 474
Transit Systems, 682-684
TRANSPORTATION (chap. 19), 652-684
    air, 659-666
    freight and intermodalism, 658-659
    general policy, 653-658
    government, 337
    maritime, 666-672
    motor vehicles, 672-680

rail, 680-682
transit systems, 682-684
Transportation Communications International Union, 682
Transportation Department (DOT), 653
    Airline Information, 660
    airline safety hotline, 12
    auto safety hotline, 12
    Aviation Analysis, 660
    Aviation and International Affairs, 653, 660
    boating hotline, 12
    Bureau of Transportation Statistics, 653
    congressional liaison, 704
    Consumer Affairs, 14, 654, 660
    Environment, Energy, and Safety, 654
    Environmental Division, 275, 654
    equal employment opportunity contact, 226
    Federal Aviation Administration. *See that heading.*
    Federal Highway Administration. *See that heading.*
    Federal Railroad Administration. *See that heading.*
    Federal Transit Administration, 682, 683
    financial officer, 332
    fraud and abuse hotline, 334
    freedom of information contact, 82
    general counsel, 494
    hazardous materials, chemical, and oil spills, 12
    Information, 653
    information officer, 78
    Information Technology, Financial, and Secretarial Audits, 660
    inspector general, 334
    Intelligence and Security, 581, 654
    Intermodalism, 658
    International Aviation, 453
    Internet world wide web site, 84
    library, 184
    Maritime Administration. *See that heading.*
    National Highway Traffic Safety Administration. *See that heading.*
    National Response Center, 293, 670
    organization (chart), 654
    personnel office, 320
    procurement officer, 326
    publications office, 79
    Research and Special Programs Administration, 262, 653
    Saint Lawrence Seaway Development Corp., 455, 671
    secretary, 653
    small and disadvantaged business contact, 167
    Surface Transportation Board, 499, 658, 667, 681, 683
    toll-free numbers, 12
    Transportation Policy, 656
    U.S. Coast Guard. *See that heading.*
Transportation Institute, 670
Travel and Tourism, 124-125
    Americans abroad, 454-455
    government, 337
Travel Industry Assn. of America, 125
Treasurer of the United States, 137
Treasury Department, 129, 137
    Bureau of Alcohol, Tobacco, and Firearms. *See that heading.*
    Bureau of Engraving and Printing, 137
    Bureau of the Public Debt, 138, 149
    Comptroller of the Currency. *See that heading.*
    congressional liaison, 704

U.S. Wheat Associates, 51
USA Rice Federation, 51
USA Today, 90
USDA. *See Agriculture Department.*
USDA Graduate School, 187, 209
    International Institute for Training and Education, 448
USIA. *See U.S. Information Agency.*
USO (United Service Organizations), 526, 585
UTC, The Telecommunications Assn., 76
Utilities, public, 255-256
Utility Workers Union of America, 247, 425

Vegetables and fruits, 49-50
Very Special Arts, 198, 639
Veterans, 545-554
    appeals of VA decisions, 549-550
    education and economic opportunity, 550-551
    health care and VA hospitals, 551-553
    spouses, dependents, and survivors, 553-554
    toll-free numbers, 12
Veterans Affairs Department, 546
    benefits hotline, 13
    Board of Veterans Appeals, 549
    Center for Women Veterans, 545
    Committee on the Readjustment of Vietnam Veterans and
        Other War Veterans, 551
    Compensation and Pension Service, 547
    congressional liaison, 704
    Congressional Liaison Service, 707
    Consumer Affairs, 14
    debt management hotline, 13
    Education Service, 550
    equal employment opportunity contact, 226
    financial officer, 332
    fraud and abuse hotline, 13, 334
    freedom of information contact, 82
    general counsel, 494
    Information, 546
    information officer, 78
    inspector general, 334
    Internet world wide web site, 84
    library, 184
    life insurance information, 13
    Loan Guaranty Service, 550
    National Cemetery System, 542, 547
    National Center for Veteran Analysis and Statistics, 547
    organization (chart), 546
    Persian Gulf hotline, 13
    personnel office, 320
    Policy and Planning, 547
    procurement officer, 326
    Public Affairs, 858
    publications office, 79
    secretary, 546
    small and disadvantaged business contact, 167
    toll-free numbers, 13
    Veterans Benefits Administration, 547, 858
    Veterans Health Administration, 552
    Vocational Rehabilitation and Counseling Service, 551
Veterans Benefits Administration, 547
    regional offices, 858
Veterans' Employment and Training Service (DOL), 551
    Operations and Programs, 551
Veterans Health Administration, 552
    Academic Affiliations, 552

Dentistry, 552
Facilities Management, 552
Geriatrics and Extended Care, 552
Mental Health Strategic Health Care, 552
Patient Care Services, 552
Policy Planning and Performance, 552
Readjustment Counseling, 552
Research and Development, 552
Voluntary Service, 552
Veterans of Foreign Wars of the United States
    Appeals, 550
    Military Claims, 550
    National Veterans Service, 549
Veterans of the Battle of the Bulge, 549
Veterans of World War I of the U.S.A., 549
Vice President of the United States, 329
    President of the Senate, 702
Vietnam Veterans in Congress, 696
Vietnam Veterans of America, 549
Virgin Islands, Delegate to Congress, 489
Virgin Islands, Department of Tourism, 489
Virginia Railway Express, 683
Visa services, 451
Vision care, 373-375
Vision Council of America, 375
VISTA (Volunteers in Service to America), 24, 205, 626
Visual arts, 112-113
Visually impaired persons, 644-645
Vocational education, 209-210
    veterans programs, 550-551
Vocational Industrial Clubs of America, 210
Voice of America, 448
Voluntarism, 23-28
Volunteers in Overseas Cooperative Assistance, 471
Volunteers in Technical Assistance, 471
Voters for Choice, 504, 711
Voting and political participation, 691-693

Wages and salaries
    congressional, 703-705
    federal employees, 324-325
    federal wage standards, 216-217
    military personnel, 533-534
Wall Street Journal, 90
Wallace Institute for Alternative Agriculture, 44
Walter Reed Army Institute of Research, 385, 532
    Combined Military Diagnostic Retrovirology Service, 388
Warren Grant Magnuson Clinical Center, 385
    Transfusion Medicine, 388, 389
Washington Alert, 688
Washington area history and culture, 119-121
Washington Area Music Assn., 111
Washington Business Group on Health, 357
Washington Center, 178
Washington Center for Politics and Journalism, 178
Washington colleges and universities (box), 187
Washington History, 120
Washington Institute for Near East Policy, 486
Washington International Trade Assn., 468
Washington Legal Foundation, 496
Washington media contacts (box), 90
Washington Metropolitan Area Transit Authority, 683
Washington Office on Africa, 474
Washington Office on Latin America, 483
Washington Post, 90, 688